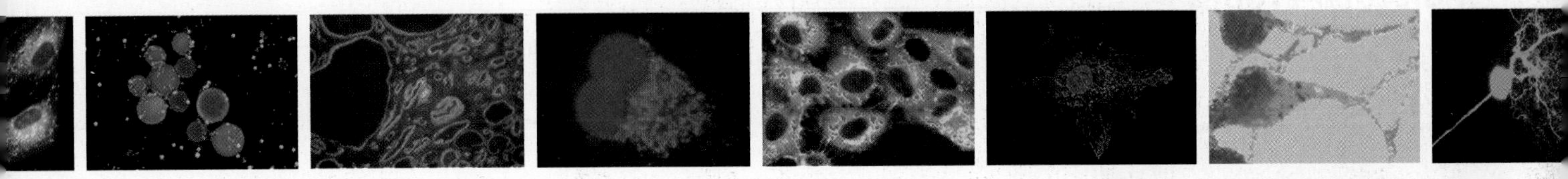

The Handbook

A Guide to Fluorescent Probes and Labeling Technologies

Tenth Edition

by Richard P. Haugland, Ph.D.

Michelle T.Z. Spence, Ph.D., Editor
Iain Johnson, Ph.D., Technical Information Coordinator
Aaron Basey, Content Management

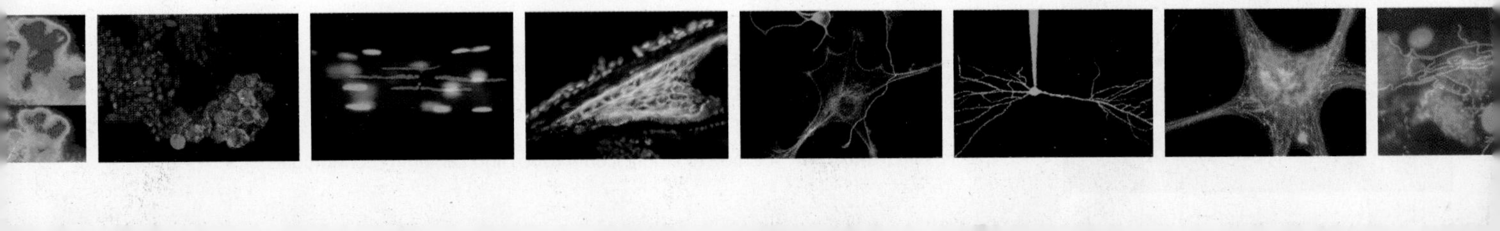

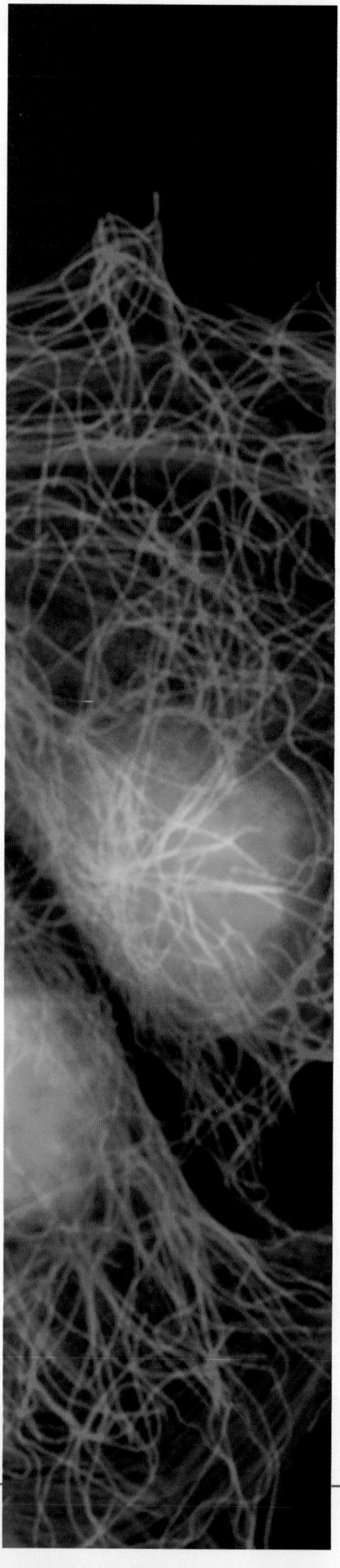

Editor

Michelle T.Z. Spence, Ph.D.

Editorial Assistance

Jay Gregory, Ph.D., Jennifer Bordun, Coleen Miller, Ph.D., Grace Richter, Ph.D.

Technical Information Coordinator

Iain Johnson, Ph.D.

Content Management

Kumi Hagimoto, Aaron Basey

Publication Design

Lynn Soderberg, Isamu Sato

Graphics Production and Layout

Lynn Soderberg, Isamu Sato, Kathleen Simpson, Kelly Christensen,
Joanna deFelice, Lynda Gansel, Marci Cardon, Ginger Bellino, Lydia Jablonski

Publications Production Manager

Rakar West

Legal

Koren Anderson, Ph.D., Renee Taylor

Fulfillment, Circulation, Distribution

Ginger Bellino

The Handbook would not have been possible without the help of our dedicated staff, including those in the following departments: Accounting, Administration Support, Business Development, Commercial, Corporate, Customer Service, Facilities, Human Resources, Imaging, Information Services, Intellectual Property, Marketing Communications, Operations, Packaging, Product Administration, Program Management, Purchasing, Quality Assurance, Quality Control, Regulatory/Safety, Research and Development, Shipping, Strategic Marketing, Technical Service.

First Edition published 1978. Second Edition 1981. Third Edition 1985. Fourth Edition 1989. Fifth Edition 1992. Sixth Edition 1996. Seventh Edition 1999 (on CD only). Eighth Edition 2000 (on CD only). Ninth Edition 2002. Tenth Edition 2005.

ISBN 0-9710636-4-8

Printed in the United States of America.

Table of Contents

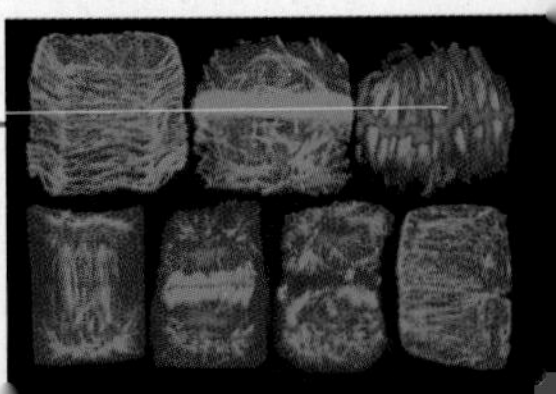

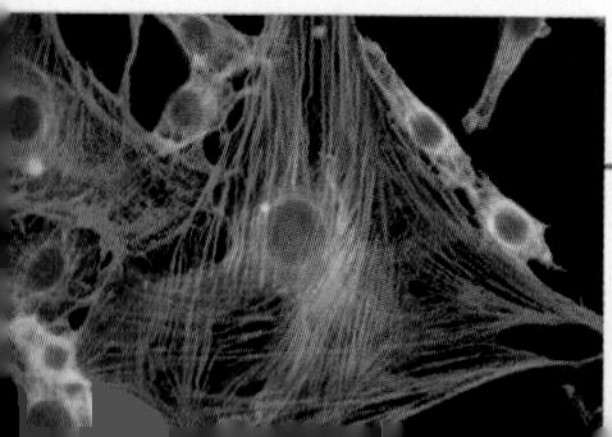

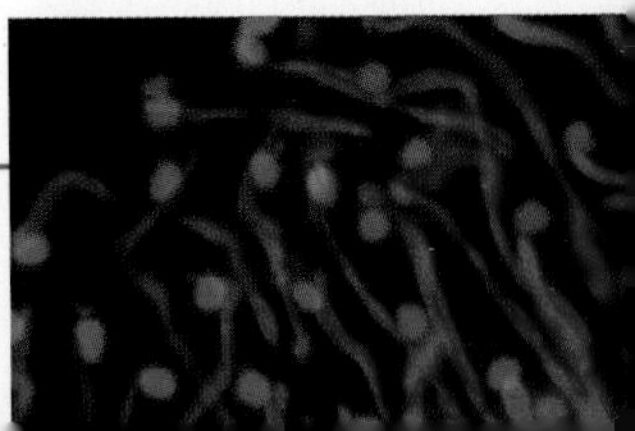

Product Highlight and Technical Focus Notes

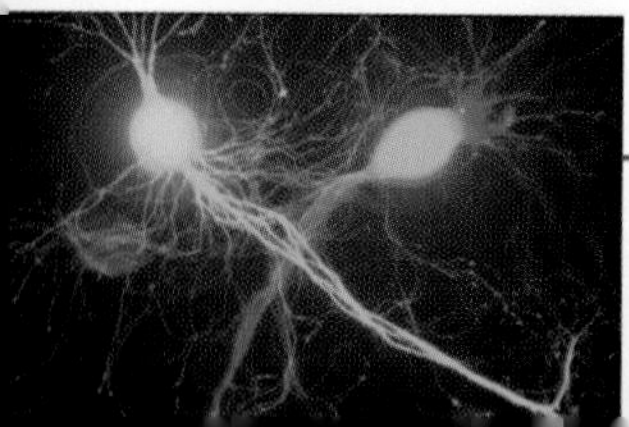

Technical Service

Do you have questions about Molecular Probes products or their applications? Our technical service scientists are ready to help you find the right answers. You are our very best source of information about product performance and emerging methodologies, and we value your inquiries.

Please refer to the inside back cover of *The Handbook* to find contact information for the distributor or branch office nearest you.

Custom Synthesis and Bulk Sales

Custom Synthesis

Molecular Probes offers a variety of specialty manufacturing and research services for the diagnostic, pharmaceutical and biotechnology industries, including:

- Custom synthesis — From milligram to kilogram quantities, we can provide a wide selection of fluorophores, fluorescent dye conjugates, fluorescent microspheres, and other organic compounds (e.g., crosslinking reagents).
- Custom conjugations — We have a laboratory dedicated to producing protein conjugates, many of which we sell as regular catalog items. We also custom conjugate antibodies and other proteins to fluorescent dyes, biotin, enzymes or other molecules. Our custom conjugation service is efficient and confidential, and we guarantee the quality of our work.

Bulk Sales

We offer special discounts on orders of large quantities of our standard reagents, whether delivered in bulk or in special packaging. Please contact our Custom and Bulk Sales Department for details about our services and for a schedule of prices. More information is also available at our Web site: **probes.invitrogen.com/about/custom** and **probes.invitrogen.com/about/custom/conjugations**.

Please refer to the inside back cover of *The Handbook* to find contact information for the distributor or branch office nearest you.

Licensing and Business Development

Molecular Probes has extensive patent coverage for many novel technologies, and several of these patents are available for license. We are looking for partners who can expand our marketing and technical capabilities. Technologies that are available for license include:

- Highly sensitive nucleic acid stains for gels, cells, solutions, capillary and flow cytometric detection
- Superior protein stains for gels, solutions, and capillary electrophoresis
- Bright fluorescent labels for proteins, peptides, nucleic acids, polysaccharides and small molecules
- Efficient fluorescence quencher dyes for coupling to many biological materials
- Fluorescent microspheres that can be customized to fit your needs
- Highly selective fluorescent stains for organelles
- One-step fluorescence-based assays for microbial and mammalian cell viability
- Fluorogenic enzyme substrates for cell- or tissue-based detection on microplates or in solution

Put the capabilities of our bioscientists and organic chemists to work for you. We welcome your inquiries at probesbusdev@invitrogen.com. Molecular Probes is ISO 9002 certified.

Be the first to know!

Our E-Mail Newsletter Delivers the Latest Information

ProbesOnline, our monthly e-mail newsletter, introduces new products and describes new work being done with classic products. *ProbesOnline* is your source for information before it is available anywhere else.

Subscribing is easy — just follow the link in the Literature section of our Web site. Our software will automatically add your return e-mail address to the subscription list.

Molecular Probes is committed to e-mail privacy and rational use of Internet bandwidth. We will not share your e-mail address with anyone without your permission, and we will keep *ProbesOnline* file sizes small.

Navigating *The Handbook*

Overview

The Handbook is divided into 23 chapters, each discussing a product group with common properties or applications. Each chapter is subdivided into sections, grouping products by more narrowly defined properties or applications. If a product has multiple applications, it may appear in more than one location.

Where possible, we have cited the literature for particular applications. For some products, we have speculated on possible applications. We advise researchers to use appropriate caution when approaching such areas of novel discovery.

Product Lists

Product lists contain the catalog numbers, names and unit sizes of the products discussed in each section. Product lists, arranged alphabetically by product name, can be found at the end of each section. (See also the Master Product List at the back of the book.)

probes.invitrogen.com

More Information Available Online

For the most up-to-date product information, including pricing and availability, visit the Molecular Probes Web site. There you'll find our online ordering service and our browsable *Handbook*, as well as informative product pages, an extensive bibliography, and a gallery of images featuring Molecular Probes products in action.

Order online

- Real-time pricing and availability
- 24-hour accessibility
- Order status and history

Read The Handbook *online*

- Fully searchable
- Links to online resources
- Printer-friendly format available

Download technical resources

- Technical information, protocols, and MSDS
- Chemical and spectral data
- Searchable, product-specific bibliographies

Browse additional features

- Gallery
- New products and announcements
- Base:dye ratio and K_d calculators
- Useful links to other sites
- Free downloadable screensaver

Data Tables

Most sections of *The Handbook* include tables of technical data, listing the chemical and spectroscopic properties of products described in the section. See page iii for definitions of data table contents.

More Information Online

For a review of the additional information available at our Web site, see "More Information Available Online" below.

Finding a Product of Interest

The Handbook includes products released by Molecular Probes through September 2004. Additional products and search capabilities are available through our Web site (probes.invitrogen.com). All information, including price and availability, is subject to change without notice.

If you know the name of the product you want: Find the product by name in the Master Product List. The product list is arranged alphabetically, by product name and alternative name. This list will refer you to all *Handbook* sections that discuss the product.

If you know only the catalog number of the product you want, but not its name: Look for the catalog number in the Master Product List. First locate the group of catalog numbers with the same alpha identifier as the product of interest and then scan this group for the correct number (because products are arranged alphabetically by name, catalog numbers are not in numerical order). The product list will refer you directly to all *Handbook* sections that discuss this product. Alternatively, you may use the search features available through our Web site (probes.invitrogen.com) to obtain the name of any of our current products given only the catalog number.

If you know neither the name nor the catalog number of the product you want: Scan the index for the words that best describe the applications in which the product is used. The index will refer you to page numbers on which the topics are discussed. Alternatively, review the table of contents for the chapter or section title that most closely relates to your application.

If you know only part of a product name or are searching for a product introduced after publication of *The Handbook*: Search Molecular Probes' up-to-date product list through our Web site (probes.invitrogen.com). The product search feature allows you to search our entire product list, including products that have been added since the completion of *The Handbook*, using a partial product name, complete product name or catalog number. Several product-specific bibliographies can also be obtained from our Web site.

If you still cannot find the product you are looking for or need advice on choosing a product: Please contact our Technical Service Department by phone or e-mail (see page i for more information on technical service).

Definitions of Data Table Contents

Cat #: The alpha-numeric catalog number for a particular product. Data tables are organized first in alphabetical order using the alpha identifier of the catalog number, and second in numerical order using the numeric identifier of the catalog number (e.g., A47, B153, B438, C194, etc.). The Master Product Index shows all sections in which products are discussed in the text. In most cases, data tables do not list kits, protein conjugates, dextran conjugates, gel and blot stains, ChromaTide® nucleotides and FluoSpheres® polystyrene microspheres.

MW: Molecular weight (MW) for the anhydrous compound, except in a few cases for which the exact degree of hydration has been determined and is specified in the name of the product. We caution that products may not be completely anhydrous upon receipt, even if they are represented in this form by the chemical structure and MW value. For compounds isolated and sold in salt form, MW is inclusive of counterions unless noted otherwise. In some cases (e.g., nucleotide derivatives, some peptides and proteins), the exact salt form has not been established, and consequently the MW value is approximate, denoted by a preceding "approximately" symbol (~). In general, we recommend measuring the absorbance of a solution and calculating concentration with the extinction coefficient rather than using these MW values.

Storage: Recommended storage conditions for products. Abbreviations are as follows:

A	Material may be air sensitive
AA	Air sensitive, use under a N_2 or Ar atmosphere
D	Desiccation *recommended*
DD	Desiccation *required*
F or FF	Store at ≤-20°C
L	Protect material from long-term exposure to light; may be exposed to light for short periods of time
LL	Protect material from light *at all times*
MIXED	Contains components with incompatible storage requirements; store components separately as indicated
NC	Storage conditions are not critical; store at ≤25°C
RO	Store at ≤6°C; if frozen, AVOID FREEZE-THAW CYCLES
RR	Store at 2–6°C; DO NOT FREEZE
RT	Store at room temperature or below (2–25°C); DO NOT FREEZE
UF	Store at ≤-70°C

Many products may remain at ambient temperature for short periods of time (e.g., during shipment) without any loss of product performance, but should be stored as indicated upon arrival. Storage information is also printed on all product container labels.

Soluble: Recommended solvent for preparing stock solutions of at least 1 mM. Recommendations are based on the best knowledge and experience of our technical staff, but have not necessarily been tested. If a pH is indicated, the product generally ionizes and should be dissolved in aqueous buffer in the specified pH range. Please send any alternate suggestions and corrections to this information based on practical experience to probestech@invitrogen.com. Abbreviations for solvents are defined below (see Solvent).

Abs: The longest-wavelength (unless noted otherwise) absorption maximum (in nanometers) in the solvent listed in the column headed Solvent.

EC: Molar extinction coefficient (in $cm^{-1}M^{-1}$) determined at the wavelength listed in the column headed Abs. Values above 10,000 $cm^{-1}M^{-1}$ are rounded to the nearest 1000. In most cases, extinction coefficients have not been rigorously determined, and the values may vary somewhat among production lots.

Em: Fluorescence emission maximum (in nanometers) in the solvent listed in the column headed Solvent. Em values are generally not corrected for instrument response characteristics, resulting in small variations when compared to measurements in other laboratories. Considerable environment-dependent variation of Em occurs for some products; when known, this is indicated with a footnote.

Solvent: Solvent used for acquisition of spectroscopic data, including Abs, EC and Em. Solubility of the product in this solvent is not necessarily any greater than is required to obtain an absorption spectrum (i.e. 10 µM or less). In some cases, it is necessary to prepare a stock solution in a different solvent and then to dilute the sample into the indicated solvent to measure spectra. Refer to the column headed Soluble for recommended solvents for preparing stock solutions. Abbreviations are as follows:

$CHCl_3$	Chloroform
DMF	Dimethylformamide
DMSO	Dimethylsulfoxide
EtOAc	Ethyl acetate
EtOH	Ethanol
H_2O	Unbuffered water
pH 7	pH 7 aqueous buffer
H_2O/DNA	Spectra measured for probes bound to DNA in aqueous solution
MeCN	Acetonitrile
MeOH	Methanol
THF	Tetrahydrofuran

Data for ion indicators are usually listed for aqueous solutions both with and without the target ion. The indicator dissociation constant for the target ion, in most cases determined in Molecular Probes' laboratories, is listed in a separate column headed $\mathbf{K_d}$ or for pH indicators, $\mathbf{pK_a}$.

Product: Catalog numbers or references to footnotes indicating products that are generated by enzymatic or chemical conversion of the parent compound in the course of standard applications.

Notes: Extensions to the listed data, identified by numbers (1, 2, etc.). For example, in cases where a product exists in two forms (e.g., substrate/enzymatic product, free/bound, unreacted/reacted), data for one form is listed in the table and for the other form in a footnote. Other spectroscopic parameters reported in some footnotes include fluorescence quantum yields (QY) and excited state lifetimes (τ; units = seconds × 10^{-9} = nanoseconds). We do not routinely determine QY and τ for our products, but include this data in the footnotes when it is known.

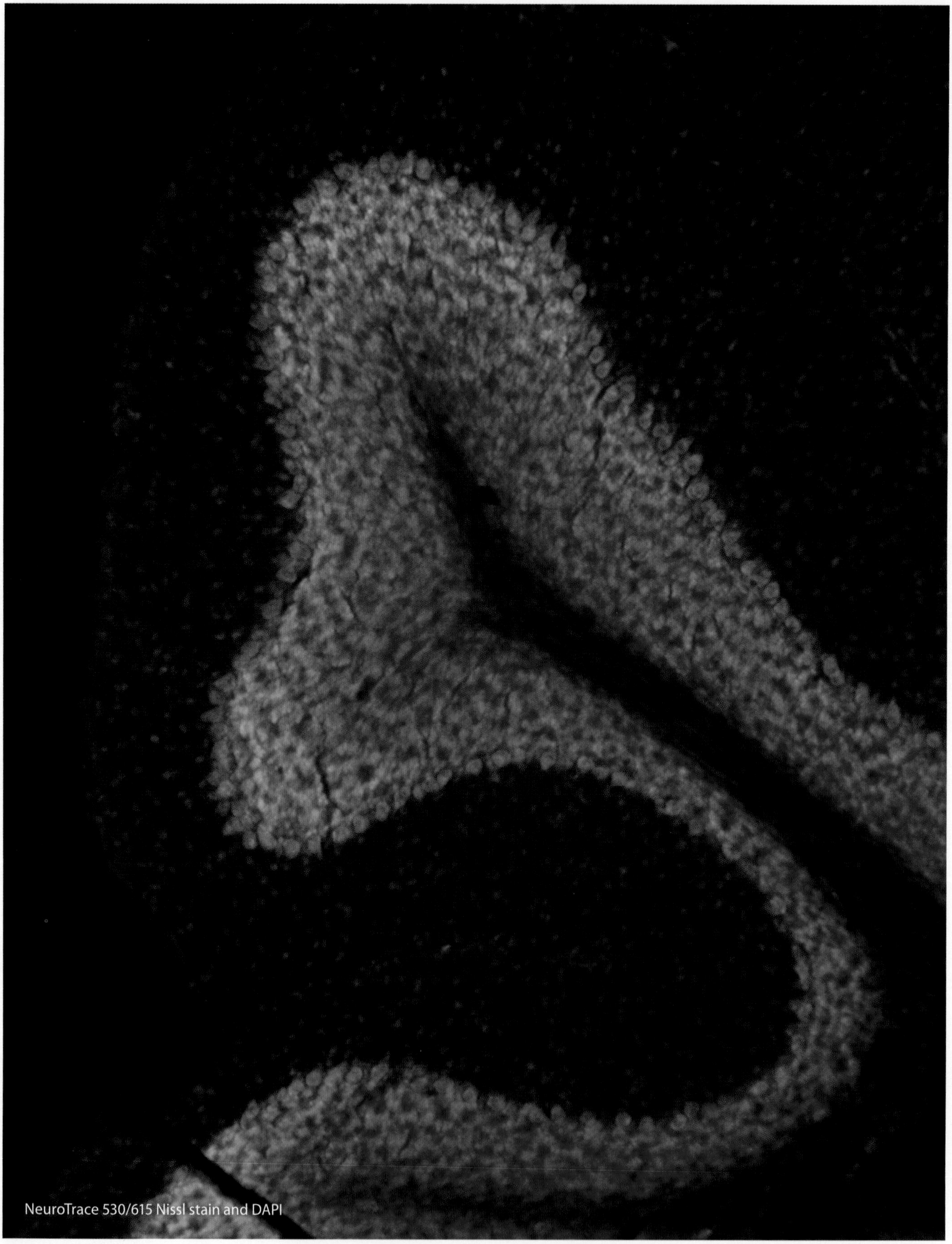

NeuroTrace 530/615 Nissl stain and DAPI

Introduction to Fluorescence Techniques

Fluorescent probes enable researchers to detect particular components of complex biomolecular assemblies, including live cells, with exquisite sensitivity and selectivity. The purpose of this introduction is to briefly outline fluorescence techniques for newcomers to the field.

The Fluorescence Process

Fluorescence is the result of a three-stage process that occurs in certain molecules (generally polyaromatic hydrocarbons or heterocycles) called fluorophores or fluorescent dyes. A fluorescent probe is a fluorophore designed to localize within a specific region of a biological specimen or to respond to a specific stimulus. The process responsible for the fluorescence of fluorescent probes and other fluorophores is illustrated by the simple electronic-state diagram (Jablonski diagram) shown in Figure 1.

Stage 1 : Excitation

A photon of energy $h\upsilon_{EX}$ is supplied by an external source such as an incandescent lamp or a laser and absorbed by the fluorophore, creating an excited electronic singlet state (S_1'). This process distinguishes fluorescence from chemiluminescence, in which the excited state is populated by a chemical reaction.

Stage 2 : Excited-State Lifetime

The excited state exists for a finite time (typically 1–10 nanoseconds). During this time, the fluorophore undergoes conformational changes and is also subject to a multitude of possible interactions with its molecular environment. These processes have two important consequences. First, the energy of S_1' is partially dissipated, yielding a relaxed singlet excited state (S_1) from which fluorescence emission originates. Second, not all the molecules initially excited by absorption (Stage 1) return to the ground state (S_0) by fluorescence emission. Other processes such as collisional quenching, fluorescence resonance energy transfer (FRET) (see Note 1.2 "Technical Focus: Fluorescence Resonance Energy Transfer (FRET)" in Section 1.3) and intersystem crossing (see below) may also depopulate S_1. The fluorescence quantum yield, which is the ratio of the number of fluorescence photons emitted (Stage 3) to the number of photons absorbed (Stage 1), is a measure of the relative extent to which these processes occur.

Stage 3 : Fluorescence Emission

A photon of energy $h\upsilon_{EM}$ is emitted, returning the fluorophore to its ground state S_0. Due to energy dissipation during the excited-state lifetime, the energy of this photon is lower, and therefore of longer wavelength, than the excitation photon $h\upsilon_{EX}$. The difference in energy or wavelength represented by ($h\upsilon_{EX} - h\upsilon_{EM}$) is called the Stokes shift. The Stokes shift is fundamental to the sensitivity of fluorescence techniques because it allows emission photons to be detected against a low background, isolated from excitation photons. In contrast, absorption spectrophotometry requires measurement of transmitted light relative to high incident light levels at the same wavelength.

Fluorescence Spectra

The entire fluorescence process is cyclical. Unless the fluorophore is irreversibly destroyed in the excited state (an important phenomenon known as photobleaching, see below), the same fluorophore can be repeatedly excited and detected. The fact that a single fluorophore can generate many thousands of detectable photons is fundamental to the high sensitivity of fluorescence detection techniques. For polyatomic molecules in solution, the discrete electronic transitions represented by $h\upsilon_{EX}$ and $h\upsilon_{EM}$ in Figure 1 are replaced by rather broad energy spectra called the fluorescence excitation spectrum and fluorescence emission spectrum, respectively. The bandwidths of these spectra are parameters of particular importance for applications in which two or more different fluorophores are simultaneously detected (see below). With few exceptions, the fluorescence excitation spectrum of a single fluorophore species in dilute solution is identical to its absorption spectrum. Under the same conditions, the fluorescence emission spectrum is independent of the excitation wavelength, due to the partial dissipation of excitation energy during the excited-state lifetime, as illustrated in Figure 1. The emission intensity is proportional to the amplitude of the fluorescence excitation spectrum at the excitation wavelength (Figure 2).

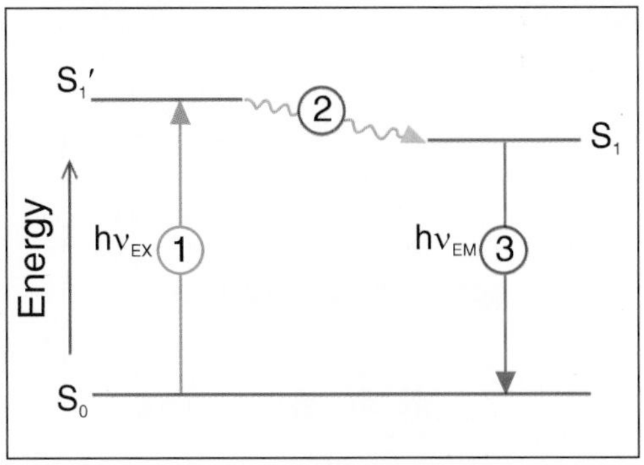

Figure 1 Jablonski diagram illustrating the processes involved in the creation of an excited electronic singlet state by optical absorption and subsequent emission of fluorescence. The labeled stages 1, 2 and 3 are explained in the adjoining text.

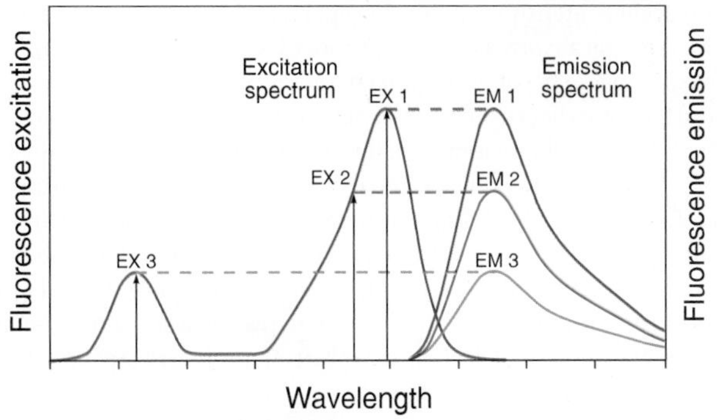

Figure 2 Excitation of a fluorophore at three different wavelengths (EX 1, EX 2, EX 3) does not change the emission profile but does produce variations in fluorescence emission intensity (EM 1, EM 2, EM 3) that correspond to the amplitude of the excitation spectrum.

Fluorescence Detection

Fluorescence Instrumentation

Four essential elements of fluorescence detection systems can be identified from the preceding discussion: 1) an excitation source, 2) a fluorophore, 3) wavelength filters to isolate emission photons from excitation photons and 4) a detector that registers emission photons and produces a recordable output, usually as an electrical signal or a photographic image. Regardless of the application, compatibility of these four elements is essential for optimizing fluorescence detection.

Fluorescence instruments are primarily of four types, each providing distinctly different information:

- **Spectrofluorometers and microplate readers** measure the *average* properties of bulk (µL to mL) samples.
- **Fluorescence microscopes** resolve fluorescence as a function of spatial coordinates in two or three dimensions for microscopic objects (less than ~0.1 mm diameter).
- **Fluorescence scanners**, including microarray readers, resolve fluorescence as a function of spatial coordinates in two dimensions for macroscopic objects such as electrophoresis gels, blots and chromatograms.
- **Flow cytometers** measure fluorescence per cell in a flowing stream, allowing subpopulations within a large sample to be identified and quantitated.

Other types of instrumentation that use fluorescence detection include capillary electrophoresis apparatus, DNA sequencers and microfluidic devices. Each type of instrument produces different measurement artifacts and makes different demands on the fluorescent probe. For example, although photobleaching is often a significant problem in fluorescence microscopy, it is not a major impediment in flow cytometry or DNA sequencers because the dwell time of individual cells or DNA molecules in the excitation beam is short.

Fluorescence Signals

Fluorescence intensity is quantitatively dependent on the same parameters as absorbance — defined by the Beer–Lambert law as the product of the molar extinction coefficient, optical path length and solute concentration — as well as on the fluorescence quantum yield of the dye and the excitation source intensity and fluorescence collection efficiency of the instrument. In dilute solutions or suspensions, fluorescence intensity is linearly proportional to these parameters. When sample absorbance exceeds about 0.05 in a 1 cm pathlength, the relationship becomes nonlinear and measurements may be distorted by artifacts such as self-absorption and the inner-filter effect.[1] Because fluorescence quantitation is dependent on the instrument, fluorescent reference standards are essential for calibrating measurements made at different times or using different instrument configurations.[2–4] To meet these requirements, Molecular Probes offers high-precision fluorescent microsphere reference standards for fluorescence microscopy and flow cytometry and a set of ready-made fluorescent standard solutions for spectrofluorometry (Section 23.1, Section 23.2).

A spectrofluorometer is extremely flexible, providing continuous ranges of excitation and emission wavelengths. Laser-scanning microscopes and flow cytometers, however, require probes that are excitable at a single fixed wavelength. In contemporary instruments, the excitation source is usually the 488 nm spectral line of the argon-ion laser. As shown in Figure 3, separation of the fluorescence emission signal (S1) from Rayleigh-scattered excitation light (EX) is facilitated by a large fluorescence Stokes shift (i.e., separation of A1 and E1). Biological samples labeled with fluorescent probes typically contain more than one fluorescent species, making signal-isolation issues more complex. Additional optical signals, represented in Figure 3 as S2, may be due to background fluorescence or to a second fluorescent probe.

Background Fluorescence

Fluorescence detection sensitivity is severely compromised by background signals, which may originate from endogenous sample constituents (referred to as autofluorescence) or from unbound or nonspecifically bound probes (referred to as reagent background). Detection of autofluorescence can be minimized either by selecting filters that reduce the transmission of E2 relative to E1 or by selecting probes that absorb and emit at longer wavelengths. Although narrowing the fluorescence detection bandwidth increases the resolution of E1 and E2, it also compromises the overall fluorescence intensity detected. Signal distortion caused by autofluorescence of cells, tissues and biological fluids is most readily minimized by using probes that can be excited at >500 nm. Furthermore, at longer wavelengths, light scattering by dense media such as tissues is much reduced, resulting in greater penetration of the excitation light.[5]

Multicolor Labeling Experiments

A multicolor labeling experiment entails the deliberate introduction of two or more probes to simultaneously monitor different biochemical functions. This technique has major applications in flow cytometry,[6,7] DNA sequencing,[8,9] fluorescence *in situ* hybridization [10,11] and fluorescence microscopy.[12,13] Signal isolation and data analysis are facilitated by maximizing the spectral separation of the multiple emissions (E1 and E2 in Figure 3). Consequently, fluorophores with narrow spectral bandwidths, such as Molecular Probes' Alexa Fluor® dyes (Section 1.3) and BODIPY® dyes (Section 1.4), are particularly useful in multicolor applications.[8] An ideal combination of dyes for multicolor labeling would exhibit strong absorption at a coincident excitation wavelength and well-separated emission spectra (Figure 3). Unfortunately, it is not easy to find single dyes with the requisite combination of a large extinction coefficient for absorption and a large Stokes shift [14] (see Note 6.2 "Technical Focus: Limitations of Low Molecular Weight Dyes" in Section 6.5).

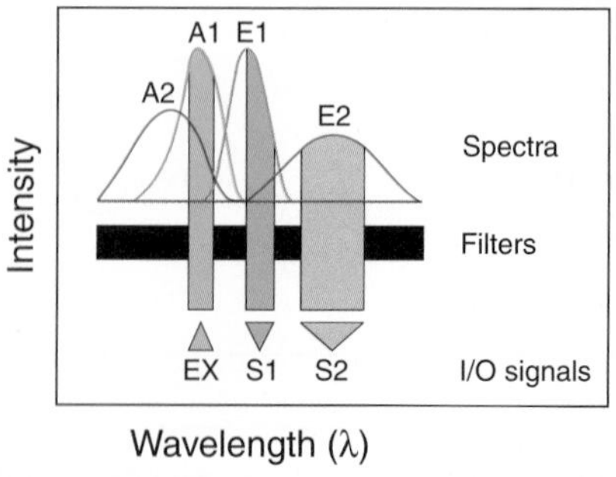

Figure 3 Fluorescence detection of mixed species. Excitation (EX) in overlapping absorption bands A1 and A2 produces two fluorescent species with spectra E1 and E2. Optical filters isolate quantitative emission signals S1 and S2.

Ratiometric Measurements

In some cases, for example the Ca^{2+} indicators fura-2 and indo-1 (Section 19.2) and the pH indicators BCECF and SNARF® (Section 20.2), the free and ion-bound forms of fluorescent ion indicators have different emission or excitation spectra. With this type of indicator, the ratio of the optical signals (S1 and S2 in Figure 3) can be used to monitor the association equilibrium and to calculate ion concentrations. Ratiometric measurements eliminate distortions of data caused by photobleaching and variations in probe loading and retention, as well as by instrumental factors such as illumination stability.[15] (see Note 19.1 "Technical Focus: Loading and Calibration of Intracellular Ion Indicators" in Section 19.1).

Fluorescence Output of Fluorophores

Comparing Different Dyes

Fluorophores currently used as fluorescent probes offer sufficient permutations of wavelength range, Stokes shift and spectral bandwidth to meet requirements imposed by instrumentation (e.g., 488 nm excitation), while allowing flexibility in the design of multicolor labeling experiments (Figure 4). The fluorescence output of a given dye depends on the efficiency with which it absorbs and emits photons, and its ability to undergo repeated excitation/emission cycles. Absorption and emission efficiencies are most usefully quantified in terms of the molar extinction coefficient (ε) for absorption and the quantum yield (QY) for fluorescence. Both are constants under specific environmental conditions. The value of ε is specified at a single wavelength (usually the absorption maximum), whereas QY is a measure of the total photon emission over the entire fluorescence spectral profile. Fluorescence intensity per dye molecule is proportional to the product of ε and QY. The range of these parameters among fluorophores of current practical importance is approximately 5000 to 200,000 $cm^{-1}M^{-1}$ for ε and 0.05 to 1.0 for QY. Phycobiliproteins such as R-phycoerythrin (Section 6.4) have multiple fluorophores on each protein and consequently have much larger extinction coefficients (on the order of 2×10^6 $cm^{-1}M^{-1}$) than low molecular weight fluorophores.

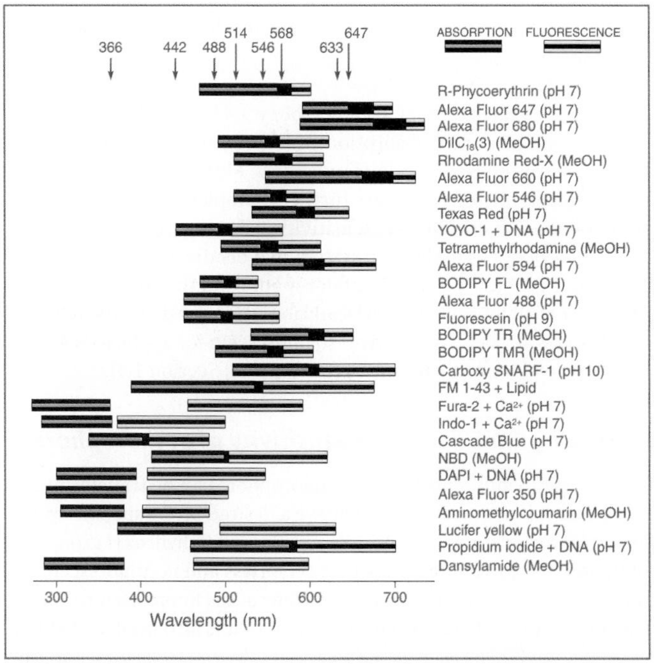

Figure 4 Absorption and fluorescence spectral ranges for 28 fluorophores of current practical importance. The range encompasses only those values of the absorbance or the fluorescence emission that are >25% of the maximum value. Fluorophores are arranged vertically in rank order of the maximum molar extinction coefficient (ε_{max}), in either methanol or aqueous buffer as specified. Some important excitation source lines are indicated on the upper horizontal axis.

Photobleaching

Under high-intensity illumination conditions, the irreversible destruction or photobleaching of the excited fluorophore becomes the factor limiting fluorescence detectability. The multiple photochemical reaction pathways responsible for photobleaching of fluorescein have been investigated and described in considerable detail.[16,17] Some pathways include reactions between adjacent dye molecules, making the process considerably more complex in labeled biological specimens than in dilute solutions of free dye. In all cases, photobleaching originates from the triplet excited state, which is created from the singlet state (S_1, Figure 1) via an excited-state process called intersystem crossing.

The most effective remedy for photobleaching is to maximize detection sensitivity, which allows the excitation intensity to be reduced. Detection sensitivity is enhanced by low-light detection devices such as CCD cameras, as well as by high–numerical aperture objectives and the widest bandpass emission filters compatible with satisfactory signal isolation. Alternatively, a less photolabile fluorophore may be substituted in the experiment. Molecular Probes' Alexa Fluor® 488 dye is an important fluorescein substitute that provides significantly greater photostability than fluorescein (Figure 1.46, Figure 1.9; Figure 1.10, Figure 1.11), yet is compatible with standard fluorescein optical filters. Antifade reagents such as Molecular Probes' *SlowFade*® and ProLong® products (Section 23.1) can also be applied to reduce photobleaching; however, they are usually incompatible with live cells. In general, it is difficult to predict the necessity for and effectiveness of such countermeasures because photobleaching rates are dependent to some extent on the fluorophore's environment.[17–19]

Signal Amplification

The most straightforward way to enhance fluorescence signals is to increase the number of fluorophores available for detection. Fluorescent signals can be amplified using 1) avidin–biotin or antibody–hapten secondary detection techniques, 2) enzyme-labeled secondary detection reagents in conjunction with fluorogenic substrates[20,21] or 3) probes that contain multiple fluorophores such as phycobiliproteins and Molecular Probes' FluoSpheres® fluorescent microspheres. Our most sensitive reagents and methods for signal amplification are discussed in Chapter 6.

Simply increasing the probe concentration can be counterproductive and often produces marked changes in the probe's chemical and optical characteristics. It is important to note that the effective intracellular concentration of probes loaded by bulk permeabilization methods (see Note 19.1 "Technical Focus: Loading and Calibration of Intracellular Ion Indicators" in Section 19.1) is usually much higher (>10-fold) than the extracellular incubation concentration. Also, increased labeling of proteins or membranes ultimately leads to precipitation of the protein or gross changes in membrane permeability. Antibodies labeled with more than four to six fluorophores per protein may exhibit reduced specificity and reduced binding affinity. Furthermore, at high degrees of substitution, the extra fluorescence obtained per added fluorophore typically decreases due to self-quenching (Figure 1.54).

Environmental Sensitivity of Fluorescence

Fluorescence spectra and quantum yields are generally more dependent on the environment than absorption spectra and extinction coefficients. For example, coupling a single fluorescein label to a protein typically reduces fluorescein's QY ~60% but only decreases its ε by ~10%. Interactions either between two adjacent fluorophores or between a fluorophore and other species in the surrounding environment can produce environment-sensitive fluorescence.

Fluorophore–Fluorophore Interactions

Fluorescence quenching can be defined as a bimolecular process that reduces the fluorescence quantum yield without changing the fluorescence emission spectrum; it can result from transient excited-state interactions (collisional quenching) or from formation of nonfluorescent ground-state species. Self-quenching is the quenching of one fluorophore by another; it therefore tends to occur when high loading concentrations or labeling densities are used (Figure 1.54, Figure 1.76). Molecular Probes' DQ™ substrates (Section 10.4) are heavily labeled and therefore highly quenched biopolymers that exhibit dramatic fluorescence enhancement upon enzymatic cleavage [22] (Figure 10.56). Studies of the self-quenching of carboxyfluorescein show that the mechanism involves energy transfer to nonfluorescent dimers.[23]

Fluorescence resonance energy transfer (FRET, see Section 1.3) is a strongly distance-dependent excited-state interaction in which emission of one fluorophore is coupled to the excitation of another.

Some excited fluorophores interact to form excimers, which are excited-state dimers that exhibit altered emission spectra. Excimer formation by the polyaromatic hydrocarbon pyrene is described in Section 13.2 (see especially Figure 13.8).

Because they all depend on the interaction of adjacent fluorophores, self-quenching, FRET and excimer formation can be exploited for monitoring a wide array of molecular assembly or fragmentation processes such as membrane fusion (see Note 14.3 "Technical Focus: Assays of Volume Change, Membrane Fusion and Membrane Permeability" in Section 14.3), nucleic acid hybridization (Section 8.5), ligand–receptor binding and polypeptide hydrolysis.

Other Environmental Factors

Many other environmental factors exert influences on fluorescence properties. The three most common are:

- Solvent polarity (solvent in this context includes interior regions of cells, proteins, membranes and other biomolecular structures)
- Proximity and concentrations of quenching species
- pH of the aqueous medium

Fluorescence spectra may be strongly dependent on solvent. This characteristic is most often observed with fluorophores that have large excited-state dipole moments, resulting in fluorescence spectral shifts to longer wavelengths in polar solvents. Representative fluorophores include the aminonaphthalenes such as prodan, badan (Figure 2.28) and dansyl, which are effective probes of environmental polarity in, for example, a protein's interior.[24]

Binding of a probe to its target can dramatically affect its fluorescence quantum yield (see Note 13.3 "Product Highlight: Monitoring Protein-Folding Processes with Anilinonaphthalenesulfonate Dyes" in Section 13.5). Probes that have a high fluorescence quantum yield when bound to a particular target but are otherwise effectively nonfluorescent yield extremely low reagent background signals (see above). Molecular Probes' ultrasensitive SYBR® Green, SYBR® Gold, SYTO®, PicoGreen®, RiboGreen® and OliGreen® nucleic acid stains (Chapter 8) are prime examples of this strategy. Similarly, fluorogenic enzyme substrates, which are nonfluorescent or have only short-wavelength emission until they are converted to fluorescent products by enzymatic cleavage (see below), allow sensitive detection of enzymatic activity.

Extrinsic quenchers, the most ubiquitous of which are paramagnetic species such as O_2 and heavy atoms such as iodide, reduce fluorescence quantum yields in a concentration-dependent manner. If quenching is caused by collisional interactions, as is usually the case, information on the proximity of the fluorophore and quencher and their mutual diffusion rate can be derived. This quenching effect has been used productively to measure chloride-ion flux in cells (Section 21.2). Many fluorophores are also quenched by proteins. Examples are NBD, fluorescein and BODIPY® dyes, in which the effect is apparently due to charge-transfer interactions with aromatic amino acid residues.[25–27] Consequently, antibodies raised against these fluorophores are effective and highly specific fluorescence quenchers (Section 7.4).

Fluorophores such as BCECF and carboxy SNARF®-1 that have strongly pH-dependent absorption and fluorescence characteristics can be used as physiological pH indicators. Fluorescein and hydroxycoumarins (umbelliferones) are further examples of this type of fluorophore. Structurally, pH sensitivity is due to a reconfiguration of the fluorophore's π-electron system that occurs upon protonation. Molecular Probes' BODIPY® FL fluorophore and the Alexa Fluor® 488 dye, both of which lack protolytically ionizable substituents, provide spectrally equivalent alternatives to fluorescein for applications requiring a pH-*in*sensitive probe (Section 1.3, Section 1.4).

Modifying Environmental Sensitivity of a Fluorophore

The environmental sensitivity of a fluorophore can be transformed by structural modifications to achieve a desired probe specificity. For example, conversion of the prototropic 3′- and 6′-hydroxyl groups of fluorescein to acetate esters yields colorless and nonfluorescent fluorescein diacetate. This derivatization causes fluorescein to adopt the nonfluorescent lactone configuration that is also prevalent at low pH [28] (Figure 20.1); cleavage of the acetates by esterases under appropriate pH conditions releases anionic fluorescein, which is strongly colored and highly fluorescent. Fluorogenic substrates for other hydrolytic enzymes can be created by replacing acetates with other appropriate functional groups such as sugar ethers (glycosides, Section 10.2) or phosphate esters (Section 10.3). Furthermore, unlike fluorescein, fluorescein diacetate is uncharged and therefore somewhat membrane permeant. This property forms the basis of an important noninvasive method for loading polar fluorescent indicators into cells in the form of membrane-permeant precursors that can be activated by intracellular esterases [29] (see Note 19.1 "Technical Focus: Loading and Calibration of Intracellular Ion Indicators" in Section 19.1).

References

1. Analyst 119, 417 (1994); **2.** Methods Cell Biol 42 Pt B, 605 (1994); **3.** Methods Cell Biol 30, 113 (1989); **4.** Luminescence Applications in Biol, Chem, Environ and Hydrol Sciences, Goldberg MC, Ed. pp. 98–126 (1989); **5.** J Microsc 176, 281 (1994); **6.** Methods Cell Biol 41, 61 (1994); **7.** Methods 2, 192 (1991); **8.** Science 271, 1420 (1996); **9.** Anal Biochem 223, 39 (1994); **10.** Proc Natl Acad Sci U S A 89, 1388 (1992); **11.** Cytometry 11, 126 (1990); **12.** Methods Cell Biol 38, 97 (1993); **13.** Methods Cell Biol 30, 449 (1989); **14.** Optical Microscopy for Biology, Herman B, Jacobson K, Eds. pp. 143–157 (1990); **15.** Methods Cell Biol 56, 237 (1998); **16.** Biophys J 70, 2959 (1996); **17.** Biophys J 68, 2588 (1995); **18.** J Cell Biol 100, 1309 (1985); **19.** J Org Chem 38, 1057 (1973); **20.** Cytometry 23, 48 (1996); **21.** J Histochem Cytochem 43, 77 (1995); **22.** Anal Biochem 251, 144 (1997); **23.** Anal Biochem 172, 61 (1988); **24.** Nature 319, 70 (1986); **25.** Biophys J 69, 716 (1995); **26.** Biochemistry 16, 5150 (1977); **27.** Immunochemistry 14, 533 (1977); **28.** Spectrochim Acta A 51, 7 (1995); **29.** Proc Natl Acad Sci U S A 55, 134 (1966).

Selected Books and Articles

The preceding discussion has introduced some general principles to consider when selecting a fluorescent probe. Application-specific details are addressed in subsequent chapters of this *Handbook.* For in-depth treatments of fluorescence techniques and their biological applications, the reader is referred to the many excellent books and review articles listed below.

Principles of Fluorescence Detection

Albani, J.R., *Absorption et fluorescence: Principes et applications*, Lavoisier (2001). This book is the first on absorption and fluorescence to be published in the French language.

Brand, L. and Johnson, M.L., Eds., *Fluorescence Spectroscopy (Methods in Enzymology, Volume 278)*, Academic Press (1997).

Cantor, C.R. and Schimmel, P.R., *Biophysical Chemistry Part 2*, W.H. Freeman (1980) pp. 433–465.

Dewey, T.G., Ed., *Biophysical and Biochemical Aspects of Fluorescence Spectroscopy*, Plenum Publishing (1991).

Guilbault, G.G., Ed., *Practical Fluorescence, Second Edition*, Marcel Dekker (1990).

Lakowicz, J.R., Ed., *Topics in Fluorescence Spectroscopy: Techniques (Volume 1, 1991); Principles (Volume 2, 1991); Biochemical Applications (Volume 3, 1992); Probe Design and Chemical Sensing (Volume 4, 1994); Nonlinear and Two-Photon Induced Fluorescence (Volume 5, 1997); Protein Fluorescence (Volume 6, 2000); DNA Technology (Volume 7, 2003)*; Plenum Publishing.

Lakowicz, J.R., *Principles of Fluorescence Spectroscopy, Second Edition*, Plenum Publishing (1999).

Mathies, R.A., Peck, K. and Stryer, L., "Optimization of high-sensitivity fluorescence detection," Anal Chem 62, 1786–1791 (1990).

Powe, A.M., Fletcher, K.A., St. Luce, N.N., Lowry, M., Neal, S., McCarroll, M.E., Oldham, P.B., McGown, L.B. and Warner, I.M., "Molecular fluorescence, phosphorescence, and chemiluminescence spectrometry," Anal Chem 76, 4614–4634 (2004).

Royer, C.A., "Approaches to teaching fluorescence spectroscopy," Biophys J 68, 1191–1195 (1995).

Sharma, A. and Schulman, S.G., *Introduction to Fluorescence Spectroscopy*, John Wiley and Sons (1999).

Valeur, B., *Molecular Fluorescence: Principles and Applications*, John Wiley and Sons (2002).

Fluorophores and Fluorescent Probes

Berlman, I.B., *Handbook of Fluorescence Spectra of Aromatic Molecules, Second Edition*, Academic Press (1971).

Czarnik, A.W., Ed., *Fluorescent Chemosensors for Ion and Molecule Recognition (ACS Symposium Series 538)*, American Chemical Society (1993).

Drexhage, K.H., "Structure and properties of laser dyes" in *Dye Lasers, Third Edition*, F.P. Schäfer, Ed., Springer-Verlag, (1990) pp. 155–200.

Giuliano, K.A., Post, P.L., Hahn, K.M. and Taylor, D.L., "Fluorescent protein biosensors: measurement of molecular dynamics in living cells," Annu Rev Biophys Biomol Struct 24, 405-434 (1995).

Green, F.J., *The Sigma-Aldrich Handbook of Stains, Dyes and Indicators*, Aldrich Chemical Company (1990).

Griffiths, J., *Colour and Constitution of Organic Molecules*, Academic Press (1976).

Haugland, R.P., "Antibody conjugates for cell biology" in *Current Protocols in Cell Biology*, J.S. Bonifacino, M. Dasso, J. Lippincott-Schwartz, J.B. Harford and K.M. Yamada, Eds., John Wiley and Sons (2000) pp. 16.5.1–16.5.22.

Haugland, R.P., "Spectra of fluorescent dyes used in flow cytometry," Meth Cell Biol 42, 641–663 (1994).

Hermanson, G.T., *Bioconjugate Techniques*, Academic Press (1996). **Available from Molecular Probes** (B7884, Section 23.6).

Johnson, I.D., Ryan, D. and Haugland, R.P., "Comparing fluorescent organic dyes for biomolecular labeling" in *Methods in Nonradioactive Detection*, G.C. Howard, Ed., Appleton and Lange (1993) pp. 47–68.

Johnson, I.D., "Fluorescent probes for living cells," Histochem J 30, 123–140 (1998).

Kasten, F.H., "Introduction to fluorescent probes: properties, history and applications" in *Fluorescent and Luminescent Probes for Biological Activity*, W.T. Mason, Ed., Academic Press (1993) pp. 12–33.

Krasovitskii, B.M. and Bolotin, B.M., *Organic Luminescent Materials*, VCH Publishers (1988).

Lakowicz, J.R., Ed., *Topics in Fluorescence Spectroscopy: Probe Design and Chemical Sensing (Volume 4)*, Plenum Publishing (1994).

Mason, W.T., Ed., *Fluorescent and Luminescent Probes for Biological Activity*, Second Edition, Academic Press (1999). **Available from Molecular Probes** (F14944, Section 23.6).

Marriott, G., Ed., *Caged Compounds (Methods in Enzymology, Volume 291)*, Academic Press (1998).

Tsien, R.Y., "The green fluorescent protein," Annu Rev Biochem 67, 509–544 (1998).

Waggoner, A.S., "Fluorescent probes for cytometry" in *Flow Cytometry and Sorting, Second Edition*, M.R. Melamed, T. Lindmo and M.L. Mendelsohn, Eds., Wiley-Liss (1990) pp. 209–225.

Wells, S. and Johnson, I., "Fluorescent labels for confocal microscopy" in *Three-Dimensional Confocal Microscopy: Volume Investigation of Biological Systems*, J.K. Stevens, L.R. Mills and J.E. Trogadis, Eds., Academic Press (1994) pp. 101–129.

Fluorescence Microscopy

Allan, V., Ed., *Protein Localization by Fluorescence Microscopy: A Practical Approach*, Oxford University Press (1999).

Andreeff, M. and Pinkel, D., Eds., *Introduction to Fluorescence* In Situ *Hybridization: Principles and Clinical Applications*, John Wiley and Sons (1999).

Conn, P.M., Ed., *Confocal Microscopy (Methods in Enzymology, Volume 307)*, Academic Press (1999).

Denk, W. and Svoboda, K., "Photon upmanship: why multiphoton imaging is more than a gimmick," Neuron 18, 351–357 (1997).

Diaspro, A., Ed., *Confocal and Two-Photon Microscopy: Foundations, Applications and Advances*, John Wiley and Sons (2001).

Goldman, R.D. and Spector, D.L., Eds., *Live Cell Imaging: A Laboratory Manual*, Cold Spring Harbor Laboratory Press (2004).

Herman, B., *Fluorescence Microscopy, Second Edition*, BIOS Scientific Publishers (1998).

Inoué, S. and Spring, K.R., *Video Microscopy, Second Edition*, Plenum Publishing (1997).

Matsumoto, B., Ed., *Cell Biological Applications of Confocal Microscopy, Second Edition (Methods in Cell Biology, Volume 70)*, Academic Press (2003).

Michalet, X., Kapanidis, A.N., Laurence, T., Pinaud, F., Doose, S., Pflughoefft, M. and Weiss S., "The power and prospects of fluorescence microscopies and spectroscopies," Annu Rev Biophys Biomolec Struct 32, 161–182 (2003).

Murphy, D.B., *Fundamentals of Light Microscopy and Electronic Imaging*, John Wiley and Sons (2001). **Available from Molecular Probes** (F24840, Section 23.6).

Pawley, J.B., Ed., *Handbook of Biological Confocal Microscopy, Second Edition*, Plenum Publishing (1995).

Paddock, S., Ed., *Confocal Microscopy (Methods in Molecular Biology, Volume 122)*, Humana Press (1998). **Available from Molecular Probes** (C14946, Section 23.6).

Periasamy, A., Ed., *Methods in Cellular Imaging*, Oxford University Press (2001).

Rizzuto, R., and Fasolato, C., Eds., *Imaging Living Cells*, Springer-Verlag (1999).

Sheppard, C.J.R. and Shotton, D.M., *Confocal Laser Scanning Microscopy*, BIOS Scientific Publishers (1997).

Stevens, J.K., Mills, L.R. and Trogadis, J.E., Eds., *Three-Dimensional Confocal Microscopy: Volume Investigation of Biological Systems*, Academic Press (1994).

Taylor, D.L. and Wang, Y.L., Eds., *Fluorescence Microscopy of Living Cells in Culture, Parts A and B (Methods in Cell Biology, Volumes 29 and 30)*, Academic Press (1989).

Toomre, D. and Manstein, D.J., "Lighting up the cell surface with evanescent wave microscopy," Trends Cell Biol 11, 298–303 (2001).

Tsien, R.Y., " Imagining imaging's future," Nat Rev Mol Cell Biol 4, SS16–SS21 (2003).

Wang, X.F. and Herman, B., Eds., *Fluorescence Imaging Spectroscopy and Microscopy*, John Wiley and Sons (1996).

Yuste, R., Lanni, F. and Konnerth, A., *Imaging Neurons: A Laboratory Manual*, Cold Spring Harbor Laboratory Press (2000).

Flow Cytometry

Darzynkiewicz, Z., Crissman, H.A. and Robinson, J.P., Eds., *Cytometry, Third Edition Parts A and B (Methods in Cell Biology, Volumes 63 and 64)*, Academic Press (2001).

Davey, H.M. and Kell, D.B., "Flow cytometry and cell sorting of heterogeneous microbial populations: the importance of single-cell analyses," Microbiological Rev 60, 641–696 (1996).

Gilman-Sachs, A., "Flow cytometry," Anal Chem 66, 700A–707A (1994).

Givan, A.L., *Flow Cytometry: First Principles, Second Edition*, John Wiley and Sons (2001).

Herzenberg, L.A., Parks, D., Sahaf, B., Perez, O., Roederer, M. and Herzenberg, L.A., "The history and future of the fluorescence activated cell sorter and flow cytometry: a view from Stanford," Clin Chem 48, 1819–1827 (2002).

Jaroszeski, M.J. and Heller, R., Eds., *Flow Cytometry Protocols (Methods in Molecular Biology, Volume 91)*, Humana Press (1997).

Lloyd, D., Ed., *Flow Cytometry in Microbiology*, Springer-Verlag (1993).

Melamed, M.R., Lindmo, T. and Mendelsohn, M.L., Eds., *Flow Cytometry and Sorting, Second Edition*, Wiley-Liss (1990).

Ormerod, M.G., Ed., *Flow Cytometry: A Practical Approach, Third Edition*, Oxford University Press (2000).

Robinson, J.P., Ed., *Current Protocols in Cytometry*, John Wiley and Sons (1997).

Shapiro, H.M., "Optical measurement in cytometry: light scattering, extinction, absorption and fluorescence," Meth Cell Biol 63, 107–129 (2001).

Shapiro, H.M., *Practical Flow Cytometry, Fourth Edition*, Wiley-Liss (2003).

Weaver, J.L., "Introduction to flow cytometry," Methods 21, 199–201 (2000). This journal issue also contains 10 review articles on various flow cytometry applications.

Other Fluorescence Measurement Techniques

Goldberg, M.C., Ed., *Luminescence Applications in Biological, Chemical, Environmental and Hydrological Sciences (ACS Symposium Series 383)*, American Chemical Society (1989).

Gore, M., Ed., *Spectrophotometry and Spectrofluorimetry: A Practical Approach, Second Edition*, Oxford University Press (2000).

Hemmilä, I.A., *Applications of Fluorescence in Immunoassays*, John Wiley and Sons (1991).

Patton, W.F., "A thousand points of light: the application of fluorescence detection technologies to two-dimensional gel electrophoresis and proteomics," Electrophoresis 21, 1123–1144 (2000).

Rampal, J.B., Ed., *DNA Arrays: Methods and Protocols (Methods in Molecular Biology, Volume 170)*, Humana Press (2001). **Available from Molecular Probes** (D24835, Section 23.6).

Schena, M., Ed., *DNA Microarrays: A Practical Approach*, Oxford University Press (1999).

Schena, M., Ed., *Microarray Biochip Technology*, BioTechniques Press (2000).

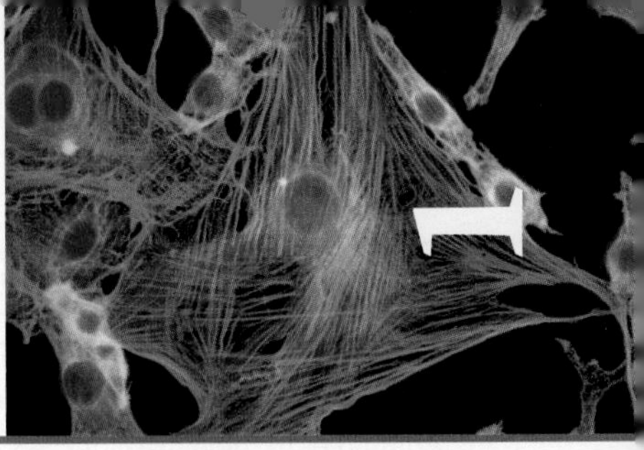

Chapter 1

Fluorophores and Their Amine-Reactive Derivatives

1.1 Introduction to Amine Modification

Molecular Probes provides a full spectrum of fluorophores and haptens for labeling biopolymers and derivatizing low molecular weight molecules. Chapters 1–5 describe the chemical and spectral properties of the reactive reagents we offer, whereas the remainder of this *Handbook* is primarily devoted to our diverse collection of fluorescent probes and their applications in cell biology, immunology, biochemistry, biophysics, microbiology, molecular biology, genomics, proteomics and neuroscience.

Common Applications for Amine-Reactive Probes

Labeling Biopolymers

Amine-reactive probes are widely used to modify proteins, peptides, ligands, synthetic oligonucleotides and other biomolecules. In contrast to our thiol-reactive reagents (Chapter 2), which frequently serve as probes of protein structure and function, amine-reactive dyes are most often used to prepare bioconjugates for immunochemistry, fluorescence *in situ* hybridization (FISH), cell tracing, receptor labeling and fluorescent analog cytochemistry.[1] In these applications, the stability of the chemical bond between the dye and biomolecule is particularly important because the conjugate is typically stored and used repeatedly over a relatively long period of time. Moreover, these conjugates are often subjected to rigorous incubation, hybridization and washing steps that demand a strong dye–biomolecule linkage.

Our selection of amine-reactive fluorophores for modifying biomolecules covers the entire visible and near-infrared spectrum (Table 1.1, Table 1.2). An up-to-date bibliography is available for most of our amine-reactive probes on our web site (probes.invitrogen.com). Also available are other product-specific bibliographies, as well as keyword searches of the over 50,000 literature references in our extensive bibliography database. Chapter 1 discusses the properties of Molecular Probes' most important proprietary fluorophores, including our premier sets of Alexa Fluor® dyes (Section 1.3) and BODIPY® dyes (Section 1.4), our Oregon Green® and Rhodamine Green™ dyes (Section 1.5), the red-fluorescent Rhodamine Red™-X and Texas Red® dyes (Section 1.6) and the UV light–excitable Cascade Blue®, Cascade Yellow™, Marina Blue®, Pacific Blue™, bimane and AMCA-X fluorophores (Section 1.7). Our essentially nonfluorescent QSY® dyes (Section 1.6, Section 1.8) have strong visible absorption, making them excellent acceptors for fluorescence resonance energy transfer (FRET) applications (see Note 1.2 "Technical Focus: Fluorescence Resonance Energy Transfer (FRET)" in Section 1.3).

Table 1.1 — Molecular Probes' amine-reactive dyes

Fluorophore	COOH *	SE *	Other *	Abs (nm)	Em (nm)	Notes
Alexa Fluor® 350		A10168		346	442	• Higher fluorescence per attached dye than AMCA
Alexa Fluor® 405		A30000 A30100		402	421	• Cascade Blue® derivative containing a spacer between the fluorophore and the reactive SE • Near-perfect match to the 405 nm spectral line of the blue diode laser
Alexa Fluor® 430		A10169		433	539	• Large Stokes shift
Alexa Fluor® 488		A20000 † A20100 †	A30005 (TFP)	495	519	• Bright and photostable fluorescein substitute • Fluorescence output unmatched by any other spectrally similar dye • pH-insensitive fluorescence between pH 4 and 10 • Ideal for excitation by the 488 nm spectral line of the argon-ion laser • As compared with the SE, the TFP ester is less susceptible to spontaneous hydrolysis during conjugation reactions
Alexa Fluor® 500		A30001 †		503	525	• Designed to be optically separated from the Alexa Fluor® 514 dye using the Zeiss META system or similar spectral imaging instruments with linear-unmixing software
Alexa Fluor® 514		A30002 †		518	540	• Designed to be optically separated from the Alexa Fluor® 500 or the Alexa Fluor® 488 dye using the Zeiss META system or similar spectral imaging instruments with linear-unmixing software • Optimal dye for the 514 nm spectral line of the argon-ion laser
Alexa Fluor® 532		A20001 A20101MP		531	554	• Bright and photostable dye with spectra intermediate between those of fluorescein and tetramethylrhodamine • Fluorescence output unmatched by any other spectrally similar dye • pH-insensitive fluorescence between pH 4 and 10 • Ideal for excitation by the 532 nm frequency-doubled principal line output of the Nd:YAG laser
Alexa Fluor® 546		A20002 † A20102 †		556	575	• Bright and photostable tetramethylrhodamine or Cy3 substitute • Fluorescence output unmatched by any other spectrally similar dye • pH-insensitive fluorescence between pH 4 and 10 • Less prone to aggregation than tetramethylrhodamine • Ideal for excitation by the 546 nm spectral line of the mercury-arc lamp

Table 1.1 — Molecular Probes' amine-reactive dyes — continued

Fluorophore	COOH *	SE *	Other *	Abs (nm)	Em (nm)	Notes
Alexa Fluor® 555		A20009 A20109		555	565	• Red-orange fluorescence • Bright and photostable tetramethylrhodamine or Cy3 substitute • Spectrally identical to Cy3
Alexa Fluor® 568		A20003 † A20103 †		578	603	• Bright and photostable Lissamine rhodamine B substitute • Fluorescence output unmatched by any other spectrally similar dye • pH-insensitive fluorescence between pH 4 and 10 • Ideal for excitation by the 568 nm spectral line of the Ar–Kr mixed-gas laser
Alexa Fluor® 594		A20004 † A20104 †		590	617	• Bright and photostable Texas Red® dye substitute • Fluorescence output unmatched by any other spectrally similar dye • pH-insensitive fluorescence between pH 4 and 10 • Ideal for excitation by the 594 nm spectral line of the He–Ne laser
Alexa Fluor® 610		A30003 A30103		612	628	• Bright and photostable Texas Red® dye substitute • Fluorescence output unmatched by any other spectrally similar dye • pH-insensitive fluorescence between pH 4 and 10 • Easily differentiated from green fluorophores • Still visible by eye, unlike longer-wavelength fluorophores
Alexa Fluor® 633		A20005 † A20105 †		632	647	• Far-red fluorescence • Good spectral separation from green fluorophores • pH-insensitive fluorescence between pH 4 and 10
Alexa Fluor® 635				633	647	• Far-red fluorescence • Absorption spectra does not split into two peaks upon protein conjugation • Good spectral separation from green fluorophores • pH-insensitive fluorescence between pH 4 and 10
Alexa Fluor® 647		A20006 A20106		650	668	• Far-red fluorescence • Produces conjugates that are brighter than those of the Cy5 dye • pH-insensitive fluorescence between pH 4 and 10
Alexa Fluor® 660		A20007 A20107		663	690	• Far-red fluorescence • Good spectral separation from green and red-orange fluorophores • pH-insensitive fluorescence between pH 4 and 10
Alexa Fluor® 680		A20008 A20108		682	702	• Far-red fluorescence • Good separation from red fluorophores — useful for three- and four-color applications • pH-insensitive fluorescence between pH 4 and 10
Alexa Fluor® 700		A20010 A20110		696	719	• Far-red fluorescence • Good separation from red fluorophores — useful for three- and four-color applications • pH-insensitive fluorescence between pH 4 and 10
Alexa Fluor® 750		A20011 A20111		752	779	• Far-red fluorescence • Good separation from red fluorophores — useful for three- and four-color applications • pH-insensitive fluorescence between pH 4 and 10 • Spectrally similar to the Cy7 dye
AMCA		A6118 (X)		349	448	• Widely used blue-fluorescent labeling dye • Compact structure
Bimane	B30250	B30251		380	458	• Blue-fluorescent dye • Small size
BODIPY® 493/503		D2191		500	506	• pH-insensitive fluorescence • Narrow spectral bandwidth • Higher 488 nm absorptivity than the BODIPY® FL fluorophore
BODIPY® FL	D2183 ‡ D3834 (C_5)	D2184 D6140 (SSE) D6141 (CASE) D6102 (X) D6184 (C_5)	B10006 (STP)	505	513	• BODIPY® substitute for fluorescein • pH-insensitive fluorescence • Narrow spectral bandwidth • Succinimidyl ester with a cysteic acid spacer (BODIPY® FL, CASE; D6141) is the preferred reactive BODIPY® FL dye for protein conjugation
BODIPY® R6G		D6180		528	550	• BODIPY® substitute with spectra similar to rhodamine 6G • pH-insensitive fluorescence • Narrow spectral bandwidth
BODIPY® 530/550		D2187		534	554	• pH-insensitive fluorescence • Narrow spectral bandwidth

Table 1.1 — Molecular Probes' amine-reactive dyes — continued

Fluorophore	COOH *	SE *	Other *	Abs (nm)	Em (nm)	Notes
BODIPY® TMR		D6117 (X)	B10002 (STP)	542	574	• BODIPY® substitute for tetramethylrhodamine • pH-insensitive fluorescence • Narrow spectral bandwidth
BODIPY® 558/568		D2219		558	569	• pH-insensitive fluorescence • Narrow spectral bandwidth
BODIPY® 564/570		D2222		565	571	• pH-insensitive fluorescence • Narrow spectral bandwidth
BODIPY® 576/589		D2225		576	590	• pH-insensitive fluorescence • Narrow spectral bandwidth
BODIPY® 581/591		D2228		584	592	• pH-insensitive fluorescence • Narrow spectral bandwidth
BODIPY® TR		D6116 (X)	B10003 (STP)	589	617	• BODIPY® substitute for the Texas Red® fluorophore • pH-insensitive fluorescence
BODIPY® 630/650		D10000 (X)		625	640	• pH-insensitive fluorescence • Ideal for excitation by the 633 nm spectral line of the He–Ne laser
BODIPY® 650/665		D10001 (X)	B10005 (STP)	646	660	• pH-insensitive fluorescence • Longest-wavelength BODIPY® dye currently available • Ideal for excitation by the 647 nm spectral line of the krypton-ion laser
2′,4,4′,5′,7,7′-hexachlorofluorescein (HEX)		C20091 (SE)		535	556	• Succinimidyl ester derivative (6-HEX, SE; C20091) is widely used for automated DNA sequencing
Cascade Blue® dye			C2284 (AA)	400	420	• Resistant to quenching upon protein conjugation • Water soluble
Cascade Yellow™ dye		C10164		402	545	• Large Stokes shift • High molar absorptivity
Dansyl		D6104 (X)	D21 (SC)	340	520 ‡	• Environment-sensitive fluorescence • Large Stokes shift
Dapoxyl® dye		D10161 D10162	D10160 (SC)	373	551 ‡	• Environment-sensitive fluorescence • Large Stokes shift
Dialkylamino-coumarin	D126 D1421	D374 D1412		375 435	470 § 475 **	• Longer-wavelength alternatives to AMCA
4′,5′-Dichloro-2′,7′-dimethoxy-fluorescein (JOE)		C6171MP		522	550	• Succinimidyl ester derivative (6-JOE, SE; C6171MP) is widely used for automated DNA sequencing
2′,7′-Dichloro-fluorescein	C368 †			510	532	• pH-insensitive fluorescence at pH >6
Eosin			E18 (ITC)	524	544	• Useful for DAB photoconversion • Phosphorescent
Erythrosin			E30150 (ITC)	530	555	• Phosphorescent
Fluorescein	C1359 C1360 C1904 †	C2210 C6164 C1311 † F6106 (X) F2181 (X) † F6129 (X) † F6130 (EX) C20050 (C)	D16 (DTA) F143 (ITC) F1906 (ITC) F1907 (ITC)	494	518	• Most widely used green-fluorescent labeling dye • Absorption overlaps the 488 nm spectral line of the argon-ion laser • Prone to photobleaching • pH-sensitive fluorescence between pH 5–8 • Succinimidyl ester derivative (5-FAM, SE; C2210) is widely used for automated DNA sequencing • Fluorescein-5-EX succinimidyl ester (F6130) is the preferred reactive fluorescein for protein conjugation
Hydroxycoumarin	H185 H1428	H1193		385	445 ††	• pH-sensitive fluorescence • Compact structure
Lissamine rhodamine B			L20 (SC) † L1908 (SC) †	570	590	• Optimal for 568 nm excitation • Photostable
Malachite green			M689 (ITC)	630	none	• Nonfluorescent photosensitizer
Marina Blue® dye		M10165		365	460	• Strongly fluorescent at neutral pH, unlike 7-hydroxycoumarins • Optimal for 365 nm excitation of the mercury-arc lamp
Methoxycoumarin	M1420MP	M1410		340	405	• pH-insensitive alternative to 7-hydroxycoumarins
Naphthofluorescein	C652 †	C653 †		605	675	• Very long-wavelength excitation and emission • pH-sensitive fluorescence
NBD		S1167 (X)	F486 (AH)	465	535	• Environment-sensitive fluorescence • Compact structure

Table 1.1 — Molecular Probes' amine-reactive dyes — continued

Fluorophore	COOH *	SE *	Other *	Abs (nm)	Em (nm)	Notes
Oregon Green® 488	O6146	O6147 O6149	O6080 (ITC) †	496	524	• Photostable fluorescein substitute • pH-insensitive fluorescence at pH >6
Oregon Green® 514	O6138	O6139		511	530	• Exceptionally photostable • pH-insensitive fluorescence at pH >6
Pacific Blue™ dye		P10163		410	455	• Strongly fluorescent at neutral pH, unlike 7-hydroxycoumarins
PyMPO		S6110		415	570	• Large Stokes shift
Pyrene		P6115 P130 P6114 (CASE)	P24 (SC) P10167 (STP)	345	378	• Long excited-state lifetime • Spectral shifts due to excimer emission
QSY® 7		Q10193		560	none	• Essentially nonfluorescent quencher • Broad visible-wavelength absorption • Efficient energy transfer acceptor from green and orange fluorophores
QSY® 9		Q20131		562	none	• Essentially nonfluorescent quencher • Spectrally similar to QSY® 7, but with enhanced water solubility • Efficient energy-transfer acceptor from green and orange fluorophores
QSY® 21		Q20132		661	none	• Essentially nonfluorescent quencher • Long-wavelength absorption • An efficient energy transfer acceptor from red and near-infrared fluorophores
QSY® 35		Q20133		475	none	• Nonfluorescent quencher • Spectrally similar to dabcyl • An efficient energy transfer acceptor from blue and green fluorophores
Rhodamine 6G		C6127 C6128 C6157 †		525	555	• Excited by the 514 nm spectral line of the Ar-ion laser • Spectra intermediate between those of fluorescein and tetramethylrhodamine
Rhodamine Green™ dye		R6107 † R6112 † R6113 (X) †		502	527	• Photostable fluorescein substitute • pH-insensitive fluorescence
Rhodamine Red™ dye		R6160 (X) †		570	590	• Conjugates are generally more fluorescent than those of Lissamine rhodamine B sulfonyl chloride and the succinimidyl ester is more stable in H_2O
2′,4′,5′,7′-Tetra-bromosulfone-fluorescein		C6166		528	544	• Eosin derivative useful for DAB photoconversion
2′,4,7,7′-Tetra-chlorofluorescein, succinimidyl ester (TET)		C20092		521	536	• Succinimidyl ester derivative (6-TET, SE; C20092) is widely used for automated DNA sequencing
Tetramethyl-rhodamine (TMR)	C6121 C6122 C300 †	C2211 C6123 C1171 † T6105 (X) †	T1480 (ITC) T1481 (ITC) T490 (ITC) †	555	580	• pH-insensitive fluorescence • Good photostability • Prone to aggregation • Succinimidyl ester derivative (6-TAMRA, SE; C6123) is widely used for automated DNA sequencing
Texas Red® dye		T6134 (X) † T20175 (X)	T353 (SC) † T1905 (SC) † T10125 (STP)	595	615	• Good spectral separation from green fluorophores • Texas Red®-X succinimidyl ester typically yields higher fluorescence per attached dye than Texas Red® sulfonyl chloride and is more stable in H_2O
X-rhodamine	C6124 C6156	C6125 C6126 C1309 †	X491 (ITC) †	580	605	• Succinimidyl ester derivative (6-ROX, SE; C6126) is widely used for automated nucleic acid sequencing

The absorption (Abs) and fluorescence emission (Em) maxima listed in this table are for the goat anti–mouse IgG antibody or dextran conjugates in aqueous buffer. Full spectra for many dyes are available from our web site (probes.invitrogen.com). * COOH = carboxylic acid; SE = succinimidyl ester; (AA) = acetyl azide; (AH) = aryl halide; (C_5) = pentanoic acid; (CASE) = cysteic acid; succinimidyl ester; (DTA) = dichlorotriazine; (EX) = seven-atom spacer that is more hydrophilic than X; (ITC) = isothiocyanate; (SC) = sulfonyl chloride; (SSE) = sulfosuccinimidyl ester; (STP) = 4-sulfotetrafluorophenyl ester; (TFP) = tetrafluorophenyl ester; (X) = an aminohexanoyl spacer between the dye and SE. † Mixed isomers. ‡ Emission spectra of dansyl and Dapoxyl® conjugates may vary considerably depending on the dye attachment site and the degree of labeling. § Spectral maxima for D374. ** Spectral maxima for D1412. †† Spectral maxima for H1193.

Preparing the Optimal Bioconjugate

The preferred bioconjugate usually has a high fluorescence yield (or, in the case of a haptenylated conjugate, a suitable degree of labeling) yet retains the critical parameters of the unlabeled biomolecule, such as solubility, selective binding to a receptor or nucleic acid, activation or inhibition of a particular enzyme or the ability to incorporate into a biological membrane. Frequently, however, conjugates with the highest degree of labeling precipitate or bind nonspecifically. It may therefore be necessary to have a less-than-maximal fluorescence yield to preserve function or binding specificity. Although conjugating dyes to biomolecules is usually rather easy, preparing the *optimal* conjugate may require extensive experimentation. Thus, for the most critical assays, we recommend that researchers consider preparing and optimizing their own conjugates. We offer a detailed protocol describing how to use our amine-reactive dyes for labeling biomolecules. The procedure is straightforward and requires no special equipment. Following conjugation, it is very important to remove as much unconjugated labeling reagent as possible, usually by gel filtration, dialysis, bioconjugate precipitation and resolubilization, HPLC or a combination of these techniques. The presence of free dye, particularly if it remains chemically reactive, can greatly complicate subsequent experiments with the bioconjugate.

With the exception of the phycobiliproteins (Section 6.4, Table 6.2), fluorescent microspheres (Section 6.5, Table 6.7), Zenon® Antibody Labeling Kits (Section 7.3, Table 7.13) and ULYSIS Nucleic Acid Labeling Kits (Section 8.2, Table 8.8), virtually all the dyes used to prepare Molecular Probes' fluorescent bioconjugates are amine-reactive reagents and almost all are described in this chapter. We have also developed useful kit formats for labeling proteins with several of our most important dyes, or alternatively with biotin or DSB-X™ biotin. Section 1.2 and Table 1.3 include a complete description of these kits, including our Alexa Fluor® and FluoReporter® Protein Labeling Kits, as well as our Zenon® Antibody Labeling Kits (Section 7.3) for the rapid and quantitative labeling of antibodies from a purified antibody fraction or from a crude antibody preparation such as serum, ascites fluid or a hybridoma supernatant.

Alternatively, Molecular Probes prepares custom fluorescent conjugates for research use; contact our Custom and Bulk Sales Department for more information. Conjugations with phycobiliproteins and fluorescent polystyrene microspheres require unique procedures that are described in Section 6.4 and Section 6.5, respectively.

Molecular Probes also has what are probably the best reagents and kits for labeling oligonucleotides and nucleic acids (see details in Section 8.2), including:

- ARES™ DNA Labeling Kits (Section 8.2, Table 8.9), which permit the indirect labeling of DNA with a wide variety of our amine-reactive dyes
- Alexa Fluor® Oligonucleotide Amine Labeling Kits (Section 8.2, Table 8.10) for efficient labeling of 5′-amine-derivatized DNA or RNA oligonucleotides with our premier dyes
- ULYSIS Nucleic Acid Labeling Kits (Section 8.2, Table 8.8), which make labeling of nucleic acids as easy as protein labeling
- ChromaTide® UTP, ChromaTide® dUTP, aha-dUTP and ChromaTide® OBEA-dCTP nucleotides labeled with several of our best dyes or with biotin (Section 8.2; Table 8.6, Table 8.7), which can be incorporated into nucleic acids by a variety of enzymatic methods[2–5]

In addition, we offer amine-reactive versions of our SYBR® dyes (Section 8.2), which can be conjugated to oligonucleotides, nucleic acids, peptides or proteins that interact with nucleic acids or affinity matrices. The SYBR® dyes remain essentially nonfluorescent until complexed to nucleic acids.

Derivatizing Low Molecular Weight Molecules

Some amine-reactive probes described in this chapter are also important reagents for various bioanalytical applications, including amine quantitation, protein and nucleic acid sequencing and chromatographic and electrophoretic analysis of low molecular weight molecules. Reagents that are particularly useful for derivatizing low molecular weight amines — including fluorescamine, *o*-phthaldialdehyde, our ATTO-TAG™ reagents, NBD chloride and dansyl chloride — are discussed in Section 1.8. However, many of the reactive dyes described in Sections 1.2 to 1.7 can also be used as derivatization reagents; likewise, most of the derivatization reagents in Section 1.8 can be utilized for biomolecule conjugation.

Reactivity of Amino Groups

The amine-reactive probes described in this chapter are mostly acylating reagents that form carboxamides, sulfonamides or thioureas upon reaction with amines. The kinetics of the reaction depends on the reactivity and concentration of both the acylating reagent and the amine. Of course, buffers that contain free amines such as Tris and glycine must be avoided when using *any* amine-reactive probe. Ammonium sulfate that has been used for protein precipitation must also be removed before performing dye conjugations. In addition, high concentrations of nucleophilic thiols should be avoided because they may react with the reagent to form an unstable intermediate that could consume the dye. Reagents for reductive alkylation of amines (Figure 3.22) are described in Chapter 2 and Chapter 3.

The most significant factors affecting an amine's reactivity are its class and its basicity. Virtually all proteins have lysine residues, and most have a free amine at the N-terminus. Aliphatic amines such as lysine's ε-amino group are moderately basic and reactive with most acylating reagents. However, the concentration of the free base form of aliphatic amines below pH 8 is very low; thus, the kinetics of acylation reactions of amines by isothiocyanates, succinimidyl esters and other reagents are strongly pH dependent. A pH of 8.5 to 9.5 is usually optimal for modifying lysine residues. In contrast, the α-amino group at a protein's N-terminus usually has a pK_a of ~7, so it can sometimes be selectively modified by reaction at near neutral pH. Furthermore, although amine acylation should usually be carried out above pH 8.5, the acylation reagents tend to degrade in the presence of water, with the rate increasing as the pH increases. Protein modification by succinimidyl esters can typically be done at pH 8.5, whereas isothiocyanates usually require a pH >9 for optimal conjugations; this high pH may be a factor when working with base-sensitive proteins. DNA and most polysaccharides can be modified at a relatively basic pH if necessary.

Aromatic amines, which are uncommon in biomolecules, are very weak bases and thus unprotonated at pH 7. Modification of aromatic amines requires a highly reactive reagent, such as an isocyanate, isothiocyanate, sulfonyl chloride or acid halide, but can be done at any pH above ~4. A tyrosine residue (Section 3.1) can be selectively modified to form an *o*-aminotyrosine aromatic amine, which can then be reacted at a relatively low pH with certain amine-reactive probes[6–8] (Figure 3.3).

In aqueous solution, acylating reagents are virtually unreactive with the amide group of peptide bonds and the side-chain amides of glutamine and asparagine residues, the guanidinium group of arginine, the imidazolium group of histidine and the nonbasic amines, such as adenosine or guanosine, found in nucleotides and nucleic acids. The ULYSIS Kits described in Section 8.2 provide an alternative method for direct modification of guanosine residues in nucleic acids.

Isothiocyanates

Molecular Probes does not sell any isocyanate (R–NCO) reagents because they are very susceptible to deterioration during storage. However, some acyl azides (Section 3.1) are readily converted to isocyanates (Figure 3.7), which react with amines to form ureas. As an alternative to the unstable isocyanates, we offer a selection of isothiocyanates (R–NCS), which are moderately reactive but quite stable in water and most solvents. Isothiocyanates form thioureas upon reaction with amines (Figure 1.1). Although the thiourea product is reasonably stable, it has been reported that antibody conjugates prepared from fluorescent isothiocyanates deteriorate over time,[9] prompting us to use fluorescent succinimidyl esters and sulfonyl halides almost exclusively for synthesizing our bioconjugates. The thiourea formed by the reaction of fluorescein isothiocyanate (FITC) with amines is also susceptible to conversion to a guanidine by concentrated ammonia.[10] Despite the growing number of choices in amine-reactive fluorophores, fluorescein isothiocyanate and tetramethylrhodamine isothiocyanate (TRITC) are still widely used reactive fluorescent dyes for preparing fluorescent bioconjugates.

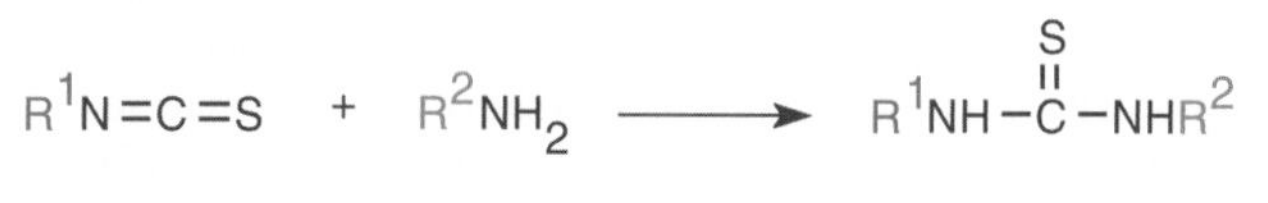

Figure 1.1 Reaction of a primary amine with an isothiocyanate.

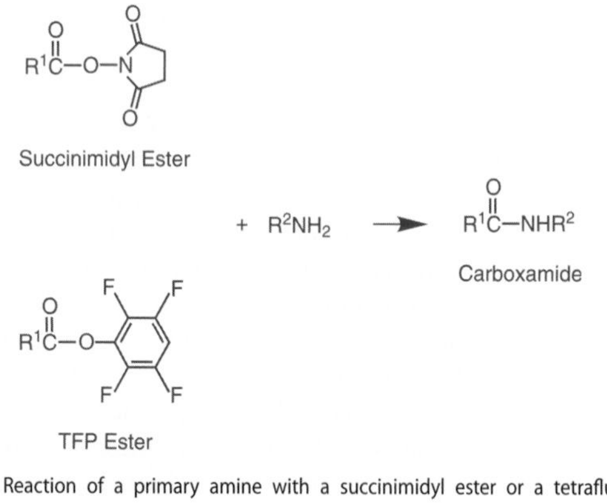

Figure 1.2 Reaction of a primary amine with a succinimidyl ester or a tetrafluorophenyl (TFP) ester.

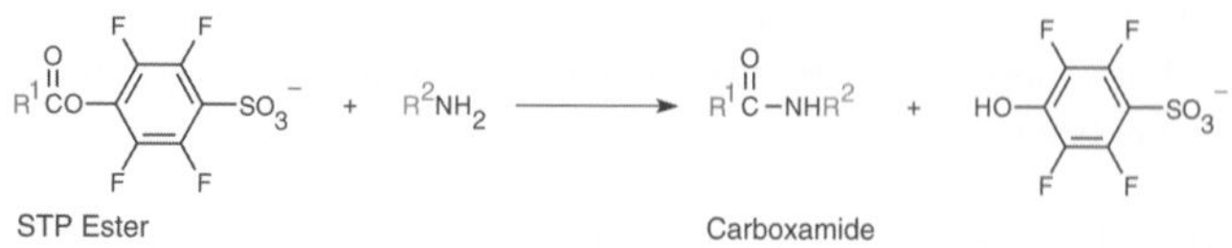

Figure 1.3 Reaction of a primary amine with an STP ester.

Active Esters and Carboxylic Acids

Succinimidyl Esters

Succinimidyl esters are excellent reagents for amine modification because the amide bonds they form (Figure 1.2) are as stable as peptide bonds. Molecular Probes has available over 100 succinimidyl esters of fluorescent dyes and nonfluorescent molecules, most of which have been developed within our own laboratories (Table 1.1, Table 1.2). These reagents are generally stable during storage if well desiccated, and show good reactivity with aliphatic amines and very low reactivity with aromatic amines, alcohols, phenols (including tyrosine) and histidine. Succinimidyl esters will also react with thiols in organic solvents to form thioesters. If formed in a protein, a thioester may transfer the acyl moiety to a nearby amine. Succinimidyl ester hydrolysis can compete with conjugation, but this side reaction is usually slow below pH 9.

Carboxylic Esters and Their Conversion into Sulfosuccinimidyl Esters and STP Esters

Some succinimidyl esters may not be compatible with a specific application because they can be quite insoluble in aqueous solution. To overcome this limitation, Molecular Probes also offers carboxylic acid derivatives of some of its fluorophores, which can be converted into sulfosuccinimidyl esters or STP esters. These sulfonated reagents have higher water solubility than simple succinimidyl esters and sometimes eliminate the need for organic solvents in the conjugation reaction. However, they are also more polar than succinimidyl esters, which makes them less likely to react with buried amines in proteins or to penetrate cell membranes. Because of their combination of reactivity and polarity, sulfosuccinimidyl esters are not easily purified by chromatographic means and thus only a few are currently available from Molecular Probes. Sulfosuccinimidyl esters can generally be prepared *in situ* simply by dissolving the carboxylic acid dye in an amine-free buffer that contains *N*-hydroxysulfosuccinimide (NHSS, H2249; Section 3.3) and 1-ethyl-3-(3-dimethylaminopropyl)carbodiimide (EDAC, E2247; Section 3.3). Addition of NHSS to the buffer has been shown to enhance the yield of carbodiimide-mediated conjugations[11] (Figure 3.24). STP esters (Figure 1.3) are prepared in the same way from 4-sulfo-2,3,5,6-tetrafluorophenol[12] (S10490, Section 3.3), and we find them to be more readily purified by chromatography than their sulfosuccinimidyl ester counterparts. The carboxylic acids may also be useful for preparing acid chlorides and anhydrides, which, unlike succinimidyl esters, can be used to modify aromatic amines and alcohols.

Tetrafluorophenyl (TFP) Esters

2,4,5,6-Tetrafluorophenyl (TFP) esters (Figure 1.2) appear to be more resistant to nonspecific hydrolysis than either succinimidyl esters (Figure 1.16) or sulfosuccinimidyl esters but to retain equal or superior reactivity with amines. At this time, the important Alexa Fluor® 488 carboxylic acid is the only fluorescent TFP ester available from Molecular Probes (A30005, Section 1.3).

Carbonyl Azides

Section 3.1 describes coumarin, fluorescein and tetramethylrhodamine carbonyl azides (D1446, M1445, F6218, T6219). Like succinimidyl esters, carbonyl azides are active esters that can react with amines to yield amides; however, a more common application of carbonyl azides is thermal rearrangement to a labile isocyanate (which can react with both aliphatic and aromatic amines to form ureas) for derivatizing alcohols and phenols (Section 3.1, Figure 3.7).

Sulfonyl Chlorides

Sulfonyl chlorides, including the dansyl, pyrene, Lissamine rhodamine B and Texas Red® derivatives, are highly reactive. These reagents are quite unstable in water, especially at the higher pH required for reaction with aliphatic amines. For example, we have determined that dilute Texas Red® sulfonyl chloride is totally hydrolyzed within 2–3 minutes in pH 8.3 aqueous solution at room temperature.[13] Protein modification by this reagent is best done at low temperature. Once conjugated, however, the sulfonamides that are formed (Figure 1.4) are extremely stable; they even survive complete protein hydrolysis (for example, dansyl end-group analysis[14]). Sulfonyl chlorides can also react with phenols (including tyrosine), aliphatic alcohols (including polysaccharides), thiols (such as cysteine) and imidazoles (such as histidine), but these reactions are not common in proteins or in aqueous solution. Sulfonyl chloride conjugates of thiols and imidazoles are generally unstable, and conjugates of aliphatic alcohols are subject to nucleophilic displacement.[15] Note that sulfonyl chlorides are unstable in dimethylsulfoxide (DMSO) and should never be used in that solvent.[16]

Other Amine-Reactive Reagents

Aldehydes react with amines to form Schiff bases. Notable aldehyde-containing reagents described in Section 1.7 include *o*-phthaldialdehyde (OPA), naphthalenedicarboxaldehyde (NDA) and the 3-acylquinolinecarboxaldehyde (ATTO-TAG™) reagents CBQCA and FQ devised by Novotny and collaborators.[17–19] All of these reagents are useful for the sensitive quantitation of amines in solution, as well as by HPLC and capillary electrophoresis. In addition, certain arylating reagents such as NBD chloride, NBD fluoride and dichlorotriazines react with both amines and thiols, forming bonds with amines that are particularly stable.

Figure 1.4 Reaction of a primary amine with a sulfonyl chloride.

References

1. Methods Cell Biol 29, 1 (1989); **2.** Genes Chromosomes Cancer 27, 418 (2000); **3.** J Cell Biol 151, 353 (2000); **4.** Anal Biochem 269, 21 (1999); **5.** Cytometry 20, 172 (1995); **6.** Eur J Biochem 132, 339 (1983); **7.** Biochem Int 22, 125 (1990); **8.** Biochemistry 18, 3589 (1979); **9.** Bioconjug Chem 6, 447 (1995); **10.** Bioconjug Chem 9, 627 (1998); **11.** Anal Biochem 156, 220 (1986); **12.** Tetrahedron Lett 40, 1471 (1999); **13.** Bioconjug Chem 7, 482 (1996); **14.** Methods Biochem Anal 18, 259 (1970); **15.** J Phys Chem 83, 3305 (1979); **16.** J Org Chem 31, 3880 (1966); **17.** Anal Chem 63, 408 (1991); **18.** Anal Chem 63, 413 (1991); **19.** J Chromatogr 499, 579 (1990).

1.2 Kits for Labeling Proteins and Nucleic Acids

Molecular Probes provides a vast number of stand-alone reagents for preparation of bioconjugates, most of which are described in detail in other sections of this chapter. This section describes the many specialized kits that we have developed for labeling proteins and nucleic acids with our premier dyes and haptens (Table 1.2, Table 1.3). As an alternative to direct conjugation of primary antibodies with our reactive dyes and haptens, we strongly recommend using our exclusive Zenon® technology (Section 7.3) to form labeled antibody complexes (Figure 7.59) (see Note 7.1 "Product Highlight: Guide to Labeling Antibodies with Alexa Fluor® Dyes" in Section 7.2). Zenon® labeling can be completed in minutes in quantitative yield starting with as little as submicrogram quantities of the antibody, and the conjugate brightness can be easily adjusted by modifying the stoichiometry of the reagents. Although technically not amine-reactive reagents, the Zenon® Antibody Labeling Kits that employ our dyes and biotin derivatives are listed in both Table 1.2 and Table 7.13.

Kits for Labeling Proteins with a Fluorescent Dye or Biotin

FluoReporter® Protein Labeling Kits

The FluoReporter® Protein Labeling Kits (Table 1.2, Table 1.3) facilitate research-scale preparation of protein conjugates labeled with some of our best dyes. Typically, labeling and purifying conjugates with the FluoReporter® Protein Labeling Kits can be completed in under three hours, with very little hands-on time. First, the amount of dye necessary for the desired protein sample is calculated using the guidelines outlined in the kit protocol. After dissolving the dye in DMSO, the calculated amount of dye is added to the protein and the reaction is incubated for 1–1.5 hours. Purification is easily accomplished using convenient spin columns designed for use with proteins

Table 1.2 — Succinimidyl esters and kits for labeling proteins and nucleic acids

Label	Fluorescence Color (Abs/Em) *	Succinimidyl Ester or Tetrafluorophenyl (TFP) Ester	Protein Labeling Kits	Zenon® Mouse IgG_1 Labeling Kit	Zenon® Mouse IgG_{2a} Labeling Kit
Alexa Fluor® 350	Blue (346/442)	A10168	A10170 (P), A20180 (Mab)	Z25000	Z25100
Marina Blue®	Blue (365/460)	M10165		Z25040	
Alexa Fluor® 405	Blue (402/421)	A30000, A30100		Z25013	Z25113
Pacific Blue™	Blue (410/455)	P10163		Z25041	
Alexa Fluor® 430	Yellow-green (433/539)	A10169	A10171 (P)	Z25001	
Fluorescein-EX	Green (494/518)	F6130	F10240 (P), F6433 (F)	Z25042	
FITC	Green (494/518)		F6434 (F)		
Alexa Fluor® 488	Green (495/519)	A20000 †, A20100 †, A30005 (TFP)	A10235 ‡ (P), A20181 ‡ (Mab)	Z25002, Z25090 (TSA)	Z25102
Oregon Green® 488	Green (496/524)	O6147, O6149	O10241 (P), F6153 (F)	Z25043	
Alexa Fluor® 500	Green (503/525)	A30001 †			
Oregon Green® 514	Green (511/530)	O6139	F6155 (F)		
Alexa Fluor® 514	Yellow-green (518/540)	A30002 †			
Alexa Fluor® 532	Yellow (532/554)	A20001, A20101MP	A10236 (P), A20182 (Mab)	Z25003	
Alexa Fluor® 546	Orange (556/573)	A20002 †, A20102 †	A10237 (P), A20183 (Mab)	Z25004	Z25104
Alexa Fluor® 555	Red-orange (555/565)	A20009, A20109	A20174 (P), A20187 (Mab)	Z25005	Z25105
Tetramethylrhodamine	Red-orange (555/580)	C2211, C6123, C1171 †, T6105 † (X)	F6163 (F)		
Rhodamine Red™-X	Red-orange (570/590)	R6160	F6161 (F)		
Alexa Fluor® 568	Red-orange (578/603)	A20003 †, A20103 †	A10238 (P), A20184 (Mab)	Z25006, Z25091 (TSA)	Z25106
Alexa Fluor® 594	Red (590/617)	A20004 †, A20104 †	A10239 (P), A20185 (Mab)	Z25007	Z25107
Texas Red®-X	Red (595/615)	T6134 †, T20175	T10244 (P), F6162 (F)	Z25045	
Alexa Fluor® 610	Red (612/628)	A30003, A30103			
Alexa Fluor® 633 §	Far-red (632/647)	A20005 †, A20105 †	A20170 (P)		
Alexa Fluor® 635 §	Far-red (633/647)				
Alexa Fluor® 647 §	Far-red (650/668)	A20006, A20106	A20173 (P), A20186 (Mab)	Z25008	Z25108
Alexa Fluor® 660 §	Near infrared (663/690)	A20007, A20107	A20171 (P)	Z25009	Z25109
Alexa Fluor® 680 §	Near infrared (679/702)	A20008, A20108	A20172 (P)	Z25010	Z25110
Alexa Fluor® 700 §	Near infrared (702/723)	A20010, A20110		Z25011	
Alexa Fluor® 750 §	Near infrared (749/775)	A20011, A20111			
Biotin-XX	NA	B1606, B6353	F2610 (FMB), F6347 (FB)	Z25052	Z25152
DNP–biotin	NA (364/none)	B2604	F6348 (F)		
DSB-X™ biotin	NA	NA	D20655 (D)	Z25053	

* Approximate absorption (Abs) and fluorescence emission (Em) maxima for conjugates, in nm. † Mixed isomers. ‡ These Alexa Fluor® 488 protein labeling kits contain the amine-reactive Alexa Fluor® 488 carboxylic acid TFP ester, whereas the Alexa Fluor® 488 kits for labeling nucleic acid and oligonucleotide contain the Alexa Fluor® 488 succinimidyl ester. § Human vision is insensitive to light beyond ~650 nm, and therefore it is not possible to view the far-red–fluorescent dyes by looking through the eyepiece of a conventional fluorescence

of molecular weight ≥30,000 daltons. The kit components, number of conjugations and conjugation principles are summarized in Table 1.3.

Easy-to-Use Protein Labeling Kits

Our easy-to-use protein labeling kits (Table 1.2, Table 1.3) provide a nearly effortless way to label proteins, especially IgG antibodies, with a fluorescent dye (Figure 1.5) (see Note 7.1 "Product Highlight: Guide to Labeling Antibodies with Alexa Fluor® Dyes" in Section 7.2). Simply add ~1 mg of protein (in a volume of ~500 µL and free of amine-containing buffers such as Tris) to one of the three included vials, which contain a premeasured quantity of amine-reactive dye and a magnetic stir bar. Because the reactive dyes used in these kits are water soluble, no organic solvents are required. Purification is accomplished on a gravity-feed size-exclusion column, which is supplied with the kit. Labeling and purification can be completed in about two hours, with very little hands-on time. The kit components, number of conjugations and conjugation principles are summarized in Table 1.3.

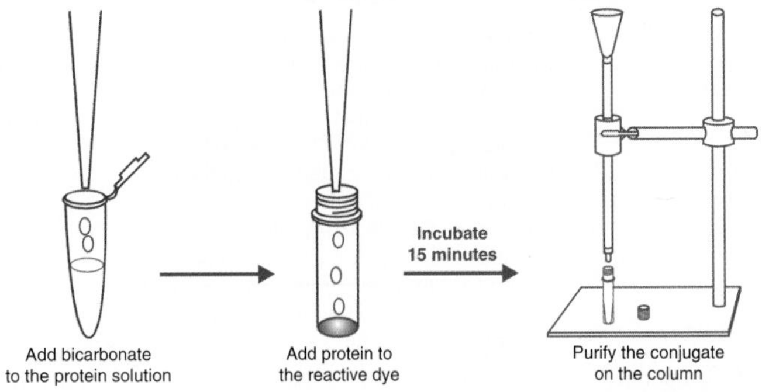
Incubate
15 minutes
Add bicarbonate
to the protein solution
Add protein to
the reactive dye
Purify the conjugate
on the column

Figure 1.5 Illustration of the three simple steps in the protocol for Molecular Probes' easy-to-use Protein Labeling Kits, which provide a convenient method for covalently labeling most proteins.

Zenon® Mouse IgG_{2b} Labeling Kit	Zenon® Rabbit IgG Labeling Kit	Zenon® Goat IgG Labeling Kit	Zenon® Human IgG Labeling Kit	ULYSIS Nucleic Acid Labeling Kit	ARES™ DNA Labeling Kit	Oligonucleotide Amine Labeling Kit
Z25200	Z25300		Z25400		A21675	A20190
	Z25340					
Z25213	Z25313					
	Z25341			U21658		
	Z25301					
	Z25342					
Z25202	Z25302	Z25602	Z25402	U21650	A21665	A20191
	Z25343			U21659		
	Z25303			U21651	A21666	A20192
Z25204	Z25304			U21652	A21667	A20193
Z25205	Z25305	Z25605	Z25405		A21677	A20197
Z25206	Z25306	Z25606		U21653	A21668	A20194
Z25207	Z25307	Z25607	Z25407	U21654	A21669	A20195
	Z25345					
Z25208	Z25308	Z25608	Z25408	U21660	A21676	A20196
Z25209	Z25309			U21656	A21671	
Z25210	Z25310			U21657	A21672	
	Z25311					
	Z25312					
Z25252	Z25352		Z25452			

microscope. (D) = DSB-X™ Biotin Protein Labeling Kit. (F) = FluoReporter® Protein Labeling Kit. (FB) = FluoReporter® Biotin-XX Protein Labeling Kit. (FMB) = FluoReporter® Mini-Biotin-XX Protein Labeling Kit. (Mab) = Monoclonal Antibody Labeling Kit. (P) = Easy-to-Use Protein Labeling Kit. (TFP) = Tetrafluorophenyl ester. (TSA) = Enhanced with TSA technology. (X) = An aminohexanoyl spacer between the dye and the SE. NA = Not applicable.

Table 1.3 — Molecular Probes' kits for protein and nucleic acid labeling

Kit Name	Kit Components	# Labelings	Conjugation Principle
Easy-to-Use Protein Labeling Kit	• Three vials of the succinimidyl ester of the corresponding fluorescent dye, each containing a magnetic stir bar • Sodium bicarbonate • Gravity-feed columns, a size-exclusion resin and concentrated elution buffer for conjugate purification • Column funnels, foam column holders, disposable pipettes and collection tubes • An easy-to-follow protocol for conjugation, purification and determination of the degree of labeling	Three ~1 mg protein samples of a 150,000-dalton protein, such as an IgG	A buffered solution of the protein is added to one of the three vials of the amine-reactive dye. The reactive dye has a succinimidyl ester moiety that reacts efficiently with primary amines of proteins to form stable dye–protein conjugates. Purification of the conjugate can be accomplished on the included gravity-feed size-exclusion columns.
FluoReporter® Protein Labeling Kit	• Five vials of the amine-reactive dye • Anhydrous DMSO • Reaction tubes, each containing a stir bar • Ten spin columns • Collection tubes • A detailed protocol	5 to 10 protein samples of 0.2 to 2 mg each in 200 µL volumes	The amount of dye necessary for the desired protein sample is calculated using the guidelines outlined in the kit protocol. The reactive dye has a succinimidyl ester moiety that reacts efficiently with primary amines of proteins to form stable dye–protein conjugates. Purification of the conjugate can be easily accomplished using the included spin columns.
Monoclonal Antibody Labeling Kit	• Five vials of the succinimidyl ester of the corresponding fluorescent dye • Sodium bicarbonate • Five spin columns and collection tubes • An easy-to-follow protocol for conjugation, purification and determination of the degree of labeling	Five labelings of ~100 µg each of carrier-free monoclonal IgG samples (although other proteins can be labeled)	A buffered solution of the protein is added to one of the five vials of amine-reactive dye. The reactive dye has a succinimidyl ester moiety that reacts efficiently with primary amines of proteins to form stable dye–protein conjugates. The conjugate can be purified on the included size-exclusion spin columns.
Zenon® Antibody Labeling Kit	See Section 7.3	See Section 7.3	See Section 7.3
ULYSIS Nucleic Acid Labeling Kit	• ULS labeling reagent and appropriate solvent • Labeling buffer • Deoxyribonuclease I (DNase I), for digesting DNA longer than 1000 base-pairs prior to labeling • DNase I storage and reaction buffers • Control DNA from calf thymus • Nuclease-free H_2O • A detailed protocol for preparing fluorescent DNA hybridization probes for chromosome *in situ* hybridization and dot-blot hybridization	20 labelings of 1 µg DNA	The ULS reagent reacts with the *N*-7 position of guanine residues to provide a stable coordination complex between the nucleic acid and the fluorophore label. Separation of the labeled nucleic acids from the unreacted ULS complex can be accomplished through a simple procedure using a spin column (not provided).
ARES™ DNA Labeling Kit	• 5-(3-Aminoallyl)-dUTP • Amine-reactive fluorescent dye and appropriate solvent • Sodium bicarbonate • Nuclease-free H_2O • A detailed protocol for labeling DNA using reverse transcriptase or nick translation	5 to 10 labelings of 1–5 µg DNA	In the first step, an amine-modified nucleotide, 5-(3-aminoallyl)-dUTP, is incorporated into DNA using conventional enzymatic labeling methods. In the second step, the amine-modified DNA is chemically labeled using an amine-reactive fluorescent dye. The amine-modified DNA can be purified using a commercially available purification kit (not provided).
Oligonucleotide Amine Labeling Kit	• Three vials of the amine-reactive dye • DMSO • Three vials of labeling buffer • A detailed protocol	Three labelings of 50 µg each of an amine-modified oligonucleotide	The reactive dye used in the labeling has an amine-reactive succinimidyl ester moiety that reacts efficiently with an amine-modified oligonucleotide. Following the labeling reaction, the conjugate can be purified from the reaction mixture by preparative gel electrophoresis or reverse-phase HPLC.
FluoReporter® Biotin-XX Protein Labeling Kit	• Biotin-XX, succinimidyl ester • DMSO • Gel filtration column • Avidin–HABA complex • Biotinylated goat IgG • A detailed protocol	Five biotinylation reactions, each with 5–20 mg of protein	The biotin-XX succinimidyl ester (SE) reacts with primary amines of proteins or other biomolecules to form stable biotin conjugates. The biotin-XX SE has a 14-atom spacer that enhances the binding of biotin derivatives to avidin's relatively deep binding sites. A gel filtration column is provided for purifying the labeled proteins from excess biotin reagent. After purification, the degree of biotinylation can be estimated using the included avidin–biotin displacement assay.
FluoReporter® Mini-Biotin-XX Protein Labeling Kit	• Biotin-XX, sulfosuccinimidyl ester • Reaction tubes, each containing a stir bar • Five spin columns • Collection tubes • Dialysis tubing • A detailed protocol	Five biotinylation reactions of 0.1 to 3 mg each	The biotin-XX sulfosuccinimidyl ester (SSE) is water soluble and reacts with primary amines of proteins or other biomolecules to form stable biotin conjugates. The biotin-XX SSE has a 14-atom spacer that enhances the binding of biotin derivatives to avidin's relatively deep binding sites. Ready-to-use spin columns are included for purification of the biotinylated protein from excess reagents.

Monoclonal Antibody Labeling Kits

Molecular Probes' Monoclonal Antibody Labeling Kits (Table 1.2, Table 1.3) provide researchers with a simple yet efficient means to label small amounts of IgG antibodies with our superior Alexa Fluor® dyes (Figure 1.6). Unlike polyclonal antibodies and most other commercially available proteins, monoclonal antibodies are typically only available in small quantities. These kits contain everything needed to perform five separate labeling reactions. Simply dissolve the carrier-free monoclonal antibody at ~1 mg/mL in the provided buffer, then add it to one of the five vials of amine-reactive dye. No organic solvents are required. Purification is accomplished on a size-exclusion spin column optimized for proteins of molecular weight ≥30,000 daltons. Labeling and purification can be completed in less than two hours. The kit components, number of conjugations and conjugation principles are summarized in Table 1.3. Mouse monoclonal antibodies in serum, in ascites fluid or diluted with carrier proteins should not be labeled with these kits; however, such antibody preparations can be efficiently labeled with our Zenon® Mouse IgG Labeling Kits (Section 7.3, Table 7.13). Similarly, our Zenon® Rabbit IgG, Goat IgG and Human IgG Labeling Kits (Section 7.3, Table 7.13) can be used to efficiently prepare labeling complexes from antibodies produced in these animals.

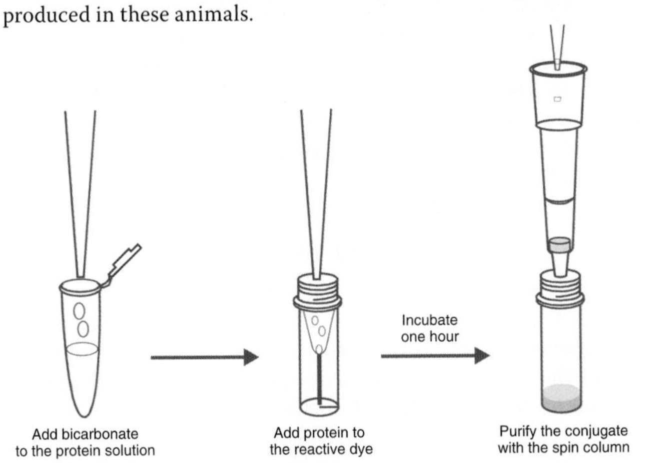
Add bicarbonate to the protein solution
Add protein to the reactive dye
Incubate one hour
Purify the conjugate with the spin column

Figure 1.6 Illustration of the three simple steps in the protocol for Molecular Probes' Monoclonal Antibody Labeling Kits, which provide a convenient method for covalently labeling small amounts of IgG antibodies.

FluoReporter® Biotin-XX Protein Labeling Kit

The FluoReporter® Biotin-XX Protein Labeling Kit (F2610, Table 1.3) is designed for five biotinylation reactions, each with 5 to 20 mg of protein; up to 100 mg of protein may be labeled. A gel filtration column is provided for purifying the labeled proteins from excess biotin reagent. Once purified, the degree of biotinylation can be determined using the included avidin–biotin displacement assay; biotinylated goat IgG is provided as a standard. The kit components, number of conjugations and conjugation principles are summarized in Table 1.3.

FluoReporter® Mini-Biotin-XX Protein Labeling Kit

The FluoReporter® Mini-Biotin-XX Protein Labeling Kit (F6347, Table 1.3) permits efficient biotinylation of small amounts of antibodies or other proteins. The water-soluble biotin-XX sulfosuccinimidyl ester has a 14-atom spacer (Figure 1.7) that enhances the binding of biotin derivatives to avidin's relatively deep binding sites. The ready-to-use spin columns provide a convenient method of purifying the biotinylated protein from excess reagents. The kit components, number of conjugations and conjugation principles are summarized in Table 1.3.

DSB-X™ Biotin Protein Labeling Kit

Our unique DSB-X™ biotin technology, which is described in detail in Section 7.6, permits the facile reversal of the virtually irreversible

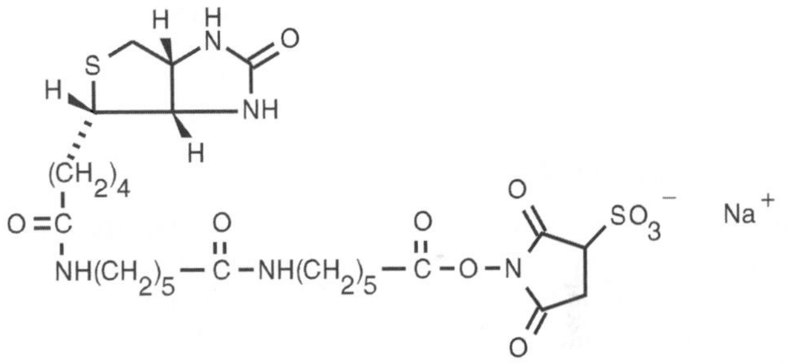

Figure 1.7 B6352 6-((6-((biotinoyl)amino)hexanoyl)amino)hexanoic acid, sulfosuccinimidyl ester, sodium salt (biotin-XX, SSE).

Table 1.3 — Molecular Probes' kits for protein and nucleic acid labeling — continued

Kit Name	Kit Components	# Labelings	Conjugation Principle
DSB-X™ Protein Labeling Kit	• DSB-X™ biotin, succinimidyl ester (five vials) • DMSO for dissolving the succinimidyl ester • Reaction tubes • Purification resin, spin columns and collection tubes for small-scale purifications • Dialysis tubing for larger-scale separations • A detailed protocol for conjugations and purifications	Five protein conjugations of 0.5–3 mg each	DSB-X™ biotin succinimidyl ester, a derivative of desthiobiotin with an additional seven-atom spacer, reacts with amine groups of biomolecules to form stable amides. The DSB-X™ biotin conjugate can be detected with avidin or streptavidin derivatives. Binding is almost totally reversed by addition of free biotin at neutral pH and normal ionic strength. Materials are included for both small- and large-scale preparations.
FluoReporter® Biotin/DNP Protein Labeling Kit	• DNP-X–biocytin-X, succinimidyl ester (five vials) • DMSO for dissolving the succinimidyl ester • Reaction tubes • Spin columns and collection tubes for small-scale purifications • A detailed protocol	5 to 10 labeling reactions of 0.2–2 mg of protein each.	The FluoReporter® Biotin/DNP Protein Labeling Kit is similar to our other FluoReporter® Protein Labeling Kits, except that it contains DNP-X–biocytin-X succinimidyl ester as the reactive label. When proteins are labeled with this chromophoric biotin derivative, the degree of biotinylation can be readily assessed from the extinction coefficient of DNP ($\epsilon_{360\ nm}$ = 15,000 $cm^{-1}M^{-1}$). An additional feature of the conjugates labeled with DNP-X–biocytin-X succinimidyl ester is that they can be recognized by avidin derivatives (or anti-biotin antibodies) and by anti-DNP antibodies, enabling researchers to choose among several detection techniques suitable for fluorescence and electron microscopy.

biotin–avidin interaction under extremely gentle conditions.[1] DSB-X™ biotin succinimidyl ester, a derivative of desthiobiotin (Figure 4.1) with an additional seven-atom spacer, reacts with amine groups of biomolecules to form stable amides. The DSB-X™ biotin conjugate can be detected with any of the avidin or streptavidin derivatives described in Section 7.6. Binding is almost totally reversed by addition of free biotin (B1595, B20656; Section 4.2) at neutral pH and normal ionic strength. Significantly, DSB-X™ biotin–conjugated biopolymers can be separated from complex mixtures using agarose affinity matrices (Figure 7.99) or the streptavidin conjugate of our Captivate™ ferrofluid superparamagnetic particles (C21476, Section 7.6, Figure 7.107). Magnetic separation can include cells targeted by the DSB-X™ biotin conjugate. Our DSB-X™ Bioconjugate Isolation Kits #1 and #2 (D20658, D20659; Section 7.6) provide the reagents and protocols for using DSB-X™ biotin conjugates. The DSB-X™ Biotin Protein Labeling Kit (D20655) contains the reagents required for five protein conjugations of 0.5–3 mg each. The kit components, number of conjugations and conjugation principles are summarized in Table 1.3.

FluoReporter® Biotin/DNP Protein Labeling Kit

The FluoReporter® Biotin/DNP Protein Labeling Kit (F6348, Table 1.2) provides the necessary reagents for labeling proteins with DNP-X–biocytin-X succinimidyl ester (Figure 4.4). The degree of biotinylation of proteins labeled with this reagent can be assessed from the optical absorbance of DNP (ε = 15,000 $cm^{-1}M^{-1}$ at ~360 nm). The conjugates are recognized by both avidin derivatives and anti-DNP antibodies, permitting a choice of detection techniques. Sufficient reagents are supplied for 5 to 10 labeling reactions of 0.2–2 mg of protein each.

Zenon® Antibody Labeling Kits

Our Zenon® Antibody Labeling Kits (Table 1.2, Table 7.13), which are described in detail in Section 7.3, are useful for the rapid and quantitative labeling of antibodies with dyes (including phycobiliproteins and their tandem conjugates), haptens (including both biotin and DSB-X™ biotin) and enzymes (Figure 7.59). Zenon® Antibody Labeling Kits are designed to label intact antibodies in amounts from less than 1 µg to as much as 50 µg, starting with a purified antibody fraction or with a crude antibody preparation such as serum, ascites fluid or a hybridoma supernatant. Multicolor labeling using multiple antibodies derived from the same species in the same protocol and using Zenon® labeled antibody complexes combined with direct conjugates are both very practical approaches. The Zenon® antibody labeling technology is discussed further in Section 7.3.

Nucleic Acid Labeling Kits

ARES™ DNA Labeling Kits

The ARES™ DNA Labeling Kits (Table 1.2, Table 8.9) provide a versatile, two-step method for labeling DNA with several of our premier fluorescent dyes[2] (Figure 8.45). In the first step, an amine-modified nucleotide, 5-(3-aminoallyl)-dUTP (Figure 8.47), is incorporated into DNA using conventional enzymatic labeling methods. This step ensures relatively uniform labeling of the probe with primary amine groups. The aminoallyl dUTP substrate used in this reaction is taken up efficiently by reverse transcription or nick translation, for which we provide the protocols; other enzymatic methods are also likely to be compatible. In the second step, the amine-modified DNA is chemically labeled using an amine-reactive fluorescent dye. This chemical reaction varies little in its efficiency from dye to dye, so that it is possible to use any combination of the ARES™ Kits, with their broad selection of the brightest and most photostable dyes, and obtain consistent DNA labeling. The labeling protocols provided generally result in about one dye per 12–15 bases, which we have determined to be optimal for fluorescence *in situ* hybridization (FISH) and dot-blot hybridization. See Section 8.2 for a complete description of the ARES™ Kits and Section 8.5 for applications of nucleic acid probes prepared using the ARES™ reagents.

Alexa Fluor® Oligonucleotide Amine Labeling Kits

The Alexa Fluor® Oligonucleotide Amine Labeling Kits (Section 8.2; Table 1.2, Table 1.3, Table 8.10) provide the reagents required for labeling synthetic oligonucleotides that have amine groups incorporated at their 5′-terminus. Following purification by standard chromatographic or electrophoretic procedures, these singly labeled oligonucleotides can serve as primers for a variety of applications. The dye-labeled oligonucleotides may also serve as either fluorescence resonance energy transfer (FRET) acceptors or donors in hybridization reactions (see Note 1.2 "Technical Focus: Fluorescence Resonance Energy Transfer (FRET)" in Section 1.3). The kit components, number of conjugations and conjugation principles are summarized in Table 1.3.

ULYSIS Nucleic Acid Labeling Kits

The ULYSIS Alexa Fluor® Nucleic Acid Labeling Kits (Section 8.2; Table 1.2, Table 1.3, Table 8.8) combine several of our Alexa Fluor® fluorophores with the versatile, patented Universal Linkage System (ULS) platinum-based chemistry developed at KREATECH Diagnostics, resulting in a simple, fail-safe method for producing fluorescent hybridization probes. The ULS method is based on the use of a platinum dye complex, patented by KREATECH Biotechnology BV, that forms a stable adduct with the *N*-7 position of guanine and, to a lesser extent, adenine bases in DNA, RNA, PNA and oligonucleotides (Figure 8.42). The labeling reaction takes only 15 minutes, and separation of the labeled nucleic acids from the unreacted ULS complex can be accomplished through use of a simple spin-column procedure (Figure 8.43). The kit components, number of conjugations and conjugation principles are summarized in Table 1.3.

In addition to the ULYSIS Alexa Fluor® Nucleic Acid Labeling Kits, we offer ULYSIS Kits containing our Pacific Blue™ and Oregon Green® 488 dyes (Table 1.2, Table 8.8). Probes labeled using the ULYSIS Kits are stable indefinitely and hybridize effectively to target DNA. The ULS method has been used to prepare labeled probes for dot, Southern and Northern blot analysis, RNA and DNA *in situ* hybridization, multicolor FISH, comparative genome hybridization (CGH) and microarray analysis.

References

1. Anal Biochem 308, 343 (2002); **2.** Biotechniques 36, 114 (2004).

Product List — 1.2 Kits for Labeling Proteins and Nucleic Acids

Cat #	Product Name	Unit Size
A20180	Alexa Fluor® 350 Monoclonal Antibody Labeling Kit *5 labelings*	1 kit
A20181	Alexa Fluor® 488 Monoclonal Antibody Labeling Kit *5 labelings*	1 kit
A20182	Alexa Fluor® 532 Monoclonal Antibody Labeling Kit *5 labelings*	1 kit
A20183	Alexa Fluor® 546 Monoclonal Antibody Labeling Kit *5 labelings*	1 kit
A20187	Alexa Fluor® 555 Monoclonal Antibody Labeling Kit *5 labelings*	1 kit
A20184	Alexa Fluor® 568 Monoclonal Antibody Labeling Kit *5 labelings*	1 kit
A20185	Alexa Fluor® 594 Monoclonal Antibody Labeling Kit *5 labelings*	1 kit
A20186	Alexa Fluor® 647 Monoclonal Antibody Labeling Kit *5 labelings*	1 kit
A20190	Alexa Fluor® 350 Oligonucleotide Amine Labeling Kit *3 labelings*	1 kit
A20191	Alexa Fluor® 488 Oligonucleotide Amine Labeling Kit *3 labelings*	1 kit
A20192	Alexa Fluor® 532 Oligonucleotide Amine Labeling Kit *3 labelings*	1 kit
A20193	Alexa Fluor® 546 Oligonucleotide Amine Labeling Kit *3 labelings*	1 kit
A20197	Alexa Fluor® 555 Oligonucleotide Amine Labeling Kit *3 labelings*	1 kit
A20194	Alexa Fluor® 568 Oligonucleotide Amine Labeling Kit *3 labelings*	1 kit
A20195	Alexa Fluor® 594 Oligonucleotide Amine Labeling Kit *3 labelings*	1 kit
A20196	Alexa Fluor® 647 Oligonucleotide Amine Labeling Kit *3 labelings*	1 kit
A10170	Alexa Fluor® 350 Protein Labeling Kit *3 labelings*	1 kit
A10171	Alexa Fluor® 430 Protein Labeling Kit *3 labelings*	1 kit
A10235	Alexa Fluor® 488 Protein Labeling Kit *3 labelings*	1 kit
A10236	Alexa Fluor® 532 Protein Labeling Kit *3 labelings*	1 kit
A10237	Alexa Fluor® 546 Protein Labeling Kit *3 labelings*	1 kit
A20174	Alexa Fluor® 555 Protein Labeling Kit *3 labelings*	1 kit
A10238	Alexa Fluor® 568 Protein Labeling Kit *3 labelings*	1 kit
A10239	Alexa Fluor® 594 Protein Labeling Kit *3 labelings*	1 kit
A20170	Alexa Fluor® 633 Protein Labeling Kit *3 labelings*	1 kit
A20173	Alexa Fluor® 647 Protein Labeling Kit *3 labelings*	1 kit
A20171	Alexa Fluor® 660 Protein Labeling Kit *3 labelings*	1 kit
A20172	Alexa Fluor® 680 Protein Labeling Kit *3 labelings*	1 kit
A21675	ARES™ Alexa Fluor® 350 DNA Labeling Kit *10 labelings*	1 kit
A21665	ARES™ Alexa Fluor® 488 DNA Labeling Kit *10 labelings*	1 kit
A21666	ARES™ Alexa Fluor® 532 DNA Labeling Kit *10 labelings*	1 kit
A21667	ARES™ Alexa Fluor® 546 DNA Labeling Kit *10 labelings*	1 kit
A21677	ARES™ Alexa Fluor® 555 DNA Labeling Kit *10 labelings*	1 kit
A21668	ARES™ Alexa Fluor® 568 DNA Labeling Kit *10 labelings*	1 kit
A21669	ARES™ Alexa Fluor® 594 DNA Labeling Kit *10 labelings*	1 kit
A21676	ARES™ Alexa Fluor® 647 DNA Labeling Kit *10 labelings*	1 kit
A21671	ARES™ Alexa Fluor® 660 DNA Labeling Kit *5-10 labelings*	1 kit
A21672	ARES™ Alexa Fluor® 680 DNA Labeling Kit *5-10 labelings*	1 kit
D20655	DSB-X™ Biotin Protein Labeling Kit *5 labelings*	1 kit
F6348	FluoReporter® Biotin/DNP Protein Labeling Kit *5-10 labelings*	1 kit
F2610	FluoReporter® Biotin-XX Protein Labeling Kit *5 labelings of 5-20 mg protein each*	1 kit
F6434	FluoReporter® FITC Protein Labeling Kit *5-10 labelings*	1 kit
F6433	FluoReporter® Fluorescein-EX Protein Labeling Kit *5-10 labelings*	1 kit
F6347	FluoReporter® Mini-biotin-XX Protein Labeling Kit *5 labelings of 0.1-3 mg protein each*	1 kit
F6153	FluoReporter® Oregon Green® 488 Protein Labeling Kit *5-10 labelings*	1 kit
F6155	FluoReporter® Oregon Green® 514 Protein Labeling Kit *5-10 labelings*	1 kit
F6161	FluoReporter® Rhodamine Red™-X Protein Labeling Kit *5-10 labelings*	1 kit
F6163	FluoReporter® Tetramethylrhodamine Protein Labeling Kit *5-10 labelings*	1 kit
F6162	FluoReporter® Texas Red®-X Protein Labeling Kit *5-10 labelings*	1 kit
F10240	Fluorescein-EX Protein Labeling Kit *3 labelings*	1 kit
O10241	Oregon Green® 488 Protein Labeling Kit *3 labelings*	1 kit
T10244	Texas Red®-X Protein Labeling Kit *3 labelings*	1 kit
U21650	ULYSIS® Alexa Fluor® 488 Nucleic Acid Labeling Kit *20 labelings*	1 kit
U21651	ULYSIS® Alexa Fluor® 532 Nucleic Acid Labeling Kit *20 labelings*	1 kit
U21652	ULYSIS® Alexa Fluor® 546 Nucleic Acid Labeling Kit *20 labelings*	1 kit
U21653	ULYSIS® Alexa Fluor® 568 Nucleic Acid Labeling Kit *20 labelings*	1 kit
U21654	ULYSIS® Alexa Fluor® 594 Nucleic Acid Labeling Kit *20 labelings*	1 kit
U21660	ULYSIS® Alexa Fluor® 647 Nucleic Acid Labeling Kit *20 labelings*	1 kit
U21656	ULYSIS® Alexa Fluor® 660 Nucleic Acid Labeling Kit *20 labelings*	1 kit
U21657	ULYSIS® Alexa Fluor® 680 Nucleic Acid Labeling Kit *20 labelings*	1 kit

For current prices or to order online, visit probes.invitrogen.com

Product List — 1.2 Kits for Labeling Proteins and Nucleic Acids — continued

Cat #	Product Name	Unit Size
U21659	ULYSIS® Oregon Green® 488 Nucleic Acid Labeling Kit *20 labelings*	1 kit
U21658	ULYSIS® Pacific Blue™ Nucleic Acid Labeling Kit *20 labelings*	1 kit
Z25400	Zenon® Alexa Fluor® 350 Human IgG Labeling Kit *50 labelings*	1 kit
Z25000	Zenon® Alexa Fluor® 350 Mouse IgG_1 Labeling Kit *50 labelings*	1 kit
Z25100	Zenon® Alexa Fluor® 350 Mouse IgG_{2a} Labeling Kit *50 labelings*	1 kit
Z25200	Zenon® Alexa Fluor® 350 Mouse IgG_{2b} Labeling Kit *50 labelings*	1 kit
Z25300	Zenon® Alexa Fluor® 350 Rabbit IgG Labeling Kit *50 labelings*	1 kit
Z25013	Zenon® Alexa Fluor® 405 Mouse IgG_1 Labeling Kit *50 labelings*	1 kit
Z25113	Zenon® Alexa Fluor® 405 Mouse IgG_{2a} Labeling Kit *50 labelings*	1 kit
Z25213	Zenon® Alexa Fluor® 405 Mouse IgG_{2b} Labeling Kit *50 labelings*	1 kit
Z25313	Zenon® Alexa Fluor® 405 Rabbit IgG Labeling Kit *50 labelings*	1 kit
Z25001	Zenon® Alexa Fluor® 430 Mouse IgG_1 Labeling Kit *50 labelings*	1 kit
Z25301	Zenon® Alexa Fluor® 430 Rabbit IgG Labeling Kit *50 labelings*	1 kit
Z25602	Zenon® Alexa Fluor® 488 Goat IgG Labeling Kit *50 labelings*	1 kit
Z25402	Zenon® Alexa Fluor® 488 Human IgG Labeling Kit *50 labelings*	1 kit
Z25002	Zenon® Alexa Fluor® 488 Mouse IgG_1 Labeling Kit *50 labelings*	1 kit
Z25102	Zenon® Alexa Fluor® 488 Mouse IgG_{2a} Labeling Kit *50 labelings*	1 kit
Z25202	Zenon® Alexa Fluor® 488 Mouse IgG_{2b} Labeling Kit *50 labelings*	1 kit
Z25302	Zenon® Alexa Fluor® 488 Rabbit IgG Labeling Kit *50 labelings*	1 kit
Z25003	Zenon® Alexa Fluor® 532 Mouse IgG_1 Labeling Kit *50 labelings*	1 kit
Z25303	Zenon® Alexa Fluor® 532 Rabbit IgG Labeling Kit *50 labelings*	1 kit
Z25004	Zenon® Alexa Fluor® 546 Mouse IgG_1 Labeling Kit *50 labelings*	1 kit
Z25104	Zenon® Alexa Fluor® 546 Mouse IgG_{2a} Labeling Kit *50 labelings*	1 kit
Z25204	Zenon® Alexa Fluor® 546 Mouse IgG_{2b} Labeling Kit *50 labelings*	1 kit
Z25304	Zenon® Alexa Fluor® 546 Rabbit IgG Labeling Kit *50 labelings*	1 kit
Z25605	Zenon® Alexa Fluor® 555 Goat IgG Labeling Kit *50 labelings*	1 kit
Z25405	Zenon® Alexa Fluor® 555 Human IgG Labeling Kit *50 labelings*	1 kit
Z25005	Zenon® Alexa Fluor® 555 Mouse IgG_1 Labeling Kit *50 labelings*	1 kit
Z25105	Zenon® Alexa Fluor® 555 Mouse IgG_{2a} Labeling Kit *50 labelings*	1 kit
Z25205	Zenon® Alexa Fluor® 555 Mouse IgG_{2b} Labeling Kit *50 labelings*	1 kit
Z25305	Zenon® Alexa Fluor® 555 Rabbit IgG Labeling Kit *50 labelings*	1 kit
Z25006	Zenon® Alexa Fluor® 568 Mouse IgG_1 Labeling Kit *50 labelings*	1 kit
Z25106	Zenon® Alexa Fluor® 568 Mouse IgG_{2a} Labeling Kit *50 labelings*	1 kit
Z25206	Zenon® Alexa Fluor® 568 Mouse IgG_{2b} Labeling Kit *50 labelings*	1 kit
Z25306	Zenon® Alexa Fluor® 568 Rabbit IgG Labeling Kit *50 labelings*	1 kit
Z25607	Zenon® Alexa Fluor® 594 Goat IgG Labeling Kit *50 labelings*	1 kit
Z25407	Zenon® Alexa Fluor® 594 Human IgG Labeling Kit *50 labelings*	1 kit
Z25007	Zenon® Alexa Fluor® 594 Mouse IgG_1 Labeling Kit *50 labelings*	1 kit
Z25107	Zenon® Alexa Fluor® 594 Mouse IgG_{2a} Labeling Kit *50 labelings*	1 kit
Z25207	Zenon® Alexa Fluor® 594 Mouse IgG_{2b} Labeling Kit *50 labelings*	1 kit
Z25307	Zenon® Alexa Fluor® 594 Rabbit IgG Labeling Kit *50 labelings*	1 kit
Z25020	Zenon® Alexa Fluor® 610–R-Phycoerythrin Mouse IgG_1 Labeling Kit *10 labelings*	1 kit
Z25608	Zenon® Alexa Fluor® 647 Goat IgG Labeling Kit *50 labelings*	1 kit
Z25408	Zenon® Alexa Fluor® 647 Human IgG Labeling Kit *50 labelings*	1 kit
Z25008	Zenon® Alexa Fluor® 647 Mouse IgG_1 Labeling Kit *50 labelings*	1 kit
Z25108	Zenon® Alexa Fluor® 647 Mouse IgG_{2a} Labeling Kit *50 labelings*	1 kit
Z25208	Zenon® Alexa Fluor® 647 Mouse IgG_{2b} Labeling Kit *50 labelings*	1 kit
Z25308	Zenon® Alexa Fluor® 647 Rabbit IgG Labeling Kit *50 labelings*	1 kit
Z25021	Zenon® Alexa Fluor® 647–R-Phycoerythrin Mouse IgG_1 Labeling Kit *10 labelings*	1 kit
Z25121	Zenon® Alexa Fluor® 647–R-Phycoerythrin Mouse IgG_{2a} Labeling Kit *10 labelings*	1 kit
Z25221	Zenon® Alexa Fluor® 647–R-Phycoerythrin Mouse IgG_{2b} Labeling Kit *10 labelings*	1 kit
Z25009	Zenon® Alexa Fluor® 660 Mouse IgG_1 Labeling Kit *50 labelings*	1 kit
Z25109	Zenon® Alexa Fluor® 660 Mouse IgG_{2a} Labeling Kit *50 labelings*	1 kit
Z25209	Zenon® Alexa Fluor® 660 Mouse IgG_{2b} Labeling Kit *50 labelings*	1 kit
Z25309	Zenon® Alexa Fluor® 660 Rabbit IgG Labeling Kit *50 labelings*	1 kit
Z25010	Zenon® Alexa Fluor® 680 Mouse IgG_1 Labeling Kit *50 labelings*	1 kit
Z25110	Zenon® Alexa Fluor® 680 Mouse IgG_{2a} Labeling Kit *50 labelings*	1 kit
Z25210	Zenon® Alexa Fluor® 680 Mouse IgG_{2b} Labeling Kit *50 labelings*	1 kit

For current prices or to order online, visit probes.invitrogen.com

Cat #	Product Name	Unit Size
Z25310	Zenon® Alexa Fluor® 680 Rabbit IgG Labeling Kit *50 labelings*	1 kit
Z25022	Zenon® Alexa Fluor® 680–R-Phycoerythrin Mouse IgG_1 Labeling Kit *10 labelings*	1 kit
Z25011	Zenon® Alexa Fluor® 700 Mouse IgG_1 Labeling Kit *50 labelings*	1 kit
Z25311	Zenon® Alexa Fluor® 700 Rabbit IgG Labeling Kit *50 labelings*	1 kit
Z25030	Zenon® Alexa Fluor® 700–Allophycocyanin Mouse IgG_1 Labeling Kit *10 labelings*	1 kit
Z25312	Zenon® Alexa Fluor® 750 Rabbit IgG Labeling Kit *50 labelings*	1 kit
Z25031	Zenon® Alexa Fluor® 750–Allophycocyanin Mouse IgG_1 Labeling Kit *10 labelings*	1 kit
Z25606	Zenon® Alexa Fluor® 568 Goat IgG Labeling Kit *50 labelings*	1 kit
Z25090	Zenon® Alexa Fluor® 488 Mouse IgG_1 Labeling Kit *enhanced with TSA™ technology* *25 labelings*	1 kit
Z25091	Zenon® Alexa Fluor® 568 Mouse IgG_1 Labeling Kit *enhanced with TSA™ technology* *25 labelings*	1 kit
Z25050	Zenon® Alkaline Phosphatase Mouse IgG_1 Labeling Kit *25 labelings*	1 kit
Z25150	Zenon® Alkaline Phosphatase Mouse IgG_{2a} Labeling Kit *25 labelings*	1 kit
Z25250	Zenon® Alkaline Phosphatase Mouse IgG_{2b} Labeling Kit *25 labelings*	1 kit
Z25350	Zenon® Alkaline Phosphatase Rabbit IgG Labeling Kit *25 labelings*	1 kit
Z25451	Zenon® Allophycocyanin Human IgG Labeling Kit *25 labelings*	1 kit
Z25051	Zenon® Allophycocyanin Mouse IgG_1 Labeling Kit *25 labelings*	1 kit
Z25151	Zenon® Allophycocyanin Mouse IgG_{2a} Labeling Kit *25 labelings*	1 kit
Z25251	Zenon® Allophycocyanin Mouse IgG_{2b} Labeling Kit *25 labelings*	1 kit
Z25351	Zenon® Allophycocyanin Rabbit IgG Labeling Kit *25 labelings*	1 kit
Z25452	Zenon® Biotin-XX Human IgG Labeling Kit *50 labelings*	1 kit
Z25052	Zenon® Biotin-XX Mouse IgG_1 Labeling Kit *50 labelings*	1 kit
Z25152	Zenon® Biotin-XX Mouse IgG_{2a} Labeling Kit *50 labelings*	1 kit
Z25252	Zenon® Biotin-XX Mouse IgG_{2b} Labeling Kit *50 labelings*	1 kit
Z25352	Zenon® Biotin-XX Rabbit IgG Labeling Kit *50 labelings*	1 kit
Z25053	Zenon® DSB-X™ Biotin Mouse IgG_1 Labeling Kit *50 labelings*	1 kit
Z25042	Zenon® Fluorescein Mouse IgG_1 Labeling Kit *50 labelings*	1 kit
Z25342	Zenon® Fluorescein Rabbit IgG Labeling Kit *50 labelings*	1 kit
Z25454	Zenon® Horseradish Peroxidase Human IgG Labeling Kit *25 labelings*	1 kit
Z25054	Zenon® Horseradish Peroxidase Mouse IgG_1 Labeling Kit *25 labelings*	1 kit
Z25154	Zenon® Horseradish Peroxidase Mouse IgG_{2a} Labeling Kit *25 labelings*	1 kit
Z25254	Zenon® Horseradish Peroxidase Mouse IgG_{2b} Labeling Kit *25 labelings*	1 kit
Z25354	Zenon® Horseradish Peroxidase Rabbit IgG Labeling Kit *25 labelings*	1 kit
Z25040	Zenon® Marina Blue® Mouse IgG_1 Labeling Kit *50 labelings*	1 kit
Z25340	Zenon® Marina Blue® Rabbit IgG Labeling Kit *50 labelings*	1 kit
Z25043	Zenon® Oregon Green® 488 Mouse IgG_1 Labeling Kit *50 labelings*	1 kit
Z25343	Zenon® Oregon Green® 488 Rabbit IgG Labeling Kit *50 labelings*	1 kit
Z25041	Zenon® Pacific Blue™ Mouse IgG_1 Labeling Kit *50 labelings*	1 kit
Z25341	Zenon® Pacific Blue™ Rabbit IgG Labeling Kit *50 labelings*	1 kit
Z25455	Zenon® R-Phycoerythrin Human IgG Labeling Kit *25 labelings*	1 kit
Z25055	Zenon® R-Phycoerythrin Mouse IgG_1 Labeling Kit *25 labelings*	1 kit
Z25155	Zenon® R-Phycoerythrin Mouse IgG_{2a} Labeling Kit *25 labelings*	1 kit
Z25255	Zenon® R-Phycoerythrin Mouse IgG_{2b} Labeling Kit *25 labelings*	1 kit
Z25355	Zenon® R-Phycoerythrin Rabbit IgG Labeling Kit *25 labelings*	1 kit
Z25045	Zenon® Texas Red®-X Mouse IgG_1 Labeling Kit *50 labelings*	1 kit
Z25345	Zenon® Texas Red®-X Rabbit IgG Labeling Kit *50 labelings*	1 kit
Z25460	Zenon® Tricolor Human IgG Labeling Kit #1 *for green, orange and deep red fluorescence imaging* *3 x 10 labelings*	1 kit
Z25470	Zenon® Tricolor Human IgG Labeling Kit #2 *for blue, green and red fluorescence imaging* *3 x 10 labelings*	1 kit
Z25060	Zenon® Tricolor Mouse IgG_1 Labeling Kit #1 *for green, orange and deep red fluorescence imaging* *3 x 10 labelings*	1 kit
Z25070	Zenon® Tricolor Mouse IgG_1 Labeling Kit #2 *for blue, green and red fluorescence imaging* *3 x 10 labelings*	1 kit
Z25080	Zenon® Tricolor Mouse IgG_1 Labeling Kit #3 *for flow cytometry, 488 nm excitation* *3 x 10 labelings*	1 kit
Z25160	Zenon® Tricolor Mouse IgG_{2a} Labeling Kit #1 *for green, orange and deep red fluorescence imaging* *3 x 10 labelings*	1 kit
Z25170	Zenon® Tricolor Mouse IgG_{2a} Labeling Kit #2 *for blue, green and red fluorescence imaging* *3 x 10 labelings*	1 kit
Z25180	Zenon® Tricolor Mouse IgG_{2a} Labeling Kit #3 *for flow cytometry, 488 nm excitation* *3 x 10 labelings*	1 kit
Z25260	Zenon® Tricolor Mouse IgG_{2b} Labeling Kit #1 *for green, orange and deep red fluorescence imaging* *3 x 10 labelings*	1 kit
Z25270	Zenon® Tricolor Mouse IgG_{2b} Labeling Kit #2 *for blue, green and red fluorescence imaging* *3 x 10 labelings*	1 kit
Z25280	Zenon® Tricolor Mouse IgG_{2b} Labeling Kit #3 *for flow cytometry, 488 nm excitation* *3 x 10 labelings*	1 kit
Z25360	Zenon® Tricolor Rabbit IgG Labeling Kit #1 *for green, orange and deep red fluorescence imaging* *3 x 10 labelings*	1 kit
Z25370	Zenon® Tricolor Rabbit IgG Labeling Kit #2 *for blue, green and red fluorescence imaging* *3 x 10 labelings*	1 kit

For current prices or to order online, visit probes.invitrogen.com

1.3 Alexa Fluor® Dyes Spanning the Visible and Infrared Spectrum

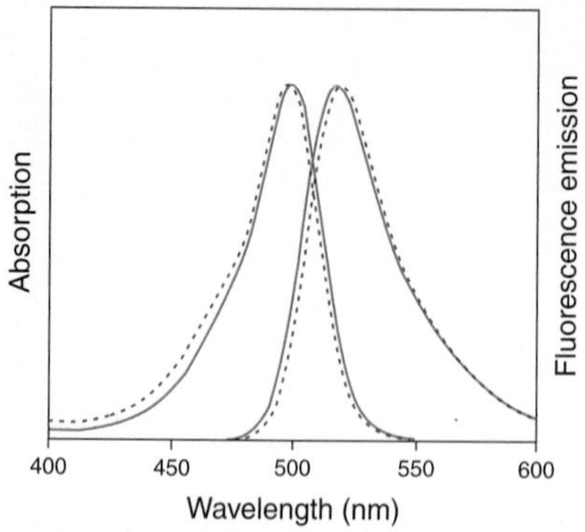

Figure 1.8 Absorption and fluorescence emission spectra of fluorescein goat anti–mouse IgG antibody (F2761, (—)) and Alexa Fluor® 488 goat anti–mouse IgG antibody (A11001, (---)). The fluorescence intensity of the Alexa Fluor® 488 conjugate was significantly higher than that of the fluorescein conjugate. The data are normalized to show the spectral similarity.

Molecular Probes' Alexa Fluor® dyes set new standards for fluorophores and the bioconjugates prepared from them (see Note 1.1 "Product Highlight: The Alexa Fluor® Dye Series — Peak Performance across the Visible Spectrum"). The absorption spectra (Figure 1.34, Figure 1.17, Figure 1.24) of these superior fluorescent dyes — Alexa Fluor® 350, Alexa Fluor® 405, Alexa Fluor® 430, Alexa Fluor® 488, Alexa Fluor® 500, Alexa Fluor® 514, Alexa Fluor® 532, Alexa Fluor® 546, Alexa Fluor® 555, Alexa Fluor® 568, Alexa Fluor® 594, Alexa Fluor® 610, Alexa Fluor® 633, Alexa Fluor® 635, Alexa Fluor® 647, Alexa Fluor® 660, Alexa Fluor® 680, Alexa Fluor® 700 and Alexa Fluor® 750 dyes — cover the entire spectrum and match the principal output wavelengths of common excitation sources.[1,2]

With spectra almost identical to those of fluorescein (Figure 1.8), but with far greater fluorescence in its conjugates and significantly better photostability, the Alexa Fluor® 488 dye is indisputably the best green-fluorescent reactive dye available. Spectra of the Alexa Fluor® 555 dye are an almost perfect match to those of the Cy3 dye (Figure 1.18), but bioconjugates of the Alexa Fluor® 555 dye are more fluorescent (Figure 1.29) and more photostable (Figure 1.20) than those of the Cy3 dye. Similarly, spectra of the Alexa Fluor® 647 conjugates substantially match those of the Cy5 dye (Figure 1.25) and the Alexa Fluor® 680 and Alexa Fluor® 750 dyes match the spectral properties of the Cy5.5 and Cy7 dyes, respectively (Figure 1.26, Figure 1.27); however, the Alexa Fluor® dyes usually provide superior performance, particularly in their protein and nucleic acid conjugates. Tandem conjugates of the Alexa Fluor® dyes with other dyes to form bifluorophores (DyeMer™ conjugates; Section 7.2, Section 7.6) and with R-phycoerythrin and allophycocyanin (Section 6.4) further expand the utility of the Alexa Fluor® dyes in multicolor applications (Figure 6.34, Figure 6.37).

Our exclusive Zenon® Antibody Labeling Kits, which are available for most of the Alexa Fluor® dyes (Table 1.2, Table 7.13), make it possible to rapidly and quantitatively label antibodies from a purified antibody fraction or from a crude antibody preparation such as serum, ascites fluid or a hybridoma supernatant (Figure 7.59). The Zenon® Antibody Labeling Kits and the Zenon® technology are described in detail in Section 7.3.

The Alexa Fluor® series of dyes shares several significant attributes, including:

- High absorbance at wavelengths of maximal output of common excitation sources
- Bright and unusually photostable fluorescence of their bioconjugates
- Good water solubility of the reactive dyes for ease of conjugation and resistance of the conjugates to precipitation and aggregation
- Insensitivity of their spectra to pH over a broad range
- Well-differentiated spectra, providing many options for multicolor detection and fluorescence resonance energy transfer (see Note 1.2 "Technical Focus: Fluorescence Resonance Energy Transfer (FRET)")
- Extremely high FRET efficiency, with calculated R_0 values of up to 84 Å between pairs of Alexa Fluor® dyes (Table 1.4) and up to 77 Å between Alexa Fluor® dyes and some nonfluorescent quenchers (Table 1.10)

Table 1.4 — R_0 values for some Alexa Fluor® dyes *

Donor	Acceptor					
	Alexa Fluor® 488	Alexa Fluor® 546	Alexa Fluor® 555	Alexa Fluor® 568	Alexa Fluor® 594	Alexa Fluor® 647
Alexa Fluor® 350	50					
Alexa Fluor® 488	NA	64	70	62	60	56
Alexa Fluor® 546		NA		70	71	74
Alexa Fluor® 555			NA		47	51
Alexa Fluor® 568				NA		82
Alexa Fluor® 594					NA	85
Alexa Fluor® 647						NA

* R_0 values in angstroms (Å) represent the distance at which fluorescence resonance energy transfer from the donor dye to the acceptor dye is 50% efficient. Values were calculated from spectroscopic data as outlined (see Note 1.2 "Technical Focus: Fluorescence Resonance Energy Transfer (FRET)" in Section 1.3). NA = Not applicable.

Note 1.1 — Product Highlight

The Alexa Fluor® Dye Series — Peak Performance across the Visible Spectrum

The Alexa Fluor® dyes — a series of superior fluorescent dyes that span the visible spectrum — represent a major breakthrough in the development of fluorescent labeling reagents,[1,2] especially when combined with our multipurpose Zenon® technology (Section 7.3) and nucleic acid detection methods (Section 8.5). These dyes, without exception, produce the best and brightest conjugates we have ever tested. Benefits of the Alexa Fluor® dyes and their conjugates include:

- **Brightness** — Alexa Fluor® conjugates exhibit more intense fluorescence than other spectrally similar conjugates
- **Photostability** — Alexa Fluor® conjugates are more photostable than most other fluorescent conjugates, allowing more time for image capture (Figure 1.10, Figure 1.11)
- **Instrument compatibility** — Absorption spectra of the Alexa Fluor® conjugates are matched to the principal output wavelengths of common excitation sources
- **Color selection** — Alexa Fluor® conjugates are available in several distinct fluorescent colors, ranging from blue to red
- **pH insensitivity** — Alexa Fluor® dyes remain highly fluorescent over a broad pH range
- **Water solubility** — Alexa Fluor® reactive dyes have good water solubility, so protein conjugations can be performed without organic solvents, and the conjugates are relatively resistant to precipitation during storage

Alexa Fluor® 350 Dye — Bright Blue and UV Light–Excitable

The blue-fluorescent Alexa Fluor® 350 dye produces conjugates that are typically greater than 50% more fluorescent than conjugates prepared from AMCA (Figure 7.34). Furthermore, because Alexa Fluor® 350 conjugates have slightly shorter-wavelength emission maxima than AMCA conjugates (442 nm versus 448 nm), the fluorescence of Alexa Fluor® 350 conjugates is better separated from that of commonly used green fluorophores (Figure 1.94, Figure 7.2).

Alexa Fluor® 405 Dye — A Near-Perfect Match to the Blue Laser Diode

With excitation/emission maxima of 402/421 nm, our Alexa Fluor® 405 dye (Figure 7.3) is a near-perfect match to the 405 nm spectral line of the blue diode laser recently developed for fluorescence microscopy and flow cytometry. The Alexa Fluor® 405 succinimidyl ester is an amine-reactive derivative of our Cascade Blue® dye, which was previously available in amine-reactive form only as an acetyl azide. Not only is it offered at higher purity than is Cascade Blue® acetyl azide, but the Alexa Fluor® 405 succinimidyl ester also contains a 4-piperidinecarboxylic acid spacer that separates the fluorophore from its reactive moiety, minimizing any interactions between the fluorophore and the biomolecule to which it is conjugated.

Alexa Fluor® 430 Dye — Absorption at 430 nm with a High Stokes Shift

Few reactive dyes that absorb between 400 nm and 450 nm have appreciable fluorescence beyond 500 nm in aqueous solution. Our Alexa Fluor® 430 dye fills this spectral gap. Excitation near its absorption maximum at ~430 nm is accompanied by strong emission near 540 nm (Figure 7.4, Figure 7.96).

Alexa Fluor® 488 Dye — The Best Green Fluorophore

Protein conjugates prepared with the Alexa Fluor® 488 dye are far superior to conjugates of fluorescein, and are indeed much better than conjugates of any other green fluorophore that we have tested, including those of the Cy2 dye (Figure 7.39). Not only are Alexa Fluor® 488 conjugates significantly brighter than fluorescein conjugates (Figure 1.13), they are *much* more photostable (Figure 1.9, Figure 1.10, Figure 1.11, Figure 1.53). Furthermore, fluorescence of the Alexa Fluor® 488 fluorophore is independent of pH from 4 to 10. This pH insensitivity is a major improvement over fluorescein, which emits fluorescence that is significantly affected by pH (Figure 1.12, Figure 7.42, Figure 7.5).

Alexa Fluor® 500 and Alexa Fluor® 514 Dyes — Two Green Fluorophores for Optical Separation Systems

The green-fluorescent Alexa Fluor® 500 and Alexa Fluor® 514 dyes are specifically designed to be detected simultaneously with other green fluorophores, despite their spectral overlap (Figure 7.6, Figure 7.7). Though they appear similar in color by eye, the Alexa Fluor® 500 dye can be optically separated from the Alexa Fluor® 514 dye using the Zeiss META system or similar spectral imaging instruments with linear-unmixing software; these instruments have the capability of differentiating between fluorescence emission maxima <5 nm apart. Similarly, the fluorescent signal from the Alexa Fluor® 514 dye can be resolved from both the Alexa Fluor® 488 and the Alexa Fluor® 500 fluorescence emissions. Furthermore, the photostable and pH-insensitive Alexa Fluor® 514 dye is probably the best fluorophore available for the 514 nm spectral line of the argon-ion laser.

Alexa Fluor® 532 Dye — The Optimal Dye for 532 nm Excitation Sources

With excitation and emission spectra intermediate between those of the green-fluorescent Alexa Fluor® 488 dye and orange-fluorescent Alexa Fluor® 546 dye (Figure 7.8), the Alexa Fluor® 532 dye and its conjugates are ideal for use with 532 nm excitation sources, including the frequency-doubled Nd:YAG laser (Figure 11.17).

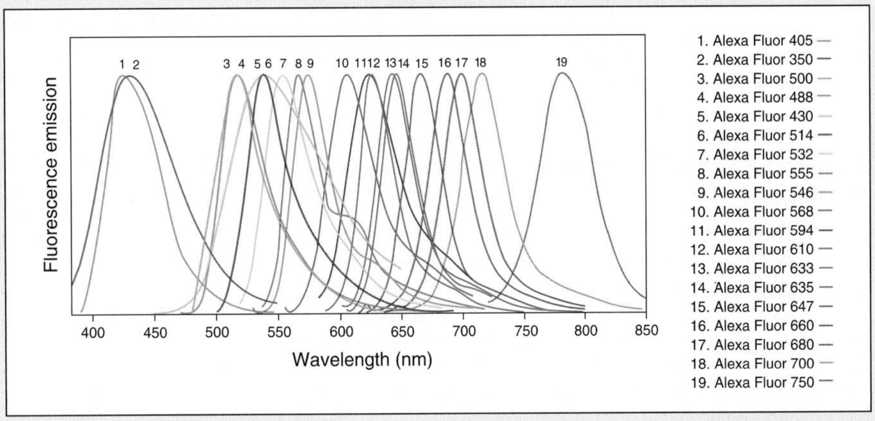

Emission spectra for the Alexa Fluor® dye series.

continued on next page

Important Licensing Information
These products may be covered by one or more Limited Use Label Licenses (See the Invitrogen Web site, www.invitrogen.com, or the Molecular Probes Web site, probes.invitrogen.com). By the use of these products you accept the terms and conditions of all applicable Limited Use Label Licenses. All products are for research use only. CAUTION: Not intended for human or animal diagnostic or therapeutic uses.

continued from previous page

Alexa Fluor® 546 Dye — A More Fluorescent Alternative to Cy3 and Tetramethylrhodamine

Conjugates prepared with the Alexa Fluor® 546 dye are perfect for applications that require fluorescent probes that emit in the orange region of the spectrum. These intensely fluorescent conjugates outperform conjugates of tetramethylrhodamine (TRITC and TAMRA) and Cy3 (Figure 1.23, Figure 12.27) and are readily excited by the strong 546 nm emission of mercury-arc lamps (Figure 7.9, Figure 7.91).

Alexa Fluor® 555 Dye — A Superior Alternative to the Cy3 Dye

Spectra of the Alexa Fluor® 555 conjugates virtually match those of the Cy3 dye (Figure 1.18, Figure 7.10), resulting in an optimal match to filters designed for that dye. However, total fluorescence of Alexa Fluor® 555 conjugates is higher (Figure 1.22, Figure 1.29). The Alexa Fluor® 555 dye is also more photostable than Cy 3 (Figure 1.20), providing researchers with additional time for image capture.[1]

Alexa Fluor® 568 Dye — Perfect for 568 nm Excitation Sources

The red-orange–fluorescent Alexa Fluor® 568 dye is optimally excited by the 568 nm spectral line of the Ar–Kr mixed-gas laser used in many confocal laser-scanning microscopes. Alexa Fluor® 568 conjugates are considerably brighter than Lissamine Rhodamine B conjugates or even Rhodamine Red™-X conjugates, which have similar excitation and emission maxima (Figure 1.19, Figure 7.11).

Alexa Fluor® 594 Dye — A Superior Alternative to the Texas Red® Dye

Conjugates prepared from the Alexa Fluor® 594 dye emit in the red region of the spectrum (Figure 7.12), making them particularly useful for multilabeling experiments in combination with green-fluorescent probes. Alexa Fluor® 594 conjugates are much more fluorescent than are Texas Red® conjugates (Figure 1.21, Figure 7.42).

Alexa Fluor® 610 Dye — The Red Jewel of the Alexa Fluor® Dyes

Our bright and photostable Alexa Fluor® 610 dye emits an intense red fluorescence that can be visualized with the same optics used for the Texas Red® and Alexa Fluor® 594 dyes. With excitation/emission maxima of 612/628 nm (Figure 7.13), the Alexa Fluor® 610 dye can be easily differentiated from green fluorophores, making it an ideal candidate for multicolor labeling. Unlike the fluorescence of the Alexa Fluor® 633 dye and longer-wavelength fluorophores, fluorescence of the Alexa Fluor® 610 dye can still be seen with the human eye. We have principally utilized the Alexa Fluor® 610 dye to prepare tandem conjugates of phycobiliproteins with improved spectral properties (Section 6.4).

Alexa Fluor® 633 Dye — The Optimal Dye for the 633 nm He–Ne Laser Line

Far-red–fluorescent dyes are among the most sought-after labels for fluorescence imaging because their spectra are well beyond the range of most sample autofluorescence. The growing popularity of the 633 nm spectral line of the He–Ne laser and the 635 nm spectral line of red diode lasers prompted us to create compatible dyes. Although their fluorescence is not visible to the human eye, Alexa Fluor® 633 conjugates are bright and photostable, with peak absorption centered at 632 nm and a peak emission at 650 nm[1] (Figure 7.14).

Alexa Fluor® 647 Dye — A Superior Alternative to the Cy5 Dye

Spectra of the Alexa Fluor® 647 conjugates virtually match those of the Cy5 dye (Figure 1.25), resulting in an optimal match to optical filters designed for that dye. However, total fluorescence of the secondary antibody conjugates of the Alexa Fluor® 647 dye is significantly higher than that of Cy5 conjugates supplied by other companies (Figure 1.32, Figure 1.30, Figure 1.31). Also, unlike the Cy5 dye, the Alexa Fluor® 647 dye has very little change in absorbance or fluorescence spectra when conjugated to most proteins, oligonucleotides and nucleic acids (Figure 1.33), thus yielding greater total fluorescence at the same degree of substitution.[1]

Alexa Fluor® 660 Dye — An Excellent Dye for the 647 nm Krypton-Ion Laser Line

The Alexa Fluor® 660 dye is optimally excited by the 647 nm spectral line of the krypton-ion laser and well excited by the 633 nm spectral line of the He–Ne laser. Protein conjugates of the Alexa Fluor® 660 dye produce bright far-red–fluorescence emission, with a peak at 690 nm. The wide separation of its emission from that of other fluorophores allows use of the Alexa Fluor® 660 dye with other fluorescent labels, including the Alexa Fluor® 546 and Cy3 dyes and phycoerythrin conjugates (Figure 7.17). The Alexa Fluor® 660 dye is the dye of choice as a "second label" with allophycocyanin (APC) conjugates in flow cytometry applications.

Alexa Fluor® 680 Dye — An Alternative to the Cy5.5 Dye

With a peak excitation at 679 nm and maximum emission at 702 nm, the Alexa Fluor® 680 dye is spectrally similar to the Cy5.5 dye (Figure 1.26). Fluorescence emission of the Alexa Fluor® 680 dye is well separated from that of other commonly used red fluorophores, such as the tetramethylrhodamine, Texas Red®, R-phycoerythrin, Alexa Fluor® 594 and Alexa Fluor® 647 dyes, making it ideal for three- and four-color labeling[1] (Figure 7.18).

Alexa Fluor® 700 Dye — The Optimal Dye for Far-Red Diode Lasers

With an absorption maximum at 696 nm, the Alexa Fluor® 700 dye can be excited with a xenon-arc lamp, far-red diode lasers or dye-pumped lasers operating in the 675–700 nm range. The Alexa Fluor® 700 dye provides infrared fluorescence emission, with a peak at 719 nm (Figure 7.19).

Alexa Fluor® 750 Dye — Our Longest-Wavelength Alexa Fluor® Dye

Spectrally similar to the Cy7 dye (Figure 1.27), the Alexa Fluor® 750 dye is the longest-wavelength Alexa Fluor® dye currently available. Its fluorescence emission maximum at 779 nm is well separated from commonly used far-red fluorophores such as Alexa Fluor® 647, Alexa Fluor® 660 or allophycocyanin (APC), facilitating multicolor analysis. With a peak excitation at ~752 nm, conjugates of the Alexa Fluor® 700 dye are well excited by a xenon-arc lamp or dye-pumped lasers operating in the 720–750 nm range (Figure 7.20).

References

1. J Histochem Cytochem 51, 1699 (2003); **2.** J Histochem Cytochem 47, 1179 (1999).

Note 1.2 — Technical Focus

Fluorescence Resonance Energy Transfer (FRET)

Fluorescence resonance energy transfer (FRET) is a distance-dependent interaction between the electronic excited states of two dye molecules in which excitation is transferred from a donor molecule to an acceptor molecule *without emission of a photon*. The efficiency of FRET is dependent on the inverse sixth power of the intermolecular separation,[1] making it useful over distances comparable with the dimensions of biological macromolecules. Thus, FRET is an important technique for investigating a variety of biological phenomena that produce changes in molecular proximity.[2–11] When FRET is used as a contrast mechanism, colocalization of proteins and other molecules can be imaged with spatial resolution beyond the limits of conventional optical microscopy.[12,13]

Primary Conditions for FRET

- Donor and acceptor molecules must be in close proximity (typically 10–100 Å).
- The absorption spectrum of the acceptor must overlap the fluorescence emission spectrum of the donor (see Figure).
- Donor and acceptor transition dipole orientations must be approximately parallel.

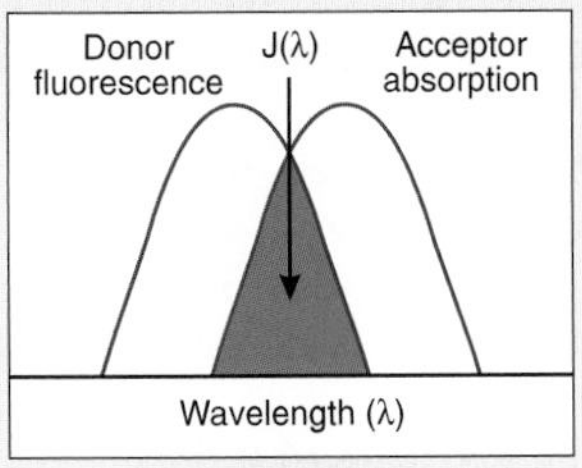

Schematic representation of the FRET spectral overlap integral.

Förster Radius

The distance at which energy transfer is 50% efficient (i.e., 50% of excited donors are deactivated by FRET) is defined by the Förster radius (R_o). The magnitude of R_o is dependent on the spectral properties of the donor and acceptor dyes (see Table):

$$R_o = [8.8 \times 10^{23} \cdot \kappa^2 \cdot n^{-4}\, QY_D \cdot J(\lambda)]^{1/6}\ Å$$

where κ^2 = dipole orientation factor (range 0–4; $\kappa^2 = {}^2/_3$ for randomly oriented donors and acceptors)

QY_D = fluorescence quantum yield of the donor in the absence of the acceptor

n = refractive index

$J(\lambda)$ = spectral overlap integral (see figure)

$= \int \varepsilon_A(\lambda) \cdot F_D(\lambda) \cdot \lambda^4 d\lambda\ cm^3M^{-1}$

where ε_A = extinction coefficient of acceptor

F_D = fluorescence emission intensity of donor as a fraction of the total integrated intensity

Typical Values of R_o

Donor	Acceptor	R_o (Å)
Fluorescein	Tetramethylrhodamine	55
IAEDANS	Fluorescein	46
EDANS	Dabcyl	33
Fluorescein	Fluorescein	44
BODIPY® FL	BODIPY® FL	57
Fluorescein	QSY® 7 and QSY® 9 dyes	61

Donor/Acceptor Pairs

In most applications, the donor and acceptor dyes are different, in which case FRET can be detected by the appearance of sensitized fluorescence of the acceptor or by quenching of donor fluorescence. When the donor and acceptor are the same, FRET can be detected by the resulting fluorescence depolarization.[14] Typical values of R_o for some dye pairs are listed in the table above and more extensive compilations are in Table 1.4 and Table 1.10. Note that because the component factors of R_o (see above) are dependent on the environment, the actual value observed in a specific experimental situation is somewhat variable. Extensive compilations of R_o values can be found in the literature.[3,8,9,11] Nonfluorescent acceptors such as dabcyl and our QSY® dyes (Table 1.9) have the particular advantage of eliminating the potential problem of background fluorescence resulting from direct (i.e., nonsensitized) acceptor excitation. FRET efficiencies from several donor dyes to the QSY® 7 quencher in molecular beacon hybridization probes have been calculated.[15] Probes incorporating fluorescent donor–nonfluorescent acceptor combinations have been developed primarily for detecting proteolysis [16] (Figure 10.10) and nucleic acid hybridization [15,17,18] (Figure 8.113, Figure 8.114).

Selected Applications of FRET

- Structure and conformation of proteins [19–24]
- Spatial distribution and assembly of protein complexes [25–29]
- Receptor/ligand interactions [30–34]
- Immunoassays [35,36]
- Probing interactions of single molecules [37]
- Structure and conformation of nucleic acids [38–43]
- Real-time PCR assays and SNP detection [44–49] (Figure 8.115, Figure 8.116, Figure 8.117)
- Detection of nucleic acid hybridization [17,18,50–53] (Figure 8.113)
- Primer-extension assays for detecting mutations [54] (Figure 8.116)
- Automated DNA sequencing [55–57]
- Distribution and transport of lipids [58–60]
- Membrane fusion assays [61–64] (see Note 13.1 "Technical Focus: Lipid-Mixing Assays of Membrane Fusion" in Section 13.2)
- Membrane potential sensing [65]
- Fluorogenic protease substrates [16,66–69]
- Indicators for cyclic AMP [70,71] and zinc [72]

References

1. Proc Natl Acad Sci U S A 58, 719 (1967); **2.** Biophys J 84, 3992 (2003); **3.** Resonance Energy Transfer Theory and Data, Van der Meer BS, et al. pp. 133–168 (1994); **4.** J Struct Biol 115, 175 (1995); **5.** Photochem Photobiol 38, 487 (1983); **6.** Annu Rev Biochem 47, 819 (1978); **7.** Methods Enzymol 246, 300 (1995); **8.** Anal Biochem 218, 1 (1994); **9.** Methods Enzymol 48, 347 (1978); **10.** Scanning 17, 72 (1995); **11.** J Muscle Res Cell Motil 8, 97 (1987); **12.** Methods 24, 289 (2001); **13.** Biophys J 74, 2702 (1998); **14.** Biophys J 69, 1569 (1995); **15.** Nucleic Acids Res 30, e122 (2002); **16.** Science 247, 954 (1990); **17.** Nat Biotechnol 14, 303 (1996); **18.** Nat Biotechnol 16, 49 (1998); **19.** Biophys J 74, 3111 (1998); **20.** Biochemistry 35, 4795 (1996); **21.** Biochemistry 34, 8693 (1995); **22.** Biochemistry 34, 6475 (1995); **23.** J Biol Chem 273, 9119 (1998); **24.** J Biol Chem 268, 15588 (1993); **25.** Biochemistry 34, 7904 (1995); **26.** Biochemistry 33, 13102 (1994); **27.** Biochemistry 33, 5539 (1994); **28.** J Photochem Photobiol B 12, 323 (1992); **29.** J Biol Chem 264, 8699 (1989); **30.** J Recept Signal Transduct Res 22, 333 (2002); **31.** Biochemistry 33, 11875 (1994); **32.** J Cell Physiol 159, 176 (1994); **33.** Biophys J 60, 307 (1991); **34.** J Biol Chem 259, 5717 (1984); **35.** Anal Biochem 174, 101 (1988); **36.** Anal Biochem 108, 156 (1980); **37.** Proc Natl Acad Sci U S A 93, 6264 (1996); **38.** Biochemistry 37, 2979 (1998); **39.** Biochemistry 37, 8173 (1998); **40.** Anal Biochem 221, 306 (1994); **41.** Biophys J 66, 99 (1994); **42.** Nucleic Acids Res 22, 920 (1994); **43.** Science 266, 785 (1994); **44.** Nucleic Acids Res 28, 3752 (2000);

continued on next page

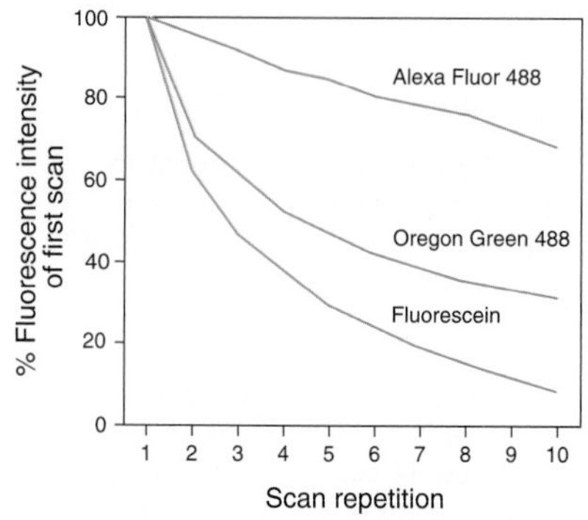

Figure 1.9 Photobleaching resistance of the green-fluorescent Alexa Fluor® 488, Oregon Green® 488 and fluorescein dyes, as determined by laser-scanning cytometry. EL4 cells were labeled with biotin-conjugated anti-CD44 antibody and detected by Alexa Fluor® 488 (S11223), Oregon Green® 488 (S6368) or fluorescein (S869) streptavidin (Section 7.6). The cells were then fixed in 1% paraformaldehyde, washed and wet-mounted. After mounting, cells were scanned 10 times on a laser-scanning cytometer; laser power levels were 25 mW for the 488 nm spectral line of the argon-ion laser. Scan durations were approximately five minutes apiece, and each repetition was started immediately after completion of the previous scan. Data are expressed as percentages derived from the mean fluorescence intensity (MFI) of each scan divided by the MFI of the first scan. Data contributed by Bill Telford, Experimental Transplantation and Immunology Branch, National Can-

continued from previous page

45. Nat Biotechnol 17, 804 (1999); **46.** Biotechniques 27, 342 (1999); **47.** Genome Res 6, 986 (1996); **48.** Nucleic Acids Res 25, 2516 (1997); **49.** Genome Res 11, 163 (2001); **50.** Biochemistry 34, 285 (1995); **51.** Nucleic Acids Res 22, 662 (1994); **52.** Nonisotopic DNA Probe Techniques, Kricka LR, Ed. pp. 311–352 (1992); **53.** Proc Natl Acad Sci U S A 85, 8790 (1988); **54.** Proc Natl Acad Sci U S A 94, 10756 (1997); **55.** Anal Biochem 255, 32 (1998); **56.** Anal Chem 67, 3676 (1995); **57.** Proc Natl Acad Sci U S A 92, 4347 (1995); **58.** Biochemistry 34, 4846 (1995); **59.** Biochemistry 31, 2865 (1992); **60.** J Biol Chem 258, 5368 (1983); **61.** Biochemistry 37, 2361 (1998); **62.** Biochim Biophys Acta 1189, 175 (1994); **63.** Methods Enzymol 221, 239 (1993); **64.** Biochemistry 20, 4093 (1981); **65.** Biophys J 69, 1272 (1995); **66.** FEBS Lett 413, 379 (1997); **67.** Techniques in Protein Chemistry V, Crabb JW, Ed. pp. 493–500 (1994); **68.** Biochemistry 37, 11434 (1998); **69.** Bioconjug Chem 4, 537 (1993); **70.** Nature 349, 694 (1991); **71.** Fluorescent and Luminescent Probes for Biological Activity, Mason WT, Ed. pp. 133–149 (1993); **72.** J Am Chem Soc 118, 6514 (1996).

Features of the Alexa Fluor® Dyes

Alexa Fluor® 488 Dye

Based on our testing, publications[2–5] and results reported by customers, the Alexa Fluor® 488 dye is by far the best fluorescein (FITC or FAM) substitute available for most applications (see Note 1.3 "Product Highlight: Customer Testimonials for the Alexa Fluor® Dyes"). It is probably the best dye available for single-molecule detection of bioconjugates, for fluorescence correlation spectroscopy (see Note 1.4 "Technical Focus: Fluorescence Correlation Spectroscopy (FCS)") and for fluorescence polarization measurements (see Note 1.5 "Technical Focus: Fluorescence Polarization (FP)" in Section 1.4). This green-fluorescent dye exhibits several unique features:

- Fluorescence spectra almost identical to those of fluorescein, with excitation/emission maxima of 495/519 nm (Figure 1.8) and a fluorescence lifetime of ~4.1 nanoseconds
- Strong absorption, with an extinction coefficient greater than 65,000 $cm^{-1}M^{-1}$
- Much greater photostability than fluorescein (Figure 1.9), allowing more time for observation and image capture (Figure 1.10, Figure 1.11)
- pH-insensitive fluorescence between pH 4 and 10 (Figure 1.12)

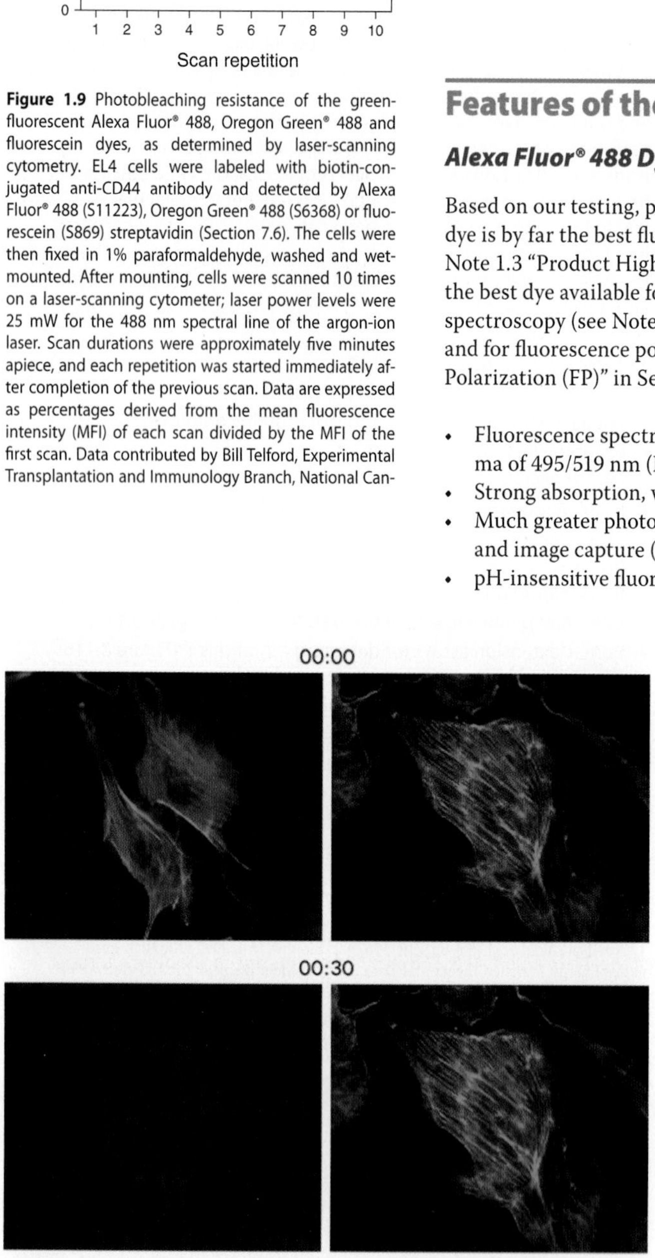

Figure 1.10 Bovine pulmonary artery endothelial cells (BPAEC) were labeled with fluorescein phalloidin (left panels, F432), or Alexa Fluor® 488 phalloidin (right panels, A12379), which labels filamentous actin, and mounted in PBS. The cells were placed under constant illumination on the microscope with an FITC filter set using a 60× objective. Images were acquired at one-second intervals for 30 seconds. Under these illumination conditions, fluorescein photobleached to about 20% of its initial value in 30 seconds; the fluorescence of Alexa Fluor® 488 phalloidin stayed at the initial value under the same illumination conditions.

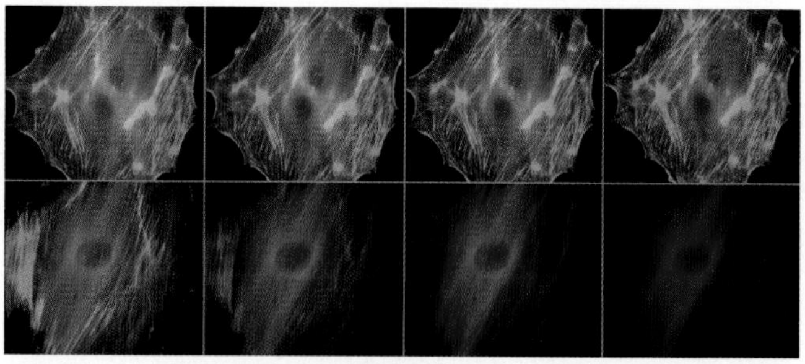

Figure 1.11 Comparison of the photobleaching rates of the Alexa Fluor® 488 and Alexa Fluor® 546 dyes and the well-known fluorescein and Cy3 fluorophores. The cytoskeleton of bovine pulmonary artery endothelial cells (BPAEC) was labeled with (top series) Alexa Fluor® 488 phalloidin (A12379) and mouse monoclonal anti-α-tubulin antibody (A11126) in combination with Alexa Fluor® 546 goat anti-mouse IgG antibody (A11003) or (bottom series) fluorescein phalloidin (F432) and the anti-α-tubulin antibody in combination with a commercially available Cy3 goat anti-mouse IgG antibody. The pseudocolored images were taken at 30-second intervals (0, 30, 90, and 210 seconds of exposure). The images were acquired with bandpass filter sets appropriate for fluorescein and rhodamine.

- Water solubility, with no organic co-solvents required in labeling reactions, suggesting that the succinimidyl ester of Alexa Fluor® 488 carboxylic acid (A20000, A20100) may be the ideal reagent for labeling amines of exposed cell-surface proteins of live cells[6]
- Superior fluorescence output per protein conjugate, surpassing that of any other spectrally similar fluorophore-labeled protein, including fluorescein conjugates (Figure 1.13) and Cy2 conjugates of antibodies (Figure 1.14)
- Utility as a fluorescence anisotropy probe for measuring protein–protein interactions[7] (see Note 1.5 "Technical Focus: Fluorescence Polarization (FP)" in Section 1.4)

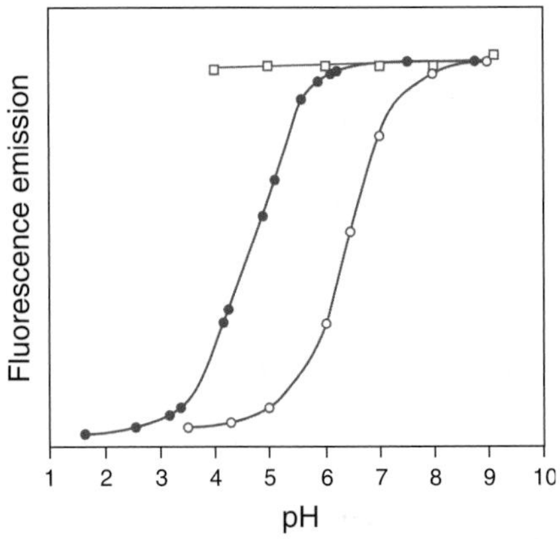

Figure 1.12 Comparison of pH-dependent fluorescence of the Oregon Green® 488 (●), carboxyfluorescein (○) and Alexa Fluor® 488 (□) fluorophores. Fluorescence intensities were measured for equal concentrations of the three dyes using excitation/emission at 490/520 nm.

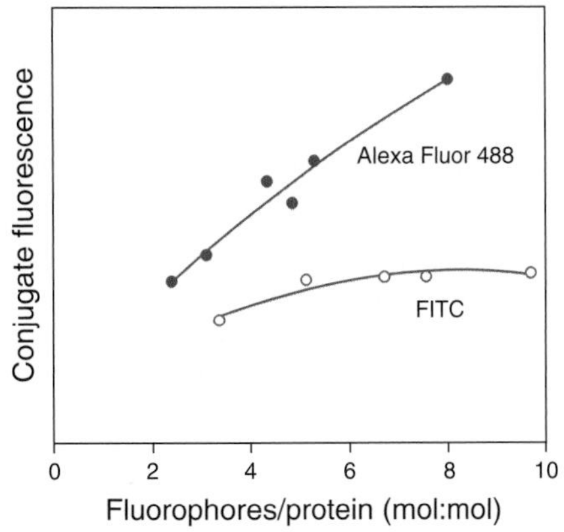

Figure 1.13 Comparison of the relative fluorescence of goat anti-mouse IgG antibody conjugates prepared from the Alexa Fluor® 488 dye and from fluorescein isothiocyanate (FITC). Conjugate fluorescence is determined by measuring the fluorescence quantum yield of the conjugated dye relative to that of a reference dye and multiplying by the dye:protein labeling ratio.

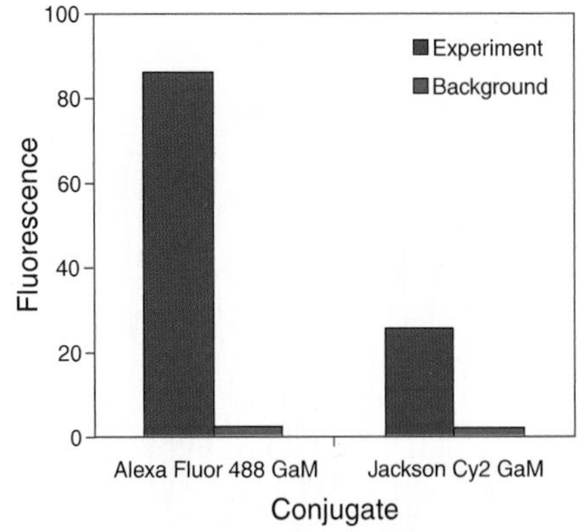

Figure 1.14 Brightness comparison of Molecular Probes' Alexa Fluor® 488 goat anti-mouse IgG antibody with Cy2 goat anti-mouse IgG antibody from Jackson ImmunoResearch. Human blood was blocked with normal goat serum and incubated with an anti-CD3 mouse monoclonal antibody; cells were washed, resuspended and incubated with either Alexa Fluor® 488 or Cy2 goat anti-mouse IgG antibody at equal concentration. Red blood cells were lysed, and the samples were analyzed with a flow cytometer equipped with a 488 nm argon-ion laser and a 525 ± 10 nm bandpass emission filter.

Note 1.3 — Product Highlight

Customer Testimonials for the Alexa Fluor® Dyes

"I have been using Alexa Fluor® 594 in place of Texas Red® and have found it to be perhaps five times as sensitive with less background ... another investigator in the lab had no results at all until he used Alexa Fluor® 594 and is now getting excellent results."

Warren R. Clark, Senior Biological Scientist
University of Florida
Gainesville, Florida USA

"I have been extremely impressed with the quality of the Alexa Fluor® dyes. They have made it possible to do fluorescent (confocal) analysis on certain antigens that had not previously been possible with the standard fluorophores (FITC, rhodamine, Texas Red®)."

Ray Grill, Assistant Project Neuroscientist
University of California, San Diego
San Diego, California USA

"I just tried the Alexa Fluor® 488 actin in live tissue culture cells. I was very pleased with the results. On the whole, the labeled actin incorporated into actin stress fibers very well. If anyone asks for feedback on Alexa Fluor® 488 actin, I would be happy to recommend it."

Louise Cramer, Group Leader,
MRC-Laboratory for Molecular Cell Biology
University College London
London, England

"I am using the Alexa Fluor® 488 hydrazide salt for intracellular injections and it is truly great ... better than Lucifer yellow in brightness, photostability and [it exhibits] less bleedthrough to other channels ... it is by far my first choice."

Johan Wassélius, Department of Ophthalmology
University Hospital
Lund, Sweden

"I use Alexa Fluor® 488, 568 and 594 secondary antibody conjugates instead of FITC or TRITC because of their great photostability ... staining with Alexa Fluor® 488 [provides] the possibility of long time exposure for serial laser scanning or photomicrography."

Olaf Anhenn, Department of Pathology
Ruhr-University
Bochum, Germany

"All of the Alexa Fluor® dyes are superior to anything out there. [They are the] best reagents since sliced bread. FITC has been banned from this lab."

Joe Goodhouse, Department of Molecular Biology
Princeton University
Princeton, New Jersey USA

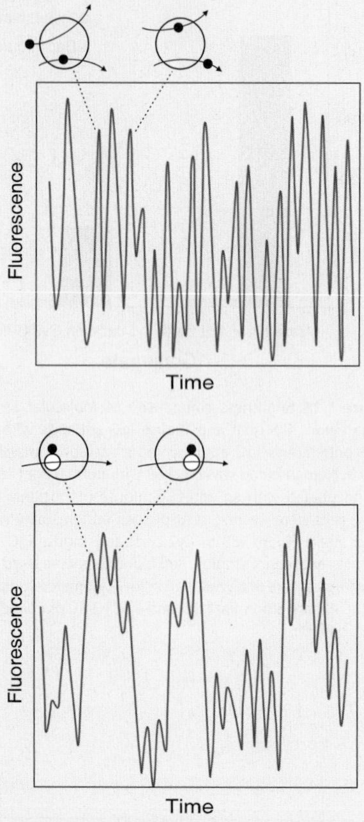

Figure 1. Physical origins of fluorescence correlation spectroscopy data. Free fluorescent ligands move in and out of the detection volume (open circle) and are detected as a series of short, randomized fluorescence bursts (top panel). Macromolecule-bound ligands are less mobile, producing a more slowly fluctuating (i.e., more highly autocorrelated) time-dependent fluorescence pattern (bottom panel).

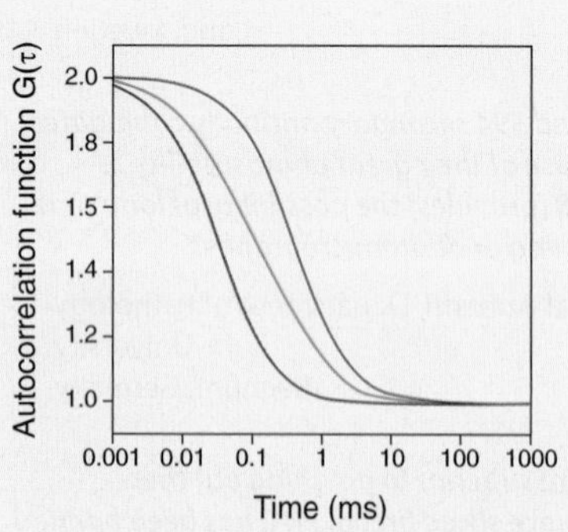

Figure 2. Simulated FCS autocorrelation functions representing a low molecular weight ligand (left curve, blue), macromolecule-bound ligand (right curve, red) and a 1:1 mixture of free and bound ligand (middle curve, green).

Note 1.4 — Technical Focus

Fluorescence Correlation Spectroscopy (FCS)

Fluorescence correlation spectroscopy (FCS) is a technique in which spontaneous fluorescence intensity fluctuations are measured in a microscopic detection volume of about 10^{-15} L (1 femtoliter) defined by a tightly focused laser beam.[1–3] Renewed interest in FCS in recent years has been stimulated by the fact that it is inherently miniaturized and therefore applicable for high-throughput screening applications.[4] Fluorescence intensity fluctuations measured by FCS represent changes in either the number or the fluorescence quantum yield of molecules resident in the detection volume (Figure 1). Small, rapidly diffusing molecules produce rapidly fluctuating intensity patterns, whereas larger molecules produce more sustained bursts of fluorescence.

This situation is in marked contrast to conventional fluorescence photometry carried out in sample volumes of around 0.1–1.0 mL (~10^8 times larger than FCS measurement volumes) that report only the macroscopic average of diffusion-dependent intensity fluctuations. In a typical FCS measurement, fluorescence intensity is recorded for a small number of molecules in the detection volume (e.g., 3 molecules/femtoliter, equivalent to ~5 nM macroscopic concentration) over a time range from about 1 microsecond to 1 second. The time-dependent fluorescence intensity (F(t)) is then analyzed in terms of its temporal autocorrelation function (G (τ)), which compares the fluorescence intensity at time t with the intensity at (t + τ), where τ is a variable interval, averaged over all data points in the time series (denoted by < >):

$$G(\tau) = \frac{\langle \delta F(t) \bullet \delta F(t+\tau) \rangle}{\langle F(t) \rangle^2}$$

The autocorrelation function contains information about equilibrium concentrations, reaction kinetics and diffusion rates of molecules in the sample. The initial amplitude of the autocorrelation function is inversely proportional to the number of molecules in the detection volume. The autocorrelation function decays from its initial value with a time-dependence that is determined by molecular diffusion rates. For example, free fluorescent ligands exhibit faster autocorrelation decay than slower-moving complexed ligands (Figure 2):

Probes and Applications for FCS

FCS is applicable for monitoring a multitude of biomolecular association and dissociation processes (see Table below). Because FCS is intrinsically sensitive to the mass changes occurring in these processes, probe design and selection is generally less critical than it is in assays based on macroscopic fluorescence intensity changes generated by dye–dye interactions (FRET, self-quenching etc.) or environment-dependent fluorescence enhancement. Dyes that perform well in confocal laser-scanning microscopy are usually among the best choices for FCS applications. Laser sources used for excitation in FCS include the 488 nm argon-ion spectral line, the 543 nm and 633 nm He–Ne laser spectral lines and the 568 nm and 647 nm Ar–Kr laser spectral lines. Dyes with appreciable rates of triplet state population via intersystem crossing are generally not well suited for FCS measurement because this process results in an additional submillisecond autocorrelation decay component.[5]

Recent Technical Developments in FCS

Two-photon excitation (TPE) has been applied to FCS for reasons similar to those that have motivated its use in fluorescence microscopy — inherent spatial confinement of excitation, diminished photobleaching and phototoxicity, less scattering and better optical penetration in turbid media.[6,7] Dual-color cross-correlation FCS[8] measures the cross-correlation of the time-dependent fluorescence intensities of two spectrally distinct dyes, instead of the conventional autocorrelation for a single dye. This approach has the advantage that cross-correlated fluorescence is only generated by molecules or complexes labeled with both dyes, allowing quantitation of interacting molecules without reference to their diffusion characteristics. In practice, discrimination based on mass in conventional FCS requires that the interacting components should have a molecular weight ratio of at least 1:7. FCS measurements using TPE in combination with dual-color cross-correlation have recently been reported.[9]

References

1. Biochemistry 41, 697 (2002); **2.** Proc Natl Acad Sci U S A 94, 11753 (1997); **3.** Topics in Fluorescence Spectroscopy, Lakowicz JR, Ed. 1: Techniques, 337 (1991); **4.** J Biomol Screen 4, 335 (1999); **5.** J Phys Chem 99, 13368 (1995); **6.** Biophys J 77, 2251 (1999); **7.** Biophys J 71, 410 (1996); **8.** Biophys J 72, 1878 (1997); **9.** Proc Natl Acad Sci U S A 97, 10377 (2000).

continued on next page

continued from previous page

Applications of fluorescence correlation spectroscopy

Detected process	References
Nucleic acid fragmentation	Anal Biochem 260, 166 (1998); Proc Natl Acad Sci U S A 95, 1416 (1998); Proc Natl Acad Sci U S A 95, 1421 (1998)
Nucleic acid hybridization	Biochemistry 35, 10182 (1996); Nucleic Acids Res 23, 1795 (1995)
PCR product formation	Biochemistry 37, 12971 (1998); Biotechniques 25, 706 (1998); Proc Natl Acad Sci U S A 93, 12805 (1996)
Lateral segregation of lipids in bilayer membranes	Cytometry 36, 176 (1999); Proc Natl Acad Sci U S A 96, 8461 (1999)
Molecular diffusion in the nucleus and cytoplasm	Biophys J 75, 2547 (1998); Proc Natl Acad Sci U S A 95, 6043 (1998)
Protein–protein interactions	Biochem Biophys Res Commun 267, 300 (2000); Biochemistry 38, 13759 (1999); Biochemistry 38, 8402 (1999); Chem Biol 6, 53 (1999); Cytometry 36, 247 (1999); Biophys Chem 75, 151 (1998)
Binding equilibria for drugs and other low molecular weight ligands	Biochemistry 38, 5082 (1999); Biochemistry 38, 8671 (1999); J Biomol Screen 4, 355 (1999); Biophys J 73, 2195 (1997); Biophys Chem 58, 3 (1996)
Clustering of membrane-bound receptors	Biophys J 70, 2001 (1996); Biophys J 65, 1135 (1993); Chem Phys Lipids 50, 253 (1989)

The monosuccinimidyl ester of Alexa Fluor® 488 carboxylic acid is a mixture of two isomers and is available in a 1 mg or 5 mg unit size (A20000, A20100). The isomerically pure 5-isomer of the Alexa Fluor® 488 dye is also available as an amine-reactive tetrafluorophenyl (TFP) ester (A30005, Figure 1.15). TFP esters are an improvement over the succinimidyl ester (NHS ester or SE) chemistry typically used to attach fluorophores or haptens to the primary amines of biomolecules. Both reactive chemistries produce the same strong amide bond between the dye or hapten and the compound of interest (Figure 1.2), but TFP esters are less susceptible to spontaneous hydrolysis during conjugation reactions (Figure 1.16). The Alexa Fluor® 488 carboxylic acid TFP ester is stable for several hours at the basic pH typically used for reactions — far outlasting succinimidyl esters. The amine-reactive Alexa Fluor® 488 succinimidyl ester is a component of several labeling kits for proteins, nucleic acids and oligonucleotides (Section 1.2; Table 1.2, Table 1.5); the Alexa Fluor® 488 carboxylic acid TFP ester is the amine-reactive dye included in the Alexa Fluor® 488 Monoclonal Antibody Labeling Kit (A20181) and the Alexa Fluor® 488 Protein Labeling Kit (A10235).

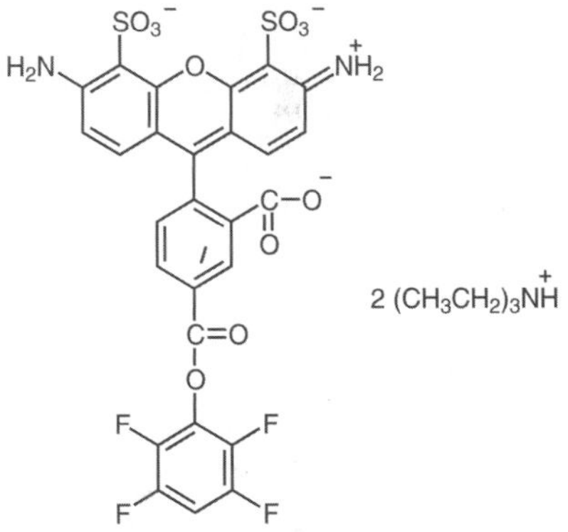

Figure 1.15 A30005 Alexa Fluor 488 carboxylic acid, 2,3,5,6-tetrafluorophenyl ester (Alexa Fluor 488 5-TFP).

Alexa Fluor® 500 and Alexa Fluor® 514 Dyes

Sophisticated detection systems demand highly specialized Alexa Fluor® dyes. Instruments such as the Zeiss META system, with the capacity to differentiate between fluorescence emission maxima <5 nm apart, greatly expand the palette of fluorescent colors available for multicolor labeling experiments. To keep up with the capabilities and demands of these advancing technologies, Molecular Probes has developed the Alexa Fluor® 500 and Alexa Fluor® 514 dyes, with visually similar but spectrally distinct emission profiles (Figure 1.17, Figure 7.6, Figure 7.7). Like

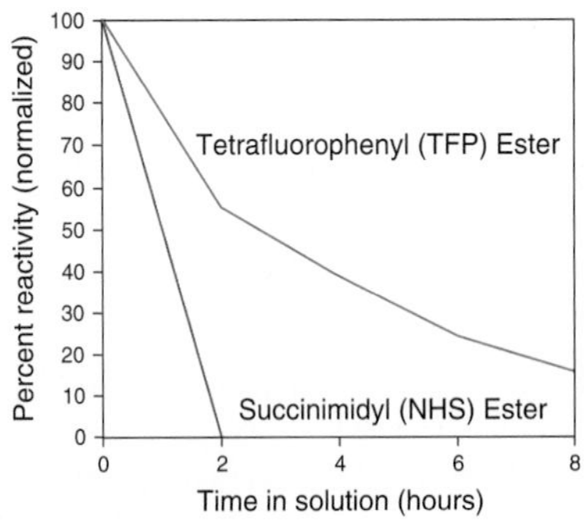

Figure 1.16 Stability of the tetrafluorophenyl (TFP) and succinimidyl (NHS) esters at basic pH (8.0–9.0).

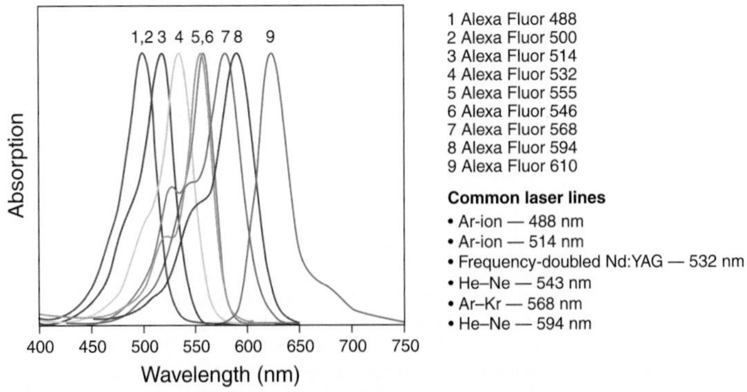

Figure 1.17 Absorption spectra of our intermediate-wavelength light-absorbing Alexa Fluor® dyes.

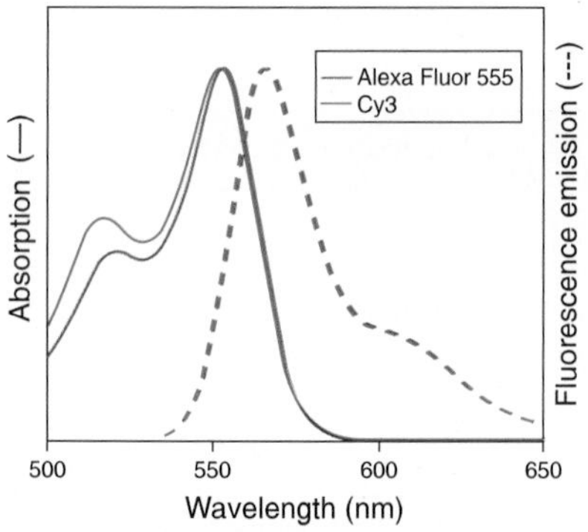

Figure 1.18 Comparison of the absorption and fluorescence emission spectra of the Alexa Fluor® 555 and Cy3 dyes. Spectra have been normalized to the same intensity for comparison purposes.

our Alexa Fluor® 488 dye, these two green-fluorescent Alexa Fluor® dyes are superior to fluorescein in both brightness and photostability, and they can be detected with standard fluorescein, Oregon Green® dye or Alexa Fluor® 488 dye filter sets (Section 23.5, Table 23.9). However, the Alexa Fluor® 500 and Alexa Fluor® 514 dyes are specifically designed to be detected simultaneously with other green fluorophores, despite their spectral overlap. Though they appear similar in color by eye, the Alexa Fluor® 500 dye can be optically separated from the Alexa Fluor® 514 dye using the Zeiss META system or similar spectral imaging instruments with linear-unmixing software. Similarly, the fluorescent signal from the Alexa Fluor® 514 dye can be resolved from both the Alexa Fluor® 488 and the Alexa Fluor® 500 fluorescence emissions. Additionally, the Alexa Fluor® 514 dye is one the brightest and most photostable dyes available for excitation by the 514 nm spectral line of the argon-ion laser. Both the Alexa Fluor® 500 and the Alexa Fluor® 514 dyes are available as succinimidyl esters (A30001, A30002) and as antibody (Section 7.2, Table 7.1) and streptavidin conjugates (Section 7.6, Table 7.22).

Table 1.5 — Alexa Fluor® active esters and kits for labeling proteins and nucleic acids

Fluorescent Color	Alexa Fluor® Dye	Abs/Em *	Succinimidyl Ester or Tetrafluorophenyl Ester (TFP)	Kits for Proteins			
				Protein Labeling Kit	Monoclonal Antibody	Zenon® Mouse IgG_1 Labeling Kit	Zenon® Mouse IgG_{2a} Labeling Kit
Blue	Alexa Fluor® 350	346/442	A10168 †	A10170	A20180	Z25000	Z25100
Blue	Alexa Fluor® 405	402/421	A30000 ‡ A30100 †			Z25013	Z25113
Yellow-green	Alexa Fluor® 430	434/539	A10169 †	A10171		Z25001	
Green	Alexa Fluor® 488	495/519	A20000 ‡ § A20100 † § A30005 (TFP)	A10235 **	A20181 **	Z25002	Z25102
Green	Alexa Fluor® 500	503/525	A30001 ‡ §				
Yellow-green	Alexa Fluor® 514	518/540	A30002 ‡ §				
Yellow	Alexa Fluor® 532	531/554	A20001 ‡ A20101MP †	A10236	A20182	Z25003	
Orange	Alexa Fluor® 546	556/573	A20002 ‡ § A20102 † §	A10237	A20183	Z25004	Z25104
Red-orange	Alexa Fluor® 555	555/565	A20009 ‡ A20109 †	A20174	A20187	Z25005	Z25105
Red-orange	Alexa Fluor® 568	578/603	A20003 ‡ § A20103 † §	A10238	A20184	Z25006	Z25106
Red	Alexa Fluor® 594	590/617	A20004 ‡ § A20104 † §	A10239	A20185	Z25007	Z25107
Red	Alexa Fluor® 610	612/628	A30003 ‡ A30103 †				
Far-red	Alexa Fluor® 633 ††	632/647	A20005 ‡ § A20105 † §	A20170			
Far-red	Alexa Fluor® 635 ††	633/647					
Far-red	Alexa Fluor® 647 ††	650/668	A20006 ‡ A20106 †	A20173	A20186	Z25008	Z25108
Near infrared	Alexa Fluor® 660 ††	663/690	A20007 ‡ A20107 †	A20171		Z25009	Z25109
Near infrared	Alexa Fluor® 680 ††	679/702	A20008 ‡ A20108 †	A20172		Z25010	Z25110
Near infrared	Alexa Fluor® 700 ††	702/723	A20010 ‡ A20110 †			Z25011	
Near infrared	Alexa Fluor® 750 ††	749/775	A20011 ‡ A20111 †				

* Approximate absorption (Abs) and fluorescence emission (Em) maxima for conjugates, in nm. † 5 mg unit size. ‡ 1 mg unit size. § Mixed isomers. ** These Alexa Fluor® 488 protein labeling kits contain the amine-reactive Alexa Fluor® 488 carboxylic acid TFP ester, whereas the Alexa Fluor® 488 kits for labeling nucleic acid and oligonucleotide contain the Alexa Fluor® 488 succinimidyl ester. †† Human vision is insensitive to light beyond ~650 nm, and therefore it is not possible to view the far-red–fluorescent dyes by looking through the eyepiece of a conventional fluorescence microscope. Succinimidyl Ester — With the exception of Alexa Fluor® 350 and Alexa Fluor® 430 dyes, which are packaged in 5 mg unit sizes, most of the Alexa Fluor® succinimidyl esters are available in both 1 mg or 5 mg quantities with a guaranteed ≥50% reactive dye per vial. Actual purity may significantly exceed 50%. Tetrafluorophenyl Ester — The Alexa Fluor® 488 dye is also available as an amine-reactive TFP ester, which produces the same strong amide bond between the dye and the compound of interest as does the succinimidyl ester, but TFP esters are less susceptible to spontaneous hydrolysis during storage and conjugation reactions. Protein Labeling Kit — Complete,

Alexa Fluor® 532, Alexa Fluor® 546, Alexa Fluor® 555, Alexa Fluor® 568, Alexa Fluor® 594 and Alexa Fluor® 610 Dyes

These yellow- to orange- to red-fluorescent Alexa Fluor® dyes (Figure 1.17) provide strong visible fluorescence that contrasts well with the green fluorescence of the Alexa Fluor® 488 dye; consequently, they are frequently used in combination with green-fluorescent dyes. Five of our Alexa Fluor® dyes have been utilized for simultaneous seven-color fluorescence imaging in tissue samples.[8] The Alexa Fluor® 532 dye (Figure 7.8) is readily excited by the frequency-doubled output of the Nd:YAG laser. Both the Alexa Fluor® 546 and Alexa Fluor® 555 dyes have spectra that are similar to tetramethylrhodamine and the Cy3 dye; the spectra of the Alexa Fluor® 555 dye are an almost exact match to those of the Cy3 dye (Figure 1.18). We have observed that, unlike most other Alexa Fluor® dyes, antifade reagents provide little protective effect for conjugates of the Alexa Fluor® 546 dye; the spectrally similar Alexa Fluor® 555 dye is a good substitute for the Alexa Fluor® 546 dye in many applications. The Alexa Fluor® 568 (Figure 1.19) and Alexa Fluor® 594 dyes have absorption and fluorescence emission maxima similar to the

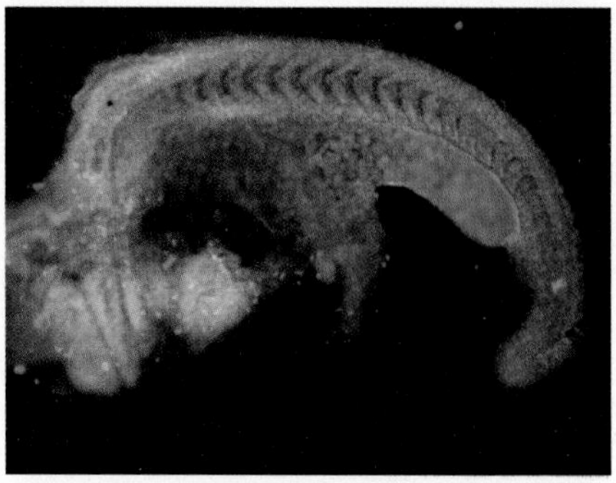

Figure 1.19 Neuronal cells in a 22-hour zebrafish embryo were identified with anti–HuC/HuD mouse monoclonal antibody (A21271) and visualized with red-orange–fluorescent Alexa Fluor® 568 goat anti–mouse IgG antibody (A11004). The nuclei were stained with blue-fluorescent DAPI (D1306, D3571, D21490).

Kits for Proteins				Kits for Nucleic Acids and Oligonucleotides		
Zenon® Mouse IgG_{2b} Labeling Kit	Zenon® Rabbit IgG Labeling Kit	Zenon® Goat IgG Labeling Kit	Zenon® Human IgG Labeling Kit	ULYSIS Nucleic Acid Labeling Kit	ARES™ DNA Labeling Kit	Oligonucleotide Amine Labeling Kit
Z25200	Z25300		Z25400		A21675	A20190
Z25213	Z25313					
	Z25301					
Z25202	Z25302	Z25602	Z25402	U21650	A21665	A20191
	Z25303			U21651	A21666	A20192
Z25204	Z25304			U21652	A21667	A20193
Z25205	Z25305	Z25605	Z25405		A21677	A20197
Z25206	Z25306	Z25606		U21653	A21668	A20194
Z25207	Z25307	Z25607	Z25407	U21654	A21669	A20195
Z25208	Z25308	Z25608	Z25408	U21660	A21676	A20196
Z25209	Z25309			U21656	A21671	
Z25210	Z25310			U21657	A21672	
	Z25311					
	Z25312					

easy-to-use kit designed for 3 reactions, each reaction optimized to label ~1 mg of protein. Monoclonal Antibody Labeling Kit — Complete ready-to-use kit designed for 5 reactions, each reaction optimized to label ~100 µg of an IgG. Zenon® Antibody Labeling Kits - Simple, rapid (~10 minutes) and quantitative method to label antibodies (Section 7.3). ULYSIS Nucleic Acid Labeling Kit — Convenient means to create fluorophore-labeled hybridization probes from any DNA source without enzymatic incorporation of labeled nucleotides. Each kit provides sufficient material for 20 labeling reactions of 1 µg of DNA. ARES™ DNA Labeling Kit — Aminoallyl dUTP is enzymatically incorporated, then the Alexa Fluor® dye is covalently attached to the amino group. Each kit provides sufficient material for 5–10 labeling reactions of 1–5 µg of DNA. Oligonucleotide Amine Labeling Kit — Designed to label oligonucleotides synthesized with an amine group on the 3′ or 5′ end. Each kit provides sufficient materials for 3 labeling reactions of 50 µg of DNA.

Lissamine rhodamine B and Texas Red® dyes, respectively. The Alexa Fluor® 610 dye emits an intense red fluorescence that, unlike the Alexa Fluor® 633 dye and longer-wavelength fluorophores, can still be seen with the human eye. Each of these yellow-, orange- and red-fluorescent Alexa Fluor® dyes exhibits several features that distinguish them from spectrally similar fluorophores:

- Excitation/emission maxima of ~531/554 nm for the Alexa Fluor® 532 dye (Figure 7.8), ~556/573 nm for the Alexa Fluor® 546 dye (Figure 7.9), ~555/565 nm for the Alexa Fluor® 555 dye (Figure 7.10), ~578/603 nm for the Alexa Fluor® 568 dye (Figure 7.11), ~590/617 nm for the Alexa Fluor® 594 dye (Figure 7.12) and ~612/628 nm for the Alexa Fluor® 610 dye (Figure 7.13), with fluorescence lifetimes for the Alexa Fluor® 546, Alexa Fluor® 568 and Alexa Fluor® 594 dyes of approximately 4.0, 3.6 and 3.9 nanoseconds, respectively
- Strong absorption, with extinction coefficients greater than 80,000 $cm^{-1}M^{-1}$ for the Alexa Fluor® 532, Alexa Fluor® 546, Alexa Fluor® 568 and Alexa Fluor® 594 dyes and greater than 130,000 $cm^{-1}M^{-1}$ for the Alexa Fluor® 555 and Alexa Fluor® 610 dyes
- Fluorescence that is more photostable than that of other spectrally similar dyes, allowing more time for observation and image capture (Figure 1.20)
- pH-insensitive fluorescence over a broad range
- Water solubility, therefore permitting labeling reactions to be performed without organic solvents
- Superior fluorescence output per protein or nucleic acid conjugate, surpassing that of any other spectrally similar fluorophore-labeled protein (Figure 1.21), including Cy3 dye–labeled proteins (Figure 1.22, Figure 1.23)

Isomeric mixtures of the amine-reactive monosuccinimidyl esters of the Alexa Fluor® 546, Alexa Fluor® 568 and Alexa Fluor® 594 dyes and the isomer-free monosuccinimidyl esters of the Alexa Fluor® 532, Alexa Fluor® 555 and Alexa Fluor® 610 dyes are available as separate reagents in either a 1 mg or 5 mg unit size or as components of several labeling kits (Table 1.2, Table 1.5). The contents and utility of these protein and nucleic acid labeling kits are discussed in detail in Section 1.2.

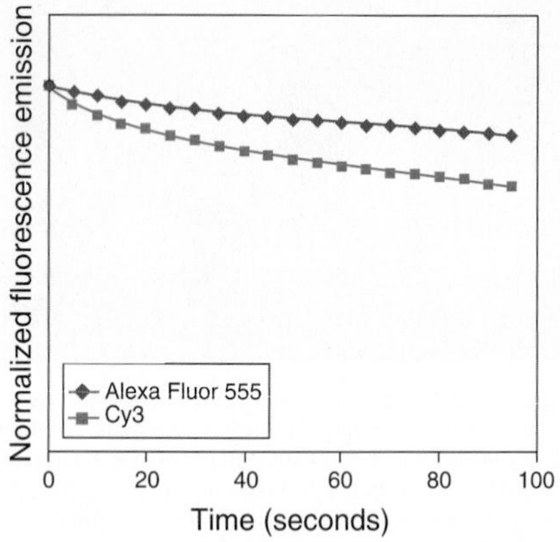

Figure 1.20 Photobleaching profiles of the Alexa Fluor® 555 and Cy3 dyes were obtained by placing equal molar concentrations of the free dyes into capillary tubes; the samples were continuously illuminated and data points were collected every five seconds. Fluorescence has been normalized to the same initial intensity.

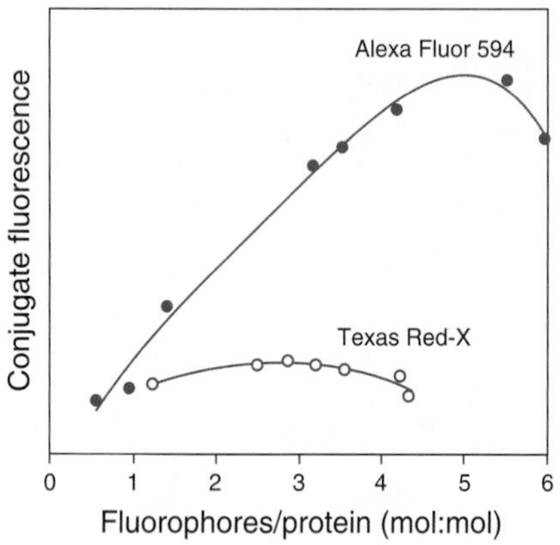

Figure 1.21 Comparison of the relative fluorescence of Alexa Fluor® 594 and Texas Red®-X goat anti-mouse IgG antibody F(ab')$_2$ fragment conjugates at different dye:protein ratios.

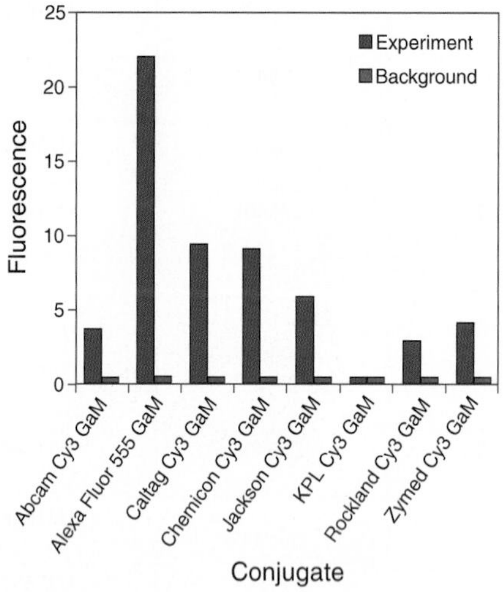

Figure 1.22 Brightness comparison of Molecular Probes' Alexa Fluor® 555 goat anti-mouse IgG antibody with Cy3 goat anti-mouse IgG antibody conjugates commercially available from several other companies. Human blood was blocked with normal goat serum and incubated with an anti-CD3 mouse monoclonal antibody; cells were washed, resuspended and incubated with either the Alexa Fluor® 555 or Cy3 goat anti-mouse IgG antibody at equal concentrations. Red blood cells were lysed and the samples were analyzed with a flow cytometer equipped with a 488 nm argon-ion laser and a 585 ± 21 nm bandpass emission filter.

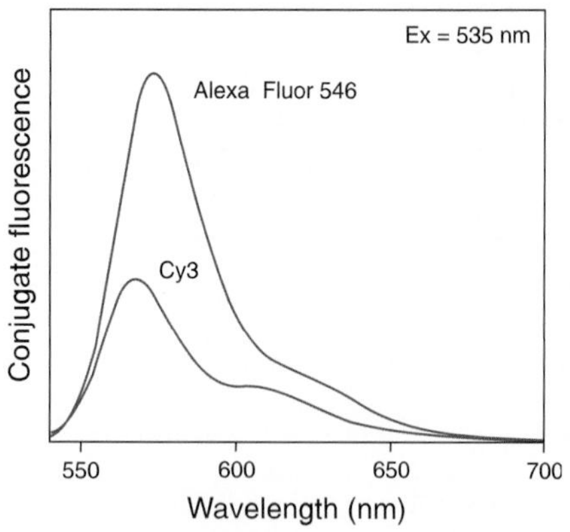

Figure 1.23 Fluorescence output from an Alexa Fluor® 546 goat anti-mouse IgG antibody (dye:protein ratio = 5.7) and a commercially available Cy3 goat anti-mouse IgG antibody (dye:protein ratio = 3.8). Antibody concentrations were adjusted to give equal absorbance at the excitation wavelength (535 nm). The relative fluorescence quantum yield of Alexa Fluor® 546 conjugates is higher than that of Cy3 conjugates, even at high dye:protein ratios that would typically result in self-quenching effects with most other protein-labeling dyes.

For labeling amine-modified DNA or RNA probes in microarray-based experiments, we offer the Alexa Fluor® 555 and the Alexa Fluor® 594 reactive dye decapacks (A32756, A32751), which provide our outstanding Alexa Fluor® 555 and Alexa Fluor® 594 succinimidyl esters, respectively, conveniently packaged in 10 single-use vials. This specially packaged amine-reactive dye can be used in conjunction with our aminohexylacrylamido-dUTP (aha-dUTP, A32760; Section 8.2), aminoallyl dUTP or aminoallyl UTP (A21664, A21663; Section 8.2) nucleotides or with commercially available aminoallyl nucleotide–based nucleic acid labeling kits. The monoreactive, single-isomer Alexa Fluor® 555 succinimidyl ester produces high-efficiency labeling of aminoallyl-modified DNA or RNA — up to one dye every 12 bases. With excitation/emission maxima of 555/565 nm, the Alexa Fluor® 555 succinimidyl ester matches one of the most popular wavelength channels used to scan microarrays.[9] Conjugates of the Alexa Fluor® 594 succinimidyl ester (excitation/emission maxima ~590/617 nm) exhibit very little spectral overlap with green-fluorescent conjugates and are efficiently excited by the 568 nm line of the Ar–Kr laser and by the 594 nm line of the orange He–Ne laser. Furthermore, the Alexa Fluor® 555/Alexa Fluor® 647 dye pair have been shown to display higher signal correlation coefficients than the Cy3/Cy5 dye pair in two-color DNA microarray assays.[10] Each single-use vial contains sufficient Alexa Fluor® succinimidyl ester to optimally label the amount of cDNA produced from reverse transcription of either 20 µg of total RNA or 1–5 µg of poly(A)+ RNA, in the presence of aminoallyl dUTP. We also offer the Alexa Fluor® 647 reactive dye decapack (A32757, see below), and, for added convenience, a combination set of the Alexa Fluor® 555 and Alexa Fluor® 647 reactive dye decapacks (A32755) that contains 10 vials of each succinimidyl ester and is sufficient for 10 two-color labeling reactions.

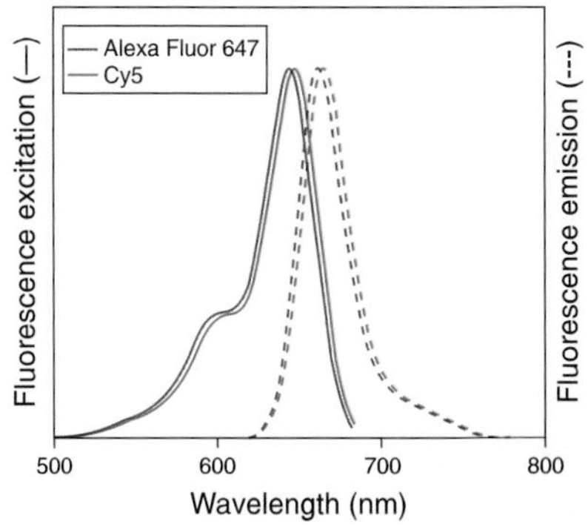

Figure 1.25 Comparison of the fluorescence spectra of the Alexa Fluor® 647 and Cy5 dyes. Spectra have been normalized to the same intensity for comparison purposes.

Alexa Fluor® 633, Alexa Fluor® 635, Alexa Fluor® 647, Alexa Fluor® 660, Alexa Fluor® 680, Alexa Fluor® 700 and Alexa Fluor® 750 Dyes

A long-term goal at Molecular Probes has been to develop superior dyes that can be excited by long-wavelength excitation sources, including the red He–Ne laser (at 633 nm), krypton-ion laser (at 647 nm) and laser diodes. It has particularly been a challenge to prepare reactive dyes whose fluorescence is not significantly quenched on conjugation. The Alexa Fluor® 633, Alexa Fluor® 635, Alexa Fluor® 647,[11] Alexa Fluor® 660, Alexa Fluor® 680, Alexa Fluor® 700 and Alexa Fluor® 750 dyes (Figure 1.24) meet our goals in several ways:[1]

- An excellent spectral match to common long-wavelength excitation sources, with very high extinction coefficients — typically >165,000 cm^{-1}M^{-1} but up to >230,000 cm^{-1}M^{-1} for the Alexa Fluor® 750 dye
- Spectra of the Alexa Fluor® 647, Alexa Fluor® 680 and Alexa Fluor® 750 conjugates that virtually match those of the Cy5 dye (Figure 1.25), Cy5.5 dye (Figure 1.26) and Cy7 dye (Figure 1.27), respectively, resulting in an optimal match to optical filters designed for these dyes (Table 23.9)

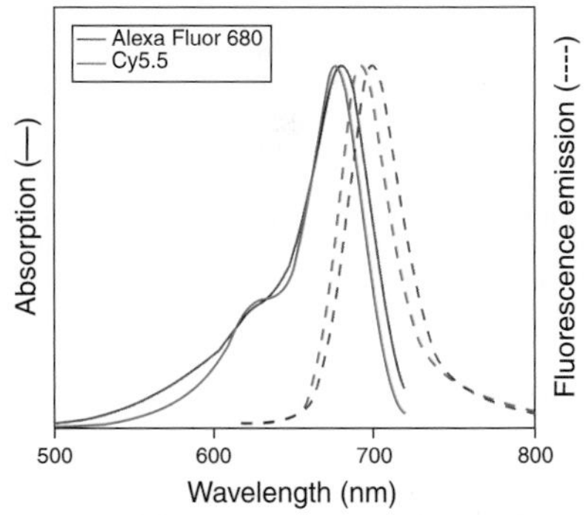

Figure 1.26 Comparison of the fluorescence spectra of the unconjugated Alexa Fluor® 680 and Cy5.5 dyes. Spectra have been normalized to the same intensity for comparison purposes.

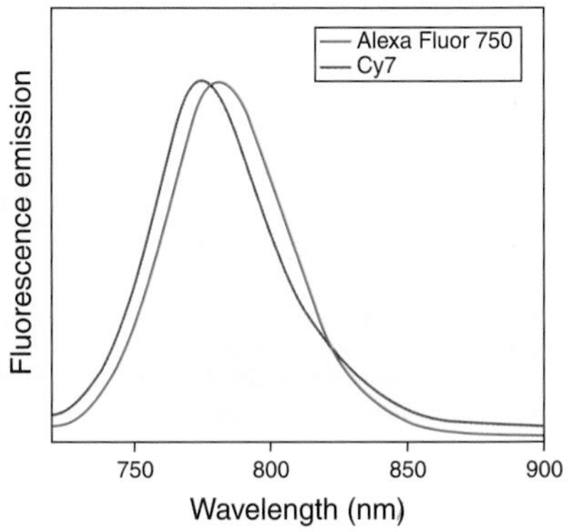

Figure 1.27 Comparison of the fluorescence emission spectra of the Alexa Fluor® 750 and Cy7 dyes. Spectra have been normalized to the same intensity for comparison purposes.

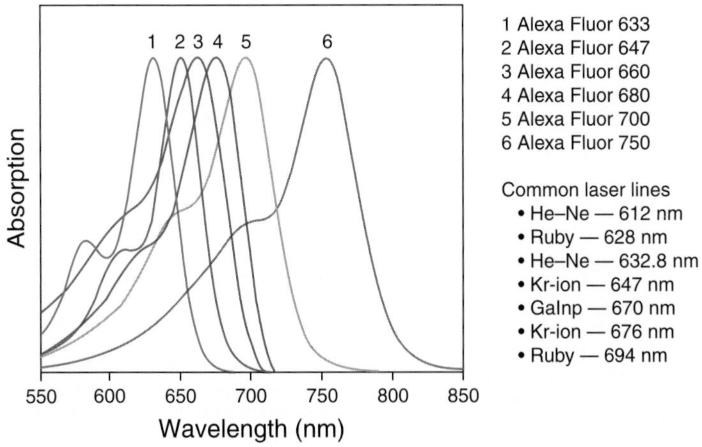

Figure 1.24 Absorption spectra of our long-wavelength light–absorbing Alexa Fluor® dyes. The Alexa Fluor® 635 dye, available conjugated to antibodies, streptavidin and phalloidin, is not included here but its absorption spectrum is very similar to that of the Alexa Fluor® 633 dye.

- Photostability of the Alexa Fluor® 633 and Alexa Fluor® 647 conjugates that exceeds that of Cy5, allophycocyanin and PBXL-3 conjugates (Figure 1.28)
- Unusually low fluorescence quenching upon conjugation to proteins, even at relatively high degrees of substitution (Figure 1.29, Figure 1.13, Figure 1.30), resulting in protein conjugates that are typically at least three to four times brighter than those of Cy5, Cy5.5, Cy7 and similar dyes [12,13] but that are, in some cases, as much as 40-fold brighter at equal antibody concentrations (Figure 1.26, Figure 1.30, Figure 1.31, Figure 1.32)
- Fluorescence of the nucleotide, oligonucleotide and nucleic acid conjugates of the Alexa Fluor® 647 dye that usually exceeds that of the Cy5 dye conjugates (Section 8.2, Section 8.5)
- Unlike the Cy5 dye, very little change in absorbance or fluorescence spectra when conjugated to most proteins, oligonucleotides and nucleic acids (Figure 1.33), thus yielding significantly greater total fluorescence at the same degrees of substitution (Figure 1.30, Figure 1.31, Figure 1.32)
- Reasonable water solubility of their succinimidyl esters, permitting conjugations to be done without addition of organic solvents, if desired
- Chemistry that permits synthesis of pure, singly reactive dyes, thus avoiding crosslinking reactions

Fluorescence of these long-wavelength Alexa Fluor® dyes is not visible to the human eye but is readily detected by most imaging systems. Pictures of these dyes throughout this *Handbook* have been pseudocolored to represent the staining that is observed with sensitive detection equipment.

An isomeric mixture of the amine-reactive succinimidyl ester of the Alexa Fluor® 633 dye and the isomer-free monosuccinimidyl esters of the Alexa Fluor® 647, Alexa Fluor® 660, Alexa Fluor® 680, Alexa Fluor® 700 and Alexa Fluor® 750 dyes are available as stand-alone reagents in either a 1 mg or 5 mg unit size (Table 1.2), and in most cases, as components of kits that permit facile labeling of proteins, oligonucleotides and nucleic acids (Table 1.2, Table 1.5). These kits and their contents are described in detail in Section 1.2. The Alexa Fluor® 635 dye, which is currently only available as antibody (Table 7.1, Figure 7.15) and streptavidin (Table 7.22) conjugates, typically produces brighter protein conjugates than does the Alexa Fluor® 633 dye because the absorption spectrum of the Alexa Fluor® 635 dye does not split into two peaks upon protein conjugation, as do the absorption spectra of the Alexa Fluor® 633, Cy5 and tetramethylrhodamine dyes (Figure 1.71). The spectral characteristics of thirteen different red-fluorescent fluorophores, including the Alexa Fluor® 647 and BODIPY® 630/660 (Section 1.4) dyes,

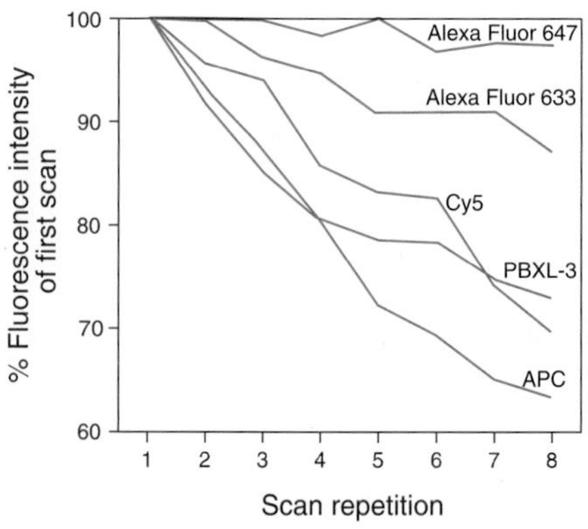

Figure 1.28 Photobleaching resistance of the red-fluorescent Alexa Fluor® 647, Alexa Fluor® 633, PBXL-3 and Cy5 dyes and the allophycocyanin fluorescent protein, as determined by laser-scanning cytometry. EL4 cells were labeled with biotin-conjugated anti-CD44 antibody and detected by Alexa Fluor® 647 (S21374), Alexa Fluor® 633 (S21375), PBXL-3, Cy5 or allophycocyanin (APC, S868) streptavidin (Section 7.6). The cells were then fixed in 1% paraformaldehyde, washed and wet-mounted. After mounting, cells were scanned eight times on a laser-scanning cytometer; laser power levels were 18 mW for the 633 nm spectral line of the He–Ne laser. Scan durations were approximately five minutes apiece, and each repetition was started immediately after completion of the previous scan. Data are expressed as percentages derived from the mean fluorescence intensity (MFI) of each scan divided by the MFI of the first scan. Data contributed by Bill Telford, Experimental Transplantation and Immunology Branch, National Cancer Institute.

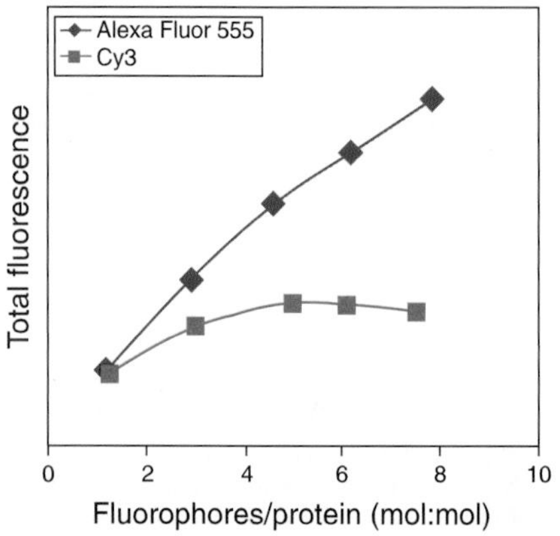

Figure 1.29 Comparison of the relative fluorescence of goat anti–rabbit IgG antibody conjugates of the Alexa Fluor® 555 and Cy3 dyes (prepared by Molecular Probes, Inc.) at different dye:protein ratios in the conjugate.

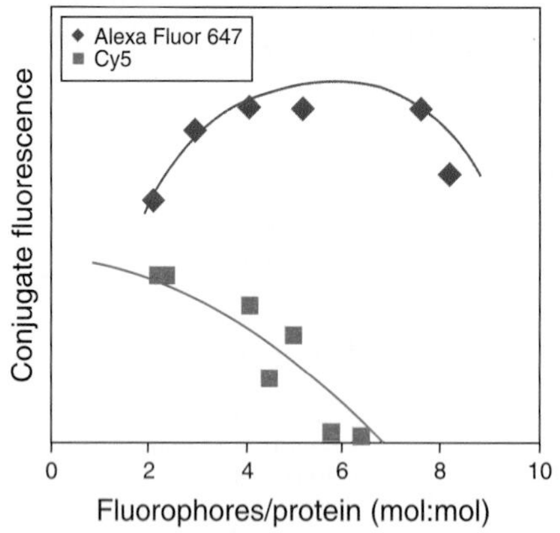

Figure 1.30 Comparison of the brightness of Alexa Fluor® 647 and Cy5 dye antibody conjugates (prepared by Molecular Probes, Inc.). More Alexa Fluor® 647 dye molecules can be attached to proteins and nucleic acids without significant quenching, thus yielding conjugates that are much brighter than those possible using the Cy5 dye.

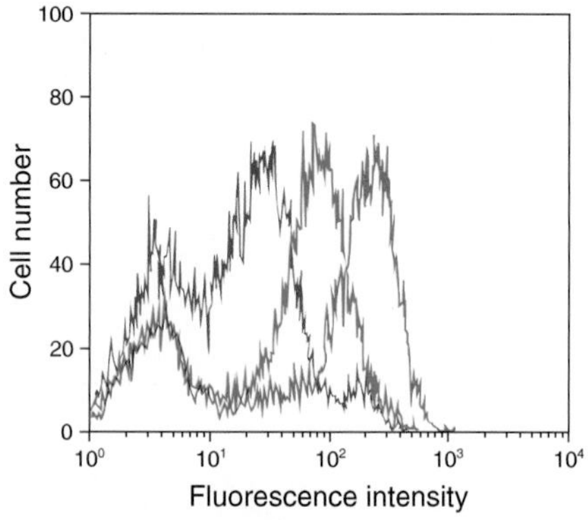

Figure 1.31 Flow cytometry was used to compare the brightness of Molecular Probes' Alexa Fluor® 647 goat anti–mouse IgG antibody (red, A21235) with commercially available Cy5 goat anti–mouse IgG antibody from Jackson ImmunoResearch Laboratories (green) and Amersham-Pharmacia Biotech (blue). Human blood was blocked with normal goat serum and incubated with an anti-CD3 mouse monoclonal antibody; cells were washed, resuspended and incubated with either an Alexa Fluor® 647 or Cy5 goat anti–mouse IgG secondary antibody at equal concentration. Red blood cells were lysed and the samples were analyzed on a flow cytometer equipped with a 633 nm He–Ne laser and a longpass emission filter (>650 nm).

have been evaluated in different surrounding media to assess the influence of polarity, viscosity and detergent concentration and to facilitate probe choice in fluorescence-based assays.[11]

For labeling amine-modified DNA or RNA probes in microarray-based experiments, we offer the Alexa Fluor® 647 reactive dye decapack (A32757), which provides our outstanding Alexa Fluor® 647 succinimidyl ester conveniently packaged in 10 single-use vials. This specially packaged amine-reactive dye can be used in conjunction with our aminohexylacrylamido-dUTP (aha-dUTP, A32760; Section 8.2), aminoallyl dUTP or aminoallyl UTP (A21664, A21663; Section 8.2) nucleotides or with commercially available aminoallyl nucleotide–based nucleic acid labeling kits. The Alexa Fluor® 647 succinimidyl ester produces high-efficiency labeling of aminoallyl-modified DNA or RNA — up to one dye every 12 bases. With excitation/emission maxima of 650/668 nm, the Alexa Fluor® 647 succinimidyl ester matches one of the most popular wavelength channels used to scan microarrays. Furthermore, the Alexa Fluor® 555/Alexa Fluor® 647 dye pair have been shown to display higher signal correlation coefficients than the Cy3/Cy5 dye pair in two-color DNA microarray assays.[10] Each single-use vial contains sufficient Alexa Fluor® succinimidyl ester to optimally label the amount of cDNA produced from reverse transcription of either 20 µg of total RNA or 1–5 µg of poly(A)+ RNA, in the presence of aminoallyl dUTP. We also offer the Alexa Fluor® 555 and Alexa Fluor® 594 reactive dye decapacks (A32756, A32751; see above), and, for added convenience, a combination set of the Alexa Fluor® 555 and Alexa Fluor® 647 reactive dye decapacks (A32755) that contains 10 vials of each succinimidyl ester and is sufficient for 10 two-color labeling reactions.

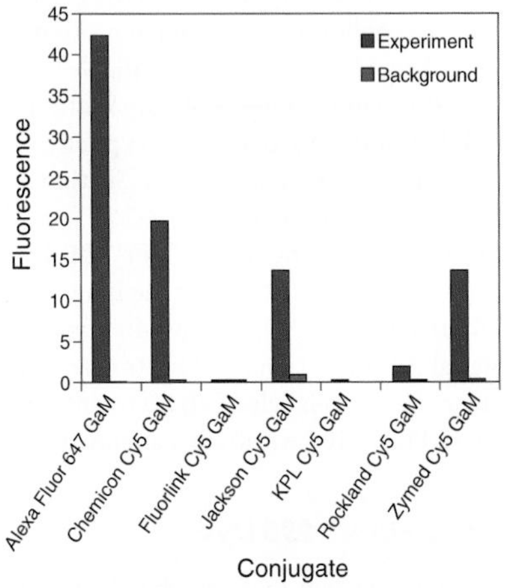

Figure 1.32 Brightness comparison of Molecular Probes' Alexa Fluor® 647 goat anti-mouse IgG antibody with Cy5 goat anti-mouse IgG antibody conjugates commercially available from other companies. Human blood was blocked with normal goat serum and incubated with an anti-CD3 mouse monoclonal antibody; cells were washed, resuspended and incubated with either Alexa Fluor® 647 or Cy5 goat anti-mouse IgG antibody at an equal concentration. Red blood cells were lysed and the samples were analyzed with a flow cytometer equipped with a 633 nm He–Ne laser and a longpass emission filter (>650 nm).

Alexa Fluor® 350 Dye

The sulfonated coumarin derivative, Alexa Fluor® 350 carboxylic acid succinimidyl ester (Figure 1.91), is more water soluble than either AMCA succinimidyl ester or AMCA-X succinimidyl ester (A6118, Section 1.7) and yields protein conjugates that are more fluorescent than those prepared from its nonsulfonated analog (Figure 7.34). Alexa Fluor® 350 protein conjugates are optimally excited at 346 nm (Figure 1.34, Figure 1.93) and exhibit bright blue fluorescence at wavelengths slightly shorter than AMCA or AMCA-X conjugates (442 nm versus 448 nm), which reduces the dye's spectral overlap with the emission of fluorescein.

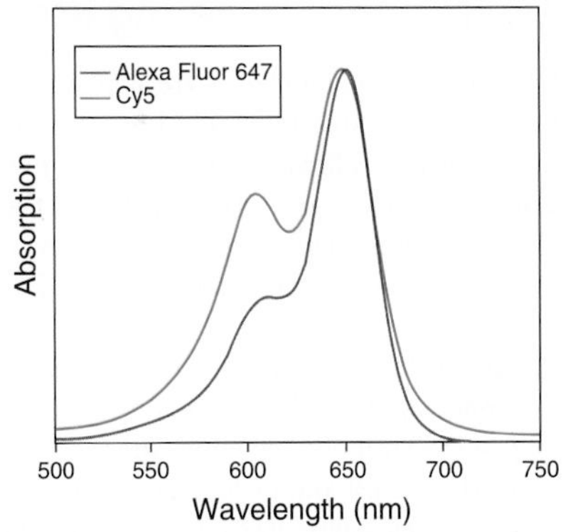

Figure 1.33 The absorption spectra of the Cy5 dye conjugates of both proteins and nucleic acids show an additional peak at about 600 nm when compared to the spectrum of the free dye. However, light absorbed by the Cy5 dye conjugates at this wavelength does not result in fluorescence. Alexa Fluor® 647 dye conjugates of proteins do not exhibit this spectral anomaly. Spectra have been normalized to the same peak intensity for comparison purposes.

Alexa Fluor® 405 Dye

With excitation/emission maxima of 402/421 nm (Figure 1.34, Figure 7.3), our Alexa Fluor® 405 dye is a near-perfect match to the 405 nm spectral line of the blue diode laser recently developed for fluorescence microscopy and flow cytometry. The Alexa Fluor® 405 succinimidyl ester is an amine-reactive derivative of our Cascade Blue® dye, which was previously available in amine-reactive form only as its acetyl azide (C2284, Section 1.7). Not only is it offered at higher purity than is Cascade Blue® acetyl azide, but the Alexa Fluor® 405 succinimidyl ester also contains a 4-piperidinecarboxylic acid spacer that separates the fluorophore from its reactive moiety (Figure 1.103). This spacer enhances the reactivity of the succinimidyl ester and minimizes any interactions between the fluorophore and the biomolecule to which it is conjugated. As with conjugates of Cascade Blue® acetyl azide, the Alexa Fluor® 405 conjugates show minimal spectral overlap

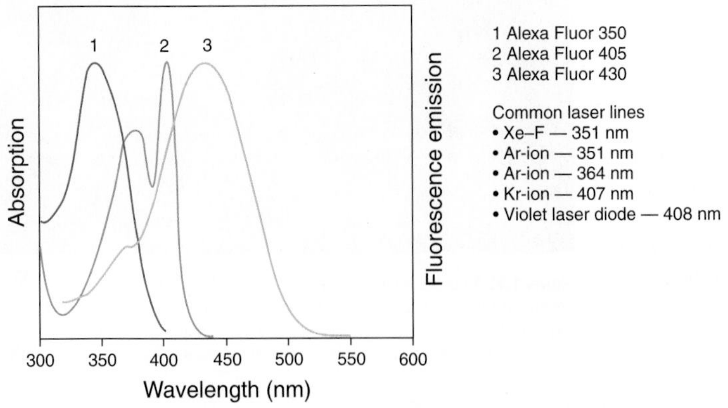

Figure 1.34 Absorption spectra of our short-wavelength light-absorbing Alexa Fluor® dyes.

with green fluorophores, making them ideal for multicolor applications. Moreover, with its longer-wavelength excitation maximum, the Alexa Fluor® 405 dye is potentially brighter than UV light–excitable blue fluorophores, whose signal is often obscured by autofluorescence. The Alexa Fluor® 405 dye is available as a succinimidyl ester (A30000, A30100), a maleimide (A30458, Section 2.3), a thiol-reactive mercurial (Hg-Link™ Alexa Fluor® 405 phenylmercury, H30461; Section 2.3) and a cadaverine (A30675, Section 3.3), as well as conjugated to secondary antibodies (Section 7.2, Table 7.1) and streptavidin (Section 7.6, Table 7.22). The Alexa Fluor® 405 dye is also recognized by our anti–Alexa Fluor® 405/Cascade Blue® dye antibody (A5760, Section 7.4). In addition, Alexa Fluor® 405 tyramide is used in the Tyramide Signal Amplification (TSA) Kits (Section 6.2, Table 6.1), and Alexa Fluor® 405 dye–labeled Fab fragments are provided in the Zenon® Alexa Fluor® 405 Antibody Labeling Kits (Section 7.3, Table 7.13).

Alexa Fluor® 430 Dye

Few reactive dyes that absorb between 400 nm and 450 nm have appreciable fluorescence beyond 500 nm in aqueous solution. Our Alexa Fluor® 430 dye fills this spectral gap (Figure 1.34, Figure 1.35, Figure 7.4). Excitation near its absorption maximum at 431 nm is accompanied by strong yellow-green fluorescence, with an emission maximum at 541 nm. The coumarin-based amine-reactive succinimidyl ester of Alexa Fluor® 430 carboxylic acid (A10169) is available, as well as Alexa Fluor® 430 conjugates of secondary antibodies (A11063, A11064; Section 7.2) and streptavidin (S11237, Section 7.6). Alexa Fluor® 430 dye–labeled Fab fragments are provided in the Zenon® Alexa Fluor® 430 Antibody Labeling Kits (Section 7.3, Table 7.13).

Alexa Fluor® Labeling Reagents and Kits

All of our Alexa Fluor® dyes are available as amine-reactive succinimidyl esters (Table 1.2, Table 1.5), and the Alexa Fluor® 488 dye is additionally available as its single-isomer, hydrolysis-resistant tetrafluorophenyl (TFP) ester (A30005). Most of the Alexa Fluor® dyes are also offered as components of several protein and nucleic acid labeling kits (Table 1.2) that are principally discussed in Section 1.2, including:

- Easy-to-Use Protein Labeling Kits (Section 1.2, Table 1.5)
- Monoclonal Antibody Labeling Kits (Section 1.2, Table 1.5)
- Zenon® Antibody Labeling Kits (Section 7.3; Table 1.2, Table 7.13) for the easiest and fastest method of preparing labeled antibody complexes, particularly on a microgram or submicrogram scale
- ARES™ DNA Labeling Kits (Section 1.2, Table 1.5; Section 8.2)
- Alexa Fluor® Oligonucleotide Amine Labeling Kits (Section 1.2, Table 1.5; Section 8.2, Table 8.10)
- ULYSIS Nucleic Acid Labeling Kits (Section 8.2, Table 8.8), which utilize Alexa Fluor® conjugates of a guanosine-reactive platinum compound for labeling of intact nucleic acids

These kits and their components are described in detail in the sections and tables indicated above. In addition, we offer several ChromaTide® UTP, ChromaTide® dUTP, aha-dUTP and ChromaTide® OBEA-dCTP nucleotides (Table 8.6, Table 8.7) that include our Alexa Fluor® dyes for enzyme-catalyzed incorporation into nucleic acids. The ChromaTide® and aha-dUTP nucleotides are described in Section 8.2.

Purity of the Alexa Fluor® carboxylic acid succinimidyl esters when prepared and when packaged in a 5 mg unit size (Table 1.2) is usually >80–95% by HPLC. However, Alexa Fluor® dyes tenaciously bind water, and packaging of these products in smaller unit sizes — the 1 mg stand-alone reagents and the multiple vials used in all kits — may result in some loss of reactivity. The Alexa Fluor® 488 tetrafluorophenyl (TFP) ester (A30005) has somewhat better resistance to water and may be the preferred amine-reactive form reactive of this exceptional reagent. Our specifications for stand-alone Alexa Fluor® carboxylic acid succinimidyl esters that are sold in a 1 mg size or as a component of a labeling kit require the product to have reactivity ≥50% after packaging. As part of our quality control protocol, we test the suitability of the reactive Alexa Fluor® reagents in the 1 mg unit size and in all of our Alexa Fluor® protein and nucleic acid labeling kits after packaging; however, we recommend that all of the Alexa Fluor® carboxylic acid succinimidyl esters and Alexa Fluor® protein and nucleic acid labeling kits be used soon after receipt.

Several Alexa Fluor® dyes are also available as thiol-reactive maleimides and mercurials (Section 2.2, Table 2.1) and as aldehyde- and ketone-reactive hydrazides and hydroxylamines (Section 3.2, Table 3.1). The Alexa Fluor® hydrazides and hydroxylamines are also important probes for intracellular tracing (Section 14.3; Figure 3.16, Figure 14.23). Although some of the Alexa Fluor® dyes are mixtures of two isomers, all the reactive Alexa Fluor® dyes contain only a single reactive moiety.

The Alexa Fluor® fluorophores, reactive dyes, conjugates and their applications are the subject of several patents and patent applications filed by Molecular Probes, Inc., and are offered for research purposes only. Molecular Probes welcomes inquiries about licensing these products and technology for resale or other commercial uses. Custom conjugations of the Alexa Fluor® fluorophores are also available. Please contact our Custom and Bulk Sales Department.

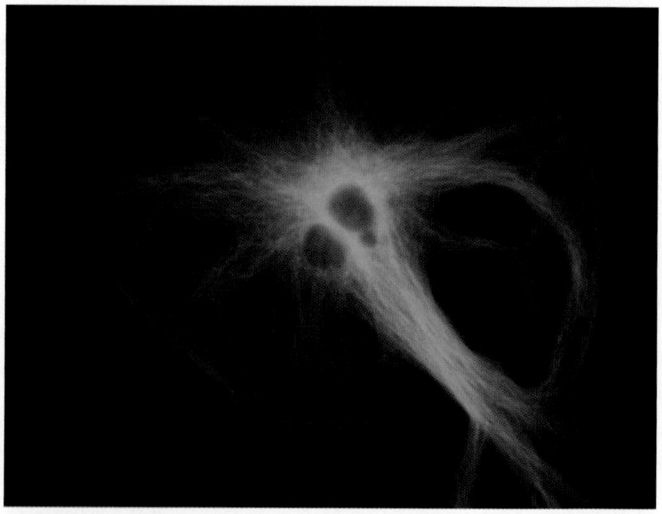

Figure 1.35 A bovine pulmonary artery endothelial (BPAE) cell labeled with mouse monoclonal anti–α-tubulin antibody (A11126) in combination with Alexa Fluor® 430 goat anti–mouse IgG antibody (A11063) to stain microtubules. The image was acquired using a longpass filter set allowing excitation at 455 ± 35 nm and emission at wavelengths greater than 515 nm.

Alexa Fluor® Bioconjugates and Tandem Conjugates

Alexa Fluor® Bioconjugates

For immunofluorescence, receptor labeling, nucleic acid synthesis, cell tracing and many other applications, we offer Alexa Fluor® dyes in a wide variety of bioconjugates, including those of:

- Tandem conjugates of R-phycoerythrin (R-PE) and allophycocyanin (APC) for multicolor applications that employ a single laser as an excitation source (Section 6.4; Figure 6.34, Figure 6.37)
- Zenon® labeling reagents (Section 7.3; Table 1.2, Table 7.13), for quick and convenient labeling of antibodies for multicolor applications
- Secondary antibodies (Section 7.2, Table 7.1)
- Protein A and protein G (Section 7.2, Table 7.12)
- FluoroNanogold antibody and streptavidin conjugates (Section 7.2, Section 7.6)
- Anti-fluorescein/Oregon Green® antibody for simultaneously amplifying and photostabilizing the signal of fluorescein- or Oregon Green® dye–conjugated probes (A11090, Section 7.4) and for changing the green fluorescence of these probes to red fluorescence (A11091, A21250; Section 7.4; Figure 7.72, Figure 7.73)
- Anti-biotin and anti–dinitrophenyl-KLH antibodies (Section 7.4)
- Primary antibodies, including the CD3, CD4 and CD8 antibodies (Section 7.5)
- Anti–green-fluorescent protein antibody (anti-GFP; A21311, A21312; Section 7.5)
- An antibody to the epitope tag hemagglutinin (anti-HA; A21287, A21288; Section 7.5)
- Anti–glutathione *S*-transferase antibody (A11131, Section 7.5)
- Avidin and streptavidin (Section 7.6, Table 7.22)
- Lectins (Section 7.7, Table 7.23)
- UTP, dUTP, aha-dUTP and OBEA-dCTP nucleotides (Section 8.2) for enzyme-mediated incorporation into nucleic acids
- Panomer™ 9 random oligodeoxynucleotide and oligodeoxythymidine-18 (dT_{18}) conjugates (Section 8.5, Table 8.18)
- Phalloidin, F-actin and DNase I (Section 11.1, Table 11.1)
- An antibody to glial fibrillary acidic protein (anti-GFAP, Section 11.2)
- Anti–OxPhos Complex IV antibody (anti–complex I of cytochrome oxidase, Section 12.2)
- Dextrans (Section 14.5)
- Bovine serum albumin, parvalbumin, soybean trypsin inhibitor, α-crystallin and cholera toxin subunit B (Section 14.7)
- Anti-bromodeoxyuridine antibody and kits for following cell proliferation and apoptosis (Section 15.4, Section 15.5)
- Annexin V (Section 15.5)
- Fibrinogen and methotrexate (Section 15.6)
- Lipopolysaccharides (Section 16.1, Table 16.1)
- Acetylated low-density lipoprotein (Section 16.1)
- *Escherichia coli, Staphylococcus aureus* and *zymosan A* BioParticles®, epidermal growth factor, histones and transferrin (Section 16.1; Table 16.2, Table 16.3)
- Angiotensin II, neuromedin C and substance P (Section 16.2)
- α-Bungarotoxin (Section 16.2, Table 16.4)
- Apamin (Section 16.3)
- Calmodulin (Section 17.3)

Alexa Fluor® Tandem Conjugates of Phycobiliproteins

We have conjugated R-phycoerythrin with an Alexa Fluor® 610 dye and with our Alexa Fluor® 647 and Alexa Fluor® 680 dyes — and in turn conjugated these fluorescent proteins to antibodies or streptavidin, yielding tandem conjugates that permit simultaneous multicolor labeling and detection of multiple targets with excitation by a single excitation source — the 488 nm spectral line of the argon-ion laser (Section 6.4, Figure 6.34). Additionally, our Alexa Fluor® 680, Alexa Fluor® 700 and Alexa Fluor® 750 tandem conjugates of allophycocyanin can be combined with allophycocyanin or Alexa Fluor® 647 bioconjugates for multicolor measurements using excitation by the lasers that emit at 633 to 650 nm (Figure 6.37). Zenon® Antibody Labeling Kits for the rapid and quantitative labeling of antibodies with the tandem phycobiliprotein dyes are also available (Section 7.3, Table 7.13).

DyeMer™ Bifluorophores

Our DyeMer™ 488/605, DyeMer™ 488/615 and DyeMer™ 488/630 conjugates of secondary antibodies (Section 7.2, Table 7.1) and of streptavidin (Section 7.6, Table 7.22) are optimized for use in flow cytometry applications. The red-orange–fluorescent DyeMer™ 488/605, red-fluorescent DyeMer™ 488/615 and far-red–fluorescent DyeMer™ 488/630 conjugates are each labeled with a unique bifluorophore comprising two covalently linked fluorophores that act as a donor–acceptor pair for fluorescence resonance energy transfer (FRET). When the green-fluorescent donor dye is excited with the 488 nm spectral line of the argon-ion laser, efficient energy transfer produces fluorescence of the long-wavelength acceptor dye, which emits at 611, 617 or 630 nm (Figure 7.31, Figure 7.32, Figure 7.33). Any fluorescence from the donor dye due to incomplete FRET can easily be compensated for by setting up compensation circuits to remove unwanted signals. Although their total fluorescence is not as intense as that of the phycobiliprotein tandem conjugates, the DyeMer™ conjugates exhibit minimal lot-to-lot variation and less interference at the antigen- or biotin-binding site due to the relatively small size of the DyeMer™ bifluorophores. Moreover, their fluorescence can be excited either at 488 nm or at their longer-wavelength absorption maximum. Because there is some green fluorescence emitted from the donor dye, the DyeMer™ conjugates were not developed for imaging applications. By carefully choosing bandpass filters that block this green fluorescence or by using a green-fluorescent label for the most abundant target to keep exposure times short, these DyeMer™ conjugates can be successfully applied to multicolor fluorescence microscopy experiments.

Signal Amplification with Alexa Fluor® Dyes

Tyramide Signal Amplification

Tyramide signal amplification (TSA) technology, which was developed by NEN (now a part of PerkinElmer Corporation) and licensed to Molecular Probes for in-cell and in-tissue applications, permits significant amplification of cellular targets by a horseradish peroxidase (HRP)–mediated scheme (Figure 6.5). Molecular Probes has introduced several TSA Kits (Section 6.2, Table 6.1), including kits that utilize Alexa Fluor® 350 tyramide (Figure 1.36), Alexa Fluor® 405 tyramide, Alexa Fluor® 488 tyramide (Figure 1.37, Figure 1.38), Alexa Fluor® 546 tyramide, Alexa Fluor® 555 tyramide, Alexa Fluor® 568 tyramide (Figure 1.39), Alexa Fluor® 594 tyramide or Alexa Fluor® 647 tyramide (Figure 1.40) as the amplification reagent. The HRP-catalyzed immobilization of a fluorescent tyramide can yield far greater total fluorescence than would ever be possible with direct labeling of the target — enabling detection of very low-abundance receptors (Figure 6.10) — and can be used in either live- or fixed-cell preparations. TSA also permits use of greatly decreased quantities of precious antibodies or nucleic acid probes. Our TSA Kits are listed in Table 6.1 and are extensively discussed in Section 6.2.

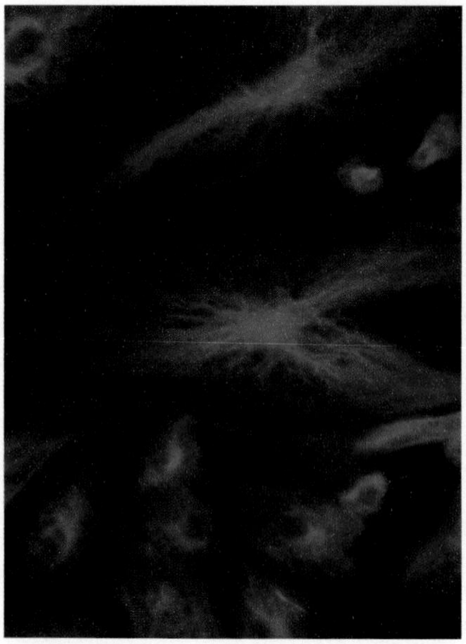

Figure 1.36 Fixed and permeabilized bovine pulmonary artery endothelial (BPAE) cells labeled with mouse monoclonal anti–α-tubulin antibody (A11126) and detected using TSA Kit #7 with the HRP conjugate of goat anti–mouse IgG antibody and Alexa Fluor® 350 tyramide (T20912).

Antibody-Based Signal Amplification Kits

Although the direct fluorescence signal of Alexa Fluor® conjugates tends to be significantly greater than that of other dyes with comparable spectra, we have also developed two kits that take further advantage of the superior brightness and photostability of Alexa Fluor® 488 dye– and Alexa Fluor® 594 dye–labeled reagents. These Alexa Fluor® Signal Amplification Kits are designed to substantially increase the signals obtained by immunofluorescence techniques (Figure 7.50), thus permitting detection of low-abundance targets. The Alexa Fluor® 488 Signal Amplification Kit for Fluorescein-Conjugated Probes (A11053) dramatically enhances the fluorescence and photostability of virtually any fluoresceinated probe (Figure 7.49). The Alexa Fluor® 488 Signal Amplification Kit for Mouse Antibodies (A11054) can be used to sensitively detect mouse primary antibodies. The similar Alexa Fluor® 568 and Alexa Fluor® 594 Signal Amplification Kits for Mouse Antibodies (A11066, A11067) provide ultrasensitive immunofluorescent detection at longer wavelengths. For additional details about these kits, see Section 7.2 and our product literature.

Alexa Fluor® Conjugates of Anti-Fluorescein/Oregon Green® Antibody

Our Alexa Fluor® 488 dye–labeled rabbit anti-fluorescein/Oregon Green® antibody (A11090, Section 7.4) can be used to enhance the green-fluorescent signal of the fluorescein (or Oregon Green®) hapten without changing its fluorescence color. Thus, this conjugate allows researchers to take advantage of the superior photostability of the Alexa Fluor® 488 dye, while utilizing existing fluorescein- or Oregon Green® dye–labeled probes and fluorescein-compatible optics (Table 23.9). The Alexa Fluor® 594 dye–labeled rabbit anti-fluorescein/Oregon Green® antibody

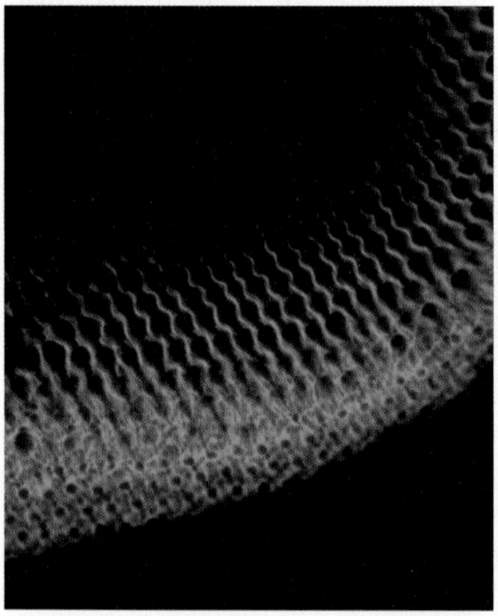

Figure 1.37 A zebrafish retina cryosection labeled with the mouse monoclonal antibody FRet 6 and detected using TSA Kit #9 with the HRP conjugate of goat anti–mouse IgG antibody and Alexa Fluor® 488 tyramide (T20912).

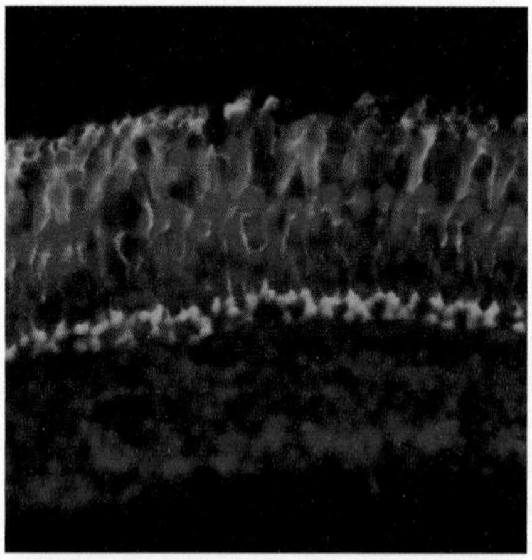

Figure 1.38 A zebrafish retina cryosection labeled with the mouse monoclonal antibody FRet 43 and detected using TSA Kit #9 with the HRP conjugate of goat anti–mouse IgG antibody and green-fluorescent Alexa Fluor® 488 tyramide (T20912). The nuclei were counterstained with blue-fluorescent Hoechst 33258 (H1398, H3569, H21491).

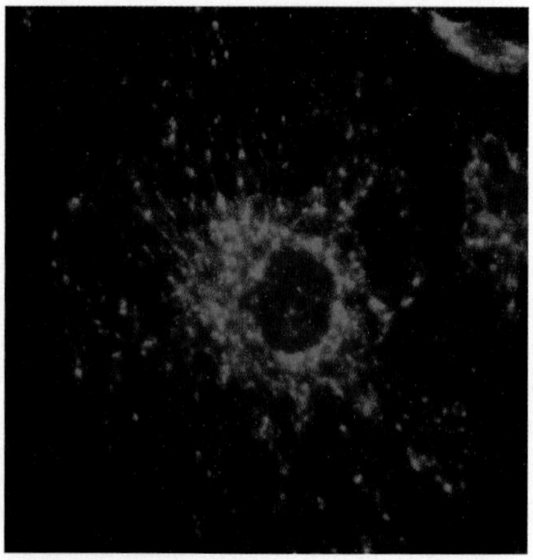

Figure 1.39 Fixed and permeabilized bovine pulmonary artery endothelial cells (BPAEC) labeled with anti–OxPhos Complex IV subunit I (human) antibody (anti–cytochrome oxidase subunit I) (A6403) and detected using TSA Kit #4 with the HRP conjugate of goat anti–mouse IgG antibody and Alexa Fluor® 568 tyramide (T20914).

(A11091) can be used to convert the green fluorescence of fluorescein or Oregon Green® conjugates into exceptionally photostable red fluorescence (Figure 7.72), and to amplify the signal from fluorescein and Oregon Green® conjugates by as much as 100-fold (Figure 7.73).

Antibodies to the Alexa Fluor® 488 and Alexa Fluor® 405 Dyes

We offer a rabbit polyclonal antibody to the Alexa Fluor® 488 dye (A11094, Section 7.4) that quenches the dye's fluorescence and can be used in various signal amplification schemes, potentially including further amplification of the signal from the TSA Kits that contain Alexa Fluor® 488 tyramide (T20912, T20922, T20932; Section 6.2) or from Alexa Fluor® conjugates of proteins or nucleic acids. As expected, the rabbit polyclonal antibody to the Cascade Blue® dye that we developed (A5760, Section 7.4) strongly interacts with the Alexa Fluor® 405 dye, making it useful for various fluorescence quenching and amplification schemes. Our Zenon® Rabbit IgG Labeling Kits (Section 7.3, Table 7.13) can also be used to prepare fluorescent dye–, biotin- or enzyme-labeled complexes of these rabbit IgG antibodies for use in various detection and amplification schemes.

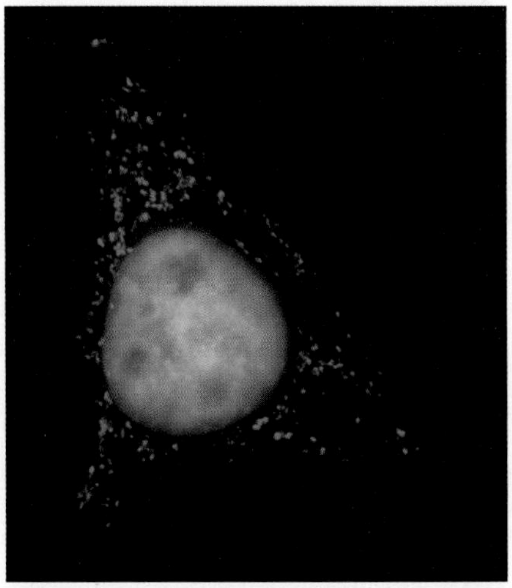

Figure 1.40 Fixed and permeabilized bovine pulmonary artery endothelial cells (BPAEC) labeled with anti–OxPhos Complex IV subunit I (human) antibody (anti–cytochrome oxidase subunit I) (A6403) and detected using TSA Kit #6 with the HRP conjugate of goat anti–mouse IgG antibody and Alexa Fluor® 647 tyramide (T20916). The image was deconvolved using Huygens software (Scientific Volume Imaging, www.svi.nl).

References

1. J Histochem Cytochem 51, 1699 (2003); **2.** J Histochem Cytochem 47, 1179 (1999); **3.** Cytometry 41, 316 (2000); **4.** J Bacteriol 182, 2793 (2000); **5.** J Histochem Cytochem 47, 1213 (1999); **6.** Electrophoresis 25, 779 (2004); **7.** Anal Biochem 308, 18 (2002); **8.** J Histochem Cytochem 48, 653 (2000); **9.** Biotechniques 36, 114 (2004); **10.** Anal Biochem 331, 243 (2004); **11.** Bioconjug Chem 14, 195 (2003); **12.** J Immunol Methods 271, 17 (2002); **13.** Bioconjug Chem 11, 696 (2000).

Data Table — 1.3 Alexa Fluor Dyes Spanning the Visible and Near-Infrared Spectrum

Cat #	MW	Storage	Soluble	Abs	EC	Em	Solvent	Notes
A10168	410.35	F,D,L	H_2O, DMSO	346	19,000	445	pH 7	1
A10169	701.75	F,D,L	H_2O, DMSO	430	15,000	545	pH 7	1
A20000, A20100	643.41	F,DD,L	H_2O, DMSO	494	73,000	517	pH 7	1, 2
A20001, A20101	723.77	F,DD,L	H_2O, DMSO	530	81,000	555	pH 7	1
A20002, A20102	1079.39	F,DD,L	H_2O, DMSO	554	112,000	570	pH 7	1
A20003, A20103	791.80	F,DD,L	H_2O, DMSO	578	88,000	602	pH 7	1, 3
A20004, A20104	819.85	F,DD,L	H_2O, DMSO	590	92,000	617	pH 7	1, 4
A20005, A20105	~1200	F,DD,L	H_2O, DMSO	621	159,000	639	MeOH	1, 5, 6
A20006, A20106	~1250	F,DD,L	H_2O, DMSO	651	270,000	672	MeOH	1, 7
A20007, A20107	~1100	F,DD,L	H_2O, DMSO	668	132,000	698	MeOH	1, 8
A20008, A20108	~1150	F,DD,L	H_2O, DMSO	684	183,000	707	MeOH	1, 9
A20009, A20109	~1250	F,DD,L	H_2O, DMSO	555	155,000	572	MeOH	1
A20010, A20110	~1400	F,DD,L	H_2O, DMSO	702	196,000	723	MeOH	1
A20011, A20110	~1300	F,DD,L	H_2O, DMSO	749	240,000	782	MeOH	1
A30000, A30100	1028.26	F,DD,L	H_2O, DMSO	400	35,000	424	pH 7	1, 10
A30001	700.43	F,DD,L	H_2O, DMSO	502	71,000	525	pH 7	1
A30002	713.69	F,DD,L	H_2O, DMSO	517	80,000	542	pH 7	1
A30003, A30103	1171.66	F,DD,L	H_2O, DMSO	604	138,000	623	MeOH	1
A30005	884.91	F,DD,L	H_2O, DMSO	494	72,000	520	pH 7	1, 2

For definitions of the contents of this data table, see "Navigating this Handbook" in the introductory pages.

Notes

1. This sulfonated succinimidyl ester derivative is water soluble and may be dissolved in buffer at ~pH 8 for reaction with amines. Long-term storage in water is NOT recommended due to hydrolysis.
2. The fluorescence lifetime (τ) of the Alexa Fluor® 488 dye in pH 7.4 buffer at 20°C is 4.1 nanoseconds. Data provided by the SPEX Fluorescence Group, Jobin Yvon Inc.
3. The fluorescence lifetime (τ) of the Alexa Fluor® 568 dye in pH 7.4 buffer at 20°C is 3.6 nanoseconds. Data provided by the SPEX Fluorescence Group, Jobin Yvon Inc.
4. The fluorescence lifetime (τ) of the Alexa Fluor® 594 dye in pH 7.4 buffer at 20°C is 3.9 nanoseconds. Data provided by the SPEX Fluorescence Group, Jobin Yvon Inc.
5. Alexa Fluor® 633 dye–labeled proteins typically exhibit two absorption peaks at about ~580 and ~630 nm. Fluorescence excitation is more efficient at the 630 nm absorption peak.
6. The fluorescence lifetime (τ) of the Alexa Fluor® 633 dye in H_2O at 20°C is 3.2 nanoseconds. Data provided by LJL BioSystems/Molecular Devices Corporation.
7. The fluorescence lifetime (τ) of the Alexa Fluor® 647 dye in H_2O at 20°C is 1.0 nanoseconds and 1.5 nanoseconds in EtOH (Bioconjug Chem 14, 195 (2003)).
8. The fluorescence lifetime (τ) of the Alexa Fluor® 660 dye in pH 7.5 buffer at 20°C is 1.2 nanoseconds. Data provided by Pierre-Alain Muller, Max Planck Institute for Biophysical Chemistry, Göttingen.
9. The fluorescence lifetime (τ) of the Alexa Fluor® 680 dye in pH 7.5 buffer at 20°C is 1.2 nanoseconds. Data provided by Pierre-Alain Muller, Max Planck Institute for Biophysical Chemistry, Göttingen.
10. The Alexa Fluor® 405 and Cascade Blue® dyes have a second absorption peak at about 376 nm with EC ~80% of the 395–400 nm peak.

Product List — 1.3 Alexa Fluor Dyes Spanning the Visible and Near-Infrared Spectrum

Cat #	Product Name	Unit Size
A10168	Alexa Fluor® 350 carboxylic acid, succinimidyl ester	5 mg
A30000	Alexa Fluor® 405 carboxylic acid, succinimidyl ester	1 mg
A30100	Alexa Fluor® 405 carboxylic acid, succinimidyl ester	5 mg
A10169	Alexa Fluor® 430 carboxylic acid, succinimidyl ester	5 mg
A20000	Alexa Fluor® 488 carboxylic acid, succinimidyl ester *mixed isomers*	1 mg
A20100	Alexa Fluor® 488 carboxylic acid, succinimidyl ester *mixed isomers*	5 mg
A30001	Alexa Fluor® 500 carboxylic acid, succinimidyl ester *mixed isomers*	1 mg
A30002	Alexa Fluor® 514 carboxylic acid, succinimidyl ester *mixed isomers*	1 mg
A20001	Alexa Fluor® 532 carboxylic acid, succinimidyl ester	1 mg
A20101MP	Alexa Fluor® 532 carboxylic acid, succinimidyl ester	5 mg
A20002	Alexa Fluor® 546 carboxylic acid, succinimidyl ester	1 mg
A20102	Alexa Fluor® 546 carboxylic acid, succinimidyl ester	5 mg
A20009	Alexa Fluor® 555 carboxylic acid, succinimidyl ester	1 mg
A20109	Alexa Fluor® 555 carboxylic acid, succinimidyl ester	5 mg
A20003	Alexa Fluor® 568 carboxylic acid, succinimidyl ester *mixed isomers*	1 mg
A20103	Alexa Fluor® 568 carboxylic acid, succinimidyl ester *mixed isomers*	5 mg
A20004	Alexa Fluor® 594 carboxylic acid, succinimidyl ester *mixed isomers*	1 mg
A20104	Alexa Fluor® 594 carboxylic acid, succinimidyl ester *mixed isomers*	5 mg
A30003	Alexa Fluor® 610 carboxylic acid, succinimidyl ester *6-isomer*	1 mg
A30103	Alexa Fluor® 610 carboxylic acid, succinimidyl ester *6-isomer*	5 mg
A20005	Alexa Fluor® 633 carboxylic acid, succinimidyl ester	1 mg
A20105	Alexa Fluor® 633 carboxylic acid, succinimidyl ester	5 mg
A20006	Alexa Fluor® 647 carboxylic acid, succinimidyl ester	1 mg
A20106	Alexa Fluor® 647 carboxylic acid, succinimidyl ester	5 mg
A20007	Alexa Fluor® 660 carboxylic acid, succinimidyl ester	1 mg
A20107	Alexa Fluor® 660 carboxylic acid, succinimidyl ester	5 mg
A20008	Alexa Fluor® 680 carboxylic acid, succinimidyl ester	1 mg
A20108	Alexa Fluor® 680 carboxylic acid, succinimidyl ester	5 mg
A20010	Alexa Fluor® 700 carboxylic acid, succinimidyl ester	1 mg
A20110	Alexa Fluor® 700 carboxylic acid, succinimidyl ester	5 mg
A20011	Alexa Fluor® 750 carboxylic acid, succinimidyl ester	1 mg
A20111	Alexa Fluor® 750 carboxylic acid, succinimidyl ester	5 mg
A30005	Alexa Fluor® 488 carboxylic acid, 2,3,5,6-tetrafluorophenyl ester (Alexa Fluor® 488 5-TFP) *5-isomer*	1 mg
A20181	Alexa Fluor® 488 Monoclonal Antibody Labeling Kit *5 labelings*	1 kit
A20182	Alexa Fluor® 532 Monoclonal Antibody Labeling Kit *5 labelings*	1 kit
A20183	Alexa Fluor® 546 Monoclonal Antibody Labeling Kit *5 labelings*	1 kit
A20187	Alexa Fluor® 555 Monoclonal Antibody Labeling Kit *5 labelings*	1 kit
A20184	Alexa Fluor® 568 Monoclonal Antibody Labeling Kit *5 labelings*	1 kit
A20185	Alexa Fluor® 594 Monoclonal Antibody Labeling Kit *5 labelings*	1 kit
A20186	Alexa Fluor® 647 Monoclonal Antibody Labeling Kit *5 labelings*	1 kit
A20191	Alexa Fluor® 488 Oligonucleotide Amine Labeling Kit *3 labelings*	1 kit
A20192	Alexa Fluor® 532 Oligonucleotide Amine Labeling Kit *3 labelings*	1 kit
A20193	Alexa Fluor® 546 Oligonucleotide Amine Labeling Kit *3 labelings*	1 kit
A20197	Alexa Fluor® 555 Oligonucleotide Amine Labeling Kit *3 labelings*	1 kit
A20194	Alexa Fluor® 568 Oligonucleotide Amine Labeling Kit *3 labelings*	1 kit
A20195	Alexa Fluor® 594 Oligonucleotide Amine Labeling Kit *3 labelings*	1 kit
A20196	Alexa Fluor® 647 Oligonucleotide Amine Labeling Kit *3 labelings*	1 kit
A10170	Alexa Fluor® 350 Protein Labeling Kit *3 labelings*	1 kit
A10171	Alexa Fluor® 430 Protein Labeling Kit *3 labelings*	1 kit
A10235	Alexa Fluor® 488 Protein Labeling Kit *3 labelings*	1 kit
A10236	Alexa Fluor® 532 Protein Labeling Kit *3 labelings*	1 kit
A10237	Alexa Fluor® 546 Protein Labeling Kit *3 labelings*	1 kit
A20174	Alexa Fluor® 555 Protein Labeling Kit *3 labelings*	1 kit
A10238	Alexa Fluor® 568 Protein Labeling Kit *3 labelings*	1 kit
A10239	Alexa Fluor® 594 Protein Labeling Kit *3 labelings*	1 kit
A20170	Alexa Fluor® 633 Protein Labeling Kit *3 labelings*	1 kit
A20173	Alexa Fluor® 647 Protein Labeling Kit *3 labelings*	1 kit
A20171	Alexa Fluor® 660 Protein Labeling Kit *3 labelings*	1 kit
A20172	Alexa Fluor® 680 Protein Labeling Kit *3 labelings*	1 kit
A32756	Alexa Fluor® 555 reactive dye decapack *for microarrays* *set of 10 vials*	1 set

For current prices or to order online, visit probes.invitrogen.com

Cat #	Product Name	Unit Size
A32751	Alexa Fluor® 594 reactive dye decapack *for microarrays* *set of 10 vials*	1 set
A32757	Alexa Fluor® 647 reactive dye decapack *for microarrays* *set of 10 vials*	1 set
A32755	Alexa Fluor® 555 and Alexa Fluor® 647 reactive dye decapacks *for microarrays* *set of 2 x 10 vials* *includes A32756 and A32757 decapacks*	1 set
A21665	ARES™ Alexa Fluor® 488 DNA Labeling Kit *10 labelings*	1 kit
A21666	ARES™ Alexa Fluor® 532 DNA Labeling Kit *10 labelings*	1 kit
A21667	ARES™ Alexa Fluor® 546 DNA Labeling Kit *10 labelings*	1 kit
A21677	ARES™ Alexa Fluor® 555 DNA Labeling Kit *10 labelings*	1 kit
A21668	ARES™ Alexa Fluor® 568 DNA Labeling Kit *10 labelings*	1 kit
A21669	ARES™ Alexa Fluor® 594 DNA Labeling Kit *10 labelings*	1 kit
A21676	ARES™ Alexa Fluor® 647 DNA Labeling Kit *10 labelings*	1 kit
A21671	ARES™ Alexa Fluor® 660 DNA Labeling Kit *5-10 labelings*	1 kit
A21672	ARES™ Alexa Fluor® 680 DNA Labeling Kit *5-10 labelings*	1 kit
U21650	ULYSIS® Alexa Fluor® 488 Nucleic Acid Labeling Kit *20 labelings*	1 kit
U21651	ULYSIS® Alexa Fluor® 532 Nucleic Acid Labeling Kit *20 labelings*	1 kit
U21652	ULYSIS® Alexa Fluor® 546 Nucleic Acid Labeling Kit *20 labelings*	1 kit
U21653	ULYSIS® Alexa Fluor® 568 Nucleic Acid Labeling Kit *20 labelings*	1 kit
U21654	ULYSIS® Alexa Fluor® 594 Nucleic Acid Labeling Kit *20 labelings*	1 kit
U21660	ULYSIS® Alexa Fluor® 647 Nucleic Acid Labeling Kit *20 labelings*	1 kit
U21656	ULYSIS® Alexa Fluor® 660 Nucleic Acid Labeling Kit *20 labelings*	1 kit
U21657	ULYSIS® Alexa Fluor® 680 Nucleic Acid Labeling Kit *20 labelings*	1 kit
Z25400	Zenon® Alexa Fluor® 350 Human IgG Labeling Kit *50 labelings*	1 kit
Z25000	Zenon® Alexa Fluor® 350 Mouse IgG_1 Labeling Kit *50 labelings*	1 kit
Z25100	Zenon® Alexa Fluor® 350 Mouse IgG_{2a} Labeling Kit *50 labelings*	1 kit
Z25200	Zenon® Alexa Fluor® 350 Mouse IgG_{2b} Labeling Kit *50 labelings*	1 kit
Z25300	Zenon® Alexa Fluor® 350 Rabbit IgG Labeling Kit *50 labelings*	1 kit
Z25013	Zenon® Alexa Fluor® 405 Mouse IgG_1 Labeling Kit *50 labelings*	1 kit
Z25113	Zenon® Alexa Fluor® 405 Mouse IgG_{2a} Labeling Kit *50 labelings*	1 kit
Z25213	Zenon® Alexa Fluor® 405 Mouse IgG_{2b} Labeling Kit *50 labelings*	1 kit
Z25313	Zenon® Alexa Fluor® 405 Rabbit IgG Labeling Kit *50 labelings*	1 kit
Z25001	Zenon® Alexa Fluor® 430 Mouse IgG_1 Labeling Kit *50 labelings*	1 kit
Z25301	Zenon® Alexa Fluor® 430 Rabbit IgG Labeling Kit *50 labelings*	1 kit
Z25602	Zenon® Alexa Fluor® 488 Goat IgG Labeling Kit *50 labelings*	1 kit
Z25402	Zenon® Alexa Fluor® 488 Human IgG Labeling Kit *50 labelings*	1 kit
Z25002	Zenon® Alexa Fluor® 488 Mouse IgG_1 Labeling Kit *50 labelings*	1 kit
Z25102	Zenon® Alexa Fluor® 488 Mouse IgG_{2a} Labeling Kit *50 labelings*	1 kit
Z25202	Zenon® Alexa Fluor® 488 Mouse IgG_{2b} Labeling Kit *50 labelings*	1 kit
Z25302	Zenon® Alexa Fluor® 488 Rabbit IgG Labeling Kit *50 labelings*	1 kit
Z25003	Zenon® Alexa Fluor® 532 Mouse IgG_1 Labeling Kit *50 labelings*	1 kit
Z25303	Zenon® Alexa Fluor® 532 Rabbit IgG Labeling Kit *50 labelings*	1 kit
Z25004	Zenon® Alexa Fluor® 546 Mouse IgG_1 Labeling Kit *50 labelings*	1 kit
Z25104	Zenon® Alexa Fluor® 546 Mouse IgG_{2a} Labeling Kit *50 labelings*	1 kit
Z25204	Zenon® Alexa Fluor® 546 Mouse IgG_{2b} Labeling Kit *50 labelings*	1 kit
Z25304	Zenon® Alexa Fluor® 546 Rabbit IgG Labeling Kit *50 labelings*	1 kit
Z25605	Zenon® Alexa Fluor® 555 Goat IgG Labeling Kit *50 labelings*	1 kit
Z25405	Zenon® Alexa Fluor® 555 Human IgG Labeling Kit *50 labelings*	1 kit
Z25005	Zenon® Alexa Fluor® 555 Mouse IgG_1 Labeling Kit *50 labelings*	1 kit
Z25105	Zenon® Alexa Fluor® 555 Mouse IgG_{2a} Labeling Kit *50 labelings*	1 kit
Z25205	Zenon® Alexa Fluor® 555 Mouse IgG_{2b} Labeling Kit *50 labelings*	1 kit
Z25305	Zenon® Alexa Fluor® 555 Rabbit IgG Labeling Kit *50 labelings*	1 kit
Z25006	Zenon® Alexa Fluor® 568 Mouse IgG_1 Labeling Kit *50 labelings*	1 kit
Z25106	Zenon® Alexa Fluor® 568 Mouse IgG_{2a} Labeling Kit *50 labelings*	1 kit
Z25206	Zenon® Alexa Fluor® 568 Mouse IgG_{2b} Labeling Kit *50 labelings*	1 kit
Z25306	Zenon® Alexa Fluor® 568 Rabbit IgG Labeling Kit *50 labelings*	1 kit
Z25607	Zenon® Alexa Fluor® 594 Goat IgG Labeling Kit *50 labelings*	1 kit
Z25407	Zenon® Alexa Fluor® 594 Human IgG Labeling Kit *50 labelings*	1 kit
Z25007	Zenon® Alexa Fluor® 594 Mouse IgG_1 Labeling Kit *50 labelings*	1 kit
Z25107	Zenon® Alexa Fluor® 594 Mouse IgG_{2a} Labeling Kit *50 labelings*	1 kit
Z25207	Zenon® Alexa Fluor® 594 Mouse IgG_{2b} Labeling Kit *50 labelings*	1 kit
Z25307	Zenon® Alexa Fluor® 594 Rabbit IgG Labeling Kit *50 labelings*	1 kit
Z25020	Zenon® Alexa Fluor® 610–R-Phycoerythrin Mouse IgG_1 Labeling Kit *10 labelings*	1 kit
Z25608	Zenon® Alexa Fluor® 647 Goat IgG Labeling Kit *50 labelings*	1 kit
Z25408	Zenon® Alexa Fluor® 647 Human IgG Labeling Kit *50 labelings*	1 kit

For current prices or to order online, visit probes.invitrogen.com

Product List — 1.3 Alexa Fluor Dyes Spanning the Visible and Near-Infrared Spectrum — continued

Cat #	Product Name	Unit Size
Z25008	Zenon® Alexa Fluor® 647 Mouse IgG_1 Labeling Kit *50 labelings*	1 kit
Z25108	Zenon® Alexa Fluor® 647 Mouse IgG_{2a} Labeling Kit *50 labelings*	1 kit
Z25208	Zenon® Alexa Fluor® 647 Mouse IgG_{2b} Labeling Kit *50 labelings*	1 kit
Z25308	Zenon® Alexa Fluor® 647 Rabbit IgG Labeling Kit *50 labelings*	1 kit
Z25021	Zenon® Alexa Fluor® 647–R-Phycoerythrin Mouse IgG_1 Labeling Kit *10 labelings*	1 kit
Z25121	Zenon® Alexa Fluor® 647–R-Phycoerythrin Mouse IgG_{2a} Labeling Kit *10 labelings*	1 kit
Z25221	Zenon® Alexa Fluor® 647–R-Phycoerythrin Mouse IgG_{2b} Labeling Kit *10 labelings*	1 kit
Z25009	Zenon® Alexa Fluor® 660 Mouse IgG_1 Labeling Kit *50 labelings*	1 kit
Z25109	Zenon® Alexa Fluor® 660 Mouse IgG_{2a} Labeling Kit *50 labelings*	1 kit
Z25209	Zenon® Alexa Fluor® 660 Mouse IgG_{2b} Labeling Kit *50 labelings*	1 kit
Z25309	Zenon® Alexa Fluor® 660 Rabbit IgG Labeling Kit *50 labelings*	1 kit
Z25010	Zenon® Alexa Fluor® 680 Mouse IgG_1 Labeling Kit *50 labelings*	1 kit
Z25110	Zenon® Alexa Fluor® 680 Mouse IgG_{2a} Labeling Kit *50 labelings*	1 kit
Z25210	Zenon® Alexa Fluor® 680 Mouse IgG_{2b} Labeling Kit *50 labelings*	1 kit
Z25310	Zenon® Alexa Fluor® 680 Rabbit IgG Labeling Kit *50 labelings*	1 kit
Z25022	Zenon® Alexa Fluor® 680–R-Phycoerythrin Mouse IgG_1 Labeling Kit *10 labelings*	1 kit
Z25011	Zenon® Alexa Fluor® 700 Mouse IgG_1 Labeling Kit *50 labelings*	1 kit
Z25311	Zenon® Alexa Fluor® 700 Rabbit IgG Labeling Kit *50 labelings*	1 kit
Z25030	Zenon® Alexa Fluor® 700–Allophycocyanin Mouse IgG_1 Labeling Kit *10 labelings*	1 kit
Z25312	Zenon® Alexa Fluor® 750 Rabbit IgG Labeling Kit *50 labelings*	1 kit
Z25031	Zenon® Alexa Fluor® 750–Allophycocyanin Mouse IgG_1 Labeling Kit *10 labelings*	1 kit
Z25606	Zenon® Alexa Fluor® 568 Goat IgG Labeling Kit *50 labelings*	1 kit
Z25090	Zenon® Alexa Fluor® 488 Mouse IgG_1 Labeling Kit *enhanced with TSA™ technology* *25 labelings*	1 kit
Z25091	Zenon® Alexa Fluor® 568 Mouse IgG_1 Labeling Kit *enhanced with TSA™ technology* *25 labelings*	1 kit

For current prices or to order online, visit probes.invitrogen.com

1.4 BODIPY® Dye Series

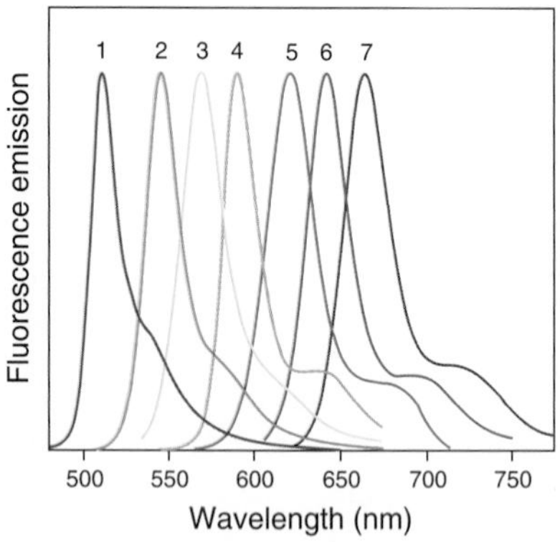

Figure 1.41 Normalized fluorescence emission spectra of **1**) BODIPY® FL, **2**) BODIPY® R6G, **3**) BODIPY® TMR, **4**) BODIPY® 581/591, **5**) BODIPY® TR, **6**) BODIPY® 630/650 and **7**) BODIPY® 650/665 fluorophores in methanol.

Overview of Our BODIPY® Fluorophores

Our patented BODIPY® fluorophores have spectral characteristics that are often superior to those of fluorescein, tetramethylrhodamine, Texas Red® and longer-wavelength dyes and may be substituted for these dyes in some applications. With derivatives that span the visible spectrum (Figure 1.41), BODIPY® dyes are proving to be extremely versatile. We use them to generate fluorescent conjugates of proteins, nucleotides, oligonucleotides and dextrans, as well as to prepare fluorescent enzyme substrates, fatty acids, phospholipids, lipopolysaccharides, receptor ligands and polystyrene microspheres. BODIPY® dyes are unusual in that they are relatively nonpolar and the chromophore is electrically neutral (Figure 1.42). These properties sometimes enhance the affinity of their ligand conjugates for receptors, as long as the overall conjugate is not too lipophilic. BODIPY® dye conjugates of low molecular weight molecules also tend to be more permeant to live cells than are conjugates of charged fluorophores (Section 14.2). In addition, oligonucleotide conjugates of several of our BODIPY® dyes have been reported to be useful for DNA sequencing[1–3] (Section 8.2, Table 8.1), in part because the dye exhibits minimal effect on the mobility of the fragment during electrophoresis. And with their high peak intensity, reactive BODIPY® dyes are among the most detectable amine-derivatization reagents available for HPLC and capillary electrophoresis.[4] The BODIPY® dyes are more useful than most other long-wavelength dyes, including fluoresceins and carbocyanines, for assays that measure fluorescence polarization[5–8] (see Note 1.5 "Technical Focus: Fluorescence Polarization (FP)"). Furthermore, BODIPY® dyes have exceptionally large cross-sections for excitation by multiphoton excitation sources.[9,10]

Amine-reactive BODIPY® dyes (Table 1.6) are discussed below; thiol-reactive BODIPY® dyes are included in Section 2.2. Other reactive BODIPY® dyes useful for derivatizing aldehydes, ketones and carboxylic acids are described in Section 3.2 and Section 3.3. Applications of some thiol-reactive BODIPY® dyes for cell tracing are discussed in Section 14.2.

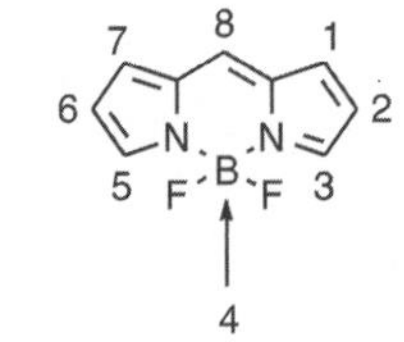

Figure 1.42 The structure and numbering of the BODIPY® fluorophore, 4,4-difluoro-4-bora-3a,4a-diaza-*s*-indacene.

The core structure of the BODIPY® fluorophore is shown in Figure 1.42. Solutions of the alkyl-substituted derivatives have a green, fluorescein-like fluorescence. However, when substituents that yield additional conjugation are added to the parent molecule, both the absorption and emission spectra of the resulting derivatives can shift to significantly longer wavelengths, with emission maxima of greater than 750 nm now possible with some BODIPY® derivatives. Our goal has been to develop BODIPY® dyes that are optimal for the major excitation sources and that match the common optical filter sets (Table 23.9). Accordingly, our best BODIPY® substitutes for the fluorescein, rhodamine 6G, tetramethylrhodamine and Texas Red® fluorophores are BODIPY® FL, BODIPY® R6G, BODIPY® TMR and BODIPY® TR, respectively (Figure 1.43). Because there are so many BODIPY® dyes, we have had to develop a systematic strategy for naming them. Except for BODIPY® FL, BODIPY® R6G, BODIPY® TMR and BODIPY® TR, we now identify these dyes with the registered trademark BODIPY® followed by the approximate absorption/emission maxima in nm (determined in methanol); for example, the BODIPY® 581/591 dye.

The BODIPY® fluorophores, reactive dyes and conjugates are covered by several patents issued to Molecular Probes. These products are offered for research purposes only. Molecular Probes welcomes inquiries about licensing these products for resale or other commercial uses. Custom conjugations of the various BODIPY® fluorophores are also available from Molecular Probes; please contact our Custom and Bulk Sales Department. Custom-conjugated oligonucleotides are available through our licensees (Licensing).

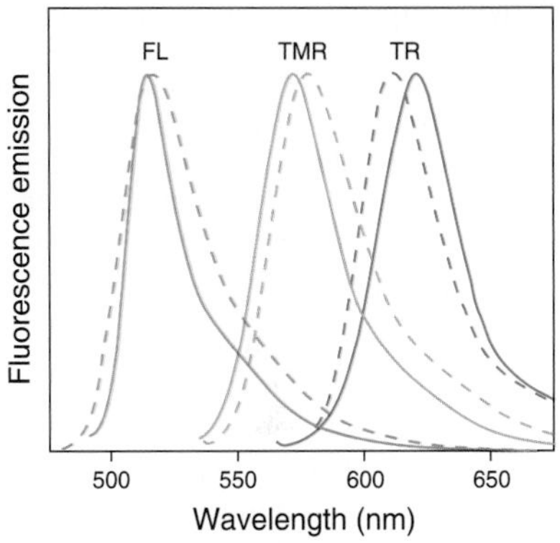

Figure 1.43 Normalized fluorescence emission spectra of goat anti–mouse IgG antibody conjugates of fluorescein (FL), tetramethylrhodamine (TMR) and the Texas Red® (TR) dyes, shown by dashed lines (---), as compared with goat anti–mouse IgG antibody conjugates of BODIPY® FL, BODIPY® TMR and BODIPY® TR dyes, respectively, shown by solid lines (—).

BODIPY® FL Dye: A Substitute for Fluorescein

With the most fluorescein-like spectra of the BODIPY® dyes, the green-fluorescent BODIPY® FL fluorophore (Figure 1.44) (excitation/emission maxima ~503/512 nm) has several characteristics [11,12] that make it potentially superior to fluorescein in some applications. These include:

- High extinction coefficient (ε >80,000 $cm^{-1}M^{-1}$)
- High fluorescence quantum yield (often approaching 1.0, even in water)
- Spectra that are relatively insensitive to solvent polarity and pH [11]

Table 1.6 — Amine-reactive BODIPY® dyes

BODIPY® Dye	Abs *	Em *	COOH	STP	Succinimidyl Ester
BODIPY® 493/503	500	506			D2191
BODIPY® FL	505	513	D2183 (C_3) D3834 (C_5)	B10006	D2184 (C_3) D6140 (SSE) D6141 (CASE) D6102 (X) D6184 (C_5)
BODIPY® R6G	528	550			D6180
BODIPY® 530/550	534	554			D2187
BODIPY® TMR	542	574		B10002	D6117 (X)
BODIPY® 558/568	558	569			D2219
BODIPY® 564/570	565	571			D2222
BODIPY® 576/589	576	590			D2225
BODIPY® 581/591	584	592			D2228
BODIPY® TR	589	617		B10003	D6116 (X)
BODIPY® 630/650-X †	625	640			D10000
BODIPY® 650/655-X †	646	660		B10005	D10001

* Approximate absorption (Abs) and fluorescence (Em) maxima, in nm, for the goat anti–mouse IgG antibody or dextran conjugates in aqueous buffer. † Not recommended for derivatizing proteins. COOH = Carboxylic acid. C_3 = Propionic acid. C_5 = Pentanoic acid. SSE = Sulfosuccinimidyl ester. CASE = Cysteic acid, succinimidyl ester. X = Aminohexanoyl spacer separating the dye and the SE. STP = 4-Sulfotetrafluorophenyl ester.

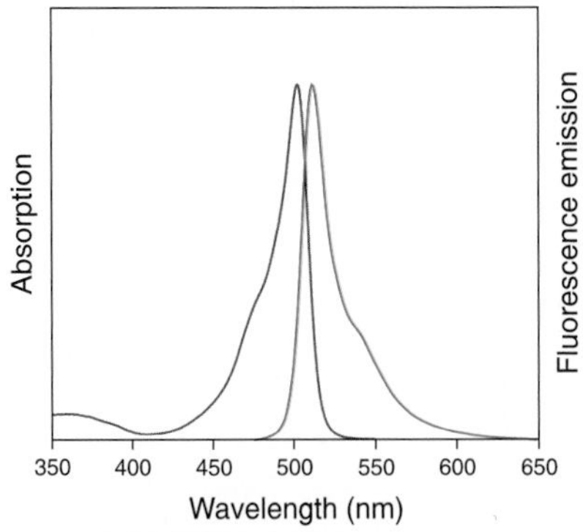

Figure 1.44 Absorption and fluorescence emission spectra of BODIPY® FL propionic acid, succinimidyl ester in methanol.

Note 1.5 — Technical Focus

Fluorescence Polarization (FP)

Principles

Fluorescence polarization measurements provide information on molecular orientation and mobility and processes that modulate them, including receptor–ligand interactions, proteolysis, protein–DNA interactions, membrane fluidity and muscle contraction (Figure 1).

Because polarization is a general property of fluorescent molecules (with certain exceptions such as lanthanide chelates), polarization-based readouts are somewhat less dye-dependent and less susceptible to environmental interferences such as pH changes than assays based on fluorescence intensity measurements. Experimentally, the degree of polarization is determined from measurements of fluorescence intensities parallel and perpendicular with respect to the plane of linearly polarized excitation light, and is expressed in terms of fluorescence polarization (P) or anisotropy (r):

$$P = \frac{(F_{\parallel} - F_{\perp})}{(F_{\parallel} + F_{\perp})} \qquad r = \frac{(F_{\parallel} - F_{\perp})}{(F_{\parallel} + 2F_{\perp})}$$

where $F_{\parallel}$ = fluorescence intensity parallel to the excitation plane
$F_{\perp}$ = fluorescence intensity perpendicular to the excitation plane

Note that both P and r are ratio quantities with no nominal dependence on dye concentration. Because of the ratio formulation, fluorescence intensity variations due to the presence of colored sample additives tend to cancel and produce relatively minor inteferences.[1] P has physically possible values ranging from –0.33 to 0.5. In practice, these limiting values are rarely attained. Measured values of P in bioanalytical applications typically range from 0.01 to 0.3 or 10 to 300 mP (mP = P/1000). This measurement range is not as narrow as it might appear to be because very precise measurements (P ± 0.002 or ± 2 mP) are readily obtainable with modern instrumentation.

Dependence of Fluorescence Polarization on Molecular Mobility

Interpretation of the dependence of fluorescence polarization on molecular mobility is usually based on a model derived in 1926 from the physical theory of Brownian motion by Perrin.[2,3]

$$\left(\frac{1}{P} - \frac{1}{3}\right) = \left(\frac{1}{P_0} - \frac{1}{3}\right)\left(1 + \frac{\tau}{\phi}\right)$$

where P_o is the fundamental polarization of the dye (for fluorescein, rhodamine and BODIPY® dyes, P_o is close to the theoretical maximum of 0.5), τ is the excited-state lifetime of the dye and ϕ is the rotational correlation time of the dye or dye conjugate. These relationships can be expressed in terms of fluorescence anisotropy in an equivalent and mathematically simpler manner. For a hydrodynamic sphere, ϕ can be estimated as follows:

$$\phi = \frac{\eta V}{RT}$$

where η = solvent viscosity, T = temperature, R = gas constant and V = molecular volume of the fluorescent dye or dye conjugate. In turn, V can be estimated from the molecular weight of the dye or dye

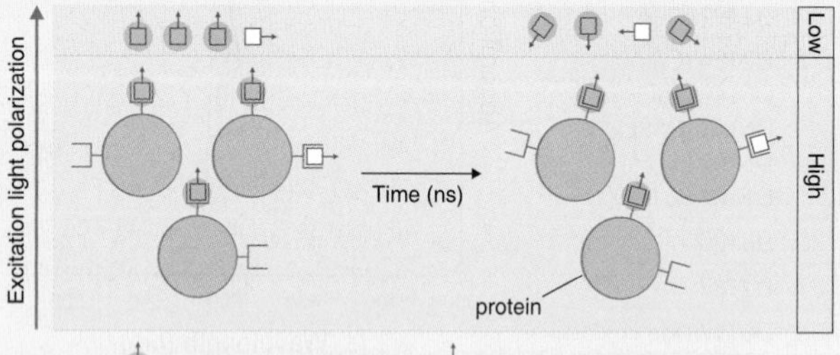

Figure 1. Physical basis of fluorescence polarization assays. Dye molecules with their absorption transition vectors (arrows) aligned parallel to the electric vector of linearly polarized light (along the vertical page axis) are selectively excited. For dyes attached to small, rapidly rotating molecules, the initially photoselected orientational distribution becomes randomized prior to emission, resulting in low fluorescence polarization. Conversely, binding of the low molecular weight tracer to a large, slowly rotating molecule results in high fluorescence polarization. Fluorescence polarization therefore provides a direct readout of the extent of tracer binding to proteins, nucleic acids and other biopolymers.

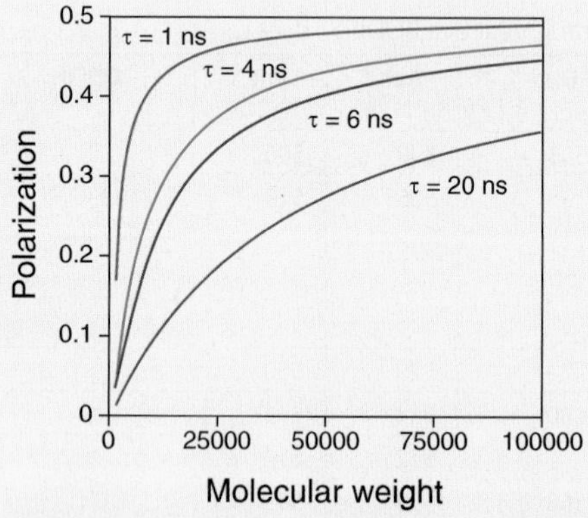

Figure 2. Simulation of the relationship between molecular weight (MW) and fluorescence polarization (P). Simulations are shown for dyes with various fluorescence lifetimes (τ): 1 ns (cyanine dyes) in purple, 4 ns (fluorescein and Alexa Fluor® 488 dyes) in red, 6 ns (some BODIPY® dyes) in green and 20 ns (dansyl dyes) in blue. At MW = 1000, P = 0.167 for τ = 1 ns, P = 0.056 for τ = 4 ns, P = 0.039 for τ = 6 ns and P = 0.012 for τ = 20 ns. Simulations assume P_o (the fundamental polarization) = 0.5 and rigid attachment of dyes to spherical carriers.

continued on next page

continued from previous page

conjugate with appropriate adjustments for hydration. Simulations of these relationships are shown in Figure 2, leading to the following general conclusions:

- Fluorescence polarization increases as molecular weight increases.
- Fluorescence polarization increases as solvent viscosity increases.
- Fluorescence polarization decreases as the excited state lifetime of the dye (τ) increases.

Note that these simulations assume that the dye is rigidly attached to a spherical carrier. When conventional parameter estimates for proteins in aqueous solutions are used, ϕ is found to increase by about 1 ns per 2400 dalton increase of molecular weight.[4]

Dyes for Fluorescence Polarization Assays

Tracers used in fluorescence polarization assays include peptides, drugs and cytokines that are modified by the attachment of a fluorescent dye. Depolarization due to flexibility in the attachment of the dye, sometimes referred to as the "propeller effect", distorts the relationships between P and molecular weight shown in Figure 2. For this reason, it is generally preferable to use reactive dyes without aliphatic linkers between the fluorophore and the reactive group in the preparation of tracers for fluorescence polarization–based assays.[5,6] A key factor in the performance of fluorescence polarization–based assays is the extent to which the biological activity of the tracer is perturbed by the dye modification. Molecular Probes' BODIPY® dyes generally produce less perturbation of receptor-binding affinity and other activity parameters than conventional dyes such as fluorescein and rhodamine.[7,8] Furthermore, these BODIPY® dyes usually have longer excited-state lifetimes than fluorescein and rhodamine dyes, making their fluorescence polarization sensitive to binding interactions over a larger molecular weight range (Figure 2). The long-wavelength BODIPY® TMR and BODIPY® TR dyes also tend to minimize assay interferences due to intrinsically fluorescent sample contaminants.[7]

Applications

Fluorescence polarization measurements have long been a valuable biophysical research tool for investigating processes such as membrane lipid mobility, myosin reorientation and protein–protein interactions at the molecular level.[9–12] Immunoassays that have been developed and used extensively for clinical diagnostics represent the largest group of bioanalytical applications.[13,14] The more recent advent of microplate readers equipped with polarizing optics has led to the adoption of fluorescence polarization as a readout mode for high-throughput screening.[15–17] Some typical bioanalytical applications of fluorescence polarization–based assays are summarized below.

References

1. Anal Biochem 247, 83 (1997); **2.** J Phys Radium 7, 390 (1926); **3.** Fluorescence and Phosphorescence Analysis, Hercules DM, Ed. 217 (1966); **4.** Biophysical Chemistry, Part 2, Cantor CR, Schimmel PR, Eds 454 (1980); **5.** Anal Biochem 249, 29 (1997); **6.** Anal Biochem 247, 77 (1997); **7.** J Biomol Screen 5, 329 (2000); **8.** Endocrinology 138, 296 (1997); **9.** Methods 19, 222 (1999); **10.** Biophys J 71, 3330 (1996); **11.** Chem Phys Lipids 64, 99 (1993); **12.** Methods Enzymol 246, 283 (1995); **13.** Immunochemistry 7, 799 (1970); **14.** Immunochemistry 10, 219 (1973); **15.** J Biomol Screen 5, 297 (2000); **16.** High Throughput Screening: The Discovery of Bioactive Substances, Devlin J, Ed. 389 (1997); **17.** J Biomol Screen 6, 275 (2001).

Examples of fluorescence polarization–based assays

Assay Target	Tracer	References
Ligand binding to neurokinin 1 (NK1) receptor	Fluorescein-labeled substance P	Biochemistry 33, 13079 (1994)
Ligand binding to melanocortin G-protein–coupled receptors	BODIPY® TMR dye–labeled NDP-αMSH	J Biomol Screen 5, 329 (2000)
Ligand binding to B2 bradykinin receptor, a G-protein–coupled receptor	BODIPY® TMR dye–labeled HOE140	J Biomol Screen 7, 111 (2002)
Ligand binding to estrogen receptors	Fluorescein-labeled estradiol	J Biomol Screen 5, 77 (2000)
Ligand binding to tyrosine kinase Src homology domains	Fluorescein- and BODIPY® TR dye–labeled phosphopeptides	Anal Biochem 275, 62 (1999); Anal Biochem 247, 77 (1997)
Substrate binding to protein farnesyltransferase	Oregon Green® 488 dye–labeled peptide	Biochemistry 38, 13138 (1999)
β-Lactam antibiotic binding to penicillin-binding proteins	BODIPY® FL dye–labeled penicillin V	Antimicrob Agents Chemother 43, 1124 (1999)
Protein kinase activity	Fluorescently labeled phosphopeptide	Anal Biochem 278, 206 (2000); Methods 22, 61 (2000)
Nonspecific protease activity	BODIPY® FL dye–labeled casein	Anal Biochem 243, 1 (1996)
Detection of specific PCR products	Fluorescein-labeled oligonucleotide	Gene 259, 123 (2000)
Ligation and cleavage of RNA by ribozymes	Fluorescein- or tetramethylrhodamine-labeled oligoribonucleotide	Biotechniques 29, 344 (2000)
SNP detection by allele-specific primer extension	Fluorescent ddNTP	Genome Res 9, 492 (1999)
Protein–protein and protein–nucleic acid interactions	Alexa Fluor® 488 dye–labeled human Factor VIIa, Oregon Green® 488 dye–labeled soluble human tissue factor and Oregon Green® 514 dye–labeled oligonucleotide	Anal Biochem 308, 18 (2002)

- Narrow emission bandwidth (Figure 1.43), resulting in a higher peak intensity than that of fluorescein
- Unique red shift in fluorescence emission at high dye concentrations — a property that can be used to detect regions of high probe density (Figure 12.51)
- Relatively long excited-state lifetime (typically 4 nanoseconds or longer), making the BODIPY® FL dye useful for fluorescence polarization–based assays (see Note 1.5 "Technical Focus: Fluorescence Polarization (FP)")
- Little or no spectral overlap with longer-wavelength dyes such as tetramethylrhodamine and Texas Red® dye (Figure 1.43), making BODIPY® FL one of the preferred green-fluorescent dyes for multicolor applications [13] (Figure 1.45)
- Greater photostability than fluorescein in some environments [14] (Figure 1.46)
- A large two-photon cross-section for multiphoton excitation [9,10] (Figure 1.47)
- Lack of ionic charge

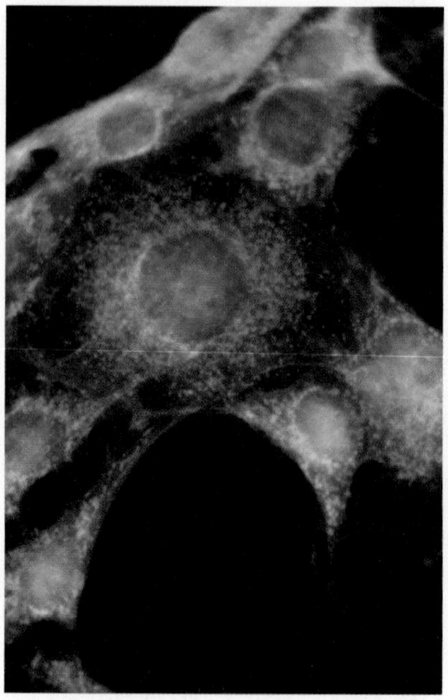

Figure 1.45 NIH 3T3 cells stained with MitoTracker® CMXRos (M7512), BODIPY® FL phallacidin (B607) and POPO™-1 (P3580). The cells were incubated with MitoTracker® CMXRos, which stains mitochondria red. After the fixed cells were permeabilized with acetone, they were stained with BODIPY® FL phallacidin, which labels F-actin green, and with POPO™-1, which labels nuclei blue. This photomicrograph was obtained with a single exposure through an Omega Optical triple bandpass filter set.

Longer-Wavelength BODIPY® Dyes

We have found that it is possible to synthesize BODIPY® fluorophores with altered spectral properties by simply changing the substituents on the parent molecule. This discovery has led to creation of a series of longer-wavelength BODIPY® dyes with fluorescence spectra that span the visible spectrum (Figure 1.41). The BODIPY® R6G (excitation/emission maxima ~528/547 nm), BODIPY® TMR (excitation/emission maxima ~543/569 nm) and BODIPY® TR (excitation/emission maxima ~592/618 nm) fluorophores are spectrally similar to the rhodamine 6G (R634, Section 12.2), tetramethylrhodamine and Texas Red® fluorophores, respectively, and are thus compatible with standard optical filter sets designed for these important dyes (Table 23.9). The red fluorescence of the BODIPY® 581/591 fluorophore shifts to green fluorescence upon peroxidation, a feature that has been exploited for ratiometric measurements of lipid oxidation in live cells [15] (Section 18.2). The BODIPY® 630/650-X and BODIPY® 650/665-X fluorophores are the longest-wavelength amine-reactive BODIPY® fluorophores currently available. The spectral properties of these longer-wavelength BODIPY® derivatives retain most of the advantages of the BODIPY® FL fluorophore, including narrow bandwidths, high extinction coefficients, good fluorescence quantum yields and relatively long excited-state lifetimes (>3 nanoseconds for the BODIPY® 630/650 dye [16–18]). Like the BODIPY® FL fluorophore, however, most of these dyes have a small Stokes shift, which may require that they be excited or detected at suboptimal wavelengths. Nevertheless, even when suboptimal excitation is required, the BODIPY® dyes are among the most intensely fluorescent dyes available. The spectral characteristics of 13 different red-fluorescent fluorophores, including the Alexa Fluor® 647 (Section 1.3) and BODIPY® 630/660 dyes, have been evaluated in different surrounding media to assess the influence of polarity, viscosity and detergent concentration and to facilitate probe choice in fluorescence-based assays.[16]

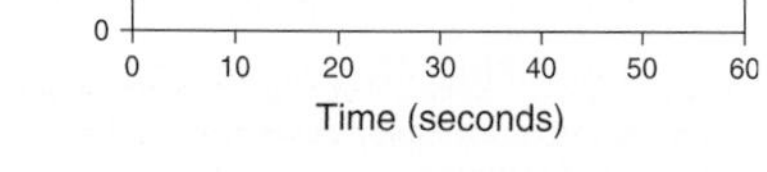

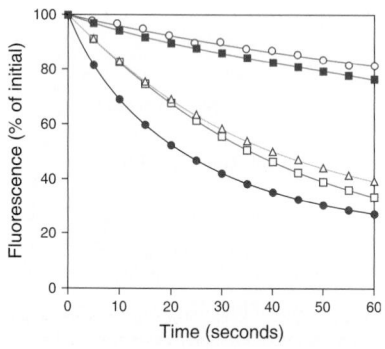

Figure 1.46 Comparison of photostability of green-fluorescent antibody conjugates. The following fluorescent goat anti–mouse IgG antibody conjugates were used to detect mouse anti–human IgG antibody labeling of human anti-nuclear antibodies in HEp-2 cells on prefixed test slides (INOVA Diagnostics Corp.): Oregon Green® 514 (O6383, ■), Alexa Fluor® 488 (A11001, ○), BODIPY® FL (B2752, △), Oregon Green® 488 (O6380, □) or fluorescein (F2761, ●). Samples were continuously illuminated and viewed on a fluorescence microscope using a fluorescein longpass filter set. Images were acquired every 5 seconds. For each conjugate, three data sets, representing different fields of view, were averaged and then normalized to the same initial fluorescence intensity value to facilitate comparison.

Amine-Reactive BODIPY® Dyes

BODIPY® Dye Succinimidyl Esters

Molecular Probes offers an extensive selection of amine-reactive BODIPY® dyes (Table 1.6), including succinimidyl esters of several BODIPY® propionic acids and of one BODIPY® pentanoic acid. In addition, we have prepared the reactive succinimidyl esters of:

- BODIPY® FL-X (D6102)
- BODIPY® R6G-X (D6186)
- BODIPY® TMR-X (D6117)
- BODIPY® TR-X (D6116)
- BODIPY® 630/650-X (D10000)
- BODIPY® 650/665-X (D10001)

These reactive dyes contain an additional seven-atom aminohexanoyl spacer ("X") between the fluorophore and the succinimidyl ester group. This spacer helps to separate the fluorophore from its point of attachment, potentially reducing the interaction of the fluorophore with the biomolecule to which it is conjugated and making it more accessible to secondary detection reagents such as anti-dye antibodies.[19–21] BODIPY® TMR-X SE has been conjugated to a series of peptide ligands for use in a high-throughput fluorescence polarization assay of ligand binding to G protein–coupled receptors.[22] Several BODIPY® succinimidyl esters have been conjugated to aminoacyl tRNAs for metabolic incorporation into proteins through *in vitro* translation.[23,24] For amplifying the BODIPY® FL dye signal or converting it into an electron-dense signal, we offer an unlabeled anti–BODIPY® FL rabbit polyclonal antibody (A5770, Section 7.4). This antibody crossreacts with some other BODIPY® dyes, but not with other fluorophores, and therefore should not be used for simultaneous detection of more than one dye based on the BODIPY® fluorophore.

The BODIPY® propionic acid succinimidyl esters (D2184, D2187, D2191, D2219, D2222, D2225, D2228, D6180) and BODIPY® FL pentanoic acid succinimidyl ester (D6184) are particularly useful for preparing conjugates of peptides, nucleotides, oligonucleotides,[25] drugs, toxins, sphingolipids and other low molecular weight ligands that contain aliphatic amines and for derivatizing amines in various high-resolution separation technologies (Section 1.7). Our BODIPY® 630/650-X and BODIPY® 650/665-X succinimidyl esters (D10000, D10001) are quite fluorescent when conjugated to nucleotides[18] and oligonucleotides, and can be excited by near-infrared excitation sources. In addition to their use in preparing bioconjugates, at least two of our BODIPY® dye succinimidyl esters — BODIPY® FL-X SE and BODIPY® TR-X SE — are very useful for quantitative and extremely sensitive protein staining on blots and arrays, and we have therefore utilized these amine-reactive BODIPY® derivatives in our DyeChrome™ Western Blot Stain Kits (Section 9.4, Figure 9.62).

Figure 1.47 An experiment illustrating ordinary (single-photon) excitation of fluorescence and two-photon excitation. The cuvette contains a solution of the dye safranin O, which normally emits yellow light when excited by green light. The upper lens focuses green (543 nm) light from a CW helium–neon laser into the cuvette, producing the expected conical pattern of excitation (fading to the left). The lower lens focuses pulsed infrared (1046 nm) light from a neodymium–YLF laser. In two-photon absorption, the excitation is proportional to the square of the intensity; thus, the emission is confined to a small point focus (see arrow), which can be positioned anywhere in the cuvette by moving the illuminating beam. Image contributed by Brad Amos, Science Photo Library, London.

Water-Soluble BODIPY® FL Succinimidyl Esters and STP Esters

The moderate lipophilicity of the BODIPY® propionic acid succinimidyl esters discussed above requires their dissolution in an organic solvent before use in conjugations. Although these reactive dyes are very useful for preparing conjugates of amines in organic solvents, they are less suitable for use with proteins than our water-soluble amine-reactive BODIPY® dyes. We usually use the succinimidyl ester of BODIPY® FL cysteic acid (BODIPY® FL, CASE; D6141), which contains a sulfonated spacer that appears to decrease the interaction between the fluorophore and the protein (Figure 1.48) and thus reduce the quenching in our protein conjugates. Both this cysteic acid derivative and the sulfosuccinimidyl ester of BODIPY® FL propionic acid (BODIPY® FL, SSE; D6140) are quite soluble in water and potentially useful for preparing conjugates of most proteins, amine-modified oligonucleotides and other biomolecules. Sulfosuccinimidyl esters of biotin (B6352, B6353; Section 4.2) are sometimes employed as cell-impermeant probes for selectively labeling the outer membrane of cells in topological studies;[26–28] these sulfonated BODIPY® FL succinimidyl esters and the STP esters described below may be similarly useful.

Molecular Probes has introduced water-soluble STP esters[29] of some of our most popular BODIPY® dyes:

- BODIPY® FL, STP ester (B10006)
- BODIPY® TMR, STP ester (B10002)
- BODIPY® TR-X, STP ester (B10003)
- BODIPY® 650/665-X, STP ester (B10005)

STP esters, which are prepared by coupling a carboxylic acid and 4-sulfo-2,3,5,6-tetrafluorophenol (S10490, Section 3.3, Figure 1.3), are more readily purified than sulfosuccinimidyl esters but equally amine reactive. They are more suitable than the corresponding BODIPY® dye succinimidyl esters for amine conjugation in aqueous solution.

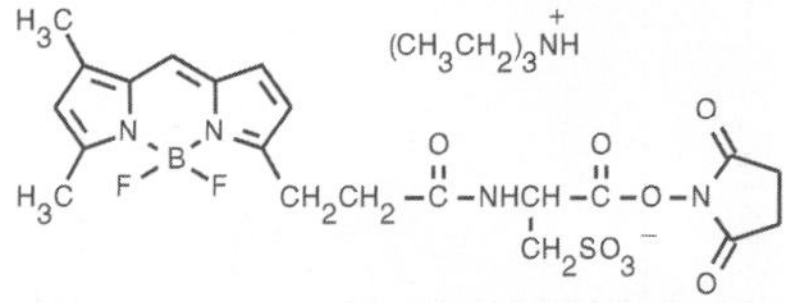

Figure 1.48 D6141 *N*-(4,4-difluoro-5,7-dimethyl-4-bora-3a,4a-diaza-*s*-indacene-3-propionyl)cysteic acid, succinimidyl ester, triethylammonium salt (BODIPY® FL, CASE).

BODIPY® Carboxylic Acids

Two green-fluorescent BODIPY® carboxylic acids (D2183, D3834) are available. These carboxylic acid derivatives can be converted to fluorescent esters,[30] acid halides or amides using standard chemical techniques.

BODIPY® Dye Conjugates

The versatility of the BODIPY® fluorophore is demonstrated by its incorporation into literally hundreds of products listed in this *Handbook*, including many of our FluoSpheres® and TransFluoSpheres® microspheres (Section 6.5), enzyme substrates (Chapter 10) and several of our imaging and flow cytometry standards (Section 23.1, Section 23.2).

Peptides and Proteins

As is common with many fluorescent dyes, conjugation of BODIPY® dyes to proteins is sometimes accompanied by significant fluorescence quenching. Because of this potential problem, we do *not* recommend using the simple BODIPY® propionic acid succinimidyl esters discussed above for preparing most protein conjugates, although peptides labeled with a single BODIPY® dye can be quite fluorescent and are quite useful for fluorescence polarization–based assays [31,32] (see Note 9.2 "Technical Focus: Labeling Small Peptides with Amine-Reactive Dyes in Organic Solvents" in Section 9.5). Molecular Probes prepares conjugates of its BODIPY® dyes with an exceptionally wide variety of peptides, proteins and polysaccharides, including:

- Antibodies (Section 7.4; Table 7.1; Figure 1.49, Figure 23.22)
- Pepstatin A, a membrane-permeant analog of this important cathepsin D inhibitor (P12271, Section 10.4)
- Phallacidin and phalloidin for staining F-actin filaments (B607, B3475, B7464, B12382; Section 11.1; Table 11.1; Figure 1.45, Figure 1.50, Figure 23.18)
- Cholesterol (C3927MP, Section 13.3)
- Dextran (D7168, Section 14.5)
- Bovine serum albumin, for use as a tracer (A2750, Section 14.7)
- *Escherichia coli*, *Staphylococcus aureus* and zymosan A (*Saccharomyces cerevisiae*) BioParticles® conjugates (E2864, S2854, Z2844; Section 16.1; Table 16.3)
- Acetylated and non-acetylated low-density lipoproteins (L3485, L3483; Section 16.1)
- Lipopolysaccharides (L23350, L23355; Section 16.1; Table 16.1)
- Transferrin (T2873, Section 16.1, Table 16.2)
- Apamin, a probe for K^+ channels (A13542, Section 16.3)

In addition, Molecular Probes prepares conjugates of proteins (and of starch) that are so heavily labeled that they are almost nonfluorescent (Figure 10.56). Use of the EnzChek® Kits and DQ™ reagents that incorporate these bioconjugates as fluorogenic enzyme substrates is described later in this section and in Section 10.4.

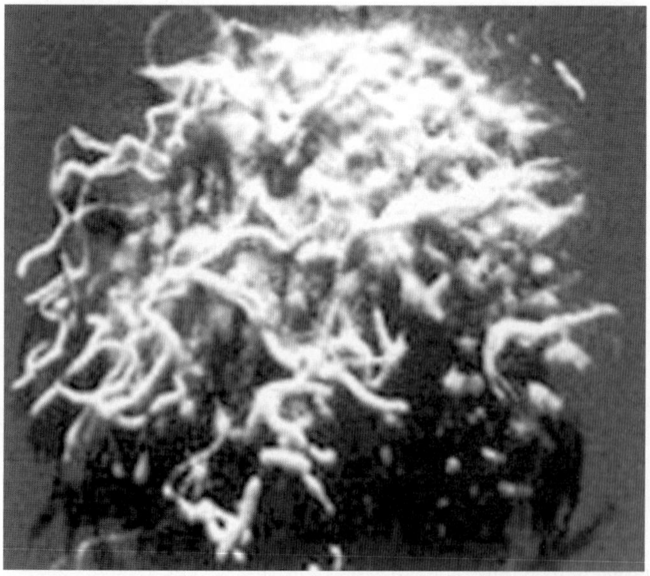

Figure 1.49 Microtubules from the first cleavage stage of a sea urchin embryo were stained with a monoclonal anti-α-tubulin primary antibody and subsequently visualized with BODIPY® FL goat anti-rabbit IgG antibody (B2766). Image contributed by Isao Uemura, Tokyo Metropolitan University, and provided courtesy of Yokogawa Electric Corporation.

BODIPY® Dye Conjugates of Nucleotides and Oligonucleotides

With the exception of guanosine nucleotides (see below), fluorescence quenching is usually not a problem if the BODIPY® derivative is conjugated to nucleotides, oligonucleotides, peptides or low molecular weight amines in which the stoichiometry of modification is 1:1. Oligonucleotide conjugates of the BODIPY® dyes are among the brightest derivatives available for DNA sequencing, nucleic acid hybridization [33] and other applications. BODIPY® FL dye–labeled oligonucleotide primers also have lower photodestruction rates than fluorescein-labeled primers, improving the detectability of labeled DNA in sequencing gels.[14] Oligonucleotide conjugates of several of our BODIPY® dyes have been shown to be useful for DNA sequencing [1–3] (Section 8.2, Table 8.11), in part because the dye exhibits minimal effect on the mobility of the fragment during electrophoresis. Molecular Probes also offers an assortment of BODIPY® dye–labeled ChromaTide® nucleotides for enzyme-mediated incorporation into nucleic acids (Section 8.2; Table 8.6, Table 8.7) or for use as structural probes of nucleotide-binding proteins (Section 17.3).

BODIPY® Dye Conjugates of Lipids and Receptor Ligands

BODIPY® dye conjugates of other molecules — lipids, toxins, steroids, drug analogs, receptor probes, enzyme substrates and the like — often have quantum yields approaching unity, especially in organic solvents. The lack of ionic charge makes several of these derivatives useful for staining receptors in live cells.

Our BODIPY® derivatives of low molecular weight ligands include analogs of:

- Cytochalasin B and cytochalasin D, which are actin-polymerization inhibitors (C12376, C12377, C12378; Section 11.1)
- Paclitaxel (Taxol), for staining tubulin in isolated preparations (P7500, P7501; Section 11.2)
- Vinblastine, a microtubule-disrupting agent (V12390, Section 11.2)
- Brefeldin A, a fungal metabolite (B7447, B7449; Section 12.4; Figure 12.50)

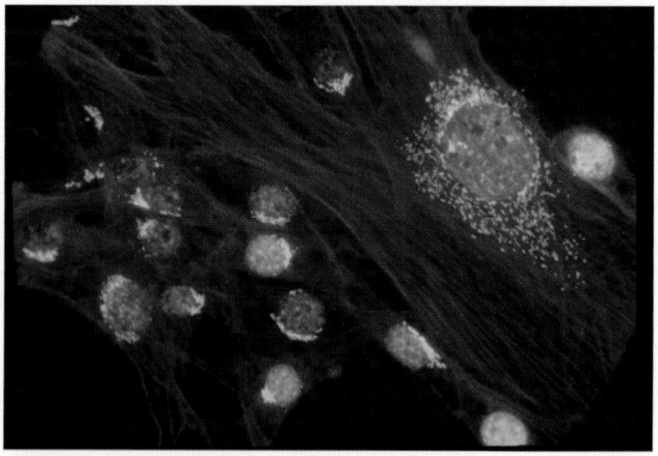

Figure 1.50 Mouse fibroblasts that were fixed, permeabilized and then labeled with BODIPY® TR-X phalloidin (B7464), DAPI (D1306, D3571, D21490) and a rabbit anti–Golgi complex antibody (provided by Vivek Malhotra, UC San Diego) in conjunction with BODIPY® FL goat anti–rabbit IgG antibody (B2766). The triple-labeled cells were photographed through an Omega Optical RGB triple-bandpass filter set.

- Phospholipids and fatty acids, numerous versions of which are described in Section 13.2
- Phosphatidylinositol phosphate derivatives for applications in following signal transduction (Section 13.2, Section 17.4; Table 17.3; Figure 17.35)
- Sphingolipids, including several ceramide (Figure 12.52), sphingomyelin, ganglioside G_{M1}, galactocerebroside, glucocerebroside, ceramide, glucosyl ceramide and lactosyl ceramide derivatives (Section 13.3)
- Vancomycin, an antibiotic (V34850, Section 15.2)
- Penicillin V (B13233, B13234; Section 15.2)
- Verapamil, for investigating multidrug resistance (B7431, Section 15.6)
- Forskolin, an adenylate cyclase activator (B7469, Section 15.6)
- Methotrexate (M23272, Section 15.6)
- Lipopolysaccharides (L23350, L23355; Section 16.1)
- Hyaluronic acid (H23379, Section 16.1)
- Prazosin, an α_1-adrenergic receptor probe (B7433, B7434; Section 16.2)
- Pirenzepine analogs for staining muscarinic receptors (B7436, B7437; Section 16.2)
- Ouabain and digoxigenin, both of which are cardiac glycosides (B23461, B23460; Section 16.3)
- Glibenclamide, a probe for potassium channels (B7439, B13540; Section 16.3)
- Ivermectin, an antiparasitic agent that binds to glutamate-gated chloride-ion channels (B13510, Section 16.3)
- A dihydropyridine drug that is selective for Ca^{2+} channels (D7443, S7445; Section 16.3)
- Ryanodine, an important calcium-mobilizing agent (B7505, Section 16.3)
- Amiloride, an inhibitor of the Na^+/H^+ antiporter of vertebrate cells (B6905, Section 16.3)
- Thapsigargin, which promotes Ca^{2+} release by inhibiting the endoplasmic reticulum Ca^{2+}-ATPase (B7487, B13800; Section 17.2)
- Phospholipase substrates (Section 17.4)

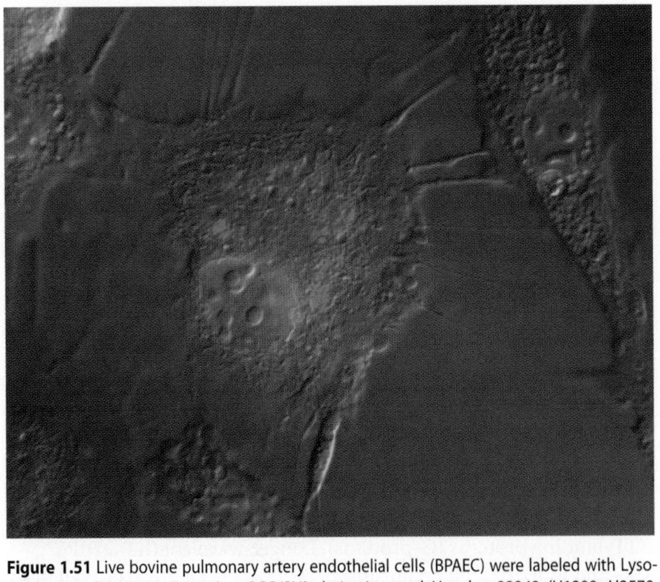

Figure 1.51 Live bovine pulmonary artery endothelial cells (BPAEC) were labeled with LysoTracker® Red DND-99 (L7528), a BODIPY® derivative, and Hoechst 33342 (H1399, H3570, H21492). The cells were then imaged by fluorescence and differential interference contrast (DIC) microscopy.

In addition to the BODIPY® dye conjugates of receptor ligands in the list above, we have utilized BODIPY® dyes for synthesis of several LysoTracker® (Figure 1.51) and LysoSensor™ dyes, as well as BODIPY® FL histamine (B22461, Figure 12.39), that are extremely useful probes for labeling acidic organelles in live cells. These products are discussed in Section 12.3.

BODIPY® Dye Conjugates as Enzyme Substrates and for High-Throughput Screening Applications

EnzChek® Kits and DQ™ Reagents as Fluorogenic Enzyme Substrates

We have found BODIPY® dye conjugates to be very useful reagents for numerous bioanalytical screening applications. In particular, we have utilized the tendency of BODIPY® dyes to quench their fluorescence on conjugation to certain biopolymers to our advantage (Figure 10.56) in the following enzyme-assay kits and reagents:

- EnzChek® Protease Assay Kits, which contain almost nonfluorescent casein derivatives that are heavily labeled with either the green-fluorescent BODIPY® FL dye (E6638, R22130; Section 10.4) or red-fluorescent BODIPY® TR-X dye (E6639, R22131; Section 10.4)
- EnzChek® Elastase Assay Kit (E12056, Section 10.4), with DQ™ elastin, a quenched BODIPY® FL conjugate
- EnzChek® Amylase Assay Kit (E11954, Section 10.2), containing a highly quenched BODIPY® FL starch derivative
- Almost nonfluorescent bovine serum albumin conjugates, DQ™ Green BSA (D12050, Section 10.4) and DQ™ Red BSA (D12051, Section 10.4), which yield intense green or red fluorescence upon enzyme-catalyzed hydrolysis (Figure 16.5)
- DQ™ ovalbumin (D12053, Section 10.4), a heavily labeled BODIPY® FL dye conjugate of ovalbumin

Conjugation of either the BODIPY® FL dye (excitation/emission maxima 500/506 nm) or BODIPY® TR dye (excitation/emission maxima 589/617 nm) to a biopolymer at high degrees of substitution (DOS) results in almost total quenching of the conjugate's fluorescence; they typically exhibit <3% of the fluorescence of the corresponding free dyes. Enzyme-catalyzed hydrolysis relieves this quenching, yielding brightly fluorescent BODIPY® FL dye– or BODIPY® TR-X dye–labeled peptides (Figure 10.56), or, in the case of the BODIPY® FL amylase substrate in the EnzChek® Amylase Assay Kit, BODIPY® FL dye–labeled carbohydrates. The increase in fluorescence, which can be measured with a spectrofluorometer, minifluorometer or fluorescence microplate reader, is proportional to enzymatic activity. The DQ™ ovalbumin and DQ™ BSA substrates are particularly suitable for the study of receptor labeling and antigen processing. Ovalbumin is efficiently processed through mannose receptor–mediated endocytosis by antigen-presenting cells and is widely used for studying antigen processing. The BSA conjugates can be targeted to Fc receptors by complexing the DQ™ BSA reagents with our anti-BSA antibody (A11133, Section 7.5). Upon endocytosis and proteolysis, highly fluorescent peptides are released within intracellular vacuoles. DQ™ ovalbumin appears to be an excellent indicator of macrophage-mediated antigen processing in flow cytometry or microscopy assays.

EnzChek® Polarization Assay Kit for Proteases

When a fluorescent molecule tethered to a protein is excited by polarized fluorescent light, the polarization of fluorescence emission is dependent on the rate of molecular tumbling. Upon proteolytic cleavage of the fluorescently labeled protein, the smaller peptides that result tumble faster and the emitted light is depolarized relative to the light measured from the intact conjugate (see Note 1.5 "Technical Focus: Fluorescence Polarization (FP)"). The EnzChek® Polarization Assay Kit for Proteases (E6658, Section 10.4) contains green-fluorescent BODIPY® FL casein with an optimal degree of labeling for fluorescence polarization–based protease assays. Fluorescence polarization technology is more sensitive than many other nonradioactive assays for proteases and allows measurements to be taken in real time, permitting the collection of kinetics data. Our BODIPY® FL dye has an adequate fluorescence lifetime and pH-insensitive fluorescence — two prerequisites for successful measurement of protease activity by fluorescence polarization.

Lipophilic BODIPY® Substrates for Phospholipases and Other Enzymes

The low polarity of the BODIPY® fluorophore makes probes containing these dyes excellent analogs of biological lipids (Chapter 13). Consequently, these probes are well tolerated by enzymes that metabolize lipids, including phospholipases and enzymes that act on sphingolipids (Section 17.4, Table 17.2). In most cases, lack of a spectral shift in the metabolic product's fluorescence requires use of an easy extraction and chromatographic separation step to detect product formation, with quantitation possible by photography or with a fluorescence- or absorption-based scanner. Useful lipophilic substrates based on our BODIPY® dyes include:

- PED6 (D23739, Section 17.4), a fluorogenic substrate for phospholipase A_2 (PLA_2) that incorporates a BODIPY® FL dye–labeled *sn*-2 acyl chain and a dinitrophenyl quencher group.[34–36] Cleavage of the dye-labeled acyl chain by PLA_2 eliminates the intramolecular quenching effect of the dinitrophenyl group, resulting in increased fluorescence[36] (Figure 17.24). PED6 is useful for high-throughput assays and even for detecting PLA_1 activity *in vivo* in some organisms (Figure 17.27).
- The phospholipase A substrate bis-BODIPY®-glycerophosphocholine (bis-BODIPY® FL C_{11}-PC, B7701; Section 17.4), which has been specifically designed to allow continuous monitoring of PLA action and to be spectrally compatible with argon-ion laser excitation sources. When this probe is incorporated into cell membranes, the proximity of the BODIPY® FL fluorophores on adjacent phospholipid acyl chains causes fluorescence self-quenching. Separation of the fluorophores upon hydrolytic cleavage of one of the acyl chains by either PLA_1 or PLA_2 results in increased fluorescence[37] (Figure 17.24).
- A 1-*O*-alkyl–substituted phospholipid containing the BODIPY® FL fluorophore (D3771, Section 17.4), which is a useful substrate for a phospholipase A_2–specific chromatographic assay.[38,39]
- BODIPY® FL C_5-HPC (D3803, Section 17.4), which has been used to quantitatively delineate a discontinuous increase of Ca^{2+}-dependent cytosolic phospholipase A_2 ($cPLA_2$) activity during zebrafish embryogenesis.[40]
- BODIPY® FL, BODIPY® TMR-X and BODIPY® TR-X phosphatidylinositol derivatives and their phosphate esters (Section 17.4, Table 17.3), fluorescent analogs of important cell signaling molecules.[41,42]
- BODIPY® FL C_{12}-galactosylceramide (D7519), BODIPY® FL C_5-glucocerebroside (D7548) and BODIPY® FL C_{12}-glucocerebroside (D7547), which have been shown to be converted back to the fluorescent ceramide by either galactosylceramidase or glucocerebrosidase.[43–45] In addition, purified G_{M1} ganglioside β-galactosidase removes the terminal galactose residue from lactosylceramides like our BODIPY® FL C_5-lactosylceramide (D13951), yielding the corresponding glucosylceramide.[46] These substrates are described further in Section 17.4.
- BODIPY® FL C_5-sphingomyelin[47,48] (D3522, Section 13.3) and BODIPY® FL C_{12}-sphingomyelin[49] (D7711, Section 13.3), which are substrates for sphingomyelinase.
- BODIPY® FL C_5-ganglioside G_{M1}[50,51] (B13950, Section 17.4), a potential neuraminidase (sialidase) substrate. A structurally similar BODIPY® ganglioside is a known neuraminidase substrate in MDCK cells.[52]
- BODIPY® FL C_5-ceramide (D3521) and related BODIPY® and NBD ceramides in Section 13.3, structural markers for the Golgi complex (Section 12.4) that are metabolized in live cells to a variety of fluorescent sphingolipids, which can then be extracted and chromatographically characterized.[50,53]

BODIPY® Dye–Based Substrates for Chloramphenicol Acetyltransferase

Chloramphenicol acetyltransferase (CAT), an enzyme that is encoded by an important reporter gene, can acetylate chloramphenicol derivatives that incorporate the BODIPY® fluorophore (Figure 10.71). The acetylated products are readily separated from the substrate by thin-layer chromatography (Figure 10.70) and quantitated by photography, fluorometry or with a plate scanner. Our original *FAST* CAT® Chloramphenicol Acetyltransferase Assay Kit[54,55] (F2900) and improved *FAST* CAT® (deoxy) Chloramphenicol Acetyltransferase Assay Kit (F6616) utilize a green-fluorescent BODIPY® FL substrate and the *FAST* CAT® Yellow (deoxy) Chloramphenicol Acetyltransferase Assay Kit (F6617) utilizes a yellow-fluorescent BODIPY® TMR 1-deoxychloramphenicol substrate. These products are described in detail in Section 10.6 and in the associated product literature.

BODIPY® Dye–Labeled Nucleotides as Enzyme Substrates and for High-Throughput Screening Applications

Molecular Probes offers BODIPY® dye–labeled ChromaTide® nucleotides, including both UTP and dUTP derivatives (Section 8.2; Table 8.6, Table 8.7). These nucleotide analogs are readily incorporated into DNA or RNA by a variety of enzymes. Among these derivatives is the BODIPY® FL-14-dUTP conjugate (C7614, Section 8.2), which has been used as a terminal deoxynucleotidyl transferase (TdT) substrate in the detection of apoptotic cells (TUNEL assay, Section 15.5; Figure 15.84).

In addition to the ChromaTide® nucleotides labeled with BODIPY® dyes, we have prepared BODIPY® FL conjugates of ATP, AMPPNP, GTP and GMPPNP that are labeled through the ribose moieties (A12410, B22355, G12411, B22356; Section 17.3). In this case, BODIPY® FL GTP and BODIPY® FL GMPPNP both show significant fluorescence quenching (Figure 17.16) that is relieved by binding to GTP-binding proteins (G-proteins). Longer-wavelength BODIPY® R6G and BODIPY® TR conjugates of ATP and GTP are also available (A22352, G22350, G22351; Section 17.3).

For protein-binding studies that require nonhydrolyzable nucleotides, we offer the BODIPY® FL fluorophore linked through the γ-thiol of ATP-γ-*S* (A22184, Figure 17.17) and the BODIPY® FL, BODIPY® 515/530 and BODIPY® TR fluorophores linked through the γ-thiol of GTP-γ-*S*[56] (G22183, G35779, G35780; Section 17.3). Like BODIPY® FL GMPPNP, the fluorescence of the BODIPY® GTP-γ-*S* thioesters is quenched ~90% relative to that of the free dye but is recovered upon protein binding to at least some G-proteins.[56] The green-fluorescent BODIPY® FL GTP-γ-*S* has been used to detect GTP-binding proteins separated by capillary electrophoresis.[57] BODIPY® 515/530 GTP-γ-*S* thioester also exhibits green fluorescence and has a greater fluorescence increase upon protein binding, as compared with the BODIPY® FL GTP-γ-*S* thioester. The BODIPY® TR GTP-γ-*S* thioester is a red-fluorescent analog with spectral properties similar to the Texas Red® dye.

We also offer the green-fluorescent BODIPY® FL GTP-γ-*NH* amide (G35778, Section 17.3) as another choice for protein-binding studies. Although this analog exhibits less fluorescence enhancement upon protein binding, it is reportedly the best of the three green-fluorescent GTP-γ analogs for directly monitoring nucleotide exchange.[58] The different linker lengths of the green-fluorescent GTP-γ analogs (six-carbon for BODIPY® FL GTP-γ-*NH* amide, four- carbon for BODIPY® FL GTP-γ-*S* and one-carbon for BODIPY® 515/530 GTP-γ-*S*) may be useful for understanding protein active-site geometries.

In addition to their potential use for binding studies, our patented BODIPY® FL ATP-γ-*S* and BODIPY® FL GTP-γ-*S* thioesters are important substrates for Fhit (Figure 17.18), a member of the histidine triad superfamily of nucleotide-binding proteins that bind and cleave diadenosine polyphosphates.[59–61] Fhit, one of the most frequently inactivated proteins in lung cancer, functions as a tumor suppressor by inducing apoptosis.[60,62,63] These BODIPY® nucleotides should be especially useful for screening potential Fhit inhibitors and activators.

Conjugates of BODIPY® Dyes for Fluorescence Polarization–Based Assays

The relatively long fluorescence lifetimes (typically >4 nanoseconds) at visible wavelengths, good anisotropy properties, high molar absorptivity and fluorescence intensity and lack of pH sensitivity in the spectra of the BODIPY® dyes have been shown to make these dyes the preferred fluorophores for high-throughput, fluorescence polarization–based assays (see Note 1.5 "Technical Focus: Fluorescence Polarization (FP)"). BODIPY® dye conjugates of nucleotides, peptides and drug analogs are available from Molecular Probes or are readily prepared from the chemically reactive BODIPY® dyes. Fluorescence polarization–based assays for G-protein–coupled receptors, kinases and phosphatases and for high-affinity receptors are particularly important when screening for new drug candidates. Our EnzChek® Polarization Assay Kit for Proteases (E6658, Section 10.4), which contains green-fluorescent BODIPY® FL casein with an optimal degree of labeling, is particularly useful for fluorescence polarization–based protease assays.

Additional Methods of Analysis Using BODIPY® Dye Conjugates

In addition to their general utility for the intensity-based and fluorescence polarization–based assays described above, the BODIPY® dyes are near optimal for a variety of other bioanalytical techniques:

- The spectral variety and high absorbance of the BODIPY® dyes (Figure 1.41) permits their use as efficient donor or acceptor dyes for numerous assays that use fluorescence resonance energy transfer, including internally quenched endopeptidase substrates[64] (Section 10.4), nucleic acid hybridization assays (Section 8.5) and receptor-binding assays (see Note 1.2 "Technical Focus: Fluorescence Resonance Energy Transfer (FRET)" in Section 1.3).
- BODIPY® dye conjugates of peptides are readily separated by chromatographic means and can be used to detect the activity of enzymes that catalyze secondary modifications, such as phosphorylation/dephosphorylation, glycosylation/deglycosylation, oxidation/reduction, myristoylation, farnesylation and peptide–peptide crosslinking.
- Hydrolysis of peptides that are singly labeled with BODIPY® dyes to smaller peptides can be detected chromatographically with extremely high sensitivity.
- In several instances, we have observed significant fluorescence enhancement or quenching of BODIPY® dye–labeled probes on binding to receptors or in hybridization assays that may permit sensitive, high-throughput assays that do not require separation steps.
- With their high peak intensity and narrow emission spectra, reactive BODIPY® dyes are among the most detectable amine-derivatization reagents available for HPLC and capillary electrophoresis; thus, amine-containing metabolites can be derivatized with succinimidyl esters of the BODIPY® dyes (Table 1.6) for ultrasensitive analysis.

References

1. Biotechniques 25, 446 (1998); **2.** Science 271, 1420 (1996); **3.** Nucleic Acids Res 20, 2471 (1992); **4.** Anal Chem 67, 139 (1995); **5.** J Biochem Biophys Methods 42, 137 (2000); **6.** Anal Biochem 275, 62 (1999); **7.** Jpn J Physiol 45, 673 (1995); **8.** Anal Biochem 243, 1 (1996); **9.** J Opt Soc Am B 13, 481 (1996); **10.** J Microsc 190, 298 (1998); **11.** J Am Chem Soc 116, 7801 (1994); **12.** Optical Microscopy for Biology, Herman B, Jacobson K, Eds. pp. 143–157 (1990); **13.** J Microsc 168, 219 (1992); **14.** Electrophoresis 13, 542 (1992); **15.** FEBS Lett 453, 278 (1999); **16.** Bioconjug Chem 14, 195 (2003); **17.** Biophys J 83, 605 (2002); **18.** Bioimaging 6, 14 (1998); **19.** Biochim Biophys Acta 1104, 9 (1992); **20.** Biochim Biophys Acta 776, 217 (1984); **21.** Biochemistry 21, 978 (1982); **22.** J Recept Signal Transduct Res 22, 333 (2002); **23.** Nat Biotechnol 21, 1093 (2003); **24.** Anal Biochem 326, 25 (2004); **25.** Nucleosides Nucleotides 18, 411 (1999); **26.** Biotechniques 18, 56 (1995); **27.** J Cell Biol 127, 2081 (1994); **28.** J Cell Biol 127, 2021 (1994); **29.** Tetrahedron Lett 40, 1471 (1999); **30.** Anal Biochem 156, 220 (1986); **31.** Endocrinology 138, 296 (1997); **32.** Lett Pept Sci 1, 235 (1995); **33.** Anal Chem 69, 3915 (1997); **34.** Science 292, 1385 (2001); **35.** Science 288, 1160 (2000); **36.** Anal Biochem 276, 27 (1999); **37.** J Biol Chem 267, 21465 (1992); **38.** Anal Biochem 286, 277 (2000); **39.** Anal Biochem 218, 136 (1994); **40.** J Biol Chem 274, 19338 (1999); **41.** Biochem J 379, 527 (2004); **42.** Proc Natl Acad Sci U S A 97, 11286 (2000); **43.** Frontiers in Bioactive Lipids, Vanderhoek JV, Ed. pp. 203–213 (1996); **44.** J Cell Biol 125, 769 (1994); **45.** Methods Enzymol 312, 293 (2000); **46.** J Neurochem 73, 1375 (1999); **47.** Chem Phys Lipids 102, 55 (1999); **48.** Biophys J 72, 37 (1997); **49.** J Cell Biol 140, 39 (1998); **50.** Methods Enzymol 312, 523 (2000); **51.** J Biol Chem 276, 24985 (2001); **52.** Lancet 354, 901 (1999); **53.** J Cell Biol 113, 1267 (1991); **54.** Biotechniques 8, 170 (1990); **55.** Anal Biochem 197, 401 (1991); **56.** J Biol Chem 276, 29275 (2001); **57.** Anal Chem 75, 4297 (2003); **58.** Proc Natl Acad Sci U S A 101, 2800 (2004); **59.** Proc Natl Acad Sci U S A 100, 1592 (2003); **60.** Curr Biol 10, 907 (2000); **61.** J Biol Chem 275, 4555 (2000); **62.** Am J Pathol 156, 419 (2000); **63.** J Natl Cancer Inst 92, 338 (2000); **64.** Nat Biotechnol 18, 1071 (2000).

Data Table — 1.4 BODIPY Dye Series

Cat #	MW	Storage	Soluble	Abs	EC	Em	Solvent	Notes
B10002	648.31	F,D,L	H_2O, DMSO	541	60,000	569	MeCN	1, 2
B10003	787.49	F,D,L	H_2O, DMSO	587	61,000	618	MeCN	1, 2
B10005	796.48	F,D,L	H_2O, DMSO	647	102,000	665	MeCN	1, 2
B10006	542.19	F,D,L	H_2O, DMSO	502	80,000	510	MeOH	1, 2
D2183	292.09	F,L	DMSO, MeCN	505	91,000	511	MeOH	1
D2184	389.16	F,D,L	DMSO, MeCN	502	82,000	510	MeOH	1, 3
D2187	513.31	F,D,L	DMSO, MeCN	534	77,000	551	MeOH	1
D2191	417.22	F,D,L	DMSO, MeCN	500	79,000	509	MeOH	1
D2219	443.23	F,D,L	DMSO, MeCN	559	97,000	568	MeOH	1
D2222	463.25	F,D,L	DMSO, MeCN	563	142,000	569	MeOH	1
D2225	426.19	F,D,L	DMSO, MeCN	575	83,000	588	MeOH	1
D2228	489.28	F,D,L	DMSO, MeCN	581	136,000	591	MeOH	4
D3834	320.15	F,L	DMSO, MeCN	505	96,000	511	MeOH	1
D6101	407.27	F,L	DMSO, MeCN	504	82,000	510	MeOH	1
D6102	502.32	F,D,L	DMSO, MeCN	504	85,000	510	MeOH	1
D6103	336.10	F,L	DMSO, MeCN	509	94,000	515	MeOH	1
D6116	634.46	F,D,L	DMSO, MeCN	588	68,000	616	MeOH	1, 5
D6117	608.45	F,D,L	DMSO, MeCN	544	60,000	570	MeOH	1
D6140	491.20	F,D,L	H_2O, DMSO	502	75,000	510	MeOH	1, 6
D6141	641.49	F,D,L	H_2O, DMSO	504	82,000	511	MeOH	1, 6
D6144	546.96	F,D,L	DMSO, MeCN	530	64,000	545	MeOH	1
D6180	437.21	F,D,L	DMSO, MeCN	528	70,000	547	MeOH	1
D6184	417.22	F,D,L	DMSO, MeCN	504	87,000	511	MeOH	1
D6186	550.37	F,D,L	DMSO, MeCN	529	73,000	547	MeOH	1
D10000	660.50	F,D,L	DMSO, MeCN	625	101,000	640	MeOH	1, 7
D10001	643.45	F,D,L	DMSO, MeCN	646	102,000	660	MeOH	1

For definitions of the contents of this data table, see "Navigating *The Handbook*" in the introductory pages.

Notes

1. The absorption and fluorescence spectra of BODIPY® derivatives are relatively insensitive to the solvent.
2. This sulfotetrafluorophenyl (STP) ester derivative is water-soluble and may be dissolved in buffer at ~pH 8 for reaction with amines. Long-term storage in water is NOT recommended due to hydrolysis.
3. The fluorescence lifetime (τ) of D2184 in MeOH at 20°C is 5.7 nanoseconds. Data provided by the SPEX Fluorescence Group, Jobin Yvon Inc.
4. Oxidation of the polyunsaturated butadienyl portion of the BODIPY® 581/591 dye results in a shift of the fluorescence emission peak from ~590 nm to ~510 nm (Methods Enzymol 319, 603 (2000); FEBS Lett 453, 278 (1999)).
5. The fluorescence lifetime (τ) of D6116 in MeOH at 20°C is 5.4 nanoseconds. Data provided by the SPEX Fluorescence Group, Jobin Yvon Inc.
6. This sulfonated succinimidyl ester derivative is water-soluble and may be dissolved in buffer at ~pH 8 for reaction with amines. Long-term storage in water is NOT recommended due to hydrolysis.
7. The fluorecence lifetime (τ) of the BODIPY® 630/650 dye at 20°C is 3.9 nanoseconds in H_2O and 4.4 nanoseconds in EtOH (Bioconjug Chem 14, 195 (2003)).

Product List — 1.4 BODIPY Dye Series

Cat #	Product Name	Unit Size
B10006	BODIPY® FL, STP ester, sodium salt	5 mg
B10002	BODIPY® TMR, STP ester, sodium salt	5 mg
B10003	BODIPY® TR-X, STP ester, sodium salt	5 mg
B10005	BODIPY® 650/665-X, STP ester, sodium salt	5 mg
D6144	2,6-dibromo-4,4-difluoro-5,7-dimethyl-4-bora-3a,4a-diaza-*s*-indacene-3-propionic acid, succinimidyl ester (BODIPY® FL Br_2, SE)	5 mg
D6103	4,4-difluoro-4-bora-3a,4a-diaza-*s*-indacene-3,5-dipropionic acid (BODIPY® 500/510)	5 mg
D3834	4,4-difluoro-5,7-dimethyl-4-bora-3a,4a-diaza-*s*-indacene-3-pentanoic acid (BODIPY® FL C_5)	1 mg
D6184	4,4-difluoro-5,7-dimethyl-4-bora-3a,4a-diaza-*s*-indacene-3-pentanoic acid, succinimidyl ester (BODIPY® FL C_5, SE)	5 mg
D2183	4,4-difluoro-5,7-dimethyl-4-bora-3a,4a-diaza-*s*-indacene-3-propionic acid (BODIPY® FL)	5 mg
D2184	4,4-difluoro-5,7-dimethyl-4-bora-3a,4a-diaza-*s*-indacene-3-propionic acid, succinimidyl ester (BODIPY® FL, SE)	5 mg
D6140	4,4-difluoro-5,7-dimethyl-4-bora-3a,4a-diaza-*s*-indacene-3-propionic acid, sulfosuccinimidyl ester, sodium salt (BODIPY® FL, SSE)	5 mg
D6101	6-((4,4-difluoro-5,7-dimethyl-4-bora-3a,4a-diaza-*s*-indacene-3-propionyl)amino)hexanoic acid (BODIPY® FL-X)	5 mg
D6102	6-((4,4-difluoro-5,7-dimethyl-4-bora-3a,4a-diaza-*s*-indacene-3-propionyl)amino)hexanoic acid, succinimidyl ester (BODIPY® FL-X, SE)	5 mg
D6141	*N*-(4,4-difluoro-5,7-dimethyl-4-bora-3a,4a-diaza-*s*-indacene-3-propionyl)cysteic acid, succinimidyl ester, triethylammonium salt (BODIPY® FL, CASE)	5 mg
D6117	6-((4,4-difluoro-1,3-dimethyl-5-(4-methoxyphenyl)-4-bora-3a,4a-diaza-*s*-indacene-2-propionyl)amino)hexanoic acid, succinimidyl ester (BODIPY® TMR-X, SE)	5 mg
D2187	4,4-difluoro-5,7-diphenyl-4-bora-3a,4a-diaza-*s*-indacene-3-propionic acid, succinimidyl ester (BODIPY® 530/550, SE)	5 mg
D6180	4,4-difluoro-5-phenyl-4-bora-3a,4a-diaza-*s*-indacene-3-propionic acid, succinimidyl ester (BODIPY® R6G, SE)	5 mg
D6186	6-((4,4-difluoro-5-phenyl-4-bora-3a,4a-diaza-*s*-indacene-3-propionyl)amino)hexanoic acid, succinimidyl ester (BODIPY® R6G-X, SE)	5 mg
D2228	4,4-difluoro-5-(4-phenyl-1,3-butadienyl)-4-bora-3a,4a-diaza-*s*-indacene-3-propionic acid, succinimidyl ester (BODIPY® 581/591, SE)	5 mg
D2225	4,4-difluoro-5-(2-pyrrolyl)-4-bora-3a,4a-diaza-*s*-indacene-3-propionic acid, succinimidyl ester (BODIPY® 576/589, SE)	5 mg
D10001	6-(((4,4-difluoro-5-(2-pyrrolyl)-4-bora-3a,4a-diaza-*s*-indacene-3-yl)styryloxy)acetyl)aminohexanoic acid, succinimidyl ester (BODIPY® 650/665-X, SE)	5 mg
D2222	4,4-difluoro-5-styryl-4-bora-3a,4a-diaza-*s*-indacene-3-propionic acid, succinimidyl ester (BODIPY® 564/570, SE)	5 mg
D2191	4,4-difluoro-1,3,5,7-tetramethyl-4-bora-3a,4a-diaza-*s*-indacene-8-propionic acid, succinimidyl ester (BODIPY® 493/503, SE)	5 mg
D2219	4,4-difluoro-5-(2-thienyl)-4-bora-3a,4a-diaza-*s*-indacene-3-propionic acid, succinimidyl ester (BODIPY® 558/568, SE)	5 mg
D6116	6-(((4-(4,4-difluoro-5-(2-thienyl)-4-bora-3a,4a-diaza-*s*-indacene-3-yl)phenoxy)acetyl)amino)hexanoic acid, succinimidyl ester (BODIPY® TR-X, SE)	5 mg
D10000	6-(((4,4-difluoro-5-(2-thienyl)-4-bora-3a,4a-diaza-*s*-indacene-3-yl)styryloxy)acetyl)aminohexanoic acid, succinimidyl ester (BODIPY® 630/650-X, SE)	5 mg

For current prices or to order online, visit probes.invitrogen.com

1.5 Fluorescein, Oregon Green® and Rhodamine Green™ Dyes

Spectral Properties of Fluorescein

The amine-reactive fluorescein derivatives (Table 1.7) have been the most common fluorescent derivatization reagents for covalently labeling proteins. In addition to its relatively high absorptivity, excellent fluorescence quantum yield and good water solubility, fluorescein (F1300, Figure 1.52) has an excitation maximum (494 nm) that closely matches the 488 nm spectral line of the argon-ion laser, making it an important fluorophore for confocal laser-scanning microscopy[1] and flow cytometry applications. In addition, fluorescein's protein conjugates are not inordinately susceptible to precipitation. Because it can be prepared in high purity, fluorescein is one of the five dyes in our Reference Dye Sampler Kit (R14782, Section 23.1). Molecular Probes is also the source of the NIST-traceable fluorescein standard (F36915) described below.

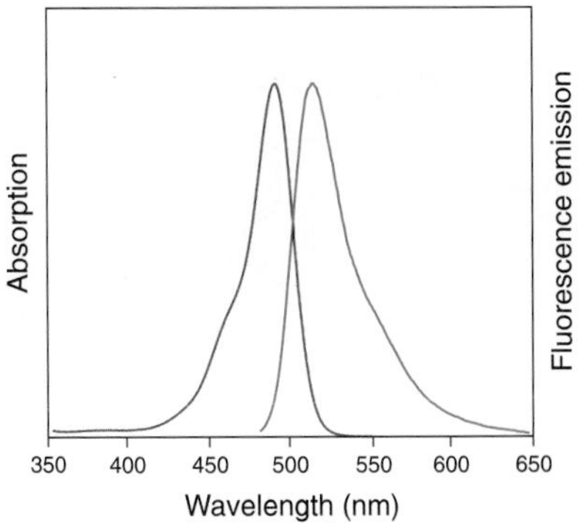

Figure 1.52 Absorption and fluorescence emission spectra of fluorescein in pH 9.0 buffer.

Limitations of Fluoresceins

Unfortunately, fluorescein-based dyes and their conjugates have several drawbacks, including:

- A relatively high rate of photobleaching[2] (Figure 1.9, Figure 1.10, Figure 1.11, Figure 1.46, Figure 1.53, Figure 7.23, Figure 11.8)
- pH-sensitive fluorescence[3] (pK_a ~6.4) that is significantly reduced below pH 7 (Figure 1.12)
- A relatively broad fluorescence emission spectrum (Figure 1.43), limiting their utility in some multicolor applications
- A tendency toward quenching of their fluorescence on conjugation to biopolymers, particularly at high degrees of substitution[4,5] (Figure 1.54)

The photobleaching and pH sensitivity of fluorescein makes quantitative measurements with this fluorophore problematic. Furthermore, fluorescein's relatively high photobleaching rate limits the sensitivity that can be obtained, a significant disadvantage for applications requiring ultrasensitive detection, such as DNA sequencing (Section 8.2), fluorescence *in situ* hybridization (Section 8.5) and localization of low-abundance receptors. These limitations have encouraged the development of alternative fluorophores. However, because of the widespread availability of optical filter sets designed to efficiently excite and detect fluorescein's fluorescence (Section 23.5, Table 23.9) and the near-optimal match of fluorescein dyes to the 488 nm spectral line of the argon-ion laser, useful fluorescein substitutes must closely replicate fluorescein's spectra.

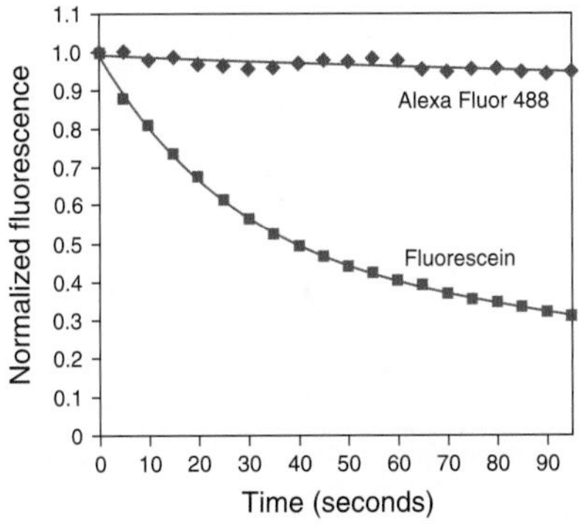

Figure 1.53 Photobleaching profiles of cells stained with Alexa Fluor® 488 or fluorescein conjugates of goat anti-mouse IgG antibody $F(ab')_2$ fragment (A11017, F11021) were used to detect HEp-2 cells probed with human anti-nuclear antibodies. Samples were continuously illuminated and images were collected every 5 seconds with a cooled CCD camera. Normalized intensity data demonstrate the difference in photobleaching rates.

There are no new dyes available that completely solve fluorescein's photobleaching problems, but Molecular Probes has developed some excellent dyes whose spectra mimic those of fluorescein — the Alexa Fluor® 488 (Section 1.3), BODIPY® FL (Section 1.4), Oregon Green® 488, Oregon Green® 514 and Rhodamine Green™ dyes (this section). These dyes are much more photostable than fluorescein and have less or no pH sensitivity in the physiological pH range. When compared with fluorescein, all of these dyes exhibit the same or slightly longer-wavelength spectra (absorption maxima ~490–515 nm) and comparably high fluorescence quantum yields. Alternatively, where they can be used, our yellow-green fluorescent FluoSpheres® microspheres (Section 6.5) provide a means of preparing bioconjugates that have a combination of fluorescence intensity and photostability far superior to that of any simple dye conjugate.

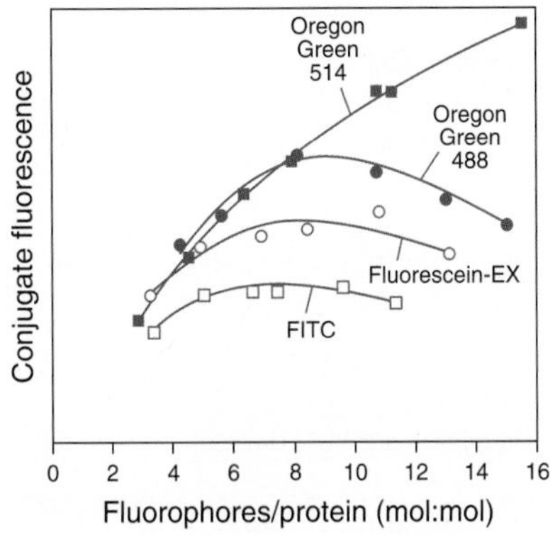

Figure 1.54 Comparison of relative fluorescence as a function of the number of fluorophores attached per protein for goat anti-mouse IgG antibody conjugates prepared using Oregon Green® 514 carboxylic acid succinimidyl ester (O6139 ■), Oregon Green® 488 carboxylic acid succinimidyl ester (O6147, ●), fluorescein-5-EX succinimidyl ester (F6130, ○) and fluorescein isothiocyanate (FITC, F143, F1906, F1907, □). Conjugate fluorescence is determined by measuring the fluorescence quantum yield of the conjugated dye relative to that of the free dye and multiplying by the number of fluorophores per protein.

NIST-Traceable Fluorescein Standard

The National Institute of Standards and Technology (NIST) chose a high-grade fluorescein synthesized by Molecular Probes to create Standard Reference Material 1932 (SRM 1932), a certified fluorescein solution. Molecular Probes now offers a NIST-traceable fluorescein standard (F36915) that not only meets the stringent criteria established by NIST, but is also directly traceable to SRM 1932. We supply our NIST-traceable fluorescein standard as a calibrated 50 µM solution of fluorescein in 100 mM sodium borate buffer, pH 9.5; under these conditions,

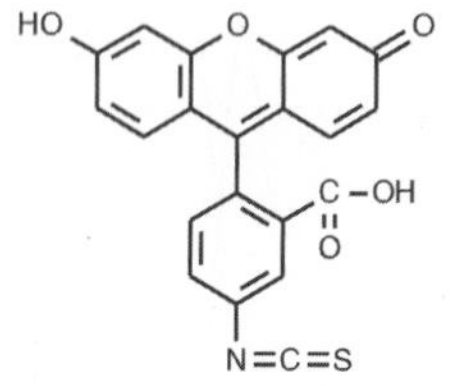

Figure 1.55 F143 fluorescein-5-isothiocyanate (FITC 'Isomer I').

fluorescein is completely ionized[6] and is therefore in its most fluorescent form (Figure 20.1, Figure 20.2), exhibiting an extremely high quantum yield of 0.93 (Section 20.2).

Academic researchers and industry scientists alike can use our NIST-traceable fluorescein standard to assess day-to-day or experiment-to-experiment variation in fluorescence-based instrumentation, as well as to determine the Molecules of Equivalent Soluble Fluorophore (MESF) value for an experimental solution. The MESF value is defined not as the actual number of dye molecules present, but rather as the number of fluorophores that would yield a fluorescence intensity equivalent to that of the experimental solution when analyzed on the same instrument under the same conditions.[7–9] Consequently, the MESF value is an important tool for characterizing the fluorescence intensity of a solution containing spectrally similar dye molecules attached to antibodies, nucleic acids, microspheres or other substrates that might enhance or diminish the fluorescence. When its pH is carefully matched with that of the experimental solution, our NIST-traceable fluorescein standard can be used for accurate MESF determinations of a wide range of green-fluorescent dye solutions and on an assortment of fluorescence-based instruments.

Reactive Derivatives of Fluorescein

Single-Isomer Fluorescein Isothiocyanate (FITC) Preparations

Despite the availability of alternative amine-reactive fluorescein derivatives that yield conjugates with superior stability and comparable spectra, fluorescein isothiocyanate (FITC) remains one

Table 1.7 — Amine-reactive xanthene derivatives in this section

Fluorophore (Abs/Em) *	COOH	Succinimidyl Ester	Other	Protein and Nucleic Acid Labeling Kits	Notes
Eosin (524/544)			E18 (ITC)[5]		• Useful for DAB photoconversion • Phosphorescent
Erythrosin (530/555)			E30150 (ITC)[5]		• Phosphorescent
Fluorescein (494/518)	C1359[5] C1360[6] C1904[M]	C2210 [5] C6164 [6] C1311 [M] F6106 (X)[6] F2181 (X)[M] F6129 (X)[M] F6130 (EX)[5] C20050 (C)[5]	F143 (ITC)[5] F1906 (ITC)[5] F1907 (ITC)[5] D16 (DTA)[5]	F6433 (F) F6434 (F) F10240 (P) Z25042 (Z) Z25342 (Z)	• Most widely used green-fluorescent labeling dye • Absorption overlaps the 488 nm spectral line of the argon-ion laser • Prone to photobleaching • pH-sensitive spectra between pH 5 and pH 8 • Common donor in FRET applications that utilize tetramethylrhodamine as the acceptor
HEX (535/556)		C20091 [6]			• Traditional fluorophore used in automated DNA sequencing
JOE (520/548)		C6171MP [6]			• Traditional fluorophore used in automated DNA sequencing • pH-insensitive spectra at pH >6
Oregon Green® 488 (496/524)	O6146[5]	O6147 [5] O6149 [6] O6185 (X)[6]	O6080[M]	F6153 (F) O10241 (P) Z25043 (Z) Z25342 (Z) U21659 (U)	• Photostable fluorescein substitute • pH-insensitive spectra at pH >6 • Recognized by anti-fluorescein antibodies
Oregon Green® 514 (511/530)	O6138[M]	O6139 [6]		F6155 (F)	• Photostable fluorescein substitute • pH-insensitive spectra at pH >6
Rhodamine Green™ (502/527)		R6107 [M] R6112 (TFA)[M] R6113 (X)[M]			• Photostable fluorescein substitute • pH-insensitive spectra
2′,4′,5′,7′-Tetrabromosulfone-fluorescein (528/544)		C6166 [5]			• Eosin derivative • Useful for DAB photoconversion
TET (521/536)		C20092 [6]			• pH-insensitive spectra at pH >6

* The numbers in parentheses reflect the absorption (Abs) and fluorescence emission (Em) maxima, in nm, of the goat anti–mouse IgG antibody or dextran conjugates in aqueous buffer. These values were obtained from the Molecular Probes data tables. COOH = Carboxylic acid. ITC = Isothiocyanate. X = Aminohexanoyl spacer separating the dye and SE. EX = A seven-atom spacer that is more hydrophilic than X. C = Caged; the probe is nonfluorescent until the caging group is removed by UV illumination. DTA = Dichlorotriazine. TFA = Trifluoroacetyl protected. 5 = 5-Isomer. 6 = 6-Isomer. M = Mixture of 5- and 6-isomers. F = FluoReporter® Protein Labeling Kit (Section 1.2). P = Easy-to-Use Protein Labeling Kit (Section 1.2). Z = Zenon® Antibody Labeling Kit (Section 7.3). U = ULYSIS Nucleic Acid Labeling Kit (Section 8.2).

of the most popular fluorescent labeling reagents. The synthesis of fluorescein isothiocyanate, carboxyfluorescein (FAM, see below) and similar fluorescein-derived reagents yields a mixture of isomers at the 5- and 6-positions of fluorescein's "bottom" ring (Figure 1.55). Spectra of the two isomers are almost indistinguishable in both wavelength and intensity. However, the isomers may differ in the geometry of their binding to proteins, and the conjugates may elute under different chromatographic conditions or migrate differently in an electrophoretic gel when the dyes are used for high-resolution DNA sequencing. Thus, certain applications may require the single-isomer preparations. Many fluorescein (and rhodamine) probes are available from Molecular Probes either as a mixture of isomers or as purified single isomers.

The 5-isomer or "isomer I" of FITC (F143, Figure 1.55, Figure 1.56) is the most widely used FITC isomer, probably because it is easier to isolate in pure form. Because isothiocyanates may deteriorate during storage, we recommend purchasing the 5-isomer of FITC specially packaged in individual vials (F1906, F1907). FITC is readily soluble in aqueous solutions that have a pH above 6. FITC is also available in our FluoReporter® FITC Protein Labeling Kit (F6434, Table 1.2). This kit and its components are described in Section 1.2.

In addition to its widespread use for preparing immunoreagents, FITC has a multitude of other applications. Oligonucleotide conjugates of FITC are frequently employed as hybridization probes.[10] Peptide conjugates of FITC and other fluorescent isothiocyanates are susceptible to Edman degradation, making them useful for high-sensitivity amino acid sequencing;[11] FITC-labeled amino acids and peptides have been separated by capillary electrophoresis, with a detection limit of fewer than 1000 molecules.[12,13] FITC has also been used to detect proteins in gels[14–16] and on nitrocellulose membranes,[17–19] and FITC is a selective inhibitor of several membrane ATPases.[20–22] Furthermore, fluorescein-to-fluorescein excited-state energy transfer leads to self-quenching (see Note 1.2 "Technical Focus: Fluorescence Resonance Energy Transfer (FRET)" in Section 1.3). This self-quenching has permitted scientists to follow the assembly of fluorescein-labeled C9 complement protein from its subunits.[23,24] The degree of substitution of proteins by FITC has been accurately determined by matrix-assisted laser desorption/ionization time-of-flight (MALDI-TOF) mass spectrometry.[25] FITC — and probably Oregon Green® isothiocyanate (O6080) and eosin isothiocyanate (E118, see below) — at a concentration of 2–500 nM can be used as a highly selective marker of eosinophils.[26]

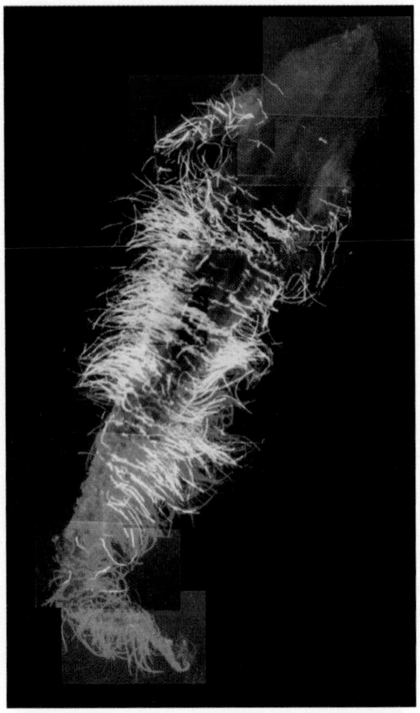

Figure 1.56 Two proteobacterial symbionts localized with phylotype-specific 16S rRNA–directed oligonucleotide probes labeled with either fluorescein-5-isothiocyanate (F143, F1906, F1907) or Texas Red® sulfonyl chloride (T353, T1905). The filamentous bacteria are attached to a hair-like structure secreted from a pore on the dorsal surface of the deep-sea hydrothermal vent polychaete *Alvinella pompejana*. Image contributed by M. Cottrell and C. Cary, College of Marine Studies, University of Delaware.

Mixed-Isomer and Single-Isomer Preparations of Carboxyfluorescein (FAM) Succinimidyl Ester

Although many other companies still prepare their fluorescein bioconjugates with FITC, Molecular Probes prefers to use amine-reactive succinimidyl esters of carboxyfluorescein (commonly called FAM), which yield carboxamides that are more resistant to hydrolysis. We offer both mixed-isomer and single-isomer preparations of FAM (FluoroPure™ Grade, C1904; C1359, C1360) and FAM succinimidyl esters (C1311, C2210, C6164). A study comparing the relative conjugation rate of several reactive fluorescein derivatives with a protein or L-lysine and the stability of the resulting conjugates concluded that the succinimidyl ester of carboxyfluorescein showed superior performance, followed by fluorescein dichlorotriazine (DTAF, see below). FITC was both the slowest to react and yielded the least stable conjugates;[27] however, the degree of labeling was most easily controlled with FITC.[27] The succinimidyl ester of 5-FAM (C2210) is reported to react much faster than FITC when used to derivatize small biomolecules prior to separation by capillary electrophoresis.[28]

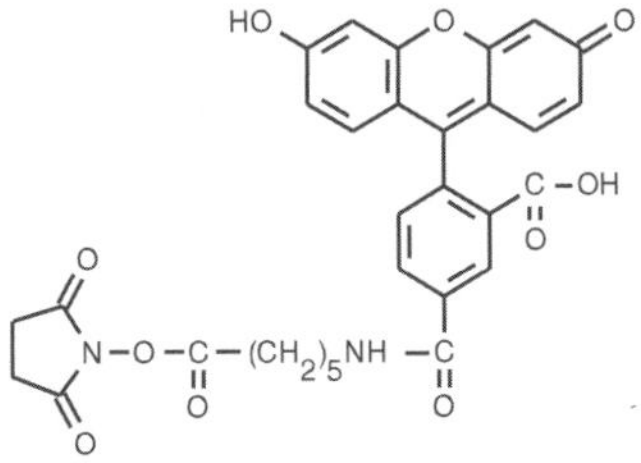

Figure 1.57 F6106 6-(fluorescein-5-carboxamido)-hexanoic acid, succinimidyl ester (5-SFX).

Succinimidyl Esters of Fluorescein with Spacer Groups

We also prepare succinimidyl esters of fluorescein that contain aliphatic spacers between the fluorophore and the reactive group. These include mixed-isomer (F2181, F6129) and single-isomer (F6106) preparations of fluorescein-X succinimidyl ester (SFX), which contains a seven-atom aminohexanoyl spacer ("X") between the FAM fluorophore and the succinimidyl ester (Figure 1.57). In addition, we offer fluorescein-5-EX succinimidyl ester (F6130), which contains a seven-atom spacer that is somewhat more hydrophilic than is the spacer in SFX (Figure 1.58). These spacers separate the fluorophore from the biomolecule to which it is conjugated, potentially reducing the quenching that typically occurs upon conjugation. We have determined that conjugates of some proteins prepared with fluorescein-5-EX succinimidyl ester are up to twice as fluorescent as the corresponding conjugates labeled with FITC at the same degree of labeling (Figure 1.54). Consequently, we now recommend this fluorescein derivative as the preferred dye

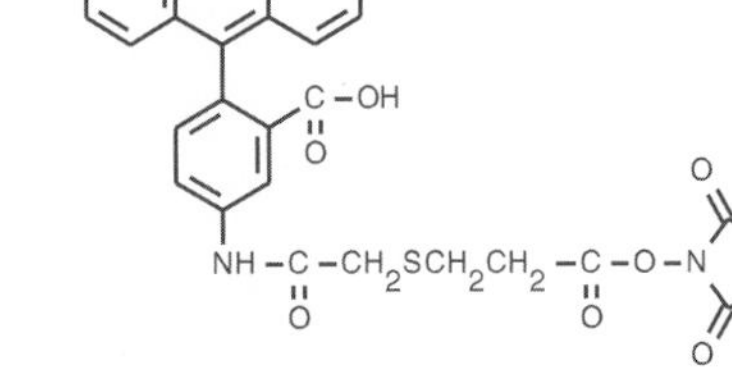

Figure 1.58 F6130 fluorescein-5-EX, succinimidyl ester.

for preparing most fluoresceinated proteins. Fluorescein-5-EX succinimidyl ester is also available in our convenient FluoReporter® Fluorescein-EX Protein Labeling Kit (F6433) and Fluorescein-EX Protein Labeling Kit (F10240). See Section 1.2 and Table 1.3 for more details about these labeling kits.

The spacers in our SFX and fluorescein-5-EX succinimidyl esters may also make the fluorophore more accessible to secondary detection reagents.[29–31] For example, the spacers should make the fluorescein moiety more available for quenching by our polyclonal and monoclonal anti-fluorescein/Oregon Green® antibodies, a technique used to determine the accessibility of the fluorophore in proteins, membranes and cells.[30,32] Fluorescein is frequently used as a hapten on a primary detection reagent that can be either amplified or converted into a longer-wavelength or electron-dense signal with the appropriate secondary detection reagent. Section 7.4 describes our extensive selection of antibodies to fluorescein and other dyes.

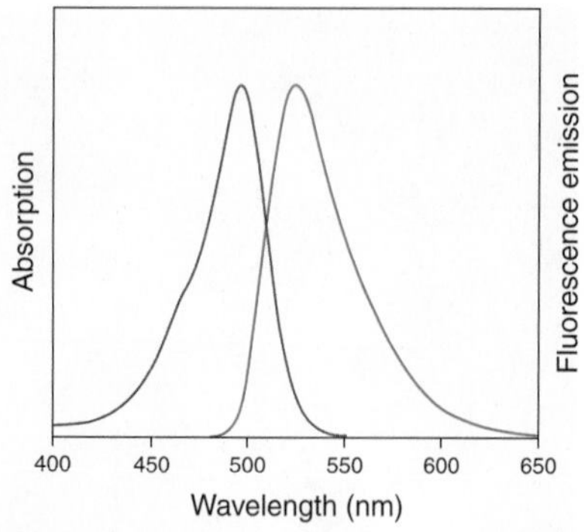

Figure 1.60 Absorption and fluorescence emission spectra of Oregon Green® 488 goat anti–mouse IgG antibody in pH 8.0 buffer.

Fluorescein Dichlorotriazine (DTAF)

The 5-isomer of fluorescein dichlorotriazine (5-DTAF, D16) is highly reactive with proteins[33,34] and is commonly used to prepare biologically active fluorescein tubulin.[35] Unlike other reactive fluoresceins, 5-DTAF also reacts directly with polysaccharides and other alcohols in aqueous solution at pH above 9, but cannot be used to modify alcohols in the presence of better nucleophiles such as amines or thiols.[36] Polysaccharides that have been modified by DTAF (or other fluorescein derivatives) are readily radioiodinated.[37]

Caged Fluorescein

"Caged" probes are those that can liberate an active species upon illumination with ultraviolet light (Section 5.3). Caged versions of nucleotides, drugs and ion indicators are particularly common. Caged fluorescent dyes can be utilized as polar tracers whose fluorescence can be spatially and temporally "turned on" by illumination. Conjugation of the succinimidyl ester of our water-soluble, caged carboxyfluorescein β-alanine-carboxamide (C20050, Figure 1.59) to a biomolecule of interest produces an essentially nonfluorescent probe that yields a green-fluorescent fluorescein-labeled product only after ultraviolet illumination. We have utilized this amine-reactive reagent to prepare conjugates of goat anti–mouse IgG and goat anti–rabbit IgG antibodies (G21061, G21080; Section 7.2). Unlike dye-labeled antibodies, brief ultraviolet illumination of these conjugates results in an increase in fluorescence at the labeling site, a property that may be useful in overcoming high autofluorescence in the sample. Furthermore, photolysis of caged fluorescein conjugates releases a fluorescein dye that can serve as a hapten for our anti-fluorescein/Oregon Green® antibodies (Section 7.4, Figure 7.74).

Oregon Green® 488 and Oregon Green® 514 Dyes

Spectral Properties of the Oregon Green® Dyes

Our patented Oregon Green® 488 and Oregon Green® 514 dyes are fluorinated analogs of fluoresceins. The absorption and emission spectra of the Oregon Green® 488 dye (2′,7′-difluorofluorescein; D6145) perfectly match those of fluorescein (Figure 1.60). With additional fluorination of the "bottom" ring of fluorescein, the Oregon Green® 514 dye exhibits a moderate shift in

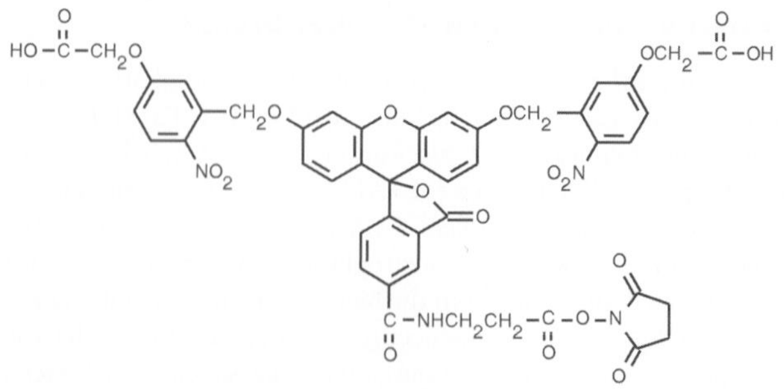

Figure 1.59 C20050 5-carboxyfluorescein-bis-(5-carboxymethoxy-2-nitrobenzyl) ether, β-alanine-carboxamide, succinimidyl ester (CMNB-caged carboxyfluorescein, SE).

its absorption and fluorescence spectra of about 15 nm relative to those of fluorescein or the Oregon Green® 488 dye. Because of the near match of their absorption maxima on proteins (~498 nm and ~512 nm) to the strong 488 nm and 514 nm spectral lines of the argon-ion laser, the Oregon Green® 488 and Oregon Green® 514 fluorophores are important dyes for both confocal laser-scanning microscopy and flow cytometry applications. Furthermore, sophisticated detection systems, such as the Zeiss META system, use linear-unmixing software to differentiate between fluorescence emission maxima <5 nm apart, greatly expanding the palette of fluorescent colors available for multicolor labeling experiments and permitting the use of the Oregon Green® 514 dye in combination with other green-fluorescent dyes.

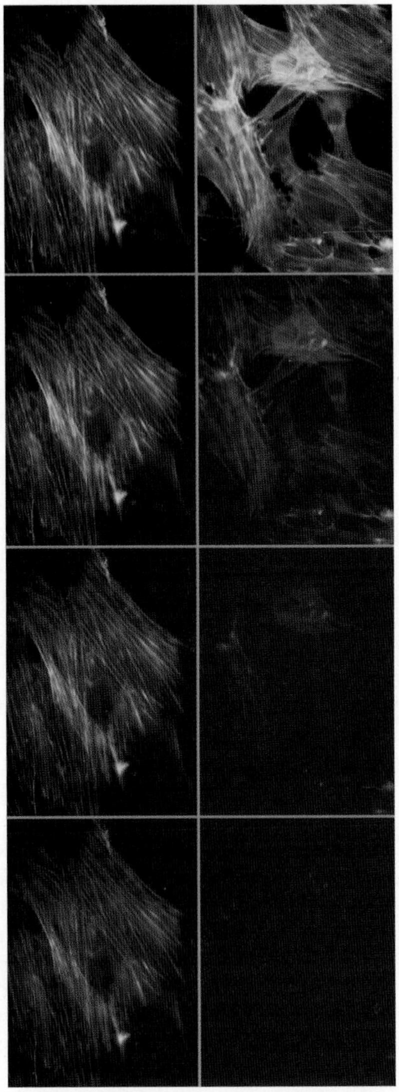

Figure 1.61 Photostability comparison of Oregon Green® 514 phalloidin (O7465, left series) and fluorescein phalloidin (F432, right series). CRE BAG 2 fibroblasts were fixed with formaldehyde, then permeabilized with acetone and stained with the fluorescent phallotoxin. Samples were illuminated continuously and viewed on a fluorescence microscope equipped with a fluorescein longpass optical filter set. Images acquired at 1, 10, 20 and 30 seconds after the start of illumination (top to bottom) demonstrate the superior photostability of the Oregon Green® 514 fluorophore.

Advantages of the Oregon Green® Dyes

Bioconjugates prepared from the Oregon Green® 488 and Oregon Green® 514 dyes share several advantages over those of other fluorescein dyes. These include:

- Fluorescence of protein conjugates prepared from the Oregon Green® 488 and Oregon Green® 514 dyes is not appreciably quenched, even at relatively high degrees of labeling (Figure 1.54).
- Conjugates of the Oregon Green® 488 and Oregon Green® 514 fluorophores are more photostable than those of fluorescein (Figure 1.46). The superior photostability of the Oregon Green® 488 dye and, in particular, the Oregon Green® 514 conjugates permits the acquisition of many more photons before the photodestruction of the dye, making the Oregon Green® dyes particularly useful substitutes for fluoresceins for fluorescence imaging applications (Figure 1.61).
- Oregon Green® dyes have a lower pK_a (pK_a = 4.7 versus 6.4 for fluorescein) (Figure 1.12), making their fluorescence essentially pH insensitive in the physiological pH range. However, the pH sensitivity of the Oregon Green® dyes in the weakly acidic range (pH 4 to 6) also makes these dyes useful as pH indicators for acidic organelles of live cells (Section 20.3).
- Oregon Green® dyes are excellent haptens for anti-fluorescein/Oregon Green® antibodies (Section 7.4, Table 4.2), making Oregon Green® bioconjugates useful in a variety of signal amplification schemes.

Both Oregon Green® 488 and Oregon Green® 514 dyes have also proven useful as fluorescence anisotropy probes for measuring protein–protein and protein–nucleic acid interactions.[38]

Reactive Oregon Green® Dyes

We have prepared a variety of reactive derivatives that enable researchers to take advantage of the excellent spectral properties of the Oregon Green® 488 and Oregon Green® 514 dyes (Table 1.7). These include the FITC analog, Oregon Green® 488 isothiocyanate (F_2FITC, O6080), and the single-isomer succinimidyl esters of Oregon Green® 488 carboxylic acid (O6147, O6149) and Oregon Green® 514 carboxylic acid (O6139), as well as the 5-isomer of Oregon Green® 488 carboxylic acid (O6146, Figure 1.62) and the mixed-isomer preparation of Oregon Green® 514 carboxylic acid (O6138, Figure 1.63). The 6-isomer of Oregon Green® 488-X succinimidyl ester (O6185, Figure 1.64) contains a seven-atom aminohexanoyl spacer ("X") between the fluorophore and the succinimidyl ester group. This spacer helps to separate the fluorophore from its point of attachment, potentially reducing the interaction of the fluorophore with the biomolecule to which it is conjugated and making it more accessible to secondary detection reagents, such as anti-dye antibodies (Section 7.4). Oregon Green® 488 iodoacetamide (O6010) and Oregon Green® 488 maleimide (O6034), which are useful for thiol conjugation, are described in

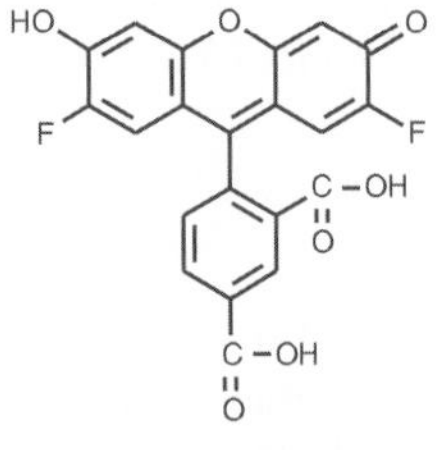

Figure 1.62 O6146 Oregon Green® 488 carboxylic acid.

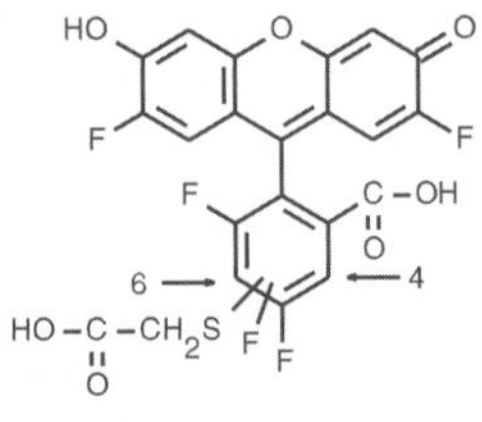

Figure 1.63 O6138 Oregon Green® 514 carboxylic acid.

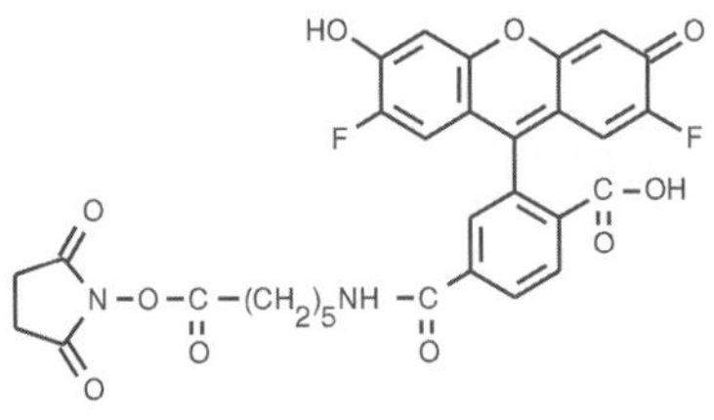

Figure 1.64 O6185 Oregon Green® 488-X, succinimidyl ester.

Section 2.2. We also offer Oregon Green® 488 cadaverine (O10465, Section 3.3) for synthesizing conjugates and labeling carboxylic acids.

The Oregon Green® fluorophores, reactive dyes and conjugates are patented by Molecular Probes, Inc., and are offered for research purposes only. Molecular Probes welcomes inquiries about licensing these products for resale or other commercial uses. Custom conjugations of the Oregon Green® 488 fluorophore are also available. Please contact our Custom and Bulk Sales Department.

Oregon Green® Protein and Nucleic Acid Labeling Kits

To facilitate direct labeling of biomolecules, we offer several types of labeling kits that incorporate reactive versions of our Oregon Green® dyes. These kits are easy to use and give reliable conjugations in minimal time. Our Oregon Green® protein and nucleic acid labeling kits, which are described in detail in the indicated sections, include the:

- FluoReporter® Oregon Green® 488 and Oregon Green® 514 Protein Labeling Kits (F6153, F6155; Section 1.2)
- Easy-to-Use Oregon Green® 488 Protein Labeling Kit (O10241, Section 1.2)
- Zenon® Oregon Green® 488 Antibody Labeling Kits (Section 7.3, Table 7.13)
- ULYSIS Oregon Green® 488 Nucleic Acid Labeling Kit (U21659, Section 8.2)

Oregon Green® 488 Tyramide Signal Amplification Kits

Tyramide signal amplification (TSA) utilizes horseradish peroxidase conjugates to yield significant amplification of targets (Figure 6.5). Our TSA Kits #9 (T20919) and #29 (T20939), which are described in Section 6.2, contain Oregon Green® 488 tyramide and horseradish peroxidase conjugates of either goat anti–mouse IgG antibody or streptavidin. Once deposited, the Oregon Green® 488 tyramide can serve as a hapten for further amplification by using a second round of TSA (Figure 6.5) or our ELF® technology (Section 6.3).

Conjugates of Oregon Green® Dyes

When directly compared with their fluorescein analogs, Oregon Green® 488 and Oregon Green® 514 conjugates typically have higher fluorescence yields and greater resistance to photobleaching. We have used succinimidyl esters of the Oregon Green® 488 and Oregon Green® 514 carboxylic acids to prepare conjugates of:

- Antibodies (Table 7.1) and protein A (Table 7.12), which are described in Section 7.2
- Streptavidin and NeutrAvidin biotin-binding protein (Section 7.6, Table 7.22)
- Lectins (Section 7.7, Table 7.23)
- ChromaTide® dUTP (C7630, Section 8.2, Table 8.7) for synthesis of labeled DNA
- Phalloidin and DNase I (Section 11.1, Table 11.1, Figure 11.7) for staining actin in fixed cells
- Tubulin (T12391, Section 11.2)
- Paclitaxel (Taxol) for staining tubulin filaments in live cells (Flutax-2, P22310; Section 11.2; Figure 11.22)
- DHPE, a phospholipid (O12650, Section 13.2)
- Biocytin (O12920, Section 14.3)
- Dextrans (Section 14.5, Table 14.4)
- Annexin V (A13200, Section 15.5)
- Polymyxin B (P13236, Section 15.2)
- Collagen IV and gelatin (C13185, G13186; Section 15.6)
- Transferrin (T13341), epidermal growth factor (E7498) and fibrinogen (F7496). See Section 16.1 for details on these products.
- α-Bungarotoxin (B7488, Section 16.2)
- Shuttle PIP carriers for transport of fluorescent phosphatidylinositol polyphosphates into living cells (Section 17.4, Figure 17.35)
- BAPTA, a calcium chelator (Section 19.3, Section 19.4)

Fluorescein Derivatives for Genetic Analysis

In addition to the single isomers of the succinimidyl ester of carboxyfluorescein, 5-FAM (C2210) and 6-FAM (C6164), Molecular Probes offers the fluorescein derivatives JOE, HEX and TET for genetic analysis (Figure 1.65). These dyes are important for automated DNA sequencing applications.[39] They are also commonly used as fluorescent donors to label primers and hybridization probes (Section 8.2, Section 8.5; Table 8.11), often in combination with the rhodamine-based fluorescent acceptors ROX (C6125, C6126) and TAMRA[40–42] (C6121, C6122; Table 8.11). The nonfluorescent quenchers dabcyl (D2245), dabsyl (D1537) and the QSY® dyes (Table 1.9) can also be used as energy acceptors in conjunction with these fluorophores. Furthermore, sophisticated detection systems, such as the Zeiss META system, use linear-unmixing software to differentiate between fluorescence emission maxima <5 nm apart, greatly expanding the palette of fluorescent colors available for multicolor labeling experiments and permitting the use of these dyes and their conjugates in combination with other green- or orange-fluorescent dyes.

JOE

Chemical modifications of the xanthene ring of fluoresceins typically shift the dye's absorption and emission maxima to longer wavelengths (Figure 1.65). We offer a single-isomer preparation of the succinimidyl ester of 6-carboxy-4′,5′-dichloro-2′,7′-dimethoxyfluorescein (6-JOE, SE; C6171MP; Figure 1.66). 6-JOE is one of the traditional fluorophores (i.e., 5-FAM, 6-JOE, 6-TAMRA and 6-ROX) used in automated DNA sequencing (Section 8.2, Table 8.11).

TET

Like JOE, the succinimidyl ester of 6-carboxy-2′,4,7,7′-tetrachlorofluorescein (TET, SE; C20092) has a chlorinated xanthene ring, but also additional chlorination of the "bottom" ring (Figure 1.66). As a result, TET has red-shifted absorption and emission maxima of 521 and 536 nm, respectively (Figure 1.65). TET and FAM are often used simultaneously as FRET donors to TAMRA for RT-PCR and SSP-PCR applications.[40–43]

HEX

With excitation and emission maxima of 535 and 556 nm, respectively, the isomer-free succinimidyl ester of 6-carboxy-2′,4,4′,5′,7,7′-hexachlorofluorescein (HEX, SE; C20091) has the longest wavelengths of these chlorinated fluorescein derivatives (Figure 1.65). The HEX dye has four chlorine atoms on the xanthene ring and two on the lower ring (Figure 1.66). HEX is often employed in multiplexed DNA sequencing for classical genotyping[44,45] (Section 8.2, Table 8.11) and in pathological forensics.[39] HEX has also been used in conjunction with the FAM and TET dyes in a 5'-exonuclease assay to detect three different *Candida* species in a single reaction tube.[40]

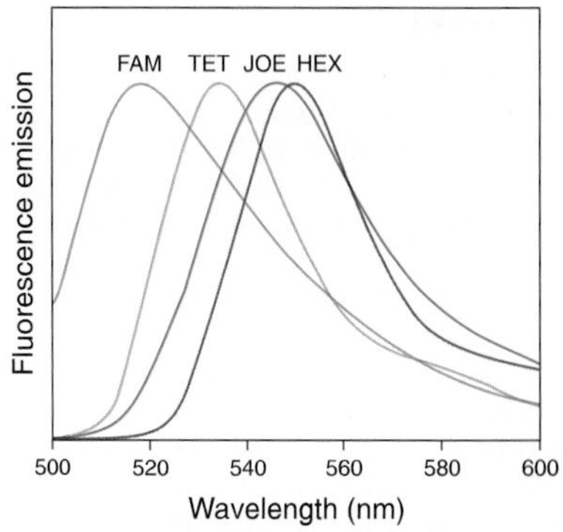

Figure 1.65 Normalized emission spectra of 5-FAM SE (C2210, green), 6-TET SE (C20092, orange), 6-JOE SE (C6171MP, red), and 6-HEX SE (C20091, blue).

Eosins and Erythrosins: Phosphorescent Probes and Photosensitizers

Eosin and Erythrosin

The reactive eosin (2′,4′,5′,7′-tetrabromofluorescein) and erythrosin (2′,4′,5′,7′-tetraiodofluorescein) dyes are usually not chosen for their fluorescence properties — the fluorescence quantum yield of eosin is typically only about 10–20% that of fluorescein, and erythrosin is even less fluorescent — but rather for their ability to act as phosphorescent probes or as photosensitizers. With their high quantum yields (~0.57) for singlet oxygen generation, eosin and its conjugates can be used as effective photooxidizers of diaminobenzidine (DAB) in high-resolution electron microscopy studies (see Note 14.2 "Product Highlight: Fluorescent Probes for Photoconversion of Diaminobenzidine Reagents" in Section 14.3). Like their thiol-reactive counterparts in Section 2.2, eosin and erythrosin isothiocyanates (E18, E30150) are particularly useful as phosphorescent probes for measuring the rotational properties of proteins, virus particles and other biomolecules in solution and in membranes. In addition, they are employed for fluorescence resonance energy transfer (FRET) studies (see Note 1.2 "Technical Focus: Fluorescence Resonance Energy Transfer (FRET)" in Section 1.3) and for fluorescence recovery after photobleaching (FRAP) measurements of lateral diffusion.

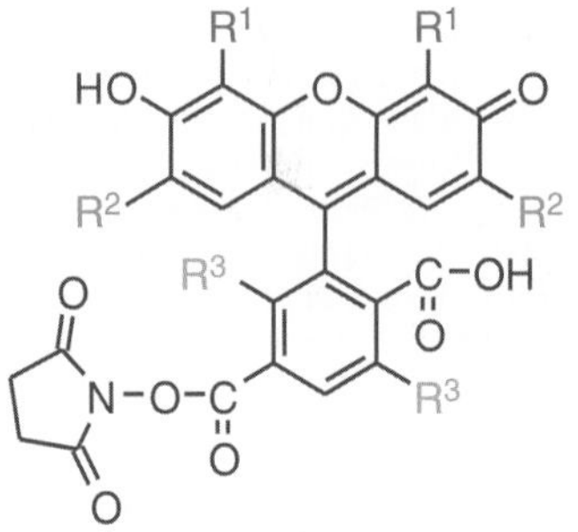

	R^1	R^2	R^3
JOE	Cl	OCH_3	H
HEX	Cl	Cl	Cl
TET	H	Cl	Cl

Figure 1.66 Structures of 6-JOE SE (C6171MP), 6-HEX SE (C20091) and 6-TET SE (C20092).

An Eosin Analog

In 5-carboxy-2′,4′,5′,7′-tetrabromosulfonefluorescein, the carboxylic acid usually found in eosin dyes is replaced by a sulfonic acid (Figure 1.67). The resulting dye is somewhat more photostable than eosin, but is likely to have a similar triplet yield. Because the ability to generate singlet oxygen is lost when a dye bleaches, it is possible that conjugates prepared from the succinimidyl ester of this dye (C6166) will produce singlet oxygen for longer periods, potentially making them more useful than eosin conjugates for photoconversion studies.

Rhodamine Green™ Dyes

Reactive Rhodamine Green™ Dyes

The Rhodamine Green™ dye, which is the nonsulfonated analog of our important Alexa Fluor® 488 dye, offers a combination of desirable properties, including good photostability, a high extinction coefficient (>75,000 $cm^{-1}M^{-1}$) and a high fluorescence quantum yield, particu-

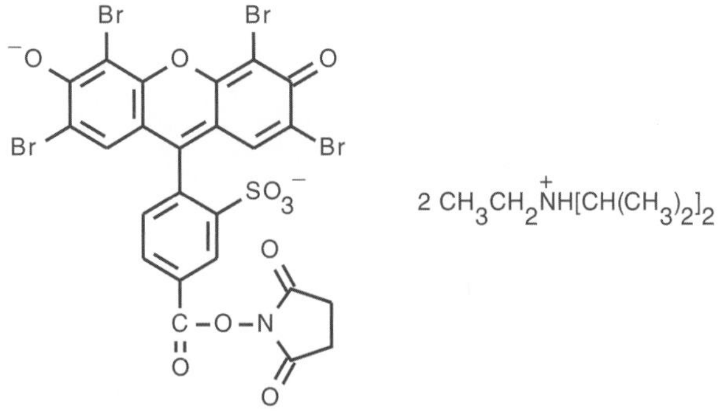

Figure 1.67 C6166 5-carboxy-2′,4′,5′,7′-tetrabromosulfonefluorescein, succinimidyl ester, bis-(diisopropylethylammonium) salt.

larly in its nucleotide and nucleic acid conjugates. The Rhodamine Green™ fluorophore — our trademark for carboxyrhodamine 110 — is even more photostable than the Oregon Green® 488 dye and about equivalent in photostability to the Oregon Green® 514 dye (Figure 1.46). Moreover, the fluorescence of its conjugates is completely insensitive to pH between 4 and 9 (Figure 1.12).

Reactive versions of the Rhodamine Green™ dye (Table 1.7) were originally developed by Molecular Probes for use in DNA sequencing and other applications. Conjugates of the Rhodamine Green™ fluorophore with amines can be prepared either directly from its succinimidyl ester (5(6)-CR 110, SE; R6107) or indirectly from its TFA-protected derivative (5(6)-CR 110 TFA, SE; R6112; Figure 1.68). The succinimidyl ester of the Rhodamine Green™-X dye (R6113) has an additional seven-atom aminohexanoyl spacer ("X") to potentially reduce interaction of the fluorophore and its reaction site. The absorption and fluorescence emission maxima of Rhodamine Green™ conjugates are red-shifted about 7 nm compared with those of fluorescein; however, they remain compatible with standard fluorescein optical filter sets (Table 23.9). The Rhodamine Green™ fluorophore has been used to label the peptide gastrin;[46] however, in general, Rhodamine Green™ succinimidyl esters are much less suitable for protein conjugations than are succinimidyl esters of the Alexa Fluor® and Oregon Green® dyes. Rhodamine Green™ dye–labeled probes have been frequently used for fluorescence correlation spectroscopy[47–50] (see Note 1.4 "Technical Focus: Fluorescence Correlation Spectroscopy (FCS)" in Section 1.3).

Rhodamine Green™ Conjugates

Although the Rhodamine Green™ dye is one of the most photostable of the fluorescein substitutes, its fluorescence when conjugated to proteins is often substantially quenched, and these conjugates also tend to precipitate from solution. Therefore, we do not recommend any of the Rhodamine Green™ succinimidyl esters for preparing protein conjugates. However, when conjugated to dextrans, nucleotides and oligonucleotides, the Rhodamine Green™ fluorophore remains quite fluorescent. Molecular Probes currently has available Rhodamine Green™ dextran conjugates (Section 14.5, Table 14.4) and ChromaTide® Rhodamine Green™ dUTP (C7629; Section 8.2; Table 8.6, Table 8.7).

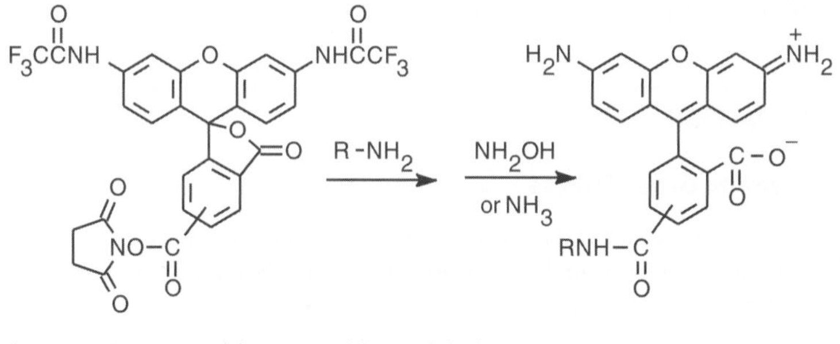

Figure 1.68 Conjugation of the succinimidyl ester of Rhodamine Green™ TFA (R6112) to an amine, followed by deprotection of the fluorophore with either hydroxylamine or ammonia.

References

1. Three-Dimensional Confocal Microscopy, Stevens JK, Mills LR, Trogadis JE, Eds. pp. 101–129 (1994); **2.** Biophys J 68, 2588 (1995); **3.** Spectrochim Acta A 51, 7 (1995); **4.** Anal Biochem 173, 59 (1988); **5.** Clin Chem 25, 1554 (1979); **6.** J Fluorescence 6, 147 (1996); **7.** J Res Natl Inst Stand Technol 107, 83 (2002); **8.** J Res Natl Inst Stand Technol 106, 381 (2001); **9.** J Res Natl Inst Stand Technol 107, 83 (2002); **10.** J Histochem Cytochem 38, 467 (1990); **11.** Biosci Biotechnol Biochem 58, 300 (1994); **12.** J Chromatogr 480, 141 (1989); **13.** Science 242, 562 (1988); **14.** Anal Biochem 174, 38 (1988); **15.** Anal Biochem 132, 334 (1983); **16.** Agr Biol Chem 41, 2059 (1977); **17.** Anal Biochem 177, 263 (1989); **18.** Anal Biochem 164, 303 (1987); **19.** Electrophoresis 8, 25 (1987); **20.** J Biol Chem 259, 9532 (1984); **21.** Biochim Biophys Acta 731, 9 (1983); **22.** Biochim Biophys Acta 626, 255 (1980); **23.** Biochemistry 23, 3260 (1984); **24.** Biochemistry 23, 3248 (1984); **25.** Anal Biochem 269, 312 (1999); **26.** Cytometry 36, 77 (1999); **27.** Bioconjug Chem 6, 447 (1995); **28.** J Chromatogr A 809, 203 (1998); **29.** Biochim Biophys Acta 1104, 9 (1992); **30.** Biochim Biophys Acta 776, 217 (1984); **31.** Biochemistry 21, 978 (1982); **32.** Biochemistry 30, 1692 (1991); **33.** J Immunol Methods 17, 361 (1977); **34.** J Immunol Methods 13, 305 (1976); **35.** Methods Enzymol 134, 519 (1986); **36.** Carbohydr Res 30, 251 (1973); **37.** J Biomed Mater Res 40, 275 (1998); **38.** Anal Biochem 308, 18 (2002); **39.** Genome Res 6, 1170 (1996); **40.** J Clin Microbiol 37, 165 (1999); **41.** Genome Res 6, 995 (1996); **42.** Mol Cell Probes 14, 249 (2000); **43.** Tissue Antigens 54, 508 (1999); **44.** Anim Genet 31, 396 (2000); **45.** Electrophoresis 18, 2871 (1997); **46.** Lett Pept Sci 1, 235 (1995); **47.** J Immunol Methods 260, 117 (2002); **48.** J Biol Chem 274, 29025 (1999); **49.** J Biomol Screen 4, 335 (1999); **50.** Biophys J 72, 1878 (1997).

Data Table — 1.5 Fluorescein, Oregon Green and Rhodamine Green Dyes

Cat #	MW	Storage	Soluble	Abs	EC	Em	Solvent	Notes
C301	691.91	L	pH >6, DMF	519	100,000	542	pH 9	1
C1311	473.39	F,D,L	DMF, DMSO	495	74,000	519	pH 9	2
C1359	376.32	L	pH >6, DMF	492	79,000	518	pH 9	2
C1360	376.32	L	pH >6, DMF	492	81,000	515	pH 9	2
C1904	376.32	L	pH >6, DMF	492	78,000	517	pH 9	2, 3
C2210	473.39	F,D,L	DMF, DMSO	494	78,000	520	pH 9	2
C6164	473.39	F,D,L	DMF, DMSO	496	83,000	516	pH 9	2
C6166	1083.52	F,D,L	DMF, DMSO	529	89,000	544	pH 9	
C6171MP	602.34	F,D,L	DMF, DMSO	520	75,000	548	pH 12	4
C20050	962.79	F,D,LL	DMSO	289	9,500	none	MeOH	5, 6
C20091	680.07	F,D,L	DMF, DMSO	533	98,000	550	pH 9	7
C20092	611.18	F,D,L	DMF, DMSO	521	99,000	536	pH 9	8
D16	495.28	F,D,L	pH >6, DMF	492	83,000	516	pH 9	2, 9
D6145	368.29	L	pH >6, DMF	490	87,000	514	pH 9	10
E18	704.97	F,DD,L	pH >6, DMF	521	95,000	544	pH 9	1, 11
E30150	892.97	F,DD,L	pH >6, DMF	529	90,000	554	pH 9	1, 11
F143	389.38	F,DD,L	pH >6, DMF	494	77,000	519	pH 9	2, 11, 12
F1300	332.31	L	pH >6, DMF	490	93,000	514	pH 9	2
F1906	389.38	F,DD,L	pH >6, DMF	494	77,000	519	pH 9	2, 11, 12
F1907	389.38	F,DD,L	pH >6, DMF	494	77,000	519	pH 9	2, 11, 12
F2181	586.55	F,D,L	DMF, DMSO	494	74,000	520	pH 9	2
F6106	586.55	F,D,L	DMF, DMSO	494	75,000	521	pH 9	2
F6129	586.55	F,D,L	DMF, DMSO	494	74,000	520	pH 9	2
F6130	590.56	F,D,L	DMF, DMSO	491	86,000	515	pH 9	2
F36915	332.31	RO,L	see Notes	490	93,000	514	pH 9.5	2, 13
O6080	425.36	F,DD,L	DMF, DMSO	493	78,000	520	pH 9	10, 11
O6135	448.35	L	pH >6, DMF	497	84,000	517	pH 9	14
O6138	512.36	L	pH >6, DMF	506	86,000	526	pH 9	15, 16
O6139	609.43	F,D,L	DMF, DMSO	506	85,000	526	pH 9	15, 16
O6146	412.30	L	pH >6, DMF	492	85,000	518	pH 9	10, 17
O6147	509.38	F,D,L	DMF, DMSO	495	76,000	521	pH 9	10, 17
O6149	509.38	F,D,L	DMF, DMSO	496	82,000	516	pH 9	10, 17
O6185	622.53	F,D,L	DMF, DMSO	494	84,000	517	pH 9	10
R6107	507.89	F,D,L	DMF, DMSO	504	78,000	532	MeOH	
R6112	663.44	F,D,L	DMF, DMSO	<300		none		18
R6113	621.05	F,D,L	DMF, DMSO	503	74,000	528	MeOH	

For definitions of the contents of this data table, see "Navigating *The Handbook*" in the introductory pages.

Notes

1. Eosin and erythrosin derivatives also exhibit phosphorescence with an emission maximum at ~680 nm. The phosphorescence lifetime is ~1 millisecond for eosin and 0.5 milliseconds for erythrosin (Biochem J 183, 561 (1979); Spectroscopy 5, 20 (1990)). Fluorescence lifetimes (τ) are 1.4 nanoseconds (QY = 0.2) for eosin and 0.1 nanoseconds (QY = 0.02) for erythrosin (J Am Chem Soc 99, 4306 (1977)).
2. Absorption and fluorescence of fluorescein derivatives are pH-dependent. Extinction coefficients and fluorescence quantum yields decrease markedly at pH <7.
3. This product is specified to equal or exceed 98% analytical purity by HPLC.
4. Absorption and fluorescence of C6171MP are pH-dependent (pK_a ~11.5). Fluorescence is maximal at pH >12.
5. All photoactivatable probes are sensitive to light. They should be protected from illumination except when photolysis is intended.
6. This product is colorless and nonfluorescent until it is activated by ultraviolet photolysis. Photoactivation generates a fluorescein derivative with spectral characteristics similar to C1359.
7. Absorption and fluorescence of C20091 are pH-dependent (pK_a ~3.0). Fluorescence is maximal at pH >4.
8. Absorption and fluorescence of C20092 are pH-dependent (pK_a ~4.5). Fluorescence is maximal at pH >6.
9. Unstable in water. Use immediately.
10. Absorption and fluorescence of Oregon Green® 488 derivatives are pH-dependent only in moderately acidic solutions (pH <5).
11. Isothiocyanates are unstable in water and should not be stored in aqueous solution.
12. The extinction coefficient of fluorescein isothiocyanate decreases about 10% on protein conjugation (J Immunol Methods 5, 103 (1974)). The fluorescence lifetime (τ) is 3.8 nanoseconds.
13. F36915 consists of a fluorescein solution in 100 mM sodium borate buffer pH 9.5. The concentration of fluorescein is set spectrophotometrically to be equivalent to that of NIST Standard Reference Material (SRM) 1932.
14. Absorption and fluorescence of Oregon Green® 500 dyes are pH-dependent only in moderately acidic solutions (pH <5).
15. Absorption and fluorescence of Oregon Green® 514 derivatives are pH-dependent only in moderately acidic solutions (pH <5).
16. The fluorescence lifetime (τ) of the Oregon Green® 514 dye in pH 9.0 buffer at 20°C is 4.2 nanoseconds. Data provided by the SPEX Fluorescence Group, Jobin Yvon Inc.
17. The fluorescence lifetime (τ) of the Oregon Green® 488 dye (O6146) in pH 9.0 buffer at 20°C is 4.1 nanoseconds. Data provided by the SPEX Fluorescence Group, Jobin Yvon Inc.
18. R6112 is converted to R6107 by cleavage of the trifluoroacetyl protecting groups.

Product List — 1.5 Fluorescein, Oregon Green and Rhodamine Green Dyes

Cat #	Product Name	Unit Size
C6171MP	6-carboxy-4',5'-dichloro-2',7'-dimethoxyfluorescein, succinimidyl ester (6-JOE, SE)	5 mg
C301	5-(and-6)-carboxyeosin *mixed isomers*	100 mg
C1359	5-carboxyfluorescein (5-FAM) *single isomer*	100 mg
C1360	6-carboxyfluorescein (6-FAM) *single isomer*	100 mg
C1904	5-(and-6)-carboxyfluorescein (5(6)-FAM) *FluoroPure™ grade* *mixed isomers*	100 mg
C20050	5-carboxyfluorescein-bis-(5-carboxymethoxy-2-nitrobenzyl) ether, β-alanine-carboxamide, succinimidyl ester (CMNB-caged carboxyfluorescein, SE)	1 mg
C2210	5-carboxyfluorescein, succinimidyl ester (5-FAM, SE) *single isomer*	10 mg
C6164	6-carboxyfluorescein, succinimidyl ester (6-FAM, SE) *single isomer*	10 mg
C1311	5-(and-6)-carboxyfluorescein, succinimidyl ester (5(6)-FAM, SE) *mixed isomers*	100 mg
C20091	6-carboxy-2',4,4',5',7,7'-hexachlorofluorescein, succinimidyl ester (6-HEX, SE) *single isomer*	5 mg
C6166	5-carboxy-2',4',5',7'-tetrabromosulfonefluorescein, succinimidyl ester, bis-(diisopropylethylammonium) salt	5 mg
C20092	6-carboxy-2',4,7,7'-tetrachlorofluorescein, succinimidyl ester (6-TET, SE) *single isomer*	5 mg
D16	5-(4,6-dichlorotriazinyl)aminofluorescein (5-DTAF) *single isomer*	100 mg
D6145	2',7'-difluorofluorescein (Oregon Green® 488)	10 mg
E18	eosin-5-isothiocyanate	100 mg
E30150	erythrosin-5-isothiocyanate	10 mg
F6434	FluoReporter® FITC Protein Labeling Kit *5-10 labelings*	1 kit
F6433	FluoReporter® Fluorescein-EX Protein Labeling Kit *5-10 labelings*	1 kit
F6153	FluoReporter® Oregon Green® 488 Protein Labeling Kit *5-10 labelings*	1 kit
F6155	FluoReporter® Oregon Green® 514 Protein Labeling Kit *5-10 labelings*	1 kit
F1300	fluorescein *reference standard*	1 g
F6106	6-(fluorescein-5-carboxamido)hexanoic acid, succinimidyl ester (5-SFX) *single isomer*	5 mg
F2181	6-(fluorescein-5-(and-6)-carboxamido)hexanoic acid, succinimidyl ester (5(6)-SFX) *mixed isomers*	10 mg
F6129	6-(fluorescein-5-(and-6)-carboxamido)hexanoic acid, succinimidyl ester (5(6)-SFX) *mixed isomers* *special packaging*	10 x 1 mg
F10240	Fluorescein-EX Protein Labeling Kit *3 labelings*	1 kit
F6130	fluorescein-5-EX, succinimidyl ester	10 mg
F143	fluorescein-5-isothiocyanate (FITC 'Isomer I')	1 g
F1906	fluorescein-5-isothiocyanate (FITC 'Isomer I') *special packaging*	10 x 10 mg
F1907	fluorescein-5-isothiocyanate (FITC 'Isomer I') *special packaging*	10 x 100 mg
F36915	fluorescein *NIST-traceable standard* *nominal concentration 50 µM* *special packaging*	5 x 1 mL
O6146	Oregon Green® 488 carboxylic acid *5-isomer*	5 mg
O6147	Oregon Green® 488 carboxylic acid, succinimidyl ester *5-isomer*	5 mg
O6149	Oregon Green® 488 carboxylic acid, succinimidyl ester *6-isomer*	5 mg
O6080	Oregon Green® 488 isothiocyanate (F_2FITC) *mixed isomers*	5 mg
O10241	Oregon Green® 488 Protein Labeling Kit *3 labelings*	1 kit
O6185	Oregon Green® 488-X, succinimidyl ester *6-isomer*	5 mg
O6135	Oregon Green® 500 carboxylic acid *5-isomer*	5 mg
O6138	Oregon Green® 514 carboxylic acid	5 mg
O6139	Oregon Green® 514 carboxylic acid, succinimidyl ester	5 mg
R6107	Rhodamine Green™ carboxylic acid, succinimidyl ester, hydrochloride (5(6)-CR 110, SE) *mixed isomers*	5 mg
R6112	Rhodamine Green™ carboxylic acid, trifluoroacetamide, succinimidyl ester (5(6)-CR 110 TFA, SE) *mixed isomers*	5 mg
R6113	Rhodamine Green™-X, succinimidyl ester, hydrochloride *mixed isomers*	5 mg
U21659	ULYSIS® Oregon Green® 488 Nucleic Acid Labeling Kit *20 labelings*	1 kit
Z25042	Zenon® Fluorescein Mouse IgG_1 Labeling Kit *50 labelings*	1 kit
Z25342	Zenon® Fluorescein Rabbit IgG Labeling Kit *50 labelings*	1 kit
Z25043	Zenon® Oregon Green® 488 Mouse IgG_1 Labeling Kit *50 labelings*	1 kit
Z25343	Zenon® Oregon Green® 488 Rabbit IgG Labeling Kit *50 labelings*	1 kit

For current prices or to order online, visit probes.invitrogen.com

1.6 Long-Wavelength Rhodamines, Texas Red® Dyes and QSY® Quenchers

This section includes dyes that have absorption maxima beyond about 520 nm, extending to nearly 800 nm. Significant exceptions, however, are the long-wavelength Alexa Fluor® dyes, which are all discussed in Section 1.3, the long-wavelength BODIPY® dyes — BODIPY® TMR, BODIPY® TR, BODIPY® 630/650 and BODIPY® 650/665 — which are described in Section 1.4 and the 2′,4′,5′,7′-tetrabromofluorescein (eosin), 2′,4′,5′,7′-tetraiodofluorescein (erythrosin), TET, JOE and HEX dyes, which also absorb maximally beyond 520 nm but are discussed with other fluoresceins in Section 1.5. The versatile Alexa Fluor® and BODIPY® dyes provide demonstrably superior performance relative to the dyes in this section in many applications.

Molecular Probes' long-wavelength light–emitting dyes (Table 1.8) are among the most photostable fluorescent labeling reagents available. Moreover, spectra of most of the dyes are not affected by changes in pH between 4 and 10, an important advantage over the fluoresceins for many biological applications. Dyes in this spectral range are important for certain multicolor applications, such as DNA sequencing, detection on microarrays and fluorescence *in situ* hybridization, which demand a greater number of fluorophores with distinct spectra. The most common members of this group have been the tetramethylrhodamines — including the reactive isothiocyanate (TRITC) and carboxylic acid (TAMRA) derivatives — as well as the X-rhodamines. The X prefix of the X-rhodamines, which include Texas Red® derivatives, refers to the fluorophore's extra julolidine rings (Figure 1.69). These rings prevent rotation about the nitrogen atoms, resulting in a shift in the fluorophore's spectra to longer wavelengths and usually an increase in its fluorescence quantum yield. Our unique patented diarylrhodamine derivatives — the QSY® 7, QSY® 9 and QSY® 21 dyes — are essentially nonfluorescent compounds that have strong absorption in the visible spectrum (Figure 1.70). They are probably the best chromophores available for use as fluorescence quenchers in many bioassays. These QSY® dyes complement the QSY® 35 dye — a totally nonfluorescent quencher based on the NBD fluorophore that absorbs maximally near 475 nm and the dabcyl and dansyl quenchers (Section 1.8).

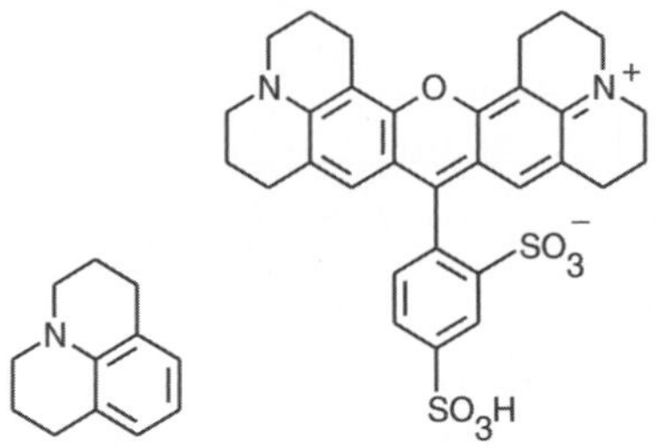

Julolidine   Sulforhodamine 101

Figure 1.69 The amine substituents of X-rhodamine, sulforhodamine 101 and Texas Red® dyes are rigidified in a julolidine ring structure.

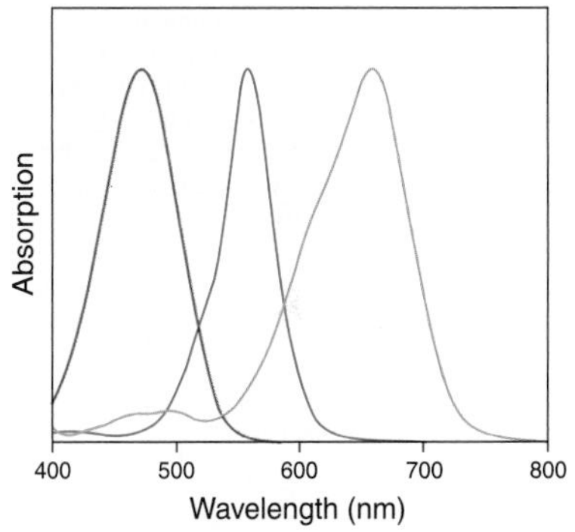

Figure 1.70 Normalized absorption spectra of the QSY® 35 (blue), QSY® 7 (red) and QSY® 21 (orange) dyes. The QSY® 7 and QSY® 9 dyes have essentially identical spectra.

Table 1.8 — Amine-reactive orange- and red-fluorescent fluorophores in this section

Fluorophore (Abs/Em) *	Succinimidyl Ester	Other	Protein Labeling Kits	Notes
Lissamine rhodamine B (570/590)		L20 (SC)M L1908 (SC)M		• Optimal for 568 nm excitation • Photostable
Naphthofluorescein (602/672)	C653 M	C652 (COOH)M		• Very long-wavelength excitation and emission • pH-sensitive fluorescence, with a high pK_a (~7.6)
Rhodamine 6G (525/555)	C6127 5 C6128 6 C6157 M			• Excited by the 514 nm spectral line of the argon-ion laser • Spectra intermediate between those of fluorescein and TMR
Rhodamine Red™-X (580/590)	R6160 (X)5		F6161 (F)	• Conjugates of Rhodamine Red™-X are generally more fluorescent than those of Lissamine rhodamine B, and the succinimidyl ester is more stable in H_2O
Tetramethylrhodamine (555/580)	C2211 5 C6123 6 C1171 M T6105 (X)M	C6121 (COOH)5 C6122 (COOH)6 C300 (COOH)M T1480 (ITC)5 T1481 (ITC)6 T490 (ITC)M	F6163 (F)	• pH-insensitive fluorescence • Good photostability • Conjugates are prone to aggregation • Succinimidyl ester derivative (6-TAMRA, SE; C6123) is widely used for automated DNA sequencing
Texas Red® dye (595/615)	T6134 (X)M T20175 (X)5	T353 (SC)M T1905 (SC)M T10125 (STP)M	F6162 (F) T10244 (P) Z25045 (Z) Z25345 (Z)	• Good spectral separation from green fluorophores • Texas Red®-X succinimidyl ester typically yields greater fluorescence per attached dye than Texas Red® sulfonyl chloride and is more stable in H_2O
X-rhodamine (580/605)	C6125 5 C6126 6 C1309 M	C6124 (COOH)5 C6156 (COOH)6 X491 (ITC)M		• Succinimidyl ester derivative (6-ROX, SE; C6126) is widely used for automated nucleic acid sequencing

* The numbers in parentheses reflect the absorption (Abs) and fluorescence emission (Em) maxima, in nm, of the goat anti–mouse IgG antibody or dextran conjugates in aqueous buffer. These values were obtained from the Molecular Probes data tables. SC = Sulfonyl chloride. COOH = Carboxylic acid. X = Aminohexanoyl spacer separating the dye and the SE. ITC = Isothiocyanate. STP = 4-Sulfotetrafluorophenyl ester. 5 = 5-Isomer. 6 = 6-Isomer. S = Single isomer. M = Mixed isomers. F = FluoReporter® Protein Labeling Kit (Section 1.2). P = Easy-to-Use Protein Labeling Kit (Section 1.2). Z = Zenon® Antibody Labeling Kit (Section 7.3).

Tetramethylrhodamine

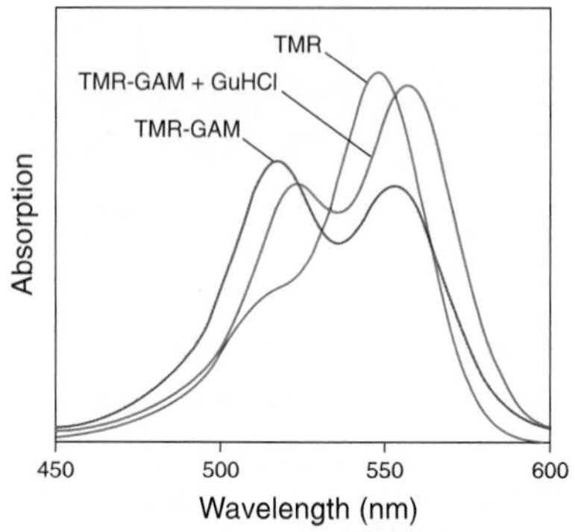

Figure 1.71 Effect of protein conjugation on the absorption spectrum of tetramethylrhodamine. The absorption spectrum of tetramethylrhodamine conjugated to goat anti–mouse IgG antibody (TMR-GAM, T2762) shows an additional peak at about 520 nm when compared with the spectrum of the same concentration of the free dye (TMR). Partial unfolding of the protein in the presence of 4.8 M guanidine hydrochloride (TMR-GAM + GuHCl) results in a spectrum more similar to that of the free dye.

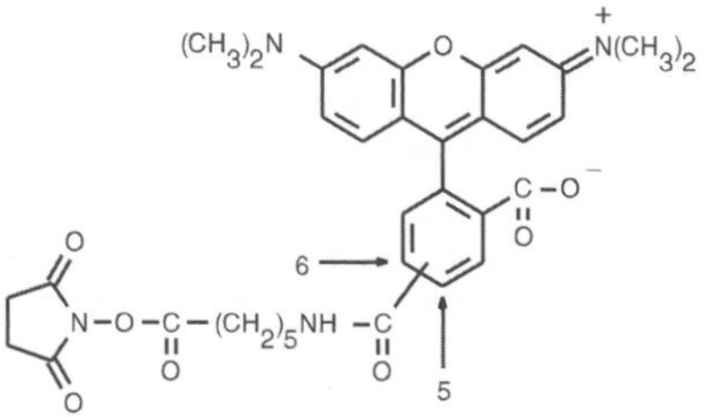

Figure 1.72 T6105 6-(tetramethylrhodamine-5-(and-6)-carboxamido)hexanoic acid, succinimidyl ester (5(6)-TAMRA-X, SE).

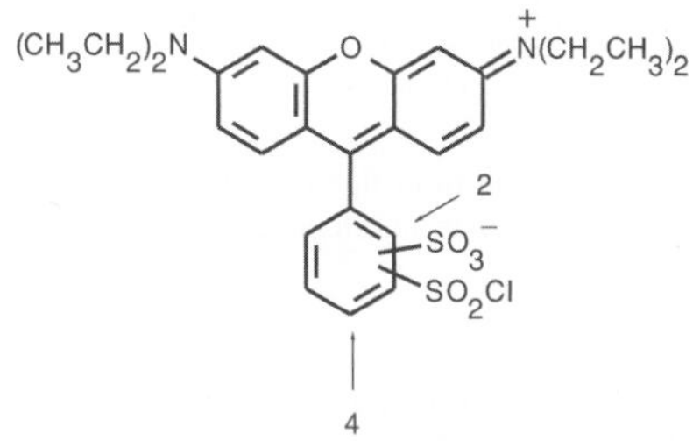

Figure 1.73 L20 Lissamine rhodamine B sulfonyl chloride.

Tetramethylrhodamine (TMR) has been an important fluorophore for preparing protein conjugates, especially fluorescent antibody and avidin derivatives used in immunochemistry, although we now strongly recommend using conjugates of our Alexa Fluor® 546 and Alexa Fluor® 555 dyes (Section 1.3) instead of the tetramethylrhodamine conjugates for applications in this spectral range. Under the name TAMRA, the carboxylic acid of TMR has also achieved prominence as a dye for oligonucleotide labeling and automated DNA sequencing applications [1–3] (Section 8.2, Table 8.11). Because it can be prepared in high purity, the 5-isomer of TAMRA (C6121) is one of the five dyes in our Reference Dye Sampler Kit (R14782, Section 23.1). The detection limit of TMR-labeled amino acids by capillary electrophoresis is reported to be ~600 molecules.[4] The fluorescence quantum yield of TMR conjugates is usually only about one-fourth that of fluorescein conjugates. However, because TMR is readily excited by the intense 546 nm spectral line from mercury-arc lamps used in most fluorescence microscopes and is intrinsically more photostable than fluorescein, TMR conjugates often appear brighter than the corresponding fluorescein conjugates. TMR is also efficiently excited by the 543 nm spectral line of the green He–Ne laser, which is increasingly being used for analytical instrumentation. TMR conjugates are not as well excited by the 568 nm spectral line of the Ar–Kr mixed-gas laser used in many confocal laser-scanning microscopes.

A significant limitation of the TMR dyes TAMRA and TRITC as protein-labeling reagents is that the absorption spectrum of TMR-labeled proteins is frequently complex (Figure 1.71), usually splitting into two absorption peaks at about 520 and 550 nm,[5] so that the actual degree of labeling is difficult to determine. Excitation at wavelengths in the range of the short-wavelength peak fails to yield the expected amount of fluorescence, indicating that it arises from a nonfluorescent dye aggregate. Furthermore, when the TMR-labeled protein conjugate is denatured by guanidine hydrochloride, the long-wavelength absorption increases, the short-wavelength peak mostly disappears and the fluorescence yield almost doubles[6] (Figure 1.71). This change in the absorption spectrum indicates that the extinction coefficient of TMR probably decreases upon conjugation to proteins. The absorption spectra of TMR-labeled nucleotides and of other probes such as our rhodamine phalloidin (R415, Section 11.1) do *not* split into two peaks, indicating a labeling ratio of one dye molecule per biomolecule. The emission spectrum of TMR conjugates does not vary much with the degree of labeling.[5] An improved method for estimating the degree of substitution of TRITC conjugates has been described.[6] Unlike TMR-labeled proteins, protein conjugates of our Alexa Fluor® 546 and Alexa Fluor® 555 dyes (Section 1.3) show normal absorption spectra (Figure 7.9) and are also more fluorescent than either TMR or Cy3 protein conjugates (Figure 1.22).

Mixed-Isomer and Single-Isomer TRITC Preparations

Our tetramethylrhodamine isothiocyanate (TRITC) is of the highest quality available from any commercial source. Both our mixed-isomer (T490) and single-isomer (T1480, T1481) TRITC preparations typically have extinction coefficients above 80,000 $cm^{-1}M^{-1}$, whereas some competitive sources of TRITC have extinction coefficients reported to be below 50,000 $cm^{-1}M^{-1}$. TRITC is widely used by other companies to prepare most of their so-called "rhodamine" immunoconjugates; however, they also often employ reactive versions of rhodamine B or Lissamine rhodamine B, which have somewhat different spectra, resulting in some confusion in matching the product name to the correct fluorophore.

Succinimidyl Esters of Carboxytetramethylrhodamine (TAMRA)

Almost all of Molecular Probes' TMR conjugates are prepared using succinimidyl esters of carboxytetramethylrhodamine (TAMRA), rather than TRITC, because bioconjugates from succinimidyl esters are more stable and often more fluorescent. We offer the mixed-isomer (C300) and single-isomer (C6121, C6122) preparations of TAMRA, as well as the corresponding mixed-isomer (C1171) and single-isomer (C2211, C6123) TAMRA succinimidyl esters. The single-isomer preparations of TAMRA are most important for high-resolution techniques such as DNA sequencing[2] and separation of TAMRA-labeled carbohydrates by capillary electrophoresis.[7] 6-TAMRA is one of the traditional fluorophores (5-FAM, 6-JOE, 6-TET, 6-HEX, 6-TAMRA and 6-ROX) used in automated DNA sequencing [1–3,8] (Section 8.2, Table 8.11). Our FluoReporter® Tetramethylrhodamine Protein Labeling Kit (F6163, Section 1.2) supplies the mixed-isomer 5(6)-TAMRA succinimidyl ester for preparing TMR-labeled proteins.

We have also prepared the mixed-isomer TAMRA-X succinimidyl ester (5(6)-TAMRA-X, SE; T6105), which contains a seven-atom aminohexanoyl spacer ("X") between the reactive group and the fluorophore (Figure 1.72). This spacer helps to separate the fluorophore from its point of attachment, potentially reducing the interaction of the fluorophore with the biomolecule to which it is conjugated and making it more accessible to secondary detection reagents.[9–11] Polyclonal anti-tetramethylrhodamine and anti–Texas Red® dye antibodies that recognize the tetramethylrhodamine, Rhodamine Red™-X, X-rhodamine and Texas Red® fluorophores are available (Section 7.4).

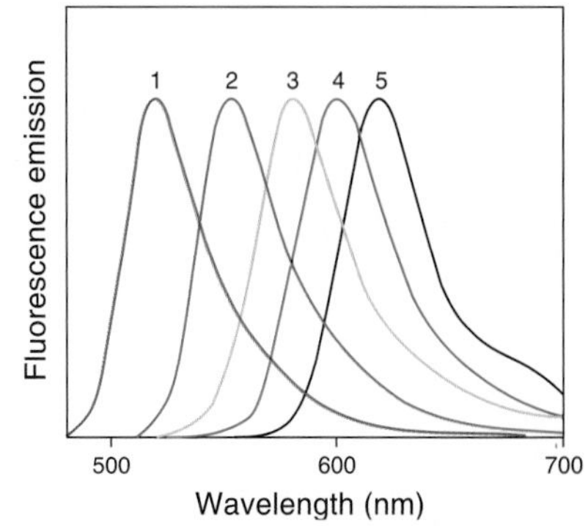

Figure 1.74 Normalized fluorescence emission spectra of goat anti–mouse IgG antibody conjugates of 1) fluorescein, 2) rhodamine 6G, 3) tetramethylrhodamine, 4) Lissamine rhodamine B and 5) Texas Red® dyes.

Lissamine Rhodamine B and Rhodamine Red™-X Dyes

Lissamine Rhodamine B Sulfonyl Chloride

Lissamine rhodamine B sulfonyl chloride (L20, L1908; Figure 1.73) is much less expensive than Texas Red® sulfonyl chloride (see below), and the fluorescence emission spectrum of its protein conjugates lies between those of tetramethylrhodamine and Texas Red® conjugates (Figure 1.74). Although the absorption spectral shift relative to tetramethylrhodamine is not large, it is sufficient to permit conjugates of Lissamine rhodamine B to be excited by the 568 nm spectral line of the Ar–Kr mixed-gas laser used in many confocal laser-scanning microscopes. Furthermore, the protein conjugates of Lissamine rhodamine B are easier to purify and more chemically stable than are the conjugates of tetramethylrhodamine. Like Texas Red® sulfonyl chloride, Lissamine rhodamine B sulfonyl chloride is actually a mixture of isomeric sulfonyl chlorides.

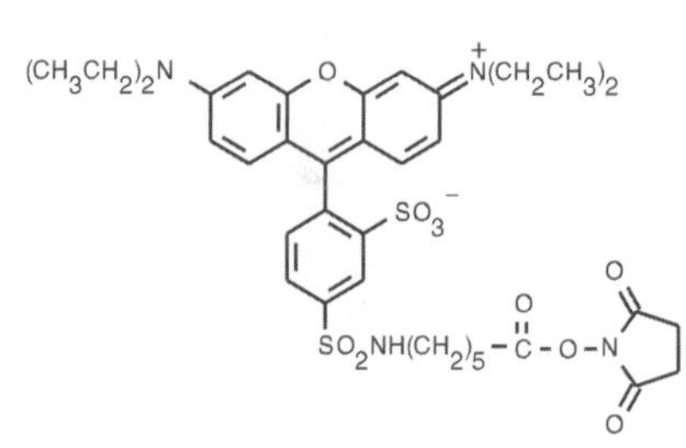

Figure 1.75 R6160 Rhodamine Red™-X, succinimidyl ester.

Rhodamine Red™-X Succinimidyl Ester

Lissamine rhodamine B sulfonyl chloride is unstable, particularly in aqueous solution, making it somewhat difficult to achieve reproducible conjugations using this dye. Unlike Lissamine rhodamine B sulfonyl chloride, which is a mixture of isomeric sulfonyl chlorides (Figure 1.73), our patented Rhodamine Red™-X succinimidyl ester (R6160, Figure 1.75) is isomerically pure. Rhodamine Red™-X succinimidyl ester is resistant to hydrolysis at the pH typically used for conjugation and provides a spacer between the fluorophore and the reactive site. Moreover, we have found that protein conjugates of the Rhodamine Red™-X dye are frequently brighter than those of Lissamine rhodamine B (Figure 1.76), and are less likely to precipitate during storage.[12] Rhodamine Red™-X succinimidyl ester is used in our FluoReporter® Rhodamine Red™-X Protein Labeling Kit (F6161). See Section 1.2 for further information on this kit.

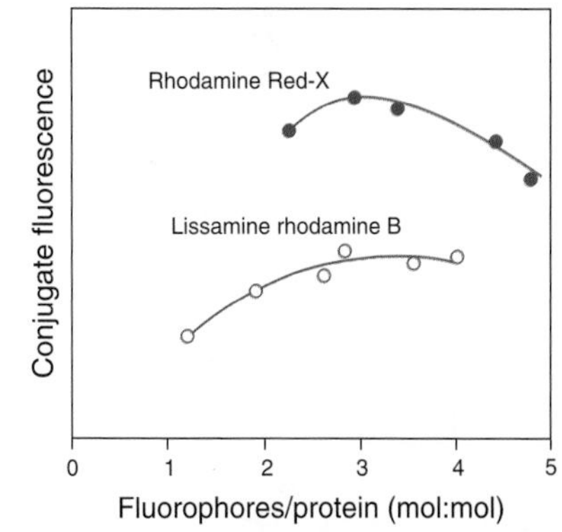

Figure 1.76 Comparison of the relative fluorescence of goat anti–mouse IgG antibody conjugates of Rhodamine Red™-X succinimidyl ester (R6160, ●) and Lissamine rhodamine B sulfonyl chloride (L20, L1908, ○). Conjugate fluorescence is determined by measuring the fluorescence quantum yield of the conjugated dye relative to that of the free dye and multiplying by the number of fluorophores per protein. Higher numbers of fluorophores attached per protein are attainable with Rhodamine Red™-X dye due to the lesser tendency of this dye to induce protein precipitation (Bioconjug Chem 7, 482 (1996)).

X-Rhodamine

The derivatives of carboxy-X-rhodamine (ROX) — a dye originally developed at Molecular Probes in 1986 — are widely used for oligonucleotide labeling and automated DNA sequencing applications (Section 8.2, Table 8.11). Conjugates of this dye and of the similar isothiocyanate (5(6)-XRITC, X491; Figure 1.77) have longer-wavelength spectra (Figure 1.78) than the spectra of Lissamine rhodamine B, but somewhat shorter-wavelength spectra than those of Texas Red®

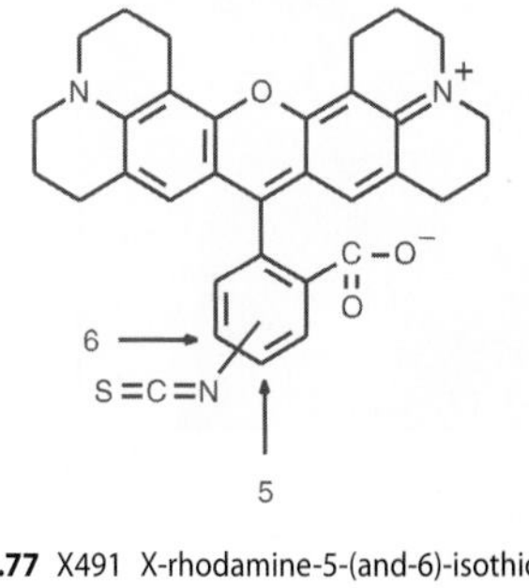

Figure 1.77 X491 X-rhodamine-5-(and-6)-isothiocyanate (5(6)-XRITC).

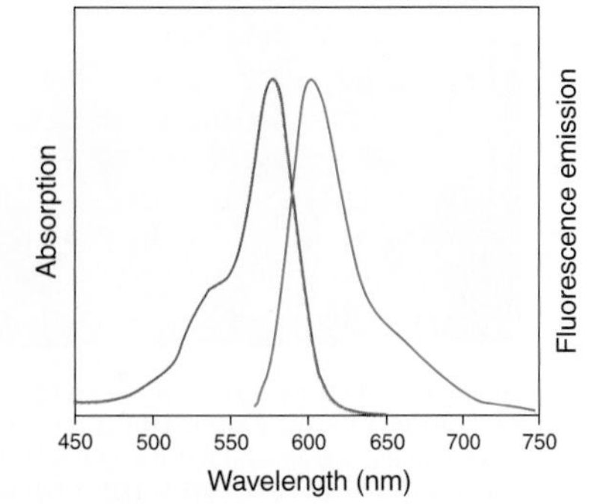

Figure 1.78 Absorption and fluorescence emission spectra of 5-carboxy-X-rhodamine (5-ROX) in pH 7.0 buffer.

conjugates (Figure 1.79). Both the pure 5-isomer (C6124) and 6-isomer (C6156) of ROX are available, as are mixed-isomer (C1309, Figure 1.80) and single-isomer (C6125, C6126) preparations of the succinimidyl ester of ROX.

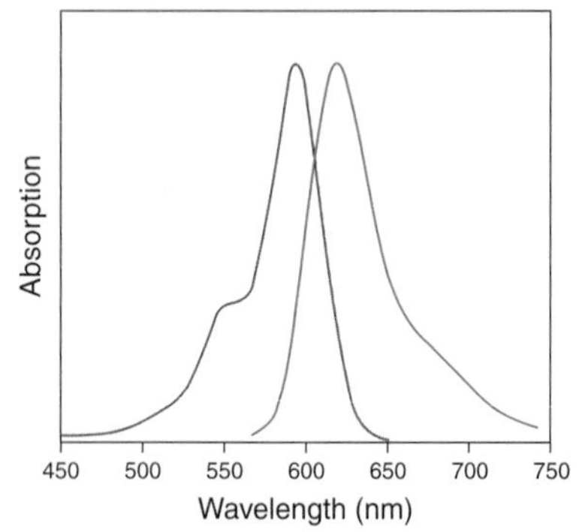

Figure 1.79 Absorption and fluorescence emission spectra of the Texas Red® conjugate of bovine serum albumin in pH 7.0 buffer.

Texas Red® and Texas Red®-X Dyes

The Texas Red® fluorophore emits at a longer wavelength than do either tetramethylrhodamine or Lissamine rhodamine B (Figure 1.74), making Texas Red® conjugates among the most commonly used long-wavelength "third labels" in fluorescence microscopy (Figure 1.81, Figure 11.7, Figure 11.10, Figure 11.12). Unlike the other rhodamines, the Texas Red® fluorophore exhibits very little spectral overlap with fluorescein (Figure 1.74), and its fluorescence can be distinguished from that of phycoerythrins.[13–15] Moreover, the fluorescence quantum yield of Texas Red® conjugates is usually higher than that of tetramethylrhodamine or Lissamine rhodamine B conjugates. When the correct optical filter sets are used (Section 23.5, Table 23.9), Texas Red® conjugates are brighter and have lower background than conjugates of the other commonly used red-fluorescent dyes, except the Alexa Fluor® 594 dye. Texas Red® conjugates are particularly well suited for excitation by the 568 nm spectral line of the Ar–Kr mixed-gas laser now used in many confocal laser-scanning microscopes, or the 594 nm spectral line of the orange He–Ne laser.

Texas Red® Sulfonyl Chloride

Texas Red® sulfonyl chloride is Molecular Probes' trademarked mixture of isomeric sulfonyl chlorides (Figure 1.82) of sulforhodamine 101.[16] This reagent is quite unstable in water, especially at the higher pH required for reaction with aliphatic amines. For example, dilute solutions of Texas Red® sulfonyl chloride are totally hydrolyzed within 2–3 minutes in pH 8.3 aqueous solution at room temperature.[12] Protein modification by this reagent is best done at low temperature. Once conjugated, however, the sulfonamides that are formed (Figure 1.4) are extremely stable; they even survive complete protein hydrolysis. Because Texas Red® sulfonyl chloride rapidly degrades upon exposure to moisture, Molecular Probes offers this reactive dye specially packaged as a set of 10 vials (T1905), each containing approximately 1 mg of Texas Red® sulfonyl chloride for small-scale conjugations. We also offer the 10 mg unit size packaged in a single vial (T353) for larger-scale conjugations. Each milligram of Texas Red® sulfonyl chloride modifies approximately 8–10 mg of protein. Note that sulfonyl chlorides are unstable in dimethylsulfoxide (DMSO) and should never be used in that solvent.[17] Polyclonal anti-tetramethylrhodamine and anti–Texas Red® antibodies that recognize tetramethylrhodamine, Rhodamine Red™, X-rhodamine and Texas Red® fluorophores are available (Section 7.4, Table 4.2).

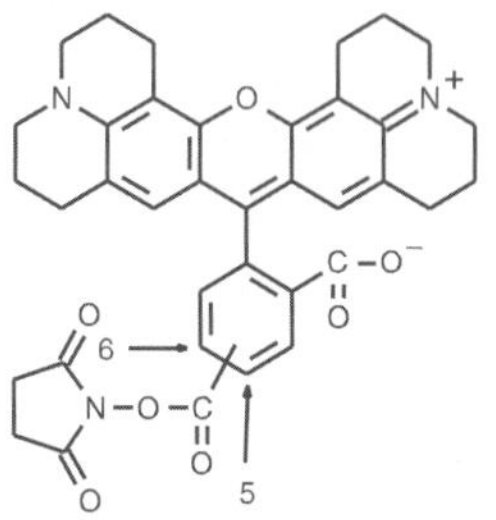

Figure 1.80 C1309 5-(and-6)-carboxy-X-rhodamine, succinimidyl ester (5(6)-ROX, SE).

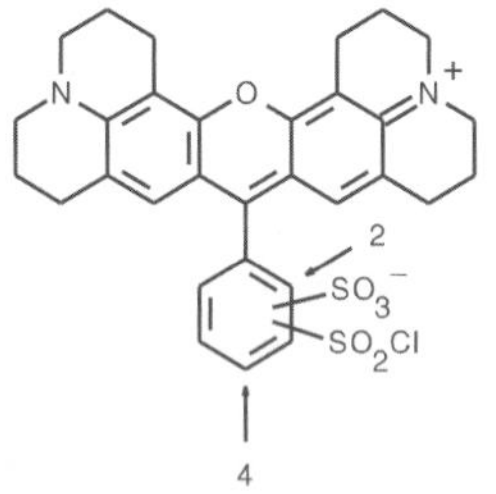

Figure 1.82 T353 Texas Red® sulfonyl chloride.

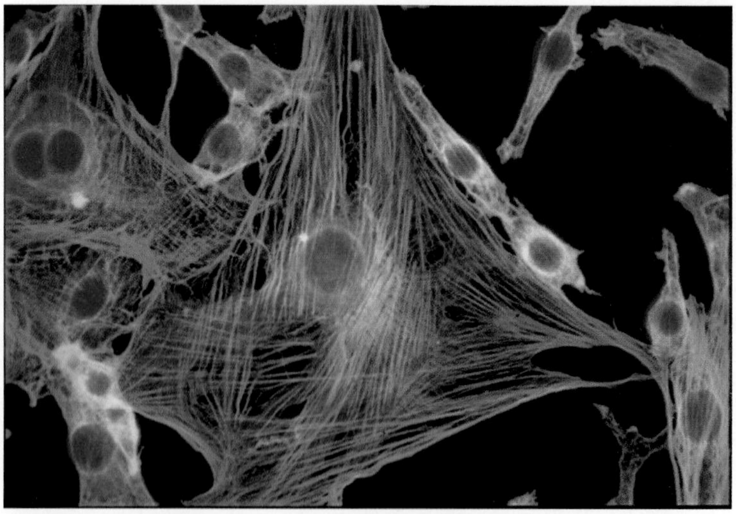

Figure 1.81 Photomicrograph of mouse fibroblasts that have been formaldehyde-fixed, acetone-permeabilized and triple-stained with the F-actin–specific probe BODIPY® FL phallacidin (B607), with mouse monoclonal anti–β-tubulin antibody in conjunction with Texas Red® goat anti–mouse IgG antibody (T862) and with DAPI (D1306, D3571, D21490). The image was obtained by taking multiple exposures through bandpass optical filter sets appropriate for fluorescein, Texas Red® dye and DAPI using a 100X Plan Apochromat objective.

Texas Red®-X Succinimidyl Ester

Texas Red® sulfonyl chloride's susceptibility to hydrolysis and low solubility in water may complicate its conjugation to some biomolecules. To overcome this difficulty, Molecular Probes has developed and patented Texas Red®-X succinimidyl ester, which contains an additional seven-atom aminohexanoyl spacer ("X") between the fluorophore and its reactive group.[12] The single-isomer preparation of Texas Red®-X succinimidyl ester (T20175, Figure 1.83) is preferred over the mixed-isomer product (T6134) when the dye is used to prepare conjugates of low molecular weight peptides, oligonucleotides and receptor ligands that are to be purified by high-resolution techniques. Also, because isomers of a reactive dye may differ in their binding geometry, certain applications such as fluorescence resonance energy transfer (FRET) may benefit from the use of single-isomer reactive dyes[18] (see Note 1.2 "Technical Focus: Fluorescence Resonance Energy Transfer (FRET)" in Section 1.3). Thiol-reactive Texas Red® derivatives that are based on a similar synthetic approach are described in Section 2.2. Texas Red®-X succinimidyl ester offers significant advantages over Texas Red® sulfonyl chloride for the preparation of bioconjugates:

- In the absence of amines, greater than 80% of Texas Red®-X succinimidyl ester's reactivity is retained in pH 8.3 solution after one hour at room temperature.[12]
- Much less Texas Red®-X succinimidyl ester (usually half or less of the amount of Texas Red® sulfonyl chloride) is required to yield the same degree of labeling, making the effective costs of these two reagents about the same.
- Conjugations with Texas Red®-X succinimidyl ester are more reproducible.
- Unlike Texas Red® sulfonyl chloride, which can form unstable products with tyrosine, histidine, cysteine and other residues in proteins, the Texas Red®-X succinimidyl ester reacts almost exclusively with amines.
- Protein conjugates prepared with Texas Red®-X succinimidyl ester have a higher fluorescence yield than those with the same labeling ratio prepared with Texas Red® sulfonyl chloride (Figure 1.84).
- We have noted a decreased tendency of Texas Red®-X protein conjugates to precipitate during the reaction or upon storage.

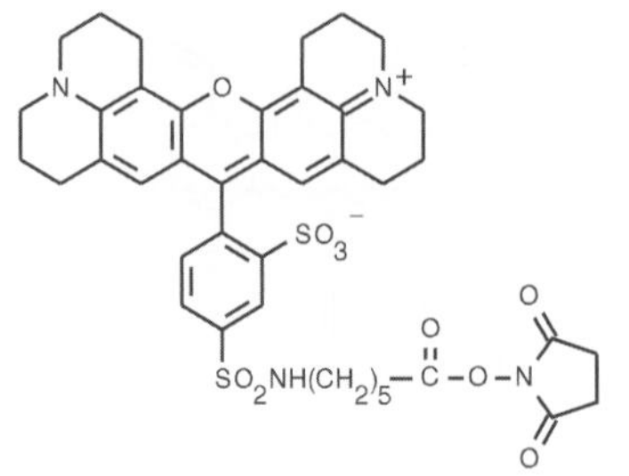

Figure 1.83 T20175 Texas Red®-X, succinimidyl ester.

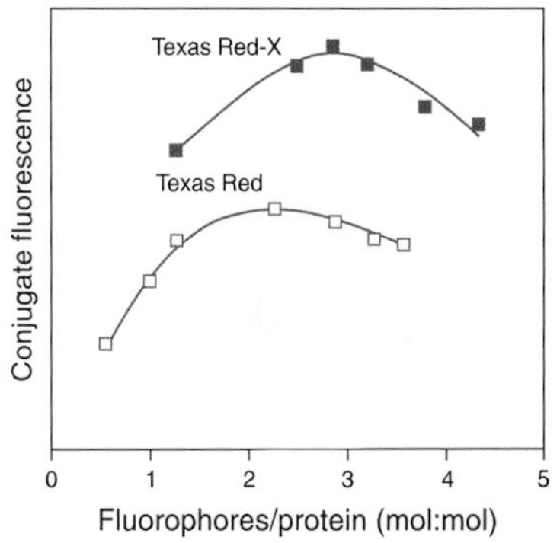

Figure 1.84 Comparison of the relative fluorescence of goat anti–mouse IgG antibody conjugates of Texas Red®-X succinimidyl ester (T6134, ■) and Texas Red® sulfonyl chloride (T353, □). Conjugate fluorescence was determined by measuring the fluorescence quantum yield of the conjugated dye relative to that of the free dye and multiplying by the number of fluorophores per protein. Higher numbers of fluorophores attached per protein are attainable with the Texas Red®-X dye due to the lesser tendency of this dye to induce protein precipitation (Bioconjug Chem 7, 482 (1996)).

Texas Red®-X STP Ester

Molecular Probes has prepared the water-soluble 4-sulfo-2,3,5,6-tetrafluorophenyl (STP) ester of the Texas Red®-X dye[19] (T10125). STP esters, which are prepared by coupling a carboxylic acid and 4-sulfo-2,3,5,6-tetrafluorophenol (S10490, Section 3.3, Figure 3.29), react rapidly with amines on proteins (Figure 1.3) under the same conditions as succinimidyl esters but are much more water soluble. STP esters are also available for some of our BODIPY® dyes (Section 1.4).

Texas Red® C_2-Dichlorotriazine

Texas Red® C_2-dichlorotriazine (T30200) is a reactive dye with absorption/emission maxima of ~588/601 nm. Dichlorotriazines readily modify amines in proteins, and they are among the few reactive groups that are reported to react directly with polysaccharides and other alcohols in aqueous solution, provided that the pH is >9 and that other nucleophiles are absent.[20–23]

Texas Red®-X Conjugates and Texas Red®-X Labeling Kits

Because of the advantages of Texas Red®-X succinimidyl ester, we have converted some of our Texas Red® conjugates to the Texas Red®-X conjugates. Consequently, we have prepared Texas Red®-X conjugates of:

- Antibodies (Section 7.2, Table 7.1)
- Streptavidin (S6370, Section 7.6, Table 7.22)
- Wheat germ agglutinin (W21405, Section 7.7)
- dUTP (C7631, Section 8.2)
- Phalloidin (T7471, Section 11.1, Table 11.1)
- Polymyxin B (P13237, Section 15.2)
- Methotrexate (M23273, Section 15.6)

Protein conjugates of the Texas Red®-X dye are readily prepared using our FluoReporter® Texas Red®-X Protein Labeling Kit (F6162) and Texas Red®-X Protein Labeling Kit (T10244). See Section 1.2 for further information on these kits. Our Zenon® Texas Red®-X Antibody Labeling Kits for mouse IgG_1 and rabbit IgG antibodies (Z25045, Z25345; Section 7.3) permit the rapid and quantitative labeling of antibodies from a purified antibody fraction or from a crude antibody preparation such as serum, ascites fluid or a hybridoma supernatant with the Texas Red®-X dye. Polyclonal anti-tetramethylrhodamine and anti–Texas Red® antibodies that recognize tetramethylrhodamine, Rhodamine Red™, X-rhodamine and Texas Red® fluorophores are available (Section 7.4, Table 7.18).

Reactive Texas Red®-X dyes and their conjugates are patented by Molecular Probes. They are offered for research purposes only. We welcome inquiries about Licensing these products for resale or other commercial uses.

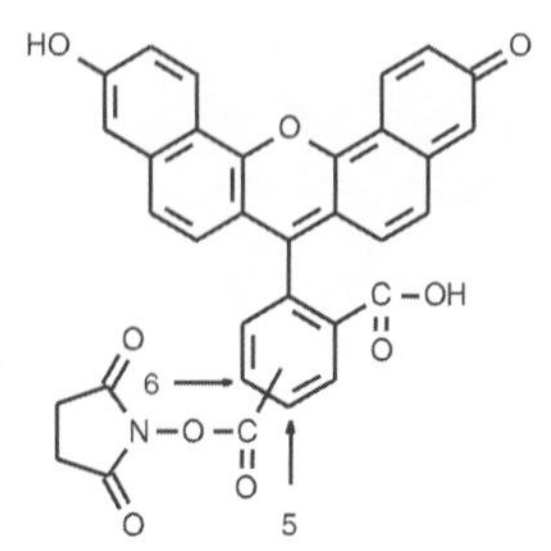

Figure 1.85 C653 5-(and-6)-carboxynaphthofluorescein, succinimidyl ester.

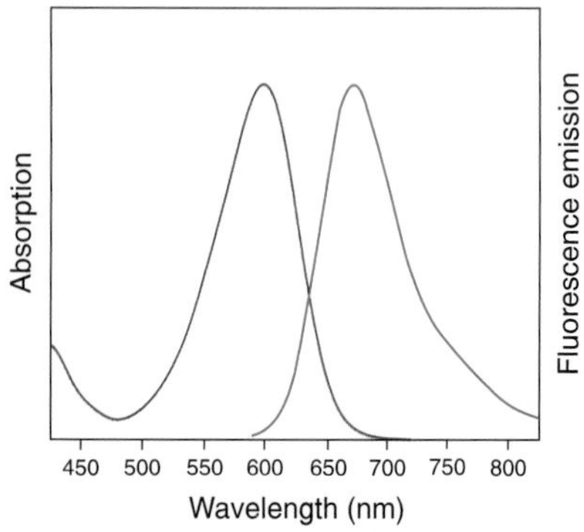

Figure 1.86 Absorption and fluorescence emission spectra of 5-(and-6)-carboxynaphthofluorescein in pH 10.0 buffer.

Naphthofluorescein

Naphthofluorescein carboxylic acid and its succinimidyl ester (C652, C653; Figure 1.85) have emission maxima of approximately 660 nm in aqueous solution at pH 10 (Figure 1.86). However, their fluorescence is pH dependent (pK_a ~7.6), requiring a relatively alkaline pH for maximal fluorescence.

Carboxyrhodamine 6G

The excitation and emission spectra of carboxyrhodamine 6G (CR 6G) fall between those of fluorescein and tetramethylrhodamine (Figure 1.74). With a peak absorption at ~520 nm, conjugates prepared from the mixed-isomer (C6157) or single-isomer (C6127, C6128) preparations of CR 6G succinimidyl esters are an excellent match to the 514 nm spectral line of the argon-ion laser. They also tend to exhibit a higher fluorescence quantum yield than tetramethylrhodamine conjugates, as well as excellent photostability. As with the Rhodamine Green™ dyes, the carboxyrhodamine 6G dyes are more suitable for preparing nucleotide and oligonucleotide conjugates than for preparing protein conjugates. Oligonucleotide conjugates of the CR 6G dye have spectroscopic and electrophoretic properties that are superior to the JOE dye (C6171MP, Section 1.5) that is often used for DNA sequencing (Section 8.2, Table 8.11).

Table 1.9 — Molecular Probes' nonfluorescent quenchers and photosensitizers

Dye	Abs *	Extinction Coefficient †	Amine-reactive ‡	Notes
Dabcyl	453	32,000	D2245 (SE)	• Broad and intense visible-wavelength absorption • Efficient energy transfer acceptor from blue- and green-fluorescent dyes in FRET applications
Dabsyl	466	33,000	D1537 (SC)	• Sulfonyl chlorides form very stable conjugates • Broad and intense visible-wavelength absorption
Malachite green	628	76,000	M689 (ITC)	• Nonfluorescent photosensitizer
QSY® 7	560	90,000	Q10193 (SE)	• Essentially nonfluorescent quencher • Broad visible-wavelength absorption • Efficient energy transfer acceptor from UV light–excited green- and orange-fluorescent dyes in FRET applications
QSY® 9	562	88,000	Q20131 (SE)	• Essentially nonfluorescent quencher • Spectrally similar to QSY® 7, but with enhanced water solubility • Efficient energy transfer acceptor from UV light–excited green- and orange-fluorescent dyes in FRET applications
QSY® 21	661	90,000	Q20132 (SE)	• Essentially nonfluorescent quencher • Long-wavelength absorption • An efficient energy transfer acceptor from red- and near-infrared–fluorescent dyes in FRET applications
QSY® 35	475	23,000	Q20133 (SE) §	• Nonfluorescent quencher • Spectrally similar to dabcyl • An efficient energy transfer acceptor from blue- and green-fluorescent dyes in FRET applications

* Absorption (Abs) maxima, in nm. † Molar extinction coefficient in $cm^{-1}M^{-1}$ determined at the wavelength listed in the column headed Abs. These values were obtained from Molecular Probes' data tables and may vary with the environment, particularly for the QSY® 35 dye. ‡ SE = Succinimidyl ester. SC = Sulfonyl chloride. ITC = Isothiocyanate.

One of our reactive BODIPY® dyes (BODIPY® R6G; D6180, D6186; Section 1.4) has spectra similar to carboxyrhodamine 6G but with narrower absorption and emission spectra (Figure 1.41), which may be advantageous for multicolor applications.

QSY® Dyes: The Best Fluorescence Quenchers

Dyes that quench the fluorescence of visible light–excited fluorophores are increasingly important for use in proximity studies (see Note 1.2 "Technical Focus: Fluorescence Resonance Energy Transfer (FRET)" in Section 1.3) and in a wide variety of assays, such as those based on DNA hybridization (Section 8.5). Our QSY® 7, QSY® 9 and QSY® 21 dyes (Table 1.9) are diarylrhodamine derivatives that have several properties that make them superior to the commonly used dabcyl chromophore (Section 1.8) when preparing bioconjugates for use in energy transfer–based assays:

- Broad absorption in the visible-light spectrum, with an absorption maximum near 560 nm for both the QSY® 7 and QSY® 9 dyes and near 660 nm for the QSY® 21 dye (Figure 1.70)
- Extinction coefficients that are typically in excess of 90,000 $cm^{-1}M^{-1}$
- Absorption spectra of the conjugates that are insensitive to pH between 4 and 10
- Fluorescence quantum yields typically <0.001 in aqueous solution (In a few isolated cases, we have observed that some QSY dyes can exhibit fluorescence when placed in a rigidifying environment such as glycerol.)
- Efficient quenching of the fluorescence emission of donor dyes by the QSY® 7 and QSY® 9 dyes, including blue-fluorescent coumarins, any of our green- or orange-fluorescent dyes, and conjugates of the Texas Red® and Alexa Fluor® 594 dyes
- Quenching of all red-fluorescent dyes by the exceptionally long-wavelength light–absorbing QSY® 21 dye (Table 1.10)
- Quenching of most green and red fluorophores that is more effective at far greater distances than is possible with dabcyl quenchers (Table 1.10, Figure 8.51)
- Residual fluorescence of the conjugates, at close spatial separations, that is typically lower than in conjugates that use dabcyl as the quencher
- High chemical stability of the conjugates and very good resistance to photobleaching

The distance at which energy transfer is 50% efficient (i.e., 50% of excited donors are deactivated by fluorescence resonance energy transfer) is defined by the Förster radius (R_0). The magnitude of R_0 is dependent on the spectral properties of the donor and acceptor dyes. Förster distances (R_0) calculated for energy transfer from various Alexa Fluor® dyes to QSY® and dabcyl quenchers are listed in Table 1.10. FRET efficiencies from several donor dyes to the QSY® 7 quencher in molecular beacon hybridization probes have also been calculated.[24]

For preparing bioconjugates of the QSY® dyes, Molecular Probes offers the amine-reactive QSY® 7 (Figure 1.87), QSY® 9 and QSY® 21 succinimidyl esters (Q10193, Q20131, Q20132), the thiol-reactive QSY® 7 C_5-maleimide[25] and QSY® 9 C_5-maleimide (Q10257, Q30457; Section 2.2), an aldehyde- and ketone-reactive QSY® 9 hydrazide (Q30626) and a QSY® 7 aliphatic amine (Q10464, Section 3.3) that can be coupled to carboxylic acids and other functional groups.

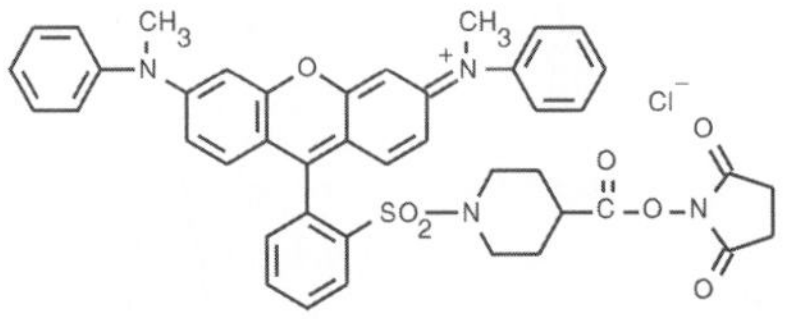

Figure 1.87 Q10193 QSY® 7 carboxylic acid, succinimidyl ester.

Table 1.10 — R_0 values for QSY® and dabcyl quenchers *

Donor	Acceptor			
	QSY® 35	dabcyl	QSY® 7 and QSY® 9	QSY® 21
Alexa Fluor® 350	47	50		
Alexa Fluor® 488	44	49	64	
Alexa Fluor® 546	25	29	67	
Alexa Fluor® 555			45	
Alexa Fluor® 568			56	75
Alexa Fluor® 594				77
Alexa Fluor® 647				69

* R_0 values in angstroms (Å) represent the distance at which fluorescence resonance energy transfer from the donor dye to the acceptor dye is 50% efficient. Values were calculated from spectroscopic data, as outlined (see Note 1.2 "Technical Focus: Fluorescence Resonance Energy Transfer (FRET)" in Section 1.3).

We also have prepared a QSY® 7 derivative of α-FMOC lysine (Q21930, Section 9.5) for automated synthesis of peptides that contain this important quencher.

These QSY® dyes, their conjugates and their use as fluorescence quenchers are patented by Molecular Probes, Inc. We welcome inquiries about licensing these products for resale or other commercial uses.

In addition to the QSY® 7, QSY® 9 and QSY® 21 dyes, Molecular Probes has available other quenchers that absorb maximally below 500 nm, including the QSY® 35 dye, dabcyl and dabsyl dyes (Table 1.9). These products are described in Section 1.8.

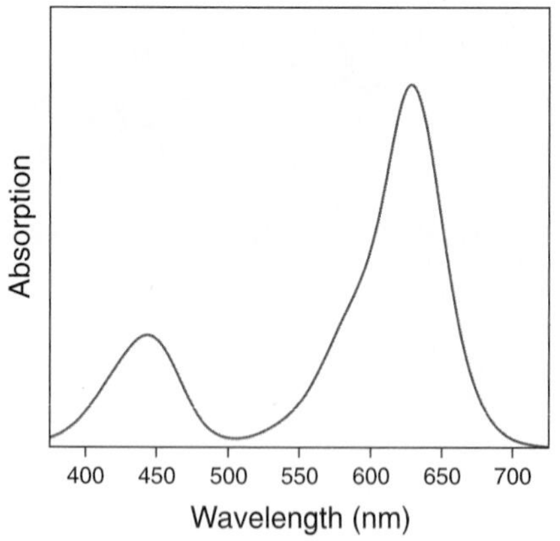

Figure 1.88 Absorption spectrum of malachite green isothiocyanate in acetonitrile.

Nonfluorescent Malachite Green

Malachite green is a nonfluorescent photosensitizer that absorbs at long wavelengths (~630 nm, Figure 1.88). Its photosensitizing action can be targeted to particular cellular sites by conjugating malachite green isothiocyanate (M689, Figure 1.89) to specific antibodies. Enzymes and other proteins within ~10 Å of the binding site of the malachite green–labeled antibody can then be selectively destroyed upon irradiation with long-wavelength light.[26,27] Studies by Jay and colleagues have demonstrated that this photoinduced destruction of enzymes in the immediate vicinity of the chromophore is apparently the result of localized production of hydroxyl radicals, which have short lifetimes that limit their diffusion from the site of their generation.[28] Earlier studies had supported a thermal mechanism of action.[29–31]

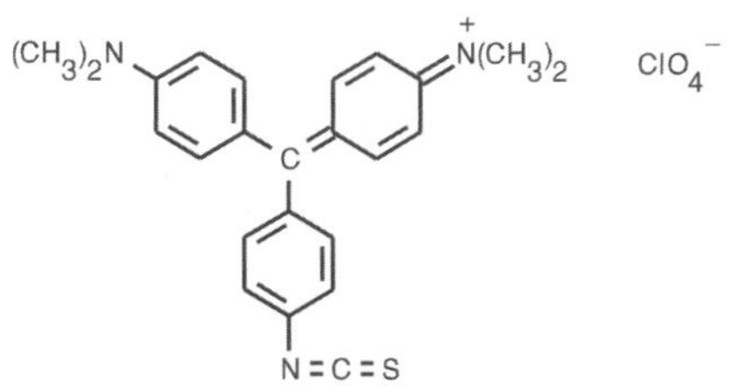

Figure 1.89 M689 malachite green isothiocyanate.

NANOGOLD Sulfosuccinimidyl Ester

In collaboration with Nanoprobes, Inc. (www.nanoprobes.com), Molecular Probes offers NANOGOLD and Alexa Fluor® FluoroNanogold particles, small metal cluster complexes of gold particles for research applications in light or electron microscopy.[32] The NANOGOLD and Alexa Fluor® FluoroNanogold clusters are discrete chemical compounds, not gold colloids. NANOGOLD mono(sulfosuccinimidyl ester) (N20130) permits attachment of these very small (1.4 nm) yet uniformly sized gold particles to biomolecules in the same way that one reacts a succinimidyl ester of a dye (Figure 1.90). This product, which is supplied as a set of five vials of a powder that has been lyophilized from pH 7.5 HEPES buffer, is resuspended with the protein in deionized water at room temperature or below, then any excess NANOGOLD mono(sulfosuccinimidyl ester) is removed by gel filtration and the conjugate is stored frozen. 100 nanomoles of NANOGOLD mono(sulfosuccinimidyl ester) is sufficient to label about 100 µg of a protein with a MW of 100,000. Excess reagent should not be stored, and the conjugation mixture must be free of thiols or amine-containing buffers. NANOGOLD and Alexa Fluor® FluoroNanogold conjugates of antibodies and streptavidin are described in Section 7.2 and Section 7.6, respectively, along with reagents and methods for silver enhancement to amplify electron microscopic detection. In addition to being used for ultrastructural studies, NANOGOLD conjugates are extremely effective excited-state energy transfer quenchers with an enhanced ability to detect single-base mismatches in beacon technology[33] (Figure 8.113). We also supply NANOGOLD monomaleimide (N20345, Section 2.2, Figure 2.22).

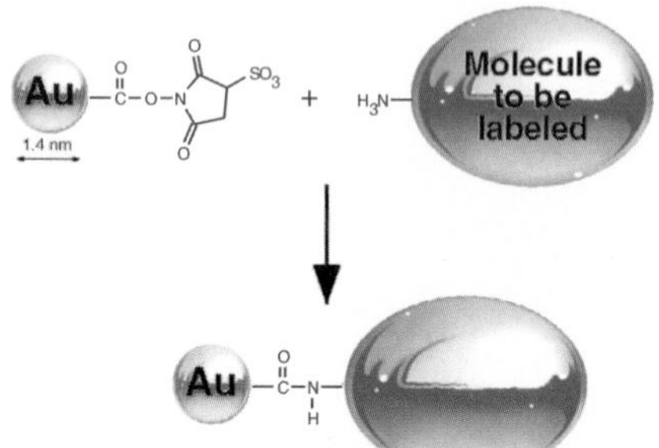

Figure 1.90 Reaction of NANOGOLD mono(sulfosuccinimidyl ester) (N20130) with a primary amine. Image courtesy of Nanoprobes, Inc.

References

1. Anal Biochem 223, 39 (1994); **2.** Nucleic Acids Res 20, 2471 (1992); **3.** Proc Natl Acad Sci U S A 86, 9178 (1989); **4.** J Chromatogr 608, 117 (1992); **5.** Anal Biochem 80, 585 (1977); **6.** J Immunol Methods 143, 263 (1991); **7.** J Chromatogr B Biomed Appl 657, 307 (1994); **8.** Anal Biochem 238, 165 (1996); **9.** Biochim Biophys Acta 1104, 9 (1992); **10.** Biochim Biophys Acta 776, 217 (1984); **11.** Biochemistry 21, 978 (1982); **12.** Bioconjug Chem 7, 482 (1996); **13.** Acta Histochem 89, 85 (1990); **14.** Proc Natl Acad Sci U S A 85, 3546 (1988); **15.** Cell Biophys 7, 129 (1985); **16.** J Immunol Methods 50, 193 (1982); **17.** J Org Chem 31, 3880 (1966); **18.** Proc Natl Acad Sci U S A 97, 13021 (2000); **19.** Tetrahedron Lett 40, 1471 (1999); **20.** Eur J Cell Biol 74, 376 (1997); **21.** Anal Biochem 247, 348 (1997); **22.** J Biomed Mater Res 40, 275 (1998); **23.** Carbohydr Res 30, 251 (1973); **24.** Nucleic Acids Res 30, e122 (2002); **25.** Proc Natl Acad Sci U S A 100, 13308 (2003); **26.** J Cell Biol 134, 1197 (1996); **27.** Nature 376, 686 (1995); **28.** Proc Natl Acad Sci U S A 91, 2659 (1994); **29.** Biophys J 61, 956 (1992); **30.** Biophys J 61, 631 (1992); **31.** Proc Natl Acad Sci U S A 85, 5454 (1988); **32.** J Histochem Cytochem 48, 471 (2000); **33.** Nat Biotechnol 19, 365 (2001).

Data Table — 1.6 Long-Wavelength Rhodamines, Texas Red® Dyes and QSY® Quenchers

Cat #	MW	Storage	Soluble	Abs	EC	Em	Solvent	Notes
C300	466.92	L	DMF, DMSO	540	95,000	565	MeOH	1
C652	476.44	L	pH >6, DMF	598	49,000	668	pH 10	2
C653	573.51	F,D,L	DMF, DMSO	602	42,000	672	pH 10	2
C1171	527.53	F,D,L	DMF, DMSO	546	95,000	576	MeOH	1, 3
C1309	631.68	F,D,L	DMF, DMSO	576	80,000	601	MeOH	1
C2211	527.53	F,D,L	DMF, DMSO	546	95,000	579	MeOH	1, 3
C2213	494.97	D,L	pH >6, DMF	518	90,000	543	MeOH	
C6109	494.97	D,L	pH >6, DMF	520	101,000	546	MeOH	
C6121	430.46	L	pH >6, DMF	542	91,000	568	MeOH	1
C6122	430.46	L	pH >6, DMF	540	103,000	564	MeOH	1
C6123	527.53	F,D,L	DMF, DMSO	547	91,000	573	MeOH	1, 3
C6124	635.80	F,L	pH >6, DMF	567	92,000	591	MeOH	1
C6125	631.68	F,D,L	DMF, DMSO	574	78,000	602	MeOH	1
C6126	631.68	F,D,L	DMF, DMSO	575	82,000	602	MeOH	1
C6127	555.59	F,D,L	pH >6, DMF	524	108,000	557	MeOH	
C6128	555.59	F,D,L	DMF, DMSO	524	102,000	550	MeOH	
C6156	534.61	F,L	pH >6, DMF	570	113,000	590	MeOH	1
C6157	555.59	F,D,L	DMF, DMSO	524	92,000	552	MeOH	
L20	577.11	F,DD,L	DMF, MeCN	568	88,000	583	MeOH	4
L1908	577.11	F,DD,L	DMF, MeCN	568	88,000	583	MeOH	4
M689	485.98	F,DD,L	DMF, DMSO	629	75,000	none	MeCN	5
Q10193	791.32	F,D,L	DMSO	560	90,000	none	MeOH	
Q20131	951.43	F,D,L	H_2O, DMSO	562	88,000	none	MeOH	6
Q20132	815.34	F,D,L	DMSO	661	90,000	none	MeOH	
R6160	768.90	F,D,L	DMF, DMSO	560	129,000	580	MeOH	
T353	625.15	F,DD,L	DMF, MeCN	588	84,000	601	$CHCl_3$	4
T490	443.52	F,DD,L	DMF, DMSO	544	84,000	572	MeOH	3, 5
T1480	443.52	F,DD,L	DMF, DMSO	543	99,000	571	MeOH	3, 5
T1481	443.52	F,DD,L	DMF, DMSO	544	90,000	572	MeOH	3, 5
T1905	625.15	F,DD,L	DMF, MeCN	587	85,000	602	$CHCl_3$	4
T6105	640.69	F,D,L	DMF, DMSO	543	92,000	571	MeOH	1, 3
T6134	816.94	F,D,L	DMF, DMSO	583	112,000	603	MeOH	
T10125	969.97	F,D,L	H_2O, DMSO	585	92,000	605	MeOH	7
T20175	816.94	F,D,L	DMF, DMSO	587	96,000	602	MeOH	
T30200	796.74	F,D,L	DMF, DMSO	583	87,000	604	MeOH	
X491	547.67	F,DD,L	DMF, DMSO	572	92,000	596	MeOH	5

For definitions of the contents of this data table, see "Navigating *The Handbook*" in the introductory pages.

Notes

1. Abs and Em for TAMRA and ROX dyes in pH 8 buffer are red-shifted approximately 8 nm compared to MeOH, with EC lower by ~10%.
2. Absorption and fluorescence of naphthofluorescein derivatives are pH-dependent. Both the absorption and emission spectra shift to much shorter wavelengths at pH <8. Fluorescence quantum yield ~0.14 at pH 9.5 (Cytometry 10, 151 (1989)).
3. Tetramethylrhodamine protein conjugates often exhibit two absorption peaks at about 520 and 545 nm. The 520 nm peak is due to nonfluorescent dye aggregates (J Immunol Methods 143, 263 (1991); J Phys Chem B 102, 1820 (1998)).
4. Do NOT dissolve in DMSO.
5. Isothiocyanates are unstable in water and should not be stored in aqueous solution.
6. This sulfonated succinimidyl ester derivative is water-soluble and may be dissolved in buffer at ~pH 8 for reaction with amines. Long-term storage in water is NOT recommended due to hydrolysis.
7. This sulfotetrafluorophenyl (STP) ester derivative is water-soluble and may be dissolved in buffer at ~pH 8 for reaction with amines. Long-term storage in water is NOT recommended due to hydrolysis.

Product List — 1.6 Long-Wavelength Rhodamines, Texas Red® Dyes and QSY® Quenchers

Cat #	Product Name	Unit Size
C652	5-(and-6)-carboxynaphthofluorescein *mixed isomers*	100 mg
C653	5-(and-6)-carboxynaphthofluorescein, succinimidyl ester *mixed isomers*	25 mg
C6109	5-carboxyrhodamine 6G, hydrochloride (5-CR 6G) *single isomer*	5 mg
C2213	6-carboxyrhodamine 6G, hydrochloride (6-CR 6G) *single isomer*	5 mg
C6127	5-carboxyrhodamine 6G, succinimidyl ester (5-CR 6G, SE) *single isomer*	5 mg
C6128	6-carboxyrhodamine 6G, succinimidyl ester (6-CR 6G, SE) *single isomer*	5 mg
C6157	5-(and-6)-carboxyrhodamine 6G, succinimidyl ester (5(6)-CR 6G, SE) *mixed isomers*	5 mg
C6121	5-carboxytetramethylrhodamine (5-TAMRA) *single isomer*	10 mg
C6122	6-carboxytetramethylrhodamine (6-TAMRA) *single isomer*	10 mg
C300	5-(and-6)-carboxytetramethylrhodamine (5(6)-TAMRA) *mixed isomers*	100 mg
C2211	5-carboxytetramethylrhodamine, succinimidyl ester (5-TAMRA, SE) *single isomer*	5 mg
C6123	6-carboxytetramethylrhodamine, succinimidyl ester (6-TAMRA, SE) *single isomer*	5 mg
C1171	5-(and-6)-carboxytetramethylrhodamine, succinimidyl ester (5(6)-TAMRA, SE) *mixed isomers*	25 mg
C6124	5-carboxy-X-rhodamine, triethylammonium salt (5-ROX) *single isomer*	10 mg
C6156	6-carboxy-X-rhodamine (6-ROX) *single isomer*	10 mg
C6125	5-carboxy-X-rhodamine, succinimidyl ester (5-ROX, SE) *single isomer*	5 mg
C6126	6-carboxy-X-rhodamine, succinimidyl ester (6-ROX, SE) *single isomer*	5 mg
C1309	5-(and-6)-carboxy-X-rhodamine, succinimidyl ester (5(6)-ROX, SE) *mixed isomers*	25 mg
F6161	FluoReporter® Rhodamine Red™-X Protein Labeling Kit *5-10 labelings*	1 kit
F6163	FluoReporter® Tetramethylrhodamine Protein Labeling Kit *5-10 labelings*	1 kit
F6162	FluoReporter® Texas Red®-X Protein Labeling Kit *5-10 labelings*	1 kit
L20	Lissamine™ rhodamine B sulfonyl chloride *mixed isomers*	1 g
L1908	Lissamine™ rhodamine B sulfonyl chloride *mixed isomers* *special packaging*	10 x 10 mg
M689	malachite green isothiocyanate	10 mg
N20130	NANOGOLD® mono(sulfosuccinimidyl ester) *special packaging*	5 x 6 nmol
Q10193	QSY® 7 carboxylic acid, succinimidyl ester	5 mg
Q20131	QSY® 9 carboxylic acid, succinimidyl ester	5 mg
Q20132	QSY® 21 carboxylic acid, succinimidyl ester	5 mg
R6160	Rhodamine Red™-X, succinimidyl ester *5-isomer*	5 mg
T6105	6-(tetramethylrhodamine-5-(and-6)-carboxamido)hexanoic acid, succinimidyl ester (5(6)-TAMRA-X, SE) *mixed isomers*	10 mg
T1480	tetramethylrhodamine-5-isothiocyanate (5-TRITC; G isomer)	5 mg
T1481	tetramethylrhodamine-6-isothiocyanate (6-TRITC; R isomer)	5 mg
T490	tetramethylrhodamine-5-(and-6)-isothiocyanate (5(6)-TRITC) *mixed isomers*	10 mg
T30200	Texas Red® C_2-dichlorotriazine	5 mg
T353	Texas Red® sulfonyl chloride *mixed isomers*	10 mg
T1905	Texas Red® sulfonyl chloride *mixed isomers* *special packaging*	10 x ~1 mg
T10244	Texas Red®-X Protein Labeling Kit *3 labelings*	1 kit
T10125	Texas Red®-X, STP ester, sodium salt *mixed isomers*	5 mg
T6134	Texas Red®-X, succinimidyl ester *mixed isomers*	5 mg
T20175	Texas Red®-X, succinimidyl ester *single isomer*	2 mg
X491	X-rhodamine-5-(and-6)-isothiocyanate (5(6)-XRITC) *mixed isomers*	10 mg
Z25045	Zenon® Texas Red®-X Mouse IgG_1 Labeling Kit *50 labelings*	1 kit
Z25345	Zenon® Texas Red®-X Rabbit IgG Labeling Kit *50 labelings*	1 kit

For current prices or to order online, visit probes.invitrogen.com

1.7 Coumarins, Pyrenes and Other Ultraviolet Light–Excitable Fluorophores

Shorter-wavelength amine-reactive fluorophores are infrequently used for preparing bioconjugates because dyes excited with longer wavelengths, and therefore lower energy, are widely available and less likely to cause photodamage to labeled biomolecules. Moreover, many cells and tissues autofluoresce when excited with ultraviolet (UV) light and thus preclude the use of blue-fluorescent conjugates in a number of applications. However, for certain multicolor fluorescence applications, including immunofluorescence, nucleic acid and protein microarrays, *in situ* hybridization and neuronal tracing, a blue-fluorescent probe provides a contrasting color that is easily distinguished from the green, yellow, orange or red fluorescence of the longer-wavelength probes. The short-wavelength reactive dyes that we recommend for preparing the brightest blue-fluorescent bioconjugates are the Cascade Blue®, Marina Blue®, Pacific Blue™, AMCA-X, Alexa Fluor® 350 and Alexa Fluor® 405 derivatives (Table 1.11). Our Alexa Fluor® 430 dye fills a spectral void because it exhibits the rare combination of absorbance between 400 nm and 450 nm and fluorescence emission beyond 500 nm (Figure 7.4, Figure 7.38). The amine-reactive naphthalene, pyrene and Dapoxyl® derivatives are important for the production of environment-sensitive probes for protein structural studies (Table 1.12); their thiol-reactive counterparts are discussed in Section 2.3. Many of our UV light–excitable reactive dyes are more commonly employed for such bioanalytical techniques as HPLC derivatization, amino acid sequencing and protein determination and are therefore discussed in Section 1.8.

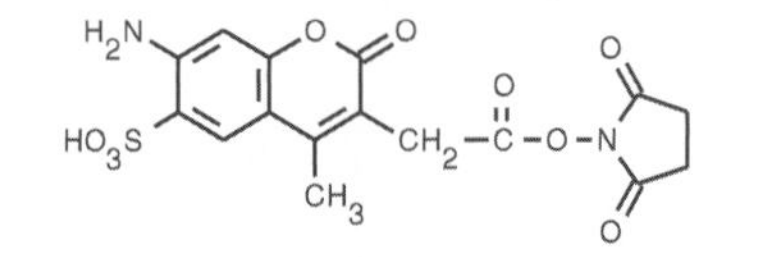

Figure 1.91 A10168 Alexa Fluor® 350 carboxylic acid, succinimidyl ester.

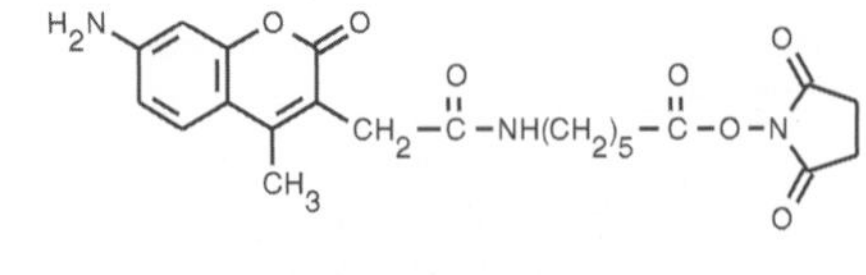

Figure 1.92 A6118 6-((7-amino-4-methylcoumarin-3-acetyl)amino)hexanoic acid, succinimidyl ester (AMCA-X, SE).

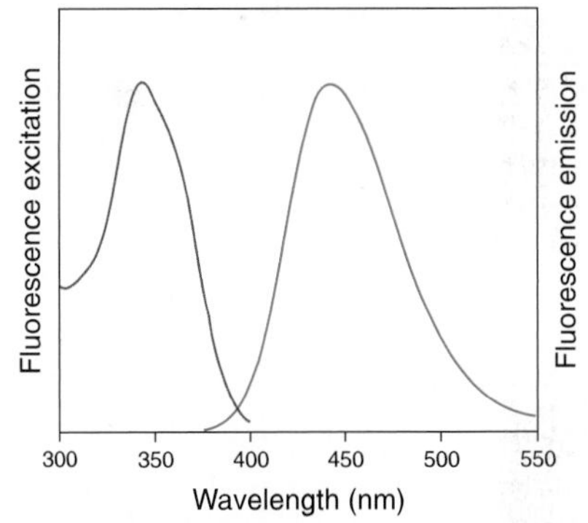

Figure 1.93 Fluorescence excitation and emission spectra of Alexa Fluor® 350 goat anti–mouse IgG antibody in pH 8.0 buffer.

Coumarin Derivatives

Alexa Fluor® 350 and AMCA-X Dyes

Although conjugates of the Cascade Blue® dye generally have a higher absorptivity and fluorescence quantum yield than the corresponding aminocoumarin conjugates, the limited spectral sensitivity of the human eye to the shorter-wavelength fluorescence of Cascade Blue® conjugates may make aminocoumarin conjugates appear visibly brighter when viewed through a microscope. Derivatives of various 7-aminocoumarins have been the most widely used labeling reagents for preparing these conjugates.[1] For preparing brightly blue-fluorescent conjugates of proteins and nucleic acids, we offer two important amine-reactive 7-aminocoumarin derivatives: Alexa Fluor® 350 carboxylic acid succinimidyl ester[2,3] (A10168) and AMCA-X succinimidyl ester (AMCA-X, SE; A6118).

The sulfonated coumarin derivative, Alexa Fluor® 350 carboxylic acid succinimidyl ester (Figure 1.91), is more water soluble than either AMCA succinimidyl ester or AMCA-X succinimidyl ester (Figure 1.92) and yields protein conjugates that are more fluorescent than those prepared from its nonsulfonated analog (Figure 7.34). Alexa Fluor® 350 protein conjugates are optimally excited at 346 nm and have bright blue fluorescence emission (Figure 1.34, Figure 1.93, Figure 1.94) at wavelengths slightly shorter than AMCA or AMCA-X conjugates (Figure 10.4) (442 nm versus 448 nm), which reduces the dye's spectral overlap with the emission of fluorescein.

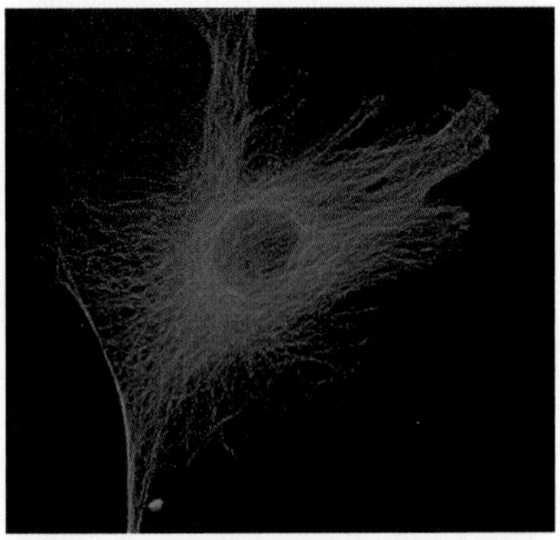

Figure 1.94 The microtubules of fixed bovine pulmonary artery endothelial cells (BPAEC) localized with mouse monoclonal anti–α-tubulin antibody (A11126), which was visualized with Alexa Fluor® 350 goat anti–mouse IgG antibody (A11045). The image was acquired using a longpass filter set appropriate for DAPI. The image was deconvolved using Huygens software (Scientific Volume Imaging, www.svi.nl).

Conjugates of the Alexa Fluor® 350 dye with antibodies (Section 7.2, Table 7.1), avidins (Section 7.6, Table 7.22), lectins (Section 7.7, Table 7.23), Panomer™ 9 random oligodeoxynucleotide (P21679, Section 8.5), phalloidin (A22281, Section 11.1) and annexin V (A23202, Section 15.5) are available. A thiol-reactive Alexa Fluor® 350 maleimide (A30505) is described in Section 2.3 and Alexa Fluor® 350 hydrazide (A10439, Section 3.2) is also available. Alexa Fluor® 350 tyramide is used in several of our Tyramide Signal Amplification (TSA) Kits (Section 6.3, Table 6.1, Figure 6.5), and the TSA method undoubtedly provides the strongest blue fluorescence possible for site-specific labeling with currently available technology.

AMCA-X succinimidyl ester contains a seven-atom aminohexanoyl spacer ("X") between the fluorophore and the reactive group. This spacer separates the fluorophore from the biomolecule to which it is conjugated, potentially reducing the quenching that typically occurs upon conjugation and making the dye more available for recognition by secondary detection reagents.

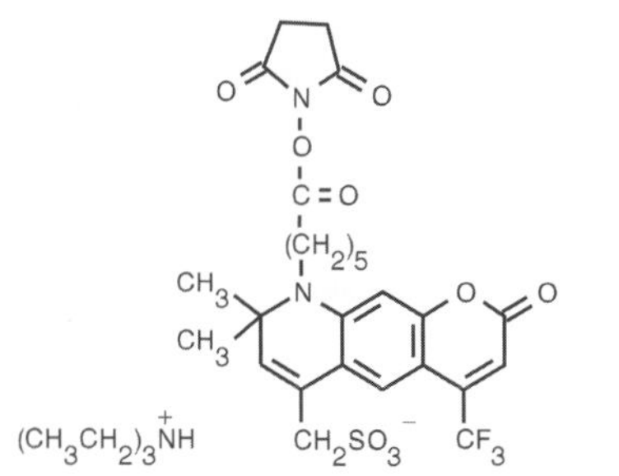

Figure 1.95 A10169 Alexa Fluor® 430 carboxylic acid, succinimidyl ester.

Slightly longer-wavelength conjugates can be prepared from the isothiocyanate (DACITC, D10166), succinimidyl esters (D374, D1412) or free acids (D126, D1421) of 7-dialkylaminocoumarins.[4,5]

The Alexa Fluor® 350 dye and its conjugates are patented by Molecular Probes and are offered for research purposes only. We welcome inquiries about licensing these products for resale or other commercial uses.

Alexa Fluor® 430 Dye

Few reactive dyes that absorb between 400 nm and 450 nm have appreciable fluorescence beyond 500 nm in aqueous solution. Our Alexa Fluor® 430 dye fills this spectral gap.[2] Excitation near its absorption maximum at 431 nm is accompanied by strong green fluorescence with an emission maximum at 541 nm (Figure 1.34, Figure 7.4). The amine-reactive succinimidyl ester of Alexa Fluor® 430 carboxylic acid (A10169, Figure 1.95) is available, as well as Alexa Fluor® 430 conjugates of secondary antibodies (A11063, A11064; Section 7.2) and streptavidin (S11237, Section 7.6).

Table 1.11 — Amine-reactive blue-fluorescent dyes, protein and nucleic acid labeling kits

Fluorophore	Abs *	Em *	Amine-Reactive Dyes	Protein and Nucleic Acid Labeling Kits	Notes
Alexa Fluor® 350	346	442	A10168 (SE)	A10171 (P) A20180 (Mab) A20190 (O) A21675 (A) Z25000 (Z) Z25100 (Z) Z25200 (Z) Z25300 (Z)	• Higher fluorescence per attached dye than AMCA • Protein conjugates emit at slightly shorter wavelengths than AMCA or AMCA-X
Alexa Fluor® 405	402	421	A30000 (SE) A30100 (SE)	Z25013 (Z) Z25113 (Z) Z25213 (Z) Z25313 (Z)	• Cascade Blue® derivative containing a spacer between the fluorophore and the reactive SE • Near-perfect match to the 405 nm spectral line of the blue diode laser
AMCA-X	353	442	A6118 (SE)		• Widely used blue-fluorescent labeling dye • Compact structure
Bimane	380	458	B30250 (COOH)		• Blue-fluorescent dye • Small size
Cascade Blue®	400	420	C2284 (AA)		• Resistant to quenching upon protein conjugation • Trisulfonated pyrene
Dialkylaminocoumarin	375 435	470[1] 475[2]	D126 (COOH) D1421 (COOH) D374 (SE) D1412 (SE)		• Longer-wavelength alternatives to AMCA
Hydroxycoumarin	385 360	445[3] 455[4]	H185 (COOH) H1428 (COOH) H1193 (SE)		• pH-sensitive fluorescence • Compact structure
Marina Blue®	365	460	M10165 (SE)	Z25040 (Z) Z25340 (Z)	• Optimal for 365 nm excitation sources
Methoxycoumarin	358	410	M1410 (SE) M1420MP (COOH)		• pH-insensitive fluorescence • Compact structure
Pacific Blue™	410	455	P10163 (SE)	U21658 (U) Z25041 (Z) Z25341 (Z)	• Longer-wavelength alternative to the Alexa Fluor® 350 and AMCA-X dyes

* The absorption (Abs) and fluorescence emission (Em) maxima, in nm, listed in this table are for the goat anti-mouse IgG antibody or dextran conjugates in aqueous buffer. These values were obtained from the Molecular Probes data tables. SE = Succinimidyl ester. AA = Acetyl azide. COOH = Carboxylic acid. ITC = Isothiocyanate. P = Easy-to-Use Protein Labeling Kit (Section 1.2). Mab = Monoclonal Antibody Labeling Kit (Section 1.2). Z = Zenon® Antibody Labeling Kit (Section 7.3). U = ULYSIS Nucleic Acid Labeling Kit (Section 8.2). A = ARES™ DNA Labeling Kit (Section 8.2). O = Oligonucleotide Amine Labeling Kit (Section 8.2). **1.** Spectral maxima for D374. **2.** Spectral maxima for D1412. **3.** Spectral maxima for H1193. **4.** Spectral maxima for 7-hydroxy-4-methylcoumarin-3-acetic acid, succinimidyl ester.

Alexa Fluor® and Zenon® Labeling Kits

For easy and trouble-free labeling of proteins with succinimidyl esters of the Alexa Fluor® 350 and Alexa Fluor® 430 carboxylic acids, we offer Alexa Fluor® 350 and Alexa Fluor® 430 Protein Labeling Kits (A10170, A10171; Table 1.2). These kits, which are described in greater detail in Section 1.2, contain everything that is required to perform three separate labeling reactions and to purify the resulting conjugates (Table 1.3, Figure 1.5). Our Alexa Fluor® 350 Monoclonal Antibody Labeling Kit (A20180) can be used to prepare blue-fluorescent conjugates of monoclonal antibodies, as well as of other proteins in limited quantities (~100 µg per conjugation).

Our exclusive Zenon® Alexa Fluor® 350 and Zenon® Alexa Fluor® 430 Antibody Labeling Kits (Table 7.13) permit the rapid and quantitative labeling of antibodies from a purified antibody fraction or from a crude antibody preparation such as serum, ascites fluid or a hybridoma supernatant. The Zenon® Antibody Labeling Kits and the Zenon® technology are described in detail in Section 7.3

Marina Blue® and Pacific Blue™ Dyes

Our patented Marina Blue® and Pacific Blue™ dyes, both of which are based on the 6,8-difluoro-7-hydroxycoumarin fluorophore, exhibit bright blue fluorescence emission near 460 nm.[6] The Marina Blue® dye is optimally excited by the intense 365 nm spectral line of the mercury-arc lamp, whereas the Pacific Blue™ dye maximally absorbs at ~415 nm (Table 1.2, Table 1.1, Table 1.11). Significantly, the pK_a values of these 6,8-difluoro-7-hydroxycoumarin derivatives are 2–3 log units lower than those of the corresponding 7-hydroxycoumarins (Figure 1.96). Thus, the Marina Blue® and Pacific Blue™ dyes yield conjugates that are strongly fluorescent, even at neutral pH. For preparing bioconjugates, we offer amine-reactive succinimidyl esters of the Marina Blue® and Pacific Blue™ dyes (M10165, P10163; Figure 1.97, Figure 1.98).

Marina Blue® and Pacific Blue™ conjugates of various antibodies (Section 7.2, Table 7.1), avidins (Section 7.6, Table 7.22), wheat germ agglutinin (W11260, Section 7.7), Panomer™ 9 random oligodeoxynucleotide (P21678, Section 8.5) and phospholipids (M12652, P22652; Section 13.2) are available. Custom conjugations of the Marina Blue® and Pacific Blue™ fluorophores are also available from Molecular Probes; please contact our Custom and Bulk Sales Department.

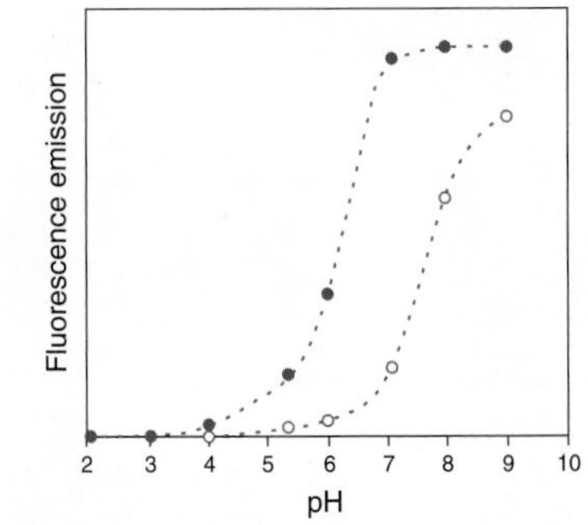

Figure 1.96 Comparison of the pH-dependent fluorescence changes produced by attachment of electron-withdrawing fluorine atoms to a hydroxycoumarin. 7-Hydroxy-4-methylcoumarin-3-acetic acid (○, H1428) and 6,8-difluoro-7-hydroxy-4-methylcoumarin (●, D6566) demonstrate the decrease of the pK_a from ~7.4 to ~6.2. Fluorescence intensities were measured for equal concentrations of the two dyes using excitation/emission at 360/450 nm.

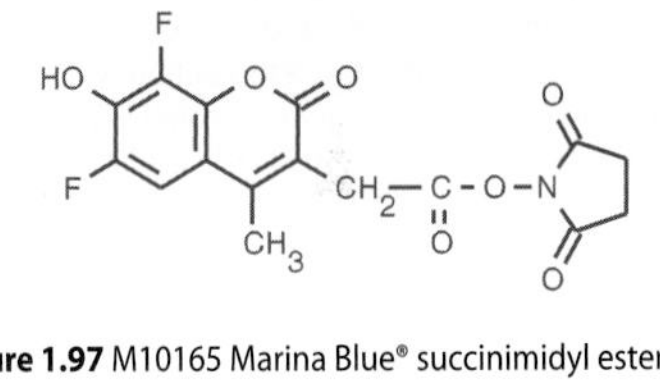

Figure 1.97 M10165 Marina Blue® succinimidyl ester.

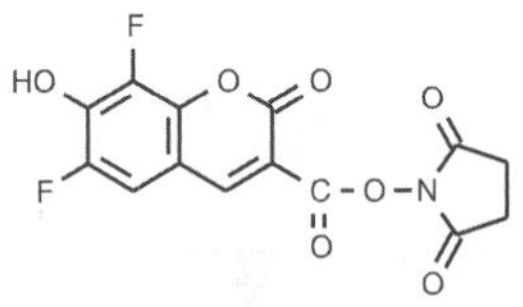

Figure 1.98 P10163 Pacific Blue™ succinimidyl ester.

Table 1.12 — Amine-reactive, environment-sensitive fluorophores

Fluorophore	Abs *	Em *	Succinimidyl Ester	Other	Notes
Cascade Yellow™	409	558	C10164		• Fluorescence emission spectrum shifts to shorter wavelengths in nonpolar solvents
Dansyl	335	518	D6104 (X)	D21 (SC)	• Sulfonyl chloride is nonfluorescent until it reacts with amines • Weak fluorescence in aqueous solutions
Dapoxyl®	395	601	D10161 D10162	D10160 (SC)	• Very low fluorescence in water • Large Stokes shifts (up to ~200 nm) • Large extinction coefficients of Dapoxyl® derivatives in some solvents [1]
NBD	466	535	S1167 (X)	C20260 (AH) F486 (AH)	• NBD amine derivatives have low fluorescence in water; emission spectra and quantum yields in other solvents are variable [2]
PyMPO	415	570	S6110		• Fluorescence emission spectrum shifts to shorter wavelengths in nonpolar solvents
Pyrene	340	376	P6115 P130 P6114 (CASE)	P10167 (STP)	• Forms excited-state dimers (excimers) that emit at longer wavelengths (~470 nm) than the lone excited fluorophore • Extremely long fluorescence lifetime (can be >100 ns)

Absorption (Abs) and Emission (Em) maxima, in nm, are for conjugates. X = Aminohexanoyl spacer separating the dye and the SE. CASE = Cysteic acid separating the dye and the SE. SC = Sulfonyl chloride. AH = Aryl halide. STP = 4-Sulfotetrafluorophenyl ester.

Pacific Blue™ Tyramide Signal Amplification Kits

Tyramide signal amplification (TSA) utilizes horseradish peroxidase conjugates to yield significant amplification of targets (Figure 6.5). Our TSA Kits #10, #20 and #30 (Table 6.1, Figure 1.99), which are described in Section 6.2, contain Pacific Blue™ tyramide and horseradish peroxidase conjugates of a goat anti–mouse IgG antibody, goat anti–rabbit IgG antibody and streptavidin, respectively.

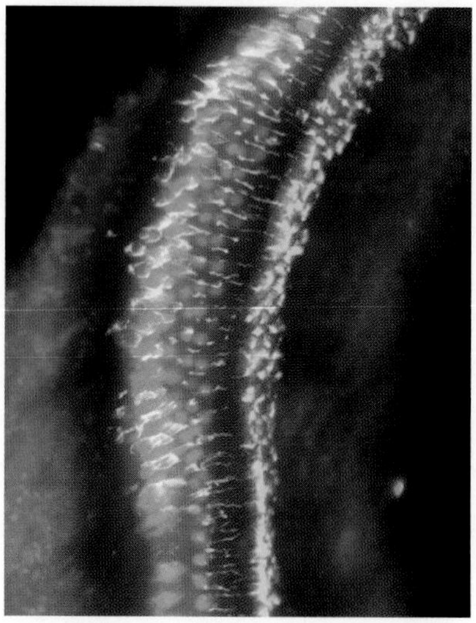

Figure 1.99 A zebrafish retina cryosection was labeled with the mouse monoclonal antibody FRet 43, which was detected using TSA Kit #10 (T20920) with the HRP conjugate of goat anti-mouse IgG antibody and Pacific Blue™ tyramide. The nuclei were counterstained with the SYTOX® Orange nucleic acid stain (S11368).

Zenon® Antibody Labeling Kits with the Marina Blue® and Pacific Blue™ Dyes

The Zenon® Marina Blue® and Zenon® Pacific Blue™ Antibody Labeling Kits (Table 7.13) enable the researcher to rapidly prepare labeled antibody complexes starting with extremely small quantities — as little as submicrogram quantities — of the antibody. The Zenon® Marina Blue® and Zenon® Pacific Blue™ Antibody Labeling Kits and the Zenon® technology are described in detail in Section 7.3.

Alexa Fluor® 350 and Pacific Blue™ Nucleic Acid Labeling Kits

Our ARES™ Alexa Fluor® 350 DNA Labeling Kit (A21675) and ULYSIS Pacific Blue™ Nucleic Acid Labeling Kit (U21658) permit facile incorporation of our blue-fluorescent Alexa Fluor® 350 and Pacific Blue™ dyes into nucleic acids.

Other Hydroxycoumarin and Alkoxycoumarin Derivatives

The hydroxycoumarins (H185, H1193, H1428) exhibit pH-sensitive spectral properties, but the methoxycoumarins (M1410, M1420MP) do not.[7,8] Hydroxycoumarins are often used to prepare reactive intermediates for the synthesis of radioiodinated materials.[8,9] The spectral properties of the hydroxycoumarins allow their quantitation prior to radioiodination.[9]

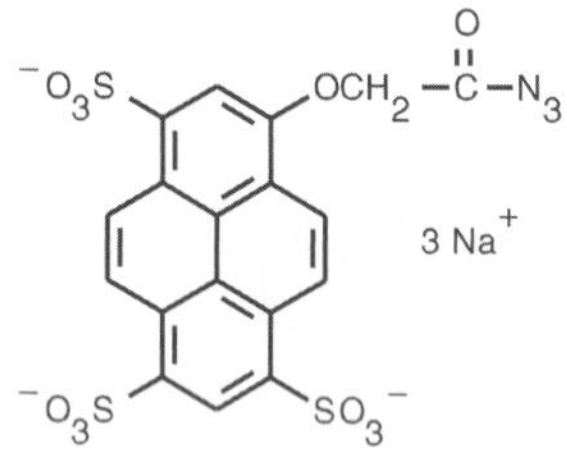

Figure 1.100 C2284 Cascade Blue® acetyl azide, trisodium salt.

Cascade Blue® and other Pyrene Derivatives

Cascade Blue® Acetyl Azide

Cascade Blue® acetyl azide is the amine-reactive derivative of the trademarked and patented sulfonated pyrene[10] that Molecular Probes uses to prepare its blue-fluorescent Cascade Blue® dye–labeled proteins and dextrans. The high polarity of this reagent makes it difficult to purify to homogeneity; however, we offer a Cascade Blue® acetyl azide preparation (C2284, Table 1.11, Figure 1.100) that is ~60% reactive and packaged according to the net weight of the reactive dye. The remaining constituents are inorganic salts or unreactive forms of the dye that can readily be removed following conjugation. As compared with the aminocoumarin derivatives, the Cascade Blue® fluorophore shows less spectral overlap with fluorescein (Figure 1.101), an important advantage for multicolor applications. In addition, this reactive Cascade Blue® derivative has high absorptivity (Figure 1.102), is highly fluorescent and, unlike most dyes, resists quenching upon protein conjugation (Figure 7.35). Even at low degrees of labeling, Cascade Blue® conjugates are significantly more fluorescent than are those of 7-amino-4-methylcoumarin-3-acetic acid (AMCA),[10] and they remain preferred reagents for multicolor flow cytometry.[11–13] Although a standard DAPI/Hoechst optical filter set can be used with Cascade Blue® conjugates, the fluorescence will be brighter when viewed through optical filters optimized for the spectral properties of the Cascade Blue® dye (Table 23.9).

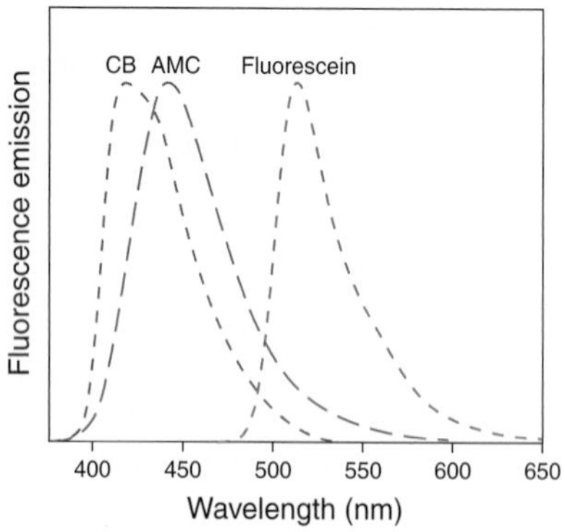

Figure 1.101 Normalized fluorescence emission spectra of Cascade Blue® (CB), 7-amino-4-methylcoumarin (AMC) and fluorescein in aqueous solutions.

In addition to its use for preparing protein conjugates, the membrane-impermeant, very water-soluble Cascade Blue® acetyl azide may be useful for identifying proteins located on extracellular cell surfaces. Molecular Probes offers Cascade Blue® derivatives that can be immobilized with aldehyde-based fixatives for use as polar tracers (Section 14.3) and Cascade Blue® conjugates of a variety of proteins, a nucleotide (Section 8.2) and a dextran (Section 14.5), as well as an antibody directed against the Cascade Blue® fluorophore (A5760, Section 7.4).

Alexa Fluor® 405 Dye

With excitation/emission maxima of 402/421 nm (Figure 1.34, Figure 7.3), our Alexa Fluor® 405 dye is a near-perfect match to the 405 nm spectral line of the blue diode laser recently developed for fluorescence microscopy and flow cytometry. The Alexa Fluor® 405 succinimidyl ester is an amine-reactive derivative of our Cascade Blue® dye, which was previously available in amine-reactive form only as its acetyl azide. Not only is it offered at higher purity than is Cascade Blue® acetyl azide, but the Alexa Fluor® 405 succinimidyl ester also contains a 4-piperidinecarboxylic acid spacer that separates the fluorophore from its reactive moiety (Figure 1.103). This spacer enhances the reactivity of the succinimidyl ester and minimizes any interactions between the fluorophore and the biomolecule to which it is conjugated. As with conjugates of Cascade Blue® acetyl azide, the Alexa Fluor® 405 conjugates show minimal spectral overlap with green fluorophores, making them ideal for multicolor applications. Moreover, with its longer excitation maximum, the Alexa Fluor® 405 dye is potentially brighter than UV light–excitable blue fluorophores, whose signal is often obscured by autofluorescence. The Alexa Fluor® 405 dye is available as a succinimidyl ester (A30000, A30100), a maleimide (A30458, Section 2.3), a thiol-reactive mercurial (Hg-Link™ Alexa Fluor® 405 phenylmercury, H30461; Section 2.3) and a cadaverine (A30675, Section 3.3), as well as conjugated to secondary antibodies (Section 7.2, Table 7.1) and streptavidin (Section 7.6, Table 7.22). It is also recognized by our anti–Alexa Fluor® 405/Cascade Blue® dye antibody (A5760, Section 7.4). In addition, Alexa Fluor® 405 tyramide is used in several of our Tyramide Signal Amplification (TSA) Kits (Section 6.3, Table 6.1, Figure 6.5).

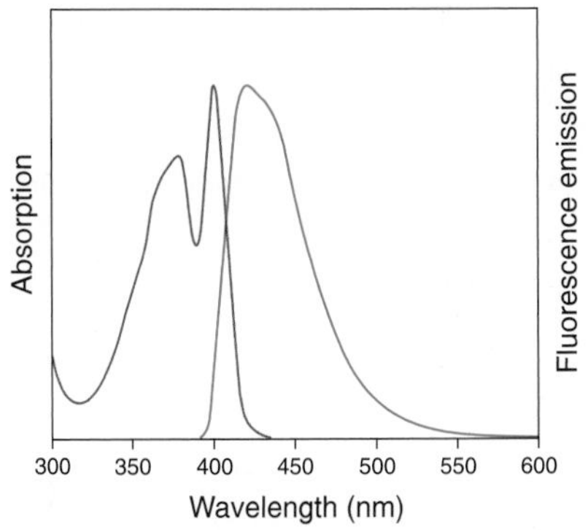

Figure 1.102 Absorption and fluorescence emission spectra of Cascade Blue® dye–labeled bovine serum albumin (BSA) in pH 7.0 buffer.

Other Pyrenes

Conjugates of the pyrene succinimidyl esters (P130, P6114, P6115) have exceptionally long excited-state lifetimes (sometimes >100 nanoseconds) and relatively short-wavelength spectra. These amine-reactive pyrene derivatives have primarily been used for labeling polynucleotides [14–17] and for studying protein conformation;[18,19] pyrene derivatives have also been utilized as oxygen sensors.[20,21] The pyrene moiety of pyrenebutyric acid succinimidyl ester (P130) has been noncovalently adsorbed onto carbon nanotubes, resulting in functionalization of the nanotube with an amine-reactive group that is useful for protein immobilization.[22] The long fluorescence lifetime of pyrenebutyric acid (1-pyrenebutanoic acid) permits time-gating of the fluorescence, which is a useful technique for discriminating between the dye signal and sample autofluorescence,[23] and has been exploited for fluorescence immunoassays.[24] For preparing pyrene conjugates with long fluorescence lifetimes, we recommend our more water-soluble succinimidyl ester of *N*-(1-pyrenebutanoyl)cysteic acid (P6114, Figure 1.104) or 4-sulfo-2,3,5,6-tetrafluorophenyl (STP) ester of 1-pyrenebutanoic acid [25] (P10167). The amine-reactive 1-pyrenesulfonyl chloride (P24, Section 1.8) is primarily used as a derivatization reagent.

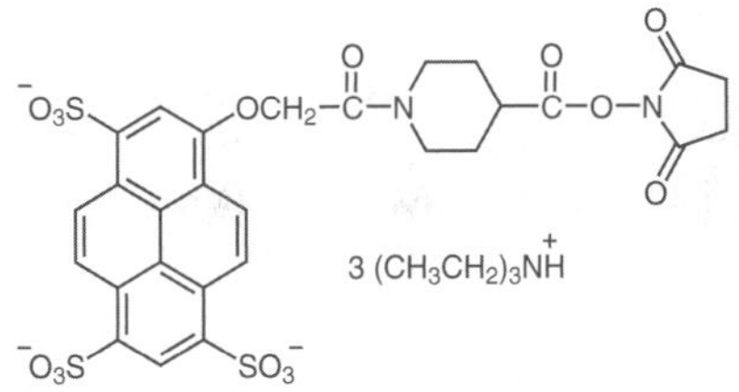

Figure 1.103 A30000 Alexa Fluor® 405 carboxylic acid, succinimidyl ester.

Pyrene dyes frequently form excited-state dimers (excimers) with fluorescence emission at longer wavelengths than the monomers (Figure 13.8). This property has been used to detect protein interactions,[26–29] nucleic acid hybridization,[30] triple-helix formation [14] and phospholipase activity (Section 17.4), as well as to detect transition metal ions.[31] Aliphatic polyamines derivatized with pyrenebutyric acid succinimidyl ester (P130) have been differentiated from pyrene-labeled monoamines by HPLC using this fluorescent excimer formation.[32]

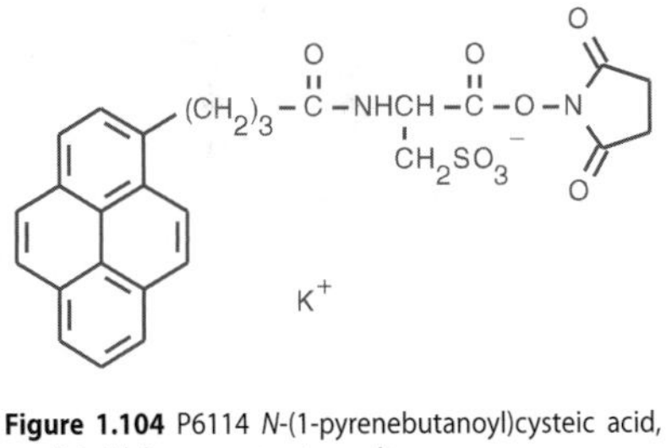

Figure 1.104 P6114 *N*-(1-pyrenebutanoyl)cysteic acid, succinimidyl ester, potassium salt.

Naphthalenes, Including Dansyl Chloride

Naphthalene-based probes tend to have emission spectra that are sensitive to the environment and exhibit weak fluorescence in aqueous solution. Spectra of environment-sensitive probes respond to perturbations in the local environment (Table 1.12). For example, changes in solvation that occur because of ligand binding, protein assembly or protein denaturation can often evoke changes in the fluorescence properties of these probes. This property has made dansyl chloride (5-dimethylaminonaphthalene-1-sulfonyl chloride, D21) and other naphthalene-based dyes important tools for protein structural studies.

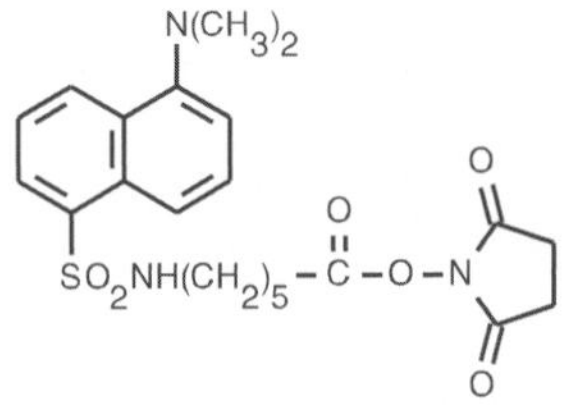

Figure 1.105 D6104 6-((5-dimethylaminonaphthalene-1-sulfonyl)amino)hexanoic acid, succinimidyl ester (dansyl-X, SE).

Dansyl chloride is nonfluorescent until it reacts with amines. The resulting dansyl amides have environment-sensitive fluorescence quantum yields and emission maxima, along with large Stokes shifts. Despite the weak absorptivity (ε ~4000 $cm^{-1}M^{-1}$ at 330–340 nm) and moderate fluorescence quantum yield of dansyl sulfonamides, dansyl chloride is widely used as a derivatization reagent for end-group analysis of proteins, amino acid analysis and HPLC detection (Section 1.8). The succinimidyl ester of dansylaminohexanoic acid (dansyl-X, SE; D6104; Figure 1.105) contains a seven-atom spacer ("X") that places the dansyl fluorophore further from its reaction site, potentially reducing the interaction of the fluorophore with the biomolecule to which it is conjugated and enhancing accessibility to antibody binding.[33–35] A rabbit polyclonal antibody to the 1,5-dansyl fluorophore (A6398) that significantly enhances the dye's fluorescence is described in Section 7.4.

Conjugates of two isomers of dansyl chloride (2,5-dansyl chloride, D22; 2,6-dansyl chloride, D23) have smaller Stokes shifts and appreciably longer fluorescence lifetimes (up to ~30 nanoseconds) than conjugates of 1,5-dansyl chloride, making these isomers among the best available probes for fluorescence depolarization studies.[36] These dyes are particularly useful for preparing fluorescent drug or ligand analogs that are expected to bind to hydrophobic sites in proteins or membranes. The lipophilicity of these reagents may also facilitate the labeling of sites within the membrane-spanning portions of cellular proteins.

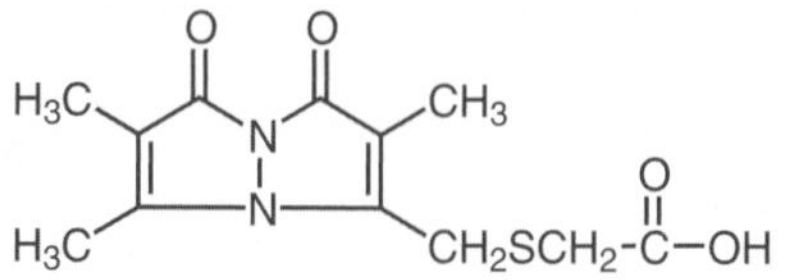

Figure 1.106 B30250 bimane mercaptoacetic acid (carboxymethylthiobimane).

Bimane Derivative

Bimane mercaptoacetic acid (carboxymethylthiobimane, B30250) and its amine-reactive succinimidyl ester (B30251) are blue-fluorescent dyes with excitation/emission maxima of ~380/458 nm. Bimane's small size (Figure 1.106) reduces the likelihood that the label will interfere with the function of the biomolecule, an important advantage for site-selective probes.

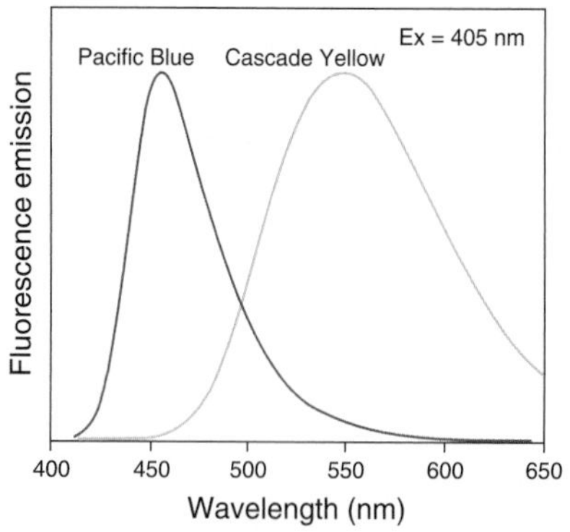

Figure 1.109 Normalized fluorescence emission spectra of Pacific Blue™ goat anti-mouse IgG antibody (P10993) and a Cascade Yellow™ goat anti-mouse IgG antibody conjugate prepared with the Cascade Yellow™ succinimidyl ester (C10164). Both fluorescent conjugates are excited at 405 nm. When samples containing equal concentrations of antibody are compared, the peak fluorescence intensity of the Pacific Blue™ conjugate at 456 nm is nine times greater than that of the Cascade Yellow™ conjugate at 548 nm.

Pyridyloxazole Derivatives

The pyridyloxazole derivatives — including the succinimidyl ester (PyMPO, SE; S6110; Figure 1.107) and the thiol-reactive maleimide (M6026, Section 2.2) — fill the spectral gap between UV light–excited dyes and the fluoresceins. These derivatives of the laser dye PyMPO exhibit absorption maxima near 415 nm and unusually high Stokes shifts, with emission at 560–580 nm.[37] Like the naphthalene-based dyes, the pyridyloxazole dyes exhibit environment-sensitive fluorescence spectra. PyMPO SE has been used to synthesize fluorescent gramicidin derivatives for following ion-channel-gating processes.[38]

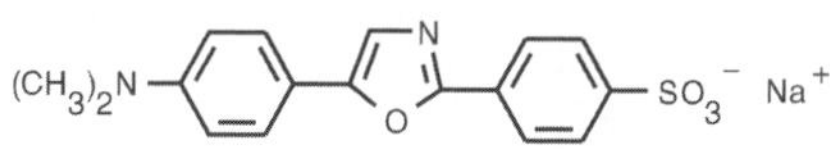

Figure 1.110 D12800 Dapoxyl® sulfonic acid, sodium salt.

Cascade Yellow™ Dye

Like the Alexa Fluor® 430 and Pacific Blue™ dyes described above, the Cascade Yellow™ dye exhibits an excitation maximum that falls between those of the UV light–excited dyes and the fluoresceins. This sulfonated pyridyloxazole (PyMPO) laser dye (Figure 1.108) exhibits an absorption maximum near 410 nm and an unusually high Stokes shift, with relatively strong emission at 550–570 nm [37,39,40] (Figure 7.38). The large Stokes shift permits detection at a wavelength well beyond that of most sample autofluorescence, and allows multiple fluorophores to be excited at the same wavelengths and detected at different wavelengths. For example, protein conjugates of Cascade Yellow™ succinimidyl ester (C10164) can be simultaneously excited at 405 nm with Pacific Blue™ conjugates, and then separately detected at longer wavelengths (Figure 1.109). Cascade Yellow™ and Cascade Blue® antibody conjugates, along with several phycobiliprotein tandem conjugates, are utilized in an 11-color polychromatic flow cytometry technique.[11,12]

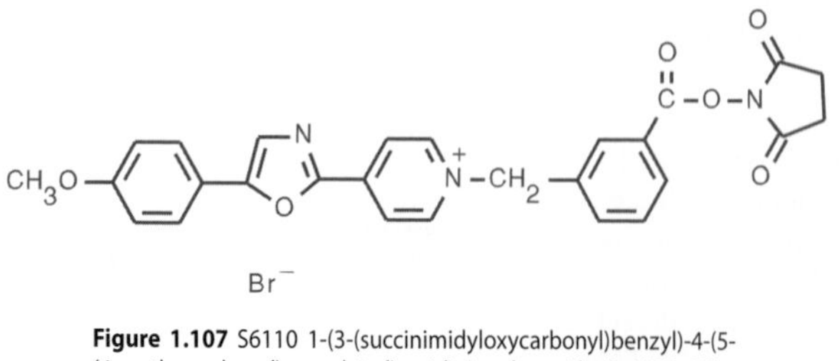

Figure 1.107 S6110 1-(3-(succinimidyloxycarbonyl)benzyl)-4-(5-(4-methoxyphenyl)oxazol-2-yl)pyridinium bromide (PyMPO, SE).

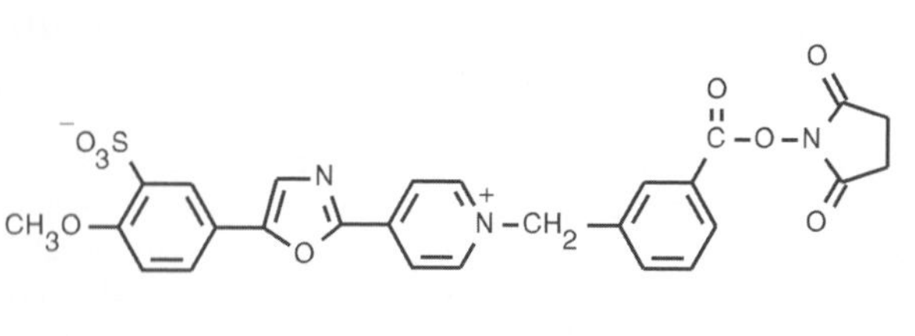

Figure 1.108 C10164 Cascade Yellow™ succinimidyl ester.

Dapoxyl® Dye

Our Dapoxyl® dye (Figure 1.110) is a particularly versatile derivatization reagent and precursor to environment-sensitive probes.[41] Like the Cascade Yellow™ dye, the Dapoxyl® dye exhibits an exceptionally large Stokes shift, with excitation/emission maxima of ~370/580 nm (Figure 1.111). Sulfonamides from Dapoxyl® sulfonyl chloride (D10160) have much higher extinction coefficients than those of dansyl chloride (~26,000 $cm^{-1}M^{-1}$ versus about 4000 $cm^{-1}M^{-1}$) and equal or greater quantum yields when dissolved in organic solvents; however, the fluorescence of Dapoxyl® derivatives is very environment sensitive and their fluorescence in water is very low, suggesting that Dapoxyl® conjugates may be useful as probes for conformational changes, denaturation, phosphorylation state and phase changes. The huge Stokes shifts (up to ~200 nm) and large extinction coefficients of Dapoxyl® derivatives in some solvents, and the close match of their absorption to the intense 365 nm spectral line of the mercury-arc lamp, make the reactive Dapoxyl® derivatives advantageous derivatization reagents for chromatographic and electrophoretic analysis. In addition to Dapoxyl® sulfonyl chloride, we offer the amine-reactive succinimidyl esters (D10161, D10162), the thiol-reactive bromoacetamide derivative (D10300, Section 2.3) and the carboxylic acid–reactive (2-aminoethyl)sulfonamide (D10460, Section 3.3) Dapoxyl® derivatives. We have also exploited the environment-sensitive fluorescence of the Dapoxyl® dye (Figure 1.112) to develop a novel acidotropic probe for lysosomes and other acidic organelles (LysoTracker® Blue-White DPX, L12490; Section 12.3; Figure 1.113), as well as a highly selective and photostable stain for the endoplasmic reticulum (ER-Tracker™ Blue-White DPX, E12353; Section 12.4; Figure 1.114).

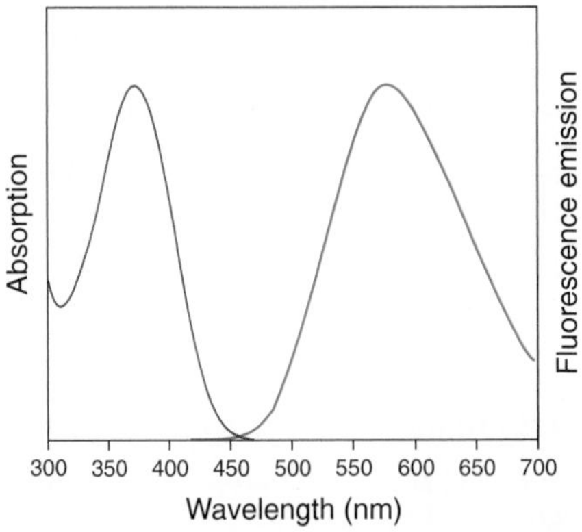

Figure 1.111 Absorption and fluorescence emission spectra of Dapoxyl® (2-aminoethyl)sulfonamide in methanol.

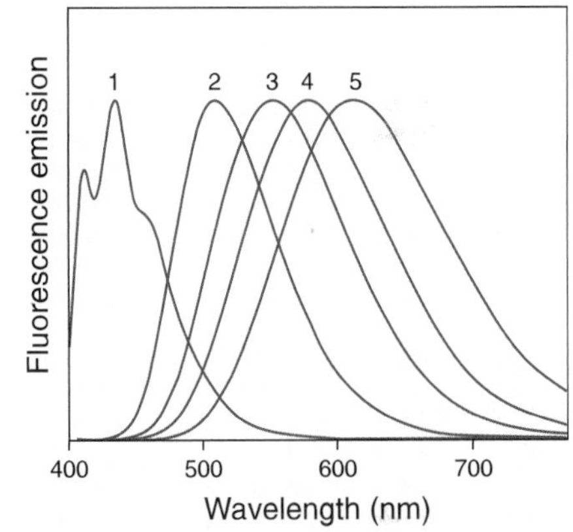

Figure 1.112 Normalized fluorescence emission spectra of Dapoxyl® (2-aminoethyl)sulfonamide (D10460) in 1) hexane, 2) chloroform, 3) acetone, 4) acetonitrile and 5) 1:1 acetonitrile: water.

UV Light–Excitable Microspheres

Molecular Probes' blue-fluorescent and blue-green–fluorescent FluoSpheres® beads (Section 6.5, Table 6.7) are intensely fluorescent (Figure 1.115) and biologically inert. These microspheres can be conjugated to a variety of proteins for use in labeling targets or may be directly useful as tracers (Section 14.6).

We have also prepared luminescent microspheres containing europium or platinum chelates (Section 6.5, Table 6.8). These luminescent microspheres are excited in the UV and have extremely high Stokes shifts with long-lived, narrow emission near 610 nm for the europium-based microspheres (Figure 6.47) or near 650 nm for the platinum-based microspheres (Figure 6.48). Time-resolved measurements of these microspheres permit essentially background-free measurements of their luminescence.

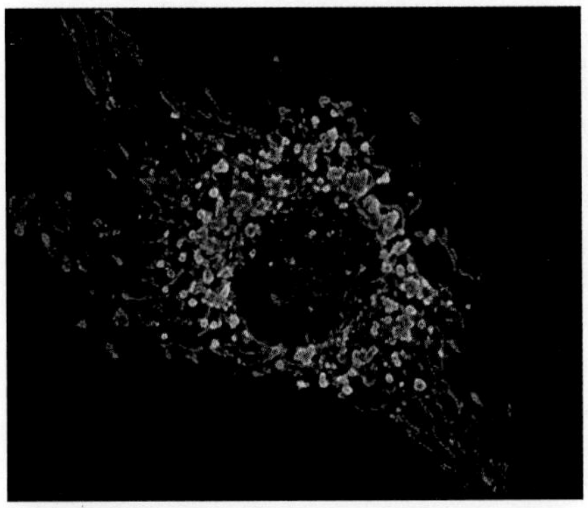

Figure 1.113 Live bovine pulmonary artery endothelial cells (BPAEC) stained simultaneously with 50 nM LysoTracker® Blue-White DPX (L12490), a Dapoxyl® derivative, and 100 nM MitoTracker® CMXRos (M7512) at room temperature. This multiple-exposure image was acquired using longpass filter sets appropriate for DAPI and tetramethyrhodamine. The image was deconvolved using Huygens software (Scientific Volume Imaging, www.svi.nl). 3-D reconstruction was performed using Imaris software (Bitplane AG, www.bitplane.com).

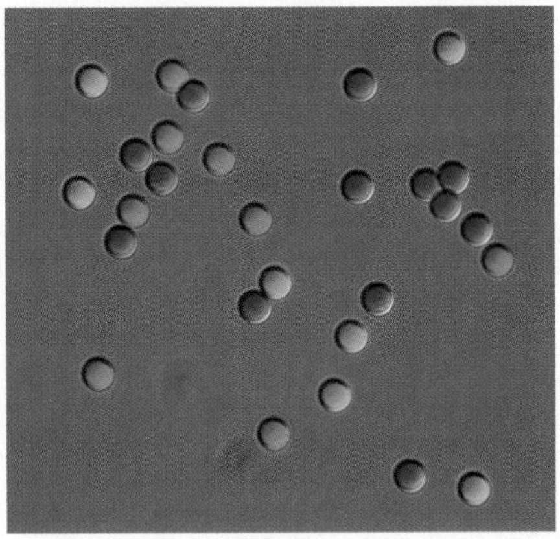

Figure 1.115 A photomicrograph of a multicolor mixture of Molecular Probes' FluoSpheres® fluorescent microspheres overlaid with a differential interference contrast (DIC) image of the same field. Molecular Probes applies its proprietary fluorescent dye technology to produce a range of intensely fluorescent FluoSpheres® microspheres labeled with biotin, streptavidin and NeutrAvidin biotin-binding protein, providing important tools for improving the sensitivity of flow cytometry applications and immunodiagnostic assays.

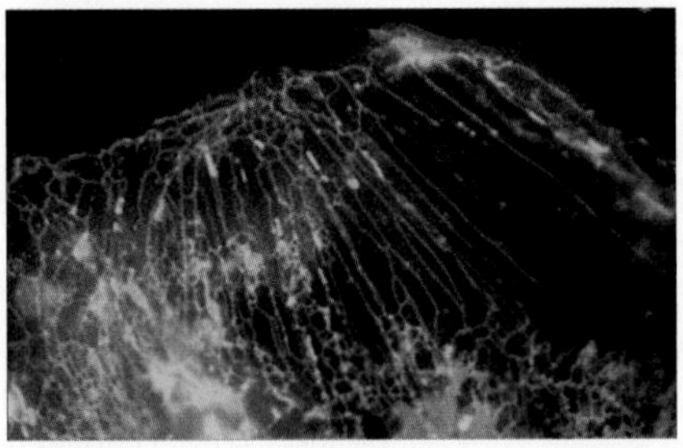

Figure 1.114 Live bovine pulmonary artery endothelial cells (BPAEC) stained with ER-Tracker™ Blue-White DPX (E12353), a Dapoxyl® derivative. This image was acquired using a DAPI bandpass optical filter.

References

1. Histochem J 18, 497 (1986); **2.** J Histochem Cytochem 47, 1179 (1999); **3.** Bioorg Med Chem Lett 9, 2229 (1999); **4.** J Biol Chem 271, 31160 (1996); **5.** Biochemistry 27, 8889 (1988); **6.** Bioorg Med Chem Lett 8, 3107 (1998); **7.** Anal Chem 40, 803 (1968); **8.** 12 (1949); **9.** FEBS Lett 182, 185 (1985); **10.** Anal Biochem 198, 119 (1991); **11.** Nat Med 7, 245 (2001); **12.** Nat Biotechnol 20, 155 (2002); **13.** Cytometry 29, 328 (1997); **14.** Biochemistry 36, 14836 (1997); **15.** Nucleic Acids Res 21, 5085 (1993); **16.** EMBO J 11, 3777 (1992); **17.** Anal Biochem 183, 231 (1989); **18.** Biochemistry 30, 4298 (1991); **19.** Biochemistry 29, 3082 (1990); **20.** Anal Chem 59, 279 (1987); **21.** Mikrochim Acta 1, 153 (1984); **22.** J Am Chem Soc 123, 3838 (2001); **23.** J Biochem Biophys Methods 29, 157 (1994); **24.** Anal Biochem 174, 101 (1988); **25.** Tetrahedron Lett 40, 1471 (1999); **26.** Biochemistry 26, 4922 (1987); **27.** Biochemistry 24, 6631 (1985); **28.** J Biol Chem 255, 11296 (1980); **29.** J Biol Chem 253, 3757 (1978); **30.** Photochem Photobiol 62, 836 (1995); **31.** Tetrahedron Lett 36, 1451 (1995); **32.** Anal Chem 72, 4199 (2000); **33.** Biochim Biophys Acta 1104, 9 (1992); **34.** Biochim Biophys Acta 776, 217 (1984); **35.** Biochemistry 21, 978 (1982); **36.** J Biochem Biophys Methods 5, 1 (1981); **37.** IEEE J Quantum Electronics 16, 777 (1980); **38.** Bioconjug Chem 12, 594 (2001); **39.** Cytometry 33, 435 (1998); **40.** Cytometry 36, 36 (1999); **41.** Photochem Photobiol 66, 424 (1997).

Data Table — 1.7 Coumarins, Pyrenes and Other Ultraviolet Light-Excitable Fluorophores

Cat #	MW	Storage	Soluble	Abs	EC	Em	Solvent	Notes
A6118	443.46	F,D,L	DMF, DMSO	353	19,000	442	MeOH	
A10168	410.35	F,D,L	H_2O, DMSO	346	19,000	445	pH 7	1
A10169	701.75	F,D,L	H_2O, DMSO	430	15,000	545	pH 7	1
A30000	1028.26	F,DD,L	H_2O, DMSO	400	35,000	424	pH 7	1, 2, 3
B30250	282.31	F,D,L	DMSO	380	5,700	458	MeOH	
B30251	379.39	F,D,L	DMSO	380	5,800	460	MeOH	
C2284	607.42	F,D,LL	H_2O, MeOH	396	29,000	410	MeOH	2, 4
C10164	563.54	F,D,L	DMF, DMSO	409	24,000	558	MeOH	5
D21	269.75	F,DD,L	DMF, MeCN	372	3,900	none	$CHCl_3$	6, 7
D22	269.75	F,DD,L	DMF, MeCN	403	2,900	none	MeOH	7, 8
D23	269.75	F,DD,L	DMF, MeCN	380	16,000	none	$CHCl_3$	7, 8
D126	247.25	L	pH >6, DMF	370	22,000	459	MeOH	
D374	344.32	F,D,L	DMF, MeCN	376	22,000	468	MeOH	
D1412	358.35	F,D,L	DMF, MeCN	432	56,000	472	MeOH	
D1421	261.28	L	pH >6, DMF	409	33,000	473	pH 9	
D6104	461.53	F,D,L	DMF, MeCN	335	4,200	518	MeOH	
D10160	362.83	F,DD,L	DMF, MeCN	403	22,000	see Notes	MeOH	7, 9
D10161	405.41	F,D,L	DMF, DMSO	395	20,000	601	MeOH	10
D10162	512.54	F,D,L	DMF, DMSO	373	26,000	574	MeOH	5
D10166	260.31	F,DD,L	DMF, MeCN	400	36,000	476	MeOH	11, 12
H185	206.15	L	pH >6, DMF	386	29,000	448	pH 10	13
H1193	303.23	F,D,L	DMF, MeCN	419	36,000	447	MeOH	
H1428	234.21	L	pH >6, DMF	360	19,000	455	pH 10	
M1410	317.25	F,D,L	DMF, MeCN	358	26,000	410	MeOH	
M1420MP	220.18	L	pH >6, DMF	336	20,000	402	pH 9	
M10165	367.26	F,D,L	DMF, MeCN	362	19,000	459	pH 9	
P24	300.76	F,DD,L	DMF, MeCN	350	28,000	380	MeOH	7, 14
P130	385.42	F,D,L	DMF, DMSO	340	43,000	376	MeOH	15
P6114	574.65	F,D,L	H_2O, DMSO	341	38,000	376	MeOH	1, 15
P6115	357.36	F,D,L	DMF, DMSO	340	44,000	376	MeOH	15
P10163	339.21	F,D,L	DMF, MeCN	416	46,000	451	pH 9	
P10167	538.44	F,D,L	H_2O, DMSO	340	46,000	376	MeOH	15, 16
S6110	582.41	F,D,L	DMF, DMSO	415	26,000	570	MeOH	5

For definitions of the contents of this data table, see "Navigating *The Handbook*" in the introductory pages.

Notes

1. This sulfonated succinimidyl ester derivative is water-soluble and may be dissolved in buffer at ~pH 8 for reaction with amines. Long-term storage in water is NOT recommended due to hydrolysis.
2. The Alexa Fluor® 405 and Cascade Blue® dyes have a second absorption peak at about 376 nm with EC ~80% of the 395–400 nm peak.
3. A30100 is an alternative packaging of A30000 but is otherwise identical.
4. Unstable in water. Use immediately.
5. Fluorescence emission spectrum shifts to shorter wavelengths in nonpolar solvents.
6. D21 butylamine derivative has Abs = 337 nm (EC = 5300 $cm^{-1}M^{-1}$), Em = 492 nm in $CHCl_3$. Em and QY are highly solvent dependent: Em = 496 nm (QY = 0.45) in dioxane, 536 nm (QY = 0.28) in MeOH and 557 nm (QY = 0.03) in H_2O (Biochemistry 6, 3408 (1967)). EC typically decreases upon conjugation to proteins (EC = 3400 $cm^{-1}M^{-1}$ at 340 nm) (Biochemistry 25, 513 (1986)). Fluorescence lifetimes (τ) of protein conjugates are typically 12–20 nanoseconds (Arch Biochem Biophys 133, 263 (1969); Arch Biochem Biophys 128, 163 (1968)).
7. Do NOT dissolve in DMSO.
8. D22 butylamine derivative: Abs = 375 nm (EC = 3100 $cm^{-1}M^{-1}$), Em = 470 nm in MeOH. D23 butylamine derivative: Abs = 375 nm (EC = 13,000 $cm^{-1}M^{-1}$), Em = 419 nm in $CHCl_3$.
9. D10160 fluorescence is very weak. Reaction product with butylamine has Abs = 373 nm (EC = 26,000 $cm^{-1}M^{-1}$), Em = 551 nm.
10. D10161 butylamine derivative: Abs = 367 nm (EC = 25,000 $cm^{-1}M^{-1}$), Em = 574 nm in MeOH. QY of the derivative is approximately 15-fold higher than the unreacted reagent.
11. Isothiocyanates are unstable in water and should not be stored in aqueous solution.
12. D10166 butylamine derivative: Abs = 376 nm (EC = 25,000 $cm^{-1}M^{-1}$), Em = 469 nm in MeOH. QY of the derivative is approximately 6-fold higher than the unreacted reagent.
13. H185 Abs = 339 nm (EC = 19,000 $cm^{-1}M^{-1}$), Em = 448 nm at pH 4.
14. Spectra of the reaction product with butylamine.
15. Pyrene derivatives exhibit structured spectra. The absorption maximum is usually about 340 nm with a subsidiary peak at about 325 nm. There are also strong absorption peaks below 300 nm. The emission maximum is usually about 376 nm with a subsidiary peak at 396 nm. Excimer emission at about 470 nm may be observed at high concentrations.
16. This sulfotetrafluorophenyl (STP) ester derivative is water-soluble and may be dissolved in buffer at ~pH 8 for reaction with amines. Long-term storage in water is NOT recommended due to hydrolysis.

Product List — 1.7 Coumarins, Pyrenes and Other Ultraviolet Light-Excitable Fluorophores

Cat #	Product Name	Unit Size
A10168	Alexa Fluor® 350 carboxylic acid, succinimidyl ester	5 mg
A30000	Alexa Fluor® 405 carboxylic acid, succinimidyl ester	1 mg
A30100	Alexa Fluor® 405 carboxylic acid, succinimidyl ester	5 mg
A10169	Alexa Fluor® 430 carboxylic acid, succinimidyl ester	5 mg
A20180	Alexa Fluor® 350 Monoclonal Antibody Labeling Kit *5 labelings*	1 kit
A20190	Alexa Fluor® 350 Oligonucleotide Amine Labeling Kit *3 labelings*	1 kit
A10170	Alexa Fluor® 350 Protein Labeling Kit *3 labelings*	1 kit
A10171	Alexa Fluor® 430 Protein Labeling Kit *3 labelings*	1 kit
A6118	6-((7-amino-4-methylcoumarin-3-acetyl)amino)hexanoic acid, succinimidyl ester (AMCA-X, SE)	10 mg
A21675	ARES™ Alexa Fluor® 350 DNA Labeling Kit *10 labelings*	1 kit
B30250	bimane mercaptoacetic acid (carboxymethylthiobimane)	5 mg
B30251	bimane mercaptoacetic acid, succinimidyl ester	5 mg
C2284	Cascade Blue® acetyl azide, trisodium salt	5 mg
C10164	Cascade Yellow™ succinimidyl ester	5 mg
D10161	Dapoxyl® carboxylic acid, succinimidyl ester	5 mg
D10162	Dapoxyl® 3-sulfonamidopropionic acid, succinimidyl ester	10 mg
D10160	Dapoxyl® sulfonyl chloride	10 mg
D1421	7-diethylaminocoumarin-3-carboxylic acid	100 mg
D1412	7-diethylaminocoumarin-3-carboxylic acid, succinimidyl ester	25 mg
D126	7-dimethylaminocoumarin-4-acetic acid (DMACA)	100 mg
D374	7-dimethylaminocoumarin-4-acetic acid, succinimidyl ester (DMACA, SE)	25 mg
D10166	7-dimethylamino-4-methylcoumarin-3-isothiocyanate (DACITC)	10 mg
D6104	6-((5-dimethylaminonaphthalene-1-sulfonyl)amino)hexanoic acid, succinimidyl ester (dansyl-X, SE)	25 mg
D21	5-dimethylaminonaphthalene-1-sulfonyl chloride (dansyl chloride)	1 g
D22	2-dimethylaminonaphthalene-5-sulfonyl chloride	100 mg
D23	2-dimethylaminonaphthalene-6-sulfonyl chloride	100 mg
H185	7-hydroxycoumarin-3-carboxylic acid *reference standard*	100 mg
H1193	7-hydroxycoumarin-3-carboxylic acid, succinimidyl ester	25 mg
H1428	7-hydroxy-4-methylcoumarin-3-acetic acid	100 mg
M10165	Marina Blue® succinimidyl ester	5 mg
M1420MP	7-methoxycoumarin-3-carboxylic acid	100 mg
M1410	7-methoxycoumarin-3-carboxylic acid, succinimidyl ester	25 mg
P10163	Pacific Blue™ succinimidyl ester	5 mg
P6115	1-pyreneacetic acid, succinimidyl ester	25 mg
P10167	1-pyrenebutanoic acid, STP ester, sodium salt	5 mg
P130	1-pyrenebutanoic acid, succinimidyl ester	100 mg
P6114	*N*-(1-pyrenebutanoyl)cysteic acid, succinimidyl ester, potassium salt	5 mg
P24	1-pyrenesulfonyl chloride	100 mg
S6110	1-(3-(succinimidyloxycarbonyl)benzyl)-4-(5-(4-methoxyphenyl)oxazol-2-yl)pyridinium bromide (PyMPO, SE)	5 mg
U21658	ULYSIS® Pacific Blue™ Nucleic Acid Labeling Kit *20 labelings*	1 kit
Z25400	Zenon® Alexa Fluor® 350 Human IgG Labeling Kit *50 labelings*	1 kit
Z25000	Zenon® Alexa Fluor® 350 Mouse IgG_1 Labeling Kit *50 labelings*	1 kit
Z25100	Zenon® Alexa Fluor® 350 Mouse IgG_{2a} Labeling Kit *50 labelings*	1 kit
Z25200	Zenon® Alexa Fluor® 350 Mouse IgG_{2b} Labeling Kit *50 labelings*	1 kit
Z25300	Zenon® Alexa Fluor® 350 Rabbit IgG Labeling Kit *50 labelings*	1 kit
Z25013	Zenon® Alexa Fluor® 405 Mouse IgG_1 Labeling Kit *50 labelings*	1 kit
Z25113	Zenon® Alexa Fluor® 405 Mouse IgG_{2a} Labeling Kit *50 labelings*	1 kit
Z25213	Zenon® Alexa Fluor® 405 Mouse IgG_{2b} Labeling Kit *50 labelings*	1 kit
Z25313	Zenon® Alexa Fluor® 405 Rabbit IgG Labeling Kit *50 labelings*	1 kit
Z25001	Zenon® Alexa Fluor® 430 Mouse IgG_1 Labeling Kit *50 labelings*	1 kit
Z25301	Zenon® Alexa Fluor® 430 Rabbit IgG Labeling Kit *50 labelings*	1 kit
Z25040	Zenon® Marina Blue® Mouse IgG_1 Labeling Kit *50 labelings*	1 kit
Z25340	Zenon® Marina Blue® Rabbit IgG Labeling Kit *50 labelings*	1 kit
Z25041	Zenon® Pacific Blue™ Mouse IgG_1 Labeling Kit *50 labelings*	1 kit
Z25341	Zenon® Pacific Blue™ Rabbit IgG Labeling Kit *50 labelings*	1 kit

For current prices or to order online, visit probes.invitrogen.com

1.8 Reagents for Analysis of Low Molecular Weight Amines

Not only are low molecular weight amines abundantly distributed in nature, but numerous drugs, synthetic probes and other molecules of interest also contain amino groups. The sensitive detection, identification and quantitation of amines are important applications of many of the reactive fluorophores in this section. Some of these reagents have also been used to indirectly detect carbohydrates, carboxylic acids, thiols and cyanide.

The preferred reagents for detecting and quantitating amines in solution or on amine-containing polymers are those that are nonfluorescent but form fluorescent conjugates stoichiometrically with amines. It is usually difficult to compare the sensitivity for amine detection of the different reagents because it depends heavily on the equipment and detection technology used. However, many of the assays are rapid, reliable and adaptable to a variety of different sample types and instrumentation.

Fluorescamine

Fluorescamine (F2332; FluoroPure™ Grade, F20261) is intrinsically nonfluorescent but reacts rapidly with primary aliphatic amines, including those in peptides and proteins, to yield a blue-green–fluorescent derivative [1,2] (Figure 1.116). Modifications to the reaction protocol permit fluorescamine to be used to detect those amino acids containing secondary amines,[3] such as proline. Excess reagent is rapidly converted to a nonfluorescent product by reaction with water,[4] making fluorescamine useful for determining protein concentrations of solutions.[5,6] Fluorescamine can also be used to detect proteins in gels and to analyze low molecular weight amines by TLC, HPLC and capillary electrophoresis.[7,8] An optimized procedure that employs fluorescamine for amino acid analysis in microplates has been published.[9] In addition, chiral separation of fluorescamine-labeled amino acids has been optimized using capillary electrophoresis in the presence of hydroxypropyl-β-cyclodextran, a method designed for use in extraterrestrial exploration on Mars.[10]

Dialdehydes: OPA and NDA

Analyte Detection with OPA and NDA

The homologous aromatic dialdehydes *o*-phthaldialdehyde [11] (OPA, P2331MP) and naphthalene-2,3-dicarboxaldehyde [12] (NDA, N1138) are essentially nonfluorescent until reacted with a primary amine in the presence of excess cyanide or a thiol, such as 2-mercaptoethanol, 3-mercaptopropionic acid or the less obnoxious sulfite,[13] to yield a fluorescent isoindole (Figure 1.117, Figure 1.118). Modified protocols that use an excess of an amine and limiting amounts of other nucleophiles permit the determination of carboxylic acids [14] and thiols,[15] as well as of cyanide in blood, urine and other samples.[16–19] Without an additional nucleophile, NDA forms fluorescent adducts with both hydrazine and methylated hydrazines [20] (excitation/emission maxima ~403/500 nm).

Sensitivity of NDA

Amine adducts of NDA have longer-wavelength spectral characteristics and greater sensitivity than the amine adducts of OPA. The stability and detectability of the amine derivatives of NDA are also superior;[21,22] the detection of glycine with NDA and cyanide is reported to be 50-fold more sensitive than with OPA and 2-mercaptoethanol.[12] The limit for electrochemical detection of the NDA adduct of asparagine has been determined to be as low as 36 attomoles [23,24] (36×10^{-18} moles). An optimized procedure that uses NDA for amino acid analysis in microplates has been published.[9]

Applications for OPA and NDA

OPA and NDA are used extensively for both pre- and postcolumn derivatization of amines (and thiols) separated by HPLC [25] or by capillary electrophoresis.[26–30] The amines in a single cell have been analyzed by capillary electrophoresis using a sequence of on-capillary lysis, derivatization with NDA and cyanide and laser-excited detection.[31,32] A capillary electrophoresis method based on NDA derivatization has also been developed to follow stimulated release of amines from individual neurons and small groups of isolated neurons.[33] NDA derivatives can be excited at 442 nm by the He–Cd laser.[26]

ATTO-TAG™ Reagents

Sensitivity of ATTO-TAG™ CBQCA and ATTO-TAG™ FQ

Molecular Probes exclusively offers ATTO-TAG™ CBQCA (A6222, A2333) and ATTO-TAG™ FQ (A10192, A2334) for ultrasensitive detection of primary amines, including those in peptides, amino acid homopolymers and glycoproteins. These reagents combine high sensitivity, visible-wavelength excitation and freedom from background fluorescence, making them useful for research, analytical and forensic applications. Developed by Novotny and collaborators, the ATTO-TAG™ reagents are similar to OPA and NDA in that they rapidly react with amines in the presence of cyanide or thiols to form highly fluorescent isoindoles [34–44] (Figure 1.119).

The ATTO-TAG™ CBQCA reagent reacts specifically with amines to form charged conjugates that can be analyzed by electrophoresis techniques. Carbohydrates lacking amines can be detected fol-

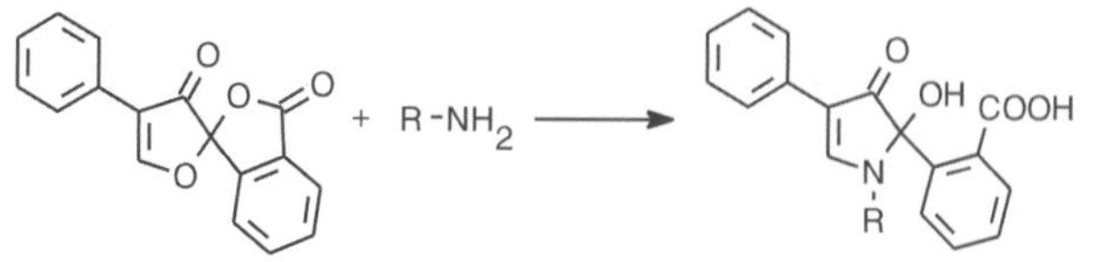

Figure 1.116 Fluorogenic amine-derivatization reaction of fluorescamine (F2332, F20261).

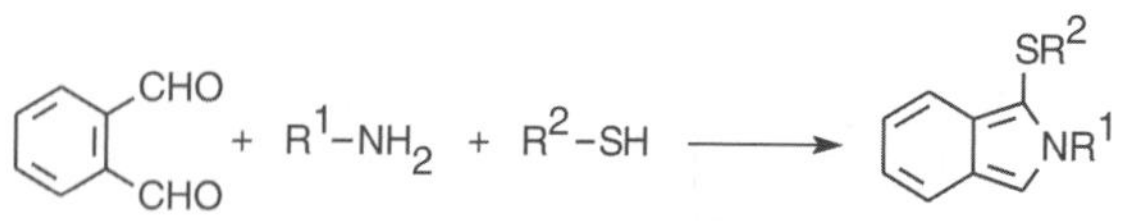

Figure 1.117 Fluorogenic amine-derivatization reaction of *o*-phthaldialdehyde (OPA) (P2331MP).

lowing reductive amination with ammonia and $NaCNBH_3$.[43,45,46] ATTO-TAG™ CBQCA conjugates are maximally excited at ~456 nm or by the 442 nm spectral line of the He–Cd laser, with peak emission at ~550 nm, whereas ATTO-TAG™ FQ conjugates are maximally excited at ~480 nm or by the 488 nm spectral line of the argon-ion laser, with peak emission at ~590 nm. In capillary zone electrophoresis, the sensitivity of amine detection of the laser-induced fluorescence should be in the subattomole range ($<10^{-18}$ moles) for ATTO-TAG™ CBQCA and subfemtomole range ($<10^{-15}$ moles) for ATTO-TAG™ FQ.[47,48] Sensitivity for detection of reductively aminated glucose using ATTO-TAG™ CBQCA is reported to be 75 zeptomoles[49] (75×10^{-21} moles). Similar ultrasensitive detection of CBQCA-derivatized amino acids by capillary electrophoresis has been reported.[50]

ATTO-TAG™ reagents can, of course, be used in HPLC and other modes of chromatography with either absorption or fluorescence detection. The principal limitation to obtaining ultrasensitive detection using the ATTO-TAG™ reagents and all other chemical derivatization reagents is that relatively high concentrations of the derivatizing reagent are required to obtain adequate kinetics and sufficient modification of the analyte. One particularly useful technique employs ATTO-TAG™ FQ for the solid-phase derivatization of dilute solutions (~10^{-8} M) of peptides that have been immobilized on Immobilon CD membranes.[51] This method permits the quantitative derivatization and analysis by capillary electrophoresis of only a few picomoles of the analyte. A very sensitive assay that uses ATTO-TAG™ CBQCA for rapid quantitation of protein amines (C6667) is described in Section 9.2.

ATTO-TAG™ Reagents and Kits

Cyclodextrins have been reported to amplify the signal from ATTO-TAG™ CBQCA conjugates up to 10-fold[44,52,53] so we include β-cyclodextrin in our ATTO-TAG™ Amine Derivatization Kits (A2333, A2334). The kits contain:

- 5 mg of ATTO-TAG™ CBQCA (in Kit A2333) or ATTO-TAG™ FQ (in Kit A2334)
- Potassium cyanide
- β-Cyclodextrin
- A protocol for amine modification

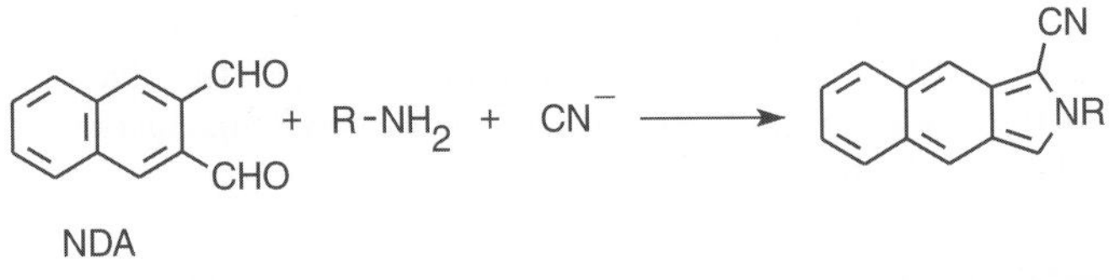

Figure 1.118 Fluorogenic amine-derivatization reaction of naphthalene-2,3-dicarboxaldehyde (NDA) (N1138).

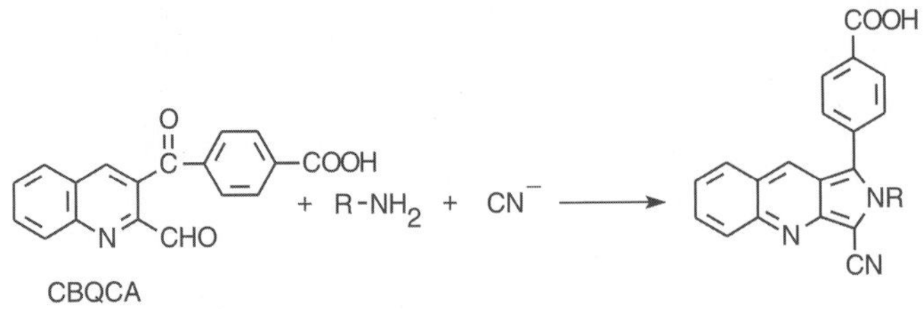

Figure 1.119 Fluorogenic amine-derivatization reaction of CBQCA (A6222, A2333).

The ATTO-TAG™ CBQCA and ATTO-TAG™ FQ Amine Derivatization Kits supply sufficient reagents for derivatizing approximately 150 and 100 samples, respectively, depending on the amine concentration and sample volume. We also offer both the ATTO-TAG™ CBQCA and the ATTO-TAG™ FQ derivatization reagents separately (CBQCA, A6222; FQ, A10192).

7-Nitrobenz-2-Oxa-1,3-Diazole (NBD) Derivatives

NBD chloride (FluoroPure™ Grade, C20260; Figure 1.120) was first introduced in 1968 as a fluorogenic derivatization reagent for amines.[54] It also reacts with thiols and alcohols, although these adducts absorb and emit at shorter wavelengths and are less fluorescent than amine derivatives.[55] NBD fluoride (F486) usually yields the same products as NBD chloride but is much more reactive;[56] for example, the reaction of NBD fluoride with glycine is reported to be 500 times faster than the reaction of NBD chloride with glycine.[57] Unlike OPA and fluorescamine, both NBD chloride and NBD fluoride react with secondary amines and are therefore capable of derivatizing proline and hydroxyproline.[56,58] NBD chloride and NBD fluoride are extensively used as derivatization reagents for chromatographic analysis of amino acids[59] and other low molecular weight amines.[60] NBD fluoride has also been used for the enantiomeric separation of D,L-amino acids on a chiral column[61] and by capillary electrophoresis using cyclodextrin chiral selectors, as well as for the ultramicroanalysis of reducing carbohydrates.[62,63]

The absorption and fluorescence emission spectra, quantum yields and extinction coefficients of NBD conjugates are all markedly dependent on solvent;[64,65] in particular, the fluorescence quantum yield in water of NBD adducts of amines can be very low (<0.01), particularly of secondary amines. NBD adducts of aromatic amines are essentially nonfluorescent, a property that we have utilized to prepare our QSY® 35 quenchers (see below). Fluorescence of lysine-modified NBD-labeled actin is sensitive to polymerization.[66] Inactivation of certain ATPases by NBD chloride apparently involves a tyrosine modification followed by intramolecular migration of the label to a lysine residue.[67,68] NBD is also a functional analog of the dinitrophenyl hapten, and its fluorescence is quenched upon binding to anti-dinitrophenyl antibodies[65] (Section 7.4). NBD aminohexanoic acid (NBD-X, N316) and its succinimidyl ester (NBD-X, SE; S1167) are precursors to NBD-labeled phospholipids (Section 13.2), NBD C_6-ceramide (N1154, Section 12.4) and other probes.

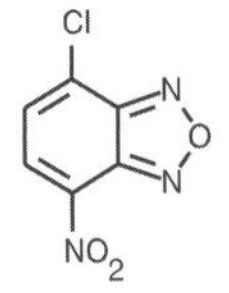

Figure 1.120 C20260 4-chloro-7-nitrobenz-2-oxa-1,3-diazole (NBD chloride; 4-chloro-7-nitrobenzofurazan).

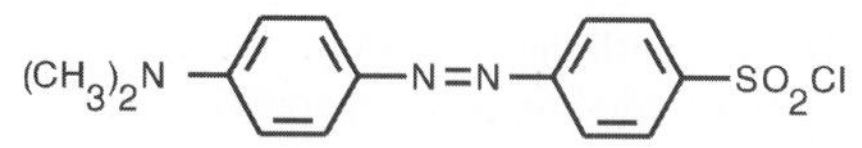

Figure 1.121 D1537 4-dimethylaminoazobenzene-4′-sulfonyl chloride (dabsyl chloride).

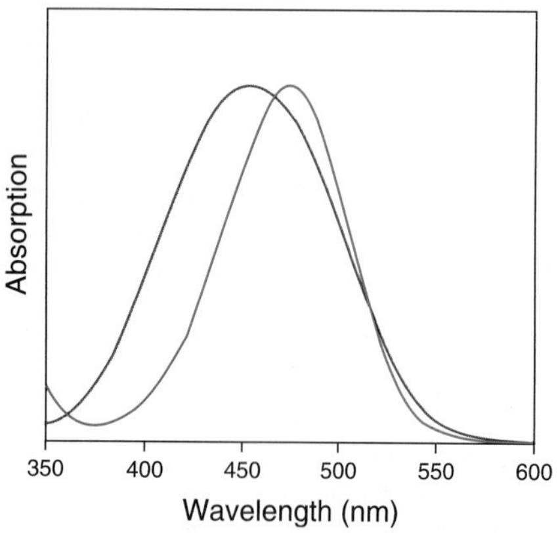

Figure 1.122 Normalized absorption spectra of the succinimidyl esters of the dabcyl (D2245, blue) and QSY® 35 (Q20133, red) dyes. The molar absorptivity of the QSY® 35 dye, however, is almost four times that of the dabcyl chromophore.

Dansyl Chloride and Other Sulfonyl Chlorides

Many of the sulfonyl chlorides described in Section 1.7, including dansyl chloride (D21), 1-pyrenesulfonyl chloride (P24) and Dapoxyl® sulfonyl chloride (D10160), react with amines to yield blue- or blue-green–fluorescent sulfonamides and are particularly useful as chromatographic derivatization reagents. They react with both aliphatic and aromatic amines to yield very stable derivatives. In addition, they are generally good acceptors for fluorescence resonance energy transfer (FRET) from tryptophan, as well as good donors to longer-wavelength dyes such as dabsyl chloride (D1537) and our QSY® dyes (Section 1.6) (see Note 1.2 "Technical Focus: Fluorescence Resonance Energy Transfer (FRET)" in Section 1.3). Fluorescence of dansyl conjugates in aqueous solutions can be enhanced by adding cycloheptaamylose.[69] Although dansyl chloride is the most commonly used of these reagents, the stronger absorption of 1-pyrenesulfonamides and huge Stokes shift of Dapoxyl® sulfonamides[70] (Figure 1.111) should make these sulfonyl chlorides more sensitive reagents for amine analysis. Note that sulfonyl chlorides are unstable in dimethylsulfoxide (DMSO) and should never be used in that solvent.[71]

Dansyl Chloride

Since its development by Weber in 1951,[72] dansyl chloride (D21, Section 1.7) has been used extensively to determine the N-terminal amino acid residue of proteins and to prepare fluorescent derivatives of drugs, amino acids, oligonucleotides and proteins for detection by numerous chromatographic methods.[73] Nonfluorescent dansyl chloride reacts with amines to form fluorescent dansyl amides that exhibit large Stokes shifts, along with environment-sensitive fluorescence quantum yields and emission maxima.

Dapoxyl® Sulfonyl Chloride

Sulfonamides from Dapoxyl® sulfonyl chloride (D10160, Section 1.7) have much higher extinction coefficients than those of dansyl chloride (~22,000 $cm^{-1}M^{-1}$ versus ~4000 $cm^{-1}M^{-1}$) and equal or greater quantum yields when dissolved in organic solvents; however, Dapoxyl® derivatives have very low fluorescence in water. The huge Stokes shifts (up to ~200 nm) and large extinction coefficients of Dapoxyl® derivatives in some solvents[70] (Figure 1.111), and the close match of their absorption to the intense 365 nm emission of the mercury-arc lamp, make the reactive Dapoxyl® derivatives advantageous derivatization reagents for chromatographic and electrophoretic analysis.[74]

Pyrene Sulfonyl Chloride

The absorptivity (and therefore ultimate fluorescence output) of dansyl derivatives is weak compared with that of the more strongly UV light–absorbing fluorophores such as pyrene. Thus, 1-pyrenesulfonyl chloride (P24, Section 1.7) should have greater sensitivity for detection of amines. The fluorescence lifetime of pyrenesulfonamides can also be relatively long (up to ~30 nanoseconds), making them useful for fluorescence anisotropy measurements.[75] Fluorescence polarization measurements of DNA probes labeled with 1-pyrenesulfonyl chloride permit homogeneous detection of hybridization.[76]

Chromophoric Sulfonyl Chloride

Dabsyl chloride (D1537, Figure 1.121) is a common amine-derivatization reagent for detecting proteins by HPLC,[77,78] as well as by gel and capillary electrophoresis.[79–81] Conjugates of dabsyl chloride have broad and intense visible absorption, making them useful as acceptors in FRET applications (see Note 1.2 "Technical Focus: Fluorescence Resonance Energy Transfer (FRET)" in Section 1.3).

FITC and Benzofuran Isothiocyanates

Isothiocyanates for preparing bioconjugates have been described in several sections of this chapter. However, FITC (F143, F1906, F1907; Section 1.5) and benzofuran (D1332) isothiocyanates can also be used for derivatizing low molecular weight amines and, like phenyl isothiocyanate, for microsequencing of peptides as their thiohydantoins.[82] A unique method for specific derivatization of the N-terminus of peptides by FITC has been described.[83] FITC-labeled amino acids and peptides have been separated by capillary electrophoresis with a detection limit of fewer than 1000 molecules.[84,85]

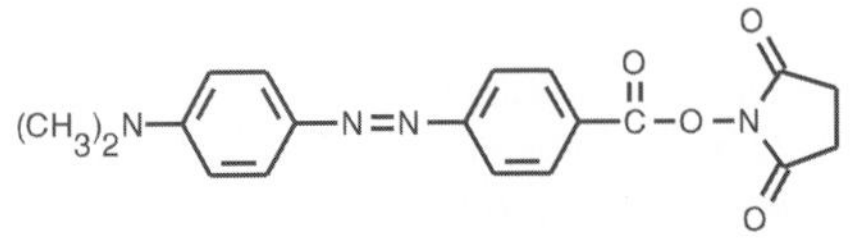

Figure 1.123 D2245 4-((4-(dimethylamino)phenyl)azo)benzoic acid, succinimidyl ester (dabcyl, SE).

Succinimidyl Esters and Carboxylic Acids

Succinimidyl esters have a high selectivity for reaction with aliphatic amines. Most of the succinimidyl ester reagents described elsewhere in this chapter can be used to derivatize low molecular weight amines for separation by chromatography or capillary electrophoresis. The Alexa Fluor®, BODIPY®, Oregon Green® and fluorescein derivatives usually yield the greatest sensitivity, particularly when the conjugate is detected following laser excitation. Use of single isomers of these reactive dyes is essential for all high-resolution analyses. Analysis by capillary electrophoresis shows that carboxyfluorescein succinimidyl ester reacts faster and yields more stable amine conjugates than FITC or DTAF.[86] The UV light–excitable coumarins described in Section 1.7 have good absorptivity at ~320–420 nm, with purple to bright blue emission at 400–500 nm. Aliphatic polyamines derivatized with 1-pyrenebutanoic acid succinimidyl ester (P130, Section 1.7) have been differentiated from pyrene-labeled monoamines by HPLC using their fluorescent excimer formation.[87]

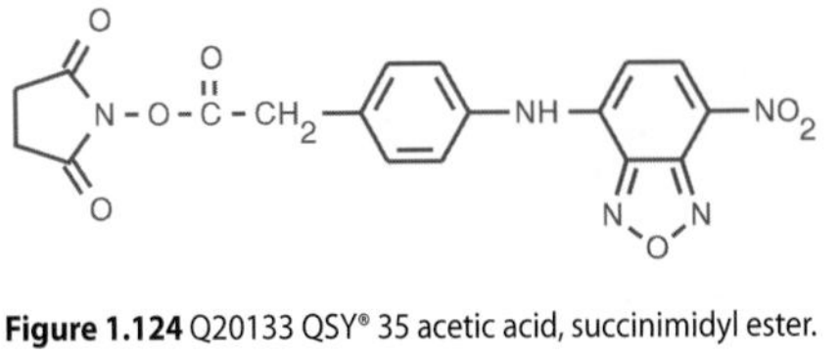

Figure 1.124 Q20133 QSY® 35 acetic acid, succinimidyl ester.

The Smallest Reactive Fluorophore

Both *N*-methylisatoic anhydride (M25) and the succinimidyl ester of *N*-methylanthranilic acid (S128) are useful precursors for preparing esters or amides of the small *N*-methylanthranilic acid fluorophore. The small size of this fluorophore should reduce the likelihood that the label will interfere with the function of the biomolecule, an important advantage when designing site-selective probes. These amine-acylating reagents are often used to prepare fluorescent derivatives of biologically active peptides and toxins[88–91] and, in combination with a quencher, to prepare fluorogenic endoprotease substrates.[92,93] *N*-methylisatoic anhydride also reacts with the ribose moiety of ribonucleotides to yield fluorescent MANT nucleotide analogs[94–96] (Section 17.3, Figure 17.19).

Chromophoric Succinimidyl Esters: Fluorescence Quenchers

Dabcyl has broad and intense visible absorption (Figure 1.122) but no fluorescence, making it useful as an acceptor in FRET applications (see Note 1.2 "Technical Focus: Fluorescence Resonance Energy Transfer (FRET)" in Section 1.3). Biomolecules double-labeled with dabcyl and the appropriate fluorophore can be used to monitor proteolytic cleavage, conformational changes and other dynamic spatial movements. Dabcyl succinimidyl ester (dabcyl, SE; D2245; Figure 1.123) is particularly useful in preparing quenched fluorogenic substrates for proteases, including our HIV protease (Figure 10.10) and renin substrates[97–99] (H2930, R2931; Section 10.4), papain,[100,101] Alzheimer's disease–associated proteases[102] and others.[103–106] Fluorogenic substrates using this quenching group have also been prepared for interleukin-1β–converting enzyme (ICE),[107] a cysteine protease that is proposed to function in the onset of apoptosis.[108] The dabcyl chromophore has been used as the quencher in donor–acceptor labeled oligonucleotides in "molecular beacons"[109–112] (Figure 8.113); unfolding of these probes upon hybridization leads to recovery of the donor dye's fluorescence (Section 8.5).

QSY® 35 acetic acid succinimidyl ester (Q20133) is an essentially nonfluorescent nitrobenzoxadiazole (NBD) derivative (Figure 1.124). Like the QSY® 7, QSY® 9 and QSY® 21 dyes (Section 1.6, Figure 1.70), the QSY® 35 dye has stronger absorption at longer wavelengths than does the dabcyl dye (Figure 1.122), making it a very good acceptor from most blue-fluorescent dyes (Table 1.10). A peptide containing the QSY® 35 quencher paired with the blue-fluorescent 7-hydroxy-4-methyl-3-acetylcoumarin fluorophore has proven useful in a fluorescence resonance energy transfer (FRET) assay for *Bacillus anthracis* lethal factor protease.[113] A QSY® 35 iodoacetamide (Q20348, Section 2.2) and aliphatic methylamine (Q20540, Section 3.3) are available, as is an FMOC-protected QSY® 35 amino acid (Q21931, Section 9.5) for automated preparation of FRET-based protease substrates (Section 10.4).

N-(t-BOC)-Aminooxyacetic Acid TFP Ester

The tetrafluorophenyl ester (TFP) of *N*-(*t*-BOC)-aminooxyacetic acid (B30300) is an amine-reactive protected hydroxylamine that is useful for synthesizing new aldehyde- and ketone-reactive probes in an organic solvent. Following coupling to aliphatic amines, the *t*-BOC group can be quantitatively removed with trifluoroacetic acid. The resultant hydroxylamine can then spontaneously react with aldehydes, the reducing ends of saccharides and oligosaccharides and abasic sites in oligonucleotides to form stable adducts (Section 3.2).

Biotinylation, Desthiobiotinylation, Crosslinking and Thiolation Reagents

Molecular Probes offers a number of succinimidyl esters that are useful for preparing biotin and desthiobiotin (DSB-X™ biotin) conjugates or for crosslinking biomolecules and thiolation of amines. These products are described in Chapter 4 and Chapter 5. Uses of reactive dyes as haptens are discussed in Section 4.2.

References

1. Arch Biochem Biophys 163, 390 (1974); **2.** Science 178, 871 (1972); **3.** Biochem Biophys Res Commun 50, 352 (1973); **4.** Arch Biochem Biophys 163, 400 (1974); **5.** Clin Chim Acta 157, 73 (1986); **6.** J Lipid Res 27, 792 (1986); **7.** J Chromatogr 502, 247 (1990); **8.** J Chromatogr 548, 319 (1991); **9.** Anal Biochem 297, 128 (2001); **10.** J Chromatogr A 1021, 191 (2003); **11.** Proc Natl Acad Sci U S A 72, 619 (1975); **12.** Anal Chem 59, 1096 (1987); **13.** J Chromatogr A 668, 323 (1994); **14.** Anal Biochem 189, 122 (1990); **15.** J Chromatogr 564, 258 (1991); **16.** J Chromatogr 582, 131 (1992); **17.** Anal Chim Acta 225, 351 (1989); **18.** Biomed Chromatogr 3, 209 (1989); **19.** Anal Sci 2, 491 (1986); **20.** Analyst 119, 1907 (1994); **21.** Anal Chem 59, 411 (1987); **22.** J Org Chem 51, 3978 (1986); **23.** Anal Biochem 178, 202 (1989); **24.** Anal Chem 61, 432 (1989); **25.** Anal Biochem 180, 279 (1989); **26.** Anal Chem 67, 4261 (1995); **27.** Anal Chem 63, 417 (1991); **28.** J Chromatogr 540, 343 (1991); **29.** Anal Chem 62, 2189 (1990); **30.** Science 242, 224 (1988); **31.** Anal Chem 67, 58 (1995); **32.** Science 246, 57 (1989); **33.** Anal Chem 71, 28 (1999); **34.** J Chromatogr B Biomed Sci Appl 695, 67 (1997); **35.** J Neurosci Methods 65, 33 (1996); **36.** Anal Chem 66, 3512 (1994); **37.** Anal Chem 66, 3477 (1994); **38.** Anal Chem 65, 563 (1993); **39.** Electrophoresis 14, 373 (1993); **40.** Anal Chem 63, 413 (1991); **41.** Anal Chem 63, 408 (1991); **42.** J Chromatogr 559, 223 (1991); **43.** Proc Natl Acad Sci U S A 88, 2302 (1991); **44.** J Chromatogr 499, 579 (1990); **45.** Anal Chem 66, 3466 (1994); **46.** Proc Natl Acad Sci U S A 90, 9451 (1993); **47.** Electrophoresis 19, 2175 (1998); **48.** Anal Chem 69, 3015 (1997); **49.** J Chromatogr A 716, 221 (1995); **50.** Anal Chim Acta 299, 319 (1995); **51.** Electrophoresis 16, 534 (1995); **52.** J Chromatogr A 716, 335 (1995); **53.** J Chromatogr 519, 189 (1990); **54.** Biochem J 108, 155 (1968); **55.** FEBS Lett 6, 346 (1970); **56.** Anal Chim Acta 130, 377 (1981); **57.** Anal Chim Acta 170, 81 (1985); **58.** J Chromatogr 278, 167 (1983); **59.** Anal Biochem 116, 471 (1981); **60.** Anal Chim Acta 290, 3 (1994); **61.** Biomed Chromatogr 9, 10 (1995); **62.** J Liquid Chromatography 17, 1883 (1994); **63.** Eur J Cancer 30A, 1352 (1994); **64.** Photochem Photobiol 54, 361 (1991); **65.** Biochemistry 16, 5150 (1977); **66.** J Biol Chem 269, 3829 (1994); **67.** Eur J Biochem 142, 387 (1984); **68.** J Biol Chem 259, 14378 (1984); **69.** Chem Pharm Bull (Tokyo) 22, 2413 (1974); **70.** J Photochem Photobiol A 131, 95 (2000); **71.** J Org Chem 31, 3880 (1966); **72.** Biochem J 51, 155 (1952); **73.** J Liquid Chromatography 12, 2733 (1989); **74.** Photochem Photobiol 66, 424 (1997); **75.** J Colloid Interface Sci 135, 435 (1990); **76.** Anal Biochem 241, 238 (1996); **77.** J Chromatogr 553, 123 (1991); **78.** Methods Enzymol 91, 41 (1983); **79.** Anal Chem 62, 2193 (1990); **80.** Anal Biochem 141, 121 (1984); **81.** Anal Biochem 128, 412 (1983); **82.** Anal Biochem 141, 446 (1984); **83.** J Chromatogr 608, 239 (1992); **84.** J Chromatogr 480, 141 (1989); **85.** Science 242, 562 (1988); **86.** Bioconjug Chem 6, 447 (1995); **87.** Anal Chem 72, 4199 (2000); **88.** Peptides 13, 663 (1992); **89.** J Neurosci Methods 13, 119 (1985); **90.** J Biol Chem 259, 6117 (1984); **91.** J Biol Chem 258, 11948 (1983); **92.** Anal Biochem 212, 58 (1993); **93.** Anal Biochem 162, 213 (1987); **94.** Biochemistry 30, 422 (1991); **95.** Biochemistry 29, 3309 (1990); **96.** J Biol Chem 257, 13354 (1982); **97.** Anal Biochem 210, 351 (1993); **98.** Science 247, 954 (1990); **99.** Tetrahedron Lett 31, 6493 (1990); **100.** Arch Biochem Biophys 306, 304 (1993); **101.** FEBS Lett 297, 100 (1992); **102.** Bioorg Med Chem Lett 2, 1665 (1992); **103.** Drug Des Discov 15, 3 (1997); **104.** FEBS Lett 413, 379 (1997); **105.** Anal Biochem 204, 96 (1992); **106.** J Med Chem 35, 3727 (1992); **107.** Pept Res 7, 72 (1994); **108.** Science 267, 1445 (1995); **109.** Nat Biotechnol 16, 49 (1998); **110.** Appl Environ Microbiol 63, 1143 (1997); **111.** Nat Biotechnol 14, 303 (1996); **112.** Proc Natl Acad Sci U S A 95, 8602 (1998); **113.** Proc Natl Acad Sci U S A 99, 6603 (2002).

Data Table — 1.8 Reagents for Analysis of Low Molecular Weight Amines

Cat #	MW	Storage	Soluble	Abs	EC	Em	Solvent	Notes
A176	250.30	L	DMSO	366	8,900	414	MeOH	
A448	276.74	F,DD,L	DMF, MeCN	382	4,000	421	MeOH	1, 2
A1139	234.25	L	EtOH	546	ND	570	MeOH	3, 4
A2333	305.29	F,D,L	MeOH	465	ND	560	MeOH	4, 5, 6, 7
A2334	251.24	F,D,L	EtOH	486	ND	591	MeOH	7, 8
A6222	305.29	F,D,L	MeOH	465	ND	560	MeOH	4, 5, 6
A10192	251.24	F,L	EtOH	486	ND	591	MeOH	4, 8
B30300	339.24	F,D	DMSO	<300		none		
C20260	199.55	F,D,L	DMF, MeCN	336	9,800	none	MeOH	9, 10, 11
D1332	294.37	F,DD,L	DMF, MeCN	348	38,000	425	MeOH	12
D1537	323.80	F,DD,L	DMF, MeCN	466	33,000	none	MeOH	2, 13
D2245	366.38	F,D,L	DMF, DMSO	453	32,000	none	MeOH	14
F486	183.10	F,D,L	MeCN, $CHCl_3$	328	8,000	none	MeOH	9, 10
F2332	278.26	F,D,L	MeCN	380	7,800	464	MeCN	15

Cat #	MW	Storage	Soluble	Abs	EC	Em	Solvent	Notes
F20261	278.26	F,D,L	MeCN	380	8,400	464	MeCN	11, 15
M25	177.16	D	DMF, DMSO	316	3,500	386	MeOH	16
N316	294.27	L	DMSO	467	23,000	539	MeOH	10
N1138	184.19	L	DMF, MeCN	419	9,400	493	see Notes	17
P2331MP	134.13	L	EtOH	334	5,700	455	pH 9	18
Q20133	411.33	F,D,L	DMSO	475	23,000	none	MeOH	
S128	248.24	F,D,L	DMF, MeCN	368	6,500	437	MeOH	
S1167	391.34	F,D,L	DMF, DMSO	466	22,000	535	MeOH	10

For definitions of the contents of this data table, see "Navigating *The Handbook*" in the introductory pages.

Notes

1. Spectra of the reaction product with butylamine.
2. Do NOT dissolve in DMSO.
3. Spectra of A1139 with butylamine + cyanide. Absorption spectrum has multiple peaks. Unreacted reagent Abs = 361 nm (EC = 5400 $cm^{-1}M^{-1}$), Em = 410 nm in MeOH.
4. ND = not determined.
5. Spectral data are for the reaction product with glycine in the presence of cyanide. Unreacted reagent in MeOH: Abs = 254 nm (EC = 46,000 $cm^{-1}M^{-1}$), nonfluorescent.
6. Solubility in methanol is improved by addition of base (e.g., 1–5% (v/v) 0.2 M KOH).
7. Data represent the reactive dye component of this labeling kit.
8. Spectral data are for the reaction product with glycine in the presence of cyanide. Unreacted reagent in MeOH: Abs = 282 nm (EC = 21,000 $cm^{-1}M^{-1}$), nonfluorescent.
9. Spectra for primary aliphatic amine derivative of NBD chloride in MeOH: Abs = 465 nm (EC = 22,000 $cm^{-1}M^{-1}$), Em = 535 nm (QY = 0.3). Spectra for secondary aliphatic amine derivative in MeOH: Abs = 485 nm (EC = 25,000 $cm^{-1}M^{-1}$), Em = 540 nm (QY <0.1). Aromatic amine derivatives are nonfluorescent. All NBD amine derivatives are almost nonfluorescent in water and have strongly solvent-dependent emission spectra. NBD fluoride yields the same derivatives as NBD chloride but is more reactive.
10. Fluorescence of NBD and its derivatives in water is relatively weak. QY and τ increase and Em decreases in aprotic solvents and other nonpolar environments relative to water (Biochemistry 16, 5150 (1977); Photochem Photobiol 54, 361 (1991)).
11. This product is specified to equal or exceed 98% analytical purity by HPLC.
12. Spectra of this compound are in methanol containing a trace of KOH.
13. D1537 is nonfluorescent both before and after reaction with amines. Reation product with butylamine has Abs = 435 nm (EC = 31,000 $cm^{-1}M^{-1}$) in MeOH.
14. D2245 is nonfluorescent both before and after reaction with amines. Reaction product with butylamine has Abs = 428 nm (EC = 32,000 $cm^{-1}M^{-1}$) in MeOH.
15. Fluorescamine spectra are for the reaction product with butylamine. The fluorescence quantum yield and lifetime of the butylamine adduct in EtOH are 0.23 and 7.5 nanoseconds, respectively (Arch Biochem Biophys 163, 390 (1974)). The unreacted reagent is nonfluorescent (Abs = 234 nm, EC = 28,000 $cm^{-1}M^{-1}$ in MeCN).
16. The amide reaction product of M25 with butylamine has Abs = 353 nm (EC = 5900 $cm^{-1}M^{-1}$), Em = 426 nm in MeOH. Ester reaction products with alcohols have Abs = 350 nm (EC = 5700 $cm^{-1}M^{-1}$), Em = 446 nm in water (pH 8).
17. Spectral data are for the reaction product with glycine in the presence of cyanide, measured in pH 7.0 buffer/MeCN (40:60) (Anal Chem 59, 1102 (1987)). Unreacted reagent in MeOH: Abs = 279 nm (EC = 5500 $cm^{-1}M^{-1}$), Em = 330 nm.
18. Spectral data are for the reaction product of P2331MP with alanine and 2-mercaptoethanol. The spectra and stability of the adduct depend on the amine and thiol reactants (Biochim Biophys Acta 576, 440 (1979)). Unreacted reagent in H_2O: Abs = 257 nm (EC = 1000 $cm^{-1}M^{-1}$).

Product List — 1.8 Reagents for Analysis of Low Molecular Weight Amines

Cat #	Product Name	Unit Size
A1139	anthracene-2,3-dicarboxaldehyde (ADA)	25 mg
A176	9-anthracenepropionic acid	100 mg
A448	2-anthracenesulfonyl chloride	100 mg
A2333	ATTO-TAG™ CBQCA Amine-Derivatization Kit	1 kit
A6222	ATTO-TAG™ CBQCA derivatization reagent (CBQCA; 3-(4-carboxybenzoyl)quinoline-2-carboxaldehyde)	10 mg
A2334	ATTO-TAG™ FQ Amine-Derivatization Kit	1 kit
A10192	ATTO-TAG™ FQ derivatization reagent (FQ; 3-(2-furoyl)quinoline-2-carboxaldehyde)	10 mg
B30300	*N*-(*t*-BOC)-aminooxyacetic acid, tetrafluorophenyl ester	25 mg
C20260	4-chloro-7-nitrobenz-2-oxa-1,3-diazole (NBD chloride; 4-chloro-7-nitrobenzofurazan) *FluoroPure™ grade*	100 mg
D1537	4-dimethylaminoazobenzene-4′-sulfonyl chloride (dabsyl chloride)	100 mg
D1332	*N*-(4-(6-dimethylamino-2-benzofuranyl)phenylisothiocyanate	25 mg
D2245	4-((4-(dimethylamino)phenyl)azo)benzoic acid, succinimidyl ester (dabcyl, SE)	100 mg
F2332	fluorescamine	100 mg
F20261	fluorescamine *FluoroPure™ grade*	100 mg
F486	4-fluoro-7-nitrobenz-2-oxa-1,3-diazole (NBD fluoride; 4-fluoro-7-nitrobenzofurazan)	25 mg
M25	*N*-methylisatoic anhydride *high purity*	1 g
N1138	naphthalene-2,3-dicarboxaldehyde (NDA)	100 mg
N316	6-(*N*-(7-nitrobenz-2-oxa-1,3-diazol-4-yl)amino)hexanoic acid (NBD-X)	100 mg
P2331MP	*o*-phthaldialdehyde (OPA) *high purity*	1 g
Q20133	QSY® 35 acetic acid, succinimidyl ester	5 mg
S128	succinimidyl *N*-methylanthranilate	100 mg
S1167	succinimidyl 6-(*N*-(7-nitrobenz-2-oxa-1,3-diazol-4-yl)amino)hexanoate (NBD-X, SE)	25 mg

For current prices or to order online, visit probes.invitrogen.com

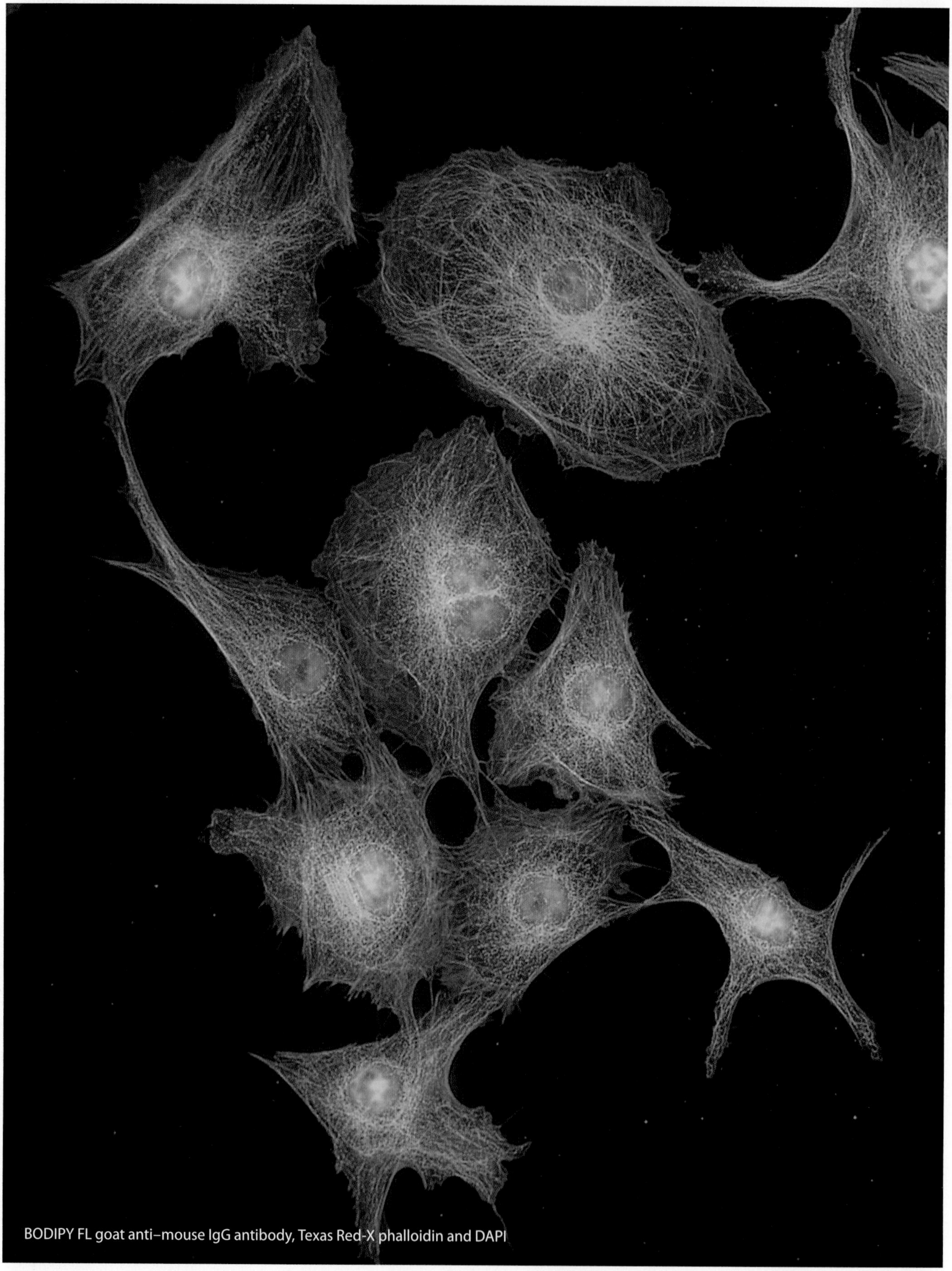

BODIPY FL goat anti–mouse IgG antibody, Texas Red-X phalloidin and DAPI

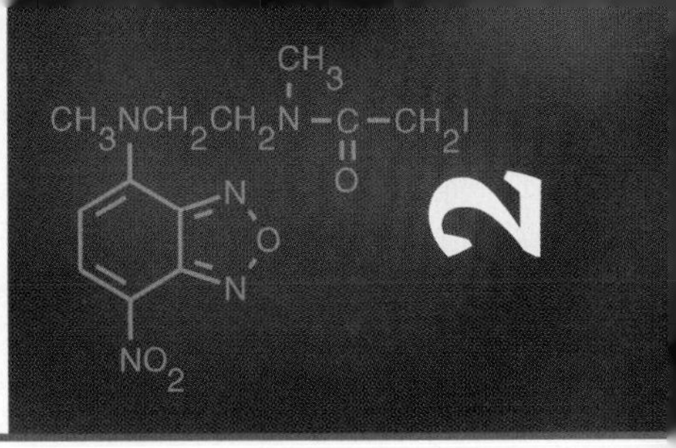

Chapter 2

Thiol-Reactive Probes

2.1 Introduction to Thiol Modification and Detection

Common Applications for Thiol-Reactive Probes

Labeling Biopolymers

In contrast to the amine-reactive reagents described in Chapter 1, thiol-reactive dyes are principally used to prepare fluorescent peptides, proteins and oligonucleotides for probing biological structure, function and interactions. Because the thiol functional group is not very common in most proteins and can be labeled with high selectivity, thiol-reactive reagents often provide a means of selectively modifying a protein at a defined site. Thiol-reactive probes can be used to:

- Analyze the topography of proteins in biological membranes using polar thiol-reactive fluorescent reagents
- Determine distances within the protein or between the protein and a ligand using excited-state energy transfer (see Note 1.2 "Technical Focus: Fluorescence Resonance Energy Transfer (FRET)" in Section 1.3)
- Follow changes in protein conformation using environment-sensitive probes
- Site-selectively label proteins in order to study protein–protein and protein–nucleic acid interactions using fluorescence anisotropy [1] (see Note 1.5 "Technical Focus: Fluorescence Polarization (FP)" in Section 1.4)

Thiol-reactive dyes can also be reacted with thiolated primers for DNA sequencing,[2,3] with thiouridine-modified tRNA for studying its association with protein synthesis machinery [4,5] and with thiol-containing proteins to facilitate their electrophoretic detection.[6]

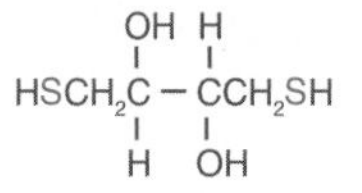

dithiothreitol (DTT)

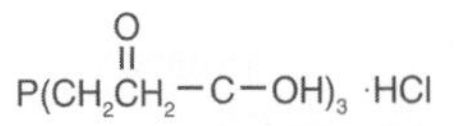

tris-(2-carboxyethyl)phosphine, hydrochloride (TCEP)

Figure 2.1 Structural comparison of the reducing agents DTT and TCEP. Unlike DTT (dithiothreitol, D1532), TCEP (tris-(2-carboxyethyl)phosphine, hydrochloride; T2556) does not contain a free thiol, and therefore does not require removal before reaction with a thiol-reactive probe.

Derivatizing Low Molecular Weight Molecules

Several of the thiol-reactive probes described in this chapter are also useful for derivatizing low molecular weight thiols for various analytical assays that employ chromatographic and electrophoretic separation. An extensive review by Shimada and Mitamura describes the use of several of our thiol-reactive reagents for derivatizing thiol-containing compounds.[7]

Quantitating Thiols

Thiols play a principal role in maintaining the appropriate oxidation–reduction state of proteins, cells and organisms. However, the susceptibility of thiols to oxidation can lead to the formation of disulfides and higher oxidation products, often with loss of biological activity. Measuring the oxidation state of thiols within live cells is complicated by the extraordinarily high concentration of reduced glutathione in cells, which makes them difficult to assay with reagents that stoichiometrically react with the thiol (Section 15.6). However, good reagents and methods have been described for the quantitative assay of thiols (and disulfides) in solution, a few of which are described below.

Reactivity of Thiol Groups

In proteins, thiol groups (also called mercaptans or sulfhydryls) are present in cysteine residues. Thiols can also be generated by selectively reducing cystine disulfides with reagents such as dithiothreitol [8] (DTT, D1532) or 2-mercaptoethanol (β-mercaptoethanol), each of which must then be removed by dialysis or gel filtration before reaction with the thiol-reactive probe.[9] Unfortunately, removal of DTT or 2-mercaptoethanol is sometimes accompanied by air oxidation of the thiols back to the disulfides. Reformation of the disulfide bond can be avoided by using the reducing agent tris-(2-carboxyethyl)phosphine [10,11] (TCEP, T2556), which usually does not need to be removed prior to thiol modification because it does not contain thiols (Figure 2.1); however, TCEP has been reported to react with haloacetamides or maleimides under certain conditions.[10,12,13] TCEP is more stable at a higher pH and at higher temperatures [14] than is DTT and for a longer period of time in buffers without metal chelators such as EGTA; DTT is more stable than TCEP in solutions that contain metal chelators.[10] TCEP

Figure 2.2 Reaction of a thiol with an alkyl halide.

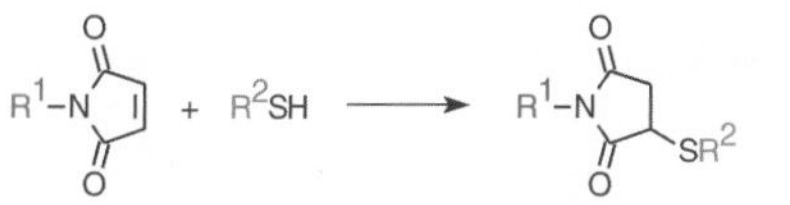

Figure 2.3 Reaction of a thiol with a maleimide.

is also more stable in the presence of Ni^{2+} levels that commonly contaminate proteins eluted from Ni^{2+} affinity columns and that rapidly oxidize DTT.[10] Spin labels in TCEP are two to four times more stable than those in DTT, an advantage for electron paramagnetic resonance (EPR) spectroscopy.[10] In addition, TCEP is used to stabilize solutions of ascorbic acid.[15] TCEP is generally impermeable to cell membranes and to the hydrophobic protein core, permitting its use for the selective reduction of disulfides that have aqueous exposure. The pH-insensitive and less polar phosphine derivative tris-(2-cyanoethyl)phosphine (T6052) may yield greater reactivity with buried disulfides.

The common thiol-reactive functional groups are primarily alkylating reagents, including iodoacetamides, maleimides, benzylic halides and bromomethylketones. Arylating reagents such as NBD halides react with thiols or amines by a similar substitution of the aromatic halide by the nucleophile. Reaction of any of these functional groups with thiols usually proceeds rapidly at or below room temperature in the physiological pH range (pH 6.5–8.0) to yield chemically stable thioethers.

Molecular Probes has introduced both the TS-Link™ and Hg-Link™ series of reagents for reversible thiol modification (Section 2.2, Section 2.3). The TS-Link™ reagents are water-soluble thiosulfates that react stoichiometrically with thiols to form mixed disulfides (Figure 2.9). The Hg-Link™ reagents combine some of our best Alexa Fluor® dyes with organic mercurials to provide reagents that rapidly react with thiols to form fluorescent adducts. Disulfide and mercury–thiol bonds can be reduced by DTT. TCEP reduces disulfides but apparently not mercury–thiol bonds.[14]

Thiols also react with many of the amine-reactive reagents described in Chapter 1, including isothiocyanates and succinimidyl esters. However, the products appear to be insufficiently stable to be useful for routine modification of thiols in proteins. Although the thiol–isothiocyanate product (a dithiocarbamate) can react with an adjacent amine to yield a thiourea, the dithiocarbamate is more likely to react with water, consuming the reactive reagent without forming a covalent adduct.

Several reagents have also been developed for introducing thiols into proteins, nucleic acids and lipids, permitting the use of any of the fluorescent or chromophoric thiol-reactive reagents described in this chapter for their covalent modification. Because the selective introduction of thiols is particularly important for crosslinking two biomolecules, these reagents are discussed in Chapter 5.

Iodoacetamides

Iodoacetamides readily react with all thiols, including those found in peptides, proteins and thiolated polynucleotides, to form thioethers (Figure 2.2); they are somewhat more reactive than bromoacetamides. However, when a protein's cysteine residues are blocked or absent, iodoacetamides can sometimes react with methionine residues.[16,17] They may also react with histidine[18] or tyrosine, but generally only if free thiols are absent. Although iodoacetamides can react with the free base form of amines, most aliphatic amines, except the α-amino group at a protein's N-terminus, are protonated and thus relatively unreactive below pH 8. In addition, iodoacetamides react with thiolated oligonucleotide primers, as well as with thiophosphates and thiouridine residues present in certain nucleic acids,[2,4,5,19] but usually not with the common nucleotides.

Iodoacetamides are intrinsically unstable in light, especially in solution; reactions should therefore be carried out under subdued light. Adding cysteine, glutathione or mercaptosuccinic acid to the reaction mixture will quench the reaction of thiol-reactive probes, forming highly water-soluble adducts that are easily removed by dialysis or gel filtration. Although the thioether bond formed when an iodoacetamide reacts with a protein thiol is very stable, the bioconjugate loses its fluorophore during amino acid hydrolysis, yielding *S*-carboxymethylcysteine.

Maleimides

Maleimides are excellent reagents for thiol-selective modification, quantitation and analysis. In this reaction, the thiol is added across the double bond of the maleimide to yield a thioether (Figure 2.3). Applications of these fluorescent and chromophoric analogs of *N*-ethylmaleimide

(NEM) strongly overlap those of iodoacetamides, although maleimides apparently do not react with methionine, histidine or tyrosine. Reaction of maleimides with amines usually requires a higher pH than reaction of maleimides with thiols. Hydrolysis of the maleimide to an unreactive product can compete significantly with thiol modification, particularly above pH 8. Furthermore, once formed, maleimide adducts can hydrolyze to an isomeric mixture of maleamic acid adducts, which may cause a significant change in the fluorescence properties of the conjugate,[20] or they can ring-open by nucleophilic reaction with an adjacent amine to yield crosslinked products.[21] This latter reaction can potentially be enhanced by raising the pH above 9 after conjugation. Several maleimides — including 7-diethylamino-3-(4′-maleimidylphenyl)-4-methylcoumarin (CPM, D346) and *N*-(7-dimethylamino-4-methylcoumarin-3-yl)maleimide (DACM, D10251), as well as the pyrene and stilbene derivatives — are not appreciably fluorescent until after conjugation with thiols, and may therefore be useful for thiol quantitation.

Other Thiol-Reactive Reagents

A variety of other thiol-reactive probes are available, including alkyl halides and arylating agents (NBD chloride, ABD fluoride) and the fluorescent disulfides BODIPY® FL L-cystine (B20340, Section 2.2, Figure 2.8) and *N,N*′-didansyl-L-cystine (D146, Section 2.3). Symmetric disulfides undergo a thiol–disulfide interchange reaction to yield a new asymmetric disulfide (Figure 2.4), a reaction that is freely reversible and thiol-*specific*. Thiosulfates ($R–S–SO_3^-$), including our water-soluble TS-Link™ reagents (Section 2.2, Section 2.3), are similar to disulfides in that they stoichiometrically react with thiols to form disulfides (Figure 2.9); however, unlike the reaction of the BODIPY® FL cystine and dansyl cystine probes with a free thiol, no excess of the TS-Link™ reagent is required to drive the equilibrium. Similarly, reaction of thiols with the Hg-Link™ phenylmercury reagents does not require excess of the Hg-Link™ reagent and yields a reversible mercury–thiol bond (Figure 2.6). The covalent adducts from the fluorescent cystine, TS-Link™ and Hg-Link™ thiol-reactive probes are, in general, more stable than those from iodoacetamides or maleimides, which are somewhat sensitive to hydrolysis at the amide linkage connecting the fluorophore to its reactive group. Thiol-reactive probes with specialty applications are described in later chapters (see Note 2.1 “Product Highlight: Thiol-Reactive Probes Discussed in Other Chapters of *The Handbook*”).

Reagents for Quantitating Thiols

Thiol and Sulfide Quantitation Kit

Ultrasensitive colorimetric quantitation of both protein and nonprotein thiols is now possible using our Thiol and Sulfide Quantitation Kit (T6060). In this assay, which is based on a method reported by Singh,[22,23] thiols or sulfides reduce a disulfide-inhibited derivative of papain, stoichiometrically releasing the active enzyme (Figure 5.7). Activity of the enzyme is then measured using the chromogenic papain substrate L-BAPNA. Although thiols and inorganic sulfides can also be quantitated using 5,5′-dithiobis-(2-nitrobenzoic acid) (DTNB or Ellman's reagent, D8451), the enzymatic amplification step in the Thiol and Sulfide Quantitation Kit enables researchers to detect as little as 0.2 nanomoles of thiols or sulfides — a sensitivity that is about 100-fold better than that achieved with DTNB. Thiols in proteins and potentially other high molecular weight molecules can be detected indirectly by incorporating the disulfide cystamine into the reaction mixture. Cystamine undergoes an exchange reaction with protein thiols, yielding 2-mercaptoethylamine (cysteamine), which then releases active papain. The Thiol and Sulfide Quantitation Kit contains:

- Papain-$SSCH_3$, the disulfide-inhibited papain derivative
- L-BAPNA, a chromogenic papain substrate
- DTNB (Ellman's reagent), for calibrating the assay
- Cystamine
- L-Cysteine, a thiol standard
- Buffer
- Detailed protocols for measuring thiols, inorganic sulfides and maleimides

$$R^1S\text{-}SR^1 + R^2SH \longrightarrow R^1S\text{-}SR^2 + R^1SH$$

Symmetric disulfide — Mixed disulfide

Figure 2.4 Reaction of a thiol with a symmetric disulfide (e.g., didansyl-L-cystine, D146).

Note 2.1 — Product Highlight

Thiol-Reactive Probes Discussed in Other Chapters of The Handbook

Molecular Probes offers a number of other thiol-reactive probes with special applications. For example, our DetectaGene™ β-galactosidase substrates and our CellTracker™ and MitoTracker® probes are mildly thiol-reactive chloromethyl derivatives that show superior cellular retention when compared with their non-chloromethyl counterparts. These and other thiol-reactive probes are discussed in the chapter appropriate for their application.

- Chapter 4 — Biotin Derivatives and Haptens: Including thiol-reactive biotinylation and haptenylation reagents.
- Chapter 5 — Crosslinking and Photoactivatable Reagents: Including several reagents that contain maleimide groups for crosslinking biomolecules or synthesizing thiol-reactive probes, as well as reagents for introducing thiols into biopolymers.
- Chapter 10 — Enzyme Substrates: Including fluorogenic substrates for glycosidases, proteases and microsomal dealkylase that contain mildly thiol-reactive chloromethyl or pentafluorobenzoyl groups.
- Chapter 12 — Probes for Organelles: Including thiol-reactive MitoTracker® mitochondrion-selective probes.
- Chapter 14 — Fluorescent Tracers of Cell Morphology and Fluid Flow: Including thiol-reactive CellTracker™ probes.
- Chapter 18 — Probes for Reactive Oxygen Species, Including Nitric Oxide: Including a cell-permeant, thiol-reactive derivative of dichlorodihydrofluorescein.
- Chapter 20 — pH Indicators: Including a thiol-reactive, cell-permeant derivative of the SNARF®-1 pH indicator.

Sufficient reagents are provided for approximately 50 assays using standard 1 mL cuvettes or 250 assays using a microplate format. This kit can also be used to detect phosphines, sulfites and cyanide (Section 21.2) with detection limits of about 0.5, 1 and 5 nanomoles, respectively.

Ellman's Reagent (DTNB) for Quantitating Thiols

Ellman's reagent (5,5′-dithiobis-(2-nitrobenzoic acid) or DTNB; D8451) is an important reagent for quantitating thiols in proteins, cells and plasma by absorption measurements.[24] It readily forms a mixed disulfide with thiols, liberating the chromophore 5-mercapto-2-nitrobenzoic acid[25] (absorption maximum 410 nm, $\varepsilon \sim 13{,}600\ cm^{-1}M^{-1}$). Only protein thiols that are accessible to this water-soluble reagent are modified.[26,27] Inaccessible thiols can usually be quantitated by carrying out the titration in the presence of 6 M guanidinium chloride. DTNB conjugates of glutathione and other thiols can be separated by HPLC and quantitated based on their absorbance.[28]

Other Fluorometric Reagents for Quantitating Thiols

Several of the "fluorescent" maleimides described in Section 2.3 actually have very low fluorescence until they react with thiols to form fluorescent adducts, permitting their use for both the quantitation of thiols and their semiquantitative localization in cellular organelles. Monobromobimane (M1378, M20381; Section 2.3) is also essentially nonfluorescent until it reacts with thiols and can be used for their quantitation.

In addition, most of the fluorescent thiol-reactive reagents in this chapter can be used as derivatization reagents for analyzing thiols by techniques such as HPLC that utilize a separation step. 5-(Bromomethyl)fluorescein (B1355, Section 2.2) is the reagent with the greatest intrinsic sensitivity for this application. See Section 15.6 for a further discussion of methods to quantitate reduced glutathione in cells.

References

1. Anal Biochem 308, 18 (2002); **2.** Nucleic Acids Res 16, 2203 (1988); **3.** Nucleic Acids Res 15, 4593 (1987); **4.** Biochemistry 24, 692 (1985); **5.** J Mol Biol 156, 113 (1982); **6.** Anal Biochem 160, 376 (1987); **7.** J Chromatogr B Biomed Appl 659, 227 (1994); **8.** Eur J Biochem 168, 169 (1987); **9.** Methods Enzymol 143, 246 (1987); **10.** Anal Biochem 273, 73 (1999); **11.** J Org Chem 56, 2648 (1991); **12.** Anal Biochem 318, 325 (2003); **13.** Anal Biochem 282, 161 (2000); **14.** Anal Biochem 325, 137 (2004); **15.** Anal Biochem 282, 89 (2000); **16.** Biochemistry 25, 5036 (1986); **17.** Biochemistry 25, 4887 (1986); **18.** Biochemistry 20, 7021 (1981); **19.** Biochemistry 22, 1208 (1983); **20.** Biophys J 50, 75 (1986); **21.** Biochemistry 15, 2863 (1976); **22.** Bioconjug Chem 5, 348 (1994); **23.** Anal Biochem 213, 49 (1993); **24.** Biochem J 89, 296 (1963); **25.** Methods Enzymol 233, 380 (1994); **26.** Methods Enzymol 143, 44 (1987); **27.** Methods Enzymol 91, 49 (1983); **28.** Anal Biochem 138, 95 (1984).

Data Table — 2.1 Introduction to Thiol Modification and Detection

Cat #	MW	Storage	Soluble	Abs	Em
D1532	154.24	D	H_2O	<300	none
D8451	396.35	D	pH >6	324	none
T2556	286.65	D	pH >5	<300	none
T6052	193.19	D	MeCN	<300	none

For definitions of the contents of this data table, see "Navigating *The Handbook*" in the introductory pages.

Product List — 2.1 Introduction to Thiol Modification and Detection

Cat #	Product Name	Unit Size
D8451	5,5′-dithiobis-(2-nitrobenzoic acid) (DTNB; Ellman's reagent)	10 g
D1532	dithiothreitol (DTT)	1 g
T6060	Thiol and Sulfide Quantitation Kit *50-250 assays*	1 kit
T2556	tris-(2-carboxyethyl)phosphine, hydrochloride (TCEP)	1 g
T6052	tris-(2-cyanoethyl)phosphine	1 g

For current prices or to order online, visit probes.invitrogen.com

2.2 Thiol-Reactive Probes Excited with Visible Light

Among all the thiol-reactive probes, the Alexa Fluor®, BODIPY®, fluorescein, Oregon Green®, tetramethylrhodamine and Texas Red® derivatives have the strongest absorptivity and highest fluorescence quantum yields. This combination of attributes makes these compounds the preferred reagents for preparing protein and low molecular weight ligand conjugates to study the diffusion, structural properties and interactions of proteins and ligands using techniques such as:

- Fluorescence recovery after photobleaching (FRAP)
- Fluorescence polarization (FP) (see Note 1.5 "Technical Focus: Fluorescence Polarization (FP)" in Section 1.4)
- Fluorescence correlation spectroscopy (FCS) (see Note 1.4 "Technical Focus: Fluorescence Correlation Spectroscopy (FCS)" in Section 1.3)
- Fluorescence resonance energy transfer (FRET) (see Note 1.2 "Technical Focus: Fluorescence Resonance Energy Transfer (FRET)" in Section 1.3)

In this section and in Section 2.3, thiol-reactive reagents with similar spectra, rather than the same reactive group, are generally discussed together. The probes described in this section have visible absorption maxima beyond 410 nm; thiol-reactive probes with peak absorption below 410 nm are described in Section 2.3. Table 2.1 summarizes this section's thiol-reactive probes excited with visible light.

Table 2.1 — Thiol-reactive dyes excited with visible light

Derivative	Abs *	Em *	Maleimide	Haloacetamide	Bromomethyl	Halide
Alexa Fluor® 488	495	519	A10254^M			
Alexa Fluor® 532	532	553	A10255			
Alexa Fluor® 546	556	575	A10258^M			
Alexa Fluor® 568	578	603	A20341^M			
Alexa Fluor® 594	590	617	A10256^M			
Alexa Fluor® 555	555	565	A20346			
Alexa Fluor® 633	632	647	A20342^M			
Alexa Fluor® 647	650	665	A20347			
Alexa Fluor® 660	663	690	A20343			
Alexa Fluor® 680	679	702	A20344			
BODIPY® FL	505	513	B10250	D6003		
BODIPY® TMR	544	570		D6012		
BODIPY® 493/503	493	503			B2103	
BODIPY® 499/508	499	508	D20350			
BODIPY® 507/545	508	543		D6004		
BODIPY® 530/550	534	554		D2006		
BODIPY® 577/618	577	618	D20351			
BODIPY® 630/650	625	640			B22802	
4-Dimethylaminophenylazophenyl	419	NA	D1521			
Eosin	524	544	E118^5	E30450^5		
Fluo-4	494	516		F36200		
Fluorescein	494	518	F150^5	I30451^5, I30452^6	B1355^5	
Lucifer yellow	426	531		L1338		
NBD	478	541		I9 †, D2004		F486, F6053 ‡, C20260
Oregon Green® 488	496	524	O6034^5	O6010^M		
PyMPO	415	570	M6026			
QSY® 7	560	NA	Q10257			
QSY® 35	475	NA		Q20348		
Rhodamine Red™	570	590	R6029^M			
Sulfonerhodamine	555	580		B10621 §		
Tetramethylrhodamine	555	580	T6027^5 T6028^6	T6006^5		
Texas Red®	595	615	T6008^M		T6009^M	

* Absorption (Abs) and emission (Em) maxima, in nm. † Iodoacetate ester. ‡ Like the NBD probes, ABD-F (F6053) is a benz-2-oxa-1,3-diazole, except that it is sulfonated (i.e., an SBD probe) instead of nitrated (i.e., an NBD probe); its reaction product with dimethylaminoethanethiol has abs/em maxima of 376/510 nm. § Bifunctional crosslinker. 5 = 5-Isomer. 6 = 6-Isomer. M = Mixed isomers. NA = Not applicable.

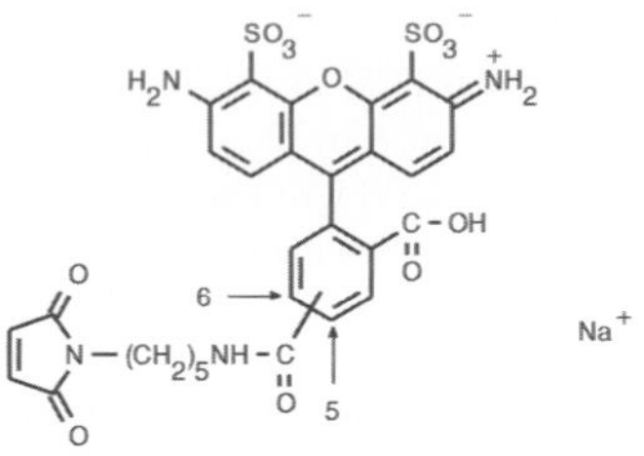

Figure 2.5 A10254 Alexa Fluor® 488 C_5-maleimide.

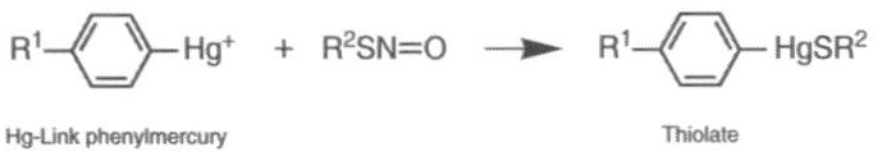

Figure 2.6 Reaction of an Hg-Link™ phenylmercury compound with a nitrosylated thiol.

Alexa Fluor® Derivatives

Alexa Fluor® Maleimides

Molecular Probes' patented Alexa Fluor® dyes set new standards for fluorescent dyes and the bioconjugates prepared from them (see Note 1.1 "Product Highlight: The Alexa Fluor® Dye Series — Peak Performance across the Visible Spectrum" in Section 1.3). The Alexa Fluor® dyes exhibit several unique features:

- Strong absorption, with extinction coefficients greater than 65,000 $cm^{-1}M^{-1}$
- Excellent photostability (Figure 1.9, Figure 1.28), providing more time for observation and image capture than spectrally similar dyes allow (Figure 1.10, Figure 1.11)
- pH-insensitive fluorescence between pH 4 and 10
- Superior fluorescence output per protein conjugate, surpassing that of any other spectrally similar fluorophore-labeled protein, including fluorescein, tetramethylrhodamine, Cy3, Cy5 and Texas Red® conjugates [1]

For labeling thiol groups, we offer thiol-reactive Alexa Fluor® dyes that span the visible spectrum:

- Alexa Fluor® 350 C_5-maleimide (A20380, Section 2.3)
- Alexa Fluor® 405 C_5-maleimide (A30458, Section 2.3)
- Alexa Fluor® 488 C_5-maleimide [2–5] (A10254, Figure 2.5)
- Alexa Fluor® 532 C_5-maleimide (A10255)
- Alexa Fluor® 546 C_5-maleimide [2,6] (A10258)
- Alexa Fluor® 555 C_2 maleimide (A20346)
- Alexa Fluor® 568 C_5-maleimide (A20341)
- Alexa Fluor® 594 C_5-maleimide [7–9] (A10256)
- Alexa Fluor® 633 C_5-maleimide (A20342)
- Alexa Fluor® 647 C_2-maleimide (A20347)
- Alexa Fluor® 660 C_2-maleimide (A20343)
- Alexa Fluor® 680 C_2-maleimide (A20344)

The Alexa Fluor® maleimides are particularly useful for labeling thiol-containing proteins on the surface of live cells, where their polarity permits the sensitive detection of exposed thiols.[3,10] Subsequent to labeling, the Alexa Fluor® protein conjugates can be electrophoretically separated and then detected without additional staining. In addition, protein labeling with Alexa Fluor® 488 C_5-maleimide has been used to investigate the thermodynamics of protein–protein interactions by fluorescence anisotropy.[11]

Hg-Link™ Alexa Fluor® Phenylmercury Reagents

The Hg-Link™ Alexa Fluor® reagents are phenylmercury compounds that react with thiol groups to form stable mercury–thiol bonds. This reaction occurs under the same conditions used for maleimide and iodoacetamide reactions with thiols, but unlike maleimides and iodoacetamides, Hg-Link™ reagents can react with nitrosylated thiols [12] (SNO) (Saville reaction, Figure 2.6). Furthermore, in contrast to the stable thioether bond formed by iodoacetamides and maleimides, the mercury–thiol bond is reversible with 0.1 M HCl [13] or reducing agents such as 50 mM DTT; however, it is apparently not reduced by TCEP.[14] Alexa Fluor® Hg-Link™ reagents also react faster with thiols than do the commonly used thiol-reactive *N*-ethylmaleimide (NEM) and the chromogenic disulfide DTNB [15] (Ellman's reagent). We currently offer:

- Hg-Link™ Alexa Fluor® 350 phenylmercury (H30460, Section 2.3)
- Hg-Link™ Alexa Fluor® 405 phenylmercury (H30461, Section 2.3)
- Hg-Link™ Alexa Fluor® 488 phenylmercury (H30462)
- Hg-Link™ Alexa Fluor® 555 phenylmercury (H30463)
- Hg-Link™ Alexa Fluor® 594 phenylmercury (H30464)
- Hg-Link™ Alexa Fluor® 647 phenylmercury (H30465)

Nitrosylation has important biological effects — for example, nitrosylation of cysteine residues in caspases and in HIV-1 protease inhibits the activity of these enzymes [16] — making SNO detection useful in the study of several disease states. Although antibodies to nitrosothiols are employed for SNO detection, Hg-Link™ Alexa Fluor® dyes could potentially be used for direct SNO detection in gels, cells and tissues. A nonfluorescent thiol-reactive compound such as NEM could first be used to block free sulfhydryls, and then a fluorescent Hg-Link™ reagent could be used to label the SNO-modified proteins and peptides. Because the binding of Hg-Link™ reagents is reversible, SNO modification could still be confirmed with an appropriate antibody.

The Hg-Link™ Alexa Fluor® reagents may also be useful for the sensitive detection of homocysteine levels in urine. With higher extinction coefficients and longer wavelengths than the UV-excitable fluorophore dansyl, which is commonly used to detect homocysteine,[17] Alexa Fluor® Hg-Link™ reagents are less affected by autofluorescence from proteins and other biomolecules. Elevated homocysteine levels are an indicator of cardiovascular disease and vitamin B_{12} deficiency.[18]

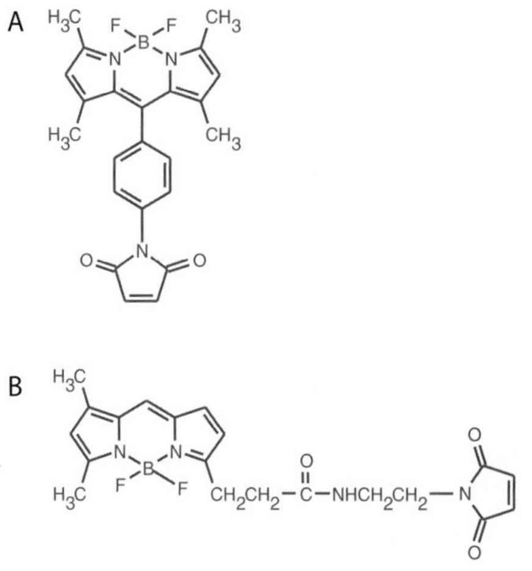

Figure 2.7 Comparison of the fluorophore orientation relative to the reactive moiety of two spectrally similar thiol-reactive BODIPY® dyes, A) BODIPY® 499/508 maleimide (D20350) and B) BODIPY® FL N-(2-aminoethyl)maleimide (B10250).

BODIPY® Derivatives

BODIPY® Maleimides, Iodoacetamides and Methyl Bromides

Like their amine-reactive BODIPY® counterparts (Section 1.4), BODIPY® iodoacetamides, BODIPY® maleimides and BODIPY® methyl bromides yield thiol adducts with several important properties:

- High extinction coefficients (ε >60,000 $cm^{-1}M^{-1}$)
- High fluorescence quantum yields, often approaching 1.0, even in water
- Narrow emission bandwidths (Figure 1.43)
- Good photostability
- Spectra that are relatively insensitive to solvent polarity and insensitive to the pH of the medium [19]
- Lack of ionic charge, which is especially useful when preparing membrane probes and cell-permeant reagents

Our selection of patented thiol-reactive BODIPY® reagents includes:

- BODIPY® FL maleimide and BODIPY® FL iodoacetamide [20–23] (B10250, Figure 2.7; D6003), which exhibit spectral characteristics very similar to fluorescein
- BODIPY® 507/545 iodoacetamide (D6004)
- BODIPY® 530/550 iodoacetamide [23] (D2006)
- BODIPY® TMR cadaverine iodoacetamide (D6012)
- BODIPY® 493/503 methyl bromide [23] (B2103)
- BODIPY® 630/650 methyl bromide (B22802), with very long-wavelength spectra

Two additional symmetric maleimidylphenyl BODIPY® derivatives are available with excitation/emission maxima of ~499/508 nm (D20350, Figure 2.7) or ~577/618 nm (D20351). All of the thiol-reactive BODIPY® probes are suitable for labeling cysteine residues in proteins and thiolated oligonucleotides and for detecting thiol conjugates separated by HPLC and capillary electrophoresis using ultrasensitive laser-scanning techniques.[19] The BODIPY® probes are chemically stable between about pH 3 and pH 10, although they are less stable to extremes of pH than are fluorescein and Alexa Fluor® derivatives.

BODIPY® FL L-Cystine

We have attached the BODIPY® FL fluorophore to the amino groups of the disulfide-linked amino acid cystine to create a reagent for reversible, thiol-specific labeling of proteins, thiolated oligonucleotides and cells.[24] BODIPY® FL L-cystine (B20340) is virtually nonfluorescent due to interactions between the two fluorophores; however, thiol-specific exchange to form a mixed disulfide results in significant enhancement of the green fluorescence (Figure 2.8).

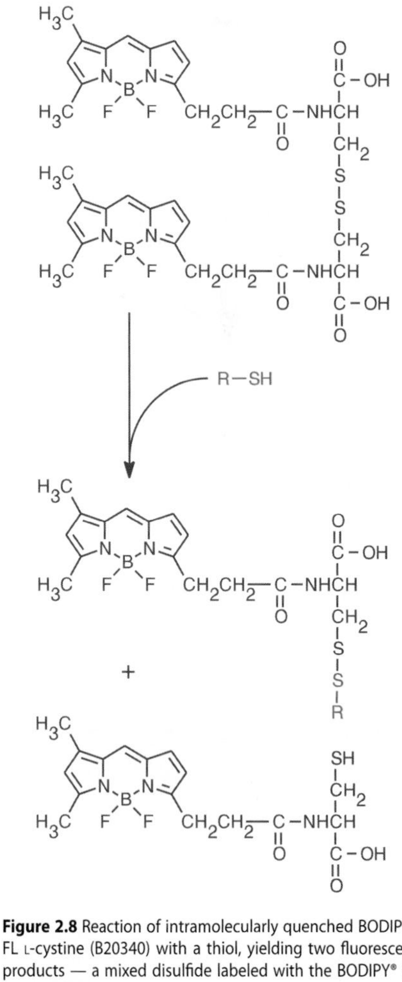

Figure 2.8 Reaction of intramolecularly quenched BODIPY® FL L-cystine (B20340) with a thiol, yielding two fluorescent products — a mixed disulfide labeled with the BODIPY® FL dye and a BODIPY® FL cysteine derivative.

TS-Link™ BODIPY® Thiosulfate Reagents

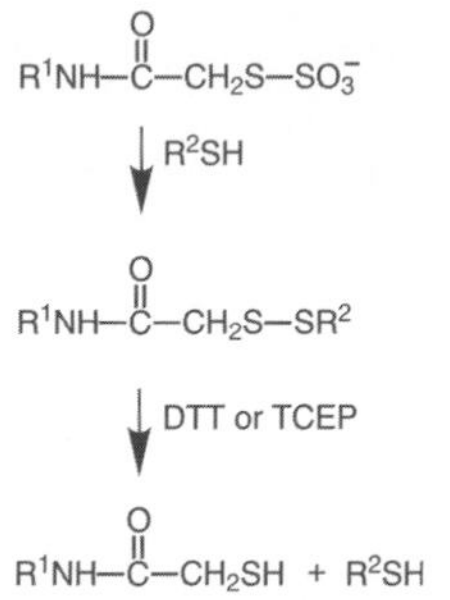

Figure 2.9 Reaction of a TS-Link™ reagent with a thiol, followed by removal of the label with a reducing agent.

The TS-Link™ BODIPY® reagents are water-soluble thiosulfates that react readily and selectively with free thiols to form disulfide bonds (Figure 2.9). In contrast to the thioether bonds formed by maleimides and iodoacetamides, the disulfide bond formed by the TS-Link™ reagents is reversible — the TS-Link™ BODIPY® fluorophore can easily be removed using a reducing agent such as dithiothreitol (DTT, D1532; Section 2.1) or tris-(2-carboxyethyl)phosphine (TCEP, T2556; Section 2.1), leaving the molecule of interest unchanged. These TS-Link™ reagents yield the same disulfide products as methanethiosulfonates [25] (MTS reagents), but they are much more polar and water soluble and may therefore selectively react with residues on the surface of a protein or live cell. We currently offer:

- TS-Link™ BODIPY® FL C_2-thiosulfate (T30453)
- TS-Link™ BODIPY® TMR C_5-thiosulfate (T30454)
- TS-Link™ BODIPY® TR C_5-thiosulfate (T30455)
- TS-Link™ BODIPY® 630/650 C_5-thiosulfate (T30456)

We also offer TS-Link™ bimane thiosulfate (T30502, Section 2.3), TS-Link™ DSB-X™ biotin C_5-thiosulfate (TS-Link™ desthiobiotin-X C_5-thiosulfate, T30754; Section 4.2) and TS-Link™ TFP-X thiosulfate (T30875, Section 5.2).

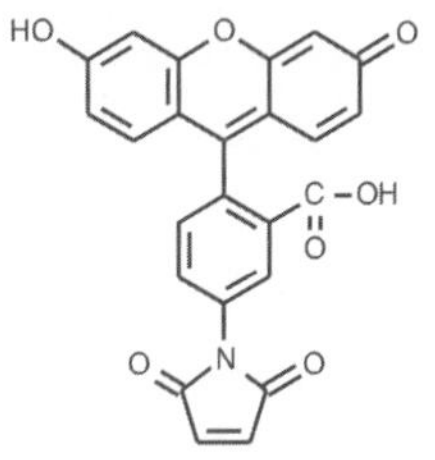

Figure 2.10 F150 fluorescein-5-maleimide.

Fluorescein Derivatives, Including Thiol-Reactive Oregon Green® Dyes

Fluorescein Derivatives

The excellent water solubility of the fluorescein iodoacetamide single isomers (I30451, I30452) and fluorescein-5-maleimide (F150, Figure 2.10) at pH 7 makes it easy to prepare green-fluorescent thiol conjugates of biomolecules. Fluorescein maleimide and 5-iodoacetamidofluorescein (one of the five original products offered by Molecular Probes when it started business in 1975) have been the most extensively used visible wavelength–excitable, thiol-reactive dyes for modification of proteins, nucleic acids and other biopolymers. Following conjugation to thiols, fluorescein-5-maleimide (and other fluoresceins) can be radioiodinated.[26] When compared with these iodoacetamide and maleimide derivatives, 5-(bromomethyl)fluorescein (B1355, Figure 2.11) reacts more slowly with thiols of peptides, proteins and thiolated nucleic acids but forms stronger thioether bonds that are expected to remain stable under the conditions required for complete amino acid analysis. With the possible exception of our Alexa Fluor® maleimides and the thiol-reactive BODIPY® dyes described above, 5-(bromomethyl)fluorescein has the highest intrinsic detectability of all thiol-reactive probes, particularly for instrumentation that uses the 488 nm spectral line of the argon-ion laser. Furthermore, its negative charges should make capillary electrophoretic separation of 5-bromomethylfluorescein adducts possible.

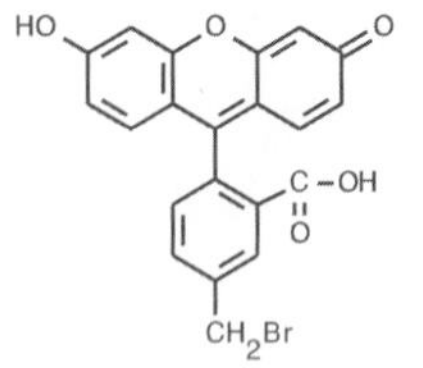

Figure 2.11 B1355 5-(bromomethyl)fluorescein.

Oregon Green® 488 Derivatives

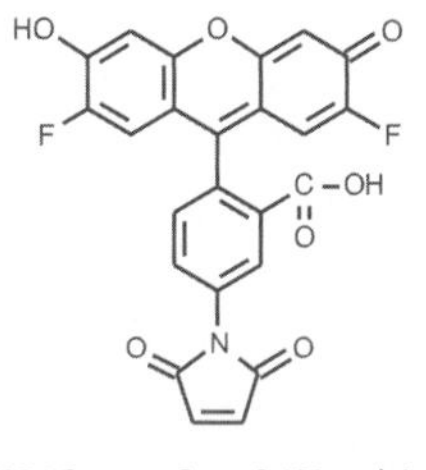

Figure 2.12 O6034 Oregon Green® 488 maleimide.

One of our fluorescein substitutes — the Oregon Green® 488 dye (2′,7′-difluorofluorescein, D6145; Section 1.5) — has absorption and emission spectra that are a perfect match to those of fluorescein. In addition to the Oregon Green® 488 isothiocyanate, carboxylic acid and succinimidyl ester derivatives (Section 1.5), we have synthesized the isomeric mixture of Oregon Green® 488 iodoacetamide (O6010) and the single-isomer Oregon Green® 488 maleimide (O6034, Figure 2.12). These thiol-reactive probes yield conjugates that have several important advantages when directly compared with fluorescein conjugates, including:

- Greater photostability (Figure 1.46)
- A lower pK_a (pK_a of 4.8 for 2′,7′-difluorofluorescein versus 6.4 for fluorescein) (Figure 1.12)
- Higher fluorescence and less quenching at comparable degrees of substitution (Figure 1.54)
- Utility as fluorescence anisotropy probes for measuring protein–protein and protein–nucleic acid interactions [11] (see Note 1.5 "Technical Focus: Fluorescence Polarization (FP)" in Section 1.4)

Fluo-4 Iodoacetamide: A Thiol-Reactive Calcium Indicator

To create unique fluorescent Ca^{2+}-sensitive probes, we offer a thiol-reactive Ca^{2+} indicator — fluo-4 iodoacetamide (F36200) — that can react with sulfhydryl groups on proteins, peptides and thiol-modified surfaces. The fluo-4 Ca^{2+} indicator is an analog of the fluo-3 Ca^{2+} indicator with the two chlorine substituents replaced by fluorines (Section 19.3). This fairly minor structural modification results in increased fluorescence excitation at 488 nm and consequently higher signal levels for confocal laser-scanning microscopy, flow cytometry and microplate screening applications.

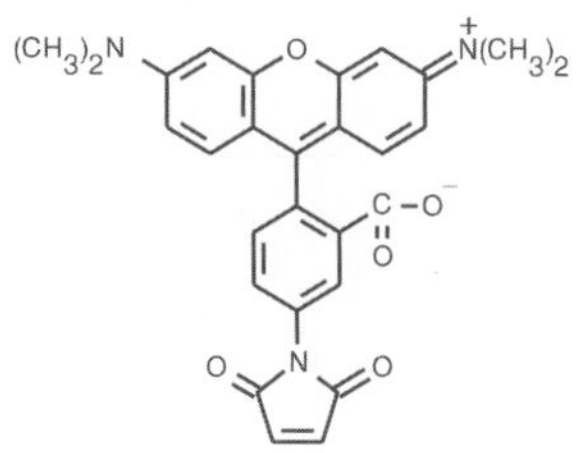

Figure 2.13 T6027 tetramethylrhodamine-5-maleimide.

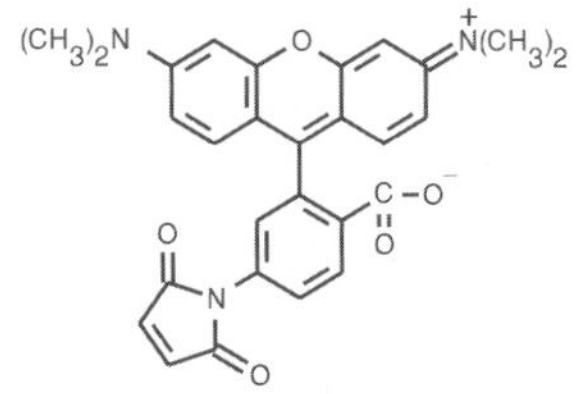

Figure 2.14 T6028 tetramethylrhodamine-6-maleimide.

Eosin Derivatives

Although eosin iodoacetamide (E30450) and eosin maleimide (E118) are much less fluorescent than the corresponding fluorescein derivatives, they are more phosphorescent and better photosensitizers.[27] With eosin's high quantum yield of 0.57 for singlet oxygen generation,[28–30] eosin conjugates can be used as effective photooxidizers of diaminobenzidine (DAB) in high-resolution electron microscopy studies[31,32] (see Note 14.2 "Product Highlight: Fluorescent Probes for Photoconversion of Diaminobenzidine Reagents" in Section 14.3).

Currently, the principal application of eosin conjugates, including those prepared with the thiol-reactive derivatives in this chapter and the amine-reactive derivatives in Section 1.5, is to follow localized rotational motions in proteins, protein assemblies and proteins in membranes using phosphorescence anisotropy.[33–35] Eosin (excitation/emission maxima ~519/540 nm) derivatives efficiently absorb the fluorescence from fluorescein and other fluorophores such as the BODIPY® FL, Alexa Fluor® 488, Oregon Green® 488, dansyl and coumarin dyes, making them good acceptors in FRET techniques[36] (see Note 1.2 "Technical Focus: Fluorescence Resonance Energy Transfer (FRET)" in Section 1.3). Although usually selectively reactive with thiols, eosin maleimide reportedly also reacts with a specific lysine residue of the band-3 protein in human erythrocytes, inhibiting anion exchange in these cells.[37,38]

Rhodamine Derivatives, Including Thiol-Reactive Texas Red® Dyes

Tetramethylrhodamine Derivatives

Tetramethylrhodamine iodoacetamide (TMRIA) and tetramethylrhodamine maleimide yield photostable, pH-insensitive, red-orange–fluorescent thiol conjugates.[39,40] However, the iodoacetamide and maleimide derivatives are difficult to prepare in pure form and different batches of our mixed-isomer products have contained variable mixtures of the 5- and 6-isomers. Apparently certain cytoskeletal proteins preferentially react with individual isomers, leading to complications in the interpretation of labeling results.[41–44] Consequently, we now prepare the 5-isomer of TMRIA (T6006) and the 5-isomer (T6027, Figure 2.13) and 6-isomer (T6028, Figure 2.14) of tetramethylrhodamine maleimide. TMRIA is reported to predominantly label SH-1 (Cys-707) of the myosin heavy chain in skinned muscle fibers.[45] The product bibliographies for the single-isomer preparations of TMRIA and tetramethylrhodamine maleimide contain literature references for both the corresponding single-isomer and mixed-isomer products.

A Rhodamine-Based Crosslinking Reagent

The thiol-reactive homobifunctional crosslinker bis-((*N*-iodoacetyl)piperazinyl)sulfonerhodamine (B10621) is derived from a relatively rigid rhodamine dye (Figure 5.8). This crosslinker, which is similar to a thiol-reactive rhodamine-based crosslinking reagent that was used to label regulatory light-chains of chicken gizzard myosin for fluorescence polarization experiments,[46] should also be useful for proximity studies. Researchers have attached bis-((*N*-iodoacetyl)pipe razinyl)sulfonerhodamine to the kinesin motor domain and then, using polarized fluorescence microscopy, have determined the orientation of kinesin bound to microtubules in the presence of a nonhydrolyzable ATP analog.[47]

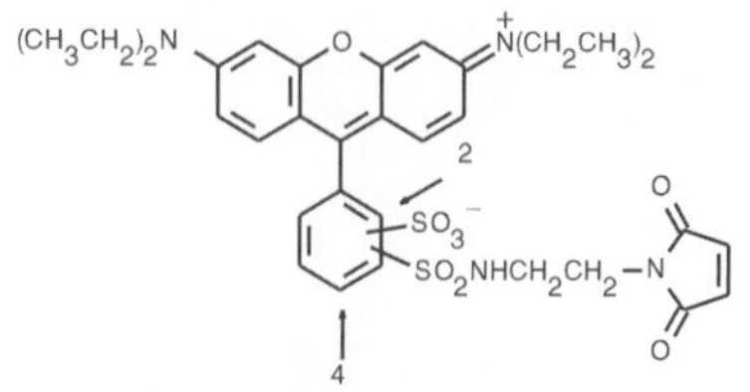

Figure 2.15 R6029 Rhodamine Red C_2-maleimide.

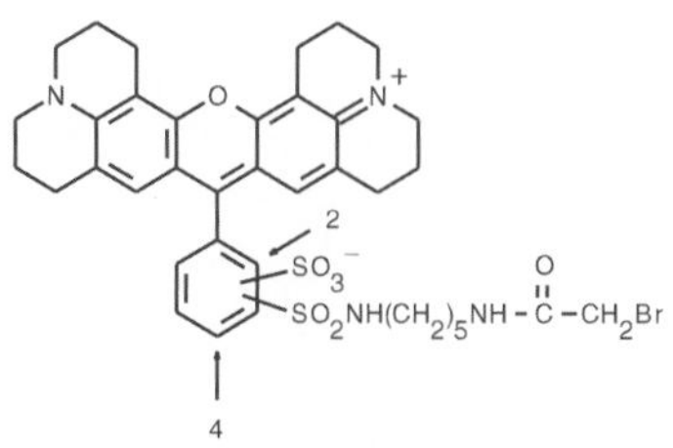

Figure 2.16 T6009 Texas Red® C_5-bromoacetamide.

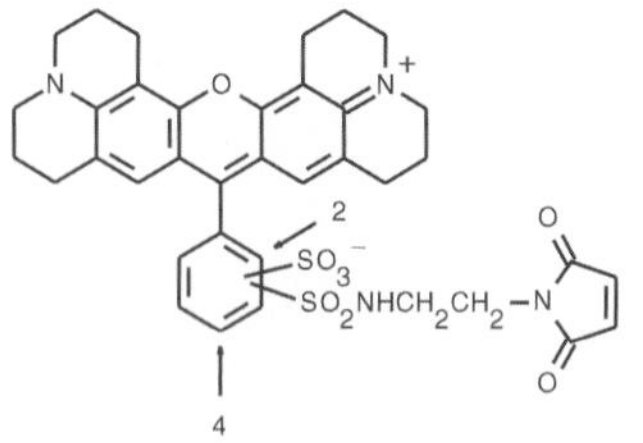

Figure 2.17 T6008 Texas Red® C_2-maleimide.

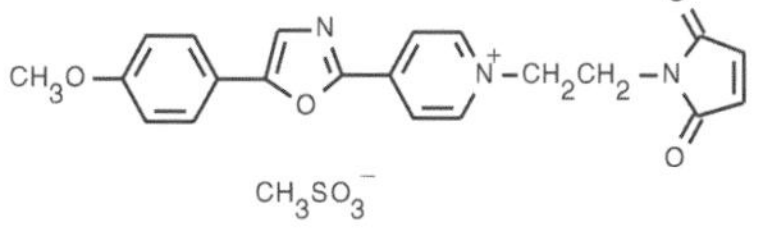

Figure 2.18 M6026 1-(2-maleimidylethyl)-4-(5-(4-methoxyphenyl)oxazol-2-yl)pyridinium methanesulfonate (PyMPO maleimide).

Rhodamine Red™ Derivative

We offer a maleimide derivative of our Rhodamine Red™ fluorophore (R6029), which is a preferred dye for excitation (Figure 7.25) by the 568 nm spectral line of the Ar–Kr mixed-gas laser used in some confocal laser-scanning microscopes. This maleimide is a mixture of two isomeric sulfonamides (Figure 2.15).

Texas Red® Derivatives

Conjugates of the bromoacetamide and maleimide derivatives of our Texas Red® fluorophore (T6009, T6008) have very little spectral overlap with fluorescein or Alexa Fluor® 488 conjugates, yet can be excited by the 568 nm spectral line of the Ar–Kr mixed-gas laser (Figure 1.74). Thus, Texas Red® conjugates are useful as a second label in multicolor applications or as energy transfer acceptors from green-fluorescent dyes. Bromoacetamides are only slightly less reactive with thiols than are iodoacetamides. The Texas Red® bromoacetamide (Figure 2.16) and maleimide (Figure 2.17) derivatives are mixtures of the corresponding two isomeric sulfonamides.

Pyridyloxazole Derivatives

The pyridyloxazole derivatives — including the thiol-reactive maleimide [48,49] (M6026, Figure 2.18) and the amine-reactive succinimidyl ester (PyMPO, SE; S6110) — fill the spectral gap between UV-excited dyes and the fluoresceins. These derivatives of the laser dye PyMPO exhibit environment-sensitive fluorescence spectra, absorption maxima near 415 nm and unusually high Stokes shifts, with emission at ~560–580 nm.[50]

Benzoxadiazole Derivatives, Including NBD Probes

NBD Chloride and NBD Fluoride

Benz-2-oxa-1,3-diazoles (also called benzofurazans) are a diverse group of reactive dyes that include both nitrated derivatives of the NBD series and sulfonated analogs of the SBD series. NBD chloride (FluoroPure™ Grade, C20260; Figure 3.2) and the more reactive NBD fluoride (F486) are common reagents for amine modification (Section 1.8). However, they also react with thiols [51–53] and cysteine in several proteins [54–58] to yield thioethers. NBD conjugates of thiols usually have much shorter-wavelength absorption and weaker fluorescence than do NBD conjugates of amines.[53] Selective modification of cysteines in the presence of reactive lysines and tyrosines is promoted by carrying out the reaction at pH <7;[59,60] however, NBD conjugates of thiols are often unstable, resulting in time-dependent label migration to adjacent lysine residues.[53,60]

ABD-F: An SBD Probe

Thiol conjugates of the SBD probe 7-fluorobenz-2-oxa-1,3-diazole-4-sulfonamide [61,62] (ABD-F, F6053) are much more stable in aqueous solution than are the thiol conjugates prepared from NBD chloride or NBD fluoride.[61] ABD-F is nonfluorescent until reacted with thiols and therefore can be used to quantitate thiols in solution,[63] as well as thiols separated by HPLC [64] or TLC.[65] ABD-F also reportedly reacts slowly with the hydroxy group of some tyrosine residues as well as α-amino groups in some proteins, forming products that are nonfluorescent but can be detected by absorbance at 385 nm.[66] ABD-F labels the thiols of thionein only in the presence of the chelating agent EDTA, which removes the bound Zn^{2+} ions.[67] ABD–cysteine conjugates are very stable to acid hydrolysis but labeling is partially reversed in basic solution containing DTT [68,69] (D1532; Section 2.1). ABD-F can also be combined with tributylphosphine for the determination of disulfides in peptides and proteins.[70–72] As possible alternatives to the malodorous tributylphosphine, we recommend tris-(2-carboxyethyl)phosphine (TCEP, T2556; Section 2.1), which selectively reduces only those disulfides located on protein or live-cell surfaces due to its high polarity, or the less polar tris-(2-cyanoethyl)phosphine (T6052, Section 2.1).

IANBD Ester and IANBD Amide

When conjugating the NBD fluorophore to thiols located in hydrophobic sites of proteins, we recommend using the NBD iodoacetate ester (IANBD ester, I9) or, preferably, the more hydrolytically stable NBD iodoacetamide[73] (IANBD amide, D2004; Figure 2.19). These reactive reagents exhibit appreciable fluorescence only after reaction with thiols that are buried or unsolvated, and this fluorescence is highly sensitive to changes in the solvation level of the fluorophore.

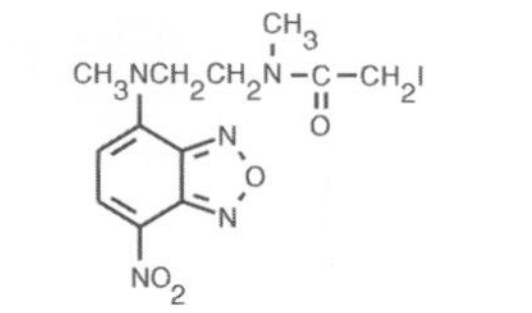

Figure 2.19 D2004 *N,N'*-dimethyl-*N*-(iodoacetyl)-*N'*-(7-nitrobenz-2-oxa-1,3-diazol-4-yl)ethylenediamine (IANBD amide).

Lucifer Yellow Iodoacetamide

Lucifer yellow CH is a well-known polar tracer for neurons (Section 14.3). Its iodoacetamide derivative (L1338) similarly has high water solubility and visible absorption and emission spectra similar to those of lucifer yellow CH (Figure 2.20, Figure 14.24). As with our Alexa Fluor® maleimides (see above) and the stilbene iodoacetamide and maleimide (A484, A485; Section 2.3), a principal application of lucifer yellow iodoacetamide is the labeling of exposed thiols of proteins in solution, as well as in the outer membrane of live cells.[74–76] Lucifer yellow iodoacetamide has also been used as a fluorescence energy acceptor from stilbene iodoacetamide to follow subunit assembly of α-crystallin.[77]

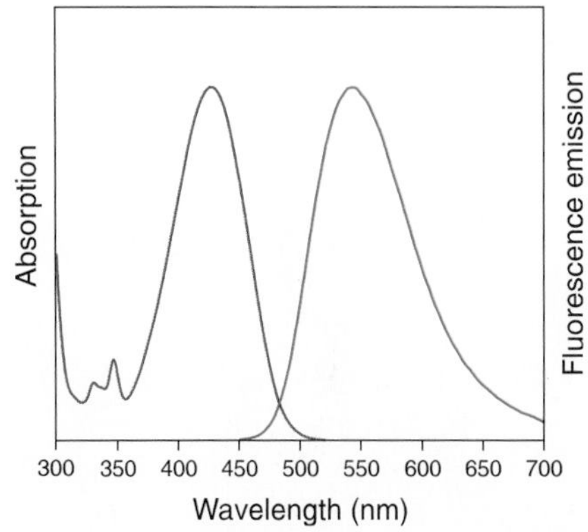

Figure 2.20 Absorption and fluorescence emission spectra of lucifer yellow CH in water.

Chromophoric Maleimides and Iodoacetamides

QSY® 7 C_5-maleimide[78] (Q10257, Figure 2.21) and QSY® 9 C_5-maleimide (Q30457) are essentially nonfluorescent, thiol-reactive diarylrhodamines with absorption spectra similar to those of our QSY® 7 and QSY® 9 succinimidyl esters (Q10193, Q20131; Section 1.6; Figure 1.70), respectively; the QSY® 7 and QSY® 9 chromophores are spectrally similar but the QSY® 9 dye exhibits enhanced water solubility. The principal applications of these QSY® maleimides are as quenchers for fluorescent donor dyes in FRET studies (see Note 1.2 "Technical Focus: Fluorescence Resonance Energy Transfer (FRET)" in Section 1.3). Most FRET detection is based on the interaction between fluorescent donor and acceptor dyes. However, the use of nonfluorescent acceptor dyes avoids the background fluorescence that often results from direct (i.e., nonsensitized) excitation of the acceptor dye. The broad and strong absorption of the QSY® 7 and QSY® 9 dyes in the visible-light spectrum (absorption maximum ~560 nm, ε ~90,000 $cm^{-1}M^{-1}$) yields extraordinarily efficient quenching of donors that have blue, green, orange or red fluorescence at relatively long spatial separations (Table 1.10). A QSY® 7 amine derivative for modifying carboxylic acids (Q10464, Figure 3.25) is described in Section 3.3. We also have prepared a QSY® 7 derivative of α-FMOC lysine (Q21930, Section 9.5) for automated synthesis of peptides that contain this important quencher.

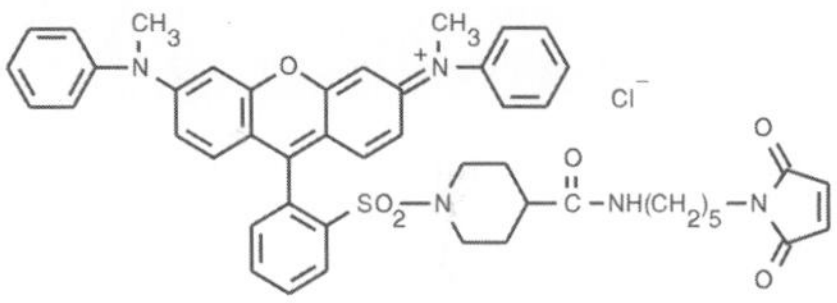

Figure 2.21 Q10257 QSY® 7 C_5-maleimide.

QSY® 35 iodoacetamide (Q20348) is an essentially nonfluorescent thiol-reactive analog of the amine-reactive nitrobenzoxazole (NBD) dye. QSY® 35 derivatives absorb light maximally near 470 nm (Figure 1.70), making their conjugates excellent FRET acceptors from UV light–excited fluorescent dyes. The amine-reactive QSY® 35 acetic acid succinimidyl ester (Q20133) is described in Section 1.8. A QSY® 35 aliphatic amine is also available (Q20540, Section 3.3), as is a QSY® 35 FMOC-protected amino acid for automated peptide synthesis of fluorogenic protease substrates (Q21931, Section 9.5).

The broad visible absorption of the chromophoric maleimide DABMI (D1521) conjugates makes DABMI another useful nonfluorescent thiol-reactive acceptor for fluorescence resonance energy transfer studies.[79,80] This reagent is also used to derivatize thiols for HPLC detection.[81,82]

Labeling Cell-Surface Thiols and Disulfides

Polar reagents for labeling cell-surface thiols of proteins include the stilbene iodoacetamide and maleimide[83] (A484, A485; Section 2.3), lucifer yellow iodoacetamide (L1338), 5-iodoacetamidofluorescein (5-IAF, I30451), fluorescein-5-maleimide (F150), and maleimidylpropionyl biocytin[83] (M1602, Section 4.2). However, we now recommend the sulfonated rhodamine dyes Alexa Fluor® 488 C_5-maleimide[3] (A10254) and Alexa Fluor® 594 C_5-maleimide (A10256) as the preferred reagents. Their high water solubility, selectivity for thiols, strong absorption of visible light and high resistance to photobleaching should result in high fluorescence yields and signifi-

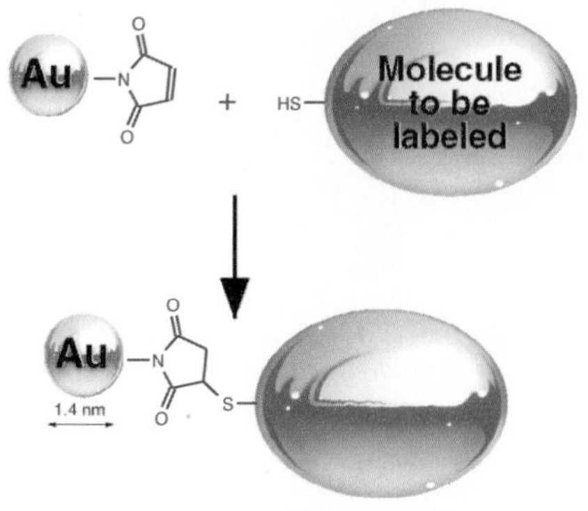

Figure 2.22 Reaction of NANOGOLD monomaleimide (N20345) with a thiol. Image courtesy of Nanoprobes, Inc.

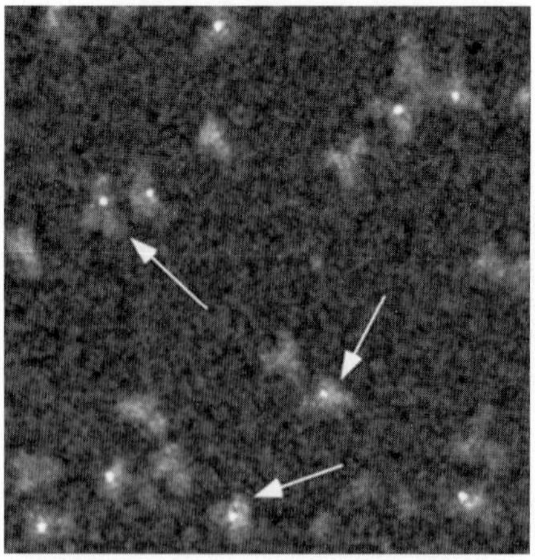

Figure 2.23 Scanning transmission electron microscope (STEM) image indicating that labeling with NANOGOLD monomaleimide (N20345, arrows) occurs specifically at a hinge-thiol site on the IgG molecule. Image courtesy of Nanoprobes, Inc.

cantly better detectability of their conjugates. Following electrophoretic separation, protein conjugates can be detected in gels by their visible fluorescence. Our antibodies to lucifer yellow, fluorescein (which strongly crossreacts with the Oregon Green® fluorophore), the Alexa Fluor® 405 dye (which crossreacts with the Cascade Blue® fluorophore) and the Alexa Fluor® 488 dye (Section 7.4, Table 7.18) may facilitate isolation and detection of proteins labeled with the thiol-reactive lucifer yellow, fluorescein (or Oregon Green®), Alexa Fluor® 405 (or Cascade Blue®) and Alexa Fluor® 488 derivatives, respectively, following blotting onto nitrocellulose membranes.

Disulfides in peptides and proteins can be reduced to thiols by a variety of reagents (Section 5.2). The three negative charges of the phosphine TCEP (T2556, Section 2.1) render it membrane impermeant, which makes it particularly useful for selective reduction of disulfides on the cell's outer membrane. The less polar tris-(2-cyanoethyl)phosphine (T6052, Section 2.1) may be a useful complementary reagent for reducing intramembrane and intracellular disulfides. Unlike DTT (D1532, Section 2.1), phosphines do not contain thiols and therefore may not need to be removed prior to thiol modification.

NANOGOLD Monomaleimide

In collaboration with Nanoprobes, Inc. (www.nanoprobes.com), Molecular Probes offers NANOGOLD particles, small metal cluster complexes of gold particles for research applications in light or electron microscopy.[84,85] The NANOGOLD clusters are discrete chemical compounds, not gold colloids. NANOGOLD monomaleimide (N20345) permits attachment of these very small (1.4 nm) yet uniformly sized gold particles to biomolecules in the same way that one reacts the maleimide of a dye with a biomolecule (Figure 2.22, Figure 2.23). The product, which is supplied as a set of five vials of a powder lyophilized from pH 7.5 HEPES buffer, is resuspended with the thiol-containing protein in deionized water at room temperature or below, then any excess NANOGOLD monomaleimide is removed by gel filtration and the conjugate is stored frozen.[86,87] 100 nanomoles of NANOGOLD monomaleimide is sufficient to label about 100 µg of a 100,000-dalton protein, and the conjugation mixture must be free of thiols or amine-containing buffers. In addition to its many uses for light and electron microscopy, NANOGOLD monomaleimide has been shown to be an extremely efficient quencher for dyes in molecular beacons — probes that can be used for homogeneous fluorescence *in situ* hybridization assays[88] (Figure 8.113). NANOGOLD conjugates of antibodies and streptavidin are described in Section 7.2 and Section 7.6, respectively, along with reagents and methods for silver enhancement to amplify electron microscopy detection.[88] We also supply NANOGOLD mono(sulfosuccinimidyl ester) (N20130, Section 1.6, Figure 1.90).

References

1. J Histochem Cytochem 51, 1699 (2003); **2.** Biochemistry 40, 5065 (2001); **3.** J Cell Biol 148, 755 (2000); **4.** J Biol Chem 275, 40163 (2000); **5.** Proc Natl Acad Sci U S A 96, 13944 (1999); **6.** Science 290, 333 (2000); **7.** Biochemistry 39, 15225 (2000); **8.** Proc Natl Acad Sci U S A 96, 15062 (1999); **9.** Science 283, 1152 (1999);**10.** Proc Natl Acad Sci U S A 100, 4001 (2003); **11.** Anal Biochem 308, 18 (2002); **12.** Analyst 83, 670 (1958); **13.** J Chromatogr 160, 239 (1978); **14.** Anal Biochem 325, 137 (2004); **15.** Pharmacol Toxicol 62, 278 (1988); **16.** Curr Med Chem 7, 821 (2000); **17.** Lancet 338, 1043 (1991); **18.** Cardiovasc Drugs Ther 16, 391 (2002); **19.** J Am Chem Soc 116, 7801 (1994); **20.** Biophys J 74, 11 (1998); **21.** Biochemistry 38, 976 (1999); **22.** J Biol Chem 273, 22950 (1998); **23.** J Biol Chem 269, 12880 (1994); **24.** Biochemistry 25, 5468 (1986); **25.** J Biol Chem 278, 50136 (2003); **26.** Anal Biochem 253, 175 (1997); **27.** J Gen Microbiol 139, 841 (1993); **28.** Adv Photochem 18, 315 (1993); **29.** Photochem Photobiol 37, 271 (1983); **30.** J Am Chem Soc 99, 4306 (1977); **31.** J Cell Biol 126, 901 (1994); **32.** J Cell Biol 126, 877 (1994); **33.** Biochemistry 30, 3538 (1991); **34.** Biochemistry 29, 10023 (1990); **35.** Spectroscopy 5, 20 (1990); **36.** Nucleic Acids Res 20, 5205 (1992); **37.** Biochemistry 29, 8283 (1990); **38.** Biochim Biophys Acta 1025, 199 (1990); **39.** Biophys J 65, 113 (1993); **40.** Biochemistry 28, 2204 (1989); **41.** Biophys J 74, 3093 (1998); **42.** Biophys J 74, 3083 (1998); **43.** Biophys J 68, 78S (1995); **44.** Biochemistry 31, 12431 (1992); **45.** Biophys J 71, 3330 (1996); **46.** Bioconjug Chem 9, 160 (1998); **47.** Biophys J 81, 2851 (2001); **48.** Biochemistry 39, 14183 (2000); **49.** J Biol Chem 274, 1683 (1999); **50.** IEEE J Quantum Electronics 16, 777 (1980); **51.** Anal Chem 57, 1864 (1985); **52.** Anal Chem 55, 1786 (1983); **53.** FEBS Lett 6, 346 (1970); **54.** Arch Biochem Biophys 281, 6 (1990); **55.** Biochemistry 29, 10613 (1990); **56.** Biochemistry 29, 7309 (1990); **57.** J Biochem (Tokyo) 107, 563 (1990); **58.** Biochim Biophys Acta 956, 217 (1988); **59.** J Biol Chem 266, 13777 (1991); **60.** J Biol Chem 258, 5419 (1983); **61.** Anal Chim Acta 290, 3 (1994); **62.** Anal Chem 56, 2461 (1984); **63.** Chem Pharm Bull (Tokyo) 38, 2290 (1990); **64.** J Chromatogr 514, 189 (1990); **65.** J Chromatogr 502, 230 (1990); **66.** Anal Biochem 314, 166 (2003); **67.** Proc Natl Acad Sci U S A 98, 5556 (2001); **68.** J Chromatogr A 798, 47 (1998); **69.** Techniques in Protein Chemistry V, Crabb JW, Ed. pp. 189–194 (1994); **70.** Anal Biochem 233, 181 (1996); **71.** Anal Biochem 214, 128 (1993); **72.** J Biol Chem 264, 7185 (1989); **73.** J Biol Chem 270, 5395 (1995); **74.** Am J Pathol 148, 405 (1996); **75.** Biochem Soc Trans 23, 38S (1995); **76.** J Fluorescence 3, 33 (1993); **77.** J Biol Chem 272, 29511 (1997); **78.** Proc Natl Acad Sci U S A 100, 13308 (2003); **79.** Biochemistry 34, 6475 (1995); **80.** Biochemistry 33, 13102 (1994); **81.** J Chromatogr 414, 11 (1987); **82.** Biochem J 211, 163 (1983); **83.** Biochemistry 36, 6777 (1997); **84.** Microsc Res Tech 42, 2 (1998); **85.** J Histochem Cytochem 48, 471 (2000); **86.** J Biol Chem 275, 30458 (2000); **87.** J Biol Chem 275, 30465 (2000); **88.** Nat Biotechnol 19, 365 (2001).

Data Table — 2.2 Thiol-Reactive Probes Excited with Visible Light

Cat #	MW	Storage	Soluble	Abs	EC	Em	Solvent	Notes
A10254	720.66	F,DD,L	H_2O, DMSO	493	72,000	516	pH 7	1, 2
A10255	812.88	F,DD,L	H_2O, DMSO	528	78,000	552	MeOH	1
A10256	908.97	F,DD,L	H_2O, DMSO	588	96,000	612	pH 7	1, 3
A10258	1034.37	F,DD,L	H_2O, DMSO	554	93,000	570	pH 7	1
A20341	880.92	F,DD,L	H_2O, DMSO	575	92,000	600	pH 7	1, 4
A20342	~1300	F,DD,L	H_2O, DMSO	622	143,000	640	MeOH	1
A20343	~900	F,DD,L	H_2O, DMSO	668	112,000	697	MeOH	1, 5
A20344	~1000	F,DD,L	H_2O, DMSO	684	175,000	714	MeOH	1, 6
A20346	~1250	F,DD,L	H_2O, DMSO	556	158,000	572	MeOH	1
A20347	~1300	F,DD,L	H_2O, DMSO	651	265,000	671	MeOH	1, 7
B1355	425.23	F,D,L	pH >6, DMF	492	81,000	515	pH 9	8
B2103	341.00	F,D,L	DMSO, MeCN	533	62,000	561	$CHCl_3$	9, 10
B10250	414.22	F,D,L	DMSO, MeCN	504	79,000	510	MeOH	10
B10621	840.47	F,D,L	DMSO	549	88,000	575	MeOH	11
B20340	788.44	F,D,L	DMSO	504	132,000	511	MeOH	12
B22802	449.14	F,D,L	DMSO, MeCN	658	73,000	678	$CHCl_3$	13
C20260	199.55	F,D,L	DMF, MeCN	336	9,800	none	MeOH	14, 15
D1521	320.35	F,D,L	DMF, MeCN	419	34,000	none	MeOH	16
D2004	419.18	F,D,L	DMF, DMSO	478	25,000	541	MeOH	11, 16
D2006	626.25	F,D,L	DMSO, MeCN	534	69,000	552	MeOH	10, 11
D6003	417.00	F,D,L	DMSO, MeCN	502	76,000	510	MeOH	10, 11
D6004	431.03	F,D,L	DMSO, MeCN	508	69,000	543	MeOH	10, 11
D6012	650.31	F,D,L	DMSO, MeCN	544	63,000	570	MeOH	10, 11
D10620	585.92	F,D,L	DMSO, MeCN	509	103,000	516	MeOH	10, 11
D20350	419.24	F,D,L	DMSO	499	88,000	508	MeOH	17
D20351	575.38	F,D,L	DMSO	577	60,000	618	MeOH	17
E118	742.95	F,D,L	pH >6, DMF	524	103,000	545	MeOH	1, 18
E6051	458.41	F,D,L	DMSO	412	26,000	564	MeOH	19
E30450	830.84	F,D,L	pH >6, DMF	519	100,000	540	pH 9	1, 11, 18
F150	427.37	F,D,L	pH >6, DMF	492	83,000	515	pH 9	1, 8, 20
F486	183.10	F,D,L	MeCN, $CHCl_3$	328	8,000	none	MeOH	14
F6053	217.17	F,D,L	DMF, DMSO	320	4,800	none	MeOH	21
F36200	1223.19	F,D,L	pH >6	494	76,000	518	H_2O/Ca^{2+}	1, 11, 22, 23
H30462	852.21	F,DD,L	H_2O, DMSO	494	80,000	518	pH 7	1
H30463	~1200	F,DD,L	H_2O, DMSO	555	155,000	572	MeOH	1
H30464	1062.50	F,DD,L	H_2O, DMSO	588	92,000	617	pH 7	1
H30465	~1200	F,DD,L	H_2O, DMSO	651	270,000	672	MeOH	1
I9	406.14	F,D,L	DMF, MeCN	472	23,000	536	MeOH	11, 16
I30451	515.26	F,D,L	pH >6, DMF	492	78,000	515	pH 9	1, 8, 11
I30452	515.26	F,D,L	pH >6, DMF	491	82,000	516	pH 9	1, 8, 11
L1338	659.51	F,D,L	H_2O	426	11,000	531	pH 7	11
M6026	471.48	F,D,L	DMSO	412	23,000	561	MeOH	19
O6010	551.24	F,D,L	pH >6, DMF	491	68,000	516	pH 9	1, 11, 24
O6034	463.35	F,D,L	pH >6, DMF	491	81,000	515	pH 9	1, 24
Q10257	858.45	F,D,L	DMSO	560	92,000	none	MeOH	
Q20348	453.20	F,D,L	DMSO	475	24,000	none	MeOH	11
Q30457	1083.30	F,D,L	H_2O, DMSO	562	90,000	none	MeOH	1
R6029	680.79	F,D,L	DMSO	560	119,000	580	MeOH	
T6006	825.22	F,D,L	DMSO	543	87,000	567	MeOH	11
T6008	728.83	F,D,L	DMSO	582	112,000	600	MeOH	
T6009	811.80	F,D,L	DMSO	583	115,000	603	MeOH	
T6027	481.51	F,D,L	DMSO	541	95,000	567	MeOH	
T6028	481.51	F,D,L	DMSO	541	91,000	567	MeOH	
T30453	510.31	F,D,L	DMSO	503	80,000	510	MeOH	
T30454	658.52	F,D,L	DMSO	544	58,000	570	MeOH	
T30455	684.53	F,D,L	DMSO	589	63,000	617	MeOH	
T30456	710.57	F,D,L	DMSO	625	93,000	640	MeOH	

For definitions of the contents of this data table, see "Navigating *The Handbook*" in the introductory pages.

Notes

1. Aqueous stock solutions should be used within 24 hours; long-term storage is NOT recommended.
2. The fluorescence lifetime (τ) of the Alexa Fluor® 488 dye in pH 7.4 buffer at 20°C is 4.1 nanoseconds. Data provided by the SPEX Fluorescence Group, Jobin Yvon Inc.
3. The fluorescence lifetime (τ) of the Alexa Fluor® 594 dye in pH 7.4 buffer at 20°C is 3.9 nanoseconds. Data provided by the SPEX Fluorescence Group, Jobin Yvon Inc.
4. The fluorescence lifetime (τ) of the Alexa Fluor® 568 dye in pH 7.4 buffer at 20°C is 3.6 nanoseconds. Data provided by the SPEX Fluorescence Group, Jobin Yvon Inc.
5. The fluorescence lifetime (τ) of the Alexa Fluor® 660 dye in pH 7.5 buffer at 20°C is 1.2 nanoseconds. Data provided by Pierre-Alain Muller, Max Planck Institute for Biophysical Chemistry, Göttingen.
6. The fluorescence lifetime (τ) of the Alexa Fluor® 680 dye in pH 7.5 buffer at 20°C is 1.2 nanoseconds. Data provided by Pierre-Alain Muller, Max Planck Institute for Biophysical Chemistry, Göttingen.
7. The fluorescence lifetime (τ) of the Alexa Fluor® 647 dye in H_2O at 20°C is 1.0 nanoseconds and 1.5 nanoseconds in EtOH (Bioconjug Chem 14, 195 (2003)).
8. Absorption and fluorescence of fluorescein derivatives are pH-dependent. Extinction coefficients and fluorescence quantum yields decrease markedly at pH <7.
9. B2103 spectra are for the unreacted reagent. The thiol adduct has Abs = 493 nm, Em = 503 nm in MeOH.
10. The absorption and fluorescence spectra of BODIPY® derivatives are relatively insensitive to the solvent.
11. Iodoacetamides in solution undergo rapid photodecomposition to unreactive products. Minimize exposure to light prior to reaction.

Data Table — 2.2 Thiol-Reactive Probes Excited with Visible Light — continued

12. Fluorescence emission of B20340 is relatively weak until the disulfide linkage between its two BODIPY® FL fluorophores is reductively cleaved.
13. B22802 spectral data are for the unreacted reagent. The thiol adduct has Abs = 629 nm, Em = 647 nm in dichloromethane (CH_2Cl_2).
14. Spectra of 2-mercaptoethanol adduct of NBD chloride in MeOH: Abs = 425 nm (EC = 13,000 $cm^{-1}M^{-1}$), Em = 520 nm. NBD fluoride yields the same derivatives as NBD chloride but is more reactive.
15. This product is specified to equal or exceed 98% analytical purity by HPLC.
16. Spectral data of the 2-mercaptoethanol adduct.
17. Spectral data are for the unreacted reagent and are essentially unchanged upon reaction with thiols.
18. Eosin and erythrosin derivatives also exhibit phosphorescence with an emission maximum at ~680 nm. The phosphorescence lifetime is ~1 millisecond for eosin and 0.5 milliseconds for erythrosin.

Product List — 2.2 Thiol-Reactive Probes Excited with Visible Light

Cat #	Product Name	Unit Size
A10254	Alexa Fluor® 488 C_5-maleimide	1 mg
A10255	Alexa Fluor® 532 C_5-maleimide	1 mg
A10258	Alexa Fluor® 546 C_5-maleimide	1 mg
A20346	Alexa Fluor® 555 C_2-maleimide	1 mg
A20341	Alexa Fluor® 568 C_5-maleimide	1 mg
A10256	Alexa Fluor® 594 C_5-maleimide	1 mg
A20342	Alexa Fluor® 633 C_5-maleimide	1 mg
A20347	Alexa Fluor® 647 C_2-maleimide	1 mg
A20343	Alexa Fluor® 660 C_2-maleimide	1 mg
A20344	Alexa Fluor® 680 C_2-maleimide	1 mg
B10621	bis-((*N*-iodoacetyl)piperazinyl)sulfonerhodamine	5 mg
B10250	BODIPY® FL *N*-(2-aminoethyl)maleimide	5 mg
B20340	BODIPY® FL L-cystine	1 mg
B22802	8-bromomethyl-4,4-difluoro-3,5-bis-(2-thienyl)-4-bora-3a,4a-diaza-*s*-indacene (BODIPY® 630/650 methyl bromide)	1 mg
B2103	8-bromomethyl-4,4-difluoro-1,3,5,7-tetramethyl-4-bora-3a,4a-diaza-*s*-indacene (BODIPY® 493/503 methyl bromide)	5 mg
B1355	5-(bromomethyl)fluorescein	10 mg
C20260	4-chloro-7-nitrobenz-2-oxa-1,3-diazole (NBD chloride; 4-chloro-7-nitrobenzofurazan) *FluoroPure™ grade*	100 mg
D10620	4,4-difluoro-3,5-di(iodoacetamidomethyl)-4-bora-3a,4a-diaza-*s*-indacene (BODIPY® FL bis-(methyleneiodoacetamide))	5 mg
D20351	4,4-difluoro-3,5-bis(4-methoxyphenyl)-8-(4-maleimidylphenyl)-4-bora-3a,4a-diaza-*s*-indacene (BODIPY® 577/618 maleimide)	5 mg
D6003	*N*-(4,4-difluoro-5,7-dimethyl-4-bora-3a,4a-diaza-*s*-indacene-3-yl)methyl)iodoacetamide (BODIPY® FL C_1-IA)	5 mg
D6012	*N*-(5-((4,4-difluoro-1,3-dimethyl-5-(4-methoxyphenyl)-4-bora-3a,4a-diaza-*s*-indacene-2-propionyl)amino)pentyl)iodoacetamide (BODIPY® TMR cadaverine IA)	5 mg
D2006	*N*-(4,4-difluoro-5,7-diphenyl-4-bora-3a,4a-diaza-*s*-indacene-3-propionyl)-*N*′-iodoacetylethylenediamine (BODIPY® 530/550 IA)	5 mg
D6004	*N*-(4,4-difluoro-1,3,5,7-tetramethyl-4-bora-3a,4a-diaza-*s*-indacene-2-yl)iodoacetamide (BODIPY® 507/545 IA)	5 mg
D20350	4,4-difluoro-1,3,5,7-tetramethyl-8-(4-maleimidylphenyl)-4-bora-3a,4a-diaza-*s*-indacene (BODIPY® 499/508 maleimide)	5 mg
D1521	4-dimethylaminophenylazophenyl-4′-maleimide (DABMI)	100 mg
D2004	*N,N*′-dimethyl-*N*-(iodoacetyl)-*N*′-(7-nitrobenz-2-oxa-1,3-diazol-4-yl)ethylenediamine (IANBD amide)	25 mg
E30450	eosin-5-iodoacetamide	25 mg
E118	eosin-5-maleimide	25 mg
E6051	1-(2,3-epoxypropyl)-4-(5-(4-methoxyphenyl)oxazol-2-yl)pyridinium trifluoromethanesulfonate (PyMPO epoxide)	5 mg
F36200	fluo-4 iodoacetamide, pentapotassium salt	500 µg
F150	fluorescein-5-maleimide	25 mg
F6053	7-fluorobenz-2-oxa-1,3-diazole-4-sulfonamide (ABD-F)	10 mg
F486	4-fluoro-7-nitrobenz-2-oxa-1,3-diazole (NBD fluoride; 4-fluoro-7-nitrobenzofurazan)	25 mg
H30462	Hg-Link™ Alexa Fluor® 488 phenylmercury	1 mg
H30463	Hg-Link™ Alexa Fluor® 555 phenylmercury, disodium salt	1 mg
H30464	Hg-Link™ Alexa Fluor® 594 phenylmercury, sodium salt	1 mg
H30465	Hg-Link™ Alexa Fluor® 647 phenylmercury, disodium salt	1 mg
I30451	5-iodoacetamidofluorescein (5-IAF)	25 mg
I30452	6-iodoacetamidofluorescein (6-IAF)	25 mg
I9	*N*-((2-(iodoacetoxy)ethyl)-*N*-methyl)amino-7-nitrobenz-2-oxa-1,3-diazole (IANBD ester)	100 mg
L1338	lucifer yellow iodoacetamide, dipotassium salt	25 mg
M6026	1-(2-maleimidylethyl)-4-(5-(4-methoxyphenyl)oxazol-2-yl)pyridinium methanesulfonate (PyMPO maleimide)	5 mg
N20345	NANOGOLD® monomaleimide *special packaging*	5 x 6 nmol
O6010	Oregon Green® 488 iodoacetamide *mixed isomers*	5 mg
O6034	Oregon Green® 488 maleimide	5 mg
Q10257	QSY® 7 C_5-maleimide	5 mg
Q30457	QSY® 9 C_5-maleimide	5 mg
Q20348	QSY® 35 iodoacetamide	5 mg

For current prices or to order online, visit probes.invitrogen.com

Cat #	Product Name	Unit Size
R6029	Rhodamine Red™ C_2-maleimide	5 mg
T6006	tetramethylrhodamine-5-iodoacetamide dihydroiodide (5-TMRIA) *single isomer*	5 mg
T6027	tetramethylrhodamine-5-maleimide *single isomer*	5 mg
T6028	tetramethylrhodamine-6-maleimide *single isomer*	5 mg
T6008	Texas Red® C_2-maleimide	5 mg
T6009	Texas Red® C_5-bromoacetamide	5 mg
T30456	TS-Link™ BODIPY® 630/650 C_5-thiosulfate, sodium salt	5 mg
T30453	TS-Link™ BODIPY® FL C_2-thiosulfate, sodium salt	5 mg
T30454	TS-Link™ BODIPY® TMR C_5-thiosulfate, sodium salt	5 mg
T30455	TS-Link™ BODIPY® TR C_5-thiosulfate, sodium salt	5 mg

For current prices or to order online, visit probes.invitrogen.com

2.3 Thiol-Reactive Probes Excited with Ultraviolet Light

The thiol-reactive dyes described in this section have their longest-wavelength absorption peaks at less than 410 nm (Table 2.2). Typically, these dyes exhibit blue fluorescence and have much weaker absorption than the dyes described in Section 2.2, with extinction coefficients often below 20,000 $cm^{-1}M^{-1}$. Furthermore, photostability of UV light–excitable dyes is generally less than that of visible light–excitable dyes. The strong environmental dependence of the emission spectra and quantum yields of several of the dyes — especially the coumarin, benzoxadiazole (NBD probes and ABD-F, Section 2.2), aminonaphthalene (e.g., dansyl) and Dapoxyl® fluorophores — makes some of these thiol-reactive probes useful for investigating protein structure and assembly, following protein transport through membranes and studying ligand binding to receptors. As discussed below, the spectra of certain dyes tend to be particularly sensitive to ligand and metal binding, protein association and chaotropic reagents. When protein conjugates of these dyes are denatured or undergo a change in conformation, a decrease in fluorescence intensity and a shift in emission to longer wavelengths are often observed.

Coumarin Derivatives

Alexa Fluor® 350 C_5-Maleimide

Alexa Fluor® 350 C_5-maleimide (A30505), a thiol-reactive, sulfonated coumarin derivative, produces protein conjugates that are optimally excited at 346 nm and have bright blue fluorescence emission (Figure 7.2) at wavelengths slightly shorter than AMCA or AMCA-X conjugates (Figure 10.4) (emission maximum ~442 nm versus 448 nm), which reduces the dye's spectral overlap with the emission of fluorescein. Like our other Alexa Fluor® dyes, Alexa Fluor® 350 C_5-maleimide offers unrivaled brightness and pH-independent fluorescence, as well as water solubility and a low degree of quenching upon conjugation (see Note 1.1 "Product Highlight: The Alexa Fluor® Dye Series — Peak Performance across the Visible Spectrum" in Section 1.3).

Hg-Link™ Alexa Fluor® 350 Phenylmercury Reagent

We also offer the Hg-Link™ Alexa Fluor® 350 phenylmercury reagent (H30460), which forms a stable bond with a free thiol. This reaction occurs under the same conditions used for maleimide and iodoacetamide reactions with thiols, but unlike maleimides and iodoacetamides, Hg-Link™ reagents can react with nitrosylated thiols [1] (SNO) (Saville reaction, (Figure 2.6); see Section 2.2 for more information on phenylmercury compounds and a complete list of Hg-Link™ dyes).

Other Coumarin Maleimides and Iodoacetamides

In addition to thiol-reactive Alexa Fluor® 350 derivatives, Molecular Probes has available several blue-fluorescent thiol-reactive coumarins (Table 2.2). 7-Diethylamino-3-(4′-maleimidylphenyl)-4-methylcoumarin (CPM, D346; Figure 2.24) and the corresponding iodoacetamide (DCIA, D404) are among the brightest UV light–excitable fluorescent thiol reagents available. CPM and DCIA are spectrally similar to *N*-(7-dimethylamino-4-methylcoumarin-3-yl)maleimide (DACM, D10251) and iodoacetamide (DACIA, D10252), but they yield conjugates that are more fluorescent than the corresponding DACM and DACIA adducts. The coumarin fluorophore is an excellent fluorescence energy acceptor from tryptophan and a good donor to fluorescein, eosin, Alexa Fluor® 488, selected BODIPY® dyes [2] and our essentially nonfluorescent QSY® 7, QSY® 9 and QSY® 35 quenchers (Section 1.6, Section 1.7, Section 2.2, Section 3.3), making these thiol-reactive coumarins especially valuable for studying protein structure and for detecting protein–membrane interactions. Fluorescence emission of the coumarin conjugates is moderately sensitive to environment.

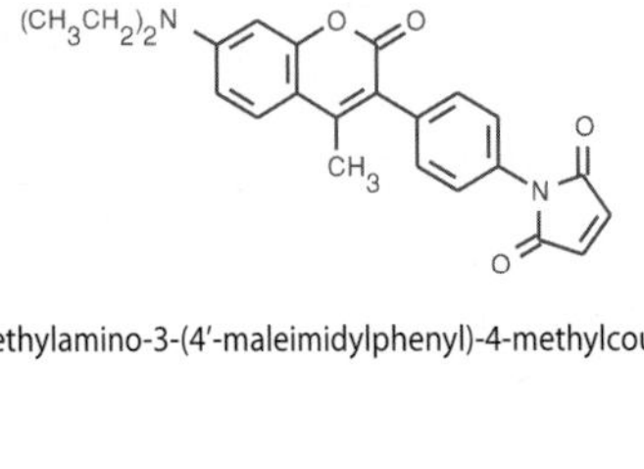

Figure 2.24 D346 7-diethylamino-3-(4′-maleimidylphenyl)-4-methylcoumarin (CPM).

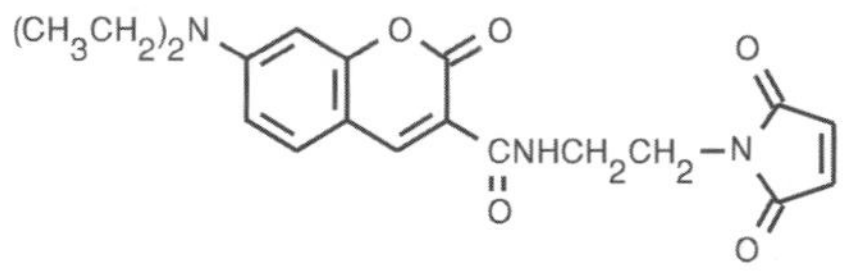

Figure 2.25 D10253 7-diethylamino-3-((((2-maleimidyl)-ethyl)amino)carbonyl)coumarin (MDCC).

Unlike MDCC (described below), which is intrinsically fluorescent, the maleimides DACM and CPM are essentially nonfluorescent until they react with thiols, permitting thiol quantitation without a separation step. CPM has been used to follow the release of picomoles of thiols from acetylthiocholine by acetylcholinesterase [3–5] and to determine cystamine, cysteamine [6] and thiol content of proteins, cells and plasma.[7–10] CPM can also be used to quantitate thiols using a fluorescence microplate reader.[11] Furthermore, nucleolar protein staining by CPM has been used to distinguish highly proliferating cancer cells in a flow cytometry assay.[12] In addition to modifying proteins, CPM reacts with thiophosphorylated RNA [13] and thiolated oligonucleotides.[14,15] Similar to CPM, DACM is an important derivatization and quantitation reagent for low molecular weight thiols.[16–21] DACM has also been extensively used as a probe for protein structure,[22–25] as a fluorescence energy transfer donor and acceptor [26] and as a tool for localizing thiols in cells and tissues.[27]

We also offer 7-diethylamino-3-((((2-maleimidyl)ethyl)amino)carbonyl)coumarin (MDCC, D10253; Figure 2.25) and the corresponding iodoacetamide (IDCC, D20382). When conjugated to a mutant phosphate-binding protein,[28] MDCC has proven useful for direct, real-time measurement of inorganic phosphate release during enzymatic reactions.[29–33] An IDCC conjugate of a mutant nucleoside diphosphate kinase has been used as a fluorescent sensor of the phosphorylation state of the kinase and of the purine nucleoside diphosphate concentrations in real time.[34] Both MDCC and IDCC are also useful reagents for general labeling of thiols with bright blue fluorescence.

Table 2.2 — Thiol-reactive dyes excited with ultraviolet light

Derivative	Abs *	Em *	Alkyl Halide or Haloacetamide	Maleimide	Other
Alexa Fluor® 350	346	442		A30505	
Alexa Fluor® 405	402	412		A30458	
Anilinonaphthalene †	326	462	IAANS, I7	MIANS, M8	
Benzophenone	282	NA		B1508	
Bimane	375	456	B30500		
Dansyl †	328	563			D146 ‡ D151 §
Dapoxyl® †	374	572	D10300		
Dibromobimane	394	490			bBBr, D1379 **
Diethylaminocoumarin	384	470	DCIA, D404 IDCC, D20382	CPM, D346 ** MDCC, D10253	
Dimethylaminocoumarin	376	465	DACIA, D10252	DACM, D10251 **	
Dimethylamino-naphthalene †	391	500	badan, B6057		acrylodan, A433
Monobromobimane	394	490			mBBr, M1378 ** mBBr, M20381 **†† qBBr, M1380 **
Monochlorobimane	394	490			mBCl, M1381MP **
Naphthalene †	336	490	IAEDANS, I14		
Pyrene †	339	384	P29 P2007MP	P28	
Stilbene †	329	408	A484	A485	

* Approximate absorption (Abs) and emission (Em) maxima, in nm, for the reagent (if fluorescent) or the fluorescent thiol adduct. † Environment-sensitive fluorophore. ‡ Disulfide; undergoes a thiol–disulfide interchange to form a mixed disulfide. § Dansyl aziridine. ** Very weakly fluorescent until reacted with thiols. †† FluoroPure™ grade. NA = Not applicable.

Pyrene Derivatives

Alexa Fluor® 405 C_5-Maleimide

With excitation/emission maxima of 402/421 nm (Figure 1.34, Figure 7.3), our Alexa Fluor® 405 dye is a near-perfect match to the 405 nm spectral line of the blue diode laser recently developed for fluorescence microscopy and flow cytometry. The Alexa Fluor® 405 C_5-maleimide (A30458) is a thiol-reactive derivative of our Cascade Blue® dye, which was not previously available in a thiol-reactive form. As with conjugates of Cascade Blue® acetyl azide, the Alexa Fluor® 405 conjugates show minimal spectral overlap with green fluorophores, making them ideal for multicolor applications (Figure 1.101). Moreover, with its longer-wavelength excitation maximum, the Alexa Fluor® 405 dye is potentially brighter than UV light–excitable blue fluorophores, whose signal is often obscured by autofluorescence. The Alexa Fluor® 405 dye is also recognized by our anti–Alexa Fluor® 405/Cascade Blue® dye antibody (A5760, Section 7.4).

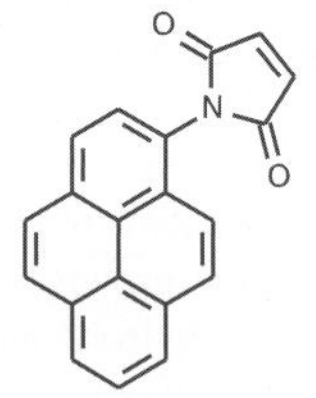

Figure 2.26 P28 N-(1-pyrene)maleimide.

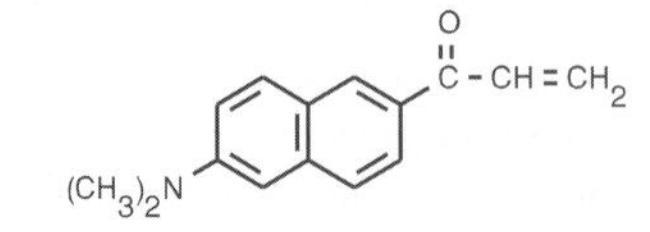

Figure 2.27 A433 6-acryloyl-2-dimethylaminonaphthalene (acrylodan).

Hg-Link™ Alexa Fluor® 405 Phenylmercury Reagent

We also offer the Hg-Link™ Alexa Fluor® 405 phenylmercury compound (H30461), which forms a stable bond with a free thiol. This reaction occurs under the same conditions used for maleimide and iodoacetamide reactions with thiols, but unlike maleimides and iodoacetamides, Hg-Link™ reagents can react with nitrosylated thiols [1] (SNO) (Saville reaction, (Figure 2.6); see Section 2.2 for more information on phenylmercury compounds and a complete list of Hg-Link™ dyes).

Pyrene Maleimide

Not only is *N*-(1-pyrene)maleimide (pyrene maleimide, P28) essentially nonfluorescent until it has reacted with thiols, but once excited, pyrene–thiol conjugates can interact to form excited-state dimers (excimers) that emit at longer wavelengths than the lone excited fluorophore. Pyrene maleimide conjugates often have very long fluorescence lifetimes (>100 nanoseconds), giving proximal pyrene rings within 6–10 Å of each other ample time to form the spectrally altered excimer (Figure 13.8). Excimers may form between labeled sites in a single protein, as they do in tropomyosin,[35–38] lens crystallins,[39] apolipophorin III[40] and sarcoplasmic reticulum ATPase,[41,42] or between sites in interacting biomolecules. Excimer formation can be used to monitor diffusion or to define interacting molecules within a functional unit of assembled biomolecules. Despite its low solubility in water, pyrene maleimide has been conjugated to a wide variety of proteins[43–47] and used as an HPLC derivatization reagent for thiols and reduced disulfides.[48] In several papers, *N*-(1-pyrene)maleimide (P28, Figure 2.26) has been incorrectly named *N*-(3-pyrene)maleimide or variants of that nomenclature.

Pyrene Iodoacetamide Derivatives

Fluorescence of the actin monomer labeled with pyrene iodoacetamide (P29) has been demonstrated to change upon polymerization, making this probe an excellent tool for following the kinetics of actin polymerization.[49–51] Pyrene iodoacetamide has been cited for this application in literally hundreds of publications. Using pyrene iodoacetamide, researchers have investigated the influence of several actin-binding proteins and of cytochalasin on the rate of actin polymerization. Conjugates of *N*-(1-pyrenemethyl)iodoacetamide (P2007MP) have the longest excited-state fluorescence lifetimes (>100 nanoseconds) of all reported thiol-reactive probes. The tendency of doubly pyrene dye–labeled nucleic acid probes to form excited-state dimers with altered fluorescence emission enables their use in homogeneous hybridization assays.[52,53] Excimer formation has also been observed in pyrene iodoacetamide–labeled carbonic anhydrase II.[54]

Naphthalene Derivatives, Including Thiol-Specific Didansyl Cystine

Acrylodan and Its Bromoacetyl Analog

Although acrylodan (A433, Figure 2.27) and 6-bromoacetyl-2-dimethylaminonaphthalene (badan, B6057) generally react with thiols more slowly than do iodoacetamides or maleimides, they form very strong thioether bonds that are expected to remain stable under conditions required for complete amino acid analysis. The fluorescence emission peak and intensity of these adducts (Figure 2.28) are particularly sensitive to conformational changes or ligand binding, making these dyes some of the most useful thiol-reactive probes for protein structure studies.[55–58] For example, the acrylodan conjugate of an intestinal fatty acid–binding protein, ADIFAB (A3880, Section 17.4), is a sensor for free fatty acids[59] (Figure 17.42). Also, myosin regulatory light chain labeled with acrylodan shows a spectral response upon phosphorylation by myosin light chain kinase.[60] The environment-sensitive spectral shifts of acrylodan and badan conjugates (Figure 2.28) may make these probes useful for distinguishing thiols that are located in membranes versus those exposed to aqueous solvation in cells.

IAANS and MIANS

To develop appreciable fluorescence, both the reactive anilinonaphthalenesulfonate iodoacetamide (IAANS, I7; Figure 2.29) and maleimide (MIANS, also called Mal-ANS; M8) must be reacted with thiols that are located in hydrophobic sites. Often, however, buried unsolvated thiol residues are exceptionally reactive, allowing these sites to be selectively modified by these reagents. The environment-sensitive fluorescence properties of the protein conjugates of MIANS and IAANS are similar to those of the structurally related probes 1,8-ANS and 2,6-TNS (A47, T53; Section 13.5). The fluorescence intensity, and to a lesser extent, the emission wavelengths of the conjugates, tend to be very sensitive to substrate binding, folding and unfolding of the protein, changes in ionic strength and association of the labeled protein with other proteins, membranes or nucleic acids. Both IAANS and MIANS have been widely used for protein structural studies, particularly of contractile proteins.[61–63]

IAEDANS

The fluorescence of IAEDANS (I14) is quite dependent upon environment, although much less so than that of IAANS and MIANS conjugates. Its conjugates frequently respond to ligand binding by undergoing spectral shifts and changes in fluorescence intensity that are determined by the degree of aqueous solvation. Advantages of this reagent include high water solubility above pH 4 and a relatively long fluorescence lifetime (sometimes >20 nanoseconds, although commonly 10–15 nanoseconds), making the conjugates useful for fluorescence polarization and rotational studies[64–67] (see Note 1.5 "Technical Focus: Fluorescence Polarization (FP)" in Section 1.4). In addition, because it has a large Stokes shift[68] and an emission that overlaps well with the absorption of fluorescein, Alexa Fluor® 488, Oregon Green® dyes and BODIPY® FL dyes, IAEDANS is an excellent reagent for fluorescence resonance energy transfer (FRET) measurements[69,70] of proximity up to about 60 Å (see Note 1.2 "Technical Focus: Fluorescence Resonance Energy Transfer (FRET)" in Section 1.3). IAEDANS usually reacts with thiols; however, it has been reported to react with a lysine residue in tropomyosin.[71]

Dansyl Aziridine

Another probe with environment-sensitive spectral propeties, dansyl aziridine (D151), forms very strong thioether bonds that remain stable under conditions required for complete amino acid analysis. Although it reacts with a methionine residue in troponin C,[72] dansyl aziridine is primarily a thiol-reactive reagent. The fluorescence of the calmodulin and troponin C conjugates of dansyl aziridine is sensitive to Ca^{2+} binding.[73–76]

N,N′-Didansyl-L-Cystine

Disulfides such as *N,N′*-didansyl-L-cystine (D146) are the only type of fluorescent thiol-*specific* reagents available. Disulfide derivatives undergo a thiol–disulfide interchange reaction to form mixed disulfides[77] (Figure 2.4). The fluorescent disulfide that is initially formed, however, can subsequently transfer its fluorophore to neighboring thiols. The disulfide linkage formed by didansyl cystine can also be cleaved with reagents such as DTT or TCEP (D1532, T2556; Section 2.1).

Dapoxyl® Derivatives

Our Dapoxyl® dyes have good absorptivity and exceptionally high environmental sensitivity.[78] Although optimally excited in the UV near 370 nm, their emission maxima range from about 450 nm to 650 nm, depending on the solvent (Figure 1.112). Dapoxyl® (2-bromoacetamidoethyl)sulfonamide[79] (D10300, Figure 2.30) alkylates a thiol group;

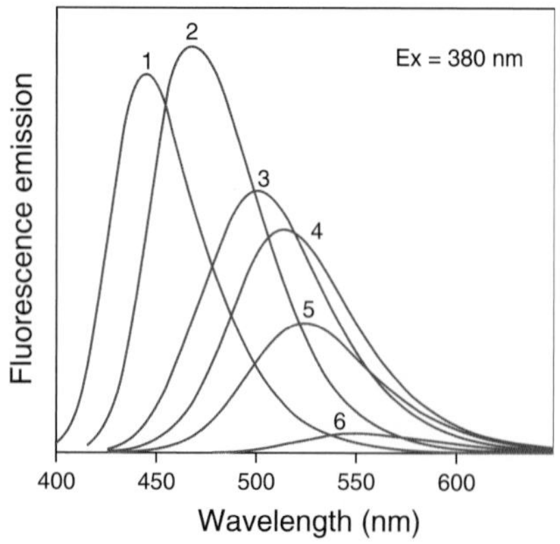

Figure 2.28 Fluorescence emission spectra of the 2-mercaptoethanol adduct of badan (B6057) in: 1) toluene, 2) chloroform, 3) acetonitrile, 4) ethanol, 5) methanol and 6) water. Each solution contains the same concentration of the adduct. Excitation of all samples is at 380 nm.

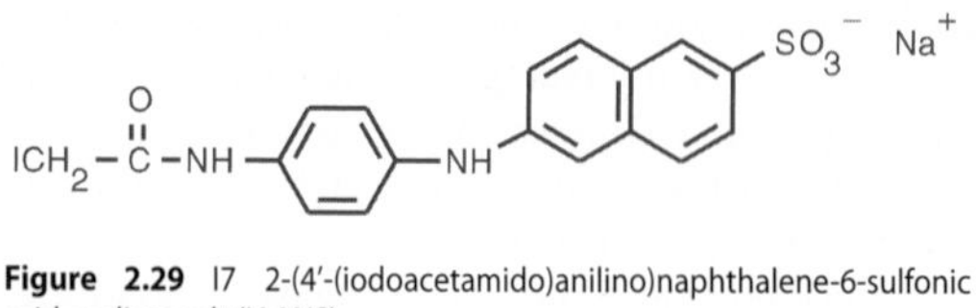

Figure 2.29 I7 2-(4′-(iodoacetamido)anilino)naphthalene-6-sulfonic acid, sodium salt (IAANS).

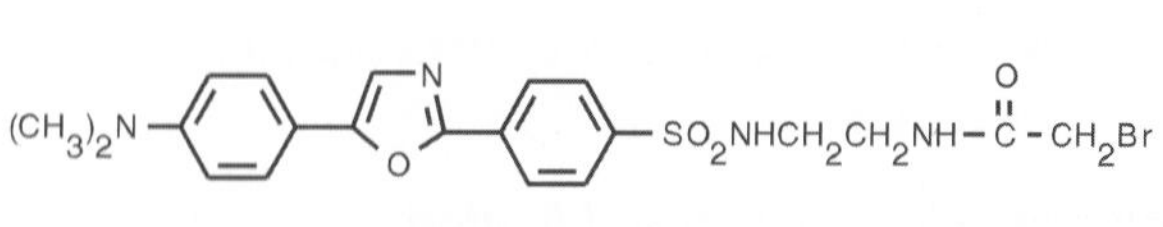

Figure 2.30 D10300 Dapoxyl (2-bromoacetamidoethyl)sulfonamide.

amine-reactive Dapoxyl® derivatives are described in Section 1.7, and a carboxylic acid–reactive Dapoxyl® derivative is described in Section 3.3.

Bimanes for Thiol Derivatization

Monobromobimane and Monochlorobimane

The monobromobimanes (M1378, M20381, M1380), which are essentially nonfluorescent until conjugated, readily react with several low molecular weight thiols, including glutathione,[80–82] *N*-acetylcysteine,[83] mercaptopurine,[84] peptides[85] and plasma thiols,[86] as well as with carboxylic acids (Section 3.3). Although monobromobimane (M1378; FluoroPure™ Grade, M20381; Figure 2.31) is the most extensively used bimane derivative, monobromotrimethylammoniobimane (M1380, Figure 2.32) contains a positive charge, thus permitting separation of its conjugates by electrophoresis[87] or cation-exchange chromatography.[88] The membrane permeability of this charged bimane, as well as its ability to access sites within a protein, may differ from that of the uncharged bimane probes.[89,90] These reagents, which were originally described by Kosower and colleagues,[91,92] are also useful for detecting the distribution of protein thiols in cells before and after chemical reduction of disulfides.[93] Both monobromobimane and the more thiol-selective monochlorobimane (M1381MP) have been extensively used for detecting glutathione in live cells (Section 15.6). Monobromobimane can also be used to derivatize thiol-containing proteins prior to separation by isoelectric focusing without appreciably modifying the protein's electrophoretic mobility.[94]

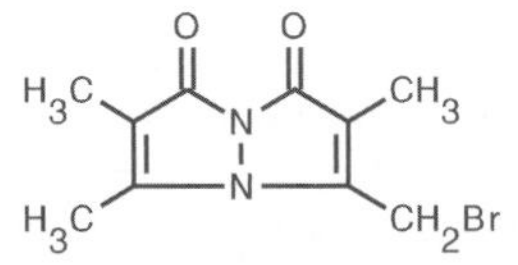

Figure 2.31 M1378 monobromobimane (mBBr).

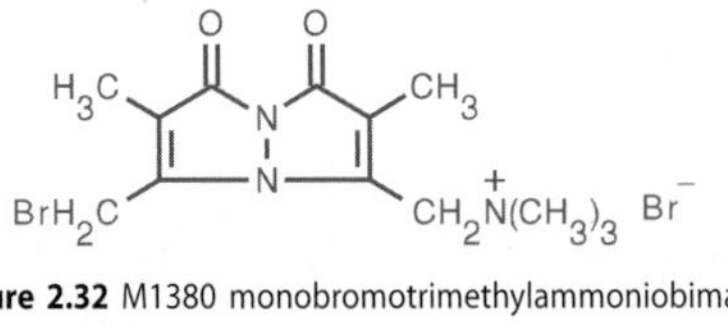

Figure 2.32 M1380 monobromotrimethylammoniobimane bromide (qBBr).

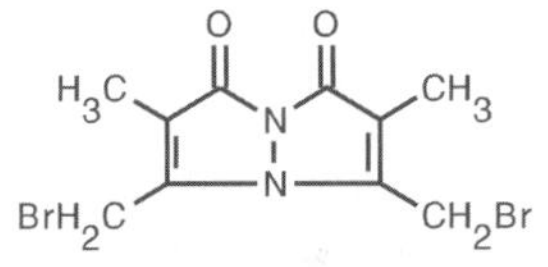

Figure 2.33 D1379 dibromobimane (bBBr).

Dibromobimane

Dibromobimane (D1379, Figure 2.33) is an interesting crosslinking reagent for proteins[95] because it is unlikely to fluoresce until *both* of its alkylating groups have reacted. It has been used to crosslink thiols in myosin,[96–99] hemoglobin,[100] *Escherichia coli* lactose permease[101] and mitochondrial ATPase.[102] Dibromobimane was also used to probe for the proximity of dual-cysteine mutagenesis sites in ArsA ATPase[103] and to crosslink thiols in actin,[104] myosin[96] and P-glycoprotein.[105,106]

Bimane Iodoacetamide and Bimane C_3-Maleimide

Bimane iodoacetamide (B30500) and bimane C_3-maleimide (B30501) are blue-fluorescent thiol-reactive fluorophores with excitation/emission maxima of ~375/456 nm. The small size of the bimane fluorophore reduces the likelihood that the label will interfere with the function of the biomolecule, an important advantage for site-selective probes.

TS-Link™ Bimane Thiosulfate

We also offer TS-Link™ bimane thiosulfate (T30502), which is a water-soluble thiosulfate that reacts readily and selectively with a free thiol to form a disulfide bond (Figure 2.9). In contrast to the thioether bonds formed by maleimides and iodoacetamides, the disulfide bond formed by this TS-Link™ reagent is reversible — the TS-Link™ bimane fluorophore can easily be removed using a reducing agent such as dithiothreitol (DTT, D1532; Section 2.1) or tris-(2-carboxyethyl)phosphine (TCEP, T2556; Section 2.1), leaving the molecule of interest unchanged. In addition to TS-Link™ bimane thiosulfate, we prepare TS-Link™ BODIPY® thiosulfates (Section 2.2), as well as TS-Link™ DSB-X™ biotin C_5-thiosulfate (TS-Link™ desthiobiotin-X C_5-thiosulfate, T30754; Section 4.2) and TS-Link™ TFP-X thiosulfate (T30875, Section 5.2).

Polar Reagents for Determining Thiol Accessibility

Like IAEDANS (I14), the iodoacetamide and maleimide derivatives of stilbene (A484, A485) have high water solubility and are readily conjugated to thiols. Their combination of high polarity and membrane impermeability makes these polysulfonated dyes useful for determining whether thiol-containing proteins and polypeptide chains are exposed at the extracellular or cytoplasmic membrane surface. Stilbene protein adducts are charged and can be detected by gel or capillary electrophoresis. Our long-wavelength Alexa Fluor® maleimides (Section 2.2),

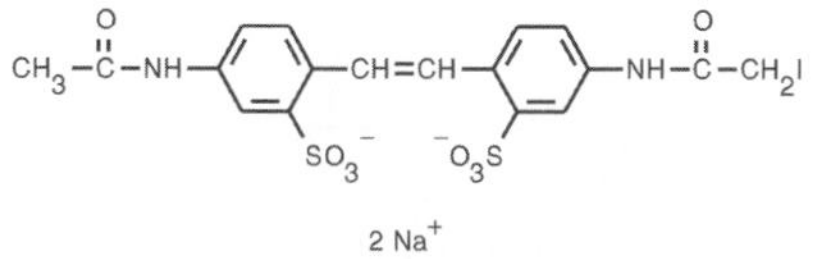

Figure 2.34 A484 4-acetamido-4'-((iodoacetyl)amino)stilbene-2,2'-disulfonic acid, disodium salt.

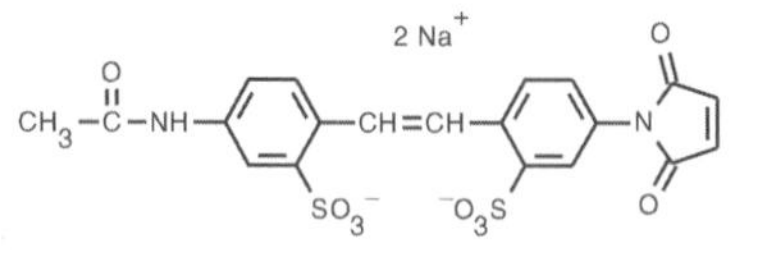

Figure 2.35 A485 4-acetamido-4'-maleimidylstilbene-2,2'-disulfonic acid, disodium salt.

which are also sulfonated polar dyes, are expected to have similar properties and applications but to be more fluorescent and have stronger absorption than these UV light–excited dyes.

The sulfonated stilbene iodoacetamide (A484, Figure 2.34) was used to label single-cysteine mutants of staphylococcal α-hemolysin in order to determine structural changes that occur during oligomerization and pore formation [107] and of the lipid-binding region of *E. coli* pyruvate oxidase in order to detect conformational changes upon substrate binding.[108] It has also been used as a fluorescence donor to a lucifer yellow iodoacetamide (L1338, Section 2.2) conjugate of α-crystalline.[109] Similarly, *E. coli* SecA variants containing single cysteine residues have been probed with the sulfonated stilbene maleimide (A485, Figure 2.35) to systematically study the topology of this inner membrane protein.[110] Lucifer yellow iodoacetamide reacts with the single exposed thiol of low-density lipoproteins (LDL) without reacting with the two buried thiols of the lipoprotein(a) component, whereas acrylodan (A433) reacts with all three thiols.[111] Lucifer yellow iodoacetamide has also been used in a flow cytometric assay of accessible thiols on the cell surface.[112]

1,10-Phenanthroline Iodoacetamide for Preparing Metal-Binding Conjugates

Conjugation of 1,10-phenanthroline iodoacetamide (P6879) to thiol-containing ligands confers the metal-binding properties of this important complexing agent on the ligand. For example, the covalent copper–phenanthroline complex of oligonucleotides or nucleic acid–binding molecules in combination with hydrogen peroxide acts as a chemical nuclease to selectively cleave DNA or RNA [113–117] (Section 8.7).

References

1. Analyst 83, 670 (1958); **2.** Biochem Biophys Res Commun 207, 508 (1995); **3.** J Biol Chem 272, 15373 (1997); **4.** Biochemistry 29, 10640 (1990); **5.** Anal Biochem 133, 450 (1983); **6.** Anal Biochem 170, 432 (1988); **7.** Anal Biochem 154, 186 (1986); **8.** Cytometry 3, 349 (1983); **9.** J Histochem Cytochem 29, 1377 (1981); **10.** J Histochem Cytochem 29, 314 (1981); **11.** Toxicol Appl Pharmacol 100, 485 (1989); **12.** J Histochem Cytochem 41, 1413 (1993); **13.** Biochemistry 30, 4821 (1991); **14.** Anal Biochem 191, 295 (1990); **15.** Proc Natl Acad Sci U S A 87, 1744 (1990); **16.** Chem Pharm Bull 23, 1385 (1975); **17.** Chem Pharm Bull 25, 1289 (1977); **18.** Anal Biochem 79, 83 (1977); **19.** Chem Pharm Bull 25, 1678 (1977); **20.** Melanoma Res 1, 33 (1991); **21.** J Chromatogr 380, 301 (1986); **22.** Biochem J 266, 453 (1990); **23.** Biochemistry 37, 615 (1998); **24.** Anal Biochem 84, 313 (1978); **25.** Biochem J 283, 567 (1992); **26.** Cytometry 15, 106 (1994); **27.** J Histochem Cytochem 27, 942 (1979); **28.** The bacterial clone for expressing the mutant phosphate-binding protein is available from Martin Webb, National Institute for Medical Research, London, UK; **29.** Biochemistry 37, 10381 (1998); **30.** Biophys J 74, 3120 (1998); **31.** J Physiol 501, 125 (1997); **32.** FEBS Lett 364, 59 (1995); **33.** Biochemistry 33, 8262 (1994); **34.** Biochemistry 40, 5087 (2001); **35.** Biochemistry 26, 4922 (1987); **36.** Biochemistry 24, 6631 (1985); **37.** J Biol Chem 255, 11296 (1980); **38.** J Biol Chem 253, 3757 (1978); **39.** J Biol Chem 265, 14277 (1990); **40.** Biochemistry 39, 6594 (2000); **41.** Biophys J 51, 513 (1987); **42.** Eur J Biochem 130, 5 (1983); **43.** Biophys J 74, 1115 (1998); **44.** J Biochem (Tokyo) 117, 881 (1995); **45.** Eur J Biochem 204, 783 (1992); **46.** J Biol Chem 266, 5508 (1991); **47.** Arch Biochem Biophys 266, 622 (1988); **48.** J Chromatogr 564, 258 (1991); **49.** J Biochem (Tokyo) 116, 236 (1994); **50.** J Muscle Res Cell Motil 4, 253 (1983); **51.** Eur J Biochem 114, 33 (1981); **52.** Nucleic Acids Symp Ser 83 (1997); **53.** Photochem Photobiol 62, 836 (1995); **54.** FEBS Lett 420, 63 (1997); **55.** Eur J Biochem 268, 800 (2001); **56.** Biochemistry 35, 973 (1996); **57.** Biochemistry 34, 11864 (1995); **58.** J Biol Chem 270, 9911 (1995); **59.** J Biol Chem 267, 23495 (1992); **60.** J Biol Chem 269, 12880 (1994); **61.** J Biol Chem 275, 20610 (2000); **62.** J Biol Chem 274, 20133 (1999); **63.** J Biol Chem 267, 14941 (1992); **64.** Biochemistry 24, 3731 (1985); **65.** Biochim Biophys Acta 773, 321 (1984); **66.** Proc Natl Acad Sci U S A 73, 133 (1976); **67.** Biochemistry 12, 2250 (1973); **68.** Biochemistry 12, 4154 (1973); **69.** Biopolymers 27, 821 (1988); **70.** J Muscle Res Cell Motil 8, 97 (1987); **71.** Eur J Biochem 187, 155 (1990); **72.** Biochim Biophys Acta 1479, 247 (2000); **73.** Biophys J 76, 1480 (1999); **74.** Biochemistry 36, 970 (1997); **75.** Biochemistry 33, 8464 (1994); **76.** Methods Enzymol 102, 148 (1983); **77.** Science 185, 1176 (1974); **78.** Photochem Photobiol 66, 424 (1997); **79.** Anal Commun 36, 175 (1999); **80.** J Biol Chem 263, 14107 (1988); **81.** J Am Chem Soc 108, 4527 (1986); **82.** J Pharm Pharmacol 35, 384 (1983); **83.** Anal Lett 21, 741 (1988); **84.** J Chromatogr 309, 409 (1984); **85.** Histochemistry 86, 281 (1987); **86.** J Chromatogr 424, 141 (1988); **87.** Anal Biochem 107, 1 (1980); **88.** Anal Biochem 111, 357 (1981); **89.** Arch Biochem Biophys 282, 307 (1990); **90.** J Leukoc Biol 45, 177 (1989); **91.** Methods Enzymol 143, 76 (1987); **92.** Proc Natl Acad Sci U S A 76, 3382 (1979); **93.** Mol Reprod Dev 37, 318 (1994); **94.** Anal Biochem 209, 57 (1993); **95.** Anal Biochem 225, 174 (1995); **96.** Proc Natl Acad Sci U S A 97, 1461 (2000); **97.** Biochem Biophys Res Commun 152, 1 (1988); **98.** Biochemistry 26, 1889 (1987); **99.** Proc Natl Acad Sci U S A 82, 1658 (1985); **100.** Biochim Biophys Acta 622, 201 (1980); **101.** Proc Natl Acad Sci U S A 93, 10123 (1996); **102.** FEBS Lett 150, 207 (1982); **103.** J Biol Chem 271, 24465 (1996); **104.** J Mol Biol 299, 421 (2000);**105.** J Biol Chem 274, 35388 (1999); **106.** Kidney Int 51, 1797 (1997); **107.** FEBS Lett 356, 66 (1994); **108.** Biochemistry 36, 11564 (1997); **109.** J Biol Chem 272, 29511 (1997); **110.** J Biol Chem 272, 23239 (1997); **111.** Biochemistry 30, 11245 (1991); **112.** Biochem Soc Trans 23, 38S (1995); **113.** Biochemistry 37, 1350 (1998); **114.** Biochemistry 36, 7951 (1997); **115.** Nucleic Acids Res 22, 4789 (1994); **116.** Bioconjug Chem 4, 69 (1993); **117.** Proc Natl Acad Sci U S A 86, 9702 (1989).

Data Table — 2.3 Thiol-Reactive Probes Excited with Ultraviolet Light

Cat #	MW	Storage	Soluble	Abs	EC	Em	Solvent	Notes
A433	225.29	L	DMF, MeCN	391	20,000	500	MeOH	1
A484	624.33	F,D,L	H_2O	329	39,000	408	pH 8	2, 3
A485	536.44	F,D	H_2O	322	35,000	411	pH 8	2
A30458	1095.39	F,DD,L	H_2O, DMSO	400	34,000	424	pH 7	4, 5
A30505	578.68	F,DD,L	H_2O, DMSO	345	17,000	444	pH 7	5
B6057	292.17	F,L	DMF, MeCN	387	21,000	520	MeOH	6
B30500	375.17	F,D,L	DMSO	375	5,800	456	MeOH	3
B30501	358.35	F,D,L	DMSO	375	5,700	458	MeOH	
D146	706.86	L	pH >6	328	8,400	563	pH 7	7
D151	276.35	F,D,L	DMF, MeCN	340	4,100	543	MeOH	8
D346	402.45	F,D,L	DMSO	384	33,000	469	MeOH	9
D404	490.34	F,D,L	DMSO	384	31,000	470	MeOH	2, 3
D1379	350.01	L	DMF, MeCN	391	6,100	see Notes	MeOH	10
D10251	298.30	F,D,L	DMSO	383	27,000	463	MeOH	11
D10252	386.19	F,D,L	DMSO	376	24,000	465	MeOH	3
D10253	383.40	F,D,L	DMSO	419	50,000	466	MeOH	12
D10300	507.40	F,D,L	DMSO	374	24,000	572	MeOH	13
D10301	583.74	F,D,L	DMF, DMSO	374	24,000	574	MeOH	13
D20382	471.29	F,D,L	DMSO	420	49,000	470	MeOH	3, 14
H30460	631.02	F,DD,L	H_2O, DMSO	347	19,000	445	pH 7	5
H30461	990.30	F,DD,L	H_2O, DMSO	400	34,000	424	pH 7	4, 5
I7	504.27	F,D,L	DMF	326	27,000	462	MeOH	2, 3
I14	434.25	F,D,L	pH >6, DMF	336	5,700	490	pH 8	3, 15
M8	416.38	F,D,L	DMSO, DMF	322	27,000	417	MeOH	16
M1378	271.11	F,L	DMF, MeCN	398	5,000	see Notes	pH 7	10
M1380	409.12	L	H_2O	378	5,500	see Notes	pH 7	10, 17
M1381MP	226.66	F,L	DMSO	380	6,000	see Notes	MeOH	10
M20381	271.11	F,L	DMF, MeCN	398	5,000	see Notes	pH 7	10, 18
P4	400.22	F,D,L	DMF, MeCN	341	43,000	376	MeOH	3, 19
P28	297.31	F,D,L	DMF, DMSO	338	40,000	375	MeOH	19, 20
P29	385.20	F,D,L	DMF, DMSO	339	26,000	384	MeOH	2, 3
P2007MP	399.23	F,D,L	DMSO	341	41,000	377	MeOH	2, 3, 19
P6878	316.16	F,D,L	DMSO	270	29,000	none	$CHCl_3$	
P6879	363.16	F,D,L	DMSO	270	28,000	none	$CHCl_3$	3
T30502	383.37	F,D,L	DMSO	375	5,700	458	MeOH	

For definitions of the contents of this data table, see "Navigating *The Handbook*" in the introductory pages.

Notes

1. Fluorescence of unconjugated A433 is weak, increasing markedly upon reaction with thiols. Em (QY) for the 2-mercaptoethanol adduct are: 540 nm (0.18) in H_2O, 513 nm (0.57) in MeOH, 502 nm (0.79) in EtOH, 468 nm (0.78) in MeCN, 435 nm (0.83) in dioxane (J Biol Chem 258, 7541 (1983)).
2. Spectral data of the 2-mercaptoethanol adduct.
3. Iodoacetamides in solution undergo rapid photodecomposition to unreactive products. Minimize exposure to light prior to reaction.
4. The Alexa Fluor® 405 and Cascade Blue® dyes have a second absorption peak at about 376 nm with EC ~80% of the 395–400 nm peak.
5. Aqueous stock solutions should be used within 24 hours; long-term storage is NOT recommended.
6. Em for 2-mercaptoethanol adduct of B6057: 550 nm in H_2O (pH 7), 523 nm in MeOH, 514 nm in EtOH, 502 nm in MeCN, 469 nm in $CHCl_3$, 457 nm in dioxane, 445 nm in toluene. Abs is relatively independent of solvent.
7. D146 thiol conjugate has EC = 4000 $cm^{-1}M^{-1}$. Em = 527 nm on G-actin, shifting to 520 nm upon polymerization (Arch Biochem Biophys 142, 333 (1971)).
8. D151 conjugated to calmodulin with and without Ca^{2+} has Em = 532 nm and 550 nm, respectively (Methods Enzymol 102, 148 (1983)). On troponin I, Em = 500 nm (with Ca^{2+}) and 550 nm (without Ca^{2+}) (Biochemistry 21, 5669 (1982)). Fluorescence lifetimes of these conjugates are 14 to 20 nsec (Ca^{2+}-dependent).
9. Spectral data are for the 2-mercaptoethanol adduct. The unreacted reagent is nonfluorescent, Abs = 384 nm (EC = 32,000 $cm^{-1}M^{-1}$) in MeOH.
10. Bimanes are almost nonfluorescent until reacted with thiols. For monobromobimane conjugated to glutathione, Abs = 394 nm, Em = 490 nm (QY ~0.1–0.3) in pH 8 buffer (Methods Enzymol 143, 76 (1987); Methods Enzymol 251, 133 (1995)).
11. Spectral data are for the 2-mercaptoethanol adduct. The unreacted reagent is nonfluorescent, Abs = 381 nm (EC = 27,000 $cm^{-1}M^{-1}$) in MeOH.
12. QY increases on reaction with thiols; Abs, EC and Em are unchanged (J Chem Soc Perkin Trans I 2975 (1994)).
13. Fluorescence emission spectrum shifts to shorter wavelengths in nonpolar solvents.
14. Spectral data are for the unreacted reagent and are essentially unchanged upon reaction with thiols (J Chem Soc Perkin Trans I 2975 (1994)).
15. The 2-mercaptoethanol adduct of I14 has essentially similar spectral characteristics in aqueous solution (Biochemistry 12, 4154 (1973)). Fluorescence lifetime (τ) = 21 nsec when conjugated to myosin subfragment-1 (Biochemistry 12, 2250 (1973)).
16. Spectral data are for the 2-mercaptoethanol adduct. The unreacted reagent is nonfluorescent, Abs = 443 nm (EC = 13,000 $cm^{-1}M^{-1}$) in MeOH.
17. Unstable in water. Use immediately.
18. This product is specified to equal or exceed 98% analytical purity by HPLC.
19. Pyrene derivatives exhibit structured spectra. The absorption maximum is usually about 340 nm with a subsidiary peak at about 325 nm. There are also strong absorption peaks below 300 nm. The emission maximum is usually 376 nm with a subsidiary peak at 396 nm. Excimer emission at about 470 nm may be observed at high concentrations.
20. Fluorescence of unreacted P28 is weak. Em data represent the 2-mercaptoethanol adduct.

Product List — 2.3 Thiol-Reactive Probes Excited with Ultraviolet Light

Cat #	Product Name	Unit Size
A484	4-acetamido-4′-((iodoacetyl)amino)stilbene-2,2′-disulfonic acid, disodium salt	25 mg
A485	4-acetamido-4′-maleimidylstilbene-2,2′-disulfonic acid, disodium salt	25 mg
A433	6-acryloyl-2-dimethylaminonaphthalene (acrylodan)	25 mg
A30505	Alexa Fluor® 350 C_5-maleimide	1 mg
A30458	Alexa Fluor® 405 C_5-maleimide	1 mg
B30501	bimane C_3-maleimide	5 mg
B30500	bimane iodoacetamide	5 mg
B6057	6-bromoacetyl-2-dimethylaminonaphthalene (badan)	10 mg
D10300	Dapoxyl® (2-bromoacetamidoethyl)sulfonamide	10 mg
D10301	Dapoxyl® 2-(3-(2-pyridyldithio)propionamidoethyl)sulfonamide	10 mg
D1379	dibromobimane (bBBr)	25 mg
D146	*N,N′*-didansyl-L-cystine	100 mg
D20382	7-diethylamino-3-((((2-iodoacetamido)ethyl)amino)carbonyl)coumarin (IDCC)	5 mg
D404	7-diethylamino-3-((4′-(iodoacetyl)amino)phenyl)-4-methylcoumarin (DCIA)	25 mg
D10253	7-diethylamino-3-((((2-maleimidyl)ethyl)amino)carbonyl)coumarin (MDCC)	5 mg
D346	7-diethylamino-3-(4′-maleimidylphenyl)-4-methylcoumarin (CPM)	25 mg
D10252	*N*-(7-dimethylamino-4-methylcoumarin-3-yl)iodoacetamide (DACIA)	10 mg
D10251	*N*-(7-dimethylamino-4-methylcoumarin-3-yl)maleimide (DACM)	10 mg
D151	5-dimethylaminonaphthalene-1-sulfonyl aziridine (dansyl aziridine)	100 mg
H30460	Hg-Link™ Alexa Fluor® 350 phenylmercury	1 mg
H30461	Hg-Link™ Alexa Fluor® 405 phenylmercury, disodium salt	1 mg
I7	2-(4′-(iodoacetamido)anilino)naphthalene-6-sulfonic acid, sodium salt (IAANS)	100 mg
I14	5-((((2-iodoacetyl)amino)ethyl)amino)naphthalene-1-sulfonic acid (1,5-IAEDANS)	100 mg
M8	2-(4′-maleimidylanilino)naphthalene-6-sulfonic acid, sodium salt (MIANS)	100 mg
M1378	monobromobimane (mBBr)	25 mg
M20381	monobromobimane (mBBr) *FluoroPure™ grade*	25 mg
M1380	monobromotrimethylammoniobimane bromide (qBBr)	25 mg
M1381MP	monochlorobimane (mBCl)	25 mg
P6878	*N*-(1,10-phenanthrolin-5-yl)bromoacetamide	5 mg
P6879	*N*-(1,10-phenanthrolin-5-yl)iodoacetamide	5 mg
P29	*N*-(1-pyrene)iodoacetamide	100 mg
P28	*N*-(1-pyrene)maleimide	100 mg
P2007MP	*N*-(1-pyrenemethyl)iodoacetamide (PMIA amide)	25 mg
P4	1-pyrenemethyl iodoacetate (PMIA ester)	100 mg
T30502	TS-Link™ bimane thiosulfate, sodium salt	5 mg

For current prices or to order online, visit probes.invitrogen.com

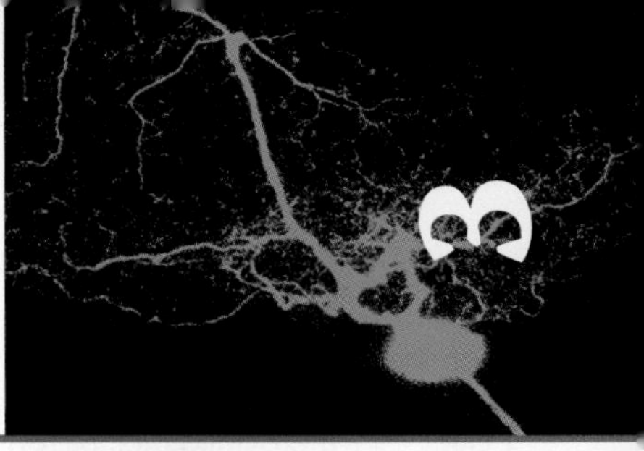

Chapter 3

Reagents for Modifying Groups Other Than Thiols or Amines

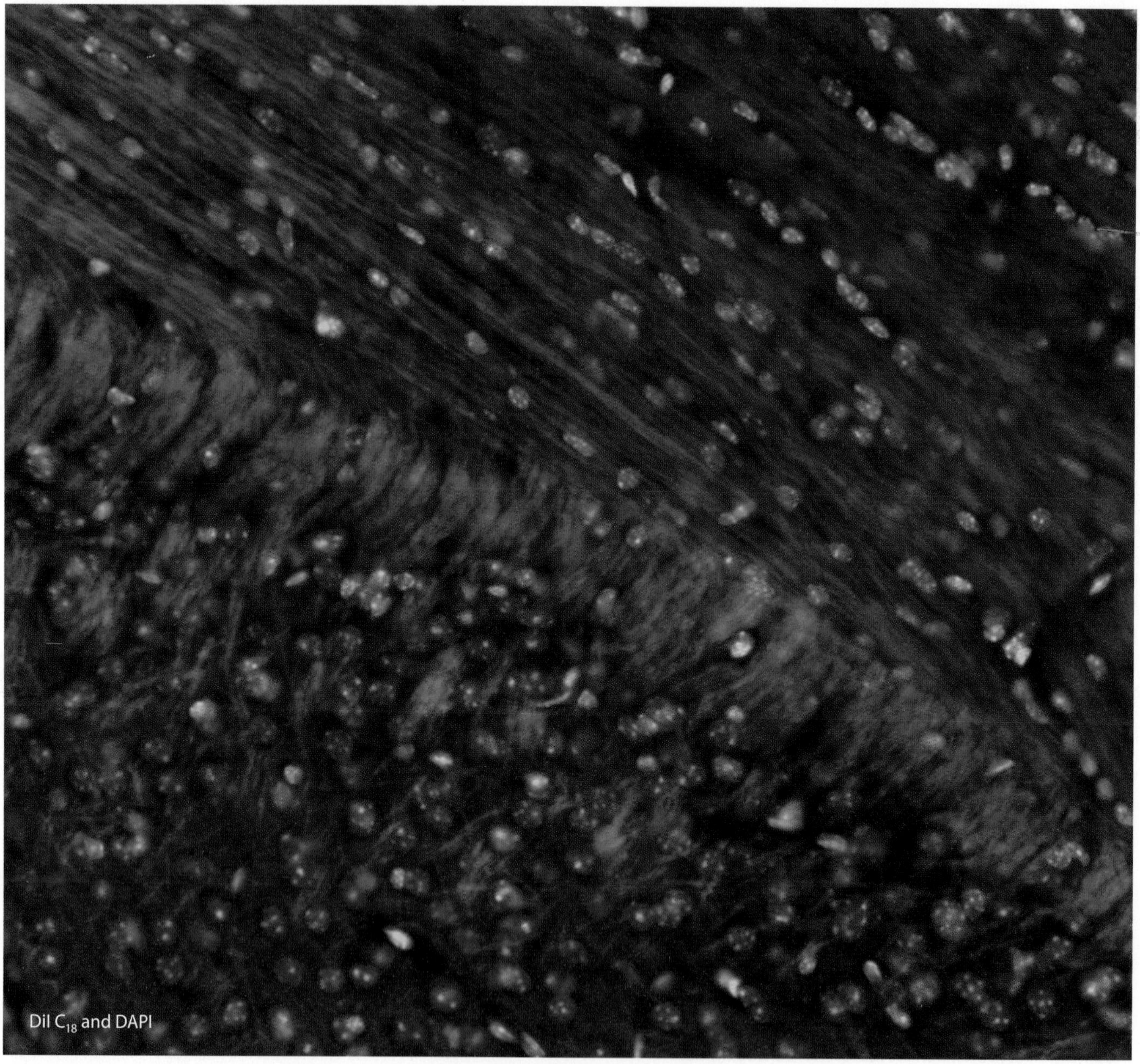
DiI C_{18} and DAPI

3.1 Reagents for Modifying Alcohols

Alcohols in Proteins: Serine, Threonine and Tyrosine Residues

Although alcohols (including phenols such as tyrosine and the hydroxyl groups in serine, threonine, sterols and carbohydrates) are abundant in biomolecules, their chemical reactivity in aqueous solution is extremely low. Few reagents are selective for alcohols in aqueous solution, especially in the presence of more reactive nucleophiles such as thiols and amines. It is therefore difficult to selectively modify serine, threonine and tyrosine residues in proteins except when they exhibit unusual reactivity, such as by residing at an enzyme's active site.

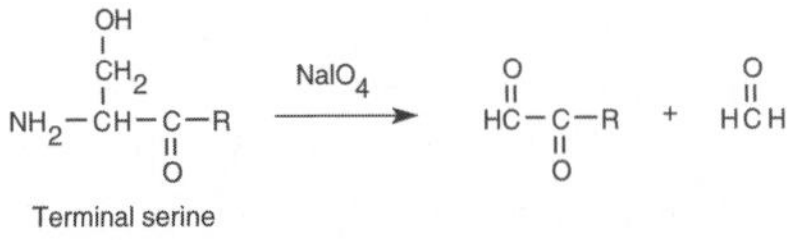

Figure 3.1 Sodium periodate oxidation of an N-terminal serine residue to an aldehyde, with the release of formaldehyde. The aldehyde thus formed from the protein can be subsequently modified with a variety of hydrazine, hydroxylamine or amine derivatives.

Serine and Threonine Residues

Nonacylated N-terminal serine and threonine residues in peptides and proteins can be oxidized with periodate to yield aldehydes [1–8] (Figure 3.1) that can be subsequently modified with a variety of hydrazine, hydroxylamine or amine derivatives (Section 3.2, Table 3.1). Some reports have described the labeling of certain serine and threonine residues in myosin by 9-anthroylnitrile [9–13] (A1440). In addition, the tripeptide sequences of certain peptides such as gonadotropin-releasing hormone (GnRH) — wherein serine, threonine or tyrosine residues are separated from a histidine residue by a single amino acid — can be selectively acylated by the succinimidyl ester or sulfosuccinimidyl ester of biotin-X (B1582, B6353; Section 4.2; Figure 4.7) or by the Bolton–Hunter reagent.[14–17] This property may also permit selective modification of these sequences (Ser-X-His, Thr-X-His and Tyr-X-His) in peptides and proteins with fluorescent succinimidyl esters (Chapter 1). *O*-acylation versus *N*-acylation can be detected by treatment with hydroxylamine, which cleaves esters but usually not amides.[14]

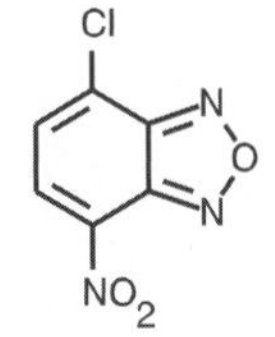

Figure 3.2 C20260 4-chloro-7-nitrobenz-2-oxa-1,3-diazole (NBD chloride; 4-chloro-7-nitrobenzofurazan).

Tyrosine Residues

Modification of tyrosine residues is sometimes a side reaction when proteins are reacted with sulfonyl chlorides, iodoacetamides or other reactive dyes described in Chapter 1 and Chapter 2. For example, NBD chloride (C20260, Section 1.8, Figure 3.2) reacts with an active-site tyrosine in monoamine oxidase enzymes, causing strong inhibition.[18] NBD chloride also reacts with the tyrosine residues in glutathione *S*-transferase,[19] bacterial F_1-ATPase,[20] mitochondrial F_1-ATPase [21,22] and chloroplast H^+-ATPase.[23] The covalent adduct of NBD chloride with phenols has shorter-wavelength absorption than does that with amines.

Tyrosine residues in some proteins can be selectively modified by initial nitration of the *ortho* position of its phenol using tetranitromethane, and then reduction of the *o*-nitrotyrosine with sodium dithionite ($Na_2S_2O_4$) to form an *o*-aminotyrosine (Figure 3.3). Although much less reactive than aliphatic amines, the aromatic amine of *o*-aminotyrosine can react with most amine-reactive reagents (except succinimidyl esters) between pH 5 and 7.[24] This indirect method has been used to selectively modify tyrosine residues in actin with dansyl chloride, dabsyl chloride and NBD fluoride [25–27] (D21, Section 1.7; D1537, F486; Section 1.8).

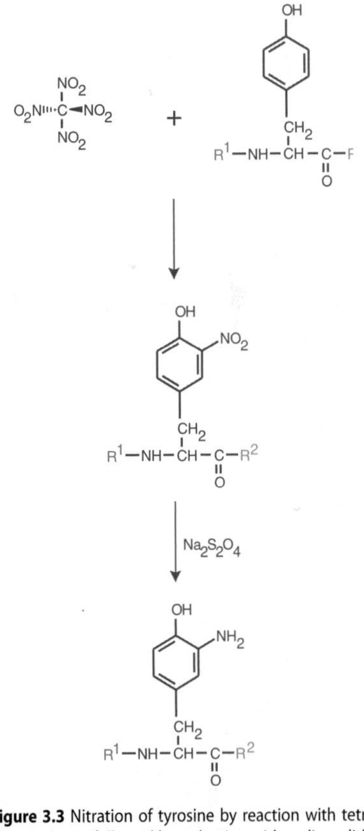

Figure 3.3 Nitration of tyrosine by reaction with tetranitromethane, followed by reduction with sodium dithionite, to yield an *o*-aminotyrosine.

Nitration of tyrosine residues by nitric oxide occurs naturally in cells through the intermediacy of peroxynitrite radicals (Section 18.3, Table 18.1), yielding derivatives that can be reduced to *o*-aminotyrosine and subsequently detected using amine-reactive reagents.[28,29] Carcinogenic nitro compounds and nitrosamines also yield tyrosine derivatives that can be detected similarly.[30] The presence of nitrotyrosine has been detected in patients with myocardial inflammation,[29,31] acute lung injury,[32] atherosclerosis [33] and a number of other diseases or conditions. Our rabbit anti-nitrotyrosine antibody (A21285, Section 7.4) may be of utility for detecting and separating proteins containing nitrotyrosine residues.

Another method for modifying tyrosine groups in peptides is to convert the phenol group in tyrosine residues to a salicylaldehyde derivative, and then to react the salicylaldehyde with 1,2-diamino-4,5-dimethoxybenzene (D1463, Section 3.2) to form a fluorescent benzimidazole.[34–36] The salicylaldehyde generated in this Reimer–Tiemann reaction [37] can also potentially react with hydrazine and hydroxylamine derivatives (Section 3.2) to yield fluorescent derivatives, though this reaction has apparently not yet been reported.

The tyramide signal amplification (TSA) technology (Section 6.2), which was developed by NEN (now a part of PerkinElmer Corporation) and licensed to Molecular Probes for in-cell and in-tissue applications, permits significant amplification of the detectability of targets by a horseradish peroxidase–mediated scheme (Figure 6.5). In the TSA method, the labeled tyramide becomes covalently linked to tyrosine residues in or near the target. Molecular Probes has introduced an extensive selection of TSA Kits (Table 6.1) that utilize one of our Alexa Fluor® tyramides, Pacific Blue™ tyramide, Oregon Green® 488 tyramide, biotin-XX tyramide, DSB-X™ biotin tyramide or DNP-X tyramide as the amplification reagents.

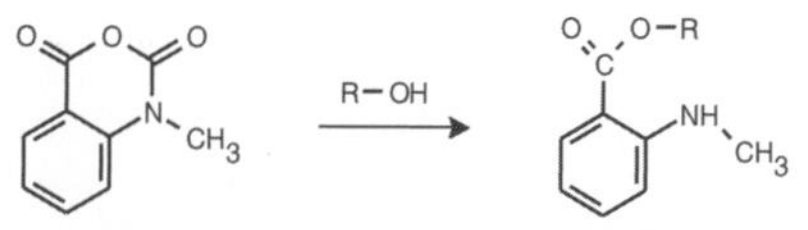

Figure 3.4 Reaction of *N*-methylisatoic anhydride (M25) with an alcohol to produce a blue-fluorescent (~350/446 nm) *N*-methylanthraniloyl (MANT) ester.

Alcohols in Carbohydrates

As with derivatization of alcohols in proteins, it is difficult to selectively modify most carbohydrates in aqueous solution because of their low reactivity and the competing hydrolysis of the reactive reagents. However, several reagents are available for derivatizing reducing sugars (which contain a low equilibrium concentration of the reactive aldehyde function), as well as for modifying aldehydes and ketones obtained by periodate oxidation of various carbohydrates. To pursue this labeling approach, see Section 3.2 for a description of our aldehyde- and ketone-reactive reagents.

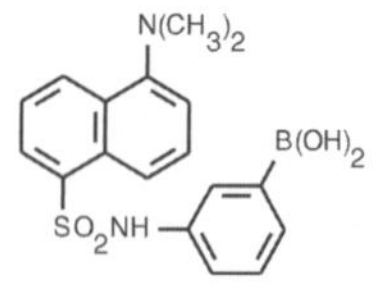

Figure 3.5 D2281 *m*-dansylaminophenylboronic acid.

Dichlorotriazines

Dichlorotriazines readily modify amines in proteins, and they are among the few reactive groups that are reported to react directly with polysaccharides and other alcohols in aqueous solution, provided that the pH is >9 and that other nucleophiles are absent.[38–41] We offer the 5-isomer of fluorescein dichlorotriazine (5-DTAF, D16), with absorption/emission maxima of ~492/516 nm, as well as Texas Red® C_2-dichlorotriazine (T30200), with absorption/emission maxima of ~588/601 nm.

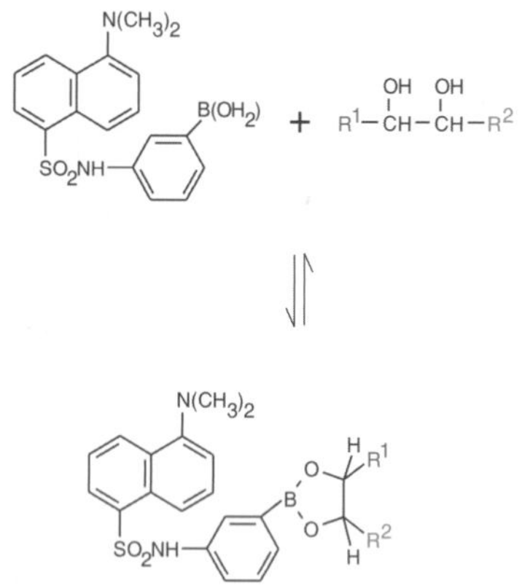

Figure 3.6 Reaction of m-dansylaminophenylboronic acid (D2281) with a vicinal diol to form a reversible fluorescent cyclic complex.

N-*Methylisatoic Anhydride*

In the absence of other reactive functional groups, *N*-methylisatoic anhydride (M25) will convert ribonucleotides and certain other carbohydrates[42] to fluorescent esters with excitation/emission maxima of ~350/446 nm in mildly basic aqueous solution[43–47] (Section 17.3). The compactness and moderate environmental sensitivity of this fluorophore, which is a synthetic precursor to blue-fluorescent *N*-methylanthraniloyl (MANT) amides and esters,[46] may be advantageous for preparing site-selective probes. Low molecular weight alcohols are better derivatized by this reagent in aprotic organic solvents[48–50] (Figure 3.4).

Dansyl Aminophenylboronic Acid

m-Dansylaminophenylboronic acid (D2281, Figure 3.5) reacts with vicinal diols (hydroxyl groups on adjacent carbon atoms) and certain amino alcohols to form cyclic complexes[51,52] (Figure 3.6) that have a fluorescence intensity and peak emission dependent on the environment of the dansyl fluorophore. This interesting reagent binds reversibly to cell-wall carbohydrates and probably glycoproteins,[52] as well as to glycosylated (but not deglycosylated) human serum albumin.[53] Moreover, it specifically inhibits certain serine hydrolases that have adjacent histidine residues, including subtilisin,[54] lipoprotein lipase,[55] human milk lipase[56] and the β-lactamase from *Enterobacter cloacae* P99.[57] Dansylaminophenylboronic acid is also used as an HPLC derivatization reagent for vicinal diols[58] and as a detection reagent for glycolipids analyzed by thin-layer chromatography.[59]

Alcohol Modification in Organic Solvents

Two functional groups — acyl azides and acyl nitriles — react directly with aliphatic amines to yield the same products as do the corresponding succinimidyl esters. However, when reacted in organic solvents, these reagents can also form derivatives of alcohols and phenols, making them extremely useful for sensitive analysis of alcohols by HPLC or capillary electrophoresis.

Isocyanates Prepared from Acyl Azides

Alcohols are much easier to modify in anhydrous organic solvents than in aqueous solution. Perhaps the most effective reagents are isocyanates, which are much more reactive with alcohols (and amines) than are isothiocyanates but are not sufficiently stable to permit their sale. Fortunately, isocyanates can often be prepared by Curtius rearrangement of acyl azides (Figure 3.7). When an acyl azide and alcohol are heated together in an organic solvent such as toluene, dioxane or DMF at 80°C, the acyl azide will rearrange to form an isocyanate that then reacts with the alcohol to form a stable urethane. As little as 50 femtograms of the urethane conjugates prepared from the coumarin derivatives 7-methoxycoumarin-3-carbonyl azide (M1445) and 7-diethylaminocoumarin-3-carbonyl azide (D1446) can be detected using an HPLC fluorescence detector.[60,61] Alcohol conjugates (urethanes) prepared from the single-isomer carbonyl azides of fluorescein diacetate (F6218) and tetramethylrhodamine (T6219) may provide even higher sensitivity, particularly with instruments that employ the argon-ion laser. Following rearrangement and alcohol conjugation, the acetates of the fluorescein derivative can be removed by hydrolysis at pH 9–10. The diacetate of fluorescein-5-carbonyl azide has been used to synthesize a fluorogenic substrate for the anandamide transmembrane carrier.[62] Tetramethylrhodamine-5-carbonyl azide has been successfully conjugated to the hydrophobic poly(ε-caprolactone) (PCL) block of a diblock copolymer micelle in order to follow its cellular internalization.[63]

Acyl Nitriles

9-Anthroylnitrile (A1440) reacts with alcohols, such as steroids and acylglycerols, in organic solvents to yield carboxylate esters that are useful for HPLC.[64,65] To optimize solid-phase organic synthesis, 9-anthroylnitrile has been used to quantitate the absolute amount of resin-bound hydroxyl groups directly on solid support.[66] In addition, 9-anthroylnitrile has been reported to be useful for the selective labeling of certain serine and threonine residues in myosin.[9–13] The lipophilicity of 9-anthroylnitrile may make it useful for modifying hydroxyl groups of proteins and hydroxylated fatty acids that are buried within cell membranes.

References

1. Biochem J 108, 883 (1968); **2.** Biochem J 95, 180 (1965); **3.** Biochem J 94, 17 (1965); **4.** Bioconjug Chem 7, 38 (1996); **5.** Bioconjug Chem 4, 537 (1993); **6.** Bioconjug Chem 3, 138 (1992); **7.** Bioconjug Chem 5, 636 (1994); **8.** J Biol Chem 269, 7224 (1994); **9.** Biochemistry 35, 16061 (1996); **10.** Biochemistry 33, 6867 (1994); **11.** J Biol Chem 265, 18791 (1990); **12.** J Biol Chem 265, 18786 (1990); **13.** J Biol Chem 264, 18188 (1989); **14.** J Biol Chem 267, 5060 (1992); **15.** Biochem Biophys Res Commun 218, 377 (1996); **16.** Anal Biochem 219, 240 (1994); **17.** Biochem Biophys Res Commun 196, 461 (1993); **18.** J Neurochem 55, 813 (1990); **19.** J Biol Chem 266, 13777 (1991); **20.** J Biol Chem 265, 2483 (1990); **21.** Biochim Biophys Acta 1057, 208 (1991); **22.** J Biol Chem 264, 1361 (1989); **23.** Z Naturforsch [C] 49, 204 (1994); **24.** Eur J Biochem 60, 67 (1975); **25.** Eur J Biochem 132, 339 (1983); **26.** Biochem Int 22, 125 (1990); **27.** Biochemistry 18, 3589 (1979); **28.** Anal Biochem 259, 127 (1998); **29.** Proc Natl Acad Sci U S A 94, 3211 (1997); **30.** Chem Res Toxicol 10, 1420 (1997); **31.** Crit Care Med 25, 812 (1997); **32.** Am J Respir Crit Care Med 151, 1250 (1995); **33.** Biol Chem Hoppe Seyler 375, 81 (1994); **34.** J Chromatogr 430, 271 (1988); **35.** J Chromatogr 356, 171 (1986); **36.** J Chromatogr 344, 267 (1985); **37.** Pharmazie 33, 467 (1978); **38.** Eur J Cell Biol 74, 376 (1997); **39.** Anal Biochem 247, 348 (1997); **40.** J Biomed Mater Res 40, 275 (1998); **41.** Carbohydr Res 30, 251 (1973); **42.** Anal Biochem 284, 167 (2000); **43.** Biochemistry 30, 422 (1991); **44.** Biochemistry 29, 3309 (1990); **45.** Biochim Biophys Acta 742, 496 (1983); **46.** J Biol Chem 257, 13354 (1982); **47.** Arch Biochem Biophys 155, 70 (1973); **48.** Anal Biochem 234, 31 (1996); **49.** Synthesis 39, 266 (1982); **50.** J Org Chem 24, 1214 (1959); **51.** Science 217, 166 (1982); **52.** Biochem Biophys Res Commun 96, 157 (1980); **53.** Clin Chim Acta 149, 13 (1985); **54.** FEBS Lett 133, 36 (1981); **55.** Biochim Biophys Acta 746, 217 (1983); **56.** J Mol Catalysis 52, 317 (1989); **57.** Biochemistry 28, 6875 (1989); **58.** Anal Chim Acta 228, 101 (1990); **59.** J Lipid Res 36, 1848 (1995); **60.** Chem Pharm Bull 33, 1164 (1985); **61.** J Lipid Res 38, 429 (1997); **62.** J Pharmacol Exp Ther 293, 289 (2000); **63.** Bioconjug Chem 13, 1259 (2002); **64.** Anal Chim Acta 147, 397 (1983); **65.** J Chromatogr 276, 289 (1983); **66.** Anal Chem 71, 4564 (1999).

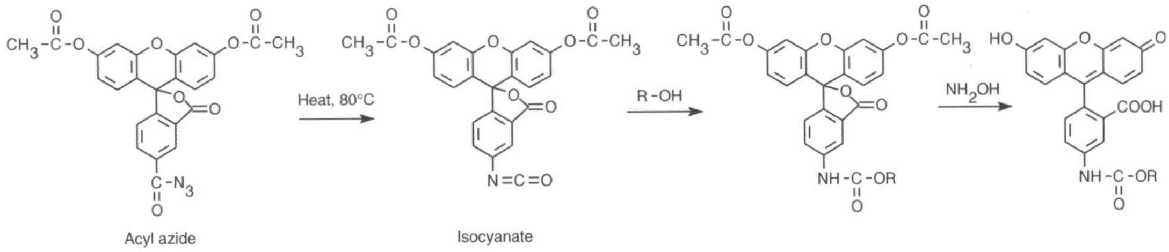

Figure 3.7 Derivatization of an alcohol using the diacetate of fluorescein-5-carbonyl azide (F6218). This process consists of three steps: 1) rearrangement of the acyl azide to an isocyanate, 2) reaction of the isocyanate with an alcohol to form a urethane and 3) deprotection of the nonfluorescent urethane derivative using hydroxylamine.

Data Table — 3.1 Reagents for Modifying Alcohols

Cat #	MW	Storage	Soluble	Abs	EC	Em	Solvent	Notes
A1440	231.25	F,D,L	DMF, MeCN	361	7,500	470	MeOH	1
D16	495.28	F,D,L	pH >6, DMF	492	83,000	516	pH 9	2, 3
D1446	286.29	F,D,L	DMF, MeCN	436	57,000	478	MeOH	
D2281	370.23	D,L	DMF, DMSO	337	4,600	517	MeOH	4
D10402	463.31	F,D,L	DMF, DMSO	376	22,000	570	MeOH	5
F6218	485.41	FF,D	DMF, MeCN	<300		none		
M25	177.16	D	DMF, DMSO	316	3,500	386	MeOH	6
M1445	245.19	FF,D,L	DMF, MeCN	360	25,000	415	MeOH	
T6219	455.47	FF,D,L	DMF, MeCN	545	90,000	578	MeOH	
T30200	796.74	F,D,L	DMF, DMSO	583	87,000	604	MeOH	

For definitions of the contents of this data table, see "Navigating *The Handbook*" in the introductory pages.

Notes

1. The absorption spectrum of A1440 has subsidiary peaks at 380 nm and 344 nm. Emission spectrum is unstructured. Ester derivatives formed by reaction with alcohols have essentially similar spectra.
2. Unstable in water. Use immediately.
3. Absorption and fluorescence of fluorescein derivatives are pH-dependent. Extinction coefficients and fluorescence quantum yields decrease markedly at pH <7.
4. Fluorescence of D2281 when bound to proteins is typically blue shifted (Em ~490 nm).
5. Fluorescence emission spectrum shifts to shorter wavelengths in nonpolar solvents.
6. The amide reaction product of M25 with butylamine has Abs = 353 nm (EC = 5900 $cm^{-1}M^{-1}$), Em = 426 nm in MeOH. Ester reaction products with alcohols have Abs = 350 nm (EC = 5700 $cm^{-1}M^{-1}$), Em = 446 nm in water (pH 8).

Product List — 3.1 Reagents for Modifying Alcohols

Cat #	Product Name	Unit Size
A1440	9-anthroylnitrile	25 mg
D2281	*m*-dansylaminophenylboronic acid	100 mg
D10402	Dapoxyl® 3-sulfonamidophenylboronic acid	5 mg
D16	5-(4,6-dichlorotriazinyl)aminofluorescein (5-DTAF) *single isomer*	100 mg
D1446	7-diethylaminocoumarin-3-carbonyl azide	25 mg
F6218	fluorescein-5-carbonyl azide, diacetate	10 mg
M1445	7-methoxycoumarin-3-carbonyl azide	25 mg
M25	*N*-methylisatoic anhydride *high purity*	1 g
T6219	tetramethylrhodamine-5-carbonyl azide	5 mg
T30200	Texas Red® C_2-dichlorotriazine	5 mg

For current prices or to order online, visit probes.invitrogen.com

3.2 Hydrazines, Hydroxylamines and Aromatic Amines for Modifying Aldehydes and Ketones

Aldehydes and ketones are present in a number of low molecular weight molecules such as drugs, steroid hormones, reducing sugars and metabolic intermediates (e.g., pyruvate and α-ketoglutarate). Except for polysaccharides containing free reducing sugars, biopolymers generally lack aldehyde and ketone groups. Even those aldehydes and ketones that are found in the open-ring form of simple carbohydrates are usually in equilibrium with the closed-ring form of the sugar. The infrequent occurrence of aldehydes and ketones has stimulated the development of techniques to selectively introduce these functional groups into certain biomolecules, thus providing unique sites for chemical modification and greatly extending the applications of the probes found in this section. Experimental protocols designed to directly express ketone-containing carbohydrates on cell surfaces have led to the introduction of the reagents ManLev and ManLev tetraacetate (see below) for metabolic labeling of cell-surface glycoproteins.[1–6] Fluorescent modification of aldehyde or carboxylic acid groups in carbohydrates is also frequently utilized for their analysis by HPLC, capillary electrophoresis[7] and other methods.

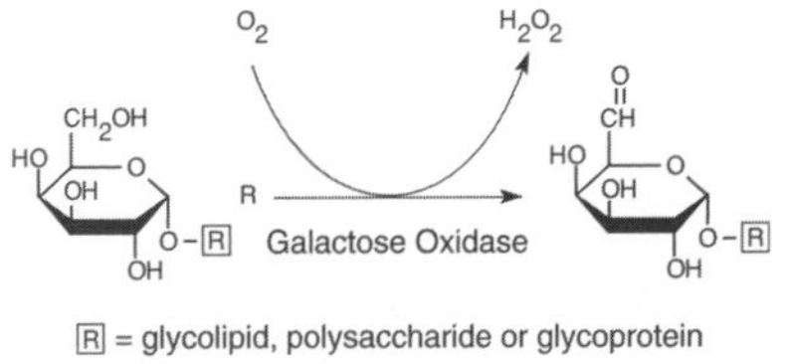

Figure 3.8 Oxidation of the terminal galactose residue of a glycoprotein, glycolipid or polysaccharide results in the generation of an aldehyde, which can react with hydrazines, hydroxylamines or primary amine–containing compounds.

Introducing Aldehydes and Ketones into Biomolecules

Periodate Oxidation

The most common method for introducing aldehydes and ketones into polysaccharides and glycoproteins (including antibodies) is by periodate-mediated oxidation of vicinal diols. In addition, alkenes from unsaturated fatty acids and ceramides can be converted to glycols by osmium tetroxide and then oxidized by periodate to aldehydes. Periodate will also oxidize certain β-aminoethanol derivatives such as the hydroxylysine residues in collagen, as well as methionine (to its sulfoxide) and certain thiols (usually to disulfides). These other reactions, however, usually occur at a slower rate than oxidation of vicinal diols. Periodate oxidation of the 3′-terminal ribose provides one of the few methods of selectively modifying RNA.[8,9] Periodate-oxidized ribonucleotides can subsequently be converted to fluorescent nucleic acid probes by reaction with fluorescent hydrazines, hydroxylamines and amines.[10] Furthermore, N-terminal serine and threonine residues of peptides and proteins can be selectively oxidized by periodate to aldehyde groups[11–14] (Figure 3.1), thus allowing highly selective modification of certain proteins such as corticotrophin[15,16] and β-lactamase.[17] Moreover, because antibodies are glycosylated at sites distant from the antigen-binding region, modification of periodate-oxidized antibodies by hydrazines and hydroxylamines usually does not inactivate the antibody, as sometimes occurs with FITC, TRITC and Texas Red® sulfonyl chloride labeling. Researchers have also used some of the hydrazine derivatives described in this section to detect periodate-oxidized glycoproteins in gels.[18] Our Pro-Q® Emerald 300 and Pro-Q® Emerald 488 Glycoprotein Stain Kits for Gels and for Blots (Section 9.4, Table 9.8) are based on periodate oxidation of glycoproteins. The Pro-Q® Emerald 300 and Pro-Q® Emerald 488 reagents provide sensitivity and linearity of response for glycoprotein detection that is superior to any previous technology (Figure 9.52).

Enzyme-Mediated Oxidation with Galactose Oxidase

A second specific method for introducing aldehydes into biomolecules is through the use of galactose oxidase, an enzyme that oxidizes terminal galactose residues to aldehydes, particularly in glycoproteins.[19–23] This method was used to label live corn and rose protoplasts with hydrazine derivatives and aromatic amines.[24] The introduction of galactose residues can be especially advantageous for structural studies because it provides a means of selectively labeling specific sites on biomolecules. For example, galactose has been specifically inserted into the carbohydrate moiety of rhodopsin using a galactosyl transferase.[23] Galactose oxidase–modified lipopolysaccharides (LPS) have been modified with Alexa Fluor® 488 hydrazide (A10436) to probe for LPS-binding sites on cells.[25] Because galactose oxidase–mediated oxidation liberates a molecule of hydrogen peroxide for each molecule of aldehyde that is formed (Figure 3.8), horseradish peroxidase–catalyzed oxidation of the Amplex® Red reagent to red-fluorescent resorufin by hydrogen peroxide provides a ready means by which the number of aldehyde residues introduced into a biomolecule, including on a cell surface, can be quantitated. The Amplex® Red Galactose/Galactose Oxidase Assay Kit (A22179) provides the reagents and a general protocol for this assay of introduced aldehyde residues.

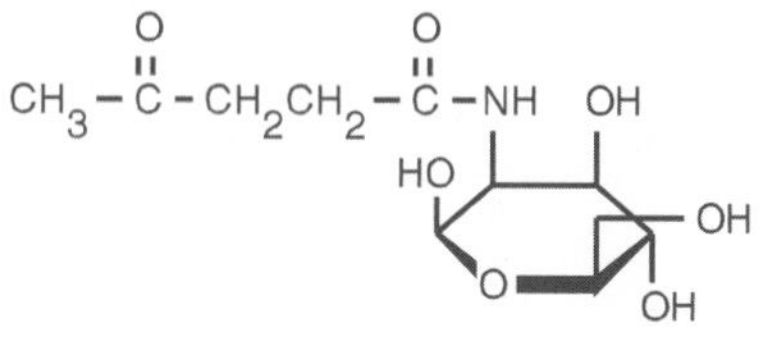

Figure 3.9 L20492 N-levulinoyl-D-mannosamine (ManLev).

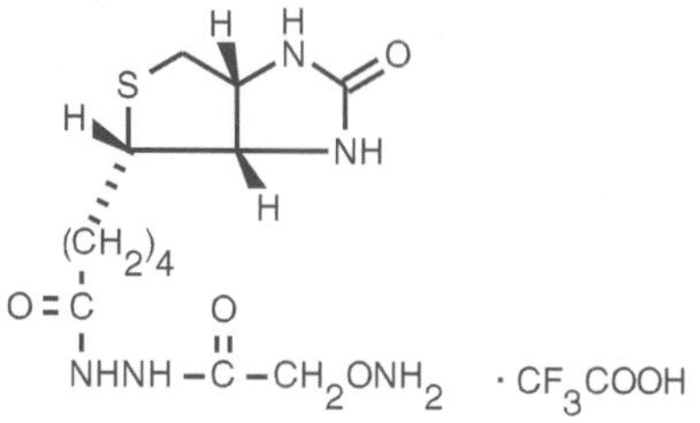

Figure 3.10 A10550 *N*-(aminooxyacetyl)-*N*′-(D-biotinoyl) hydrazine, trifluoroacetic acid salt (ARP).

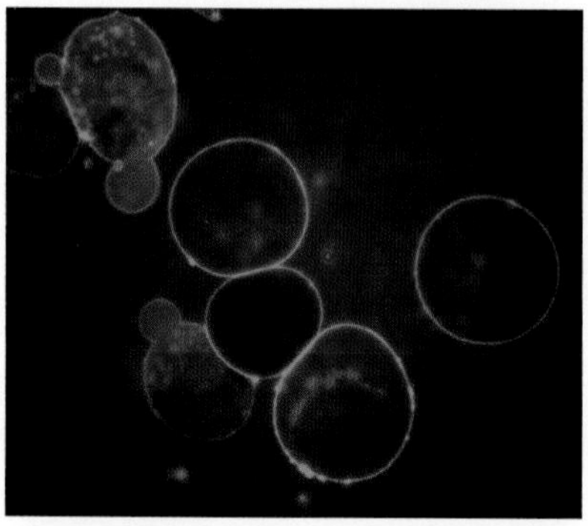

Figure 3.11 Metabolic labeling of cell-surface glycoproteins. Jurkat cells were cultured for 24 hours in the presence of 25 µM ManLev tetraacetate (L20493). Following treatment, the cell surface–expressed, ketone-containing glycoproteins were reacted with a biotin-containing ketone-reactive reagent, ARP (A10550), and then visualized by incubation with Alexa Fluor® 488 streptavidin (S11223). The metabolically labeled glycoproteins were detected using a fluorescence microscope equipped with a filter set appropriate for FITC. No fluorescence was observed in control cells that were not treated with ManLev tetraacetate (data not shown).

Metabolic Incorporation of Ketone-Containing Carbohydrates

The oligosaccharide components of cell-surface glycoproteins play a role in the interactions that regulate many important biological processes, from cell–cell adhesion to signal transduction. Because modification of these surface groups affects the behavior of the cell,[26] strategies that introduce alternative surface groups to the cell provide researchers with novel methods for tagging specific cell populations. Sialic acids are the most abundant terminal components of oligosaccharides on mammalian cell-surface glycoproteins and are synthesized from the six-carbon precursor *N*-acetylmannosamine.[27] When cells in culture are incubated with 25 mM *N*-levulinoyl-D-mannosamine (ManLev, L20492; Figure 3.9) or — much more efficiently — with 25 µM ManLev tetraacetate (L20493), this ketone-containing monosaccharide serves as a substrate in the oligosaccharide synthesis pathway, resulting in ketone-tagged cell-surface oligosaccharides.[1,3,5,6,28–30] Because ketones are rare in cells, reaction with 2 mM biotinylated aldehyde-reactive probe (ARP, A10550; Section 4.2, Figure 3.10) followed by a fluorescent avidin or streptavidin conjugate (Section 7.6, Table 7.22) provides a means of identifying and tracing tagged cells either by imaging (Figure 3.11) or by flow cytometry. We find that the biotin hydroxylamine ARP is much more reactive than the biotin hydrazides; fluorescent hydrazides and hydroxylamines usually are not suitable for this detection because the required concentrations can result in their internalization in live cells by pinocytosis.

Coupling Hydrazines and Amines to Amine-Containing Biomolecules without Introducing Aldehydes and Ketones

Common tissue fixatives such as formaldehyde and glutaraldehyde can be used to couple hydrazine and amine derivatives to proteins and other amine-containing polymers. For example, lucifer yellow CH (L453) can be conjugated to surrounding biomolecules by common aldehyde-based fixatives in order to preserve the dye's staining pattern during subsequent tissue manipulations.[31] Glutaraldehyde has also been used to couple biotin hydrazides (Section 4.2) directly to nucleic acids,[32] a reaction that is potentially useful for conjugating fluorescent hydrazine and hydroxylamine derivatives to DNA.

Introducing a Hydroxylamine into a Biomolecule

The tetrafluorophenyl (TFP) ester of *N*-(*t*-BOC)-aminooxyacetic acid (B30300) is an amine-reactive protected hydroxylamine that is useful for synthesizing new aldehyde- and ketone-reactive probes in an organic solvent. Following coupling to aliphatic amines, the *t*-BOC group can be quantitatively removed with trifluoroacetic acid. The resultant hydroxylamine probe can then spontaneously react with aldehydes, the reducing ends of saccharides and oligosaccharides and abasic sites in oligonucleotides to form stable adducts.

Hydrazines and Hydroxylamines

Reactivity of Hydrazine and Hydroxylamine Derivatives

Although certain aromatic amines such as 8-aminonaphthalene-1,3,6-trisulfonic acid (ANTS, A350), 2-aminoacridone (A6289) and 8-aminopyrene-1,3,6-trisulfonic acid (APTS, A6257; Figure 3.12) have been extensively utilized to modify reducing sugars for analysis and sequencing, the most reactive reagents for forming stable conjugates of aldehydes and ketones are usually hydrazine derivatives, including hydrazides, semicarbazides and carbohydrazides (Figure 3.13), as well as hydroxylamine derivatives. Hydrazine derivatives react with ketones to yield relatively stable hydrazones (Figure 3.14), and with aldehydes to yield hydrazones that are somewhat less stable, though they may be formed faster. Hydroxylamine derivatives (aminooxy compounds) react with aldehydes and ketones to yield oximes. Both hydrazones and oximes can be reduced with sodium borohydride ($NaBH_4$) to further increase the stability of the linkage. Hydrazine and hydroxylamine derivatives also have amine-like reactivity and, in some cases, can be coupled to water-soluble carbodiimide–activated carboxylic acid groups in drugs, peptides and proteins;[33–35] see Section 3.3 for more details. Because the fluorescence of the hydrazide- and hydroxylamine-containing reagents usually does not change significantly upon reaction with aldehydes or ketones, especially after chemical reduction, the excess reagent required to drive the equilibrium reaction must be separated from the conjugate by washing, gel filtration, dialysis or other separation techniques.

Fluorescent Hydrazine and Hydroxylamine Derivatives Excited with Visible Light

Molecular Probes offers a large number of fluorescent hydrazine and hydroxylamine derivatives for reaction with aldehydes or ketones (Table 3.1). The most extensively used visible light–excitable fluorescent hydrazine derivative, fluorescein-5-thiosemicarbazide (F121, Figure 3.15), has been coupled to a wide variety of biomolecules, including:

- L-Aspartase-α-decarboxylase [36]
- Enzyme-oxidized live plant protoplasts [24]
- Immunoglobulins [37]
- Na^+/K^+-ATPase glycoprotein [38]
- Periodate-oxidized glycoproteins in gels [18]
- Periodate-oxidized RNA [8,9,39–42]
- Thrombin and antithrombin [43]

Although fluorescein-5-thiosemicarbazide is the conventional fluorescent aldehyde- and ketone-reactive reagent, several other hydrazine and hydroxylamine derivatives are likely brighter and more photostable in the same applications:

- Alexa Fluor® 488 (Figure 3.16), Alexa Fluor® 555, Alexa Fluor® 568, Alexa Fluor® 594 (Figure 14.44), Alexa Fluor® 633 and Alexa Fluor® 647 hydrazides (A10436, A20501MP, A10437, A10438, A30634, A20502)
- Alexa Fluor® 488 and Alexa Fluor® 647 hydroxylamines (A30629, A30632)
- Fluorescein hydrazide with an extra spacer between the fluorophore and the reactive group [44] (C356)
- BODIPY® FL hydrazide (D2371, Figure 3.17)
- Texas Red® hydrazide (T6256), which is >90% single isomer by HPLC

HPLC detection of progesterone and 17-hydroxyprogesterone after derivatization with BODIPY® FL hydrazide proved to be over 50 times more sensitive than reported HPLC methods with

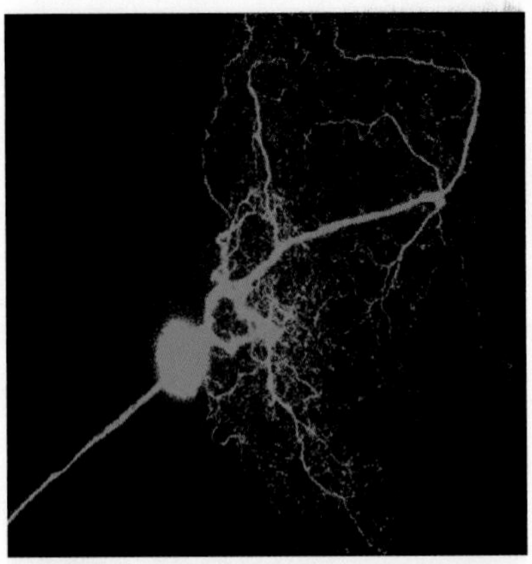

Figure 3.16 The APR motor neuron of a larval moth, *Manduca sexta*, labeled by the intracellular injection of Alexa Fluor® 488 hydrazide, sodium salt (A10436, A10440). This pseudocolored image was created by combining 21 optical sections obtained using a scanning confocal microscope equipped with a bandpass filter appropriate for fluorescein. The image was contributed by Jack Gray and Walter Metcalfe, Institute of Neuroscience, University of Oregon.

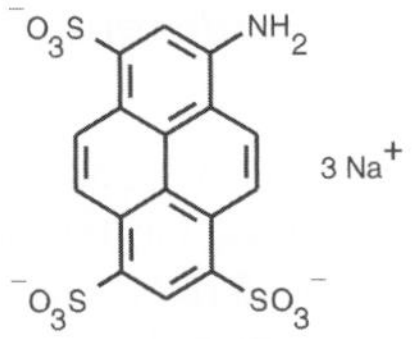

Figure 3.12 A6257 8-aminopyrene-1,3,6-trisulfonic acid, trisodium salt (APTS).

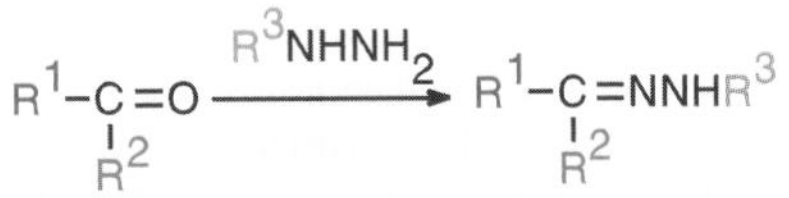

Figure 3.14 Modifying aldehydes and ketones with hydrazine derivatives.

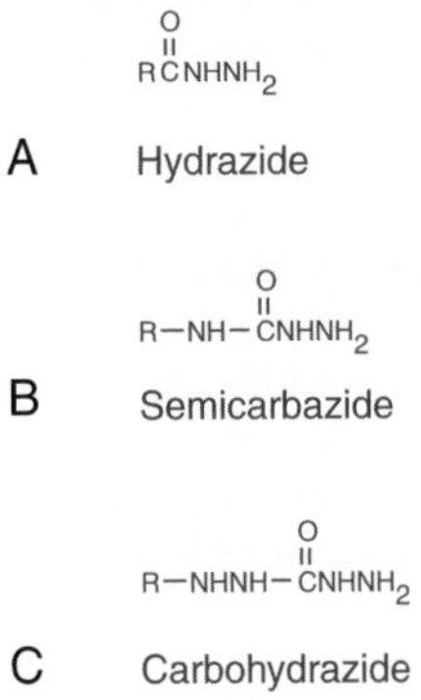

Figure 3.13 Structures of A) a hydrazide, B) a semicarbazide and C) a carbohydrazide.

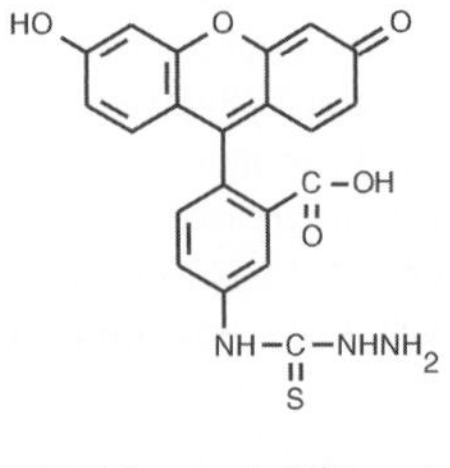

Figure 3.15 F121 fluorescein-5-thiosemicarbazide.

dansyl hydrazine.[45] Texas Red® hydrazide was used to assay the extent of periodate oxidation of saccharide units in glycoproteins[46] and to detect proteins on blots.[47] Because they are more photostable than the fluorescein derivatives, the Alexa Fluor®, BODIPY® and Texas Red® hydrazides should be among the most sensitive reagents for detecting aldehydes and ketones in laser-excited chromatographic methods. However, with the exception of the Alexa Fluor® 555 and Alexa Fluor® 647 hydrazides and the Alexa Fluor® 647 hydroxylamine, the Alexa Fluor® reagents are mixed isomers and may resolve into multiple peaks when analyzed with high-resolution techniques.

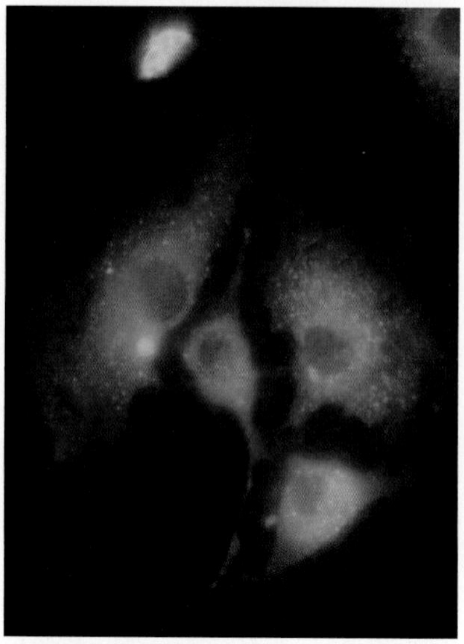

Figure 3.17 BODIPY® FL hydrazide (D2371) loaded into CRE BAG 2 cells with the aid of the Influx™ pinocytic cell-loading reagent (I14402). The existing endosomes were then counterstained with LysoTracker® Red DND-99 (L7528) to demonstrate the selective rupture of only the Influx™ reagent–induced pinocytic vesicles. The double-exposure image was acquired using bandpass filters appropriate for fluorescein and the Texas Red® dye.

Fluorescent Hydrazine and Hydroxylamine Derivatives Excited with UV Light

Dansyl hydrazine (D100) has been by far the most widely used UV light–excitable hydrazine probe for derivatizing aldehydes and ketones for chromatographic analysis. It has been used to modify:

- Bile acids[48–50]
- Glycoproteins[51–53]
- Oligosaccharides[54]
- Reducing sugars[55–59]
- RNA[60–62]
- Steroids[50,63–66]

A unique application that has been reported for dansyl hydrazine, but that is likely a general reaction of hydrazine derivatives, is the detection of *N*-acetylated or *N*-formylated proteins through transfer of the acyl group to the fluorescent hydrazide.[67,68] Although dansyl hydrazine has been widely used as a derivatization reagent, our 7-diethylaminocoumarin and pyrene hydrazides (D355, P101) have much higher absorptivity and fluorescence, which should make their conjugates about 10 times more detectable than those of dansyl hydrazine.

We also offer the shorter-wavelength derivatization reagent, FMOC hydrazine (F6290), which was employed in the HPLC determination of neutral and amino monosaccharides in glycoproteins.[69,70] The FMOC-derivatized sugar hydrazones were detected by fluorescence (excitation/emission wavelengths 270/320 nm) with a detection limit of 0.05–0.4 picomoles and by UV absorption (at 263 nm) with a detection limit of 1–3 picomoles.[69] FMOC hydrazine has been used to analyze blood sugars[71] and reducing sugars in aqueous samples such as urine.[72]

Lucifer Yellow, Cascade Blue® and Alexa Fluor® 350 Hydrazides and Alexa Fluor® 350 Hydroxylamine

Lucifer yellow CH (L453) is most commonly used as an aldehyde-fixable neuronal tracer with visible absorption and emission (Figure 2.20). This membrane-impermeant hydrazide also reacts with periodate-oxidized cell-surface glycoproteins,[38,73] oxidized ribonucleotides[74] and gangliosides.[75] Our patented Cascade Blue® hydrazide (C687) exhibits high absorptivity (ϵ >28,000 $cm^{-1}M^{-1}$), fluorescence quantum yield (0.54) and water solubility[76] (~1%). Like Cascade Blue® hydrazide, Alexa Fluor® 350 hydrazide (A10439) and Alexa Fluor® 350 hydroxylamine (A30627) also have high water solubility and bright blue fluorescence. These sulfonated pyrene and coumarin derivatives have applications similar to those of lucifer yellow CH.[77] See Section 14.3 for a discussion of the use of these probes as aldehyde-fixable polar tracers.

NBD Methylhydrazine

NBD methylhydrazine (*N*-methyl-4-hydrazino-7-nitrobenzofurazan, M20490) has been used to monitor aldehydes and ketones in tobacco smoke[78] and automobile exhaust[79] and also to measure nitrite in water[80] (Section 21.2). NBD methylhydrazine reacts with carbonyl compounds in acidic media, forming the corresponding hydrazones (Figure 3.18). Following separation by HPLC, the hydrazones can be detected either by UV/VIS spectroscopy (using wavelengths corresponding to the absorption maxima of the relevant hydrazone) or by fluorescence spectroscopy using excitation/emission maxima of ~470/560 nm.

QSY® 9 Hydrazide

QSY® 9 hydrazide (Q30626) is an essentially nonfluorescent, aldehyde- and ketone-reactive diarylrhodamine with an absorption spectrum similar to that of our QSY® 9 succinimidyl ester (Q20131, Section 1.7, Figure 1.70). The principal application of QSY® 9 hydrazide is expected to be as a quencher for fluorescent donor dyes in fluorescence resonance energy transfer (FRET) studies (see Note 1.2 "Technical Focus: Fluorescence Resonance Energy Transfer (FRET)" in Section 1.3). Most FRET detection is based on the interaction between fluorescent donor and acceptor dyes. However, the use of nonfluorescent acceptor dyes avoids the background fluorescence that often results from direct (i.e., nonsensitized) excitation of the acceptor dye. The broad and strong absorption of the QSY® 9 dye in the visible-light spectrum (absorption maximum ~562 nm, ε ~88,000 $cm^{-1}M^{-1}$, Figure 1.70) yields extraordinarily efficient quenching of donors that have blue, green, orange or red fluorescence at relatively long spatial separations (Table 1.10).

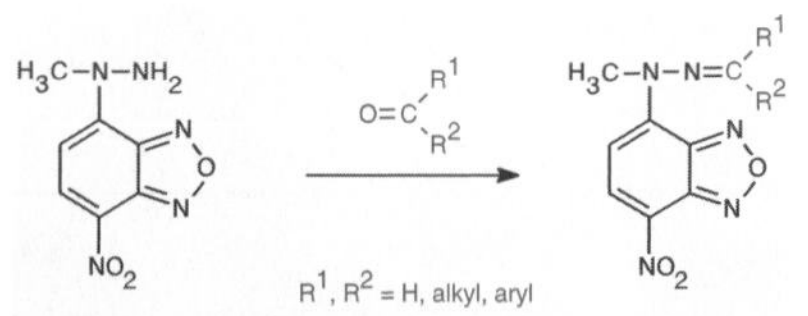

Figure 3.18 Reaction scheme illustrating the principle of ketone and aldehyde detection by NBD methylhydrazine (M20490).

Table 3.1 — Molecular Probes' hydrazine, hydroxylamine and amine derivatives

Derivative	Hydrazines *	Hydroxylamines *	Cadaverines *	Other Amines *
Acridone				A6289 †
Alexa Fluor® 350	A10439	A30627	A30674	
Alexa Fluor® 405			A30675	
Alexa Fluor® 488	A10436	A30629	A30676	
Alexa Fluor® 555	A20501MP		A30677	
Alexa Fluor® 568	A10437		A30680	
Alexa Fluor® 594	A10438		A30678	
Alexa Fluor® 633	A30634			
Alexa Fluor® 647	A20502	A30632	A30679	
ARP ‡ §		A10550		
4-Azido-2,3,5,6-tetrafluorobenzyl				A10662
Bimane				B30633
Biotin and DSB-X biotin §	B1603, B2600, D20653	A10550 ‡	A1594, B1596	A1593, B1592, N6356
t-BOC		B30300		M6248
BODIPY® FL	D2371			D2390
BODIPY® TR			D6251	
Cascade Blue®	C687			C621
Coumarin	D355			A191 †
Dansyl	D100		D113	D112
Dapoxyl®				D10460
2,3-Diaminonaphthalene				D7918 †
Dimethoxybenzene				D1463 †
Dinitrophenyl				D1552
Eosin				A117
Fluo-4			F36201	
Fluorescein	C356, F121		A10466	A1351, A1353, A1363
FMOC	F6290			
Lucifer yellow	L453			A1339
Naphthalene				A91, A350 †, A22840 †
NBD	M20490			
Oregon Green® 488			O10465	
Pyrene	P101			A6257 †, P2421
QSY® 7				Q10464
QSY® 9	Q30626			
QSY® 35				Q20540
Rhodamine			A1318	L2424
Texas Red®	T6256		T2425	

* Hydrazine, hydroxylamine and aromatic amine derivatives are discussed in Section 3.2, and aliphatic amine der-ivatives are discussed in Section 3.3, except for D1552, which appears in Section 12.3, and A10662, which appears in Section 5.3. † Aromatic amines used extensively for modifying aldehydes and ketones. ‡ ARP is the abbreviation for *N*-(aminooxyacetyl)-*N'*-(D-biotinoyl)hydrazine. § Biotin and desthiobiotin (DSB-X™ biotin) derivatives are listed in Section 4.2.

Figure 3.19 Lipopolysaccharide staining with the Pro-Q® Emerald 300 Lipopolysaccharide Gel Stain Kit. Lipopolysaccharides (LPS) were electrophoresed through a 13% acrylamide gel and stained using the Pro-Q® Emerald 300 Lipopolysaccharide Gel Stain Kit (P20495). From left to right, the lanes contain: CandyCane™ glycoprotein molecular weight standards (~250 ng/band), blank, 4, 1 and 0.25 µg of LPS from *Escherichia coli* smooth serotype 055:B5 and 4, 1 and 0.25 µg of LPS from *E. coli* rough mutant EH100 (Ra mutant).

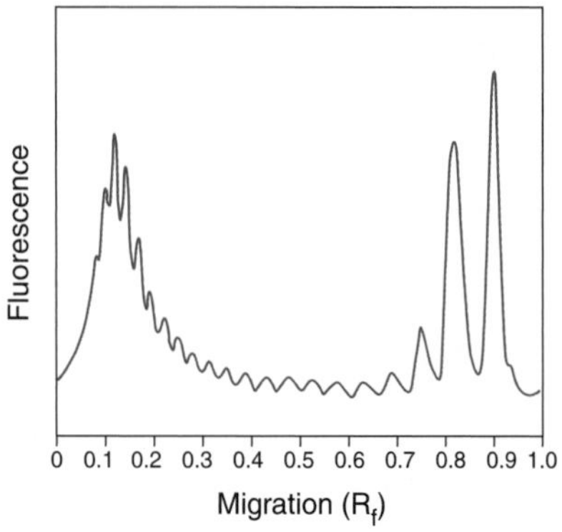

Figure 3.20 Characterization of lipopolysaccharides. Lipopolysaccharides (LPS) from *Escherichia coli* smooth serotype 055:B5 were loaded onto a 13% polyacrylamide gel. Following electrophoresis, the gel was stained using the Pro-Q® Emerald 300 Lipopolysaccharide Gel Stain Kit (P20495), and the fluorescence was measured for the lane. A plot of fluorescence signal versus the relative distance from the dye front shows a characteristic laddering profile for smooth-type LPS.

Biotin Hydrazides and Biotin Hydroxylamine

In addition to the fluorescent hydrazine and hydroxylamine derivatives, we offer several nonfluorescent biotin and DSB-X biotin hydrazides (B1603, B2600, D20653; Section 4.2) and the biotin hydroxylamine derivative ARP (A10550, Section 4.2), each of which can be detected using fluorescent dye– or enzyme-labeled avidin or streptavidin (Section 7.6, Table 7.22). We recommend the biotin hydroxylamine derivative ARP (aldehyde-reactive probe, (A10550, Figure 3.10) as the most efficient reagent for incorporating biotins into aldehyde- or ketone-containing cell surfaces. ARP has been used to modify the exposed aldehyde group at abasic sites in DNA — those apurinic sites and apyrimidinic lesions thought to be important intermediates in carcinogenesis [81–84] (Figure 8.147). Abasic sites are generated spontaneously or can be caused by free radicals, ionizing radiation or mutagens like methyl methanesulfonate (MMS). A quick and sensitive microplate assay for abasic sites can be performed using ARP. In addition, ARP is membrane permeant, permitting detection of abasic sites in live cells.[85,86] Once the aldehyde groups in abasic sites are modified by ARP and the cells are fixed and permeabilized, the resulting biotinylated DNA can be detected with fluorescent dye– or enzyme-conjugated streptavidin conjugates (Section 7.6, Table 7.22). ARP has also been used to immobilize IgG antibodies on streptavidin-coated monolayer surfaces with their binding sites oriented toward the solution phase.[87] As compared with an amine-reactive biotinylation reagent, which randomly biotinylates lysines in the IgG molecule, ARP reacts with the carbohydrate domain in the Fc region of the IgG molecule, allowing the specific orientation of the IgG on the streptavidin-coated surface and optimizing the antibody microarray for protein expression profiling. In addition, DSB-X™ biotin hydrazide (D20653, Section 4.2), which has moderate affinity for avidin and streptavidin that is rapidly reversed by low concentrations of free biotin, can be used to produce a DSB-X™ biotin–labeled molecule that reversibly binds avidin or streptavidin affinity matrices (Section 7.6) or the superparamagnetic Captivate™ ferrofluid conjugate of streptavidin (C21476, Section 7.6).

Labeling Cell-Surface Carbohydrates

Cell membrane–impermeant reagents are important probes for assessing the topology of peptide and protein exposure on the surface of live cells. Some of the reagents in this chapter are useful for this application. Periodate- or galactose oxidase–mediated oxidation of cell-surface glycoproteins and polysaccharides can be used to selectively introduce aldehyde residues on the cell surface; these can then be reacted with a membrane-impermeant hydrazide. The high polarity of our Alexa Fluor® hydrazides (A10436, A10437, A10438, A10439, A20501MP, A20502, A30634), Alexa Fluor® hydroxylamines (A30627, A30629, A30632), lucifer yellow CH (L453) and Cascade Blue® hydrazide (C687) make them the preferred labeling reagents. These methods have been used to label plant protoplasts with lucifer yellow CH and Texas Red® hydrazide [24] (T6256) and to label erythrocyte ghosts with fluorescein-5-thiosemicarbazide (F121), lucifer yellow CH, 1-pyrenebutanoic acid hydrazide (P101) and several other dyes.[38] Our anti-dye antibodies and avidin derivatives (Section 7.4, Section 7.6) may facilitate isolation and detection of the modified residues.

Staining Lipopolysaccharides in Gels

Molecular Probes' Pro-Q® Emerald 300 Lipopolysaccharide Gel Stain Kit (P20495) provides a simple, rapid and highly sensitive method for staining lipopolysaccharides (LPS) in gels (Figure 3.19, Figure 3.20, Figure 3.21). LPS, also known as endotoxins, are a family of complex glycolipid molecules located on the surface of gram-negative bacteria. LPS play a large role in protecting the bacterium from host defense mechanisms and antibiotics. The structure of this important class of molecules can be analyzed by SDS-polyacrylamide gel electrophoresis, during which the heterogeneous mixture of polymers separates into a characteristic ladder pattern. This ladder has conventionally been detected using silver staining.[88–90] However, despite the long and complex procedures required, silver staining provides poor sensitivity and cannot differentiate LPS from proteins in the sample. An alternative staining method that makes use of the reaction of the carbohydrates with detectable hydrazides obtains higher sensitivity, but requires blotting to a membrane and time- and labor-intensive procedures.[91–95]

By comparison, the staining technology used in the Pro-Q® Emerald 300 Lipopolysaccharide Gel Stain Kit vastly simplifies detection of LPS in SDS-polyacrylamide gels. The key to this novel methodology is our bright green-fluorescent Pro-Q® Emerald 300 dye, which covalently binds to periodate-oxidized carbohydrates of LPS. This dye allows the detection of as little as 200 pg of LPS in just a few hours. The sensitivity is at least 50–100 times that of silver staining and requires much less hands-on time. This dye is also used in our Pro-Q® Emerald 300 and Multiplexed Proteomics® Glycoprotein Stain Kits (P21855, P21857, M33307; Section 9.4) and may be useful for detection of other molecules containing carbohydrates or aldehydes. The bright green fluorescence is easy to visualize using a simple UV transilluminator. To detect contaminating proteins in the sample, the same gel can also be stained with SYPRO® Ruby protein gel stain (S12000, S12001, S21900; Section 9.3). The Pro-Q® Emerald 300 Lipopolysaccharide Gel Stain Kit contains:

- Pro-Q® Emerald 300 reagent
- Pro-Q® Emerald 300 staining buffer
- Oxidizing reagent (periodic acid)
- Smooth LPS standard from *Escherichia coli* serotype 055-B5
- A detailed protocol

Sufficient materials are supplied to stain ten 8 cm × 10 cm gels, 0.5–0.75 mm thick.

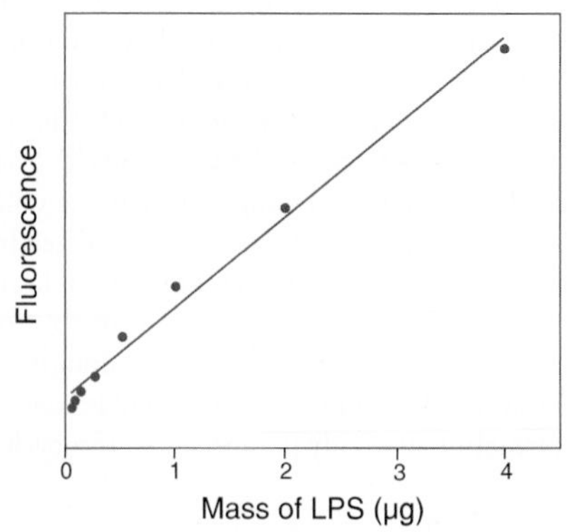

Figure 3.21 Linearity of the Pro-Q® Emerald 300 stain for lipopolysaccharide (LPS) detection. A dilution series of lipopolysaccharides from *Escherichia coli* smooth serotype 055:B5 was loaded onto a 13% polyacrylamide gel. Following electrophoresis, the gel was stained using the Pro-Q® Emerald 300 Lipopolysaccharide Gel Stain Kit (P20495) and the same band from each lane was quantitated using a CCD camera. A plot of the fluorescence intensity versus the mass of LPS loaded shows a linear range over two orders of magnitude.

Aromatic Amines

Primary aliphatic and aromatic amines (Table 3.1) can be coupled reversibly to aldehydes and ketones to form hydrolytically unstable Schiff bases [19] (Figure 3.22). The reversibility of this modification makes reagents that contain amines less desirable unless the Schiff base is reduced to a stable amine derivative by sodium borohydride [96,97] or sodium cyanoborohydride.[98] Chemical reduction also retains the amine's original charge. Sequencing of carbohydrate polymers using fluorescent derivatives has usually relied on derivatization of the reducing end of the polymer with a fluorescent amine.[99] Certain aromatic amines have been extensively utilized for coupling to aldehydes, ketones, monosaccharides and the reducing end of carbohydrate polymers:

- 2-Aminoacridone (A6289) forms conjugates that can be separated by HPLC [100,101] or, as their borate complexes, by polyacrylamide gel electrophoresis,[99,102,103] capillary electrophoresis [104–106] and micellar electrokinetic capillary chromatography [107,108] (MECC). Starting with as little as 25 µg of a glycoprotein, researchers have efficiently released and purified the carbohydrates, and then derivatized them with 2-aminoacridone for subsequent structural analysis.[109] 2-Aminoacridone derivatives of oligosaccharides have been directly analyzed by MALDI-TOF mass spectrometry.[110] 2-Aminoacridone is also used to prepare fluorogenic substrates for proteases.[111]
- 7-Amino-4-methylcoumarin (A191), which is a common base of protease substrates (Section 10.4), can be used for the reductive derivatization of oligosaccharides.[112,113]
- 8-Aminopyrene-1,3,6-trisulfonic acid (APTS, A6257) has been extensively used to derivatize carbohydrates prior to separation by gel or capillary electrophoresis.[114–121] Among the amines we offer, APTS is the aromatic amine that has the most favorable combination of strong absorbance, high quantum yield and ionic charge.
- ANTS (A350) and 7-aminonaphthalene-1,3-disulfonic acid (ANDS; FluoroPure™ Grade, A22840) have high ionic charges, permitting electrophoretic separation of the degradation products of complex oligosaccharides.[122] Carboxylated polysaccharides have been coupled to the aromatic amine of ANDS preceding electrophoretic analysis.[7,99,122–126]

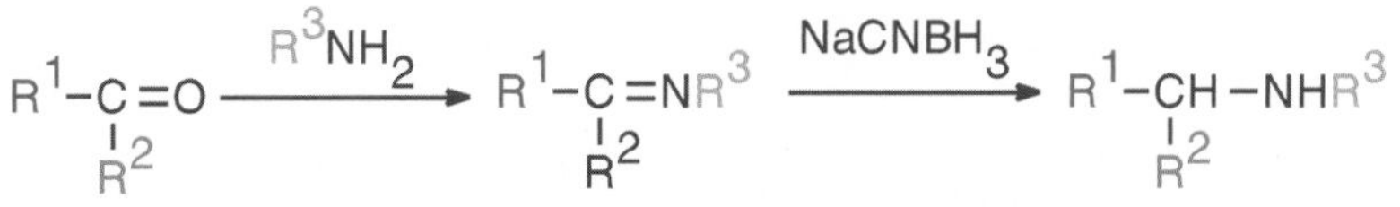

Figure 3.22 Modifying aldehydes and ketones with amine derivatives.

The aromatic diamine 1,2-diamino-4,5-dimethoxybenzene (DDB, D1463), which forms heterocyclic compounds with certain aldehydes and ketones, has been used to selectively detect aromatic aldehydes in the presence of aliphatic aldehydes, including carbohydrates.[127] It has also been employed for fluorometric determination of ascorbic acid,[128,129] lactic acid,[130] α-keto acids [131–133] and *N*-acetylneuraminic acids [134] by HPLC. Endogenous leucine-enkephalin and other tyrosine-containing peptides can be detected by HPLC at concentrations as low as 5.6 picomoles per gram of rat brain tissue using a Reimer–Tiemann reaction followed by derivatization with DDB.[135] The dimly fluorescent aromatic diamine 2,3-diaminonaphthalene (D7918) may be similarly useful for detection of ketones and α-keto acids through formation of highly fluorescent heterocycles.

Alternatively, aldehydes and ketones can be transformed into primary aliphatic amines by reductive amination with ammonia, ethylenediamine or other nonfluorescent diamines.[136] This chemistry is particularly useful because the products can then be coupled with any of the amine-reactive reagents described in Chapter 1 such as the succinimidyl esters of TAMRA [137] (C1171, C6121, C6122; Section 1.6). Derivatization by succinimidyl esters has been extensively utilized for tagging oligosaccharides that are to be separated by capillary zone electrophoresis with laser-induced fluorescence detection.[137–140]

References

1. Methods Enzymol 327, 260 (2000); **2.** Science 276, 1128 (1997); **3.** J Biol Chem 273, 31168 (1998); **4.** Curr Opin Chem Biol 2, 49 (1998); **5.** Science 276, 1125 (1997); **6.** Glycobiology 10, 1049 (2000); **7.** Anal Biochem 244, 283 (1997); **8.** Biochemistry 30, 4821 (1991); **9.** Biochemistry 19, 5947 (1980); **10.** Bioconjug Chem 5, 436 (1994); **11.** Bioconjug Chem 7, 38 (1996); **12.** J Biol Chem 269, 7224 (1994); **13.** Bioconjug Chem 4, 537 (1993); **14.** Bioconjug Chem 3, 262 (1992); **15.** Biochem J 94, 17 (1965); **16.** Biochem J 83, 91 (1962); **17.** Bioconjug Chem 5, 636 (1994); **18.** Anal Biochem 161, 245 (1987); **19.** Methods Enzymol 247, 30 (1994); **20.** Anal Biochem 170, 271 (1988); **21.** Methods Enzymol 138, 429 (1987); **22.** Biochem Biophys Res Commun 92, 1215 (1980); **23.** J Supramol Struct 6, 291 (1977); **24.** Protoplasma 139, 117 (1987); **25.** Cytometry 41, 316 (2000); **26.** Cell 1, 147 (1974); **27.** Glycobiology 1, 187 (1991); **28.** Biotechniques 31, 384 (2001); **29.** Nat Biotechnol 19, 553 (2001); **30.** Glycobiology 11, 11R (2001); **31.** Nature 292, 17 (1981); **32.** Chem Pharm Bull (Tokyo) 37, 1831 (1989); **33.** Biochim Biophys Acta 897, 384 (1987); **34.** Ann NY Acad Sci 463, 214 (1984); **35.** Biochemistry 22, 5 (1983); **36.** Biochem J 323, 661 (1997); **37.** J Immunol Methods 109, 289 (1988); **38.** Biochemistry 24, 322 (1985); **39.** J Mol Biol 221, 441 (1991); **40.** Eur Biophys J 16, 45 (1988); **41.** Biochemistry 25, 5298 (1986); **42.** Eur J Biochem 142, 261 (1984); **43.** Biochim Biophys Acta 785, 1 (1984); **44.** Eur J Biochem 213, 1205 (1993); **45.** Analyst 123, 2339 (1998); **46.** J Chromatogr 587, 171 (1991); **47.** J Biol Chem 273, 9894 (1998); **48.** J Chromatogr 272, 261 (1983); **49.** J Chromatogr 260, 115 (1983); **50.** J Chromatogr 217, 349 (1981); **51.** Anal Biochem 157, 100 (1986); **52.** Anal Biochem 96, 208 (1979); **53.** Anal Biochem 73, 192 (1976); **54.** Anal Biochem 146, 143 (1985); **55.** J Chromatogr 464, 343 (1989); **56.** J Chromatogr 333, 123 (1985); **57.** J Chromatogr 256, 27 (1983); **58.** Anal Biochem 114, 153 (1981); **59.** J Chromatogr 139, 343 (1977); **60.** Biochemistry 30, 5238 (1991); **61.** Eur J Biochem 129, 211 (1982); **62.** Nucleic Acids Res 8, 3229 (1980); **63.** Chromatographia 19, 452 (1984); **64.** J Chromatogr 233, 61 (1982); **65.** J Chromatogr 232, 1 (1982); **66.** J Chromatogr 226, 1 (1981); **67.** J Cell Biol 106, 1607 (1988); **68.** Anal Biochem 29, 186 (1969); **69.** J Chromatogr 646, 45 (1993); **70.** Anal Biochem 195, 160 (1991); **71.** J Pharm Biomed Anal 16, 1059 (1998); **72.** J Chromatogr A 730, 99 (1996); **73.** Biochem Biophys Res Commun 112, 872 (1983); **74.** Biochemistry 27, 6039 (1988); **75.** J Cell Biol 100, 721 (1985); **76.** Anal Biochem 198, 119 (1991); **77.** Physiol Res 46, 407 (1997); **78.** Fresenius J Anal Chem 366, 396 (2000); **79.** Anal Chem 71, 1893 (1999); **80.** Anal Chem 71, 3003 (1999); **81.** Anal Biochem 267, 331 (1999); **82.** Biochemistry 11, 3610 (1972); **83.** Biochemistry 31, 3703 (1992); **84.** Biochemistry 32, 8276 (1993); **85.** Proc Natl Acad Sci U S A 97, 686 (2000); **86.** J Biol Chem 275, 6741 (2000); **87.** Anal Biochem 312, 113 (2003); **88.** J Clin Microbiol 28, 2627 (1990); **89.** Microbiol Immunol 35, 331 (1991); **90.** J Biochem Biophys Methods 26, 81 (1993); **91.** Electrophoresis 19, 2398 (1998); **92.** Appl Environ Microbiol 61, 2845 (1995); **93.** Electrophoresis 20, 462 (1999); **94.** Electrophoresis 21, 526 (2000); **95.** Anal Biochem 188, 285 (1990); **96.** Biochemistry 26, 2162 (1987); **97.** Biochim Biophys Acta 597, 285 (1980); **98.** Biochim Biophys Acta 670, 181 (1981); **99.** Anal Biochem 222, 270 (1994); **100.** Anal Chem 70, 2530 (1998); **101.** Anal Chem 69, 4985 (1997); **102.** Anal Biochem 216, 243 (1994); **103.** Anal Biochem 196, 238 (1991); **104.** Anal Biochem 240, 68 (1996); **105.** Electrophoresis 17, 406 (1996); **106.** Anal Biochem 230, 115 (1995); **107.** Anal Chem 68, 4424 (1996); **108.** J chem soc chem commun (14), 1691 (1994); **109.** Anal Biochem 262, 197 (1998); **110.** Rapid Commun Mass Spectrom 11, 1635 (1997); **111.** Anal Biochem 171, 393 (1988); **112.** Biophys J 71, 2040 (1996); **113.** Anal Biochem 128, 41 (1983); **114.** Anal Biochem 283, 125 (2000); **115.** Anal Chem 69, 4554 (1997); **116.** Biomed Chromatogr 10, 285 (1996); **117.** Electrophoresis 17, 681 (1996); **118.** Electrophoresis 17, 412 (1996); **119.** Electrophoresis 17, 347 (1996); **120.** LC-GC 14, 788 (1996); **121.** Nature 380, 461 (1996); **122.** Anal Biochem 283, 136 (2000); **123.** J Chromatogr A 792, 75 (1997); **124.** Methods Enzymol 230, 250 (1994); **125.** Electrophoresis 12, 94 (1991); **126.** Biochem J 270, 705 (1990); **127.** Anal Chim Acta 134, 39 (1982); **128.** Chem Pharm Bull (Tokyo) 33, 3499 (1985); **129.** J Chromatogr 344, 351 (1985); **130.** J Chromatogr 566, 1 (1991); **131.** Chem Pharm Bull 35, 687 (1987); **132.** Anal Chim Acta 172, 167 (1985); **133.** J Chromatogr 344, 33 (1985); **134.** Anal Biochem 164, 138 (1987); **135.** J Chromatogr 430, 271 (1988); **136.** Proc Natl Acad Sci U S A 88, 2302 (1991); **137.** J Chromatogr B Biomed Appl 657, 307 (1994); **138.** Anal Biochem 227, 368 (1995); **139.** Carbohydr Res 296, 203 (1996); **140.** J Biomol Screen 4, 239 (1999).

Data Table — 3.2 Hydrazines, Hydroxylamines and Aromatic Amines for Modifying Aldehydes and Ketones

Cat #	MW	Storage	Soluble	Abs	EC	Em	Solvent	Notes
A191	175.19	L	DMF, DMSO	351	18,000	430	MeOH	
A350	427.33	L	H_2O	353	7,200	520	H_2O	
A1642	191.25	D,A	EtOH	<300		none		
A6257	523.39	D,L	H_2O	424	19,000	505	pH 7	
A6289	246.70	D,L	DMF, DMSO	425	5,200	531	MeOH	1
A10436	570.48	D,L	H_2O	493	71,000	517	pH 7	
A10437	730.74	D,L	H_2O	576	86,000	599	pH 7	2
A10438	758.79	D,L	H_2O	588	97,000	613	pH 7	2
A10439	349.29	L	H_2O, DMSO	345	13,000	445	pH 7	
A20501MP	~1150	D,L	H_2O	554	150,000	567	pH 7	
A20502	~1200	D,L	H_2O	649	250,000	666	pH 7	
A22840	341.39	L	H_2O	350	4,200	450	pH 7	3
A30627	584.52	F,D,L	H_2O, DMSO	353	20,000	437	MeOH	4
A30629	895.07	F,D,L	H_2O, DMSO	494	77,000	518	pH 7	4
A30632	~1220	F,D,L	H_2O, DMSO	651	250,000	672	MeOH	4
A30634	~950	D,L	H_2O, DMSO	624	110,000	643	pH 7	
B30300	339.24	F,D	DMSO	<300		none		
C356	493.49	L	pH >7, DMF	492	78,000	516	pH 8	5
C687	596.44	L	H_2O	399	30,000	421	H_2O	6, 7
D100	265.33	L	EtOH	336	4,400	534	MeOH	
D355	275.31	D,L	MeCN, DMF	420	46,000	468	MeOH	
D1463	241.12	D,L	EtOH	298	3,100	359	MeOH	
D2371	306.12	F,D,L	MeOH, MeCN	503	71,000	510	MeOH	8
D7918	158.20	L	DMSO, MeOH	340	5,100	377	MeOH	9
D10430	358.41	L	DMF, DMSO	374	27,000	583	MeOH	10
F121	421.43	D,L	pH >7, DMF	492	85,000	516	pH 9	5
F6290	254.29	F,D	DMF, DMSO	299	5,800	309	MeOH	11
L453	457.24	L	H_2O	428	12,000	536	H_2O	12
L20492	277.27	F,DD	H_2O	<300		none		
L20493	445.42	F,DD	DMSO	<300		none		13
M10432	284.22	L	H_2O, DMSO	362	19,000	460	pH 9	
M20490	209.16	F,L	MeCN	487	24,000	none	MeOH	14
P101	302.38	D,L	MeCN, DMF	341	43,000	376	MeOH	15
Q30626	933.12	F,D,L	H_2O, DMSO	562	90,000	none	MeOH	
T6256	620.74	F,L	DMF	582	109,000	602	MeOH	

For definitions of the contents of this data table, see "Navigating *The Handbook*" in the introductory pages.

Notes

1. Spectra of this compound are in methanol containing a trace of KOH.
2. Maximum solubility in water is ~8% for A10437 and A10438.
3. This product is specified to equal or exceed 98% analytical purity by HPLC.
4. Aqueous stock solutions should be used within 24 hours; long-term storage is NOT recommended.
5. Absorption and fluorescence of fluorescein derivatives are pH-dependent. Extinction coefficients and fluorescence quantum yields decrease markedly at pH <7.
6. The Alexa Fluor® 405 and Cascade Blue® dyes have a second absorption peak at about 376 nm with EC ~80% of the 395–400 nm peak.
7. Maximum solubility in water is ~1% for C687, ~1% for C3221 and ~8% for C3239.
8. The absorption and fluorescence spectra of BODIPY® derivatives are relatively insensitive to the solvent.
9. Fluorescence of D7918 is weak. Reaction with α-ketoaldehydes yields fluorescent benzoquinoxaline derivatives (Abs = 365 nm, Em = 540 nm in H_2O (pH 8)) (J Chromatogr B Biomed Sci Appl 729, 237 (1999)).
10. Fluorescence emission spectrum shifts to shorter wavelengths in nonpolar solvents.
11. F6290 has stronger absorption at 264 nm (EC = 20,000 $cm^{-1}M^{-1}$). This peak is usually used for excitation in fluorescence-detected HPLC or capillary electrophoresis.
12. Maximum solubility in water is ~8% for L453, ~6% for L682 and ~1% for L1177.
13. This product is supplied as a ready-made solution in the solvent indicated under "Soluble."
14. NBD methylhydrazine reacts with aldehydes and ketones in the presence of strong acid, yielding weakly fluorescent hydrazone products (Anal Chem 71, 1893 (1999)). Abs = 493 nm, Em = 552 nm in MeOH for reaction product with acetone.
15. Pyrene derivatives exhibit structured spectra. The absorption maximum is usually about 340 nm with a subsidiary peak at about 325 nm. There are also strong absorption peaks below 300 nm. The emission maximum is usually about 376 nm with a subsidiary peak at 396 nm. Excimer emission at about 470 nm may be observed at high concentrations.

Product List — 3.2 Hydrazines, Hydroxylamines and Aromatic Amines for Modifying Aldehydes and Ketones

Cat #	Product Name	Unit Size
A1642	2-acetamido-4-mercaptobutanoic acid hydrazide (AMBH)	100 mg
A30627	Alexa Fluor® 350 C_5-aminooxyacetamide, trifluoroacetate salt (Alexa Fluor® 350 hydroxylamine)	1 mg
A30629	Alexa Fluor® 488 C_5-aminooxyacetamide, bis(triethylammonium) salt (Alexa Fluor® 488 hydroxylamine)	1 mg
A30632	Alexa Fluor® 647 C_5-aminooxyacetamide, bis(triethylammonium) salt (Alexa Fluor® 647 hydroxylamine)	1 mg
A10439	Alexa Fluor® 350 hydrazide, sodium salt	5 mg
A10436	Alexa Fluor® 488 hydrazide, sodium salt	1 mg
A20501MP	Alexa Fluor® 555 hydrazide, tris(triethylammonium) salt	1 mg
A10437	Alexa Fluor® 568 hydrazide, sodium salt	1 mg
A10438	Alexa Fluor® 594 hydrazide, sodium salt	1 mg
A30634	Alexa Fluor® 633 hydrazide, bis(triethylammonium) salt	1 mg
A20502	Alexa Fluor® 647 hydrazide, tris(triethylammonium) salt	1 mg
A6289	2-aminoacridone, hydrochloride	25 mg
A191	7-amino-4-methylcoumarin *reference standard*	100 mg
A22840	7-aminonaphthalene-1,3-disulfonic acid, potassium salt (ANDS) *FluoroPure™ grade*	1 g
A350	8-aminonaphthalene-1,3,6-trisulfonic acid, disodium salt (ANTS)	1 g
A6257	8-aminopyrene-1,3,6-trisulfonic acid, trisodium salt (APTS)	10 mg
B30300	*N*-(*t*-BOC)-aminooxyacetic acid, tetrafluorophenyl ester	25 mg
C356	5-(((2-(carbohydrazino)methyl)thio)acetyl)aminofluorescein	25 mg
C687	Cascade Blue® hydrazide, trisodium salt	10 mg
D10430	Dapoxyl® sulfonyl hydrazine	10 mg
D1463	1,2-diamino-4,5-dimethoxybenzene, dihydrochloride (DDB)	100 mg
D7918	2,3-diaminonaphthalene	100 mg
D355	7-diethylaminocoumarin-3-carboxylic acid, hydrazide (DCCH)	25 mg
D2371	4,4-difluoro-5,7-dimethyl-4-bora-3a,4a-diaza-*s*-indacene-3-propionic acid, hydrazide (BODIPY® FL hydrazide)	5 mg
D100	5-dimethylaminonaphthalene-1-sulfonyl hydrazine (dansyl hydrazine)	100 mg
F6290	*N*-(9-fluorenylmethoxycarbonyl) hydrazine (FMOC hydrazine)	25 mg
F121	fluorescein-5-thiosemicarbazide	100 mg
L20492	*N*-levulinoyl-D-mannosamine (ManLev)	25 mg
L20493	*N*-levulinoyl-D-mannosamine, tetraacetate (ManLev tetraacetate) *5 mM solution in DMSO*	500 µL
L453	lucifer yellow CH, lithium salt	25 mg
M10432	Marina Blue® hydrazide	5 mg
M20490	*N*-methyl-4-hydrazino-7-nitrobenzofurazan (NBD methylhydrazine)	25 mg
P20495	Pro-Q® Emerald 300 Lipopolysaccharide Gel Stain Kit *10 minigels*	1 kit
P101	1-pyrenebutanoic acid, hydrazide	100 mg
Q30626	QSY® 9 hydrazide	5 mg
T6256	Texas Red® hydrazide *>90% single isomer*	5 mg

For current prices or to order online, visit probes.invitrogen.com

3.3 Derivatization Reagents for Carboxylic Acids and Glutamine

Carboxylic acids can be converted to esters, amides, acyl hydrazides or hydroxamic acids, all of which are discussed in this section. Alternatively, the half-protected *tert*-butyloxycarbonyl (*t*-BOC) propylenediamine derivative (M6248) is useful for converting organic solvent–soluble carboxylic acids into aliphatic amines. Following coupling of the half-protected aliphatic diamine to an activated carboxylic acid, the *t*-BOC group can be quantitatively removed with trifluoroacetic acid (Figure 3.23). The resultant aliphatic amine can then be modified with any of the amine-reactive reagents described in Chapter 1 or coupled to solid-phase matrices for affinity chromatography.

Coupling Hydrazines, Hydroxylamines and Amines to Carboxylic Acids

Modification in Aqueous Solutions

The carboxylic acids of water-soluble biopolymers such as proteins can be coupled to hydrazines, hydroxylamines and amines (Table 3.1) in aqueous solution using water-soluble carbodiimides such as 1-ethyl-3-(3-dimethylaminopropyl)carbodiimide (EDAC, E2247). Including *N*-hydroxysulfosuccinimide (H2249) in the reaction mixture has been shown to improve the coupling efficiency of EDAC-mediated protein–carboxylic acid conjugations [1] (Figure 3.24). To reduce intra- and interprotein coupling to lysine residues,[2] which is a common side reaction, carbodiimide-mediated coupling should be performed in a concentrated protein solution at a low pH, using a large excess of the nucleophile.[3–6] EDAC has been shown to be impermeable to membranes of live cells, which permits its use to distinguish between cytoplasmic and lumenal sites of reaction.[7] EDAC may also be useful for conjugating fluorescent aliphatic amines to cell-surface proteins. Fluoresceinyl glycine amide (5-(aminoacetamido)fluorescein, A1363) and various hydrazines and hydroxylamines may be the best probes for this application because they are more likely to remain reactive at a lower pH than are aliphatic amines such as the cadaverines.[8] Fluoresceinyl glycine amide has been coupled to the carboxylic acid of a cyclosporin derivative by EDAC.[9] Quantitative analysis of carboxylic acids, including sugar carboxylates, in aqueous solution using 1-naphthylethylenediamine and *o*-phthaldialdehyde (P2331MP, Section 1.8) has also been reported.[10]

ANTS (A350, Section 3.2) and 7-aminonaphthalene-1,3-disulfonic acid (ANDS; FluoroPure™ Grade, A22840; Section 3.2) have high ionic charges, which permit electrophoretic separation of their products with complex oligosaccharides.[11] Carboxylated polysaccharides have been coupled to the aromatic amine of ANDS preceding electrophoretic analysis.[11–17] Several of the fluorescent hydrazine and hydroxylamine derivatives described in Section 3.2 should have similar utility for carbodiimide-mediated derivatization of carboxylic acids.

Modification in Organic Solvents

Peptide synthesis research has led to the development of numerous methods for coupling carboxylic acids to amines in organic solution. One such method involves the conversion of carboxylic acids to succinimidyl esters or mixed anhydrides. Dicyclohexylcarbodiimide and diisopropylcarbodiimide are widely used to promote amide formation in organic solution. Another recommended derivatization method for coupling organic solvent–soluble carboxylic acids, including peptides, to aliphatic amines without racemization is the combination of 2,2′-dipyridyldisulfide and triphenylphosphine.[18,19] Unlike fluorescent aliphatic amines, fluorescent aromatic amines

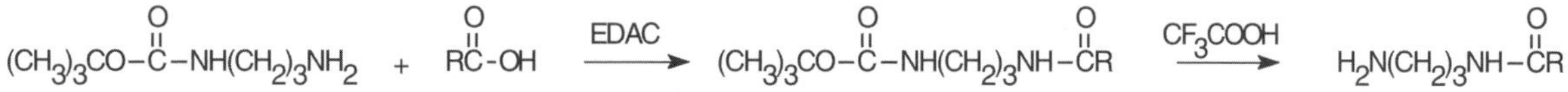

Figure 3.23 Conversion of a carboxylic acid group into an aliphatic amine. The activated carboxylic acid is derivatized with a half-protected aliphatic diamine (mono-*N*-(*t*-BOC)-propylenediamine, M6248), usually in an organic solvent, followed by removal of the *t*-BOC–protecting group with trifluoroacetic acid.

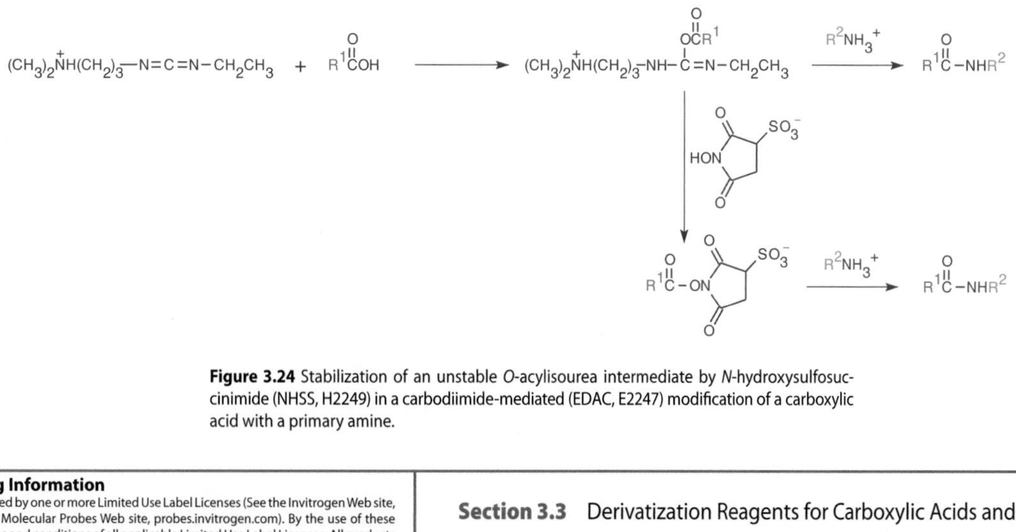

Figure 3.24 Stabilization of an unstable *O*-acylisourea intermediate by *N*-hydroxysulfosuccinimide (NHSS, H2249) in a carbodiimide-mediated (EDAC, E2247) modification of a carboxylic acid with a primary amine.

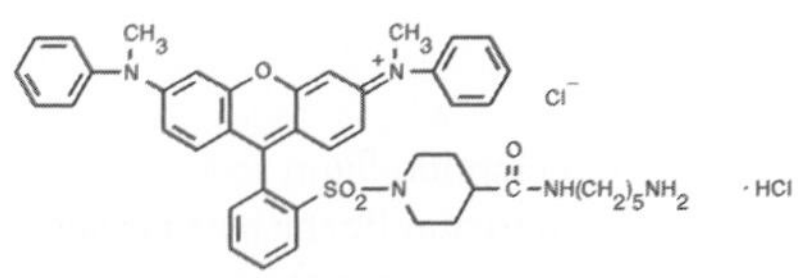

Figure 3.25 Q10464 QSY® 7 amine, hydrochloride.

such as those derived from 7-amino-4-methylcoumarin (A191) and 2-aminoacridone (A6289, Section 3.2) exhibit a shift in their absorption and emission (if any) to much shorter wavelengths upon forming carboxamides. This property makes these aromatic amines preferred reagents for preparing peptidase substrates (Section 10.4). Aromatic amines can generally be coupled to acid halides and anhydrides, with organic solvents usually required for efficient reaction. 5-Aminoeosin (A117) is the key precursor to a wide variety of eosin-based probes.

Hydrazine, Hydroxylamine and Aliphatic Amine Derivatives

Molecular Probes provides a wide selection of carboxylic acid–reactive reagents (Table 3.1), including several different Dapoxyl®, Alexa Fluor®, BODIPY®, fluorescein, Oregon Green®, rhodamine, Texas Red® and QSY® hydrazine derivatives, hydroxylamine derivatives and amine derivatives, all of which are particularly useful for synthesizing drug analogs and as probes for fluorescence polarization immunoassays [20–22] (see Note 1.5 "Technical Focus: Fluorescence Polarization (FP)" in Section 1.4). These probes all require a coupling agent such as a carbodiimide to react with carboxylic acids; they do not spontaneously react with carboxylic acids in solution. They do, however, react spontaneously with the common amine-reactive functional groups described in Section 1.1, including succinimidyl esters and isothiocyanates. Some of the more important probes and their potential applications include:

- Alexa Fluor® hydrazides (A10436, A10437, A10438, A10439, A30634, A20501MP, A20502; Section 3.2), Alexa Fluor® hydroxylamines (A30627, A30629, A30632; Section 3.2) and Alexa Fluor® cadaverines (A30674, A30675, A30676, A30677, A30678, A30679, A30680), our brightest and most photostable carboxylic acid–reactive probes
- BODIPY® aliphatic amines (D2390, D6251), for preparing pH-insensitive probes, such as BODIPY® FL etoposide,[23] from carboxylic acid derivatives
- Isomeric aminomethylfluoresceins (A1351, A1353), which are readily coupled to activated carboxylic acids [20,24]
- Dapoxyl® (2-aminoethyl)sulfonamide (D10460) for preparing conjugates with strong UV absorption and a Stokes shift of ~200 nm (Figure 1.111)
- Dansyl ethylenediamine (D112), dansyl cadaverine (D113), Dapoxyl® (2-aminoethyl)sulfonamide (D10460) and Lissamine rhodamine B ethylenediamine (L2424), for carboxylic acid derivatization [25] and glutamine transamidation reactions [26]
- Bimane amine (B30633), a small blue-fluorescent dye for carboxylic acid derivatization
- EDANS (A91), for preparing radioactive IAEDANS,[22,27] energy transfer–quenched substrates for endopeptidases (Section 10.4), labeled sugar carboxylates [28] and an ATP substrate analog for DNA-dependent RNA polymerase [29]
- 1-Pyrenemethylamine (P2421), for synthesizing new probes that have excited-state lifetimes of ~100 nanoseconds and also for preparing derivatives of carboxylic acids for chromatographic analysis
- QSY® 7 amine (Q10464, Figure 3.25) and QSY® 35 methylamine (Q20540), which are essentially nonfluorescent dyes with strong visible absorption (Figure 1.70) for preparing highly efficient quenchers (Table 1.10) for bioassays based on fluorescence resonance energy transfer (FRET) (see Note 1.2 "Technical Focus: Fluorescence Resonance Energy Transfer (FRET)" in Section 1.3)
- Hydrazine (Section 3.2) and amine derivatives of lucifer yellow (A1339), Alexa Fluor® 405 (A30675) and Cascade Blue® (C621) dyes, which are precursors of highly fluorescent, water-soluble probes
- Hydrazine and amine derivatives of biotin and desthiobiotin (Section 4.2), which are versatile intermediates for synthesizing biotin- and desthiobiotin-containing probes [3,30]
- Fluo-4 cadaverine (F36201), an amine-containing Ca^{2+} indicator (Section 19.3) that can react with aldehydes, ketones and activated esters to form unique Ca^{2+}-sensitive fluorescent probes

Enzyme-Catalyzed Transamidation

A special enzyme-catalyzed transamidation reaction of glutamine residues in some proteins and peptides — including actin,[31] melittin,[32] rhodopsin[33] and factor XIII[26,34] — enables their selective modification by amine-containing probes. The NH_2 group of certain glutamine residues can be replaced with an aliphatic amine to form a labeled glutamine amide — a reaction that can be catalyzed by a transglutaminase enzyme[32,33] (Figure 3.26). This unique method for selective protein modification requires formation of a complex consisting of the glutamine residue, the aliphatic amine probe and the enzyme. It has been found that a short aliphatic spacer in the amine probe enhances the reaction. The cadaverine ($–NH(CH_2)_5NH–$) spacer is usually optimal. Although dansyl cadaverine (D113) has been probably the most widely used reagent,[32,33,35] Alexa Fluor® cadaverines (A30674, A30675, A30676, A30677, A30678, A30679, A30680), Oregon Green® 488 cadaverine (O10465), fluorescein cadaverine[36–41] (A10466), tetramethylrhodamine cadaverine[42] (A1318), Texas Red® cadaverine (T2425) and BODIPY® TR cadaverine (D6251) are the most fluorescent transglutaminase substrates available. The intrinsic transglutaminase activity in sea urchin eggs has been used to covalently incorporate dansyl cadaverine during embryonic development.[43] Two biotin cadaverines (A1594, B1596; Section 4.2) are also available for transglutaminase-mediated reactions.[44–46] Amine-terminated peptides and fluorescent and biotin hydrazides, including Cascade Blue® hydrazide, have been successfully incorporated into protein fragments by transamidation during enzyme-catalyzed proteolysis.[47]

Transamidation of cell-surface glutamine residues by the combination of a transglutaminase enzyme and a fluorescent or biotinylated aliphatic amine can form stable amides.[33] Impermeability of the enzyme restricts this reaction to a limited number of proteins on the cell surface. This technique was used to selectively label erythrocyte band 3 protein with dansyl cadaverine (D113) and proteins of the extracellular matrix with fluorescein cadaverine[39,40] (A10466). Following protease treatment, the dansylated peptides were isolated using an anti-dansyl affinity column.[48]

Modification of Proteins with Fluorescent Carbodiimides

When carboxylic acids are reacted with carbodiimides in the absence of a nucleophile, they may rearrange to form a stable *N*-acylurea (Figure 3.27). If the carbodiimide contains a fluorophore such as in the naphthyl carbodiimide NCD-4 (C428), then the fluorophore will be specifically incorporated into the protein. This reaction has been used to label:

- Chloroplast-coupling factor[49,50]
- Cytochrome *bc*1 complex[51]
- Mitochondrial proton-channel protein[52]
- Plant tonoplast ATPase[53]
- Proteins in the sarcoplasmic reticulum[54–57]
- An inorganic pyrophosphatase[58]

A similar mechanism of labeling may occur in some dicyclohexylcarbodiimide (DCC)–inhibited proteins, in which DCC appears to react with a carboxyl residue within a very hydrophobic sequence of the protein.[59]

Esterification Reagents for Carboxylic Acids

Biologically important molecules, especially the nonchromophoric fatty acids, bile acids and prostaglandins, are typically esterified by carboxylic acid–reactive reagents in organic solvents. Esterification of carboxylic acids in aqueous solution is usually not possible, and esters tend to be unstable in water. Fluorescent derivatization reagents for biomedical chromatography have been extensively discussed in reviews.[60,61]

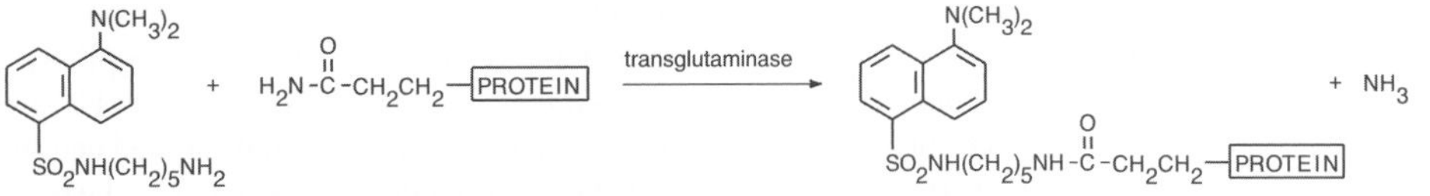

Figure 3.26 Transglutaminase-mediated labeling of a protein using dansyl cadaverine (D113).

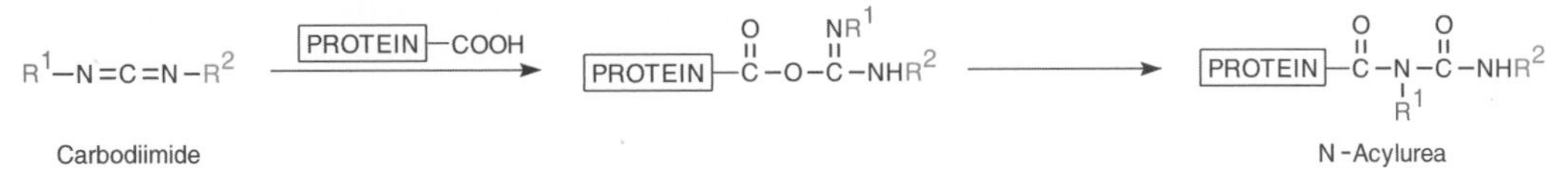

Figure 3.27 Carbodiimide modification of a carboxylic acid group in a protein, followed by rearrangement to yield a stable *N*-acylurea.

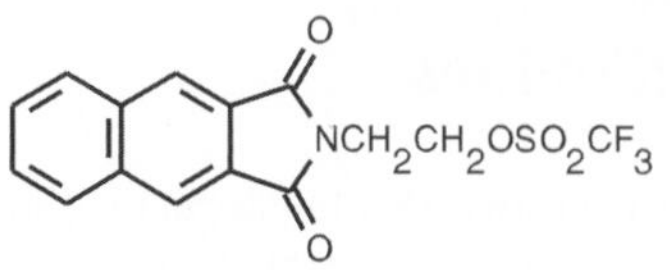

Figure 3.28 N2461 2-(2,3-naphthalimino)ethyl trifluoromethanesulfonate.

Fluorescent Diazoalkanes

HPLC derivatization reagents for carboxylic acids include two fluorescent analogs of the common esterification reagent diazomethane. Diazoalkanes react without the addition of catalysts and may be useful for direct carboxylic acid modification of proteins and synthetic polymers. Fluorescent diazoalkanes also react with phosphates [62] and potentially with lipid-associated carboxylic acids in membrane-bound proteins or with free fatty acids.

The fluorescent diazomethyl derivative 9-anthryldiazomethane (ADAM, A1400) has been commonly used to derivatize biomolecules. Unfortunately, ADAM is not very stable and may decompose during storage. 1-Pyrenyldiazomethane [63–66] (PDAM, P1405) is recommended as a replacement for ADAM because it has much better chemical stability. Moreover, the detection limit for PDAM conjugates is reported to be about 20–30 femtomoles, which is five times better than reported for detection of ADAM conjugates.[64] ADAM and PDAM have been used to detect several types of acids, including:

- Amino acids [66,67]
- Arachidonic acid [68]
- Bile acids [69]
- Fatty acids [64,70–75]
- Okadaic acid [76]
- Prostaglandins [77,78]
- Steroid acids [79]

In addition, fatty acids derivatized with these reagents have been used to measure phospholipase A_2 activity [73] (Section 17.4). It has been reported that photolysis of pyrenemethyl esters liberates the free carboxylic acid,[66] making PDAM a potential protecting group for carboxylic acids. To optimize solid-phase organic synthesis, PDAM has been used to quantitate the absolute amount of resin-bound carboxyl groups directly on solid support.[80]

Fluorescent Alkyl Halides

The low nucleophilicity of carboxylic acids requires that they be converted to anions (typically cesium or quaternary ammonium are used as counterions) before they can be esterified with alkyl halides in organic solvents. Panacyl bromide (A1122) has been used to derivatize prostaglandins,[81–83] fatty acids [84] and biotin,[85,86] and it also reacts with phosphonic acids.[87] Conjugates of 6-bromoacetyl-2-dimethylaminonaphthalene (badan, B6057) have a high Stokes shift, as well as spectral properties that are very environment-sensitive. 5-(Bromomethyl)fluorescein [88,89] (B1355), BODIPY® 493/503 methyl bromide (B2103) and BODIPY® 630/650 methyl bromide (B22802) have the strongest absorptivity and fluorescence of the currently available carboxylic acid–derivatization reagents.[88] Molecular Probes' BODIPY® 493/503 methyl bromide and BODIPY® 630/650 methyl bromide may react with anions of carboxylic acids during heating in an organic solvent such as methanol or acetonitrile. The high absorptivity, electrical neutrality and intense fluorescence of their conjugates may make the BODIPY® 493/503 and BODIPY® 630/650 methyl bromides the preferred reagents for carboxylic acid determinations. Esters and thioethers of BODIPY® 630/650 methyl bromide can be excited by the red He–Ne laser and 635 nm laser diodes and have near-infrared fluorescence emission.

All of the alkyl halides in this section also react with thiol groups, including those in proteins.[90,91] Although more commonly used as thiol-reactive reagents, the monobromobimanes (M1378, M1380, M20381; Section 2.3) have been reported to react with carboxylic acids in organic solvents.[92] The coumarin iodoacetamide DCIA (D404, Section 2.3) has also been used to derivatize carboxylic acids;[93] other iodoacetamides in Chapter 2 will probably react similarly.

Fluorescent Trifluoromethanesulfonate

2-(2,3-Naphthalimino)ethyl trifluoromethanesulfonate (N2461, Figure 3.28) reacts rapidly with the anions of carboxylic acids in acetonitrile to give adducts that are reported to be detectable by absorption at 259 nm down to 100 femtomoles and by fluorescence at 394 nm down to 4 femtomoles.[94] This naphthalimide sulfonate ester will likely react with other nucleophiles too, including thiols, amines, phenols (e.g., tyrosine) and probably histidine. 2-(2,3-Naphthalimino)ethyl trifluoromethanesulfonate has been used for the sensitive fluorometric detection of carnitine and acylcarnitines in tissue.[95]

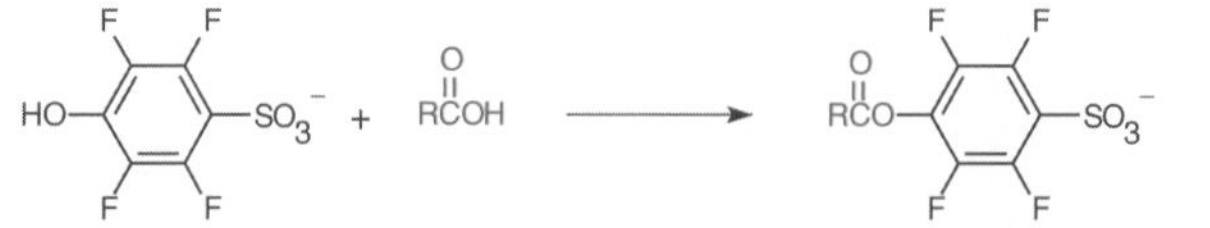

Figure 3.29 4-Sulfo-2,3,5,6-tetrafluorophenol (STP, S10490) can be used to prepare water-soluble activated esters from various carboxylic acids.

4-Sulfo-2,3,5,6-Tetrafluorophenol (STP) and *N*-Hydroxysulfosuccinimide (NHSS)

4-Sulfo-2,3,5,6-tetrafluorophenol (STP, S10490) and *N*-hydroxysulfosuccinimide (NHSS, H2249) can be used to prepare water-soluble activated esters from various carboxylic acids (Figure 3.29). Coupling typically involves a carbodiimide such as EDAC (E2247) and is performed in an organic solvent. Scientists at Molecular Probes have found that the resulting STP esters are much easier to purify and more stable than activated esters prepared from *N*-hydroxysulfosuccinimide.[96] NHSS esters of biotin and other derivatives considerably increase the aqueous solubility of the reagents.[97] Molecular Probes offers a variety of amine-reactive STP esters, which are discussed in Chapter 1.

References

1. Anal Biochem 156, 220 (1986); **2.** Biochemistry 33, 6867 (1994); **3.** J Histochem Cytochem 38, 377 (1990); **4.** J Planar Chromatogr 2, 65 (1989); **5.** Biochim Biophys Acta 897, 384 (1987); **6.** Biochemistry 22, 5 (1983); **7.** J Biol Chem 275, 977 (2000); **8.** Methods Enzymol 25B, 616 (1972); **9.** Bioconjug Chem 3, 32 (1992); **10.** Anal Biochem 219, 189 (1994); **11.** Anal Biochem 283, 136 (2000); **12.** Anal Biochem 244, 283 (1997); **13.** J Chromatogr A 792, 75 (1997); **14.** Anal Biochem 222, 270 (1994); **15.** Methods Enzymol 230, 250 (1994); **16.** Electrophoresis 12, 94 (1991); **17.** Biochem J 270, 705 (1990); **18.** J Chromatogr 645, 75 (1993); **19.** Tetrahedron Lett 22, 1901 (1970); **20.** Anal Biochem 162, 89 (1987); **21.** Clin Chem 31, 1193 (1985); **22.** Biochemistry 12, 4154 (1973); **23.** Biochem Pharmacol 53, 715 (1997); **24.** Bioconjug Chem 5, 459 (1994); **25.** Biochim Biophys Acta 1085, 223 (1991); **26.** Anal Biochem 44, 221 (1971); **27.** J Labelled Compounds Radiopharmaceut 20, 1265 (1983); **28.** Biosci Biotechnol Biochem 61, 1836 (1997); **29.** Arch Biochem Biophys 246, 564 (1986); **30.** Ann NY Acad Sci 463, 214 (1984); **31.** Biochemistry 27, 938 (1988); **32.** FEBS Lett 278, 51 (1991); **33.** Biochemistry 17, 2163 (1978); **34.** Anal Biochem 131, 419 (1983); **35.** Anal Biochem 201, 270 (1992); **36.** Toxicol in Vitro 13, 773 (1999); **37.** J Biol Chem 274, 430 (1999); **38.** Biochem J 331, 105 (1998); **39.** Exp Cell Res 239, 119 (1998); **40.** Histochem J 29, 593 (1997); **41.** Biochemistry 27, 3483 (1988); **42.** Biochemistry 27, 4512 (1988); **43.** Biochemistry 29, 5103 (1990); **44.** J Biol Chem 273, 11991 (1998); **45.** J Biol Chem 269, 24596 (1994); **46.** Anal Biochem 205, 166 (1992); **47.** J Biol Chem 271, 28399 (1996); **48.** J Biol Chem 269, 22907 (1994); **49.** Biochemistry 29, 9879 (1990); **50.** Biochemistry 28, 3063 (1989); **51.** Arch Biochem Biophys 352, 193 (1998); **52.** Biochemistry 24, 7366 (1985); **53.** Plant Physiol 95, 707 (1991); **54.** Eur J Biochem 253, 339 (1998); **55.** Biochim Biophys Acta 979, 113 (1989); **56.** Biochim Biophys Acta 827, 419 (1985); **57.** Biochim Biophys Acta 730, 201 (1983); **58.** Plant Cell Physiol 39, 1045 (1998); **59.** Trends Biochem Sci 9, 309 (1984); **60.** J Chromatogr B Biomed Appl 659, 139 (1994); **61.** J Chromatogr B Biomed Appl 659, 85 (1994); **62.** Anal Biochem 179, 127 (1989); **63.** J Lipid Res 38, 1913 (1997); **64.** Anal Chem 60, 2067 (1988); **65.** J Chromatogr 456, 421 (1988); **66.** Tetrahedron Lett 28, 679 (1987); **67.** J Chromatogr 348, 425 (1985); **68.** J Chromatogr 357, 199 (1986); **69.** J Chromatogr 413, 247 (1987); **70.** Biochim Biophys Acta 1046, 277 (1990); **71.** J Chromatogr 526, 331 (1990); **72.** J Chromatogr 380, 247 (1986); **73.** J Biol Chem 263, 5724 (1988); **74.** Fresenius Z Anal Chem 329, 47 (1987); **75.** Anal Biochem 107, 116 (1980); **76.** Toxicon 29, 21 (1991); **77.** J Liquid Chromatography 11, 1273 (1988); **78.** J Chromatogr 253, 271 (1982); **79.** J Chromatogr 564, 27 (1991); **80.** Anal Chem 71, 4564 (1999); **81.** Prostaglandins 42, 355 (1991); **82.** J Chromatogr 427, 209 (1988); **83.** Anal Biochem 165, 220 (1987); **84.** J Liq Chromatogr 16, 2915 (1993); **85.** Methods Enzymol 279, 286 (1997); **86.** Anal Biochem 200, 89 (1992); **87.** Anal Chem 59, 1056 (1987); **88.** Anal Chem 68, 327 (1996); **89.** Biomed Chromatogr 10, 193 (1996); **90.** J Biol Chem 272, 17444 (1997); **91.** J Biol Chem 271, 19964 (1996); **92.** J Org Chem 46, 1666 (1981); **93.** Anal Chem 59, 1203 (1987); **94.** J Chromatogr 508, 133 (1990); **95.** Anal Biochem 231, 315 (1995); **96.** Tetrahedron Lett 40, 1471 (1999); **97.** Biochemistry 21, 3950 (1982).

Data Table — 3.3 Derivatization Reagents for Carboxylic Acids and Glutamine

Cat #	MW	Storage	Soluble	Abs	EC	Em	Solvent	Notes
A91	288.30	L	pH >10, DMF	335	5,900	493	pH 8	
A117	662.91	L	pH >6, DMF	523	109,000	542	MeOH	
A191	175.19	L	DMF, DMSO	351	18,000	430	MeOH	1
A434	807.14	D,L	pH >6, DMF	515	93,000	540	pH 8	
A1122	419.27	F,D,L	DMF, MeCN	362	8,500	494	MeOH	
A1318	514.62	F,D,L	DMF, EtOH	544	78,000	571	MeOH	
A1339	491.57	L	H_2O	425	12,000	532	H_2O	
A1340	533.65	L	H_2O	426	11,000	531	H_2O	
A1351	397.81	L	pH >6, DMF	492	80,000	516	pH 9	2
A1353	397.81	L	pH >6, DMF	492	68,000	516	pH 9	2
A1363	404.38	L	pH >6, DMF	491	80,000	515	pH 9	2
A1364	418.40	L	pH >6, DMF	494	81,000	517	pH 9	2
A1400	218.26	FF,D,L	DMF, MeCN	364	6,100	411	MeOH	
A10461	249.23	L	DMSO	480	29,000	538	MeOH	3
A10466	653.38	D,L	pH >6, DMF	493	82,000	517	pH 9	2
A30674	397.45	F,D,L	H_2O	353	20,000	437	MeOH	
A30675	666.58	F,D,L	H_2O	399	29,000	422	H_2O	4
A30676	640.61	F,D,L	H_2O	493	73,000	516	pH 7	
A30677	~950	F,D,L	H_2O	555	155,000	572	MeOH	
A30678	806.94	F,D,L	H_2O	588	105,000	612	pH 7	
A30679	~1000	F,D,L	H_2O	651	245,000	672	MeOH	
A30680	812.95	F,D,L	H_2O	578	93,000	602	pH 7	
B1355	425.23	F,D,L	pH >6, DMF	492	81,000	515	pH 9	
B2103	341.00	F,D,L	DMSO, MeCN	533	62,000	561	$CHCl_3$	
B6057	292.17	F,L	DMF, MeCN	387	21,000	520	MeOH	
B22802	449.14	F,D,L	DMSO, MeCN	658	73,000	678	$CHCl_3$	
B30633	207.23	F,D,L	DMSO	375	6,000	458	MeOH	
C428	292.40	F,D	DMF, MeCN	333	8,900	414	$CHCl_3$	5
C621	624.49	L	H_2O	399	30,000	423	H2O	4
D112	293.38	L	EtOH, DMF	335	4,600	526	MeOH	
D113	335.46	L	EtOH, DMF	335	4,600	518	MeOH	
D2390	370.64	F,D,L	DMSO, MeCN	503	76,000	510	MeOH	6
D2391	494.78	F,D,L	DMSO, MeCN	534	60,000	551	MeOH	6
D6251	544.85	F,D,L	DMSO, MeCN	588	64,000	616	MeOH	6
D10460	386.47	L	DMF, DMSO	373	23,000	571	MeOH	7
E2247	191.70	F,D	H_2O	<300		none		
F36201	1055.26	F,D,L	pH >6	494	78,000	518	H_2O/Ca^{2+}	8, 9
H2249	217.13	D	H_2O	<300		none		
L2424	600.75	L	DMF, DMSO	561	122,000	581	MeOH	
M6248	174.24	D,A	DMF, MeCN	<300		none		
N2461	373.30	FF,DD,L	DMF, $CHCl_3$	260	59,000	395	MeOH	
O10465	496.47	F,D,L	pH >6, DMF	494	75,000	521	pH 9	10
P244	274.36	L	DMF, $CHCl_3$	341	41,000	376	MeOH	
P1405	242.28	FF,L	DMF, MeCN	340	41,000	375	MeOH	
P2421	267.76	L	DMF, DMSO	340	39,000	376	MeOH	11
P6254	295.81	L	DMF, DMSO	340	41,000	376	MeOH	11
P6281	~5000	NC	H_2O, MeOH	<300		none		
Q10464	814.87	L	DMSO	560	92,000	none	MeOH	
Q20540	399.29	L	DMSO, DMF	472	24,000	none	MeOH	
S10490	268.11	D	H_2O	<300		none		
T2425	690.87	L	DMF	591	85,000	612	pH 9	

For definitions of the contents of this data table, see "Navigating *The Handbook*" in the introductory pages.

Notes

1. A191 in aqueous solution (pH 7.0): Abs = 342 nm (EC = 16,000 $cm^{-1}M^{-1}$), Em = 441 nm.
2. Absorption and fluorescence of fluorescein derivatives are pH-dependent. Extinction coefficients and fluorescence quantum yields decrease markedly at pH <7.
3. Fluorescence of NBD and its derivatives in water is relatively weak. QY and τ increase and Em decreases in aprotic solvents and other nonpolar environments relative to water (Biochemistry 16, 5150 (1977); Photochem Photobiol 54, 361 (1991)).
4. The Alexa Fluor® 405 and Cascade Blue® dyes have a second absorption peak at about 376 nm with EC ~80% of the 395–400 nm peak.
5. Spectra are for the reaction product with acetic acid.
6. The absorption and fluorescence spectra of BODIPY® derivatives are relatively insensitive to the solvent.
7. Fluorescence emission spectrum shifts to shorter wavelengths in nonpolar solvents.
8. Spectra measured in 100 mM KCl, 10 mM MOPS, pH 7.2 containing 39 µM free Ca^{2+} (H_2O/Ca^{2+}).
9. $K_d(Ca^{2+})$ for F36200 and F36201 is 950 nM measured in 100 mM KCl, 10 mM MOPS, pH 7.2, 0 to 39 µM free Ca^{2+} at 22°C.
10. Absorption and fluorescence of Oregon Green® 488 derivatives are pH-dependent only in moderately acidic solutions (pH <5).
11. Pyrene derivatives exhibit structured spectra. The absorption maximum is usually about 340 nm with a subsidiary peak at about 325 nm. There are also strong absorption peaks below 300 nm. The emission maximum is usually about 376 nm with a subsidiary peak at 396 nm. Excimer emission at about 470 nm may be observed at high concentrations.

Product List — 3.3 Derivatization Reagents for Carboxylic Acids and Glutamine

Cat #	Product Name	Unit Size
A30674	Alexa Fluor® 350 cadaverine	1 mg
A30675	Alexa Fluor® 405 cadaverine, trisodium salt	1 mg
A30676	Alexa Fluor® 488 cadaverine, sodium salt	1 mg
A30677	Alexa Fluor® 555 cadaverine, disodium salt	1 mg
A30680	Alexa Fluor® 568 cadaverine, diammonium salt	1 mg
A30678	Alexa Fluor® 594 cadaverine	1 mg
A30679	Alexa Fluor® 647 cadaverine, disodium salt	1 mg
A1363	5-(aminoacetamido)fluorescein (fluoresceinyl glycine amide)	10 mg
A1364	4'-((aminoacetamido)methyl)fluorescein	10 mg
A117	5-aminoeosin	100 mg
A1339	*N*-(2-aminoethyl)-4-amino-3,6-disulfo-1,8-naphthalimide, dipotassium salt (lucifer yellow ethylenediamine)	25 mg
A91	5-((2-aminoethyl)amino)naphthalene-1-sulfonic acid, sodium salt (EDANS)	1 g
A191	7-amino-4-methylcoumarin *reference standard*	100 mg
A1351	4'-(aminomethyl)fluorescein, hydrochloride	25 mg
A1353	5-(aminomethyl)fluorescein, hydrochloride	10 mg
A1318	5-(and-6)-((*N*-(5-aminopentyl)amino)carbonyl)tetramethylrhodamine (tetramethylrhodamine cadaverine) *mixed isomers*	10 mg
A1340	*N*-(5-aminopentyl)-4-amino-3,6-disulfo-1,8-naphthalimide, dipotassium salt (lucifer yellow cadaverine)	25 mg
A434	5-((5-aminopentyl)thioureidyl)eosin, hydrochloride (eosin cadaverine)	25 mg
A10466	5-((5-aminopentyl)thioureidyl)fluorescein, dihydrobromide salt (fluorescein cadaverine)	25 mg
A10461	3*S*-(4-(3-aminopyrrolidin-1-yl))-7-nitrobenz-2-oxa-1,3-diazole ((*S*)-NBD-APy)	10 mg
A1122	4-(9-anthroyloxy)phenacyl bromide (panacyl bromide)	100 mg
A1400	9-anthryldiazomethane (ADAM)	25 mg
B30633	bimane amine	5 mg
B6057	6-bromoacetyl-2-dimethylaminonaphthalene (badan)	10 mg
B22802	8-bromomethyl-4,4-difluoro-3,5-bis-(2-thienyl)-4-bora-3a,4a-diaza-*s*-indacene (BODIPY® 630/650 methyl bromide)	1 mg
B2103	8-bromomethyl-4,4-difluoro-1,3,5,7-tetramethyl-4-bora-3a,4a-diaza-*s*-indacene (BODIPY® 493/503 methyl bromide)	5 mg
B1355	5-(bromomethyl)fluorescein	10 mg
C621	Cascade Blue® ethylenediamine, trisodium salt	10 mg
C428	*N*-cyclohexyl-*N'*-(4-(dimethylamino)naphthyl)carbodiimide (NCD-4)	25 mg
D10460	Dapoxyl® (2-aminoethyl)sulfonamide	10 mg
D2390	4,4-difluoro-5,7-dimethyl-4-bora-3a,4a-diaza-*s*-indacene-3-propionyl ethylenediamine, hydrochloride (BODIPY® FL EDA)	5 mg
D2391	4,4-difluoro-5,7-diphenyl-4-bora-3a,4a-diaza-*s*-indacene-3-propionyl ethylenediamine, hydrochloride (BODIPY® 530/550 EDA)	5 mg
D6251	5-(((4-(4,4-difluoro-5-(2-thienyl)-4-bora-3a,4a-diaza-*s*-indacene-3-yl)phenoxy)acetyl)amino)pentylamine, hydrochloride (BODIPY® TR cadaverine)	5 mg
D112	5-dimethylaminonaphthalene-1-(*N*-(2-aminoethyl))sulfonamide (dansyl ethylenediamine)	100 mg
D113	5-dimethylaminonaphthalene-1-(*N*-(5-aminopentyl))sulfonamide (dansyl cadaverine)	100 mg
E2247	1-ethyl-3-(3-dimethylaminopropyl)carbodiimide, hydrochloride (EDAC)	100 mg
F36201	fluo-4 cadaverine, pentapotassium salt	500 µg
H2249	*N*-hydroxysulfosuccinimide, sodium salt (NHSS)	100 mg
L2424	Lissamine™ rhodamine B ethylenediamine	10 mg
M6248	mono-*N*-(*t*-BOC)-propylenediamine	1 g
N2461	2-(2,3-naphthalimino)ethyl trifluoromethanesulfonate	100 mg
O10465	Oregon Green® 488 cadaverine *5-isomer*	5 mg
P6281	poly(ethylene glycol) methyl ether, amine-terminated, average MW 5000	1 g
P244	1-pyrenebutanol	100 mg
P2421	1-pyrenemethylamine, hydrochloride (1-aminomethylpyrene, hydrochloride)	100 mg
P6254	1-pyrenepropylamine, hydrochloride	5 mg
P1405	1-pyrenyldiazomethane (PDAM)	25 mg
Q10464	QSY® 7 amine, hydrochloride	5 mg
Q20540	QSY® 35 methylamine	5 mg
S10490	4-sulfo-2,3,5,6-tetrafluorophenol, sodium salt (STP)	100 mg
T2425	Texas Red® cadaverine (Texas Red® C_5)	5 mg

For current prices or to order online, visit probes.invitrogen.com

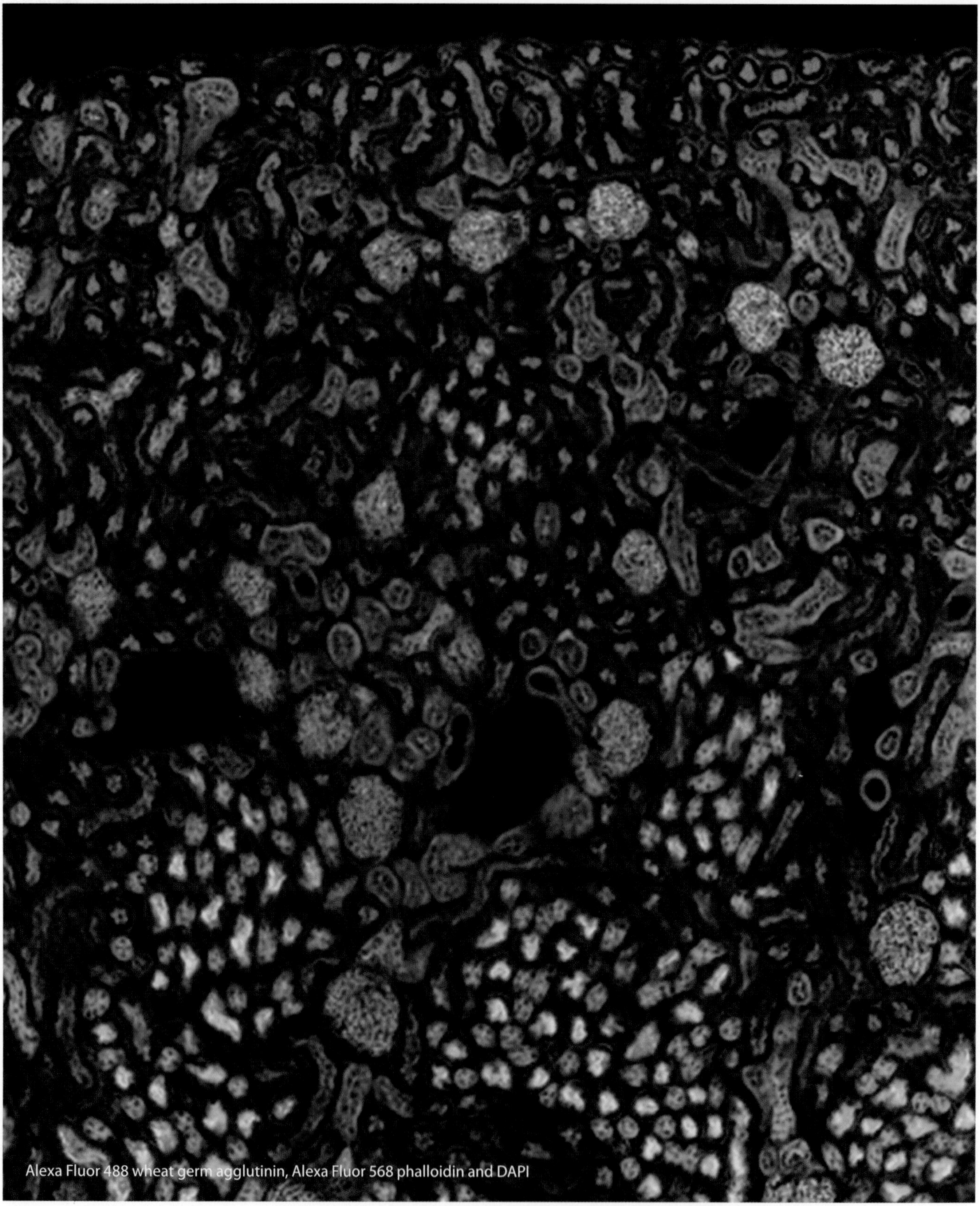

Alexa Fluor 488 wheat germ agglutinin, Alexa Fluor 568 phalloidin and DAPI

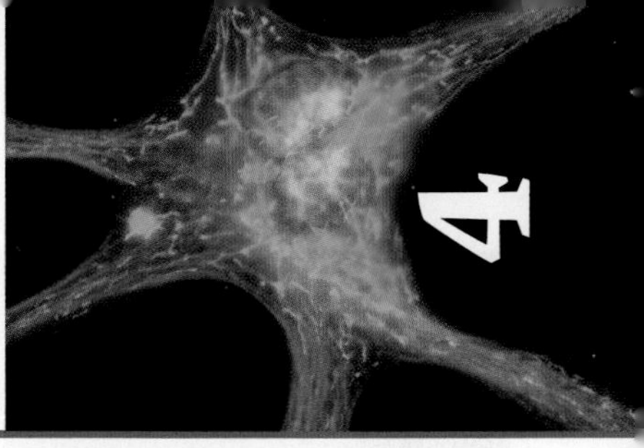

Chapter 4

Biotin Derivatives and Haptens

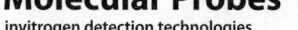

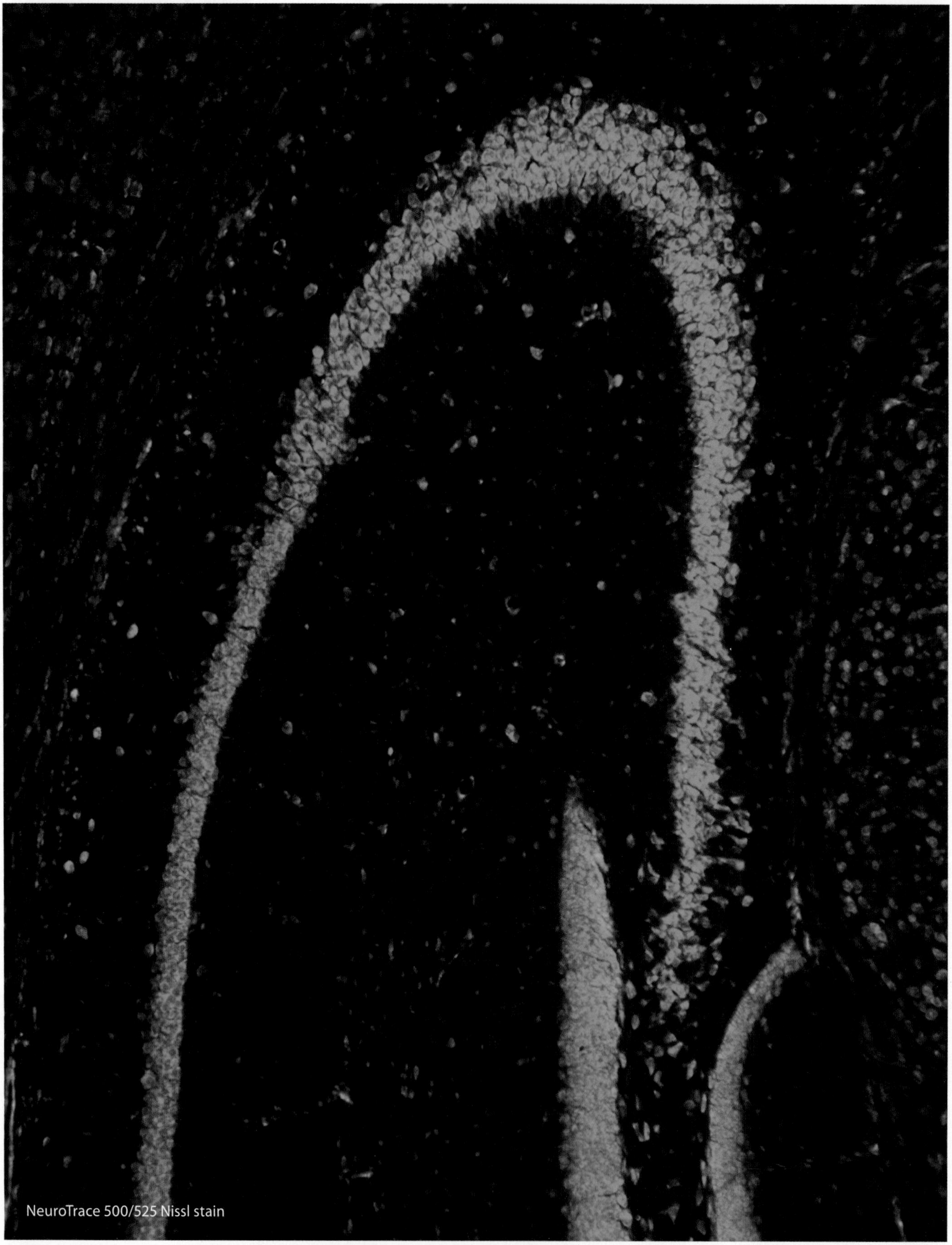
NeuroTrace 500/525 Nissl stain

4.1 Introduction to Avidin–Biotin and Antibody–Hapten Techniques

The high affinity and specificity of avidin–biotin and antibody–hapten interactions have been exploited for diverse applications in immunology, histochemistry, *in situ* hybridization (Section 8.5), affinity chromatography and many other areas.[1–4] Biotinylation (Table 4.1) and haptenylation (Table 4.2) reagents provide the "tag" that transforms poorly detectable molecules into probes that can be recognized by a labeled detection reagent or an affinity-capture matrix. Once tagged with biotin or a hapten, a molecule of interest — such as an antibody, lectin, drug, polynucleotide, polysaccharide or receptor ligand — can be used to probe complex solutions, cells and tissues, as well as protein and nucleic acid blots and arrays. This tagged molecule can then be detected with the appropriate avidin or anti-hapten antibody conjugate that has been labeled with a fluorophore, fluorescent microsphere (Section 6.5), enzyme, chromophore, magnetic particle or colloidal gold (Section 7.6). Biotinylated molecules can also be captured with various forms of immobilized streptavidin, such as our streptavidin agarose (S951, Section 7.6), CaptAvidin™ agarose (C21386, Section 7.6) and Captivate™ ferrofluid magnetic particles (C21476, Section 7.6), or stained for electron microscopy with NANOGOLD or Alexa Fluor® FluoroNanogold 1.4 nm gold cluster streptavidin (N24918, A24926, A24927, Section 7.6).

Although binding of biotin to native avidin or streptavidin is essentially irreversible, appropriately modified avidins can bind biotinylated probes reversibly, making them valuable reagents for isolating and purifying biotinylated molecules from complex mixtures.[5,6] CaptAvidin™ biotin-binding protein (C21385, Section 7.6) is our newest avidin derivative.[6] Selective nitration of tyrosine residues in the four biotin-binding sites of avidin considerably reduces the affinity of the protein for biotinylated molecules above pH 9. Consequently, biotinylated probes can be adsorbed at neutral pH or below and released at ~pH 10 [5,6] (Figure 7.99). CaptAvidin™ agarose (C21386, Section 7.6) is particularly useful for separating and purifying biotin conjugates from complex mixtures.[6]

In contrast to the modified avidin of our CaptAvidin™ products, our unique DSB-X™ biotin technology (Section 7.6) employs a modified biotin to provide a means of labeling and separating biomolecules, including live cells, under extremely gentle conditions.[7] The DSB-X™ biotin reagents, which are derivatives of desthiobiotin (Figure 4.1) with an additional seven-atom 'X' spacer, have moderate affinity for avidin and streptavidin that is rapidly reversed by low concentrations of free biotin or desthiobiotin at neutral pH and room temperature (Figure 7.103). This technique permits capture and release of DSB-X™ biotin–labeled molecules using our DSB-X™ Biotin Bioconjugate Isolation Kits #1 and #2 (D20658, D20659; Section 7.6; Figure 7.109) or Captivate™ ferrofluid streptavidin (C21476, Section 7.6).

Avidin–biotin and antibody–hapten techniques are compatible with flow cytometry and light, electron and fluorescence microscopy, as well as with solution-based methods such as enzyme-linked immunosorbent assays (ELISAs). Moreover, avidin–biotin and antibody–hapten techniques are frequently combined for simultaneous, multicolor detection of multiple targets in a complex solution, cell or tissue sample. Furthermore, by judicious choice of detection reagents and sandwich protocols, these techniques can be employed to amplify the signal from low-abundance analytes. For example, the bridging method is a common immunohistochemical technique for signal amplification and improved tissue penetration in which avidin or streptavidin serves as a bridge between two biotinylated molecules.

This chapter is devoted to our biotinylation, desthiobiotinylation (DSB-X™ biotinylation) and haptenylation reagents (Section 4.2) and our biotin and desthiobiotin (DSB-X™ biotin) conjugates (Section 4.3). Section 7.2 and Section 7.6 describe our large assortment of labeled antibody (Table 7.1) and avidin (Table 7.22) probes, respectively; we offer the largest selection of fluorescent secondary reagents available from any commercial source. Furthermore, our unique Zenon® Antibody Labeling Kits permit the rapid and quantitative labeling of even extremely small quantities of primary antibodies with biotin, DSB-X™ biotin or a wide variety of fluorophores and enzymes (Section 7.3, Table 7.13, Figure 7.59). Where they can be used, our avidin- and biotin-coated FluoSpheres® and TransFluoSpheres® fluorescent microspheres (Section 6.5) provide an alternative detection technology that offers a combination of fluorescence intensity and photostability far superior to that of any simple dye conjugate.

Both the tyramide signal amplification (TSA) technology (Section 6.2), which was developed by NEN (now a part of PerkinElmer Corporation) and licensed to Molecular Probes for in-cell and in-tissue applications, and our Enzyme-Labeled Fluorescence (ELF®) technology (Section 6.3) take advantage of the high affinity and specificity of the avidin–biotin interaction. Several of our ELF® 97 Kits utilize an application-specific ELF® 97 phosphatase substrate and either alkaline phosphatase streptavidin or a biotinylated alkaline phosphatase plus a streptavidin bridge to yield much greater fluorescence at the site of biotinylated molecules than is possible with direct dye conjugates of avidin. Additionally, Molecular Probes has introduced several TSA Kits (Section 6.2, Table 6.1) that contain a labeled tyramide and a horseradish peroxidase conjugate of either streptavidin or a secondary antibody for amplifying the detectability of biotinylated or antibody-labeled molecules (Figure 6.30). TSA Kits are available containing biotin-XX tyramide, DSB-X™ biotin tyramide or 2,4-dinitrophenyl-X (DNP-X) tyramide as the amplification reagent. We also offer TSA Kits containing one of our Alexa Fluor® tyramides, Pacific

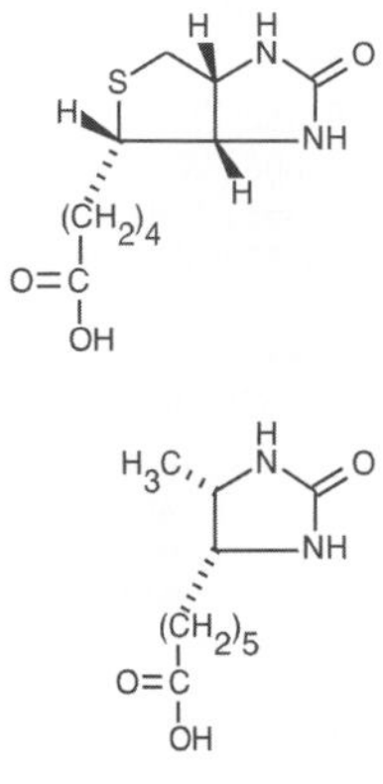

Figure 4.1 Comparison of the structures of D-biotin (top) and D-desthiobiotin (bottom).

Blue™ tyramide or Oregon Green® 488 tyramide as the direct detection reagents. Further amplification can also sometimes be achieved by combining TSA with ELF® or a second round of TSA (Figure 6.5) to yield the greatest fluorescence intensity in cells and tissues, while retaining high spatial resolution.

Mammalian cells and tissues contain biotin-dependent carboxylases, which are required for a variety of metabolic functions. These biotin-containing enzymes often produce substantial background signals when biotin–avidin or biotin–streptavidin detection systems are used to identify cellular targets[8] (Figure 4.2, Figure 12.27). The reagents in our Endogenous Biotin-Blocking Kit (E21390), which is described in Section 7.6, can be used to minimize interference from endogenous biotin in these techniques.

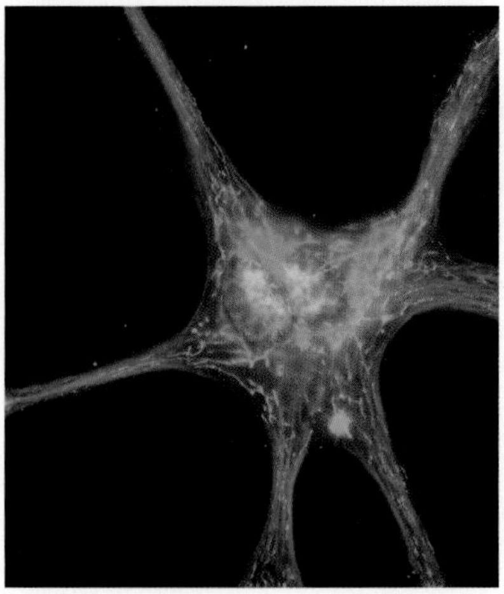

Figure 4.2 The cytoskeleton of a fixed and permeabilized bovine pulmonary artery endothelial cell detected using mouse monoclonal anti–α-tubulin antibody (A11126), visualized with Alexa Fluor® 647 goat anti–mouse IgG antibody (A21235) and pseudocolored magenta. Endogenous biotin in the mitochondria was labeled with green-fluorescent Alexa Fluor® 488 streptavidin (S11223) and DNA was stained with blue-fluorescent DAPI (D1306, D3571, D21490).

References

1. Clin Chem 37, 625 (1991); **2.** Methods Biochem Anal 26, 1 (1980); **3.** Methods Enzymol 184, (Complete Volume) (1990); **4.** Anal Biochem 171, 1 (1988); **5.** Biochem J 316, 193 (1996); **6.** Anal Biochem 243, 257 (1996); **7.** Anal Biochem 308, 343 (2002); **8.** J Histochem Cytochem 45, 1053 (1997).

4.2 Biotinylation and Haptenylation Reagents

Molecular Probes is the primary manufacturer of a diverse array of biotinylation (Table 4.1) and haptenylation (Table 4.2) reagents for labeling biomolecules. In addition, our DSB-X™ biotin technology (Section 7.6) employs a modified biotin to provide a means of labeling and separating biomolecules, including live cells, under extremely gentle conditions.[1,2] Biotinylated molecules, as well as DSB-X™ biotin–labeled molecules prepared using our DSB-X™ Biotin Protein Labeling Kit (D20655, Section 1.2), can be subsequently detected with fluorescent dye or enzyme conjugates of avidins (Section 7.6, Table 7.22) or with NANOGOLD streptavidin gold clusters (N24918, A24925, A24926; Section 7.6). These biotinylated and DSB-X™ biotin–labeled molecules are also readily captured and separated from solutions with streptavidin agarose (S951, Section 7.6, Figure 7.103), CaptAvidin™ agarose (C21386, Section 7.6) or the streptavidin conjugate of Captivate™ ferrofluid superparamagnetic particles (C21476, Section 7.6). Adsorption of DSB-X™ biotin–labeled molecules or cells onto affinity matrices can be rapidly reversed at neutral pH and room temperature by adding free biotin to the solution (Figure 7.99).

Reviews of the methods that we use to prepare biotinylated[3,4] and fluorescent[5] conjugates of antibodies have been published. To make the labeling reactions particularly easy, we have developed some very useful kits for labeling proteins with biotin, DSB-X™ biotin, 2,4-dinitrophenyl (DNP) or a choice of several different fluorophores, as described below. Each of the protein labeling kits contains the preferred reactive dye or hapten — many of which have spacers to reduce interactions between the label and the biomolecule — along with a detailed protocol for preparing the conjugates. In most cases, these kits also provide the separation media for purifying labeled protein conjugates from the reaction mixture.

Table 4.1 — Biotinylation and desthiobiotinylation reagents

Derivatizing Reagent	Cat #
Aliphatic amine	A1593, A1594, B1596, N6356
Carboxylic acid	B1595, B20656, B1592, D20652, D20657
DNP-X-biocytin-X, SE	B2604, F6348 (F)
FMOC	B20651 (B)
Hydrazide	B1603 (B), B2600 (XX), D20653 (X)(D)
Hydroxylamine	ARP, A10550
Iodoacetamide	B1591
Maleimide	M1602 (B)
Nitrilotriacetic acid (NTA)	B11790
Succinimidyl ester (SE)	B1513, B1582 (X), B1606 (XX), B6353 (SSE)(X), B6352 (SSE)(XX), F2610 (F), F6347 (F), D20655 (DK)

SE = Succinimidyl ester. F = FluoReporter® Protein Labeling Kit (Section 1.2). B = Biocytin. XX = Aminohexanoylaminohexanoyl spacer separating the biotin and the reactive moiety. X = Aminohexanoyl spacer separating the biotin or desthiobiotin and the reactive moiety. D = DSB-X™ biotin. SSE = Sulfosuccinimidyl ester. DK = DSB-X™ Biotin Protein Labeling Kit (Section 1.2).

Our ARES™ DNA Labeling Kits (Section 8.2, Table 8.9, Figure 8.45), ULYSIS Nucleic Acid Labeling Kits (Section 8.2, Table 8.8, Figure 8.42), Alexa Fluor® Oligonucleotide Amine Labeling Kits (Section 8.2, Table 8.10), ChromaTide® UTP, dUTP and dCTP nucleotides (Section 8.2; Table 8.6, Table 8.7) and 5-aminohexylacrylamido-dUTP (aha-dUTP) nucleotides (Section 8.2, Table 8.7) yield probes whose labels can, in many cases, be utilized as haptens in various signal amplification schemes.

Our exclusive Zenon® technology (Section 7.3) permits the quantitative biotinylation and desthiobiotinylation of even submicrogram quantities of an antibody in less than 10 minutes (Figure 7.59). The Zenon® Biotin-XX and DSB-X™ Biotin Antibody Labeling Kits (Table 7.13) provide the reagents and detailed instructions for this labeling. Also available are numerous other Zenon®

Table 4.2 — Selected haptenylation reagents and their anti-hapten antibodies

Cat #	Preferred Reactive Hapten(s)	Unlabeled and Labeled Anti-Hapten Antibodies * (Cat #)
A30000 A30100	Alexa Fluor® 405, SE	Anti–Alexa Fluor® 405/Cascade Blue® dye (A5760)
A20000 A20100	Alexa Fluor® 488, SE	Anti–Alexa Fluor® 488 dye (A11094)
A2952	3-Amino-3-deoxydigoxigenin hemisuccinamide, SE	Anti-digoxigenin (available from other suppliers)
B1582 B1606 B6352 B6353	Biotin-X, SE Biotin-XX, SE Biotin-XX, SSE Biotin-X, SSE	Anti-biotin (A11242, A31800, A31801)
D6102 B10006	BODIPY® FL-X, SE BODIPY® FL, STP ester	Anti–BODIPY® FL dye (A5770) †
C2284	Cascade Blue® acetyl azide	Anti–Alexa Fluor® 405/Cascade Blue® dye (A5760)
D6104	Dansyl-X, SE	Anti-dansyl (A6398)
D2248	DNP-X, SE	Anti-DNP (A6423, A6430, A6435); Alexa Fluor® 488 anti–DNP-KLH (A11097)
B2604	DNP-X–biocytin-X, SE	Anti-DNP (A6423, A6430, A6435); anti-biotin (A11242, A31800, A31801)
D20655	DSB-X™ biotin, SE	Anti-biotin (A11242, A31800, A31801)
F2181 F6130	Fluorescein 5(6)-SFX Fluorescein-EX, SE	Anti-fluorescein/Oregon Green® dye (A889, A982, A6413, A6421, A11090, A11091, A21253, A21254) †
L1338	Lucifer yellow iodoacetamide	Anti–lucifer yellow dye (A5750, A5751)
O6185	Oregon Green® 488-X, SE	Anti-fluorescein/Oregon Green® dye (A889, A982, A6413, A6421, A11090, A11091, A21253, A21254) †
T6105	5(6)-TAMRA-X, SE	Anti-tetramethylrhodamine (A6397); anti–Texas Red® dye (A6399) †
R6160	Rhodamine Red™-X, SE	Anti-tetramethylrhodamine (A6397); anti–Texas Red® dye (A6399) †
T6134 T10125	Texas Red®-X, SE Texas Red®-X, STP ester	Anti-tetramethylrhodamine (A6397); anti–Texas Red® dye (A6399) †

* See Section 7.4 for a description of these anti-hapten antibodies. † Both the anti-tetramethylrhodamine and the anti–Texas Red® dye antibodies crossreact with tetramethylrhodamine, Lissamine rhodamine, Rhodamine Red™ and Texas Red® fluorophores. Therefore, these fluorophores should not be used simultaneously to generate separate signals in a multicolor experiment. Similarly, the anti–BODIPY® FL dye antibody may crossreact with other BODIPY® dyes, and the anti-fluorescein/Oregon Green® dye antibody crossreacts with both fluorescein and Oregon Green® dyes.

Antibody Labeling Kits (Table 7.13) for labeling mouse, rabbit, goat and human IgG antibodies with many of our brightest proprietary fluorescent dyes, as well as with phycobiliproteins and enzyme labels. An outstanding feature of the Zenon® technology is that it potentially permits the use of multiple antibodies derived from the same species in the same protocol.

A Variety of Biotinylation Reagents

The primary building blocks for preparing biotinylation reagents are biotin (B1595, B20656), biotin-X and biotin-XX, where "X" represents a seven-atom aminohexanoyl spacer between biotin and the reactive carboxylic acid. This spacer helps to separate the biotin moiety from its point of attachment, potentially reducing the interaction of biotin with the biomolecule to which it is conjugated and enhancing its ability to bind to the relatively deep biotin binding sites in avidin[2] (Figure 4.3). We also offer biocytin (ε-biotinoyl-L-lysine, B1592), biotin ethylenediamine (A1593), biotin cadaverine (A1594), biotin-X cadaverine (B1596), DSB-X™ desthiobiocytin (ε-desthiobiotinoyl-L-lysine, D20652) and DSB-X™ biotin ethylenediamine (D30752), each of which contains a primary amine that allows it to be fixed in cells with aldehyde-based fixatives, facilitating subsequent detection with conjugates of avidin and streptavidin (Section 7.6) or with our anti-biotin monoclonal antibody (Section 7.4). Biocytin derivatives, including probes that contain both biotin and fluorophore moieties, are commonly employed as microinjectable cell tracers and are discussed in Section 4.3 and Section 14.3. D-Desthiobiotin (D20657) is the biological precursor to D-biotin[6,7] and a key reagent in our important DSB-X™ biotin technology (Section 7.6).

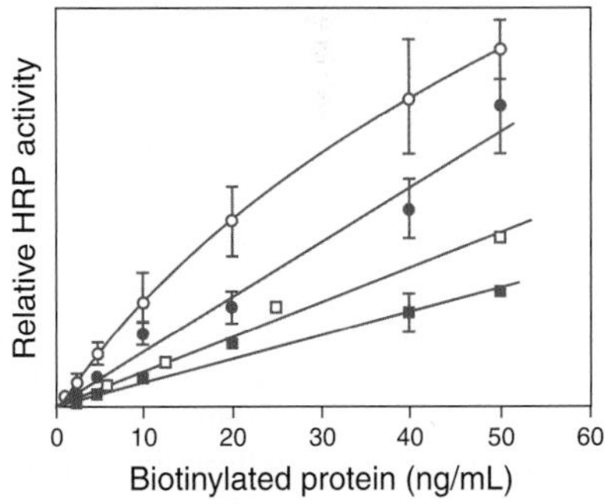

Figure 4.3 ELISA-type assay comparing the binding capacity of bovine serum albumin (BSA) and goat anti–mouse IgG antibody (GAM) biotinylated with either biotin-X succinimidyl ester (B1582) or biotin-XX succinimidyl ester (B1606). The assay was developed using horseradish peroxidase streptavidin (S911, 0.2 µg/mL) and o-phenylenediamine dihydrochloride (OPD). The moles of biotin per mole of protein were: 4.0 biotin-X/GAM (●), 4.4 biotin-XX/GAM (○), 6.7 biotin-X/BSA (■) and 6.2 biotin-XX/GAM (□). Error bars on some data points have been omitted for clarity. Reprinted with permission from Methods Mol Biol 45, 223 (1995).

Amine-Reactive Biotinylation Reagents

Although Molecular Probes' biotin succinimidyl ester (B1513) can be used to biotinylate amines in peptides, proteins and other biomolecules,[8] we strongly recommend the biotin-X and biotin-

XX succinimidyl esters (B1582, B1606), and especially the water-soluble biotin-X and biotin-XX sulfosuccinimidyl esters (B6353, B6352), because their additional 7- and 14-atom spacers greatly facilitate binding to avidin and to anti-biotin antibodies (Figure 4.3). Molecular Probes uses biotin-X succinimidyl ester or the biotin-XX derivative to prepare all of its biotinylated protein and dextran conjugates. Red blood cells that were biotinylated with biotin-X succinimidyl ester — but surprisingly not those modified with biotin-X sulfosuccinimidyl ester — could be detected in circulation for almost 100 days after injection into dogs.[9]

The sulfosuccinimidyl esters of biotin-X and biotin-XX (B6353, B6352) have been extensively used as topological probes to label proteins in the outer membrane surface,[10] yielding labeled proteins that can be separated by electrophoresis, blotted onto membranes and then detected with a fluorophore- or enzyme-conjugated avidin derivative (Section 7.6). We utilize biotin-XX sulfosuccinimidyl ester as a component in our FluoReporter® Cell-Surface Biotinylation Kit (F20650, see below). Our alkaline phosphatase streptavidin–containing Pro-Q® Western Blot Stain Kits (P21862, P21865; Section 9.4), Amplex® Gold Western Blot Stain Kit #3 (A21892, Section 9.4) and DyeChrome™ Western Blot Stain Kits (D21883, D21886; Section 9.4) use biotinylated reagents to provide sensitivity similar to that of enhanced chemiluminescence but with permanent labeling.

Reactive DSB-X™ Biotin Derivatives

Our unique DSB-X™ biotin technology (Section 4.1) permits the readily reversible binding of DSB-X™ biotin–labeled biomolecules to avidin and streptavidin derivatives,[1] including dye, enzyme and NANOGOLD or Alexa Fluor® FluoroNanogold 1.4 nm gold cluster (N24918, A24925, A24926; Section 7.6) conjugates, affinity matrices and our Captivate™ ferrofluid streptavidin (C21476, Section 7.6). The DSB-X™ biotin reagents, which are derivatives of desthiobiotin (Figure 4.1), have a moderate affinity for avidins, making DSB-X™ biotin an ideal ligand for transient immobilization of avidin and streptavidin conjugates (Figure 7.109). DSB-X™ biotin succinimidyl ester, which is a component of both the DSB-X™ Biotin Protein Labeling Kit (D20655) described below, can be conjugated to amine-containing molecules in the same way as the biotin succinimidyl esters. Our DSB-X™ biotin C_2-iodoacetamide (D30753) and TS-Link™ DSB-X™ biotin C_5-thiosulfate (T30754) are thiol-reactive derivatives for labeling proteins and thiol-modified oligonucleotides. In addition, we offer DSB-X™ biotin hydrazide (D20653), DSB-X™ desthiobiocytin (D20652) and DSB-X™ biotin ethylenediamine (D30752), reactive derivatives of DSB-X™ biotin that should be useful as fixable polar tracers in neurons and other cells (Section 14.3). See Section 7.6 for a complete discussion of our DSB-X™ biotin technology and its uses.

Amine-Reactive Chromophoric Biotin Derivative

Determining a protein's degree of biotinylation is relatively difficult because of the lack of visible absorbance by the biotin molecule. To facilitate this determination, Molecular Probes offers an amine-reactive chromophoric derivative, biotin-X 2,4-dinitrophenyl-X-L-lysine succinimidyl ester (DNP-X–biocytin-X, SE; B2604; Figure 4.4). Following protein conjugation, the extent of biotinylation is easily determined from the absorbance of the DNP chromophore ($\varepsilon_{360\ nm}$ = 15,000 $cm^{-1}M^{-1}$). Incorporation of the DNP moiety into the biotinylating reagent does not affect its complexation with avidin or with anti-biotin antibodies. Our FluoReporter® Biotin/DNP Protein Labeling Kit (F6348), described below, contains sufficient DNP-X–biocytin-X SE for 5 to 10 protein labeling reactions of 0.2–2 mg each.

The DNP-X–biocytin-X succinimidyl ester is a unique amine-reactive reagent with versatile applications. Because this reagent comprises both DNP and biotin moieties (Figure 4.4), molecules labeled with it may be probed with Molecular Probes' anti-DNP or anti-biotin antibodies (Section 7.4, Table 7.19) or with our avidin conjugates (Section 7.6), thus facilitating correlated fluorescence and electron microscopy studies. This chromophoric biotin is also very useful for preparing conjugates for Molecular Devices' patented Threshold Immuno-Ligand Assay System. The Threshold System is designed to quantitate DNA and protein impurities in biopharmaceuticals by a urease-mediated signal amplification system that employs a silicon sensor to convert the chemical signal into an electronic signal.[11]

Thiol-Reactive Biotinylation Reagents

Although amine-reactive reagents are more commonly employed, the thiol-reactive biotin iodoacetamide[12] (B1591), biotin maleimide[13–15] (M1602) and DSB-X™ biotin C_2-iodoacetamide (D30753) derivatives can also be used to label proteins and thiol-modified oligonucleotides. Electrophoretically separated thiolated proteins treated with biotin maleimide have been detected in Western blots by an avidin–alkaline phosphatase conjugate.[16] Biotin iodoacetamide was used as an enzyme substrate in an unusual chemical reaction catalyzed by a ribozyme.[17]

We also offer TS-Link™ DSB-X™ biotin C_5-thiosulfate (TS-Link™ desthiobiotin-X C_5-thiosulfate, T30754), which is a water-soluble thiosulfate that reacts readily and selectively with a free thiol to form a disulfide bond (Figure 2.9). In contrast to the thioether bonds formed by maleimides and iodoacetamides, the disulfide bond formed by this TS-Link™ reagent is reversible — the TS-Link™ DSB-X™ hapten can easily be removed using a reducing agent such as dithiothreitol (DTT, D1532; Section 2.1) or tris-(2-carboxyethyl)phosphine (TCEP, T2556; Section 2.1), leaving the molecule of interest unchanged. In addition to TS-Link™ DSB-X™ biotin C_5-thiosulfate, we prepare fluorescent TS-Link™ BODIPY® thiosulfates (Section 2.2), as well as TS-Link™ bimane thiosulfate (T30502, Section 2.3) and TS-Link™ TFP-X thiosulfate (T30875, Section 5.2).

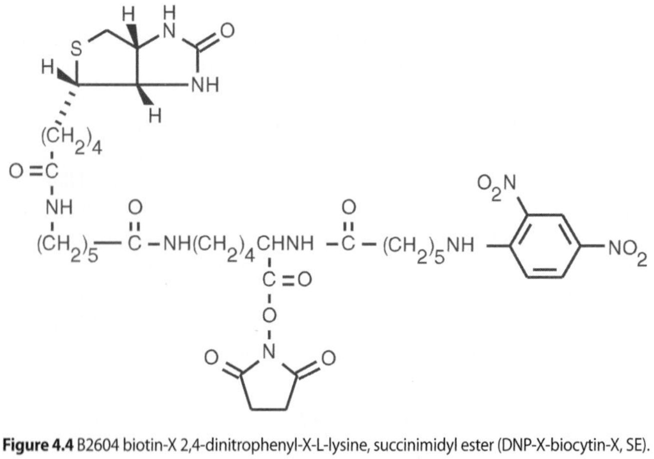

Figure 4.4 B2604 biotin-X 2,4-dinitrophenyl-X-L-lysine, succinimidyl ester (DNP-X-biocytin-X, SE).

Convenient Kits for Biotinylating Proteins

FluoReporter® Mini-Biotin-XX Protein Labeling Kit

Molecular Probes' FluoReporter® Mini-Biotin-XX Protein Labeling Kit (F6347, Table 1.3) provides a method for efficiently biotinylating small amounts of antibodies or other proteins. The water-soluble biotin-XX sulfosuccinimidyl ester contained in this kit readily reacts with a protein's amines to yield a biotin moiety that is linked to the protein through two aminohexanoyl chains ("XX"). This 14-atom spacer has been shown to enhance the binding of biotin derivatives to avidin's relatively deep binding sites (Figure 4.3). Each FluoReporter® Mini-Biotin-XX Labeling Kit contains:

- Biotin-XX, sulfosuccinimidyl ester
- Reaction tubes, each containing a magnetic spin bar
- Spin columns plus collection tubes
- Dialysis tubing (molecular weight cut-off ~12,000–14,000 daltons)
- A protocol for preparing and purifying the biotinylated protein

The ready-to-use spin columns provide an extremely convenient method of purifying the biotinylated protein from excess biotinylation reagents. Alternatively, the researcher may choose to remove excess reagents by dialysis, thereby avoiding further dilution of the biotinylated protein. The FluoReporter® Mini-Biotin-XX Protein Labeling Kit contains sufficient reagents for five biotinylation reactions of 0.1–3 mg of protein each. The Zenon® Biotin-XX Antibody Labeling Kits (Table 7.13) are a useful alternative for rapid and quantitative modification of antibodies with biotin. See Section 7.3 for a complete description of our Zenon® technology and Zenon® Antibody Labeling Kits.

FluoReporter® Biotin-XX Protein Labeling Kit

We also offer the FluoReporter® Biotin-XX Protein Labeling Kit (F2610, Table 1.3) for larger-scale biotinylation reactions. Once the labeled protein is purified from excess biotin reagent, its degree of biotinylation can be determined using an avidin–biotin displacement assay;[18,19] biotinylated goat IgG is provided as a control. The FluoReporter® Biotin-XX Protein Labeling Kit supplies:

- Biotin-XX, succinimidyl ester
- Dimethylsulfoxide (DMSO)
- Gel filtration column
- Avidin–HABA complex
- Biotinylated goat IgG
- A protocol for preparing and purifying the biotinylated protein, as well as for quantitating the degree of labeling

The FluoReporter® Biotin-XX Protein Labeling Kit provides sufficient reagents for five labeling reactions of 5–20 mg of protein each.

FluoReporter® Biotin/DNP Protein Labeling Kit

The FluoReporter® Biotin/DNP Protein Labeling Kit (F6348, Table 1.3) is similar to our other FluoReporter® Protein Labeling Kits, except that it contains DNP-X–biocytin-X succinimidyl ester as the reactive label. When proteins are labeled with this chromophoric biotin derivative, the degree of biotinylation can be readily assessed from the extinction coefficient of DNP ($\varepsilon_{360\ nm}$ = 15,000 $cm^{-1}M^{-1}$). An additional feature of the conjugates labeled with DNP-X–biocytin-X succinimidyl ester is that they can be recognized by avidin derivatives (or anti-biotin antibodies) and by anti-DNP antibodies, enabling researchers to choose among several detection techniques suitable for fluorescence and electron microscopy. Each FluoReporter® Biotin/DNP Protein Labeling Kit contains:

- DNP-X–biocytin-X, succinimidyl ester
- Dimethylsulfoxide (DMSO)
- Reaction tubes, each containing a magnetic spin bar
- Spin columns plus collection tubes
- A protocol for preparing and purifying the protein conjugate, as well as for quantitating the degree of labeling

The FluoReporter® Biotin/DNP Protein Labeling Kit supplies sufficient reagents for 5 to 10 labeling reactions of 0.2–2 mg of protein each.

DSB-X™ Biotin Protein Labeling Kit

Our unique DSB-X™ biotin technology, which is described in detail in Section 7.6, permits the facile reversal of the virtually irreversible biotin–avidin interaction under extremely gentle conditions.[1] DSB-X™ biotin succinimidyl ester, a derivative of desthiobiotin (Figure 4.1) with an additional seven-atom spacer, reacts with amine groups of biomolecules to form stable amides. The DSB-X™ biotin conjugate can be detected with any of the avidin or streptavidin derivatives described in Section 7.6. Binding is almost totally reversed by addition of free biotin (B1595, B20656; Section 4.2) at neutral pH and normal ionic strength. Significantly, DSB-X™ biotin–conjugated biopolymers can be separated from complex mixtures using agarose affinity matrices (Figure 7.99) or our Captivate™ ferrofluid superparamagnetic particles (Figure 7.107). Magnetic separation can include cells targeted by the DSB-X™ biotin conjugate. Our DSB-X™ Bioconjugate Isolation Kits #1 and #2 (D20658, D20659; Section 7.6) provide the reagents and protocols for using DSB-X™ biotin conjugates. The DSB-X™ Biotin Protein Labeling Kit (D20655, Table 1.3) contains the reagents required for five protein conjugations of 0.5–3 mg each, including:

- DSB-X™ biotin, succinimidyl ester
- Dimethylsulfoxide (DMSO)
- Reaction tubes
- Purification resin, spin columns and collection tubes for small-scale purifications
- Dialysis tubing for larger-scale purifications
- A detailed protocol for conjugations and purifications

As an alternative to direct labeling of primary antibodies with the DSB-X™ biotin succinimidyl ester, our Zenon® DSB-X™ Biotin Mouse IgG_1 Labeling Kit (Z25053, Section 7.3) gives rapid and quantitative complex formation with any whole mouse IgG_1 monoclonal antibody.

FluoReporter® Cell-Surface Biotinylation Kit

Biotin-XX sulfosuccinimidyl ester is a membrane-impermeant, amine-reactive compound that may be used to label proteins exposed on the surface of live cells[10] (Figure 4.5). The sulfosuccinimidyl ester forms an extremely stable conjugate with cell-surface proteins,[20] and the biotin provides a convenient hapten for subsequent isolation or analysis with an avidin-based protein, including streptavidin, NeutrAvidin and CaptAvidin™ biotin-binding proteins and the Captivate™ ferrofluid streptavidin conjugate (C21476, Section 7.6). Cell-surface biotinylation techniques have been employed to differentially label proteins in the apical and basolateral plasma membranes of epithelial cells.[21,22] These techniques are also well suited for studying internalization of membrane proteins[23] and cell-surface targeting of proteins.[24–26] The FluoReporter® Cell-Surface Biotinylation Kit (F20650) provides a convenient method to label proteins exposed on the cell surface including, but not limited to, membrane proteins. This kit includes:

- Biotin-XX sulfosuccinimidyl ester
- Anhydrous DMSO for preparing stable stock solutions
- A detailed protocol for cell-surface biotinylation

The supplied protocol for cell-surface biotinylation is easy to perform and can be completed in less than one hour. Biotinylated proteins can be subsequently identified using the reagents in some of our Pro-Q®, Amplex® Gold and DyeChrome™ Western Blot Kits (Section 9.4).

Oligohistidine Fusion Protein Detection

The oligohistidine domain is a Ni^{2+}-binding moiety comprising four to six consecutive histidine residues. Biotin-X nitrilotriacetic acid (biotin-X NTA, B11790; Figure 4.6) is designed to detect oligohistidine fusion proteins immobilized on nitrocellulose membranes. The nitrilotriacetic acid moiety of biotin-X NTA chelates Ni^{2+} that is associated with oligohistidine domains. Once bound, the complex can be detected using standard enzyme-linked streptavidin methods. McMahan and Burgess have shown that biotin-X NTA can be used to detect less than 0.1 picomole of an oligohistidine fusion protein using horseradish peroxidase streptavidin and chemiluminescence techniques.[27] An additional benefit of biotin-X NTA is that it can be removed from the oligohistidine fusion protein at pH 4.8, allowing the blot to be reanalyzed with another probe. In addition to biotin-X NTA as a stand-alone reagent (B11790), Molecular Probes has utilized biotin-X NTA in its Pro-Q® Oligohistidine Blot Stain Kits (P21878, P21879), which are discussed in detail in Section 9.4. We have also developed the Pro-Q® Sapphire Oligohistidine Gel Stains (P21876, P21877; Section 9.4), which can detect oligohistidine fusion proteins without blotting (Figure 9.74, Figure 9.75). In addition, Molecular Probes offers the Penta·His mouse IgG monoclonal antibody (P21315, Section 9.4), which provides a sensitive method for specific detection of fusion proteins that have an oligohistidine domain comprising five or six consecutive histidine residues on blots and in cells.

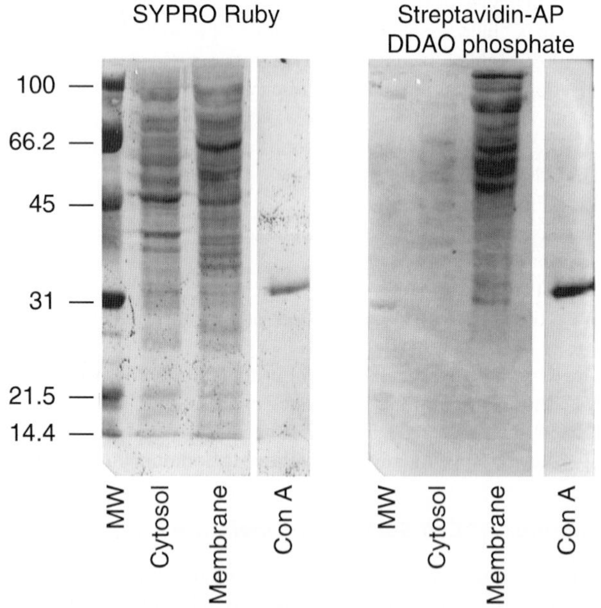

Figure 4.5 Identification of cell-surface proteins in Jurkat cells labeled with the FluoReporter® Cell-Surface Biotinylation Kit (F20650). The labeled cells were fractionated by differential detergent extraction into membrane and cytosolic fractions. The proteins were then precipitated with acetone, separated on an SDS-polyacrylamide gel and blotted onto a PVDF membrane. Total proteins and biotinylated proteins were differentially stained using the Pro-Q® Western Blot Stain Kit #6 (P21862). Total proteins were detected with the SYPRO® Ruby protein blot stain component of the kit (left panel); biotinylated proteins were identified with alkaline phosphatase streptavidin in combination with the red-fluorescent substrate, DDAO phosphate (right panel). MW = protein molecular weight markers; Con A = biotinylated concanavalin A.

Pro-Q® Oligohistidine Blot Stain Kits

The Pro-Q® Oligohistidine Blot Stain Kits (P21878, P21879; Section 9.4) include biotin-X nitrilotriacetic acid (biotin-X NTA, B11790), which chelates Ni^{2+} associated with oligohistidine domains. The blot is incubated with a complex of biotin-X NTA, Ni^{2+} and alkaline phosphatase streptavidin. The complex binds to the oligohistidine domain and is then detected by reaction with a fluorogenic phosphatase substrate, either DDAO phosphate (Kit #1, P21878) or ELF® 39 phosphate (Kit #2, P21879). The enzymatic reactions produce fluorescent products within minutes. Both fluorogenic detection methods have sensitivity rivaling that of ECL detection, but the signals can be imaged several times and are stable indefinitely on dried blots. The green-fluorescent ELF® 39 product (Kit #2) forms a permanent precipitate, whereas the red-fluorescent DDAO (Kit #1) can be washed off for further processing of the blot.

Pro-Q® Sapphire Oligohistidine Gel Stains

The Pro-Q® Sapphire 365 oligohistidine stain and Pro-Q® Sapphire 488 oligohistidine stain (P21876, P21877; Section 9.4) use proprietary reagents that allow detection of oligohistidine fusion proteins directly in the gel (Figure 9.74), eliminating the need to blot the proteins to a membrane for immunodetection. Both reagents use one of Molecular Probes' state-of-the-art fluorescent dyes conjugated to a nitrilotriacetic acid (NTA) moiety. The NTA moiety binds to oligohistidine domains, providing a simple and highly specific detection method. As little as 50 ng of oligohistidine fusion protein can be detected. Pro-Q® Sapphire 365 dye is excited by UV light, and its blue fluorescence can be visualized using standard UV transilluminators; Pro-Q® Sapphire 488 dye can also be excited by UV light, but it is optimally

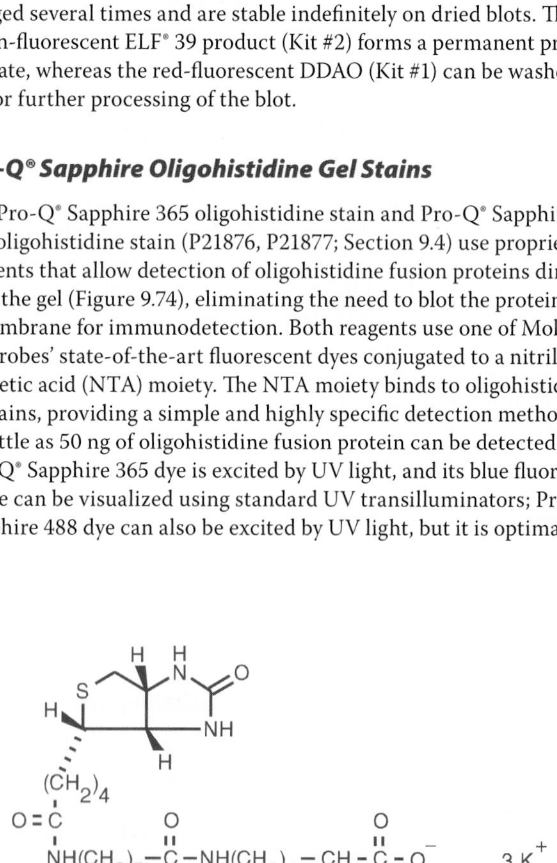

Figure 4.6 B11790 biotin-X nitrilotriacetic acid, tripotassium salt (biotin-X NTA).

excited by ~488 nm light, and its green fluorescence can be visualized using laser scanners. Both dyes are compatible with subsequent staining using SYPRO® Ruby protein gel stain, permitting oligohistidine fusion protein and total-protein detection on the same gel.

Biotinylation of Other Biomolecules

Histidine, Serine and Threonine Modification

Tripeptide sequences of certain peptides such as gonadotropin releasing hormone (GnRH), wherein serine, threonine or tyrosine residues are separated from a histidine residue by a single amino acid, can be selectively acylated by the succinimidyl ester or sulfosuccinimidyl ester of biotin-X (B1582, B6353). The reaction probably involves formation of an acyl histidine intermediate, followed by intramolecular transfer of the label (Figure 4.7). *O*-acylation can be detected by treating the conjugate with hydroxylamine, which cleaves esters of biotin but not amides.[28] N-terminal serine and threonine residues of proteins can be oxidized by periodate and then biotinylated with biotin hydrazine derivatives (B1603, B2600, D20653), which are described below.

Labeling with Biotin Hydrazides and Biotin Hydroxylamine (ARP)

As described in Section 3.2, aldehydes generated by periodate oxidation of vicinal diols in glycoproteins (Figure 9.49), polysaccharides and RNA or of N-terminal serine and threonine residues in proteins can be biotinylated using biotin-XX hydrazide (B2600). Biocytin hydrazide (B1603) reacts similarly and may be preferred because of its higher water solubility.[14,29] As with our other DSB-X™ biotin reagents (Section 7.6), DSB-X™ biotin hydrazide (desthiobiotin-X hydrazide, D20653) can be used to produce a DSB-X™ biotin–labeled molecule that exhibits easily reversible binding to avidin- or streptavidin-labeled reagents. Biotin hydrazides have been used to quantitate periodate-oxidized glycoproteins on electroblots,[30] as well as to biotinylate:

- Antibodies[31,32]
- Calmodulin[33]
- Cytidine residues[34]
- Erythropoietin[35]
- Glucagon[36]
- Glycoproteins,[37,38] sialic acid and carbohydrates[29]
- Low-density lipoproteins[39] (LDL)
- Nucleic acid hybridization probes[40,41]
- Steroids[42]

The biotin-containing hydroxylamine derivative ARP (aldehyde-reactive probe, A10550) has been used to modify the exposed aldehyde group at abasic sites in DNA — those apurinic sites and apyrimidinic lesions thought to be important intermediates in carcinogenesis[43–46] (Figure 8.147). Abasic sites are generated spontaneously or can be caused by free radicals, ionizing radiation or mutagens like methyl methanesulfonate (MMS). A quick and sensitive microplate assay for abasic sites can be performed using ARP. In addition, ARP is membrane permeant, permitting detection of abasic sites in live cells.[47,48] Once the aldehyde group in an abasic site is modified by ARP and the cells are fixed and permeabilized, the resulting biotinylated DNA can be detected with fluorescent dye– or enzyme-conjugated streptavidin conjugates (Section 7.6, Table 7.22). ARP has also been used to immobilize IgG antibodies on streptavidin-coated monolayer surfaces with their binding sites oriented toward the solution phase.[49] As compared with an amine-reactive biotinylation reagent, which randomly biotinylates lysines in the IgG molecule, ARP reacts with the carbohydrate domain in the Fc region of the IgG molecule, allowing the specific orientation of the IgG on the streptavidin-coated surface and optimizing the antibody microarray for protein expression profiling. We have determined that ARP and other hydroxylamine derivatives react with aldehydes and ketones faster than do the hydrazine derivatives.

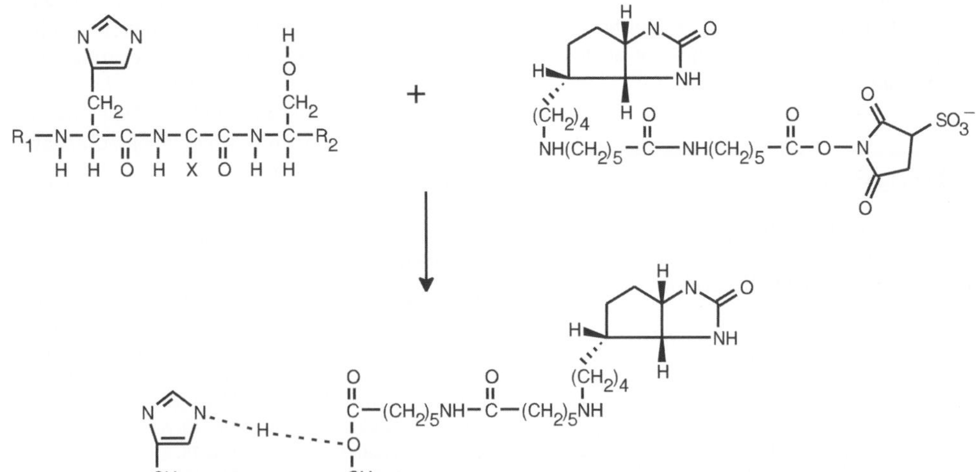

Figure 4.7 Nucleophilic attack of serine on the carbonyl group (C=O) of biotin-X, SSE (B6353) results in the stable *O*-acylated derivative. In addition to histidine-x-serine, this stable intermediate can be formed in the presence of linear sequences of histidine-x-tyrosine and histidine-x-threonine, where "x" refers to any amino acid.

Tyramide Signal Amplification Technology

The tyramide signal amplification (TSA) technology (Section 6.2), which was developed by NEN (now a part of PerkinElmer Corporation) and licensed to Molecular Probes for in-cell and in-tissue applications, permits significant amplification of the detectability of targets by a horseradish peroxidase (HRP)–mediated scheme (Figure 6.5). In the TSA method, the labeled tyramide becomes covalently linked to tyrosine residues in or near the target. Molecular Probes has introduced a wide selection of TSA Kits, including those that utilize either biotin-XX tyramide or DSB-X™ biotin tyramide as the amplification reagent (Section 6.2), those that utilize 2,4-dinitrophenyl-X (DNP-X) tyramide and those that utilize one of our Alexa Fluor® tyramides, Pacific Blue™ tyramide or Oregon Green® 488 tyramide as the direct detection reagents. Our antibodies to the Alexa Fluor® 488 and Oregon Green® fluorophores or to the biotin and DNP haptens (Section 7.4, Table 7.18) can be used in further amplification schemes of these tyramides. The TSA Kits containing the HRP–streptavidin conjugate (Table 6.1) can be used to amplify detection of any biotinylated probe.

Biotinylation of Carboxylic Acids

The biotin amines and hydrazides can be coupled to chemically activated carboxylic acids (Figure 3.23). The amine-containing biotin derivatives (B1592, A1593, A1594, B1596, N6356) are versatile intermediates for coupling biotin to DNA, carboxylic acids [50,51] and other biomolecules.[12] The biotin cadaverines (A1594, B1596) and potentially our unique norbiotinamine [52] (N6356, Figure 4.8) are useful for transglutaminase-mediated modification of glutamine residues in cells and certain proteins [53,54] (Section 3.3, Figure 3.26) and for the microplate assay of transglutaminase activity.[55–57]

Synthesis of Biotinylated and Desthiobiotinylated Peptides

Biocytin is a naturally occurring amino acid derivative (ε-D-biotinoyl-L-lysine). The FMOC derivative of biocytin (B20651) can be used in automated synthesis of biotinylated peptides. The reagent can also be attached to the synthesis resin as the first residue to provide for automated synthesis of C-terminal biotinylated or desthiobiotinylated peptides. Other reagents for automated synthesis of labeled peptides are described in Section 9.5.

Haptenylation Reagents

A prerequisite for multicolor applications such as fluorescence *in situ* hybridization is the availability of multiple hapten molecules, along with their complementary binding proteins. The avidin–biotin system can provide only single-color detection, whereas antibody–hapten methods can generate a number of unique signals, limited only by the specificity of the antibody–hapten detection and the ability to distinguish the signals from different antibodies. The characteristics of a suitable hapten include a unique chemical structure that is not commonly found in cells, a high degree of antigenicity that elicits good antibody production, and a means for incorporating the hapten into the detection system. Molecular Probes' ever-increasing selection of haptenylation reagents enables researchers to covalently attach haptens to nucleotides, proteins, enzymes and other biomolecules.

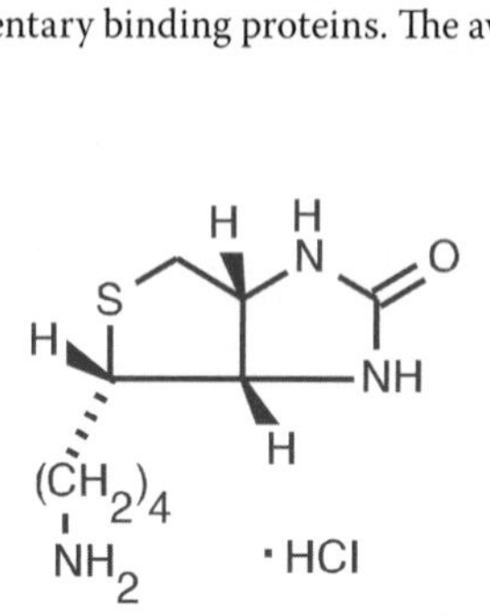

Figure 4.8 N6356 norbiotinamine, hydrochloride.

In addition to our wide range of biotinylation reagents discussed above, Molecular Probes provides some unique haptenylation reagents, including an amine-reactive version of digoxigenin (A2952), dinitrophenyl-X [58] (DNP-X, SE; D2248) and several fluorophores (Table 4.2). The succinimidyl ester derivative of digoxigenin has been shown to inhibit the Na^+/K^+-ATPase by binding to the cardiac steroid receptor site.[59] We usually recommend haptenylation reagents that contain spacers between the hapten and the reactive groups to reduce potential interactions with the biomolecule to which it is conjugated and to make the hapten maximally available to secondary detection reagents. Most of the preferred haptenylation reagents in Table 4.2 possess this feature.

DNP-X–biocytin-X succinimidyl ester (B2604) can be used to simultaneously incorporate both a hapten and biotin into a biomolecule (Figure 4.4), enabling researchers to readily determine the degree of substitution from the absorbance of the DNP chromophore. Likewise, using a fluorophore as a hapten offers significant advantages for determining the degree of labeling. Fluorescein has been found to be an excellent hapten for *in situ* hybridization because it binds with high affinity to its anti-fluorescein antibody.[60–62] Anti-fluorescein antibodies crossreact with all of the Oregon Green® dyes (Section 1.5), permitting their use with conjugates prepared from these dyes. By adding antibodies that recognize the Alexa Fluor® 488, dansyl, tetramethylrhodamine and Texas Red® fluorophores to our line of detection reagents (Section 7.4), we have greatly expanded the number of potential haptens. Because the anti-tetramethylrhodamine and anti–Texas Red® dye antibodies crossreact with the tetramethylrhodamine, Lissamine rhodamine, Rhodamine Red™ and Texas Red® fluorophores, these antibody–fluorophore combinations should not be used simultaneously to generate separate signals in a multicolor experiment. Similarly, our antibody to the BODIPY® FL dye crossreacts with some of the other BODIPY® dyes and therefore should not be used for simultaneous detection of more than one dye based on the BODIPY® fluorophore.

References

1. Anal Biochem 308, 343 (2002); **2.** Biochemistry 21, 978 (1982); **3.** Methods Mol Biol 80, 173 (1998); **4.** Methods Mol Biol 45, 223 (1995); **5.** Methods Mol Biol 45, 205 (1995); **6.** Biochemistry 40, 8343 (2001); **7.** Biochemistry 40, 8352 (2001); **8.** Proc Natl Acad Sci U S A 71, 3537 (1974); **9.** Ann Hematol 74, 231 (1997); **10.** Cell Biology: A Laboratory Handbook, 2nd Ed., Vol. 4, Celis JE, Ed. pp. 341–350 (1998); **11.** Anal Chem 63, 850 (1991); **12.** Biochem J 251, 935 (1988); **13.** Anal Biochem 161, 262 (1987); **14.** Biochem Biophys Res Commun 136, 80 (1986); **15.** Anal Biochem 149, 529 (1985); **16.** Radiat Res 117, 326 (1989); **17.** Nature 374, 777 (1995); **18.** FEBS Lett 328, 165 (1993); **19.** Methods Enzymol 18, 418 (1970); **20.** Bioconjug Chem 6, 447 (1995); **21.** J Neurochem 77, 1301 (2001); **22.** J Cell Sci 109, 3025 (1996); **23.** Cell Biology: A Laboratory Handbook, 2nd Ed., Vol. 1, Celis JE, Ed. pp. 341–350 (1998); **24.** J Cell Biol 153, 957 (2001); **25.** J Virol 75, 4744 (2001); **26.** J Biol Chem 274, 36801 (1999); **27.** Anal Biochem 236, 101 (1996); **28.** J Biol Chem 267, 5060 (1992); **29.** Anal Biochem 170, 271 (1988); **30.** Anal Biochem 163, 204 (1987); **31.** Immunol Lett 8, 273 (1984); **32.** J Immunol Methods 168,

References — continued

209 (1994); **33.** Biochem J 275, 733 (1991); **34.** Biochem Biophys Res Commun 142, 519 (1987); **35.** Blood 74, 952 (1989); **36.** Biochim Biophys Acta 631, 49 (1980); **37.** J Cell Biol 111, 2909 (1990); **38.** Methods Enzymol 138, 429 (1987); **39.** Biochem J 229, 785 (1985); **40.** Chem Pharm Bull (Tokyo) 37, 1831 (1989); **41.** Nucleic Acids Res 14, 6227 (1986); **42.** J Steroid Biochem 35, 633 (1990); **43.** Anal Biochem 267, 331 (1999); **44.** Biochemistry 11, 3610 (1972); **45.** Biochemistry 31, 3703 (1992); **46.** Biochemistry 32, 8276 (1993); **47.** Proc Natl Acad Sci U S A 97, 686 (2000); **48.** J Biol Chem 275, 6741 (2000); **49.** Anal Biochem 312, 113 (2003); **50.** J Histochem Cytochem 38, 377 (1990); **51.** Ann NY Acad Sci 463, 214 (1984); **52.** Bioconjug Chem 7, 271 (1996); **53.** Biochem J 313, 803 (1996); **54.** J Biol Chem 269, 24596 (1994); **55.** Anal Biochem 223, 88 (1994); **56.** J Biol Chem 269, 28309 (1994); **57.** Anal Biochem 205, 166 (1992); **58.** Eur J Cell Biol 56, 223 (1991); **59.** Eur J Biochem 227, 61 (1995); **60.** Nucleic Acids Res 19, 3237 (1991); **61.** J Histochem Cytochem 38, 467 (1990); **62.** Fluorescein Hapten: An Immunological Probe, Voss EW, Ed. (Complete Volume) (1984).

Data Table — 4.2 Biotinylation and Haptenylation Reagents

Cat #	MW	Storage	Soluble	Abs	EC	Em	Solvent	Notes
A1593	367.30	NC	DMF, DMSO	<300		none		
A1594	442.50	NC	DMF, DMSO	<300		none		
A2952	586.68	F,D	DMF, DMSO	<300		none		
A10550	445.41	F,D	H_2O, DMSO	<300		none		
A20000	643.41	F,DD,L	H_2O, DMSO	494	73,000	517	pH 7	1, 2, 3
A30000	1028.26	F,DD,L	H_2O, DMSO	400	35,000	424	pH 7	4, 5
B1513	341.38	F,D	DMF, DMSO	<300		none		
B1582	454.54	F,D	DMF, DMSO	<300		none		
B1591	454.33	F,D	DMF, DMSO	<300		none		6
B1592	372.48	NC	H_2O	<300		none		
B1595	244.31	NC	pH >6, DMF	<300		none		
B1596	555.65	NC	DMF, DMSO	<300		none		
B1597	399.55	NC	DMF, DMSO	<300		none		
B1603	386.51	D	pH >6, DMF	<300		none		
B1606	567.70	F,D	DMF, DMSO	<300		none		
B2600	484.66	D	DMF, DMSO	<300		none		
B2604	861.97	F,D,L	DMF	362	15,000	none	pH 8	
B6350	499.67	D	pH >6, DMF	<300		none		
B6352	669.74	F,D	DMF, pH >6	<300		none		1
B6353	556.58	F,D	DMF, pH >6	<300		none		1
B11790	715.98	D	H_2O, DMSO	<300		none		
B20651	594.72	F,D	DMF, MeCN	<300		none		
B20656	244.31	RO	pH >6	<300		none		7
C2284	607.42	F,D,LL	H_2O, MeOH	396	29,000	410	MeOH	4, 8
D2248	394.34	F,D,L	DMF, DMSO	348	18,000	none	MeOH	
D6102	502.32	F,D,L	DMSO, MeCN	504	85,000	510	MeOH	9
D6104	461.53	F,D,L	DMF, MeCN	335	4,200	518	MeOH	
D20652	342.44	NC	H_2O	<300		none		
D20653	341.45	D	DMSO	<300		none		
D20657	214.26	RO	pH >6	<300		none		7
D30752	405.97	F,DD	DMF, DMSO	<300		none		
D30753	537.44	F,D	DMSO	<300		none		6
F2181	586.55	F,D,L	DMF, DMSO	494	74,000	520	pH 9	10
F6130	590.56	F,D,L	DMF, DMSO	491	86,000	515	pH 9	10
L1338	659.51	F,D,L	H_2O	426	11,000	531	pH 7	6
M1602	523.60	F,D	pH >6, DMF	<300		none		
N6356	251.77	D	DMF, pH <6	<300		none		
O6185	622.53	F,D,L	DMF, DMSO	494	84,000	517	pH 9	11
R6160	768.90	F,D,L	DMF, DMSO	560	129,000	580	MeOH	
T6105	640.69	F,D,L	DMF, DMSO	543	92,000	571	MeOH	
T6134	816.94	F,D,L	DMF, DMSO	583	112,000	603	MeOH	
T10125	969.97	F,D,L	H_2O, DMSO	585	92,000	605	MeOH	12
T20175	816.94	F,D,L	DMF, DMSO	587	96,000	602	MeOH	
T30754	587.72	F,D	DMSO	<300		none		

For definitions of the contents of this data table, see "Navigating *The Handbook*" in the introductory pages.

Notes

1. This sulfonated succinimidyl ester derivative is water-soluble and may be dissolved in buffer at ~pH 8 for reaction with amines. Long-term storage in water is NOT recommended due to hydrolysis.
2. The fluorescence lifetime (τ) of the Alexa Fluor® 488 dye in pH 7.4 buffer at 20°C is 4.1 nanoseconds. Data provided by the SPEX Fluorescence Group, Jobin Yvon Inc.
3. A20100 is an alternative packaging of A20000 but is otherwise identical.
4. The Alexa Fluor® 405 and Cascade Blue® dyes have a second absorption peak at about 376 nm with EC ~80% of the 395–400 nm peak.
5. A30100 is an alternative packaging of A30000 but is otherwise identical.
6. Iodoacetamides in solution undergo rapid photodecomposition to unreactive products. Minimize exposure to light prior to reaction.
7. This product is supplied as a ready-made solution in the solvent indicated under "Soluble."
8. Unstable in water. Use immediately.
9. The absorption and fluorescence spectra of BODIPY® derivatives are relatively insensitive to the solvent.
10. Absorption and fluorescence of fluorescein derivatives are pH-dependent. Extinction coefficients and fluorescence quantum yields decrease markedly at pH <7.
11. Absorption and fluorescence of Oregon Green® 488 derivatives are pH-dependent only in moderately acidic solutions (pH <5).
12. This sulfotetrafluorophenyl (STP) ester derivative is water-soluble and may be dissolved in buffer at ~pH 8 for reaction with amines. Long-term storage in water is NOT recommended due to hydrolysis.

Product List — 4.2 Biotinylation and Haptenylation Reagents

Cat #	Product Name	Unit Size
A30000	Alexa Fluor® 405 carboxylic acid, succinimidyl ester	1 mg
A30100	Alexa Fluor® 405 carboxylic acid, succinimidyl ester	5 mg
A20000	Alexa Fluor® 488 carboxylic acid, succinimidyl ester *mixed isomers*	1 mg
A20100	Alexa Fluor® 488 carboxylic acid, succinimidyl ester *mixed isomers*	5 mg
A2952	3-amino-3-deoxydigoxigenin hemisuccinamide, succinimidyl ester	5 mg
A1593	*N*-(2-aminoethyl)biotinamide, hydrobromide (biotin ethylenediamine)	25 mg
A10550	*N*-(aminooxyacetyl)-*N'*-(D-biotinoyl) hydrazine, trifluoroacetic acid salt (ARP)	10 mg
A1594	*N*-(5-aminopentyl)biotinamide, trifluoroacetic acid salt (biotin cadaverine)	25 mg
B1592	biocytin (ε-biotinoyl-L-lysine)	100 mg
B1603	biocytin hydrazide	25 mg
B1595	D-biotin	1 g
B20656	D-biotin *50 mM aqueous solution*	10 mL
B1582	6-((biotinoyl)amino)hexanoic acid, succinimidyl ester (biotin-X, SE; biotinamidocaproate, *N*-hydroxysuccinimidyl ester)	100 mg
B6353	6-((biotinoyl)amino)hexanoic acid, sulfosuccinimidyl ester, sodium salt (Sulfo-NHS-LC-Biotin; biotin-X, SSE)	25 mg
B1597	2-(((*N*-(biotinoyl)amino)hexanoyl)amino)ethylamine (biotin-X ethylenediamine)	10 mg
B2600	6-((6-((biotinoyl)amino)hexanoyl)amino)hexanoic acid, hydrazide (biotin-XX hydrazide)	25 mg
B1606	6-((6-((biotinoyl)amino)hexanoyl)amino)hexanoic acid, succinimidyl ester (biotin-XX, SE)	100 mg
B6352	6-((6-((biotinoyl)amino)hexanoyl)amino)hexanoic acid, sulfosuccinimidyl ester, sodium salt (biotin-XX, SSE)	25 mg
B1596	5-(((*N*-(biotinoyl)amino)hexanoyl)amino)pentylamine, trifluoroacetic acid salt (biotin-X cadaverine)	10 mg
B6350	ε-(6-(biotinoyl)amino)hexanoyl-L-lysine, hydrazide (biocytin-X hydrazide)	25 mg
B20651	ε-biotinoyl-α-(9-fluorenylmethoxycarbonyl)-L-lysine (FMOC biocytin)	25 mg
B1591	*N*-(biotinoyl)-*N'*-(iodoacetyl)ethylenediamine	25 mg
B1513	D-biotin, succinimidyl ester (succinimidyl D-biotin)	100 mg
B2604	biotin-X 2,4-dinitrophenyl-X-L-lysine, succinimidyl ester (DNP-X-biocytin-X, SE)	5 mg
B11790	biotin-X nitrilotriacetic acid, tripotassium salt (biotin-X NTA)	5 mg
C2284	Cascade Blue® acetyl azide, trisodium salt	5 mg
D20657	D-desthiobiotin *50 mM aqueous solution*	10 mL
D6102	6-((4,4-difluoro-5,7-dimethyl-4-bora-3a,4a-diaza-*s*-indacene-3-propionyl)amino)hexanoic acid, succinimidyl ester (BODIPY® FL-X, SE)	5 mg
D6104	6-((5-dimethylaminonaphthalene-1-sulfonyl)amino)hexanoic acid, succinimidyl ester (dansyl-X, SE)	25 mg
D2248	6-(2,4-dinitrophenyl)aminohexanoic acid, succinimidyl ester (DNP-X, SE)	25 mg
D30753	DSB-X™ biotin C_2-iodoacetamide (desthiobiotin-X C_2-iodoacetamide)	5 mg
D30752	DSB-X™ biotin ethylenediamine (desthiobiotin-X ethylenediamine, hydrochloride)	1 mg
D20653	DSB-X™ biotin hydrazide	5 mg
D20655	DSB-X™ Biotin Protein Labeling Kit *5 labelings*	1 kit
D20652	DSB-X™ desthiobiocytin (ε-desthiobiotinoyl-L-lysine)	5 mg
F6348	FluoReporter® Biotin/DNP Protein Labeling Kit *5-10 labelings*	1 kit
F2610	FluoReporter® Biotin-XX Protein Labeling Kit *5 labelings of 5-20 mg protein each*	1 kit
F20650	FluoReporter® Cell-Surface Biotinylation Kit	1 kit
F6347	FluoReporter® Mini-biotin-XX Protein Labeling Kit *5 labelings of 0.1-3 mg protein each*	1 kit
F2181	6-(fluorescein-5-(and-6)-carboxamido)hexanoic acid, succinimidyl ester (5(6)-SFX) *mixed isomers*	10 mg
F6130	fluorescein-5-EX, succinimidyl ester	10 mg
L1338	lucifer yellow iodoacetamide, dipotassium salt	25 mg
M1602	N^{α}-(3-maleimidylpropionyl)biocytin	25 mg
N6356	norbiotinamine, hydrochloride	10 mg
O6185	Oregon Green® 488-X, succinimidyl ester *6-isomer*	5 mg
R6160	Rhodamine Red™-X, succinimidyl ester *5-isomer*	5 mg
T6105	6-(tetramethylrhodamine-5-(and-6)-carboxamido)hexanoic acid, succinimidyl ester (5(6)-TAMRA-X, SE) *mixed isomers*	10 mg
T10125	Texas Red®-X, STP ester, sodium salt *mixed isomers*	5 mg
T6134	Texas Red®-X, succinimidyl ester *mixed isomers*	5 mg
T20175	Texas Red®-X, succinimidyl ester *single isomer*	2 mg
T30754	TS-Link™ DSB-X™ biotin C_5-thiosulfate (TS-Link™ desthiobiotin-X C_5-thiosulfate, sodium salt)	5 mg

For current prices or to order online, visit probes.invitrogen.com

4.3 Biotin and Desthiobiotin Conjugates

Molecular Probes prepares a wide array of biotin and desthiobiotin conjugates, all of which are included in this section's product list. We will also custom-conjugate biotin, desthiobiotin (DSB-X™), fluorophores or other haptens to proteins or other biomolecules of interest (see Note 4.1 "Product Highlight: Custom Immunogen Preparation"); contact our Custom and Bulk Sales Department to request a quote.

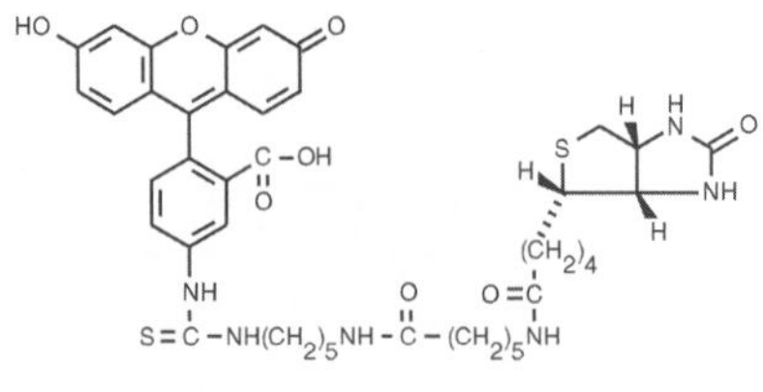

Figure 4.9 B13705-((N-(5-(N-(6-(biotinoyl)amino)hexanoyl)-amino)pentyl)thioureidyl)fluorescein (fluorescein biotin).

Fluorescent Biotin Derivatives

Fluorescein Biotin and Biotin-4-Fluorescein

Fluorescein biotin (B1370, Figure 4.9) was developed by Molecular Probes as an alternative to radioactive biotin for detecting and quantitating biotin-binding sites by either fluorescence or absorbance.[1] A fluorescence polarization–based assay that employs competitive binding of fluorescein biotin to assess the degree of protein biotinylation has been reported[2] (see Note 1.5 "Technical Focus: Fluorescence Polarization (FP)" in Section 1.4). A similar derivative was used for determining avidin and biotin concentrations by fluorescence depolarization.[3] Several other methods for quantitating avidin and biotin have been reported (see Note 4.2 "Technical Focus: Quantitation of Biotin and Avidin").

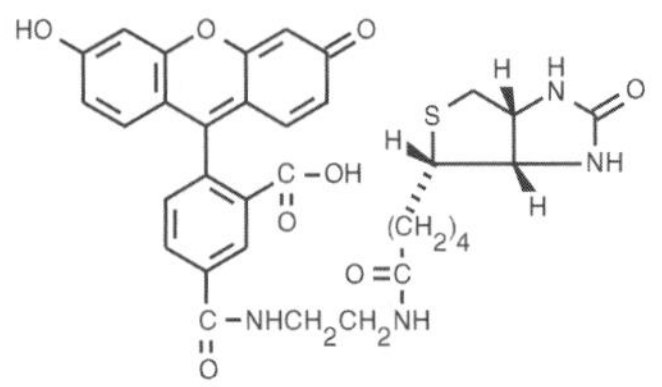

Figure 4.10 B10570 biotin-4-fluorescein.

Our biotin-4-fluorescein (B10570, Figure 4.10) offers a substantially improved method for quantitating biotin-binding sites. Biotin-4-fluorescein binds to avidin much faster than does conventional fluorescein biotin, allowing for rapid analysis.[4,5] The strong quenching associated with avidin binding to biotin-4-fluorescein can be used to easily measure the concentration of avidin or streptavidin[6] (Figure 4.11).

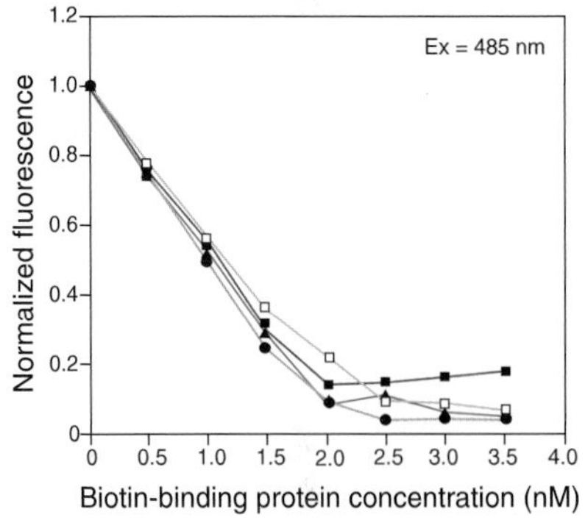

Figure 4.11 Quantitation of biotin-binding sites with 8 nM biotin-4-fluorescein (B10570). Both the fluorescence and absorbance of biotin-4-fluorescein are quenched upon binding to one of the four biotin-binding sites of streptavidin (S888, pink), avidin (A887, A2667; dark blue), or the streptavidin conjugates of the Alexa Fluor® 633 dye (S21375, orange) and alkaline phosphatase (S921, light blue). As a result, when a known concentration of biotin-4-fluorescein is added to a known amount of streptavidin, one can estimate the number of biotin-binding sites.

Other Fluorescent Biotin Derivatives

In addition to supplying nonfluorescent biocytin (ε-biotinoyl-L-lysine, B1592, Section 4.2) and desthiobiocytin (ε-desthiobiotinoyl-L-lysine, D20652, Section 4.2), we offer lucifer yellow cadaverine biotin-X[7] (L2601), lucifer yellow biocytin[8] (L6950), Alexa Fluor® 488 biocytin (A12924), Alexa Fluor® 546 biocytin[9] (A12923), Alexa Fluor® 594 biocytin[8] (A12922), Oregon Green® 488 biocytin[8] (O12920) and tetramethylrhodamine biocytin[8] (T12921) — reagents that incorporate a fluorophore and biotin moiety in the same molecule. As with fluorescein biotin and biotin-4-fluorescein, which are described above, these reagents can be employed for detecting and quantitating biotin-binding proteins, but we anticipate that their principal use will be as polar cell tracers and as tracers for cell–cell communication (Section 14.3). It has been reported that our lucifer yellow cadaverine biotin-X is well retained in aldehyde-fixed tissues, even after sectioning, extraction with detergents and several washes.[10] Because these fluorescent biocytin conjugates contain free primary amines, they should be more efficiently fixed by formaldehyde and glutaraldehyde. Once these probes are fixed, the researcher can choose to detect them directly by fluorescence or indirectly with labeled avidin conjugates (Section 7.6, Table 7.22) or with labeled anti-fluorophore or anti-biotin antibodies (Section 7.4; Table 7.18, Table 7.19).

Note 4.1 — Product Highlight

Custom Immunogen Preparation

Low molecular weight molecules (<2000 daltons) or haptens generally will not elicit an immune response unless conjugated to a carrier protein such as bovine serum albumin (BSA) or keyhole limpet hemocyanin (KLH). Preparing these immunogens often requires introducing reactive groups into the haptens through chemical synthesis. Molecular Probes has considerable experience synthesizing reactive chemical species, including reactive forms of drugs, natural products and herbicides. In addition to their use for preparing immunogens, these reactive haptens can be used to generate new detection reagents and site-selective probes, as well as affinity matrices for isolating antibodies and receptors. We provide our custom services on an exclusive or nondisclosure basis when requested. Please contact our Custom and Bulk Sales Department for further information.

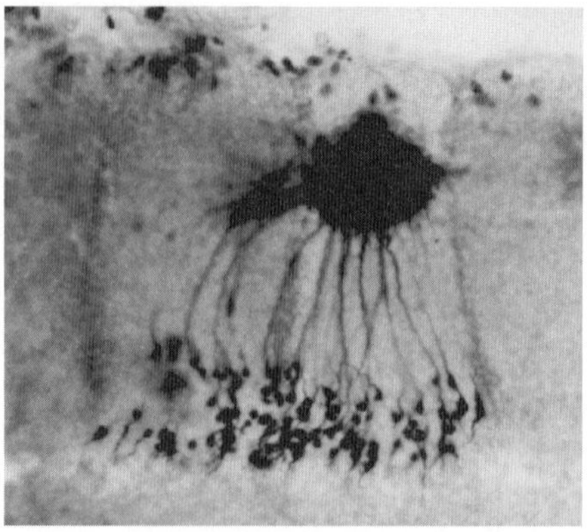

Figure 4.12 Motor neuron in a three-day chick embryo labeled with lysine-fixable, biotinylated 3000 MW dextran (BDA-3000, D7135). Filled neurons were detected with biotinylated horseradish peroxidase (P917) and diaminobenzidine using standard avidin/streptavidin bridging techniques. Reprinted with permission from J Neurosci Methods 50, 95 (1993).

Note 4.2 — Technical Focus

Quantitation of Biotin and Avidin

The amount of free biotin in solution has been measured by several methods, including a microplate reader–based assay in which free biotin competes with biotinylated bovine serum albumin (BSA) for binding avidin–β-galactosidase,[1] as well as a sensitive fluorometric displacement assay for the biotin–avidin interaction that employs 2,6-ANS[2] (A50, Section 13.5). Biotin and low molecular weight biotin derivatives have also been quantitated by their fluorescence enhancement of fluorescein streptavidin (S869, Section 7.6), a technique employed in an HPLC-based binding assay with a reported sensitivity of 97 pg and 149 pg for biotin and biocytin, respectively.[3] We have determined that our Oregon Green® 514 conjugate of streptavidin (S6369, Section 7.6) has an approximately 15-fold increase in fluorescence on binding of biotin, which makes it our most sensitive reagent for biotin determination. In addition, the degree of protein biotinylation has been determined using fluorescein biotin (B1370) in a fluorescence polarization assay that can detect about 2–20 nM biotinylated BSA.[4] Our biotin-4-fluorescein (B10570) offers a substantially improved method for quantitating biotin-binding sites. Biotin-4-fluorescein binds avidin much faster than conventional fluorescein biotin (B1370), allowing for rapid analysis.[5] The strong quenching associated with avidin binding to biotin-4-fluorescein can be used to easily measure avidin and streptavidin concentrations[6] (Figure 4.11).

References

1. Biotechniques 13, 543 (1992); **2.** Anal Biochem 151, 178 (1985); **3.** Anal Chem 67, 1014 (1995); **4.** Clin Chem 40, 2112 (1994); **5.** Biochim Biophys Acta 1427, 33 (1999); **6.** Biochim Biophys Acta 1427, 44 (1999).

Biotinylated Dextrans

In addition to the low molecular weight biotinylated tracers described above, Molecular Probes prepares biotinylated versions of a wide variety of dextrans (Figure 4.12, Table 14.4), including dextrans that are double-labeled with fluorophores and biotin moieties for correlated fluorescence and electron microscopy studies. See Section 14.5 for a discussion of the applications of these reagents, particularly as cell tracers.

Biotinylated and DSB-X™ Biotin–Labeled Proteins

Our biotinylated primary and secondary antibodies, $F(ab')_2$ fragments, phycobiliproteins and enzymes are invaluable detection reagents for a broad assortment of assays; for more information, see Chapter 6 and Chapter 7. Biotinylated R-phycoerythrin (P811) and biotinylated horseradish peroxidase (P917) can be used in combination with an avidin or streptavidin bridge to amplify the detection of biotinylated targets. Biotinylated transferrin (T23363, Section 16.1) can be used to follow the intracellular trafficking of this important iron-carrying protein.[11]

Antibody Conjugates of DSB-X™ Biotin

In addition to our biotinylated antibodies, Molecular Probes has prepared conjugates of several secondary antibodies with DSB-X™ biotin (Figure 4.1). These are listed in the product list for this section and in Table 7.10. Targets complexed with DSB-X™ biotin–labeled antibodies can be selectively detected with avidin or streptavidin conjugates or isolated on affinity matrices, including streptavidin agarose (S951, D20658; Section 7.6) and Captivate™ ferrofluid streptavidin superparamagnetic particles (C21476, Section 7.6), and then rapidly released with D-biotin (B1595, B20656; Section 4.2) under extremely gentle conditions[12] (Figure 7.103). See Section 7.6 for a complete description of our unique DSB-X™ biotin technology.

Zenon® Antibody Labeling Kits

We have applied our exceptional Zenon® technology (Section 7.3) in several Zenon® Biotin-XX and Zenon® DSB-X™ Biotin Antibody Labeling Kits (Table 7.13) that effectively permit the rapid and quantitative formation of biotin-XX or DSB-X™ biotin (desthiobiotin) conjugates of even submicrogram quantities of antibody (Figure 7.59). Mouse IgG_1 antibodies to cell-surface proteins that are indirectly labeled with the Zenon® DSB-X™ Biotin Mouse IgG_1 Labeling Kit (Z25053) can potentially be used to selectively capture and release viable rare cells from a complex mixture with our Captivate™ ferrofluid streptavidin (C21476, Section 7.6). The Zenon® Labeling Kits and the Zenon® technology are described in detail in Section 7.3.

BioGEE: A Biotinylated Glutathione Analog

Biotinylated glutathione ethyl ester (BioGEE, G36000) is a cell-permeant, biotinylated glutathione analog for detecting glutathiolation. Under conditions of oxidative stress, cells may transiently incorporate glutathione into proteins. Stressed cells incubated with BioGEE will also incorporate this biotinylated glutathione derivative into proteins, facilitating the identification of oxidation-sensitive proteins.[13] Once these cells are fixed and permeabilized, glutathiolation levels can be detected with a fluorescent streptavidin conjugate (Section 7.6, Table 7.22) using either flow cytometry or fluorescence microscopy. Proteins glutathiolated with BioGEE can also be extracted and analyzed by mass spectrometry or by Western blotting methods in conjunction with fluorophore- or enzyme-labeled streptavidin conjugates.

DSB-X™ Biotin Agarose

DSB-X™ biotin agarose is the matrix provided in our DSB-X™ Bioconjugate Isolation Kit #2 (D20659). The moderate affinity of avidin and streptavidin conjugates for DSB-X™ biotin agarose permits their selective isolation from solutions and facile release by either D-biotin or D-desthiobiotin.[12] Protein–protein conjugations of avidins to enzymes, antibodies and phycobiliproteins can be separated from any unconjugated protein labels by adsorption onto DSB-X™ agarose and then released with a biotin derivative (Figure 7.109). The DSB-X™ Bioconjugate Isolation Kit #2 includes:

- DSB-X™ biotin agarose
- Separate solutions of D-biotin and D-desthiobiotin for elution of the column
- Unfilled chromatography columns
- A detailed protocol for isolation and release of avidin and streptavidin conjugates

Our DSB-X™ biotin agarose has a binding capacity of approximately 9 mg (~170 nanomoles) streptavidin per milliliter of sedimented gel. Solutions of D-biotin and D-desthiobiotin are also available separately (B20656, D20657; Section 4.2).

Biotinylated Microspheres

Biotinylated FluoSpheres® microspheres have significant potential for signal amplification techniques, as described in Section 6.5. Like biotinylated R-phycoerythrin (P811, see above), they can be used with bridging techniques to detect biotinylated targets. Our intensely fluorescent FluoSpheres® microspheres are much brighter and more photostable than low molecular weight dye conjugates.

Biotin-XX Panomer™ 9 Random Oligonucleotide

Our Panomer™ 9 random-sequence oligodeoxynucleotides (Section 8.5, Table 8.18) are covalently labeled on the 5′-terminus with one of our proprietary fluorescent dyes, with a nonfluorescent QSY® 7 quencher dye or with biotin-XX. The biotin-XX Panomer™ 9 random oligonucleotide (P21689) is useful as a primer for synthesizing biotin-labeled DNA via Klenow DNA polymerase or reverse transcriptase. Following these reactions, the biotin label can be detected with any of our avidin-based reagents (Section 7.6, Table 7.22) or the biotinylated probe can be captured with streptavidin agarose (S951, Section 7.6), CaptAvidin™ agarose (C21386, Section 7.6) or the Captivate™ ferrofluid streptavidin superparamagnetic particles (C21476, Section 7.6).

Biotin-X-aha-dUTP

Nucleic acids labeled with biotin have generally been the most common nonisotopic probes used in hybridization techniques (Section 8.5). Nucleoside triphosphate analogs such as our ChromaTide® and aha-dUTP nucleotides (Section 8.2; Table 8.6, Table 8.7) are important reagents for preparing labeled nucleic acids for use as hybridization probes. The biotinylated aminohexylacrylamido-dUTP (aha-dUTP) derivative (B32766) contains a long 11-atom spacer between the biotin and its attachment point on the nucleic acid to facilitate its detection and signal amplification by fluorophore and enzyme conjugates of avidin and streptavidin (Section 7.6, Table 7.22). Biotin conjugates can also be detected with anti-biotin antibodies, which we provide unlabeled or conjugated to our bright green-fluorescent Alexa Fluor® 488 dye or our intensely red-fluorescent Alexa Fluor® 594 dye (A11242, A31801, A31800; Section 7.4). Our proprietary Tyramide Signal Amplification (TSA) Kits containing the streptavidin conjugate of horseradish peroxidase (HRP) and one of our Alexa Fluor® tyramides, Pacific Blue™ tyramide, Oregon Green® 488 tyramide or dinitrophenyl (DNP)-X tyramide (Section 6.2, Table 6.1) permit ultrasensitive HRP-amplified detection of low-abundance targets in cells.

Biotinylated Site-Selective Probes

Biotin conjugates of moderately low molecular weight ligands permit amplified detection of ligand binding. They may also be useful for immobilizing receptor ligands on streptavidin agarose (S951, D20658), CaptAvidin™ agarose (C21386, Figure 7.99) or Captivate™ ferrofluid streptavidin (C21476) for affinity isolation of receptors. See Section 7.6 for a description of these products and affinity isolation methods that use biotin- or DSB-X™ biotin–labeled reagents.

Our biotinylated ligands include the:

- Biotin-X conjugate of annexin V (A13204, Section 15.5), for detecting the externalization of phosphatidylserine, an early indicator of apoptosis
- Biotin-XX conjugate of α-bungarotoxin[14,15] (B1196, Section 16.2), for labeling the α-subunit of the acetylcholine receptor
- Biotin-XX conjugate of epidermal growth factor (EGF)[16–19] (E3477), as well as biotinylated EGF complexed with Alexa Fluor® 488 streptavidin (E13345, Figure 16.11), Alexa Fluor® 555 streptavidin (E35350), Alexa Fluor® 647 streptavidin (E35351) or Texas Red® streptavidin (E3480, Figure 16.12), for labeling EGF receptors (Section 16.1)
- Biotin-XX conjugate of transferrin[11] (T23363, Section 16.1), for following intracellular trafficking of this iron-carrying protein
- Biotin-XX conjugate of phalloidin[20,21] (B7474, Section 11.1), for labeling F-actin
- Biotin-XX conjugate of isolectin IB_4 from *Griffonia simplicifolia*, for detecting α-galactosyl moieties in microglia and other glycoproteins (Section 7.7, Figure 7.117, Figure 7.116)
- Biotin-XX cholera toxin subunit B (C34779, Section 7.7), which binds to galactosyl moieties and is a marker of lipid rafts — regions of cell membranes high in ganglioside G_{M1} that are thought to be important in cell signaling

- Biotin-XX tyramide and DSB-X™ biotin tyramide, which are the amplification reagents used in six of our TSA Kits (Section 6.2, Table 6.1) for high-sensitivity detection of targets in cells and tissues. The reagents are not available separately.

Biotinylated Lipids

Our extensive selection of labeled phospholipids includes phospholipid derivatives of biotin and biotin-X (B1550, B1616). These biotinylated lipids, which are described in Section 5.2, can be used to prepare liposomes that retain high affinity for avidin conjugates.[22]

References

1. Biochim Biophys Acta 1381, 203 (1998); **2.** Clin Chem 40, 2112 (1994); **3.** Anal Chem 60, 853 (1988); **4.** Biotechniques 27, 592 (1999); **5.** Biochim Biophys Acta 1427, 33 (1999); **6.** Biochim Biophys Acta 1427, 44 (1999); **7.** J Neurosci Methods 53, 23 (1994); **8.** Bioconjug Chem 11, 584 (2000); **9.** Anal Chem 75, 1147 (2003); **10.** J Neurosci Methods 46, 59 (1993); **11.** J Cell Biol 149, 901 (2000); **12.** Anal Biochem 308, 343 (2002); **13.** Biochemistry 39, 11121 (2000); **14.** J Cell Biol 125, 661 (1994); **15.** J Biol Chem 268, 25108 (1993); **16.** J Histochem Cytochem 42, 307 (1994); **17.** J Histochem Cytochem 41, 313 (1993); **18.** J Histochem Cytochem 40, 1353 (1992); **19.** Anal Biochem 188, 97 (1990); **20.** J Cell Biol 130, 591 (1995); **21.** Anal Biochem 200, 199 (1992); **22.** Methods Enzymol 149, 119 (1987).

Data Table — 4.3 Biotin and Desthiobiotin Conjugates

Cat #	MW	Storage	Soluble	Abs	EC	Em	Solvent	Notes
A12922	1141.31	D,L	DMSO, H_2O	591	80,000	618	pH 7	
A12923	1209.66	D,L	DMSO, H_2O	556	99,000	572	pH 7	
A12924	974.98	D,L	DMSO, H_2O	494	62,000	520	pH 7	
B1196	~8400	F,D	H_2O	<300		none		1
B1370	831.01	L	DMF, pH >6	494	75,000	518	pH 9	2
B1550	1019.45	FF,D	see Notes	<300		none		3
B1616	1132.61	FF,D	see Notes	<300		none		3
B6357	347.49	D	DMSO, H_2O	<300		none		
B7474	~1300	F	MeOH, H_2O	<300		none		1, 4
B10570	644.70	L	DMSO	494	68,000	523	pH 9	2
B32766	1041.78	FF	H_2O	<300		none		5
D7146	see Notes	F,LL	H_2O	352	ND	519	H_2O	6, 7, 8, 9
D7147	see Notes	F,LL	H_2O	352	ND	521	H_2O	6, 7, 8, 9
E3477	~6600	FF,D	H_2O	<300		none		1
E3480	see Notes	FF,D,L	H_2O	596	ND	612	pH 7	9, 10
E13345	see Notes	FF,D,L	H_2O	497	ND	520	pH 8	9, 11
E35350	see Notes	FF,D,L	H_2O	554	ND	568	pH 7	9, 12
E35351	see Notes	FF,D,L	H_2O	653	ND	671	pH 7	9, 13
G36000	561.67	F,D	DMSO	<300		none		
L2601	873.10	D,L	H_2O	428	11,000	531	H_2O	
L6950	850.03	D,L	H_2O	428	11,000	532	pH 7	
O12920	887.39	L	DMSO, H_2O	495	66,000	522	pH 9	14
T12921	869.09	D,L	DMSO	554	103,000	581	pH 7	

For definitions of the contents of this data table, see "Navigating *The Handbook*" in the introductory pages.

Notes

1. α-Bungarotoxin, EGF and phallotoxin conjugates have approximately 1 label per peptide.
2. Absorption and fluorescence of fluorescein derivatives are pH-dependent. Extinction coefficients and fluorescence quantum yields decrease markedly at pH <7.
3. Chloroform is the most generally useful solvent for preparing stock solutions of phospholipids (including sphingomyelins). Glycerophosphocholines are usually freely soluble in ethanol. Most other glycerophospholipids (phosphoethanolamines, phosphatidic acids and phosphoglycerols) are less soluble in ethanol, but solutions up to 1–2 mg/mL should be obtainable, using sonication to aid dispersion if necessary. Labeling of cells with fluorescent phospholipids can be enhanced by addition of cyclodextrins during incubation (J Biol Chem 274, 35359 (1999)).
4. Although this phallotoxin is water-soluble, storage in water is not recommended, particularly in dilute solution.
5. This product is supplied as a ready-made solution in the solvent indicated under "Soluble."
6. The molecular weight is nominally as specified in the product name but may have a broad distribution.
7. All photoactivatable probes are sensitive to light. They should be protected from illumination except when photolysis is intended.
8. This product is colorless and nonfluorescent until it is activated by ultraviolet photolysis. Photoactivation generates a fluorescein derivative with spectral characteristics similar to C1359.
9. ND = not determined.
10. E3480 is a complex of E3477 with Texas Red® streptavidin, which typically incorporates 3 dyes/streptavidin (MW ~52,800).
11. E13345 is a complex of E3477 with Alexa Fluor® 488 streptavidin, which typically incorporates 5 dyes/streptavidin (MW ~52,800).
12. E35350 is a complex of E3477 with Alexa Fluor® 555 streptavidin, which typically incorporates 3 dyes/streptavidin (MW ~52,800).
13. E35351 is a complex of E3477 with Alexa Fluor® 647 streptavidin, which typically incorporates 3 dyes/streptavidin (MW ~52,800).
14. Absorption and fluorescence of Oregon Green® 488 derivatives are pH-dependent only in moderately acidic solutions (pH <5).

Product List — 4.3 Biotin and Desthiobiotin Conjugates

Cat #	Product Name	Unit Size
A12924	Alexa Fluor® 488 biocytin, disodium salt (biocytin Alexa Fluor® 488)	250 µg
A12923	Alexa Fluor® 546 biocytin, sodium salt (biocytin Alexa Fluor® 546)	250 µg
A12922	Alexa Fluor® 594 biocytin, sodium salt (biocytin Alexa Fluor® 594)	250 µg
A13204	annexin V, biotin-X conjugate *100 assays*	500 µL
A21301MP	anti-bromodeoxyuridine, mouse IgG_1, monoclonal PRB-1, biotin-XX conjugate (anti-BrdU, biotin conjugate)	350 µL
A6435	anti-dinitrophenyl-KLH, rabbit IgG fraction, biotin-XX conjugate *2 mg/mL*	0.5 mL
A982	anti-fluorescein/Oregon Green®, rabbit IgG fraction, biotin-XX conjugate *1 mg/mL*	0.5 mL
A21272	anti-HuC/HuD neuronal protein (human), mouse IgG_{2b}, monoclonal 16A11, biotin-XX conjugate	100 µg
A5751	anti-lucifer yellow, rabbit IgG fraction, biotin-XX conjugate *3 mg/mL*	0.5 mL
A21371	anti-α-tubulin (bovine), mouse IgG_1, monoclonal 236-10501, biotin-XX conjugate	50 µg
B32766	biotin-aha-dUTP *1 mM in TE buffer*	25 µL
B10570	biotin-4-fluorescein	5 mg
B1370	5-((*N*-(5-(*N*-(6-(biotinoyl)amino)hexanoyl)amino)pentyl)thioureidyl)fluorescein (fluorescein biotin)	5 mg
B1616	*N*-((6-(biotinoyl)amino)hexanoyl)-1,2-dihexadecanoyl-*sn*-glycero-3-phosphoethanolamine, triethylammonium salt (biotin-X DHPE)	5 mg
B1550	*N*-(biotinoyl)-1,2-dihexadecanoyl-*sn*-glycero-3-phosphoethanolamine, triethylammonium salt (biotin DHPE)	10 mg
B11027	biotin-XX $F(ab')_2$ fragment of goat anti-mouse IgG (H+L) *2 mg/mL*	250 µL
B21078	biotin-XX $F(ab')_2$ fragment of goat anti-rabbit IgG (H+L) *2 mg/mL*	250 µL
B2763	biotin-XX goat anti-mouse IgG (H+L) *2 mg/mL*	0.5 mL
B2770	biotin-XX goat anti-rabbit IgG (H+L) *2 mg/mL*	0.5 mL
B7474	biotin-XX phalloidin	50 U
B6357	*S*-biotinylhomocysteine	5 mg
B1196	α-bungarotoxin, biotin-XX conjugate	500 µg
C34779	cholera toxin subunit B (recombinant), biotin-XX conjugate	100 µg
D7135	dextran, biotin, 3000 MW, lysine fixable (BDA-3000)	10 mg
D7134	dextran, biotin, 3000 MW, neutral	10 mg
D1956	dextran, biotin, 10,000 MW, lysine fixable (BDA-10,000)	25 mg
D1957	dextran, biotin, 70,000 MW, lysine fixable (BDA-70,000)	25 mg
D7142	dextran, biotin, 500,000 MW, lysine fixable (BDA-500,000)	10 mg
D7146	dextran, DMNB-caged fluorescein and biotin, 10,000 MW, lysine fixable	5 mg
D7147	dextran, DMNB-caged fluorescein and biotin, 70,000 MW, lysine fixable	5 mg
D7156	dextran, fluorescein and biotin, 3000 MW, anionic, lysine fixable (micro-emerald)	5 mg
D7178	dextran, fluorescein and biotin, 10,000 MW, anionic, lysine fixable (mini-emerald)	10 mg
D7162	dextran, tetramethylrhodamine and biotin, 3000 MW, lysine fixable (micro-ruby)	5 mg
D3312	dextran, tetramethylrhodamine and biotin, 10,000 MW, lysine fixable (mini-ruby)	10 mg
D20659	DSB-X™ Bioconjugate Isolation Kit #2 *with DSB-X™ biotin agarose* *5 isolations*	1 kit
D20698	DSB-X™ biotin donkey anti-goat IgG (H+L) *2 mg/mL*	0.5 mL
D20699	DSB-X™ biotin donkey anti-sheep IgG (H+L) *2 mg/mL*	0.5 mL
D20692	DSB-X™ biotin $F(ab')_2$ fragment of goat anti-mouse IgG (H+L) *2 mg/mL*	250 µL
D20696	DSB-X™ biotin $F(ab')_2$ fragment of goat anti-rabbit IgG (H+L) *2 mg/mL*	250 µL
D20701	DSB-X™ biotin goat anti-chicken IgG (H+L) *2 mg/mL*	0.5 mL
D20700	DSB-X™ biotin goat anti-human IgG (H+L) *2 mg/mL*	0.5 mL
D20690	DSB-X™ biotin goat anti-mouse IgG (H+L) *2 mg/mL*	0.5 mL
D20691	DSB-X™ biotin goat anti-mouse IgG (H+L) *highly cross-adsorbed* *2 mg/mL*	0.5 mL
D20693	DSB-X™ biotin goat anti-mouse IgM (µ chain) *2 mg/mL*	250 µL
D20694	DSB-X™ biotin goat anti-rabbit IgG (H+L) *2 mg/mL*	0.5 mL
D20695	DSB-X™ biotin goat anti-rabbit IgG (H+L) *highly cross-adsorbed* *2 mg/mL*	0.5 mL
D20697	DSB-X™ biotin goat anti-rat IgG (H+L) *2 mg/mL*	0.5 mL
E3477	epidermal growth factor, biotin-XX conjugate (biotin EGF)	20 µg
E13345	epidermal growth factor, biotinylated, complexed to Alexa Fluor® 488 streptavidin (Alexa Fluor® 488 EGF complex)	100 µg
E35350	epidermal growth factor, biotinylated, complexed to Alexa Fluor® 555 streptavidin (Alexa Fluor® 555 EGF complex)	100 µg
E35351	epidermal growth factor, biotinylated, complexed to Alexa Fluor® 647 streptavidin (Alexa Fluor® 647 EGF complex)	100 µg
E3480	epidermal growth factor, biotinylated, complexed to Texas Red® streptavidin (Texas Red® EGF complex)	100 µg
F8766	FluoSpheres® biotin-labeled microspheres, 0.04 µm, yellow-green fluorescent (505/515) *1% solids*	0.4 mL
F8767	FluoSpheres® biotin-labeled microspheres, 0.2 µm, yellow-green fluorescent (505/515) *1% solids*	0.4 mL
F8769	FluoSpheres® biotin-labeled microspheres, 1.0 µm, nonfluorescent *1% solids*	0.4 mL
F8768	FluoSpheres® biotin-labeled microspheres, 1.0 µm, yellow-green fluorescent (505/515) *1% solids*	0.4 mL
G36000	glutathione ethyl ester, biotin amide (BioGEE) *glutathiolation detection reagent* *special packaging*	10 x 100 µg
I21414	isolectin GS-IB_4 from *Griffonia simplicifolia*, biotin-XX conjugate	500 µg

For current prices or to order online, visit probes.invitrogen.com

Product List — 4.3 Biotin and Desthiobiotin Conjugates — continued

Cat #	Product Name	Unit Size
L6950	lucifer yellow biocytin, potassium salt (biocytin lucifer yellow)	5 mg
L2601	lucifer yellow cadaverine biotin-X, dipotassium salt	10 mg
O12920	Oregon Green® 488 biocytin (biocytin Oregon Green® 488)	5 mg
P21689	Panomer™ 9 random oligodeoxynucleotide, biotin-XX conjugate	10 nmol
P917	peroxidase from horseradish, biotin-XX conjugate	10 mg
P811	R-phycoerythrin, biotin-XX conjugate *4 mg/mL*	0.5 mL
T12921	5-(and-6)-tetramethylrhodamine biocytin (biocytin TMR)	5 mg
T23363	transferrin from human serum, biotin-XX conjugate	5 mg
Z25452	Zenon® Biotin-XX Human IgG Labeling Kit *50 labelings*	1 kit
Z25052	Zenon® Biotin-XX Mouse IgG_1 Labeling Kit *50 labelings*	1 kit
Z25152	Zenon® Biotin-XX Mouse IgG_{2a} Labeling Kit *50 labelings*	1 kit
Z25252	Zenon® Biotin-XX Mouse IgG_{2b} Labeling Kit *50 labelings*	1 kit
Z25352	Zenon® Biotin-XX Rabbit IgG Labeling Kit *50 labelings*	1 kit
Z25053	Zenon® DSB-X™ Biotin Mouse IgG_1 Labeling Kit *50 labelings*	1 kit

For current prices or to order online, visit probes.invitrogen.com

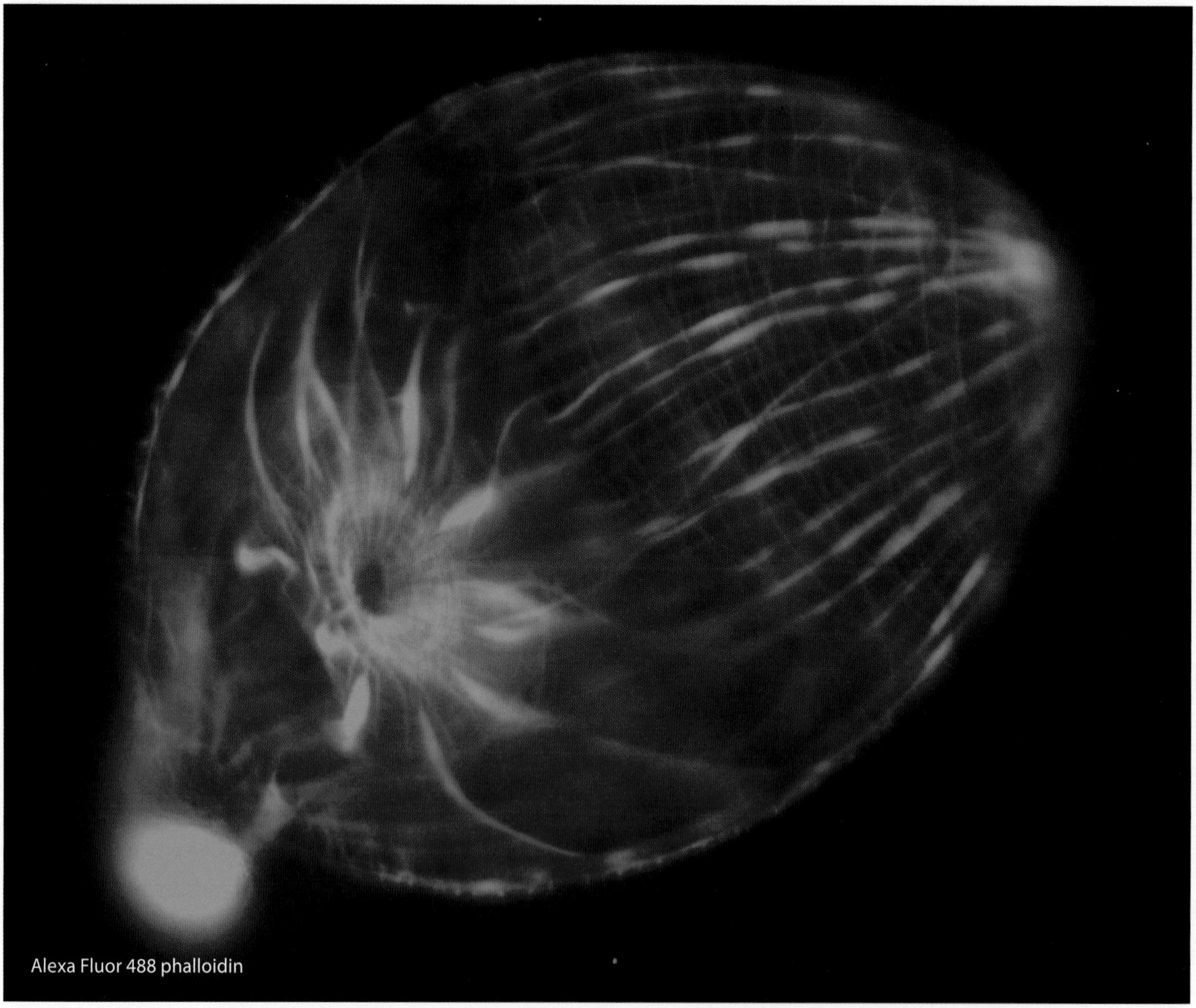

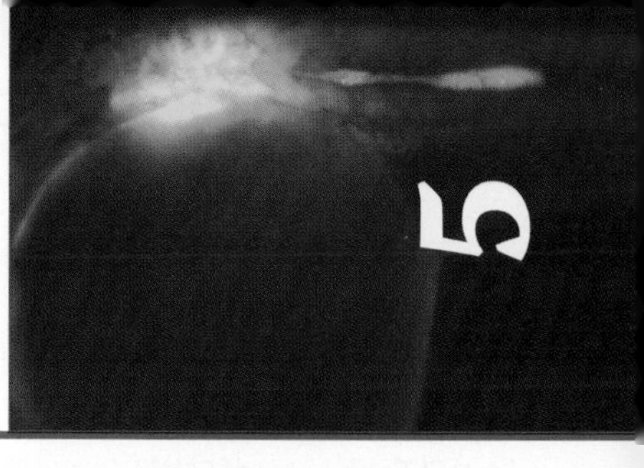

Chapter 5

Crosslinking and Photoactivatable Reagents

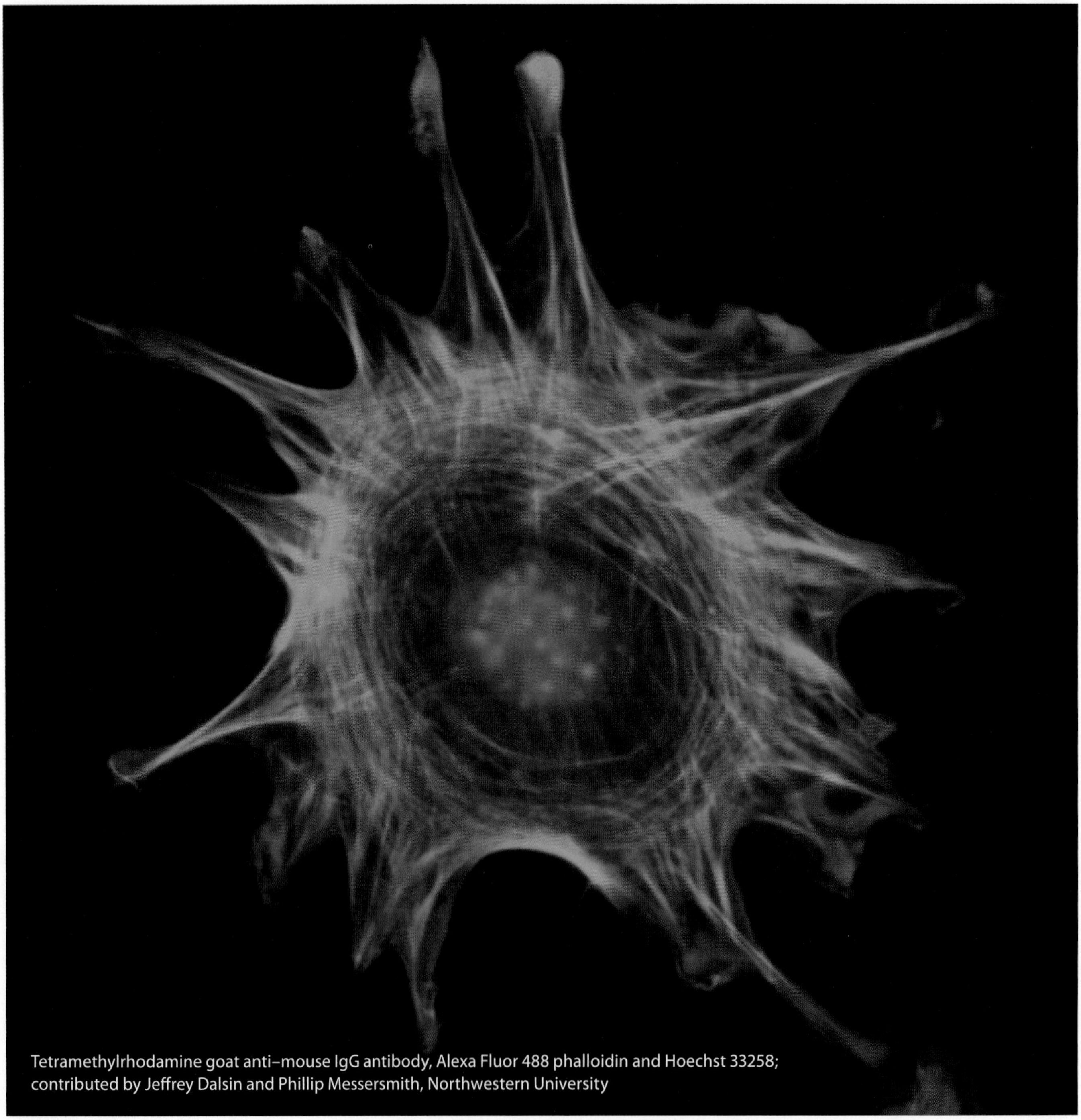

Tetramethylrhodamine goat anti–mouse IgG antibody, Alexa Fluor 488 phalloidin and Hoechst 33258; contributed by Jeffrey Dalsin and Phillip Messersmith, Northwestern University

5.1 Introduction to Crosslinking and Photoactivatable Reagents

Chemical and Photoreactive Crosslinkers

Bifunctional "crosslinking" reagents contain two reactive groups, thereby providing a means of covalently linking two target groups. The reactive groups in a chemical crosslinking reagent (Section 5.2) typically belong to the classes of functional groups — including succinimidyl esters, maleimides and iodoacetamides — described in Chapter 1, Chapter 2 and Chapter 3. In contrast, one of the reactive groups in each of our photoreactive crosslinking reagents (Section 5.3) requires light activation before reacting with a target group. Crosslinking of a biopolymer (such as an antibody, enzyme, avidin or nucleic acid) to a low molecular weight molecule (such as a drug, toxin, peptide or oligonucleotide) or to another biopolymer yields a stable heteroconjugate. This bioconjugate can serve as a detection reagent in a wide variety of research and diagnostic assays (Section 6.1) or as an immunogen designed to elicit antibody production. Crosslinking reagents are also useful for probing the spatial relationships and interactions within and between biomolecules.

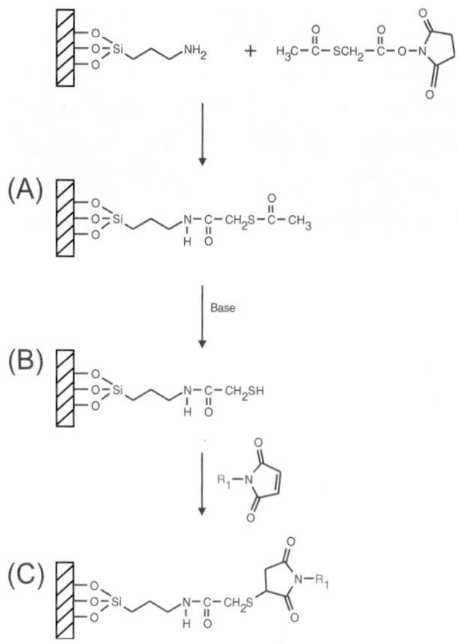

Figure 5.1 Schematic illustration of the heterobifunctional crosslinker succinimidyl acetylthioacetate (SATA, S1553): A) attachment to an aminosilane-modified surface, B) deprotection with base and C) reaction with a thiol-reactive biomolecule.

In homobifunctional crosslinking reagents (Section 5.2), the reactive groups are identical. These reagents couple like functional groups — typically two thiols, two amines, two acids or two alcohols — and are predominantly used to form intramolecular crosslinks or to prepare polymers from monomers. When used to conjugate two different biomolecules, for example an enzyme to an antibody, these relatively nonspecific reagents tend to yield high molecular weight aggregates.

In heterobifunctional crosslinking reagents (Section 5.2, Table 5.1), the reactive groups have dissimilar chemistry, allowing the formation of crosslinks between unlike functional groups (Figure 5.1). As with homobifunctional crosslinking reagents, heterobifunctional crosslinking reagents can still form multiple intermolecular crosslinks to yield high molecular weight aggregates, but conjugations that use these reagents can be more easily controlled so as to optimize the stoichiometry of the target molecules. Thus, heterobifunctional crosslinking reagents are very useful for preparing conjugates between two different biomolecules.

The photoreactive crosslinking reagents (Section 5.3) are a special subset of the heterobifunctional crosslinking reagents. Upon UV illumination, these reagents react with nucleophiles or form C-H insertion products (Figure 5.12, Figure 5.13, Figure 5.14).

An additional variation is the "zero-length" crosslinking reagent — a reagent that forms a chemical bond between two groups without itself being incorporated into the product (Figure 3.23). The water-soluble carbodiimide EDAC (E2247, Section 5.2), which is used to couple carboxylic acids to amines, is an example of a zero-length crosslinking reagent.

A noncovalent interaction between two molecules that has very slow dissociation kinetics can also function as a crosslink. For example, reactive derivatives of phospholipids can be used to link the liposomes or cell membranes in which they are incorporated to antibodies or enzymes. Biotinylation and haptenylation reagents (Chapter 4) can also be thought of as heterobifunctional crosslinking reagents because they comprise a chemically reactive group as well as a biotin or hapten moiety that binds with high affinity to avidin or an anti-hapten antibody, respectively. Similarly, avidin, streptavidin, NeutrAvidin biotin-binding protein and CaptAvidin™ biotin-binding protein (Section 7.6) can tightly bind up to four molecules of a biotinylated target, and immunoglobulin G (IgG) can bind up to two haptens.

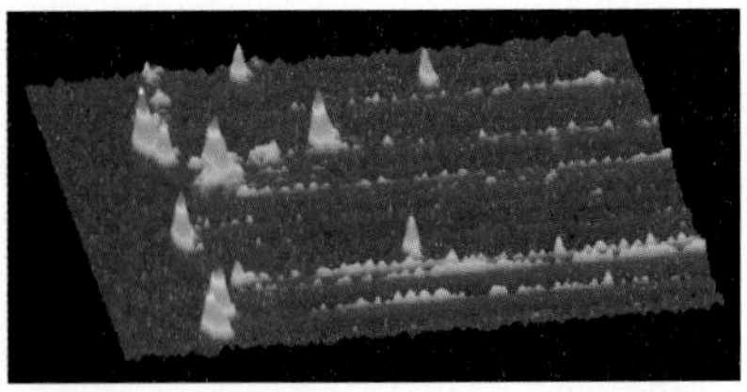

Figure 5.2 Confocal linescan image of calcium "puffs" in a *Xenopus* oocyte. Oregon Green® 488 BAPTA-1 (O6806) was used as the calcium indicator and Ca^{2+} liberation was evoked by flash photolysis of NPE-caged Ins 1,4,5-P_3 (I23580). Image contributed by Ian Parker and Nick Callamaras, University of California at Irvine.

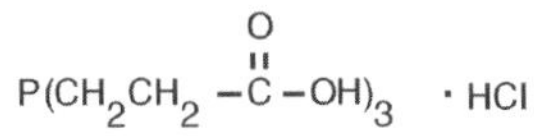

Figure 5.3 T2556 tris-(2-carboxyethyl)phosphine, hydrochloride (TCEP).

Photoactivatable (Caged) Probes

In addition to the photoreactive crosslinking reagents that are briefly mentioned above and described in detail in Section 5.3, Molecular Probes is the principal supplier of photoactivatable probes. Flash photolysis of photoactivatable or "caged" probes provides a means of controlling the release — both spatially and temporally — of biologically active products or other reagents of interest.[1–7] The chemical caging process may also confer membrane permeability on the caged ligand, as is the case for caged cAMP[8] and caged luciferin.[9] Molecular Probes' extensive selection of caged nucleotides, chelators, second messengers (Figure 5.2) and neurotransmitters has tremendous potential for use with both live cells and isolated proteins (Section 5.3).

We prepare caged versions of biologically active molecules, as well as caged fluorescent dyes that are essentially nonfluorescent until after photolysis. These caged fluorophores have proven useful for photoactivation of fluorescence (PAF) experiments, which are analogous to fluorescence recovery after photobleaching (FRAP) experiments except that the fluorophore is activated upon illumination rather than bleached. Measuring the bright fluorescent signal of the photoactivated fluorophore against a dark background is intrinsically more sensitive than measuring a dark photobleached region against a bright field.[2,10] We have also introduced secondary antibody conjugates of CMNB-caged fluorescein (Section 7.2) that simultaneously form the fluorescein hapten and develop strong green fluorescence following brief illumination with UV light (Figure 7.74).

Table 5.1 — Molecular Probes' heterobifunctional crosslinkers

Cat #	Crosslinker	Reactivity			
		Thiol (R_1-SH)	Amine (R_1-NH_2)	Aldehyde or Ketone	Photoreactive *
S1534	succinimidyl *trans*-4-(maleimidylmethyl) cyclohexane-1-carboxylate (SMCC)	✓	✓		
T30875	TS-Link™ TFP-X thiosulfate	✓	✓		
S1531	succinimidyl 3-(2-pyridyldithio)propionate (SPDP)	✓	✓		
P6317	*N*-((2-pyridyldithio)ethyl)-4-azidosalicylamide (PEAS; AET)	✓			✓
A2522	4-azido-2,3,5,6-tetrafluorobenzoic acid, succinimidyl ester (ATFB, SE)		✓		✓
A10661	4-azido-2,3,5,6-tetrafluorobenzoic acid, STP ester, sodium salt (ATFB, STP ester)		✓		✓
A10662	4-azido-2,3,5,6-tetrafluorobenzyl amine, hydrochloride			✓	✓
B1508	benzophenone-4-maleimide	✓			✓
B1526	benzophenone-4-isothiocyanate		✓		✓
B1577	4-benzoylbenzoic acid, succinimidyl ester		✓		✓

* Reacts nonspecifically with available sites upon UV illumination.

References

1. Photochem Photobiol Sci 1, 441 (2002); 2. Methods Enzymol 291, 63 (1998); 3. Methods Enzymol 291, 30 (1998); 4. Curr Opin Neurobiol 6, 379 (1996); 5. Biological Applications of Photochemical Switches, Morrison H, Ed. pp. 243–305 (1993); 6. Optical Microscopy: Emerging Methods and Applications, Herman B, Lemasters JJ, Eds. pp. 27–85 (1993); 7. Annu Rev Physiol 55, 755 (1993); 8. Nature 310, 74 (1984); 9. Biotechniques 15, 848 (1993); 10. Cell Biology: A Laboratory Handbook, 2nd Ed., Vol. 3, Celis JE, Ed. pp. 127–135 (1998).

5.2 Chemical Crosslinking Reagents

The most common schemes for forming a well-defined heteroconjugate involve the indirect coupling of an amine group on one biomolecule to a thiol group on a second biomolecule, usually by a two- or three-step reaction sequence. The high reactivity of thiols (Chapter 2) and — with the exception of a few proteins such as β-galactosidase — their relative rarity in most biomolecules make thiol groups ideal targets for controlled chemical crosslinking. If neither molecule contains a thiol group, then one or more can be introduced using one of several thiolation methods. The thiol-containing biomolecule is then reacted with an amine-containing biomolecule using a heterobifunctional crosslinking reagent such as one of those described in Amine–Thiol Crosslinking, below.

Thiolation of Biomolecules

Introducing Thiol Groups

Several methods are available for introducing thiols into biomolecules, including the reduction of intrinsic disulfides, as well as the conversion of amine or carboxylic acid groups to thiol groups:

- Disulfide crosslinks of cystines in proteins can be reduced to cysteine residues by dithiothreitol[1] (DTT, D1532), tris-(2-carboxyethyl)phosphine (TCEP, T2556; Figure 5.3) or tris-(2-cyanoethyl)phosphine (T6052). However, reduction may result in loss of protein activity or specificity. Excess DTT must be carefully removed under conditions that prevent reformation of the disulfide,[2] whereas excess TCEP usually does not need to be removed before carrying out the crosslinking reaction. TCEP is also more stable at higher pH values and at higher temperatures than is the air-sensitive DTT reagent.[3]
- Amines can be indirectly thiolated by reaction with succinimidyl 3-(2-pyridyldithio)propionate[4] (SPDP, S1531), followed by reduction of the 3-(2-pyridyldithio)propionyl conjugate with DTT or TCEP (Figure 5.4). Reduction releases the 2-pyridinethione chromophore, which can be used to determine the degree of thiolation.
- Amines can be indirectly thiolated by reaction with succinimidyl acetylthioacetate[5] (SATA, S1553), followed by removal of the acetyl group with 50 mM hydroxylamine or hydrazine at near-neutral pH (Figure 5.1). This reagent is most useful when disulfides are essential for activity, as is the case for some peptide toxins.
- Amines can be indirectly thiolated by reaction with the very water-soluble TS-Link™ TFP-X thiosulfate (T30875), followed by reduction with DTT or TCEP (Figure 5.5).
- Thiols can be incorporated at carboxylic acid groups by an EDAC-mediated reaction with cystamine, followed by reduction of the disulfide with DTT or TCEP;[6,7] see Amine–Carboxylic Acid Crosslinking below.
- Tryptophan residues in thiol-free proteins can be oxidized to mercaptotryptophan residues, which can then be modified by iodoacetamides or maleimides.[8–10]

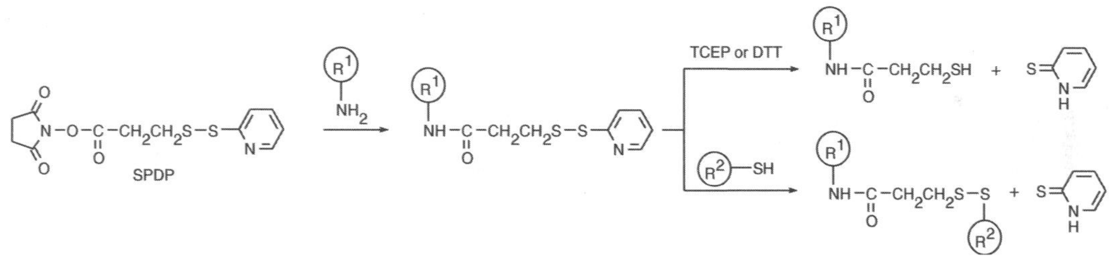

Figure 5.4 SPDP derivatization reactions. SPDP (S1531) reacts with an amine-containing biomolecule at pH 7 to 9, yielding a pyridyldithiopropionyl mixed disulfide. The mixed disulfide can then be reacted with a reducing agent such as DTT (D1532) or TCEP (T2556) to yield a 3-mercaptopropionyl conjugate or with a thiol-containing biomolecule to form a disulfide-linked tandem conjugate. Either reaction can be quantitated by measuring the amount of 2-pyridinethione chromophore released during the reaction.

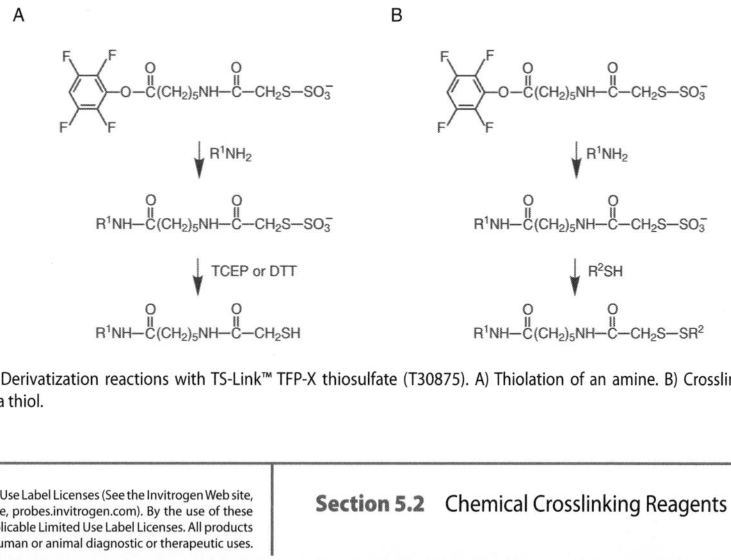

Figure 5.5 Derivatization reactions with TS-Link™ TFP-X thiosulfate (T30875). A) Thiolation of an amine. B) Crosslinking of an amine and a thiol.

Our preferred reagent combination for protein thiolation is SPDP/DTT or SPDP/TCEP.[11] Molecular Probes uses SPDP to prepare a reactive R-phycoerythrin derivative (P806, Section 6.4), providing researchers with the optimal number of pyridyldisulfide groups for crosslinking the phycobiliprotein to thiolated antibodies, enzymes and other biomolecules through disulfide linkages.[12] More commonly, the pyridyldisulfide groups are first reduced to thiols, which are then reacted with maleimide- or iodoacetamide-derivatized proteins (Figure 5.4, Figure 5.6). SPDP can also be used to thiolate oligonucleotides[13] and — like all of the thiolation reagents in this section — to introduce the highly reactive thiol group into peptides, onto cell surfaces or onto affinity matrices for subsequent reaction with fluorescent, enzyme-coupled or other thiol-reactive reagents (Chapter 2). In addition, because the 3-(2-pyridyldithio)propionyl conjugate releases the 2-pyridinethione chromophore upon reduction, SPDP is useful for quantitating the number of reactive amines in an affinity matrix.[14]

Measuring Thiolation of Biomolecules

To ensure success in forming heterocrosslinks, it is important to know that a molecule has the proper degree of thiolation. We generally find that two to three thiol residues per protein are optimal. Following removal of excess reagents, the degree of thiolation in proteins or other molecules thiolated with SPDP can be directly determined by measuring release of the 2-pyridinethione chromophore[4] ($\varepsilon_{343\,nm}$ ~8000 $cm^{-1}M^{-1}$).

Alternatively, the degree of thiolation and presence of residual thiols in a solution can be assessed using 5,5′-dithiobis-(2-nitrobenzoic acid) (DTNB, Ellman's reagent; D8451), which stoichiometrically yields the 5-mercapto-2-nitrobenzoic acid chromophore ($\varepsilon_{410\,nm}$ ~13,600 $cm^{-1}M^{-1}$) upon reaction with a thiol group.[15,16] DTNB can also be used to quantitate residual phosphines in aqueous solutions, including TCEP;[17] in this case, two molecules of 5-mercapto-2-nitrobenzoic acid are formed per reaction with one molecule of a phosphine.

Thiol and Sulfide Quantitation Kit

Ultrasensitive colorimetric quantitation of both protein and nonprotein thiols is now possible using our Thiol and Sulfide Quantitation Kit (T6060). In this assay, which is based on a method reported by Singh,[18,19] thiols reduce a disulfide-inhibited derivative of papain, stoichiometrically releasing the active enzyme. Activity of the enzyme is then measured using the chromogenic papain substrate L-BAPNA (Figure 5.7). Although thiols can also be quantitated using DTNB (Ellman's reagent, see above), the enzymatic amplification step in our quantitation kit enables researchers to detect as little as 0.2 nanomoles of a thiol — a sensitivity that is about 100-fold better than that achieved with DTNB. Thiols in proteins and potentially in other high molecular weight molecules can be detected indirectly by incorporating the disulfide cystamine into the solution. Cystamine undergoes

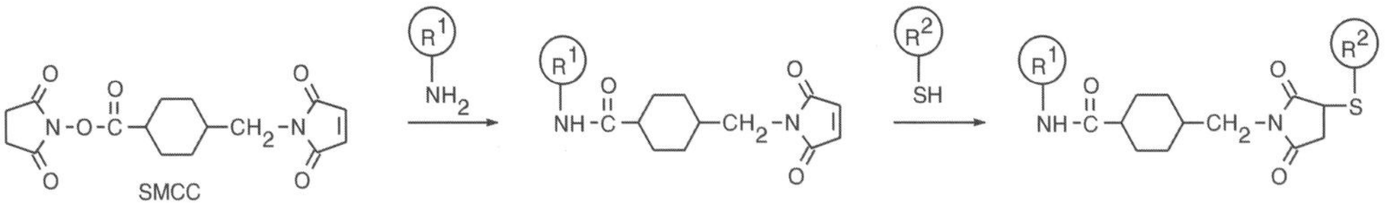

Figure 5.6 Two-step reaction sequence for crosslinking biomolecules using the heterobifunctional crosslinker SMCC (S1534).

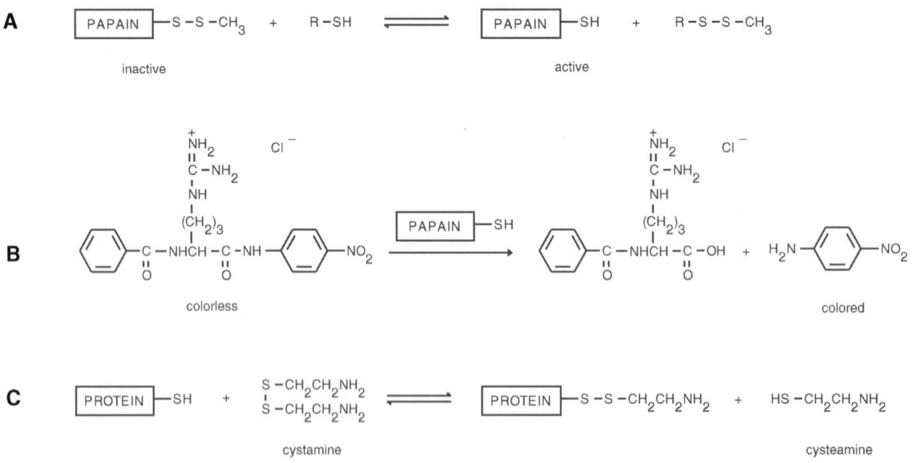

Figure 5.7 Chemical basis for thiol detection using the Thiol and Sulfide Quantitation Kit (T6060): A) the inactive disulfide derivative of papain, papain–$SSCH_3$, is activated in the presence of thiols; B) active papain cleaves the substrate L-BAPNA, releasing the *p*-nitroaniline chromophore; C) protein thiols, often poorly accessible, exchange with cystamine to generate 2-mercaptoethylamine (cysteamine), which is easily detected.

an exchange reaction with protein thiols, yielding 2-mercaptoethylamine (cysteamine), which then releases active papain. All traces of reducing agents must be removed before determining free thiols in proteins. The Thiol and Sulfide Quantitation Kit contains:

- Papain–$SSCH_3$, the disulfide-inhibited papain derivative
- L-BAPNA, a chromogenic papain substrate
- DTNB (Ellman's reagent), for calibrating the assay
- Cystamine
- L-Cysteine, a thiol standard
- Buffer
- A detailed protocol for measuring thiols, inorganic sulfides and maleimides

Sufficient reagents are provided for approximately 50 assays using 1 mL assay volumes and standard cuvettes or 250 assays using a microplate format. This kit can also be used to detect phosphines, sulfites and cyanides, with detection limits of about 0.5, 1 and 5 nanomoles, respectively.

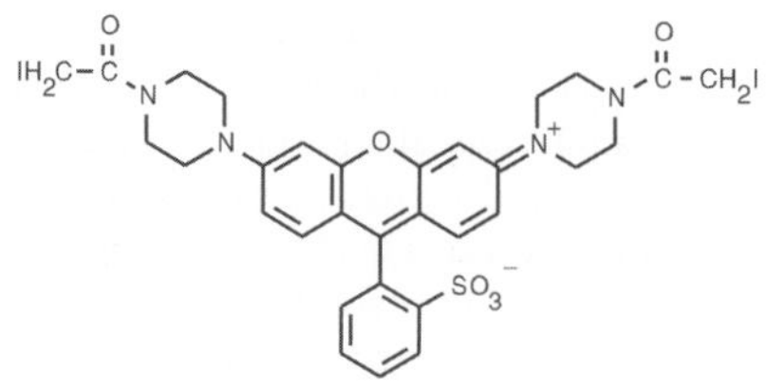

Figure 5.8 B10621 bis-((*N*-iodoacetyl)piperazinyl)sulfonerhodamine.

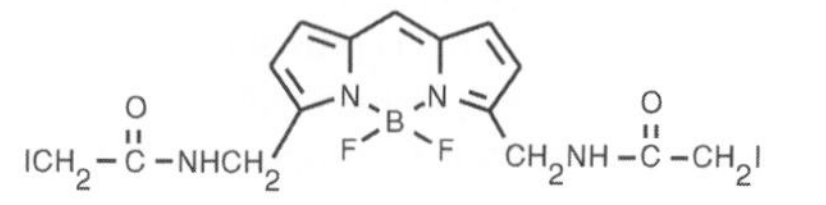

Figure 5.9 D10620 4,4-difluoro-3,5-di(iodoacetamidomethyl)-4-bora-3a,4a-diaza-*s*-indacene (BODIPY® FL bis-(methyleneiodoacetamide)).

Thiol–Thiol Crosslinking

Oxidation

Thiol residues in close proximity can be oxidized to disulfides by either an intra- or intermolecular reaction. In many circumstances, however, this oxidation reaction is reversible and difficult to control.

Fluorescent Thiol–Thiol Crosslinkers

Dibromobimane (bBBr, D1379) is an interesting crosslinking reagent for proteins because it is unlikely to fluoresce until both of its alkylating groups have reacted.[20] It has been used to crosslink thiols in myosin,[21] actin,[22] hemoglobin,[23] *Escherichia coli* lactose permease[24] and mitochondrial ATPase.[25] It has also been shown to intramolecularly crosslink thiols in a complex of nebulin and calmodulin.[26] In addition, dibromobimane has been used to probe for the proximity of dual-cysteine mutagenesis sites in ArsA ATPase[27] and P-glycoprotein.[28–30] Dibromobimane, a stimulator of the ATPase activity of a cysteine-free P glycoprotein, was used with cysteine-scanning mutagenesis to identify amino acid residues important for function.[31]

In addition to dibromobimane, we offer two other thiol–thiol crosslinkers. The thiol-reactive homobifunctional crosslinker bis-((*N*-iodoacetyl)piperazinyl)sulfonerhodamine (B10621) is derived from a relatively rigid rhodamine dye (Figure 5.8). This crosslinker, which is similar to a thiol-reactive rhodamine-based crosslinking reagent that was used to label regulatory light-chains of chicken gizzard myosin for fluorescence polarization experiments,[32] may also be useful for proximity studies. Researchers have attached bis-((*N*-iodoacetyl)piperazinyl)sulfonerhodamine to the kinesin motor domain and then, using polarized fluorescence microscopy, have determined the orientation of kinesin bound to microtubules in the presence of a nonhydrolyzable ATP analog.[33] BODIPY® FL bis-(methyleneiodoacetamide) (D10620, Figure 5.9) is a novel bifunctional thiol-reactive probe that can be used for biophysical studies of protein–protein and protein–nucleic acid interactions. The two iodoacetamide groups of the probe were recently used to anchor the BODIPY® FL fluorophore to two nearby cysteine residues of calmodulin, thereby constraining rotation of the dye and permitting fluorescence anisotropy measurements of the interaction of labeled calmodulin with various targets.[34]

Amine–Amine Crosslinking

The scientific literature contains numerous references to reagents that form crosslinks between amines of biopolymers. Homobifunctional amine crosslinkers include glutaraldehyde, bis(imido esters), bis(succinimidyl esters), diisocyanates and diacid chlorides.[35] However, these reagents tend to yield high molecular weight aggregates, making them unsuitable for reproducibly preparing well-defined conjugates between two different amine-containing biomolecules. Such conjugates are more commonly prepared by thiolating one or more amines on one of the biomolecules and converting one or more amines on the second biomolecule to a thiol-reactive functional group such as a maleimide or iodoacetamide, as described below in Amine–Thiol Crosslinking. For example, glutaraldehyde is still used by some companies and research laboratories to couple horseradish peroxidase, which has only six lysine residues,[36] to proteins with a larger numbers of lysine residues. However, this practice can result in variable molecular weights and batch-to-batch inconsistency. Consequently, we prepare our horseradish peroxidase conjugates (Section 7.2, Section 7.6) using SPDP- and SMCC-mediated reactions (Figure 5.4, Figure 5.6).

Direct amine–amine crosslinking routinely occurs during fixation of proteins, cells and tissues with formaldehyde or glutaraldehyde. These common aldehyde-based fixatives are also used to crosslink amine and hydrazine derivatives to proteins and other amine-containing polymers. For example, lucifer yellow CH (L453, Section 14.3) is nonspecifically conjugated to surrounding biomolecules by aldehyde-based fixatives in order to preserve the dye's staining pattern during subsequent tissue manipulations.[37] Also, biotin hydrazides (Section 4.2) have been directly coupled to nucleic acids with glutaraldehyde,[38,39] a reaction that is potentially useful for conjugating fluorescent hydrazides and hydroxylamines to DNA.

Amine–Thiol Crosslinking

Indirect crosslinking of the amines in one biomolecule to the thiols in a second biomolecule is the predominant method for forming a heteroconjugate. If one of the biomolecules does not already contain one or more thiol groups, it is necessary to introduce them using one of the thiolation procedures described above in Thiolation of Biomolecules. Thiol-reactive groups such as maleimides are typically introduced into the second biomolecule by modifying a few of its amines with a heterobifunctional crosslinker containing both a succinimidyl ester and a maleimide. The maleimide-modified biomolecule is then reacted with the thiol-containing biomolecule to form a stable thioether crosslink. Chromatographic methods are usually employed to separate the higher molecular weight heteroconjugate from the unconjugated biomolecules.

Introducing Maleimides at Amines

Succinimidyl *trans*-4-(maleimidylmethyl)cyclohexane-1-carboxylate[40] (SMCC, S1534) is our reagent of choice for introducing thiol-reactive groups at amine sites because of the superior chemical stability of its maleimide and its ease of use[41] (Figure 5.6).

Introducing Disulfides at Amines

Our preferred method for preparing heteroconjugates employs the thiolation reagent SPDP (S1531). The pyridyldisulfide intermediate that is initially formed by reaction of SPDP with amines can form an unsymmetrical disulfide through reaction with a second thiol-containing molecule[4,12] (Figure 5.4). The thiol-containing target can be a molecule such as β-galactosidase that contains intrinsic thiols or a molecule in which thiols have been introduced using one of the thiolation procedures described above in Thiolation of Biomolecules. In either case, it is essential that all reducing agents, such as DTT and TCEP, are absent. The heteroconjugate's disulfide bond is about as stable and resistant to reduction as disulfides found in proteins; it can be reduced with DTT or TCEP to generate two thiol-containing biomolecules.

TS-Link™ TFP-X Thiosulfate: A Versatile Reagent for Thiolation and Crosslinking

TS-Link™ TFP-X thiosulfate (T30875) is a heterobifunctional crosslinker in which the tetrafluorophenyl (TFP) portion of the molecule will react with an aliphatic primary amine and the thiosulfate can react reversibly with a free thiol to form a disulfide (Figure 5.5). Presumably, the reactions with amines and thiols can occur in either order, depending on the pH, with the crosslinking efficiency controlled by the geometry and proximity of the reactive sites. Alternatively, TS-Link™ TFP-X thiosulfate can be used to thiolate amines, as described above (Figure 5.5).

Protein–Protein Crosslinking Kit

Our Protein–Protein Crosslinking Kit (P6305) provides all of the reagents and purification media required to perform three protein–protein conjugations in which neither protein contains thiol residues. The chemistry used to thiolate the amines of one of the proteins with SPDP and to convert the amines of the second protein to thiol-reactive maleimides with SMCC is shown in Figure 5.4 and Figure 5.6, respectively. Included in the kit are:

- SPDP, for thiolating amines
- SMCC, for converting amines to thiol-reactive maleimides
- TCEP, for reducing the pyridyldisulfide intermediate
- *N*-ethylmaleimide (NEM), for capping residual thiols
- Six reaction tubes, each containing a magnetic stir bar
- Spin columns plus collection tubes
- Dimethylsulfoxide (DMSO)
- A detailed crosslinking protocol

The Protein–Protein Crosslinking Kit was designed to prepare and purify protein–protein conjugates; however, it can be readily modified for generating peptide–protein or enzyme–nucleic acid conjugates or for conjugating biomolecules to affinity matrices.

Molecular Probes has considerable experience in preparing protein–protein conjugates and will apply this expertise to a researcher's particular application through our custom synthesis service. We provide custom conjugation services on an exclusive or nondisclosure basis when requested. For more information or a quote, please contact our Custom and Bulk Sales Department.

Assaying Maleimide- and Iodoacetamide-Modified Biomolecules

The potential instability of maleimide derivatives and the photosensitivity of iodoacetamide derivatives may make it advisable to assay the modified biomolecule for thiol reactivity before conjugation with a thiol-containing biomolecule. SAMSA fluorescein (A685, Figure 5.10), which is currently our only fluorescent reagent that can generate a free thiol group, was designed for assaying whether a biomolecule is adequately labeled with a heterobifunctional maleimide or iodoacetamide crosslinker. Brief treatment of SAMSA fluorescein with NaOH at pH 10 liberates a free thiol. By adding base-treated SAMSA fluorescein to a small aliquot of the crosslinker-modified biomolecule, the researcher can check to see whether the biomolecule has been sufficiently labeled before proceeding to the next step. The degree of modification can be approximated from either the absorbance or the fluorescence of the conjugate following quick purification on a gel-filtration column.

Alternatively, thiol reactivity of the modified biomolecule can be assayed using the reagents provided in our Thiol and Sulfide Quantitation Kit (T6060), a product that is described above.[18,19] Once unconjugated reagents have been removed, a small aliquot of the maleimide- or iodoacetamide-modified biomolecule can be reacted with excess cysteine. Thiol-reactive groups can then be quantitated by determining the amount of cysteine consumed in this reaction with the Thiol and Sulfide Quantitation Kit.

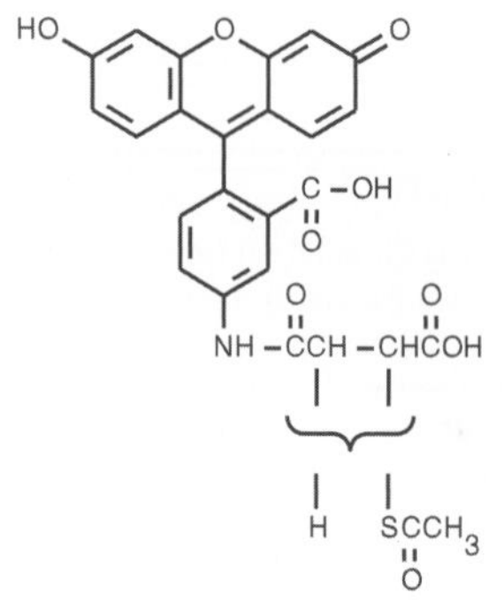

Figure 5.10 A685 5-((2-(and-3)-*S*-(acetylmercapto)succinoyl)amino)fluorescein (SAMSA fluorescein).

Amine–Carboxylic Acid and Thiol–Carboxylic Acid Crosslinking

1-Ethyl-3-(3-dimethylaminopropyl)carbodiimide (EDAC, E2247) can react with biomolecules to form "zero-length" crosslinks, usually within a molecule or between subunits of a protein complex. In this chemistry, the crosslinking reagent is not incorporated into the final product. The water-soluble carbodiimide EDAC crosslinks a specific amine and carboxylic acid between subunits of allophycocyanin, thereby stabilizing its assembly.[42] Molecular Probes uses EDAC to stabilize allophycocyanin in its allophycocyanin conjugates (Section 6.4). EDAC has also been used to form intramolecular crosslinks in myosin subfragment-1,[43] intermolecular crosslinks in actomyosin,[44] intersubunit crosslinks of chloroplast subunits[45] and crosslinks between proteins and DNA.[46] Addition of *N*-hydroxysuccinimide or *N*-hydroxysulfosuccinimide (NHSS, H2249) is reported to enhance the yield of carbodiimide-mediated conjugations,[47] indicating the *in situ* formation of a succinimidyl ester–activated protein (Figure 3.24). EDAC has been reported to be impermeant to cell membranes,[48] which should permit selective surface labeling of cellular carboxylic acids with fluorescent amines.

Reaction of carboxylic acids with cystamine ($H_2NCH_2CH_2S{-}SCH_2CH_2NH_2$) and EDAC followed by reduction with DTT results in thiolation at carboxylic acids.[7] This indirect route to amine–carboxylic acid coupling is particularly suited to acidic proteins with few amines, carbohydrate polymers,[6] heparin, poly(glutamic acid) and synthetic polymers lacking amines. The thiolated biomolecules can also be reacted with any of the probes described in Chapter 2.

Crosslinking Amines to Acrylamide Polymers

The succinimidyl ester of 6-((acryloyl)amino)hexanoic acid (acryloyl-X, SE; A20770) reacts with amines of proteins, amine-modified nucleic acids and other biomolecules to yield acrylamides that can be copolymerized into polyacrylamide matrices or on surfaces, such as in microarrays and in biosensors. For example, streptavidin acrylamide (S21379, Section 7.6) copolymerizes with acrylamide on polymeric surfaces to create a uniform monolayer of the immobilized protein. The streptavidin can then bind biotinylated ligands, including biotinylated hybridization probes, enzymes, antibodies and drugs.[49]

Crosslinking Liposomes and Cell Membranes to Biomolecules

All of the chemical crosslinkers described above form covalent bonds with their targets. However, reagents used to crosslink liposomes, cell membranes and potentially other lipid assemblies to biomolecules typically comprise a phospholipid derivative to anchor one end of the crosslink in the lipid layer and a reactive group at the other end to attach the membrane assembly to the target biomolecule.

Chemically Reactive and Biotinylated Phospholipids

Molecular Probes offers a maleimide-containing phospholipid (MMCC DHPE, M1618; Figure 5.11) that can be incorporated into liposomes, then coupled to thiolated antibodies,[50] streptavidin,[51] lectins[52] and other proteins.[53,54] Similarly, our phospholipid derivatives of biotin and biotin-X (B1550, B1616) can be used to prepare liposomes that have high affinity for avidin conjugates.[55–57]

Applications for Liposome Bioconjugates

Liposome bioconjugates are versatile reagents that can serve as a means of targeted delivery — either of the contents of the liposome's aqueous cavity or of the components in its lipid membrane — to a particular site recognized by its biomolecule tag. Representative applications include:

- Following receptor-mediated endocytosis of liposomes by flow cytometry[58]
- Loading liposomes with fluorescent dyes, including any of the polar tracers described in Section 14.3, for amplified detection in imaging and flow cytometry[59–62]
- Measuring anti-protein antibody using antigen-bearing liposomes in a liposome immunelysis assay (LILA)[63]
- Studying lateral and structural organization at aqueous interfaces[64–67]
- Targeting delivery of enzyme inhibitors[68] and oligodeoxyribonucleotides[69] into cells

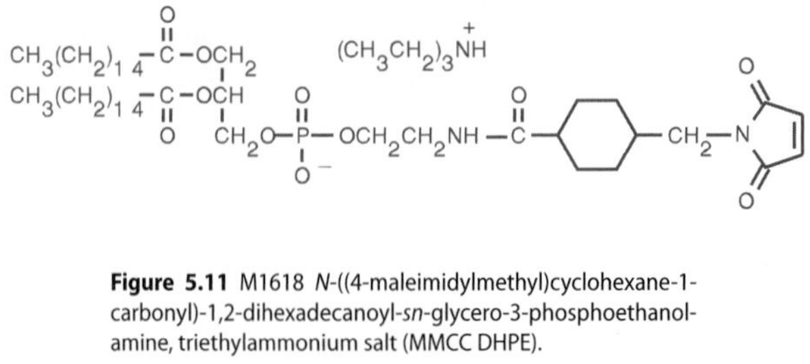

Figure 5.11 M1618 *N*-((4-maleimidylmethyl)cyclohexane-1-carbonyl)-1,2-dihexadecanoyl-*sn*-glycero-3-phosphoethanolamine, triethylammonium salt (MMCC DHPE).

References

1. Bioconjug Chem 12, 421 (2001); **2.** Methods Enzymol 143, 246 (1987); **3.** Anal Biochem 325, 137 (2004); **4.** Biochem J 173, 723 (1978); **5.** Anal Biochem 132, 68 (1983); **6.** Biosci Biotechnol Biochem 61, 1836 (1997); **7.** Biochim Biophys Acta 1038, 382 (1990); **8.** Biochim Biophys Acta 971, 307 (1988); **9.** Biochim Biophys Acta 971, 298 (1988); **10.** J Biol Chem 255, 10884 (1980); **11.** Methods Mol Biol 45, 235 (1995); **12.** J Cell Biol 93, 981 (1982); **13.** Nucleic Acids Res 17, 4404 (1989); **14.** J Biochem Biophys Methods 12, 349 (1986); **15.** Methods Enzymol 233, 380 (1994); **16.** Methods Enzymol 91, 49 (1983); **17.** Anal Biochem 220, 5 (1994); **18.** Bioconjug Chem 5, 348 (1994); **19.** Anal Biochem 213, 49 (1993); **20.** Anal Biochem 225, 174 (1995); **21.** Proc Natl Acad Sci U S A 97, 1461 (2000); **22.** J Mol Biol 299, 421 (2000); **23.** Biochim Biophys Acta 622, 201 (1980); **24.** Proc Natl Acad Sci U S A 93, 10123 (1996); **25.** FEBS Lett 150, 207 (1982); **26.** Biochemistry 40, 7903 (2001); **27.** J Biol Chem 271, 24465 (1996); **28.** J Biol Chem 275, 39272 (2000); **29.** J Biol Chem 274, 35388 (1999); **30.** Kidney Int 51, 1797 (1997); **31.** J Biol Chem 272, 31945 (1997); **32.** Bioconjug Chem 9, 160 (1998); **33.** Biophys J 81, 2851 (2001); **34.** Biophys J 74, A380, abstract #200 (1998); **35.** Methods Enzymol 172, 584 (1989); **36.** Eur J Biochem 96, 483 (1979); **37.** Nature 292, 17 (1981); **38.** Nucleic Acids Res 17, 4899 (1989); **39.** Chem Pharm Bull (Tokyo) 37, 1831 (1989); **40.** Eur J Biochem 101, 395 (1979); **41.** Anal Biochem 198, 75 (1991); **42.** Cytometry 8, 91 (1987); **43.** Biochemistry 33, 6867 (1994); **44.** Biophys J 68, 35S (1995); **45.** Biochim Biophys Acta 1101, 97 (1992); **46.** J Mol Biol 123, 149 (1978); **47.** Anal Biochem 156, 220 (1986); **48.** J Biol Chem 275, 977 (2000); **49.** Anal Biochem 282, 200 (2000); **50.** Biol Cell 47, 111 (1983); **51.** Anal Biochem 207, 341 (1992); **52.** Cell Biol Int Rep 9, 1123 (1985); **53.** J Immunol Methods 132, 25 (1990); **54.** Methods Enzymol 149, 111 (1987); **55.** Biophys J 75, 2352 (1998); **56.** Biophys J 70, 57 (1996); **57.** Methods Enzymol 149, 119 (1987); **58.** Biochem J 214, 189 (1983); **59.** J Fluorescence 3, 33 (1993); **60.** J Immunol Methods 121, 1 (1989); **61.** Cytometry 8, 562 (1987); **62.** J Immunol Methods 100, 59 (1987); **63.** J Immunol Methods 75, 351 (1984); **64.** Biophys J 68, 312 (1995); **65.** Biophys J 66, 305 (1994); **66.** Biophys J 65, 2160 (1993); **67.** J Membr Biol 135, 83 (1993); **68.** J Cell Biol 102, 1630 (1986); **69.** Proc Natl Acad Sci U S A 87, 2448 (1990).

Data Table — 5.2 Chemical Crosslinking Reagents

Cat #	MW	Storage	Soluble	Abs	EC	Em	Solvent	Notes
A685	521.50	F,D,L	pH >6, DMF	491	78,000	515	pH 9	
A1642	191.25	D,A	EtOH	<300		none		
A20770	282.30	F,D,L	DMSO	<300		none		
B1550	1019.45	FF,D	see Notes	<300		none		1
B1616	1132.61	FF,D	see Notes	<300		none		1
B10621	840.47	F,D,L	DMSO	549	88,000	575	MeOH	2
D1379	350.01	L	DMF, MeCN	391	6,100	see Notes	MeOH	3
D1532	154.24	D	H_2O	<300		none		
D8451	396.35	D	pH >6	324	18,000	none	pH 8	4
D10620	585.92	F,D,L	DMSO, MeCN	509	103,000	516	MeOH	2, 5
E2247	191.70	F,D	H_2O	<300		none		
H2249	217.13	D	H_2O	<300		none		
M1618	1012.40	FF,D	see Notes	<300		none		1
P1619MP	990.43	FF,D	see Notes	281	4,900	none	MeOH	1
S1531	312.36	F,D	DMF, MeCN	282	4,700	none	MeOH	6
S1534	334.33	F,D	DMF, MeCN	<300		none		
S1553	231.22	F,D	DMF, MeCN	<300		none		
T2556	286.65	D	pH >5	<300		none		
T6052	193.19	D	MeCN	<300		none		
T30875	455.37	F,D	DMSO, H_2O	<300		none		7

For definitions of the contents of this data table, see "Navigating *The Handbook*" in the introductory pages.

Notes

1. Chloroform is the most generally useful solvent for preparing stock solutions of phospholipids (including sphingomyelins). Glycerophosphocholines are usually freely soluble in ethanol. Most other glycerophospholipids (phosphoethanolamines, phosphatidic acids and phosphoglycerols) are less soluble in ethanol, but solutions up to 1–2 mg/mL should be obtainable, using sonication to aid dispersion if necessary. Labeling of cells with fluorescent phospholipids can be enhanced by addition of cyclodextrins during incubation (J Biol Chem 274, 35359 (1999)).
2. Iodoacetamides in solution undergo rapid photodecomposition to unreactive products. Minimize exposure to light prior to reaction.
3. Bimanes are almost nonfluorescent until reacted with thiols. For monobromobimane conjugated to glutathione, Abs = 394 nm, Em = 490 nm (QY ~0.1–0.3) in pH 8 buffer (Methods Enzymol 143, 76 (1987); Methods Enzymol 251, 133 (1995)).
4. D8451 reaction product with thiols has Abs = 410 nm (EC = 14,000 $cm^{-1}M^{-1}$) (Methods Enzymol 233, 380 (1994)).
5. The absorption and fluorescence spectra of BODIPY® derivatives are relatively insensitive to the solvent.
6. After conjugation of S1531 the degree of substitution can be determined by measuring the amount of 2-pyridinethione formed by treatment with DTT (D1532) or TCEP (T2556) from its absorbance at 343 nm (EC = 8000 $cm^{-1}M^{-1}$) (Biochem J 173, 723 (1978)).
7. Aqueous stock solutions should be used within 24 hours; long-term storage is NOT recommended.

Product List — 5.2 Chemical Crosslinking Reagents

Cat #	Product Name	Unit Size
A1642	2-acetamido-4-mercaptobutanoic acid hydrazide (AMBH)	100 mg
A685	5-((2-(and-3)-*S*-(acetylmercapto)succinoyl)amino)fluorescein (SAMSA fluorescein) *mixed isomers*	25 mg
A20770	6-((acryloyl)amino)hexanoic acid, succinimidyl ester (acryloyl-X, SE)	5 mg
B1616	*N*-((6-(biotinoyl)amino)hexanoyl)-1,2-dihexadecanoyl-*sn*-glycero-3-phosphoethanolamine, triethylammonium salt (biotin-X DHPE)	5 mg
B1550	*N*-(biotinoyl)-1,2-dihexadecanoyl-*sn*-glycero-3-phosphoethanolamine, triethylammonium salt (biotin DHPE)	10 mg
B10621	bis-((*N*-iodoacetyl)piperazinyl)sulfonerhodamine	5 mg
D1379	dibromobimane (bBBr)	25 mg
D10620	4,4-difluoro-3,5-di(iodoacetamidomethyl)-4-bora-3a,4a-diaza-*s*-indacene (BODIPY® FL bis-(methyleneiodoacetamide))	5 mg
D8451	5,5′-dithiobis-(2-nitrobenzoic acid) (DTNB; Ellman's reagent)	10 g
D1532	dithiothreitol (DTT)	1 g
E2247	1-ethyl-3-(3-dimethylaminopropyl)carbodiimide, hydrochloride (EDAC)	100 mg
H2249	*N*-hydroxysulfosuccinimide, sodium salt (NHSS)	100 mg
M1618	*N*-((4-maleimidylmethyl)cyclohexane-1-carbonyl)-1,2-dihexadecanoyl-*sn*-glycero-3-phosphoethanolamine, triethylammonium salt (MMCC DHPE)	5 mg
P6305	Protein-Protein Crosslinking Kit *3 conjugations*	1 kit
P1619MP	*N*-((2-pyridyldithio)propionyl)-1,2-dihexadecanoyl-*sn*-glycero-3-phosphoethanolamine, triethylammonium salt (PDP DHPE)	5 mg
S1553	succinimidyl acetylthioacetate (SATA)	100 mg
S1534	succinimidyl *trans*-4-(maleimidylmethyl)cyclohexane-1-carboxylate (SMCC)	100 mg
S1531	succinimidyl 3-(2-pyridyldithio)propionate (SPDP)	100 mg
T6060	Thiol and Sulfide Quantitation Kit *50-250 assays*	1 kit
T2556	tris-(2-carboxyethyl)phosphine, hydrochloride (TCEP)	1 g
T6052	tris-(2-cyanoethyl)phosphine	1 g
T30875	TS-Link™ TFP-X thiosulfate, sodium salt	5 mg

For current prices or to order online, visit probes.invitrogen.com

5.3 Photoactivatable Reagents, Including Photoreactive Crosslinkers and Caged Probes

This section describes two types of photoactivatable probes: products that form short-lived, high-energy intermediates that can chemically couple to nearby residues, and "caged" probes that are designed to be biologically inactive until UV light–mediated photolysis releases a natural product. Photolysis of each of these photoactivatable probes can be accomplished with high spatial and temporal resolution.

Nonfluorescent Photoreactive Crosslinking Reagents

In contrast to chemical crosslinking reagents (Section 5.2), which are often used to prepare bioconjugates, photoreactive crosslinking reagents are important tools for determining the proximity of two sites. Thus, these probes can be employed to define relationships between two reactive groups on a protein, on a ligand and its receptor or on separate biomolecules within an assembly. In the lattermost case, photoreactive crosslinking reagents can potentially reveal interactions among proteins, nucleic acids and membranes in live cells. The general scheme for defining spatial relationships usually involves photoreactive crosslinking reagents that contain a chemically reactive group as well as a photoreactive group. These crosslinkers are first chemically reacted with one molecule, for example a receptor ligand, and then this modified molecule is coupled to a second molecule, for example the ligand's receptor, using UV illumination. Depending on the reactive properties of the chemical and photoreactive groups, these crosslinkers can be used to couple like or unlike functional groups.

Molecular Probes offers three types of photoreactive reagents for covalent labeling:

- Simple aryl azides that upon illumination (usually at <360 nm) generate reactive intermediates that form bonds with nucleophilic groups (Figure 5.12)
- Fluorinated aryl azides that upon UV photolysis generate reactive nitrenes, thereby producing more C–H insertion products than the simple aryl azides (Figure 5.13)
- Benzophenone derivatives that can be repeatedly excited at <360 nm until they generate covalent adducts, without loss of reactivity (Figure 5.14)

Simple Aryl Azide Crosslinker

The "transferable" aryl azide *N*-((2-pyridyldithio)ethyl)-4-azidosalicylamide (PEAS, P6317; Figure 5.15) is a unique reagent for assessing protein–protein or protein–nucleic acid interactions. This aryl azide undergoes disulfide–thiol interchange of its pyridyldisulfide groups with the thiol groups of biomolecules to form mixed disulfides in the same way as SPDP [1] (S1531, Section 5.2). UV photolysis induces covalent crosslinking to residues or biomolecules adjacent to the crosslinker. The mixed disulfide can then be cleaved with DTT or TCEP (D1532, T2556; Section 5.2). If the phenolic PEAS reagent is radioiodinated before the coupling and photolysis steps, then only the resulting target biomolecule will be radioactive at the conclusion of the reaction.

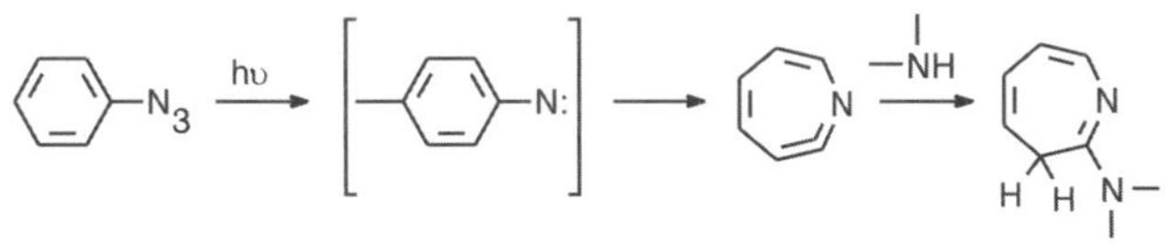

Figure 5.12 Photoreactive crosslinking reaction of a simple aryl azide.

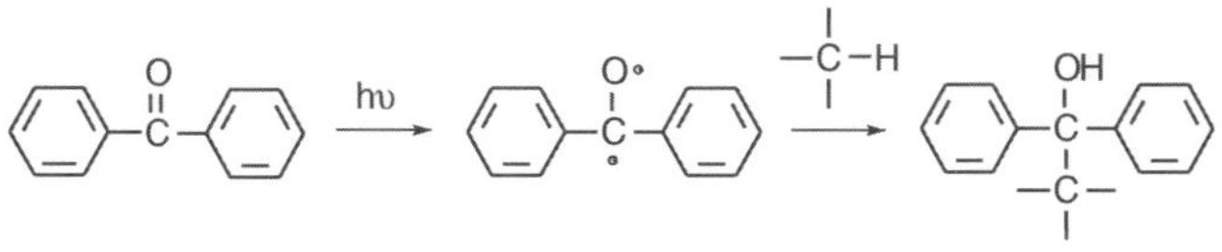

Figure 5.14 Photoreactive crosslinking reaction of a benzophenone derivative.

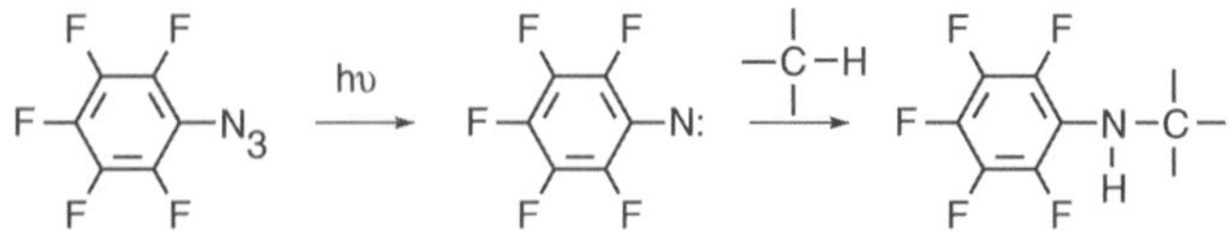

Figure 5.13 Photoreactive crosslinking reaction of a fluorinated aryl azide.

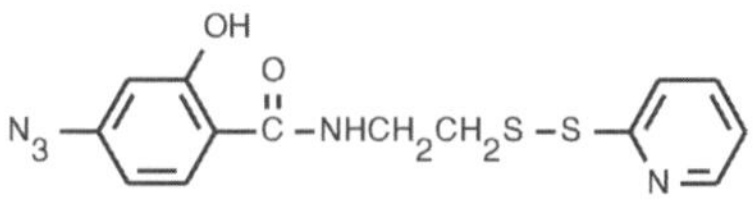

Figure 5.15 P6317 *N*-((2-pyridyldithio)ethyl)-4-azidosalicylamide (PEAS; AET).

Fluorinated Aryl Azides: True Nitrene-Generating Reagents

Although the simple aryl azides may be initially photolyzed to electron-deficient aryl nitrenes, it has been shown that these rapidly ring-expand to form dehydroazepines — molecules that tend to react with nucleophiles rather than form C–H insertion products.[2,3] In contrast, Keana and Cai have shown that the photolysis products of the fluorinated aryl azides are clearly aryl nitrenes[4] and undergo characteristic nitrene reactions such as C–H bond insertion with high efficiency. Moreover, conjugates prepared from the amine-reactive succinimidyl ester (A2522) or the more water-soluble STP ester (A10661) of 4-azido-2,3,5,6-tetrafluorobenzoic acid may have quantum yields for formation of photocrosslinked products that are superior to those of the nonfluorinated aryl azides. An important application of these reactive derivatives of 4-azido-2,3,5,6-tetrafluorobenzoic acid is the photofunctionalization of polymer surfaces[5,6] (Figure 5.16). 4-Azido-2,3,5,6-tetrafluorobenzyl amine (A10662) is a useful building block for other fluorinated photoreactive reagents.

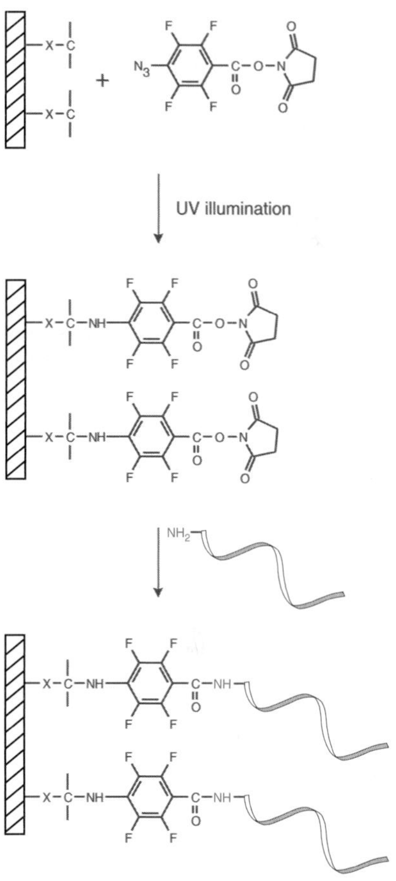

Figure 5.16 Schematic showing attachment of an amine-modified oligonucleotide to a surface using the photoreactive crosslinking reagent 4-azido-2,3,5,6-tetrafluorobenzoic acid, succinimidyl ester (ATFB, SE; A2522).

Benzophenone-Based Photoreactive Reagents

Benzophenones generally have higher crosslinking yields than the aryl azide photoreactive reagents.[7] Benzophenone maleimide (B1508) has been used for efficient irreversible protein crosslinking of actin,[8] calmodulin,[9,10] myosin,[11,12] tropomyosin,[13] troponin,[14–17] ATP synthase[18,19] and other proteins. The succinimidyl ester of 4-benzoylbenzoic acid (B1577) and benzophenone isothiocyanate (B1526) have proven useful for synthesizing photoreactive peptides[20–23] and oligonucleotides.[24,25] Benzophenone-labeled ATP and GTP probes are described below.

Other Photoreactive Reagents

Ethidium Monoazide for Photoreactive Fluorescent Labeling of Nucleic Acids

Ethidium monoazide (E1374) can be photolyzed in the presence of DNA or RNA to yield fluorescently labeled nucleic acids, both in solution and in cells.[26–29] The efficiency of the irreversible photolytic coupling of ethidium monoazide, which intercalates into nucleic acids like ethidium bromide, is unusually high[30] (>40%). Photolabeling of DNA can be used to follow its transport,[31] phase transitions[32] and diffusion.[33] In addition to its utility for studying DNA dynamics, the membrane-impermeant ethidium monoazide is reported to label only those cells with compromised membranes and can therefore serve as a fixable cell viability probe. A mixed population of live and dead cells labeled with this reagent retains its staining pattern after aldehyde-based fixation,[34,35] thereby reducing the investigator's exposure to potentially pathogenic cells during cell viability analysis. Also, leukocyte phagocytosis was investigated by flow cytometry using ethidium monoazide–labeled *Candida albicans.*[36] Multiphoton-targeted photochemistry of vertebrate cells labeled with ethidium monoazide was used to selectively inactivate gene expression.[37] Photolyzed ethidium monoazide is reported to activate topoisomerase II–mediated single- and double-stranded DNA cleavage.[38]

Bimane Azide for Photoaffinity Labeling of Proteins

Bimane azide (B30600) is a small blue-fluorescent photoreactive alkyl azide (excitation/emission maxima ~375/458 nm) for photoaffinity labeling of proteins, potentially including membrane proteins from within the membrane. This reactive fluorophore's small size may reduce the likelihood that the label will interfere with the function of the biomolecule, an important advantage for site-selective probes.

Photoreactive ATP and GTP Derivatives for Labeling Nucleotide-Binding Proteins

Functional ion channels can be assembled from both homomeric and heteromeric combinations of the seven P2X receptor subunits so far identified ($P2X_{1-7}$). Due to the lack of specific agonists or antagonists for P2X receptors, it is difficult to determine which receptor subtypes mediate particular cellular responses. One of the most potent and widely used P2X receptor agonists,

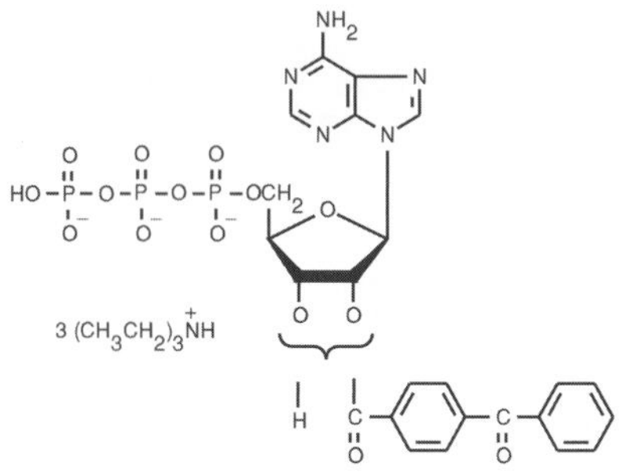

Figure 5.17 B22358 2′-(or-3′)-*O*-(4-benzoylbenzoyl)-adenosine 5′-triphosphate, tris(triethylammonium) salt (BzBzATP).

BzBzATP (2′-(or 3′-)*O*-(4-benzoylbenzoyl)adenosine 5′-triphosphate, B22358; Figure 5.17), is available from Molecular Probes,[39–42] along with the corresponding GTP derivative (B22357). Both BzBzATP and BzBzGTP have more general applications for site-directed irreversible modification of nucleotide-binding proteins via photoaffinity labeling.[43,44]

Caged Probes and Their Photolysis

Flash photolysis of photoactivatable or "caged" probes provides a means of controlling the release — both spatially and temporally — of biologically active products or other reagents of interest.[45–51] The chemical caging process may also confer membrane permeability on the caged ligand, as is the case for caged cAMP[52] and caged luciferin.[53] Molecular Probes' extensive selection of caged nucleotides, chelators, second messengers (Figure 5.2) and neurotransmitters has tremendous potential for use with both live cells and isolated proteins.

The caging moiety (Table 5.2) is designed to *maximally* interfere with the binding or activity of the molecule. It is detached in microseconds to milliseconds by flash photolysis at ≤360 nm, resulting in a pulse of the active product. Uncaging can easily be accomplished with UV illumination in the fluorescence microscope or with a UV laser or UV flashlamp. The availability of low-cost UV lasers[54] and UV flashlamps[55] should facilitate photolysis experiments in many laboratories (Table 5.3). A high-resolution, confocal laser-scanning microscope and flash photolysis system for physiological studies has been described.[56] The effects of photolytic release are frequently monitored either with fluorescent probes that measure calcium, pH, other ions or membrane potential, or with electrophysiological techniques.

To date, most of the caged reagents described in the literature have been derivatives of *o*-nitrobenzylic compounds. The nitrobenzyl group is synthetically incorporated into the biologically active molecule by linkage to a heteroatom (usually *O*, *S* or *N*) as an ether, thioether, ester (including phosphate or thiophosphate esters), amine or similar functional group. Both the structure of the nitrobenzylic compound and the atom to which it is attached affect the efficiency and wavelength required for uncaging. We currently use six different photolabile protecting groups in our caged probes.[47] Their properties are summarized in Table 5.2.

Table 5.2 — Properties of six different caging groups

Probe	Uncaging Rate *	Photolysis Quantum Yield *	Inertness of Photolysis By-product	Confers Water Solubility	Long-Wavelength Absorption (≥360 nm)
CNB	++++	+++++	+++++	+++++	++
NPE	+++	+++	+++	+	++
DMNB	+++	+++	++	+	+++++
DMNPE	+++	+++	+++	+	+++++
CMNB	+++	+++	+	++++	+++
CMNCBZ	++	+++	+	++++	+++

+++++ = Optimal response. + = Poor response. * Both the structure of the nitrobenzyl moiety and the atom to which it is attached have some effect on the efficiency and wavelength required for uncaging.

Table 5.3 — Suppliers of instrumentation for photolysis of caged compounds

Company	Location	Web Site
Cairn Research Ltd.	Faversham, UK	www.cairnweb.com/
Intracellular Imaging, Inc.	Cincinnati, OH, USA	www.intracellular.com/
Fryer Company, Inc.	Huntley, IL, USA	www.fryerco.com/prairie/
Hi-Tech Scientific	Salisbury, UK	www.hi-techsci.co.uk/
Photonic Instruments, Inc.	Arlington Heights, IL, USA	www.photonic-instruments.com/
Prairie Technologies, LLC	Middleton, WI, USA	www.prairie-technologies.com/
Rapp OptoElectronic	Hamburg, Germany	www.rapp-opto.com/
T.I.L.L. Photonics	Martinsried, Germany	www.till-photonics.com/

- Probes caged with our patented α-carboxy-2-nitrobenzyl (CNB) caging group generally have the most advantageous properties. These include good water solubility, very fast uncaging rates in the microsecond range, high photolysis quantum yields (from 0.2–0.4) and biologically inert photolytic by-products. Although the absorption maximum of the CNB caging group is near 260 nm, its absorption spectrum tails out to approximately 360 nm, allowing successful photolysis using light with wavelengths ≤360 nm.
- The 1-(2-nitrophenyl)ethyl (NPE) caging group has properties similar to those of CNB and can also be photolyzed at ≤360 nm.
- As compared with CNB and NPE, the 4,5-dimethoxy-2-nitrobenzyl (DMNB) and 1-(4,5-dimethoxy-2-nitrophenyl)ethyl (DMNPE) caging groups have longer-wavelength absorption (absorption maximum ~355 nm) and therefore absorb 340–360 nm light more efficiently. However, photolysis rates and quantum yields of DMNB- and DMNPE-caged probes are generally lower than those obtained for CNB-caged probes.
- The 5-carboxymethoxy-2-nitrobenzyl (CMNB) and ((5-carboxymethoxy-2-nitrobenzyl)-oxy)carbonyl (CMNCBZ) caging groups provide an absorption maximum of intermediate wavelength (absorption maximum ~310 nm), while imparting significant water solubility to the caged probe. Their photolysis rate and quantum yield are intermediate between those of CNB- and DMNB-caged probes.

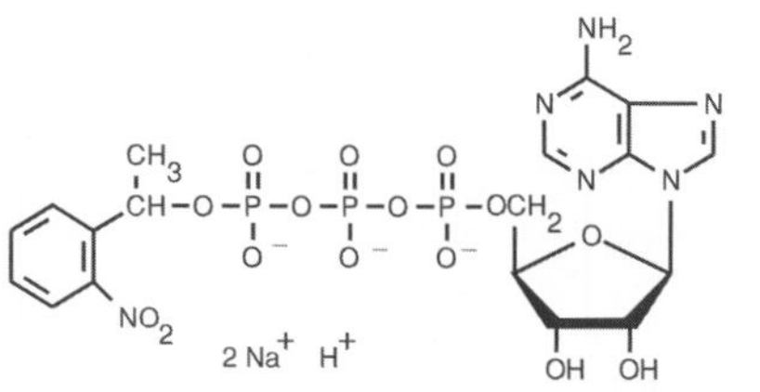

Figure 5.18 A1048 adenosine 5′-triphosphate, P^3-(1-(2-nitrophenyl)ethyl) ester, disodium salt (NPE-caged ATP).

Experiments utilizing probes caged with any of the above caging groups, except the CNB caging group, may require the addition of dithiothreitol (DTT, D1532; Section 2.1). This reducing reagent prevents the potentially cytotoxic reaction between amines and the 2-nitrosobenzoyl photolytic by-products.[57]

Molecular Probes' caged probes provide researchers with important tools for delivering physiological stimuli by naturally active biomolecules with spatial and temporal precision that far exceeds that of microinjection or perfusion. Caged dyes can also serve as tracers with fluorescence that can be "turned on" by brief exposure to ultraviolet light.

Caged Nucleotides and Caged Phosphates

Photoactivatable nucleotides and phosphates have contributed significantly to our understanding of cytoskeleton dynamics, signal transduction pathways and other critical cellular processes.[49] Some of our caged nucleotides are available with a choice of caging group:

- Caged ATP (A1048, Figure 5.18; A1049), which has been shown to release ATP in skinned muscle fibers,[58–60] sarcoplasmic reticulum vesicles,[61] submitochondrial particles[62] and membrane fragments containing Na^+/K^+-ATPase[63]
- Caged ADP (A7056), which has been used to investigate the molecular basis of contraction of skeletal muscle fibers,[64] as well as transport by an ADP/ATP carrier[65]
- Caged cAMP (D1037), which is cell-permeant and rapidly photolyzed to cAMP[52,66,67]
- Caged GTP-γ-*S* (G1053), a probe for studying regulatory proteins such as G-proteins[57,68,69]
- Caged inositol 1,4,5-triphosphate[70–73] (I23580) and caged cADP-ribose[74,75] (C7074, (Section 17.2)) — important probes for second messenger studies
- Caged phosphate[76–79] (N7065), which can be used to produce a pulse of phosphate and to generate a photolysis-dependent proton release that results in a rapid drop in pH

Caged Ca^{2+}, Caged Ca^{2+} Chelators and Caged Ionophores

Caged ions and caged chelators can be used to influence the ionic composition of both solutions and cells, particularly for ions such as Ca^{2+} that are present at low concentrations under normal physiological conditions.

Caged Ca^{2+} Reagents

Developed by Ellis-Davies and Kaplan,[80] nitrophenyl EGTA (NP-EGTA) is a photolabile Ca^{2+} chelator that exhibits a high selectivity for Ca^{2+} ions, a dramatic increase in its K_d for Ca^{2+} upon illumination (from 80 nM to 1 mM) and a high photolysis quantum yield (0.23). NP-EGTA's affinity for Ca^{2+} *decreases* ~12,500-fold upon photolysis. Furthermore, its K_d for Mg^{2+} of 9 mM makes NP-EGTA essentially insensitive to physiological Mg^{2+} concentrations. We exclusively

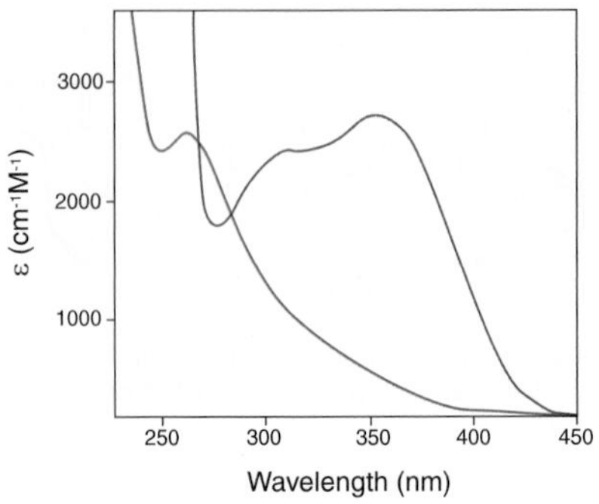

Figure 5.19 Spectral comparison of equimolar concentrations of the caged Ca^{2+} reagents NP-EGTA (N6802, red line) and DMNP-EDTA (D6814, blue line), illustrating the optimal wavelengths for photolysis and subsequent release of Ca^{2+} from these chelators. Spectra were taken in 100 mM KCl and 30 mM MOPS buffer containing 39.8 µM free Ca^{2+} at pH 7.2.

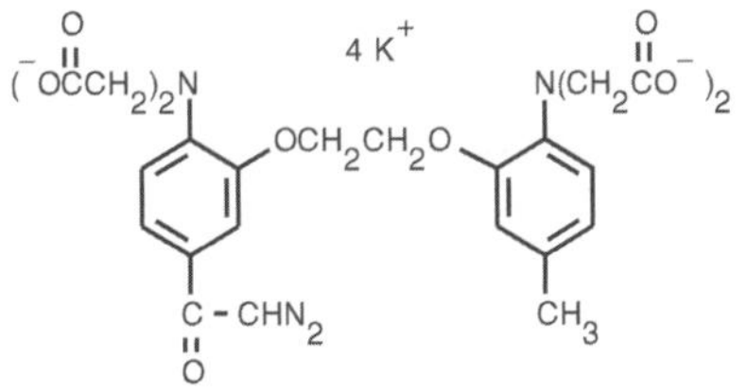

Figure 5.20 D3034 diazo-2, tetrapotassium salt.

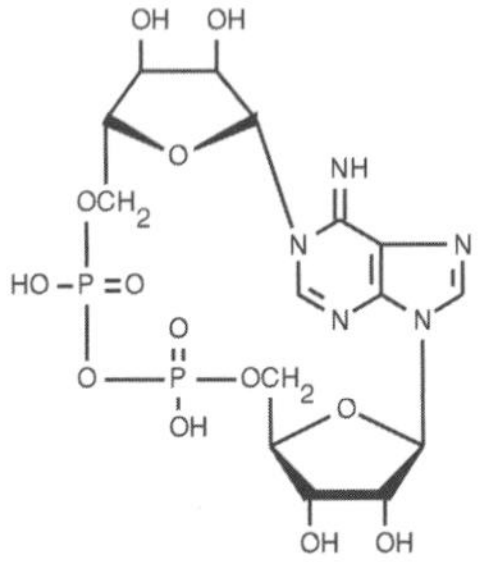

Figure 5.21 C7619 cyclic adenosine 5′-diphosphate ribose (cADP-ribose).

offer the tetrapotassium salt (N6802) and the acetoxymethyl (AM) ester (N6803) of NP-EGTA. The NP-EGTA salt can be complexed with Ca^{2+} to generate a caged Ca^{2+} reagent that will rapidly deliver Ca^{2+} upon photolysis [73,81,82] (Figure 17.4). The cell-permeant AM ester of NP-EGTA does not bind Ca^{2+} unless its AM ester groups are removed. This AM ester can serve as a photolabile chelator in cells because, once converted to NP-EGTA by intracellular esterases, it will bind free Ca^{2+} until photolyzed with UV light.

The first caged Ca^{2+} reagent described by Kaplan and Ellis-Davies was 1-(4,5-dimethoxy-2-nitrophenyl) EDTA (DMNP-EDTA, D6814), which they named DM-Nitrophen [83,84] (now a trademark of Calbiochem-Novabiochem Corp.). Because its structure more resembles that of EDTA than EGTA, we named it as a caged EDTA derivative (Figure 17.5). Upon illumination, DMNP-EDTA's affinity for Ca^{2+} *decreases* ~600,000-fold and its K_d for Ca^{2+} rises from 5 nM to 3 mM. Thus, photolysis of DMNP-EDTA complexed with Ca^{2+} results in a pulse of free Ca^{2+}. DMNP-EDTA has a stronger absorbance at longer wavelengths than does NP-EGTA (Figure 5.19), which facilitates uncaging. Furthermore, DMNP-EDTA has significantly higher affinity for Mg^{2+} (K_d = 2.5 µM) [83] than does NP-EGTA (K_d = 9 mM),[80] making it a potentially useful caged Mg^{2+} reagent. A paper by Neher and Zucker discusses the uses and limitations of DMNP-EDTA.[85] In addition to high-purity DMNP-EDTA (D6814), we have prepared its cell-permeant AM ester (D6815).

Caged Ca^{2+} Chelator

In contrast to NP-EGTA and DMNP-EDTA, diazo-2 is a photoactivatable Ca^{2+} scavenger. Diazo-2, which was introduced by Adams, Kao and Tsien,[86] exhibits a low affinity for Ca^{2+} before photolysis (K_d = 2.2 µM) that *increases* by a factor of 30 upon exposure to UV light. Diazo-2 can be microinjected as its K^+ salt (D3034, Figure 5.20) or loaded into cells as the AM ester (D3036). Upon illumination near 360 nm, the photolyzed diazo-2 binds cytosolic free Ca^{2+} within a few milliseconds. Diazo-2 has been used to rapidly decrease cytosolic Ca^{2+} in tensed frog muscle cells [87] and in rat fibroblasts.[86]

Caged 4-Bromo A-23187

We have introduced a unique tool for the study of Ca^{2+} regulation and ion transport. Our patented cell-permeant DMNPE-caged ionophore derived from 4-bromo A-23187 (B7108) can be passively loaded into cells and, at a later time, photoactivated with a UV laser or UV flashlamp to stimulate ion movement across the plasma membrane or to liberate Ca^{2+} from intracellular stores.

Caged Second Messengers

Caged Inositol 1,4,5-Triphosphate

NPE-caged Ins 1,4,5-P_3 can be used to generate rapid and precisely controlled release of Ins 1,4,5-P_3 in intact cells (Figure 5.2) and is widely employed in studies of Ins 1,4,5-P_3–mediated second messenger pathways.[70–73] Our NPE-caged Ins 1,4,5-P_3 (I23580) is a mixture of the physiologically inert, singly esterified P^4 and P^5 esters (Figure 17.2) and does not contain the somewhat physiologically active P^1 ester. NPE-caged Ins 1,4,5-P_3 exhibits essentially no biological activity prior to photolytic release of the biologically active Ins 1,4,5-P_3 (I3716, Section 17.2).

Caged Cyclic ADP-Ribose

Cyclic ADP-ribose (cADP-ribose, C7619; Figure 5.21; Section 17.2) is a potent intracellular Ca^{2+}– mobilizing agent that likely functions as a second messenger in an Ins 1,4,5-P_3–independent pathway.[88–93] Our NPE-caged cADP-ribose (C7074, Figure 5.22) induces Ca^{2+} mobilization in sea urchin egg homogenates only after photolysis, and this Ca^{2+} release is inhibited by the specific cADP-ribose antagonist 8-amino-cADP-ribose [75] (A7621, Section 17.2). Furthermore, when microinjected into live sea urchin eggs, NPE-caged cADP-ribose was shown to mobilize Ca^{2+} and activate cortical exocytosis after illumination with a mercury-arc lamp.[75]

Caged Amino Acid Neurotransmitters

Once activated, caged amino acid neurotransmitters rapidly initiate neurotransmitter action (Figure 5.23), thus providing tools for kinetic studies of receptor binding or channel opening.[45,49] We offer caged carbamylcholine [94–102] (*N*-(CNB-caged) carbachol, C13654), caged γ-aminobutyric acid [73,103–105] (*O*-(CNB-caged) GABA, A7110) and caged *N*-methyl-D-aspartic acid [106,107] (β-(CNB-caged) NMDA, M7114), as well as two caged versions of L-glutamic acid [104,108–114] (C7122, G7055), all of which are biologically inactive before photolysis.[47]

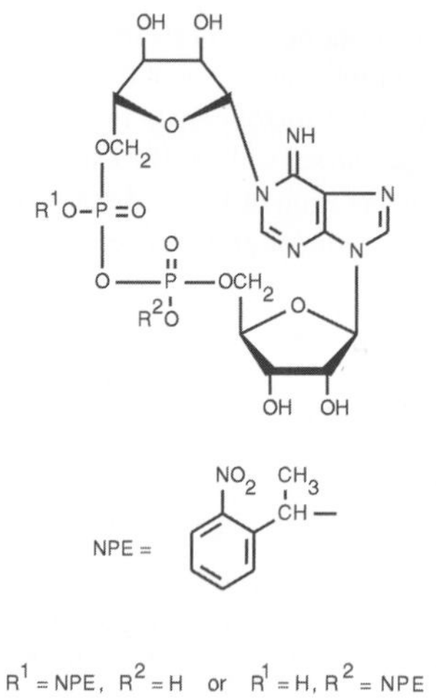

Figure 5.22 C7074 cyclic adenosine 5′-diphosphate ribose, 1-(1-(2-nitrophenyl)ethyl) ester (NPE-caged cADP-ribose).

Caged Luciferin

DMNPE-caged luciferin (L7085) readily crosses cell membranes, allowing more efficient delivery of luciferin into intact cells.[53] Once the caged luciferin is inside the cell, active luciferin can be released either instantaneously by a flash of UV light, or continuously by the action of endogenous intracellular esterases found in many cell types.

Caged Fluorescent Dyes

Photoactivatable fluorescent dyes may be one of the most useful developments in caged probe technology. In general, the caged fluorophores are colorless and nonfluorescent until photolyzed with UV light. Demonstrated and suggested applications include the study of fluid dynamics,[115–119] hydrodynamic properties of the cytoplasmic matrix, lateral diffusion in membranes and cell–cell communication. Photoactivatable fluorophores are particularly useful for investigating cell lineage because they can be injected early in development when the cells are large, and then later activated in the growing embryo when the cells of interest may be small and buried deep within the tissue.[120] Caged fluorescent dyes have also been conjugated to proteins to follow the assembly of tubulin,[121] microtubule flux [121–123] and the dynamic behavior of actin filaments.[124,125]

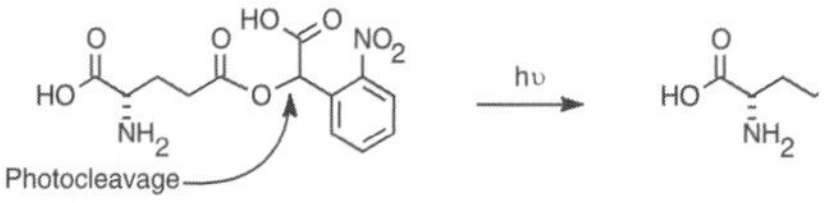

Figure 5.23 CNB-caged L-glutamic acid (G7055). The CNB-caging group is rapidly photocleaved with UV light to release L-glutamic acid.

Molecular Probes prepares a caged version of fluorescein [116,119,126,127] (F7103). We also offer a 10,000 MW dextran conjugate of DMNB-caged fluorescein [115,128,129] (D3310, Figure 5.24) and its lysine-fixable, biotinylated analog (D7146), as well as a 10,000 MW dextran conjugate of CMNCBZ-caged carboxy-Q-rhodamine (D34678) that exhibits orange fluorescence (excitation/emission maxima ~545/575 nm) after photolysis. Our caged fluorescein dextran has proven useful for analyzing regional cell movement and tissue patterning in zebrafish embryos [115] (Figure 5.24).

The succinimidyl ester of CMNB-caged carboxyfluorescein (C20050, Figure 1.59) can be used to attach the caged fluorophore to primary amine groups. The labeled probes can subsequently be photolyzed to green-fluorescent conjugates. Once photolyzed, the fluorescein dye is recognized by our anti-fluorescein/Oregon Green® antibodies (Section 7.4, Figure 7.74). This succinimidyl ester is reasonably water soluble above pH 6.

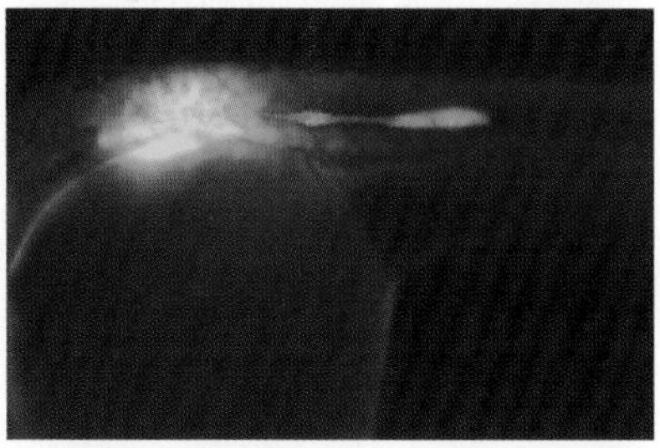

Figure 5.24 A zebrafish embryo that was injected with a 1% solution (in 0.2 M KCl) of DMNB-caged fluorescein 10,000 MW dextran (D3310) at the two-cell stage and then allowed to grow for 19 hours. The posterior lateral line placode was then exposed to a five-second pulse from an epifluorescence microscope fitted with a DAPI optical filter set. After six hours of further development, the labeled primordium has migrated caudally, away from the activation site. Image contributed by Walter K. Metcalfe, Institute of Neuroscience, University of Oregon.

Protein Conjugates of CMNB-Caged Fluorescein

The goat anti–mouse IgG antibody and goat anti–rabbit IgG antibody conjugates of CMNB-caged fluorescein (G21061, G21080) are unique reagents for labeling targets in cells and on arrays. Unlike directly fluorescent reagents, these caged secondary detection reagents allow determination of the background fluorescence prior to photolysis simply by exciting the sample through optical bandpass filters typically used for fluorescein (Table 23.9). Photoactivation of the CMNB-caged fluorescein conjugates by brief UV light illumination results in a large increase in the visible fluorescence, with the optical characteristics typical of fluorescein. Using digital imaging technology, researchers can detect probe binding to the target by determining in which pixels the fluorescence increased upon illumination (Figure 7.74). We have utilized this procedure as part of a scheme to simultaneously or sequentially measure multiple signals from fluorophores that have strong spectral overlap.

Kit for Caging Carboxylic Acid

Using organic synthesis methods, researchers can cage a diverse array of molecules. One of the preferred caging groups is the 1-(4,5-dimethoxy-2-nitrophenyl)ethyl (DMNPE) ester. Because the diazoethane precursor to DMNPE esters is unstable, we offer a kit (D2516) for the generation of 1-(4,5-dimethoxy-2-nitrophenyl)diazoethane and the subsequent preparation of DMNPE esters. This kit includes:

- 25 mg of the hydrazone precursor
- MnO_2 for oxidation
- Celite for filtration of the reaction mixture
- A detailed protocol for caging carboxylic acids

A wide range of compounds containing a weak oxy acid (with a pK_a between 3 and 7), including carboxylic acids, phenols and phosphates, should react with the diazoethane to form the DMNPE-caged analogs[57] (Figure 5.25).

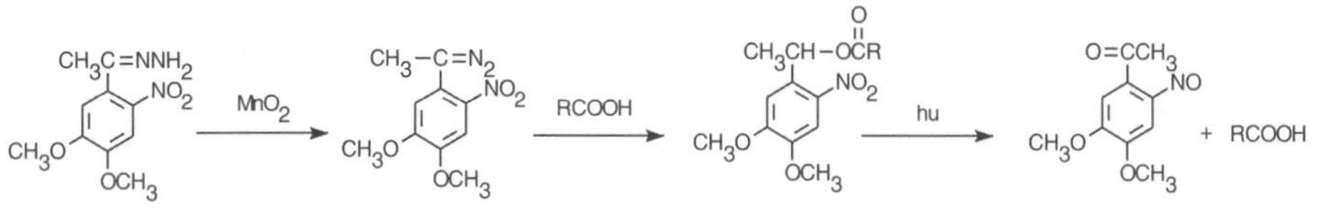

Figure 5.25 Caging of a carboxylic acid using the hydrazone precursor of DMNPE, a reagent that is provided in Molecular Probes' 1-(4,5-Dimethoxy-2-nitrophenyl)diazoethane Generation Kit (D2516).

References

1. Bioconjug Chem 7, 380 (1996); **2.** Annu Rev Biochem 62, 483 (1993); **3.** Adv Photochem 17, 69 (1992); **4.** J Org Chem 55, 3640 (1990); **5.** Bioconjug Chem 5, 151 (1994); **6.** J Am Chem Soc 115, 814 (1993); **7.** Biochemistry 33, 5661 (1994); **8.** Arch Biochem Biophys 240, 627 (1985); **9.** Biochemistry 33, 518 (1994); **10.** J Biol Chem 263, 542 (1988); **11.** Arch Biochem Biophys 288, 584 (1991); **12.** J Biol Chem 266, 2272 (1991); **13.** Biochemistry 25, 7633 (1986); **14.** J Muscle Res Cell Motil 19, 479 (1998); **15.** Biochemistry 35, 11026 (1996); **16.** Science 247, 1339 (1990); **17.** Biochemistry 26, 7042 (1987); **18.** J Biol Chem 273, 15162 (1998); **19.** J Biol Chem 271, 28341 (1996); **20.** J Virol 38, 840 (1981); **21.** J Protein Chem 3, 479 (1985); **22.** Proc Natl Acad Sci U S A 83, 483 (1986); **23.** Biochemistry 32, 2741 (1993); **24.** Nucleic Acids Res 26, 1421 (1998); **25.** Bioconjug Chem 10, 56 (1999); **26.** Biochemistry 30, 5644 (1991); **27.** Photochem Photobiol 43, 7 (1986); **28.** J Biol Chem 259, 11090 (1984); **29.** Photochem Photobiol 36, 31 (1982); **30.** Biochemistry 20, 1887 (1981); **31.** J Biol Chem 269, 4910 (1994); **32.** Biochemistry 30, 10931 (1991); **33.** Macromolecules 22, 4550 (1989); **34.** Cytometry 19, 243 (1995); **35.** Cytometry 12, 133 (1991); **36.** Cytometry 11, 610 (1990); **37.** Proc Natl Acad Sci U S A 97, 9504 (2000); **38.** Biochemistry 36, 15884 (1997); **39.** Biochemistry 26, 7524 (1987); **40.** Proc Natl Acad Sci U S A 90, 10449 (1993); **41.** J Physiol 519 Pt 3, 723 (1999); **42.** Mol Pharmacol 56, 1171 (1999); **43.** J Neurochem 61, 1657 (1993); **44.** Biochemistry 28, 3989 (1989); **45.** Photochem Photobiol Sci 1, 441 (2002); **46.** Methods Enzymol 291, 63 (1998); **47.** Methods Enzymol 291, 30 (1998); **48.** Curr Opin Neurobiol 6, 379 (1996); **49.** Biological Applications of Photochemical Switches, Morrison H, Ed. pp. 243–305 (1993); **50.** Optical Microscopy: Emerging Methods and Applications, Herman B, Lemasters JJ, Eds. pp. 27–85 (1993); **51.** Annu Rev Physiol 55, 755 (1993); **52.** Nature 310, 74 (1984); **53.** Biotechniques 15, 848 (1993); **54.** J Neurosci Methods 66, 47 (1996); **55.** Pflugers Arch 411, 200 (1988); **56.** Cell Calcium 21, 441 (1997); **57.** Annu Rev Biophys Biophys Chem 18, 239 (1989); **58.** Biophys J 67, 2436 (1994); **59.** Annu Rev Physiol 52, 875 (1990); **60.** Annu Rev Physiol 52, 857 (1990); **61.** Biochim Biophys Acta 1104, 207 (1992); **62.** J Biol Chem 268, 25320 (1993); **63.** Biochim Biophys Acta 939, 197 (1988); **64.** J Mol Biol 223, 185 (1992); **65.** Biochemistry 36, 13865 (1997); **66.** Proc Natl Acad Sci U S A 98, 10481 (2001); **67.** J Membr Biol 159, 53 (1997); **68.** Am J Physiol 261, H1665 (1991); **69.** Pflugers Arch 411, 628 (1988); **70.** J Neurosci Methods 132, 81 (2004); **71.** Biotechniques 23, 268 (1997); **72.** J Physiol 487, 343 (1995); **73.** Neuron 15, 755 (1995); **74.** Methods Enzymol 291, 403 (1998); **75.** J Biol Chem 270, 7745 (1995); **76.** FEBS Lett 405, 81 (1997); **77.** J Physiol 451, 247 (1992); **78.** Biophys J 72, 1780 (1997); **79.** J Mol Biol 184, 645 (1985); **80.** Proc Natl Acad Sci U S A 91, 187 (1994); **81.** J Biol Chem 270, 23966 (1995); **82.** Science 267, 1997 (1995); **83.** Proc Natl Acad Sci U S A 85, 6571 (1988); **84.** Science 241, 842 (1988); **85.** Neuron 10, 21 (1993); **86.** J Am Chem Soc 111, 7957 (1989); **87.** FEBS Lett 255, 196 (1989); **88.** Cell Calcium 22, 11 (1997); **89.** Physiol Rev 77, 1133 (1997); **90.** Biochem J 315, 721 (1996); **91.** EMBO J 13, 2038 (1994); **92.** Mol Cell Biochem 138, 229 (1994); **93.** Science 259, 370 (1993); **94.** Proc Natl Acad Sci U S A 93, 12964 (1996); **95.** J Neurosci Methods 54, 151 (1994); **96.** Proc Natl Acad Sci U S A 91, 6629 (1994); **97.** Biochemistry 32, 3831 (1993); **98.** Biochemistry 32, 989 (1993); **99.** Biochemistry 31, 5507 (1992); **100.** Adv Exp Med Biol 287, 75 (1991); **101.** Biochemistry 28, 49 (1989); **102.** Biochemistry 25, 1799 (1986); **103.** J Org Chem 55, 1585 (1990); **104.** J Org Chem 61, 1228 (1996); **105.** J Am Chem Soc 116, 8366 (1994); **106.** Biochemistry 38, 3140 (1999); **107.** J Org Chem 60, 4260 (1995); **108.** Neuroscience 86, 265 (1998); **109.** Science 279, 1203 (1998); **110.** Proc Natl Acad Sci U S A 91, 8752 (1994); **111.** Abstr Soc Neurosci 21, 579, abstract #238.11 (1995); **112.** J Neurosci Methods 54, 205 (1994); **113.** Science 265, 255 (1994); **114.** Proc Natl Acad Sci U S A 90, 7661 (1993); **115.** Anal Chem 70, 2459 (1998); **116.** Phys Fluids 9, 717 (1997); **117.** AIAA Journal 34, 449 (1996); **118.** Exp Fluids 18, 249 (1995); **119.** Proc SPIE-Int Soc Opt Eng 2546, 160 (1995); **120.** Cell 68, 923 (1992); **121.** J Cell Biol 109, 637 (1989); **122.** J Cell Biol 126, 1455 (1994); **123.** J Cell Biol 120, 1177 (1993); **124.** J Cell Biol 122, 833 (1993); **125.** Nature 352, 126 (1991); **126.** Anal Chem 75, 1387 (2003); **127.** Exp Fluids 21, 237 (1996); **128.** Biochem Cell Biol 75, 551 (1997); **129.** Science 272, 716 (1996).

Data Table — 5.3 Photoactivatable Reagents, Including Photoreactive Crosslinkers and Caged Probes

Cat #	MW	Storage	Soluble	Abs	EC	Em	Solvent	Notes
A1048	700.30	FF,D,LL	H_2O	259	18,000	none	MeOH	1, 2, 3
A1049	760.35	FF,D,LL	H_2O	351	4,400	none	H_2O	1, 2
A1506	300.36	F,LL	DMF, MeCN	265	32,000	none	MeOH	3
A2521	235.10	F,LL	MeOH	258	17,000	none	MeOH	3
A2522	332.17	F,D,LL	DMF	273	23,000	none	EtOH	3
A6310	267.69	F,DD,LL	DMF	338	7,500	none	MeOH	4, 5
A6311	449.40	F,D,LL	DMSO	256	20,000	none	MeOH	3
A7056	614.44	FF,D,LL	H_2O	259	15,000	none	MeOH	1, 2, 3
A7109	732.83	FF,D,LL	DMSO, EtOH	370	10,000	none	MeOH	2
A7110	396.28	F,D,LL	H_2O	262	4,500	none	pH 7	2, 3
A10661	485.20	F,D,LL	H_2O	273	27,000	none	MeOH	3, 6

Cat #	MW	Storage	Soluble	Abs	EC	Em	Solvent	Notes
A10662	256.59	F,LL	DMF	250	17,000	none	MeOH	3
B1508	277.28	F,D	DMF, MeCN	260	17,000	none	MeOH	3, 7
B1526	239.29	F,DD	DMF, MeCN	300	26,000	none	MeOH	3
B1577	323.30	F,D	DMF, MeCN	256	27,000	none	MeOH	3
B7108	811.73	FF,D,LL	DMSO, EtOH	337	11,000	none	MeOH	2
B13650	619.42	F,D,LL	DMSO	262	6,600	none	pH 7	2, 3
B22357	1034.97	FF,L	H_2O	257	24,000	none	pH 7	3, 8, 9, 10
B22358	1018.97	FF,L	H_2O	260	27,000	none	pH 7	3, 8, 9, 10
B30600	233.23	F,D,L	DMSO	375	6,000	458	MeOH	
C7074	690.45	FF,D,LL	H_2O	259	16,000	none	H_2O	2, 3
C7122	326.26	F,D,LL	H_2O	266	4,800	none	pH 7	2, 3
C13654	439.34	F,D,LL	H_2O	264	4,200	none	H_2O	2, 3
C20050	962.79	F,D,LL	DMSO	289	9,500	none	MeOH	2, 11
D1037	524.38	F,D,LL	DMSO	338	6,100	none	MeOH	1, 2
D3034	710.86	F,D,LL	pH >6	369	18,000	none	pH 7.2	2, 12
D3036	846.75	F,D,LL	DMSO	342	22,000	none	MeOH	13
D3309	see Notes	F,D,LL	H_2O	353	ND	520	H_2O	2, 11, 14, 15
D3310	see Notes	F,D,LL	H_2O	353	ND	520	H_2O	2, 3, 14, 15
D3811	1541.81	FF,D,LL	see Notes	340	13,000	none	MeOH	2, 11, 16
D6814	473.39	D,LL	DMSO	348	4,200	none	pH 7.2	2, 17
D6815	761.65	F,D,LL	DMSO	333	4,600	none	MeOH	18, 19
D7060	719.55	FF,LL	H_2O, DMSO	402	24,000	none	H_2O	2, 20
D7146	see Notes	F,LL	H_2O	352	ND	519	H_2O	2, 11, 14, 15
D7147	see Notes	F,LL	H_2O	352	ND	521	H_2O	2, 11, 14, 15
D34678	see Notes	F,D,LL	H_2O	292	ND	none	H_2O	2, 14, 15, 21
E1374	420.31	F,LL	DMF, EtOH	462	5,400	625	pH 7	22
E3561	401.86	F,LL	pH 3	432	5,700	496	pH 3	23
F1501	182.11	F,D,LL	DMF, MeCN	244	17,000	none	EtOH	24
F7103	826.81	FF,D,LL	H_2O, DMSO	333	15,000	none	DMSO	2, 11, 25
G1053	799.54	FF,D,LL	H_2O	352	3,700	none	H_2O	1, 2
G2504	378.77	F,D,LL	H_2O	346	5,900	none	H_2O	2
G7055	440.29	F,D,LL	H_2O, DMSO	262	5,100	none	pH 7	2, 3
I23580	872.82	FF,D,LL	H_2O	264	4,200	none	H_2O	2, 3, 26
L7085	489.52	FF,D,LL	DMSO, DMF	334	22,000	none	MeOH	2, 27
M7114	440.29	F,D,LL	H_2O	264	5,100	none	pH 7	2, 3
M13652	517.37	F,D,LL	DMSO, MeOH	265	9,400	none	pH 7	2, 3
N6802	653.81	FF,D,LL	pH >6	260	3,500	none	pH 7.2	2, 3, 28
N6803	789.70	FF,D,LL	DMSO	250	4,200	none	MeCN	18, 29
N7065	281.20	F,D,LL	H_2O	259	5,700	none	MeOH	2, 3
P6317	347.41	F,D,LL	DMSO	271	24,000	none	MeOH	30
P7071	1089.97	D,L	pH 7	396	4,900	none	pH 7.4	2, 25, 31

For definitions of the contents of this data table, see "Navigating *The Handbook*" in the introductory pages.

Notes

1. Caged nucleotide esters are free of contaminating free nucleotides when initially prepared. However, some decomposition may occur during storage.
2. All photoactivatable probes are sensitive to light. They should be protected from illumination except when photolysis is intended.
3. This compound has weaker visible absorption at >300 nm but no discernible absorption peaks in this region.
4. Nonfluorescent until photolyzed. The photoproduct of A1156 has Abs = 350 nm and Em = 545 to 578 nm, depending on environment (Biochemistry 22, 3954 (1983)).
5. Do NOT dissolve in DMSO.
6. This sulfotetrafluorophenyl (STP) ester derivative is water-soluble and may be dissolved in buffer at ~pH 8 for reaction with amines. Long-term storage in water is NOT recommended due to hydrolysis.
7. Spectral data of the 2-mercaptoethanol adduct.
8. The molecular weight (MW) of this product is approximate because the degree of hydration and/or salt form has not been conclusively established.
9. This product is supplied as a ready-made solution in the solvent indicated under "Soluble."
10. This product can be activated by long-wavelength ultraviolet light (>300 nm) for photoaffinity labeling of proteins.
11. This product is colorless and nonfluorescent until it is activated by ultraviolet photolysis. Photoactivation generates a fluorescein derivative with spectral characteristics similar to C1359.
12. The Ca^{2+} dissociation constant of diazo-2 is 2200 nM before photolysis and 73 nM after ultraviolet photolysis. The absorption spectrum of the photolysis product is similar to that of B1204 (J Am Chem Soc 111, 7957 (1989)).
13. D3036 is converted to D3034 via hydrolysis of its acetoxymethyl ester (AM) groups.
14. The molecular weight is nominally as specified in the product name but may have a broad distribution.
15. ND = not determined.
16. Chloroform is the most generally useful solvent for preparing stock solutions of phospholipids (including sphingomyelins). Glycerophosphocholines are usually freely soluble in ethanol. Most other glycerophospholipids (phosphoethanolamines, phosphatidic acids and phosphoglycerols) are less soluble in ethanol, but solutions up to 1–2 mg/mL should be obtainable, using sonication to aid dispersion if necessary. Labeling of cells with fluorescent phospholipids can be enhanced by addition of cyclodextrins during incubation (J Biol Chem 274, 35359 (1999)).
17. $K_d(Ca^{2+})$ increases from 5 nM to 3 mM after ultraviolet photolysis. K_d values determined in 130 mM KCl, 10 mM HEPES, pH 7.1 (Proc Natl Acad Sci U S A 85, 6571 (1988)).
18. This product is intrinsically a liquid or an oil at room temperature.
19. D6815 is converted to D6814 via hydrolysis of its acetoxymethyl ester (AM) groups.
20. D7060 is converted to fluorescent HPTS (H348) upon ultraviolet photolysis.
21. This product is colorless and nonfluorescent until it is activated by ultraviolet photolysis. Photoactivation generates fluorescent carboxyrhodamine Q (Abs = 537 nm, Em = 556 nm).
22. E1374 spectral data are for the free dye. Fluorescence is weak, but intensity increases ~15-fold on binding to DNA. After photocrosslinking to DNA, Abs = 504 nm (EC ~4000 $cm^{-1}M^{-1}$), Em = 600 nm (Nucleic Acids Res 5, 4891 (1978); Biochemistry 19, 3221 (1980)).
23. E3561 spectral data are for the free dye. Fluorescence is weak and decreases in intensity on binding to DNA (Biochemistry 19, 3221 (1980)).
24. F1501 spectra are for the unreacted reagent. Much weaker absorption occurs at longer wavelengths (Abs ~450 nm, EC ~700 $cm^{-1}M^{-1}$). The reaction product with amines has Abs = 456 nm (EC = 5000 $cm^{-1}M^{-1}$) and is nonfluorescent.
25. Unstable in water. Use immediately.
26. Ultraviolet photolysis of I23580 generates I3716.

27. L7085 is converted to bioluminescent luciferin (L2911) upon ultraviolet photoactivation.
28. Kd (Ca^{2+}) increases from 80 nM to 1 mM after ultraviolet photolysis. K_d values determined in 100 mM KCl, 40 mM HEPES, pH 7.2 (Proc Natl Acad Sci U S A 91, 187 (1994)).
29. N6803 is converted to N6802 via hydrolysis of its acetoxymethyl ester (AM) groups.
30. The absorption spectrum of P6317 includes an additional shoulder at 306 nm (EC = 10,000 $cm^{-1}M^{-1}$).
31. Releases O_2 upon photolysis at 355 nm. Recommended solution pH for optimal stability is 7.4 (Proc Natl Acad Sci U S A 92, 8105 (1995)).

Product List — 5.3 Photoactivatable Reagents, Including Photoreactive Crosslinkers and Caged Probes

Cat #	Product Name	Unit Size
A7109	A-23187, 1-(4,5-dimethoxy-2-nitrophenyl)ethyl ester (DMNPE-caged A-23187)	1 mg
A7056	adenosine 5′-diphosphate, P^2-(1-(2-nitrophenyl)ethyl) ester, monopotassium salt (NPE-caged ADP)	5 mg
A1049	adenosine 5′-triphosphate, P^3-(1-(4,5-dimethoxy-2-nitrophenyl)ethyl) ester, disodium salt (DMNPE-caged ATP)	5 mg
A1048	adenosine 5′-triphosphate, P^3-(1-(2-nitrophenyl)ethyl) ester, disodium salt (NPE-caged ATP)	5 mg
A7110	γ-aminobutyric acid, α-carboxy-2-nitrobenzyl ester, trifluoroacetic acid salt (*O*-(CNB-caged) GABA)	5 mg
A6310	5-azidonaphthalene-1-sulfonyl chloride	10 mg
A1506	4-azidophenyl disulfide (4,4′-dithiobis-(phenylazide))	100 mg
A2521	4-azido-2,3,5,6-tetrafluorobenzoic acid (ATFB)	100 mg
A10661	4-azido-2,3,5,6-tetrafluorobenzoic acid, STP ester, sodium salt (ATFB, STP ester)	10 mg
A2522	4-azido-2,3,5,6-tetrafluorobenzoic acid, succinimidyl ester (ATFB, SE)	25 mg
A6311	*N*-(2-((2-(((4-azido-2,3,5,6-tetrafluoro)benzoyl)amino)ethyl)dithio)ethyl)maleimide (TFPAM-SS1)	5 mg
A10662	4-azido-2,3,5,6-tetrafluorobenzyl amine, hydrochloride	25 mg
B1526	benzophenone-4-isothiocyanate	100 mg
B1508	benzophenone-4-maleimide	100 mg
B1577	4-benzoylbenzoic acid, succinimidyl ester	100 mg
B22358	2′-(or-3′)-*O*-(4-benzoylbenzoyl)adenosine 5′-triphosphate, tris(triethylammonium) salt (BzBzATP) *5 mM in buffer*	2 mL
B22357	2′-(or-3′)-*O*-(4-benzoylbenzoyl)guanosine 5′-triphosphate, tris(triethylammonium) salt (BzBzGTP) *5 mM in buffer*	2 mL
B30600	bimane azide	5 mg
B13650	α,γ-bis-(α-carboxy-2-nitrobenzyl)-L-glutamic acid, trifluoroacetic acid salt (α,γ-bis-(CNB-caged) L-glutamic acid)	5 mg
B7108	4-bromo A-23187, 1-(4,5-dimethoxy-2-nitrophenyl)ethyl ester (DMNPE-caged Br A-23187)	1 mg
C20050	5-carboxyfluorescein-bis-(5-carboxymethoxy-2-nitrobenzyl) ether, β-alanine-carboxamide, succinimidyl ester (CMNB-caged carboxyfluorescein, SE)	1 mg
C13654	*N*-(α-carboxy-2-nitrobenzyl)carbamylcholine, trifluoroacetic acid salt (*N*-(CNB-caged) carbachol)	5 mg
C7122	*N*-(α-carboxy-2-nitrobenzyl)-L-glutamic acid (*N*-(CNB-caged) L-glutamic acid)	5 mg
C7074	cyclic adenosine 5′-diphosphate ribose, 1-(1-(2-nitrophenyl)ethyl) ester (NPE-caged cADP-ribose) *mixed isomers*	50 µg
D34678	dextran, 5-(and-6)-carboxy-Q-rhodamine, CMNCBZ-caged, 10,000 MW, anionic	5 mg
D3309	dextran, DMNB-caged fluorescein, 3000 MW, anionic	5 mg
D3310	dextran, DMNB-caged fluorescein, 10,000 MW, anionic	5 mg
D7146	dextran, DMNB-caged fluorescein and biotin, 10,000 MW, lysine fixable	5 mg
D7147	dextran, DMNB-caged fluorescein and biotin, 70,000 MW, lysine fixable	5 mg
D3036	diazo-2, AM *cell permeant* *special packaging*	20 x 50 µg
D3034	diazo-2, tetrapotassium salt *cell impermeant*	1 mg
D1037	4,5-dimethoxy-2-nitrobenzyl adenosine 3′,5′-cyclicmonophosphate (DMNB-caged cAMP)	5 mg
D7060	8-((4,5-dimethoxy-2-nitrobenzyl)oxy)pyrene-1,3,6-trisulfonic acid, trisodium salt (DMNB-caged HPTS)	5 mg
D6814	1-(4,5-dimethoxy-2-nitrophenyl)-1,2-diaminoethane-*N,N,N′,N′*-tetraacetic acid (DMNP-EDTA) *cell impermeant*	5 mg
D6815	1-(4,5-dimethoxy-2-nitrophenyl)-1,2-diaminoethane-*N,N,N′,N′*-tetraacetic acid, tetra(acetoxymethyl ester) (DMNP-EDTA, AM) *cell permeant* *special packaging*	20 x 50 µg
D2516	1-(4,5-Dimethoxy-2-nitrophenyl)diazoethane Generation Kit	1 kit
D3811	*N*-(DMNB-caged fluorescein)-1,2-dihexadecanoyl-*sn*-glycero-3-phosphoethanolamine, triethylammonium salt	1 mg
E3561	ethidium diazide chloride	5 mg
E1374	ethidium monoazide bromide (EMA)	5 mg
F7103	fluorescein bis-(5-carboxymethoxy-2-nitrobenzyl) ether, dipotassium salt (CMNB-caged fluorescein)	5 mg
F1501	4-fluoro-3-nitrophenyl azide (FNPA)	100 mg
G7055	L-glutamic acid, γ-(α-carboxy-2-nitrobenzyl) ester, trifluoroacetic acid salt (γ-(CNB-caged) L-glutamic acid)	5 mg
G2504	L-glutamic acid, α-(4,5-dimethoxy-2-nitrobenzyl) ester, hydrochloride (α-(DMNB-caged) L-glutamic acid)	5 mg
G21061	goat anti-mouse IgG (H+L), CMNB-caged fluorescein conjugate *2 mg/mL*	250 µL
G21080	goat anti-rabbit IgG (H+L), CMNB-caged fluorescein conjugate *2 mg/mL*	250 µL
G1053	guanosine 5′-*O*-(3-thiotriphosphate), $P^{3(5)}$-(1-(4,5-dimethoxy-2-nitrophenyl)ethyl) ester, triammonium salt (*S*-(DMNPE-caged) GTP-γ-S)	1 mg
I23580	D-*myo*-inositol 1,4,5-triphosphate, $P^{4(5)}$-(1-(2-nitrophenyl)ethyl) ester, tris(triethylammonium) salt (NPE-caged Ins 1,4,5-P_3)	25 µg
L7085	D-luciferin, 1-(4,5-dimethoxy-2-nitrophenyl)ethyl ester (DMNPE-caged luciferin)	5 mg
M14943	Methods in Enzymology, Volume 291: Caged Compounds. Gerard Marriott, ed. Academic Press (1998); 529 pages, hard cover	each
M7114	*N*-methyl-D-aspartic acid, β-(α-carboxy-2-nitrobenzyl) ester, trifluoroacetic acid salt (β-(CNB-caged) NMDA)	1 mg
M13652	*N*-methyl-D-aspartic acid, β-(2,2′-dinitrobenzhydryl) ester, trifluoroacetic acid salt (β-(DNBH-caged) NMDA)	1 mg
N6803	*o*-nitrophenyl EGTA, AM (NP-EGTA, AM) *cell permeant* *special packaging*	20 x 50 µg
N6802	*o*-nitrophenyl EGTA, tetrapotassium salt (NP-EGTA) *cell impermeant*	1 mg
N7065	1-(2-nitrophenyl)ethyl phosphate, diammonium salt (NPE-caged phosphate)	5 mg
P7071	(µ-peroxo) (µ-hydroxo)bis(bis(bipyridyl)cobalt(III)) perchlorate (caged oxygen)	25 mg
P6317	*N*-((2-pyridyldithio)ethyl)-4-azidosalicylamide (PEAS; AET)	10 mg

For current prices or to order online, visit probes.invitrogen.com

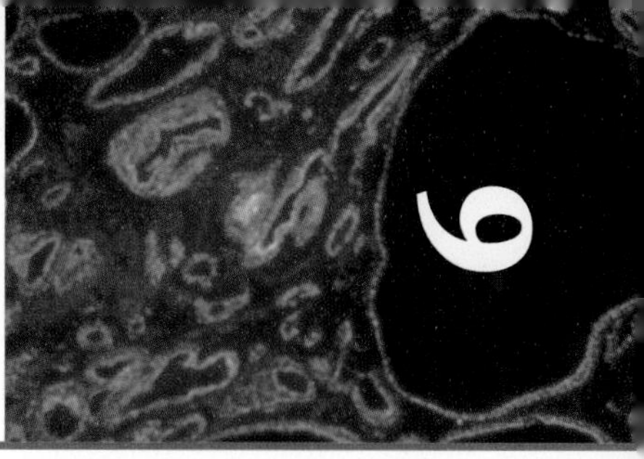

Chapter 6

Ultrasensitive Detection Technology

6.1 Introduction to Detection Methods

Fluorophore- and hapten-labeled proteins, nucleic acids, polysaccharides and lipids are important reagents for both research and diagnostic applications because they are amenable to sensitive detection techniques. Sometimes labeled biomolecules are used simply as diffusible tracers for defining the physical delimitations of the cell or tissue (Chapter 14). More commonly, however, labeled biomolecules selectively bind a particular antigen, carbohydrate, nucleic acid sequence or previously bound hapten, thus providing a means of detecting these biological targets. This section introduces the reagents and methods commonly used in fluorescence detection and some related applications; the remaining sections in this chapter focus on four novel approaches for further amplifying the signal in these methods. Section 6.2 covers tyramide signal amplification (TSA) technology,[1,2] which combines some of the best of Molecular Probes' dyes — the Alexa Fluor®, Oregon Green® and Pacific Blue™ dyes — with the important catalyzed reporter deposition (CARD) technique of NEN (now a part of PerkinElmer Life Sciences). The TSA technology (Figure 6.5, Figure 6.1), which is licensed to Molecular Probes for use in cell- and tissue-based applications, provides significant enzyme-targeted signal amplification and can potentially be combined with our ELF® technology for ultrasensitive detection of low-abundance targets.[3] Section 6.3 discusses our proprietary Enzyme-Labeled Fluorescence (ELF®) substrates, which form highly fluorescent and extremely photostable precipitates at the site of enzymatic activity (Figure 6.2). Section 6.4 focuses on phycobiliproteins, a family of highly fluorescent proteins widely used in multicolor applications, including our exclusive tandem conjugates of R-phycoerythrin with the Alexa Fluor® 610, the Alexa Fluor® 647 or the Alexa Fluor® 680 dye (Figure 6.34) and of allophycocyanin with the Alexa Fluor® 680, the Alexa Fluor® 700 or the Alexa Fluor® 750 dye (Figure 6.37). These tandem conjugates may permit simultaneous multicolor labeling and detection of up to five targets with excitation by a single excitation source (Figure 6.34). Section 6.5 describes Molecular Probes' unique set of fluorescent and luminescent microspheres (Figure 6.3, Figure 23.7), including beads labeled with biotin, streptavidin or NeutrAvidin biotin-binding protein.

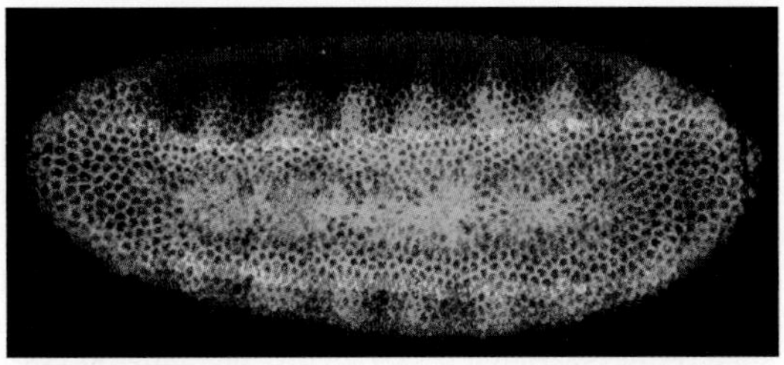

Figure 6.1 Simultaneous detection of three gene targets in a whole mount *Drosophila* embryo by fluorescence *in situ* hybridization. Pseudocolored green-fluorescent labeling represents a fluorescein-labeled cRNA probe detected using a rabbit anti-fluorescein/Oregon Green® primary antibody (A889) and an Alexa Fluor® 488 dye–labeled anti-rabbit secondary antibody (A11008). Pseudocolored yellow- and red-fluorescent labeling represents a biotinylated cRNA probe detected using HRP–streptavidin and Alexa Fluor® 568 tyramide (TSA Kit #24, T20934). Pseudocolored blue-fluorescent labeling represents a digoxigenin-labeled cRNA probe detected using a mouse anti-digoxigenin primary antibody in conjunction with an Alexa Fluor® 647 dye–labeled anti-mouse secondary antibody (A21235). The image was contributed by Ethan Bier and David Kosman, University of California, San Diego.

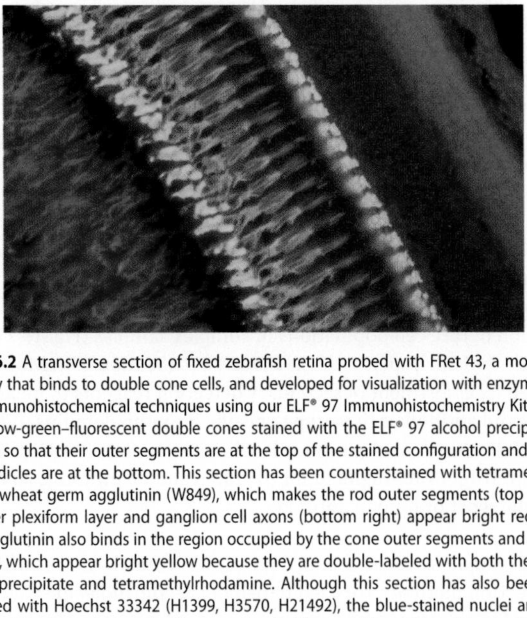

Figure 6.2 A transverse section of fixed zebrafish retina probed with FRet 43, a monoclonal antibody that binds to double cone cells, and developed for visualization with enzyme-mediated immunohistochemical techniques using our ELF® 97 Immunohistochemistry Kit (E6600). The yellow-green–fluorescent double cones stained with the ELF® 97 alcohol precipitate are oriented so that their outer segments are at the top of the stained configuration and the synaptic pedicles are at the bottom. This section has been counterstained with tetramethylrhodamine wheat germ agglutinin (W849), which makes the rod outer segments (top left) and the inner plexiform layer and ganglion cell axons (bottom right) appear bright red. Wheat germ agglutinin also binds in the region occupied by the cone outer segments and synaptic pedicles, which appear bright yellow because they are double-labeled with both the ELF® 97 alcohol precipitate and tetramethylrhodamine. Although this section has also been counterstained with Hoechst 33342 (H1399, H3570, H21492), the blue-stained nuclei are barely visible in this photomicrograph. However, the double cones' inner fibers traverse the region occupied by the Hoechst 33342 dye–stained rod nuclei, and thus appear light blue. The inner segments, myoids and nuclei of these double-cone cells are labeled only with the ELF® 97 alcohol precipitate, giving them a characteristic green appearance. The image was obtained by triple-exposure through optical filters appropriate for DAPI, tetramethylrhodamine and the ELF® precipitate. Used with permission from J Histochem Cytochem 43, 77 (1995).

Our extensive selection of fluorescent and haptenylated proteins — including antibodies, enzymes, avidins, protein A and lectins — are discussed in Chapter 7. Molecular Probes has combined its superior fluorescent dyes with quality primary and secondary detection reagents to complement the amplification reagents in this chapter. Our Zenon® technology (Section 7.3, Figure 7.59) permits rapid and quantitative antibody labeling with any fluorophore from a whole spectrum of fluorescent dyes (Table 7.13) or with horseradish peroxidase or alkaline phosphatase — key reagents for direct application of the TSA and ELF® technologies. Antibody and streptavidin conjugates of NANOGOLD and Alexa Fluor® FluoroNanogold 1.4 nm gold clusters are described in Section 7.2 and Section 7.6, as are the Captivate™ ferrofluid reagents for magnetic isolation and analysis of labeled targets, including rare cells (Figure 7.107). Our unique DSB-X™ biotin products (Section 7.6) permit facile reversibility of the biotin–avidin interaction under physiological conditions.

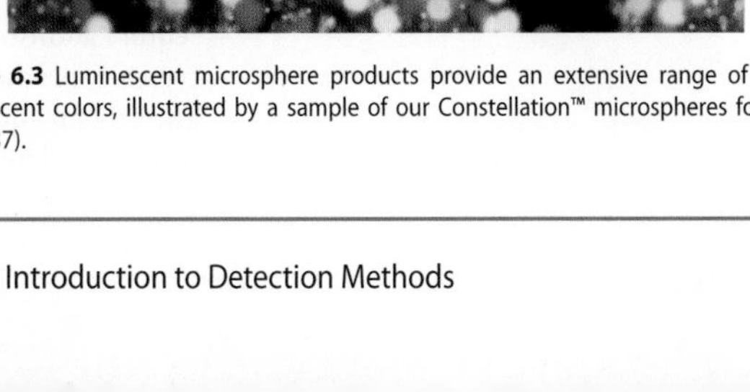

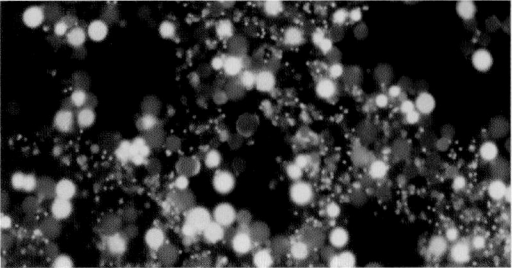

Figure 6.3 Luminescent microsphere products provide an extensive range of sizes and fluorescent colors, illustrated by a sample of our Constellation™ microspheres for imaging (C14837).

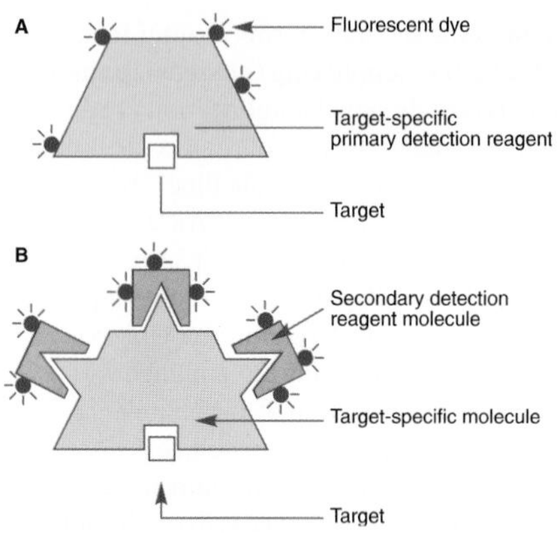

Figure 6.4 Schematic diagram of primary and secondary detection reagents. A) In primary detection methods, the target-specific molecule includes one or more detectable moieties, shown here as radiant orbs. B) In secondary detection methods, the target-specific molecule contains binding sites or haptens that can be selectively recognized by secondary detection reagents. For example, these sites might be antigenic epitopes that bind antibodies. Alternatively, the target-specific molecule might be conjugated to either biotin or fluorescent dyes, thereby creating a molecule that can be detected with any of our avidin and streptavidin conjugates or our anti–fluorescent dye antibodies (Chapter 7). As shown here, the target-specific molecule may contain multiple sites for binding the secondary detection reagent, thereby providing a simple system for amplifying the signal. Techniques in which multiple layers of secondary reagents are applied, thereby creating elaborate detection complexes, are widely used to achieve further signal amplification. The detectable moieties on the secondary reagents may be either fluorescent molecules or enzymes that can be developed for analysis by adding the appropriate substrate (Chapter 10).

Fluorescence *in situ* hybridization (FISH) methods using many fluorescent detection reagents — including some of the TSA and ELF® signal amplification technologies discussed in this chapter (Figure 6.5, Figure 6.21) — are described in Section 8.5. Reagents and methods for amplified detection of nucleic acids and proteins in gels, on membranes and on microarrays are presented in Section 8.5 and Section 9.4. We have found the ELF® technology useful for the ultrasensitive detection of protein targets on Western blots and have incorporated the ELF® 39 phosphatase substrate into several of our DyeChrome™ Western Blot Stain Kits and one of our Pro-Q® Oligohistidine Blot Stain Kits (Section 9.4). In addition, enzyme substrates (Chapter 10) can be incorporated into detection schemes that utilize reporter enzymes or enzyme conjugates, yielding an intrinsic signal amplification that can far exceed that possible with directly labeled bioconjugates.

Definitions: Detection Reagents

Primary Detection Reagents

Any easily detectable molecule that binds directly to a specific target is a primary detection reagent. Such reagents are detected either by their intrinsic fluorescence, phosphorescence, chemiluminescence, absorption, electron spin or electron density, or by virtue of a tightly associated label that confers one of these properties on the molecule. In addition to our fluorophore-labeled anti-dye antibodies (Section 7.4) and monoclonal antibodies (Section 7.5), many of the site-selective products offered by Molecular Probes can be considered primary detection reagents. These include our fluorescent lectins (Section 7.7, Table 7.23), nucleic acid stains (Chapter 8), protein and glycoprotein stains (Section 9.3, Section 9.4), phallotoxins (Section 11.1, Table 11.1), organelle probes (Chapter 12), membrane probes (Chapter 13), annexin V conjugates for detecting apoptotic cells (Section 15.5) and various drug and toxin analogs (Section 16.2, Section 16.3). These primary detection reagents can typically be detected by fluorescence microscopy, fluorometry or flow cytometry methods.

Secondary Detection Reagents

Although many biomolecules, such as antibodies and lectins, bind selectively to a biological target, they usually need to be chemically modified before they can be detected. Often the biomolecule is conjugated to a fluorescent or chromophoric dye or to a heavy atom complex such as colloidal gold or ferritin. However, the researcher may wish to avoid the time and expense required for these conjugations, choosing instead to use a secondary detection reagent, defined as any easily detectable molecule that can be indirectly linked to the molecule of interest. Typically, secondary detection reagents recognize a particular class of molecules. For example, goat anti–mouse IgG antibodies — available conjugated to a wide range of fluorophores and to biotin (Table 7.1), as well as to NANOGOLD and Alexa Fluor® FluoroNanogold 1.4 nm gold clusters — can be used to localize a tremendous variety of target-specific mouse monoclonal antibodies. The Captivate™ ferrofluid antibody conjugates (Section 7.2), which have been developed in collaboration with Immunicon Corporation (www.immunicon.com), can be used to isolate cells and proteins labeled by mouse and rabbit primary antibodies. Combination of the Captivate™ bioconjugates with the novel Captivate™ microscope-mounted magnet and yoke assembly and inserts (C24700, C24701; Section 7.2; Figure 23.56, Figure 23.57) permits the unique separation, visualization and quantitation of rare cell populations in complex samples (Figure 7.58, Figure 7.108). With the development of our superior Alexa Fluor® dyes (Section 1.3), Molecular Probes has considerably expanded its assortment of secondary detection reagents to include antibodies to many more species and antibodies to isotype-specific immunoglobulins, IgM and antibody subfragments (Section 7.2). Our Zenon® antibody labeling technology (Section 7.3) uses conjugates of an Fc-specific anti-IgG Fab fragment for the rapid and quantitative labeling of the corresponding mouse, rabbit, goat or human antibody.

Figure 6.4 compares the types of complexes formed in primary and secondary detection methods. Primary and secondary detection methods are used to detect specific molecules in cells and tissues, as well as on blots and in solution. Although secondary detection methods usually require additional steps and may sometimes yield unsatisfactory signal-to-noise ratios, they typically produce a signal that is amplified over that obtained with primary detection reagents. The scheme for secondary detection shown in Figure 6.4 represents the simplest method of secondary detection. Techniques in which multiple secondary reagents are applied to create elaborate detection complexes are widely used to achieve amplification.[4,5] Our Alexa Fluor® Signal Amplification Kits (Section 7.2, Table 7.8) permit an approximately 10-fold amplification of the signal of fluorescein-conjugated antibodies or of mouse monoclonal antibodies. Antibodies to fluorescein (and Oregon Green® dyes) that are conjugated to either R-phycoerythrin (A21250, Section 7.4) or the Alexa Fluor® 594 dye (A11091, Section 7.4) can be utilized to simultaneously amplify the signal and shift the emission of fluorescein- (or the completely crossreacting Oregon Green® dye–) labeled probes to longer wavelengths.

Common Experimental Protocols for Primary and Secondary Detection Reagents

The types of experiments commonly performed in the laboratory with primary and secondary detection methods include:

- A target-specific polyclonal or monoclonal primary antibody is first bound to its target and then detected by a fluorescently labeled polyclonal secondary antibody raised against the immunoglobulin of the primary antibody. The properties of the amine-reactive dyes used by Molecular Probes to prepare these conjugates are described in detail in Chapter 1. The secondary antibody conjugates and their applications are discussed in Section 7.2.
- A target-specific molecule such as an antibody, lectin, nucleic acid hybridization probe, drug or toxin is first conjugated to a low molecular weight hapten such as a fluorophore, digoxigenin, dinitrophenyl (DNP) or biotin; see Section 4.2 for a discussion of our haptenylation and biotinylation reagents. After binding to its target, this haptenylated biomolecule is then detected using a labeled protein that binds selectively to the hapten (Figure 6.4). Commonly used secondary detection reagents include antibodies (Section 7.2, Table 7.1), avidins and streptavidins (Section 7.6, Table 7.22) labeled with a fluorescent dye or other detectable marker.
- In nucleic acid detection, including fluorescence *in situ* hybridization (FISH, Section 8.5) and nucleic acid detection on microarrays, the hybridization probe can incorporate a fluorescent label, thereby providing a straightforward method of primary detection. Alternatively, the hybridization probe may be modified to include either a hapten that can be detected with a secondary detection reagent or an enzyme that can be detected with a fluorogenic or chromogenic substrate. Fluorescent dyes can make excellent haptens as well as detection reagents, and Molecular Probes has an extensive assortment of anti-dye antibodies (Section 7.4, Table 7.18). In most cases, the signal can be amplified several-fold using our ELF® or TSA technologies.
- In an enzyme-linked immunosorbent assay (ELISA), the primary or secondary detection reagent is usually conjugated to an enzyme. The signal is then developed through addition of a suitable fluorogenic or chromogenic enzyme substrate. Catalytic turnover of the substrate by the enzyme often results in significant amplification of the signal. Thus, enzyme-conjugated detection reagents typically provide greater sensitivity than that achieved with direct dye conjugates. The substrates used to detect the enzymatic activity — and indirectly the amount of the target — typically yield a soluble fluorophore or chromophore. An assortment of substrates for use in ELISAs is described in Chapter 10.
- Enzyme-conjugated detection reagents can also be used to localize a signal in cells or tissues (Figure 6.20). In this case, however, it is essential to use an enzyme substrate that directly yields a fluorescent, colored or electron-dense product at the site of the enzyme complex. The TSA and ELF® technologies, which are described in Section 6.2 and Section 6.3, respectively, provide a greater degree of resolution than many conventional enzyme-mediated fluorescent staining methods. Furthermore, when the TSA and ELF® technologies are combined, they can potentially provide the most sensitive assays known for detecting low-abundance targets in cells and tissues with high spatial resolution.[3]

References

1. J Immunol Methods 137, 103 (1991); **2.** J Immunol Methods 125, 279 (1989); **3.** J Histochem Cytochem 48, 1593 (2000); **4.** J Histochem Cytochem 43, 31 (1995); **2.** J 20, 75 (1988).

6.2 Tyramide Signal Amplification (TSA) Technology

Principles of Tyramide Signal Amplification

To achieve high-resolution signal amplification in cellular and tissue applications, Molecular Probes is committed to the extensive development of tyramide signal amplification (TSA) in combination with our proprietary dyes and other detection technology. TSA — sometimes called CARD, for Catalyzed Reporter Deposition — is an enzyme-mediated detection method that utilizes the catalytic activity of horseradish peroxidase (HRP) to generate high-density labeling of a target protein or nucleic acid sequence *in situ*.[1–5] The TSA method has been reported to increase the detection sensitivity up to 100-fold, as compared with conventional avidin–biotinylated enzyme complex (ABC) procedures.[3,6–12] Moreover, for multiparameter detection of targets in either live or fixed cells or tissues, TSA can be combined with several of our other important technologies, including ChromaTide® nucleotides, ULYSIS and ARES™ Nucleic Acid Labeling Kits (Section 8.2), primary and secondary antibodies, avidin and lectin conjugates (Chapter 7), Enzyme-Labeled Fluorescence (ELF®, Section 6.3), cytoskeletal stains (Chapter 11), organelle probes (Chapter 12), cell tracers and proliferation markers (Chapter 14, Chapter 15) and receptor probes (Chapter 16). Our Zenon® Horseradish Peroxidase Antibody Labeling Kits (Section 7.3, Table 7.13, Figure 7.59) are of particular utility when used in combination with TSA technology; see below for a description of our Zenon® Antibody Labeling Kits enhanced with TSA technology (Z25090, Z25091).

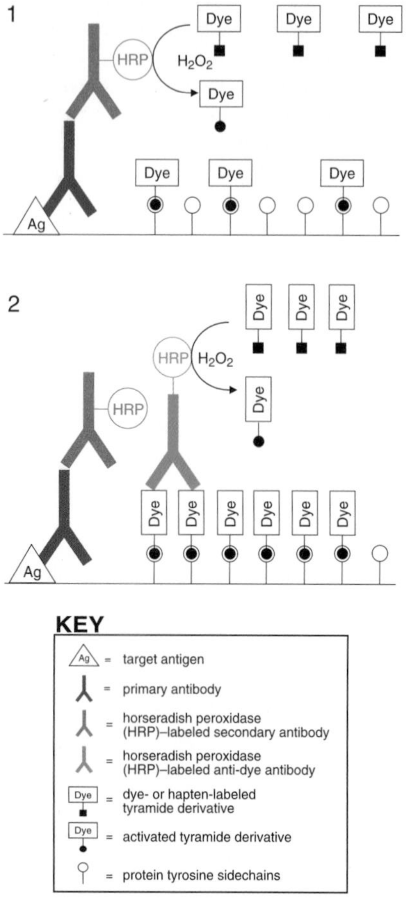

Figure 6.5 Schematic representation of TSA detection methods applied to immunolabeling of an antigen. The antigen is detected by a primary antibody, followed by a horseradish peroxidase–labeled secondary antibody in conjunction with a dye-labeled (or hapten-labeled) tyramide, resulting in localized deposition of the activated tyramide derivative (Stage 1). Further dye deposition, and therefore higher levels of signal amplification, can be generated by detecting dye deposited in stage 1 with a horseradish peroxidase–labeled anti-dye antibody in conjunction with a dye-labeled tyramide (Stage 2).

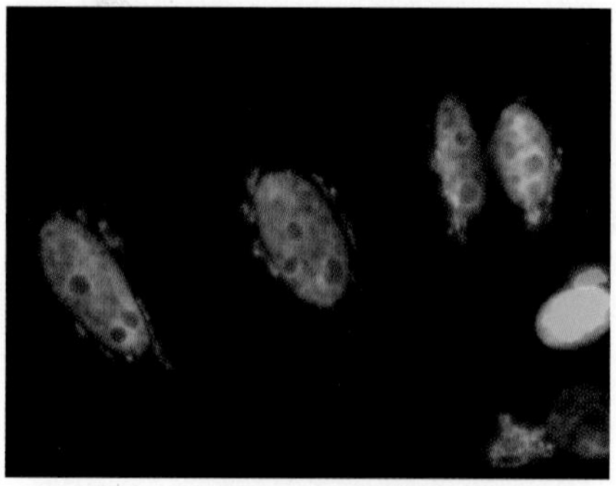

Figure 6.7 Golgi in HeLa cells detected with Alexa Fluor® 546 tyramide. Cells were fixed and permeabilized, then labeled with anti–human Golgin-97 antibody (A21270) and detected using HRP-conjugated goat anti–mouse IgG antibody and Alexa Fluor® 546 tyramide, which are components of the TSA Kit #3 (T20913). The nuclei were counterstained using DAPI (D1306, D3571, D21490). The images were acquired using filters appropriate for DAPI and Alexa Fluor® 546 and processed using MetaMorph software from Universal Imaging Corp.

TSA labeling is a combination of three (or four) elementary processes (Figure 6.5) that typically comprise:

- Binding of a probe to the target via immunoaffinity (proteins) or hybridization (nucleic acids) followed by secondary detection of the probe with an HRP-labeled antibody or streptavidin conjugate. Peroxidase conjugates of other targeting proteins such as lectins and receptor ligands are likely to be suitable for labeling targets, as is endogenous peroxidase activity.[13,14] Unconjugated HRP is also useful as a neuronal tracer; its use in combination with TSA is demonstrated in Figure 14.79.
- Activation of multiple copies of a labeled tyramide derivative by HRP. Most often a fluorescent or biotinylated tyramide has been used; however, labeling with other hapten-conjugated tyramides[15,16] or with polymeric reagents, including tyramide-conjugated gold particles, has also been reported.[17]
- Covalent coupling of the resulting highly reactive, short-lived tyramide radicals to residues (principally the phenol moiety of protein tyrosine residues) in the vicinity of the HRP–target interaction site, resulting in minimal diffusion-related loss of signal localization (Figure 6.6). In a unique application, fluorescein-labeled tyramine has been used to detect protein oxidation by reactive oxygen species (ROS, Section 18.2) in fibroblasts exposed to oxidative stress[18] and in the extracellular proteins of endothelial cells exposed to an oxidative burst from phorbol myristate acetate–activated neutrophils.[19]
- In direct TSA, the fluorescent signal can be immediately detected, resulting in both excellent spatial resolution (Figure 6.7, Figure 6.8) and high signal intensity. When using a hapten-labeled tyramide such as biotin-XX tyramide, the easily reversible DSB-X™ biotin tyramide or DNP-X tyramide (see below), a subsequent detection step is required using a bioconjugate that recognizes the hapten. This second detection step can include a dye-labeled hapten recognizer such as a fluorescent streptavidin (Section 7.6) or a fluorescent anti-hapten antibody (Section 7.4). Alternatively, the hapten-labeled tyramide can be detected using an alkaline phosphate– or HRP-labeled hapten recognizer in conjunction with a fluorogenic or chromogenic substrate (Figure 6.9), resulting in another enzyme-amplified detection step. Chemiluminescent detection of an HRP-deposited biotin tyramide has also been reported.[20] The streptavidin conjugate of NANOGOLD 1.4 nm gold clusters (N24918, Section 7.6) has been used to make biotin tyramide conjugates visible in light and electron microscopy.[21,22] Presumably, the antibody and streptavidin conjugates of Alexa Fluor® FluoroNanogold 1.4 nm gold clusters (Section 7.2, Section 7.6) can be used with hapten-labeled tyramides for correlated fluorescence, light and electron microscopy studies.

The signal amplification conferred by the turnover of multiple tyramide substrates per peroxidase label translates into practical benefits, namely ultrasensitive detection of low-abundance targets in fluorescence *in situ* hybridization,[3,23,24] immunohistochemistry,[6,25] neuroanatomical tracing[7,26] and other applications. For example, we have utilized TSA and Alexa Fluor® 488 tyramide to detect expression of low-abundance epidermal growth factor (EGF) and estrogen receptors by flow cytometry with far greater sensitivity than can be obtained using a directly labeled EGF probe (Figure 6.10) or fluorophore- or hapten-labeled antibodies to the estrogen receptor (Figure 6.11). Application of TSA resulted in significantly increased detectability of estrogen receptors in urinary bladder carcinomas, as compared with conventional immunohistochemical analysis.[27]

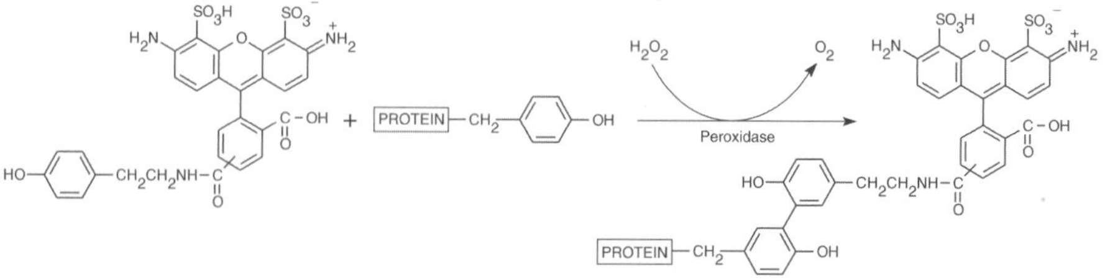

Figure 6.6 Coupling of Alexa Fluor® 488 tyramide to protein tyrosine side chains via peroxidase-mediated formation of an *O,O'*-dityrosine adduct.

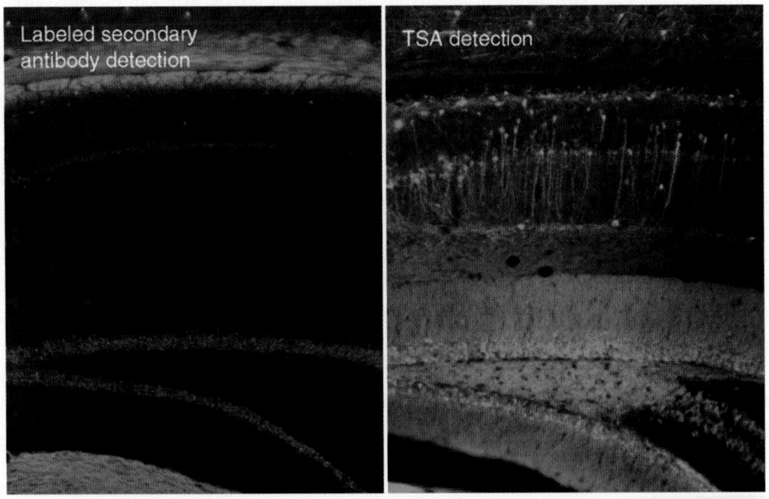

Figure 6.8 Tyramide signal amplification of immunofluorescent staining in mouse brain sections. Mice were transcardially perfused with phosphate-buffered saline followed by 4% paraformaldehyde in phosphate buffer. Thirty µm serial sections were cut in a freezing microtome and transferred to phosphate-buffered saline. Free-floating sections were incubated with 1% hydrogen peroxide to quench endogenous peroxidase activity, blocked in 5% normal goat serum, then stained with a rabbit polyclonal antibody to calbindin D-28K (Chemicon) at a 1:1000 dilution. After washing, sections were incubated with Alexa Fluor® 488 goat anti–rabbit IgG antibody (A11008) at 5 µg/mL (left panel) or HRP–goat anti–rabbit IgG antibody at 1 µg/mL, followed by Alexa Fluor® 488 tyramide (in TSA Kit #12, T20922; right panel). Sections were washed, mounted on slides, coverslipped with ProLong® antifade reagent (in Kit P7481) and imaged under identical conditions (10× magnification, 250 millisecond exposure) using a bandpass filter set appropriate for fluorescein (FITC).

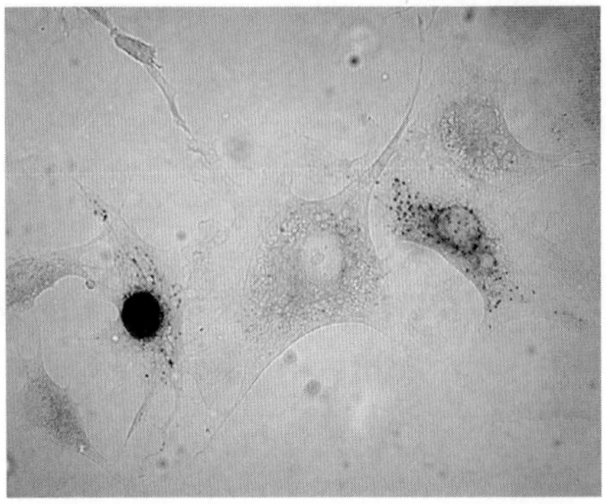

Figure 6.9 Nuclear and nonnuclear incorporation of 5-bromo-2′-deoxyuridine in live cells. Bovine pulmonary arterial endothelial (BPAE) cells were labeled with 5-bromo-2′-deoxyuridine (BrdU, B23151) applied at a concentration of 10 µM for 30 minutes. After fixation with 4% formaldehyde in phosphate-buffered saline for 30 minutes, chromatin was denatured by treatment with 2 M HCl for 20 minutes. Incorporated BrdU was detected with mouse monoclonal anti-bromodeoxyuridine antibody (A21300) followed by HRP-conjugated goat anti–mouse IgG antibody and Oregon Green® 488 tyramide (TSA Kit #9, T20919). Tyramide labeling was further amplified and converted for visualization by bright-field microscopy by detection of the Oregon Green® 488 dye hapten using the HRP conjugate of anti-fluorescein/Oregon Green® antibody (A21253) and diaminobenzidine (DAB) staining. Both nuclear and non-nuclear (presumably mitochondrial) incorporation of BrdU is clearly visible in the resulting image.

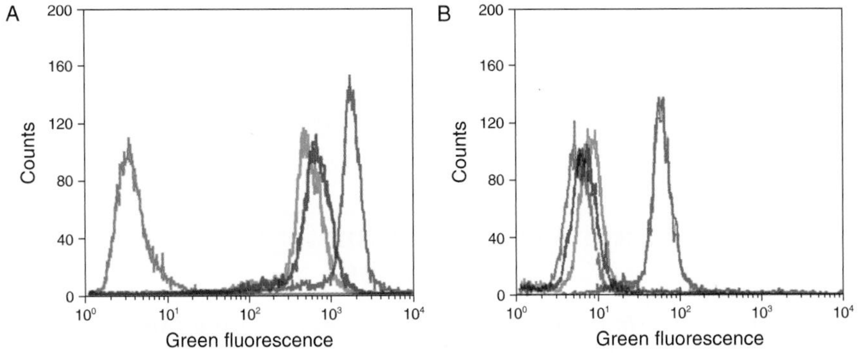

Figure 6.10 Detection of epidermal growth factor (EGF) receptors directly or with signal amplification. Cells expressing high (A431 cells, Panel A) and low (NIH 3T3 cells, Panel B) levels of EGF receptors were either directly labeled with the preformed Alexa Fluor® 488 complex of biotinylated epidermal growth factor (E13345, blue) or indirectly labeled with biotinylated EGF (E3477) followed by either Alexa Fluor® 488 streptavidin (S11223, green) or HRP-conjugated streptavidin and Alexa Fluor® 488 tyramide (purple), components of our TSA Kit #22 (T20932).

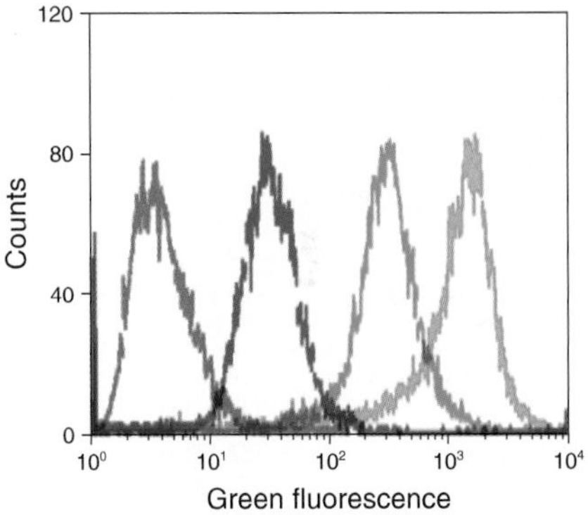

Figure 6.11 Enhancement of estrogen receptor detection sensitivity by tyramide signal amplification (TSA). SKBR3 cells with characteristically low levels of estrogen receptor expression were fixed, permeabilized and treated with H_2O_2 to inhibit endogenous peroxidase activity. A mouse anti–human estrogen receptor monoclonal antibody (Chemicon) was labeled with the Alexa Fluor® 488 dye or with biotin using our Zenon® Alexa Fluor® 488 Mouse IgG_1 Labeling Kit (Z25002) or Zenon® Biotin-XX Mouse IgG_1 Labeling Kit (Z25052), respectively. Detection of estrogen receptors using the labeled antibodies was performed on a Becton Dickinson FACScan flow cytometer with excitation at 488 nm. The cellular fluorescence intensity histograms represent detection with Alexa Fluor® 488 dye–labeled antibodies (blue), biotinylated antibodies coupled to Alexa Fluor® 488 streptavidin (S11223, green) and biotinylated antibodies coupled to HRP–streptavidin and Alexa Fluor® 488 tyramide (TSA Kit #22, T20932; orange). The red histogram represents unstained cells.

A Variety of Kits for TSA Detection

TSA Kits

We have developed numerous TSA Kits that combine the versatile tyramide signal amplification technology with our high-performance Alexa Fluor®, Oregon Green® 488 and Pacific Blue™ tyramides, as well as with biotin-XX tyramide, DSB-X™ biotin tyramide and 2,4-dinitrophenyl (DNP)-X tyramide (Table 6.1). Each kit provides sufficient materials to stain 50–150 slide preparations and includes the following components:

- Tyramide labeled with an Alexa Fluor® dye, Oregon Green® 488 dye or Pacific Blue™ dye, or with biotin-XX, DSB-X™ biotin or DNP-X
- HRP-conjugated anti–mouse IgG antibody, anti–rabbit IgG antibody or streptavidin
- Amplification reaction buffer

- H_2O_2 reaction additive
- TSA blocking reagent
- A detailed protocol for tyramide labeling

Our fluorescent dye– and hapten-labeled tyramides are not currently available as stand-alone reagents.

Zenon® Horseradish Peroxidase Antibody Labeling Kits

Our Zenon® Horseradish Peroxidase Antibody Labeling Kits, available for mouse IgG (Z25054, Z25154, Z25254), rabbit IgG (Z25354) and human IgG (Z25454), make it possible to quantitatively label even submicrogram quantities of a primary antibody with HRP immediately before it is applied to the sample (Section 7.3, Table 7.13). Antibodies labeled with HRP using these Zenon® Kits can replace the HRP–goat anti–mouse IgG and HRP–goat anti–rabbit IgG antibody conjugates in any of the TSA Kits containing these secondary detection reagents.

Zenon® Antibody Labeling Kits Enhanced with TSA Technology

For mouse IgG_1 primary antibodies, we have developed the Zenon® Mouse IgG_1 Labeling Kits enhanced with TSA technology (Z25090, Z25091), which provide the necessary reagents from both the Zenon® Horseradish Peroxidase Mouse IgG_1 Labeling Kit and the corresponding Alexa Fluor® TSA Kit, for researchers who want both the ease of labeling mouse IgG_1 antibodies with Zenon® labeling reagents and the signal amplification afforded by TSA technology. We offer these enhanced Zenon® Kits containing either the green-fluorescent Alexa Fluor® 488 tyramide or the red-orange–fluorescent Alexa Fluor® 568 tyramide (Z25090, Z25091). Each kit provides sufficient reagents for 25 labelings, including:

- Zenon® HRP mouse IgG_1 labeling reagent
- Zenon® mouse IgG blocking reagent
- Alexa Fluor® 488 tyramide (in Kit Z25090) or Alexa Fluor® 568 tyramide (in Kit Z25091)
- Dimethylsulfoxide (DMSO)
- TSA blocking reagent
- TSA amplification buffer
- Hydrogen peroxide (H_2O_2)
- A detailed protocol for Zenon® complex formation and tyramide labeling

The Zenon® HRP mouse IgG_1 labeling reagent contains Fab fragments of goat IgG antibodies directed against the Fc portion of intact mouse IgG_1 antibodies. These Fab fragments have been purified to ensure their selectivity for the Fc portion of the mouse IgG_1 antibody and then labeled with HRP. This Zenon® HRP mouse IgG_1 labeling reagent is simply mixed with any mouse IgG_1 primary antibody to form the Fab–mouse IgG_1 complexes, which can be used for immunolabeling similar to that of primary antibodies covalently labeled with HRP. TSA technology is then used to detect the target-bound Fab–mouse IgG_1 complex. Each HRP label on the Fab–mouse IgG_1 complexes can activate multiple copies of the Alexa Fluor® tyramide to produce short-lived tyramide radicals that are highly reactive with residues near the interaction site, yielding an amplified fluorescent signal with minimal diffusion.

Table 6.1 — Tyramide Signal Amplification (TSA) kits

Tyramide (Ex/Em) *	Peroxidase Conjugate		
	Anti–Mouse IgG †	Anti–Rabbit IgG †	Streptavidin
Alexa Fluor® 350 (346/442)	TSA Kit #7 (T20917)	TSA Kit #17 (T20927)	TSA Kit #27 (T20937)
Alexa Fluor® 405 (402/421)	TSA Kit #38 (T30950)	TSA Kit #39 (T30951)	TSA Kit #40 (T30952)
Pacific Blue™ (410/455)	TSA Kit #10 (T20920)	TSA Kit #20 (T20930)	TSA Kit #30 (T20940)
Alexa Fluor® 488 (495/519)	TSA Kit #2 (T20912)	TSA Kit #12 (T20922)	TSA Kit #22 (T20932)
Oregon Green® 488 (496/524)	TSA Kit #9 (T20919)	Inquire	TSA Kit #29 (T20939)
Alexa Fluor® 532 (531/554)	TSA Kit #8 (T20918)	TSA Kit #18 (T20928)	TSA Kit #28 (T20938)
Alexa Fluor® 546 (556/573)	TSA Kit #3 (T20913)	TSA Kit #13 (T20923)	TSA Kit #23 (T20933)
Alexa Fluor® 555 (555/565)	TSA Kit #40 (T30953)	TSA Kit #41 (T30954)	TSA Kit #42 (T30955)
Alexa Fluor® 568 (578/603)	TSA Kit #4 (T20914)	TSA Kit #14 (T20924)	TSA Kit #24 (T20934)
Alexa Fluor® 594 (590/617)	TSA Kit #5 (T20915)	TSA Kit #15 (T20925)	TSA Kit #25 (T20935)
Alexa Fluor® 647 (650/668)	TSA Kit #6 (T20916)	TSA Kit #16 (T20926)	TSA Kit #26 (T20936)
Biotin-XX (NA/NA)	TSA Kit #1 (T20911)	TSA Kit #11 (T20921)	TSA Kit #21 (T20931)
DSB-X™ biotin (NA/NA)	TSA Kit #31 (T20941)	TSA Kit #32 (T20942)	TSA Kit #33 (T20943)
DNP-X (NA/NA)	TSA Kit #34 (T20944)	TSA Kit #35 (T20945)	TSA Kit #36 (T20946)

*Fluorescence excitation (Ex) and emission (Em) maxima, in nm. † Host = goat. NA = Not applicable.

Applying TSA Technology to Cells and Tissues

Immunohistochemical Detection Using TSA

TSA detection can be applied to a variety of immunohistochemical specimen preparations, including crytostat sections, formaldehyde-fixed paraffin-embedded sections, plastic-embedded sections and cultured cells. In immunohistochemical applications (Figure 6.8, Figure 6.12), sensitivity enhancements derived from TSA allow primary antibody dilutions to be increased — up to a 1:1,000,000 antibody dilution was possible in one reported case,[10] although a 5- to 50-fold increase over the normal dilution factor is more common[9] — in order to reduce nonspecific background signals.[7] Additionally, the strong signal amplification provided by the TSA method can overcome relatively high autofluorescence of cells and tissues.[6] Furthermore, because TSA and diaminobenzidine (DAB) oxidation are both peroxidase-mediated reactions, TSA is readily adaptable for correlated fluorescence and electron microscopy studies.[28,29] In a very unique application, the significantly lower detection threshold of TSA, as compared with fluorescent secondary antibodies, allowed detection of two targets by primary antibodies raised in the same host species, without substantial crosstalk between the signals.[25,30] The first target was detected using TSA and a primary antibody concentration that was so low that it was essentially undetectable by fluorescent secondary antibodies. The second target was then detected by conventional secondary immunofluorescence labeling.

Fluorescence In Situ Hybridization Using TSA

The increased sensitivity afforded by TSA (Figure 6.13, Figure 6.14, Figure 8.92) can be critically important for detecting relatively short oligonucleotide probes and low-abundance mRNAs by fluorescence *in situ* hybridization[3,31] (FISH). Cosmid detection in formalin-fixed, paraffin-embedded sections is cumbersome, and the ability to use smaller cosmid probes of less than 1000 bases in conjunction with TSA detection technology is likely to be an important technique for FISH.[23] TSA is also faster than traditional FISH detection schemes, allowing definitive results to be obtained within a single day. In addition, a two-stage amplification method for ultrasensitive mRNA detection has been reported that combines TSA detection of biotinylated riboprobes with alkaline phosphatase–mediated fluorescence generation using Molecular Probes' unique ELF® 97 phosphatase substrate[32] (Section 6.3). TSA, however, is not a panacea for FISH sensitivity problems. Because both specifically and nonspecifically bound probe signals are amplified, TSA will not compensate for suboptimal hybridization conditions. Optimal probe concentrations are typically 2- to 10-fold lower for TSA-detected FISH than for conventional immunocytochemical detection procedures, again saving on the cost of expensive hybridization probes.[24] Typically, FISH probes are labeled by indirect methods that use streptavidin- or antibody-conjugated HRP. Techniques for direct labeling of oligonucleotide probes have been developed to eliminate background signals due to nonspecific binding of peroxidase conjugates.[4,33,34]

As with some other detection systems, TSA technology allows several probes to be hybridized simultaneously to identify multiple targets. Signal development using multicolored fluorescent tyramides must then be carried out sequentially, with a peroxidase inactivation step between each TSA reaction to prevent crosstalk[24] (Figure 6.13). TSA amplification followed by peroxidase inactivation through mild acid treatment with 0.01 M HCl for 10 minutes at room temperature[35] and then reapplication of TSA using a fluorescent tyramide of a different fluorescent color has been used for at least triple-labeled *in situ* hybridization.[4,35]

Detection of Biotin-XX Tyramide, DSB-X™ Biotin Tyramide and Hapten-Labeled Tyramides

When a tyramide labeled with a hapten such as biotin-XX or the readily reversible DSB-X™ biotin (Section 7.6) is used for TSA in an indirect labeling technique, a signal-generation reagent or scheme is necessary. A fluorescent tyramide such as our Oregon Green® tyramide can also be utilized as a hapten for subsequent detection and amplification by an anti-fluorescein/Oregon Green® dye antibody (Section 7.4). Various reagents and reagent combinations have been reported for detecting enzyme-deposited biotin tyramide or fluorescein tyramide that should be equally suitable for use with our biotin-XX tyramide, DSB-X™ biotin tyramide, DNP-X tyramide or Oregon Green® 488 tyramide, including:

- The streptavidin conjugate of alkaline phosphatase (S921, Section 7.6) in combination with NBT/BCIP[36,37] (N6495, B6492, N6547; Section 10.3) or ELF® 97 phosphate[32] (E6588, Section 6.3)
- Our antibodies to the DNP chromophore (Table 7.19), which are described in Section 7.4

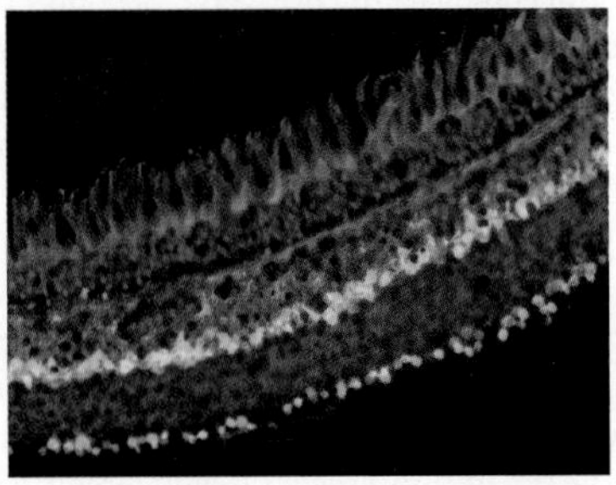

Figure 6.12 Immunohistochemical detection using tyramide signal amplification. A transverse section of fixed zebrafish retina was probed with mouse monoclonal FRet 34 antibody and subsequently developed for visualization using HRP-conjugated goat anti–mouse IgG antibody and Alexa Fluor® 488 tyramide, which are supplied in the TSA Kit #2 (T20912). The section was counterstained with the blue-fluorescent Alexa Fluor® 350 wheat germ agglutinin (W11263) and the far red–fluorescent TOTO®-3 nuclear stain (T3604).

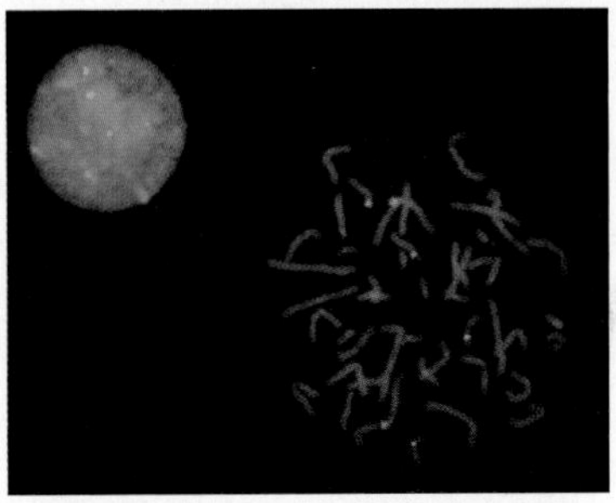

Figure 6.13 *In situ* hybridization of α-satellite probes to human chromosomes 1, 15 and 17 detected by tyramide signal amplification. α-Satellite probes to chromosomes 1, 15 and 17 were labeled by nick translation with biotin-11-dUTP, ChromaTide® Texas Red®-12-dUTP (C7631) and ChromaTide® Oregon Green® 488-5-dUTP (C7630), respectively. Following simultaneous hybridization of all three probes, the biotinylated chromosome 1 probe was detected with HRP–streptavidin conjugate and Alexa Fluor® 546 tyramide (TSA Kit #23, T20933). HRP activity from this first TSA detection step was then quenched by treatment with 1% hydrogen peroxide for 30 minutes. Lastly, the Oregon Green® 488 dye–labeled chromosome 17 probe was detected with anti-fluorescein/Oregon Green® antibody (A6421) followed by HRP-conjugated goat anti–mouse IgG antibody and Alexa Fluor® 594 tyramide (TSA Kit #5, T20915). HRP activity from this second TSA detection step was then quenched by treatment with 1% hydrogen peroxide for 30 minutes. The Texas Red® dye–labeled chromosome 15 probe was then detected with rabbit anti–Texas Red® antibody (A6399) followed by HRP-conjugated goat anti–rabbit IgG antibody and Alexa Fluor® 488 tyramide (TSA Kit #12, T20922). After counterstaining with Hoechst 33258 (H1398, H3569, H21491), the images were acquired using filters appropriate for DAPI, FITC, TRITC and the Texas Red® dye.

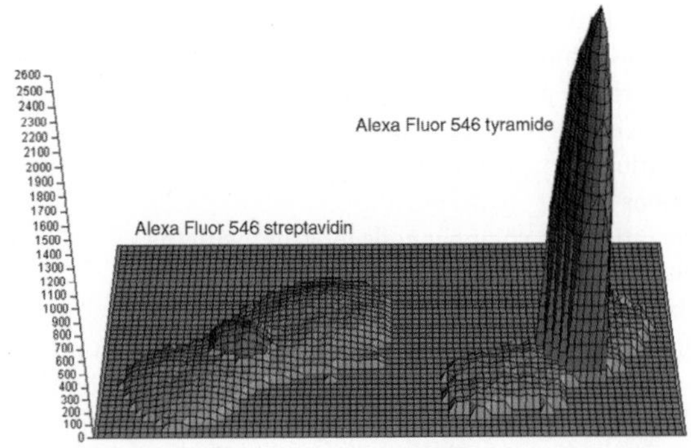

Figure 6.14 Digital image analysis comparison of *in situ*–hybridized biotinylated α-satellite probes detected using TSA Kit #23 (T20933) with HRP–streptavidin and Alexa Fluor® 546 tyramide (right) or Alexa Fluor® 546 streptavidin (S11225, left). Both images were converted to pixel intensity values using MetaMorph software (Universal Imaging Corporation) and transferred to a Microsoft Excel spreadsheet for plotting. Alexa Fluor® 546 dye and DAPI (counterstain) intensity values are shown in red and blue, respectively. Alexa Fluor® 546 dye intensity values below 35% of maximum were omitted for clarity.

- The streptavidin conjugate of HRP (S911, Section 7.6) or the rabbit anti-fluorescein/Oregon Green® antibody conjugate of HRP [30,31,38–40] (A21253, A21254; Section 7.4) in combination with a traditional chromogenic peroxidase substrate such as diaminobenzidine (DAB) [41,42] (Figure 6.9)
- Fluorescent conjugates of avidin or streptavidin, several of which are listed in Table 7.22 (Section 7.6). Our Alexa Fluor® 488 and Alexa Fluor® 594 conjugates of anti-fluorescein/Oregon Green® antibody (A11090, A11091, A11096; Section 7.4) can potentially be used to further amplify the signal (Figure 6.5) or shift the emission of the green-fluorescent Oregon Green® 488 tyramide to red fluorescence
- Diaminobenzidine (DAB) Histochemistry Kits (D22185, D22187; Section 7.2), for direct use with biotin-XX tyramide and DSB-X™ biotin tyramide or conversion of fluorescent signals to permanent staining
- NANOGOLD and Alexa Fluor® FluoroNanogold conjugates of antibodies (Section 7.2) and streptavidin (Section 7.6), for target localization using a combination of light and electron microscopy [21,43]
- The streptavidin conjugate of Captivate™ ferrofluid (C21476, Section 7.6), which can be utilized to efficiently separate low-abundance cellular targets amplified by biotin-XX tyramide or DSB-X™ biotin tyramide and the TSA technology. Binding of DSB-X™ tyramide–labeled targets to the Captivate™ ferrofluid is reversible under extremely mild conditions, potentially permitting isolation of fully viable rare cells using the unique Captivate™ microscope-mounted magnetic yoke assembly (C24700, Section 23.3) and disposable sample chambers (C24701, Section 23.3), which have been specially designed for use with the Captivate™ ferrofluid conjugates (Figure 7.58)

We have compiled several early references for biotin tyramide under the product number for our TSA Kit #21 (T20931). Some selected applications that have been reported for biotin tyramide that should work at least as well with our biotin-XX tyramide include:

- Fluorescence *in situ* hybridization (FISH) in paraffin wax–embedded sections of colon tumor cells [44]
- mRNA detection of low-abundance cytokine genes using direct HRP conjugates of hybridization probes [4,33]
- Detection of low–copy number sequences of human papillomavirus [45,46]
- Combination of mRNA *in situ* hybridization and immunohistochemical detection [47]
- Use of relatively short probes for DNA and mRNA FISH [48,49]
- *In situ* PCR amplification of HIV-1 DNA in brain tissue,[36] detection of HIV-1 p24 antigen in paraffin sections [50] and detection of HIV-1 viral DNA integration sites using FISH [51]
- Detection of low-abundance targets with mRNA probes in cryosections [31]
- Generation of a color bar code for genes with the Fiber-FISH technique [23,52]
- *In situ* hybridization in semi-thin plastic sections [38]
- Demonstration of macrophages in histochemical sections [53]
- Immunofluorescent labeling of $GABA_A$ receptor subunits in the human brain [54]
- β-Galactosidase (LacZ) detection in paraffin-embedded tissue sections [55]
- Localization of the glial cell line–derived neurotrophic factor (GDNF) and its functional receptor in the dorsal root ganglion of rat nerves [56]
- Endosome labeling using HRP-conjugated transferrin and biotin tyramide [57]
- Detection of the distribution of nitric oxide synthase in developing embryonic rat brain,[42] blood vessels of rat brain [58] and bovine aorta [59]
- Amplified detection of low-abundance targets in cultured neurites [57]
- Anterograde tracing using HRP-conjugated lectins [26,60]
- Conversion of a TSA-based detection method to an electron microscopy detection method [29]

Previously cited applications of various fluorescent tyramides that are not available from Molecular Probes include:

- Fluorescence *in situ* hybridization (FISH) [4,35]
- Double- and triple-color immunofluorescence studies using unconjugated primary antisera raised in the same species [25,61]
- Detection of chromosome-specific repeat sequences [62]
- *Escherichia coli* detection and speciation in water with a biotinylated peptide nucleic acid [63]
- Detection of cyanobacteria in a highly autofluorescent sample with a singly labeled oligonucleotide probe [64]
- Flow cytometric characterization of labeled bacteria [65]
- Localization of the HuC and HuR genes in chromosomes by FISH [66]
- Simultaneous detection of two neuropeptide receptors [40,67]
- Immunocytochemical detection of low-level incorporation of 5-bromo-2′-deoxyuridine (BrdU, B23151; Section 15.4) in dividing cells [6] (Figure 6.9)
- Localization of a scarce leptin receptor using TSA in combination with ELF® 97 phosphate [32] (Section 6.3)

Anti-fluorescein/Oregon Green® antibody conjugates of HRP (Section 7.4, Table 7.18) have been used with fluorescein-labeled probes and TSA to detect:

- Embryonic gene expression at the cellular level by FISH [68]
- An mRNA probe for a calcium transporter protein [69]
- A somatostatin receptor protein [39]
- Tissue antigens, with a 10- to 100-fold increase in sensitivity over conventional staining methods [30]
- mRNA in paraffin sections of organotypic multicellular spheroids [70]

Double and Sequential Amplification with TSA

To achieve greater signal amplification, sequential rounds of amplification can be achieved using TSA [71] (Figure 6.5) or TSA in combination with our ELF® technology [32] (Section 6.3), or using the permanent histochemical stains DAB (for HRP) or NBT/BCIP (for alkaline phosphatase). For example, in the first round biotin-XX tyramide can be deposited on a target using one of our biotin-XX tyramide TSA Kits (Table 6.1). In a subsequent step the peroxidase conjugate of streptavidin that is used in TSA Kit #21 (T20931) is used again, but this time in combination with an Alexa Fluor® tyramide, Oregon Green® 488 tyramide, Pacific Blue™ tyramide or another round of biotin-XX tyramide. Presumably, this amplification can be continued for at least a third round, although some loss of spatial resolution may result. Biotin tyramide that has first been deposited at the binding site of a biotin-labeled riboprobe using the streptavidin conjugate of HRP has been further amplified with the streptavidin conjugate of alkaline phosphatase (S921, Section 7.6) in conjunction with ELF® 97 phosphate for the ultrasensitive detection of a scarce leptin receptor mRNA.[32] In another example [72] demonstrating the versatility of the TSA technology, several labeling technologies were combined to detect the HIV-1 virus:

- Hybridization with a 15-base peptide nucleic acid probe labeled with a single fluorescein dye
- Complexation with an HRP conjugate of anti-fluorescein antibody
- Incubation with biotin tyramide
- Incubation with the streptavidin conjugate of HRP
- Re-incubation with biotin tyramide
- Detection with the Alexa Fluor® 488 conjugate of streptavidin (S11223, Section 7.6)

Alternatively, for detection by light microscopy, the sample was incubated with the streptavidin conjugate of HRP in conjunction with DAB instead of Alexa Fluor® 488 streptavidin.

DAB Histochemistry Kits

The use of HRP for enzyme-amplified immunodetection — commonly referred to as immunoperoxidase labeling — is a well-established standard histochemical technique.[73,74] The most widely used HRP substrate for these applications is diaminobenzidine (DAB), which generates a brown-colored polymeric oxidation product localized at HRP-labeled sites. The DAB reaction product can be visualized directly by bright-field light microscopy or, following osmication, by electron microscopy. We offer DAB Histochemistry Kits for detecting mouse IgG primary antibodies (D22185) and biotinylated antibodies and tracers (D22187). Each kit contains:

- Diaminobenzidine (DAB)
- HRP-labeled goat anti–mouse IgG antibody (in Kit D22185) or streptavidin (in Kit D22187) conjugate
- H_2O_2 reaction additive
- Blocking reagent
- Staining buffer
- A detailed staining protocol

Each kit provides sufficient materials to stain approximately 200 slides.

Additional Tips on Using TSA Technology

Use of the TSA technology is not without its precautions. Among these is the possibility of endogenous peroxidase activity in certain cells, especially eosinophils.[14] This activity can be at least partially blocked by incubation with 0.3–3% hydrogen peroxide for about 60 minutes. Second, when using biotin-XX tyramide or DSB-X™ biotin tyramide, endogenous biotinylated proteins are a potential problem (Figure 12.28). Third, because of the significant signal amplification capability of TSA, nonspecific binding of labeled hybridization probes, antibodies and other targeting probes can lead to unacceptably high background staining. This can be alleviated to some degree with appropriate blocking reagents,[75] and furthermore, the high sensitivity of TSA permits antibodies and nucleic acid probes to be highly diluted, far below the amount required for target saturation, thus reducing nonspecific background. Antibody and nucleic acid probe dilution can also substantially reduce the cost of an assay and the amount of an expensive or rare material required for staining.[22]

Mammalian cells and tissues contain biotin-dependent carboxylases, which are required for a variety of metabolic functions. These biotin-containing enzymes produce substantial background signals when biotin–streptavidin detection systems are used to identify cellular targets[76] (Figure 12.28). Because the TSA technology is so sensitive, we recommended preblocking endogenous biotin in cells with our Endogenous Biotin-Blocking Kit (E21390, Section 7.6) when using TSA Kits containing biotin-XX tyramide and the streptavidin conjugate of HRP. The Endogenous Biotin-Blocking Kit provides streptavidin and biotin solutions in convenient dropper bottles and an easy-to-follow protocol. Sufficient material is provided for approximately one hundred 18 mm × 18 mm glass coverslips.

Improvement of TSA detection by post-incubation heating has been reported.[32] Addition of viscosity-increasing dextran sulfate, poly(vinyl alcohol), poly(ethylene glycol) or poly(vinyl pyrrolidone) to the medium is reported to decrease diffusion of the phenoxy radical intermediate, resulting in superior localization of the signal.[71,77] Hybridization probes that are directly labeled with HRP are reportedly useful for lowering nonspecific binding when working with labeled tyramides.[4,34,62] Endogenous peroxidase can be sufficient to yield labeling at the site of this activity in cells, as in the case of eosinophils.[14] The review by Speel, Hopman and Komminoth gives additional practical suggestions and references.[3]

Our Bibliography of TSA Applications

TSA technology has been used successfully for over a decade.[1,78] Many papers have been published that report the use of biotin tyramide for indirect labeling of targets or various fluorescent tyramides for direct labeling of targets. Direct labeling methods have the considerable advantage of saving a second step in the detection scheme. Moreover, labeling targets with fluorescent tyramides instead of biotin tyramide has the further advantage of avoiding amplification of endogenous biotin in cells and tissues, such as we have observed in mitochondrial staining with streptavidin conjugates in the absence of a biotinylated probe (Figure 12.28).

We have compiled an extensive bibliography (T24831) that lists several suggested applications; continuously updated copies are available upon request from our Technical Assistance Department or through our web site (probes.invitrogen.com). However, the biotin tyramide used in most of the early references did not have the additional 14-atom spacer that we utilize in our biotin-XX tyramide to make the probe more accessible to avidin conjugates. Furthermore, none of the specific fluorescent dyes or haptens in the early references are available in kits provided by Molecular Probes, so the specific methods described in these references should be considered guides rather than definitive protocols, and results using our TSA reagents may differ from those reported. In our experience, the Alexa Fluor® 488 tyramide (Table 6.1) provides greater signal and significantly greater photostability than fluorescein tyramide, and the other Alexa Fluor® tyramides, Oregon Green® 488 tyramide and Pacific Blue™ tyramide also yield intense staining of targets.

References

1. J Immunol Methods 125, 279 (1989); **2.** Cytometry 23, 48 (1996); **3.** J Histochem Cytochem 47, 281 (1999); **4.** J Histochem Cytochem 45, 375 (1997); **5.** US Patent No 5,196,306 (1993); **6.** J Histochem Cytochem 45, 315 (1997); **7.** J Histochem Cytochem 40, 1457 (1992); **8.** Histochem Cell Biol 114, 447 (2000); **9.** J Histochem Cytochem 45, 1455 (1997); **10.** Am J Clin Pathol 106, 16 (1996); **11.** Lab Invest 73, 149 (1995); **12.** J Histochem Cytochem 42, 1635 (1994); **13.** J Histochem Cytochem 49, 155 (2001); **14.** Histochem Cell Biol 106, 447 (1996); **15.** Histochem Cell Biol 110, 571 (1998); **16.** J Histochem Cytochem 46, 771 (1998); **17.** J Histochem Cytochem 47, 421 (1999); **18.** Biochemistry 40, 7783 (2001); **19.** Med Sci Monit 7, 606 (2001); **20.** Biotechniques 23, 1076 (1997); **21.** J Histochem Cytochem 48, 933 (2000); **22.** J Histochem Cytochem 45, 359 (1997); **23.** Mutat Res 400, 287 (1998); **24.** Current Protocols in Cytometry, JP Robinson, Ed. Suppl 11, 8.9.1 (2000); **25.** Methods 18, 459 (1999); **26.** J Histochem Cytochem 46, 527 (1998); **27.** J Pathol 186, 165 (1998); **28.** J Histochem Cytochem 48, 153 (2000); **29.** J Neurosci Methods 88, 55 (1999); **30.** J Histochem Cytochem 44, 1353 (1996); **31.** J Histochem Cytochem 47, 431 (1999); **32.** J Histochem Cytochem 48, 1593 (2000); **33.** J Histochem Cytochem 46, 1249 (1998); **34.** Histochem Cell Biol 113, 175 (2000); **35.** J Histochem Cytochem 45, 1439 (1997); **36.** J Virol Methods 70, 119 (1998); **37.** J Histochem Cytochem 45, 1629 (1997); **38.** J Histochem Cytochem 46, 149 (1998); **39.** Endocrinology 138, 2632 (1997); **40.** J Histochem Cytochem 45, 1643 (1997); **41.** Brain Res 822, 251 (1999); **42.** Brain Res 788, 43 (1998); **43.** J Histochem Cytochem 47, 99 (1999); **44.** J Clin Pathol 50, 322 (1997); **45.** Diagnostic Mol Pathol 7, 76 (1998); **46.** Mod Pathol 11, 19 (1998); **47.** J Histochem Cytochem 48, 1369 (2000); **48.** Histochem Cell Biol 110, 431 (1998); **49.** Biotechniques 27, 608 (1999); **50.** J Virol Methods 67, 103 (1997); **51.** J Virol Methods 65, 19 (1997); **52.** Genomics 44, 355 (1997); **53.** Cell Tissue Res 295, 485 (1999); **54.** J Histochem Cytochem 46, 1129 (1998); **55.** J Histochem Cytochem 44, 1323 (1996); **56.** Neurosci Lett 275, 45 (1999); **57.** Eur J Cell Biol 79, 394 (2000); **58.** J Neurocytol 27, 731 (1998); **59.** Acta Histochem 99, 411 (1997); **60.** J Comp Neurol 412, 161 (1999); **61.** J Histochem Cytochem 44, 1331 (1996); **62.** Cytogenet Cell Genet 75, 258 (1996); **63.** Mol Cell Probes 13, 261 (1999); **64.** Appl Environ Microbiol 65, 1259 (1999); **65.** Appl Environ Microbiol 63, 3268 (1997); **66.** Genomics 53, 296 (1998); **67.** Regul Pept 80, 67 (1999); **68.** Histochem Cell Biol 111, 435 (1999); **69.** J Biol Chem 275, 28186 (2000); **70.** Neuropathol Appl Neurobiol 22, 548 (1996); **71.** J Histochem Cytochem 44, 389 (1996); **72.** J Pathol 194, 130 (2001); **73.** Arch Pathol Lab Med 102, 113 (1978); **74.** J Histochem Cytochem 36, 317 (1988); **75.** J Histochem Cytochem 51, 129 (2003); **76.** J Histochem Cytochem 45, 1053 (1997); **77.** Histochem Cell Biol 111, 89 (1999); **78.** J Immunol Methods 137, 103 (1991).

Product List — 6.2 Tyramide Signal Amplification (TSA) Technology

Cat #	Product Name	Unit Size
T20911	TSA™ Kit #1 *with HRP–goat anti-mouse IgG and biotin-XX tyramide* *50-150 slides*	1 kit
T20912	TSA™ Kit #2 *with HRP–goat anti-mouse IgG and Alexa Fluor® 488 tyramide* *50-150 slides*	1 kit
T20913	TSA™ Kit #3 *with HRP–goat anti-mouse IgG and Alexa Fluor® 546 tyramide* *50-150 slides*	1 kit
T20914	TSA™ Kit #4 *with HRP–goat anti-mouse IgG and Alexa Fluor® 568 tyramide* *50-150 slides*	1 kit
T20915	TSA™ Kit #5 *with HRP–goat anti-mouse IgG and Alexa Fluor® 594 tyramide* *50-150 slides*	1 kit
T20916	TSA™ Kit #6 *with HRP–goat anti-mouse IgG and Alexa Fluor® 647 tyramide* *50-150 slides*	1 kit
T20917	TSA™ Kit #7 *with HRP–goat anti-mouse IgG and Alexa Fluor® 350 tyramide* *50-150 slides*	1 kit
T20918	TSA™ Kit #8 *with HRP–goat anti-mouse IgG and Alexa Fluor® 532 tyramide* *50-150 slides*	1 kit
T20919	TSA™ Kit #9 *with HRP–goat anti-mouse IgG and Oregon Green® 488 tyramide* *50-150 slides*	1 kit
T20920	TSA™ Kit #10 *with HRP–goat anti-mouse IgG and Pacific Blue® tyramide* *50-150 slides*	1 kit
T20921	TSA™ Kit #11 *with HRP–goat anti-rabbit IgG and biotin-XX tyramide* *50-150 slides*	1 kit
T20922	TSA™ Kit #12 *with HRP–goat anti-rabbit IgG and Alexa Fluor® 488 tyramide* *50-150 slides*	1 kit
T20923	TSA™ Kit #13 *with HRP–goat anti-rabbit IgG and Alexa Fluor® 546 tyramide* *50-150 slides*	1 kit
T20924	TSA™ Kit #14 *with HRP–goat anti-rabbit IgG and Alexa Fluor® 568 tyramide* *50-150 slides*	1 kit
T20925	TSA™ Kit #15 *with HRP–goat anti-rabbit IgG and Alexa Fluor® 594 tyramide* *50-150 slides*	1 kit
T20926	TSA™ Kit #16 *with HRP–goat anti-rabbit IgG and Alexa Fluor® 647 tyramide* *50-150 slides*	1 kit
T20927	TSA™ Kit #17 *with HRP–goat anti-rabbit IgG and Alexa Fluor® 350 tyramide* *50-150 slides*	1 kit
T20928	TSA™ Kit #18 *with HRP–goat anti-rabbit IgG and Alexa Fluor® 532 tyramide* *50-150 slides*	1 kit
T20930	TSA™ Kit #20 *with HRP–goat anti-rabbit IgG and Pacific Blue® tyramide* *50-150 slides*	1 kit
T20931	TSA™ Kit #21 *with HRP–streptavidin and biotin-XX tyramide* *50-150 slides*	1 kit
T20932	TSA™ Kit #22 *with HRP–streptavidin and Alexa Fluor® 488 tyramide* *50-150 slides*	1 kit
T20933	TSA™ Kit #23 *with HRP–streptavidin and Alexa Fluor® 546 tyramide* *50-150 slides*	1 kit
T20934	TSA™ Kit #24 *with HRP–streptavidin and Alexa Fluor® 568 tyramide* *50-150 slides*	1 kit
T20935	TSA™ Kit #25 *with HRP–streptavidin and Alexa Fluor® 594 tyramide* *50-150 slides*	1 kit
T20936	TSA™ Kit #26 *with HRP–streptavidin and Alexa Fluor® 647 tyramide* *50-150 slides*	1 kit
T20937	TSA™ Kit #27 *with HRP–streptavidin and Alexa Fluor® 350 tyramide* *50-150 slides*	1 kit
T20938	TSA™ Kit #28 *with HRP–streptavidin and Alexa Fluor® 532 tyramide* *50-150 slides*	1 kit
T20939	TSA™ Kit #29 *with HRP–streptavidin and Oregon Green® 488 tyramide* *50-150 slides*	1 kit
T20940	TSA™ Kit #30 *with HRP–streptavidin and Pacific Blue® tyramide* *50-150 slides*	1 kit
T20941	TSA™ Kit #31 *with HRP–goat anti-mouse IgG and DSB-X™ biotin tyramide* *50-150 slides*	1 kit
T20942	TSA™ Kit #32 *with HRP–goat anti-rabbit IgG and DSB-X™ biotin tyramide* *50-150 slides*	1 kit
T20943	TSA™ Kit #33 *with HRP–streptavidin and DSB-X™ biotin tyramide* *50-150 slides*	1 kit
T20944	TSA™ Kit #34 *with HRP–goat anti-mouse IgG and DNP-X tyramide* *50-150 slides*	1 kit
T20945	TSA™ Kit #35 *with HRP–goat anti-rabbit IgG and DNP-X tyramide* *50-150 slides*	1 kit
T20946	TSA™ Kit #36 *with HRP–streptavidin and DNP-X tyramide* *50-150 slides*	1 kit
T30950	TSA™ Kit #37 *with HRP–goat anti-mouse IgG and Alexa Fluor® 405 tyramide* *50-150 slides*	1 kit
T30951	TSA™ Kit #38 *with HRP–goat anti-rabbit IgG and Alexa Fluor® 405 tyramide* *50-150 slides*	1 kit

For current prices or to order online, visit probes.invitrogen.com

Cat #	Product Name	Unit Size
T30952	TSA™ Kit #39 *with HRP–streptavidin and Alexa Fluor® 405 tyramide* *50-150 slides*	1 kit
T30953	TSA™ Kit #40 *with HRP–goat anti-mouse IgG and Alexa Fluor® 555 tyramide* *50-150 slides*	1 kit
T30954	TSA™ Kit #41 *with HRP–goat anti-rabbit IgG and Alexa Fluor® 555 tyramide* *50-150 slides*	1 kit
T30955	TSA™ Kit #42 *with HRP–streptavidin and Alexa Fluor® 555 tyramide* *50-150 slides*	1 kit
Z25090	Zenon® Alexa Fluor® 488 Mouse IgG_1 Labeling Kit *enhanced with TSA™ technology* *25 labelings*	1 kit
Z25091	Zenon® Alexa Fluor® 568 Mouse IgG_1 Labeling Kit *enhanced with TSA™ technology* *25 labelings*	1 kit
Z25454	Zenon® Horseradish Peroxidase Human IgG Labeling Kit *25 labelings*	1 kit
Z25054	Zenon® Horseradish Peroxidase Mouse IgG_1 Labeling Kit *25 labelings*	1 kit
Z25154	Zenon® Horseradish Peroxidase Mouse IgG_{2a} Labeling Kit *25 labelings*	1 kit
Z25254	Zenon® Horseradish Peroxidase Mouse IgG_{2b} Labeling Kit *25 labelings*	1 kit
Z25354	Zenon® Horseradish Peroxidase Rabbit IgG Labeling Kit *25 labelings*	1 kit

For current prices or to order online, visit probes.invitrogen.com

6.3 Enzyme-Labeled Fluorescence (ELF®) Signal Amplification Technology

When detecting specific biomolecules in cells, tissues and microarrays, enzyme-mediated detection methods can provide significant signal amplification due to the catalytic turnover of the fluorogenic or chromogenic substrate. For example, nitro blue tetrazolium (NBT) is frequently combined with the phosphatase substrate 5-bromo-4-chloro-3-indolyl phosphate (BCIP) (N6495, B6492, N6547; Section 10.3) to produce a colored precipitate at the site of phosphatase activity in histochemical assays, *in situ* hybridization techniques and Western, Northern and Southern blot analyses. Because fluorometric methods are potentially much more sensitive than colorimetric methods, Molecular Probes has been actively engaged in research to develop fluorogenic substrates for enzyme-mediated detection. We now have available reagents and kits to support two outstanding and complementary detection technologies — Enzyme-Labeled Fluorescence (ELF®) and tyramide signal amplification (TSA, Section 6.2) — that provide significantly enhanced detection of targets and exceptionally high photostability at the same time. Used sequentially, the TSA and ELF® technologies permit ultrasensitive detection of very low-abundance targets in cells and tissues that cannot be visualized with any other fluorescent technology.[1,2]

Our patented ELF® 97 phosphate is a substrate for both alkaline phosphatase and acid phosphatase with several unique properties that make it superior to many of the existing reagents for detecting these enzymes.[3] Upon enzymatic cleavage (Figure 6.15), this weakly blue-fluorescent substrate yields a bright yellow-green–fluorescent precipitate that exhibits an unusually large Stokes shift and excellent photostability. The ELF® 97 phosphatase substrate is a particularly powerful tool for immunohistochemistry, mRNA *in situ* hybridization[4–7] and detection of DNA on DNA chips. Unlike the radioactive signal produced by conventional methods, ELF® 97 mRNA detection signals can be developed in minutes or even seconds and can be clearly distinguished from sample pigmentation, which often obscures both radioactive and colorimetric signals. Moreover, in *in situ* hybridization applications, the yellow-green–fluorescent ELF® 97 alcohol precipitate produces a signal that is many times brighter than that achieved using either directly labeled fluorescent hybridization probes or fluorescent secondary detection methods.[8–10]

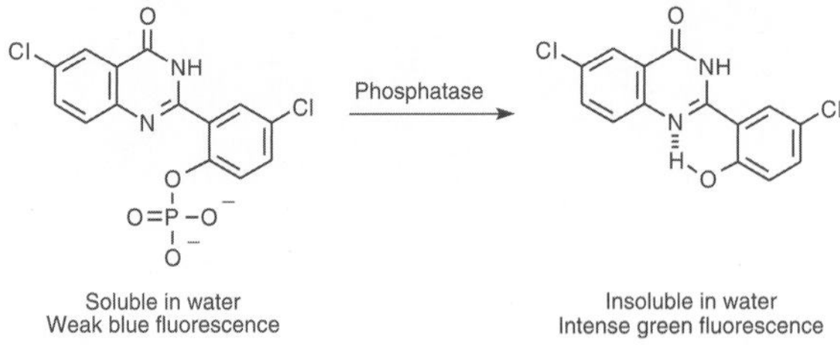

Figure 6.15 Principle of enzyme-mediated formation of the fluorescent ELF® 97 alcohol precipitate from the ELF® 97 phosphatase substrate.

Spectral Characteristics of the ELF® 97 Signal

Figure 6.15 shows conversion of the water-soluble ELF® 97 phosphatase substrate (E6588, E6589) into its hydrolysis product, the ELF® 97 alcohol (E6578), by action of a phosphatase enzyme. Under our reaction conditions, this highly insoluble planar molecule forms an intense yellow-green–fluorescent precipitate at the site of phosphatase activity. Like other crystalline fluorescent molecules containing an intramolecular hydrogen bond, the ELF® 97 alcohol precipitate provides a fluorescent signal that is not only extremely photostable but also has an exceptionally large Stokes shift.[11–13] The ELF® 97 signal is orders-of-magnitude more photostable than signals achieved using either direct or indirect detection with fluorescein conjugates[3,14] (Figure 6.16). This high photostability makes it very easy to focus and photograph ELF® 97 alcohol–labeled tissue under high magnification. For example, in tissue samples stained using reagents in the ELF® 97 Immunohistochemistry Kit, we have observed that about 40% of the ELF® 97 alcohol precipitate signal remains following two hours of constant full-power illumination from an epifluorescence microscope. Also, because the fluorescence emission of the ELF® 97 alcohol precipitate is separated from its excitation maximum by over 180 nm (Figure 6.17),

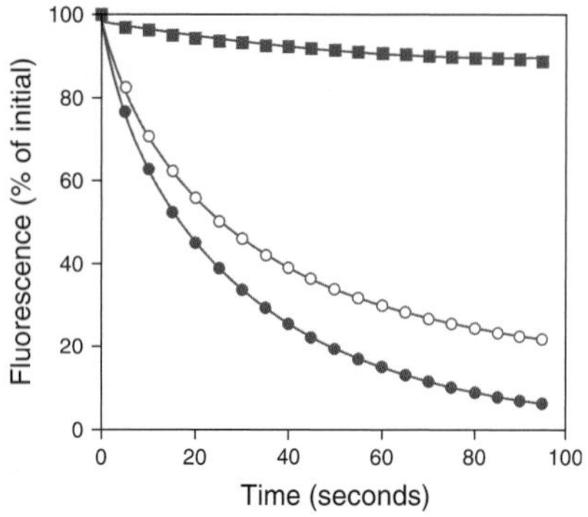

Figure 6.16 Photostability comparison for ELF® 97 alcohol– and fluorescein-labeled tubulin preparations. Tubulin in acetone-fixed CRE BAG 2 mouse fibroblasts was labeled with an anti–β-tubulin monoclonal antibody and then detected using biotin-XX goat anti–mouse IgG antibody (B2763) in conjunction with either our ELF® 97 Cytological Labeling Kit (E6603, ■) or fluorescein streptavidin (S869, ●). Alternatively, anti-tubulin labeling was detected directly using fluorescein goat anti–mouse IgG antibody (F2761, ○). The photostability of labeling produced by the three methods was compared by continuously illuminating stained samples on a fluorescence microscope using Omega Optical longpass optical filter sets. Images were acquired every 5 seconds using a Star 1 CCD camera (Photometrics); the average fluorescence intensity in the field of view was calculated with Image-1 software (Universal Imaging Corp.) and expressed as a fraction of the initial intensity. Three data sets, representing different fields of view, were averaged for each conjugate to obtain the plotted time courses.

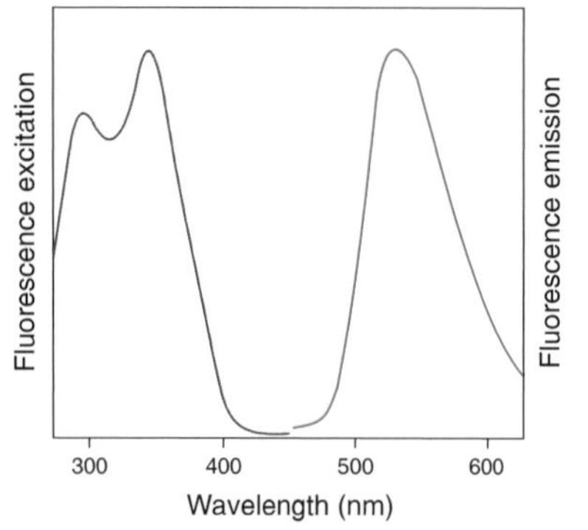

Figure 6.17 The normalized fluorescence excitation and emission spectra of the ELF® 97 alcohol precipitate (E6578), which is generated by enzymatic cleavage of the soluble ELF® 97 phosphatase substrate (E6588, E6589).

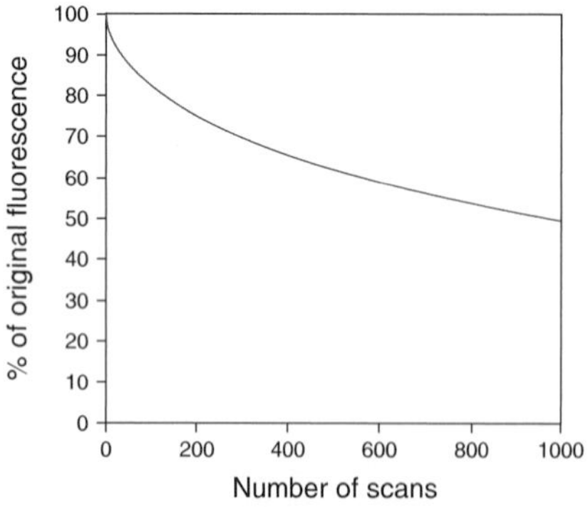

Figure 6.18 The ELF® 97 Cytological Labeling Kit (E6603) was used to label endogenous alkaline phosphatase activity of zebrafish kidney. The ELF® 97 fluorescence intensity was measured from each of 1000 consecutive scans on a confocal laser-scanning microscope (Bio-Rad MRC 1024) with UV illumination (UV/Vis Coherent Innova Enterprise Model 622 argon-ion laser, 60 mW output) using the 363 nm spectral line at 100% power with a 40× objective. Fluorescence intensity, expressed as a percentage of initial value, is plotted against scan number. In this example, 970 scans were required to reduce the signal by 50%. The figure was contributed by J. Paul Robinson and Jennie Sturgis, Purdue University.

the ELF® 97 signal can be clearly distinguished from most cell and tissue autofluorescence, which generally has a Stokes shift of much less than 100 nm.[14] As a result of its extremely high photostability, the ELF® 97 phosphate–generated signal may be the best method for immunolabeling targets to be viewed by UV-light–excited confocal laser-scanning microscopy (Figure 6.18).

The extremely high Stokes shift of the ELF® 97 alcohol precipitate makes the ELF® 97 phosphatase substrate ideal for use in multicolor applications (Figure 6.19, Figure 6.20, Figure 10.9). The ELF® 97 signal can be visualized simultaneously with blue-fluorescent probes — such as Alexa Fluor® 350 dye–, Alexa Fluor® 405 dye–, Cascade Blue® dye–, Marina Blue® dye– or Pacific Blue™ dye–labeled secondary reagents (Section 1.7) — or the DAPI and Hoechst counterstains (Section 8.6) using a fluorescence microscope fitted with a standard DAPI/Hoechst longpass optical filter set. Because the ELF® 97 alcohol precipitate and the blue-fluorescent label have distinct emission spectra, the two signals can be easily distinguished.[14] In addition, the excitation spectra of tetramethylrhodamine (TMR), Texas Red® (TR) and the Alexa Fluor® dyes that have absorption maxima beyond 530 nm are very well

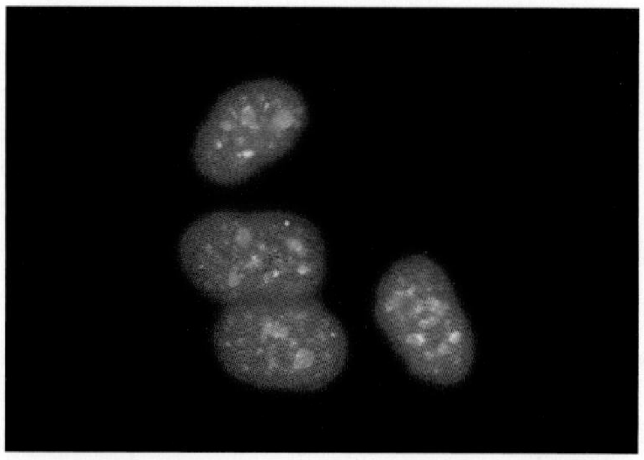

Figure 6.19 HeLa cell nuclei incubated with a mouse monoclonal antibody directed against nuclear-localized antigens (a gift from Benjamin Blencowe and Phil Sharp, Massachusetts Institute of Technology) in conjunction with Texas Red®-X streptavidin (S6370) and with a human anti-nuclear antibody in conjunction with biotin-XX goat anti–human IgG antibody. The reagents in the ELF® 97 Cytological Labeling Kit (E6603) were then used to detect the biotinylated secondary antibody. Cells were counterstained with Hoechst 33258 (H1398, H3569, H21491). Multiple exposures were taken using filters appropriate for the Texas Red® dye, fluorescein and DAPI.

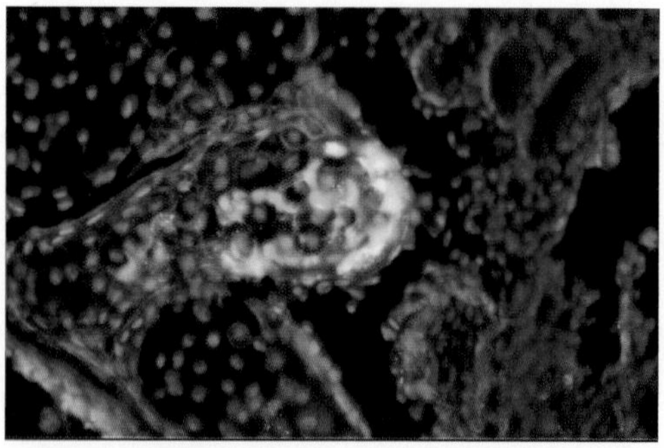

Figure 6.20 Endogenous alkaline phosphatase activity of osteoblast cells in a cartilaginous element of an adult zebrafish head cryosection. The activity was localized with the ELF® 97 Endogenous Phosphatase Detection Kit (E6601). In addition to the yellow-green fluorescence of the ELF® 97 precipitate, the section was stained with Texas Red®-X wheat germ agglutinin (W21405) and counterstained with the Hoechst 33342 nucleic acid stain (H1399, H3570, H21492). The triple-exposure image was acquired using bandpass filter sets appropriate for the ELF® precipitate, Texas Red® dye and AMCA.

separated from that of the ELF® 97 alcohol precipitate. Thus, ELF® 97 signals and the red fluorescence of tetramethylrhodamine-, Texas Red® dye– or longer-wavelength Alexa Fluor® dye–labeled secondary reagents (or a red-fluorescent counterstain such as propidium iodide) can be easily visualized sequentially with the appropriate optical filter sets without bleed-through.[14] Also, ELF® 97 alcohol signals can be distinguished from fluorescein, Oregon Green® 488 and Alexa Fluor® 488 dye signals because their excitation wavelengths do not significantly overlap (see Note 6.1 "Product Highlight: Combining ELF® 97 Staining with Other Fluorophores"). The ELF® 97 alcohol precipitate is optimally excited by UV laser–based confocal laser-scanning instruments, and its intense green fluorescence and extremely high photostability make it a preferred dye for such instruments[15] (Figure 6.16, Figure 6.18).

Applications of ELF® 97 Staining in Histochemistry

Histochemical applications often require reliable, sensitive and stable detection of targets in complex samples that may have significant background from either natural sample autofluorescence or fluorescence created during sample preparation. Many histochemical procedures utilize either enzyme-amplified detection methods in conjunction with chromophoric substrates such as 5-bromo-4-chloro-3-indolyl phosphate (BCIP), nitro blue tetrazolium (NBT) (N6495, B6492, N6547; Section 10.3) and diaminobenzidine (DAB) to yield colored precipitates at the site of labeling, or colorimetric stains such as hematoxylin/eosin staining. The ELF® technology yields staining that can be equal to or superior to NBT/BCIP staining and that forms an exceptionally persistent product. We have observed that ELF® 97 phosphate–based staining of fixed samples can persist for months to years with little if any loss of signal. ELF® 97 staining can also be combined with staining by other fluorophores to permit simultaneous analysis of multiple targets in the sample. Combination of the ELF® technology with TSA technology (Section 6.2) may provide exceptional detection limits for low-abundance targets in cells and tissues that are not possible with existing histochemical methods.[2]

Overcoming Sample Autofluorescence

The extremely high Stokes shift for the ELF® 97 alcohol precipitate — greater than 180 nm — is an important advantage for immunohistochemistry applications. Although the ELF® 97 dye is excited in the ultraviolet range where autofluorescence from cells, tissues, paraffin sections and various fixatives can be quite high,[16] the high intensity of ELF® 97 staining overcomes most of this background. Because the ELF® 97 alcohol precipitate is extremely photostable, the background can be further reduced by pre-bleaching the entire sample with ultraviolet light before measuring the specific fluorescence of the ELF® 97 alcohol precipitate. One study that used the ELF® 97 phosphatase substrate also demonstrated that filtered sunlight was more effective than UV shortwave or longwave illumination in reducing arterial autofluorescence.[17]

ELF® 97 Kits for a Wide Variety of Applications

We currently offer five ELF® 97 Kits — four application-specific kits for secondary detection and one kit designed for detecting endogenous phosphatase activity in cells and tissues:

- ELF® 97 Immunohistochemistry Kit (E6600)
- ELF® 97 Cytological Labeling Kit *with streptavidin, alkaline phosphatase conjugate* (E6603)
- ELF® 97 mRNA *In Situ* Hybridization Kit #1 (E6604)

Note 6.1 — Product Highlight

Combining ELF® 97 Staining with Other Fluorophores

Although the emission spectrum of ELF® 97 alcohol–stained targets strongly overlaps those of fluorescein and the Alexa Fluor® 488 and Oregon Green® 488 dyes, its excitation maximum is in the ultraviolet range where these green-fluorescent dyes have relatively weak absorption (Figure). The ELF® 97 alcohol — the product of the ELF® 97 phosphatase reaction — has no absorption at 480–500 nm, where these latter dyes have their peak absorption. Consequently, for samples that are doubly stained with the ELF® 97 alcohol precipitate and one of these other green-fluorescent dyes, excitation in the visible range at about 480–500 nm yields the first signal and excitation of the ELF® 97 alcohol in the ultraviolet yields the second signal.

Using digital imaging methods on a pixel-by-pixel basis, these signals can be colorized in contrasting colors. Of course, the green fluorescence of the ELF® 97 alcohol precipitate can be readily resolved from that of blue fluorescence of probes such as the DAPI and Hoechst dye nuclear stains (Section 8.6, Figure 6.2) or any orange- or red-fluorescent dye (Section 1.6) by using appropriate optical filters (Table 23.9). The green-fluorescent staining by the ELF® 97 alcohol has been shown to be distinguishable from the fluorescence of a wide variety of other fluorophores in flow cytometry.[1]

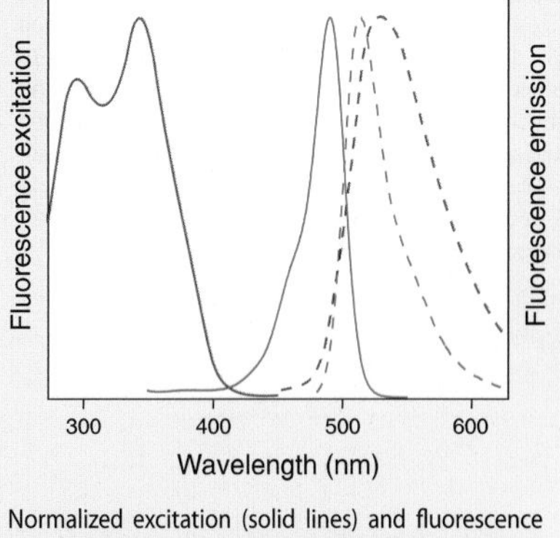

Normalized excitation (solid lines) and fluorescence emission (dashed lines) spectra of the ELF® 97 alcohol precipitate (blue) and fluorescein (red). The ELF® 97 alcohol precipitate was generated by the enzymatic cleavage of our soluble ELF® 97 phosphatase substrate (E6588, E6589).

Reference

1. Cytometry 43, 117 (2001).

- ELF® 97 mRNA *In Situ* Hybridization Kit #2 *with streptavidin, alkaline phosphatase conjugate* (E6605)
- ELF® 97 Endogenous Phosphatase Detection Kit (E6601)

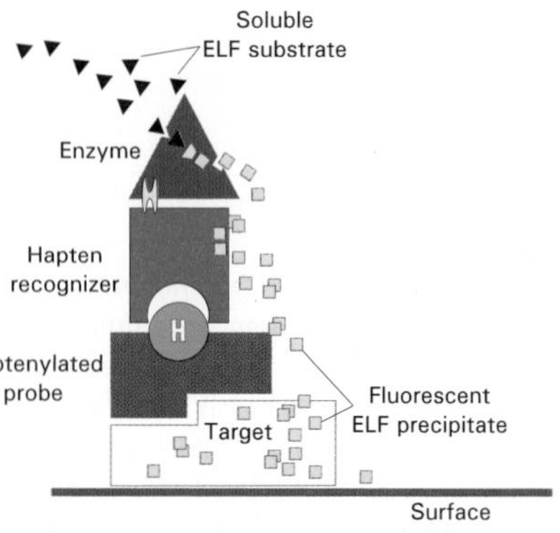

Figure 6.21 Schematic diagram of the method employed in our ELF® 97 mRNA *In Situ* Hybridization (E6604, E6605), Cytological Labeling (E6603) and Immunohistochemistry (E6600) Kits. Samples are probed with haptenylated or biotinylated target-specific probes such as antibodies or hybridization probes. Next, alkaline phosphatase conjugates of streptavidin or the hapten-specific probe are applied. Alternatively, a biotinylated antibody and biotinylated alkaline phosphatase can be used with standard bridging methods to increase the penetration in tissue, a method that is employed in our ELF® 97 Immunohistochemistry Kit. The sample is then incubated with the ELF® 97 phosphatase substrate, which forms an intense yellow-green–fluorescent ELF® 97 alcohol precipitate at the site of alkaline phosphatase activity.

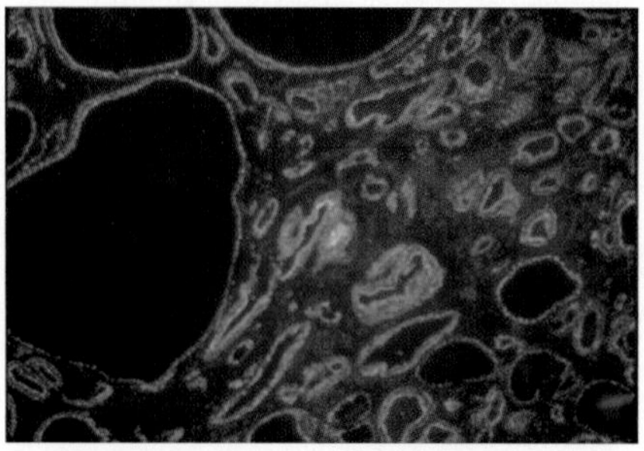

Figure 6.22 Tissue from a prostate carcinoma that has been fixed with formalin, embedded in paraffin, sectioned and hybridized with a biotinylated antisense RNA probe to gastrin-releasing peptide (GRP) receptor mRNA. Following *in situ* hybridization, the biotinylated probe was developed for visualization with alkaline phosphatase–mediated techniques using the ELF® 97 mRNA *In Situ* Hybridization Kit (E6604, E6605). Image contributed by Marty Bartholdi, Berlex Biosciences, Berlex Laboratories, Inc.

A general scheme for the secondary detection methods used to develop the ELF® 97 signal for *in situ* hybridization, cytological labeling, immunohistochemistry and microarrays is shown in Figure 6.21. Please note that the components of these ELF® 97 Kits are not interchangeable. Through the course of our product development, we have discovered that to achieve optimal sensitivity in each type of biological application requires substrate formulations, buffers and protocols that are tailored to the application. For this reason, we strongly recommend that each kit be used only for the applications for which it was developed. However, we also offer the ELF® 97 phosphate (E6588, E6589) as well as the ELF® 97 alcohol cleavage product (E6578) separately, for those researchers who want to develop their own applications. We have found that addition of 1–5 µM ELF® 97 alcohol (E6578) to the enzyme detection medium usually improves the quality of precipitation by reducing the crystal size. Addition of other components to the buffers may also be required to maximize the signal intensity and localize the signal to the target. Incorporation of the ELF® 97 phosphatase substrate into agar plates permits the detection of developing phosphatase activity in bacterial colonies, including the ability to distinguish between secreted and nonsecreted enzymes. The ELF® phosphatase substrate has also been used to assess diffusion of molecules in liver slices and rat hepatocytes [18] and to detect alkaline phosphatase activity in microemulsions.[19] A particularly promising use of the ELF® 97 phosphatase substrate is the detection of immobilized proteins and nucleic acids on microarrays.[20]

ELF® 97 mRNA In Situ *Hybridization Kits*

The optimized reagents and protocols in our ELF® 97 mRNA *In Situ* Hybridization Kits provide a rapid and sensitive assay for detecting mRNA *in situ* hybridization signals in cells and tissue sections [5–7] (Figure 6.22, Figure 8.94). In conventional mRNA *in situ* hybridization, radioactively labeled DNA or RNA probes are hybridized to the experimental sample and then detected by applying a photosensitive emulsion to the microscope slides.[21] Typically, the emulsion is exposed for days, and sometimes weeks, before it is developed and photographed using white-light microscopy. In contrast, ELF® 97 signals develop in seconds to minutes, producing a fluorescent precipitate that is significantly brighter than signals achieved either with directly labeled fluorescent nucleic acid probes or with hapten-labeled probes in combination with fluorophore-labeled secondary detection reagents.[8–10] Moreover, the fluorescent ELF® 97 signals can be clearly distinguished from sample pigmentation, which often obscures the dark silver grains in the emulsion.

The ELF® 97 mRNA *In Situ* Hybridization Kits include:

- Alkaline phosphatase streptavidin (only in Kit #2, E6605)
- ELF® wash, blocking and developing buffers
- Application-specific ELF® 97 phosphatase substrate solution
- Hoechst 33342 nucleic acid counterstain
- ELF® mounting medium
- 50 plastic coverslips
- A detailed protocol

The ELF® 97 mRNA *In Situ* Hybridization Kit #2 (E6605), which contains alkaline phosphatase streptavidin, can be used to detect biotinylated DNA probes, biotinylated RNA probes or digoxigenin-labeled probes in conjunction with a biotinylated anti-digoxigenin antibody.[22] The ELF® 97 mRNA *In Situ* Hybridization Kit #1 (E6604), which does not include alkaline phosphatase streptavidin, is designed for use with other alkaline phosphatase conjugates that have been applied to detect DNA or RNA probes labeled with haptens other than biotin. Each kit contains sufficient reagents for 50 slides or coverslips. Several other useful reagents for *in situ* hybridization are described in Section 8.5.

ELF® 97 Cytological Labeling Kit

The ELF® 97 Cytological Labeling Kit facilitates the detection of a broad range of cellular targets, including cell-surface sites, cytoplasmic organelles, nuclear antigens and cytoskeletal networks.[23] Molecular Probes' researchers have used this ELF® 97 Kit to stain both actin filaments and microtubules (Figure 6.23, Figure 6.24, Figure 6.25) and have found that resolution of the ELF® 97 signal is approximately equivalent to that achieved with direct fluorophore-labeled probes and secondary reagents, but the intensity of the ELF® 97 signal is about an order-of-magnitude greater and the photostability can be several orders-of-magnitude greater. Labeling of cell-surface receptors with the ELF® 97 Cytological Labeling Kit also results in signals that are many times brighter and more photostable than those produced by conventional methods.[8] This versatile kit can potentially be used to detect any subcellular structure that can be selectively labeled with a biotinylated or haptenylated ligand (Figure 6.26). The ELF® 97 Cytological Labeling Kit was combined with a classical hematoxylin/eosin–phloxin stain in a method to visualize glucagon in rat pancreas sections embedded in 2-hydroxyethyl methacrylate[24] (GMA). This combination of stains allowed the researchers to observe the glucagon labeled with the ELF® 97 alcohol precipitate as well as the fine cell and tissue structures characteristic of GMA-embedded sections.

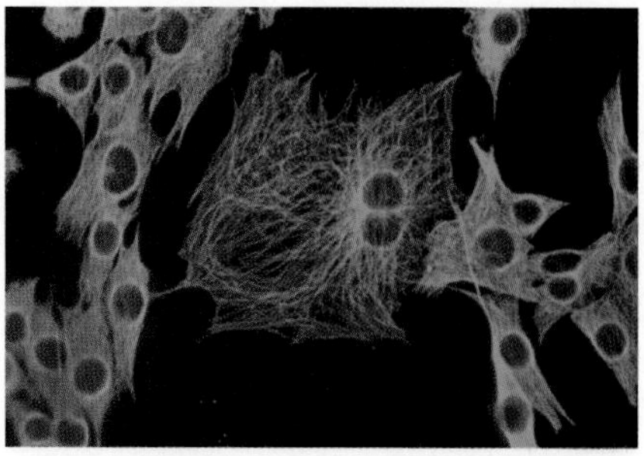

Figure 6.23 Mouse fibroblast microtubules labeled with a mouse monoclonal anti-β-tubulin antibody in conjunction with biotin-XX goat anti-mouse IgG antibody (B2763) and then developed for visualization with alkaline phosphatase–mediated techniques using the ELF® 97 Cytological Labeling Kit (E6603). This kit's novel ELF® 97 phosphatase substrate yields a yellow-green-fluorescent precipitate at the site of alkaline phosphatase activity. Prior to antibody labeling, mouse fibroblasts were fixed and permeabilized in the presence of cytoskeletal stabilizing buffer and treated with paclitaxel (P3456) to stabilize microtubule structures. The image was deconvolved using Huygens software (Scientific Volume Imaging, www.svi.nl).

The ELF® 97 Cytological Labeling Kit (E6603) includes:

- Alkaline phosphatase streptavidin
- Application-specific ELF® 97 phosphatase substrate solution plus additives
- ELF® wash, blocking and developing buffers
- ELF® mounting medium
- A detailed protocol

Each kit provides sufficient reagents for 50 slides or coverslips.

ELF® 97 Immunohistochemistry Kit

The ELF® 97 phosphatase substrate in our ELF® 97 Immunohistochemistry Kit has been specially formulated to reduce nonspecific staining in immunohistochemical preparations. In addition to a detailed protocol, this kit contains the key reagents for detecting antigens in tissue sections, including streptavidin and biotinylated alkaline phosphatase. The streptavidin provided in the kit is used to link the biotinylated alkaline phosphatase with a biotinylated secondary antibody — a common immunohistochemical technique for optimizing tissue penetration. We have used the ELF® 97 Immunohistochemistry Kit to characterize a number of antibodies generated against the zebrafish retina (Figure 6.2, Figure 6.27) and found that the ELF® 97 alcohol staining pattern was identical to that seen with fluorophore-conjugated secondary reagents.[14] The ELF® 97 signal could easily be visualized despite this tissue's considerable autofluorescence. Moreover, the staining was approximately 500 times more photostable than that produced by fluorescein-

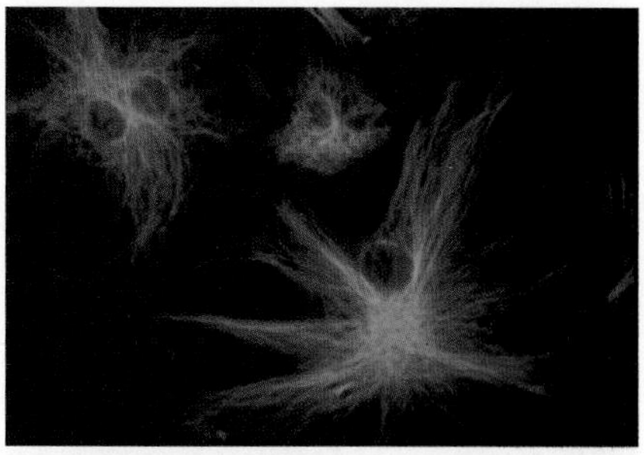

Figure 6.24 Bovine pulmonary artery endothelial cells (BPAEC) fixed and permeabilized in the presence of paclitaxel (P3456) to stabilize the microtubules. Microtubules were then labeled with mouse monoclonal anti-β-tubulin IgG and biotin-XX goat anti-mouse IgG (B2763) and visualized with the ELF® 97 Cytological Labeling Kit (E6603).

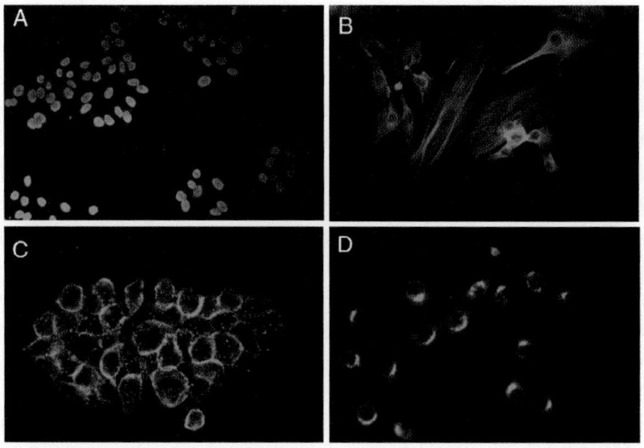

Figure 6.26 Cellular targets developed for visualization with the reagents in our ELF® 97 Cytological Labeling Kit (E6603), using the methods described in Figure 6.21. A) Nuclei in a commercial preparation of human epithelial cells (HEp-2) that have been labeled with human anti-nuclear antibodies and then incubated with biotin-XX goat anti-human IgG antibody. B) Acetone-fixed mouse fibroblast (CRE BAG 2) cells that have been treated with Triton X-100 and then incubated with biotin-XX phalloidin (B7474, Section 11.1), a probe specific for actin stress fibers. C) Formaldehyde-fixed human carcinoma cells that have been incubated with biotin-XX epidermal growth factor (E3477, Section 16.1). D) Mouse fibroblast cells that have been probed with antibodies directed against rat medial Golgi cisternae (a gift from Vivek Malhotra, University of California, San Diego) and then incubated with biotin-XX goat anti-rabbit IgG antibody (B2770, Section 7.2). In each case, the biotinylated probe was detected with alkaline phosphatase streptavidin, followed by incubation with the ELF® 97 phosphatase substrate.

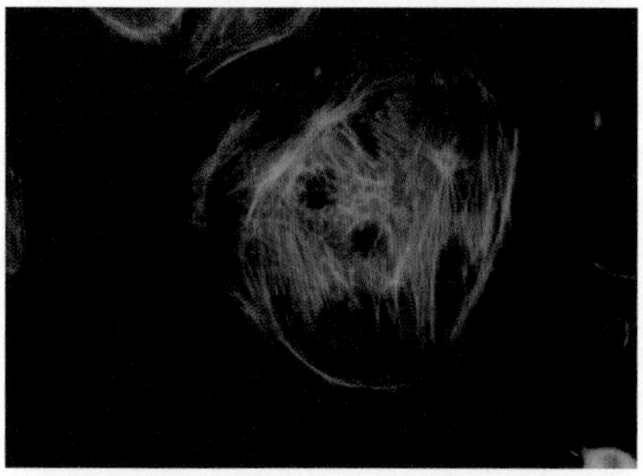

Figure 6.25 Bovine pulmonary artery endothelial cells that were fixed with acetone, treated with Triton X-100, incubated with biotin-XX phalloidin (B7474) and then developed for visualization with the ELF® Cytological Labeling Kit (E6603). Actin stress fibers were photographed through the ELF® filter set.

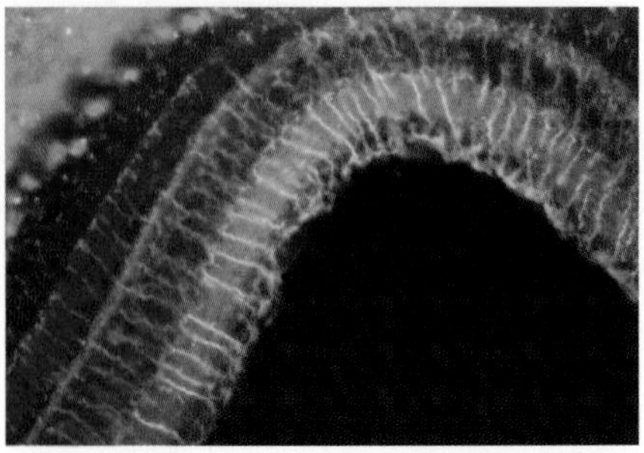

Figure 6.27 A transverse section through adult zebrafish retina that has been probed with anti–glial fibrillary acidic protein antibody (anti-GFAP antibody, A21282) and then developed for visualization with alkaline phosphatase–mediated techniques using our ELF® 97 Immunohistochemistry Kit (E6600). This kit's ELF® 97 phosphatase substrate yields an extremely photostable yellow-green signal at the site of anti-GFAP binding, clearly showing that this antibody binds to Müller cells in the zebrafish retina. The retinal section has been counterstained with Hoechst 33342 (H1399, H3570, H21492), which stains all nuclei blue, and with tetramethylrhodamine wheat germ agglutinin (W849), which stains both the inner and outer plexiform layers as well as the photoreceptor outer segments red.

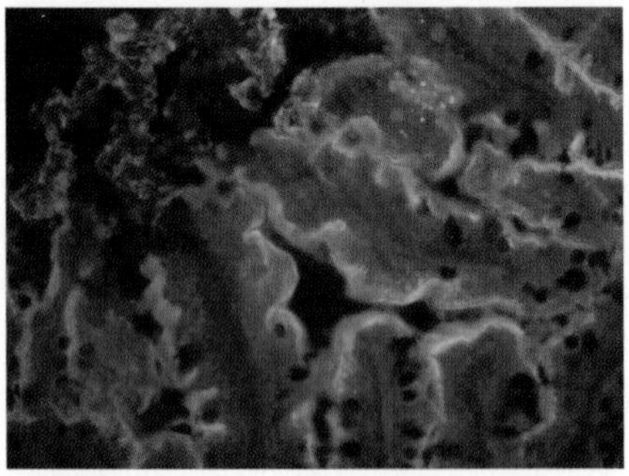

Figure 6.28 Lightly fixed adult zebrafish intestine stained with the substrate contained in the ELF® 97 Endogenous Phosphatase Detection Kit (E6601). This kit's novel ELF® substrate yields a green-fluorescent precipitate at the site of endogenous phosphatase activity. A partially digested brine shrimp, which also contains endogenous phosphatase activity, can be seen in the top left corner of this micrograph. The tissue was counterstained with propidium iodide (P1304MP, P3566, P21493) so that the entire contents of the cells fluoresce red.

labeled secondary reagents.[14] ELF® 97 phosphate has been used to measure endogenous phosphatase activity and, in combination with alkaline phosphatase–immunoconjugates, to detect intracellular cell cycle–associated proteins such as cyclin B1 by flow cytometry.[25–27] A detailed description of the proper laser and filter combinations can be found at the web site of our collaborator William Telford (http://home.ncifcrf.gov/ccr/flowcore/index.htm).

The ELF® 97 Immunohistochemistry Kit (E6600) provides sufficient reagents for preparing 50 mL of detection solution, which is adequate for staining 250 to 1000 sections. The ELF® 97 Immunohistochemistry Kit includes:

- Application-specific ELF® 97 phosphatase substrate solution
- Streptavidin
- Biotinylated alkaline phosphatase
- ELF® reaction buffer
- ELF® mounting medium
- A detailed protocol

We also offer biotin- and DSB-X™ biotin–conjugated secondary antibodies, including those of goat anti–mouse IgG and goat anti–rabbit IgG antibodies, for use in this application; see Table 7.1 for a complete list of our secondary antibodies.

Endogenous Biotin-Blocking Kit

Mammalian cells and tissues contain biotin-dependent carboxylases, which are required for a variety of metabolic functions. These biotin-containing enzymes produce substantial background signals when biotin–streptavidin detection systems are used to identify cellular targets[28] (Figure 12.27, Figure 12.28). Because the ELF® technology is so sensitive, we recommend preblocking endogenous biotin in cells with our Endogenous Biotin-Blocking Kit (E21390) when staining cells using our ELF® 97 Kits containing streptavidin conjugates. The Endogenous Biotin-Blocking Kit provides streptavidin and biotin solutions in convenient dropper bottles and an easy-to-follow protocol. Sufficient material is provided for approximately one hundred 18 mm × 18 mm glass coverslips.

ELF® 97 Endogenous Phosphatase Detection Kit

Molecular Probes' scientists have used the ELF® 97 phosphatase substrate to develop a novel fluorescence-based assay for detecting phosphatases in tissue sections and cells[8] (Figure 6.28, Figure 6.29, Figure 10.33). The ELF® 97 Endogenous Phosphatase Detection Kit provides several advantages over traditional approaches to phosphatase histochemistry. Most phosphatase substrates used in histochemistry yield colorless, soluble hydrolysis products that must be coupled with a capture reagent to generate a colored or fluorescent precipitate. This coupling step can give rise to signal diffusion and high backgrounds. In contrast, hydrolysis of ELF® 97 phosphate generates a bright yellow-green–fluorescent precipitate at the site of enzymatic activity (Figure 6.15), which not only leads to higher resolution and lower background, but also significantly reduces the amount of time required for detection.[8] The ELF® 97 alcohol precipitate shows about 10-fold higher sensitivity and much greater photostability than the Fast Red Violet LB (FRV) azo dye adduct — the product of the only other comparable fluorescent phosphatase detection method. In fact, the fluorescence signal of the ELF® 97 alcohol precipitate is up to 500 times more photostable than that of fluorescein,[14] allowing plenty of time to carefully examine and photograph samples. Use of appropriate filter sets (Table 23.9) permits facile separation of the green fluorescence of the ELF® 97 alcohol precipitate from the green fluorescence of fluorescein conjugates.

The ELF® 97 endogenous phosphatase detection system uses a simple protocol and is compatible with many types of tissue preparations, including tissue cryosections, paraffin-embedded sections and cultured cells. The fluorescence excitation and emission maxima (~365/530 nm) of the ELF® 97 alcohol precipitate are well separated, allowing researchers to easily distinguish the signal from autofluorescence and from other fluorescent labels. Using appropriate excitation filters, it is even possible to distinguish the fluorescence emission from that of other green-fluorescent dyes such as fluorescein, the Oregon Green® dyes or the Alexa Fluor® 488 dye.

Phosphatases have been commonly used as enzyme markers, allowing researchers to identify primordial germ cells,[29] to distinguish subpopulations of bone marrow stromal cells[30] and to investigate *in vitro* differentiation in carcinoma cell lines.[31–33] Because ELF® 97 phosphate is intrinsically membrane impermeant, it can be utilized as a marker for membrane integrity in which the intracellular phosphatase activity of membrane-compromised cells is detected.[34] The intense green fluorescence of the ELF® 97 alcohol precipitate (Figure 6.17) and its high photostability (Figure 6.16) permit facile localization of single cells in tissues. We have successfully used the ELF® 97 Endogenous Phosphatase Detection Kit to localize phosphatase activity in several different zebrafish tissues and in cultured rat osteosarcoma cells by fluorescence microscopy.[8] The patterns of ELF® 97 alcohol staining in intestine (Figure 6.28), kidney (Figure 6.30), ovary and gills (Figure 10.33) were essentially identical to the patterns of black precipitate produced by the conventional Gomori technique, but showed much higher spatial resolution. Using ELF® 97 phosphate and confocal laser-scanning microscopy, researchers have developed a semiautomated method for analyzing the position of transfected cells expressing the alkaline phosphatase reporter gene within a regenerating newt limb.[35] ELF® 97 phosphate was also used to detect endogenous alkaline phosphatase activity in intact rat osteosarcoma cells and primary cultures of chick chondrocytes by flow cytometry.[25,27] Furthermore, the ELF® 97 Endogenous Phosphatase Detection Kit has been used to monitor and quantitate alkaline phosphatase activity in marine phytoplankton[36,37] and bacteria.[38,39] In addition to an easy-to-follow protocol, the ELF® 97 Endogenous Phosphatase Detection Kit (E6601) provides each of the following in quantities sufficient to stain 50–250 tissue sections:

- ELF® 97 phosphatase substrate solution
- ELF® detection buffer
- ELF® mounting medium

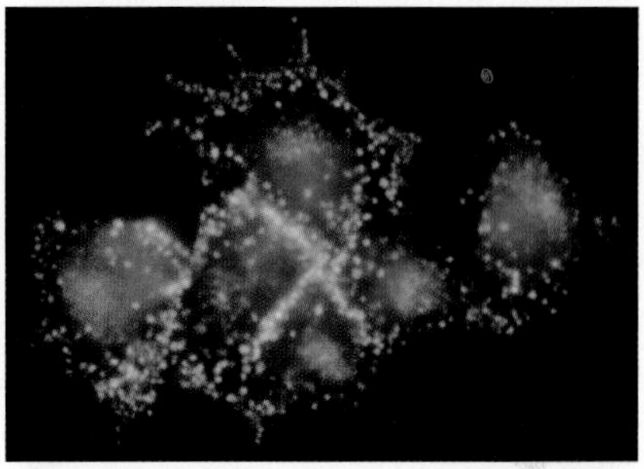

Figure 6.29 Endogenous alkaline phosphatase enzyme of osteosarcoma cells localized with the ELF® 97 Endogenous Phosphatase Detection Kit (E6601). Unlike other phosphatase substrates, the unique ELF® 97 phosphatase substrate forms a fluorescent precipitate at the site of enzymatic activity. The blue-fluorescent nucleic acid stain Hoechst 33342 (H1399, H3570, H21492) was used as a counterstain to the green fluorescence of the ELF® 97 alcohol precipitate. The double-exposure image was acquired using a bandpass filter set appropriate for ELF® 97 alcohol and a longpass filter set appropriate for DAPI.

Reagents and Accessories for the ELF® 97 Kits

Molecular Probes offers the alkaline phosphatase conjugates of streptavidin (S921, Section 7.6) and of the goat anti–mouse IgG antibody (G21060), goat anti–mouse F(ab′)$_2$ fragment (F21452), goat anti–rabbit IgG antibody (G21079), goat anti–rabbit F(ab′)$_2$ fragment (F21456) and rabbit anti–goat IgG antibody (R21458, Section 7.2, Table 7.1). Although we have not developed optimized conditions for use of these reagents in detection schemes, they may be useful for signal amplification of antibody- or biotin-labeled targets.

Our Zenon® antibody labeling technology (Section 7.3) permits the rapid and quantitative formation of dye and enzyme complexes with the Fc portion of an intact antibody (Figure 7.59). The alkaline phosphatase–antibody complexes formed with our Zenon® Alkaline Phosphatase Antibody Labeling Kits (Section 7.3, Table 7.13) can be used in combination with the ELF® 97 Kits or with other applications for alkaline phosphatase–conjugated antibodies such as ELISAs.

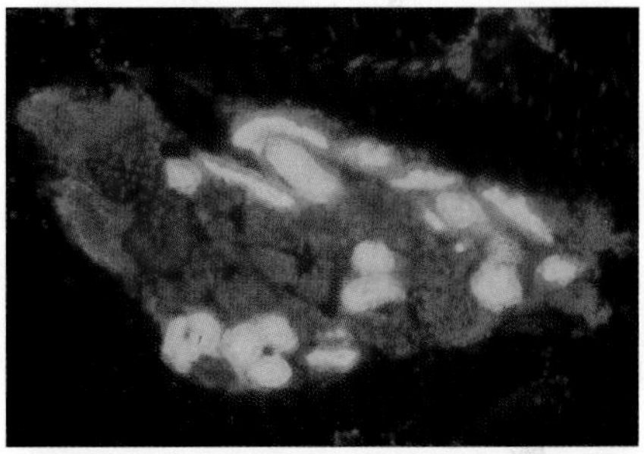

Figure 6.30 A cryostat section through adult zebrafish kidney that was incubated with the ELF® 97 phosphatase substrate in our ELF® 97 Endogenous Phosphatase Detection Kit (E6601) and counterstained with propidium iodide (P1304MP, P3566, P21493). The ELF® 97 alcohol signal, which is ordinarily green fluorescent, appears yellow in this section because the phosphatase activity is in close proximity to the nuclei, which are stained red by the propidium iodide. This double-exposure image was obtained using longpass filter sets appropriate for ELF® 97 alcohol product and tetramethylrhodamine.

ELF® 39 Phosphate, ELF® 97 Glucuronide and ELF® 97 Glucosaminide

ELF® 39 phosphate (Figure 9.65) is a phosphatase substrate that is structurally similar to ELF® 97 phosphate; however, we have found that this phosphatase substrate does not yield the finely grained precipitate that makes ELF® 97 phosphate a preferred signal amplification reagent for histochemical staining and for detection of endogenous phosphatase activity. For Western blots (and most likely for detecting nucleic acid targets on microarrays, where high spatial resolution is not particularly critical), ELF® 39 phosphate yields permanent, fluorescent staining with high sensitivity. Our DyeChrome™ Western Blot Kits #4, #5 and #6 (Section 9.4) use ELF® 39 phosphate and alkaline phosphatase–conjugated secondary antibodies or streptavidin to stain specific proteins, along with our red-fluorescent BODIPY® TR-X succinimidyl ester to detect all proteins on a blot (Figure 9.62). The Pro-Q® Oligohistidine Blot Stain Kit #2 (P21879, Section 9.4) combines a nickel complex of an oligohistidine-binding chelator (biotin NTA) with streptavidin-conjugated alkaline phosphatase and the ELF® 39 phosphatase substrate to provide selective detection of oligohistidine fusion proteins on blots.

ELF® 97 substrates for β-glucuronidase[40,41] (E6587) and chitinase/*N*-acetylglucosaminidase[42,43] (E22011) are described in Section 10.2.

ELF® Spin Filters

Like many enzyme substrates, the ELF® 97 developing solution should be filtered before use for optimal staining. The ELF® spin filters (E6606) — spin-filtration devices with a pore size of 0.2 µm — are both convenient and efficient, permitting a very small volume to be filtered without significant loss. These spin filters are recommended for use with all of our ELF® 97 Kits, as well as the DyeChrome™ and Pro-Q® Oligohistidine Kits that contain ELF® 39 phosphate (Section 9.4). These filters are equally suitable for rapid filtration of aqueous solutions of other probes.

References

1. Endocrinology 143, 239 (2002); **2.** J Histochem Cytochem 48, 1593 (2000); **3.** Proc SPIE-Int Soc Opt Eng 3602, 265 (1999); **4.** Appl Environ Microbiol 69, 2950 (2003); **5.** Trends Genet 12, 387 (1996); **6.** Trends Genet 12, 385 (1996); **7.** A Laboratory Guide to RNA: Isolation, Analysis, and Synthesis, Krieg PA, Ed. pp. 381–409 (1996); **8.** J Histochem Cytochem 47, 1443 (1999); **9.** Am J Hum Genet 55 (Suppl), A271, abstract #1585 (1994); **10.** FASEB J 8, A1444, abstract #1081 (1994); **11.** Optics Comm 64, 457 (1987); **12.** J Phys Chem 74, 4473 (1970); **13.** Anal Biochem 207, 32 (1992); **14.** J Histochem Cytochem 43, 77 (1995); **15.** Cytometry 40, 42 (2000); **16.** J Pathol 191, 452 (2000); **17.** Biotechniques 30, 794 (2001); **18.** Drug Metab Dispos 23, 1274 (1995); **19.** J Pharm Biomed Anal 18, 585 (1998); **20.** Biotechniques 27, 778 (1999); **21.** Nucleic Acid Hybridisation: A Practical Approach, Hames BD, Higgens SJ, Eds. pp. 179–202 (1985); **22.** Cell Growth Differ 13, 227 (2002); **23.** J Microsc 206, 106 (2002); **24.** J Histotechnol 21, 25 (1998); **25.** Cytometry 54A, 48 (2003); **26.** Cytometry 43, 117 (2001); **27.** Cytometry 37, 314 (1999); **28.** J Histochem Cytochem 45, 1053 (1997); **29.** Anatomical Record 118, 135 (1954); **30.** J Histochem Cytochem 40, 1059 (1992); **31.** Dev Biol 88, 279 (1981); **32.** Cell 5, 229 (1975); **33.** Proc Natl Acad Sci U S A 70, 3899 (1973); **34.** J Biol Chem 278, 36250 (2003); **35.** J Histochem Cytochem 44, 559 (1996); **36.** Appl Environ Microbiol 65, 3205 (1999); **37.** Mar Ecol Prog Ser 164, 21 (1998); **38.** J Microbiol Methods 38, 25 (1999); **39.** Appl Environ Microbiol 64, 1526 (1998); **40.** Electrophoresis 21, 497 (2000); **41.** J Biochem Biophys Methods 33, 197 (1996); **42.** Appl Environ Microbiol 66, 3566 (2000); **43.** Appl Environ Microbiol 66, 3574 (2000).

Data Table — 6.3 Enzyme-Labeled Fluorescence (ELF®) Signal-Amplification Technology

Cat #	MW	Storage	Soluble	Abs	EC	Em	Solvent	Notes
E6578	307.14	L	DMSO	345	ND	530	pH 8	1, 2, 3
E6588	431.08	F,L	H_2O	289	12,000	see Notes	pH 10	2, 4, 5
E6589	431.08	F,L	H_2O	289	12,000	see Notes	pH 10	2, 4, 5

For definitions of the contents of this data table, see "Navigating *The Handbook*" in the introductory pages.

Notes

1. ND = not determined.
2. This product is supplied as a ready-made solution in the solvent indicated under "Soluble."
3. ELF® 97 alcohol is insoluble in water. Spectral maxima listed are for an aqueous suspension; for this reason, the value of EC cannot be determined.
4. Enzymatic cleavage of this substrate yields E6578.
5. Fluorescence of the unhydrolyzed substrate is very weak.

Product List — 6.3 Enzyme-Labeled Fluorescence (ELF®) Signal-Amplification Technology

Cat #	Product Name	Unit Size
E6578	ELF® 97 alcohol *1 mM solution in DMSO*	1 mL
E6603	ELF® 97 Cytological Labeling Kit *with streptavidin, alkaline phosphatase conjugate* *50 assays*	1 kit
E6601	ELF® 97 Endogenous Phosphatase Detection Kit	1 kit
E6600	ELF® 97 Immunohistochemistry Kit	1 kit
E6604	ELF® 97 mRNA *In Situ* Hybridization Kit #1 *50 assays*	1 kit
E6605	ELF® 97 mRNA *In Situ* Hybridization Kit #2 *with streptavidin, alkaline phosphatase conjugate* *50 assays*	1 kit
E6589	ELF® 97 phosphatase substrate (ELF® 97 phosphate) *5 mM in water* *contains 2 mM azide*	1 mL
E6588	ELF® 97 phosphatase substrate (ELF® 97 phosphate) *5 mM in water* *0.2 µm filtered*	1 mL
E6606	ELF® spin filters *20 filters*	1 box
E21390	Endogenous Biotin-Blocking Kit *100 assays*	1 kit

For current prices or to order online, visit probes.invitrogen.com

6.4 Phycobiliproteins

Phycobiliproteins

Phycobiliproteins are a family of highly soluble and reasonably stable fluorescent proteins derived from cyanobacteria and eukaryotic algae. These proteins contain covalently linked tetrapyrrole groups that play a biological role in collecting light and, through fluorescence resonance energy transfer, conveying it to a special pair of chlorophyll molecules located in the photosynthetic reaction center.[1] Because of their role in light collection, phycobiliproteins have evolved to maximize both absorption and fluorescence and to minimize the quenching caused either by internal energy transfer or by external factors such as changes in pH or ionic composition.[2,3]

Phycobiliproteins have several advantages when used as fluorescent probes. These include:

- Intense long-wavelength excitation and emission to provide fluorescence that is relatively free of interference from other biological materials
- Relatively large Stokes shifts with extremely high emission quantum yields
- Fluorescence that is not quenched by external agents because the fluorophores are protected by covalent binding to the protein backbone
- Very high water solubility
- Homogeneous structure with defined molecular weights
- Multiple sites for stable conjugation to many biological and synthetic materials

Spectral Characteristics of Phycobiliproteins

B-Phycoerythrin, R-Phycoerythrin and Allophycocyanin

The phycobiliproteins B-phycoerythrin (B-PE), R-phycoerythrin (R-PE) and allophycocyanin (APC) are among the best dyes currently available for applications that require either high sensitivity or simultaneous multicolor detection.[4–6] Quantum yields up to 0.98 and extinction coefficients up to 2.4 million $cm^{-1}M^{-1}$ have been reported for these fluorescent proteins (Table 6.2). On a molar basis, the fluorescence yield is equivalent to at least 30 unquenched fluorescein or 100 rhodamine molecules at comparable wavelengths. The fluorescence of a single molecule of B-PE has been detected.[7,8] B-PE is more photostable than R-PE, but photostability of R-PE conjugates can be improved by adding 1-propyl gallate.[9]

In practical applications such as flow cytometry and immunoassays,[10,11] the sensitivity of B-PE– and R-PE–conjugated antibodies is usually 5 to 10 times greater than that of the corresponding fluorescein conjugate.[12,13] Using R-PE–conjugated streptavidin, researchers have detected fewer than 100 receptor-bound biotinylated antibodies per cell by flow cytometry.[14] A multistep amplification method utilizing a fluoresceinated opioid, biotinylated anti-fluorescein/Oregon Green® antibody (A982, Section 7.4) and a phycoerythrin conjugate of avidin (A2660) was required to detect low-abundance kappa opioid receptors by flow cytometry. In imaging applications, APC and its conjugates are both brighter and more photostable than Cy5 conjugates (Figure 6.31), likely making APC the most sensitive fluorophore currently available for detection in laser-scanning microscopes that utilize the 633 nm output of the He–Ne laser or the 647 nm spectral line of the Ar–Kr laser; our Tyramide Signal Amplification (TSA) Kits containing Alexa Fluor® 647 tyramide (Section 6.2, Table 6.1) have the potential of yielding even greater signals by a horseradish peroxidase–catalyzed signal amplification method (Figure 6.5).

Figure 6.32 and Figure 6.33 show the spectra for B-PE, R-PE and APC. R-PE can be excited efficiently at 488 nm either with an argon-ion laser or with a broadband illumination source (xenon- or mercury-arc

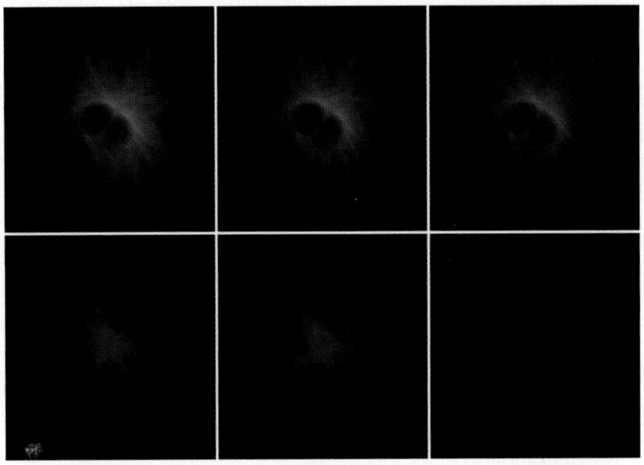

Figure 6.31 A comparison of the photobleaching rates of APC and Cy5 conjugates. The microtubules of bovine pulmonary artery endothelial cells were stained with mouse anti–α-tubulin antibody (A11126) in combination with goat anti-mouse IgG labeled antibody with either crosslinked APC (A865, top series) or the Cy5 dye (bottom series). The samples were exposed to continuous illumination, and the images were acquired at 30-second intervals with a Quantex cooled CCD camera (Photometrics) using filter sets appropriate for both APC and Cy5 dye.

Table 6.2 — Spectral data for B-PE, R-PE and APC

Cat #	Phycobiliprotein	Molecular Weight	Absorption Max (nm)	EC ($cm^{-1}M^{-1}$)	Emission Max (nm)	Fluorescence QY
P800	B-phycoerythrin	240,000	546, 565	2,410,000	575	0.98
P801	R-phycoerythrin	240,000	496, 546, 565	1,960,000	578	0.82
A803, A819	Allophycocyanin	104,000	650	700,000	660	0.68

EC = extinction coefficient. QY = quantum yield.

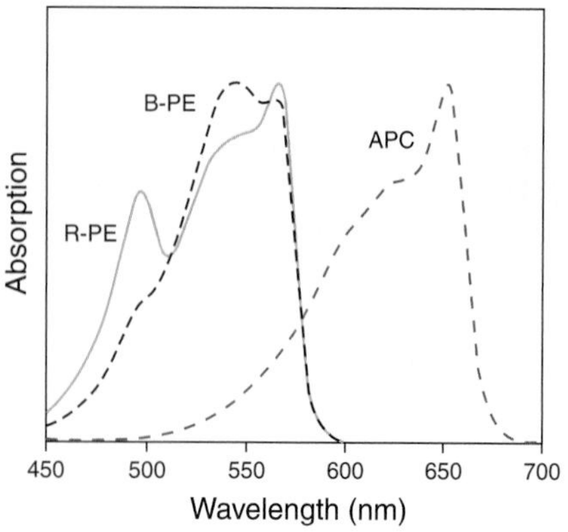

Figure 6.32 Normalized absorption spectra for B-PE, R-PE and APC.

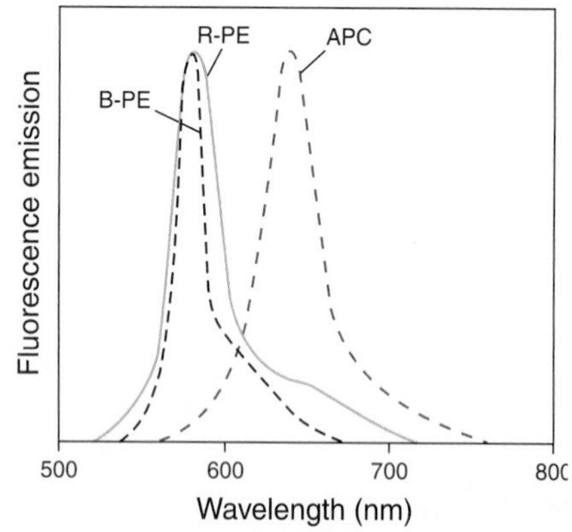

Figure 6.33 Normalized emission spectra for B-PE, R-PE and APC.

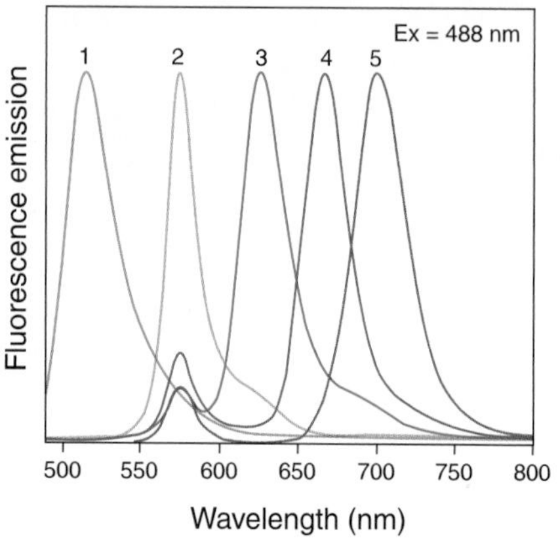

Figure 6.34 Normalized fluorescence emission spectra of 1) Alexa Fluor® 488 goat anti–mouse IgG antibody (A11001), 2) R-phycoerythrin goat anti–mouse IgG antibody (P852), 3) Alexa Fluor® 610–R-phycoerythrin goat anti–mouse IgG antibody (A20980), 4) Alexa Fluor® 647–R-phycoerythrin goat anti–mouse IgG antibody (A20990) and 5) Alexa Fluor® 680–R-phycoerythrin goat anti–mouse IgG antibody (A20983). The tandem conjugates permit simultaneous multicolor labeling and detection of up to five targets with excitation by a single excitation source — the 488 nm spectral line of the argon-ion laser.

lamps) and a standard fluorescein optical filter set (Table 23.9). With the proper emission filters, fluorescein (or any of the principal fluorescein substitutes described in Chapter 1) and R-PE can be simultaneously detected at approximately 520 nm and at wavelengths longer than 575 nm, respectively, making R-PE conjugates ideal for multicolor flow cytometry applications.[15,16] One of the fluorescent microsphere suspensions in our CompenFlow™ Flow Cytometry Compensation Kit (C7301, Section 23.2) has emission spectra that almost exactly match those of the phycoerythrins (Figure 23.36). This microsphere suspension is designed to help flow cytometry operators set up compensation circuits that properly remove unwanted phycoerythrin signals from secondary channels. Conjugates prepared from APC are ideal for use with the 633 nm spectral line of the red He–Ne laser,[11,17] or the 647 nm spectral line of the krypton-ion laser.

Tandem Conjugates of Phycobiliproteins

A phycoerythrin-labeled detection reagent can be used in combination with a green-fluorescent detection reagent to detect two different signals using simultaneous excitation with the 488 nm spectral line of the argon-ion laser.[18] By conjugating R-PE to longer-wavelength light–emitting fluorescence acceptors, an energy transfer cascade is established wherein excitation of the R-PE produces fluorescence of the acceptor dye by the process of fluorescence resonance energy transfer (FRET) (see Note 1.2 "Technical Focus: Fluorescence Resonance Energy Transfer (FRET)" in Section 1.3). This process, which occurs naturally within single molecules and assemblies of phycobiliproteins (phycobilisomes), can be quite efficient, resulting in almost total transfer of energy from the phycobiliprotein to the acceptor dye of these "tandem conjugates." Thus, it is possible to combine a green-fluorescent antibody conjugate with an R-PE conjugate, as mentioned above, and then to add tandem conjugates of R-PE with either our Alexa Fluor® 610, Alexa Fluor® 647 or Alexa Fluor® 680 dyes for simultaneous detection of up to five targets using only 488 nm excitation (Figure 6.34, Figure 6.35, Figure 6.36). We have also conjugated APC to our Alexa Fluor® 680, Alexa Fluor® 700 and Alexa Fluor® 750 dyes to provide tandem conjugates that can be excited by the He-Ne laser at 633 nm or by the krypton-ion laser at 647 nm. The Alexa Fluor® dye–APC tandem conjugates can potentially be combined with direct APC conjugates for simultaneous three- or four-color applications (Figure 6.37).

As the absorption and emission maxima of the acceptor dye move to longer wavelengths, the energy transfer efficiency from the R-PE to the bound dyes tends to decrease; also, the quantum yields of the longer-wavelength acceptor dyes in the conjugates tend to be lower than those of the shorter-wavelength dyes and to decrease further at high degrees of substitution. Consequently, the preparation of tandem conjugates necessarily involves careful optimization of both the energy transfer efficiency from the R-PE to the longer-wavelength–emitting acceptor dye and the total brightness of the tandem conjugate (Figure 6.38, Figure 6.39). For our Alexa Fluor® 647 and Alexa Fluor® 680 tandem conjugates of R-PE, the energy transfer efficiency from R-PE to the attached dye is about 99% and 98%, respectively, as determined from their fluorescence at 575 nm relative to unconjugated R-PE. The residual signal that overlaps the unquenched R-PE emission can be compensated by methods familiar to flow cytometrists.

Phycoerythrin has previously been conjugated to our Texas Red® dye to provide a third signal that is excitable at 488 nm; however, our Alexa Fluor® 610 conjugates of R-PE (A20980, A20981, S20982) have emission properties superior to those of commercially available Texas Red® conjugates of R-PE. Not only are the Alexa Fluor® 610–R-PE tandem conjugates more fluorescent than the commercially available Texas Red®–R-PE tandem conjugates, but also the fluorescence emission of Alexa Fluor® 610–R-PE tandem conjugates is shifted to somewhat longer wavelengths than is the emission of Texas Red®–R-PE conjugates, resulting in better separation from the emission of R-PE (Figure 6.39). Our Alexa Fluor® 647 (A20990, A20991, S20992) and Alexa Fluor® 680 (A20983, A20984, S20985) conjugates of R-PE have emission spectra almost identical to those of Cy5–R-PE and Cy5.5–R-PE conjugates but tend to have more intense long-wavelength emission and to require less compensation in the R-PE channel than the Cy dye–R-PE tandem conjugates (Figure 6.38, Figure 6.40).

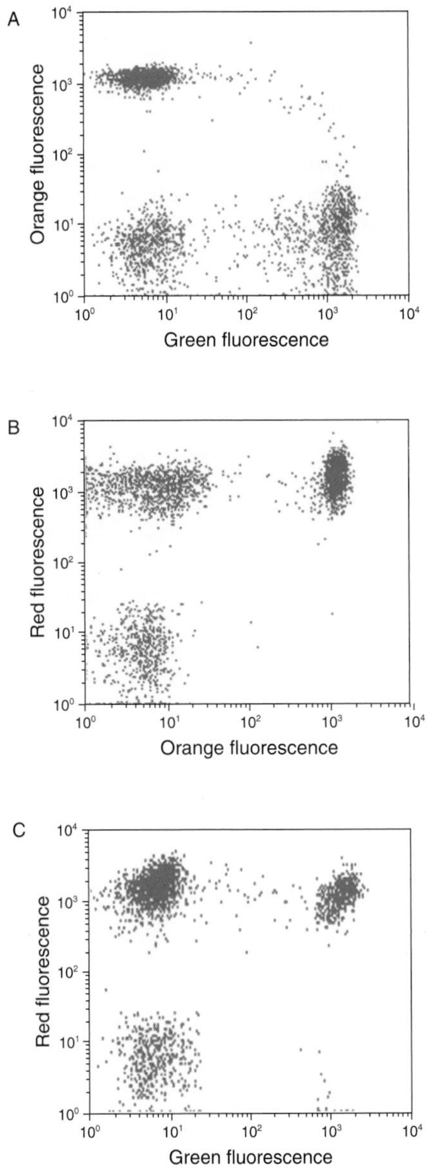

Figure 6.35 Simultaneous detection of three cell surface markers using an Alexa Fluor® 610-R-phycoerythrin tandem conjugate, Alexa Fluor® 488 dye and R-phycoerythrin labels. Lymphocytes from ammonium chloride RBC-lysed whole blood were labeled with a biotinylated mouse anti-human CD3 monoclonal antibody (Caltag Laboratories), washed with 1% BSA in PBS and then incubated with Alexa Fluor® 610-R-phycoerythrin tandem dye-labeled streptavidin (S20982). Cells were again washed and then labeled with directly conjugated primary antibodies against the CD8 and CD4 markers (Alexa Fluor® 488 dye-labeled mouse anti-human CD8 antibody (A21339) and R-phycoerythrin-conjugated mouse anti-human CD4 antibody (A21337). After a further wash in 1% BSA/PBS, labeling was analyzed on a Becton Dickinson FACScan flow cytometer using excitation at 488 nm. CD8 was detected in the green channel (525 ± 10 nm), CD4 in the orange channel (575 ± 10 nm) and CD3 in the red channel (>650 nm). The bivariate scatter plots show the expected mutually exclusive populations of CD4 and CD8 positive cells (panel A), together with co-positive CD3/CD4 (panel B) and CD3/CD8 (panel C) populations.

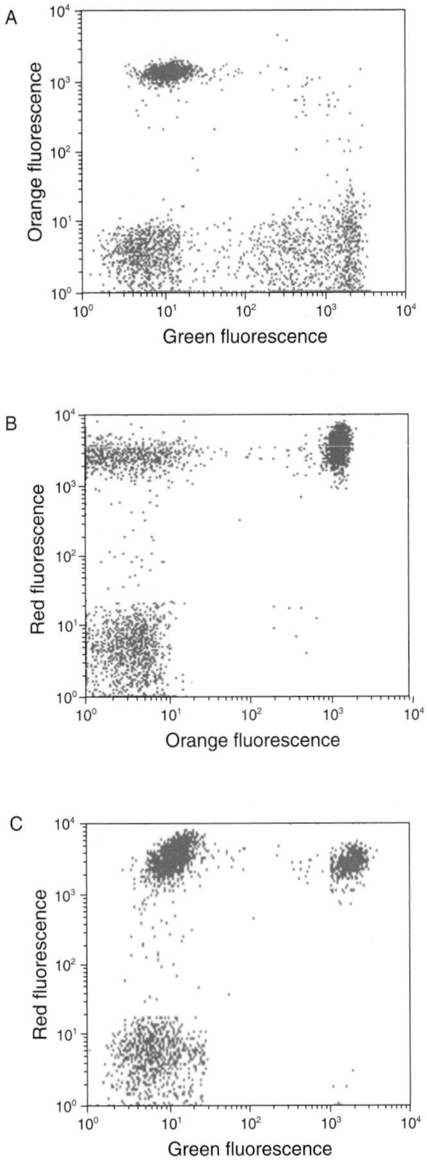

Figure 6.36 Simultaneous detection of three cell surface markers using an Alexa Fluor® 647-R-phycoerythrin tandem conjugate, Alexa Fluor® 488 dye and R-phycoerythrin labels. Lymphocytes from ammonium chloride RBC-lysed whole blood were labeled with a mouse anti-human CD3 monoclonal antibody (Caltag Laboratories), washed with 1% BSA in PBS and then incubated with a goat anti-mouse IgG antibody labeled with the Alexa Fluor® 647-R-phycoerythrin tandem dye (A20990). Cells were again washed and then labeled with directly conjugated primary antibodies against the CD8 and CD4 markers (Alexa Fluor® 488 dye-labeled mouse anti-human CD8 antibody (A21339) and R-phycoerythrin-conjugated mouse anti-human CD4 antibody (A21337). After a further wash in 1% BSA/PBS, labeling was analyzed on a Becton Dickinson FACScan flow cytometer using excitation at 488 nm. CD8 was detected in the green channel (525 ± 10 nm), CD4 in the orange channel (575 ± 10 nm) and CD3 in the red channel (>650 nm). The bivariate scatter plots show the expected mutually exclusive populations of CD4 and CD8 positive cells (panel A), together with co-positive CD3/CD4 (panel B) and CD3/CD8 (panel C) populations.

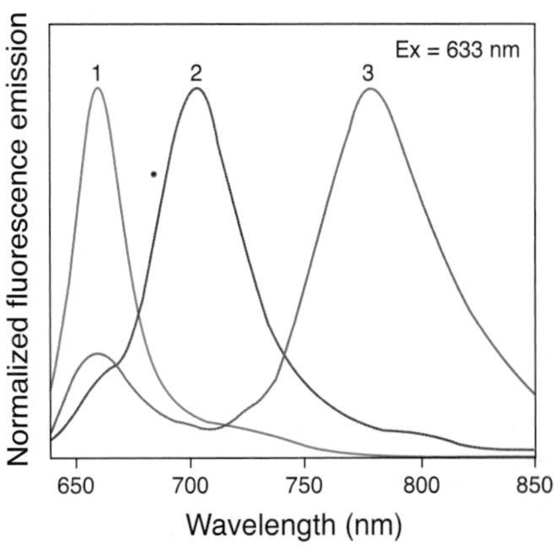

Figure 6.37 Normalized fluorescence emission spectra of 1) allophycocyanin goat anti-mouse IgG antibody (A865), 2) Alexa Fluor® 680-allophycocyanin goat anti-mouse IgG antibody (A21000) and 3) Alexa Fluor® 750-allophycocyanin goat anti-mouse IgG antibody (A21006). The tandem conjugates permit simultaneous multicolor labeling and detection of up to three targets with excitation by a single excitation source — the 633 nm spectral line of the He-Ne laser.

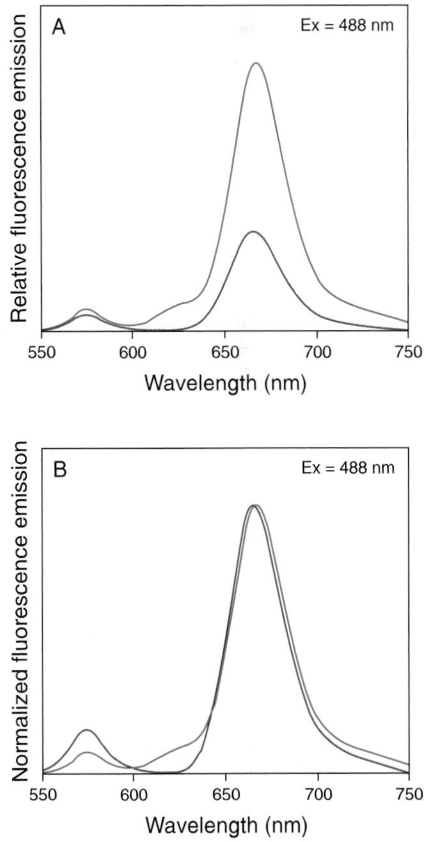

Figure 6.38 Fluorescence emission spectra of Alexa Fluor® 647-R-phycoerythrin streptavidin (S20992; red) and Cy5-R-phycoerythrin streptavidin (Caltag Laboratories; blue) tandem conjugates. Panel A shows a comparison of the spectra on a relative fluorescence intensity scale for samples prepared with equal absorbance at the excitation wavelength (488 nm). Panel B shows the same data normalized to the same peak intensity value to facilitate comparison of the spectral profiles.

Pure Phycobiliproteins

Molecular Probes was the first company to make the phycobiliproteins available for research, and we can supply bulk quantities of B-PE (P800), R-PE (P801), APC (A803), chemically crosslinked APC (A819) and their conjugates at a considerable discount.

Phycobiliproteins may undergo some loss of fluorescence upon freezing. The pure proteins are shipped in an ammonium sulfate suspension and are stable for at least one year when stored at 4°C. The conjugates and modified derivatives are shipped in solutions containing sodium azide to inhibit bacterial growth and typically have a useful life of more than six months. *All phycobiliproteins and their derivatives should be stored refrigerated, never frozen.*

Phycobiliprotein Conjugates

Reactive Phycobiliprotein Derivative

Conjugates of R-PE with other proteins are generally prepared from the pyridyldisulfide derivative of R-PE (P806). This derivative can be directly reacted with thiolated antibodies, enzymes and other biomolecules to form a disulfide linkage. More commonly, however, the pyridyldisulfide groups in this derivative are first reduced to thiols, which are then reacted with maleimide-derivatized proteins (Figure 5.4). Because the pyridyldisulfide derivative of R-PE is somewhat unstable, we recommend using it within three months of receipt. Phycobiliproteins can be conveniently crosslinked to other proteins using the reagents and protocol provided in our Protein–Protein Crosslinking Kit (P6305, Section 5.2).

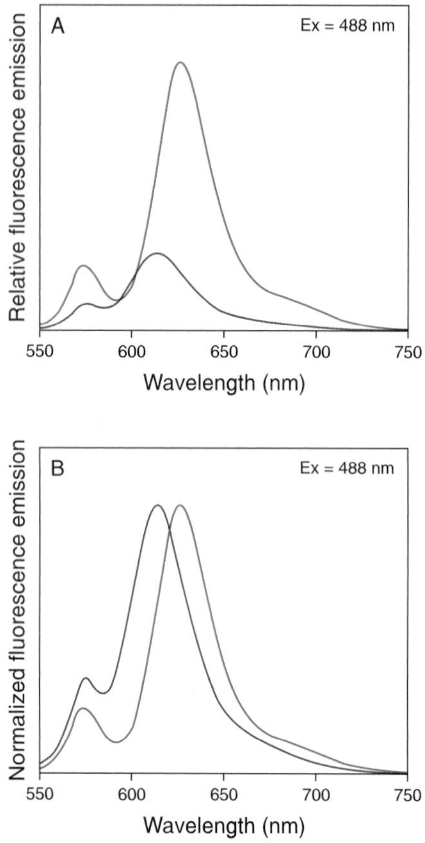

Figure 6.39 Fluorescence emission spectra of Alexa Fluor® 610–R-phycoerythrin streptavidin (S20982; red) and Texas Red®–R-phycoerythrin streptavidin (Caltag Laboratories; blue) tandem conjugates. Panel A shows a comparison of the spectra on a relative fluorescence intensity scale for samples prepared with equal absorbance at the excitation wavelength (488 nm). Panel B shows the same data normalized to the same peak intensity value to facilitate comparison of the spectral profiles.

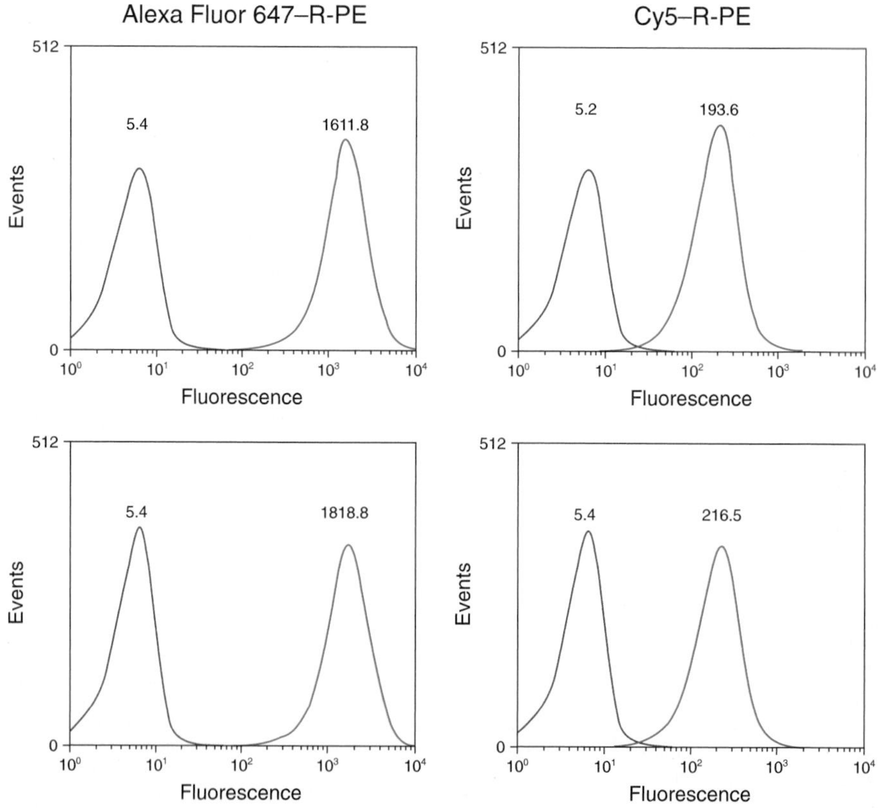

Figure 6.40 Comparison of immunofluorescent staining by R-phycoerythrin–dye tandem conjugates. EL4 cells labeled with a biotinylated anti-CD44 monoclonal antibody (Caltag Laboratories) were detected with streptavidin conjugates of Alexa Fluor® 647–R-PE (S20992) or Cy5–R-PE (Serotec). The cells were analyzed by flow cytometry on a Coulter XL cytometer using excitation at 488 nm. Data were obtained using an bandpass emission filter (675 ± 20 nm; upper panels) or a longpass emission filter (>650 nm; lower panels). In each histogram, unstained and stained cells are represented by the blue and red lines, respectively. The numbers above each peak represent mean channel fluorescence intensities. Data provided by William Telford, NCI-NIH, Bethesda, MD.

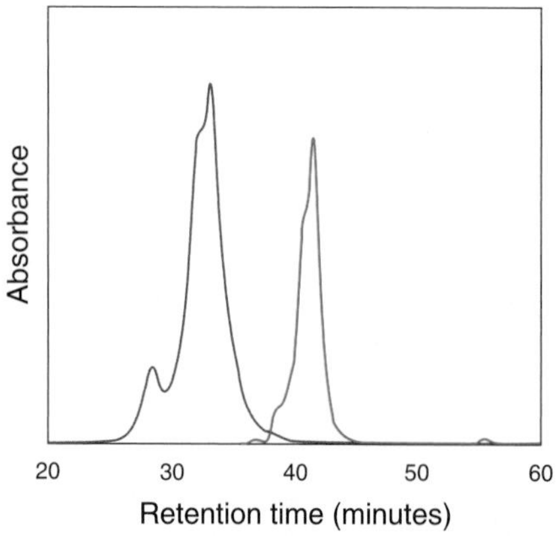

Figure 6.41 Analytical size-exclusion chromatograms of free streptavidin (S888; red curve, detected by absorption at 280 nm) and R-phycoerythrin streptavidin (SAPE; S866, S21388; blue curve, detected by absorption at 565 nm), demonstrating that the R-phycoerythrin conjugate is substantially free of unconjugated streptavidin.

Phycobiliprotein-Labeled Secondary Detection Reagents

Molecular Probes regularly prepares R-PE conjugates of the goat anti–mouse IgG (P852) and goat anti–rabbit IgG (P2771MP) antibodies and NeutrAvidin biotin-binding protein (A2660), as well as both the R-PE (SAPE, S866) and B-PE (S32350) conjugates of streptavidin. R-PE conjugates of anti–mouse IgG_1, IgG_{2a} and IgG_{2b} antibodies are also available (P21129, P21139, P21149). Our streptavidin conjugates of R-PE and B-PE have been purified to ensure that all unconjugated streptavidin has been removed (Figure 6.41), making them useful for multicolor flow cytometry and microarray assays [19–26] (Section 8.5, Figure 6.42). In addition, biotinylated R-PE (P811) can be used with standard avidin/streptavidin bridging techniques to detect biotinylated molecules.[27]

Because APC tends to dissociate into subunits when highly diluted or treated with chaotropic agents, Molecular Probes prepares all of its APC conjugates — including APC tandem conjugates, APC conjugates of the goat anti–mouse IgG (A865) and goat anti–rabbit IgG (A10931) antibodies and APC-labeled streptavidin (S868) — from chemically crosslinked APC (A819), a protein complex that does not dissociate even in strongly chaotropic salts.[28–30] We also prepare premium-grade R-PE and APC conjugates of streptavidin (S21388, S32362), which represent an even further fractionation of our R-PE streptavidin (S866) and APC streptavidin (S868), respectively.

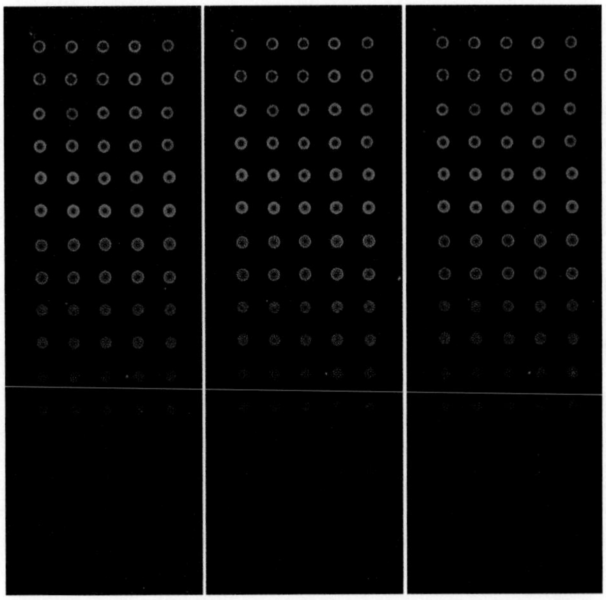

Figure 6.42 R-phycoerythrin used to detect DNA on a microarray. A DNA microarray containing a decreasing dilution of calf thymus DNA was hybridized with a biotinylated DNA probe and then incubated with R-phycoerythrin–streptavidin (SAPE; S866, S21388). After washing, the fluorescence signal was detected on a Packard ScanArray 5000 using three different detection configurations: 488 nm excitation (argon-ion laser)/570 nm emission filter (left); 543.5 nm excitation (He-Ne laser)/570 nm emission filter (middle); 543.5 nm excitation (He-Ne laser)/592 nm emission filter (right).

Secondary Detection Reagents Labeled with Alexa Fluor® Dye–Phycobiliprotein Tandem Conjugates

We have conjugated R-PE with three of our Alexa Fluor® dyes — the Alexa Fluor® 610, Alexa Fluor® 647 and Alexa Fluor® 680 dyes — and then conjugated these fluorescent proteins to antibodies or streptavidin to yield secondary detection reagents that can be excited with the 488 nm spectral line of the argon-ion laser (Table 6.3). The long-wavelength emission maxima are 628 nm for the Alexa Fluor® 610–R-PE conjugates, 668 nm for the Alexa Fluor® 647–R-PE conjugates and 702 nm for the Alexa Fluor® 680–R-PE conjugates (Figure 6.34). Emission of the Alexa Fluor® 610–R-PE conjugates is shifted to longer wavelengths by about 13 nm relative to that of Texas Red® conjugates of R-PE (Figure 6.39). This slightly longer-wavelength emission maximum significantly improves the resolution that can be obtained when using the Alexa Fluor® 610–R-PE tandem conjugates in place of Texas Red®–R-PE tandem conjugates for multicolor flow cytometry. The Alexa Fluor® 647–R-PE tandem conjugates have spectra virtually identical to those of Cy5 conjugates of R-PE but are about three-fold brighter (Figure 6.38). These tandem conjugates can potentially be used for simultaneous three-, four- or five-color labeling with a single excitation (Figure 6.34, Figure 6.35, Figure 6.36).

In addition, we have conjugated crosslinked APC (A819) to our Alexa Fluor® 680, Alexa Fluor® 700 and Alexa Fluor® 750 dyes, and then conjugated these fluorescent proteins to antibodies or streptavidin to yield secondary detection reagents that can be excited with the He–Ne laser at 633 nm or with the krypton-ion laser at 647 nm with emission beyond 700 nm (Table 6.4). The long-wavelength emission maxima are 702 nm for the Alexa Fluor® 680–APC conjugates, 719 nm for the Alexa Fluor® 700–APC conjugates and 779 nm for the Alexa Fluor® 750–APC conjugates (Figure 6.34). Our Alexa Fluor® dye–APC tandem conjugates can potentially be combined with direct APC conjugates for simultaneous three-color applications (Figure 6.37).

Table 6.3 — Tandem conjugates of R-phycoerythrin (R-PE)

Acceptor Dye (Ex/Em) *	Conjugate		
	Anti-Mouse IgG †	Anti-Rabbit IgG †	Streptavidin
Alexa Fluor® 610 (565/628)	A20980	A20981	S20982
Alexa Fluor® 647 (565/668)	A20990	A20991	S20992
Alexa Fluor® 680 (565/702)	A20983	A20984	S20985

* Fluorescence excitation and emission maxima, in nm. † Host = goat.

Table 6.4 — Tandem conjugates of allophycocyanin (APC)

Acceptor Dye (Ex/Em) *	Conjugate		
	Anti-Mouse IgG †	Anti-Rabbit IgG †	Streptavidin †
Alexa Fluor® 680 (650/702)	A21000	A21001MP	S21002
Alexa Fluor® 700 (650/719)			S21005
Alexa Fluor® 750 (650/779)	A21006		S21008

* Fluorescence excitation and emission maxima, in nm. † Host = goat.

R-Phycoerythrin Anti-Fluorescein/ Oregon Green® Antibody

Our R-PE conjugate of the rabbit anti-fluorescein/Oregon Green® antibody (A21250) has the unique utility of both shifting the green-fluorescent emission of fluorescein-labeled probes to longer wavelengths and greatly intensifying the signal (Figure 7.73). Anti-fluorescein antibodies strongly crossreact with our Oregon Green® dye conjugates, suggesting the possibility of amplifying the signal from nucleic acid probes labeled by our ULYSIS Oregon Green® 488 Nucleic Acid Labeling Kit (U21659, Section 8.2) or for further amplifying the signal of Oregon Green® 488 tyramide, which is used in TSA Kit #9 (T20919) and TSA Kit #29 (T20939) (Section 6.2, Table 6.1).

Phycobiliprotein Conjugates of Anti-CD Antibodies

Molecular Probes now offers three mouse monoclonal anti–human T-cell markers, anti-CD3, anti-CD4 and anti-CD8 antibodies. These antibodies are available unlabeled or conjugated to one of our superior Alexa Fluor® dyes (Table 7.20) or to R-PE (A21333, A21337). The approximate absorption and fluorescence emission maxima for each of these conjugates are shown in Table 7.20. Research applications for the anti-CD antibodies include:

- Identification and enumeration of $CD3^+$, $CD4^+$ and $CD8^+$ cells by flow cytometry (Figure 6.35, Figure 6.36)
- Visualization of CD^+ cells by immunohistochemistry in acetone-fixed, frozen-tissue sections; the immunoprecipitation of CD^+ fractions
- Isolation or removal of T cells by cell sorting or "bio-panning" [31]

CD3, a member of the immunoglobulin superfamily, is a cluster of differentiation (CD) cell-surface antigen associated with the T-cell receptor (TcR) of T cells and thymocytes. TcRs are specific for complexes comprising short peptides bound to and presented by the major histocompatibility complex (MHC). The human CD3/TcR complex is made up of at least five CD3 proteins (γ, δ, ε, η, ζ) in association with either alpha/beta or gamma/delta proteins of the TcR.[32,33] The TcR recognizes and binds to antigens presented by the MHC, after which the protein chains of the CD3 complex mediate activation signals. The CD3 molecule is not found on B cells; thus, its presence can be used as a marker for T cells.

Anti-CD4 and anti-CD8 antibodies can be used to differentiate helper T cells and killer T cells, both of which are $CD3^+$. Helper/inducer T cells express the cell-surface CD4 antigen, which interacts with MHC class II molecules and is the primary receptor for the human immunodeficiency virus[34] (HIV). Killer T cells express the CD8 cell-surface antigen, which interacts with MHC class I molecules. This interaction leads to the activation of the killer T cell and an increase in its avidity for the corresponding target cells.

Phycobiliprotein Conjugates of Annexin V

In collaboration with Nexins Research BV, we offer the highly fluorescent APC and R-PE conjugates of annexin V (A35110, A35111), in addition to several other fluorescent annexin V conjugates (Section 15.5). Highly fluorescent annexin V conjugates provide quick and reliable detection methods for studying the externalization of phosphatidylserine, an indicator of intermediate stages of apoptosis (Section 15.5). Vybrant® Apoptosis Assay Kits #8, #9 and #10 (V35112, V35113, V35114; Section 15.5; Table 15.4) contain either R-PE–annexin V or APC–annexin V conjugates as well as SYTOX® Green nucleic acid stain to characterize mixed populations of apoptotic and nonapoptotic cells by flow cytometry.

Custom Phycobiliprotein Conjugates

Molecular Probes has carried out hundreds of successful conjugations with phycobiliproteins, beginning soon after their use was disclosed in 1982.[6] We are experts in doing custom conjugations of phycobiliproteins to antibodies and other proteins and welcome inquiries for specific conjugates. For more information or a quote, please contact our Custom and Bulk Sales Department.

Zenon® Antibody Labeling Technology

Chemical conjugation of phycobiliproteins to antibodies and other proteins is a moderately difficult and relatively low-yield process that cannot be done on very small quantities of proteins. Our Protein–Protein Crosslinking Kit (P6305, Section 5.2) provides the reagents and a protocol for conjugations of phycobiliproteins using our recommended procedure. Instead of labeling each primary antibody, however, researchers typically use labeled secondary antibodies to detect their primary antibodies. Our exceptional Zenon® immunolabeling technology provides an easy, versatile and truly unique method of labeling antibodies with phycobiliproteins, as well as with many other premier dyes, haptens and enzymes. This enabling technology not only eliminates the need for secondary detection reagents in many applications, but also simplifies immunolabeling applications that previously were time consuming or impractical, including the use of multiple antibodies derived from the same species in the same protocol, as well as the detection of antibody binding in tissues when both the antibody and the tissue are derived from the same species. Our Zenon® reagents may eventually be the only antibody-based detection reagents needed in the laboratory for many high-throughput applications, replacing both direct conjugates of primary antibodies and dye- and enzyme-labeled secondary antibodies in a wide variety of procedures.

Zenon® immunolabeling technology, described in detail in Section 7.3, allows the rapid and quantitative preparation of antibody complexes from a purified antibody fraction or from a crude antibody preparation such as serum, ascites fluid or a hybridoma supernatant. The Zenon® antibody labeling procedure (Figure 7.59) has numerous advantages, particularly when preparing phycobiliprotein-labeled antibodies:

- Conjugations can be done on submicrogram quantities of a primary antibody.
- The reactions are usually quantitative with respect to the primary antibody.
- Labeling and purification of the complex can be completed in only minutes.
- Labeling is essentially irreversible under conditions of use.
- Multiple antibodies derived from the same species can be used in the same experiment.
- The fluorescence intensity of the cells can be adjusted by changing the ratio of labeling reagent to primary antibody, which even permits using identical dyes to detect multiple targets in cells by flow cytometry.
- Antibody complexes prepared from the Zenon® Antibody Labeling Kits can be combined with direct conjugates for multicolor labeling.

- Labeling is possible with a wide variety of fluorophores, including R-PE and APC as well as most of our Alexa Fluor® dyes (Table 7.13).
- Zenon® Antibody Labeling Kits with Alexa Fluor® dye–phycobiliprotein tandem conjugates are also available (Table 7.13), increasing the possible combinations of detection wavelengths in a multicolor experiment.
- Zenon® antibody labeling with horseradish peroxidase and alkaline phosphatase is also practical (Section 7.3) and can be used in combination with our TSA and ELF® technologies (Section 6.2, Section 6.3).

References

1. J Fluorescence 1, 135 (1991); **2.** J Biol Chem 264, 1 (1989); **3.** Methods Enzymol 167, 291 (1988); **4.** Trends Biochem Sci 9, 423 (1984); **5.** Proc Natl Acad Sci U S A 85, 7312 (1988); **6.** J Cell Biol 93, 981 (1982); **7.** Proc Natl Acad Sci U S A 86, 4087 (1989); **8.** Anal Chem 59, 2158 (1987); **9.** Anal Biochem 161, 442 (1987); **10.** J Histochem Cytochem 39, 921 (1991); **11.** Anal Lett 24, 1075 (1991); **12.** Eur Biophys J 15, 141 (1987); **13.** Clin Chem 29, 1582 (1983); **14.** J Immunol Methods 135, 247 (1990); **15.** Nat Med 7, 245 (2001); **16.** Nat Biotechnol 20, 155 (2002); **17.** Cytometry 15, 267 (1994); **18.** J Immunol Methods 243, 77 (2000); **19.** Biotechniques 31, 490 (2001); **20.** Proc Natl Acad Sci U S A 98, 8862 (2001); **21.** Proc Natl Acad Sci U S A 97, 3260 (2000); **22.** Proc Natl Acad Sci U S A 95, 3752 (1998); **23.** Proc Natl Acad Sci U S A 97, 2680 (2000); **24.** Anal Biochem 255, 188 (1998); **25.** J Biol Chem 275, 11181 (2000); **26.** Nat Biotechnol 14, 1675 (1996); **27.** J Biol Chem 265, 15776 (1990); **28.** Arch Biochem Biophys 223, 24 (1983); **29.** Biochemistry 19, 2817 (1980); **30.** Cytometry 8, 91 (1987); **31.** Immunobiology 203, 769 (2001); **32.** Leucocyte Typing IV: White Cell Differentiation Antigens, Knapp, W, et al., Ed. pp. 1049–1053 (1989); **33.** Annu Rev Immunol 6, 629 (1988); **34.** Science 271, 173 (1996).

Product List — 6.4 Phycobiliproteins

Cat #	Product Name	Unit Size
A21000	Alexa Fluor® 680–allophycocyanin goat anti-mouse IgG (H+L) *1 mg/mL*	100 µL
A21006	Alexa Fluor® 750–allophycocyanin goat anti-mouse IgG (H+L) *1 mg/mL*	100 µL
A21001MP	Alexa Fluor® 680–allophycocyanin goat anti-rabbit IgG (H+L) *1 mg/mL*	100 µL
A20980	Alexa Fluor® 610–R-phycoerythrin goat anti-mouse IgG (H+L) *1 mg/mL*	100 µL
A20990	Alexa Fluor® 647–R-phycoerythrin goat anti-mouse IgG (H+L) *1 mg/mL*	100 µL
A20983	Alexa Fluor® 680–R-phycoerythrin goat anti-mouse IgG (H+L) *1 mg/mL*	100 µL
A20981	Alexa Fluor® 610–R-phycoerythrin goat anti-rabbit IgG (H+L) *1 mg/mL*	100 µL
A20991	Alexa Fluor® 647–R-phycoerythrin goat anti-rabbit IgG (H+L) *1 mg/mL*	100 µL
A20984	Alexa Fluor® 680–R-phycoerythrin goat anti-rabbit IgG (H+L) *1 mg/mL*	100 µL
A803	allophycocyanin *4 mg/mL*	0.5 mL
A819	allophycocyanin, crosslinked (APC-XL) *4 mg/mL*	250 µL
A865	allophycocyanin, crosslinked, goat anti-mouse IgG (H+L) *1 mg/mL*	0.5 mL
A10931	allophycocyanin, crosslinked, goat anti-rabbit IgG (H+L) *1 mg/mL*	0.5 mL
A35110	annexin V, allophycocyanin conjugate (APC annexin V) *50 assays*	250 µL
A35111	annexin V, R-phycoerythrin conjugate (R-PE annexin V) *50 assays*	250 µL
A21333	anti-CD3, mouse IgG_1, monoclonal 289-13801, R-phycoerythrin conjugate *0.2 mg/mL*	0.5 mL
A21337	anti-CD4, mouse IgG_1, monoclonal 289-14120, R-phycoerythrin conjugate *0.2 mg/mL*	0.5 mL
A21250	anti-fluorescein/Oregon Green®, rabbit IgG fraction, R-phycoerythrin conjugate *2 mg/mL*	250 µL
A2660	avidin, NeutrAvidin™, R-phycoerythrin conjugate *1 mg/mL*	1 mL
P800	B-phycoerythrin *4 mg/mL*	0.5 mL
P801	R-phycoerythrin *4 mg/mL*	0.5 mL
P811	R-phycoerythrin, biotin-XX conjugate *4 mg/mL*	0.5 mL
P21129	R-phycoerythrin goat anti-mouse IgG_1 (γ1) conjugate *1 mg/mL*	250 µL
P21139	R-phycoerythrin goat anti-mouse IgG_{2a} (γ2a) conjugate *1 mg/mL*	250 µL
P21149	R-phycoerythrin goat anti-mouse IgG_{2b} (γ2b) conjugate *1 mg/mL*	250 µL
P852	R-phycoerythrin goat anti-mouse IgG (H+L) *1 mg/mL*	1 mL
P2771MP	R-phycoerythrin goat anti-rabbit IgG (H+L) *1 mg/mL*	0.5 mL
P806	R-phycoerythrin, pyridyldisulfide derivative *2 mg/mL*	1 mL
S21002	streptavidin, Alexa Fluor® 680–allophycocyanin conjugate (Alexa Fluor® 680–allophycocyanin streptavidin) *1 mg/mL*	100 µL
S21005	streptavidin, Alexa Fluor® 700–allophycocyanin conjugate (Alexa Fluor® 700–allophycocyanin streptavidin) *1 mg/mL*	100 µL
S21008	streptavidin, Alexa Fluor® 750–allophycocyanin conjugate (Alexa Fluor® 750–allophycocyanin streptavidin) *1 mg/mL*	100 µL
S20982	streptavidin, Alexa Fluor® 610–R-phycoerythrin conjugate (Alexa Fluor® 610–R-phycoerythrin streptavidin) *1 mg/mL*	100 µL
S20992	streptavidin, Alexa Fluor® 647–R-phycoerythrin conjugate (Alexa Fluor® 647–R-phycoerythrin streptavidin) *1 mg/mL*	100 µL
S20985	streptavidin, Alexa Fluor® 680–R-phycoerythrin conjugate (Alexa Fluor® 680–R-phycoerythrin streptavidin) *1 mg/mL*	100 µL
S32363	streptavidin, Alexa Fluor® 750–R-phycoerythrin conjugate (Alexa Fluor® 750–R-phycoerythrin streptavidin) *1 mg/mL*	100 µL
S32362	streptavidin, allophycocyanin conjugate *premium grade* *1 mg/mL*	250 µL
S868	streptavidin, allophycocyanin, crosslinked, conjugate *1 mg/mL*	0.5 mL
S32350	streptavidin, B-phycoerythrin conjugate *1 mg/mL*	1 mL
S866	streptavidin, R-phycoerythrin conjugate (SAPE) *1 mg/mL*	1 mL
S21388	streptavidin, R-phycoerythrin conjugate (SAPE) *premium grade* *1 mg/mL*	1 mL
Z25020	Zenon® Alexa Fluor® 610–R-Phycoerythrin Mouse IgG_1 Labeling Kit *10 labelings*	1 kit
Z25021	Zenon® Alexa Fluor® 647–R-Phycoerythrin Mouse IgG_1 Labeling Kit *10 labelings*	1 kit

For current prices or to order online, visit probes.invitrogen.com

Product List — 6.4 Phycobiliproteins — continued

Cat #	Product Name	Unit Size
Z25121	Zenon® Alexa Fluor® 647–R-Phycoerythrin Mouse IgG_{2a} Labeling Kit *10 labelings*	1 kit
Z25221	Zenon® Alexa Fluor® 647–R-Phycoerythrin Mouse IgG_{2b} Labeling Kit *10 labelings*	1 kit
Z25022	Zenon® Alexa Fluor® 680–R-Phycoerythrin Mouse IgG_1 Labeling Kit *10 labelings*	1 kit
Z25030	Zenon® Alexa Fluor® 700–Allophycocyanin Mouse IgG_1 Labeling Kit *10 labelings*	1 kit
Z25031	Zenon® Alexa Fluor® 750–Allophycocyanin Mouse IgG_1 Labeling Kit *10 labelings*	1 kit
Z25451	Zenon® Allophycocyanin Human IgG Labeling Kit *25 labelings*	1 kit
Z25051	Zenon® Allophycocyanin Mouse IgG_1 Labeling Kit *25 labelings*	1 kit
Z25151	Zenon® Allophycocyanin Mouse IgG_{2a} Labeling Kit *25 labelings*	1 kit
Z25251	Zenon® Allophycocyanin Mouse IgG_{2b} Labeling Kit *25 labelings*	1 kit
Z25351	Zenon® Allophycocyanin Rabbit IgG Labeling Kit *25 labelings*	1 kit
Z25455	Zenon® R-Phycoerythrin Human IgG Labeling Kit *25 labelings*	1 kit
Z25055	Zenon® R-Phycoerythrin Mouse IgG_1 Labeling Kit *25 labelings*	1 kit
Z25155	Zenon® R-Phycoerythrin Mouse IgG_{2a} Labeling Kit *25 labelings*	1 kit
Z25255	Zenon® R-Phycoerythrin Mouse IgG_{2b} Labeling Kit *25 labelings*	1 kit
Z25355	Zenon® R-Phycoerythrin Rabbit IgG Labeling Kit *25 labelings*	1 kit

For current prices or to order online, visit probes.invitrogen.com

6.5 FluoSpheres® and TransFluoSpheres® Fluorescent Microspheres

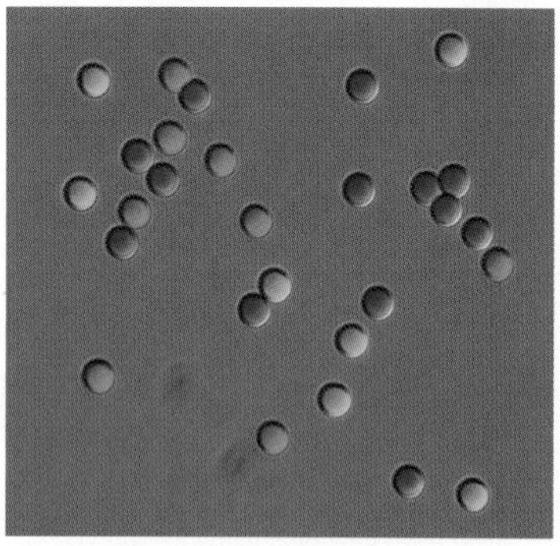

Figure 6.43 A photomicrograph of a multicolor mixture of Molecular Probes' FluoSpheres® fluorescent microspheres overlaid with a differential interference contrast (DIC) image of the same field. Molecular Probes applies its proprietary fluorescent dye technology to produce a range of intensely fluorescent FluoSpheres® microspheres labeled with biotin, streptavidin and NeutrAvidin biotin-binding protein, providing important tools for improving the sensitivity of flow cytometry applications and immunodiagnostic assays.

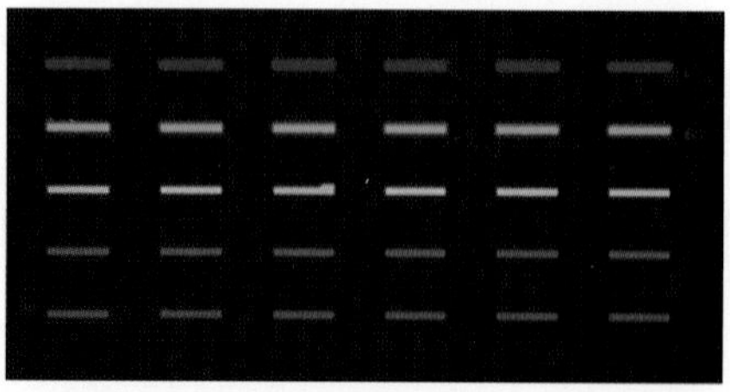

Figure 6.44 A positively charged membrane containing an approximately equal number of TransFluoSpheres® fluorescent microspheres per slot. Our proprietary TransFluoSpheres® polystyrene beads are designed to be excited with a common wavelength and then detected at a variety of longer wavelengths with minimal spectral overlap. This nylon membrane was excited with 365 nm epi-illumination and photographed through a 400 nm longpass optical filter.

Although low molecular weight reactive dyes are versatile and easy to use, they are not without limitations (see Note 6.2 "Technical Focus: Limitations of Low Molecular Weight Dyes"). For example, the fluorescence output of the dye–biomolecule conjugate is often limited by the number of dyes that can be attached to the biomolecule without disrupting its function. Our highly fluorescent microspheres — both the FluoSpheres® (Figure 6.43) and TransFluoSpheres® (Figure 6.44) beads — provide a means of overcoming this limitation. Moreover, our TransFluoSpheres® beads are designed to facilitate multicolor detection, particularly in applications that use lasers, with their inherent limited number of excitation wavelengths. TransFluoSpheres® beads contain a series of two or more proprietary dyes that have been carefully chosen to ensure excited-state energy transfer between the dyes. This unique strategy enables fine-tuning of both the excitation and emission wavelengths of the microspheres so that they match a particular instrument's excitation source and detection sensitivity and complement the spectra of other fluorophores in a multicolor experiment.

Properties of Our Fluorescent and Nonfluorescent Microspheres

Fluorescent FluoSpheres® and TransFluoSpheres® Microspheres

Molecular Probes' intensely fluorescent FluoSpheres® and TransFluoSpheres® beads are manufactured using high-quality, ultraclean polystyrene microspheres. These microspheres are internally labeled with Molecular Probes' proprietary dyes, making them the brightest fluorescent microspheres available (Table 6.5). We employ methods to ensure that each bead is heavily loaded with dye. The protective environment within the bead matrix shields the dyes from many of the environmental effects that cause photobleaching of exposed fluorophores.

The stability, uniformity and reproducibility of fluorescent microspheres, as well as the extensive selection of colors available make our microspheres the preferred standards for research and diagnostic assays that use fluorescence. We have developed several important microsphere-based products for calibrating and aligning fluorescence microscopes (Section 23.1) and flow cytometers (Section 23.2). By carefully selecting dyes that can be incorporated within the microspheres, our CompenFlow™ microspheres duplicate the spectra of widely used fluorophores such as fluorescein (Figure 23.35) or R-phycoerythrin (Figure 23.36) that are not themselves soluble in polystyrene beads.[1] Not only are our yellow-green–fluorescent beads more photostable, but their emission spectra are not affected by changes in pH, as are conventional fluorescein-labeled microspheres. Fluorescent microspheres can be fixed in formalin and embedded in paraffin if care is used to avoid extraction of the noncovalently associated dyes from the microspheres.[2]

Table 6.5 — Molecular Probes' yellow-green–fluorescent FluoSpheres® beads compared with other commercially available yellow-green–fluorescent microspheres

Supplier	Size (µm)	Fluorescence Intensity *	CV for Intensity †
Molecular Probes (F8852)	1.02	1998	4.40%
Molecular Probes (F8853)	2.07	8998	3.26%
Company A	0.84	3.7	30.28%
Company A	1.55	5.2	11.69%
Company B	1.01	12.6	2.49%
Company B	1.94	595	2.91%
Company C	0.93	116	4.62%
Company C	1.48	434	1.92%
Company D	0.85	17	5.19%
Company D	1.84	119	3.08%

* Median value for fluorescence intensity (in arbitrary units), measured for 10,000 individual beads per sample excited at 488 nm using flow cytometry. Values may vary slightly between batches of these products. † CV = coefficient of variation.

Note 6.2 — Technical Focus

Limitations of Low Molecular Weight Dyes

The argon-ion laser is the excitation source in many flow cytometers and confocal laser-scanning microscopes, as well as in certain laser scanners and DNA sequencers. In these instruments, the wavelengths used to excite green-, yellow-, orange- and red-fluorescent dyes are limited primarily to the laser's 488 and 514 nm spectral lines, which severely restricts simultaneous multicolor detection. For example, when excited at 488 or 514 nm, the Texas Red® fluorophore has a particularly low fluorescence output (see figure below) that is easily obscured by the more intense fluorescein fluorescence in a double-labeling experiment, even when detected past 600 nm. For these applications, it would be useful to have a red-fluorescent dye with an absorption maximum closer to the spectral lines of the argon-ion laser. Unfortunately, very few low molecular weight dyes have a combination of a large Stokes shift — defined as the separation of the absorption and emission maxima — and a high molar absorptivity.[1] In addition to this Stokes shift limitation, low molecular weight dyes may be impractical for some applications because they do not provide a bright enough fluorescent signal. Typically, only a limited number of dyes can be attached to a biomolecule without interfering with its binding specificity or causing it to precipitate. It may therefore be necessary to prepare a bioconjugate with a less-than-maximal fluorescence yield in order to preserve its important properties.

Molecular Probes offers three product lines that specifically address the limitations of most low molecular weight dyes. Our intensely fluorescent TransFluoSpheres® polystyrene microspheres (Section 6.5) have been especially designed to provide both a large Stokes shift and a high fluorescence yield. For instruments with argon-ion laser excitation sources, we have developed a series of five TransFluoSpheres® beads, all of which have an excitation maximum at 488 nm but that emit at different wavelengths: 560 nm, 605 nm, 645 nm, 685 nm or 720 nm (Figure 6.50). This set of TransFluoSpheres® beads enables researchers to detect five experimental parameters simultaneously with a single excitation wavelength. We also offer phycobiliproteins, a family of highly soluble red-fluorescent proteins with high quantum yields and large extinction coefficients, as well as phycobiliprotein-labeled secondary detection reagents (Section 6.4). Our tandem conjugates of R-phycoerythrin with either the Alexa Fluor® 610, Alexa Fluor® 647 and Alexa Fluor® 680 dyes (Section 6.4, Table 6.3) permit 3-, 4- and potentially even 5-color experiments using 488 nm excitation (Figure 6.34). Similarly, our Alexa Fluor® 680 (Figure 6.37), Alexa Fluor® 700 and Alexa Fluor® 750 tandem conjugates of allophycocyanin (Section 6.4, Table 6.4) may be used with APC or Alexa Fluor® 647 conjugates in simultaneous three-color experiments using the 633 nm He–Ne laser for excitation. Optimized for flow cytometry applications, the DyeMer™ 488/605, DyeMer™ 488/615 and DyeMer™ 488/630 conjugates of antibodies (Section 7.2, Table 7.1) and streptavidin (Section 7.6, Table 7.22) are labeled with synthetic bifluorophores that have highly efficient excited-state energy transfer to yield a large effective Stokes shift. These DyeMer™ conjugates are all efficiently excited at 488 nm and exhibit emission maxima at 611, 617 or 630 nm. Although their total fluorescence is not as intense as that of the phycobiliprotein tandem conjugates, the DyeMer™ conjugates exhibit minimal lot-to-lot variation and less interference at the antigen- or biotin-binding site due to the relatively small size of the DyeMer™ bifluorophores. Molecular Probes can also custom-label antibodies or other target-specific proteins with our fluorescent microspheres, phycobiliproteins, tandem conjugates of phycobiliproteins, DyeMer™ dyes or other fluorophores to provide detection reagents that match specific needs; for more information or a quotation, please contact our Custom and Bulk Sales Department.

Reference

1. Optical Microscopy for Biology, Herman B, Jacobson K, Eds. pp. 143–157 (1990).

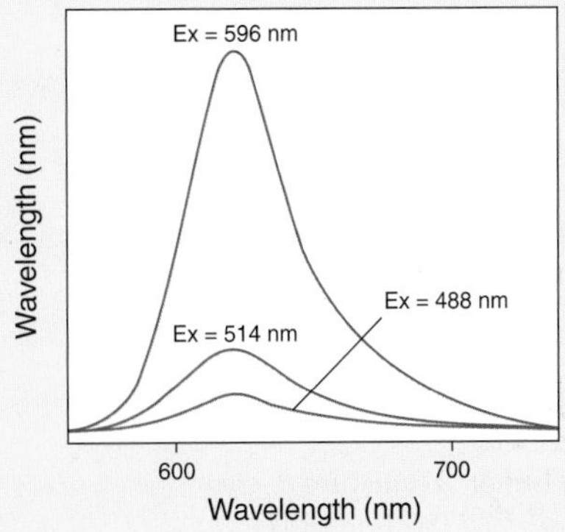

Fluorescence intensity of the Texas Red® bovine serum albumin conjugate (A23017, Section 14.7) when excited at 488, 514 and 596 nm.

We also offer fluorescent microspheres conjugated to biotin, streptavidin and NeutrAvidin biotin-binding protein, which are described below. Discounts for large-volume orders are available, as well as custom preparation of microspheres with other colors, sizes and surface coatings; please contact our Custom and Bulk Sales Department for more information. The FluoSpheres® and TransFluoSpheres® beads, their conjugates and most of our microsphere-based standards for fluorescence microscopy and flow cytometry are covered by patents. These products are offered for research purposes only. Molecular Probes welcomes inquiries about licensing these products for resale or other commercial uses.

Colored and Unstained Microspheres

In addition to our extensive line of fluorescent microspheres, Molecular Probes now offers a wide selection of colored and unstained microspheres for research applications as well as for water- and air-flow testing and bead-based diagnostic applications. Through its acquisition of Interfacial Dynamics Corporation (IDC), Molecular Probes can provide milliliter to 500-liter quantities of ultraclean microspheres with diameters from 20 nm to 10.0 µm and with more than 20 different surface functionalities; see www.idclatex.com for a complete listing of the colored and unstained microspheres available. IDC pioneered the commercial development of surfactant-free polymer particles used in bead-based assay systems and has been a key supplier of beads for Molecular Probes' fluorescent microspheres. IDC's outstanding capabilities in microsphere manufacturing allow a high level of control of the colloid engineering employed in the particle synthesis, providing unbeatable batch-to-batch consistency. Microsphere manufacturers often use surfactants to prevent aggregation. However, standards of surfactant purity are generally not very high, leading to an undefined particle surface and variable protein attachment. With the ultraclean microspheres manufactured by IDC, and now Molecular Probes, no surfactants are required to prevent aggregation, taking much of the guesswork out of stability and adsorption experiments. We can tailor-make colored and unstained microspheres of many sizes, surface chemistries, densities and volumes to meet the diverse needs of customers, including academic, industrial and government laboratories, as well as major global diagnostic companies; please contact our Custom and Bulk Sales Department for more information.

Applications for Fluorescent Microspheres

Fluorescent microspheres have been used as immunofluorescent reagents,[3–5] retrograde neuronal tracers,[6–8] microinjectable cell tracers[9,10] (Section 14.6) and standardization reagents for microscopy (Section 23.1) and flow cytometry[11] (Section 23.2). Arrays of fluorescent microspheres that differ in intensity, size or excited-state lifetime are extensively used for simultaneous assays to determine multiple analytes in a single sample.[12–19] Furthermore, fluorescent microspheres have been employed to:

- Determine blood flow in tissues[2,20–25] (Section 14.6)
- Develop high-resolution maps of regional pulmonary ventilation[26–28] (Section 14.6)
- Measure retinal and choroidal circulation[29,30]
- Define the functional diameter of alveolar microvessels using microspheres of increasing diameters[31]
- Measure the blood velocity in tumor vasculature *in vivo*[30]
- Investigate phagocytic processes[32–35] (Section 16.1)
- Detect low-abundance receptors[36–40]
- Probe specific sequences for protein binding on single DNA molecules[41]
- Develop a simultaneous assay for digoxin and theophylline[42]
- Follow the fate of transplanted cells,[43] such as donor erythrocytes, in patients who received allogenic bone marrow transplants[44]
- Quantitate lymphocyte numbers in a lymphocyte–endothelial adhesion/transendothelial migration assay[45]
- Image three different *Candida albicans* antigens simultaneously[46]
- Investigate binding mechanisms of neural cell adhesion molecules[47,48]
- Track the lateral mobility of GPI-anchored proteins in supported bilayers,[49] Thyl molecules in the plasmalemma of live fibroblasts[50] and surface receptors during cell division[51]
- Detect amines on the surface of self-assembled monolayers of a microfabricated device[52]
- Make kinesin force measurements with optical tweezers[31,53,54]
- Analyze the elasticity of single DNA molecules via optical trapping[55]
- Simultaneously screen for multiple analytes by flow cytometry[14,16–19,56,57]
- Quantitate adenovirus using a flow microsphere immunoassay[58] (FMIA)
- Detect binding of a fluorescent ligand to its receptor using microvolume fluorometry[59]

In addition, fluorescent microspheres are potentially more sensitive than colorimetric methods in most, if not all, of the major microsphere-based diagnostic test systems presently in use, including latex-agglutination tests, filter-separation tests, particle-capture ELISA methods and two-particle sandwich techniques.

FluoSpheres® Fluorescent Microspheres

A Wide Array of Fluorescent Colors

Molecular Probes' FluoSpheres® fluorescent microspheres contain dyes with excitation and emission wavelengths that cover the entire spectrum from the near UV to the near infrared. Figure 6.45 shows the normalized emission spectra for 10 fluorescent colors of FluoSpheres® beads. Because long-wavelength (>680 nm) light can penetrate tissues, our far-red– and infrared-fluorescent microspheres may allow researchers to conduct experiments that were not previously possible with beads that emit at shorter wavelengths. We would like to highlight the following FluoSpheres® products:

- Our blue-fluorescent FluoSpheres® beads with excitation/emission maxima of 350/440 nm contain an improved blue-fluorescent dye that provides superior brightness and a longer shelf life. We also offer blue-fluorescent FluoSpheres® beads with slightly shorter-wavelength fluorescence spectra (excitation/emission maxima ~365/415 nm).
- Our yellow-green–fluorescent FluoSpheres® beads have excitation/emission maxima of 505/515 nm and thus are excited very efficiently using the 488 nm spectral line of the argon-ion laser, resulting in exceptionally intense fluorescence (Table 6.5).
- Our orange-, red-orange– and red-fluorescent FluoSpheres® beads have excitation maxima of 540 nm, 565 nm and 580 nm, respectively.

- The nile red–fluorescent FluoSpheres® beads have broad excitation/emission bandwidths at 535/575 nm, making them compatible with filter sets appropriate for fluorescein, rhodamine and Texas Red® dyes.
- Our crimson- and dark red–fluorescent FluoSpheres® beads with excitation/emission maxima of 625/645 nm and 660/680 nm, respectively, are efficiently excited by the 633 nm spectral line of the He–Ne laser. Although the dark red–fluorescent beads are significantly less fluorescent than the crimson-fluorescent particles, they fluoresce at wavelengths that are longer than, and clearly distinguishable from, those of the crimson-fluorescent particles.
- The far-red–fluorescent FluoSpheres® beads with excitation/emission maxima of 690/720 nm are compatible with diode lasers — inexpensive excitation sources that are increasingly being used in fluorescence instrumentation.[60] These far-red–fluorescent beads may also prove useful for making direct fluorescence measurements in autofluorescent materials such as blood, plant tissues and marine organisms.
- The infrared-fluorescent FluoSpheres® beads with excitation/emission maxima of 715/755 nm are the longest-wavelength fluorescent microspheres currently available from any source. These beads absorb and emit at wavelengths at which most tissues are almost optically transparent.
- Our europium luminescent and platinum luminescent FluoSpheres® beads have excitation/emission maxima of 340–370/610 nm (Figure 6.47) and ~390/650 nm (Figure 6.48), respectively, and decay times of >40 microseconds for the platinum microspheres and >600 microseconds for the europium microspheres, far longer than those of conventional fluorescent probes and autofluorescent samples. The beads should be useful as standards for time-resolved microscopy and for tracing applications in highly autofluorescent samples.[61]

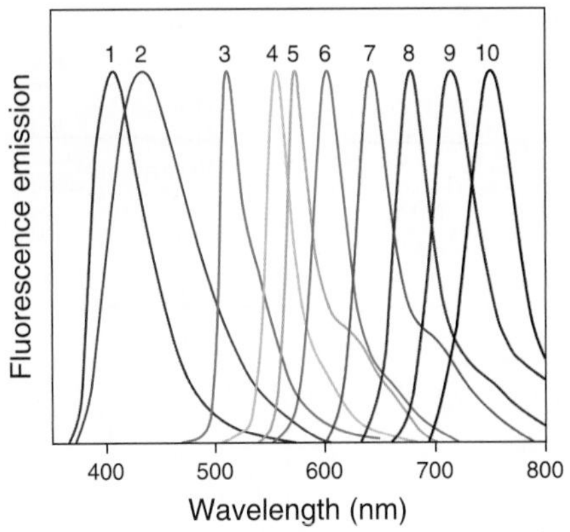

Figure 6.45 Normalized fluorescence emission spectra of our FluoSpheres® beads, named according to their excitation/emission maxima (nm): 1) blue (365/415), 2) blue (350/440), 3) yellow-green (505/515), 4) orange (540/560), 5) red-orange (565/580), 6) red (580/605), 7) crimson (625/645), 8) dark red (660/680), 9) far-red (690/720) and 10) infrared (715/755) FluoSpheres® beads.

Our FluoSpheres® beads are many times brighter than fluorescent microspheres from other companies (Table 6.5). Table 6.6 shows the approximate number of unquenched fluorescein equivalents in our yellow-green–fluorescent FluoSpheres® beads. The intensity of the beads is sufficient to allow visualization of single particles, even for our smallest microspheres, which appear as point sources (Figure 6.46); see the description of our PS-Speck™ Microscope Point Source Kit (P7220) in Section 23.1. Moreover, aqueous suspensions of FluoSpheres® beads do not fade appreciably when illuminated by a 250-watt xenon-arc lamp for 30 minutes. Indeed, most of our FluoSpheres® beads show little or no photobleaching, even when excited with the intense illumination required for fluorescence microscopy.

Although some of our FluoSpheres® beads are available in limited sizes, colors and surface functions, we will prepare custom orders upon request. Molecular Probes has considerable experience developing standards, including microsphere-based standards for companies selling fluorescence instrumentation. Additional sizes and colors of these labeled microspheres can be custom-ordered through our Custom and Bulk Sales Department. FluoSpheres® beads can also be prepared with intensities that are *lower* than those of our regular products — a desirable feature in some multicolor applications. FluoSpheres® beads with calibrated intensities are already offered in our InSpeck™ Microscope Intensity Calibration Kits (Section 23.1) and LinearFlow™ Flow Cytometry Intensity Calibration Kits (Section 23.2), which are each available in several

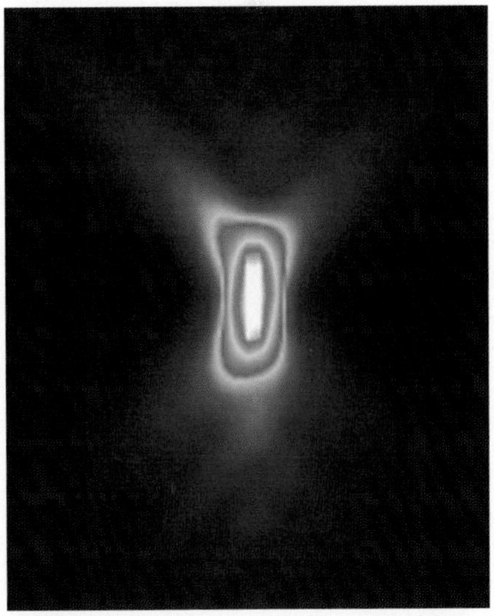

Figure 6.46 An orthogonal (x-z) pseudocolored display representing a point-spread function of a particular microscope's optics, using a microsphere from the PS-Speck™ Microscope Point Source Kit (P7220).

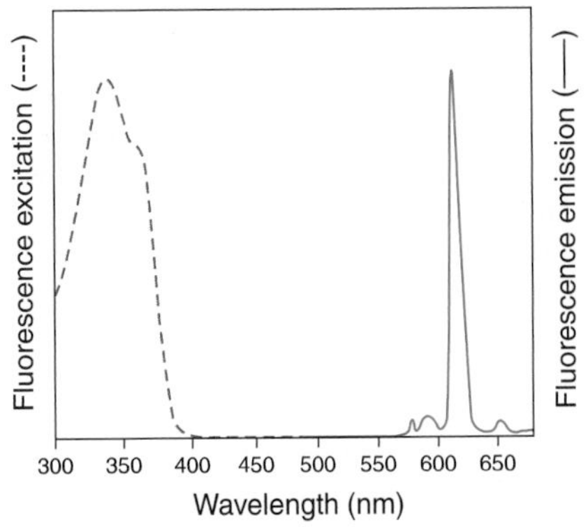

Figure 6.47 Fluorescence excitation and emission maxima of the FluoSpheres® europium luminescent microspheres (F20880, F20881, F20882, F20883, F20884, F20885).

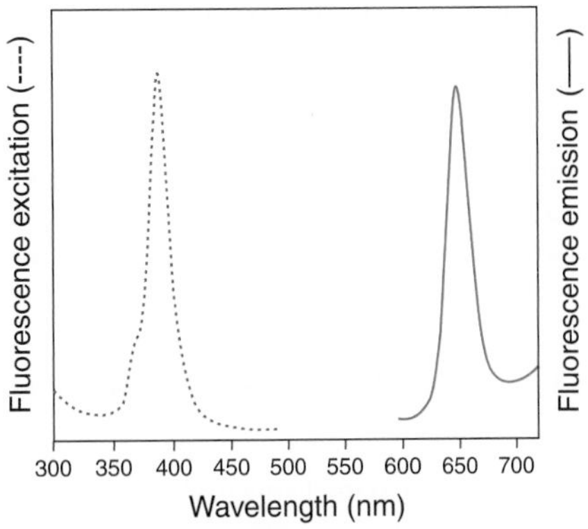

Figure 6.48 Luminescence excitation and emission spectra of the FluoSpheres® platinum luminescent microspheres (F20886, F20887, F20888, F20889, F20890, F20891).

Table 6.6 — Fluorescein equivalents in our yellow-green–fluorescent FluoSpheres® beads

Microsphere Diameter (µm)	Fluorescein Equivalents per Microsphere*
0.02	1.8×10^2
0.04	3.5×10^2
0.1	7.4×10^3
0.2	1.1×10^5
0.5	2.0×10^6
1.0	1.3×10^7
2.0	3.1×10^7
10	1.1×10^{10}
15	3.7×10^{10}

* Values may vary slightly between batches of these products.

fluorescent colors. Molecular Probes offers a variety of other microsphere reference standards designed to facilitate adjustment and calibration of fluorescence microscopes (Section 23.1) and flow cytometers (Section 23.2).

A Wide Range of Sizes

To meet the diverse needs of our customers, we offer FluoSpheres® beads in a variety of sizes (Table 6.7). The smallest microspheres are currently about 0.02 µm in diameter, with a coefficient of variation (CV) of about 20% as determined by electron microscopy. The size uniformity improves with increasing size, with the CV decreasing from ~5% for 0.1 µm FluoSpheres® beads to ~1% for those with 10–15 µm diameters. The sizes specified in the product names are nominal bead diameters; because of batch-to-batch variation in the undyed microspheres, the actual mean diameters shown on the product labels may differ from the nominal diameters, especially for the smaller microspheres. Because of their small size, 0.02–0.04 µm microspheres are effectively transparent to light in aqueous suspensions and behave very much like true solutions.

Four Different Surface Functional Groups

We prepare FluoSpheres® beads with four different surface functional groups, making them compatible with a variety of conjugation strategies. Our fluorescent dyes have negligible effect on the surface properties of the polystyrene beads or on their protein adsorption. We caution, however, that the surface properties have an important role in the functional utility of the microspheres; we cannot guarantee the suitability of a particular bead type for all applications.

- Carboxylate-modified FluoSpheres® beads have pendent carboxylic acids, making them suitable for covalent coupling of proteins and other amine-containing biomolecules using water-soluble carbodiimide reagents such as EDAC (E2247, Section 3.3). In order to both decrease nonspecific binding and provide additional functional groups for conjugation, these FluoSpheres® beads have a high density of carboxylic acids on their surfaces.
- Sulfate FluoSpheres® beads are relatively hydrophobic particles that will passively and nearly irreversibly adsorb almost any protein, including albumin, IgG, avidin and streptavidin.
- Aldehyde–sulfate FluoSpheres® beads, which are sulfate microspheres that have been modified to add surface aldehyde groups, are designed to react with proteins and other amines under very mild conditions.
- Amine-modified FluoSpheres® beads can be coupled to a wide variety of amine-reactive molecules, including the succinimidyl esters and isothiocyanates of haptens and drugs or the carboxylic acids of proteins, using a water-soluble carbodiimide. The amine surface groups can also be reacted with SPDP (S1531, Section 5.2) to yield (after reduction) microspheres with pendent sulfhydryl groups.

Fluorescent Microspheres Conjugated to Biotin, Avidin and Streptavidin

Molecular Probes offers yellow-green–fluorescent microspheres conjugated to biotin or streptavidin, and yellow-green–fluorescent, red-fluorescent, europium luminescent, platinum luminescent and nonfluorescent microspheres conjugated to NeutrAvidin biotin-binding protein (Table 6.8). NeutrAvidin biotin-binding protein has been specially processed to remove carbohydrates and lower the isoelectric point, resulting in a near-neutral protein that has significantly lower nonspecific binding than conventional avidin. These microsphere conjugates provide our customers with valuable tools for improving the sensitivity of flow cytometry applications and immunodiagnostic assays.[62] They may also be useful as tracers that can be detected with standard enzyme-mediated avidin/streptavidin methods. Additional sizes and colors of these microspheres can be custom-ordered through our Custom and Bulk Sales Department.

Fluorescent Microspheres Coated with Collagen

Fibroblasts phagocytose and then intracellularly digest collagen. These activities play an important role in the remodeling of the extracellular matrix during normal physiological turnover of connective tissues, in development, in wound repair and possibly in aging and various disorders. A well-established procedure for observing collagen phagocytosis by either flow cytometry or fluorescence microscopy involves the use of collagen-coated fluorescent microspheres, which attach to the cell surface and become engulfed by fibroblasts.[63–65] Molecular Probes

Table 6.7 — Summary of Molecular Probes' FluoSpheres® fluorescent microspheres*

Microspheres	0.02 µm	0.04 µm	0.1 µm	0.2 µm	0.5 µm	1.0 µm	2.0 µm	4.0 µm
Carboxylate-Modified Microspheres								
Europium luminescent (340–370/610)		F20880 2 mL		F20881 2 mL		F20882 2 mL		
Platinum luminescent (390/650)		F20886 2 mL		F20887 2 mL		F20888 2 mL		
Blue (365/415)	F8781 10 mL			F8805 10 mL		F8814 10 mL	F8824 2 mL	
Blue (350/440)			F8797 10 mL			F8815 10 mL		
Blue-green (430/465)						F13080 ‡ 5 mL		
Yellow-green (505/515)	F8787 10 mL	F8795 † 1 mL	F8803 10 mL	F8811 10 mL	F8813 10 mL	F8823 10 mL F13081 ‡ 5 mL	F8827 2 mL	
Nile red (535/575)	F8784 10 mL					F8819 10 mL	F8825 2 mL	
Orange (540/560)		F8792 † 1 mL	F8800 10 mL	F8809 10 mL		F8820 10 mL F13082 ‡ 5 mL		
Red-orange (565/580)		F8794 † 1 mL						
Red (580/605)	F8786 10 mL	F8793 † 1 mL	F8801 10 mL	F8810 10 mL	F8812 10 mL	F8821 10 mL F13083 ‡ 5 mL	F8826 2 mL	
Crimson (625/645)	F8782 2 mL			F8806 2 mL		F8816 2 mL		
Dark red (660/680)	F8783 2 mL	F8789 † 1 mL		F8807 2 mL				
Far-red (690/720)			F8798 1 mL					
Infrared (715/755)		F8791 † 0.4 mL	F8799 1 mL					
Sulfate Microspheres								
Blue (365/415)						F8849 10 mL		F8854 2 mL
Yellow-green (505/515)	F8845 10 mL			F8848 10 mL		F8852 10 mL	F8853 2 mL	F8859 2 mL
Red (580/605)						F8851 10 mL		F8858 2 mL
Aldehyde-Sulfate Microspheres								
Yellow-green (505/515)	F8760 10 mL					F8762 10 mL		
Amine-Modified Microspheres								
Yellow-green (505/515)				F8764 5 mL		F8765 5 mL		
Red (580/605)				F8763 5 mL				

* FluoSpheres® beads are supplied as aqueous suspensions containing 2% solids and 2 mM sodium azide, except for the 0.04 µm microspheres (†), which are supplied as aqueous suspensions containing 5% solids without preservatives; the 1 µm microspheres for tracer studies (‡), which are supplied as aqueous suspensions containing 10^{10} microspheres per mL and 0.02% thimerosal; and the europium luminescent microspheres, which are supplied as aqueous suspensions containing 0.5% solids and 2 mM sodium azide. All sizes fall within a narrow range as discussed in Section 6.5. Sizes indicated in the above tables are nominal and may vary from batch to batch. Actual sizes, as determined by electron microscopy, are specified on the product labels.

offers yellow-green–fluorescent FluoSpheres® collagen I–labeled microspheres in either 1.0 µm or 2.0 µm diameter (F20892, F20893) for use in these applications. These microspheres have collagen I from calf skin attached covalently to their surface.

Europium and Platinum Luminescent Microspheres for Time-Resolved Fluorometry

Detecting low levels of protein or DNA targets in a tissue sample or on a membrane using classic fluorochromes is sometimes difficult and prone to errors because specific fluorescence signals tend to be low and are usually mixed with nonspecific signals and autofluorescence. One approach to improve detectability is the use of time-resolved luminescence reagents, such as our FluoSpheres® europium luminescent microspheres and FluoSpheres® platinum luminescent microspheres. The FluoSpheres® europium luminescent beads contain Eu^{3+} coordination complexes with luminescence decay times of >600 microseconds — much longer that the <50 nanosecond decay time of conventional fluorophores and autofluorescence. The luminescence of the Pt^{2+} chelate in the FluoSpheres® platinum luminescent microspheres has a decay time of >40 microseconds. Thus, time-gated fluorescence detection using these microspheres results in complete rejection of autofluorescence signals.[61,66–73] In addition, both the europium luminescent and platinum luminescent microspheres feature long-wavelength emissions (610–650 nm) that are well separated from their excitation peaks (340–390 nm) (Figure 6.47, Figure 6.48). Because of this exceptionally large Stokes shift, filter combinations can be chosen that effectively isolate the desired luminescence signal.

Table 6.8 — Summary of biotin-, streptavidin- and NeutrAvidin biotin-binding protein–labeled FluoSpheres® microspheres*

Microspheres	0.04 µm	0.2 µm	1.0 µm
Biotin-Labeled Microspheres			
Yellow-green (505/515)	F8766 0.4 mL	F8767 0.4 mL	F8768 0.4 mL
Nonfluorescent			F8769 0.4 mL
Streptavidin-Labeled Microspheres			
Yellow-green (505/515)	F8780 0.4 mL		
NeutrAvidin-Labeled Microspheres			
Europium luminescent (340–370/610)	F20883 0.4 mL	F20884 0.4 mL	F20885 0.4 mL
Platinum luminescent (365/650)	F20889 0.4 mL	F20890 0.4 mL	F20891 0.4 mL
Yellow-green (505/515)	F8771 0.4 mL	F8774 0.4 mL	F8776 0.4 mL
Red (580/605)	F8770 0.4 mL		F8775 0.4 mL
Nonfluorescent	F8772 0.4 mL		F8777 0.4 mL

* The streptavidin-labeled FluoSpheres® beads are supplied as aqueous suspensions containing 0.5% solids and 5 mM sodium azide. NeutrAvidin biotin-binding protein–labeled europium luminescent FluoSpheres® are supplied as aqueous suspensions containing 0.5% solids and 0.02% thimerosal. Other NeutrAvidin biotin-binding protein– and biotin-labeled FluoSpheres® beads are supplied as aqueous suspensions containing 1% solids, 5 mM sodium azide and 0.02% Tween. All sizes fall within a narrow range as discussed in Section 6.5. Sizes indicated in the above tables are nominal and may vary from batch to batch. Actual sizes, as determined by electron microscopy, are specified on the product label.

These microspheres are available uncoated (F20880, F20881, F20882, F20886, F20887, F20888) or conjugated to NeutrAvidin biotin-binding protein (F20883, F20884, F20885, F20889, F20890, F20891), with nominal diameters of 0.04 µm, 0.2 µm or 1.0 µm. Beads labeled with NeutrAvidin biotin-binding protein can be used for the indirect detection of antigens and DNA targets in many biotin/avidin-based assays.

Fluorescent Microsphere Starter Kits

For applications requiring several different microsphere colors or sizes, we offer three types of fluorescent microsphere starter kits:

- The FluoSpheres® Fluorescent Color Kit (F10720) consists of 1 mL samples of yellow-green–, orange-, red- and dark red–fluorescent, carboxylate-modified 0.04 µm FluoSpheres® beads packaged as high-density, azide-free suspensions for microinjection.
- FluoSpheres® Size Kits contain 1 mL samples of carboxylate-modified FluoSpheres® beads in 0.02, 0.1, 0.2, 0.5, 1.0 and 2.0 µm sizes. These beads are available in yellow-green– (F8888) or red- (F8887) fluorescent colors.
- FluoSpheres® Blood Flow Determination Fluorescent Color Kits provide several different fluorescent colors of our 10 µm (F8890) or 15 µm (F8891, F8892, F21015) FluoSpheres® polystyrene microspheres (Section 14.6).

Fluorescent Microspheres for Educational Purposes

Molecular Probes' Constellation™ microspheres for imaging (C14837) can be used to demonstrate hands-on techniques with a fluorescence microscope. Constellation™ microspheres consist of a selected mixture of beads in assorted sizes and colors (Figure 6.3, Figure 23.7) that can be used to practice adjusting the focus and switching filters on a fluorescence microscope. These microspheres are stable at room temperature, so they can be conveniently stored.

TransFluoSpheres® Fluorescent Microspheres: Tools for Multicolor Detection

Advantages of TransFluoSpheres® Fluorescent Microspheres

Molecular Probes' patented TransFluoSpheres® fluorescent microspheres (Table 6.9; Figure 6.49, Figure 6.44) are specially designed to overcome the limitations imposed by modern fluorescence instrumentation. Many flow cytometers, confocal laser-scanning microscopes and laser scanners incorporate the argon-ion laser as the excitation source, thereby limiting the available excitation wavelengths to the laser's 488 nm and 514 nm spectral lines and severely restricting simultaneous multicolor detection. Ideally, it would be useful to have a series of fluorescent dyes with absorption maxima close to the argon-ion laser's spectral lines, but with emission maxima at a variety of longer wavelengths. This approach would require that some of the dyes exhibit large Stokes shifts — defined as the separation of the absorption and emission maxima. Unfortunately, very few low molecular weight dyes have a combination of a large Stokes shift and a high molar absorptivity (see Note 6.2 "Technical Focus: Limitations of Low Molecular Weight Dyes"). For example, the Texas Red® fluorophore — often used in combination with fluorescein — has a particularly low absorption at 488 nm and 514 nm. In applications that employ the argon-ion laser as an excitation source, Texas Red® conjugates have a low fluorescence output that is easily obscured by the more intense fluorescein fluorescence, even when detected past 600 nm.

Our TransFluoSpheres® beads, which incorporate two or more fluorescent dyes that undergo excited-state energy transfer, exhibit Stokes shifts that can be extremely large. Each microsphere contains a dye with an excitation peak that maximally overlaps the spectral output of a commonly used excitation source (for example, the 488 nm spectral line of the argon-ion laser; Figure 6.50). In addition, each microsphere contains one or more longer-wavelength dyes that are carefully chosen to create a relay series that can efficiently transfer the energy from the initially excited dye to the longest-wavelength acceptor dye. The proprietary dyes used in the TransFluoSpheres® beads are optimally loaded to ensure that the excitation energy is efficiently transferred from dye to dye so that essentially only the longest-wavelength dye in the series exhibits significant fluorescence. Because these TransFluoSpheres® beads fluoresce at a considerably longer wavelength than the excitation wavelength, they provide a signal that can be detected in samples with significant Rayleigh or Raman scattering or with endogenous fluorescent compounds such as bilins, flavins and certain drugs. Also, the large Stokes shifts exhibited by the TransFluoSpheres® beads allow the use of broadband filters, both to excite the sample and to detect the emission, resulting in a greater fluorescent signal (Figure 6.49).

Table 6.9 — Summary of Molecular Probes' TransFluoSpheres® fluorescent microspheres*

Excitation/ Emission (nm)	Size		
	0.04 µm	**0.1 µm**	**1.0 µm**
488/560	T8864	T8872	T8880
488/605	T8865		
488/605 NeutrAvidin-labeled	T8860	T8861	
488/645	T8867		T8883
488/645 Streptavidin-labeled	T10711		
488/685	T8868	T8876	
488/720	T8869		
543/620		T8874	
633/720	T8870	T8878	T13090†

* All TransFluoSpheres® beads are based on carboxylate-modified polystyrene microspheres and are supplied as 0.5 mL of an aqueous suspension containing 2% solids and 2 mM sodium azide, except the TransFluoSpheres® beads labeled with NeutrAvidin biotin-binding protein, which are supplied as 0.4 mL of an aqueous suspension containing 1% solids and 2 mM sodium azide, and the streptavidin-labeled beads, which are supplied as 0.4 mL of an aqueous suspension containing 0.5% solids and 2 mM sodium azide. † T13090 has a 2.0 µm diameter.

TransFluoSpheres® Beads to Match Different Excitation Sources

Molecular Probes offers TransFluoSpheres® beads that are compatible with several different excitation sources:

- Argon-ion laser–excitable TransFluoSpheres® beads (Figure 6.50) that have an excitation maximum near 488 nm but emit at 560 nm (T8864, T8872, T8880), 605 nm (T8865), 645 nm (T8867, T8883), 685 nm (T8868, T8876) or 720 nm (T8869)
- Red He–Ne laser–excitable TransFluoSpheres® beads with excitation/emission maxima of 633/720 nm (T8870, T8878)
- Green He–Ne laser–excitable TransFluoSpheres® beads with excitation/emission maxima of 543/620 nm (T8874)

The series of TransFluoSpheres® beads with 488 nm excitation enables researchers to potentially detect five experimental parameters simultaneously. TransFluoSpheres® beads can also be combined with our more traditional FluoSpheres® beads or with low molecular weight dyes for multicolor detection.[36] Using carbodiimide reagents such as EDAC (E2247, Section 3.3), researchers can couple protein or other amine-containing molecules to our carboxylate-modified TransFluoSpheres® beads, making these microspheres suitable for a wide range of applications. TransFluoSpheres® beads can be used in the major microsphere-based diagnostic test systems and in experiments that currently employ standard fluorescent microspheres to measure regional blood flow (T13090, Section 14.6), study phagocytosis (Section 16.1), detect cell-surface antigens and trace neurons.[7,29,49,74–76]

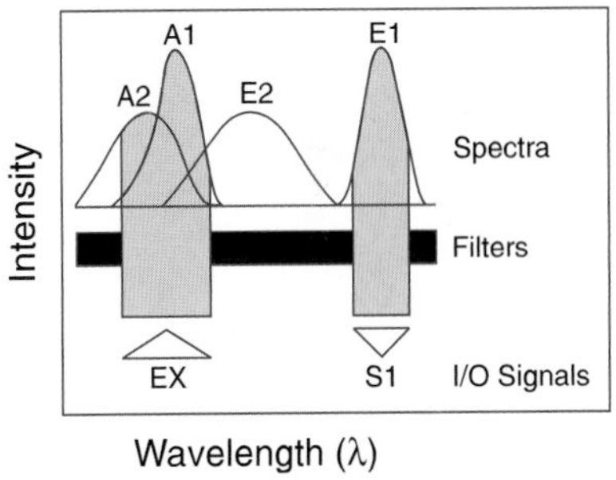

Figure 6.49 Schematic diagram of the advantages of the large Stokes shift exhibited by our TransFluoSpheres® beads. A1 and E1 represent the absorption and emission bands of a typical TransFluoSpheres® bead. The large separation of the absorption and emission maxima (Stokes shift) is characteristic of our TransFluoSpheres® beads. Unlike most low molecular weight fluorescent dyes, which show considerable overlap of their absorption and emission spectra, the TransFluoSpheres® beads can be excited (EX) across the entire absorption band A1 and the resulting fluorescence can be detected across the full emission band E1, thereby allowing the researcher to maximize the signal (S1). Moreover, because of the large Stokes shifts of the TransFluoSpheres® beads, researchers can often avoid problems associated with autofluorescence. The absorption and emission bands of a typical autofluorescent component are represented in this figure by A2 and E2. Although the endogenous fluorescent species will be excited simultaneously with the TransFluoSpheres® beads, the resulting emission (E2) does not coincide with E1 and is therefore readily rejected by suitably chosen optical filters.

We offer TransFluoSpheres® microspheres with excitation/emission maxima of 488/605 nm (T8860, T8861) conjugated to NeutrAvidin biotin- binding protein, as well as TransFluoSpheres® beads with excitation/emission maxima of 488/645 nm (T10711) conjugated to streptavidin. Flow cytometry studies demonstrate that the sensitivity of our 40 nm TransFluoSpheres® beads conjugated to streptavidin is superior to that of fluorescein streptavidin and comparable to that of R-phycoerythrin–streptavidin for detecting biotinylated epidermal growth factor (EGF) bound to EGF receptors.[36] In multicolor experiments, the long-wavelength fluorescence emission of these TransFluoSpheres® beads permits their use simultaneously with fluorescein- and R-phycoerythrin–labeled probes. For all applications requiring protein-coated microspheres, we strongly recommend using our BlockAid™ blocking solution (B10710) to reduce nonspecific binding.

If wavelength or bead-size requirements are not met by our current selection of products, we invite inquiries about custom synthesis by contacting our Custom and Bulk Sales Department. Molecular Probes can also fine-tune the excitation and emission of our microspheres to match a researcher's needs. In addition, we can covalently conjugate our TransFluoSpheres® beads to other target-specific proteins to provide detection reagents that have potentially greater sensitivity in flow cytometry applications and immunodiagnostic assays.

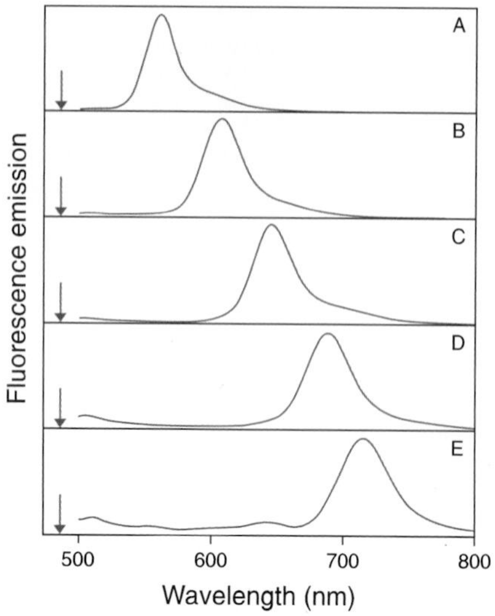

Figure 6.50 Fluorescence emission spectra of our five 488 nm light–excitable TransFluoSpheres® beads, named according to their excitation/emission maxima (nm): A) 488/560, B) 488/605, C) 488/645, D) 488/685 and E) 488/720. The arrow in each spectrum represents the 488 nm spectral line of the argon-ion laser.

BlockAid™ Blocking Solution

Molecular Probes' intensely fluorescent and highly photostable FluoSpheres® and TransFluoSpheres® microspheres have significant potential for applications requiring probes that can deliver a strong signal. Unfortunately, microspheres conjugated to proteins have hydrophobic regions that may cause them to bind to nontarget surfaces in some experimental systems. This nonspecific binding can often be relieved by the use of a blocking solution. However, we have found that microspheres require a stronger blocking solution than those in common use, and therefore we have developed the BlockAid™ blocking solution (B10710).

Our BlockAid™ reagent is a protein-based blocking solution designed for use with TransFluoSpheres® and FluoSpheres® microspheres conjugated to biotin, streptavidin, NeutrAvidin biotin-binding protein or other proteins. In our tests, BlockAid™ blocking solution was mixed with FluoSpheres® microspheres conjugated to streptavidin, which were then used to stain several different cell types for subsequent analysis by flow cytometry. We found the BlockAid™ blocking solution to be superior to blocking solutions available from other companies, as well as to several standard blocking solutions described in the scientific literature for reducing nonspecific binding of labeled microspheres. BlockAid™ blocking solution has been found to be effective in flow cytometry applications involving NIH 3T3, A431, RAW and Jurkat cell lines; however, with the HMC-1 cell line, it did not appear to offer any advantages over standard blocking solutions. We expect that BlockAid™ blocking solution will be useful for reducing the nonspecific binding of protein-coated or other macromolecule-coated microspheres in a variety of flow cytometry and microscopy applications.

Our Microsphere Bibliography

Our microsphere bibliography (M8997) contains over 1200 references, and continuously updated copies are available upon request from our Technical Assistance Department or through our web site (probes.invitrogen.com). This bibliography includes references in which microspheres from several different sources were used in a wide variety of applications. Because the source, surface properties and size of the microspheres may affect the application, the methods described in these references should be considered guides rather than definitive protocols. In particular, the bibliography lists several references that cite the use of fluorescent microspheres for retrograde tracing, and our FluoSpheres® beads have not performed consistently in this application. However, our fluorescent microspheres are guaranteed to be significantly brighter than microspheres available from other sources (Table 6.5).

References

1. Cytometry 33, 244 (1998); **2.** Biotech Histochem 73, 291 (1998); **3.** Anal Biochem 272, 165 (1999); **4.** Anal Biochem 271, 143 (1999); **5.** Science 208, 364 (1980); **6.** J Neurosci 14, 6621 (1994); **7.** J Neurosci 13, 5082 (1993); **8.** Nature 310, 498 (1984); **9.** Cell Motil Cytoskeleton 8, 293 (1987); **10.** Dev Growth Differ 28, 461 (1986); **11.** Clin Immunol Immunopathol 55, 173 (1990); **12.** J Immunol Methods 227, 41 (1999); **13.** J Immunol Methods 243, 243 (2000); **14.** Clin Chem 44, 2054 (1998); **15.** Cytometry 33, 318 (1998); **16.** Clin Chem 44, 2057 (1998); **17.** Clin Chem 43, 1799 (1997); **18.** Clin Chem 43, 1749 (1997); **19.** Methods Cell Biol 33, 613 (1990); **20.** J Neurosci Methods 122, 149 (2003); **21.** Am J Physiol 275, H110 (1998); **22.** Circ Shock 41, 156 (1993); **23.** J Appl Physiol 74, 2585 (1993); **24.** J Cereb Blood Flow Metab 13, 359 (1993); **25.** J Auton Nerv Syst 30, 159 (1990); **26.** Toxicol Appl Pharmacol 153, 28 (1998); **27.** J Appl Physiol 85, 2344 (1998); **28.** J Appl Physiol 82, 943 (1997); **29.** Ophthalmic Surg Lasers 28, 937 (1997); **30.** Ophthalmic Surg Lasers 29, 506 (1998); **31.** Methods Enzymol 292, 436 (1998); **32.** Curr Eye Res 17, 851 (1998); **33.** Cell Immunol 156, 508 (1994); **34.** J Leukoc Biol 43, 148 (1988); **35.** Science 215, 64 (1982); **36.** J Immunol Methods 219, 57 (1998); **37.** Biochim Biophys Acta 857, 61 (1986); **38.** Biochem Biophys Res Commun 181, 1223 (1991); **39.** Flow Cytometry Sorting, 2nd Ed., Melamed MR, Lindmo T, Mendelsohn ML, Eds. pp. 367–380 (1990); **40.** Am J Physiol 255, C452 (1988); **41.** Anal Chem 72, 1979 (2000); **42.** Anal Biochem 291, 219 (2001); **43.** J Histochem Cytochem 41, 1579 (1993); **44.** Br J Haematol 72, 239 (1989); **45.** Cytometry 32, 37 (1998); **46.** J Immunol Methods 116, 213 (1989); **47.** Dev Biol 149, 213 (1992); **48.** J Cell Biol 118, 937 (1992); **49.** J Membr Biol 135, 83 (1993); **50.** J Membr Biol 144, 231 (1995); **51.** J Cell Biol 127, 963 (1994); **52.** Science 268, 272 (1995); **53.** Biophotonics Int 6, 44 (1999); **54.** Science 260, 232 (1993); **55.** Biophys J 79, 1155 (2000); **56.** Cytometry 45, 27 (2001); **57.** Cytometry 44, 326 (2001); **58.** Biotechniques 27, 356 (1999); **59.** Anal Biochem 273, 20 (1999); **60.** Cytometry 15, 267 (1994); **61.** Cytometry 24, 312 (1996); **62.** Methods Enzymol 184, 353 (1990); **63.** Exp Cell Res 237, 383 (1997); **64.** J Cell Physiol 155, 461 (1993); **65.** J Cell Sci 98, 551 (1991); **66.** J Photochem Photobiol B 27, 3 (1995); **67.** Clin Chem 43, 1937 (1997); **68.** Biophys J 74, 2210 (1998); **69.** J Histochem Cytochem 44, 1091 (1996); **70.** Histochem J 31, 45 (1999); **71.** Biochemistry 37, 2372 (1998); **72.** J Histochem Cytochem 45, 1279 (1997); **73.** J Histochem Cytochem 47, 183 (1999); **74.** Biophys J 65, 2396 (1993); **75.** Brain Res 630, 115 (1993); **76.** Cytometry 13, 423 (1992).

Product List — 6.5 FluoSpheres and TransFluoSpheres Fluorescent Microspheres

Cat #	Product Name	Unit Size
B10710	BlockAid™ blocking solution *for use with microspheres*	50 mL
C14837	Constellation™ microspheres for imaging *mixture of assorted sizes and colors*	3 mL
F8760	FluoSpheres® aldehyde-sulfate microspheres, 0.02 µm, yellow-green fluorescent (505/515) *2% solids*	10 mL
F8762	FluoSpheres® aldehyde-sulfate microspheres, 1.0 µm, yellow-green fluorescent (505/515) *2% solids*	10 mL
F8763	FluoSpheres® amine-modified microspheres, 0.2 µm, red fluorescent (580/605) *2% solids*	5 mL
F8764	FluoSpheres® amine-modified microspheres, 0.2 µm, yellow-green fluorescent (505/515) *2% solids*	5 mL
F8765	FluoSpheres® amine-modified microspheres, 1.0 µm, yellow-green fluorescent (505/515) *2% solids*	5 mL
F8766	FluoSpheres® biotin-labeled microspheres, 0.04 µm, yellow-green fluorescent (505/515) *1% solids*	0.4 mL
F8767	FluoSpheres® biotin-labeled microspheres, 0.2 µm, yellow-green fluorescent (505/515) *1% solids*	0.4 mL
F8769	FluoSpheres® biotin-labeled microspheres, 1.0 µm, nonfluorescent *1% solids*	0.4 mL
F8768	FluoSpheres® biotin-labeled microspheres, 1.0 µm, yellow-green fluorescent (505/515) *1% solids*	0.4 mL
F8890	FluoSpheres® Blood Flow Determination Fluorescent Color Kit #1, polystyrene microspheres, 10 µm *seven colors, 10 mL each* *3.6x10^6 beads/mL*	1 kit
F8891	FluoSpheres® Blood Flow Determination Fluorescent Color Kit #2, polystyrene microspheres, 15 µm *seven colors, 10 mL each* *1.0x10^6 beads/mL*	1 kit
F8892	FluoSpheres® Blood Flow Determination Fluorescent Color Kit #3, polystyrene microspheres, 15 µm *five colors, 10 mL each* *1.0x10^6 beads/mL*	1 kit
F21015	FluoSpheres® Blood Flow Determination Fluorescent Color Kit #4, polystyrene microspheres, 15 µm *four colors, 10 mL each* *1.0x10^6 beads/mL*	1 kit
F8781	FluoSpheres® carboxylate-modified microspheres, 0.02 µm, blue fluorescent (365/415) *2% solids*	10 mL
F8782	FluoSpheres® carboxylate-modified microspheres, 0.02 µm, crimson fluorescent (625/645) *2% solids*	2 mL
F8783	FluoSpheres® carboxylate-modified microspheres, 0.02 µm, dark red fluorescent (660/680) *2% solids*	2 mL
F8784	FluoSpheres® carboxylate-modified microspheres, 0.02 µm, nile red fluorescent (535/575) *2% solids*	10 mL
F8786	FluoSpheres® carboxylate-modified microspheres, 0.02 µm, red fluorescent (580/605) *2% solids*	10 mL
F8787	FluoSpheres® carboxylate-modified microspheres, 0.02 µm, yellow-green fluorescent (505/515) *2% solids*	10 mL
F8789	FluoSpheres® carboxylate-modified microspheres, 0.04 µm, dark red fluorescent (660/680) *5% solids, azide free*	1 mL
F8791	FluoSpheres® carboxylate-modified microspheres, 0.04 µm, infrared fluorescent (715/755) *5% solids, azide free*	0.4 mL
F8792	FluoSpheres® carboxylate-modified microspheres, 0.04 µm, orange fluorescent (540/560) *5% solids, azide free*	1 mL
F8793	FluoSpheres® carboxylate-modified microspheres, 0.04 µm, red fluorescent (580/605) *5% solids, azide free*	1 mL
F8794	FluoSpheres® carboxylate-modified microspheres, 0.04 µm, red-orange fluorescent (565/580) *5% solids, azide free*	1 mL
F8795	FluoSpheres® carboxylate-modified microspheres, 0.04 µm, yellow-green fluorescent (505/515) *5% solids, azide free*	1 mL
F8797	FluoSpheres® carboxylate-modified microspheres, 0.1 µm, blue fluorescent (350/440) *2% solids*	10 mL
F8798	FluoSpheres® carboxylate-modified microspheres, 0.1 µm, far red fluorescent (690/720) *2% solids*	1 mL
F8799	FluoSpheres® carboxylate-modified microspheres, 0.1 µm, infrared fluorescent (715/755) *2% solids*	1 mL
F8800	FluoSpheres® carboxylate-modified microspheres, 0.1 µm, orange fluorescent (540/560) *2% solids*	10 mL
F8801	FluoSpheres® carboxylate-modified microspheres, 0.1 µm, red fluorescent (580/605) *2% solids*	10 mL
F8803	FluoSpheres® carboxylate-modified microspheres, 0.1 µm, yellow-green fluorescent (505/515) *2% solids*	10 mL
F8805	FluoSpheres® carboxylate-modified microspheres, 0.2 µm, blue fluorescent (365/415) *2% solids*	10 mL
F8806	FluoSpheres® carboxylate-modified microspheres, 0.2 µm, crimson fluorescent (625/645) *2% solids*	2 mL
F8807	FluoSpheres® carboxylate-modified microspheres, 0.2 µm, dark red fluorescent (660/680) *2% solids*	2 mL
F8809	FluoSpheres® carboxylate-modified microspheres, 0.2 µm, orange fluorescent (540/560) *2% solids*	10 mL
F8810	FluoSpheres® carboxylate-modified microspheres, 0.2 µm, red fluorescent (580/605) *2% solids*	10 mL
F8811	FluoSpheres® carboxylate-modified microspheres, 0.2 µm, yellow-green fluorescent (505/515) *2% solids*	10 mL
F8812	FluoSpheres® carboxylate-modified microspheres, 0.5 µm, red fluorescent (580/605) *2% solids*	10 mL
F8813	FluoSpheres® carboxylate-modified microspheres, 0.5 µm, yellow-green fluorescent (505/515) *2% solids*	10 mL
F8814	FluoSpheres® carboxylate-modified microspheres, 1.0 µm, blue fluorescent (365/415) *2% solids*	10 mL
F8815	FluoSpheres® carboxylate-modified microspheres, 1.0 µm, blue fluorescent (350/440) *2% solids*	10 mL
F8816	FluoSpheres® carboxylate-modified microspheres, 1.0 µm, crimson fluorescent (625/645) *2% solids*	2 mL
F8819	FluoSpheres® carboxylate-modified microspheres, 1.0 µm, nile red fluorescent (535/575) *2% solids*	10 mL
F8820	FluoSpheres® carboxylate-modified microspheres, 1.0 µm, orange fluorescent (540/560) *2% solids*	10 mL
F8821	FluoSpheres® carboxylate-modified microspheres, 1.0 µm, red fluorescent (580/605) *2% solids*	10 mL
F8823	FluoSpheres® carboxylate-modified microspheres, 1.0 µm, yellow-green fluorescent (505/515) *2% solids*	10 mL
F8824	FluoSpheres® carboxylate-modified microspheres, 2.0 µm, blue fluorescent (365/415) *2% solids*	2 mL
F8825	FluoSpheres® carboxylate-modified microspheres, 2.0 µm, nile red fluorescent (535/575) *2% solids*	2 mL
F8826	FluoSpheres® carboxylate-modified microspheres, 2.0 µm, red fluorescent (580/605) *2% solids*	2 mL
F8827	FluoSpheres® carboxylate-modified microspheres, 2.0 µm, yellow-green fluorescent (505/515) *2% solids*	2 mL
F20880	FluoSpheres® carboxylate-modified microspheres, 0.04 µm, europium luminescent (365/610) *0.5% solids*	2 mL
F20881	FluoSpheres® carboxylate-modified microspheres, 0.2 µm, europium luminescent (365/610) *0.5% solids*	2 mL
F20882	FluoSpheres® carboxylate-modified microspheres, 1.0 µm, europium luminescent (365/610) *0.5% solids*	2 mL
F20886	FluoSpheres® carboxylate-modified microspheres, 0.04 µm, platinum luminescent (390/650) *0.5% solids*	2 mL
F20887	FluoSpheres® carboxylate-modified microspheres, 0.2 µm, platinum luminescent (390/650) *0.5% solids*	2 mL
F20888	FluoSpheres® carboxylate-modified microspheres, 1.0 µm, platinum luminescent (390/650) *0.5% solids*	2 mL
F20892	FluoSpheres® collagen I-labeled microspheres, 1.0 µm, yellow-green fluorescent (505/515) *0.5% solids*	0.4 mL
F20893	FluoSpheres® collagen I-labeled microspheres, 2.0 µm, yellow-green fluorescent (505/515) *0.5% solids*	0.4 mL
F10720	FluoSpheres® Fluorescent Color Kit, carboxylate-modified microspheres, 0.04 µm *four colors, 1 mL each* *5% solids, azide free*	1 kit
F20883	FluoSpheres® NeutrAvidin™ labeled microspheres, 0.04 µm, europium luminescent (365/610) *0.5% solids*	0.4 mL

For current prices or to order online, visit probes.invitrogen.com

Product List — 6.5 FluoSpheres and TransFluoSpheres Fluorescent Microspheres — continued

Cat #	Product Name	Unit Size
F20884	FluoSpheres® NeutrAvidin™ labeled microspheres, 0.2 µm, europium luminescent (365/610) *0.5% solids*	0.4 mL
F20885	FluoSpheres® NeutrAvidin™ labeled microspheres, 1.0 µm, europium luminescent (365/610) *0.5% solids*	0.4 mL
F20889	FluoSpheres® NeutrAvidin™ labeled microspheres, 0.04 µm, platinum luminescent (390/650) *0.5% solids*	0.4 mL
F20890	FluoSpheres® NeutrAvidin™ labeled microspheres, 0.2 µm, platinum luminescent (390/650) *0.5% solids*	0.4 mL
F20891	FluoSpheres® NeutrAvidin™ labeled microspheres, 1.0 µm, platinum luminescent (390/650) *0.5% solids*	0.4 mL
F8772	FluoSpheres® NeutrAvidin™ labeled microspheres, 0.04 µm, nonfluorescent *1% solids*	0.4 mL
F8777	FluoSpheres® NeutrAvidin™ labeled microspheres, 1.0 µm, nonfluorescent *1% solids*	0.4 mL
F8770	FluoSpheres® NeutrAvidin™ labeled microspheres, 0.04 µm, red fluorescent (580/605) *1% solids*	0.4 mL
F8775	FluoSpheres® NeutrAvidin™ labeled microspheres, 1.0 µm, red fluorescent (580/605) *1% solids*	0.4 mL
F8771	FluoSpheres® NeutrAvidin™ labeled microspheres, 0.04 µm, yellow-green fluorescent (505/515) *1% solids*	0.4 mL
F8774	FluoSpheres® NeutrAvidin™ labeled microspheres, 0.2 µm, yellow-green fluorescent (505/515) *1% solids*	0.4 mL
F8776	FluoSpheres® NeutrAvidin™ labeled microspheres, 1.0 µm, yellow-green fluorescent (505/515) *1% solids*	0.4 mL
F13080	FluoSpheres® polystyrene microspheres, 1.0 µm, blue-green fluorescent (430/465) *for tracer studies* *1.0x10^{10} beads/mL*	5 mL
F13082	FluoSpheres® polystyrene microspheres, 1.0 µm, orange fluorescent (540/560) *for tracer studies* *1.0x10^{10} beads/mL*	5 mL
F13083	FluoSpheres® polystyrene microspheres, 1.0 µm, red fluorescent (580/605) *for tracer studies* *1.0x10^{10} beads/mL*	5 mL
F13081	FluoSpheres® polystyrene microspheres, 1.0 µm, yellow-green fluorescent (505/515) *for tracer studies* *1.0x10^{10} beads/mL*	5 mL
F8829	FluoSpheres® polystyrene microspheres, 10 µm, blue fluorescent (365/415) *for blood flow determination* *3.6x10^{6} beads/mL*	10 mL
F8830	FluoSpheres® polystyrene microspheres, 10 µm, blue-green fluorescent (430/465) *for blood flow determination* *3.6x10^{6} beads/mL*	10 mL
F8831	FluoSpheres® polystyrene microspheres, 10 µm, crimson fluorescent (625/645) *for blood flow determination* *3.6x10^{6} beads/mL*	10 mL
F8833	FluoSpheres® polystyrene microspheres, 10 µm, orange fluorescent (540/560) *for blood flow determination* *3.6x10^{6} beads/mL*	10 mL
F8834	FluoSpheres® polystyrene microspheres, 10 µm, red fluorescent (580/605) *for blood flow determination* *3.6x10^{6} beads/mL*	10 mL
F8836	FluoSpheres® polystyrene microspheres, 10 µm, yellow-green fluorescent (505/515) *for blood flow determination* *3.6x10^{6} beads/mL*	10 mL
F8837	FluoSpheres® polystyrene microspheres, 15 µm, blue fluorescent (365/415) *for blood flow determination* *1.0x10^{6} beads/mL*	10 mL
F8838	FluoSpheres® polystyrene microspheres, 15 µm, blue-green fluorescent (430/465) *for blood flow determination* *1.0x10^{6} beads/mL*	10 mL
F8839	FluoSpheres® polystyrene microspheres, 15 µm, crimson fluorescent (625/645) *for blood flow determination* *1.0x10^{6} beads/mL*	10 mL
F8841	FluoSpheres® polystyrene microspheres, 15 µm, orange fluorescent (540/560) *for blood flow determination* *1.0x10^{6} beads/mL*	10 mL
F8842	FluoSpheres® polystyrene microspheres, 15 µm, red fluorescent (580/605) *for blood flow determination* *1.0x10^{6} beads/mL*	10 mL
F8843	FluoSpheres® polystyrene microspheres, 15 µm, scarlet fluorescent (645/680) *for blood flow determination* *1.0x10^{6} beads/mL*	10 mL
F8844	FluoSpheres® polystyrene microspheres, 15 µm, yellow-green fluorescent (505/515) *for blood flow determination* *1.0x10^{6} beads/mL*	10 mL
F21013	FluoSpheres® polystyrene microspheres, 15 µm, carmine fluorescent (580/620) *for blood flow determination* *1.0x10^{6} beads/mL*	10 mL
F21010	FluoSpheres® polystyrene microspheres, 15 µm, green fluorescent (450/480) *for blood flow determination* *1.0x10^{6} beads/mL*	10 mL
F21012	FluoSpheres® polystyrene microspheres, 15 µm, red-orange fluorescent (565/580) *for blood flow determination* *1.0x10^{6} beads/mL*	10 mL
F21011	FluoSpheres® polystyrene microspheres, 15 µm, yellow fluorescent (515/534) *for blood flow determination* *1.0x10^{6} beads/mL*	10 mL
F8887	FluoSpheres® Size Kit #1, carboxylate-modified microspheres, red fluorescent (580/605) *six sizes, 1 mL each* *2% solids*	1 kit
F8888	FluoSpheres® Size Kit #2, carboxylate-modified microspheres, yellow-green fluorescent (505/515) *six sizes, 1 mL each* *2% solids*	1 kit
F8780	FluoSpheres® streptavidin-labeled microspheres, 0.04 µm, yellow-green fluorescent (505/515) *0.5% solids*	0.4 mL
F8845	FluoSpheres® sulfate microspheres, 0.02 µm, yellow-green fluorescent (505/515) *2% solids*	10 mL
F8848	FluoSpheres® sulfate microspheres, 0.2 µm, yellow-green fluorescent (505/515) *2% solids*	10 mL
F8849	FluoSpheres® sulfate microspheres, 1.0 µm, blue fluorescent (365/415) *2% solids*	10 mL
F8851	FluoSpheres® sulfate microspheres, 1.0 µm, red fluorescent (580/605) *2% solids*	10 mL
F8852	FluoSpheres® sulfate microspheres, 1.0 µm, yellow-green fluorescent (505/515) *2% solids*	10 mL
F8853	FluoSpheres® sulfate microspheres, 2.0 µm, yellow-green fluorescent (505/515) *2% solids*	2 mL
F8854	FluoSpheres® sulfate microspheres, 4.0 µm, blue fluorescent (365/415) *2% solids*	2 mL
F8858	FluoSpheres® sulfate microspheres, 4.0 µm, red fluorescent (580/605) *2% solids*	2 mL
F8859	FluoSpheres® sulfate microspheres, 4.0 µm, yellow-green fluorescent (505/515) *2% solids*	2 mL
T8864	TransFluoSpheres® carboxylate-modified microspheres, 0.04 µm (488/560) *2% solids*	0.5 mL
T8865	TransFluoSpheres® carboxylate-modified microspheres, 0.04 µm (488/605) *2% solids*	0.5 mL
T8867	TransFluoSpheres® carboxylate-modified microspheres, 0.04 µm (488/645) *2% solids*	0.5 mL
T8868	TransFluoSpheres® carboxylate-modified microspheres, 0.04 µm (488/685) *2% solids*	0.5 mL
T8869	TransFluoSpheres® carboxylate-modified microspheres, 0.04 µm (488/720) *2% solids*	0.5 mL
T8870	TransFluoSpheres® carboxylate-modified microspheres, 0.04 µm (633/720) *2% solids*	0.5 mL
T8872	TransFluoSpheres® carboxylate-modified microspheres, 0.1 µm (488/560) *2% solids*	0.5 mL
T8876	TransFluoSpheres® carboxylate-modified microspheres, 0.1 µm (488/685) *2% solids*	0.5 mL
T8874	TransFluoSpheres® carboxylate-modified microspheres, 0.1 µm (543/620) *2% solids*	0.5 mL
T8878	TransFluoSpheres® carboxylate-modified microspheres, 0.1 µm (633/720) *2% solids*	0.5 mL
T8880	TransFluoSpheres® carboxylate-modified microspheres, 1.0 µm (488/560) *2% solids*	0.5 mL
T8883	TransFluoSpheres® carboxylate-modified microspheres, 1.0 µm (488/645) *2% solids*	0.5 mL
T8882	TransFluoSpheres® carboxylate-modified microspheres, 1.0 µm (543/620) *2% solids*	0.5 mL
T8860	TransFluoSpheres® NeutrAvidin™ labeled microspheres, 0.04 µm (488/605) *1% solids*	0.4 mL
T8861	TransFluoSpheres® NeutrAvidin™ labeled microspheres, 0.1 µm (488/605) *1% solids*	0.4 mL
T13090	TransFluoSpheres® polystyrene microspheres, 2.0 µm (633/760) *for tracer studies* *1.0x10^{9} beads/mL*	0.5 mL
T10711	TransFluoSpheres® streptavidin-labeled microspheres, 0.04 µm (488/645) *0.5% solids*	0.4 mL

For current prices or to order online, visit probes.invitrogen.com

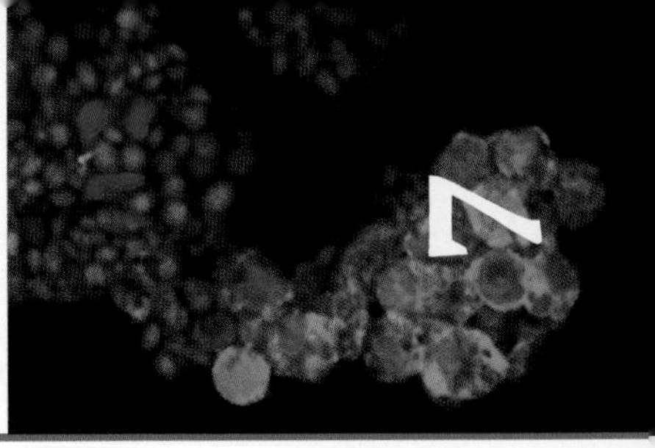

Chapter 7

Antibodies, Avidins, Lectins and Related Products

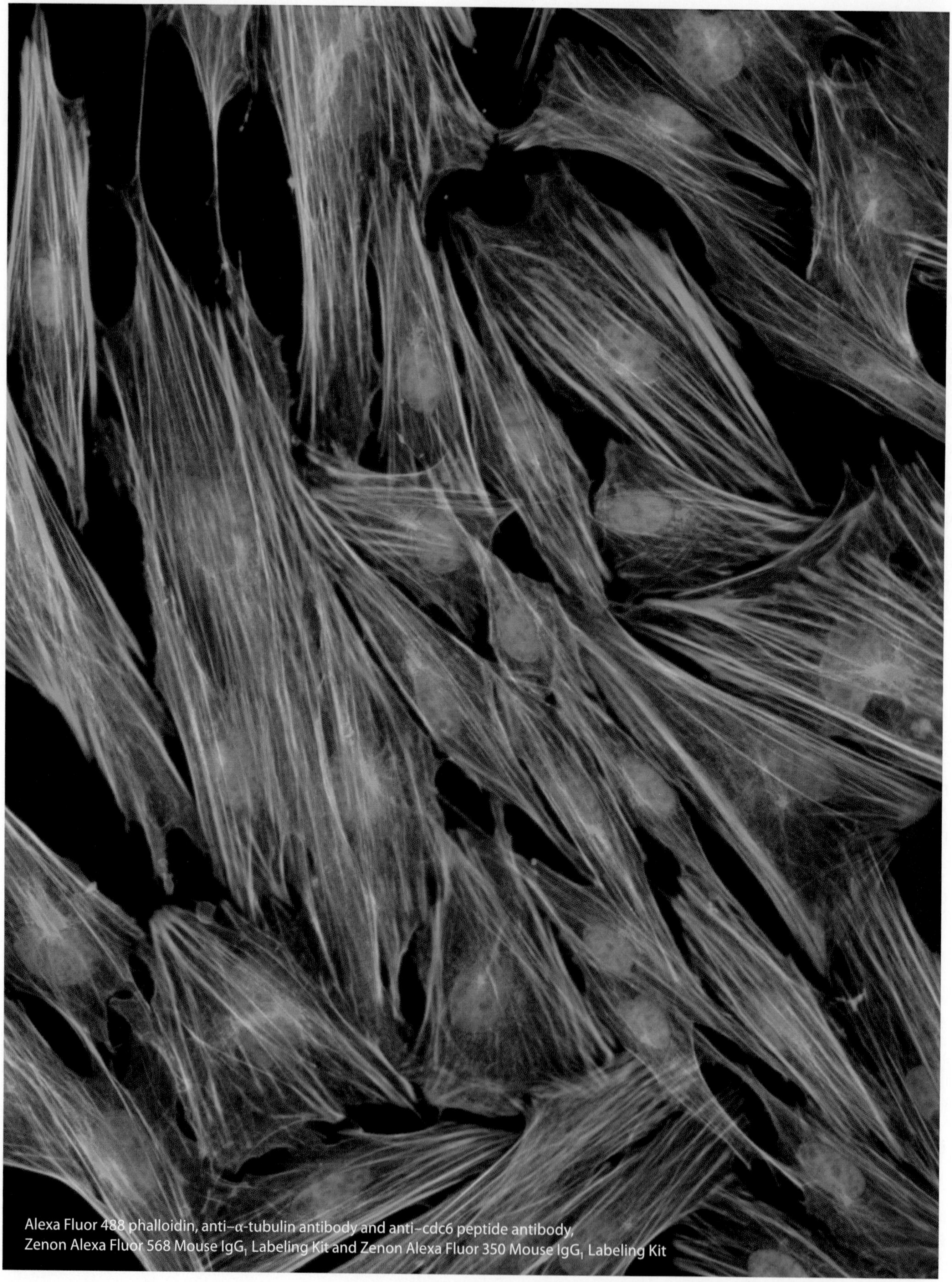

Alexa Fluor 488 phalloidin, anti–α-tubulin antibody and anti–cdc6 peptide antibody,
Zenon Alexa Fluor 568 Mouse IgG_1 Labeling Kit and Zenon Alexa Fluor 350 Mouse IgG_1 Labeling Kit

7.1 A Wide Variety of Protein Conjugates

Overview of Molecular Probes' Protein Conjugates

Antibody and Avidin Conjugates

The quality of a conjugate depends to a large degree on the quality of the protein from which it is made, as well as on the spectral properties of the fluorophore, the dye-to-protein ratio (DOS) and the methods used for the conjugate's purification. Molecular Probes uses the highest-quality proteins in its conjugates. In addition, our dyes and conjugation methods yield conjugates that are typically brighter than other commercially available conjugates (Figure 7.39, Figure 7.40, Figure 7.41), yet have low background and often have better spectral resolution. We also take exceptional care to remove unconjugated dye from the conjugate during purification. Moreover, all of our primary and secondary antibody conjugates and our avidin, streptavidin, NeutrAvidin and CaptAvidin™ biotin-binding protein conjugates are tested on cell samples to ensure low nonspecific binding and high specific staining. Table 7.1, Table 7.5 and Table 7.22 list our current offerings of fluorescent secondary immunoreagents and avidins. We also offer biotin, DSB-X™ biotin (a readily reversible version of biotin; Figure 4.1, Figure 7.103, Figure 7.104) and enzyme conjugates of some secondary antibodies (Section 7.2, Table 12.7) and anti-dye antibodies (Section 7.4, Table 7.18), as well as biotinylated enzymes and enzyme conjugates of NeutrAvidin biotin-binding protein and streptavidin (Section 7.6, Table 7.22), for use in diverse detection schemes.

Zenon® Antibody Labeling Kits and Other Protein Labeling Kits

In addition to our extensive assortment of dye- and enzyme-conjugated secondary antibodies (Section 7.2), Molecular Probes has developed the important Zenon® antibody labeling technology (Section 7.3), which utilizes a dye- or enzyme-labeled Fab fragment of an Fc-specific anti-IgG antibody to form stable complexes with the Fc portion of the corresponding mouse, rabbit, goat or human IgG antibody. Zenon® labeling methods are rapid and quantitative and can permit use of multiple antibodies derived from the same species in a single multicolor experiment (Figure 7.59, Figure 7.66, Figure 7.68).

Section 1.2 describes several protein labeling kits that can be used to directly conjugate most of our proprietary dyes to antibodies and other proteins (Table 1.2, Table 1.3). Amine-reactive versions of all of the low molecular weight fluorophores that we use to prepare our conjugates, and their spectral properties and other characteristics, are extensively described Chapter 1.

Gold Clusters and Magnetic Separation Media

In cooperation with Nanoprobes, Inc. (www.nanoprobes.com), Molecular Probes offers NANOGOLD and Alexa Fluor® FluoroNanogold 1.4 nm gold clusters covalently coupled to Fab′ fragments of secondary antibodies (Section 7.2) or streptavidin (Section 7.6) for light and electron microscopy studies. The Captivate™ ferrofluid antibody and streptavidin conjugates (Section 7.2, Section 7.6) and associated technology permit the magnetic separation of cells and cell components, and their visualization using a unique magnetic yoke and particle separation chamber (Figure 7.58).

Our Exceptional Fluorophores

Molecular Probes prepares protein conjugates of a wide variety of fluorophores, most of which have been developed in our research laboratories, ranging from the blue-fluorescent Cascade Blue®, Marina Blue® and Alexa Fluor® 350 dyes (Section 1.7) to the red-fluorescent Alexa Fluor® 594, Texas Red® and Texas Red®-X dyes and the red- to infrared-fluorescent Alexa Fluor® 633, Alexa Fluor® 635, Alexa Fluor® 647, Alexa Fluor® 660, Alexa Fluor® 680, Alexa Fluor® 700 and Alexa Fluor® 750 dyes (Section 1.3). Zenon® Antibody Labeling Kits are also available for antibody labeling with all of these dyes (Section 7.3, Table 7.13). We also prepare antibody, streptavidin and NeutrAvidin biotin-binding protein conjugates of phycobiliproteins, as well as antibodies and streptavidin labeled with our tandem conjugates of the Alexa Fluor® 610, Alexa Fluor® 647 and Alexa Fluor® 680 dyes with R-phycoerythrin (R-PE) (Section 6.4, Figure 6.34) and of allophycocyanin (APC) with the Alexa Fluor® 680, Alexa Fluor® 700 and Alexa Fluor® 750 dyes (Section 6.4, Figure 6.37). These ternary conjugates of the phycobiliprotein, a low molecular weight fluorescence resonance energy transfer acceptor and a secondary detection reagent, are particularly useful for multicolor flow cytometry measurements using a single laser, such as the 488 nm spectral line of the argon-ion laser or the 633 nm spectral line of the He–Ne laser for excitation of R-PE tandem conjugates or APC tandem conjugates, respectively. The DyeMer™ dyes are bifluorophores that have intrinsically high Stokes shifts; they absorb maximally near 488 nm with fluorescence emissions at 611, 617 or 630 nm.

Properties of the low molecular weight dyes that we use to prepare our conjugates are described in detail in Chapter 1. In particular, we would like to highlight our:

- **Alexa Fluor® conjugates.** Because of their superior brightness (Figure 7.1, Figure 7.39, Figure 7.40, Figure 7.41) and photostability (Figure 1.9, Figure 1.10, Figure 1.11, Figure 1.28, Figure 1.53), our Alexa Fluor® conjugates are rapidly becoming the preferred

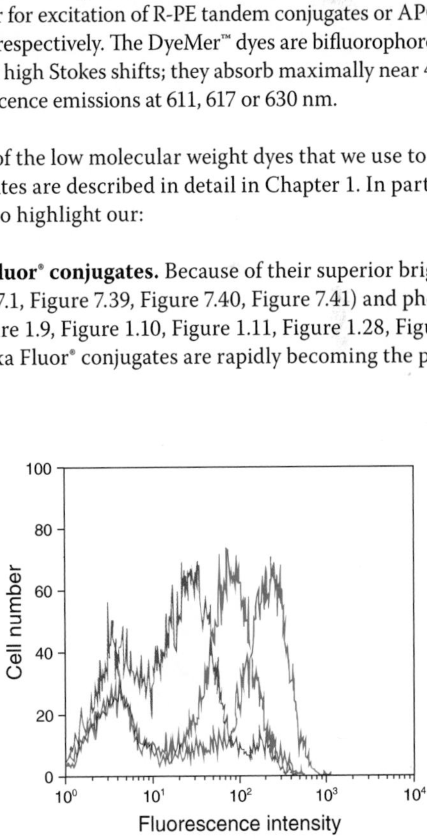

Figure 7.1 Flow cytometry was used to compare the brightness of Molecular Probes' Alexa Fluor® 647 goat anti–mouse IgG antibody (red, A21235) with commercially available Cy5 goat anti–mouse IgG antibody from Jackson ImmunoResearch Laboratories (green) and Amersham-Pharmacia Biotech (blue). Human blood was blocked with normal goat serum and incubated with an anti-CD3 mouse monoclonal antibody; cells were washed, resuspended and incubated with either an Alexa Fluor® 647 or Cy5 goat anti–mouse IgG secondary antibody at equal concentration. Red blood cells were lysed and the samples were analyzed on a flow cytometer equipped with a 633 nm He–Ne laser and a longpass emission filter (>650 nm).

Table 7.1 — Summary of Molecular Probes' secondary antibody conjugates

Antibody	Host	Blue Emission	Green Emission	Yellow Emission	Orange Emission	Red-Orange Emission	Red Emission	Far-Red Emission	Infrared Emission	Biotin	DSB-X™ biotin	Alkaline Phosphatase	Horseradish Peroxidase
Anti-mouse IgG	Goat	✓	✓	✓	✓	✓	✓	✓	✓	✓	✓	✓	✓
Anti-mouse IgM	Goat	✓	✓		✓	✓	✓	✓			✓		
Anti-rabbit IgG	Goat	✓	✓	✓	✓	✓	✓	✓	✓	✓	✓	✓	✓
Anti-rat IgG	Goat	✓	✓		✓	✓	✓	✓			✓		
Anti-rat IgM	Goat		✓				✓	✓					
Anti-guinea pig IgG	Goat		✓		✓	✓	✓	✓					
Anti-chicken IgG	Goat		✓		✓	✓	✓	✓			✓		
Anti-hamster IgG	Goat		✓		✓	✓	✓	✓					
Anti-human IgG	Goat		✓		✓	✓	✓	✓			✓		
Anti-human IgM	Goat		✓				✓	✓					
Anti-goat IgG	Donkey	✓	✓		✓	✓	✓	✓			✓		
Anti-mouse IgG	Donkey		✓		✓		✓	✓					
Anti-rabbit IgG	Donkey		✓		✓		✓	✓					
Anti-rat IgG	Donkey		✓				✓						
Anti-sheep IgG	Donkey	✓	✓		✓	✓	✓	✓			✓		
Anti-goat IgG	Rabbit		✓		✓	✓	✓	✓				✓	✓
Anti-mouse IgG	Rabbit	✓	✓		✓	✓	✓	✓		✓			✓
Anti-human IgG	Rabbit		✓										
Anti-rat IgG	Rabbit		✓				✓						
Anti-mouse IgG	Chicken		✓				✓	✓					
Anti-human IgG	Chicken		✓										
Anti-rat IgG	Chicken		✓				✓	✓					
Anti-goat IgG	Chicken		✓				✓	✓					
Anti-rabbit IgG	Chicken		✓				✓	✓					

Table 7.1A — Molecular Probes affinity-purified anti–mouse IgG conjugates, which are raised against the IgG heavy and light chains from mouse

Cat #	Label	Emission Color	Abs *	Em *
Goat Anti–Mouse IgG, Whole Antibody Cross-Adsorbed against Human IgG and Serum				
A11045	Alexa Fluor® 350	Blue	346	442
M10991	Marina Blue®	Blue	365	460
C962	Cascade Blue®	Blue	400	420
A31553	Alexa Fluor® 405	Blue	402	421
P10993	Pacific Blue™	Blue	410	455
A11063	Alexa Fluor® 430	Yellow-green	434	539
F2761	Fluorescein	Green	494	518
A11001	Alexa Fluor® 488	Green	495	519
O6380	Oregon Green® 488	Green	496	524
D31590	DyeMer™ 488/605	Red-orange	502	611
D31591	DyeMer™ 488/615	Red	502	617
D31592	DyeMer™ 488/630	Far-red	502	630
A31554	Alexa Fluor® 500	Green	503	525
B2752	BODIPY® FL	Green	505	513
O6383	Oregon Green® 514	Green	511	530
A31555	Alexa Fluor® 514	Yellow-green	518	540
A11002	Alexa Fluor® 532	Yellow	531	554
T2762	Tetramethylrhodamine	Orange	555	580
A11003	Alexa Fluor® 546	Orange	556	573
A21422	Alexa Fluor® 555	Orange	555	565
P852	R-Phycoerythrin (R-PE)	Orange	496, 546, 565	578
A20980	Alexa Fluor® 610–R-PE	Red	496, 546, 565	628
A20990	Alexa Fluor® 647–R-PE	Far-red	496, 546, 565	668
A20983	Alexa Fluor® 680–R-PE	Far-red	496, 546, 565	702
R6393	Rhodamine Red™-X	Red-orange	570	590
A11004	Alexa Fluor® 568	Red-orange	578	603
A11005	Alexa Fluor® 594	Red	590	617
T862	Texas Red®	Red	595	615
T6390	Texas Red®-X	Red	595	615
A31550	Alexa Fluor® 610	Red	612	628
A21050	Alexa Fluor® 633	Far-red	632	647
A31574	Alexa Fluor® 635	Far-red	633	647
A865	Allophycocyanin	Far-red	650	660
A21000	Alexa Fluor® 680 allophycocyanin	Far-red	650	702
A21006	Alexa Fluor® 750 allophycocyanin	Infrared	650	775
A21235	Alexa Fluor® 647	Far-red	650	668
A21054	Alexa Fluor® 660	Far-red	663	690
A21057	Alexa Fluor® 680	Far-red	679	702
A21036	Alexa Fluor® 700	Infrared	702	723
A21037	Alexa Fluor® 750	Infrared	749	775
B2763	Biotin	NA	<300	NA
D20690	DSB-X™ biotin	NA	<300	NA
G21040	Horseradish peroxidase	NA	NA	NA
G21060	Alkaline phosphatase	NA	NA	NA
Goat Anti–Mouse IgG, Whole Antibody Highly Cross-Adsorbed against Bovine, Goat, Rabbit, Rat and Human IgG and Serum				
A11029	Alexa Fluor® 488	Green	495	519
O11033	Oregon Green® 488	Green	496	524
A11030	Alexa Fluor® 546	Orange	556	573
A21424	Alexa Fluor® 555	Orange	555	565
A11031	Alexa Fluor® 568	Red-orange	578	603
A11032	Alexa Fluor® 594	Red	590	617
A21052	Alexa Fluor® 633	Far-red	632	647
A31575	Alexa Fluor® 635	Far-red	633	647

Table 7.1B — Molecular Probes' affinity-purified anti–rabbit IgG conjugates, which are raised against the IgG heavy and light chains from rabbit

Cat #	Label	Emission Color	Abs *	Em *
Goat Anti–Rabbit IgG, Whole Antibody Cross-Adsorbed against Human IgG and Serum, Mouse IgG and Serum, and Bovine Serum				
A11046	Alexa Fluor® 350	Blue	346	442
M10992	Marina Blue®	Blue	365	460
C2764	Cascade Blue®	Blue	400	420
A31556	Alexa Fluor® 405	Blue	402	421
P10994	Pacific Blue™	Blue	410	455
A11064	Alexa Fluor® 430	Yellow-green	434	539
F2765	Fluorescein	Green	494	518
A11008	Alexa Fluor® 488	Green	495	519
O6381	Oregon Green® 488	Green	496	524
D31600	DyeMer™ 488/605	Red-orange	502	611
D31601	DyeMer™ 488/615	Red	502	617
D31602	DyeMer™ 488/630	Far-red	502	630
A31557	Alexa Fluor® 500	Green	503	525
B2766	BODIPY® FL	Green	505	513
A31558	Alexa Fluor® 514	Yellow-green	518	540
A11009	Alexa Fluor® 532	Yellow	531	554
T2769	Tetramethylrhodamine	Orange	555	580
A11010	Alexa Fluor® 546	Orange	556	573
A21428	Alexa Fluor® 555	Orange	555	565
P2771MP	R-Phycoerythrin (R-PE)	Orange	496, 546, 565	578
A20981	Alexa Fluor® 610–R-PE	Red	496, 546, 565	628
A20991	Alexa Fluor® 647–R-PE	Far-red	496, 546, 565	668
A20984	Alexa Fluor® 680–R-PE	Far-red	496, 546, 565	702
R6394	Rhodamine Red™-X	Red-orange	570	590
A11011	Alexa Fluor® 568	Red-orange	578	603
A11012	Alexa Fluor® 594	Red	590	617
T2767	Texas Red®	Red	595	615
T6391	Texas Red®-X	Red	595	615
A31551	Alexa Fluor® 610	Red	612	628
A21070	Alexa Fluor® 633	Far-red	632	647
A31576	Alexa Fluor® 635	Far-red	633	647
A10931	Allophycocyanin	Far-red	650	660
A21001MP	Alexa Fluor® 680 allophycocyanin	Far-red	650	702
A21244	Alexa Fluor® 647	Far-red	650	668
A21073	Alexa Fluor® 660	Far-red	663	690
A21076	Alexa Fluor® 680	Far-red	679	702
A21038	Alexa Fluor® 700	Infrared	702	723
A21039	Alexa Fluor® 750	Infrared	749	775
B2770	Biotin	NA	<300	NA
D20694	DSB-X™ biotin	NA	<300	NA
G21079	Alkaline phosphatase	NA	NA	NA
G21234	Horseradish peroxidase	NA	NA	NA
Goat Anti–Rabbit IgG, Whole Antibody Highly Cross-Adsorbed against Bovine, Goat, Human, Mouse and Rat IgG				
A21068	Alexa Fluor® 350	Blue	346	442
A11034	Alexa Fluor® 488	Green	495	519
O11038	Oregon Green® 488	Green	496	524
A11035	Alexa Fluor® 546	Orange	556	573
A21429	Alexa Fluor® 555	Orange	555	565
A11036	Alexa Fluor® 568	Red-orange	578	603
A11037	Alexa Fluor® 594	Red	590	617
A21071	Alexa Fluor® 633	Far-red	632	647
A31577	Alexa Fluor® 635	Far-red	633	647
A21074	Alexa Fluor® 660	Far-red	663	690
A21109	Alexa Fluor® 680	Far-red	679	702

Table 7.1C — Molecular Probes' affinity-purified anti–rat IgG conjugates, which are raised against the IgG heavy and light chains from rat

Cat #	Label	Emission Color	Abs *	Em *
Goat Anti–Rat IgG, Whole Antibody Cross-Adsorbed against Mouse IgG and Serum				
A21093	Alexa Fluor® 350	Blue	346	442
A11006	Alexa Fluor® 488	Green	495	519
O6382	Oregon Green® 488	Green	496	524
A11081	Alexa Fluor® 546	Orange	556	573
A21434	Alexa Fluor® 555	Orange	555	565
A11077	Alexa Fluor® 568	Red-orange	578	603
A11007	Alexa Fluor® 594	Red	590	617
T6392	Texas Red®-X	Red	595	615
A21094	Alexa Fluor® 633	Far-red	632	647
A21247	Alexa Fluor® 647	Far-red	650	668
A21095	Alexa Fluor® 660	Far-red	663	690
A21096	Alexa Fluor® 680	Far-red	679	702
Chicken Anti–Rat IgG				
A21470	Alexa Fluor® 488	Green	495	519
A21471	Alexa Fluor® 594	Red	590	617
A21472	Alexa Fluor® 647	Far-red	650	668

*Absorption (Abs) and fluorescence emission (Em) maxima of conjugates, in nm.

Table 7.1D — Molecular Probes' affinity-purified anti–human IgG conjugates, which are raised against the IgG heavy and light chains from human

Cat #	Label	Emission Color	Abs *	Em *
Goat Anti–Human IgG, Whole Antibody Cross-Adsorbed against Mouse, Rabbit and Bovine Sera				
A11013	Alexa Fluor® 488	Green	495	519
A21089	Alexa Fluor® 546	Orange	556	573
A21433	Alexa Fluor® 555	Orange	555	565
A21090	Alexa Fluor® 568	Red-orange	578	603
A11014	Alexa Fluor® 594	Red	590	617
A21091	Alexa Fluor® 633	Far-red	632	647
A21445	Alexa Fluor® 647	Far-red	650	668
D20700	DSB-X™ biotin	NA	<300	NA
Chicken Anti–Human IgG				
A21464	Alexa Fluor® 488	Green	495	519
Rabbit Anti–Human IgG				
A21218	Alexa Fluor® 488	Green	495	519

* Absorption (Abs) and fluorescence emission (Em) maxima of conjugates, in nm.
NA = Not applicable.

Table 7.1E — Molecular Probes' affinity-purified anti–sheep IgG conjugates, which are raised against the IgG heavy and light chains from sheep

Cat #	Label	Emission Color	Abs *	Em *
Donkey Anti–Sheep IgG, Whole Antibody Cross-Adsorbed against Mouse, Rabbit, Bovine and Human Serum and Human IgG				
A21097	Alexa Fluor® 350	Blue	346	442
F2810	Fluorescein	Green	494	518
A11015	Alexa Fluor® 488	Green	495	519
A21098	Alexa Fluor® 546	Orange	556	573
A21436	Alexa Fluor® 555	Orange	555	565
A21099	Alexa Fluor® 568	Red-orange	578	603
A11016	Alexa Fluor® 594	Red	590	617
A21100	Alexa Fluor® 633	Far-red	632	647
A21448	Alexa Fluor® 647	Far-red	650	668
A21101MP	Alexa Fluor® 660	Far-red	663	690
A21102	Alexa Fluor® 680	Far-red	679	702

* Absorption (Abs) and fluorescence emission (Em) maxima of conjugates, in nm.

Table 7.1F — Molecular Probes' affinity-purified anti–goat IgG conjugates, which are raised against the IgG heavy and light chains from goat

Cat #	Label	Emission Color	Abs *	Em *
Donkey Anti–Goat IgG, Whole Antibody Cross-Adsorbed against Human, Mouse, Rabbit and Rat IgG				
A21081	Alexa Fluor® 350	Blue	346	442
A11055	Alexa Fluor® 488	Green	495	519
A11056	Alexa Fluor® 546	Orange	556	573
A21432	Alexa Fluor® 555	Orange	555	565
A11057	Alexa Fluor® 568	Red-orange	578	603
A11058	Alexa Fluor® 594	Red	590	617
A21082	Alexa Fluor® 633	Far-red	632	647
A21447	Alexa Fluor® 647	Far-red	650	668
A21083	Alexa Fluor® 660	Far-red	663	690
A21084	Alexa Fluor® 680	Far-red	679	702
Rabbit Anti–Goat IgG, Whole Antibody Cross-Adsorbed against Human and Rat IgG				
A11078	Alexa Fluor® 488	Green	495	519
A21085	Alexa Fluor® 546	Orange	556	573
A21431	Alexa Fluor® 555	Orange	555	565
A11079	Alexa Fluor® 568	Red-orange	578	603
A11080	Alexa Fluor® 594	Red	590	617
A21086	Alexa Fluor® 633	Far-red	632	647
A21446	Alexa Fluor® 647	Far-red	650	668
A21073	Alexa Fluor® 660	Far-red	663	690
A21088	Alexa Fluor® 680	Far-red	679	702
R21458	Alkaline phosphatase	NA	NA	NA
R21459	Horseradish peroxidase	NA	NA	NA
Chicken Anti–Goat IgG				
A21467	Alexa Fluor® 488	Green	495	519
A21468	Alexa Fluor® 594	Red	590	617
A21469	Alexa Fluor® 647	Far-red	650	668

* Absorption (Abs) and fluorescence emission (Em) maxima of conjugates, in nm.
NA = Not applicable.

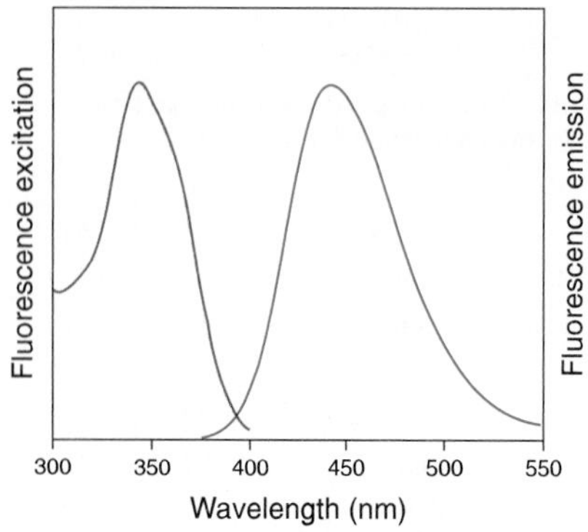

Figure 7.2 Fluorescence excitation and emission spectra of Alexa Fluor® 350 goat anti–mouse IgG antibody in pH 8.0 buffer.

reagents for all fluorescence-based immunoassays.[1,2] Furthermore, with our simplified nucleic acid labeling technology (Section 8.2) and availability of new, longer-wavelength Alexa Fluor® dyes, we anticipate significant use of the Alexa Fluor® dyes for *in situ* hybridization applications in cells and on arrays (Section 8.5). We prepare a vast number of different conjugates from our spectrally distinct Alexa Fluor® dyes: Alexa Fluor® 350 (Figure 7.2), Alexa Fluor® 405 (Figure 7.3), Alexa Fluor® 430 (Figure 7.4), Alexa Fluor® 488 (Figure 7.5), Alexa Fluor® 500 (Figure 7.6), Alexa Fluor® 514 (Figure 7.7), Alexa Fluor® 532 (Figure 7.8), Alexa Fluor® 546 (Figure 7.9), Alexa Fluor® 555 (Figure 7.10), Alexa Fluor® 568 (Figure 7.11), Alexa Fluor® 594 (Figure 7.12), Alexa Fluor® 610 (Figure 7.13), Alexa Fluor® 633 (Figure 7.14), Alexa Fluor® 635 (Figure 7.15), Alexa Fluor® 647 (Figure 7.16), Alexa Fluor® 660 (Figure 7.17), Alexa Fluor® 680 (Figure 7.18), Alexa Fluor® 700 (Figure 7.19) and Alexa Fluor® 750 (Figure 7.20) dyes, where the number refers to the near-optimal excitation wavelength for each dye. Our Alexa Fluor® 488, Alexa Fluor® 555 and Alexa Fluor® 647 goat anti–mouse IgG antibody conjugates have significantly higher total fluorescence than do all the commercially available conjugates of the spectrally similar Cy2, Cy3 and Cy5 dyes that we have tested[1,2] (Figure 7.1, Figure 7.39, Figure 7.40, Figure 7.41). These dyes and their properties are described in detail in Section 1.3.

Table 7.1G — Molecular Probes affinity-purified anti–chicken IgG conjugates, which are raised against the IgG heavy and light chains from chicken

Cat #	Label	Emission Color	Abs *	Em *
Goat Anti–Chicken IgG, Whole Antibody				
A11039	Alexa Fluor® 488	Green	495	519
A11040	Alexa Fluor® 546	Orange	556	573
A21437	Alexa Fluor® 555	Orange	555	565
A11041	Alexa Fluor® 568	Red-orange	578	603
A11042	Alexa Fluor® 594	Red	590	617
A21103	Alexa Fluor® 633	Far-red	632	647
A21449	Alexa Fluor® 647	Far-red	650	668
A21104	Alexa Fluor® 660	Far-red	663	690
D20701	DSB-X™ biotin	NA	<300	NA

* Absorption (Abs) and fluorescence emission (Em) maxima of conjugates, in nm. NA = Not applicable.

Table 7.1H — Molecular Probes' affinity-purified anti–guinea pig IgG conjugates, which are raised against the IgG heavy and light chains from guinea pig

Cat #	Label	Emission Color	Abs *	Em *
Goat Anti–Guinea Pig IgG, Whole Antibody Highly Cross-Adsorbed against Bovine, Chicken, Goat, Hamster, Human, Mouse, Rabbit, Rat and Sheep Sera				
A11073	Alexa Fluor® 488	Green	495	519
A11074	Alexa Fluor® 546	Orange	556	573
A21435	Alexa Fluor® 555	Orange	555	565
A11075	Alexa Fluor® 568	Red-orange	578	603
A11076	Alexa Fluor® 594	Red	590	617
A21105	Alexa Fluor® 633	Far-red	632	647
A21450	Alexa Fluor® 647	Far-red	650	668
A21106	Alexa Fluor® 660	Far-red	663	690

* Absorption (Abs) and fluorescence emission (Em) maxima of conjugates in nm.

Table 7.1I — Molecular Probes' affinity-purified goat anti-IgM* antibody conjugates, which are raised against the IgM μ chain

Fluorophore	Abs/Em †	Anti-Mouse	Anti-Rat	Anti-Human
Alexa Fluor® 350	346/442	A31552		
Alexa Fluor® 488	495/519	A21042	A21212	A21215
Alexa Fluor® 546	556/573	A21045		
Alexa Fluor® 555	555/565	A21426		
Alexa Fluor® 568	578/603	A21043		
Alexa Fluor® 594	590/617	A21044	A21213	A21216
Alexa Fluor® 633	632/647	A21046		
Alexa Fluor® 647	650/668	A21238	A21248	A21249
Alexa Fluor® 660	663/690	A21047		
Alexa Fluor® 680	679/702	A21048		
DSB-X™ biotin	NA	D20693		

* May also react with IgM from other species. † Absorption (Abs) and fluorescence emission (Em) maxima of conjugates, in nm. NA = Not applicable.

Table 7.1J — Molecular Probes' affinity-purified goat anti–hamster IgG antibodies

Cat #	Label	Emission Color	Abs *	Em *
Goat Anti–Hamster IgG, Whole Antibody Cross-Adsorbed against Mouse and Rat IgG				
A21110	Alexa Fluor® 488	Green	495	519
A21111	Alexa Fluor® 546	Orange	556	573
A21112	Alexa Fluor® 568	Red-orange	578	603
A21113	Alexa Fluor® 594	Red	590	617
A21114	Alexa Fluor® 633	Far-red	632	647
A21451	Alexa Fluor® 647	Far-red	650	668

* Approximate absorption (Abs) and emission (Em) maxima of conjugates, in nm.

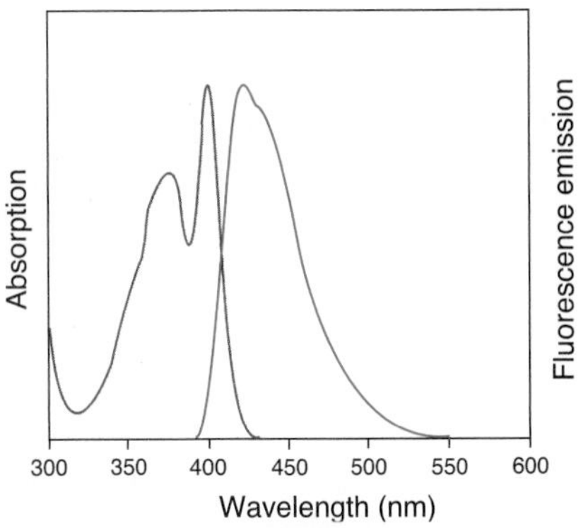

Figure 7.3 Absorption and fluorescence emission spectra of Alexa Fluor® 405 goat anti-mouse IgG antibody in pH 7.2 buffer.

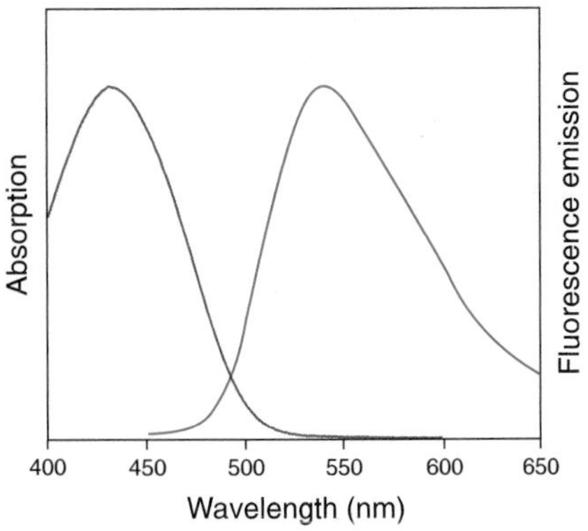

Figure 7.4 Absorption and fluorescence emission spectra of Alexa Fluor® 430 goat anti-mouse IgG antibody (A11063) in pH 7.2 buffer.

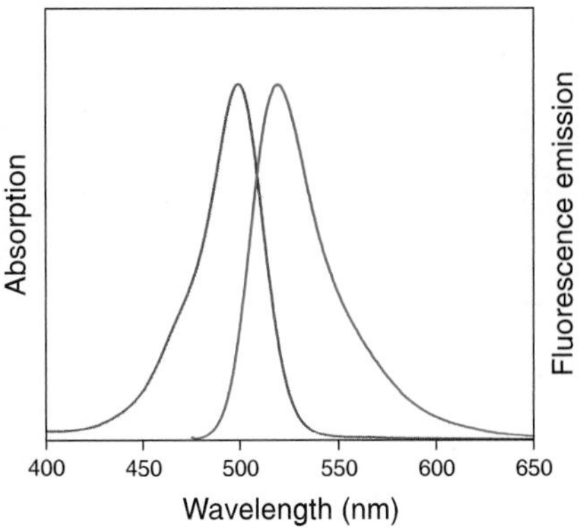

Figure 7.5 Absorption and fluorescence emission spectra of Alexa Fluor® 488 goat anti-mouse IgG antibody in pH 8.0 buffer.

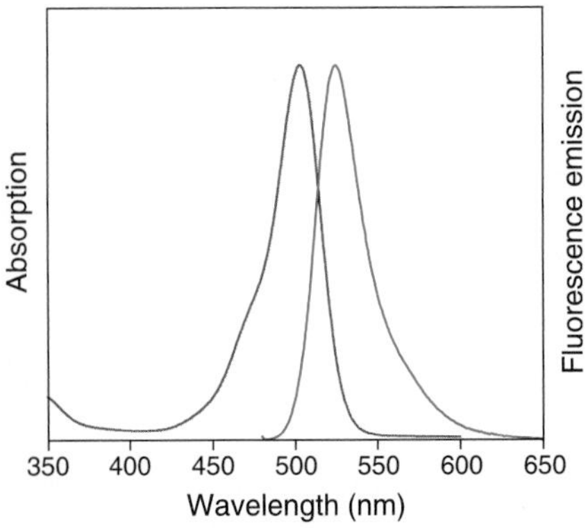

Figure 7.6 Absorption and fluorescence emission spectra of Alexa Fluor® 500 goat anti-mouse IgG antibody in pH 7.2 buffer.

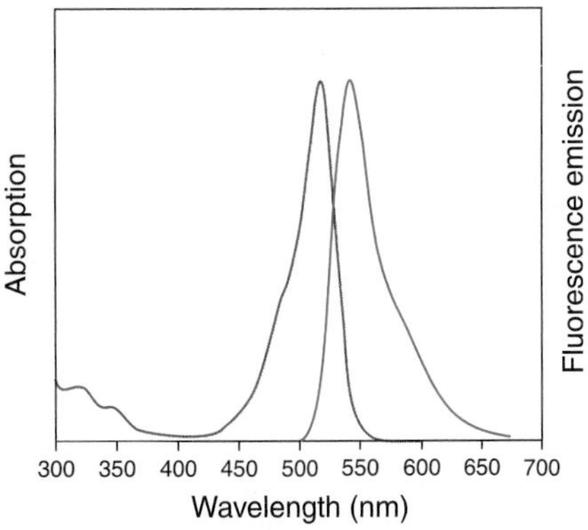

Figure 7.7 Absorption and fluorescence emission spectra of Alexa Fluor® 514 goat anti-mouse IgG antibody in pH 8.0 buffer.

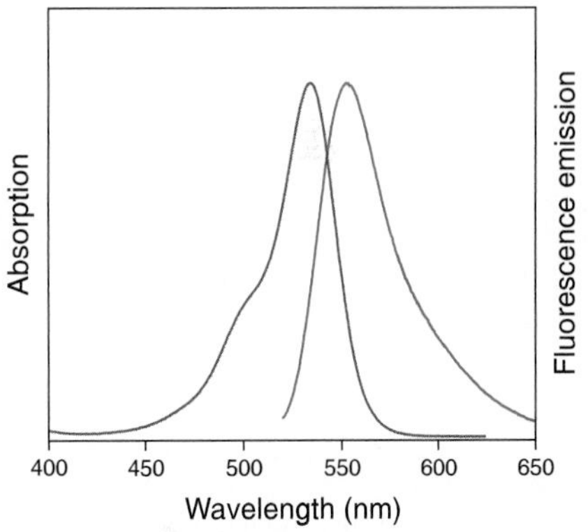

Figure 7.8 Absorption and fluorescence emission spectra of Alexa Fluor® 532 goat anti-mouse IgG antibody in pH 7.2 buffer.

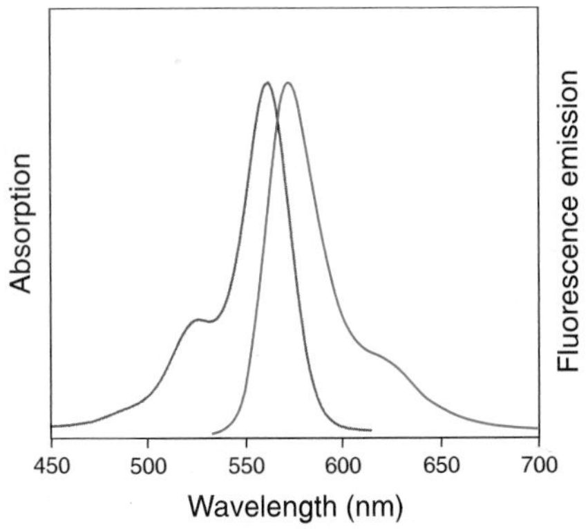

Figure 7.9 Absorption and fluorescence emission spectra of Alexa Fluor® 546 goat anti-mouse IgG antibody in pH 7.2 buffer.

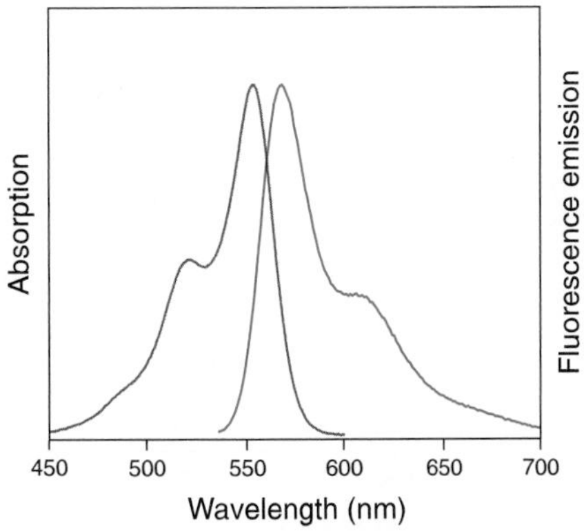

Figure 7.10 Absorption and fluorescence emission spectra of Alexa Fluor® 555 goat anti-mouse IgG antibody in pH 7.2 buffer.

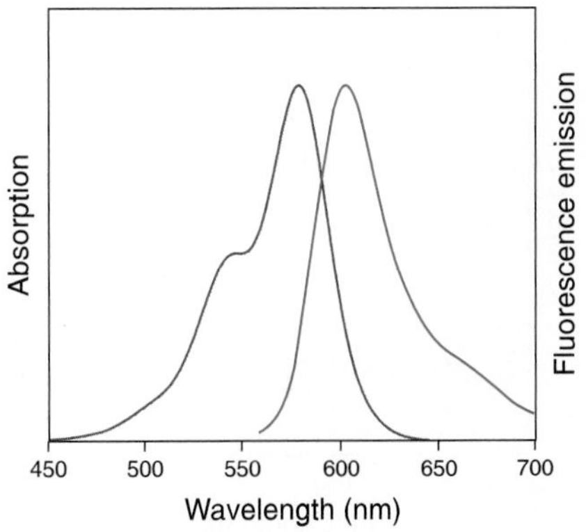

Figure 7.11 Absorption and fluorescence emission spectra of Alexa Fluor® 568 goat anti-mouse IgG antibody in pH 7.2 buffer.

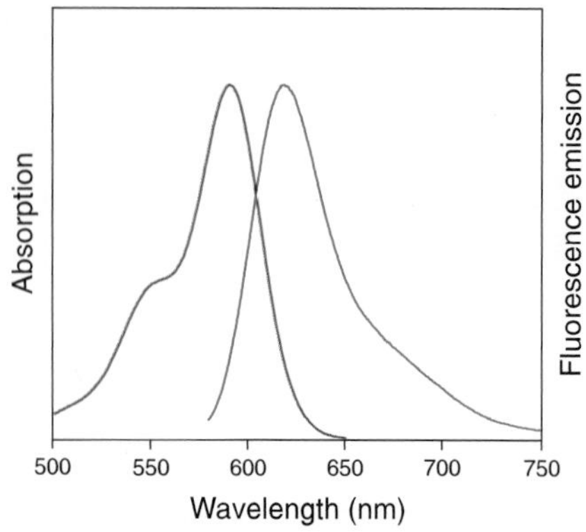

Figure 7.12 Absorption and fluorescence emission spectra of Alexa Fluor® 594 goat anti–mouse IgG antibody in pH 7.2 buffer.

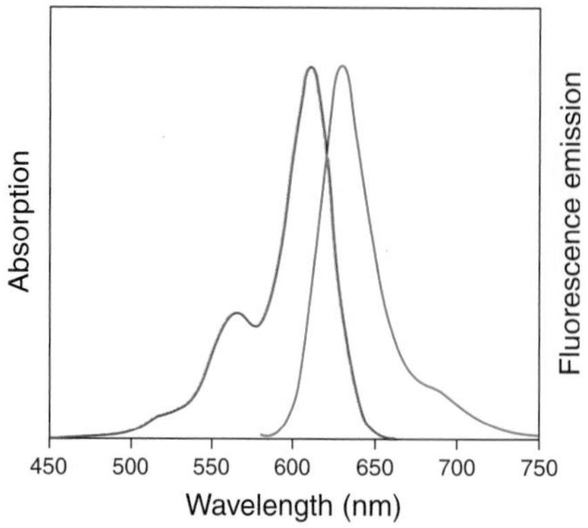

Figure 7.13 Absorption and fluorescence emission spectra of Alexa Fluor® 610 goat anti–mouse IgG antibody in pH 7.2 buffer.

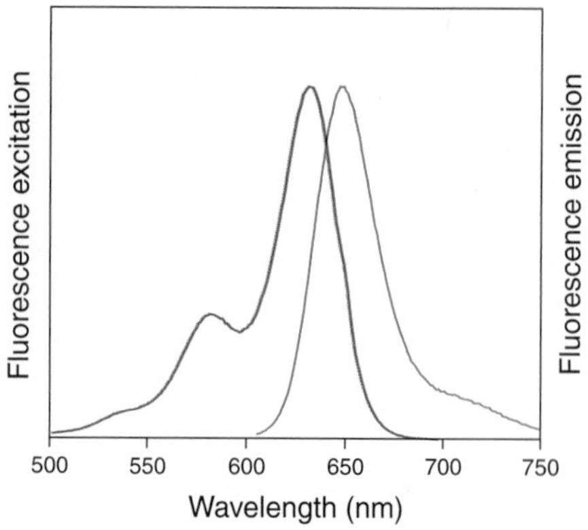

Figure 7.14 Fluorescence excitation and emission spectra of Alexa Fluor® 633 goat anti–mouse IgG antibody in pH 7.2 buffer.

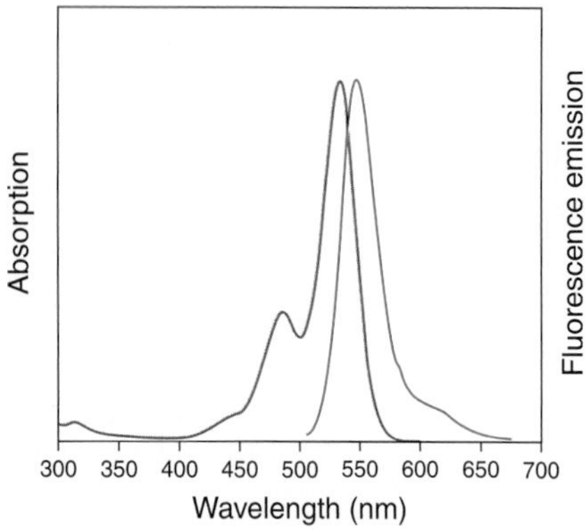

Figure 7.15 Absorption and fluorescence emission spectra of Alexa Fluor® 635 goat anti–mouse IgG antibody in pH 7.2 buffer.

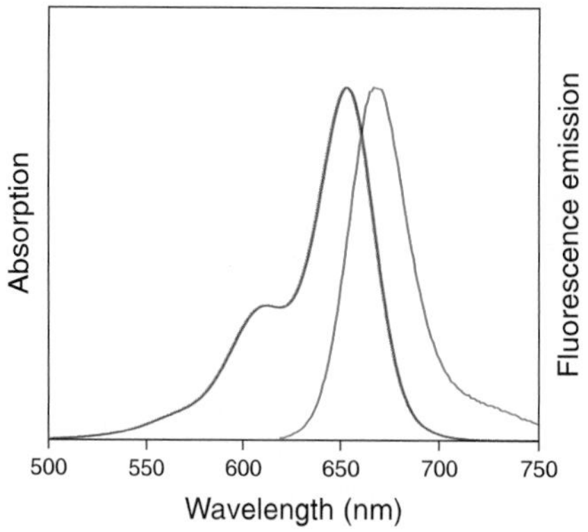

Figure 7.16 Absorption and fluorescence emission spectra of Alexa Fluor® 647 goat anti–mouse IgG antibody in pH 7.2 buffer.

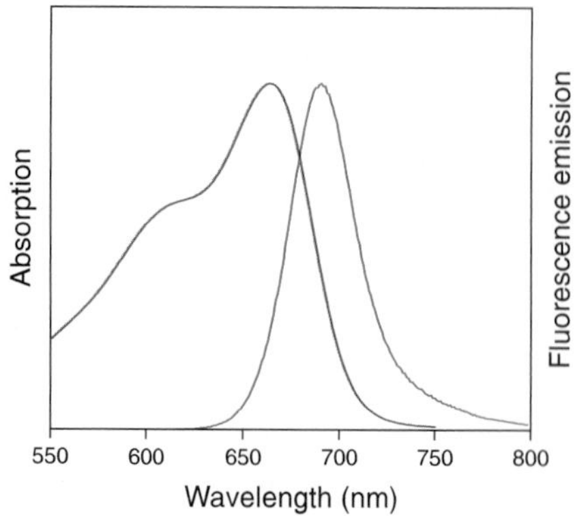

Figure 7.17 Absorption and fluorescence emission spectra of Alexa Fluor® 660 goat anti–mouse IgG antibody in pH 7.2 buffer.

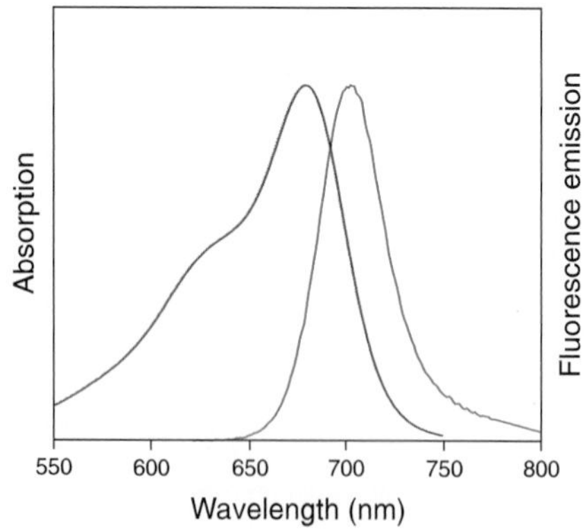

Figure 7.18 Absorption and fluorescence emission spectra of Alexa Fluor® 680 goat anti–mouse IgG antibody in pH 7.2 buffer.

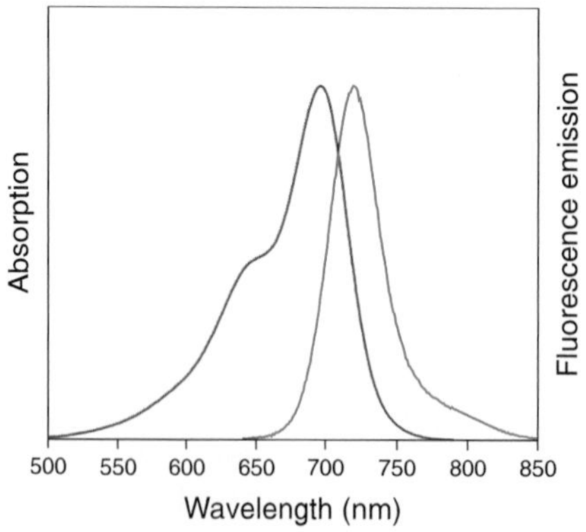

Figure 7.19 Absorption and fluorescence emission spectra of Alexa Fluor® 700 goat anti–mouse IgG antibody in pH 7.2 buffer.

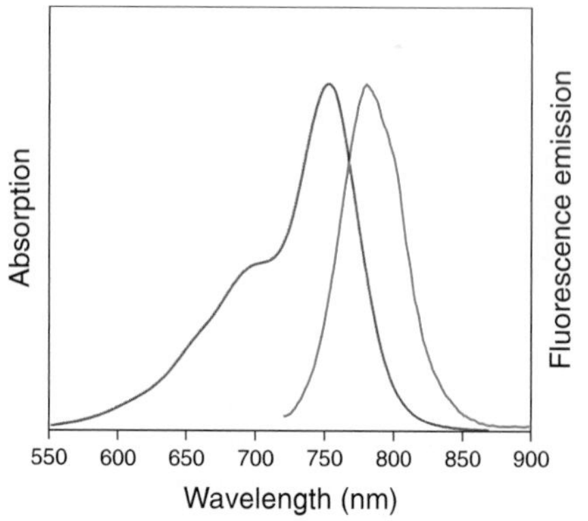

Figure 7.20 Absorption and fluorescence emission spectra of Alexa Fluor® 750 goat anti–mouse IgG antibody in pH 7.2 buffer.

- **Oregon Green® conjugates.** The Oregon Green® 488 dye has excitation and emission spectra (Figure 7.21) that are virtually identical to those of fluorescein, yet offers greater photostability and a fluorescence signal that is essentially independent of pH above pH 6 (Figure 1.12). The Oregon Green® 514 dye (Figure 7.22) is even more photostable than the Oregon Green® 488 dye (Figure 1.46, Figure 7.23). The decreased tendency of the Oregon Green® dyes to quench their fluorescence upon protein conjugation allows us to prepare conjugates that are more fluorescent than fluorescein conjugates (Figure 1.54). The available Oregon Green® dyes are listed in Table 1.6 and discussed in Section 1.5.
- **BODIPY® conjugates.** We prepare a large number of reactive BODIPY® dyes (Section 1.4, Table 1.6), and one of these — the BODIPY® FL dye — is an excellent substitute for fluorescein in some applications, although we generally recommend the Alexa Fluor® 488 and Oregon Green® 488 dyes for preparation of protein conjugates. Unlike fluorescein's fluorescence, the green fluorescence of BODIPY® FL conjugates is pH independent. In addition, the BODIPY® FL dye has an exceptionally narrow emission spectrum (Figure 7.24), making it particularly useful for multicolor applications (Figure 1.43). Because the BODIPY® FL dye is electrically neutral, BODIPY® FL conjugates have proven useful for immunofluorescence studies in eosinophils, which contain positively charged eosinophil granule proteins that cause nonspecific binding of FITC-conjugated antibodies.[3]
- **Fluorescein conjugates.** Although we feel that our Alexa Fluor® 488, Oregon Green® and BODIPY® FL dyes will provide superior performance in most applications, we continue to provide high-quality fluorescein conjugates for researchers who prefer to use fluorescein in their applications. Molecular Probes has developed a reactive fluorescein derivative that typically yields conjugates with significantly greater fluorescence than other commercially available fluorescein-labeled proteins. Figure 1.54 shows the fluorescence intensity of IgG labeled in the traditional manner using FITC, compared with that of an IgG labeled using Molecular Probes' unique fluorescein-5-EX succinimidyl ester (F6130, Section 1.4, Figure 1.58). Labeling with the fluorescein-5-EX reagent ensures that a greater signal is obtained for each IgG-bound fluorescein. Protein conjugates prepared from succinimidyl esters of fluorescein also have higher chemical stability than those prepared from fluorescein isothiocyanate[4] (FITC).

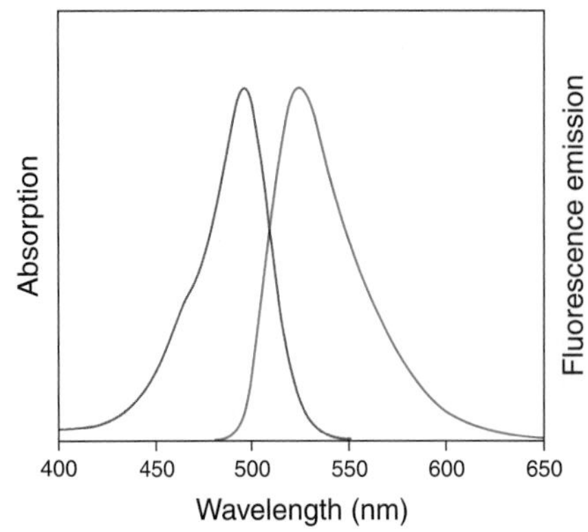

Figure 7.21 Absorption and fluorescence emission spectra of Oregon Green® 488 goat anti-mouse IgG antibody in pH 8.0 buffer.

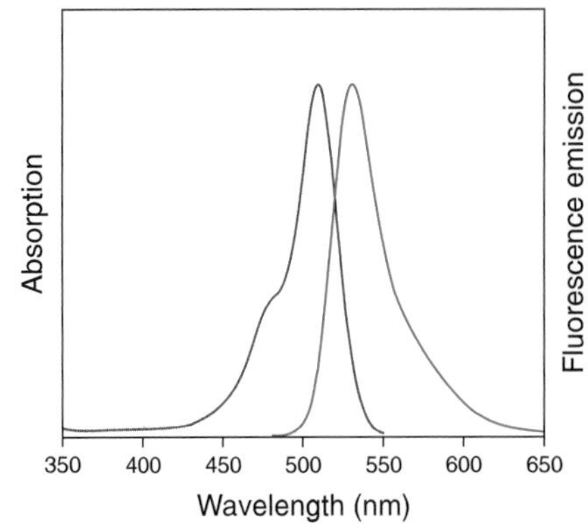

Figure 7.22 Absorption and fluorescence emission spectra of Oregon Green® 514 goat anti-mouse IgG antibody in pH 8.0 buffer.

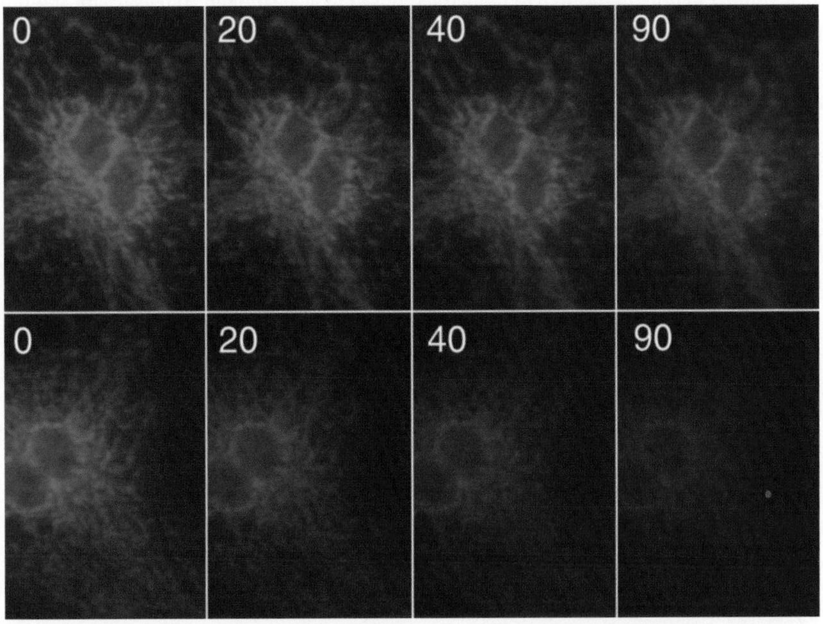

Figure 7.23 Comparison of the photostability of immunofluorescent staining by Oregon Green® 514 goat anti-mouse IgG antibody (O6383, upper series) and by fluorescein goat anti-mouse IgG antibody (F2761, lower series). Bovine pulmonary arterial endothelial cells were fixed with formaldehyde and permeabilized in cold acetone. Following blocking in 1% BSA, 1% normal goat serum, 0.1% Tween 20 in PBS, samples were incubated for one hour with 60 µg/mL mouse monoclonal anti-human cytochrome oxidase subunit I antibody (A6403, Section 7.5), after which they were rinsed and incubated with fluorescent anti-mouse IgG secondary antibodies at 10 µg/mL for 30 minutes. Samples were continuously illuminated and viewed on a fluorescence microscope using an Omega Optical fluorescein longpass filter set, a Star 1 CCD camera (Photometrics) and Image-1 software (Universal Imaging Corp.). Images acquired 0, 20, 40 and 90 seconds after the start of illumination (as indicated in the top left-hand corner of each panel) clearly demonstrate the superior photostability of the Oregon Green® 514 conjugate.

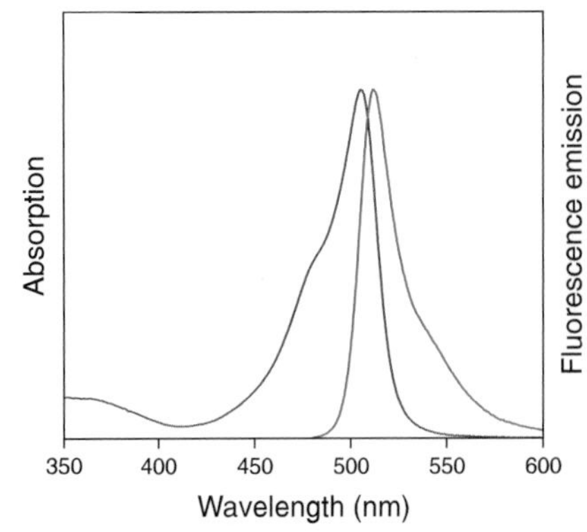

Figure 7.24 Absorption and fluorescence emission spectra of BODIPY® FL goat anti-mouse IgG antibody in pH 7.2 buffer.

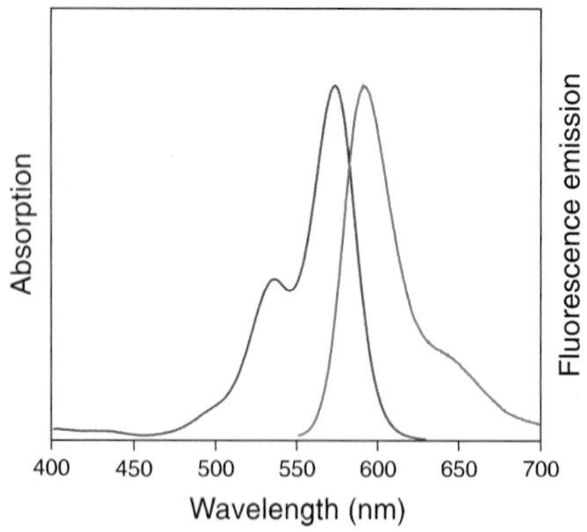

Figure 7.25 Absorption and fluorescence emission spectra of Rhodamine Red™-X goat anti-mouse IgG antibody in pH 8.0 buffer.

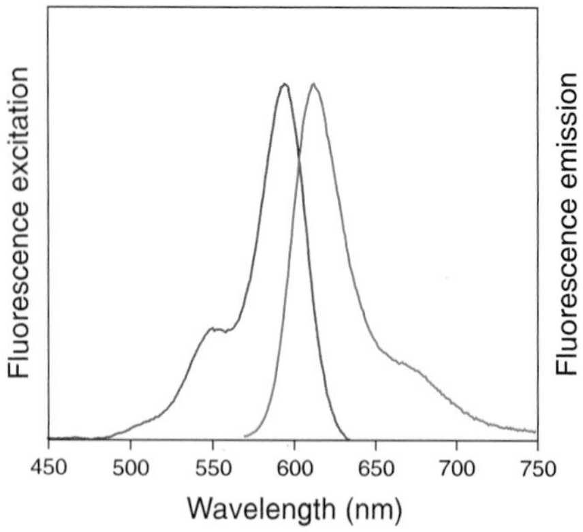

Figure 7.26 Fluorescence excitation and emission spectra of Texas Red®-X goat anti-mouse IgG antibody in pH 7.2 buffer.

- **Rhodamine Red™-X and Texas Red®-X conjugates.** Molecular Probes uses the succinimidyl esters of our patented Rhodamine Red™-X (R6160, Section 1.7; Figure 1.75, Figure 7.25) and Texas Red®-X (T6134, T20175; Section 1.7; Figure 1.83, Figure 7.26) fluorophores to prepare several detection reagents. The aminohexanoyl spacer ("X") apparently lessens the quenching that sometimes occurs when fluorescent dyes are conjugated to proteins. We have found that some of our Rhodamine Red™-X and Texas Red®-X protein conjugates are about twice as fluorescent as the corresponding conjugates prepared from Lissamine rhodamine B sulfonyl chloride and Texas Red® sulfonyl chloride [5] (Figure 1.76, Figure 1.84), thus providing a better signal-to-noise ratio. We continue to supply most of our original Texas Red® conjugates for those customers who have developed protocols using these products. Conjugates of the Texas Red® and Texas Red®-X dyes (Figure 7.26) emit at wavelengths that have little overlap with the fluorescence of fluorescein (Figure 7.27) or R-phycoerythrin (Figure 7.28) and are particularly useful for multicolor applications.[6–8] Alexa Fluor® 568 (Figure 7.11) and Rhodamine Red™-X (Figure 7.25) conjugates have maximal absorption at ~570 nm, making them the preferred probes for excitation by the 568 nm spectral line of the Ar–Kr laser used in some confocal laser-scanning microscopes.
- **Long-wavelength Alexa Fluor® conjugates.** Our Alexa Fluor® 633, Alexa Fluor® 635, Alexa Fluor® 647, Alexa Fluor® 660, Alexa Fluor® 680, Alexa Fluor® 700 and Alexa Fluor® 750 dye conjugates fill a need for bright and relatively photostable conjugates that can be excited by inexpensive, long-wavelength excitation sources such as the red He–Ne laser (633 nm) and red laser diodes.[1] Excitation and detection at long wavelengths usually results in superior rejection of sample autofluorescence. We find the Alexa Fluor® 635 dye to be the best fluorescent dye available for excitation by the red He–Ne laser at 633 nm and the 635 nm laser diode. Conjugates of the Alexa Fluor® 647 dye have fluorescence that is superior to that of the spectrally similar Cy5 dye (Figure 1.25) on both proteins (Figure 7.41) and nucleic acids (Figure 8.50). The Alexa Fluor® 680 dye has spectra virtually identical to those of the Cy5.5 dye (Figure 7.29), but its conjugates tend to be more fluorescent than those of the Cy5.5 dye. Our longest-wavelength Alexa Fluor® dye — the Alexa Fluor® 750 dye — has spectra similar to those of the Cy7 dye (Figure 7.20) and fluorescence emission that is well beyond essentially all biological autofluorescence. It may be possible to observe fluorescence of Alexa Fluor® 750 conjugates *in vivo* because biological tissues are relatively transparent to excitation light in the 700–800 nm spectral range. Using these dyes, we have prepared conjugates of a number of proteins, as well as numerous Alexa Fluor® phalloidin conjugates for staining F-actin filaments (Section 11.1, Table 11.1), the ULYSIS and ARES™ Nucleic Acid Labeling Kits (Section 8.2; Table 8.8, Table 8.9) and the Alexa Fluor® Oligonucleotide Amine Labeling Kits (Section 8.2, Table 8.10). Zenon® Antibody Labeling Kits are also available for antibody labeling with most of these dyes (Section 7.3, Table 7.13). Conjugates of the Alexa Fluor® 647, Alexa Fluor® 660, Alexa Fluor® 680, Alexa Fluor® 700 and Alexa Fluor® 750 dyes emit beyond the spectral range to which the human eye is sensitive. However, a filter combination that has been reported to be suitable for visual observation of Cy5 fluorescence [9] should also be suitable observing for Alexa Fluor® 647 conjugates. Conjugates of the Alexa Fluor® 700 and Alexa Fluor® 750 dyes may be difficult to detect without using red-enhanced photomultipliers or other suitable detection systems.

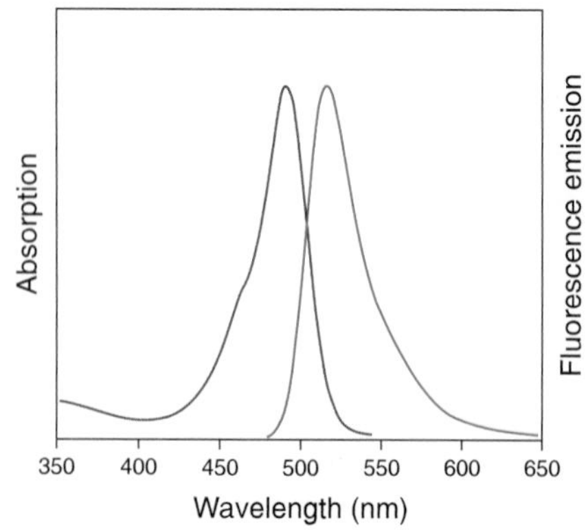

Figure 7.27 Absorption and fluorescence emission spectra of fluorescein goat anti-mouse IgG antibody in pH 8.0 buffer.

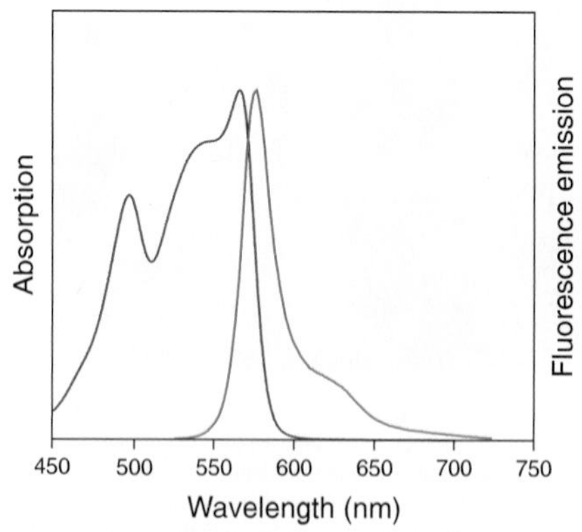

Figure 7.28 Absorption and fluorescence emission spectra of R-phycoerythrin in pH 7.5 buffer.

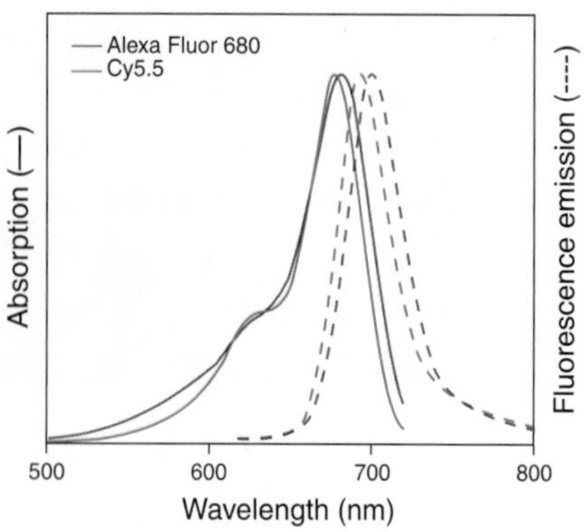

Figure 7.29 Comparison of the fluorescence spectra of the unconjugated Alexa Fluor® 680 and Cy5.5 dyes. Spectra have been normalized to the same intensity for comparison purposes.

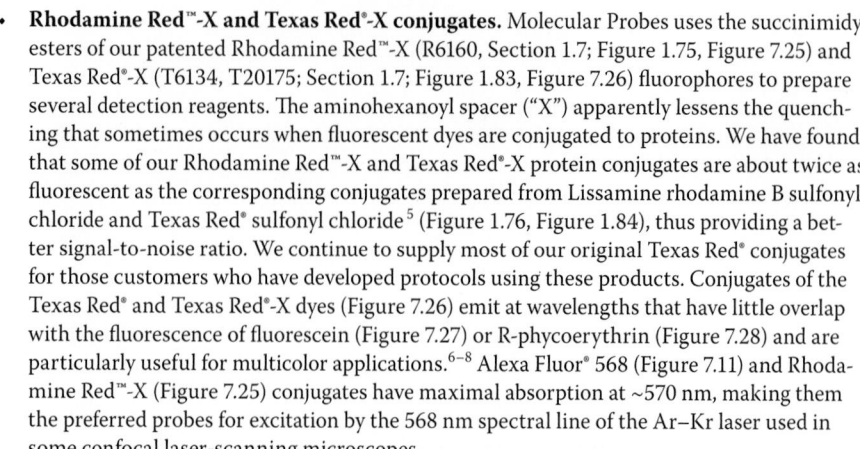

- **Phycobiliprotein conjugates.** In addition to our selection of immunoreagents labeled with organic dyes, Molecular Probes prepares phycobiliprotein-labeled secondary reagents (Section 6.4). The fluorescence yield of the red-fluorescent B- and R-phycoerythrin conjugates is theoretically equivalent to at least 30 fluorescein or 100 rhodamine molecules at comparable wavelengths. Because of the exceptional fluorescence and uniformly strong absorption for the phycoerythrins between 480 nm and 580 nm and allophycocyanin (APC) near 633 nm (Figure 6.32), phycobiliprotein-labeled detection reagents have been used extensively in flow cytometry to detect cell-specific expression of surface antigens.[10–14] Researchers used a phycobiliprotein-conjugated antibody to detect interleukin-4 in a microplate assay and found that it was the only tested fluorophore that produced an adequate signal.[15] Our streptavidin conjugate of R-phycoerythrin (SAPE; S866, S21388) has been extensively used to detect biotinylated nucleic acid probes on arrays[16–21] (Figure 6.42) and is an important reagent for "tetramer technology" (see Note 7.3 "Technical Focus: MHC Tetramer Technology" in Section 7.6). We also offer detection reagents labeled with APC (Figure 7.30) — one of the few fluorescent dyes that can be excited by the 633 nm spectral line of the He–Ne laser.[22] In imaging applications, APC is both brighter and more photostable than the spectrally similar Cy5 dye (Figure 6.31). Section 6.4 discusses the spectral properties of phycobiliproteins in more detail. Preparation of phycobiliprotein-labeled mouse, rabbit and human primary antibodies is greatly simplified by availability of Zenon® Antibody Labeling Kits (Section 7.3, Table 7.13) containing phycobiliprotein-derived labeling reagents.
- **Tandem conjugates of phycobiliproteins.** We have conjugated R-phycoerythrin (R-PE) with either the Alexa Fluor® 610, Alexa Fluor® 647 or Alexa Fluor® 680 dye, then coupled these tandem dye derivatives to antibodies or streptavidin to yield secondary detection reagents (Table 6.3) that can be excited with the 488 nm spectral line of the argon-ion laser (Section 6.4, Figure 6.34). Emission from the Alexa Fluor® 610 conjugates of R-PE is at ~630 nm, which is a slightly longer wavelength than the emission of Texas Red® dye–based tandem conjugates of R-PE[23–26] (Figure 6.39). This slightly longer-wavelength emission maximum significantly improves the resolution that can be obtained when using the Alexa Fluor® 610–R-PE tandem conjugates in place of Texas Red®–R-PE tandem conjugates for multicolor flow cytometry. The exceptionally long-wavelength emission maximum of the Alexa Fluor® 647–R-PE conjugates is at 667 nm and the energy transfer efficiency is very high (typically >98%), which results in low compensation in the red-orange fluorescence (R-PE) channel when the conjugates are used in combination with R-PE conjugates in multicolor flow cytometry applications (Figure 6.38). The Alexa Fluor® 647–R-PE and Alexa Fluor® 680–R-PE tandem conjugates have long-wavelength emission spectra that are virtually identical to those of Cy5 and Cy5.5 conjugates of R-PE, respectively, but fluorescence of our Alexa Fluor® 647–R-PE bioconjugates is substantially greater than that of commercially available Cy5–R-PE streptavidin conjugate (Figure 6.39, Figure 6.40). These tandem conjugates can be used for simultaneous three- or four-color labeling with a single excitation (Figure 6.34) and are also extremely useful for multicolor applications, including immunohistochemistry and hybridization assays, that use excitation by a longer-wavelength excitation source such as the Nd:YAG laser (at 532 nm), green He–Ne laser (at 543 nm) or krypton-ion laser (at 568 nm). In addition to the tandem conjugates of R-PE, we have prepared conjugates of either the Alexa Fluor® 680, Alexa Fluor® 700 or Alexa Fluor® 750 dye with APC and then conjugated these tandem dye derivatives to antibodies and streptavidin (Table 6.4). The Alexa Fluor® 680–APC ternary conjugates can be excited at 633–650 nm and their fluorescence detected separately from that of APC conjugates (Figure 6.37). Zenon® Mouse IgG_1 Labeling Kits containing Fab fragments labeled with the tandem phycobiliprotein conjugates are currently available (Section 7.3, Table 7.13).
- **DyeMer™ conjugates.** Our DyeMer™ 488/605, DyeMer™ 488/615 and DyeMer™ 488/630 conjugates of secondary antibodies (Section 7.2, Table 7.1) and of streptavidin (Section 7.6, Table 7.22) are optimized for use in flow cytometry applications. The red-orange–fluorescent DyeMer™ 488/605, red-fluorescent DyeMer™ 488/615 and far-red–fluorescent DyeMer™ 488/630 conjugates are each labeled with a unique bifluorophore comprising two covalently linked fluorophores that act as a donor–acceptor pair for fluorescence resonance energy transfer (FRET). When the green-fluorescent donor dye is excited with the 488 nm spectral line of the argon-ion laser, efficient energy transfer produces fluorescence of the long-wavelength acceptor dye, which emits at 611, 617 or 630 nm (Figure 7.31, Figure 7.32, Figure 7.33). Any fluorescence from the donor dye due to incomplete FRET can easily be compensated for by setting up compensation circuits to remove unwanted signals. Although their total fluorescence is not as intense as that of the phycobiliprotein tandem conjugates, the DyeMer™ conjugates exhibit mini-

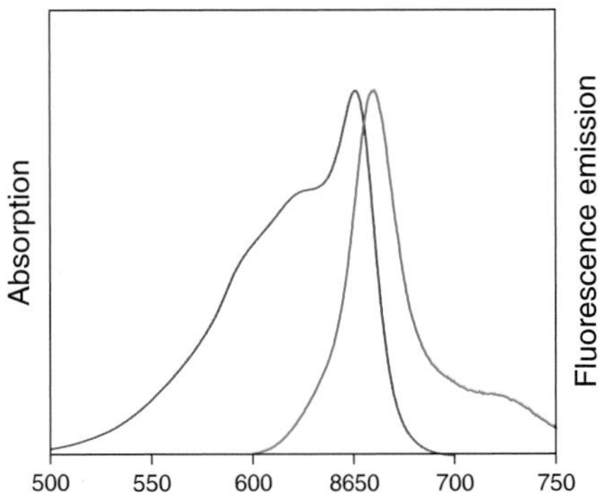

Figure 7.30 Absorption and fluorescence emission spectra of allophycocyanin in pH 7.5 buffer.

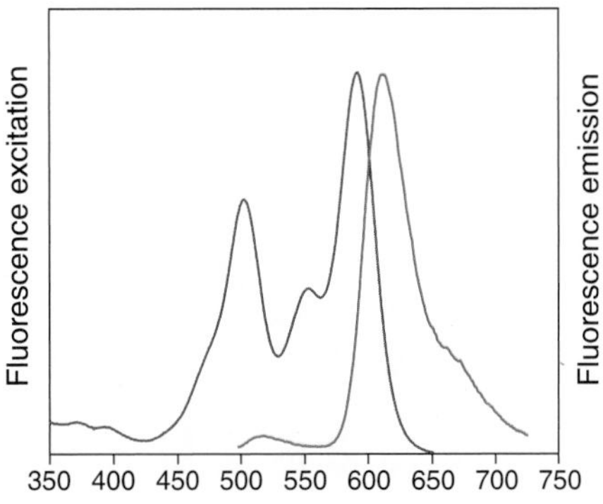

Figure 7.31 Fluorescence excitation and emission spectra of DyeMer™ 488/605 goat anti–rabbit IgG antibody in pH 7.2 buffer.

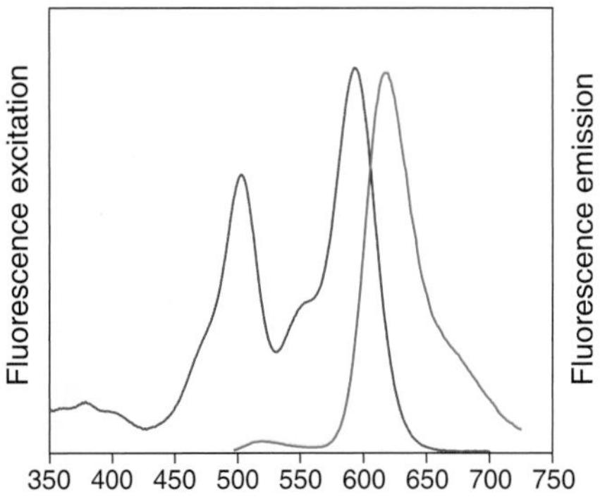

Figure 7.32 Fluorescence excitation and emission spectra of DyeMer™ 488/615 goat anti–mouse IgG antibody in pH 7.2 buffer.

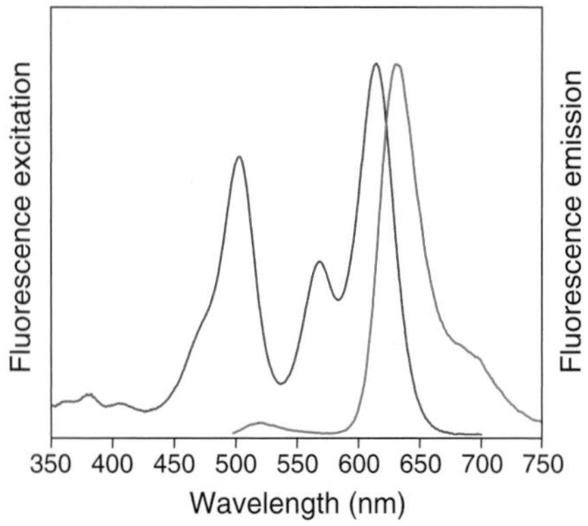

Figure 7.33 Fluorescence excitation and emission spectra of DyeMer™ 488/630 goat anti-mouse IgG antibody in pH 7.2 buffer.

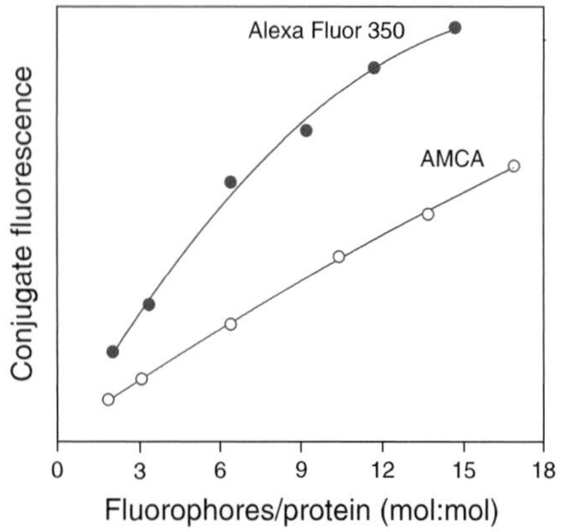

Figure 7.34 Comparison of the relative fluorescence of 7-amino-4-methylcoumarin-3-acetic acid (AMCA) streptavidin (○) and Alexa Fluor® 350 streptavidin, a sulfonated AMCA derivative (S11249, ●). Conjugate fluorescence is determined by measuring the fluorescence quantum yield of the conjugated dye relative to that of the free dye and multiplying by the number of fluorophores per protein.

mal lot-to-lot variation and less interference at the antigen- or biotin-binding site due to the relatively small size of the DyeMer™ bifluorophores. Moreover, their fluorescence can be excited either at 488 nm or at their longer-wavelength absorption maximum. Because there is some green fluorescence emitted from the donor dye, the DyeMer™ conjugates were not developed for imaging applications. By carefully choosing bandpass filters that block this green fluorescence or by using a green-fluorescent label for the most abundant target to keep exposure times short, these DyeMer™ conjugates can be successfully applied to multicolor fluorescence microscopy experiments.

- **Cascade Blue® and Alexa Fluor® 350 conjugates.** Although less frequently used because of their spectral overlap with sample autofluorescence and their generally lower fluorescence yields, blue-fluorescent fluorophores remain important for multicolor applications such as fluorescence *in situ* hybridization (FISH) and polychromatic flow cytometry.[10,11] Among the brightest UV light–excitable dyes are Molecular Probes' patented Cascade Blue® dyes and the Alexa Fluor® 350 dye — a sulfonated derivative of 7-amino-4-methylcoumarin-3-acetic acid (AMCA). We have found that protein conjugates of the Alexa Fluor® 350 dye are typically twice as fluorescent as AMCA conjugates (Figure 7.34). Furthermore, Alexa Fluor® 350 conjugates have slightly shorter-wavelength emission (Figure 7.2) than AMCA conjugates (~442 nm versus ~448 nm), thus yielding better separation of their emission from that of fluorescein or the Alexa Fluor® 488 dye. Conjugates of the Cascade Blue® dye are intrinsically brighter than AMCA[27] or Alexa Fluor® 350 conjugates and have improved spectral resolution from the emission of fluorescein (Figure 1.101), an important advantage for multicolor applications. However, the shorter emission wavelength of the Cascade Blue® conjugates (Figure 1.102) makes them appear less bright than Alexa Fluor® 350 conjugates because of the limited spectral sensitivity of the human eye to the shorter-wavelength fluorescence of the Cascade Blue® dye. Unlike many other fluorophores, such as fluorescein, the Cascade Blue® dye resists quenching upon protein conjugation (Figure 7.35). Conjugates of the Cascade Blue® dye (and the structurally similar Alexa Fluor® 405 dye) are optimally excited by the 405 nm spectral line of the blue diode laser recently developed for fluorescence microscopy and flow cytometry.
- **Marina Blue® and Pacific Blue™ conjugates.** Our patented Marina Blue® (Figure 7.36) and Pacific Blue™ (Figure 7.37) dyes, both of which are based on the 6,8-difluoro-7-hydroxycoumarin fluorophore (Figure 1.96, Figure 1.97), exhibit bright blue-fluorescent emission near 460 nm. The Marina Blue® dyes are optimally excited by the intense 365 nm spectral line of the mercury-arc lamp, whereas the Pacific Blue™ dyes maximally absorb at ~415 nm. Conjugates of the Pacific Blue™ dye are optimally excited by the 405 nm spectral line of the blue diode laser recently developed for fluorescence microscopy and flow cytometry.
- **Cascade Yellow™ conjugates.** Our yellow-fluorescent Cascade Yellow™ conjugates (Figure 7.38) absorb maximally at ~402 nm, making them near-perfect matches to the 405 nm spectral line of the blue diode laser recently developed for fluorescence microscopy and flow cytometry.

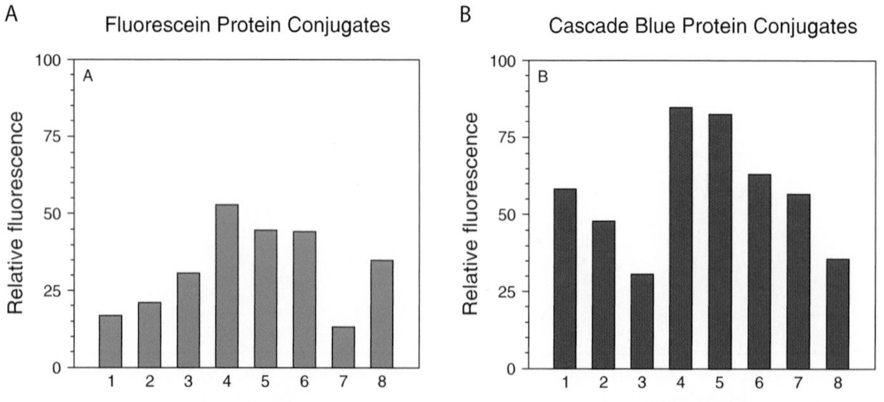

Figure 7.35 Histograms showing the fluorescence per fluorophore for A) fluorescein and B) Cascade Blue® conjugated to various proteins, relative to the fluorescence of the free dye in aqueous solution, represented by 100 on the y-axis. The proteins represented are: 1) avidin, 2) bovine serum albumin, 3) concanavalin A, 4) goat IgG, 5) ovalbumin, 6) protein A, 7) streptavidin and 8) wheat germ agglutinin.

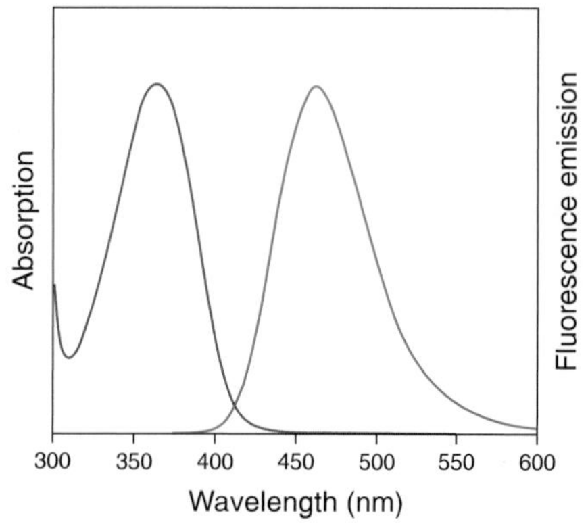

Figure 7.36 Absorption and fluorescence emission spectra of Marina Blue® goat anti-mouse IgG antibody in pH 8.0 buffer.

- **CMNB-caged fluorescein conjugates.** Our unique CMNB-caged fluorescein conjugates of the goat anti–mouse IgG and goat anti–rabbit IgG antibodies (G21061, G21080; Section 7.2) permit the fluorescent signal to be discriminated from background by photoactivation with ultraviolet light. At the same time, photoactivation creates a hapten for anti-fluorescein/Oregon Green® antibody (Section 7.4) only at sites that are illuminated (Section 7.4, Figure 7.74), a process similar to photolithography.
- **Fluorescent microspheres.** Where they can be used, conjugates of our FluoSpheres® and TransFluoSpheres® polystyrene microspheres provide the greatest versatility in selection of wavelengths and other properties[28,29] (Section 6.5, Figure 6.45). Not only are they intensely fluorescent, but TransFluoSpheres® beads also have extremely large Stokes shifts (Figure 6.49). Fluorescent microspheres labeled with biotin, streptavidin, NeutrAvidin biotin-binding protein and protein A are described in Section 6.5 and Section 7.6.
- **Tyramide signal amplification (TSA) technology.** TSA, described in Section 6.2, yields extremely high signals at the binding site of horseradish peroxidase (HRP)–conjugated probes. The method (Figure 6.5) results in catalyzed deposition of one of our Alexa Fluor® tyramide, Oregon Green® 488 tyramide or Pacific Blue™ tyramide conjugates or of biotin-XX tyramide, DSB-X™ biotin tyramide or DNP-X tyramide. The biotin-XX tyramide or DSB-X™ tyramide that is deposited on the target can be detected with a fluorescent conjugate of avidin or streptavidin (Section 7.6, Table 7.22) or can be further amplified with our ELF® technology[30] or a second round of TSA (Figure 6.5). Double amplification using TSA technology in combination with ELF® technology permits ultrasensitive detection of low-abundance targets with high spatial resolution.[30] HRP-conjugated antibodies that are useful for TSA can be rapidly and quantitatively prepared using our Zenon® Horseradish Peroxidase Antibody Labeling Kits (Section 7.3, Table 7.13).
- **Enzyme-Labeled Fluorescence (ELF®) technology.** Our ELF® detection reagents and kits, which are described in detail in Section 6.3, can be used to enhance the detection of biotinylated antibodies (Figure 6.21), biotinylated mRNA probes (Figure 8.93) and other haptenylated probes. When used in combination with alkaline phosphatase–streptavidin conjugates or alkaline phosphatase–labeled primary detection reagents, the ELF® 97 phosphatase substrate yields a yellow-green–fluorescent precipitate at the site of enzymatic activity that is much more photostable than any simple dye-labeled antibody conjugates (Figure 6.16). The Zenon® Alkaline Phosphatase Antibody Labeling Kits (Section 7.3, Table 7.13) facilitate the preparation of alkaline phosphatase–conjugated antibodies for use in combination with our ELF® technology.
- **Enzyme conjugates.** Molecular Probes offers various secondary antibody, streptavidin and NeutrAvidin conjugates of alkaline phosphatase, horseradish peroxidase and β-galactosidase, which are all prepared by methods that result in an approximate 1:1 ratio of enzyme to carrier protein, thereby ensuring the retention of both carrier-protein binding and enzymatic activity (Table 7.4). These conjugates are described in Section 7.2 and Section 7.6. Our Zenon® Alkaline Phosphatase and Horseradish Peroxidase Antibody Labeling Kits (Section 7.3, Table 7.13) permit the formation of enzyme-labeled mouse monoclonal antibodies using as little as sub-microgram quantities of the primary antibody.
- **Biotin and DSB-X™ biotin conjugates.** Biotin and DSB-X™ biotin conjugates of secondary antibodies (Table 7.10) permit the use of our fluorophore- and enzyme-labeled avidin, streptavidin and NeutrAvidin biotin-binding protein conjugates, our NANOGOLD and Alexa Fluor® FluoroNanogold streptavidin and our Captivate™ ferrofluid avidin and streptavidin products (Section 7.6), as well as the TSA and ELF® amplification technologies (Section 6.2, Section 6.3) in combination with immunolabeling methods. Binding of the DSB-X™ biotin derivatives to avidin- and streptavidin-labeled targets is fully reversible under very mild conditions (Figure 7.103, Figure 7.107). See Section 7.6 for a description of our unique DSB-X™ biotin technology.
- **Signal amplification kits.** Using antibody conjugates of our intensely fluorescent Alexa Fluor® 488 dye, Molecular Probes has developed the Alexa Fluor® 488 Signal Amplification Kit (A11053, Section 7.2), which gives a greater than 10-fold amplification of the green fluorescence of fluorescein-labeled antibodies (Figure 7.52) while at the same time considerably increasing the photostability of the stained sample. Similar kits have been developed that yield exceptionally intense green, red-orange or red fluorescence from any mouse antibody. These kits are described in Section 7.2.

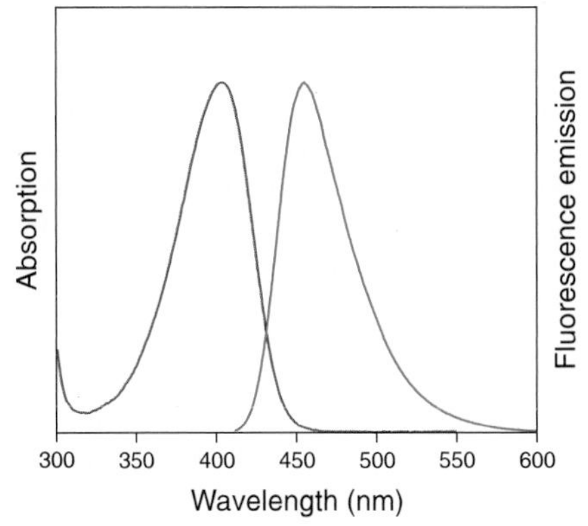

Figure 7.37 Absorption and fluorescence emission spectra of Pacific Blue™ goat anti–mouse IgG antibody in pH 8.0 buffer.

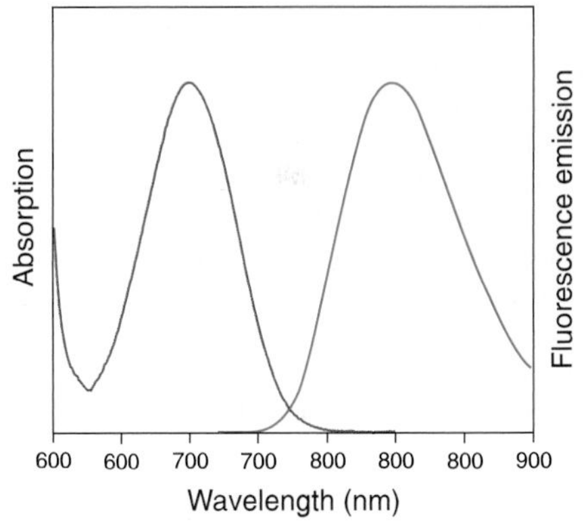

Figure 7.38 Absorption and fluorescence emission spectra of Cascade Yellow™ goat anti–mouse IgG antibody in pH 8.0 buffer.

References

1. J Histochem Cytochem 51, 1699 (2003); **2.** J Histochem Cytochem 47, 1179 (1999); **3.** J Immunol Methods 217, 113 (1998); **4.** Bioconjug Chem 6, 447 (1995); **5.** Bioconjug Chem 7, 482 (1996); **6.** Acta Histochem 89, 85 (1990); **7.** Proc Natl Acad Sci U S A 85, 3546 (1988); **8.** Cell Biophys 7, 129 (1985); **9.** J Histochem Cytochem 48, 437 (2000); **10.** Nat Med 7, 245 (2001); **11.** Nat Biotechnol 20, 155 (2002); **12.** J Cell Biol 116, 1291 (1992); **13.** J Immunol Methods 149, 159 (1992); **14.** Proc Natl Acad Sci U S A 85, 4672 (1988); **15.** J Immunol Methods 128, 109 (1990); **16.** J Biol Chem 276, 27042 (2001); **17.** Proc Natl Acad Sci U S A 98, 8862 (2001); **18.** Proc Natl Acad Sci U S A 97, 3260 (2000); **19.** Proc Natl Acad Sci U S A 97, 2680 (2000); **20.** Proc Natl Acad Sci U S A 95, 3752 (1998); **21.** Nat Biotechnol 14, 1675 (1996); **22.** Cytometry 15, 267 (1994); **23.** J Immunol Methods 138, 257 (1991); **24.** Cytometry 12, 350 (1991); **25.** J Immunol Methods 126, 69 (1990); **26.** Cytometry 10, 426 (1989); **27.** Anal Biochem 198, 119 (1991); **28.** Flow Cytometry Sorting, 2nd Ed., Melamed MR, Lindmo T, Mendelsohn ML, Eds. pp. 367–380 (1990); **29.** J Immunol Methods 219, 57 (1998); **30.** J Histochem Cytochem 48, 1593 (2000).

7.2 Secondary Immunoreagents

Molecular Probes provides scientists with an extensive and growing selection of secondary immunoreagents for use in fluorescence microscopy, flow cytometry, microplate assays, protein and nucleic acid blots and microarrays and several other techniques. Section 7.1 highlights the dyes we use to prepare several of our most important blue-, green-, orange-, red- and infrared-fluorescent secondary immunoreagents (Table 7.1), including our outstanding Alexa Fluor® conjugates (see Note 1.1 "Product Highlight: The Alexa Fluor® Dye Series — Peak Performance across the Visible Spectrum" in Section 1.3). Because of their superior brightness and photostability (Figure 1.9, Figure 1.10, Figure 1.11, Figure 1.28), the Alexa Fluor® conjugates are superior to most conventional fluorescent secondary reagents (Figure 7.39, Figure 7.40, Figure 7.41) and are the detection reagents of choice for many fluorescence-based immunoassays, *in situ* hybridization and bead-based applications (see Note 7.1 "Product Highlight: Guide to Labeling Antibodies with Alexa Fluor® Dyes"). Properties of the low molecular weight dyes that we use to prepare our conjugates are described in detail in Chapter 1, and in brief in Section 7.1. In addition to our extensive line of species-specific anti-IgG antibodies, anti-IgM antibodies, isotype-specific antibodies and $F(ab')_2$ fragments (see Note 7.2 "Technical Focus: Antibody Structure and Classification"), we prepare a variety of fluorescent conjugates of protein A and protein G — bacterial proteins that bind with high affinity to the Fc portion of various classes and subclasses of immunoglobulins from many species.

Because of the uniqueness and importance of the reagents, we have separated the discussion of our Zenon® antibody labeling technology into a separate section (Section 7.3). The Zenon® antibody labeling technology uses affinity-purified dye- or enzyme-labeled Fab fragments of Fc-specific anti-IgG antibodies for the rapid (Figure 7.60) and quantitative (Figure 7.61) labeling of an intact mouse, rabbit, goat or human IgG antibody (Figure 7.59). The Zenon® labeling method has several advantages over use of the secondary antibodies discussed in this section, including:

- The Zenon® labeling method is suitable for quantitatively labeling submicrogram amounts of an antibody in a few minutes and is not affected by the presence of non-antibody proteins or amine-containing buffers in the sample
- Multiple antibodies derived from the same species can be used in the same experiment
- The conjugate's degree of substitution and brightness can be easily adjusted
- Fluorescence colors can be mixed and matched in any combination for multicolor experiments
- The Zenon® labeled antibody complexes can be combined with labeled primary and secondary antibodies in most protocols

In many applications, the lower molecular weight of the Zenon® labeling reagents also makes them superior to labeled secondary antibodies in their ability to penetrate tissues. The fluorescence intensity of the Zenon® labeled antibody complexes, however, may be two- to threefold less than that of a labeled intact secondary antibody.

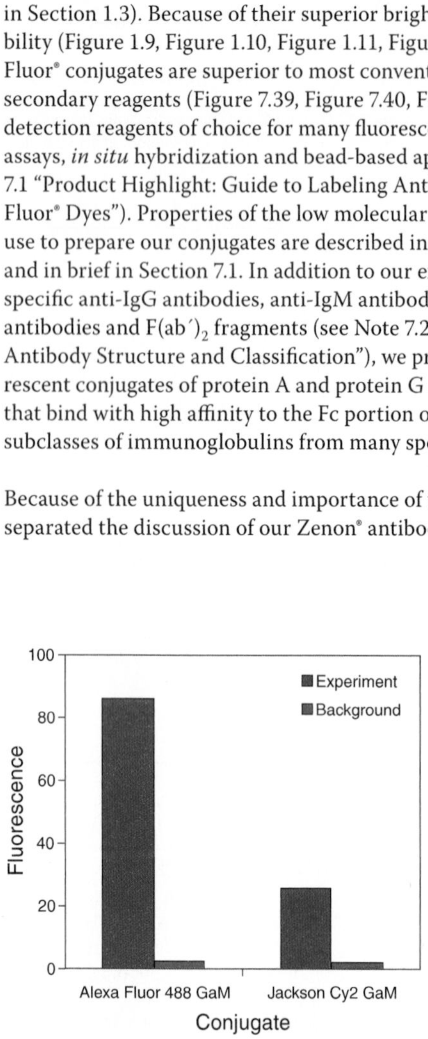

Figure 7.39 Brightness comparison of Molecular Probes' Alexa Fluor® 488 goat anti-mouse IgG antibody with Cy2 goat anti-mouse IgG antibody from Jackson ImmunoResearch. Human blood was blocked with normal goat serum and incubated with an anti-CD3 mouse monoclonal antibody; cells were washed, resuspended and incubated with either Alexa Fluor® 488 or Cy2 goat anti-mouse IgG antibody at equal concentration. Red blood cells were lysed, and the samples were analyzed with a flow cytometer equipped with a 488 nm argon-ion laser and a 525 ± 10 nm bandpass emission filter.

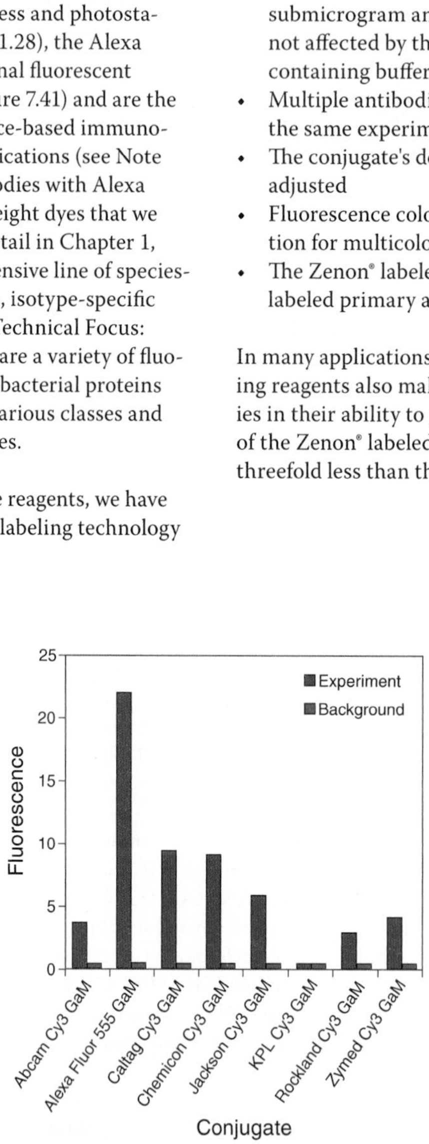

Figure 7.40 Brightness comparison of Molecular Probes' Alexa Fluor® 555 goat anti-mouse IgG antibody with Cy3 goat anti-mouse IgG antibody conjugates commercially available from several other companies. Human blood was blocked with normal goat serum and incubated with an anti-CD3 mouse monoclonal antibody; cells were washed, resuspended and incubated with either the Alexa Fluor® 555 or Cy3 goat anti-mouse IgG antibody at equal concentrations. Red blood cells were lysed and the samples were analyzed with a flow cytometer equipped with a 488 nm argon-ion laser and a 585 ± 21 nm bandpass emission filter.

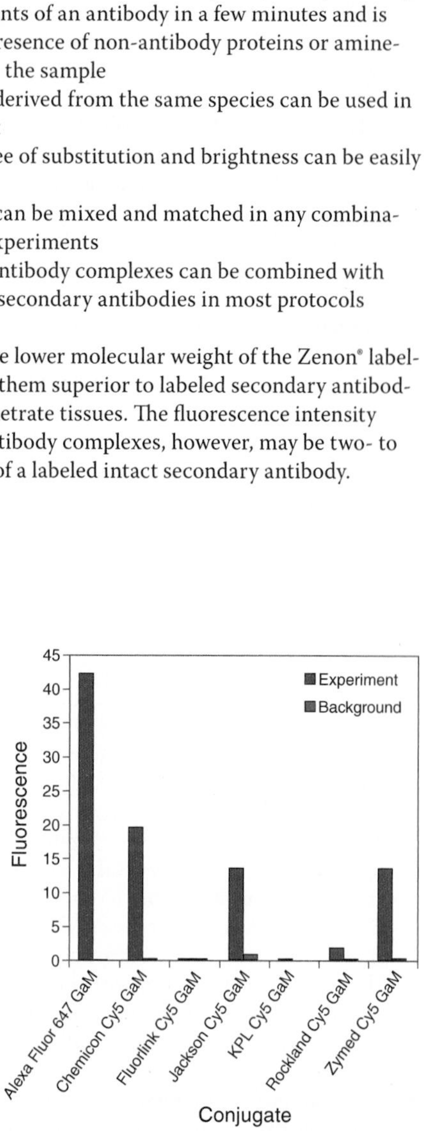

Figure 7.41 Brightness comparison of Molecular Probes' Alexa Fluor® 647 goat anti-mouse IgG antibody with Cy5 goat anti-mouse IgG antibody conjugates commercially available from other companies. Human blood was blocked with normal goat serum and incubated with an anti-CD3 mouse monoclonal antibody; cells were washed, resuspended and incubated with either Alexa Fluor® 647 or Cy5 goat anti-mouse IgG antibody at an equal concentration. Red blood cells were lysed and the samples were analyzed with a flow cytometer equipped with a 633 nm He-Ne laser and a longpass emission filter (>650 nm).

Note 7.1 — Product Highlight

Guide to Labeling Antibodies with Alexa Fluor® Dyes

Whether the experiment calls for labeled primary antibodies, labeled secondary antibodies or additional signal amplification methods, we have the tools to guarantee the brightest conjugates for every application and instrument. Each immunolabeling experiment presents its own challenges. The fluorophore or hapten label may need to be optimized to find the right match in a multiplexing application; a primary antibody present in only vanishingly small amounts may need to be labeled; or significant signal amplification may be needed to detect immunolabeling of a low-abundance target. This guide to antibody labeling can help select the solution that best fits the experiment.

Label Primary Antibodies with Alexa Fluor® Dyes

Although secondary detection methods can provide significant signal amplification, a directly labeled primary antibody often produces lower background fluorescence and less nonspecific binding. Furthermore, multiple primary antibodies of the same isotype or derived from the same species can easily be used in the same experiment when they are directly labeled. Without the signal amplification step provided by secondary detection methods, however, it is more important than ever to label the primary antibody with the brightest fluorophores available. The Alexa Fluor® dyes are a series of extremely bright and photostable fluorophores that span the spectrum from blue to far-red fluorescence (Table 1, Figure 1) (see Note 1.1 "Product Highlight: The Alexa Fluor® Dye Series — Peak Performance across the Visible Spectrum" in Section 1.3). Moreover, these dyes have been carefully chosen and optimized to be very water soluble, minimizing dye-to-dye interactions and allowing a higher degree of labeling of a monoclonal or polyclonal antibody. In addition to a wide selection of amine-reactive Alexa Fluor® dyes, we offer three different types of kits for labeling antibodies with Alexa Fluor® dyes — the Alexa Fluor® Protein Labeling Kits, the Alexa Fluor® Monoclonal Labeling Kits and the Zenon® IgG Antibody Labeling Kits (Table 1).

Immunolabel in Ten Minutes with Zenon® Antibody Labeling Technology

Our patent-pending Zenon® immunolabeling technology provides an easy, versatile and truly unique method of labeling IgG antibodies with Molecular Probes' premier dyes, haptens and enzymes, even with very small (submicrogram) amounts of starting material. The exceptional Zenon® technology takes advantage of the immunoselectivity of the antibody binding reaction by forming a complex between an intact primary IgG antibody and a fluorophore-, hapten- or enzyme-labeled Fab fragment directed against the Fc portion of the IgG (Figure 2). Each Zenon® Antibody Labeling Kit provides an isotype-specific labeled Fab fragment, as well as a blocking reagent to quantitatively prepare a labeled primary IgG in under 10 minutes. With no pre- or post-labeling purification steps required, this labeled primary antibody is now ready to stain cells or other targets in the same manner as a covalently labeled primary antibody. The Zenon® Kits contain key reagents for labeling mouse IgG_1, mouse IgG_{2a}, mouse IgG_{2b}, rabbit IgG, goat IgG and human IgG antibodies with our brightest and most popular Alexa Fluor® dyes, as well as with other fluorophores, haptens or enzymes. The Zenon® antibody labeling technology provides a means of experimenting with many different dye-antibody combinations in order to find the right one for a particular multicolor flow cytometry or imaging experiment. We also offer Zenon® Kits enhanced with tyramide signal amplification (TSA) technology for applications requiring additional sensitivity.

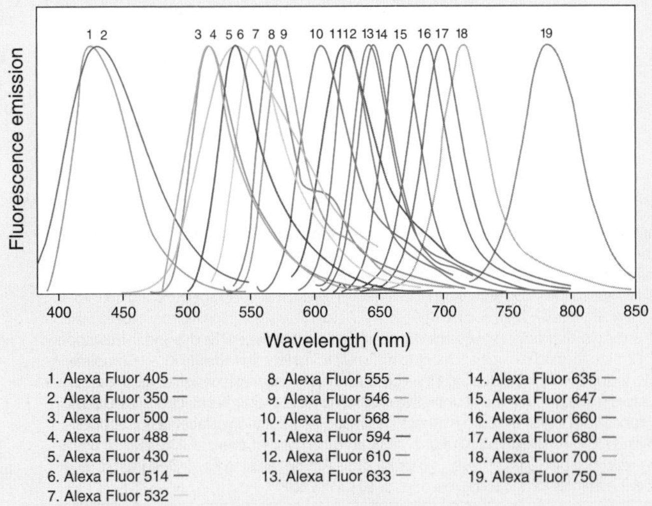

Figure 1. Emission spectra for the Alexa Fluor® dye series.

Create Covalent Alexa Fluor® Antibody Conjugates

Years of protein labeling experience are behind our Alexa Fluor® Protein Labeling Kits (for 1 mg protein samples) and Alexa Fluor® Monoclonal Antibody Labeling Kits (for 100 µg protein samples), which each contain premeasured amine-reactive Alexa Fluor® dyes along with the reagents and materials needed to purify the resulting antibody conjugates (Table 1). These protein labeling kits take advantage of the efficient and straightforward reaction chemistry of amine-reactive activated esters to selectively link an Alexa Fluor® dye to accessible primary amine groups on proteins (including the lysine side chain and amine terminus). The Alexa Fluor® NHS esters are excellent reagents for amine modification because the covalent bonds they form with the protein are as stable as the peptide bonds linking each of its amino acids. The Alexa Fluor® NHS esters are also available separately (Table 1) for optimizing a specific labeling protocol. The Alexa Fluor® 488 Protein Labeling Kit and the Alexa Fluor® 488 Monoclonal Antibody Labeling Kit each contain the amine-reactive Alexa Fluor® 488 tetrafluorophenyl (TFP) ester instead of the NHS ester. This TFP ester produces the same strong amide bond between the dye and the antibody as an NHS ester (Figure 1.2), but the TFP ester is less susceptible to spontaneous hydrolysis during the conjugation reaction. The Alexa Fluor® 488 carboxylic acid TFP ester is also available separately (Table 1).

Amplify the Signal with a Labeled Secondary Antibody

If preparing a labeled primary antibody either is not practical or does not provide enough sensitivity, then a high-quality secondary antibody can often be the solution. Although background levels may increase due to nonspecific binding of both the primary and secondary antibody, a well-chosen labeled secondary antibody often provides significant signal amplification that can overcome any increased background fluorescence. Of course, not every commercially available secondary antibody is thoroughly purified or optimally labeled. Molecular Probes provides one of the largest selections of fluorescent secondary antibodies available anywhere (Section 7.2, Table 7.1). These include the intensely fluorescent Alexa Fluor® antibody conju-

continued on next page

continued from previous page

gates, which outperform most conventional fluorescent secondary reagents across the spectrum. In the creation of each secondary antibody conjugate, we begin with the highest-quality proteins, then optimize the degree of labeling to achieve the brightest conjugates, and end with stringent testing on cell samples to ensure low nonspecific binding and high specific staining. Alexa Fluor® secondary antibodies are rapidly becoming the preferred secondary reagents in all fluorescence-based immunoassays. Several of the Alexa Fluor® antibody conjugates are also represented in the Image-iT™ FX Kits (Section 7.2, Table 7.6) — each Image-iT™ FX Kit includes one of our bright and photostable Alexa Fluor® conjugates, as well as all of the reagents needed for optimal imaging of fixed cells and tissues.

Table 1 — Alexa Fluor® active esters and kits for labeling proteins

Fluorescent Color	Alexa Fluor® Dye	Abs/Em *	Succinimidyl Ester or Tetrafluorophenyl Ester (TFP)	Kits for Proteins						
				Protein Labeling Kit	Monoclonal Antibody	Zenon® Mouse IgG_1 Labeling Kit	Zenon® Mouse IgG_{2a} Labeling Kit	Zenon® Mouse IgG_{2b} Labeling Kit	Zenon® Rabbit IgG Labeling Kit	Zenon® Human IgG Labeling Kit
Blue	Alexa Fluor® 350	346/442	A10168 †	A10170	A20180	Z25000	Z25100	Z25200	Z25300	Z25400
Blue	Alexa Fluor® 405	402/421	A30000 ‡ A30100 †			Z25013	Z25113	Z25213	Z25313	
Yellow-green	Alexa Fluor® 430	434/539	A10169 †	A10171		Z25001			Z25301	
Green	Alexa Fluor® 488	495/519	A20000 ‡ § A20100 † § A30005 (TFP)	A10235 **	A20181 **	Z25002	Z25102	Z25202	Z25302	Z25402
Green	Alexa Fluor® 500	503/525	A30001 ‡ §							
Yellow-green	Alexa Fluor® 514	518/540	A30002 ‡ §							
Yellow	Alexa Fluor® 532	531/554	A20001 ‡ A20101MP †	A10236	A20182	Z25003			Z25303	
Orange	Alexa Fluor® 546	556/573	A20002 ‡ § A20102 † §	A10237	A20183	Z25004	Z25104	Z25204	Z25304	
Red-orange	Alexa Fluor® 555	555/565	A20009 ‡ A20109 †	A20174	A20187	Z25005	Z25105	Z25205	Z25305	Z25405
Red-orange	Alexa Fluor® 568	578/603	A20003 ‡ § A20103 † §	A10238	A20184	Z25006	Z25106	Z25206	Z25306	
Red	Alexa Fluor® 594	590/617	A20004 ‡ § A20104 † §	A10239	A20185	Z25007	Z25107	Z25207	Z25307	Z25407
Red	Alexa Fluor® 610	612/628	A30003 ‡ A30103 †							
Far-red	Alexa Fluor® 633 ††	632/647	A20005 ‡ § A20105 † §	A20170						
Far-red	Alexa Fluor® 635 ††	633/647								
Far-red	Alexa Fluor® 647 ††	650/668	A20006 ‡ A20106 †	A20173	A20186	Z25008	Z25108	Z25208	Z25308	Z25408
Near Infrared	Alexa Fluor® 660 ††	663/690	A20007 ‡ A20107 †	A20171		Z25009	Z25109	Z25209	Z25309	
Near Infrared	Alexa Fluor® 680 ††	679/702	A20008 ‡ A20108 †	A20172		Z25010	Z25110	Z25210	Z25310	
Near Infrared	Alexa Fluor® 700 ††	702/723	A20010 ‡ A20110 †			Z25011			Z25311	
Near Infrared	Alexa Fluor® 750 ††	749/775	A20011 ‡ A20111 †						Z25312	

* Approximate absorption (Abs) and fluorescence emission (Em) maxima for conjugates, in nm. † 5 mg unit size. ‡ 1 mg unit size. § Mixed isomers. ** These Alexa Fluor® 488 protein labeling kits contain the amine-reactive Alexa Fluor® 488 carboxylic acid TFP ester, whereas the Alexa Fluor® 488 kits for labeling nucleic acid and oligonucleotide contain the Alexa Fluor® 488 succinimidyl ester. †† Human vision is insensitive to light beyond ~650 nm, and therefore it is not possible to view the far-red–fluorescent dyes by looking through the eyepiece of a conventional fluorescence microscope. Succinimidyl Ester — With the exception of Alexa Fluor® 350 and Alexa Fluor® 430 dyes, which are packaged in 5 mg unit sizes, most of the Alexa Fluor® succinimidyl esters are available in both 1 mg or 5 mg quantities with a guaranteed ≥50% reactive dye per vial. Actual purity may significantly exceed 50%. Tetrafluorophenyl Ester — The Alexa Fluor® 488 dye is also available as an amine-reactive TFP ester, which produces the same strong amide bond between the dye and the compound of interest as does the succinimidyl ester, but TFP esters are less susceptible to spontaneous hydrolysis during storage and conjugation reactions. Protein Labeling Kit — Complete, easy-to-use kit designed for 3 reactions, each reaction optimized to label ~1 mg of protein. Monoclonal Antibody Labeling Kit — Complete ready-to-use kit designed for 5 reactions, each reaction optimized to label ~100 µg of an IgG. Zenon® Antibody Labeling Kits - Simple, rapid (~10 minutes) and quantitative method to label antibodies (Section 7.3). ULYSIS Nucleic Acid Labeling Kit — Convenient means to create fluorophore-labeled hybridization probes from any DNA source without enzymatic incorporation of labeled nucleotides. Each kit provides sufficient material for 20 labeling reactions of 1 µg of DNA. ARES™ DNA Labeling Kit — Aminoallyl dUTP is enzymatically incorporated, then the Alexa Fluor® dye is covalently attached to the amino group. Each kit provides sufficient material for 5–10 labeling-reactions of 1–5 µg of DNA. Oligonucleotide Amine Labeling Kit — Designed to label oligonucleotides synthesized with an amine group on the 3′ or 5′ end. Each kit provides sufficient materials for 3 labeling reactions of 50 µg of DNA.

continued on next page

continued from previous page

Further Signal Enhancement with Tyramide Signal Amplification

When the target is not very abundant in the experimental sample, the signal amplification provided by a secondary antibody may not be enough. For these applications, we have developed the Tyramide Signal Amplification (TSA) Kits (Section 6.2, Table 6.1), which take advantage of the superior brightness of the Alexa Fluor® dyes to achieve the ultimate in high-resolution signal amplification. TSA technology — sometimes called CARD for catalyzed reporter deposition — is an enzyme-mediated detection method that utilizes the catalytic activity of horseradish peroxidase (HRP) to generate high-density labeling of a target protein or nucleic acid sequence *in situ* (Figure 3). TSA reportedly can amplify a signal 100-fold as compared with conventional avidin-biotinylated enzyme complex (ABC) procedures.[1–8] In the Alexa Fluor® TSA Kits, each HRP label on the HRP-conjugated secondary antibody or streptavidin activates multiple copies of an Alexa Fluor® tyramide to produce short-lived tyramide radicals that are highly reactive with nucleophilic residues near the interaction site, yielding an amplified fluorescent signal with minimal diffusion. The Alexa Fluor® TSA Kits permit ultrasensitive detection of low-abundance targets in fluorescence *in situ* hybridization (FISH), immunohistochemistry and neuroanatomical tracing experiments, as well as in flow cytometry assays, enzyme-linked immunosorbent assays (ELISAs), microarrays and other applications. For researchers who want both the ease of labeling a primary mouse IgG_1 antibody with HRP that Zenon® technology provides and the signal amplification afforded by the TSA technology, we have developed two Zenon® Mouse IgG_1 Labeling Kits enhanced with TSA technology — one containing the green-fluorescent Alexa Fluor® 488 tyramide and the other containing the red-orange–fluorescent Alexa Fluor® 568 tyramide. These kits provide the necessary reagents from both the Zenon® Horseradish Peroxidase Mouse IgG_1 Labeling Kit and the corresponding Alexa Fluor® TSA Kit, along with a detailed protocol for Zenon® complex formation and tyramide labeling. More importantly, this combination of Zenon® and TSA technologies is not limited to the mouse IgG_1 isotype and the Alexa Fluor® 488 and Alexa Fluor® 568 tyramides. Because the Zenon® Horseradish Peroxidase Antibody Labeling Kits are available for mouse IgG_1, mouse IgG_{2a}, mouse IgG_{2b}, rabbit IgG and human IgG antibodies (Section 7.3, Table 7.13), primary antibodies of any of these isotypes can be conveniently and quantitatively labeled with HRP and then used in place of the HRP-conjugated secondary antibodies in any of the TSA Kits containing these conjugates.

References

1. Lab Invest 73, 149 (1995); **2.** J Histochem Cytochem 45, 1455 (1997); **3.** J Histochem Cytochem 42, 1635 (1994); **4.** Histochem Cell Biol 114, 447 (2000); **5.** Am J Clin Pathol 106, 16 (1996); **6.** J Histochem Cytochem 40, 1457 (1992); **7.** J Histochem Cytochem 45, 315 (1997); **8.** J Histochem Cytochem 47, 281 (1999).

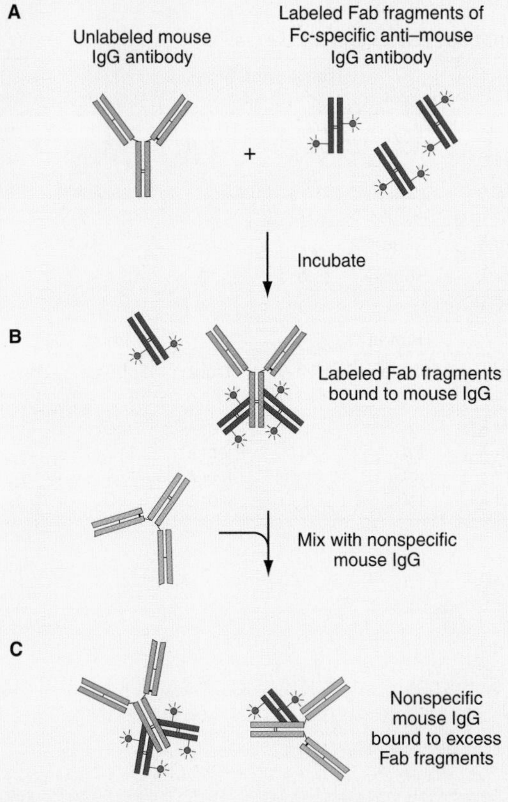

Figure 2. Labeling scheme utilized in the Zenon® Antibody Labeling Kits. An unlabeled IgG antibody is incubated with the Zenon® labeling reagent, which contains a fluorophore-labeled, Fc-specific anti-IgG Fab fragment (panel A). This labeled Fab fragment binds to the Fc portion of the IgG antibody (panel B). Excess Fab fragment is then neutralized by the addition of a nonspecific IgG (panel C), preventing crosslabeling by the Fab fragment in experiments where primary antibodies of the same type are present. Note that the Fab fragment used for labeling need not be coupled to a fluorophore, but could instead be coupled to an enzyme (such as HRP) or to biotin.

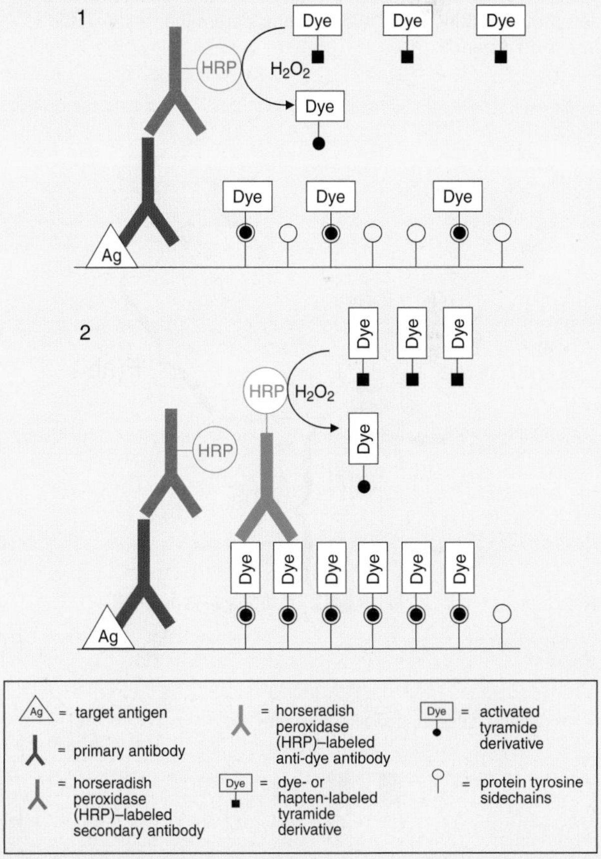

Figure 3. Schematic representation of TSA detection methods applied to immunolabeling of an antigen. The antigen is detected by a primary antibody, followed by a horseradish peroxidase–labeled secondary antibody in conjunction with a dye-labeled (or hapten-labeled) tyramide, resulting in localized deposition of the activated tyramide derivative (**Stage 1**). Further dye deposition, and therefore higher levels of signal amplification, can be generated by detecting dye deposited in stage 1 with a horseradish peroxidase–labeled anti-dye antibody in conjunction with a dye-labeled tyramide (**Stage 2**).

Note 7.2 — Technical Focus

Antibody Structure and Classification

The basic structural unit of most mammalian antibodies is a glycoprotein (MW ~150,000 daltons) composed of four polypeptide chains — two light chains, and two heavy chains, which are connected by disulfide bonds (see figure). Each light chain has a molecular weight of ~25,000 daltons and is composed of two domains, one variable domain (V_L) and one constant domain (C_L). There are two types of light chains, lambda (λ) and kappa (κ). In humans, 60% of the light chains are κ, and 40% are λ, whereas in mice, 95% of the light chains are κ and only 5% are λ. A single antibody molecule contains either κ light chains or λ light chains, but never both.

Each heavy chain has a molecular weight of ~50,000 daltons and consists of a constant and variable region. The heavy and light chains contain a number of homologous sections consisting of similar but not identical groups of amino acid sequences. These homologous units consist of about 110 amino acids and are called immunoglobulin domains. The heavy chain contains one variable domain (V_H) and either three or four constant domains (C_H1, C_H2, C_H3, and C_H4, depending on the antibody class or isotype). The region between the C_H1 and C_H2 domains is called the hinge region and permits flexibility between the two Fab arms of the Y-shaped antibody molecule, allowing them to open and close to accommodate binding to two antigenic determinants separated by a fixed distance.

The heavy chain also serves to determine the functional activity of the antibody molecule. There are five antibody classes — IgG, IgA, IgM, IgE and IgD — which are distinguished by their heavy chains γ, α, μ, ε and δ, respectively (see table). The IgD, IgE and IgG antibody classes are each made up of a single structural unit, whereas IgA antibodies may contain either one or two units and IgM antibodies consist of five disulfide-linked structural units. IgG antibodies are further divided into four subclasses (often referred to as isotypes) although the nomenclature differs slightly depending on the species producing the antibody (see table).

Structure/function studies on IgG have been aided by the discovery that the proteolytic enzymes pepsin and papain cleave the molecule into specific fragments with specific biological properties. Treatment of an IgG molecule with pepsin generates the $F(ab')_2$ fragment, which broadly encompasses the two Fab regions linked by the hinge region. Because the $F(ab')_2$ molecule is bivalent, it is capable of precipitating an antigen. Papain cleaves the IgG molecule in the hinge region between the C_H1 and C_H2 domains to yield two identical Fab fragments, which retain their antigen-binding ability, and one non-antigen-binding fragment — the fragment crystallizable (Fc) region. The Fc region is glycosylated and has many effector functions (e.g., binding complement, binding to cell receptors on macrophages and monocytes, etc.), and serves to distinguish one class of antibody from another.

Overview of antibody classes and subclasses.

Antibody	Human and Mouse					
	Light Chain	Subtype	Heavy Chain	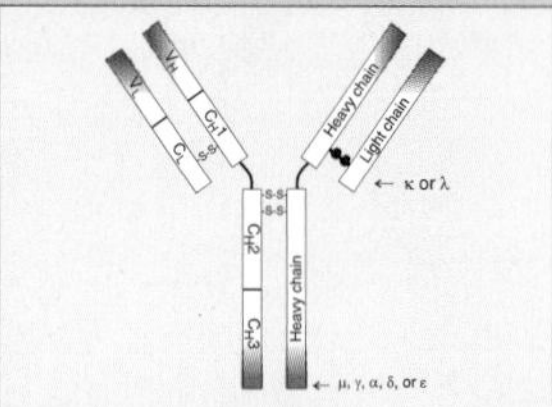		
IgA	κ or λ κ or λ	IgA_1 IgA_2	α_1 α_2			
IgE	κ or λ	None	ε			
IgD	κ or λ	None	δ			
IgM	κ or λ	None	μ			
	Human			Mouse		
IgG	Light Chain	Subtype	Heavy Chain	Light Chain	Subtype	Heavy Chain
	κ or λ κ or λ κ or λ κ or λ	IgG_1 IgG_2 IgG_3 IgG_4	γ_1 γ_2 γ_3 γ_4	κ or λ κ or λ κ or λ κ or λ	IgG_1 IgG_{2a} IgG_{2b} IgG_3	γ_1 γ_{2a} γ_{2b} γ_3

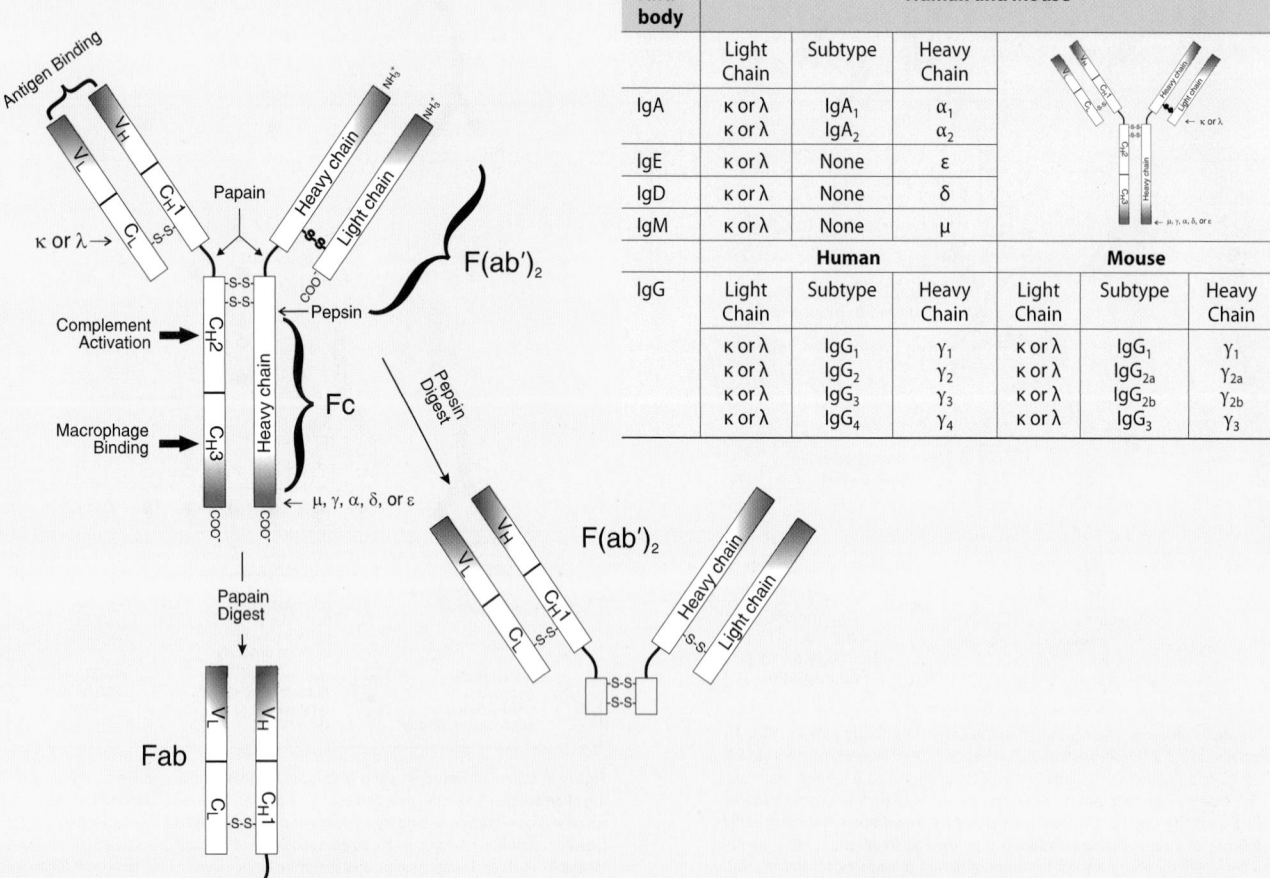

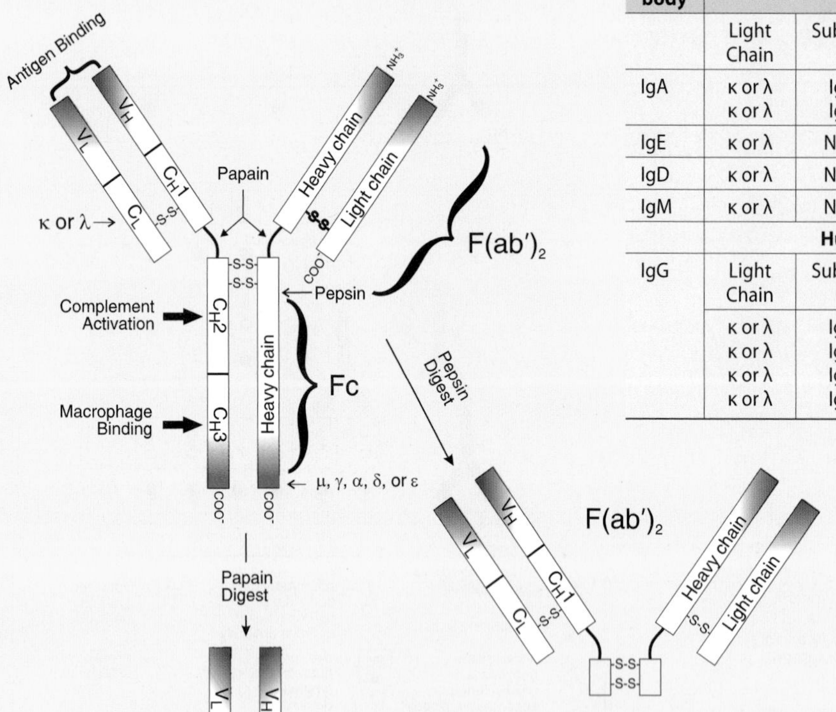

Schematic representation of an antibody molecule.

Species-Specific Secondary Antibodies

Anti-IgG Antibodies

Molecular Probes offers secondary antibody conjugates directed against IgG from a variety of species, including human, mouse, rabbit, rat, chicken, goat, guinea pig, hamster and sheep (Table 7.1). These anti-IgG antibodies are available with a wide selection of fluorophores, including our:

- Blue-fluorescent Alexa Fluor® 350 (Figure 12.9), Alexa Fluor® 405, Marina Blue®, Cascade Blue® and Pacific Blue™ dyes
- Green-fluorescent Alexa Fluor® 488 (Figure 7.42, Figure 7.43, Figure 7.44, Figure 7.45), Alexa Fluor® 500, Oregon Green® 488, Oregon Green® 514 (Figure 12.7), BODIPY® FL and fluorescein dyes
- Yellow-green–fluorescent Alexa Fluor® 430 and Alexa Fluor® 514 dyes
- Yellow-fluorescent Alexa Fluor® 532 dye (Figure 11.17)
- Orange-fluorescent Alexa Fluor® 546 (Figure 7.42), Alexa Fluor® 555 and tetramethylrhodamine dyes
- Red-orange–fluorescent Alexa Fluor® 568 and Rhodamine Red™-X dyes
- Red-fluorescent Alexa Fluor® 594 (Figure 7.46), Texas Red® and Texas Red®-X fluorophores
- Far-red–fluorescent Alexa Fluor® 633, Alexa Fluor® 635, Alexa Fluor® 647 (Figure 11.18), Alexa Fluor® 660 and Alexa Fluor® 680 dyes
- Infrared-fluorescent Alexa Fluor® 700 and Alexa Fluor® 750 dyes
- Alexa Fluor® dye–R-phycoerythrin (R-PE) tandem conjugates, which can each be excited with the 488 nm spectral line of the argon-ion laser, but exhibit long-wavelength emission maxima (627 nm for the Alexa Fluor® 610–R-PE conjugates, 667 nm for the Alexa Fluor® 647–R-PE conjugates and 702 nm for the Alexa Fluor® 680–R-PE conjugates)
- Alexa Fluor® dye–allophycocyanin (APC) tandem conjugates, which can each be excited by the He–Ne laser at 633 nm or by the krypton-ion laser at 647 nm with emission beyond 700 nm
- Red-orange–fluorescent DyeMer™ 488/605, red-fluorescent DyeMer™ 488/615 and far-red–fluorescent DyeMer™ 488/630 dyes, bifluorophores that can each be excited by the 488 nm spectral line of the argon-ion laser and emit at 605, 615 or 630 nm

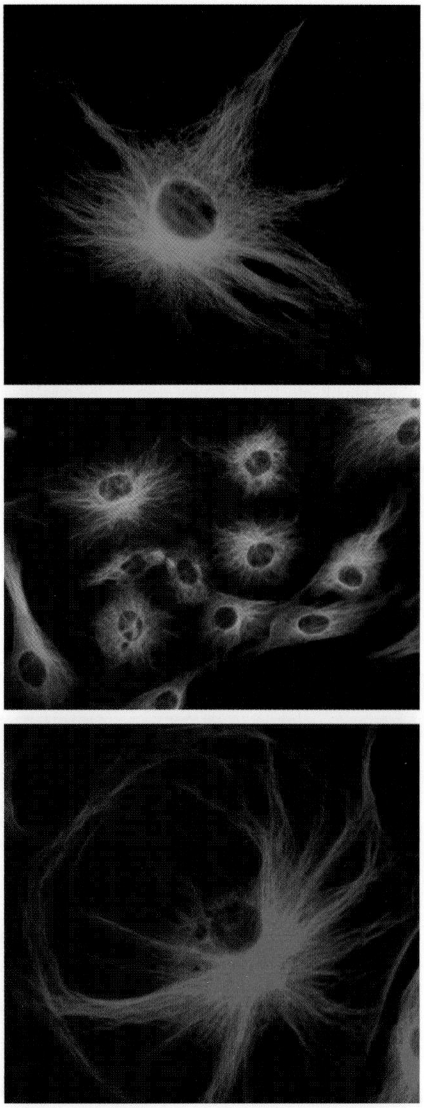

Figure 7.42 Microtubules of bovine pulmonary artery endothelial cells tagged with mouse monoclonal anti–α-tubulin antibody (A11126) and subsequently probed with: Alexa Fluor® 488 goat anti–mouse IgG antibody (A11001, top panel), Alexa Fluor® 546 goat anti–mouse IgG antibody (A11003, middle panel) or Alexa Fluor® 594 goat anti–mouse IgG antibody (A11005, bottom panel). These images were acquired using a fluorescein bandpass optical filter set, a rhodamine bandpass optical filter set and a Texas Red® bandpass optical filter set, respectively.

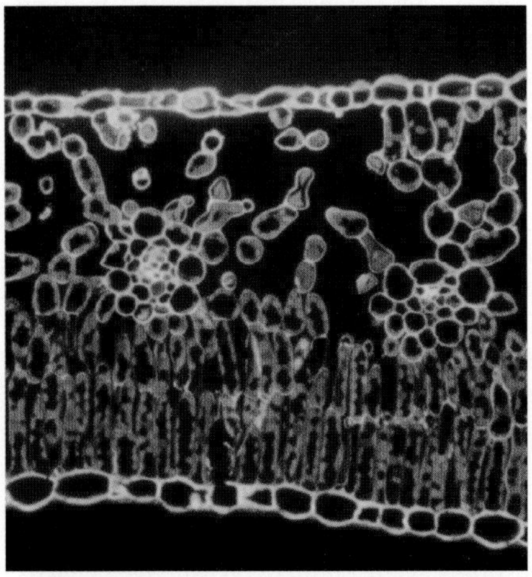

Figure 7.43 The primary cell walls in a 500 nm–thick apple leaf section identified with an antibody to the methyl-esterified regions of pectic polysaccharides or pectin, and visualized with green-fluorescent Alexa Fluor® 488 goat anti–rabbit IgG antibody (A11008). The orange regions inside the cells are due to the autofluorescent properties of chlorophyll localized in the chloroplasts. Image contributed by Paul Sutherland, EM Unit, Mount Albert Research Centre, Auckland, New Zealand.

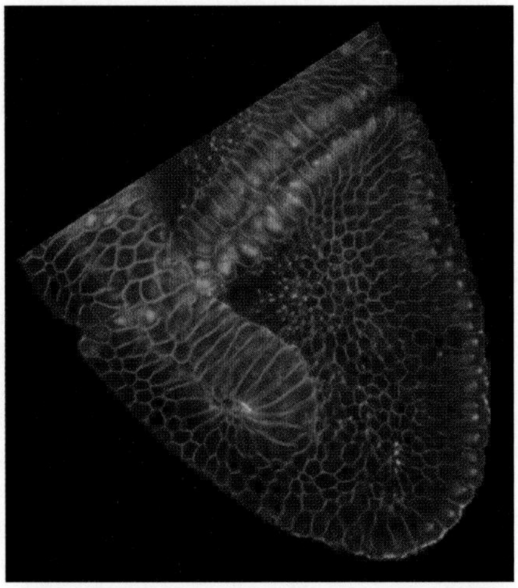

Figure 7.44 Formation of the cephalic furrow in the anterior end of a developing *Drosophila melanogaster* embryo visualized with the help of several fluorescent stains. A primary antibody to neurotactin was visualized using a red-fluorescent Cy3 dye secondary antibody (Amersham Pharmacia Biotech Ltd.). Primary antibodies to plasma membrane–bound myosin and to nuclear-localized even-skipped (Eve) protein were visualized with green-fluorescent Alexa Fluor® 488 goat anti–mouse IgG antibody (A11001) and Alexa Fluor® 488 goat anti–rabbit IgG antibody (A11008), respectively. The nuclei were stained with blue-fluorescent Hoechst 33342 (H1399, H3570, H21492). The sample was prepared by Eric Wieschaus, and the imaging was performed by Joe Goodhouse of Princeton University.

Our species-specific anti-IgG antibodies, which are raised against IgG heavy and light chains, are affinity purified and adsorbed against the sera of a number of species to minimize crossreactivity. For multilabeling experiments in which crossreactivity is critical, we offer highly cross-adsorbed goat anti–mouse IgG and goat anti–rabbit IgG antibodies. See Table 7.2 for a complete list of IgG and sera against which our anti-IgG antibodies have been cross-adsorbed.

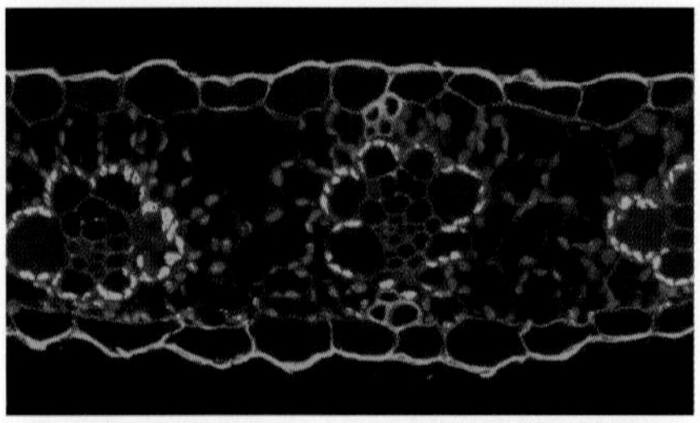

Figure 7.45 A 2.0 µm maize leaf section illustrating the immunolocalization of the enzyme ribulose bisphosphate carboxylase (rubisco) in the chloroplasts of the bundle sheath cells surrounding the vascular bundles. Maize is a C4 plant and, as a result, spatially segregates components of the photosynthetic process between the leaf mesophyll and the bundle sheath. Rubisco was localized using a rabbit anti-rubisco antibody and visualized using the highly cross-adsorbed Alexa Fluor® 488 goat anti–rabbit IgG antibody (A11034). The remaining fluorescence is due to the autofluorescence of chlorophyll, which appears red and is localized to the mesophyll plastids; lignin, which appears dull green and is localized to the xylem of the vascular bundle; and cutin, which appears bright green and is localized to the cuticle outside the epidermis. Image contributed by Todd Jones, DuPont.

Molecular Probes also offers chicken anti-mouse, -rabbit, -rat, -goat and -human secondary antibodies (Table 7.3). Chicken secondary antibodies have gained popularity because they demonstrate a lower level of nonspecific binding. Chicken IgY antibodies, which are functionally equivalent to mammalian IgG antibodies, lack a classical "Fc" domain and are not bound by protein A or protein G, nor do they bind to Fc receptors for mammalian IgG.

The CMNB-caged fluorescein conjugates of the goat anti–mouse IgG and goat anti–rabbit IgG antibodies (G21061, G21080) permit some unique experimental protocols, including the light-mediated targeted tagging of single cells or a few cells in tissues (Section 5.3) and use as a photoaddressable hapten, in a manner similar to photolithography. These conjugates are essentially colorless and nonfluorescent until illuminated with ultraviolet light, whereupon sites labeled by the caged fluorophore conjugate yield green-fluorescent staining. This photoactivated fluorescence (PAF) can be measured as an increase in signal, even in the presence of a highly autofluorescent background or other green-fluorescent probes. Furthermore, the fluorescein dye that is liberated serves as a hapten that can be specifically detected and the signal amplified by anti-fluorescein/Oregon Green® antibody conjugates (Section 7.4, Figure 7.74).

We offer the high-activity horseradish peroxidase and alkaline phosphatase conjugates of goat anti–mouse IgG, rabbit anti–mouse IgG, goat anti–rabbit IgG and rabbit anti–goat IgG antibodies (Table 7.4), as well as biotin conjugates of goat anti–mouse IgG antibody and of the $F(ab')_2$ fragments of goat anti–mouse IgG antibody and goat anti–rabbit IgG antibody (B2763, B11027, B21078). By using an avidin, streptavidin or NeutrAvidin biotin-binding protein bridge, scientists can link our biotinylated or DSB-X™ biotin–labeled secondary antibodies to a biotinylated enzyme — a method that is often preferred because it tends to reduce nonspecific staining. Links to avidin and streptavidin conjugates made through DSB-X™ biotin are readily reversible (see Section 7.6 for a description of our unique DSB-X™ biotin technology). Enzyme and hapten conjugates of secondary antibodies are also commonly used in histochemical amplification schemes such as the tyramide signal amplification (TSA) technology (Section 6.2) and Enzyme-Labeled Fluorescence (ELF®) technology (Section 6.3, Figure 9.62). Our Zenon® Alkaline Phosphatase and Horseradish Peroxidase Antibody Labeling Kits (Section 7.3, Table 7.13) permit the formation of enzyme-labeled antibodies using as little as submicrogram quantities of a primary antibody. Enzyme-conjugated antibodies are also used in a wide variety of ELISA methods, such as in our Amplex® Red ELISA Kits (see below).

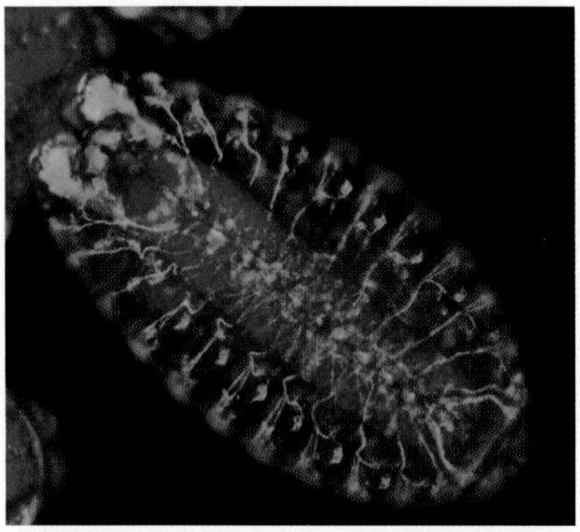

Figure 7.46 The peripheral nervous system of a wild-type (Canton-S) *Drosophila melanogaster* embryo labeled with the monoclonal 22c10 antibody (which detects a microtubule-associated protein) and subsequently visualized using green-fluorescent Alexa Fluor® 488 rabbit anti–mouse IgG antibody (A11059). The actively dividing cells of the developing denticle bands were labeled with a rabbit anti–histone-H3 antibody and visualized using red-fluorescent Alexa Fluor® 594 goat anti–rabbit IgG antibody (A11012). Finally, the nuclei, which are concentrated in the central nervous system, were counterstained with blue-fluorescent DAPI (D1306, D3571, D21490). Image contributed by Neville Cobbe, University of Edinburgh.

Anti-IgM Antibodies

In response to requests from researchers wanting to apply Alexa Fluor® dye technology to the detection of IgM monoclonal antibodies, we have added goat anti–mouse IgM, goat anti–rat IgM and goat anti–human IgM antibodies to the list of antibodies we offer as conjugates of our Alexa Fluor® dyes (Table 7.1). The anti-IgM conjugates are prepared from well-characterized antibodies that have been purified by IgM affinity chromatography and react specifically with IgM heavy chains (µ chains) (see Note 7.2 "Technical Focus: Antibody Structure and Classification"). To minimize crossreactivity, the goat anti–mouse IgM antibodies have been adsorbed against human IgG_1, IgG_{2a}, IgG_{2b}, IgG_3, IgA, human serum and purified human paraproteins. The goat anti–human IgM antibodies have been adsorbed against human IgG and IgA. Due to their large size, IgM antibodies do not diffuse well into tissue, and because the IgM µ chain is more highly conserved across different species than are IgG, IgA, or light chains, anti-IgM antibodies may react with IgM from other species.

Isotype-Specific Antibodies

Molecular Probes offers isotype-specific antibodies to aid in multilabeling experiments (Table 7.5). The Alexa Fluor® goat anti–mouse IgG isotype-specific antibodies have been cross-adsorbed against mouse IgM, IgA, pooled human sera, purified human paraproteins and other isotypes to minimize crossreactivity.

F(ab´)₂ Fragments

Our range of goat anti–mouse IgG and goat anti–rabbit IgG antibodies has been expanded to include fluorescent dye–, alkaline phosphatase–, horseradish peroxidase– and biotin-labeled F(ab´)$_2$ fragments (Table 7.1). These F(ab´)$_2$ fragments are often preferred to whole antibody conjugates because they lack the Fc region (see Note 7.2 "Technical Focus: Antibody Structure and Classification"), thereby eliminating nonspecific interactions with Fc receptor–bearing cell membranes and allowing for better penetration into tissue. Please note that the rabbit Fc region may bind nonspecifically to human tissue; consequently, Molecular Probes recommends the F(ab´)$_2$ fragment when using rabbit-derived secondary antibodies on human tissues.

Image-iT™ FX Kits: All-in-One Kits for Fluorescence Imaging of Fixed Cells

Image-iT™ FX Kits

The Image-iT™ FX Kits (Table 7.6) provide some of our best secondary detection reagents and the supporting materials needed for optimal imaging of fixed cells and tissue sections:

- Alexa Fluor® conjugates of goat anti–mouse IgG antibody, goat anti–rabbit IgG antibody or streptavidin deliver superior photostability and brightness (Table 7.7)
- ProLong® Gold antifade reagent reduces photobleaching (Figure 23.25, Figure 23.26, Figure 23.27; see Section 23.1 for more details)

Table 7.2 — Cross-adsorption chart for Molecular Probes' labeled secondary antibody conjugates

Antibody	Bovine	Chicken	Goat	Guinea Pig	Hamster	Horse	Human	Mouse	Rabbit	Rat	Sheep
Goat anti–mouse IgG							I,S				
Goat anti–mouse IgG, Highly Cross-Adsorbed	I		I				I,S		I	I	
Goat anti–mouse IgG, F(ab')$_2$ Fragment							I,S				
Goat anti–mouse IgM							A,I,P,S				
Rabbit anti–mouse IgG							S				
Rabbit anti–mouse IgG, F(ab')$_2$ Fragment							S				
Chicken anti–mouse IgG							I				
Donkey anti–mouse IgG	S	S	S	S	S	S	S		S	S	S
Goat anti–rabbit IgG	S						I,S	I,S			
Goat anti–rabbit IgG, Highly Cross-Adsorbed	I		I				I	I		I	
Goat anti–rabbit IgG, F(ab')$_2$ Fragment							P,S	H,S			
Chicken anti–rabbit IgG							I	I			
Donkey anti–rabbit IgG	S	S	S	S	S	S	S	S		S	S
Rabbit anti–goat IgG							S			S	
Rabbit anti–goat IgG, F(ab')$_2$ Fragment							S	S			
Chicken anti–goat IgG							I	I	I		
Donkey anti–goat IgG							I	I	I	I	
Goat anti–human IgG	S							S	S		
Goat anti–human IgM							A,I				
Rabbit anti–human IgG								I			
Rabbit anti–human IgG, F(ab')$_2$ Fragment								I			
Chicken anti–human IgG			I					I	I		
Goat anti–rat IgG							S	I,S			
Goat anti–rat IgM										I	
Rabbit anti–rat IgG							I				
Chicken anti–rat IgG							I		I		
Donkey anti–rat IgG	S	S	S	S	S	S	S	S	S		S<
Goat anti–chicken IgG *											
Goat anti–guinea Pig IgG, Highly Cross-Adsorbed	S	S	S		S		S	S	S	S	S
Goat anti–hamster IgG								I		I	
Donkey anti–sheep IgG	S						I,S	S	S		

* This antibody is not cross-adsorbed. A = cross-adsorbed against IgA. H = cross-adsorbed against plasmacytoma/hybridoma proteins. I = cross-adsorbed against IgG. P = cross-adsorbed against paraproteins. S = cross-adsorbed against serum.

- Image-iT™ FX signal enhancer improves the signal-to-noise ratio (Figure 7.47, Figure 7.48, Figure 23.32)
- A sample pack of two CultureWell chambered coverglasses makes sample processing more convenient (Figure 23.42, see Section 23.3 for more details)

Each Image-iT™ FX Kit provides sufficient materials to perform 50–100 assays. Furthermore, the components of each kit are available separately (Alexa Fluor® secondary antibodies, Table 7.1; Alexa Fluor® streptavidins, Section 7.6, Table 7.22; ProLong® Gold antifade reagent, P36930, Section 23.1; Image-iT™ FX signal enhancer, I36933; CultureWell chambered coverglasses, C37000, C37005; Section 23.3) for flexibility in experimental design.

Table 7.3 — Molecular Probes' affinity-purified chicken anti–mouse, –human, –goat, –rat and –rabbit IgG conjugates

Cat #	Label	Emission Color	Abs *	Em *
Chicken anti–mouse IgG				
A21200	Alexa Fluor® 488	Green	495	519
A21201	Alexa Fluor® 594	Red	590	617
A21463	Alexa Fluor® 647	Far-red	650	668
Chicken anti–rabbit IgG				
A21441	Alexa Fluor® 488	Green	495	519
A21442	Alexa Fluor® 594	Red	590	617
A21443	Alexa Fluor® 647	Far-red	650	668
Chicken anti–rat IgG				
A21470	Alexa Fluor® 488	Green	495	519
A21471	Alexa Fluor® 594	Red	590	617
A21472	Alexa Fluor® 647	Far-red	650	668
Chicken anti–goat IgG				
A21467	Alexa Fluor® 488	Green	495	519
A21468	Alexa Fluor® 594	Red	590	617
A21469	Alexa Fluor® 647	Far-red	650	668
Chicken anti–human IgG				
A21464	Alexa Fluor® 488	Green	495	519

* Approximate absorption (Abs) and fluorescence emission (Em) maxima, in nm.

Table 7.4 — Alkaline phosphatase and horseradish peroxidase enzyme conjugates and Zenon® Labeling Kits

Conjugate or Kit	Enzyme	
	Alkaline Phosphatase	Horseradish Peroxidase
Antibody (host)		
Anti–mouse IgG (goat)	G21060	G21040
Zenon® Mouse IgG_1 Labeling Kit	Z25050	Z25054
Zenon® Mouse IgG_{2a} Labeling Kit	Z25150	Z25154
Zenon® Mouse IgG_{2b} Labeling Kit	Z25250	Z25254
Anti–mouse $F(ab')_2$ fragment (goat)	F21452	F21453
Anti–mouse IgG (rabbit)		R21455
Zenon® Rabbit IgG Labeling Kit	Z25350	Z25354
Anti–rabbit IgG (goat)	G21079	G21234
Anti–rabbit $F(ab')_2$ fragment (goat)	F21456	
Anti–goat IgG (rabbit)	R21458	R21459
Anti-fluorescein/Oregon Green® (rabbit)		A21253
Anti-fluorescein/Oregon Green® $F(ab')_2$ (rabbit)		A21254
Avidin		
NeutrAvidin biotin-binding protein		A2664
Streptavidin	S921	S911

Table 7.5 — Molecular Probes' goat anti-mouse isotype-specific antibodies

Fluorophore	Abs/Em *	Goat Anti-Mouse †			
		IgG_1 (γ_1)	IgG_{2a} (γ_{2a})	IgG_{2b} (γ_{2b})	IgG_3 (γ_3)
Alexa Fluor® 350	346/442	A21120	A21130	A21140	
Alexa Fluor® 488	495/518	A21121	A21131	A21141	A21151
Alexa Fluor® 546	556/573	A21123	A21133	A21143	A21153
Alexa Fluor® 555	555/565	A21127	A21137	A21147	A21157
Alexa Fluor® 568	578/603	A21124	A21134	A21144	A21154
Alexa Fluor® 594	590/617	A21125	A21135	A21145	A21155
Alexa Fluor® 633	632/647	A21126	A21136	A21146	
Alexa Fluor® 647	650/668	A21240	A21241	A21242	
R-phycoerythrin	496/578	P21129	P21139	P21149	

* Approximate absorption (Abs) and fluorescence emission (Em) maxima, in nm.
† The Alexa Fluor® goat anti–mouse isotype-specific antibodies have been cross-adsorbed against mouse IgM, IgA, pooled sera, purified human paraproteins and the other isotypes to minimize crossreactivity.

Table 7.6 — Image-iT™ FX Kits

Fluorophore (Ex/Em) *	Goat Anti–Mouse IgG	Goat Anti–Rabbit IgG	Streptavidin
Alexa Fluor® 350 (346/442)	I37150 (Kit #1)	I37155 (Kit #6)	I37160 (Kit #11)
Alexa Fluor® 488 (495/519)	I37151 (Kit #2)	I37156 (Kit #7)	I37161 (Kit #12)
Alexa Fluor® 555 (555/565)	I37152 (Kit #3)	I37157 (Kit #8)	I37162 (Kit #13)
Alexa Fluor® 594 (590/617)	I37153 (Kit #4)	I37158 (Kit #9)	I37163 (Kit #14)
Alexa Fluor® 647 (650/668) †	I37154 (Kit #5)	I37159 (Kit #10)	I37164 (Kit #15)

* Approximate excitation (Ex) and fluorescence emission (Em) maxima, in nm.
† The fluorescence of this long-wavelength Alexa Fluor® dye is not visible to the human eye but is readily detected by most imaging systems.

Table 7.7 — Fluorescence Characteristics of the Alexa Fluor® Dyes in the Image-iT™ FX Kits

Alexa Fluor® Dyes	Ex *	Em *	Fluorescence Emission Color
Alexa Fluor® 350	346	442	Blue
Alexa Fluor® 488	495	519	Green
Alexa Fluor® 555	555	565	Orange
Alexa Fluor® 594	590	617	Red
Alexa Fluor® 647	650	668	ND

* Fluorescence excitation (Ex) and emission (Em) maxima, in nm. ND = Fluorescence of this long-wavelength Alexa Fluor® dye is not visible to the human eye but is readily detected by most imaging systems.

Image-iT™ FX Signal Enhancer

By efficiently blocking nonspecific interactions of a wide variety of fluorescent dyes with cell and tissue constituents, the Image-iT™ FX signal enhancer (I36933) dramatically improves the signal-to-noise ratio of immunolabeled cells and tissues, allowing clear visualization of targets that would normally be indistinguishable due to background fluorescence (Figure 7.47, Figure 7.48, Figure 23.32). Background staining seen with fluorescent conjugates of streptavidin, goat anti–mouse IgG antibody or goat anti–rabbit IgG antibody is largely eliminated when Image-iT™ FX signal enhancer is applied to fixed and permeabilized cells prior to staining. Image-iT™ FX signal enhancer may also effectively prevent nonspecific staining that is typically blocked with 1–2% BSA or 10% serum treatment, in some cases eliminating the need for another step in the staining protocol.

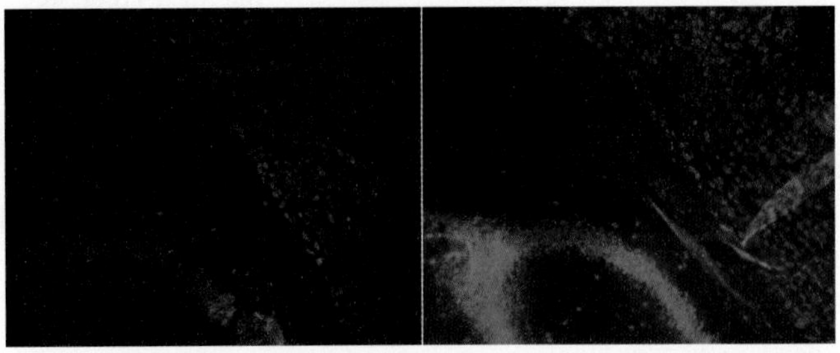

Alexa Fluor® Signal Amplification Kits

Molecular Probes' Alexa Fluor® Signal Amplification Kits are designed to substantially increase the signals obtained by immunofluorescence techniques, thus permitting detection of low-abundance targets (Figure 7.49, Figure 7.50). Each kit takes advantage of the superior brightness and photostability of Alexa Fluor® antibody conjugates. The Alexa Fluor® 488 Signal Amplification Kit for Fluorescein-Conjugated Probes (A11053) dramatically enhances the fluorescence and photostability of virtually any fluoresceinated probe. The three kits for mouse antibodies (Table 7.8) can be used to sensitively detect mouse primary antibodies. All of the Alexa Fluor® Signal Amplification Kits contain detailed protocols for staining adherent cells grown on coverslips. The kits also contain protocols for use in flow cytometry.

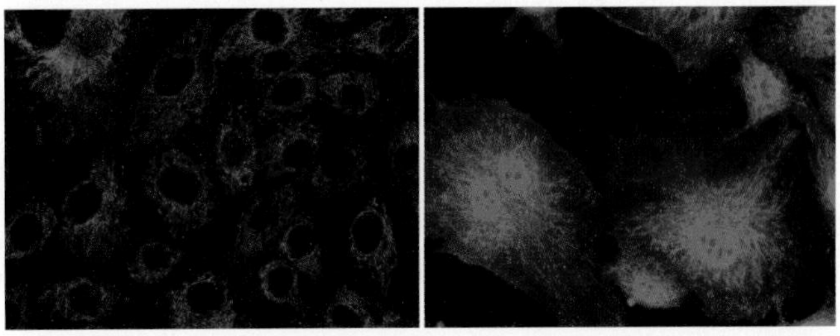

Figure 7.47 Reduced background staining afforded by Image-iT™ FX signal enhancer. Mouse brain cryosections were permeabilized and antigen retrieval was carried out. The sections were then treated for 30 minutes with Image-iT™ FX signal enhancer (I36933, left) or left untreated (right). Sections were labeled with the neural cell body selective antibody anti–Hu C/D (A21271) and visualized using TSA Kit #2 (T20912) with the HRP conjugate of goat anti–mouse IgG and Alexa Fluor® 488 tyramide. Sections were mounted using the reagents in the ProLong® Antifade Kit (P7481).

Figure 7.48 Increased label specificity and resolution provided by Image-iT™ FX signal enhancer. Fixed and permeabilized bovine pulmonary artery endothelial cells were treated with Image-iT™ FX signal enhancer (I36933, left) or left untreated (right) and then labeled with tetramethylrhodamine streptavidin (S870).

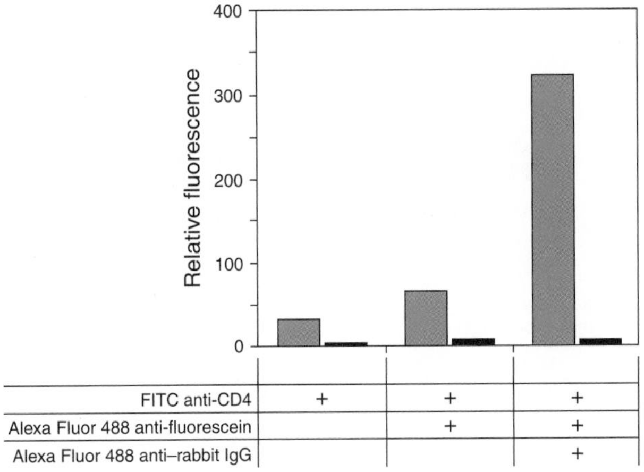

	+	+	+
FITC anti-CD4	+	+	+
Alexa Fluor 488 anti-fluorescein		+	+
Alexa Fluor 488 anti–rabbit IgG			+

Figure 7.50 An example of flow cytometry results obtained using the Alexa Fluor® 488 Signal Amplification Kit for Fluorescein- and Oregon Green® Dye–Conjugated Probes (A11053). Human T-cell leukemia cells (Jurkat) were stained with fluorescein (FITC) mouse anti-CD4 antibody and, as indicated, with Alexa Fluor® 488 rabbit anti-fluorescein/Oregon Green® antibody (A11090) and Alexa Fluor® 488 goat anti-rabbit IgG antibody (A11008). The fluorescence values of the negative controls, in which the FITC anti-CD4 antibody was omitted, are shown (black) together with the fluorescence values of the experimental samples (green). The fluorescence values represent the average signals from the population of cells analyzed.

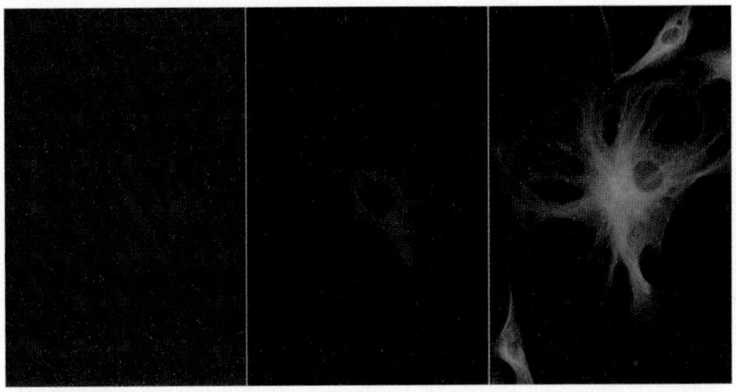

Figure 7.49 Demonstration of the amplification obtained with the Alexa Fluor® 488 Signal Amplification Kit for Fluorescein- and Oregon Green® Dye–Conjugated Probes (A11053). Bovine pulmonary artery endothelial cells were labeled with anti–α-tubulin antibody (A11126) in combination with fluorescein goat anti–mouse IgG antibody (F2761) (left panel). The center panel shows the cells after treatment with Alexa Fluor® 488 rabbit anti-fluorescein/Oregon Green® antibody (A11090), and the right panel show the cells after additional labeling with the Alexa Fluor® 488 goat anti–rabbit IgG antibody (A11008). The images were acquired using identical exposure times, and a bandpass filter set appropriate for fluorescein.

Alexa Fluor® 488 Signal Amplification Kit for Fluorescein- and Oregon Green® Dye–Conjugated Probes

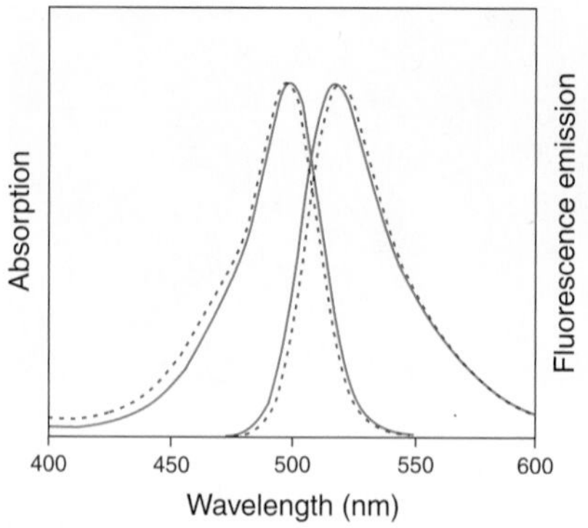

Figure 7.51 Absorption and fluorescence emission spectra of fluorescein goat anti–mouse IgG antibody (F2761, (–)) and Alexa Fluor® 488 goat anti–mouse IgG antibody (A11001, (---)). The fluorescence intensity of the Alexa Fluor® 488 conjugate was significantly higher than that of the fluorescein conjugate. The data are normalized to show the spectral similarity.

The Alexa Fluor® 488 Signal Amplification Kit for Fluorescein-Conjugated Probes (A11053) is designed to simultaneously enhance the fluorescence and the photostability of virtually any fluorescein- or Oregon Green® dye–containing probe (Figure 7.49, Figure 7.50). This kit takes advantage of the superior properties of Alexa Fluor® 488 conjugates. Alexa Fluor® 488 conjugates are considerably brighter and more photostable than fluorescein-labeled probes (Figure 1.9, Figure 1.10, Figure 1.11). In addition, the fluorescence of Alexa Fluor® 488 conjugates is not sensitive to pH over a wide pH range, unlike the fluorescence of fluorescein conjugates (Figure 1.12).

The Alexa Fluor® 488 Signal Amplification Kit for Fluorescein- and Oregon Green® Dye–Conjugated Probes uses Alexa Fluor® 488 conjugates of two different antibodies to amplify the signals from fluorescein-labeled probes. Alexa Fluor® 488 anti-fluorescein/Oregon Green® antibody, which is prepared from a rabbit IgG fraction, is first used to bind to the fluorescein- or Oregon Green® dye–labeled target. The fluorescence signal is then dramatically enhanced by addition of the Alexa Fluor® 488 goat anti–rabbit IgG antibody. Because the spectra of Alexa Fluor® 488 conjugates are remarkably similar to those of fluorescein conjugates (Figure 7.51), the kit can be used with optical filters or instrument settings appropriate for fluorescein (Section 23.5, Table 23.9). The Alexa Fluor® 488 Signal Amplification Kit for Fluorescein-Conjugated Probes can be used for fluorescence microscopy, flow cytometry, blots, microarrays and probably any other application that uses fluorescein-conjugated probes; it contains sufficient reagents for 60–120 assays by microscopy or flow cytometry.

Alexa Fluor® Signal Amplification Kits for Mouse Antibodies

Molecular Probes offers three Alexa Fluor® Signal Amplification Kits for Mouse Antibodies, permitting enhanced detection of mouse primary antibodies using conjugates of our superior Alexa Fluor® 488, Alexa Fluor® 568 and Alexa Fluor® 594 dyes, which yield green, red-orange and red fluorescence, respectively (Table 7.8). These kits each use two Alexa Fluor® conjugates to detect antibodies derived from mouse. An Alexa Fluor® rabbit anti–mouse IgG antibody conjugate is first used to bind to the mouse-derived primary antibody. The fluorescence is then dramatically enhanced by the addition of an Alexa Fluor® conjugate of a goat anti–rabbit IgG antibody (Figure 7.52). The Alexa Fluor® 488, Alexa Fluor® 568 and Alexa Fluor® 594 Signal

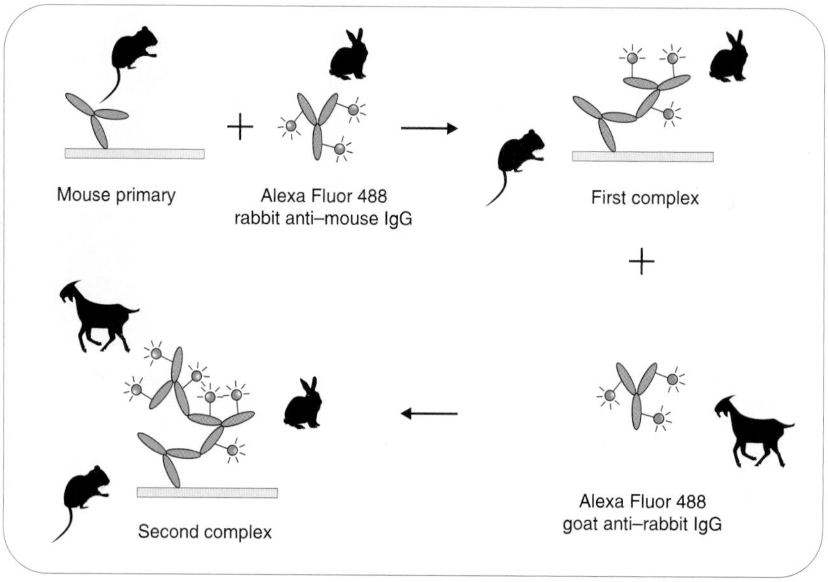

Figure 7.52 Antibody amplification scheme using our superior Alexa Fluor® conjugates, permitting enhanced detection of mouse primary antibodies. Molecular Probes offers three Alexa Fluor® Signal Amplification Kits for Mouse Antibodies containing antibody conjugates of the Alexa Fluor® 488 (A11054), Alexa Fluor® 568 (A11066) and Alexa Fluor® 594 (A11067) dyes, which yield green, red-orange and red fluorescence, respectively. These kits each use two Alexa Fluor® conjugates to detect antibodies derived from mouse. An Alexa Fluor® rabbit anti–mouse IgG antibody conjugate is first used to bind to the mouse primary antibody. The fluorescence signal is then dramatically enhanced by the addition of an Alexa Fluor® conjugate of goat anti–rabbit IgG antibody.

Amplification Kits for Mouse Antibodies can be used for both fluorescence microscopy and flow cytometry and contain sufficient materials for 60–300 assays.

Amplex® Red ELISA Kits

Molecular Probes' Amplex® Red ELISA Kits offer an extremely sensitive fluorometric or colorimetric detection method for horseradish peroxidase (HRP)–amplified enzyme-linked immunosorbent assays (ELISAs). The Amplex® Red ELISA Kit #1 (A22170) contains an HRP goat anti–mouse IgG antibody conjugate, which can be used for the ELISA detection of any mouse IgG antibody. The Amplex® Red ELISA Kit #2 (A22171) contains the versatile protein G conjugate of HRP, which can be used for the ELISA detection of IgGs from most commonly used species, including human, mouse, rabbit, goat, sheep, bovine and horse. The Amplex® Red reagent (10-acetyl-3,7-dihydroxyphenoxazine, Figure 10.58) provided in these kits is a highly sensitive and stable probe for the detection of HRP activity. In the presence of HRP, the Amplex® Red reagent reacts with hydrogen peroxide with a 1:1 stoichiometry to form the fluorescent product resorufin [1,2] (R363, Section 10.1; absorption/emission maxima ~571/585 nm, Figure 10.59). Because resorufin also has strong absorption, the assay can be performed either fluorometrically or spectrophotometrically. The Amplex® Red ELISA Kit #1 with the HRP–goat anti–mouse IgG antibody conjugate has detection limits of as little as 10 pg/microplate well of a mouse IgG by fluorometry or 50 pg/microplate well by colorimetry (Figure 7.53). The Amplex® Red ELISA Kit #2 with HRP–protein G has detection limits of as little as 1 ng/microplate well of a mouse IgG by fluorometry or 3 ng/microplate well by colorimetry (Figure 7.54) in 96-well plates.

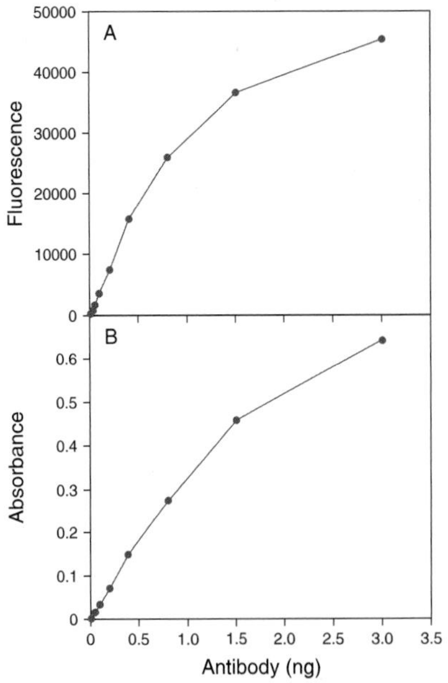

Figure 7.53 Detection of a mouse monoclonal antibody using the Amplex® Red ELISA Kit #1, with the horseradish peroxidase conjugate of goat anti–mouse IgG antibody (A22170). The wells of a microplate were first coated with an excess of a fluorescein conjugate of bovine serum albumin (BSA) and then blocked with PBS–BSA. The indicated amounts of anti-fluorescein/Oregon Green® mouse monoclonal 4-4-20 antibody (A6421) were then applied in 100 µL volumes and incubated for one hour. The wells were washed and then assayed using the reagents and protocol provided in this kit. The reactions were incubated for 50 minutes and then measured both **A)** for fluorescence (excitation/emission of 530 ± 12.5 nm/590 ± 10 nm) and **B)** for absorbance (576 ± 5 nm). The data points represent the average of three reactions. For the fluorescence plot, a background of 280 (arbitrary units) has been subtracted from each reading; for the absorption plot, a background of 0.040 has been subtracted from each reading.

Each Amplex® Red ELISA Kit contains:

- Amplex® Red reagent
- Dimethylsulfoxide (DMSO)
- Concentrated reaction buffer
- Hydrogen peroxide (H_2O_2)
- Horseradish peroxidase (HRP) conjugate of goat anti–mouse IgG antibody (in Kit #1, A22170) or of protein G (in Kit #2, A22171)
- Detailed ELISA protocols

Each kit provides sufficient reagents for approximately 1000 ELISAs using either a fluorescence- or absorption-based microplate reader and a reaction volume of 100 µL per assay. Our HRP conjugates of the goat anti–mouse IgG antibody (G21040), goat anti–rabbit IgG antibody (G21234) and protein G (P21041) are available separately. HRP conjugates of additional antibodies that can be used with the Amplex® Red reagent (A12222, A22177; Section 10.5) are listed in Table 7.4.

Gold-Labeled Immunoreagents

NANOGOLD and Alexa Fluor® FluoroNanogold Conjugates

In collaboration with Nanoprobes, Inc. (www.nanoprobes.com), Molecular Probes offers NANOGOLD and Alexa Fluor® FluoroNanogold conjugates of antibodies and streptavidin to facilitate immunoblotting, light microscopy and electron microscopy applications. These reagents include

Table 7.8 — Molecular Probes' Alexa Fluor® Signal Amplification Kits for Mouse Antibodies

Cat #	Kit	Abs *	Em *	Compatible with Filter Sets Used for	Kit Components
A11054	Alexa Fluor® 488 Signal Amplification Kit for Mouse Antibodies	495	519	Fluorescein, Oregon Green® 488	Alexa Fluor® 488 rabbit anti–mouse IgG and Alexa Fluor® 488 goat anti–rabbit IgG
A11066	Alexa Fluor® 568 Signal Amplification Kit for Mouse Antibodies	578	603	Lissamine rhodamine B, Rhodamine Red™-X dye, Tetramethylrhodamine, Cy3 dye	Alexa Fluor® 568 rabbit anti–mouse IgG and Alexa Fluor® 568 goat anti–rabbit IgG
A11067	Alexa Fluor® 594 Signal Amplification Kit for Mouse Antibodies	590	617	Texas Red® dye	Alexa Fluor® 594 rabbit anti–mouse IgG and Alexa Fluor® 594 goat anti–rabbit IgG

*Approximate absorbance (Abs) and fluorescence emission (Em) maxima of conjugates in the kit, in nm.

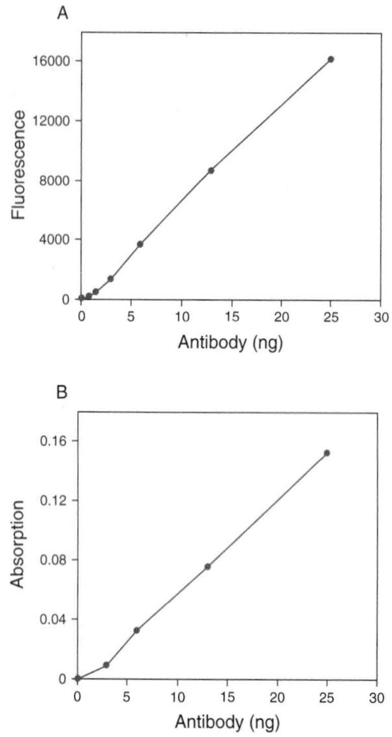

Figure 7.54 Detection of a mouse monoclonal antibody using the Amplex® Red ELISA Kit #2 (A22171). The assay can detect as little as 1 ng of a monoclonal antibody in the well of a microplate by fluorometry (panel A) or 3 ng by colorimetry (panel B). Conditions of the assay are essentially as described in the caption of Figure 7.53, except that a horseradish peroxidase conjugate of protein G was used instead of the horseradish peroxidase conjugate of goat anti–mouse IgG antibody.

affinity-purified Fab fragments of the goat anti–mouse IgG, goat anti–rabbit IgG and rabbit anti–goat IgG antibodies, as well as of streptavidin (Section 7.6, Table 7.9). Also available are NANOGOLD mono(sulfosuccinimidyl ester) (N20130, Section 1.6) and NANOGOLD monomaleimide (N20345, Section 2.2), which can be conjugated to amines (Figure 1.90) and thiols (Figure 2.22), respectively, in the same way that dyes are conjugated to proteins and nucleic acids.[3] NANOGOLD conjugates are covalently conjugated to the 1.4 nm NANOGOLD gold cluster label, whereas Alexa Fluor® FluoroNanogold conjugates are coupled to both a NANOGOLD label and either the Alexa Fluor® 488 or Alexa Fluor® 594 fluorophore, resulting in gold clusters with green or red fluorescence, respectively. Alexa Fluor® FluoroNanogold conjugates have all the advantages of the NANOGOLD cluster, with the additional benefit that they may be used for correlative fluorescence, light and electron microscopy[4,5] (Figure 7.55).

NANOGOLD gold clusters have several advantages over colloidal gold. They develop better with silver than do most gold colloids and as a result, provide higher sensitivity. Additionally, NANOGOLD particles do not have as high affinity for proteins as do gold colloids, thereby reducing any background due to nonspecific binding. Several additional advantages of NANOGOLD and Alexa Fluor® FluoroNanogold streptavidin over colloidal gold conjugates include:

- The NANOGOLD gold clusters are an extremely uniform (1.4 nm ± 10% diameter) and stable compound, not a gold colloid.
- NANOGOLD gold clusters are smaller than a complete IgG (H+L) antibody — approximately 1/15 the size of an Fab fragment — and therefore will be able to better penetrate cells and tissues, reaching antigens that are inaccessible to conjugates of larger gold particles.
- NANOGOLD conjugates contain absolutely no aggregates, as they are chromatographically purified through gel filtration columns. This feature is in sharp contrast to colloidal gold con-

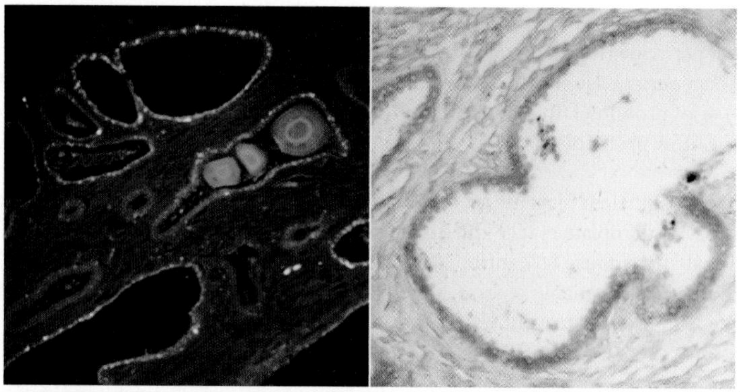

Figure 7.55 Human prostate tissue with adenocarcinoma imaged using an Alexa Fluor® 488 FluoroNanogold conjugate. Tissues were labeled with an anti-cytokeratin antibody, followed by staining with the Alexa Fluor® 488 FluoroNanogold Fab' fragment of goat anti–mouse IgG antibody (A24920). The fluorescence image in the top panel was taken with filters appropriate for fluorescein. The bottom panel shows a bright-field image of the same system, processed with the LI Silver (LIS) Enhancement Kit (L24919) to visualize the gold distribution. Image courtesy of Nanoprobes, Inc.

Table 7.9 — NANOGOLD, Alexa Fluor® FluoroNanogold and colloidal gold conjugates

Conjugate	Label (Abs/Em Maxima) *			
	NANOGOLD	Alexa Fluor® 488 FluoroNanogold (495/519)	Alexa Fluor® 488 Colloidal Gold (495/519)	Alexa Fluor® 594 FluoroNanogold (590/617)
Goat anti–mouse IgG	N24915 †	A24920 †	A31560 ‡, A31561 §	A24921 †
Goat anti–rabbit IgG	N24916 †	A24922 †	A31565 ‡, A31566 §	A24923 †
Rabbit anti–goat IgG	N24917 †	A24924 †		A24925 †
Streptavidin	N24918	A24926	A32360 ‡, A32361 §	A24927

* Approximate absorption (Abs) and fluorescence emission (Em) maxima, in nm, for conjugates. † F(ab) fragment. ‡ 5 nm colloidal gold. § 10 nm colloidal gold.

jugates, which are usually prepared by centrifugation to remove the largest aggregates and frequently contain significantly smaller aggregates.

- The ratio of NANOGOLD particle to F(ab) is nearly 1:1, making this product distinct from the 0.2–10 variable stoichiometry of most colloidal gold–antibody preparations.
- NANOGOLD cluster–stained targets develop better with silver than do most gold colloids, resulting in higher sensitivity.[6] Silver enhancement, such as the system provided in the LI Silver Enhancement Kit (L24919), is described below.

NANOGOLD and Alexa Fluor® FluoroNanogold products can be used in immunoblotting, light microscopy, and electron microscopy to provide clear visibility (Figure 7.56). Standard immunostaining methodologies can be used successfully with NANOGOLD and Alexa Fluor® FluoroNanogold immunoreagents. Also, because the concentration of antibody and gold is similar to most commercial preparations of colloidal gold antibodies, similar dilutions and blocking agents are appropriate.

Colloidal Gold Complexes

Molecular Probes offers Alexa Fluor® 488 dye–labeled colloidal gold conjugates, including affinity-purified goat anti–mouse IgG and goat anti–rabbit IgG antibodies and streptavidin (Table 7.9). These conjugates, which have been adsorbed to 5 nm or 10 nm gold colloids, may be used as probes in immunoblotting, light microscopy, fluorescence microscopy or electron microscopy. The fluorescence of these conjugates can be easily detected by standard techniques, but visualization of colloidal gold can be greatly improved using silver-enhancement methods, such as those we provide in the LI Silver Enhancement Kit (L24919) described below.

Combining fluorescent secondary detection reagents with colloidal gold to form functional complexes is difficult because the fluorescence of fluorophores such as fluorescein is significantly quenched by proximity to the colloidal gold.[7] Molecular Probes makes fluorescent colloidal gold complexes with our Alexa Fluor® 488 dye, a dye that has superior brightness and photostability. Our Alexa Fluor® 488 dye–labeled colloidal gold complexes of anti-IgG antibody and of streptavidin may be used to perform correlated immunofluorescence and electron microscopy in a two-step labeling procedure, rather than in the three-step indirect labeling procedure that is required with conventional nonfluorescent colloidal gold complexes of anti-IgG antibodies or streptavidin.[8]

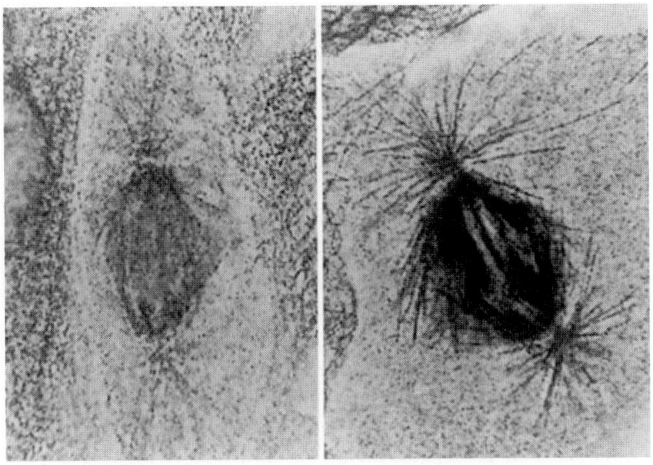

Figure 7.56 Spindle microtubules labeled with an anti-tubulin primary antibody followed by (left) goat anti–mouse IgG antibody colloidal gold or (right) NANOGOLD Fab' fragment of goat anti–mouse IgG antibody (N24915). Micrographs (magnification = 1300×) were generated by D. Vandre and R. Burry, Ohio State University. Image courtesy of Nanoprobes, Inc.

LI Silver Enhancement Kit

The LI Silver Enhancement Kit (L24919) provides a convenient, light-insensitive silver-enhancement system for use with the NANOGOLD, Alexa Fluor® FluoroNanogold and colloidal gold reagents that can be used for electron or light microscopy or to visualize gold particles on blots. LI silver is nucleated quickly by NANOGOLD gold clusters or colloidal gold, resulting in the precipitation of metallic silver and the formation of a dark brown to black signal. The system has markedly delayed self-nucleation, resulting in high contrast and very low backgrounds.

Gold particles in the presence of silver (I) ions and a reducing agent such as hydroquinone act as catalysts to reduce silver (I) ions to metallic silver (Figure 7.57). The silver is deposited onto the gold, enlarging the particles to between 30 and 100 nm in diameter. Tissues or blots stained with NANOGOLD gold clusters or colloidal gold are "developed" by this autometallographic procedure to give black staining that can be seen in a light microscope. This method — known as immunogold silver staining (IGSS) — has been widely used with the NANOGOLD cluster probe; it is one of the most sensitive immunodetection

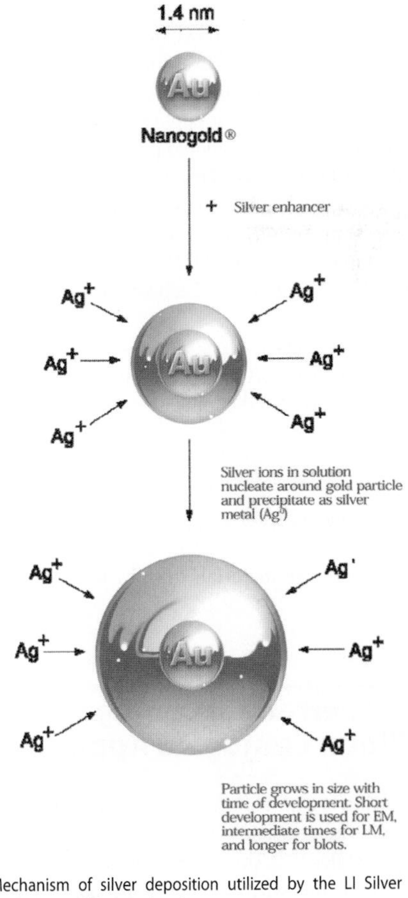

Figure 7.57 Mechanism of silver deposition utilized by the LI Silver Enhancement Kit (L24919). Image courtesy of Nanoprobes, Inc.

systems available and gives highly visible, *permanent* staining with no fading, with detection limits rivaling that of chemiluminescence and radionuclide labeling. Silver-enhanced NANOGOLD staining is compatible with double-labeling techniques, including enzyme-mediated staining. In blots, as little as 0.1 pg of a target IgG antibody can be detected using a NANOGOLD gold cluster labeled with an Fab′ fragment of a secondary antibody. NANOGOLD streptavidin (N24918, Section 7.6) has proved to be highly sensitive in detecting biotinylated nucleic acid probes in *in situ* hybridization studies.

The LI Silver Enhancement Kit (L24919), which is useful for light microscopy, gels and Western blots, is ideal for use with the NANOGOLD and Alexa Fluor® FluoroNanogold reagents and for enhancing colloidal gold products. The advantages of LI silver enhancement include:

- High-contrast signal for easy light microscope and immunoblot visibility
- Lower background than other commercial developers
- High sensitivity
- Light-insensitive signal; development can be observed under normal room lighting
- Relatively slow development (10–30 minutes) for precise monitoring of the extent of development
- Compatibility with all immunogold reagents

DAB Histochemistry Kits

The use of horseradish peroxidase (HRP) for enzyme-amplified immunodetection — commonly referred to as immunoperoxidase labeling — is a well-established standard histochemical technique.[9,10] The most widely used HRP substrate for these applications is diaminobenzidine (DAB), which generates a brown-colored polymeric oxidation product localized at HRP-labeled sites. The DAB reaction product can be visualized directly by bright-field light microscopy or, following osmication, by electron microscopy. We offer DAB Histochemistry Kits for detecting mouse IgG primary antibodies (D22185) and biotinylated antibodies and tracers (D22187, Section 7.6). Each kit contains:

- Diaminobenzidine (DAB)
- HRP-labeled goat anti–mouse IgG antibody (in Kit D22185) or streptavidin (in Kit D22187) conjugate
- H_2O_2 reaction additive
- Blocking reagent
- Staining buffer
- A detailed staining protocol

Each kit provides sufficient materials to stain approximately 200 slides.

Captivate™ Ferrofluid Conjugates and DSB-X™ Biotin Conjugate Applications

Magnetic separation is a quick, simple technique for isolating cells, organelles, proteins and nucleic acids from complex mixtures, based on bioaffinity principles.[11–14] The sample containing a target ligand to be isolated is incubated with the superparamagnetic particles coupled with the appropriate affinity reagent, e.g., streptavidin, an antibody or a complementary nucleic acid. The bound target ligand is then separated efficiently from the mixture using a high field-strength magnet.

Molecular Probes, in association with Immunicon Corporation, offers Captivate™ ferrofluid conjugates of goat anti–mouse IgG antibody (C21473), goat anti–rabbit IgG antibody (C21474) and streptavidin (C21476). Ferrofluids are superparamagnetic particles ~200 nm in diameter that respond to a magnetic field but completely demagnetize when the field is removed. The key feature of the Captivate™ ferrofluid is its small and relatively uniform particle size, which results in efficient diffusion of the ferrofluid conjugate and rapid kinetics of the binding reaction. Once added to the sample, however, no further mixing is required. Furthermore, the ferrofluid conjugates exhibit significantly higher ligand-binding capacities per mass, as compared with larger-diameter superparamagnetic particles from other suppliers. We also offer the Captivate™ microscope-mounted magnetic yoke assembly (C24700) and disposable sample chambers (C24701), which have been specially designed for use with the Captivate™ ferrofluid conjugates (Figure 7.58), for optimum capture of Captivate™ ferrofluid–tagged cells from such diverse liquid samples as culture media, blood and biological buffers.[15–17] The Captivate™ microscope-mounted magnetic yoke assembly includes one free set of 10 disposable sample chambers.

The unique particle size of the Captivate™ ferrofluid permits fluorescence microscope–based cell sorting, imaging and analysis [18] — analytical options that rival the capabilities of much more expensive instrumentation. To accomplish this, the cell suspension or blood sample is incubated with the appropriate fluorescent probes and then mixed with the Captivate™ ferrofluid conjugate. The mixture is loaded into a sample chamber, which is inserted into the magnetic yoke assembly and positioned on a microscope stage. Under influence of the strong magnetic gradient present in the chamber, cells labeled with the Captivate™ ferrofluid conjugate move quickly into position at the upper surface of the sample chamber. Cells that are not magnetically labeled sediment to the bottom. The captured cells can then be imaged and analyzed, or recovered free from unselected cells (Figure 7.58).

Molecular Probes also has available Captivate™ magnetic separators [19] for both microplates (C24702, Figure 23.58) and microtubes (C24703, Figure 23.59) that we find to be particularly useful with the Captivate™ ferrofluid products. The microplate separator is compatible with most 96-well microplates, whereas the microtube separator can accommodate six 1.5 mL microcentrifuge tubes. Both separators provide excellent separation efficiency and pull magnetic particles to one side, allowing easier removal of supernatants.

Our DSB-X™ biotin technology permits the fully reversible labeling of DSB-X™ biotin derivatives by avidin and streptavidin conjugates under extremely mild conditions [20] (Figure 7.103). DSB-X™ biotin (Figure 4.1) has moderate affinity for avidin and streptavidin; however, its binding is rapidly reversed by addition of excess D-biotin (B1595, B20656) or D-desthiobiotin (D20657). This facile reversibility has several potential applications:

- Live (or fixed) cells can be selectively isolated from a complex suspension of cells with a combination of Captivate™ ferrofluid streptavidin (C21476, Section 7.6), a DSB-X™ biotin–labeled secondary antibody (Table 7.10) and a cell-selective primary antibody, then released into fresh medium at neutral pH and physiological temperatures with D-biotin (B1595, B20656; Figure 7.107).

- Cells that have been isolated with the Captivate™ ferrofluid streptavidin by the above method retain the DSB-X™ biotin immunolabel; consequently, they can be detected and subsequently analyzed with any of our wide array of avidin and streptavidin conjugates (Section 7.6, Table 7.22).
- Targets in cells and tissues or on Western or Southern blots labeled with DSB-X™ biotin conjugates of antibodies or other DSB-X™ biotin–labeled reagents can initially be stained with fluorescent avidin or streptavidin conjugates, then the fluorescent staining can be reversed with D-biotin and the sample restained with an enzyme-conjugated avidin or streptavidin derivative in combination with a permanent stain, such as diaminobenzidine (DAB; D22185, D22187) or the combination of NBT and BCIP (N6495, B6492, N6547; Section 10.3) or with a chemiluminescent enzyme substrate such as the BOLD APB chemiluminescent substrate for membrane-based alkaline phosphatase detection (B21901, Section 9.4).
- DSB-X™ biotin conjugates can be reversibly immobilized on Captivate™ ferrofluid streptavidin or streptavidin agarose (S951, Section 7.6) and, while on the matrix, the bioconjugate — an antibody, an enzyme, an oligonucleotide or nucleic acid, a drug or some other DSB-X™ biotin conjugate — can bind to their targets, which may be from cell or tissue extracts or other sources. Gentle elution of the entire complex facilitates subsequent analysis of the affinity-isolated products by electrophoresis or other means. A potentially important application of this technique is the detection of specific protein–protein and protein–nucleic acid interactions through selective isolation and release of their intact complexes. Our DSB-X™ Biotin Bioconjugate Isolation Kit #1 (D20658, Section 7.6) contains the reagents and a protocol for isolation and recovery of complexes of DSB-X™ biotin conjugates with streptavidin agarose.

DSB-X™ biotin conjugates of antibodies and other proteins can be efficiently prepared using our DSB-X™ Biotin Protein Labeling Kit (D20655), which is described in Section 1.2. Alternatively, our Zenon® DSB-X™ Biotin Mouse IgG_1 Labeling Kit (Z25053, Section 7.3) can be used to rapidly and quantitatively prepare DSB-X™ biotin–labeled complexes of any intact mouse IgG_1 antibody (Figure 7.59).

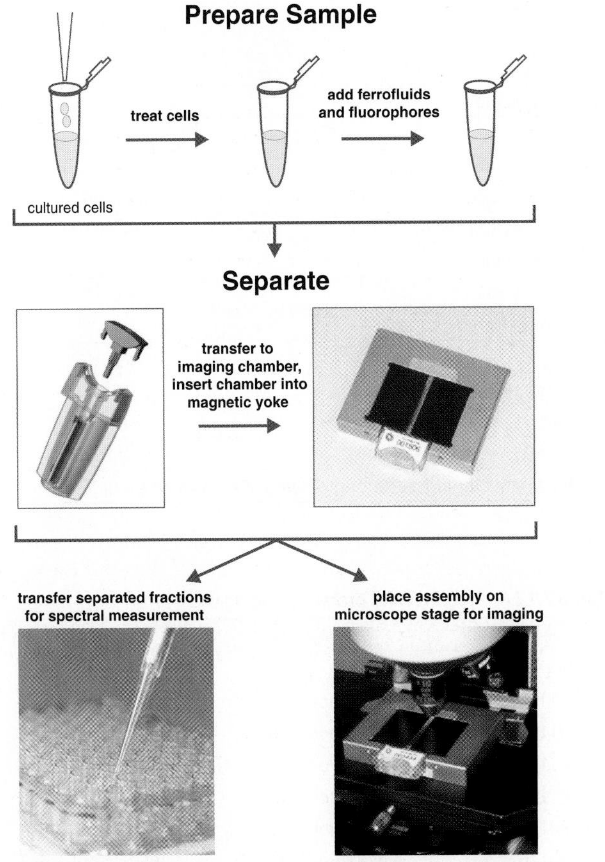

Figure 7.58 Flow chart for the magnetic separation and analysis of a cell suspension. Cells are treated with an antibody or a biotinylated or DSB-X™ biotin–labeled probe that binds to cell-surface markers. The treated cells are incubated with the appropriate Captivate™ ferrofluid conjugates, which bind to target cells. The mixture is then transferred to a chamber that is inserted into a magnetic yoke. Under the influence of a strong magnetic field, the cells bound to Captivate™ ferrofluid conjugates are rapidly separated from the unbound cells. The separate cell populations can be analyzed by both fluorometry and fluorescence microscopy.

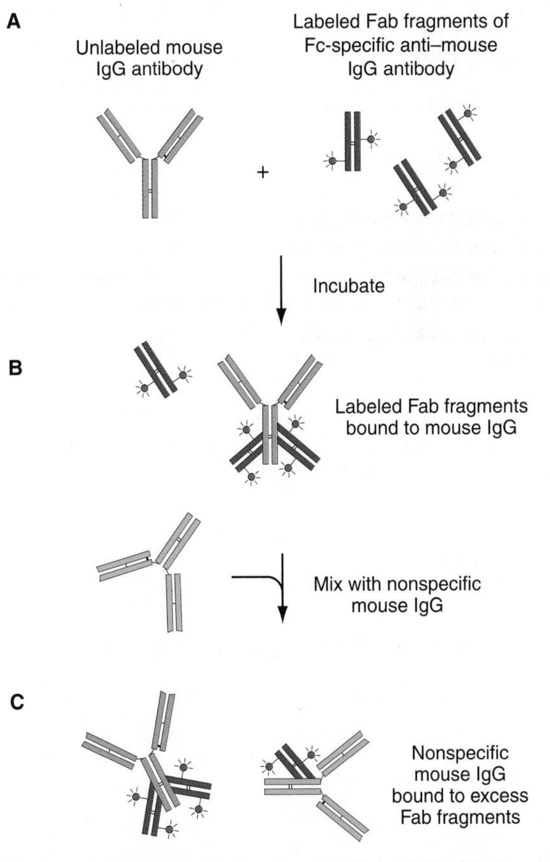

Figure 7.59 Labeling scheme utilized in the Zenon® Antibody Labeling Kits. An unlabeled IgG antibody is incubated with the Zenon® labeling reagent, which contains a fluorophore-labeled, Fc-specific anti-IgG Fab fragment (panel A). This labeled Fab fragment binds to the Fc portion of the IgG antibody (panel B). Excess Fab fragment is then neutralized by the addition of a nonspecific IgG (panel C), preventing crosslabeling by the Fab fragment in experiments where primary antibodies of the same type are present. Note that the Fab fragment used for labeling need not be coupled to a fluorophore, but could instead be coupled to an enzyme (such as HRP) or to biotin.

Table 7.10 — Molecular Probes' biotinylated and desthiobiotinylated secondary antibodies

Antibody	Host	Biotin	DSB-X™ Biotin
Anti–mouse IgG	Goat	B2763	D20690, D20691
Anti–mouse IgG, F(ab')$_2$	Goat	B11027	D20692
Anti–mouse IgM	Goat		D20693
Anti–rabbit IgG	Goat	B2770	D20694, D20695
Anti–rabbit IgG, F(ab')$_2$	Goat	B21078	D20696
Anti–rat IgG	Goat		D20697
Anti–goat IgG	Donkey		D20698
Anti–sheep IgG	Donkey		D20699
Anti–human IgG	Goat		D20700
Anti–chicken IgG	Goat		D20701

References

1. Anal Biochem 253, 162 (1997); **2.** J Immunol Methods 202, 133 (1997); **3.** J Histochem Cytochem 48, 471 (2000); **4.** J Histochem Cytochem 51, 707 (2003); **5.** Placenta 24, 557 (2003); **6.** J Microsc 199, 163 (2000); **7.** Colloidal Gold: Principles. Methods and Applications, Vol. 1, Hayat MA, Ed. pp.323–347 (1989); **8.** Proc Natl Acad Sci U S A 82, 109 (1985); **9.** J Histochem Cytochem 36, 317 (1988); **10.** Arch Pathol Lab Med 102, 113 (1978); **11.** J Biol Chem 268, 10145 (1993); **12.** J Immunol Methods 164, 61 (1993); **13.** J Immunol Methods 206, 73 (1997); **14.** Genes Cells 4, 67 (1999); **15.** Proc Natl Acad Sci U S A 95, 4589 (1998); **16.** Diagnosis 17, 1059 (1997); **17.** Magnetic Separation Techniques Applied to Cellular and Molecular Biology, Kemshead JT, Ed. pp. 47–61 (1991); **18.** Nat Biotechnol 17, 1210 (1999); **19.** These products are not manufactured by Immunicon; **20.** Anal Biochem 308, 343 (2002).

Protein A and Protein G Conjugates

Protein A and protein G are bacterial proteins that bind with high affinity to the Fc portion of various classes and subclasses of immunoglobulins from a variety of species (Table 7.11). Molecular Probes offers protein A conjugated to several different Alexa Fluor® fluorophores (Table 7.12) — the green-fluorescent Alexa Fluor® 488 (P11047), orange-fluorescent Alexa Fluor® 546 (P11049), red-orange–fluorescent Alexa Fluor® 568 (P11050), red-fluorescent Alexa Fluor® 594 (P11051) and far-red–fluorescent Alexa Fluor® 633 (P21107) and Alexa Fluor® 647 (P21462) dyes — with bright and unusually photostable fluorescence that spans the spectrum (see Note 1.1 "Product Highlight: The Alexa Fluor® Dye Series — Peak Performance across the Visible Spectrum" in Section 1.3). We also offer protein G conjugated to the Alexa Fluor® 488 dye (P11065) and to horseradish peroxidase (P21041).

Table 7.11 — Binding profiles of protein A and protein G

Antibody	Protein A	Protein G
Bovine	+	++
Cat	++	–
Chicken	–	–
Dog	++	+
Goat	+	++
Guinea pig	+	++
Horse	–	++
Human IgG$_1$, IgG$_2$, IgG$_4$	++	++
Human IgG$_3$	–	++
Human IgM, IgA, IgE	++	–
Human IgD	–	–
Mouse IgG$_1$	–	++
Mouse (others)	++	++
Pig	++	++
Rabbit	++	++
Rat	–	+
Sheep	–	++

+ Moderate binding. ++ Strong binding. - Weak or no binding.

Table 7.12 — Protein A and protein G conjugates

Cat #	Conjugate	Abs *	Em *
Protein A conjugates			
P11047	Alexa Fluor® 488	495	519
P11049	Alexa Fluor® 546	556	573
P11050	Alexa Fluor® 568	578	603
P11051	Alexa Fluor® 594	590	615
P21107	Alexa Fluor® 633	632	647
P21462	Alexa Fluor® 647	650	668
Protein G conjugates			
P11065	Alexa Fluor® 488	495	519
P21041	Horseradish peroxidase	NA	NA

* Approximate absorption (Abs) and emission (Em) maxima, in nm. NA = Not applicable.

Product List — 7.2 Secondary Immunoreagents

Cat #	Product Name	Unit Size
A21000	Alexa Fluor® 680–allophycocyanin goat anti-mouse IgG (H+L) *1 mg/mL*	100 µL
A21006	Alexa Fluor® 750–allophycocyanin goat anti-mouse IgG (H+L) *1 mg/mL*	100 µL
A21001MP	Alexa Fluor® 680–allophycocyanin goat anti-rabbit IgG (H+L) *1 mg/mL*	100 µL
A21467	Alexa Fluor® 488 chicken anti-goat IgG (H+L) *2 mg/mL*	0.5 mL
A21468	Alexa Fluor® 594 chicken anti-goat IgG (H+L) *2 mg/mL*	0.5 mL
A21469	Alexa Fluor® 647 chicken anti-goat IgG (H+L) *2 mg/mL*	0.5 mL
A21464	Alexa Fluor® 488 chicken anti-human IgG (H+L) *2 mg/mL*	0.5 mL
A21200	Alexa Fluor® 488 chicken anti-mouse IgG (H+L) *2 mg/mL*	0.5 mL
A21201	Alexa Fluor® 594 chicken anti-mouse IgG (H+L) *2 mg/mL*	0.5 mL
A21463	Alexa Fluor® 647 chicken anti-mouse IgG (H+L) *2 mg/mL*	0.5 mL
A21441	Alexa Fluor® 488 chicken anti-rabbit IgG (H+L) *2 mg/mL*	0.5 mL
A21442	Alexa Fluor® 594 chicken anti-rabbit IgG (H+L) *2 mg/mL*	0.5 mL
A21443	Alexa Fluor® 647 chicken anti-rabbit IgG (H+L) *2 mg/mL*	0.5 mL
A21470	Alexa Fluor® 488 chicken anti-rat IgG (H+L) *2 mg/mL*	0.5 mL
A21471	Alexa Fluor® 594 chicken anti-rat IgG (H+L) *2 mg/mL*	0.5 mL
A21472	Alexa Fluor® 647 chicken anti-rat IgG (H+L) *2 mg/mL*	0.5 mL
A21081	Alexa Fluor® 350 donkey anti-goat IgG (H+L) *2 mg/mL*	0.5 mL
A11055	Alexa Fluor® 488 donkey anti-goat IgG (H+L) *2 mg/mL*	0.5 mL
A11056	Alexa Fluor® 546 donkey anti-goat IgG (H+L) *2 mg/mL*	0.5 mL
A21432	Alexa Fluor® 555 donkey anti-goat IgG (H+L) *2 mg/mL*	0.5 mL
A11057	Alexa Fluor® 568 donkey anti-goat IgG (H+L) *2 mg/mL*	0.5 mL
A11058	Alexa Fluor® 594 donkey anti-goat IgG (H+L) *2 mg/mL*	0.5 mL
A21082	Alexa Fluor® 633 donkey anti-goat IgG (H+L) *2 mg/mL*	0.5 mL
A21447	Alexa Fluor® 647 donkey anti-goat IgG (H+L) *2 mg/mL*	0.5 mL
A21083	Alexa Fluor® 660 donkey anti-goat IgG (H+L) *2 mg/mL*	0.5 mL
A21084	Alexa Fluor® 680 donkey anti-goat IgG (H+L) *2 mg/mL*	0.5 mL
A21202	Alexa Fluor® 488 donkey anti-mouse IgG (H+L) *2 mg/mL*	0.5 mL
A31570	Alexa Fluor® 555 donkey anti-mouse IgG (H+L) *2 mg/mL*	0.5 mL
A21203	Alexa Fluor® 594 donkey anti-mouse IgG (H+L) *2 mg/mL*	0.5 mL
A31571	Alexa Fluor® 647 donkey anti-mouse IgG (H+L) *2 mg/mL*	0.5 mL
A21206	Alexa Fluor® 488 donkey anti-rabbit IgG (H+L) *2 mg/mL*	0.5 mL
A31572	Alexa Fluor® 555 donkey anti-rabbit IgG (H+L) *2 mg/mL*	0.5 mL
A21207	Alexa Fluor® 594 donkey anti-rabbit IgG (H+L) *2 mg/mL*	0.5 mL
A31573	Alexa Fluor® 647 donkey anti-rabbit IgG (H+L) *2 mg/mL*	0.5 mL
A21208	Alexa Fluor® 488 donkey anti-rat IgG (H+L) *2 mg/mL*	0.5 mL
A21209	Alexa Fluor® 594 donkey anti-rat IgG (H+L) *2 mg/mL*	0.5 mL
A21097	Alexa Fluor® 350 donkey anti-sheep IgG (H+L) *2 mg/mL*	0.5 mL
A11015	Alexa Fluor® 488 donkey anti-sheep IgG (H+L) *2 mg/mL*	0.5 mL
A21098	Alexa Fluor® 546 donkey anti-sheep IgG (H+L) *2 mg/mL*	0.5 mL
A21436	Alexa Fluor® 555 donkey anti-sheep IgG (H+L) *2 mg/mL*	0.5 mL
A21099	Alexa Fluor® 568 donkey anti-sheep IgG (H+L) *2 mg/mL*	0.5 mL
A11016	Alexa Fluor® 594 donkey anti-sheep IgG (H+L) *2 mg/mL*	0.5 mL
A21100	Alexa Fluor® 633 donkey anti-sheep IgG (H+L) *2 mg/mL*	0.5 mL
A21448	Alexa Fluor® 647 donkey anti-sheep IgG (H+L) *2 mg/mL*	0.5 mL
A21101MP	Alexa Fluor® 660 donkey anti-sheep IgG (H+L) *2 mg/mL*	0.5 mL
A21102	Alexa Fluor® 680 donkey anti-sheep IgG (H+L) *2 mg/mL*	0.5 mL
A11068	Alexa Fluor® 350 $F(ab')_2$ fragment of goat anti-mouse IgG (H+L) *2 mg/mL*	250 µL
A11017	Alexa Fluor® 488 $F(ab')_2$ fragment of goat anti-mouse IgG (H+L) *2 mg/mL*	250 µL
A11018	Alexa Fluor® 546 $F(ab')_2$ fragment of goat anti-mouse IgG (H+L) *2 mg/mL*	250 µL
A21425	Alexa Fluor® 555 $F(ab')_2$ fragment of goat anti-mouse IgG (H+L) *2 mg/mL*	250 µL
A11019	Alexa Fluor® 568 $F(ab')_2$ fragment of goat anti-mouse IgG (H+L) *2 mg/mL*	250 µL
A11020	Alexa Fluor® 594 $F(ab')_2$ fragment of goat anti-mouse IgG (H+L) *2 mg/mL*	250 µL
A21053	Alexa Fluor® 633 $F(ab')_2$ fragment of goat anti-mouse IgG (H+L) *2 mg/mL*	250 µL
A21237	Alexa Fluor® 647 $F(ab')_2$ fragment of goat anti-mouse IgG (H+L) *2 mg/mL*	250 µL
A21059	Alexa Fluor® 680 $F(ab')_2$ fragment of goat anti-mouse IgG (H+L) *2 mg/mL*	250 µL
A11069	Alexa Fluor® 350 $F(ab')_2$ fragment of goat anti-rabbit IgG (H+L) *2 mg/mL*	250 µL
A11070	Alexa Fluor® 488 $F(ab')_2$ fragment of goat anti-rabbit IgG (H+L) *2 mg/mL*	250 µL
A11071	Alexa Fluor® 546 $F(ab')_2$ fragment of goat anti-rabbit IgG (H+L) *2 mg/mL*	250 µL
A21430	Alexa Fluor® 555 $F(ab')_2$ fragment of goat anti-rabbit IgG (H+L) *2 mg/mL*	250 µL
A21069	Alexa Fluor® 568 $F(ab')_2$ fragment of goat anti-rabbit IgG (H+L) *2 mg/mL*	250 µL
A11072	Alexa Fluor® 594 $F(ab')_2$ fragment of goat anti-rabbit IgG (H+L) *2 mg/mL*	250 µL

For current prices or to order online, visit probes.invitrogen.com

Product List — 7.2 Secondary Immunoreagents — continued

Cat #	Product Name	Unit Size
A21072	Alexa Fluor® 633 F(ab')$_2$ fragment of goat anti-rabbit IgG (H+L) *2 mg/mL*	250 µL
A21246	Alexa Fluor® 647 F(ab')$_2$ fragment of goat anti-rabbit IgG (H+L) *2 mg/mL*	250 µL
A21075	Alexa Fluor® 660 F(ab')$_2$ fragment of goat anti-rabbit IgG (H+L) *2 mg/mL*	250 µL
A21077	Alexa Fluor® 680 F(ab')$_2$ fragment of goat anti-rabbit IgG (H+L) *2 mg/mL*	250 µL
A21222	Alexa Fluor® 488 F(ab')$_2$ fragment of rabbit anti-goat IgG (H+L) *2 mg/mL*	250 µL
A21223	Alexa Fluor® 594 F(ab')$_2$ fragment of rabbit anti-goat IgG (H+L) *2 mg/mL*	250 µL
A21204	Alexa Fluor® 488 F(ab')$_2$ fragment of rabbit anti-mouse IgG (H+L) *2 mg/mL*	250 µL
A21205	Alexa Fluor® 594 F(ab')$_2$ fragment of rabbit anti-mouse IgG (H+L) *2 mg/mL*	250 µL
A24920	Alexa Fluor® 488 FluoroNanogold™ Fab' fragment of goat anti-mouse IgG *80 µg protein/mL*	1 mL
A24921	Alexa Fluor® 594 FluoroNanogold™ Fab' fragment of goat anti-mouse IgG *80 µg protein/mL*	1 mL
A24922	Alexa Fluor® 488 FluoroNanogold™ Fab' fragment of goat anti-rabbit IgG *80 µg protein/mL*	1 mL
A24923	Alexa Fluor® 594 FluoroNanogold™ Fab' fragment of goat anti-rabbit IgG *80 µg protein/mL*	1 mL
A24924	Alexa Fluor® 488 FluoroNanogold™ Fab' fragment of rabbit anti-goat IgG *80 µg protein/mL*	1 mL
A24925	Alexa Fluor® 594 FluoroNanogold™ Fab' fragment of rabbit anti-goat IgG *80 µg protein/mL*	1 mL
A11039	Alexa Fluor® 488 goat anti-chicken IgG (H+L) *2 mg/mL*	0.5 mL
A11040	Alexa Fluor® 546 goat anti-chicken IgG (H+L) *2 mg/mL*	0.5 mL
A21437	Alexa Fluor® 555 goat anti-chicken IgG (H+L) *2 mg/mL*	0.5 mL
A11041	Alexa Fluor® 568 goat anti-chicken IgG (H+L) *2 mg/mL*	0.5 mL
A11042	Alexa Fluor® 594 goat anti-chicken IgG (H+L) *2 mg/mL*	0.5 mL
A21103	Alexa Fluor® 633 goat anti-chicken IgG (H+L) *2 mg/mL*	0.5 mL
A21449	Alexa Fluor® 647 goat anti-chicken IgG (H+L) *2 mg/mL*	0.5 mL
A21104	Alexa Fluor® 660 goat anti-chicken IgG (H+L) *2 mg/mL*	0.5 mL
A11073	Alexa Fluor® 488 goat anti-guinea pig IgG (H+L) *highly cross-adsorbed* *2 mg/mL*	0.5 mL
A11074	Alexa Fluor® 546 goat anti-guinea pig IgG (H+L) *highly cross-adsorbed* *2 mg/mL*	0.5 mL
A21435	Alexa Fluor® 555 goat anti-guinea pig IgG (H+L) *highly cross-adsorbed* *2 mg/mL*	0.5 mL
A11075	Alexa Fluor® 568 goat anti-guinea pig IgG (H+L) *highly cross-adsorbed* *2 mg/mL*	0.5 mL
A11076	Alexa Fluor® 594 goat anti-guinea pig IgG (H+L) *highly cross-adsorbed* *2 mg/mL*	0.5 mL
A21105	Alexa Fluor® 633 goat anti-guinea pig IgG (H+L) *highly cross-adsorbed* *2 mg/mL*	0.5 mL
A21450	Alexa Fluor® 647 goat anti-guinea pig IgG (H+L) *highly cross-adsorbed* *2 mg/mL*	0.5 mL
A21106	Alexa Fluor® 660 goat anti-guinea pig IgG (H+L) *highly cross-adsorbed* *2 mg/mL*	0.5 mL
A21110	Alexa Fluor® 488 goat anti-hamster IgG (H+L) *2 mg/mL*	0.5 mL
A21111	Alexa Fluor® 546 goat anti-hamster IgG (H+L) *2 mg/mL*	0.5 mL
A21112	Alexa Fluor® 568 goat anti-hamster IgG (H+L) *2 mg/mL*	0.5 mL
A21113	Alexa Fluor® 594 goat anti-hamster IgG (H+L) *2 mg/mL*	0.5 mL
A21114	Alexa Fluor® 633 goat anti-hamster IgG (H+L) *2 mg/mL*	0.5 mL
A21451	Alexa Fluor® 647 goat anti-hamster IgG (H+L) *2 mg/mL*	0.5 mL
A11013	Alexa Fluor® 488 goat anti-human IgG (H+L) *2 mg/mL*	0.5 mL
A21089	Alexa Fluor® 546 goat anti-human IgG (H+L) *2 mg/mL*	0.5 mL
A21433	Alexa Fluor® 555 goat anti-human IgG (H+L) *2 mg/mL*	0.5 mL
A21090	Alexa Fluor® 568 goat anti-human IgG (H+L) *2 mg/mL*	0.5 mL
A11014	Alexa Fluor® 594 goat anti-human IgG (H+L) *2 mg/mL*	0.5 mL
A21091	Alexa Fluor® 633 goat anti-human IgG (H+L) *2 mg/mL*	0.5 mL
A21445	Alexa Fluor® 647 goat anti-human IgG (H+L) *2 mg/mL*	0.5 mL
A21215	Alexa Fluor® 488 goat anti-human IgM (µ chain) *2 mg/mL*	250 µL
A21216	Alexa Fluor® 594 goat anti-human IgM (µ chain) *2 mg/mL*	250 µL
A21249	Alexa Fluor® 647 goat anti-human IgM (µ chain) *2 mg/mL*	250 µL
A31560	Alexa Fluor® 488 goat anti-mouse IgG, 5 nm colloidal gold conjugate *30 µg protein/mL*	0.5 mL
A31561	Alexa Fluor® 488 goat anti-mouse IgG, 10 nm colloidal gold conjugate *30 µg protein/mL*	0.5 mL
A21120	Alexa Fluor® 350 goat anti-mouse IgG$_1$ (γ1) *2 mg/mL*	250 µL
A21121	Alexa Fluor® 488 goat anti-mouse IgG$_1$ (γ1) *2 mg/mL*	250 µL
A21123	Alexa Fluor® 546 goat anti-mouse IgG$_1$ (γ1) *2 mg/mL*	250 µL
A21127	Alexa Fluor® 555 goat anti-mouse IgG$_1$ (γ1) *2 mg/mL*	250 µL
A21124	Alexa Fluor® 568 goat anti-mouse IgG$_1$ (γ1) *2 mg/mL*	250 µL
A21125	Alexa Fluor® 594 goat anti-mouse IgG$_1$ (γ1) *2 mg/mL*	250 µL
A21126	Alexa Fluor® 633 goat anti-mouse IgG$_1$ (γ1) *2 mg/mL*	250 µL
A21240	Alexa Fluor® 647 goat anti-mouse IgG$_1$ (γ1) *2 mg/mL*	250 µL
A21130	Alexa Fluor® 350 goat anti-mouse IgG$_{2a}$ (γ2a) *2 mg/mL*	250 µL
A21131	Alexa Fluor® 488 goat anti-mouse IgG$_{2a}$ (γ2a) *2 mg/mL*	250 µL
A21133	Alexa Fluor® 546 goat anti-mouse IgG$_{2a}$ (γ2a) *2 mg/mL*	250 µL
A21137	Alexa Fluor® 555 goat anti-mouse IgG$_{2a}$ (γ2a) *2 mg/mL*	250 µL

For current prices or to order online, visit probes.invitrogen.com

Cat #	Product Name	Unit Size
A21134	Alexa Fluor® 568 goat anti-mouse IgG_{2a} (γ2a) *2 mg/mL*	250 µL
A21135	Alexa Fluor® 594 goat anti-mouse IgG_{2a} (γ2a) *2 mg/mL*	250 µL
A21136	Alexa Fluor® 633 goat anti-mouse IgG_{2a} (γ2a) *2 mg/mL*	250 µL
A21241	Alexa Fluor® 647 goat anti-mouse IgG_{2a} (γ2a) *2 mg/mL*	250 µL
A21140	Alexa Fluor® 350 goat anti-mouse IgG_{2b} (γ2b) *2 mg/mL*	250 µL
A21141	Alexa Fluor® 488 goat anti-mouse IgG_{2b} (γ2b) *2 mg/mL*	250 µL
A21143	Alexa Fluor® 546 goat anti-mouse IgG_{2b} (γ2b) *2 mg/mL*	250 µL
A21147	Alexa Fluor® 555 goat anti-mouse IgG_{2b} (γ2b) *2 mg/mL*	250 µL
A21144	Alexa Fluor® 568 goat anti-mouse IgG_{2b} (γ2b) *2 mg/mL*	250 µL
A21145	Alexa Fluor® 594 goat anti-mouse IgG_{2b} (γ2b) *2 mg/mL*	250 µL
A21146	Alexa Fluor® 633 goat anti-mouse IgG_{2b} (γ2b) *2 mg/mL*	250 µL
A21242	Alexa Fluor® 647 goat anti-mouse IgG_{2b} (γ2b) *2 mg/mL*	250 µL
A21151	Alexa Fluor® 488 goat anti-mouse IgG_3 (γ3) *2 mg/mL*	250 µL
A21153	Alexa Fluor® 546 goat anti-mouse IgG_3 (γ3) *2 mg/mL*	250 µL
A21157	Alexa Fluor® 555 goat anti-mouse IgG_3 (γ3) *2 mg/mL*	250 µL
A21154	Alexa Fluor® 568 goat anti-mouse IgG_3 (γ3) *2 mg/mL*	250 µL
A21155	Alexa Fluor® 594 goat anti-mouse IgG_3 (γ3) *2 mg/mL*	250 µL
A11045	Alexa Fluor® 350 goat anti-mouse IgG (H+L) *2 mg/mL*	0.5 mL
A31553	Alexa Fluor® 405 goat anti-mouse IgG (H+L) *2 mg/mL*	0.5 mL
A11063	Alexa Fluor® 430 goat anti-mouse IgG (H+L) *2 mg/mL*	0.5 mL
A11001	Alexa Fluor® 488 goat anti-mouse IgG (H+L) *2 mg/mL*	0.5 mL
A31554	Alexa Fluor® 500 goat anti-mouse IgG (H+L) *2 mg/mL*	0.5 mL
A31555	Alexa Fluor® 514 goat anti-mouse IgG (H+L) *2 mg/mL*	0.5 mL
A11002	Alexa Fluor® 532 goat anti-mouse IgG (H+L) *2 mg/mL*	0.5 mL
A11003	Alexa Fluor® 546 goat anti-mouse IgG (H+L) *2 mg/mL*	0.5 mL
A21422	Alexa Fluor® 555 goat anti-mouse IgG (H+L) *2 mg/mL*	0.5 mL
A11004	Alexa Fluor® 568 goat anti-mouse IgG (H+L) *2 mg/mL*	0.5 mL
A11005	Alexa Fluor® 594 goat anti-mouse IgG (H+L) *2 mg/mL*	0.5 mL
A31550	Alexa Fluor® 610 goat anti-mouse IgG (H+L) *2 mg/mL*	0.5 mL
A21050	Alexa Fluor® 633 goat anti-mouse IgG (H+L) *2 mg/mL*	0.5 mL
A31574	Alexa Fluor® 635 goat anti-mouse IgG (H+L) *2 mg/mL*	0.5 mL
A21235	Alexa Fluor® 647 goat anti-mouse IgG (H+L) *2 mg/mL*	0.5 mL
A21054	Alexa Fluor® 660 goat anti-mouse IgG (H+L) *2 mg/mL*	0.5 mL
A21057	Alexa Fluor® 680 goat anti-mouse IgG (H+L) *2 mg/mL*	0.5 mL
A21036	Alexa Fluor® 700 goat anti-mouse IgG (H+L) *2 mg/mL*	0.5 mL
A21037	Alexa Fluor® 750 goat anti-mouse IgG (H+L) *2 mg/mL*	0.5 mL
A21049	Alexa Fluor® 350 goat anti-mouse IgG (H+L) *highly cross-adsorbed* *2 mg/mL*	0.5 mL
A11029	Alexa Fluor® 488 goat anti-mouse IgG (H+L) *highly cross-adsorbed* *2 mg/mL*	0.5 mL
A11030	Alexa Fluor® 546 goat anti-mouse IgG (H+L) *highly cross-adsorbed* *2 mg/mL*	0.5 mL
A21424	Alexa Fluor® 555 goat anti-mouse IgG (H+L) *highly cross-adsorbed* *2 mg/mL*	0.5 mL
A11031	Alexa Fluor® 568 goat anti-mouse IgG (H+L) *highly cross-adsorbed* *2 mg/mL*	0.5 mL
A11032	Alexa Fluor® 594 goat anti-mouse IgG (H+L) *highly cross-adsorbed* *2 mg/mL*	0.5 mL
A21052	Alexa Fluor® 633 goat anti-mouse IgG (H+L) *highly cross-adsorbed* *2 mg/mL*	0.5 mL
A31575	Alexa Fluor® 635 goat anti-mouse IgG (H+L) *highly cross-adsorbed* *2 mg/mL*	0.5 mL
A21236	Alexa Fluor® 647 goat anti-mouse IgG (H+L) *highly cross-adsorbed* *2 mg/mL*	0.5 mL
A21055	Alexa Fluor® 660 goat anti-mouse IgG (H+L) *highly cross-adsorbed* *2 mg/mL*	0.5 mL
A21058	Alexa Fluor® 680 goat anti-mouse IgG (H+L) *highly cross-adsorbed* *2 mg/mL*	0.5 mL
A31552	Alexa Fluor® 350 goat anti-mouse IgM (µ chain) *2 mg/mL*	250 µL
A21042	Alexa Fluor® 488 goat anti-mouse IgM (µ chain) *2 mg/mL*	250 µL
A21045	Alexa Fluor® 546 goat anti-mouse IgM (µ chain) *2 mg/mL*	250 µL
A21426	Alexa Fluor® 555 goat anti-mouse IgM (µ chain) *2 mg/mL*	250 µL
A21043	Alexa Fluor® 568 goat anti-mouse IgM (µ chain) *2 mg/mL*	250 µL
A21044	Alexa Fluor® 594 goat anti-mouse IgM (µ chain) *2 mg/mL*	250 µL
A21046	Alexa Fluor® 633 goat anti-mouse IgM (µ chain) *2 mg/mL*	250 µL
A21238	Alexa Fluor® 647 goat anti-mouse IgM (µ chain) *2 mg/mL*	250 µL
A21047	Alexa Fluor® 660 goat anti-mouse IgM (µ chain) *2 mg/mL*	250 µL
A21048	Alexa Fluor® 680 goat anti-mouse IgM (µ chain) *2 mg/mL*	250 µL
A31565	Alexa Fluor® 488 goat anti-rabbit IgG, 5 nm colloidal gold conjugate *30 µg protein/mL*	0.5 mL
A31566	Alexa Fluor® 488 goat anti-rabbit IgG, 10 nm colloidal gold conjugate *30 µg protein/mL*	0.5 mL
A11046	Alexa Fluor® 350 goat anti-rabbit IgG (H+L) *2 mg/mL*	0.5 mL
A31556	Alexa Fluor® 405 goat anti-rabbit IgG (H+L) *2 mg/mL*	0.5 mL
A11064	Alexa Fluor® 430 goat anti-rabbit IgG (H+L) *2 mg/mL*	0.5 mL

For current prices or to order online, visit probes.invitrogen.com

Product List — 7.2 Secondary Immunoreagents — continued

Cat #	Product Name	Unit Size
A11008	Alexa Fluor® 488 goat anti-rabbit IgG (H+L) *2 mg/mL*	0.5 mL
A31557	Alexa Fluor® 500 goat anti-rabbit IgG (H+L) *2 mg/mL*	0.5 mL
A31558	Alexa Fluor® 514 goat anti-rabbit IgG (H+L) *2 mg/mL*	0.5 mL
A11009	Alexa Fluor® 532 goat anti-rabbit IgG (H+L) *2 mg/mL*	0.5 mL
A11010	Alexa Fluor® 546 goat anti-rabbit IgG (H+L) *2 mg/mL*	0.5 mL
A21428	Alexa Fluor® 555 goat anti-rabbit IgG (H+L) *2 mg/mL*	0.5 mL
A11011	Alexa Fluor® 568 goat anti-rabbit IgG (H+L) *2 mg/mL*	0.5 mL
A11012	Alexa Fluor® 594 goat anti-rabbit IgG (H+L) *2 mg/mL*	0.5 mL
A31551	Alexa Fluor® 610 goat anti-rabbit IgG (H+L) *2 mg/mL*	0.5 mL
A21070	Alexa Fluor® 633 goat anti-rabbit IgG (H+L) *2 mg/mL*	0.5 mL
A31576	Alexa Fluor® 635 goat anti-rabbit IgG (H+L) *2 mg/mL*	0.5 mL
A21244	Alexa Fluor® 647 goat anti-rabbit IgG (H+L) *2 mg/mL*	0.5 mL
A21073	Alexa Fluor® 660 goat anti-rabbit IgG (H+L) *2 mg/mL*	0.5 mL
A21076	Alexa Fluor® 680 goat anti-rabbit IgG (H+L) *2 mg/mL*	0.5 mL
A21038	Alexa Fluor® 700 goat anti-rabbit IgG (H+L) *2 mg/mL*	0.5 mL
A21039	Alexa Fluor® 750 goat anti-rabbit IgG (H+L) *2 mg/mL*	0.5 mL
A21068	Alexa Fluor® 350 goat anti-rabbit IgG (H+L) *highly cross-adsorbed* *2 mg/mL*	0.5 mL
A11034	Alexa Fluor® 488 goat anti-rabbit IgG (H+L) *highly cross-adsorbed* *2 mg/mL*	0.5 mL
A11035	Alexa Fluor® 546 goat anti-rabbit IgG (H+L) *highly cross-adsorbed* *2 mg/mL*	0.5 mL
A21429	Alexa Fluor® 555 goat anti-rabbit IgG (H+L) *highly cross-adsorbed* *2 mg/mL*	0.5 mL
A11036	Alexa Fluor® 568 goat anti-rabbit IgG (H+L) *highly cross-adsorbed* *2 mg/mL*	0.5 mL
A11037	Alexa Fluor® 594 goat anti-rabbit IgG (H+L) *highly cross-adsorbed* *2 mg/mL*	0.5 mL
A21071	Alexa Fluor® 633 goat anti-rabbit IgG (H+L) *highly cross-adsorbed* *2 mg/mL*	0.5 mL
A31577	Alexa Fluor® 635 goat anti-rabbit IgG (H+L) *highly cross-adsorbed* *2 mg/mL*	0.5 mL
A21245	Alexa Fluor® 647 goat anti-rabbit IgG (H+L) *highly cross-adsorbed* *2 mg/mL*	0.5 mL
A21074	Alexa Fluor® 660 goat anti-rabbit IgG (H+L) *highly cross-adsorbed* *2 mg/mL*	0.5 mL
A21109	Alexa Fluor® 680 goat anti-rabbit IgG (H+L) *highly cross-adsorbed* *2 mg/mL*	0.5 mL
A21093	Alexa Fluor® 350 goat anti-rat IgG (H+L) *2 mg/mL*	0.5 mL
A11006	Alexa Fluor® 488 goat anti-rat IgG (H+L) *2 mg/mL*	0.5 mL
A11081	Alexa Fluor® 546 goat anti-rat IgG (H+L) *2 mg/mL*	0.5 mL
A21434	Alexa Fluor® 555 goat anti-rat IgG (H+L) *2 mg/mL*	0.5 mL
A11077	Alexa Fluor® 568 goat anti-rat IgG (H+L) *2 mg/mL*	0.5 mL
A11007	Alexa Fluor® 594 goat anti-rat IgG (H+L) *2 mg/mL*	0.5 mL
A21094	Alexa Fluor® 633 goat anti-rat IgG (H+L) *2 mg/mL*	0.5 mL
A21247	Alexa Fluor® 647 goat anti-rat IgG (H+L) *2 mg/mL*	0.5 mL
A21095	Alexa Fluor® 660 goat anti-rat IgG (H+L) *2 mg/mL*	0.5 mL
A21096	Alexa Fluor® 680 goat anti-rat IgG (H+L) *2 mg/mL*	0.5 mL
A21212	Alexa Fluor® 488 goat anti-rat IgM (μ chain) *2 mg/mL*	250 μL
A21213	Alexa Fluor® 594 goat anti-rat IgM (μ chain) *2 mg/mL*	250 μL
A21248	Alexa Fluor® 647 goat anti-rat IgM (μ chain) *2 mg/mL*	250 μL
A11078	Alexa Fluor® 488 rabbit anti-goat IgG (H+L) *2 mg/mL*	0.5 mL
A21085	Alexa Fluor® 546 rabbit anti-goat IgG (H+L) *2 mg/mL*	0.5 mL
A21431	Alexa Fluor® 555 rabbit anti-goat IgG (H+L) *2 mg/mL*	0.5 mL
A11079	Alexa Fluor® 568 rabbit anti-goat IgG (H+L) *2 mg/mL*	0.5 mL
A11080	Alexa Fluor® 594 rabbit anti-goat IgG (H+L) *2 mg/mL*	0.5 mL
A21086	Alexa Fluor® 633 rabbit anti-goat IgG (H+L) *2 mg/mL*	0.5 mL
A21446	Alexa Fluor® 647 rabbit anti-goat IgG (H+L) *2 mg/mL*	0.5 mL
A21087	Alexa Fluor® 660 rabbit anti-goat IgG (H+L) *2 mg/mL*	0.5 mL
A21088	Alexa Fluor® 680 rabbit anti-goat IgG (H+L) *2 mg/mL*	0.5 mL
A21218	Alexa Fluor® 488 rabbit anti-human IgG (H+L) *2 mg/mL*	0.5 mL
A21062	Alexa Fluor® 350 rabbit anti-mouse IgG (H+L) *2 mg/mL*	0.5 mL
A11059	Alexa Fluor® 488 rabbit anti-mouse IgG (H+L) *2 mg/mL*	0.5 mL
A11060	Alexa Fluor® 546 rabbit anti-mouse IgG (H+L) *2 mg/mL*	0.5 mL
A21427	Alexa Fluor® 555 rabbit anti-mouse IgG (H+L) *2 mg/mL*	0.5 mL
A11061	Alexa Fluor® 568 rabbit anti-mouse IgG (H+L) *2 mg/mL*	0.5 mL
A11062	Alexa Fluor® 594 rabbit anti-mouse IgG (H+L) *2 mg/mL*	0.5 mL
A21063	Alexa Fluor® 633 rabbit anti-mouse IgG (H+L) *2 mg/mL*	0.5 mL
A21239	Alexa Fluor® 647 rabbit anti-mouse IgG (H+L) *2 mg/mL*	0.5 mL
A21064	Alexa Fluor® 660 rabbit anti-mouse IgG (H+L) *2 mg/mL*	0.5 mL
A21065	Alexa Fluor® 680 rabbit anti-mouse IgG (H+L) *2 mg/mL*	0.5 mL
A21210	Alexa Fluor® 488 rabbit anti-rat IgG (H+L) *2 mg/mL*	0.5 mL

For current prices or to order online, visit probes.invitrogen.com

Cat #	Product Name	Unit Size
A21211	Alexa Fluor® 594 rabbit anti-rat IgG (H+L) *2 mg/mL*	0.5 mL
A20980	Alexa Fluor® 610–R-phycoerythrin goat anti-mouse IgG (H+L) *1 mg/mL*	100 µL
A20990	Alexa Fluor® 647–R-phycoerythrin goat anti-mouse IgG (H+L) *1 mg/mL*	100 µL
A20983	Alexa Fluor® 680–R-phycoerythrin goat anti-mouse IgG (H+L) *1 mg/mL*	100 µL
A20981	Alexa Fluor® 610–R-phycoerythrin goat anti-rabbit IgG (H+L) *1 mg/mL*	100 µL
A20991	Alexa Fluor® 647–R-phycoerythrin goat anti-rabbit IgG (H+L) *1 mg/mL*	100 µL
A20984	Alexa Fluor® 680–R-phycoerythrin goat anti-rabbit IgG (H+L) *1 mg/mL*	100 µL
A11053	Alexa Fluor® 488 Signal-Amplification Kit for Fluorescein- and Oregon Green® Dye–Conjugated Probes *60-120 assays*	1 kit
A11054	Alexa Fluor® 488 Signal-Amplification Kit for Mouse Antibodies *60-300 assays*	1 kit
A11066	Alexa Fluor® 568 Signal-Amplification Kit for Mouse Antibodies *60-300 assays*	1 kit
A11067	Alexa Fluor® 594 Signal-Amplification Kit for Mouse Antibodies *60-300 assays*	1 kit
A865	allophycocyanin, crosslinked, goat anti-mouse IgG (H+L) *1 mg/mL*	0.5 mL
A10931	allophycocyanin, crosslinked, goat anti-rabbit IgG (H+L) *1 mg/mL*	0.5 mL
A22170	Amplex® Red ELISA Kit #1 *with goat anti-mouse IgG, horseradish peroxidase conjugate* *1000 assays*	1 kit
A22171	Amplex® Red ELISA Kit #2 *with protein G, horseradish peroxidase conjugate* *1000 assays*	1 kit
B11027	biotin-XX F(ab')$_2$ fragment of goat anti-mouse IgG (H+L) *2 mg/mL*	250 µL
B21078	biotin-XX F(ab')$_2$ fragment of goat anti-rabbit IgG (H+L) *2 mg/mL*	250 µL
B2763	biotin-XX goat anti-mouse IgG (H+L) *2 mg/mL*	0.5 mL
B2770	biotin-XX goat anti-rabbit IgG (H+L) *2 mg/mL*	0.5 mL
B2752	BODIPY® FL goat anti-mouse IgG (H+L)	1 mg
B2766	BODIPY® FL goat anti-rabbit IgG (H+L)	1 mg
C24701	Captivate™ disposable sample chamber *for Captivate™ magnetic yoke* *set of 10*	1 set
C21473	Captivate™ ferrofluid goat anti-mouse IgG (H+L) *0.5 mg Fe/mL*	1 mL
C21474	Captivate™ ferrofluid goat anti-rabbit IgG (H+L) *0.5 mg Fe/mL*	1 mL
C24702	Captivate™ magnetic separator for 96-well microplates	each
C24703	Captivate™ magnetic separator for six microtubes	each
C24700	Captivate™ microscope-mounted magnetic yoke assembly *includes 10 sample chambers*	each
C962	Cascade Blue® goat anti-mouse IgG (H+L) *2 mg/mL*	0.5 mL
C2764	Cascade Blue® goat anti-rabbit IgG (H+L) *2 mg/mL*	0.5 mL
D22185	Diaminobenzidine (DAB) Histochemistry Kit #1 *with goat anti-mouse IgG–HRP*	1 kit
D20698	DSB-X™ biotin donkey anti-goat IgG (H+L) *2 mg/mL*	0.5 mL
D20699	DSB-X™ biotin donkey anti-sheep IgG (H+L) *2 mg/mL*	0.5 mL
D20692	DSB-X™ biotin F(ab')$_2$ fragment of goat anti-mouse IgG (H+L) *2 mg/mL*	250 µL
D20696	DSB-X™ biotin F(ab')$_2$ fragment of goat anti-rabbit IgG (H+L) *2 mg/mL*	250 µL
D20701	DSB-X™ biotin goat anti-chicken IgG (H+L) *2 mg/mL*	0.5 mL
D20700	DSB-X™ biotin goat anti-human IgG (H+L) *2 mg/mL*	0.5 mL
D20690	DSB-X™ biotin goat anti-mouse IgG (H+L) *2 mg/mL*	0.5 mL
D20691	DSB-X™ biotin goat anti-mouse IgG (H+L) *highly cross-adsorbed* *2 mg/mL*	0.5 mL
D20693	DSB-X™ biotin goat anti-mouse IgM (µ chain) *2 mg/mL*	250 µL
D20694	DSB-X™ biotin goat anti-rabbit IgG (H+L) *2 mg/mL*	0.5 mL
D20695	DSB-X™ biotin goat anti-rabbit IgG (H+L) *highly cross-adsorbed* *2 mg/mL*	0.5 mL
D20697	DSB-X™ biotin goat anti-rat IgG (H+L) *2 mg/mL*	0.5 mL
D31590	DyeMer™ 488/605 goat anti-mouse IgG (H+L) *1 mg/mL*	0.5 mL
D31591	DyeMer™ 488/615 goat anti-mouse IgG (H+L) *1 mg/mL*	0.5 mL
D31592	DyeMer™ 488/630 goat anti-mouse IgG (H+L) *1 mg/mL*	0.5 mL
D31600	DyeMer™ 488/605 goat anti-rabbit IgG (H+L) *1 mg/mL*	0.5 mL
D31601	DyeMer™ 488/615 goat anti-rabbit IgG (H+L) *1 mg/mL*	0.5 mL
D31602	DyeMer™ 488/630 goat anti-rabbit IgG (H+L) *1 mg/mL*	0.5 mL
F21452	F(ab')$_2$ fragment of goat anti-mouse IgG (H+L), alkaline phosphatase conjugate	0.5 mg
F21453	F(ab')$_2$ fragment of goat anti-mouse IgG (H+L), horseradish peroxidase conjugate	0.5 mg
F21456	F(ab')$_2$ fragment of goat anti-rabbit IgG (H+L), alkaline phosphatase conjugate	0.5 mg
F2810	fluorescein donkey anti-sheep IgG (H+L) *2 mg/mL*	0.5 mL
F11021	fluorescein F(ab')$_2$ fragment of goat anti-mouse IgG (H+L) *2 mg/mL*	250 µL
F2761	fluorescein goat anti-mouse IgG (H+L) *2 mg/mL*	0.5 mL
F2765	fluorescein goat anti-rabbit IgG (H+L) *2 mg/mL*	0.5 mL
G21060	goat anti-mouse IgG (H+L), alkaline phosphatase conjugate	1 mg
G21061	goat anti-mouse IgG (H+L), CMNB-caged fluorescein conjugate *2 mg/mL*	250 µL
G21040	goat anti-mouse IgG (H+L), horseradish peroxidase conjugate	1 mg
G21079	goat anti-rabbit IgG (H+L), alkaline phosphatase conjugate	1 mg
G21080	goat anti-rabbit IgG (H+L), CMNB-caged fluorescein conjugate *2 mg/mL*	250 µL
G21234	goat anti-rabbit IgG (H+L), horseradish peroxidase conjugate	1 mg
I37150	Image-iT™ FX Kit #1 *with Alexa Fluor® 350 goat anti-mouse IgG (A21049), ProLong® Gold antifade (P36930) and Image-iT™ FX signal enhancer (I36933)*	1 kit

For current prices or to order online, visit probes.invitrogen.com

Product List — 7.2 Secondary Immunoreagents — continued

Cat #	Product Name	Unit Size
I37151	Image-iT™ FX Kit #2 *with Alexa Fluor® 488 goat anti-mouse IgG (A11029), ProLong® Gold antifade (P36930) and Image-iT™ FX signal enhancer (I36933)*	1 kit
I37152	Image-iT™ FX Kit #3 *with Alexa Fluor® 555 goat anti-mouse IgG (A21424), ProLong® Gold antifade (P36930) and Image-iT™ FX signal enhancer (I36933)*	1 kit
I37153	Image-iT™ FX Kit #4 *with Alexa Fluor® 594 goat anti-mouse IgG (A11032), ProLong® Gold antifade (P36930) and Image-iT™ FX signal enhancer (I36933)*	1 kit
I37154	Image-iT™ FX Kit #5 *with Alexa Fluor® 647 goat anti-mouse IgG (A21236), ProLong® Gold antifade (P36930) and Image-iT™ FX signal enhancer (I36933)*	1 kit
I37155	Image-iT™ FX Kit #6 *with Alexa Fluor® 350 goat anti-rabbit IgG (A21068), ProLong® Gold antifade (P36930) and Image-iT™ FX signal enhancer (I36933)*	1 kit
I37156	Image-iT™ FX Kit #7 *with Alexa Fluor® 488 goat anti-rabbit IgG (A11034), ProLong® Gold antifade (P36930) and Image-iT™ FX signal enhancer (I36933)*	1 kit
I37157	Image-iT™ FX Kit #8 *with Alexa Fluor® 555 goat anti-rabbit IgG (A21429), ProLong® Gold antifade (P36930) and Image-iT™ FX signal enhancer (I36933)*	1 kit
I37158	Image-iT™ FX Kit #9 *with Alexa Fluor® 594 goat anti-rabbit IgG (A11037), ProLong® Gold antifade (P36930) and Image-iT™ FX signal enhancer (I36933)*	1 kit
I37159	Image-iT™ FX Kit #10 *with Alexa Fluor® 647 goat anti-rabbit IgG (A21245), ProLong® Gold antifade (P36930) and Image-iT™ FX signal enhancer (I36933)*	1 kit
I36933	Image-iT™ FX signal enhancer	10 mL
L24919	LI Silver (LIS) Enhancement Kit	1 kit
M10991	Marina Blue® goat anti-mouse IgG (H+L) *2 mg/mL*	0.5 mL
M10992	Marina Blue® goat anti-rabbit IgG (H+L) *2 mg/mL*	0.5 mL
N24915	NANOGOLD® Fab' fragment of goat anti-mouse IgG *80 µg protein/mL*	1 mL
N24916	NANOGOLD® Fab' fragment of goat anti-rabbit IgG *80 µg protein/mL*	1 mL
N24917	NANOGOLD® Fab' fragment of rabbit anti-goat IgG *80 µg protein/mL*	1 mL
O6380	Oregon Green® 488 goat anti-mouse IgG (H+L) *2 mg/mL*	0.5 mL
O11033	Oregon Green® 488 goat anti-mouse IgG (H+L) *highly cross-adsorbed* *2 mg/mL*	0.5 mL
O6381	Oregon Green® 488 goat anti-rabbit IgG (H+L) *2 mg/mL*	0.5 mL
O11038	Oregon Green® 488 goat anti-rabbit IgG (H+L) *highly cross-adsorbed* *2 mg/mL*	0.5 mL
O6382	Oregon Green® 488 goat anti-rat IgG (H+L) *2 mg/mL*	0.5 mL
O6383	Oregon Green® 514 goat anti-mouse IgG (H+L) *2 mg/mL*	0.5 mL
P10993	Pacific Blue™ goat anti-mouse IgG (H+L) *2 mg/mL*	0.5 mL
P10994	Pacific Blue™ goat anti-rabbit IgG (H+L) *2 mg/mL*	0.5 mL
P21129	R-phycoerythrin goat anti-mouse IgG_1 (γ1) conjugate *1 mg/mL*	250 µL
P21139	R-phycoerythrin goat anti-mouse IgG_{2a} (γ2a) conjugate *1 mg/mL*	250 µL
P21149	R-phycoerythrin goat anti-mouse IgG_{2b} (γ2b) conjugate *1 mg/mL*	250 µL
P852	R-phycoerythrin goat anti-mouse IgG (H+L) *1 mg/mL*	1 mL
P2771MP	R-phycoerythrin goat anti-rabbit IgG (H+L) *1 mg/mL*	0.5 mL
P11047	protein A, Alexa Fluor® 488 conjugate	1 mg
P11049	protein A, Alexa Fluor® 546 conjugate	1 mg
P11050	protein A, Alexa Fluor® 568 conjugate	1 mg
P11051	protein A, Alexa Fluor® 594 conjugate	1 mg
P21107	protein A, Alexa Fluor® 633 conjugate	1 mg
P21462	protein A, Alexa Fluor® 647 conjugate	1 mg
P11065	protein G, Alexa Fluor® 488 conjugate	1 mg
P21041	protein G, horseradish peroxidase conjugate	1 mg
R21458	rabbit anti-goat IgG (H+L), alkaline phosphatase conjugate	1 mg
R21459	rabbit anti-goat IgG (H+L), horseradish peroxidase conjugate	1 mg
R21455	rabbit anti-mouse IgG (H+L), horseradish peroxidase conjugate	1 mg
R6393	Rhodamine Red™-X goat anti-mouse IgG (H+L) *2 mg/mL*	0.5 mL
R6394	Rhodamine Red™-X goat anti-rabbit IgG (H+L) *2 mg/mL*	0.5 mL
T2762	tetramethylrhodamine goat anti-mouse IgG (H+L) *2 mg/mL*	0.5 mL
T2769	tetramethylrhodamine goat anti-rabbit IgG (H+L) *2 mg/mL*	0.5 mL
T862	Texas Red® goat anti-mouse IgG (H+L) *2 mg/mL*	0.5 mL
T2767	Texas Red® goat anti-rabbit IgG (H+L) *2 mg/mL*	0.5 mL
T6390	Texas Red®-X goat anti-mouse IgG (H+L) *2 mg/mL*	0.5 mL
T6391	Texas Red®-X goat anti-rabbit IgG (H+L) *2 mg/mL*	0.5 mL
T6392	Texas Red®-X goat anti-rat IgG (H+L) *2 mg/mL*	0.5 mL

For current prices or to order online, visit probes.invitrogen.com

7.3 Zenon® Technology: Versatile Reagents for Immunolabeling

Our exceptional Zenon® immunolabeling technology provides an easy, versatile and truly unique method of labeling antibodies with Molecular Probes' premier dyes, haptens and enzymes. This enabling technology not only eliminates the need for secondary detection reagents in many applications, but also simplifies immunolabeling applications that previously were time consuming or impractical, including the use of multiple antibodies derived from the same species in the same protocol,[1–4] as well as the detection of antibody binding in tissues when both the antibody and the tissue are derived from the same species. Moreover, Zenon® immunolabeling technology permits the rapid and quantitative preparation of antibody complexes from a purified antibody fraction or from a crude antibody preparation such as serum, ascites fluid or a hybridoma supernatant. Our Zenon® reagents may eventually be the only antibody-based detection reagents needed in the laboratory for many high-throughput applications, replacing both direct conjugates of primary antibodies and dye- and enzyme-labeled secondary antibodies in a wide variety of procedures.

The Zenon® labeling method takes advantage of the immunoselectivity of the antibody binding reaction by forming a complex between an intact primary IgG antibody and a fluorophore-, biotin- or enzyme-labeled Fab fragment directed against the Fc portion of that IgG (Figure 7.59). Simple mixing of the labeled Fab fragment, which is supplied in the Zenon® Antibody Labeling Kits, with the corresponding primary antibody quantitatively produces the Fab–antibody complex in under 10 minutes, with no pre- or postlabeling purification required. This labeled Fab–antibody complex can be immediately used to stain cells, tissues[1] and other targets in the same manner as a covalently labeled primary antibody.

We currently offer Zenon® Labeling Kits for use with mouse IgG_1, mouse IgG_{2a}, mouse IgG_{2b}, rabbit IgG, goat IgG and human IgG antibodies (see Note 7.2 "Technical Focus: Antibody Structure and Classification" in Section 7.2), each of which contains a Zenon® labeling reagent comprising Fab fragments generated from goat secondary antibodies — or in the case of the Zenon® labeling reagents for goat IgG antibodies, from rabbit secondary antibodies — directed against the Fc portion of the corresponding primary antibody and covalently labeled with an extensive assortment of detectable labels (Table 7.13). These labels include our outstanding Alexa Fluor® dyes (Section 1.3), as well as phycobiliproteins (Section 6.4), tandem conjugates of phycobiliproteins with Alexa Fluor® dyes (Section 6.4; Figure 6.34, Figure 6.37), enzymes (horseradish peroxidase and alkaline phosphatase), biotin, DSB-X™ biotin and some conventional dyes such as fluorescein. Because they are derived from secondary antibodies directed against the Fc portion of a particular antibody class (and subclass, in the case of the Zenon® Mouse IgG Labeling Kits), the Zenon® labeling reagents are selective for antibody type and species, and they form the most stable complexes when used for labeling the corresponding antibody; these reagents show quite low reactivity with antibodies isolated from other species.

Our wide selection of Zenon® Kits can be mixed and matched in the same experimental protocol and even in the same cell-labeling solution, providing the freedom to experiment with multiple dye–antibody combinations in flow cytometry and imaging applications. In addition, we offer Zenon® Mouse IgG_1 Labeling Kits enhanced with TSA technology (Z25090, Z25091), which combine the advantages of Zenon® labeling technology with the sensitivity of tyramide signal amplification (TSA). A special web site location (probes.invitrogen.com/zenon) has been established for direct access to information on our Zenon® labeling technology.

Molecular Probes' Zenon® technology has many outstanding features that will undoubtedly make it a preferred method for immunolabeling and will open several new avenues for research and development. These features, which are discussed in detail later in this section, include:

- Labeling of a primary antibody is *very* fast. The Zenon® complex is ready for use in cell-labeling protocols in less than 10 minutes. In the absence of competing antibodies of the same species, the Zenon® complex can also be stored for later use.
- Labeling can be quantitative with respect to the primary antibody. Furthermore, the extent of antibody labeling (and thus the intensity of the fluorophore or activity of a conjugated enzyme) can be adjusted by changing the molar ratio of the dye- or enzyme-labeled Fab fragment to the primary antibody. In flow cytometry, this unique property of the Zenon® reagents even permits use of the same fluorescent color to label two or more cell populations in the same sample.
- Our dye- and enzyme-labeled Fab fragments have been affinity purified during their preparation to ensure their high affinity and selectivity for the Fc portion of the corresponding primary antibody. Furthermore, our procedure for chemical labeling of the Fab fragments protects the Fc-binding site, resulting in more active labeling reagents.
- Like covalently labeled primary antibodies, the Zenon® complexes formed with the Zenon® Mouse IgG, Zenon® Rabbit IgG, Zenon® Goat IgG and Zenon® Human IgG Labeling Kits can be used to label mouse, rabbit, goat and human tissue, respectively, without introducing nonspecific background. However, the Zenon® complexes are much easier to prepare and more versatile than covalently labeled primary antibodies, and they show higher activity because only the Fc portion of the primary antibody is labeled, leaving the antigen-binding sites available for cell and tissue labeling.
- Zenon® reagents provide reliable and reproducible labeling of even submicrogram quantities of a primary antibody, resulting in very little waste of valuable reagents. Furthermore, the Zenon® Labeling Kits permit easy and efficient labeling of antibodies that are not commercially available as direct conjugates.

- Because it is based on immunoselectivity, the Zenon® labeling method does not require removal of exogenous proteins such as serum albumin or amine-containing buffers from the antibody prior to complex formation, as would be necessary with any chemical labeling procedure.
- Zenon® technology makes it very easy to change fluorescent color combinations or detection methodologies by simply using a different dye- or enzyme-labeled Fab fragment from our extensive selection of Zenon® Labeling Kits (Table 7.13). Consequently, there is no need to purchase several directly conjugated primary antibodies for multicolor experiments.
- We have determined that the fluorescence intensity, enzymatic activity and utility of the Fab–antibody complexes formed with the Zenon® Labeling Kits are usually similar to the properties of

Table 7.13 — Molecular Probes' Zenon® Labeling Kits

Label	Abs/Em *	Mouse IgG_1 Labeling Kit †	Mouse IgG_{2a} Labeling Kit †	Mouse IgG_{2b} Labeling Kit †	Rabbit IgG Labeling Kit †	Goat IgG Labeling Kit	Human IgG Labeling Kit
Alexa Fluor® dyes							
Alexa Fluor® 350	346/442	Z25000	Z25100	Z25200	Z25300		Z25400
Alexa Fluor® 405	402/421	Z25013	Z25113	Z25213	Z25313		
Alexa Fluor® 430	434/539	Z25001			Z25301		
Alexa Fluor® 488	495/519	Z25002 Z25090 ‡	Z25102	Z25202	Z25302	Z25602	Z25402
Alexa Fluor® 532	531/554	Z25003			Z25303		
Alexa Fluor® 546	556/573	Z25004	Z25104	Z25204	Z25304		
Alexa Fluor® 555	555/565	Z25005	Z25105	Z25205	Z25305	Z25605	Z25405
Alexa Fluor® 568	578/603	Z25006 Z25091 ‡	Z25106	Z25206	Z25306	Z25606	
Alexa Fluor® 594	590/617	Z25007	Z25107	Z25207	Z25307	Z25607	Z25407
Alexa Fluor® 647	650/668	Z25008	Z25108	Z25208	Z25308	Z25608	Z25408
Alexa Fluor® 660	663/690	Z25009	Z25109	Z25209	Z25309		
Alexa Fluor® 680	679/702	Z25010	Z25110	Z25210	Z25310		
Alexa Fluor® 700	702/723	Z25011			Z25311		
Alexa Fluor® 750	749/775				Z25312		
Classic dyes							
Marina Blue®	365/460	Z25040			Z25340		
Pacific Blue™	410/455	Z25041			Z25341		
Fluorescein	494/518	Z25042			Z25342		
Oregon Green® 488	496/524	Z25043			Z25343		
Texas Red®-X	595/615	Z25045			Z25345		
Biotins							
Biotin-XX	NA	Z25052	Z25152	Z25252	Z25352		Z25452
DSB-X™ biotin §	NA	Z25053					
Phycobiliproteins and Alexa Fluor® dye–phycobiliprotein tandem conjugates							
R-Phycoerythrin (R-PE)	496, 546, 565 **/578	Z25055	Z25155	Z25255	Z25355		Z25455
Alexa Fluor® 610–R-PE	496, 546, 565 **/628	Z25020					
Alexa Fluor® 647–R-PE	496, 546, 565 **/668	Z25021	Z25121	Z25221			
Alexa Fluor® 680–R-PE	496, 546, 565 **/702	Z25022					
Allophycocyanin (APC)	650/660	Z25051	Z25151	Z25251	Z25351		Z25451
Alexa Fluor® 700–APC	650/723	Z25030					
Alexa Fluor® 750–APC	650/775	Z25031					
Enzymes							
Horseradish peroxidase	NA	Z25054	Z25154	Z25254	Z25354		Z25454
Alkaline phosphatase	NA	Z25050	Z25150	Z25250	Z25350		
Tricolor labeling kits							
Kit #1: Alexa Fluor® 488, 555, 647	see above	Z25060	Z25160	Z25260	Z25360		Z25460
Kit #2: Alexa Fluor® 350, 488, 594	see above	Z25070	Z25170	Z25270	Z25370		Z25470
Kit #3: Alexa Fluor® 488, R-PE, Alexa Fluor® 647–R-PE	see above	Z25080	Z25180	Z25280			

* Approximate absorption and emission maxima, in nm. † Mouse IgG_1 primary antibodies are listed in Table 7.14, mouse IgG_{2a} primary antibodies in Table 7.15; mouse IgG_{2b} primary antibodies in Table 7.16; and rabbit IgG_1 primary antibodies in Table 7.17. ‡ These Zenon® Antibody Labeling Kits are enhanced with TSA technology. § DSB-X™ = Desthiobiotin-X. ** Multiple absorption peaks. NA = Not applicable.

directly conjugated primary antibodies. The fluorescence intensity will depend to some extent on the molar ratio of Fab fragment to antibody used during labeling.

- It should be possible to automate the preparation of an optimal Zenon® complex, which may make it practical to label minute amounts of antibodies directly in microplates or in miniaturized devices.
- Essentially any dye or other detectable label can be used in the preparation of a Zenon® labeling reagent. The Zenon® Antibody Labeling Kits containing our premier Alexa Fluor® dyes, phycobiliproteins, horseradish peroxidase (HRP), alkaline phosphatase, biotin and other labels are available (Table 7.13).

Significant Features of Molecular Probes' Zenon® Technology

Zenon® Immunolabeling Is Rapid and Quantitative

Labeling of a suitable primary antibody with the Zenon® Antibody Labeling Kits is *very* fast. The Zenon® labeling reagent contains dye- or enzyme-labeled Fab fragments that have been affinity purified to ensure their high affinity for the Fc portion of the corresponding primary antibody. We recommend incubation of the Zenon® labeling reagent with the appropriate primary antibody for five minutes, followed by a five-minute blocking reaction of any remaining labeled Fab fragments with excess nonspecific IgG. However, the actual rates of the complex formation and IgG blocking steps are likely to be even faster and may occur within the mixing time of the components (Figure 7.60).

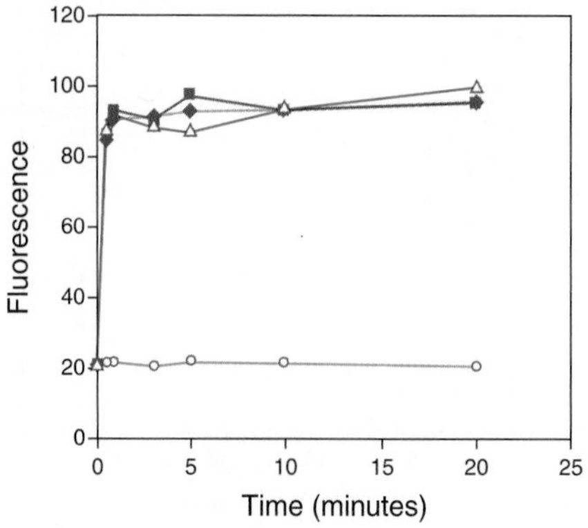

Figure 7.60 Formation of antibody–Fab complexes. An anti-biotin mouse IgG_1 monoclonal antibody (A11242) was mixed with the Zenon® Alexa Fluor® 488 labeling reagent (a component of Kit Z25002) for varying time intervals before the reaction was quenched by the addition of excess mouse IgG blocking reagent. The quenched reactions were then added to a microplate well containing biotinylated bovine serum albumin and incubated for 20 minutes. After washing, the fluorescence of the remaining bound signal was measured. Binding was found to be essentially complete in less than five minutes. Three trials are shown, along with a control (○) where no labeling reagent was added.

Fab–antibody complex formation can be quantitative with respect to the primary antibody (Figure 7.61). Furthermore, the degree of labeling (and thus the intensity of the fluorophore or activity of a conjugated enzyme) can be adjusted to some extent by changing the molar ratio of the labeled Fab fragment to the primary antibody. We find that approximately equal *weights* of a dye-labeled Fab fragment generated from a goat anti-Fc antibody (MW ~50,000 daltons) and the intact mouse primary antibody (MW ~150,000 daltons) — a 3:1 *molar* ratio of the labeled Fab fragment to the primary antibody — yields an Fab–antibody complex that is suitable for most applications. Thus, the 50 µg of labeled Fab fragments in the Zenon® labeling reagent provided in the organic dye–based Zenon® Labeling Kits is sufficient for labeling approximately 50 µg of the corresponding intact IgG antibody; we have defined "one labeling" in all of our Zenon® Labeling Kits as the amount of Zenon® labeling reagent required for labeling 1 µg of an intact primary antibody. Increasing the molar (or weight) ratio of the Zenon® labeling reagent to the antibody can yield a somewhat brighter conjugate and ensure quantitative utilization of the primary antibody, whereas decreasing the ratio can yield a somewhat less fluorescent complex.

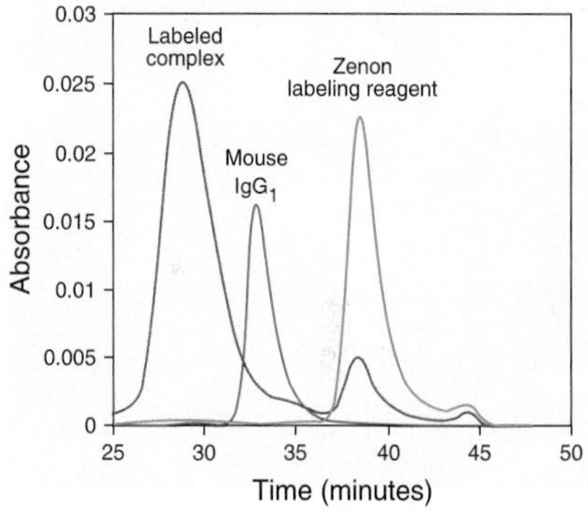

Figure 7.61 High-performance size-exclusion chromatographic analysis of the Zenon® Alexa Fluor® 488 labeling reagent (a component of Kit Z25002) binding to a mouse IgG_1 antibody. The Zenon® labeling reagent peak appears at 38 minutes; the mouse IgG_1 peak appears at 33 minutes. When combined at a molar ratio of ~5:1 (Zenon® labeling reagent: IgG_1), the IgG_1 antibody is quantitatively converted to a labeled complex, which appears as a peak at 29 minutes.

The ability to adjust the fluorescence intensity (or enzymatic activity) of a labeled complex is a feature of the Zenon® technology that is not at all practical with direct chemical labeling of antibodies. This property also permits the researcher to rapidly optimize the *best* complex for their experiment, rather than depending on the quite variable degree of substitution that is typical of covalently labeled antibodies from different commercial sources or from chemical labeling in the research laboratory. A *molar* ratio of three moles of the Zenon® labeling reagent to one mole of the primary antibody is also suitable for labeling with the phycobiliprotein- and enzyme-derived Zenon® labeling reagents. The Zenon® Labeling Kits containing a phycobiliprotein- or enzyme-labeled Fab fragment include sufficient reagents for labeling ~25 µg of an intact primary antibody; the Zenon® Labeling Kits containing an Alexa Fluor® dye–phycobiliprotein tandem conjugate include sufficient reagents for labeling ~10 µg of a primary antibody.

Zenon® Technology Simplifies the Use of Multiple Antibodies of the Same Isotype in the Same Protocol

Unlike detection with secondary antibodies, the Zenon® immunolabeling technology allows staining of a cell or tissue sample with multiple antibodies of the same isotype. Our affinity purification of the Zenon® labeling reagent (which we perform subsequent to dye or enzyme conjugation) ensures that the formation of the Fab–antibody complex is stable. Reversal of Zenon® complex formation by the excess of nonspecific IgG that is used to quench any uncom-

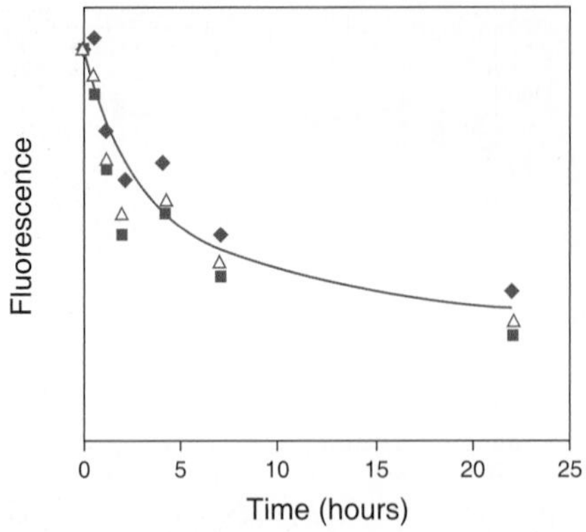

Figure 7.62 Stability of antibody–Fab complexes. An anti-biotin mouse IgG_1 monoclonal antibody (A11242) labeled with the Zenon® Alexa Fluor® 488 labeling reagent (a component of Kit Z25002) was rapidly diluted with excess mouse IgG blocking reagent. At the specified time points, a sample was removed and added to a microplate well containing biotinylated bovine serum albumin and incubated for 20 minutes. After washing, the fluorescence of the remaining bound signal was measured.

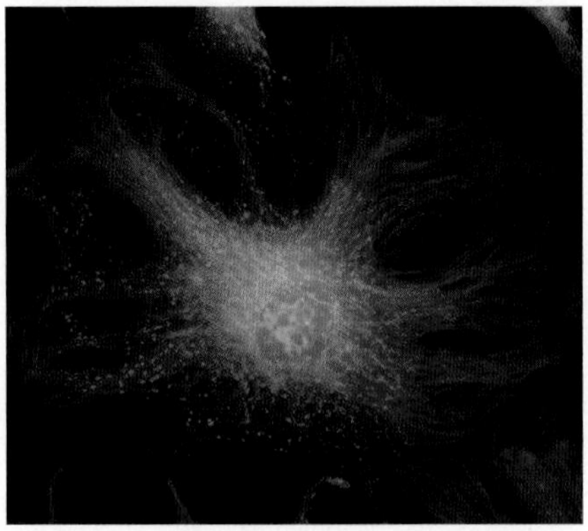

Figure 7.63 Bovine pulmonary artery endothelial cells labeled with probes for tubulin and the mitochondria. Tubulin was detected with an anti-α-tubulin mouse IgG_{2b} monoclonal antibody prelabeled with the Zenon® Alexa Fluor® 488 Mouse IgG_{2b} Labeling Kit (Z25202), and mitochondria were labeled using an anti-OxPhos Complex V subunit α, mouse IgG_{2b} monoclonal antibody (A21350) prelabeled with the Zenon® Alexa Fluor® 555 Mouse IgG_{2b} Labeling Kit (Z25205). The nucleus was stained with DAPI (D1306, D3571, D21490).

plexed Zenon® labeling reagent does occur (Figure 7.62), particularly at temperatures above room temperature. However, the stability of the complex is sufficient to allow sequential (or simultaneous) labeling of different targets in cells and tissues with multiple antibody complexes (Figure 7.63, Figure 7.64, Figure 7.68, Figure 7.71, Figure 7.85, Figure 15.78). Subsequent to staining, an aldehyde-based fixation step can permanently block the transfer of Zenon® labels between different primary antibodies and will preserve the staining pattern. Zenon® complexes can be combined with each other or with directly labeled primary antibodies, with labeled secondary antibodies to primary antibodies derived from other species, with antibodies that lack an Fc fragment and with avidin–biotin techniques (Section 7.6) for multiplexed immunolabeling. Some crossreactivity of the Zenon® labeling reagent with the Fc portion of antibodies from other species may occur unless the excess Zenon® labeling reagent is captured with the soluble nonspecific IgG included in the Zenon® Labeling Kits. Alternatively, the excess Zenon® labeling reagent from the Zenon® Mouse IgG Labeling Kits can be captured and removed entirely from the labeled complexes by agarose-immobilized mouse IgG (M25500).

Zenon® Immunolabeling Is Reliable, Even with Very Small Quantities of Reagents

Formation of the Fab–antibody complex with the Zenon® Labeling Kits is extremely reliable and reproducible, even with very small (submicrogram) amounts of primary antibody. Successful chemical labeling of submicrogram quantities of an antibody with a succinimidyl ester or an isothiocyanate of a dye is just not possible; chemical labeling and purification of proteins usually requires at least 100 µg of the carrier-free protein. Furthermore, because submicrogram amounts of an immunolabeling complex may be all that are required for an experiment, there is absolutely no waste of expensive or difficult-to-obtain antibodies when using the Zenon® Labeling Kits. Additionally, optimization of the degree of labeling by a dye or an enzyme is trivial, as compared with any chemical labeling method. Although Molecular Probes defines "one labeling" in its Zenon® Labeling Kits as the amount of Zenon® labeling reagent required for labeling 1 µg of the primary antibody, we routinely label about 0.4 µg of the primary antibody dissolved in 2 µL of a buffer.

Unfortunately, many providers of mouse monoclonal antibodies do not indicate how much of the pure antibody they provide in their products. Furthermore, these antibodies are frequently supplied diluted with an albumin or other carrier protein, which precludes estimation of the antibody concentration from the optical density at 280 nm. However, the ease of preparing Zenon® complexes makes it practical to rapidly optimize the labeling reagent, even when the amount of primary antibody in the sample is unknown.

Zenon® technology should be readily adaptable for use in microplates or miniaturized devices. Microfluidic delivery technology should permit automated formation of Zenon® complexes and staining of cells and tissues using less than nanograms of a Zenon® labeling reagent and the antibody for high-throughput applications. Because the Zenon® labeling reagent is monovalent, the Zenon® complexes are not immunoprecipitated during the labeling.

Zenon® Immunolabeling Does Not Require Antibody Pre-Purification

Unlike chemically modifying antibodies, labeling antibodies with the Zenon® Labeling Kits does not require removal of exogenous proteins such as serum albumin from the antibody. Serum albumin is frequently added to laboratory-derived or commercially supplied antibodies to help preserve the activity of dilute solutions of antibodies. Because the Zenon® labeling reagent selectively binds only to the Fc portion of the primary antibody, there should be limited or no effect of exogenous proteins that do not have an Fc fragment. Furthermore, the Zenon® labeling reagents function equally well when used to label a purified antibody or a crude antibody preparation such as serum, ascites fluid or a hybridoma supernatant. Furthermore, Zenon® labeling is usually quite successful with even dilute solutions of a primary antibody, as well as with antibodies that are dissolved in amine-containing buffers such as Tris.

Zenon® Technology Is Versatile and Cost-Effective

Once conjugated to the appropriate Fab fragment, essentially any dye or other detectable label can be used in the form of a Zenon® labeling reagent. We currently offer Zenon® Labeling Kits containing a wide selection of different fluorescent labels (Table 7.13) whose spectra span the ultraviolet, visible and near infrared (full spectra of most of these dyes are in Section 7.1). The Zenon® technology makes it particularly easy to change fluorescent colors or detection methodologies by simply using a different Zenon® labeling reagent from our extensive selection of Zenon® Labeling Kits (Table 7.13). There is no more need to purchase multiple direct conjugates of the same mouse primary antibody (such as with the cluster of differentiation (CD) antibodies) just to perform multicolor flow cytometry (Figure 7.65) and imaging protocols. Furthermore, Zenon® labeling utilizes an unlabeled primary antibody, which is usually less expensive than the directly conjugated antibody, particularly for direct conjugates of primary antibodies with phycobiliproteins and enzymes.

The Zenon® Labeling Kits that include R-phycoerythrin and allophycocyanin conjugates of the appropriate Fab fragment permit the efficient and cost-effective indirect labeling of a wide variety of primary antibodies for flow cytometry applications, including many of the CD antibodies that currently are not commercially available as direct conjugates. Molecular Probes has also developed Zenon® Labeling Kits that utilize our Alexa Fluor® dye–phycobiliprotein tandem conjugates (Section 6.4; Figure 6.34, Figure 6.37) to further expand the range of labels available (Table 7.13).

Zenon® Mouse IgG, Zenon® Rabbit IgG and Zenon® Human IgG Labeling Kits are also available for labeling antibodies with HRP or alkaline phosphatase (Table 7.13). Several applications of these Zenon® Labeling Kits for cytochemistry and histochemistry are described below. Zenon® Biotin-XX and DSB-X™ Biotin Antibody Labeling Kits are also available (Table 7.13). Our exclusive DSB-X™ biotin technology, which is described in detail in Section 7.6, permits completely reversible binding of avidin and streptavidin conjugates at neutral pH and in physiologically compatible buffers. Custom Zenon® labeling reagents and Zenon® Labeling Kits are also available from Molecular Probes. Please contact our Custom and Bulk Sales Department.

The fluorescence intensity or enzymatic activity of a Zenon® complex prepared using our protocol is usually similar to that of the corresponding directly labeled conjugate of the primary antibody, although it is typically somewhat lower than the intensity that can be obtained using a labeled secondary antibody. If necessary, the sensitivity of the assay can be greatly increased through use of a Zenon® complex in combination with a signal amplification method such as our TSA or ELF® technology (Section 6.2, Section 6.3); see below for a description of our Zenon® Mouse IgG_1 Labeling Kits enhanced with TSA technology (Z25090, Z25091).

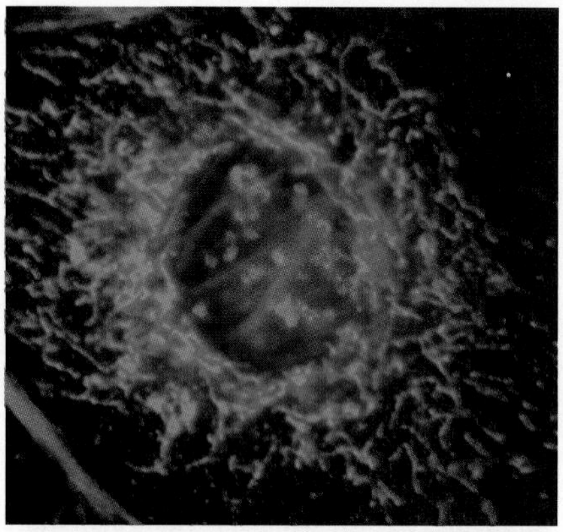

Figure 7.64 Bovine pulmonary artery endothelial cells labeled with probes for actin, mitochondria and the phosphorylated form of histone H3. Actin was labeled with blue-fluorescent Alexa Fluor® 350 phalloidin (A22281), and phosphorylated histone H3 was detected using a rabbit anti–phosphohistone H3 antibody prelabeled with the Zenon® Alexa Fluor® 555 Rabbit IgG Labeling Kit (red fluorescence, Z25305). Endogenous biotin associated with the mitochondria was labeled using streptavidin (S888) followed by a rabbit anti-streptavidin antibody prelabeled with the Zenon® Alexa Fluor® 488 Rabbit IgG Labeling Kit (green fluorescence, Z25302).

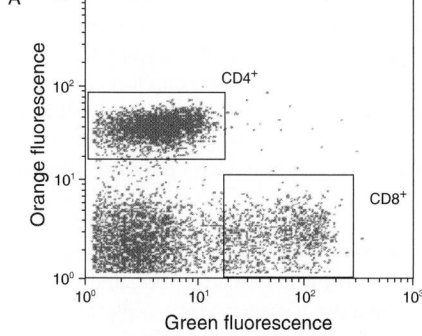

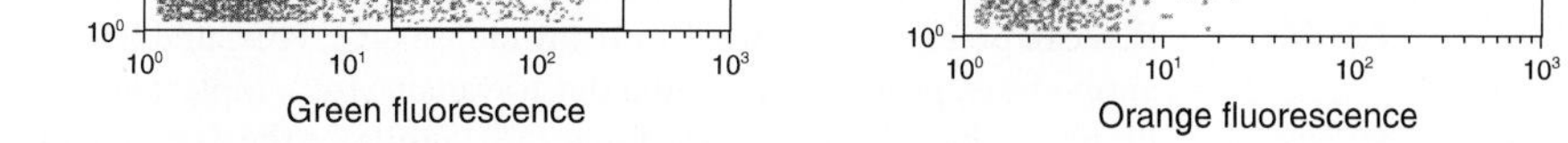

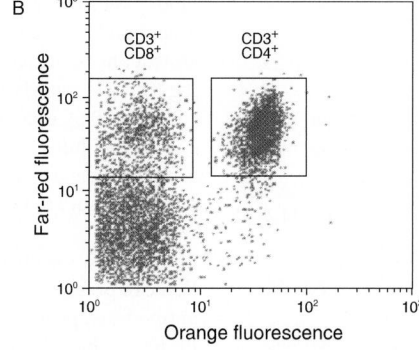

Figure 7.65 Human peripheral blood lymphocytes were stained with the following three antibodies: an anti-CD3 mouse IgG_1 antibody (A21330) prelabeled with the Zenon® Alexa Fluor® 647 Mouse IgG_1 Labeling Kit (Z25008), an anti-CD4 mouse IgG_1 antibody (A21334) prelabeled with the Zenon® R-Phycoerythrin Mouse IgG_1 Labeling Kit (Z25055) and an anti-CD8 mouse IgG_{2a} antibody (A21338) prelabeled with the Zenon® Alexa Fluor® 488 Mouse IgG_{2a} Labeling Kit (Z25102). Panels A and B show that cells can be separated by plotting the orange-fluorescent versus green-fluorescent signal or red-fluorescent versus orange-fluorescent signal, respectively, demonstrating that the Zenon® label does not transfer to other antibodies in the same sample. The samples were analyzed on a Coulter Elite flow cytometer using 488 nm excitation for R-phycoerythrin and the Alexa Fluor® 488 dye, and 633 nm excitation for the Alexa Fluor® 647 dye.

Table 7.14 — Molecular Probes' mouse IgG_1 monoclonal antibodies

Cat #	Antibody	Handbook Section(s)
Antibodies against yeast proteins		
A6427	vacuolar H^+-ATPase 60,000-dalton subunit	Section 7.5, Section 12.3
A6428	vacuolar carboxypeptidase Y	Section 7.5, Section 12.3
A6429	dolichol phosphate mannose synthase	Section 7.5
A6432	OxPhos Complex IV subunit IV	Section 7.5, Section 12.2
A6449	mitochondrial porin	Section 7.5, Section 12.2
A6457	3-phosphoglycerate kinase	Section 7.5, Section 12.3
A6458	vacuolar alkaline phosphatase	Section 7.5, Section 12.3
A21273	Pep12p	Section 7.5, Section 12.3
Antibodies against mammalian mitochondrial proteins		
A21344	OxPhos Complex I 39,000-dalton subunit	Section 7.5, Section 12.2
A21343	OxPhos Complex I 30,000-dalton subunit	Section 7.5, Section 12.2
A31857	OxPhos Complex I 20,000-dalton subunit	Section 7.5, Section 12.2
A31856	OxPhos Complex I 15,000-dalton subunit	Section 7.5, Section 12.2
A11142	OxPhos Complex II 70,000-dalton subunit	Section 7.5, Section 12.2
A21362	OxPhos Complex III core 1 subunit	Section 7.5, Section 12.2
A11143	OxPhos Complex III core 2 subunit	Section 7.5, Section 12.2
A21365	OxPhos Complex IV subunit VIa-L	Section 7.5, Section 12.2
A21366	OxPhos Complex IV subunit VIb	Section 7.5, Section 12.2
A21368	OxPhos Complex IV subunit VIIb	Section 7.5, Section 12.2
A21351	OxPhos Complex V β subunit	Section 7.5, Section 12.2
A21354	OxPhos Complex V OSCP subunit	Section 7.5, Section 12.2
A21355	OxPhos Complex V inhibitor protein	Section 7.5, Section 12.2
A21323	pyruvate dehydrogenase E1α subunit	Section 7.5, Section 12.2
A21324	pyruvate dehydrogenase E1β subunit	Section 7.5, Section 12.2
A21325	pyruvate dehydrogenase E2 subunit	Section 7.5, Section 12.2
Antibodies against other cellular proteins, epitope tags and antigens		
A11242	biotin	Section 7.4
A21300	bromodeoxyuridine (BrdU)	Section 7.5, Section 15.4
A21330	CD3	Section 7.5
A21334	CD4	Section 7.5
A21280	c-myc	Section 7.5
A21322	cyclin D3	Section 7.5, Section 15.4
A21283	desmin	Section 7.5, Section 11.2
A21270	golgin-97	Section 7.5, Section 12.4
A21282	glial fibrillary acidic protein (GFAP)	Section 7.5, Section 11.2
A11121	green-fluorescent protein (GFP)	Section 7.5
A11130	human transferrin receptor	Section 7.5, Section 16.1
A21277	HuR mRNA-binding protein	Section 7.5
P21315	Penta·His	Section 7.5, Section 9.4
A11126	α-tubulin	Section 7.5, Section 11.2

Zenon® Labeling Kits and Their Applications

Zenon® Antibody Labeling Kits for Mouse IgG, Rabbit IgG, Goat IgG and Human IgG

Molecular Probes currently offers Zenon® Labeling Kits for six classes of primary antibodies: Zenon® Mouse IgG_1 Labeling Kits, Zenon® Mouse IgG_{2a} Labeling Kits, Zenon® Mouse IgG_{2b} Labeling Kits, Zenon® Rabbit IgG Labeling Kits, Zenon® Goat IgG Labeling Kits and Zenon® Human IgG Labeling Kits. These Zenon® Labeling Kits, all of which are listed in Table 7.13, are of three types:

- Zenon® Labeling Kits that contain an affinity-purified Fab fragment of a goat anti-Fc antibody (or, in the case of the Zenon® Goat IgG Labeling Kits, a rabbit anti-Fc antibody) that has been conjugated to one of our premier Alexa Fluor® dyes (Section 1.3), to our patented Marina Blue®, Cascade Blue®, Pacific Blue™, Oregon Green® 488 and Texas Red®-X dyes or to fluorescein, biotin-XX or DSB-X™ biotin (desthiobiotin).
- Zenon® Labeling Kits with a phycobiliprotein-labeled Fab fragment of a goat anti-Fc antibody (Section 6.4) — including Zenon® Labeling Kits containing one of our five tandem conjugates of R-PE or APC with the long-wavelength Alexa Fluor® dyes — for facile labeling of primary antibodies, particularly for applications in multicolor flow cytometry.
- Zenon® Labeling Kits containing HRP or alkaline phosphatase conjugates for use in any enzyme-amplified protocol, including immunohistochemical applications, TSA (Section 6.2), ELF® (Section 6.3) and ELISAs (Section 7.2); see below for a description of our Zenon® Mouse IgG_1 Labeling Kits enhanced with TSA technology (Z25090, Z25091).

In addition to the above Zenon® Labeling Kits, we have available three different types of Zenon® Tricolor Labeling Kits for mouse IgG antibodies,[5] rabbit IgG and human IgG antibodies (Table 7.13). The Zenon® Tricolor Labeling Kit #1 contains 10 µg each of the Alexa Fluor® 488, Alexa Fluor® 555 and Alexa Fluor® 647 Zenon® labeling reagents. This kit is designed for optimal triple-antibody staining with confocal laser-scanning microscopes equipped with an Ar–Kr mixed-gas laser, but it can also be used with any suitably equipped fluorescence microscope. The Zenon® Tricolor Labeling Kit #2 contains 10 µg each of the Alexa Fluor® 350, Alexa Fluor® 488 and Alexa Fluor® 594 Zenon® labeling reagents, yielding simultaneous blue-, green- and red-fluorescent immunostaining that is useful with almost any fluorescence microscope. The Zenon® Tricolor Labeling Kit #3 is especially suitable for flow cytometry applications and contains 10 µg each of the Alexa Fluor® 488, R-phycoerythrin (R-PE) and Alexa Fluor® 647–R-PE Zenon® labeling reagents, which are all excited efficiently with an argon-ion laser and have minimal spectral overlap (Figure 6.34).

The subtype-selective Zenon® Mouse IgG_1, IgG_{2a} and IgG_{2b} Labeling Kits can presumably be used with any mouse IgG_1, IgG_{2a} and IgG_{2b} antibody, respectively, including those available from Molecular Probes (Table 7.14, Table 7.15, Table 7.16). Similarly, the Zenon® Rabbit IgG Labeling Kits, Zenon® Goat IgG Labeling Kits and Zenon® Human IgG Labeling Kits are designed for use with the rabbit IgG antibodies (Table 7.17), goat IgG antibodies and human IgG antibodies from Molecular Probes, as well as from any other commercial or research laboratory source.

Zenon® Antibody Labeling Kits Enhanced with TSA Technology

The Zenon® Mouse IgG_1 Labeling Kits enhanced with TSA technology provide exceptional target-identification capabilities. These kits provide the necessary reagents from both the Zenon® Horseradish Peroxidase Mouse IgG_1 Labeling Kit and the corresponding Alexa Fluor® TSA Kits for researchers who want both the ease of labeling mouse IgG_1 antibodies with Zenon® labeling reagents and the signal amplification afforded by the use of the TSA technology. We currently offer enhanced Zenon® Kits containing either the green-fluorescent Alexa Fluor® 488 tyramide or the red-orange–fluorescent Alexa Fluor® 568 tyramide (Z25090, Z25091). Each kit provides sufficient reagents for 25 labelings, including:

- Zenon® HRP mouse IgG_1 labeling reagent
- Zenon® mouse IgG blocking reagent
- Alexa Fluor® 488 tyramide (in Kit Z25090) or Alexa Fluor® 568 tyramide (in Kit Z25091)
- DMSO
- TSA blocking reagent
- TSA amplification buffer
- Hydrogen peroxide (H_2O_2)
- A detailed protocol for Zenon® complex formation and fluorescent tyramide labeling

The Zenon® HRP mouse IgG_1 labeling reagent contains Fab fragments of goat IgG antibodies directed against the Fc portion of intact mouse IgG_1 antibodies. These Fab fragments have been purified to ensure their selectivity for the Fc portion of the mouse IgG_1 antibody and then labeled with HRP. This Zenon® HRP mouse IgG_1 labeling reagent is simply mixed with any mouse IgG_1 primary antibody to form the Fab–mouse IgG_1 complexes, which can be used for immunolabeling similar to that of primary antibodies covalently labeled with HRP. TSA technology — an enzyme-mediated detection method that utilizes the catalytic activity of horseradish peroxidase (HRP) to generate high-density labeling of a target protein (Section 6.2) — is then used to detect the target-bound Fab–mouse IgG_1 complex. Each HRP label on the Fab–mouse IgG_1 complexes can activate multiple copies of the Alexa Fluor® tyramide to produce short-lived tyramide radicals that are highly reactive with nucleophilic residues near the interaction site, yielding an amplified fluorescent signal with minimal diffusion.

Use and Applications of Zenon® Technology

With the exception of our Zenon® Tricolor Labeling Kits, our Zenon® Labeling Kits contain sufficient reagents for 50 labelings (with the low molecular weight dye–derived Zenon® labeling reagents),

Table 7.15 — Molecular Probes' mouse IgG_{2a} monoclonal antibodies

Cat #	Antibody	Handbook Section(s)
Antibodies against yeast proteins		
A21274	late-Golgi membrane protein Vps10p	Section 7.5, Section 12.4
A6422	vacuolar H^+-ATPase 69,000-dalton subunit	Section 7.5, Section 12.3
A6426	vacuolar H^+-ATPase 100,000-dalton subunit	Section 7.5, Section 12.3
A6407	OxPhos Complex IV subunit II	Section 7.5, Section 12.2
A6408	OxPhos Complex IV subunit III	Section 7.5, Section 12.2
Antibodies against mammalian mitochondrial proteins		
A21345	OxPhos Complex II 30,000-dalton subunit	Section 7.5, Section 12.2
A21361	OxPhos Complex III 10,000-dalton subunit IV	Section 7.5, Section 12.2
A6403	OxPhos Complex IV subunit I	Section 7.5, Section 12.2
A6404	OxPhos Complex IV subunit II	Section 7.5, Section 12.2
A21347	OxPhos Complex IV subunit IV	Section 7.5, Section 12.2
A21348	OxPhos Complex IV subunit IV	Section 7.5, Section 12.2
A21363	OxPhos Complex IV subunit Va	Section 7.5, Section 12.2
A21367	OxPhos Complex IV subunit VIIa-H/L	Section 7.5, Section 12.2
A21326	pyruvate dehydrogenase E2/E3bp subunit	Section 7.5, Section 12.2
Antibodies against other cellular proteins, epitope tags and antigens		
A21338	CD8	Section 7.5
A21286	cdc6 peptide	Section 7.5, Section 15.4
A21320	cyclin D1	Section 7.5, Section 15.4
A11120	green-fluorescent protein (GFP)	Section 7.5
A6421	fluorescein/Oregon Green® dyes	Section 7.4
A21319	p21WAF1/CIP1	Section 7.5, Section 15.4

Table 7.16 — Molecular Probes' mouse IgG_{2b} monoclonal antibodies

Cat #	Antibody	Handbook Section(s)
Antibodies against yeast proteins		
A6405	OxPhos Complex IV subunit I	Section 7.5, Section 12.2
Antibodies against mammalian mitochondrial proteins		
A21359	OxPhos Complex I 17,000-dalton subunit	Section 7.5, Section 12.2
A21346	OxPhos Complex III subunit FeS	Section 7.5, Section 12.2
A21349	OxPhos Complex IV subunit Vb	Section 7.5, Section 12.2
A6401	OxPhos Complex IV subunit VIc	Section 7.5, Section 12.2
A21350	OxPhos Complex V subunit α	Section 7.5, Section 12.2
A21353	OxPhos Complex V subunit d	Section 7.5, Section 12.2
A21317	mitochondrial porin	Section 7.5, Section 12.2
A31855	mitochondrial porin	Section 7.5, Section 12.2
Antibodies against other cellular proteins, epitope tags and antigens		
A21321	cyclin D2	Section 7.5, Section 15.4
A21271	HuC/HuD	Section 7.5

25 labelings (with the R-PE–, APC-, HRP- and alkaline phosphatase–derived reagents) or 10 labelings (with the Zenon® labeling reagents containing one of five different Alexa Fluor® dye–phycobiliprotein tandem conjugates). The Zenon® Tricolor Labeling Kits #1, #2 and #3 contain sufficient reagents for 10 labelings of the same or different antibodies with each of three different Alexa Fluor® dyes. "One labeling" is defined as the amount of Zenon® labeling reagent required for labeling 1 µg of an intact mouse, rabbit, goat or human IgG antibody. However, even smaller (or larger) quantities of a primary antibody can be reliably labeled with any of the Zenon® labeling reagents. In the case of the Zenon® Labeling Kits containing low molecular weight dyes (Table 7.13), approximately equal weights of the dye-conjugated Fab fragment and the primary antibody are used, which gives an approximately 3:1 molar ratio of the Zenon® labeling reagent to the primary antibody. Our HPLC analysis of the complex indicates that our procedure yields almost complete labeling of the primary antibody in the solution, apparently within the mixing time (Figure 7.60). Use of a 5:1 molar ratio of the Zenon® labeling reagent gives an apparent 100% conversion of the primary antibody to the labeling complex (Figure 7.61) and a somewhat brighter total fluorescence when compared with the fluorescence of Zenon® complexes prepared using a 3:1 ratio. The total fluorescence intensity of the Zenon® labeling complex can be raised or lowered to some degree by using a higher or lower ratio of the Zenon® labeling reagent to the primary antibody.

For single-color labeling, it is usually not necessary to block any residual Zenon® labeling reagent that has not complexed with the primary antibody; however, in applications that involve multiple antibodies of any type (including antibodies from other species or of other isotypes that may react to a small degree with the Zenon® labeling reagent), adsorption of residual Zenon® labeling reagent is essential to avoid crossreactivity. Adsorption can be done with a solution of soluble nonspecific IgG, which is included in all of the Zenon® Labeling Kits. Alternatively, the excess Zenon® labeling reagent from the Zenon® Mouse IgG Labeling Kits can be quickly adsorbed and removed entirely from the labeled complexes using agarose-immobilized mouse IgG (M25500), which is available separately. Our mouse IgG agarose is supplied with tested protocols for its use in combination with our Zenon® technology. When the Zenon® complexes are in a solution containing the Zenon® labeling reagents adsorbed onto soluble nonspecific IgG, they should be used for staining within an hour to avoid possible transfer of the Zenon® labeling reagent to the excess nonspecific IgG. Zenon® complexes can be used with standard immunolabeling techniques; staining with Zenon® complexes can be performed sequentially or combined with each other or with additional dye- or enzyme-labeled primary antibody conjugates in a one-step, multiparameter labeling protocol. Fixation with aldehyde-based fixatives following staining is recommended to prevent transfer of the Zenon® label between antibodies.

We have demonstrated the utility of Zenon® staining for imaging in an assortment of cells (Figure 7.63, Figure 7.64, Figure 7.66, Figure 7.67, Figure 7.68, Figure 7.70, Figure 7.71, Figure 7.85, Figure 15.78)

Table 7.17 — Molecular Probes' rabbit antibodies

Cat #	Antibody	Handbook Section(s)
Antibodies against dyes and haptens		
A11094	Alexa Fluor® 488 dye	Section 7.4
A5770	BODIPY® FL dye	Section 7.4
A5760	Alexa Fluor® 405/Cascade Blue® dyes	Section 7.4
A6398	dansyl	Section 7.4
A6430	dinitrophenyl-KLH (DNP-KLH)	Section 7.4
A889	fluorescein/Oregon Green® dyes	Section 7.4
A5750	lucifer yellow dye	Section 7.4
A6397	tetramethylrhodamine	Section 7.4
A6399	Texas Red® dye	Section 7.4
Antibodies against other cellular proteins, epitope tags and antigens		
A11133	bovine serum albumin (BSA)	Section 7.5, Section 14.7
A11132	β-galactosidase	Section 7.5, Section 10.2
A5790	β-glucuronidase	Section 7.5, Section 10.2
A5800	glutathione *S*-transferase	Section 7.5, Section 9.2
A11122	green-fluorescent protein (GFP)	Section 7.5
A21285	nitrotyrosine	Section 7.4, Section 18.3
A6473	NMDA receptor subunit 2A	Section 7.5, Section 16.2
A6474	NMDA receptor subunit 2B	Section 7.5, Section 16.2
A6475	NMDA receptor subunit 2C	Section 7.5, Section 16.2
A6442	synapsin I	Section 7.5, Section 16.1, Section 17.3

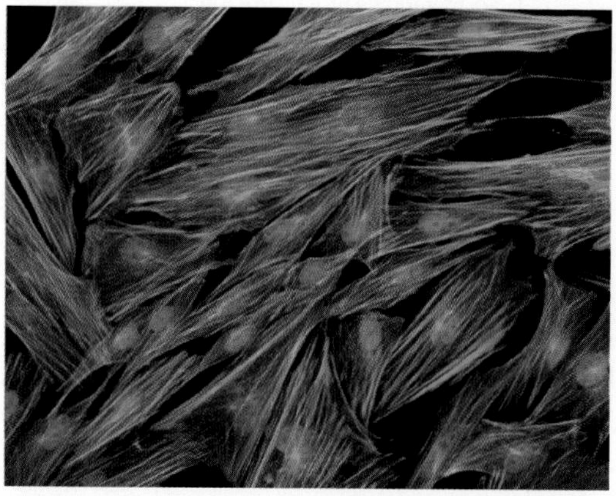

Figure 7.66 Fixed and permeabilized muntjac skin fibroblasts stained with Alexa Fluor® 488 phalloidin (A12379), an anti–α-tubulin antibody (A11126) and anti–cdc6 peptide antibody (A21286). The anti–α-tubulin antibody was prelabeled with the Zenon® Alexa Fluor® 568 Mouse IgG_1 Labeling Kit (Z25006), and the anti–cdc6 peptide antibody was prelabeled with the Zenon® Alexa Fluor® 350 Mouse IgG_1 Labeling Kit (Z25000).

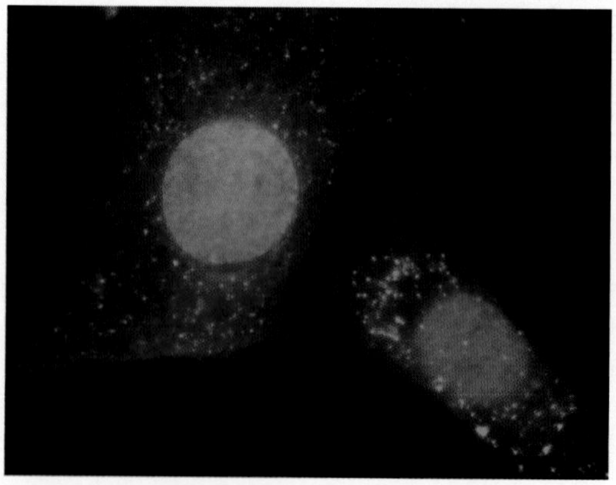

Figure 7.67 Detection of cell proliferation by BrdU incorporation. 3T3 cells were pulsed with BrdU (B23151) for 30 minutes before fixation. BrdU incorporated into the DNA of proliferating cells was detected with an anti-BrdU antibody (A21300) that was prelabeled with the Zenon® Alexa Fluor® 488 Mouse IgG_1 Labeling Kit (Z25002). The sample was mounted with the reagents in the Prolong® Antifade Kit (P7481).

and some tissues (Figure 7.69). As with the use of any antibody conjugate in tissues, staining with Zenon® complexes requires good accessibility of the antibody to the target, which can be affected by the specific conditions of fixation and permeabilization. Zenon® complexes of intact primary antibodies have somewhat higher molecular weights than direct conjugates of antibodies, potentially reducing the accessibility of the complexes to tissue antigens in some cases.

The Zenon® Allophycocyanin and R-Phycoerythrin Antibody Labeling Kits and the Zenon® Horseradish Peroxidase and Alkaline Phosphatase Antibody Labeling Kits provide a means to label a primary mouse IgG, rabbit IgG or human IgG antibody with these important labels. The Zenon® labeling method is, by far, much faster and easier than the chemical methods that we recommend for crosslinking unlike proteins (Section 5.2; Figure 5.4, Figure 5.6) and results in a much higher (essentially quantitative with respect to the primary antibody) yield of the labeled antibody complex. The Zenon® Horseradish Peroxidase and Alkaline Phosphatase Antibody Labeling Kits provide an extremely easy means to amplify the signal when combined with our many TSA reagents (Section 6.2, Table 6.1) or our Enzyme-Labeled Fluorescence (ELF® 97) Kits (Section 6.3), respectively. The Zenon® labeling reagents that contain R-PE, APC, Alexa Fluor® dye–phycobiliprotein tandem conjugates, HRP or alkaline phosphatase must not be frozen.

Important Information on Zenon® Technology

As our Zenon® antibody labeling technology is applied to different experimental systems and protocols, we are compiling a bibliography (Z25999) containing journal articles that cite the use of the Zenon® Kits; continuously updated copies are available upon request from our Technical Assistance Department or through our web site (probes.invitrogen.com). These articles can serve as guides for developing specific applications and protocols. We have extensively tested the Zenon® technology with various primary antibodies, particularly in flow cytometry (Figure 7.65) and imaging (Figure 7.63, Figure 7.64, Figure 7.66, Figure 7.67, Figure 7.68, Figure 7.70, Figure 7.71, Figure 7.85) applications and found it to be generally reliable, with no more (and sometimes less) background staining than typically occurs with directly conjugated primary antibodies. We have so far done only limited evaluation of Zenon® labeling in tissues but will report on these results as they become available.

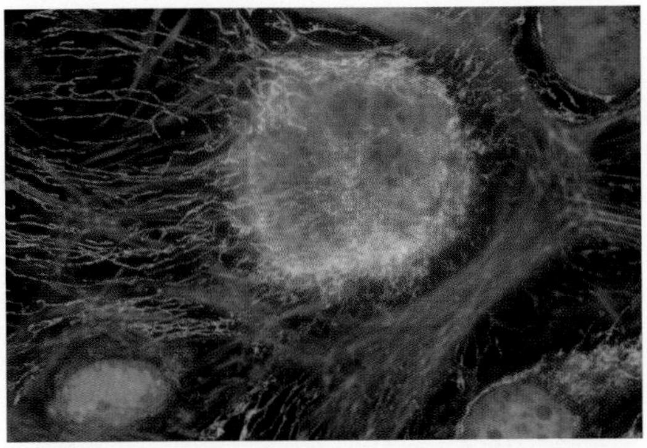

Figure 7.68 Fixed and permeabilized HeLa cells stained with Alexa Fluor® 350 phalloidin (A22281) and an anti–OxPhos Complex V inhibitor protein antibody (A21355) to label actin filaments and the mitochondria, respectively. An anti–cdc6 peptide antibody (A21286) was used to label the nucleus. The anti–OxPhos Complex V inhibitor protein antibody was labeled with the Zenon® Alexa Fluor® 488 Mouse IgG_1 Labeling Kit (Z25002), and the anti–cdc6 peptide antibody was labeled with the Zenon® Alexa Fluor® 568 Mouse IgG_1 Labeling Kit (Z25006).

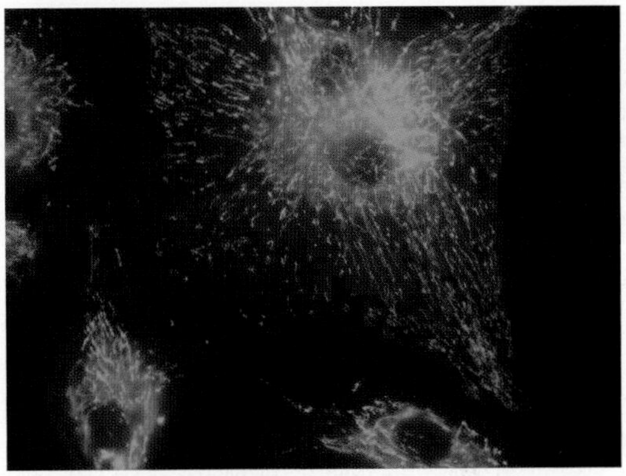

Figure 7.70 Fixed and permeabilized bovine pulmonary artery endothelial cells stained with an anti–OxPhos Complex V inhibitor protein antibody (A21355), which highlights the mitochondria. The antibody was prelabeled with the Zenon® Alexa Fluor® 488 Mouse IgG_1 Labeling Kit (Z25002).

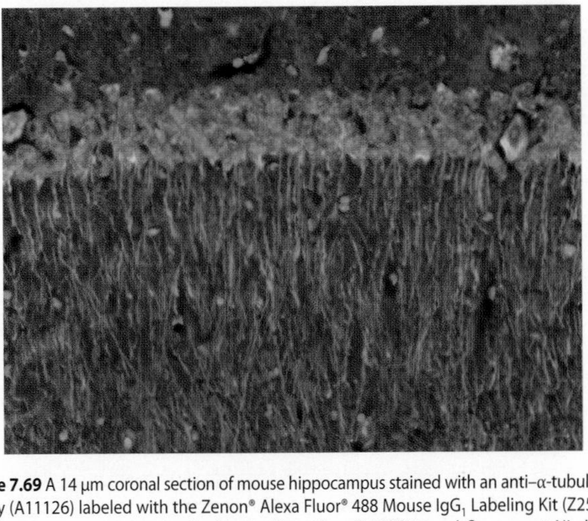

Figure 7.69 A 14 µm coronal section of mouse hippocampus stained with an anti–α-tubulin antibody (A11126) labeled with the Zenon® Alexa Fluor® 488 Mouse IgG_1 Labeling Kit (Z25002). The section was counterstained with the NeuroTrace® 530/615 red fluorescent Nissl stain (N21482) to visualize neuronal cell bodies and Hoechst 33258 (H1398, H3569, H21491) to stain nuclei.

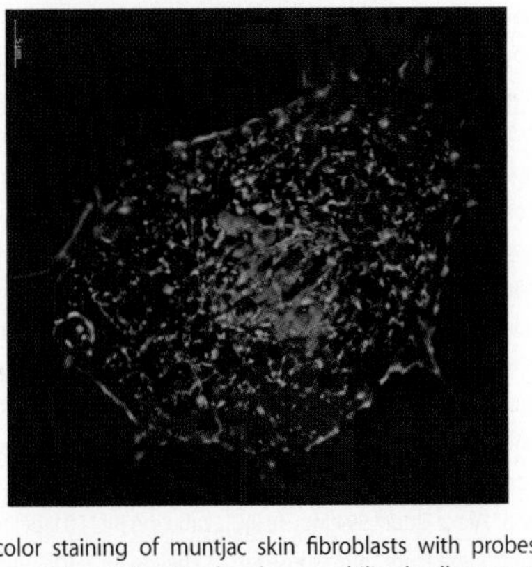

Figure 7.71 Four-color staining of muntjac skin fibroblasts with probes for cytoskeletal, nuclear and mitochondrial proteins. Fixed and permeabilized cells were stained with Alexa Fluor® 350 phalloidin (A22281), an anti–α-tubulin antibody (A11126), an anti–cdc6 peptide antibody (A21286) and an anti–OxPhos Complex V inhibitor protein antibody (A21355). The anti–OxPhos Complex V inhibitor protein antibody was prelabeled with the Zenon® Alexa Fluor® 488 Mouse IgG_1 Labeling Kit (Z25002), the anti–α-tubulin antibody was prelabeled with the Zenon® Alexa Fluor® 568 Mouse IgG_1 Labeling Kit (Z25002), and the anti–cdc6 peptide antibody was prelabeled with the Zenon® Alexa Fluor® 647 Mouse IgG_1 Labeling Kit (Z25008). The image was deconvolved using Huygens software (Scientific Volume Imaging, www.svi.nl).

Because of the importance and uniqueness of our Zenon® technology, we maintain a direct link to the latest information on these products and their applications at our web site (probes.invitrogen.com/zenon). This site includes links to complete Zenon® Labeling Kit product lists and information on applications, protocols, pictures and publications of the Zenon® technology.

Our Zenon® technology is the subject of several patents and patent applications. Licenses are available from Molecular Probes for commercial resale or high-volume uses of the Zenon® labeling reagents and methods that use these reagents. Bulk discounts are available for multiple-unit purchases of the Zenon® Labeling Kits. The stand-alone Zenon® labeling reagents are not available in bulk, except to licensees of our Zenon® technology.

References

1. Am J Physiol Renal Physiol 286, F161 (2004); **2.** Circulation 109, 1401 (2004); **3.** J Virol 78, 1552 (2004); **4.** J Neurosci 24, 4242 (2004); **5.** Mol Cell Proteomics 3, 410 (2004).

Product List — 7.3 Zenon Technology — Versatile Reagents for Immunolabeling

Cat #	Product Name	Unit Size
M25500	mouse IgG agarose *sedimented bead suspension*	1 mL
Z25400	Zenon® Alexa Fluor® 350 Human IgG Labeling Kit *50 labelings*	1 kit
Z25000	Zenon® Alexa Fluor® 350 Mouse IgG_1 Labeling Kit *50 labelings*	1 kit
Z25100	Zenon® Alexa Fluor® 350 Mouse IgG_{2a} Labeling Kit *50 labelings*	1 kit
Z25200	Zenon® Alexa Fluor® 350 Mouse IgG_{2b} Labeling Kit *50 labelings*	1 kit
Z25300	Zenon® Alexa Fluor® 350 Rabbit IgG Labeling Kit *50 labelings*	1 kit
Z25013	Zenon® Alexa Fluor® 405 Mouse IgG_1 Labeling Kit *50 labelings*	1 kit
Z25113	Zenon® Alexa Fluor® 405 Mouse IgG_{2a} Labeling Kit *50 labelings*	1 kit
Z25213	Zenon® Alexa Fluor® 405 Mouse IgG_{2b} Labeling Kit *50 labelings*	1 kit
Z25313	Zenon® Alexa Fluor® 405 Rabbit IgG Labeling Kit *50 labelings*	1 kit
Z25001	Zenon® Alexa Fluor® 430 Mouse IgG_1 Labeling Kit *50 labelings*	1 kit
Z25301	Zenon® Alexa Fluor® 430 Rabbit IgG Labeling Kit *50 labelings*	1 kit
Z25602	Zenon® Alexa Fluor® 488 Goat IgG Labeling Kit *50 labelings*	1 kit
Z25402	Zenon® Alexa Fluor® 488 Human IgG Labeling Kit *50 labelings*	1 kit
Z25002	Zenon® Alexa Fluor® 488 Mouse IgG_1 Labeling Kit *50 labelings*	1 kit
Z25102	Zenon® Alexa Fluor® 488 Mouse IgG_{2a} Labeling Kit *50 labelings*	1 kit
Z25202	Zenon® Alexa Fluor® 488 Mouse IgG_{2b} Labeling Kit *50 labelings*	1 kit
Z25302	Zenon® Alexa Fluor® 488 Rabbit IgG Labeling Kit *50 labelings*	1 kit
Z25003	Zenon® Alexa Fluor® 532 Mouse IgG_1 Labeling Kit *50 labelings*	1 kit
Z25303	Zenon® Alexa Fluor® 532 Rabbit IgG Labeling Kit *50 labelings*	1 kit
Z25004	Zenon® Alexa Fluor® 546 Mouse IgG_1 Labeling Kit *50 labelings*	1 kit
Z25104	Zenon® Alexa Fluor® 546 Mouse IgG_{2a} Labeling Kit *50 labelings*	1 kit
Z25204	Zenon® Alexa Fluor® 546 Mouse IgG_{2b} Labeling Kit *50 labelings*	1 kit
Z25304	Zenon® Alexa Fluor® 546 Rabbit IgG Labeling Kit *50 labelings*	1 kit
Z25605	Zenon® Alexa Fluor® 555 Goat IgG Labeling Kit *50 labelings*	1 kit
Z25405	Zenon® Alexa Fluor® 555 Human IgG Labeling Kit *50 labelings*	1 kit
Z25005	Zenon® Alexa Fluor® 555 Mouse IgG_1 Labeling Kit *50 labelings*	1 kit
Z25105	Zenon® Alexa Fluor® 555 Mouse IgG_{2a} Labeling Kit *50 labelings*	1 kit
Z25205	Zenon® Alexa Fluor® 555 Mouse IgG_{2b} Labeling Kit *50 labelings*	1 kit
Z25305	Zenon® Alexa Fluor® 555 Rabbit IgG Labeling Kit *50 labelings*	1 kit
Z25006	Zenon® Alexa Fluor® 568 Mouse IgG_1 Labeling Kit *50 labelings*	1 kit
Z25106	Zenon® Alexa Fluor® 568 Mouse IgG_{2a} Labeling Kit *50 labelings*	1 kit
Z25206	Zenon® Alexa Fluor® 568 Mouse IgG_{2b} Labeling Kit *50 labelings*	1 kit
Z25306	Zenon® Alexa Fluor® 568 Rabbit IgG Labeling Kit *50 labelings*	1 kit
Z25607	Zenon® Alexa Fluor® 594 Goat IgG Labeling Kit *50 labelings*	1 kit
Z25407	Zenon® Alexa Fluor® 594 Human IgG Labeling Kit *50 labelings*	1 kit
Z25007	Zenon® Alexa Fluor® 594 Mouse IgG_1 Labeling Kit *50 labelings*	1 kit
Z25107	Zenon® Alexa Fluor® 594 Mouse IgG_{2a} Labeling Kit *50 labelings*	1 kit
Z25207	Zenon® Alexa Fluor® 594 Mouse IgG_{2b} Labeling Kit *50 labelings*	1 kit
Z25307	Zenon® Alexa Fluor® 594 Rabbit IgG Labeling Kit *50 labelings*	1 kit
Z25020	Zenon® Alexa Fluor® 610–R-Phycoerythrin Mouse IgG_1 Labeling Kit *10 labelings*	1 kit
Z25608	Zenon® Alexa Fluor® 647 Goat IgG Labeling Kit *50 labelings*	1 kit
Z25408	Zenon® Alexa Fluor® 647 Human IgG Labeling Kit *50 labelings*	1 kit

For current prices or to order online, visit probes.invitrogen.com

Cat #	Product Name	Unit Size
Z25008	Zenon® Alexa Fluor® 647 Mouse IgG_1 Labeling Kit *50 labelings*	1 kit
Z25108	Zenon® Alexa Fluor® 647 Mouse IgG_{2a} Labeling Kit *50 labelings*	1 kit
Z25208	Zenon® Alexa Fluor® 647 Mouse IgG_{2b} Labeling Kit *50 labelings*	1 kit
Z25308	Zenon® Alexa Fluor® 647 Rabbit IgG Labeling Kit *50 labelings*	1 kit
Z25021	Zenon® Alexa Fluor® 647–R-Phycoerythrin Mouse IgG_1 Labeling Kit *10 labelings*	1 kit
Z25121	Zenon® Alexa Fluor® 647–R-Phycoerythrin Mouse IgG_{2a} Labeling Kit *10 labelings*	1 kit
Z25221	Zenon® Alexa Fluor® 647–R-Phycoerythrin Mouse IgG_{2b} Labeling Kit *10 labelings*	1 kit
Z25009	Zenon® Alexa Fluor® 660 Mouse IgG_1 Labeling Kit *50 labelings*	1 kit
Z25109	Zenon® Alexa Fluor® 660 Mouse IgG_{2a} Labeling Kit *50 labelings*	1 kit
Z25209	Zenon® Alexa Fluor® 660 Mouse IgG_{2b} Labeling Kit *50 labelings*	1 kit
Z25309	Zenon® Alexa Fluor® 660 Rabbit IgG Labeling Kit *50 labelings*	1 kit
Z25010	Zenon® Alexa Fluor® 680 Mouse IgG_1 Labeling Kit *50 labelings*	1 kit
Z25110	Zenon® Alexa Fluor® 680 Mouse IgG_{2a} Labeling Kit *50 labelings*	1 kit
Z25210	Zenon® Alexa Fluor® 680 Mouse IgG_{2b} Labeling Kit *50 labelings*	1 kit
Z25310	Zenon® Alexa Fluor® 680 Rabbit IgG Labeling Kit *50 labelings*	1 kit
Z25022	Zenon® Alexa Fluor® 680–R-Phycoerythrin Mouse IgG_1 Labeling Kit *10 labelings*	1 kit
Z25011	Zenon® Alexa Fluor® 700 Mouse IgG_1 Labeling Kit *50 labelings*	1 kit
Z25311	Zenon® Alexa Fluor® 700 Rabbit IgG Labeling Kit *50 labelings*	1 kit
Z25030	Zenon® Alexa Fluor® 700–Allophycocyanin Mouse IgG_1 Labeling Kit *10 labelings*	1 kit
Z25312	Zenon® Alexa Fluor® 750 Rabbit IgG Labeling Kit *50 labelings*	1 kit
Z25031	Zenon® Alexa Fluor® 750–Allophycocyanin Mouse IgG_1 Labeling Kit *10 labelings*	1 kit
Z25606	Zenon® Alexa Fluor® 568 Goat IgG Labeling Kit *50 labelings*	1 kit
Z25090	Zenon® Alexa Fluor® 488 Mouse IgG_1 Labeling Kit *enhanced with TSA™ technology* *25 labelings*	1 kit
Z25091	Zenon® Alexa Fluor® 568 Mouse IgG_1 Labeling Kit *enhanced with TSA™ technology* *25 labelings*	1 kit
Z25050	Zenon® Alkaline Phosphatase Mouse IgG_1 Labeling Kit *25 labelings*	1 kit
Z25150	Zenon® Alkaline Phosphatase Mouse IgG_{2a} Labeling Kit *25 labelings*	1 kit
Z25250	Zenon® Alkaline Phosphatase Mouse IgG_{2b} Labeling Kit *25 labelings*	1 kit
Z25350	Zenon® Alkaline Phosphatase Rabbit IgG Labeling Kit *25 labelings*	1 kit
Z25451	Zenon® Allophycocyanin Human IgG Labeling Kit *25 labelings*	1 kit
Z25051	Zenon® Allophycocyanin Mouse IgG_1 Labeling Kit *25 labelings*	1 kit
Z25151	Zenon® Allophycocyanin Mouse IgG_{2a} Labeling Kit *25 labelings*	1 kit
Z25251	Zenon® Allophycocyanin Mouse IgG_{2b} Labeling Kit *25 labelings*	1 kit
Z25351	Zenon® Allophycocyanin Rabbit IgG Labeling Kit *25 labelings*	1 kit
Z25452	Zenon® Biotin-XX Human IgG Labeling Kit *50 labelings*	1 kit
Z25052	Zenon® Biotin-XX Mouse IgG_1 Labeling Kit *50 labelings*	1 kit
Z25152	Zenon® Biotin-XX Mouse IgG_{2a} Labeling Kit *50 labelings*	1 kit
Z25252	Zenon® Biotin-XX Mouse IgG_{2b} Labeling Kit *50 labelings*	1 kit
Z25352	Zenon® Biotin-XX Rabbit IgG Labeling Kit *50 labelings*	1 kit
Z25053	Zenon® DSB-X™ Biotin Mouse IgG_1 Labeling Kit *50 labelings*	1 kit
Z25042	Zenon® Fluorescein Mouse IgG_1 Labeling Kit *50 labelings*	1 kit
Z25342	Zenon® Fluorescein Rabbit IgG Labeling Kit *50 labelings*	1 kit
Z25454	Zenon® Horseradish Peroxidase Human IgG Labeling Kit *25 labelings*	1 kit
Z25054	Zenon® Horseradish Peroxidase Mouse IgG_1 Labeling Kit *25 labelings*	1 kit
Z25154	Zenon® Horseradish Peroxidase Mouse IgG_{2a} Labeling Kit *25 labelings*	1 kit
Z25254	Zenon® Horseradish Peroxidase Mouse IgG_{2b} Labeling Kit *25 labelings*	1 kit
Z25354	Zenon® Horseradish Peroxidase Rabbit IgG Labeling Kit *25 labelings*	1 kit
Z25040	Zenon® Marina Blue® Mouse IgG_1 Labeling Kit *50 labelings*	1 kit
Z25340	Zenon® Marina Blue® Rabbit IgG Labeling Kit *50 labelings*	1 kit
Z25043	Zenon® Oregon Green® 488 Mouse IgG_1 Labeling Kit *50 labelings*	1 kit
Z25343	Zenon® Oregon Green® 488 Rabbit IgG Labeling Kit *50 labelings*	1 kit
Z25041	Zenon® Pacific Blue™ Mouse IgG_1 Labeling Kit *50 labelings*	1 kit
Z25341	Zenon® Pacific Blue™ Rabbit IgG Labeling Kit *50 labelings*	1 kit
Z25455	Zenon® R-Phycoerythrin Human IgG Labeling Kit *25 labelings*	1 kit
Z25055	Zenon® R-Phycoerythrin Mouse IgG_1 Labeling Kit *25 labelings*	1 kit
Z25155	Zenon® R-Phycoerythrin Mouse IgG_{2a} Labeling Kit *25 labelings*	1 kit
Z25255	Zenon® R-Phycoerythrin Mouse IgG_{2b} Labeling Kit *25 labelings*	1 kit
Z25355	Zenon® R-Phycoerythrin Rabbit IgG Labeling Kit *25 labelings*	1 kit
Z25045	Zenon® Texas Red®-X Mouse IgG_1 Labeling Kit *50 labelings*	1 kit
Z25345	Zenon® Texas Red®-X Rabbit IgG Labeling Kit *50 labelings*	1 kit
Z25460	Zenon® Tricolor Human IgG Labeling Kit #1 *for green, orange and deep red fluorescence imaging* *3 x 10 labelings*	1 kit
Z25470	Zenon® Tricolor Human IgG Labeling Kit #2 *for blue, green and red fluorescence imaging* *3 x 10 labelings*	1 kit

For current prices or to order online, visit probes.invitrogen.com

Product List — 7.3 Zenon Technology — Versatile Reagents for Immunolabeling — continued

Cat #	Product Name	Unit Size
Z25060	Zenon® Tricolor Mouse IgG_1 Labeling Kit #1 *for green, orange and deep red fluorescence imaging* *3 x 10 labelings*	1 kit
Z25070	Zenon® Tricolor Mouse IgG_1 Labeling Kit #2 *for blue, green and red fluorescence imaging* *3 x 10 labelings*	1 kit
Z25080	Zenon® Tricolor Mouse IgG_1 Labeling Kit #3 *for flow cytometry, 488 nm excitation* *3 x 10 labelings*	1 kit
Z25160	Zenon® Tricolor Mouse IgG_{2a} Labeling Kit #1 *for green, orange and deep red fluorescence imaging* *3 x 10 labelings*	1 kit
Z25170	Zenon® Tricolor Mouse IgG_{2a} Labeling Kit #2 *for blue, green and red fluorescence imaging* *3 x 10 labelings*	1 kit
Z25180	Zenon® Tricolor Mouse IgG_{2a} Labeling Kit #3 *for flow cytometry, 488 nm excitation* *3 x 10 labelings*	1 kit
Z25260	Zenon® Tricolor Mouse IgG_{2b} Labeling Kit #1 *for green, orange and deep red fluorescence imaging* *3 x 10 labelings*	1 kit
Z25270	Zenon® Tricolor Mouse IgG_{2b} Labeling Kit #2 *for blue, green and red fluorescence imaging* *3 x 10 labelings*	1 kit
Z25280	Zenon® Tricolor Mouse IgG_{2b} Labeling Kit #3 *for flow cytometry, 488 nm excitation* *3 x 10 labelings*	1 kit
Z25360	Zenon® Tricolor Rabbit IgG Labeling Kit #1 *for green, orange and deep red fluorescence imaging* *3 x 10 labelings*	1 kit
Z25370	Zenon® Tricolor Rabbit IgG Labeling Kit #2 *for blue, green and red fluorescence imaging* *3 x 10 labelings*	1 kit

For current prices or to order online, visit probes.invitrogen.com

7.4 Anti-Dye and Anti-Hapten Antibodies

Anti-Dye and Anti-Hapten Antibodies

In addition to being useful for direct optical detection, some fluorescent dyes and nonfluorescent ligands make excellent haptens that can be recognized by secondary detection reagents in applications such as *in situ* hybridization, enzyme-linked immunosorbent assay (ELISA) techniques and detection of labeled targets on blots (Section 9.4). Antibodies to dyes and other ligands provide unique opportunities both for signal enhancement and for correlated fluorescence and electron microscopy studies. Essentially all of the methods that use biotin and avidin reagents (Section 7.6) are also possible using dyes as haptens, as long as the corresponding anti-dye antibody is also available (Table 7.18). One advantage of using fluorescent dyes as haptens instead of biotin-based techniques is that the hapten signal is usually visible, or at least its concentration can be measured by its absorption in solution, preceding the secondary detection step. Unlike biotin, which is an endogenous ligand in mitochondria (Figure 7.98, Figure 12.27), dye-based haptens permit background-free staining of cells and tissues. Availability of noncrossreacting antibodies to a variety of haptens is essential for any multicolor application and an alternative to utilizing antibodies against multiple species of animals, which have a higher likelihood of crossreacting. Molecular Probes provides the largest assortment of anti-dye antibodies commercially available (Table 7.18), including rabbit polyclonal IgG antibodies to the fluorescein, tetramethylrhodamine, Texas Red®, dansyl, Alexa Fluor® 488, BODIPY® FL, lucifer yellow and Alexa Fluor® 405/Cascade Blue® fluorophores, as well as a goat anti-fluorescein/Oregon Green® IgG antibody (A11095). We also provide antibodies against three nonfluorescent haptens: dinitrophenyl (DNP), biotin and nitrotyrosine (Table 7.19).

Table 7.19 — Molecular Probes' anti-hapten antibodies and conjugates

Cat #	Anti-Hapten	Host	Label
A11242	Biotin	Mouse	None
A31801	Biotin	Mouse	Alexa Fluor® 488
A31800	Biotin	Mouse	Alexa Fluor® 594
A6430	Dinitrophenyl	Rabbit	None
A6435	Dinitrophenyl	Rabbit	Biotin-XX
A6423	Dinitrophenyl	Rabbit	Fluorescein
A11097	Dinitrophenyl	Rabbit	Alexa Fluor® 488
A21285	Nitrotyrosine	Rabbit	None

Table 7.18 — Anti-fluorophore antibodies and their conjugates

Cat #	Anti-Fluorophore	Host	Label
A5760	Alexa Fluor® 405/ Cascade Blue® dye	Rabbit	None
A11094	Alexa Fluor® 488 dye	Rabbit	None
A5770	BODIPY® FL dye	Rabbit	None
A6398	Dansyl	Rabbit	None
A889	Fluorescein/ Oregon Green® dye	Rabbit	None
A11095	Fluorescein/ Oregon Green® dye	Goat	None
A6421	Fluorescein/ Oregon Green® dye	Mouse (clone 4-4-20)	None
A6413	Fluorescein/ Oregon Green® dye	Rabbit, Fab fragment	None
A982	Fluorescein/ Oregon Green® dye	Rabbit	Biotin-XX
A11090	Fluorescein/ Oregon Green® dye	Rabbit	Alexa Fluor® 488 dye
A11091	Fluorescein/ Oregon Green® dye	Rabbit	Alexa Fluor® 594 dye
A11096	Fluorescein/ Oregon Green® dye	Goat	Alexa Fluor® 488 dye
A21250	Fluorescein/ Oregon Green® dye	Rabbit	R-phycoerythrin
A21253	Fluorescein/ Oregon Green® dye	Rabbit	Horseradish peroxidase
A21254	Fluorescein/ Oregon Green® dye	Rabbit $F(ab')_2$	Horseradish peroxidase
A5750	Lucifer yellow dye	Rabbit	None
A5751	Lucifer yellow dye	Rabbit	Biotin-XX
A6397	Tetramethylrhodamine and Rhodamine Red™ dye	Rabbit	None
A6399	Texas Red® and Texas Red®-X dye	Rabbit	None

Antibodies to Fluorescein and Oregon Green® Dyes

We have observed complete crossreactivity of our anti-fluorescein antibodies with the Oregon Green® 488 and Oregon Green® 514 dyes (Section 1.5). These antibodies also quench the fluorescence of the structurally similar dye resorufin (R363, Section 10.1, Figure 10.6). The high affinity and specificity of anti-fluorescein/Oregon Green® antibodies (A889, A6413, A6421, A11095) makes fluorescein and Oregon Green® dyes ideal haptens for various detection schemes.[1,2] Researchers have found that fluorescein–anti-fluorescein ELISA techniques display low nonspecific binding and are similar in sensitivity to biotin–streptavidin methods.[3]

Our anti-fluorescein/Oregon Green® rabbit polyclonal antibody (A889) and anti-fluorescein/Oregon Green® goat polyclonal antibody (A11095) can be used in combination with any of our Zenon® Rabbit IgG and Zenon® Goat IgG Labeling Kits (Section 7.3, Table 7.13), respectively, to produce fluorophore-, biotin- or enzyme-labeled antibodies. In addition to these anti-fluorescein/Oregon Green® antibodies, Molecular Probes offers an anti-fluorescein/Oregon Green® monoclonal antibody and an anti-fluorescein/Oregon Green® rabbit polyclonal Fab fragment (see Note 7.2 "Technical Focus: Antibody Structure and Classification" in Section 7.2). The high-affinity anti-fluorescein/Oregon Green® mouse IgG_{2a} monoclonal 4-4-20 antibody (A6421) may reduce nonspecific binding in ELISAs and other second-step detection assays. This antibody can also be used in combination with any of our Zenon® Mouse IgG_{2a} Labeling Kits (Section 7.3, Table 7.13) to amplify the signal or change the color of any fluorescein- or Oregon Green®–labeled primary or secondary antibody. The Fab fragment of our rabbit polyclonal anti-fluorescein/Oregon Green® antibody (A6413) provides researchers with a probe that more efficiently penetrates cell and tissue preparations. Furthermore, because the Fab fragment no longer contains the Fc portion, nonspecific interactions with Fc receptor–bearing cells are eliminated. As expected, none of our anti-fluorescein/Oregon Green® antibodies recognize the Alexa Fluor® or BODIPY® dyes.

We also offer the horseradish peroxidase (HRP) conjugate of the complete IgG (H+L) rabbit anti-fluorescein/Oregon Green® antibody (A21253) and of the $F(ab')_2$ antibody fragment (A21254). HRP conjugates are commonly used in histochemical amplification schemes such as the tyramide signal amplification (TSA) technology (Section 6.2). The TSA technology provides a greater degree of resolution than many conventional enzyme-mediated fluorescent staining methods, and sequential TSA labeling followed by Enzyme-Labeled Fluorescence (ELF®) labeling (Section 6.3 or by a second round of TSA labeling provides the most sensitive assays available for detection of low-abundance targets in cells and tissues with high spatial resolution[4] (Figure 6.5). Additionally, these anti-dye antibody conjugates of HRP can be utilized in ELISAs. Enzyme-conjugated detection reagents often provide greater sensitivity than that achieved with direct dye conjugates. The substrates used to detect the enzymatic activity — and indirectly the amount of the target — typically yield a soluble fluorophore or chromophore. Molecular Probes' assortment of substrates for use in ELISAs is described in Chapter 10.

Our Alexa Fluor® 488 dye–labeled rabbit or goat anti-fluorescein/Oregon Green® antibodies (A11090, A11096) can be used to enhance the green-fluorescent signal of the fluorescein hapten without changing its fluorescence color[5–7] (Figure 7.49). Thus, this conjugate allows researchers to take advantage of the superior photostability of the Alexa Fluor® 488 dye, while utilizing existing fluorescein-labeled probes and fluorescein-compatible optics. This strategy has been exploited in our Alexa Fluor® 488 Signal Amplification Kit for Fluorescein-Conjugated Probes (A11053; Section 7.2, Figure 7.49). Alexa Fluor® 488 dye–labeled anti-fluorescein/Oregon Green® antibodies (A11096) can be used with fluoresceinated probes to greatly enhance the photostability of the green-fluorescent signal. The Alexa Fluor® 594 dye–labeled (A11091) anti-fluorescein/Oregon Green® antibody can be used to convert the green fluorescence of fluorescein conjugates to photostable red fluorescence, or potentially to amplify the signal from fluorescein conjugates (Figure 7.72).

The R-phycoerythrin conjugate of the rabbit anti-fluorescein/Oregon Green® IgG antibody (A21250) also has the unique utility of both shifting the green-fluorescent emission of fluorescein-labeled probes to longer wavelengths and greatly intensifying the long-wavelength signal (Figure 7.73). Biotin-XX–labeled rabbit anti-fluorescein/Oregon Green® antibody (A982) is an excellent reagent for converting a fluorescence-based detection method into an enzyme-amplified light or electron microscopy technique. Biotin-XX anti-fluorescein/Oregon Green® can be combined with either the tyramide signal amplification (TSA) technology (Section 6.2, Figure 6.5) or Enzyme-Labeled Fluorescence (ELF®) technology (Section 6.3, Figure 6.21) in a variety of signal amplification schemes for cell and tissue labeling.

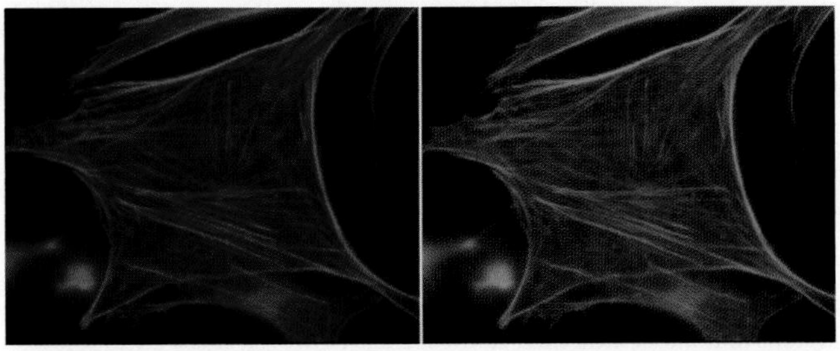

Figure 7.72 Fixed and permeabilized bovine pulmonary arterial endothelial cells were labeled with the filamentous actin (F-actin) stain, fluorescein phalloidin (F432, right). An Alexa Fluor® 594 anti-fluorescein/Oregon Green® rabbit IgG antibody (A11091) converted the green fluorescence to red (left).

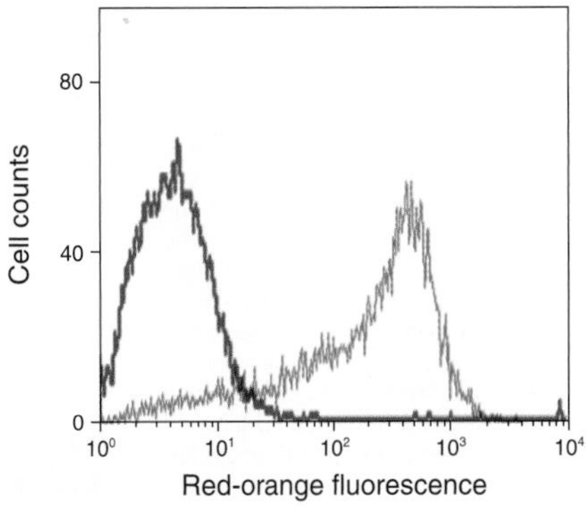

Figure 7.73 Color-shifting using a labeled anti-fluorescein/Oregon Green® antibody. Jurkat cells were first stained with a primary mouse anti–human CD3 antibody, followed by fluorescein goat anti-mouse IgG antibody (F2761), with the resultant fluorescence detected in the R-phycoerythrin (red-orange fluorescence) channel of a flow cytometer (blue curve). The weak signal was then shifted to better suit the R-phycoerythrin channel by the addition of an R-phycoerythrin conjugate of anti-fluorescein/Oregon Green® antibody (A21250). The resulting signal intensity is approximately two orders of magnitude greater (red curve) than the direct fluorescence from the first staining step (blue curve).

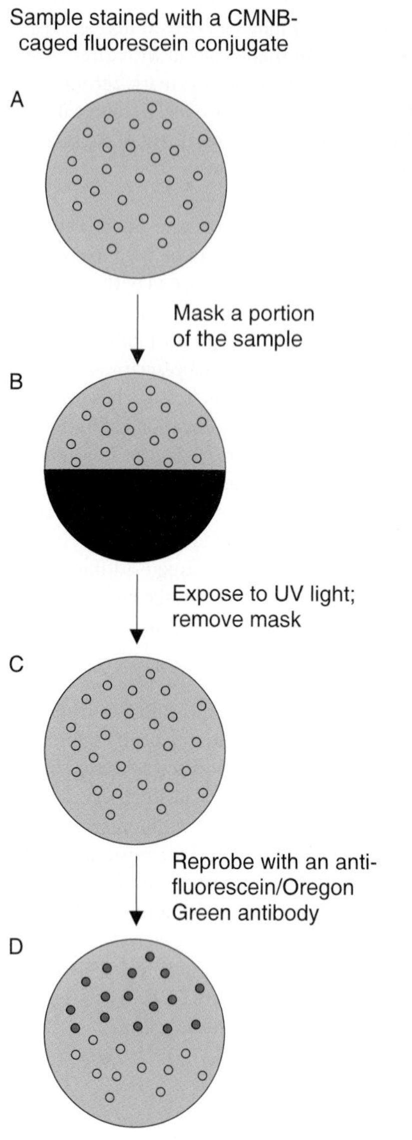
Sample stained with a CMNB-caged fluorescein conjugate
A
Mask a portion of the sample
B
Expose to UV light; remove mask
C
Reprobe with an anti-fluorescein/Oregon Green antibody
D

Figure 7.74 Schematic representation of photoactivated fluorescence combined with sample masking. Initially, no fluorescence is observed from samples stained with a CMNB-caged fluorescein-labeled secondary detection reagent (panel A). The desired mask is then placed over the sample (panel B), after which the sample is exposed to UV light. The mask is then removed; fluorescein molecules present in the unmasked portion of the sample are uncaged by the UV light and fluoresce brightly when viewed with the appropriate filters (panel C). Uncaged fluorescein may now also serve as a hapten for further signal amplification using our anti-fluorescein/Oregon Green® antibody (A889). For example, probing with the anti-fluorescein/Oregon Green® antibody followed by staining with the Alexa Fluor® 594 goat anti-mouse IgG antibody (A11005) can be used to change the color of the uncaged probe to red fluorescent (panel D).

Some of the more important applications for anti-fluorescein/Oregon Green® antibodies — almost all of which could also be carried out with any of our other anti-dye antibodies and their complementary dyes — include:

- Amplification of the signal from a fluorescein tyramide in the TSA technology [8] (Section 6.2)
- Detection of fluorescein-labeled primary antibodies [9,10]
- Development of fluorescein-labeled cell preparations for electron microscopy [11]
- Investigation of the uptake of a fluorescein dextran in kidney proximal tubules [12]
- Localization of mRNA sequences in a double *in situ* hybridization experiment in which both fluorescein- and biotin-labeled oligonucleotides were used [1]
- Preparation of an anti-fluorescein affinity matrix, which was used to immobilize a fluoresceinated protein in order to study its protein–protein interactions *in vitro* [13,14]
- Separation of fluorescein antibody–labeled cell populations by immunoadsorption [15] or magnetic separation techniques
- Assessment of the accessibility of active site–bound fluorescein probes [16]
- Investigation of the internalization pathway of fluorescein transferrin [17,18] (T2871, Section 16.1)

Ultraviolet photolysis of the nonfluorescent CMNB-caged fluorescein conjugates of goat anti–mouse IgG antibody and goat anti–rabbit IgG antibody (G21061, G21080; Section 7.2) results in formation of green-fluorescent fluorescein conjugates. The fluorescein dye that is liberated serves as a hapten that can be specifically detected and its signal amplified by anti-fluorescein/Oregon Green® antibody conjugates. This unique photoactivation procedure permits the light-mediated generation of a hapten at selected sites, a process similar in utility to photolithography (Section 7.4, Figure 7.74). The DMNB-caged fluorescein dextran conjugates (D3310, D7146; Section 14.5) may have similar utility as light-generated haptens. Caged fluorescein conjugates of other biomolecules can be prepared using the succinimidyl ester of CMNB-caged fluorescein (C20050, Section 1.4, Figure 1.59).

The anti-fluorescein/Oregon Green® antibodies can potentially be used to significantly amplify the signal from nucleic acids labeled by our Oregon Green® fluorophores or from fluorescein-labeled nucleic acid probes. These fluorescent nucleic acid probes can be prepared using ChromaTide® Oregon Green® 488-5-dUTP (C7630, Section 8.2) or the ULYSIS Oregon Green® 488 Nucleic Acid Labeling Kit (U21659, Section 8.2).

Antibody to the Alexa Fluor® 488 Dye

Molecular Probes has prepared a rabbit polyclonal antibody to our green-fluorescent Alexa Fluor® 488 dye (A11094). In a manner analogous to the anti-fluorescein/Oregon Green® antibodies, the anti–Alexa Fluor® 488 dye antibody specifically recognizes and efficiently quenches most of the fluorescence of the Alexa Fluor® 488 dye. In contrast, the anti–Alexa Fluor® 488 dye antibody does not appreciably quench the fluorescence of fluorescein, carboxytetramethylrhodamine (TAMRA) or the Alexa Fluor® 594 dye. The high affinity of the anti–Alexa Fluor® 488 dye antibody makes it potentially useful for various immunochemical applications. This antibody can be used to further amplify the signals from our Alexa Fluor® 488 tyramide–containing TSA Kits (Section 6.2, Table 6.1), as well as those of labeled nucleic acids prepared from our ARES™ Alexa Fluor® 488 Kit (A21665, Section 8.2), ULYSIS Alexa Fluor® 488 Kit (U21650, Section 8.2), Alexa Fluor® 488 Oligonucleotide Amine Labeling Kit (A20191, Section 8.2) or our ChromaTide® Alexa Fluor® 488 UTP, ChromaTide® Alexa Fluor® 488 OBEA-dCTP and ChromaTide® Alexa Fluor® 488 dUTP nucleotides (C11403, C21555, C11397; Section 8.2).

Antibodies to Tetramethylrhodamine and the Rhodamine Red™ and Texas Red® Dyes

As with the anti-fluorescein/Oregon Green® antibodies, the rabbit polyclonal antibodies to the tetramethylrhodamine and Texas Red® fluorophores (A6397, A6399) are effective reagents for binding these dye-based haptens and quenching their fluorescence. However, these antibodies strongly crossreact with some other rhodamines, including the Rhodamine Red™ and Lissamine rhodamine B dyes, and therefore cannot be used for simultaneous detection of more than one rhodamine-based dye. These anti-tetramethylrhodamine and anti–Texas Red® dye antibodies do not appear to crossreact with fluorescein or the Oregon Green® or Alexa Fluor® dyes, and our anti-fluorescein/Oregon Green® antibodies do not crossreact with tetramethylrhodamine or the Rhodamine Red™ or Texas Red® dyes. Anti-tetramethylrhodamine has been used to localize retrogradely transported tetramethylrhodamine dextrans by an immunoperoxidase-based amplification technique.[19] These antibodies should also complex with FISH probes labeled with the TAMRA, ROX, Texas Red® and Spectrum Orange dyes (Section 8.2, Section 8.5) but not with probes prepared from the sulfonated Alexa Fluor® dyes.

Antibodies to the Lucifer Yellow Dye and the Cascade Blue® and Alexa Fluor® 405 Dyes

Lucifer yellow CH (L453) and Cascade Blue® hydrazide (C687) are frequently employed as polar tracers for neuronal cell labeling (Section 14.3). Our unconjugated (A5750, A5760) and biotinylated (A5751) rabbit polyclonal antibodies to these dyes are useful in standard enzyme-mediated immunohistochemical methods for permanently labeling neuronal tissue[20–24] (see Note 14.1 "Product Highlight: Anti–Lucifer Yellow Dye, Anti–Alexa Fluor® 405/Cascade Blue® Dye and Anti–Alexa Fluor® 488 Dye Antibodies" in Section 14.3). Anti–lucifer yellow dye antibody (A5750) has also been used to follow dye coupling in smooth muscle cells by electron microscopy.[25,26] The anti–Alexa Fluor® 405/Cascade Blue® dye antibody (A5760) has been employed in Western blot analysis (Section 9.4) to identify cytoplasmic and luminal domains of the sarcoplasmic reticulum Ca^{2+}-ATPase, which had been photolabeled with Cascade Blue® aminoethyl 4-azidobenzamide.[27] Our Vybrant® Cell Lineage Tracing Kit (V22915, Section 14.5) utilizes a Cascade Blue® dextran conjugate and the anti–Alexa Fluor® 405/Cascade Blue® dye antibody for cell lineage–tracing studies (Figure 7.75). Fluorescence of nucleic acid probes prepared from ChromaTide® Cascade Blue® dUTP (C7612, Section 8.2) can be amplified using our anti–Alexa Fluor® 405/Cascade Blue® dye antibody. Also, the anti–Alexa Fluor® 405/Cascade Blue® dye antibody recognizes conjugates of our Alexa Fluor® 405 succinimidyl ester (A30000, A30100; Section 1.7), which is a derivative of our Cascade Blue® dye with a 4-piperidinecarboxylic acid spacer that separates the fluorophore from its reactive moiety.

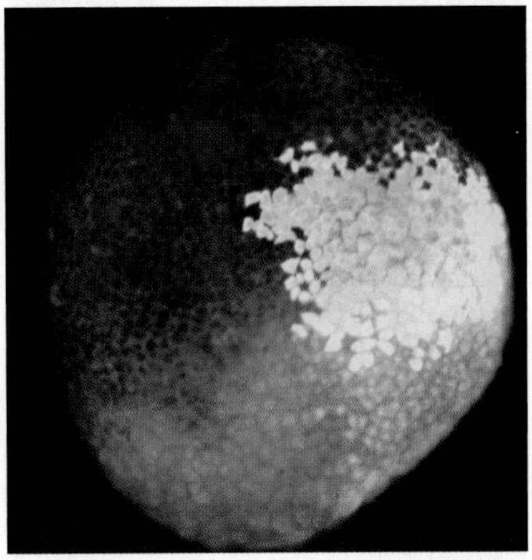

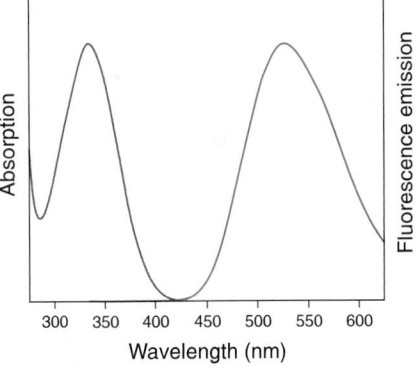

Figure 7.75 Lineage tracing in an African clawed frog (*Xenopus laevis*) embryo performed using the Vybrant® Cell Lineage Tracing Kit (V22915). Embryos at the 8-cell stage were injected with anionic, lysine-fixable Cascade Blue® 10,000 MW dextran in one dorsal-animal blastomere and allowed to develop to various stages before being fixed. The Cascade Blue® dye, which serves as an antigen in this technique, was detected with an antibody to the Cascade Blue® dye and subsequently visualized with a secondary antibody conjugated to the Alexa Fluor® 546 dye (A11010). This photographic image was taken using a bandpass filter set appropriate for rhodamine. The image was contributed by Paul Wilson, Cornell University Medical College, New York, and Greg Cox, Molecular Probes, Inc.

Antibody to the BODIPY® FL Dye

Our unlabeled rabbit polyclonal antibody to the BODIPY® FL fluorophore (A5770) crossreacts with some other BODIPY® dyes but does not crossreact appreciably with any other fluorophores. This anti–BODIPY® FL dye antibody should therefore not be used for simultaneous detection of more than one dye based on the BODIPY® fluorophore. In solution assays, we have found that the anti–BODIPY® FL dye antibody effectively quenches most of the fluorescence of the BODIPY® FL dye, but quenches the BODIPY® TR dye to a lesser degree and does not significantly quench the BODIPY® TMR dye. The anti–BODIPY® FL dye antibody has been used in a fluorescence quenching assay to determine the accessibility of BODIPY® FL dye–labeled cysteine residues in the transmembrane domain of diphtheria toxin.[28–31] This antibody should be particularly useful for detection schemes that amplify the signals from nucleic acids that have incorporated the ChromaTide® BODIPY® FL-14-UTP and ChromaTide® BODIPY® FL-14-dUTP nucleotides (C7613, C7614; Section 8.2). Other applications of the anti–BODIPY® FL dye antibody should include many of those in which the BODIPY® FL dyes are used as a simple hapten, such as those described above for anti-fluorescein/Oregon Green® antibodies.

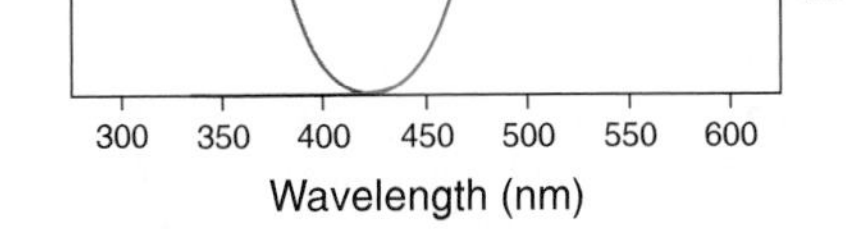

Figure 7.76 Absorption and fluorescence emission spectra of dansyl cadaverine in methanol.

Anti-Dansyl Antibody

In contrast to the other anti-fluorophore antibodies, which usually quench the fluorescence of the dye to which they bind, our rabbit polyclonal anti-dansyl antibody (A6398) typically *enhances* the fluorescence of dansyl amides by greater than 10-fold. Binding of the anti-dansyl antibody also blue shifts the emission spectrum of the fluorophore in water from ~520 nm to ~450 nm. These properties, combined with the unusually high Stokes shift of the dansyl dye (Figure 7.76), make this antibody particularly useful for determining the topography of dansyl-labeled probes, including that of dansyl-labeled phospholipids (Section 13.2) in cell and artificial membranes.[32] The dansyl hapten is preferably incorporated into biomolecules using the succinimidyl ester of dansyl-X (D6104, Section 4.2) because its aminohexanoyl spacer ("X") reduces the interaction of the fluorophore with the biomolecule to which it is conjugated and makes it more accessible to anti-dansyl antibodies.[32–34]

Efficient Quenching by Anti-Fluorophore Antibodies

Quenching Efficiencies

Except for the anti-dansyl antibody, which enhances the fluorescence of the dansyl fluorophore, all of our anti-fluorophore antibodies strongly quench the fluorescence of their complementary dyes in free solution. For example, our anti-fluorescein/Oregon Green® antibodies typically effect up to 95% quenching of the fluorescence of both fluorescein and the Oregon Green® 488 dye. The anti-fluorescein/Oregon Green® antibody also quenches some other fluorescein derivatives, such as carboxyfluorescein, Calcium Green™-1 and BCECF, making this antibody useful for reducing background fluorescence caused by leakage of these dyes from the cell.[35] However, quenching of our fluorescein-based Ca^{2+} indicators by our anti-fluorescein/Oregon Green® IgG antibody is apparently dependent on whether or not Ca^{2+} is bound; Calcium Green™-1 is quenched by 89% in the presence of 5 µM Ca^{2+}, whereas it is quenched by only 46% in the presence of 10 mM EGTA. Maximal quenching efficiencies for fluorescein analogs (all at 5 nM dye using the rabbit anti-fluorescein/Oregon Green® IgG antibody, A889) are as follows (values may vary somewhat from batch to batch) and may be different using the goat anti-fluorescein/Oregon Green® IgG antibody, A11095, the mouse monoclonal anti-fluorescein/Oregon Green®, A6421 or the rabbit IgG Fab fragment of anti-fluorescein/Oregon Green®, A6413):

- Oregon Green® 488 dye, 95%
- Oregon Green® 514 dye, 92%
- Carboxyfluorescein, 93%
- Calcium Green™-1 (in the presence of 5 µM Ca^{2+}), 89%
- Calcium Green™-1 (in the presence of 10 mM EGTA), 46%
- BCECF, 43%
- Fluo-3 (in the presence of 5 µM Ca^{2+}), 32%
- Rhodamine Green™ dye, 9%
- Calcein, <5%
- Tetramethylrhodamine, <5%

Our preparations of the anti-tetramethylrhodamine and anti–Texas Red® dye antibodies are somewhat less effective as fluorescence quenchers of their complementary fluorophores, with maximal quenching efficiencies of ~75% and ~60%, respectively. Our rabbit anti–Alexa Fluor® 488 dye IgG antibody quenches the fluorescence of the free Alexa Fluor® 488 dye by >90%. Our antibody to the BODIPY® FL fluorophore typically quenches the dye's fluorescence by ~90%. It also quenches BODIPY® TR dye fluorescence by ~45%, but does not significantly quench BODIPY® TMR dye fluorescence. Antibodies to the lucifer yellow and Alexa Fluor® 405/Cascade Blue® fluorophores quench the fluorescence of their complementary dyes by ~85% and ~80%, respectively. In addition, anti-DNP antibodies have been reported to significantly quench the fluorescence of aminonitrobenzoxadiazoles[36] (NBD amines).

Quenching Assay

Molecular Probes uses a sensitive fluorescence quenching–based assay to ensure that the concentration of specific anti-dye antibody in its purified IgG fractions is provided at a consistently high titer. As supplied, 20 µL of the antibody solution is certified to produce ≥50% of the maximal fluorescence quenching (or enhancement, in the case of anti-dansyl antibody) of 1 mL of a 50 nM solution of the corresponding dye, assayed in 100 mM sodium phosphate, pH 8.0. All maximal quenching values are determined using the free fluorophore; the maximal quenching of a fluorophore covalently bound to a protein is often significantly less due to steric hindrance.

This fluorescence quenching assay cannot be applied to our fluorophore-labeled anti-fluorescein/Oregon Green® IgG antibody conjugates or to our anti-fluorescein/Oregon Green® monoclonal antibody (A6421); these products typically contain 0.5 mg of total protein.

Applications for Fluorescence Quenching by Anti-Fluorophore Antibodies

Fluorescence quenching of dye haptens by anti-dye antibodies provides a useful measure of topography in cells, proteins and membranes. For example, researchers have used anti-fluorescein quenching assays to determine the accessibility of a fluorescein-labeled ATP-binding site in both Na^+/K^+-ATPase and Ca^{2+}/Mg^{2+}-ATPase.[16,37] Similarly, the anti–BODIPY® FL dye antibody has been employed to identify shallow- and deep-membrane–penetrating forms of diphtheria toxin T domain.[28–31] In addition, anti-fluorophore antibodies have been used as cell-impermeant probes for determining whether fluorescent dye–conjugated ligands, proteins, bacteria or other biomolecules have been internalized by endocytic or pinocytic processes[38–41] (Section 16.1). Anti-fluorophore antibodies also permit background-free observation of fusion events in an assay designed to monitor the fusion of membrane vesicles *in vitro*.[42] However, as noted above, these antibodies may quench dye-labeled proteins less effectively than they quench free dyes.

Anti-Dinitrophenyl Antibody

Because of its high affinity for the dinitrophenyl (DNP) hapten,[43,44] our anti-DNP polyclonal rabbit antibodies (Table 7.19) are excellent reagents for probing DNP-labeled molecules, including nucleic acid probes prepared using our ChromaTide® dinitrophenyl-11-dUTP nucleotide (C7610MP, Section 8.2). Unlike assays that use biotin as the hapten, it is usually easy to determine the degree of substitution of the DNP hapten in bioconjugates from the dye's visible absorption near 350 nm[45] (ε~18,000 $cm^{-1}M^{-1}$). It has been reported that human chromosomes can be probed with equal sensitivities using either biotinylated, DNP-modified or digoxigenin-modified cosmid probes.[46] Anti-DNP antibodies have been used to localize a DNP-labeled DNA probe in HIV-infected cells[47] and 2,4-dinitrophenylhydrazine-labeled proteins on blots.[48,49] Researchers have also reported using anti-DNP antibodies to probe for DNP-labeled IgG as a method for detecting sparse antigens[50] and, in conjunction with DNP-labeled bovine serum albumin (BSA), to study the Fc receptor–mediated endocytosis of IgG complexes.[51,52]

A major application of our anti-DNP antibody and its conjugates is expected to be detection of the DNP hapten that is generated by HRP-mediated deposition of DNP-X tyramide, the key reagent in our TSA Kits #34, #35 and #36 (T20944, T20945, T20946; Section 6.2). The DNP-X tyramide–containing TSA Kits have the significant advantage over biotin-XX tyramide–containing TSA Kits in that there is no endogenous DNP in cells, as is the case when biotin is the hapten (Figure 7.98, Figure 12.27).

In addition to the unlabeled anti-DNP antibody (A6430), Molecular Probes offers anti-DNP antibody conjugates of biotin-XX (A6435), fluorescein (A6423) and the Alexa Fluor® 488 dye (A11097). Our anti-DNP antibody is prepared against DNP–keyhole limpet hemocyanin (DNP-KLH) and thus the antibody and its conjugates do not crossreact with BSA, a common blocking reagent in hybridization applications.

For use in conjunction with our anti-DNP antibody, Molecular Probes offers the DNP-X succinimidyl ester (D2248, Section 4.2) for labeling proteins and amine-modified DNA. The literature also describes methods for incorporating DNP into DNA using DNP-labeled primers.[53] In addition to recognizing DNP, our anti-DNP antibody crossreacts with trinitrobenzenesulfonic acid–modified proteins, making this antibody useful both for localizing and for isolating cell-surface molecules labeled with either DNP or TNP.[53] Furthermore, anti-DNP antibodies have been reported to quench aminonitrobenzoxadiazoles (NBD amines),[36] indicating that NBD-X succinimidyl ester (S1167, Section 1.7) will also be a useful haptenylating reagent for use with this antibody.

Anti-Nitrotyrosine Antibody

Our antibody to nitrotyrosine (A21285) is raised in rabbits that have been immunized with nitrated KLH. Nitrotyrosine-modified proteins are the principal reaction products of nitric oxide (through the formation of peroxynitrite) in cells (Section 18.3). Because tyrosine residues are also conveniently converted to nitrotyrosine by reaction at near-neutral pH with tetranitromethane,[54,55] the nitrotyrosine hapten can be readily created in almost any peptide or protein that contains a tyrosine residue. A further advantage is that nitrotyrosine has pH-dependent visible absorbance (absorption maxima ~360 nm[54] and 428 nm[56]) that can be utilized to detect formation of the hapten in soluble biopolymers. Our anti-nitrotyrosine antibody is useful for detection of nitrotyrosine-containing peptides and proteins both in cells (Figure 7.77) and on Western blots (Section 18.3, Figure 18.23). This rabbit IgG antibody can be labeled with fluorophores, biotin or enzymes using any of our Zenon® Rabbit IgG Antibody Labeling Kits (Section 7.3, Table 7.13).

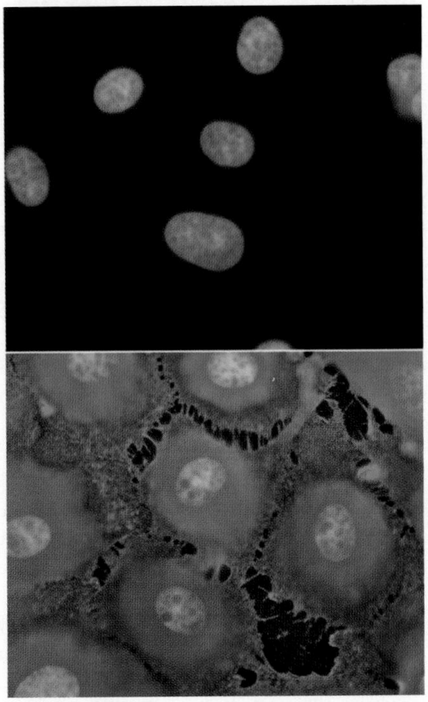

Figure 7.77 Fixed and permeabilized bovine pulmonary artery endothelial cells were treated with either degraded peroxynitrite (top panel) or ~100 µM peroxynitrite (bottom panel) for five minutes at room temperature to induce protein nitration. Nitrated tyrosine residues were detected with our rabbit anti-nitrotyrosine antibody (A21285) and visualized with the green-fluorescent Alexa Fluor® 488 goat anti–rabbit IgG antibody (A11008). Nuclei were counterstained with blue-fluorescent DAPI (D1306, D3571, D21490).

Anti-Biotin Antibody

The high affinity of avidin for biotin was first exploited in histochemical applications in the early 1970's.[57,58] The use of avidin–biotin techniques has since become standard for diverse detection schemes, although limitations of this method have also been recognized.[59,60] As an alternative to avidin-based reagents, Molecular Probes offers unlabeled, Alexa Fluor® 488 dye–labeled and Alexa Fluor® 594 dye–labeled versions of a high-affinity mouse monoclonal antibody to biotin (A11242, A31801, A31800). Our anti-biotin antibody can be used to detect biotinylated molecules in immunohistochemistry, *in situ* hybridization, ELISAs and Western blot applications. Somewhat unexpectedly, our anti-biotin antibody retains high affinity for desthiobiotin; consequently, its binding to DSB-X™ biotin bioconjugates cannot be easily reversed by addition of free D-biotin.[61]

It has been shown that certain monoclonal antibodies to biotin have biotin-binding motifs that are similar to those seen for avidin and streptavidin.[62] Anti-biotin antibody has been shown to selectively stain endogenous biotin-dependent carboxylase proteins used in fatty acid synthesis of the mitochondria.[63,64] Nonspecific staining of mitochondrial proteins by labeled avidins and by anti-biotin antibodies can be a complicating factor in using avidin–biotin techniques (Figure 7.98). This nonspecific binding can usually be blocked by pretreatment of the sample with the reagents in our Endogenous Biotin-Blocking Kit (E21390, Section 7.6).

Especially useful for indirect immunofluorescence, the green-fluorescent Alexa Fluor® 488 conjugate exhibits excitation/emission maxima similar to fluorescein, but its fluorescence is brighter, more photostable and pH insensitive. Likewise, the red-fluorescent Alexa Fluor® 594 conjugate is spectrally similar but much more fluorescent than Texas Red® conjugates, making it particularly useful for multilabeling experiments in combination with green-fluorescent probes. Because it is a mouse IgG_1 antibody, our anti-biotin antibody can be used with any of our Zenon® Mouse IgG_1 Labeling Kits (Section 7.3, Table 7.13) to create even more alternatives to avidin-based reagents for the detection of biotinylated probes.

Auxiliary Reagents for Use with Anti-Dye and Anti-Hapten Antibodies

Use of the anti-fluorophore, anti-DNP or anti-biotin antibodies requires a means for the selective incorporation of their haptens into proteins, nucleic acids, other biomolecules and cells. Hapten-labeled probes are particularly important for localizing targets in cells and organelles, on blots and in other applications. Detection with an anti-dye antibody permits significant amplification beyond what is possible with the dye itself. This method can also be used for correlated fluorescence and electron microscopy studies. Anti-fluorophore and anti-biotin antibodies may be particularly useful in combination with the TSA and ELF® technologies (Section 6.2, Section 6.3). Molecular Probes has an assortment of reactive haptens, hapten-labeled probes and hapten-labeling kits for these applications, including:

- Chemically reactive haptenylation reagents complementary to each of our anti-dye and anti-hapten antibodies (Section 4.2, Table 4.2)
- ARES™ and ULYSIS Nucleic Acid Labeling Kits and Alexa Fluor® Oligonucleotide Amine Labeling Kits (Section 8.2)
- Protein Labeling Kits for incorporating biotin, biotin/DNP, DSB-X™ biotin or a wide variety of fluorophores (Section 1.2; Table 1.2, Table 1.3)
- ChromaTide® and aha nucleotides — dUTP, aha-dUTP, OBEA-dCTP or UTP labeled with the fluorescein, Oregon Green® 488, Alexa Fluor® 488, BODIPY® FL, tetramethylrhodamine, Texas Red®, Texas Red®-X or Cascade Blue® fluorophores or the DNP dye (Section 8.2; Table 8.6, Table 8.7)
- Biotin-XX tyramide, DSB-X™ biotin tyramide, DNP-X tyramide, Oregon Green® 488 tyramide and Alexa Fluor® 488 tyramide, as components of some of our TSA Kits, for enzyme-amplified staining of cells and tissues (Section 6.2, Table 6.1)
- CellTracker™ Green CMFDA, CellTracker™ Orange CMTMR and CellTracker™ Green BODIPY®, derived from fluorescein, tetramethylrhodamine and BODIPY® FL dyes, respectively, for cell tracing (Section 14.2)
- LysoTracker® Green DND–26 (L7526) and DAMP (D1552), which are recognized by our antibodies against the BODIPY® FL dye and 2,4-dinitrophenyl (DNP), respectively, for selective staining and ultrastructural localization of intracellular compartments with low pH (Section 12.3, Table 12.7)
- MitoTracker® Orange CMTMRos and MitoTracker® Red CMXRos, both of which are recognized by the anti-tetramethylrhodamine and anti–Texas Red® dye antibodies, for selective mitochondrial staining (Section 12.2, Table 12.2)
- Biotinylated dextrans, lipids, proteins and microspheres (Section 4.3)
- Polar fluorescent tracers, including derivatives of the Alexa Fluor® 488, Oregon Green®, Cascade Blue® and lucifer yellow dyes and of biotin that can be fixed in cells by aldehyde-based fixatives (Section 14.3)
- Several fluorescent biocytin derivatives (Section 14.3), which permit detection by both avidin–biotin and fluorophore–anti-fluorophore techniques

References

1. J Histochem Cytochem 38, 467 (1990); **2.** Fluorescein Hapten: An Immunological Probe, Voss EW, Ed. (Complete Volume) (1984); **3.** J Immunol Methods 122, 115 (1989); **4.** J Histochem Cytochem 48, 1593 (2000); **5.** Appl Environ Microbiol 66, 4258 (2000); **6.** J Biol Chem 275, 11050 (2000); **7.** Mol Biol Cell 10, 4385 (1999); **8.** J Immunol Methods 137, 103 (1991); **9.** J Histochem Cytochem 38, 325 (1990); **10.** J Immunol Methods 117, 45 (1989); **11.** J Cell Biol 111, 249 (1990); **12.** Am J Physiol 258, C309 (1990); **13.** J Clin Microbiol 35, 578 (1997); **14.** J Biol Chem 257, 13095 (1982); **15.** J Immunol Methods 53, 321 (1982); **16.** FEBS Lett 253, 273 (1989); **17.** J Cell Biol 106, 1083 (1988); **18.** Proc Natl Acad Sci U S A 79, 6186 (1982); **19.** J Neurosci Methods 65, 157 (1996); **20.** Cell 81, 631 (1995); **21.** J Neurosci 15, 4851 (1995); **22.** Neuroscience Protocols, Wouterlood FG, Ed. 93-050-06, pp. 01–13 (1993); **23.** J Neurosci Methods 41, 45 (1992); **24.** Dev Biol 94, 391 (1982); **25.** Circ Res 70, 49 (1992); **26.** Endothelium-Derived Relaxing Factors, Rubanyi GM, Vanhoutte PM, Eds. pp. 117–123 (1990); **27.** Biochim Biophys Acta 1068, 27 (1991); **28.** J Biol Chem 273, 22950 (1998); **29.** Biochemistry 38, 976 (1999); **30.** Science 284, 955 (1999); **31.** J Biol Chem 272, 25091 (1997); **32.** Biochim Biophys Acta 1104, 9 (1992); **33.** Biochim Biophys Acta 776, 217 (1984); **34.** Biochemistry 21, 978 (1982); **35.** J Biol Chem 266, 24540 (1991); **36.** Biochemistry 16, 5150 (1977); **37.** Biochemistry 30, 1692 (1991); **38.** Biochemistry 30, 2888 (1991); **39.** Biochim Biophys Acta 817, 238 (1985); **40.** Biochim Biophys Acta 778, 612 (1984); **41.** J Biol Chem 259, 5661 (1984); **42.** FEBS Lett 197, 274 (1986); **43.** J Exp Med 145, 931 (1977); **44.** Adv Immunol 2, 1 (1962); **45.** J Immunol Methods 150, 193 (1992); **46.** Science 247, 64 (1990); **47.** Biotechniques 9, 186 (1990); **48.** Free Radic Biol Med 17, 429 (1994); **49.** Chem Res Toxicol 6, 430 (1993); **50.** J Histochem Cytochem 38, 69 (1990); **51.** Cell 58, 317 (1989); **52.** J Cell Biol 98, 1170 (1984); **53.** Nucleic Acids Res 18, 3175 (1990); **54.** Electrophoresis 20, 2519 (1999); **55.** Biochemistry 34, 12524 (1995); **56.** J Biol Chem 251, 308 (1976); **57.** Proc Natl Acad Sci U S A 71, 3537 (1974); **58.** Biochim Biophys Acta 264, 165 (1972); **59.** Methods Enzymol 184, (Complete Volume) (1990); **60.** Methods Biochem Anal 26, 1 (1980); **61.** Anal Biochem 308, 343 (2002); **62.** FEBS Lett 322, 47 (1993); **63.** J Histochem Cytochem 45, 1053 (1997); **64.** Histochemistry 100, 415 (1993).

Product List — 7.4 Anti-Dye and Anti-Hapten Antibodies

Cat #	Product Name	Unit Size
A11053	Alexa Fluor® 488 Signal-Amplification Kit for Fluorescein- and Oregon Green® Dye–Conjugated Probes *60-120 assays*	1 kit
A5760	anti-Alexa Fluor® 405/Cascade Blue®, rabbit IgG fraction *3 mg/mL*	0.5 mL
A11094	anti-Alexa Fluor® 488, rabbit IgG fraction *1 mg/mL*	0.5 mL
A11242	anti-biotin, mouse IgG_1, monoclonal 2F5	100 µg
A31801	anti-biotin, mouse IgG_1, monoclonal 2F5, Alexa Fluor® 488 conjugate *1 mg/mL*	100 µL
A31800	anti-biotin, mouse IgG_1, monoclonal 2F5, Alexa Fluor® 594 conjugate *1 mg/mL*	100 µL
A5770	anti-BODIPY® FL, rabbit IgG fraction *3 mg/mL*	0.5 mL
A6398	anti-dansyl, rabbit IgG fraction *1 mg/mL*	0.5 mL
A6430	anti-dinitrophenyl-KLH, rabbit IgG fraction *2 mg/mL*	0.5 mL
A11097	anti-dinitrophenyl-KLH, rabbit IgG fraction, Alexa Fluor® 488 conjugate *2 mg/mL*	0.5 mL
A6435	anti-dinitrophenyl-KLH, rabbit IgG fraction, biotin-XX conjugate *2 mg/mL*	0.5 mL
A6423	anti-dinitrophenyl-KLH, rabbit IgG fraction, fluorescein conjugate *2 mg/mL*	0.5 mL
A11095	anti-fluorescein/Oregon Green®, goat IgG fraction *1 mg/mL*	0.5 mL
A11096	anti-fluorescein/Oregon Green®, goat IgG fraction, Alexa Fluor® 488 conjugate *1 mg/mL*	0.5 mL
A6421	anti-fluorescein/Oregon Green®, mouse IgG_{2a}, monoclonal 4-4-20	0.5 mg
A6413	anti-fluorescein/Oregon Green®, rabbit IgG Fab fragment *0.5 mg/mL*	0.5 mL
A21254	anti-fluorescein/Oregon Green®, rabbit IgG $F(ab')_2$ fragment, horseradish peroxidase conjugate	250 µg
A889	anti-fluorescein/Oregon Green®, rabbit IgG fraction *1 mg/mL*	0.5 mL
A11090	anti-fluorescein/Oregon Green®, rabbit IgG fraction, Alexa Fluor® 488 conjugate *1 mg/mL*	0.5 mL
A11091	anti-fluorescein/Oregon Green®, rabbit IgG fraction, Alexa Fluor® 594 conjugate *1 mg/mL*	0.5 mL
A982	anti-fluorescein/Oregon Green®, rabbit IgG fraction, biotin-XX conjugate *1 mg/mL*	0.5 mL
A21253	anti-fluorescein/Oregon Green®, rabbit IgG fraction, horseradish peroxidase conjugate	0.5 mg
A21250	anti-fluorescein/Oregon Green®, rabbit IgG fraction, R-phycoerythrin conjugate *2 mg/mL*	250 µL
A5750	anti-lucifer yellow, rabbit IgG fraction *3 mg/mL*	0.5 mL
A5751	anti-lucifer yellow, rabbit IgG fraction, biotin-XX conjugate *3 mg/mL*	0.5 mL
A21285	anti-nitrotyrosine, rabbit IgG fraction *1 mg/mL*	0.5 mL
A6397	anti-tetramethylrhodamine, rabbit IgG fraction *1 mg/mL*	0.5 mL
A6399	anti-Texas Red®, rabbit IgG fraction *1 mg/mL*	0.5 mL

For current prices or to order online, visit probes.invitrogen.com

7.5 Primary Antibodies for Diverse Applications

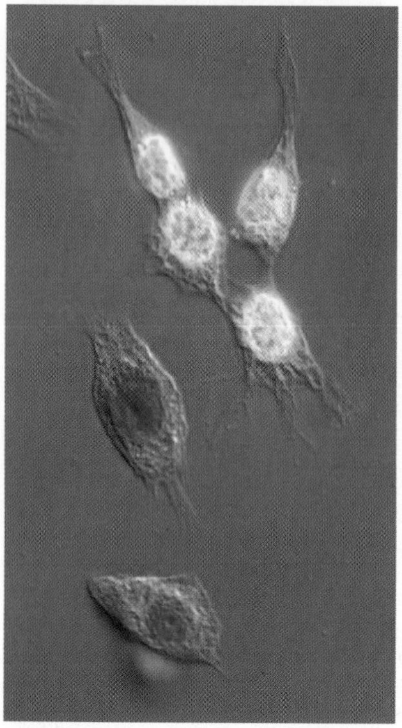

Figure 7.78 NIH 3T3 cells that were transiently transfected with a green-fluorescent protein (GFP) expression vector, then plated and allowed to attach and proliferate. The cells were fixed and labeled with our Alexa Fluor® 594 conjugate of the anti-GFP antibody (A21312). About 10% of the cells were expressing GFP and show dual labeling of both GFP (green fluorescence) and the anti-GFP antibody (red fluorescence). In this overlay of fluorescence and differential interference contrast (DIC) micrographs, the GFP-transfected cells exhibit green and red signals that overlap to yield yellow, and DAPI (D1306, D3571, D21490) stains the nuclei with a light-blue fluorescence. In the cells that are not transfected, the DAPI-stained nuclei exhibit a bright blue fluorescence.

Our polyclonal and monoclonal primary antibodies are directed toward some important reporter gene products (green-fluorescent protein (GFP), glutathione *S*-transferase (GST), glucuronidase and galactosidase) and epitope tags (oligohistidine, hemagglutinin and c-myc), as well as proteins found in the cytoskeleton, synaptic vesicles, neurons, mitochondria and yeast. Additionally, we provide monoclonal antibodies to the important cell proliferation markers BrdU, cyclins and a cdc6 peptide, to phosphatidylinositol polyphosphates, which are important in cell signaling and binding to various protein domains, and to matrix metalloproteins (MMPs), which are cell-surface proteins with a number of important biological properties. Some of these antibodies are discussed in detail in other chapters. All of our primary antibodies, other than our antibodies directed at dyes and other low molecular weight haptens, which are discussed in Section 7.4, appear in the product list for this section.

Most of our monoclonal and polyclonal antibodies to specific proteins are particularly valuable for immunostaining applications that involve detection with a fluorescent dye– or enzyme-conjugated secondary antibody (Section 7.2). We have utilized several of our mouse IgG primary antibodies (Table 7.14, Table 7.15, Table 7.16) and rabbit IgG primary antibodies (Table 7.17) in developing our exclusive Zenon® technology (Section 7.3, Table 7.13). The Zenon® antibody labeling method (Figure 7.59) is, by far, the most efficient method available for labeling small quantities of antibodies; it even permits their selective labeling in serum, ascites fluid and hybridoma supernatants. The tyramide signal amplification (TSA) and Enzyme-Labeled Fluorescence (ELF®) technologies, which are discussed in Section 6.2 and Section 6.3, respectively, are useful for detecting low-abundance targets in cells and tissues. TSA technology also permits far less antibody to be used in the detection scheme, saving the cost of expensive antibodies. The combination of mouse monoclonal antibody labeling with our Zenon® Horseradish Peroxidase Mouse IgG Labeling Kits (Section 7.3, Table 7.13) and detection with a fluorescent tyramide (Table 6.1) has the greatest potential for yielding a very high signal from a very small amount of the primary antibody or a low copy number of the target at the lowest cost to the researcher. Most of the antibodies that we offer are also useful for detecting proteins on Western blots and are compatible with our ultrasensitive DyeChrome™, Amplex® Gold or Pro-Q® Western Blot Stain Kits (Section 9.4, Table 9.7) for simultaneous staining of specific proteins and total proteins.

Polyclonal Antibodies Specific for Reporter Gene Products

Anti–Green-Fluorescent Protein Antibodies

Expression of the intrinsically fluorescent green-fluorescent protein (GFP) from the jellyfish *Aequorea victoria* has become a popular method for following gene expression and protein localization.[1–5] Molecular Probes offers a rabbit polyclonal antibody that is raised against GFP purified directly from *A. victoria*. This anti-GFP antibody, which is available as a complete serum (A6455) or as an IgG fraction (A11122), facilitates the detection of native GFP, recombinant GFP and GFP-fusion proteins by immunofluorescence (Figure 7.78), Western blot analysis[6] (Section 9.4) and immunoprecipitation. Direct conjugates made from the IgG fraction, using four of our best Alexa Fluor® dyes, are also available:

- Green-fluorescent Alexa Fluor® 488 rabbit anti-GFP antibody (A21311)
- Orange-fluorescent Alexa Fluor® 555 rabbit anti-GFP antibody (A31851)
- Red-fluorescent Alexa Fluor® 594 rabbit anti-GFP antibody (A21312)
- Far-red–fluorescent Alexa Fluor® 647 rabbit anti-GFP antibody (A31852)

Additionally, Molecular Probes offers two monoclonal anti-GFP antibodies purified from mouse hybridoma supernatants. Monoclonal 11E5 (anti-GFP, clone 11E5; A11121) is optimized for Western analysis, allowing colorimetric detection of as little as 10 ng of GFP or GFP-fusion proteins, or chemiluminescent detection of picogram quantities using the ultrasensitive BOLD APB chemiluminescent substrate for membrane-based alkaline phosphatase detection (B21901, Section 9.4). Monoclonal 3E6 (anti-GFP, clone 3E6; A11120) is useful for immunoprecipitation, immunocytochemical localization and immunosorbent assays (ELISAs). Monoclonals 11E5 and 3E6 are mouse IgG_1 and IgG_{2a} antibodies, respectively, and can therefore be labeled with a fluorophore, biotin or enzyme using the corresponding Zenon® Mouse IgG_1 or Zenon® Mouse IgG_{2a} Labeling Kits (Section 7.3, Table 7.13). The rabbit polyclonal anti-GFP antibody can be labeled with our Zenon® Rabbit IgG Labeling Kits (Section 7.3, Table 7.13).

Anti–Glutathione S-Transferase Antibody

One common partner in protein fusions is glutathione *S*-transferase (GST), a protein with natural binding specificity for glutathione that can be exploited to facilitate its purification.[7] Because the GST portion of the fusion protein retains its affinity and selectivity for glutathione, the fusion protein can be conveniently purified from the cell lysate in a single step by affinity chromatography on glutathione agarose[8–13] (Figure 9.16). For the purification of GST fusion proteins, Molecular Probes offers glutathione linked via the sulfur atom to crosslinked beaded agarose (Section 9.2), which is available as 10 mL of a sedimented bead suspension (G2879) or in a 100 mL bulk packaging (G21800). We also prepare a highly purified rabbit polyclonal anti-GST antibody (A5800) that can be used for Western blot analysis, immunodetection and immunoprecipitation of GST fusion proteins.[14,15] This highly specific and high-titer antibody, which was generated against a 260–amino acid N-terminal fragment of the *Schistosoma japonica* enzyme expressed in *Escherichia coli*, is particularly useful for detecting GST distribution in cells.[15–17] To facilitate the localization of GST and GST-fusion proteins using immunofluorescence techniques, we prepare the anti-GST antibody labeled with our green-fluorescent Alexa Fluor® 488 dye (A11131). Conjugates of the Alexa Fluor® 488 dye, which can be viewed with optical filters appropriate for fluorescein (Table 23.9), are brighter and much more photostable than fluorescein conjugates (Figure 1.9, Figure 1.10, Figure 1.11). Our Zenon® Rabbit IgG Labeling Kits (Section 7.3, Table 7.13) can also be used to prepare fluorescent dye–, biotin- or enzyme-labeled complexes of this antibody.

The Glutathione Transferase Fusion Protein Purification Kit (G21801) is designed to facilitate separation and characterization of GST-fusion proteins. This kit can be used to perform five purifications and contains:

- Glutathione agarose, linked through sulfur
- High-purity glutathione
- Rabbit polyclonal anti-GST antibody
- Purification columns
- A detailed protocol

Anti–β-Glucuronidase Antibody

The *E. coli* β-glucuronidase (GUS) gene (*uidA*) is a popular reporter gene in plants.[18–21] For Western blot and immunohistochemical analysis of transformed plant tissue[22,23] and transfected animal cells,[24] Molecular Probes prepares unlabeled rabbit anti–β-glucuronidase antibody (A5790) raised against *E. coli* type X-A β-glucuronidase. Our Zenon® Rabbit IgG Labeling Kits (Section 7.3, Table 7.13) can be used to prepare fluorescent dye–, biotin- or enzyme-labeled complexes of this antibody. Our fluorogenic and chromogenic β-glucuronidase substrates are described in Section 10.2.

Anti–β-Galactosidase Antibody

Molecular Probes has available a polyclonal antibody to the widely used reporter gene product β-galactosidase. Our rabbit anti–β-galactosidase antibody (A11132) is raised against *E. coli*–derived β-galactosidase and demonstrates high specificity for the enzyme. Whether the enzyme is used as a reporter or as a fusion protein, this antibody provides an easy tool for detecting the β-galactosidase protein. The antibody is suited to a variety of techniques, including immunoblotting, ELISA, immunoprecipitation and most immunological methods. Our Zenon® Rabbit IgG Labeling Kits (Section 7.3, Table 7.13) can be used to prepare fluorescent dye–, biotin- or enzyme-labeled complexes of this antibody. Our fluorogenic and chromogenic β-galactosidase substrates are described in Section 10.2.

Monoclonal Antibodies Specific for Epitope Tags

Epitope tagging is a powerful and versatile strategy for detecting and purifying proteins expressed by cloned genes. Protein expression vectors are often engineered with a nucleotide sequence that encodes a peptide epitope tag. Typically, a gene is cloned in-frame relative to the epitope tag such that, upon expression, a fusion protein containing the epitope tag is synthesized. Detection and purification of the epitope-tagged fusion protein can be mediated by antibodies to the engineered peptide, thus eliminating the need for antibodies to proteins from each newly cloned gene. Molecular Probes offers a series of antibodies to common epitopes, including oligohistidine, hemagglutinin (HA) and c-myc.

Penta·His Antibody

The oligohistidine domain is a Ni^{2+}-binding peptide sequence comprising a sequence of four to six histidine residues.[25,26] When the DNA sequence corresponding to an oligohistidine domain is fused in frame with a gene of interest, the resulting recombinant fusion protein can be easily purified using a nickel-chelating resin.[26,27]

In collaboration with QIAGEN, Molecular Probes has available a highly selective antibody to oligohistidine fusion proteins (Penta·His mouse monoclonal antibody, P21315). The antibody is useful for detecting sequences of five or six histidine residues, whether present at the C-terminus, the N-terminus or an internal position in a protein, in both Western blots and in immunohistochemistry.

The Penta·His antibody can detect as little as 1–2 ng in Western blot applications using fluorescent or chemiluminescent development techniques (Figure 9.77); the supplied amount (100 µg) is sufficient for 50–100 minigel blots. This antibody does not recognize tetrahistidine domains or domains in which the histidine string is interrupted by another amino acid. The antibody binds to the oligohistidine domain regardless of the surrounding amino acid context and even when the group is partially hidden, although subtle differences in the amino acid context may change the sensitivity limit for a particular fusion protein. The Penta·His antibody is directly useful for immunoprecipitation, ELISAs and immunohistochemistry. Alternatively, for subsequent detection of oligohistidine fusion proteins by almost any assay scheme, the mouse IgG_1 Penta·His antibody can be rapidly and quantitatively labeled with a fluorophore, biotin or an enzyme using the Zenon Mouse IgG_1 Labeling Kits (Section 7.3, Table 7.13).

In addition to the Penta·His antibody, Molecular Probes has developed blot stains and gel stains that can selectively detect oligohistidine fusion proteins in complex mixtures. These exceptional products, which are described in Section 9.4, include the following:

- Pro-Q® Oligohistidine Blot Stain Kit #1 — includes biotin NTA, streptavidin and DDAO phosphate (P21878)
- Pro-Q® Oligohistidine Blot Stain Kit #2 — includes biotin NTA, streptavidin and ELF® 39 phosphate (P21879)
- Pro-Q® Sapphire 365 oligohistidine gel stain (P21876)
- Pro-Q® Sapphire 488 oligohistidine gel stain (P21877)
- Pro-Q® Sapphire 532 oligohistidine gel stain (P33354)

Anti-HA Antibody

Molecular Probes' mouse monoclonal anti-hemagglutinin (HA) antibody[28] was raised against the 12–amino acid peptide CYPYDVPDYASL. It recognizes the influenza hemagglutinin epitope YPYDVPDYA, which has been used extensively as a general epitope tag in expression vectors.[29] The extreme specificity of this antibody permits unambiguous identification and quantitative analysis of the tagged protein. This antibody is effective in immunoblotting, immunofluorescence and immunoprecipitation of tagged proteins. We offer Alexa Fluor® 488 (A21287) and Alexa Fluor® 594 (A21288) conjugates of the anti-HA antibody, for those applications that require a directly conjugated antibody.

Anti–c-myc Antibody

Molecular Probes offers two antibodies to c-myc, which is commonly used in epitope tagging.[29] Our mouse monoclonal anti–c-myc antibody ($IgG_{1,\kappa}$, clone 238-19510; A21280) was raised against the peptide AEEQKLISEEDLLRKRREQLKHKLEQLRNSCA, which corresponds to amino acids 408–439 of the human c-myc protein. The chicken anti–c-myc antibody (IgY, A21281) was raised against the peptide EQKLISEEDL. These antibodies specifically react with the C-terminal epitope (AEEQKLISEEDL)[30] of human c-myc protein encoded in many expression vectors. For direct detection, the mouse monoclonal anti–c-myc antibody can be labeled with any of our Zenon® Mouse IgG_1 Labeling Kits (Section 7.3, Table 7.13). The chicken anti–c-myc antibody can be detected using any of our fluorescent anti–chicken IgG secondary antibodies (Section 7.2, Table 7.1). Chicken secondary antibodies have gained popularity because they demonstrate a lower level of nonspecific binding. Chicken IgY antibodies, which are functionally equivalent to mammalian IgG antibodies, lack a classical "Fc" domain and are not bound by protein A or protein G, nor do they bind to Fc receptors for mammalian IgG.

SelectFX™ Labeling Kits with Organelle-Specific Antibodies

SelectFX™ Alexa Fluor® 488 Endoplasmic Reticulum Labeling Kit

The SelectFX™ Alexa Fluor® 488 Endoplasmic Reticulum Labeling Kit (S34200) provides all the reagents required to fix and permeabilize mammalian cells and then label the endoplasmic reticulum (ER). To achieve ER labeling, this kit employs a primary antibody directed against an ER-associated protein, protein disulfide isomerase (PDI), and an Alexa Fluor® 488 dye–labeled secondary antibody. The Alexa Fluor® 488 dye exhibits bright green fluorescence that is compatible with filters and instrument settings appropriate for fluorescein. Each kit contains:

- Mouse IgG_{2b} anti–protein disulfide isomerase (PDI) antibody
- Highly cross-adsorbed Alexa Fluor® 488 goat anti–mouse IgG antibody
- Concentrated fixative solution
- Concentrated phosphate-buffered saline (PBS)
- Concentrated permeabilization solution
- Concentrated blocking solution
- Detailed protocols for mammalian cell preparation and staining

The SelectFX™ Alexa Fluor® 488 Endoplasmic Reticulum Labeling Kit can be used in conjunction with probes for other cell targets to achieve multicolor cell staining.

SelectFX™ Alexa Fluor® 488 Peroxisome Labeling Kit

The SelectFX™ Alexa Fluor® 488 Peroxisome Labeling Kit (S34201) provides the reagents required for labeling peroxisomes, including cell fixation and permeabilization reagents. To specifically detect peroxisomes, this kit uses an antibody directed against peroxisomal membrane protein 70 (PMP 70), which is a high-abundance integral membrane protein in peroxisomes,[31] and an Alexa Fluor® 488 dye–labeled secondary antibody; fluorescence is observed using standard fluorescein filters (Figure 12.41). PMP 70 is significantly induced by administration of hypolipidemic agents, in parallel with peroxisome proliferation and the induction of peroxisomal fatty acid β-oxidation enzymes.[31] Each kit contains:

- Rabbit IgG anti-PMP 70 antibody
- Highly cross-adsorbed Alexa Fluor® 488 goat anti–rabbit IgG antibody
- Concentrated fixative solution
- Concentrated phosphate-buffered saline (PBS)
- Concentrated permeabilization solution
- Concentrated blocking solution
- Detailed protocols for mammalian cell preparation and staining

The SelectFX™ Alexa Fluor® 488 Peroxisome Labeling Kit can be used in conjunction with probes for other cell targets to achieve multicolor cell staining.

SelectFX™ Alexa Fluor® 488 Cytochrome *c* Apoptosis Detection Kit

A distinctive feature of the early stages of programmed cell death is the disruption of active mitochondria.[32–34] This mitochondrial disruption includes changes in the membrane potential, presumably due to the opening of the mitochondrial permeability transition pore, which allows passage of ions and small molecules. The resulting equilibration of ions leads in turn to the decoupling of the respiratory chain and then the release of cytochrome *c* into the cytosol.[35,36] The SelectFX™ Alexa Fluor® 488 Cytochrome *c* Apoptosis Detection Kit (S35115) provides all the reagents required to detect cytochrome *c* in fixed cells. This kit employs an anti–cytochrome *c* primary antibody and an Alexa Fluor® 488 dye–labeled secondary antibody; fluorescence is observed using standard fluorescein filters. Each kit contains:

- Mouse IgG_1 anti–cytochrome *c* antibody
- Highly cross-adsorbed Alexa Fluor® 488 goat anti–mouse IgG antibody
- Concentrated fixative solution
- Concentrated phosphate-buffered saline (PBS)
- Concentrated permeabilization solution
- Concentrated blocking solution
- Detailed protocols for mammalian cell preparation and staining

The SelectFX™ Alexa Fluor® 488 Cytochrome *c* Apoptosis Detection Kit can be used in conjunction with probes for other cell targets to achieve multicolor cell staining.

Antibodies Specific for Proteins in the Oxidative Phosphorylation System

Oxidative phosphorylation (OxPhos) activity occurs in the mitochondria and, in mammals, is catalyzed by five large membrane-bound protein complexes, namely NADH–ubiquinol oxidoreductase (Complex I), succinate–ubiquinol oxidoreductase (Complex II), ubiquinol–cytochrome *c* oxidoreductase (Complex III), cytochrome *c* oxidase (Complex IV) and ATP synthase (Complex V). The complexes are composed of multiple subunits, some of which are encoded in the mitochondria and some in the nucleus. For example, mammalian cytochrome oxidase (COX) is composed of 13 subunits, three encoded by mitochondrial DNA (subunits I, II and III; Figure 12.29) and ten encoded by nuclear DNA. Assembly of each complex involves a coordinated association of prosthetic groups (hemes, non-heme irons, flavins and copper atoms) with some polypeptides made in the mitochondrion and others made in the cytosol and then translocated to the organelle. This complicated process is poorly defined but known to require various assembly factors, each of which is specific for a particular complex. Defects in assembly of one or more of these complexes contribute to several described mitochondrial diseases (see Note 12.2 "Technical Focus: Mitochondria in Diseases" in Section 12.2) and possibly Alzheimer's and Parkinson's diseases.[37–42]

Molecular Probes offers a range of subunit-specific anti–OxPhos Complex mouse monoclonal antibodies that recognize proteins in the oxidative phosphorylation system (Table 12.3, Table 12.4, Table 12.5; Figure 12.30) and have proven useful in the characterization and diagnosis of mitochondrial disease.[43] One set of antibodies is against the Complex IV subunits of yeast, as this is the organism of choice for studying biogenesis of cytochrome oxidase. The remaining antibodies were generated against bovine or human material and were selected because they react with high specificity for the human form of the various proteins. All of our antibodies work well on Western blots (Section 12.2, Table 12.4), and a majority can be used for immunohistochemistry, as listed in Table 12.4. These antibodies may also be employed to test other subcellular preparations for mitochondrial contamination. Stringent selection criteria were applied during the development of these monoclonal antibodies, including:

- Ability of the antibodies to detect native protein in solid-phase binding assays such as particle-concentration fluorescence immunoassays (PCFIAs) and enzyme-linked immunosorbent assays (ELISAs)
- Specificity for the appropriate denatured subunit in Western blots of whole-cell extracts and isolated mitochondria
- Where appropriate, specific mitochondrial subcellular localization of immunohistochemical reactivity in fixed cultured human cells

Detailed information, including recommended working concentrations, is provided with each product. These antibodies may be detected with many of the labeled secondary antibodies described in Section 7.2. The antibodies in this group (Table 7.15, Table 7.16, Table 7.17, Table 12.4) can be complexed with the Zenon® labeling reagents in the corresponding Zenon® Antibody Labeling Kits (Section 7.3, Table 7.13) for detecting mitochondrial targets in cells (Figure 7.80, Figure 15.78). All of our monoclonal antibodies against OxPhos subunits are described in more detail in Section 12.2.

Monoclonal Antibodies against Cytochrome Oxidase (Complex IV)

To facilitate the study of cytochrome oxidase (COX) structure and mitochondrial biogenesis, Molecular Probes offers subunit-specific mouse monoclonal anti–OxPhos Complex IV antibodies that have been derived from the human, bovine and yeast forms of COX. COX catalyzes the transfer of electrons from reduced cytochrome *c* to molecular oxygen, with a concomitant translocation of protons across the mitochondrial inner membrane.[44,45] This mitochondrial membrane–bound enzyme is composed of subunits that are encoded in both the mitochondria (COX subunits I, II and III) and the nucleus (all others), with a total of 13 subunits for mammalian COX and 11 subunits for yeast COX. The binding specificity exhibited by our anti–OxPhos Complex IV monoclonal antibody preparations allows researchers to investigate the regulation, assembly and orientation of COX subunits from a variety of organisms[46–50] (Table 12.3, Table 12.4, Table 12.5). Furthermore, because the antibodies to bovine COX also recognize the corresponding human COX subunits, the antibodies have proven valuable for analyzing human mitochondrial myopathies and related disorders.[51–54] Alexa Fluor® 488 and Alexa Fluor® 594 conjugates of the anti–COX subunit I antibody are also available for direct staining of mitochondria (A21296, A21297; Figure 7.79). Mouse monoclonal 1D6 anti–COX subunit 1 antibody (A6403), which recognizes the mitochondrial DNA–encoded COX subunit I, has been shown to be an effective tool for following mitochondrial DNA depletion in cultured fibroblasts treated with

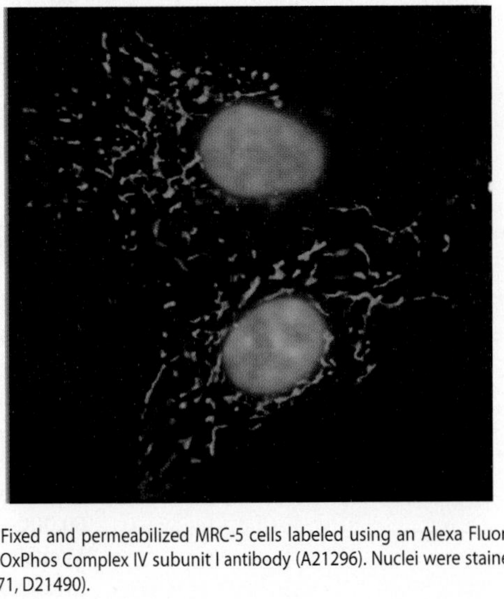

Figure 7.79 Fixed and permeabilized MRC-5 cells labeled using an Alexa Fluor® 488 conjugate of anti–OxPhos Complex IV subunit I antibody (A21296). Nuclei were stained with DAPI (D1306, D3571, D21490).

nucleoside reverse transcriptase inhibitors (NRTIs) and potentially for monitoring patients on a regimen of NRTIs for the treatment of HIV.[55]

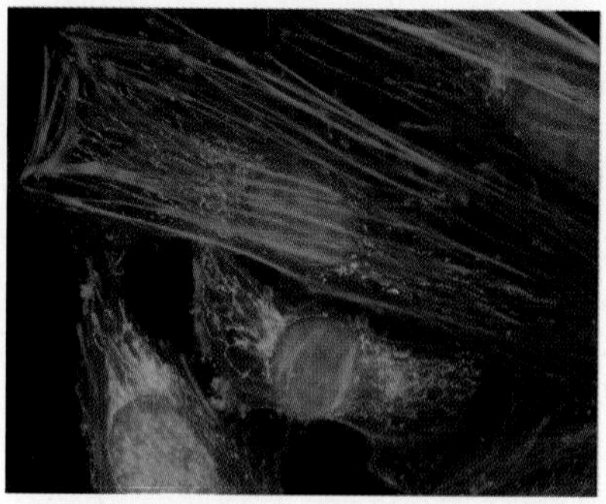

Figure 7.80 Fixed and permeabilized HeLa cells stained with Alexa Fluor® 350 phalloidin (A22281), an anti–OxPhos Complex V inhibitor protein antibody (A21355) and anti-cdc6 peptide antibody (A21286). The anti–OxPhos Complex V inhibitor protein antibody was prelabeled with the Zenon® Alexa Fluor® 488 Mouse IgG_1 Labeling Kit (Z25002) and the anti-cdc6 peptide antibody was prelabeled with the Zenon® Alexa Fluor® 568 Mouse IgG_1 Labeling Kit (Z25006).

Monoclonal Antibodies against Complexes I, II, III and V

Molecular Probes supplies a large number of monoclonal antibodies to the OxPhos Complex (Table 12.4). These include antibodies specific for individual subunits of Complexes I, II, III and V, as well as the Complex V inhibitor protein (Figure 7.80). When these monoclonal antibodies are used in combination with the set of antibodies to cytochrome *c* oxidase (Complex IV), the relative levels of all OxPhos enzyme complexes in normal and diseased tissues can be evaluated.

The mouse monoclonal 7H10 anti–OxPhos Complex V subunit (bovine) (anti–F_1F_0-ATPase subunit α, A21350) and mouse monoclonal 7E3 anti–OxPhos Complex V subunit (bovine) (anti–F_1F_0-ATPase subunit β, A21351) antibodies have also been shown to mimic angiostatin, a potent inhibitor of angiogenesis.[56] Angiostatin protein (A23375, Section 15.4), a recombinant form of natural angiostatin, targets the F_1F_0-ATP synthase and inhibits cell-surface ATP metabolism of endothelial cells, thereby blocking cell migration and proliferation that is essential for angiogenesis. This research demonstrated that these anti-ATPase antibodies had similar inhibitory effects, implying that they also compromised ATP metabolism and may function as angiostatin analogs.

Antibodies Specific for Other Mitochondrial Proteins

Anti–Mitochondrial Porin Antibodies

Mitochondrial porin is an outer-membrane protein that forms regulated channels (referred to as voltage-dependent anionic channels, or VDACs) between the cytosol and the mitochondrial intermembrane space.[57] This abundant transmembrane protein forms a small (~3 nm) pore, allowing molecules less than ~10,000 daltons to pass.[58] Due to its abundance, porin is often used as a standardization marker in Western blots when assaying for other mitochondrial proteins[59,60] and serves as an effective organelle marker for immunohistochemistry.[61] Monoclonal antibodies against both human and yeast porin are available from Molecular Probes (A21317, A31855, A6449; Table 12.6).

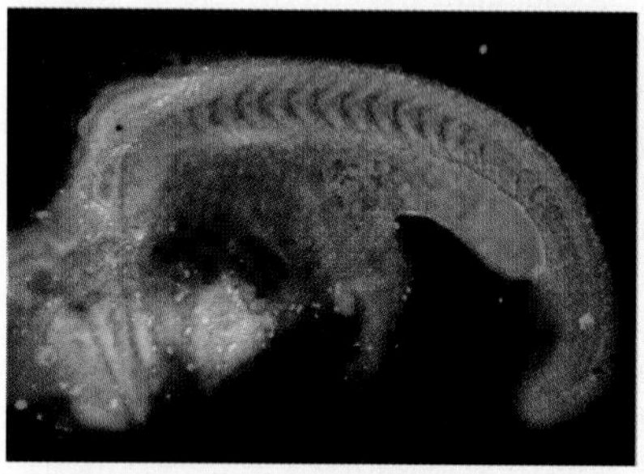

Figure 7.81 Neuronal cells in a 22-hour zebrafish embryo were identified with anti-HuC/HuD mouse monoclonal antibody (A21271) and visualized with red-orange–fluorescent Alexa Fluor® 568 goat anti–mouse IgG antibody (A11004). The nuclei were stained with blue-fluorescent DAPI (D1306, D3571, D21490).

Anti–Pyruvate Dehydrogenase Antibodies

Molecular Probes has available a series of antibodies against the human pyruvate dehydrogenase (PDH) complex (Table 12.6), a large, multienzyme assembly residing in the mitochondrial matrix and consisting of three catalytic activities: pyruvate dehydrogenase, dihydrolipoyl transacetylase and dihydrolipoyl dehydrogenase[62] (diaphorase). The PDH complex is responsible for the oxidative decarboxylation of pyruvate to form acetyl coenzyme A, which is in turn fed into the citric acid cycle. Deficiencies in the PDH complex lead to lactic acidosis;[63] severe cases can lead to developmental defects such as congenital brain malformation.[64] In addition to unlabeled subunit-specific anti-PDH antibodies, we offer the red-fluorescent Alexa Fluor® 594 conjugate of anti–PDH E1α subunit antibody (A31853), as well as the green-fluorescent Alexa Fluor® 488 conjugate of anti–PDH E2 subunit antibody (A31854).

Monoclonal Antibodies for Yeast Cell Biology

Molecular Probes provides an array of immunoreagents for researchers studying aspects of cell biology with the yeast *Saccharomyces cerevisiae* (Table 12.8). In particular, we offer monoclonal antibodies that recognize:

- Vacuolar membrane proteins — integral membrane proteins, which include alkaline phosphatase[65] (A6458) and the 100,000-dalton subunit of the yeast vacuolar H^+-ATPase[66,67] (V-ATPase, A6426), as well as peripheral membrane proteins, which include the 60,000-dalton and 69,000-dalton subunits of V-ATPase[68,69] (A6427, A6422)
- Vacuolar lumen protein — carboxypeptidase Y (A6428)
- Mitochondrial membrane proteins — porin[61,70] (A6449) and four subunits of yeast COX[49,71–73] (A6405, A6407, A6408, A6432)

- Endoplasmic reticulum membrane proteins — dolichol phosphate mannose synthase[74] (Dol-P-Man synthase, Dpm1p, A6429) and Pep12p (A21273)
- Late-Golgi compartment membrane protein (Vps10p, A21274), a receptor protein that sorts several different vacuolar proteins, including carboxypeptidase Y,[75–77] by cycling between a late-Golgi compartment and the endosome[78]
- Cytosolic protein — 3-phosphoglycerate kinase[70,74,79] (PGK, A6457)

We have selected this set of monoclonal antibodies because they are compatible with both Western blotting of denatured proteins and protein immunolocalization in fixed yeast cells. Other potential uses of these antibodies include the development of ELISAs to determine either the level of enrichment of a particular yeast organelle or the level at which the organelle contaminates a subcellular fraction. Detailed information regarding the IgG isotype and recommended working concentration is provided with each product. These monoclonal antibodies are described in Section 12.2 and Section 12.3.

Antibodies Specific for Proliferation Markers and Cell-Cycle Control Proteins

Anti-Bromodeoxyuridine Antibody (Anti-BrdU Antibody)

Incorporation of 5-bromo-2′-deoxyuridine (BrdU, B23151; Section 15.4) into newly synthesized DNA permits indirect detection of rapidly proliferating cells with fluorescent dye–labeled anti-BrdU antibodies, thereby facilitating the identification of cells that have progressed through the S phase of the cell cycle during the BrdU labeling period (Figure 15.59, Figure 15.60). In conjunction with Phoenix Flow Systems, Molecular Probes offers fluorescent conjugates of the mouse monoclonal anti-BrdU antibody PRB-1 labeled with our brightest and most photostable dyes — the Alexa Fluor® 488 (A21303), Alexa Fluor® 532 (A21307), Alexa Fluor® 546 (A21308), Alexa Fluor® 594 (A21304), Alexa Fluor® 647 (A21305) and Alexa Fluor® 660 (A21306) dyes. This anti-BrdU antibody is also available as a biotin-XX conjugate (A21301MP), as well as unlabeled (A21300). In addition to its use for detecting BrdU-labeled DNA, monoclonal PRB-1 recognizes bromouridine (BrU) incorporated into RNA, which provides one of the few methods for specific localization of RNA in cells. It should be possible to amplify the detection of very low degrees of BrdU incorporation by using the biotin-XX conjugate of anti-BrdU in conjunction with one of our streptavidin-based Tyramide Signal Amplification (TSA) Kits (Table 6.1), which are described in Section 6.2.

APO-BrdU TUNEL Assay Kit

Because DNA fragmentation is one of the most reliable methods for detecting apoptosis,[80] we have collaborated with Phoenix Flow Systems to offer the APO-BrdU TUNEL Assay Kit (A23210), which provides all the materials necessary to label and detect the DNA strand breaks of apoptotic cells.[81] When DNA strands are cleaved or nicked by nucleases, a large number of 3′-hydroxyl ends are exposed. In the APO-BrdU assay, these ends are labeled with BrdUTP and terminal deoxynucleotidyl transferase (TdT) using the terminal deoxynucleotidyl transferase dUTP nick end labeling (TUNEL) technique. Once incorporated into the DNA, BrdU is detected using an Alexa Fluor® 488 dye–labeled anti-BrdU monoclonal antibody (Figure 15.85). This kit also provides propidium iodide for determining total cellular DNA content, as well as fixed control cells for assessing assay performance.

The APO-BrdU TUNEL Assay Kit includes complete protocols for use in flow cytometry applications, though it may also be adapted for use with fluorescence microscopy. Each kit contains:

- Terminal deoxynucleotidyl transferase (TdT), for catalyzing the addition of BrdUTP at the break sites
- 5-Bromo-2′-deoxyuridine 5′-triphosphate (BrdUTP)
- Alexa Fluor® 488 dye–labeled anti-BrdU mouse monoclonal antibody PRB-1, for detecting BrdU labels
- Propidium iodide/RNase staining buffer, for quantitating total cellular DNA
- Reaction, wash and rinse buffers
- Positive control cells (a fixed human lymphoma cell line)
- Negative control cells (a fixed human lymphoma cell line)
- Detailed protocols

Sufficient reagents are provided for approximately 60 assays of 1 mL samples, each containing 1–2 × 10^6 cells/mL.

Anti–Human mRNA-Binding Protein HuR Antibody (Anti-HuR Antibody)

HuR is expressed in a wide variety of proliferating cells.[82] HuR binds to AU-rich elements (ARE) in the 3′-untranslated region of transcripts, specifically to those areas located in the 3′-UTRs of mRNAs that encode growth-regulating proteins such as c-fos, c-myc, cyclin A, cyclin B1 and NOS II.[83–86] HuR mediates the hypoxic regulation of VEGF mRNA stability and UV light–induced regulation of p21waf1 expression[87] and is likely to regulate the mRNA expression of many other cytokines and transcription factors. Our mouse IgG_1 monoclonal anti–human HuR antibody (A21277) was generated against a unique peptide from the N-terminus of HuR. Anti-HuR is suitable for immunohistochemical assays of paraffin-embedded tissue, as well as for Western blots. It can also be used in supershift assays to confirm that HuR is present in an mRNA/protein complex. Anti-HuR could prove very useful to investigators who wish to determine whether HuR regulates the expression of their mRNA. Although we have not investigated species specificity, the peptide sequence is well conserved; we therefore expect the antibody to crossreact with HuR of most species. Our Zenon® antibody labeling technology permits precomplexation of this mouse IgG_1 monoclonal antibody with a wide range of dyes or enzymes (Section 7.3, Table 7.13).

Anti–Human Neuronal Protein HuC/HuD Antibody (Anti-Hu Antibody)

Anti-Hu antibodies were originally isolated from a patient with paraneoplastic encephalomyelitis, a rare condition of selective neural tissue injury associated with small-cell lung carcinoma.[88] The antibodies bind specifically to antigens present exclusively in neuronal cells and are thus useful as markers of neuronal cells in tissue. The Hu antigen is an RNA-binding protein of the embryonic lethal abnormal vision (ELAV) family. Molecular Probes' mouse monoclonal anti–human neuronal protein HuC/HuD antibody (A21271, Figure 7.81) recognizes the ELAV family members HuC,[89] HuD[88] and Hel-N1,[90] which are all neuronal proteins. Our anti-Hu antibody does not recognize HuR, another ELAV family member that is present in

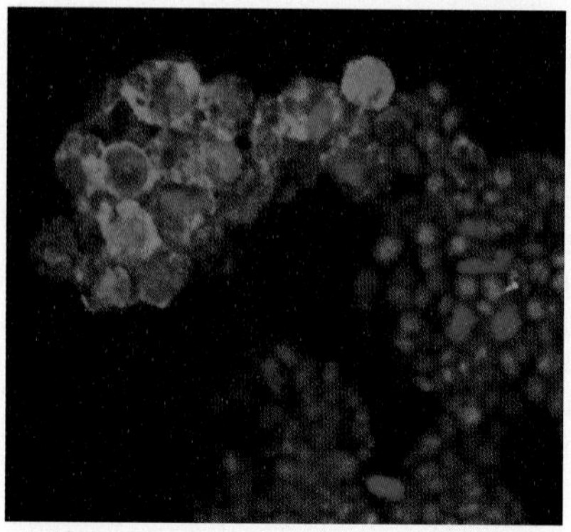

Figure 7.82 Cultured axolotl sensory neurons stained with our anti–human neuronal protein HuC/HuD antibody (anti-Hu, A21271) and detected using the red-orange–fluorescent Alexa Fluor® 546 goat anti–mouse IgG antibody (A11003). Actin was labeled using green-fluorescent Alexa Fluor® 488 phalloidin (A12379) and nuclei were stained with blue-fluorescent Hoechst 33342 (H1399, H3570, H21492). The image was contributed by Josh Gross and Linda Barlow, University of Denver, Denver, Colorado.

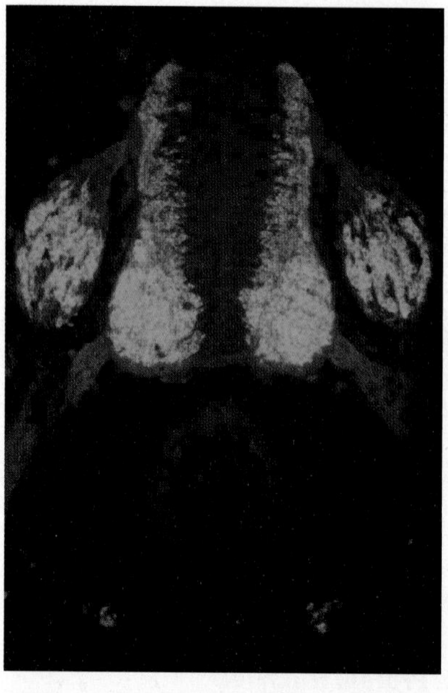

Figure 7.83 The spinal cord, dorsal root ganglia and sympathetic ganglia from the brachial region of a chick cryosection at stage 23 (Hamburger and Hamilton numbering) were identified with the mouse monoclonal anti–human neuronal protein HuC/HuD antibody (A21271) and visualized with fluorescein-labeled goat anti–mouse IgG antibody (F2761). The primary antibody recognizes an antigen localized to neuronal cell bodies and is ideal for identifying and counting neurons in both early and late development. Human, mouse, avian and zebrafish tissues have all demonstrated similar neuron-specific labeling patterns. Image contributed by Michael Marusich, Monoclonal Antibody Facility, University of Oregon, Eugene, Oregon.

all proliferating cells [82] (see above). This antibody has been shown to specifically label neuronal cells in zebrafish,[91] chick,[92] canaries [93] and humans [94] and is likely to label neuronal cells in most vertebrate species (Figure 7.82). Labeling is visible early in development, at about the time that the neurons leave the mitotic cycle.[94]

The unlabeled monoclonal anti-Hu antibody is generally used in conjunction with a secondary antibody, such as labeled goat anti–mouse IgG antibody (Section 7.2, Figure 7.83). Molecular Probes also provides a biotin-XX conjugate of the mouse IgG_{2b} monoclonal anti-Hu mouse antibody (A21272, Figure 7.84), which can be detected using streptavidin or avidin conjugates (Section 7.6, Table 7.22). The biotin conjugate is useful for staining mouse tissue in order to avoid possible background staining by a secondary anti–mouse IgG antibody.

Anti–cdc6 Peptide Antibody

The cdc6 protein, which was originally described in budding yeast, functions during eukaryotic replication initiation and is essential for DNA synthesis.[95] This 30,000-dalton protein exhibits DNA-binding properties and is thought to be involved in the assembly of minichromosome maintenance proteins onto replicating DNA.[96] cdc6 is a nuclear protein that is expressed *only* in actively replicating cells, making it an excellent marker for cell proliferation.[97,98] Quiescent cells in G_0 do not express the protein.[99] Polyclonal antibodies to cdc6 have been shown to have potential clinical applications in the assessment of tumor prognosis [100] and have been used to detect abnormal cells in Papanicolau (PAP) cervical smears with very high specificity and sensitivity.[99]

Molecular Probes offers the anti–cdc6 peptide mouse monoclonal antibody 37F4 (A21286), which is suited for immunohistochemical applications. The antibody was generated by immunizing mice with a peptide (Leu-Ser-Pro-Arg-Lys-Arg-Leu-Gly-Asp-Asp-Asn-Leu-Cys) based on a segment of the amino acid sequence of human cdc6. Molecular Probes scientists have found that this anti–cdc6 peptide antibody is an excellent marker for the nucleus, and can replace traditional nucleic acid counterstains in multicolor applications (Figure 7.66, Figure 7.85, Figure 15.78). Moreover, this antibody can be used to visualize chromatin throughout mitosis (Figure 7.86, Figure 7.87, Figure 7.88, Figure 7.89, Figure 7.90).

Anti-CD Antibodies

Molecular Probes offers three mouse monoclonal anti–human T-cell markers — the anti-CD3, anti-CD4 and anti-CD8 antibodies (Table 7.20) — which are available unlabeled or conjugated to superior Alexa Fluor® dyes or to R-phycoerythrin. Research applications for the anti-CD antibodies include: the identification and enumeration of $CD3^+$, $CD4^+$ and $CD8^+$ cells by flow cytometry (Figure 7.65); the visualization of CD^+ cells by immunohistochemistry in acetone-fixed, frozen tissue sections; the immunoprecipitation of CD^+ fractions; and the isolation or removal of T cells by cell sorting or "bio-panning."[101]

Anti-CD3 antibodies help in the identification of T cells. CD3, a member of the immunoglobulin superfamily, is a cluster of differentiation (CD) cell-surface antigen associated with the T-cell receptor (TcR) of T cells and thymocytes.[102] TcRs are specific for complexes comprising short peptides bound to and presented by the major histocompatibility complex (MHC). The human CD3/TcR complex is made up of at least five CD3 proteins (γ, δ, ε, η, ζ) in association with either α/β or γ/δ proteins of the TcR. The TcR recognizes and binds to antigens presented by the MHC,

Table 7.20 — Molecular Probes' mouse anti–human CD antibodies

Label	Abs/Em *	Anti-CD3 (IgG_1) †	Anti-CD4 (IgG_1) †	Anti-CD8 (IgG_{2a}) †
Alexa Fluor® 488	495/519	A21331	A21335	A21339
Alexa Fluor® 647 ‡	650/668	A21332	A21336	A21340
R-phycoerythrin	496, 546, 565/578 §	A21333	A21337	
Unlabeled	NA	A21330	A21334	A21338

* Approximate absorption (Abs) and fluorescence emission (Em) maxima, in nm. † Mouse monoclonal antibodies: clone 289-13801, against human CD3; clone 289-14120, against human CD4; clone 289-13804, against human CD8. ‡ Human vision is insensitive to light beyond ~650 nm; it is therefore not possible to view the fluorescence of the Alexa Fluor® 647 dye by looking through the eyepiece of a conventional fluorescence microscope. § Multiple absorption peaks. NA, not applicable.

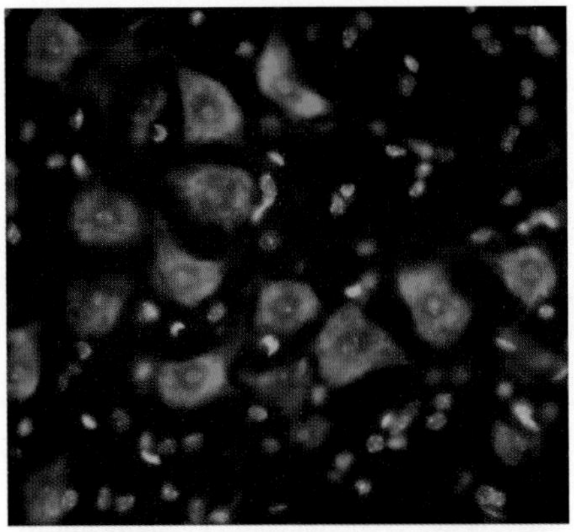

Figure 7.84 Mouse brain sections were labeled with the NeuroTrace® 500/525 green-fluorescent Nissl stain (N21480) or with our biotin-XX conjugate of anti-HuC/HuD antibody (A21272), followed by visualization with Alexa Fluor® 568 streptavidin (S11226). Both sections were counterstained with DAPI (D1306, D3571, D21490).

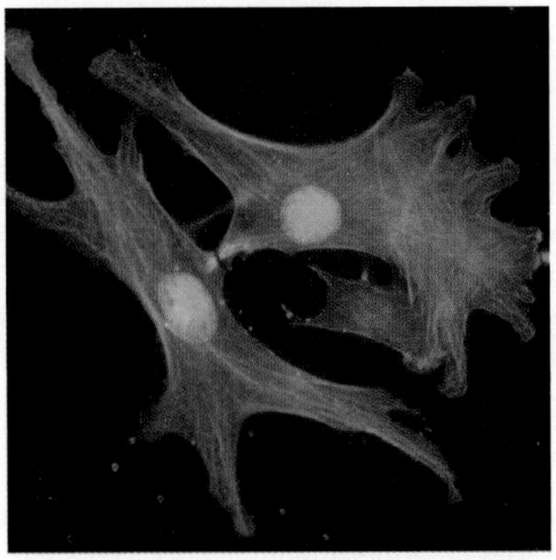

Figure 7.85 Fixed and permeabilized bovine pulmonary artery endothelial cells stained with Alexa Fluor® 350 phalloidin (A22281), an anti-α-tubulin antibody (A11126) and the anti-cdc6 peptide antibody (A21286). The anti-α-tubulin antibody was labeled with the Zenon® Alexa Fluor® 568 Mouse IgG_1 Labeling Kit (Z25006) and the anti-cdc6 peptide antibody was labeled with the Zenon® Alexa Fluor® 488 Mouse IgG_1 Labeling Kit (Z25002).

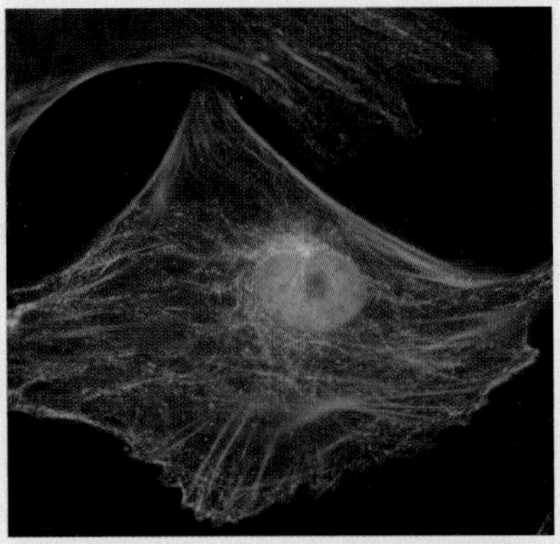

Figure 7.86 Fixed and permeabilized muntjac skin fibroblasts stained with Alexa Fluor® 350 phalloidin (A22281), an anti-α-tubulin antibody (A11126) and an anti-cdc6 peptide antibody (A21286). The anti-α-tubulin antibody was prelabeled with the Zenon® Alexa Fluor® 488 Mouse IgG_1 Labeling Kit (Z25002) and the anti-cdc6 peptide antibody was prelabeled with the Zenon® Alexa Fluor® 647 Mouse IgG_1 Labeling Kit (Z25008).

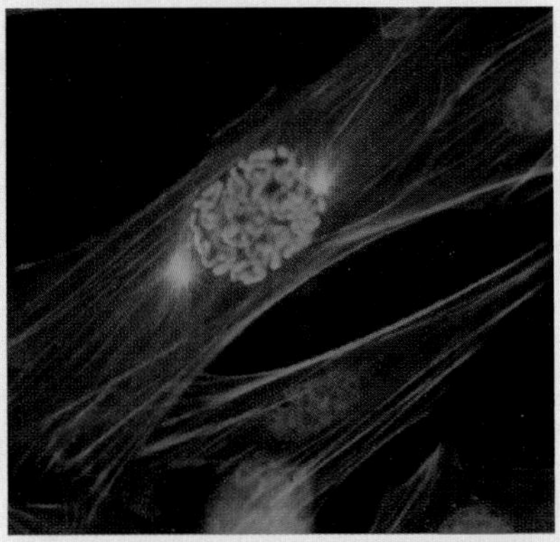

Figure 7.87 A prometaphase muntjac skin fibroblast stained with Alexa Fluor® 350 phalloidin (A22281), an anti-α-tubulin antibody (A11126) and an anti-cdc6 peptide antibody (A21286). The anti-α-tubulin antibody was prelabeled with the Zenon® Alexa Fluor® 488 Mouse IgG_1 Labeling Kit (Z25002) and the anti-cdc6 peptide antibody was prelabeled with the Zenon® Alexa Fluor® 647 Mouse IgG_1 Labeling Kit (Z25008).

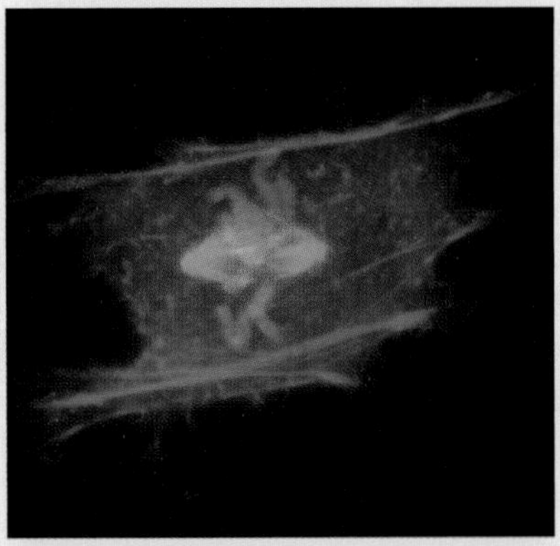

Figure 7.88 A metaphase muntjac skin fibroblast stained with Alexa Fluor® 350 phalloidin (A22281), an anti-α-tubulin antibody (A11126) and an anti-cdc6 peptide antibody (A21286). The anti-α-tubulin antibody was prelabeled with the Zenon® Alexa Fluor® 488 Mouse IgG_1 Labeling Kit (Z25002) and the anti-cdc6 peptide antibody was prelabeled with the Zenon® Alexa Fluor® 647 Mouse IgG_1 Labeling Kit (Z25008).

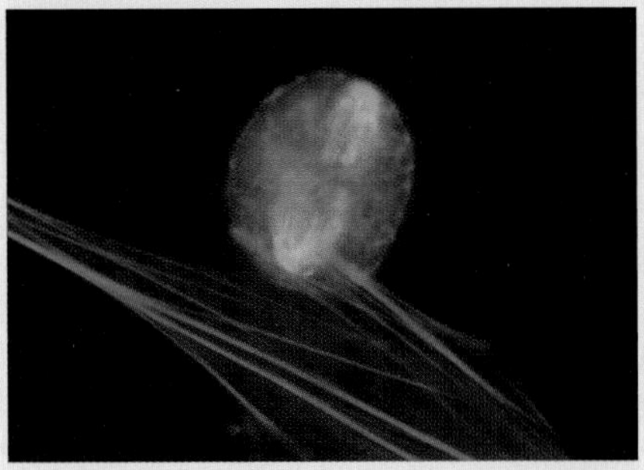

Figure 7.89 An anaphase muntjac skin fibroblast stained with Alexa Fluor® 350 phalloidin (A22281), an anti-α-tubulin antibody (A11126) and an anti-cdc6 peptide antibody (A21286). The anti-α-tubulin antibody was prelabeled with the Zenon® Alexa Fluor® 488 Mouse IgG_1 Labeling Kit (Z25002) and the anti-cdc6 peptide antibody was prelabeled with the Zenon® Alexa Fluor® 647 Mouse IgG_1 Labeling Kit (Z25008).

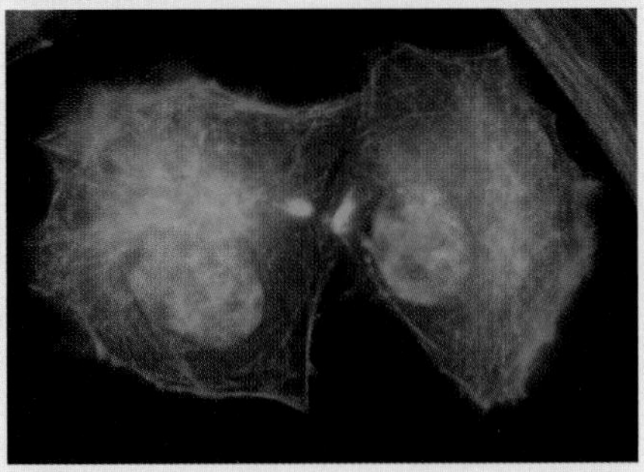

Figure 7.90 Late telophase muntjac cells stained with Alexa Fluor® 350 phalloidin (A22281), an anti-α-tubulin antibody (A11126) and an anti-cdc6 peptide antibody (A21286). The anti-α-tubulin antibody was prelabeled with the Zenon® Alexa Fluor® 488 Mouse IgG_1 Labeling Kit (Z25002), and the anti-cdc6 peptide antibody was prelabeled with the Zenon® Alexa Fluor® 647 Mouse IgG_1 Labeling Kit (Z25008).

after which the protein chains of the CD3 complex mediate activation signals. The CD3 molecule is not found on B cells; thus, its presence can be used as a marker for T cells.

Figure 7.91 The microtubules of fixed bovine pulmonary artery endothelial cells were labeled with a mouse monoclonal anti–α-tubulin antibody (A11126), which was visualized with Alexa Fluor® 546 goat anti–mouse IgG antibody (A11003). The image was acquired using a bandpass filter set appropriate for rhodamine.

Anti-CD4 and anti-CD8 antibodies can be used to differentiate between helper T cells and killer T cells, both of which are $CD3^+$. Helper/inducer T cells express the cell-surface CD4 antigen, which interacts with MHC class II molecules and is the primary receptor for the human immunodeficiency virus [103] (HIV). Killer T cells express the CD8 cell-surface antigen, which interacts with MHC class I molecules. The interaction results in the activation of the killer T cell and an increase in its avidity for the corresponding target cells.

Antibodies against D Cyclins and Cyclin-Dependent Kinase Inhibitors

Progression through the G_1 phase and into the S phase of the cell cycle is controlled in part by a series of serine/threonine kinase complexes, consisting of a cyclin regulatory subunit and catalytic subunit referred to as a cyclin-dependent kinase [104] (cdk). Binding of the cyclin to the cdk activates the complex, which promotes cell cycle progression by phosphorylation of specific target proteins. At least five proteins have been identified as G_1-phase cyclins (C, D1, D2, D3, E),[105] of which the three D cyclins form a closely related group.[106] Cyclin C has been shown to associate with cdk8,[107] while cyclin E activates cdk2.[108] The D1 and D2 cyclins can associate with both cdk4 and cdk6; activity of these complexes has been detected as early as mid-G_1 phase.[109] Cyclin D3 can also activate cdk4 and cdk6, but D3-associated cdk activity is found only at the G_1/S transition.[110]

The D cyclins in particular play an important role in regulatory decisions controlling the progression of the cell cycle; overexpression of these regulatory proteins is associated with a wide variety of proliferative diseases including breast [111,112] and gastric [113,114] cancers. For the detection of these important cell-cycle control proteins, Molecular Probes now offers a monoclonal antibody against each individual D cyclin — mouse IgG_{2a} monoclonal DCS-6 anti–cyclin D1 (A21320), mouse IgG_{2b} monoclonal DCS-5.2 anti–cyclin D2 (A21321) and mouse IgG_1 monoclonal DCS-22 anti–cyclin D3 (A21322) antibodies. Each of these antibodies is suitable for use in both Western blotting and immunohistochemical applications.

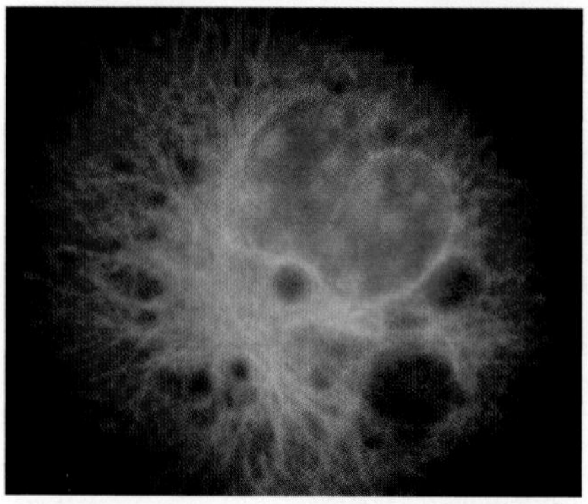

Figure 7.92 Microtubules of fixed bovine pulmonary artery endothelial cells were labeled with our mouse monoclonal anti–α-tubulin antibody (A11126), detected with the biotin-XX–conjugated $F(ab')_2$ fragment of goat anti–mouse IgG antibody (B11027) and visualized with Alexa Fluor® 488 streptavidin (S11223). The actin filaments were then labeled with orange-fluorescent Alexa Fluor® 568 phalloidin (A12380), and the cell was counterstained with blue-fluorescent Hoechst 33342 (H1399, H3570, H21492) to image the DNA, and red-fluorescent propidium iodide (P1304MP, P3566, P21493) to image the nucleolar RNA. The multiple-exposure image was acquired using bandpass filters appropriate for the Texas Red® dye, fluorescein and DAPI.

Active cyclin/cdk complexes can be inhibited by a number of different proteins, resulting in arrest of the cell cycle. In many cases these inhibitor proteins are activated by DNA damage, halting the progression through the cell cycle until repairs can be made.[115] Arrest in the G_1 phase is a result of activated Rb protein, which must be phosphorylated by a cdk in order to deactivate the protein and allow progression of the cell cycle.[116] Induction of the cdk inhibitor p21WAF1/CIP1 prevents phosphorylation of Rb, thereby maintaining arrest in G_1.[117] Studies have shown that the absence of p21WAF1/CIP1 is associated with transformed cells but not tumor-derived cell lines.[118] Our mouse IgG_{2a} monoclonal DCS-60 anti-p21WAF1/CIP1 (A21319) should be a useful tool for analysis of protein abundance and cellular localization of this important cell-cycle inhibitor.[119]

Anti-Phosphoinositide Antibodies

Research has revealed the direct action of phosphatidylinositol 4,5-biphosphate ($PtdIns(4,5)P_2$) and phosphatidylinositol 3,4,5-triphosphate ($PtdIns(3,4,5)P_3$) on a diverse array of cellular functions, including actin assembly and cytoskeletal dynamics,[120,121] vesicular protein trafficking,[122] protein kinase localization and activation,[123] cell proliferation [124] and apoptosis.[125] We offer mouse monoclonal IgM antibodies to $PtdIns(4,5)P_2$ (A21327) and $PtdIns(3,4,5)P_3$ (A21328) for immunocytochemical localization of these important lipid metabolites [126] (Figure 17.36). Both antibodies have been shown to recognize their cognate phosphoinositides in murine and human cells with only slight crossreactivity with other phosphoinositides or phospholipids. Phosphatidylinositol 3,4,5-triphosphate has been quantitated by a liposome lysis assay using a specific monoclonal antibody to $PtdIns(3,4,5)P_3$.[127]

Antibodies Specific for Structural Proteins

Anti–α-Tubulin Monoclonal Antibody

When used in conjunction with an anti–mouse IgG secondary immunoreagent (Table 7.1), Molecular Probes' mouse monoclonal anti–α-tubulin antibody (A11126) enables researchers to visualize microtubules in fixed cells (Figure 7.42, Figure 7.91, Figure 7.92, Figure 7.102, Figure 11.16) and in fixed or frozen tissue sections from various species. This mouse monoclonal antibody, which recognizes amino acid residues 69–97 of the N-terminal structural domain of bovine tubulin and most other sources of tubulin, is also useful for detecting tubulin by ELISA or Western blotting, for screening expression libraries and as a probe for the N-terminal domain of α-tubulin.

The monoclonal anti–α-tubulin antibody is available either unlabeled (A11126) or as a biotin-XX conjugate (A21371). For detecting the biotinylated antibody, Molecular Probes carries a wide variety of fluorophore- and enzyme-labeled avidin, streptavidin and NeutrAvidin biotin-binding protein conjugates, as well as NANOGOLD and Alexa Fluor® FluoroNanogold streptavidin gold clusters (Section 7.6, Table 7.22).

We have extensively used the mouse IgG_1 anti–α-tubulin antibody in the development of our important Zenon® antibody labeling technology (Section 7.3, Figure 7.59, Figure 7.85), with outstanding results (Figure 7.66, Figure 7.69, Figure 7.71, Figure 7.85).

Anti–Glial Fibrillary Acidic Protein (GFAP) Antibody

The 50,000-dalton type III intermediate filament protein known as glial fibrillary acidic protein (GFAP) is a major structural component of astrocytes and some ependymal cells.[128] GFAP associates with the calcium-binding proteins annexin II2-p11(2) and S-100.[129,130] Association with these proteins together with phosphorylation regulates GFAP polymerization. Astrocytes respond to brain injury by proliferation (astrogliosis); one of the first events to occur during astrocyte proliferation is increased GFAP expression. Molecular Probes' anti-GFAP antibody (A21282) and its Alexa Fluor® 488 and Alexa Fluor® 594 conjugates (A21294, A21295; Figure 7.93, Figure 7.94, Figure 11.25) can be used to aid in the identification of cells of glial lineage. Interestingly, antibodies to GFAP have been detected in individuals with dementia.[131] In the central and peripheral nervous system, the anti-GFAP antibody stains both astrocytes and ependymal cells, Schwann cells, satellite cells and enteric glial cells. Tumors of glial origin contain high amounts of GFAP. No positive staining is observed in skin, connective tissue, adipose tissue, lymphatic tissue, muscle, gastrointestinal tract including liver and pancreas,

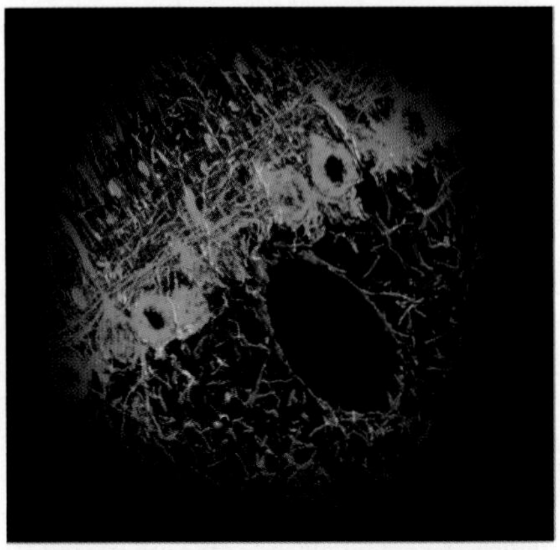

Figure 7.93 Filamentous structures of neuronal cells in a rat cerebellum, fluorescently labeled to differentiate the cell types. The cerebellum section was probed with primary antibodies to neurofilament and glial fibrillary acidic proteins (GFAP) and subsequently visualized with the green-fluorescent Alexa Fluor® 488 goat anti–mouse IgG (A11001) and red-orange–fluorescent Alexa Fluor® 568 goat anti–rabbit IgG (A11011) antibodies. This confocal micrograph was contributed by Gillian Davidson, Andrew Hubbard and Chris Guerin, Neurotoxicology Group, M.R.C Toxicology Unit, University of Leicester, Leicester, U.K.

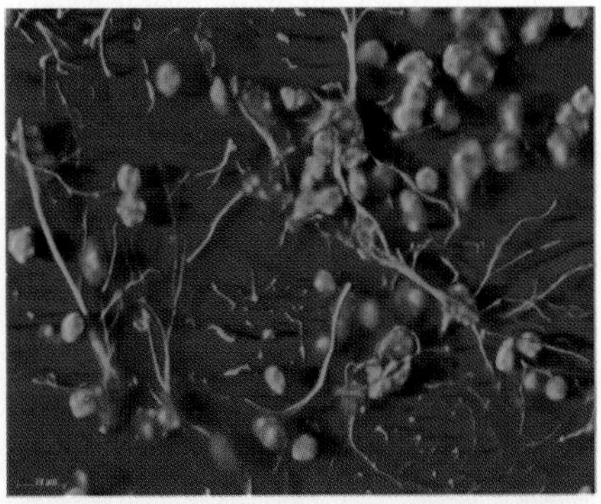

Figure 7.94 Intermediate filaments of astrocytes and ependymal cells in a 14 µm mouse brain cryosection were identified using mouse monoclonal anti–glial fibrillary acidic protein antibody (anti-GFAP, A21282) and visualized with green-fluorescent Alexa Fluor® 488 goat anti–mouse IgG antibody (A11029). Nuclei were stained with blue-fluorescent DAPI (D1306, D3571, D21490). The image was deconvolved using Huygens software (Scientific Volume Imaging, www.svi.nl). 3-D reconstruction was performed using Imaris software (Bitplane AG, www.bitplane.com).

kidney, ureter or bladder. Our anti-GFAP antibody does not cross-react with vimentin, which is frequently co-expressed in glioma cells and some astrocytes, Bergmann glial cells, gliomas or other glial cell–derived tumors. This mouse IgG_1 antibody can be used in combination with any of our Zenon® Mouse IgG_1 Labeling Kits (Section 7.3, Table 7.13).

Anti-Desmin Antibody

Desmin, whose gene belongs to the intermediate filament protein gene family,[132–134] is the main intermediate filament in mature skeletal, cardiac and smooth muscle cells (Figure 12.27). Both striated and smooth muscle cells can be labeled by an anti-desmin antibody, although not all muscle tissue contains desmin (e.g., aorta smooth muscle). Identification of desmin is useful in distinguishing habdomyosarcomas and leiomyosarcomas from other, vimentin-positive sarcomas. Molecular Probes offers a mouse IgG_1 monoclonal antibody to desmin (A21283), which can potentially be used with our fluorescent secondary antibodies (Table 7.1) or the reagents in our Zenon® Mouse IgG_1 Labeling Kits (Section 7.3, Table 7.13) as a marker for use in typing soft-tissue sarcomas. The use of anti-desmin immunohistochemical staining in cell block preparations may also be helpful in distinguishing mesothelial cells from carcinomas.[135]

Anti-Fibronectin Antibody

Fibronectin is a large glycoprotein that is found in both plasma[136] and in the extracellular matrix.[137] The protein is coded by a single gene, but alternate RNA splicing gives rise to several fibronectin isoforms that play important roles in cellular adhesion and migration, blood clotting and phagocytosis.[138] The apparent function of fibronectin is to mediate cell attachment via interactions with both cell-surface receptors and components of the extracellular matrix such as heparin, fibrinogen and collagen.[139] Molecular Probes offers a chicken IgY anti-fibronectin (human) antibody (A21316) for detecting fibronectin in Western blotting and immunohistochemistry applications (Figure 7.95), as well as several fluorescent anti–chicken IgG secondary antibodies that recognize this antibody (Section 7.2, Table 7.1).

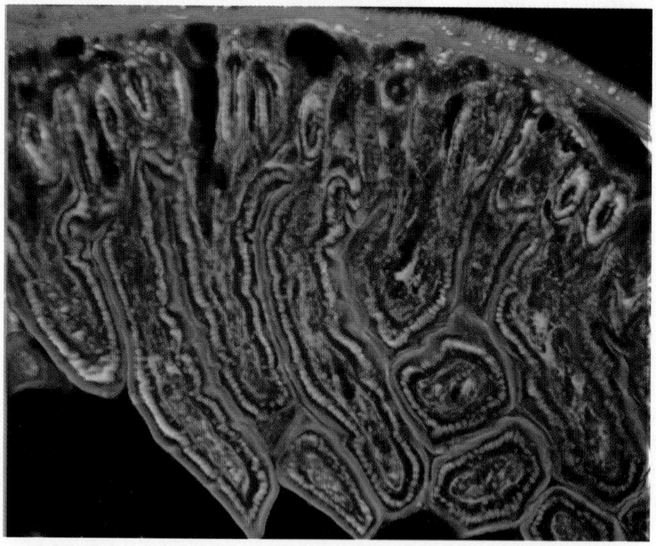

Figure 7.95 Mouse intestine cryosection showing basement membranes labeled with our chicken IgY anti-fibronectin antibody (A21316) and the Alexa Fluor® 488 goat anti–chicken IgG (A11039, green). Goblet cells and crypt cells were labeled with Alexa Fluor® 594 wheat germ agglutinin (W11262, red). The microvillar brush border and smooth muscle layers were visualized with Alexa Fluor® 680 phalloidin (A22286, pseudocolored purple). The section was counterstained with DAPI (D1306, D3571, D21490, blue).

Antibodies Specific for Neuronal Proteins

Anti–Synapsin I Antibody

Synapsin I is an actin-binding protein that is localized exclusively to synaptic vesicles and thus serves as an excellent marker for synapses in brain and other neuronal tissues.[140,141] Synapsin I inhibits neurotransmitter release, an effect that is abolished upon its phosphorylation by Ca^{2+}/calmodulin–dependent protein kinase II[142] (CaM kinase II). Antibodies directed against synapsin I have proven valuable in molecular and neurobiology research, for example, to estimate synaptic density and to follow synaptogenesis.[143–146]

Molecular Probes offers a rabbit polyclonal anti–bovine synapsin I antibody as an affinity-purified IgG fraction (A6442). This antibody was isolated from rabbits immunized against bovine brain synapsin I but is also active against human, rat and mouse forms of the antigen; it has little or no activity against synapsin II. The affinity-purified rabbit polyclonal antibody was fractionated from the serum using column chromatography in which bovine synapsin I was covalently bound to the column matrix. Affinity-purified anti–synapsin I antibody is suitable for immunohistochemistry (Figure 17.12), Western blots, enzyme-linked immunosorbent assays (ELISAs) and immunoprecipitations. Our Zenon® Rabbit IgG Labeling Kits (Section 7.3, Table 7.13) can be used to prepare fluorescent dye–, biotin- or enzyme-labeled complexes of this antibody.

Anti–NMDA Receptor Antibodies

N-methyl-D-aspartate (NMDA) receptors constitute cation channels of the central nervous system that are gated by the excitatory neurotransmitter L-glutamate.[147,148] Activation of NMDA receptors is essential for inducing long-term potentiation (LTP), a form of activity-dependent synaptic plasticity that is implicated in the learning process in animal behavioral models.[149] The biophysical properties of NMDA receptor channels contributing to LTP include Ca^{2+} permeability, voltage-dependent Mg^{2+} blocking and slow-gating kinetics.[150–153] NMDA receptor–channel activities play a role in neuronal development and in disorders such as epilepsy and ischemic neuronal cell death. As targets for ethanol, NMDA receptors may also function in the pathology of alcoholism.[154,155]

In vitro reconstitution experiments with the cloned NMDA receptor subunit 1 and any one of the four NMDA receptor subunits 2A, 2B, 2C and 2D revealed that the physical properties of the heteromeric NMDA receptor channel appear to be imparted by the particular NMDA receptor subunit 2.[156] NMDA receptor subunits 2A and 2B are detected predominantly in the hippocampus and cortex, whereas 2C is found mainly in the cerebellum. Thus, cellular expression profiles of the NMDA receptor subunits 2A, 2B, 2C and 2D may contribute to the biophysical properties of NMDA receptors in specific central neurons.

For neurobiologists, Molecular Probes offers affinity-purified rabbit polyclonal antibodies to NMDA receptor subunits 2A, 2B and 2C (A6473, A6474, A6475). The anti–NMDA receptor subunit 2A and 2B antibodies were generated against fusion proteins containing amino acid residues 1253–1391 of subunit 2A and 984–1104 of subunit 2B, respectively. These two antibodies are active against mouse, rat and human forms of the antigens and are specific for the subunit against which they were generated. In contrast, the anti–NMDA receptor subunit 2C antibody was generated against amino acid residues 25–130 of subunit 2C and recognizes the 140,000-dalton subunit 2C, as well as the 180,000-dalton subunit 2A and subunit 2B from mouse, rat and human. These three affinity-purified antibodies are suitable for immunohistochemistry (Figure 16.33), Western blots, enzyme-linked immunosorbent assays (ELISAs) and immunoprecipitations. Our Zenon® Rabbit IgG Labeling Kits (Section 7.3, Table 7.13) can be used to prepare fluorescent dye–, biotin- or enzyme-labeled complexes of these antibodies.

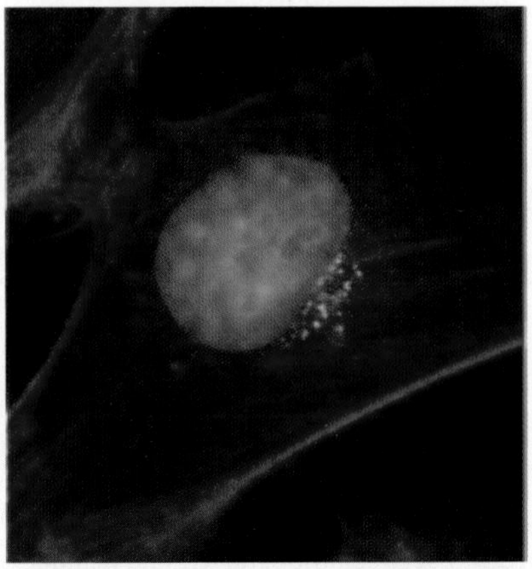

Figure 7.96 Fixed, permeabilized and RNase-treated HeLa cells were labeled with mouse monoclonal anti–human Golgin-97 antibody (A21270) and visualized with the yellow-fluorescent Alexa Fluor® 430 goat anti–mouse IgG antibody (A11063). The F-actin was labeled with red-fluorescent Alexa Fluor® 594 phalloidin (A12381) and the nuclei were stained with the SYTOX® Green nucleic acid stain (S7020). This multiple-exposure image was acquired using a Nikon Diaphot fluorescent microscope equipped with a Quantix CCD camera.

Other Polyclonal and Monoclonal Antibodies

Anti–Human Golgin-97 Antibody

Originally isolated from the serum of a patient with the autoimmune disease known as Sjögren's syndrome, anti–human golgin-97 antibodies recognize a 97,000-dalton protein called golgin-97, a member of the granin family of proteins and a peripheral membrane protein localized on the cytoplasmic face of the Golgi apparatus.[157–159] Because the antibody recognizes a protein unique to the Golgi apparatus of most vertebrate species, it is useful for immunodetection and identification of the Golgi apparatus in cells (Figure 6.7, Figure 7.96, Figure 12.5, Figure 12.53, Figure 12.54). Molecular Probes has available the purified mouse IgG_1 monoclonal anti–human golgin-97 antibody (A21270). This mouse IgG_1 antibody can be directly labeled with any of our Zenon® Mouse IgG_1 Labeling Kits (Section 7.3, Table 7.13) for applications that use multiple mouse monoclonal antibodies.

Anti–Human Transferrin Receptor Antibody

Transferrin is a monomeric serum glycoprotein (~80,000 daltons) that binds up to two Fe^{3+} atoms for delivery to vertebrate cells through receptor-mediated endocytosis.[160–162] Once iron-carrying transferrin proteins are inside endosomes, the acidic environment favors dissociation of iron from the transferrin–receptor complex. Following the release of iron, the apotransferrin is recycled to the plasma membrane, where it is released from its receptor to scavenge more iron.[163,164] Although fluorescent transferrin conjugates have been widely used to study transferrin receptor–mediated endocytosis [165–167] (Section 16.1), antibodies to the transferrin receptor have proven to be useful for localizing transferrin receptors,[168,169] following endocytic recycling pathways [167,168] and performing enzyme-linked immunosorbent assays [167] (ELISAs).

Molecular Probes' mouse monoclonal anti–human transferrin receptor antibody (A11130) should be useful for the localization of transferrin receptors by immunofluorescence techniques. This IgG_1 antibody, which is purified from ascites by protein A chromatography, recognizes the human transferrin receptor and does not block binding of transferrin to the receptor. The antibody can be complexed with the reagents in any of our Zenon® Mouse IgG_1 Labeling Kits (Section 7.3, Table 7.13) for multiplexed analyses.

Antibodies against Matrix Metalloproteinases

The matrix metalloproteinases (MMPs) constitute a family of zinc-dependent endopeptidases that function within the extracellular matrix. These enzymes are responsible for the breakdown of connective tissues and are important in bone remodeling, the menstrual cycle and repair of tissue damage. While the exact contribution of MMPs to certain pathological processes is difficult to assess, MMPs appear to have a key role in the development of arthritis and the invasion and metastasis of cancer.[170,171]

MMPs tend to have multiple substrates, with most family members having the ability to degrade several different types of collagen along with elastin, gelatin and fibronectin.[172] Most MMPs contain three major domains (Figure 7.97): a regulatory domain (which must be removed before the enzyme can be active), a catalytic domain and a hemopexin domain. The hemopexin domain aids in enzyme binding to certain substrates, although it is not necessary for the catalytic function of the enzyme.[173]

To assist researchers in the study of these important enzymes, Molecular Probes offers rabbit antibodies against MMP-1, MMP-2, MMP-3 and MMP-9 (Table 7.21). In each case, the antibody is directed at the stretch of amino acids that forms the small hinge region between the catalytic and hemopexin domains. The hinge region is highly variable among MMPs;[172] therefore, antibodies raised against this peptide sequence have very little crossreactivity with other MMPs. All of these antibodies recognize both the pro (inactive) and active forms of their respective MMP targets. They are suitable for Western blotting, immunoprecipitation and immunohistochemistry applications. Our Zenon® Rabbit IgG Labeling Kits (Section 7.3, Table 7.13) can be used to prepare fluorescent dye–, biotin- or enzyme-labeled complexes of these antibodies.

Anti–Bovine Serum Albumin Antibody

Molecular Probes has available the rabbit IgG fraction of anti–bovine serum albumin (A11133), which is useful for the detection of bovine serum albumin (BSA) in tracer studies or in protease assays. The rabbit anti-BSA antibody can then be detected with any of our fluorophore- or hapten-labeled anti–rabbit IgG antibodies. Alternatively, fluorescent dye–, biotin- or enzyme-labeled complexes of this antibody can be prepared with our Zenon® Rabbit IgG Labeling Kits (Section 7.3, Table 7.13). Precomplexation of the anti-BSA with any of our numerous BSA conjugates (Section 14.7) permits their phagocytosis via the Fc receptor (Section 16.1, Figure 16.2).

Table 7.21 — Molecular Probes' anti–matrix metalloproteinase (MMP) antibodies

Antibody	Cat #	Alternate Names for MMP
Anti–MMP-1	A21290	Collagenase 1, Interstitial Collagenase
Anti–MMP-2	A21291	Gelatinase A, 72 kDa Gelatinase, Type IV Collagenase
Anti–MMP-3	A21292	Stromelysin 1, Transin
Anti–MMP-9	A21293	Gelatinase B, 92 kDa Gelatinase, Type V Collagenase

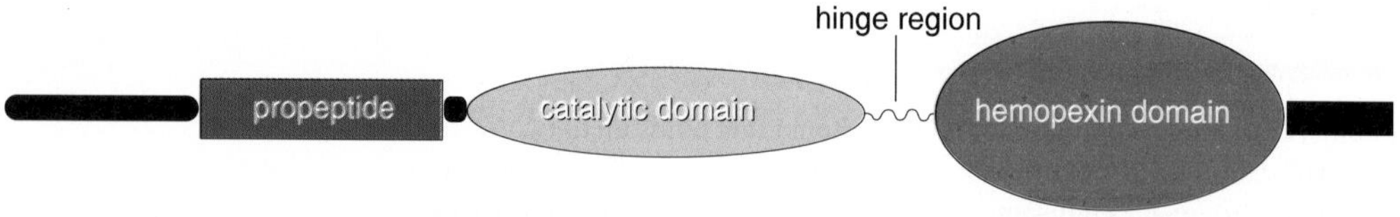

Figure 7.97 The domain structure of a typical metalloproteinase.

References

1. Nat Rev Mol Cell Biol 3, 906 (2002); **2.** Annu Rev Biochem 67, 509 (1998); **3.** Nat Biotechnol 15, 961 (1997); **4.** Nature 369, 400 (1994); **5.** Science 263, 802 (1994); **6.** J Biol Chem 273, 21054 (1998); **7.** Proc Natl Acad Sci U S A 83, 8703 (1986); **8.** Meth Mol Genet 1, 267 (1993); **9.** Biotechniques 13, 856 (1992); **10.** Biotechniques 10, 178 (1991); **11.** Nucleic Acids Res 19, 4005 (1991); **12.** Science 252, 712 (1991); **13.** Gene 67, 31 (1988); **14.** J Biol Chem 272, 8133 (1997); **15.** J Cell Biol 133, 1403 (1996); **16.** Mol Biol Cell 7, 1209 (1996); **17.** Cytometry 20, 134 (1995); **18.** Mol Gen Genet 216, 321 (1989); **19.** Mol Gen Genet 215, 38 (1988); **20.** Plant Mol Biol 10, 387 (1988); **21.** Proc Natl Acad Sci U S A 83, 8447 (1986); **22.** J Biol Chem 269, 17635 (1994); **23.** Plant Mol Biol 15, 821 (1990); **24.** Biotechniques 27, 896 (1999); **25.** DNA Cell Biol 12, 441 (1993); **26.** Protein Expr Purif 3, 263 (1992); **27.** Methods Mol Biol 130, 203 (2000); **28.** Unlabeled antibody provided by Covance Antibody Services, Inc. **29.** Methods Enzymol 194, 508 (1991); **30.** Mol Cell Biol 5, 3610 (1985); **31.** Cell Biochem Biophys 32 Spring, 131 (2000); **32.** Science 292, 624 (2001); **33.** Science 289, 1150 (2000); **34.** Trends Cell Biol 10, 369 (2000); **35.** Biochim Biophys Acta 1366, 151 (1998); **36.** Science 281, 1309 (1998); **37.** Biochim Biophys Acta 1366, 199 (1998); **38.** Biochim Biophys Acta 1366, 211 (1998); **39.** Curr Opin Cardiol 13, 190 (1998); **40.** Ann Neurol 44, S99 (1998); **41.** J Neural Transm 105, 855 (1998); **42.** Semin Liver Dis 18, 237 (1998); **43.** "Immunological approaches to the characterization and diagnosis of mitochondrial disease." R.A. Capaldi, J. Murray, L. Byrne, M.S. Janes and M.F. Marusich, Mitochondrion (2004) in press; **44.** Science 283, 1488 (1999); **45.** Annu Rev Biochem 59, 569 (1990); **46.** Biochemistry 30, 3674 (1991); **47.** Biochim Biophys Acta 1225, 95 (1993); **48.** Methods Enzymol 260, 117 (1995); **49.** J Biol Chem 268, 18754 (1993); **50.** J Biol Chem 266, 7688 (1991); **51.** Biochim Biophys Acta 1315, 199 (1996); **52.** Biochim Biophys Acta 1362, 145 (1997); **53.** Pediatr Res 28, 529 (1990); **54.** Hum Mol Genet 6, 935 (1997); **55.** J Histochem Cytochem 52, 1011 (2004); **56.** Proc Natl Acad Sci U S A 98, 6656 (2001); **57.** Biochim Biophys Acta 894, 109 (1987); **58.** J Biol Chem 273, 24406 (1998); **59.** J Biol Chem 276, 16296 (2001); **60.** Biochim Biophys Acta 1455, 35 (1999); **61.** Mol Biol Cell 9, 917 (1998); **62.** J Biol Chem 272, 5757 (1997); **63.** Biochem J 239, 89 (1986); **64.** Neurology 53, 612 (1999); **65.** J Cell Biol 136, 287 (1997); **66.** J Biol Chem 273, 29915 (1998); **67.** J Cell Biol 142, 39 (1998); **68.** J Biol Chem 272, 25928 (1997); **69.** Mol Cell Biol 16, 2700 (1996); **70.** J Cell Biol 151, 353 (2000); **71.** J Biol Chem 275, 23471 (2000); **72.** J Cell Biol 144, 915 (1999); **73.** J Bioenerg Biomembr 20, 291 (1988); **74.** J Cell Biol 143, 333 (1998); **75.** J Biol Chem 273,

References — continued

22284 (1998); **76.** J Cell Biol 140, 577 (1998); **77.** Eur J Cell Biol 70, 289 (1996); **78.** Eur J Biochem 260, 461 (1999); **79.** FEBS Lett 476, 301 (2000); **80.** Trends Cell Biol 5, 21 (1995); **81.** Proc Natl Acad Sci U S A 99, 10706 (2002); **82.** J Neuroimmunol 92, 152 (1998); **83.** EMBO J 17, 3461 (1998); **84.** EMBO J 19, 2340 (2000); **85.** J Biol Chem 275, 26040 (2000); **86.** EMBO J 17, 3448 (1998); **87.** Mol Cell Biol 20, 760 (2000); **88.** Cell 67, 325 (1991); **89.** Neurology 45, 544 (1995); **90.** Mol Cell Biol 13, 3494 (1993); **91.** Dev Genet 18, 11 (1996); **92.** Development 124, 3449 (1997); **93.** J Neurobiol 28, 82 (1995); **94.** J Neurobiol 25, 143 (1994); **95.** Biochim Biophys Acta 1280, 115 (1996); **96.** Curr Opin Cell Biol 10, 742 (1998); **97.** J Cell Sci 113, 1929 (2000); **98.** Oncogene 17, 1777 (1998); **99.** Proc Natl Acad Sci U S A 95, 14932 (1998); **100.** Clin Cancer Res 5, 2121 (1999); **101.** Immunobiology 203, 769 (2001); **102.** Annu Rev Immunol 6, 629 (1988); **103.** J Immunol 159, 3000 (1997); **104.** Cell 73, 1059 (1993); **105.** Mol Cell Biol 15, 2600 (1995); **106.** Genomics 13, 575 (1992); **107.** Oncogene 20, 551 (2001); **108.** Science 257, 1958 (1992); **109.** Mol Cell Biol 14, 2077 (1994); **110.** Mol Cell Biol 14, 2066 (1994); **111.** Int J Cancer 57, 353 (1994); **112.** Proc Natl Acad Sci U S A 90, 1112 (1993); **113.** Histopathology 36, 151 (2000); **114.** Pathol Int 48, 717 (1998); **115.** Cancer Res 55, 2910 (1995); **116.** Trends Biochem Sci 22, 14 (1997); **117.** Proc Natl Acad Sci U S A 92, 9019 (1995); **118.** J Mol Med 73, 509 (1995); **119.** Hybridoma 19, 63 (2000); **120.** Chem Phys Lipids 98, 13 (1999); **121.** Chem Phys Lipids 101, 93 (1999); **122.** J Biol Chem 274, 9129 (1999); **123.** Annu Rev Biochem 68, 965 (1999); **124.** Proc Natl Acad Sci U S A 96, 4240 (1999); **125.** J Cell Biol 151, 483 (2000); **126.** Biochem Soc Trans 27, 648 (1999); **127.** Anal Biochem 285, 270 (2000); **128.** Neurochem Res 25, 1439 (2000); **129.** Biochem Biophys Res Commun 208, 910 (1995); **130.** Biochim Biophys Acta 1313, 268 (1996); **131.** J Neurol Sci 151, 41 (1997); **132.** Proc Natl Acad Sci U S A 73, 4344 (1976); **133.** J Cell Sci 23, 243 (1977); **134.** EMBO J 1, 1649 (1982); **135.** Acta Cytol 44, 976 (2000); **136.** J Biol Chem 245, 5728 (1970); **137.** J Exp Med 147, 1054 (1978); **138.** Molecular Biology of the Cell, 3rd Ed., Alberts B, Bray D, Lewis J, Raff M, Roberts K, Watson JD pp. 986–988 (1994); **139.** Annu Rev Cell Biol 1, 67 (1985); **140.** Science 226, 1209 (1984); **141.** J Cell Biol 96, 1337 (1983); **142.** Molecular and Cellular Mechanisms of Neurotransmitter Release, Stjarne L, et al., Eds. pp. 31–45 (1994); **143.** J Neurosci 12, 1736 (1992); **144.** J Neurosci 11, 1617 (1991); **145.** J Neurosci 9, 2151 (1989); **146.** Neuron 11, 713 (1993); **147.** Neuron 12, 529 (1994); **148.** Nature 354, 31 (1991); **149.** J Neurosci 9, 3040 (1989); **150.** Nature 346, 565 (1990); **151.** Nature 325, 529 (1987); **152.** Nature 321, 519 (1986); **153.** Nature 307, 462 (1984); **154.** Mol Pharmacol 45, 324 (1994); **155.** Neurosci Lett 152, 13 (1993); **156.** Science 256, 1217 (1992); **157.** Curr Biol 9, 385 (1999); **158.** Arthritis Rheum 40, 1693 (1997); **159.** Curr Biol 9, 381 (1999); **160.** Cell 49, 423 (1987); **161.** Trends Biochem Sci 12, 350 (1987); **162.** Biochimie 68, 375 (1986); **163.** J Cell Biol 108, 1291 (1989); **164.** Cell 37, 789 (1984); **165.** J Cell Biol 140, 565 (1998); **166.** J Biol Chem 273, 2035 (1998); **167.** Mol Biol Cell 7, 355 (1996); **168.** J Biol Chem 272, 13929 (1997); **169.** J Cell Biol 135, 1749 (1996); **170.** Int J Oncol 12, 1343 (1998); **171.** Mol Med Today 4, 130 (1998); **172.** Matrix Metalloproteinases and TIMPs, Woessner JF 11 (2000); **173.** Matrix Biol 15, 511 (1997).

Product List — 7.5 Primary Antibodies for Diverse Applications

Cat #	Product Name	Unit Size
A23150	ABSOLUTE-S™ SBIP Cell Proliferation Assay Kit *with Alexa Fluor® 488 anti-BrdU* *50 assays*	1 kit
A11133	anti-albumin (bovine serum), rabbit IgG fraction (anti-BSA) *2 mg/mL*	0.5 mL
A6458	anti-alkaline phosphatase (yeast vacuolar), mouse IgG_1, monoclonal 1D3 *in conditioned culture medium*	2.5 mL
A21300	anti-bromodeoxyuridine, mouse IgG_1, monoclonal PRB-1 (anti-BrdU)	350 µL
A21303	anti-bromodeoxyuridine, mouse IgG_1, monoclonal PRB-1, Alexa Fluor® 488 conjugate (anti-BrdU, Alexa Fluor® 488 conjugate)	350 µL
A21307	anti-bromodeoxyuridine, mouse IgG_1, monoclonal PRB-1, Alexa Fluor® 532 conjugate (anti-BrdU, Alexa Fluor® 532 conjugate)	350 µL
A21308	anti-bromodeoxyuridine, mouse IgG_1, monoclonal PRB-1, Alexa Fluor® 546 conjugate (anti-BrdU, Alexa Fluor® 546 conjugate)	350 µL
A21304	anti-bromodeoxyuridine, mouse IgG_1, monoclonal PRB-1, Alexa Fluor® 594 conjugate (anti-BrdU, Alexa Fluor® 594 conjugate)	350 µL
A21305	anti-bromodeoxyuridine, mouse IgG_1, monoclonal PRB-1, Alexa Fluor® 647 conjugate (anti-BrdU, Alexa Fluor® 647 conjugate)	350 µL
A21306	anti-bromodeoxyuridine, mouse IgG_1, monoclonal PRB-1, Alexa Fluor® 660 conjugate (anti-BrdU, Alexa Fluor® 660 conjugate)	350 µL
A21301MP	anti-bromodeoxyuridine, mouse IgG_1, monoclonal PRB-1, biotin-XX conjugate (anti-BrdU, biotin conjugate)	350 µL
A6428	anti-carboxypeptidase Y (yeast vacuolar), mouse IgG_1, monoclonal 10A5 (anti-CPY)	250 µg
A21330	anti-CD3, mouse IgG_1, monoclonal 289-13801 *0.2 mg/mL*	0.5 mL
A21331	anti-CD3, mouse IgG_1, monoclonal 289-13801, Alexa Fluor® 488 conjugate *0.2 mg/mL*	0.5 mL
A21332	anti-CD3, mouse IgG_1, monoclonal 289-13801, Alexa Fluor® 647 conjugate *0.2 mg/mL*	0.5 mL
A21333	anti-CD3, mouse IgG_1, monoclonal 289-13801, R-phycoerythrin conjugate *0.2 mg/mL*	0.5 mL
A21334	anti-CD4, mouse IgG_1, monoclonal 289-14120 *0.2 mg/mL*	0.5 mL
A21335	anti-CD4, mouse IgG_1, monoclonal 289-14120, Alexa Fluor® 488 conjugate *0.2 mg/mL*	0.5 mL
A21336	anti-CD4, mouse IgG_1, monoclonal 289-14120, Alexa Fluor® 647 conjugate *0.2 mg/mL*	0.5 mL
A21337	anti-CD4, mouse IgG_1, monoclonal 289-14120, R-phycoerythrin conjugate *0.2 mg/mL*	0.5 mL
A21338	anti-CD8, mouse IgG_{2a}, monoclonal 289-13804 *0.2 mg/mL*	0.5 mL
A21339	anti-CD8, mouse IgG_{2a}, monoclonal 289-13804, Alexa Fluor® 488 conjugate *0.2 mg/mL*	0.5 mL
A21340	anti-CD8, mouse IgG_{2a}, monoclonal 289-13804, Alexa Fluor® 647 conjugate *0.2 mg/mL*	0.5 mL
A21286	anti-cdc6 peptide (human), mouse IgG_{2a}, monoclonal 37F4 *for immunohistochemistry*	100 µg
A21281	anti-c-myc, chicken IgY fraction *1 mg/mL*	100 µL
A21280	anti-c-myc, mouse IgG_1, monoclonal 289-19510 *1 mg/mL*	100 µL
A21320	anti-cyclin D1, mouse IgG_{2a}, monoclonal DCS-6	100 µg

For current prices or to order online, visit probes.invitrogen.com

Product List — 7.5 Primary Antibodies for Diverse Applications — continued

Cat #	Product Name	Unit Size
A21321	anti-cyclin D2, mouse IgG_{2b}, monoclonal DCS-5.2	100 µg
A21322	anti-cyclin D3, mouse IgG_1, monoclonal DCS-22	100 µg
A21283	anti-desmin, mouse IgG_1, monoclonal 131-15014 *1 mg/mL*	100 µL
A6429	anti-dolichol phosphate mannose synthase (yeast), mouse IgG_1, monoclonal 5C5	250 µg
A21316	anti-fibronectin (human), chicken IgY fraction *1 mg/mL*	0.5 mL
A11132	anti-β-galactosidase, rabbit IgG fraction *2 mg/mL*	0.5 mL
A21282	anti-glial fibrillary acidic protein, mouse IgG_1, monoclonal 131-17719 (anti-GFAP) *1 mg/mL*	100 µL
A21294	anti-glial fibrillary acidic protein, mouse IgG_1, monoclonal 131-17719, Alexa Fluor® 488 conjugate (anti-GFAP, Alexa Fluor® 488 conjugate) *1 mg/mL*	50 µL
A21295	anti-glial fibrillary acidic protein, mouse IgG_1, monoclonal 131-17719, Alexa Fluor® 594 conjugate (anti-GFAP, Alexa Fluor® 594 conjugate) *1 mg/mL*	50 µL
A5790	anti-β-glucuronidase, rabbit IgG fraction *2 mg/mL*	0.5 mL
A5800	anti-glutathione *S*-transferase, rabbit IgG fraction *3 mg/mL*	0.5 mL
A11131	anti-glutathione *S*-transferase, rabbit IgG fraction, Alexa Fluor® 488 conjugate *2 mg/mL*	0.5 mL
A21270	anti-golgin-97 (human), mouse IgG_1, monoclonal CDF4 (anti-Golgi)	100 µg
A11120	anti-green fluorescent protein, mouse IgG_{2a}, monoclonal 3E6 (anti-GFP, mAb 3E6)	100 µg
A11121	anti-green fluorescent protein, mouse IgG_1, monoclonal 11E5 (anti-GFP, mAb 11E5)	100 µg
A11122	anti-green fluorescent protein, rabbit IgG fraction (anti-GFP, IgG) *2 mg/mL*	100 µL
A21311	anti-green fluorescent protein, rabbit IgG fraction, Alexa Fluor® 488 conjugate (anti-GFP, IgG, Alexa Fluor® 488 conjugate) *2 mg/mL*	100 µL
A31851	anti-green fluorescent protein, rabbit IgG fraction, Alexa Fluor® 555 conjugate (anti-GFP, IgG, Alexa Fluor® 555 conjugate) *2 mg/mL*	100 µL
A21312	anti-green fluorescent protein, rabbit IgG fraction, Alexa Fluor® 594 conjugate (anti-GFP, IgG, Alexa Fluor® 594 conjugate) *2 mg/mL*	100 µL
A31852	anti-green fluorescent protein, rabbit IgG fraction, Alexa Fluor® 647 conjugate (anti-GFP, IgG, Alexa Fluor® 647 conjugate) *2 mg/mL*	100 µL
A6455	anti-green fluorescent protein, rabbit serum (anti-GFP, serum)	100 µL
A6422	anti-H^+-ATPase 69 kDa subunit (yeast vacuolar), mouse IgG_{2a}, monoclonal 8B1	250 µg
A6426	anti-H^+-ATPase 100 kDa subunit (yeast vacuolar), mouse IgG_{2a}, monoclonal 10D7	250 µg
A6427	anti-H^+-ATPase 60 kDa subunit (yeast vacuolar), mouse IgG_1, monoclonal 13D11	250 µg
A21287	anti-hemagglutinin, mouse IgG_1, monoclonal 16B12, Alexa Fluor® 488 conjugate (anti-HA, Alexa Fluor® 488 conjugate) *1 mg/mL*	100 µL
A21288	anti-hemagglutinin, mouse IgG_1, monoclonal 16B12, Alexa Fluor® 594 conjugate (anti-HA, Alexa Fluor® 594 conjugate) *1 mg/mL*	100 µL
A21271	anti-HuC/HuD neuronal protein (human), mouse IgG_{2b}, monoclonal 16A11	100 µg
A21272	anti-HuC/HuD neuronal protein (human), mouse IgG_{2b}, monoclonal 16A11, biotin-XX conjugate	100 µg
A21277	anti-HuR mRNA-binding protein (human), mouse IgG_1, monoclonal 19F12	100 µg
A21290	anti-matrix metalloproteinase-1 (hinge region), affinity-purified rabbit antibody (anti-MMP-1) *1 mg/mL*	100 µL
A21291	anti-matrix metalloproteinase-2 (hinge region), affinity-purified rabbit antibody (anti-MMP-2) *1 mg/mL*	100 µL
A21292	anti-matrix metalloproteinase-3 (hinge region), affinity-purified rabbit antibody (anti-MMP-3) *1 mg/mL*	100 µL
A21293	anti-matrix metalloproteinase-9 (hinge region), affinity-purified rabbit antibody (anti-MMP-9) *1 mg/mL*	100 µL
A6473	anti-NMDA receptor, subunit 2A (rat), rabbit IgG fraction *affinity purified*	10 µg
A6474	anti-NMDA receptor, subunit 2B (rat), rabbit IgG fraction *affinity purified*	10 µg
A6475	anti-NMDA receptor, subunit 2C (rat), rabbit IgG fraction *affinity purified*	10 µg
A21359	anti-OxPhos Complex I 17 kDa subunit, mouse IgG_{2b}, monoclonal 21C11 *human mitochondrial reactivity*	100 µg
A21343	anti-OxPhos Complex I 30 kDa subunit, mouse IgG_1, monoclonal 3F9 *human mitochondrial reactivity*	100 µg
A21344	anti-OxPhos Complex I 39 kDa subunit, mouse IgG_1, monoclonal 20C11 *human mitochondrial reactivity*	100 µg
A11142	anti-OxPhos Complex II 70 kDa subunit, mouse IgG_1, monoclonal 2E3 *human mitochondrial reactivity*	50 µg
A21345	anti-OxPhos Complex II 30 kDa subunit, mouse IgG_{2a}, monoclonal 21A11 *human mitochondrial reactivity*	100 µg
A21361	anti-OxPhos Complex III 10 kDa subunit, mouse IgG_{2a}, monoclonal 1H9 *human mitochondrial reactivity*	100 µg
A21362	anti-OxPhos Complex III core 1 subunit, mouse IgG_1, monoclonal 16D10 *human mitochondrial reactivity*	100 µg
A11143	anti-OxPhos Complex III core 2 subunit, mouse IgG_1, monoclonal 13G12 *human mitochondrial reactivity*	100 µg
A21346	anti-OxPhos Complex III subunit FeS, mouse IgG_{2b}, monoclonal 5A5 *human mitochondrial reactivity*	100 µg
A6403	anti-OxPhos Complex IV subunit I, mouse IgG_{2a}, monoclonal 1D6 (anti-cytochrome oxidase subunit I) *human mitochondrial reactivity*	100 µg
A21296	anti-OxPhos Complex IV subunit I, mouse IgG_{2a}, monoclonal 1D6, Alexa Fluor® 488 conjugate (anti-cytochrome oxidase subunit I, Alexa Fluor® 488 conjugate) *1 mg/mL* *human mitochondrial reactivity*	100 µL
A21297	anti-OxPhos Complex IV subunit I, mouse IgG_{2a}, monoclonal 1D6, Alexa Fluor® 594 conjugate (anti-cytochrome oxidase subunit I, Alexa Fluor® 594 conjugate) *1 mg/mL* *human mitochondrial reactivity*	100 µL
A6404	anti-OxPhos Complex IV subunit II, mouse IgG_{2a}, monoclonal 12C4 (anti-cytochrome oxidase subunit II) *human mitochondrial reactivity*	100 µg
A21347	anti-OxPhos Complex IV subunit IV, mouse IgG_{2a}, monoclonal 10G8 (anti-cytochrome oxidase subunit IV) *human mitochondrial reactivity*	100 µg
A21348	anti-OxPhos Complex IV subunit IV, mouse IgG_{2a}, monoclonal 20E8 (anti-cytochrome oxidase subunit IV) *human mitochondrial reactivity*	100 µg
A21363	anti-OxPhos Complex IV subunit Va, mouse IgG_{2a}, monoclonal 6E9 (anti-cytochrome oxidase subunit Va) *human mitochondrial reactivity*	100 µg
A21349	anti-OxPhos Complex IV subunit Vb, mouse IgG_{2b}, monoclonal 16H12 (anti-cytochrome oxidase subunit Vb) *human mitochondrial reactivity*	100 µg

For current prices or to order online, visit probes.invitrogen.com

Cat #	Product Name	Unit Size
A21365	anti-OxPhos Complex IV subunit VIa-L, mouse IgG_1, monoclonal 14A3 (anti-cytochrome oxidase subunit VIa-L) *human mitochondrial reactivity*	100 µg
A21366	anti-OxPhos Complex IV subunit VIb, mouse IgG_1, monoclonal 3F9 (anti-cytochrome oxidase subunit VIb) *human mitochondrial reactivity*	100 µg
A6401	anti-OxPhos Complex IV subunit VIc, mouse IgG_{2b}, monoclonal 3G5 (anti-cytochrome oxidase subunit VIc) *human mitochondrial reactivity*	100 µg
A21367	anti-OxPhos Complex IV subunit VIIa-H/L, mouse IgG_{2a}, monoclonal 6D7 (anti-cytochrome oxidase subunit VIIa-H/L) *human mitochondrial reactivity*	100 µg
A21368	anti-OxPhos Complex IV subunit VIIb, mouse IgG_1, monoclonal 2G7 (anti-cytochrome oxidase subunit VIIb) *human mitochondrial reactivity*	100 µg
A6405	anti-OxPhos Complex IV subunit I (yeast), mouse IgG_{2b}, monoclonal 11D8 (anti-cytochrome oxidase subunit I (yeast))	100 µg
A6407	anti-OxPhos Complex IV subunit II (yeast), mouse IgG_{2a}, monoclonal 4B12 (anti-cytochrome oxidase subunit II (yeast))	250 µg
A6408	anti-OxPhos Complex IV subunit III (yeast), mouse IgG_{2a}, monoclonal DA5 (anti-cytochrome oxidase subunit III (yeast))	250 µg
A6432	anti-OxPhos Complex IV subunit IV (yeast), mouse IgG_1, monoclonal 1A12 (anti-cytochrome oxidase subunit IV (yeast))	250 µg
A21355	anti-OxPhos Complex V inhibitor protein, mouse IgG_1, monoclonal 5E2 (anti-ATP synthase IP; anti-F_1F_0-ATPase IP) *human mitochondrial reactivity*	100 µg
A21350	anti-OxPhos Complex V subunit α, mouse IgG_{2b}, monoclonal 7H10 (anti-ATP synthase subunit α; anti-F_1F_0-ATPase subunit α) *human mitochondrial reactivity*	100 µg
A21351	anti-OxPhos Complex V subunit β, mouse IgG_1, monoclonal 3D5 (anti-ATP synthase subunit β; anti-F_1F_0-ATPase subunit β) *human mitochondrial reactivity*	100 µg
A21353	anti-OxPhos Complex V subunit d, mouse IgG_{2b}, monoclonal 7F9 (anti-ATP synthase subunit d; anti-F_1F_0-ATPase subunit d) *human mitochondrial reactivity*	100 µg
A21354	anti-OxPhos Complex V subunit OSCP, mouse IgG_1, monoclonal 4C11 (anti-ATP synthase subunit OSCP; anti-F_1F_0-ATPase subunit OSCP) *human mitochondrial reactivity*	100 µg
A31856	anti-OxPhos Complex I 15 kDa subunit, mouse IgG_1, monoclonal 17G3 *human mitochondrial reactivity*	100 µg
A31857	anti-OxPhos Complex I 20 kDa subunit, mouse IgG_1, monoclonal 20E9 *human mitochondrial reactivity*	100 µg
A21319	anti-p21WAF1/CIP1, mouse IgG_{2a}, monoclonal DCS-60	100 µg
A21273	anti-Pep12p (yeast), mouse IgG_1, monoclonal 2C3 *0.5 mg/mL*	100 µL
A21327	anti-phosphatidylinositol 4,5-diphosphate, mouse IgM, monoclonal 2C11 (anti-PtdIns(4,5)P_2) *1 mg/mL*	100 µL
A21328	anti-phosphatidylinositol 3,4,5-triphosphate, mouse IgM, monoclonal RC6F8 (anti-PtdIns(3,4,5)P_3) *1 mg/mL*	100 µL
A6457	anti-3-phosphoglycerate kinase (yeast), mouse IgG_1, monoclonal 22C5 (anti-PGK)	250 µg
A21317	anti-porin (human mitochondrial), mouse IgG_{2b}, monoclonal 20B12	100 µg
A31855	anti-porin (human mitochondrial), mouse IgG_{2b}, monoclonal 31HL *1 mg/mL*	100 µL
A6449	anti-porin (yeast mitochondrial), mouse IgG_1, monoclonal 16G9	250 µg
A21323	anti-pyruvate dehydrogenase E1α subunit (human mitochondrial), mouse IgG_1, monoclonal 9H9 (anti-PDH E1α subunit)	100 µg
A31853	anti-pyruvate dehydrogenase E1α subunit (human mitochondrial), mouse IgG_1, monoclonal 9H9, Alexa Fluor® 594 conjugate (anti-PDH E1α subunit, Alexa Fluor® 594 conjugate) *1 mg/mL*	100 µL
A21324	anti-pyruvate dehydrogenase E1β subunit (human mitochondrial), mouse IgG_1, monoclonal 17A5 (anti-PDH E1β subunit)	100 µg
A21325	anti-pyruvate dehydrogenase E2 subunit (human mitochondrial), mouse IgG_1, monoclonal 15D3 (anti-PDH E2 subunit)	100 µg
A21326	anti-pyruvate dehydrogenase E2/E3bp subunit (human mitochondrial), mouse IgG_{2a}, monoclonal 13G2 (anti-PDH E2/E3bp subunit)	100 µg
A31854	anti-pyruvate dehydrogenase E2 subunit (human mitochondrial), mouse IgG_1, monoclonal 15D3, Alexa Fluor® 488 conjugate (anti-PDH E2 subunit, Alexa Fluor® 488 conjugate) *1 mg/mL*	100 µL
A6442	anti-synapsin I (bovine), rabbit IgG fraction *affinity purified*	10 µg
A11130	anti-transferrin receptor (human), mouse IgG_1, monoclonal 236-15375	50 µg
A11126	anti-α-tubulin (bovine), mouse IgG_1, monoclonal 236-10501	50 µg
A21371	anti-α-tubulin (bovine), mouse IgG_1, monoclonal 236-10501, biotin-XX conjugate	50 µg
A23210	APO-BrdU™ TUNEL Assay Kit *with Alexa Fluor® 488 anti-BrdU* *60 assays*	1 kit
G21801	Glutathione Transferase Fusion Protein Purification Kit *5 purifications*	1 kit
P21315	Penta·His™ mouse IgG_1, monoclonal antibody (anti-pentahistidine) *BSA free*	100 µg
S35115	SelectFX™ Alexa Fluor® 488 Cytochrome *c* Apoptosis Detection Kit *for fixed cells*	1 kit
S34200	SelectFX™ Alexa Fluor® 488 Endoplasmic Reticulum Labeling Kit *for fixed cells*	1 kit
S34201	SelectFX™ Alexa Fluor® 488 Peroxisome Labeling Kit *for fixed cells*	1 kit

For current prices or to order online, visit probes.invitrogen.com

7.6 Avidin, Streptavidin, NeutrAvidin and CaptAvidin™ Biotin-Binding Proteins and Affinity Matrices

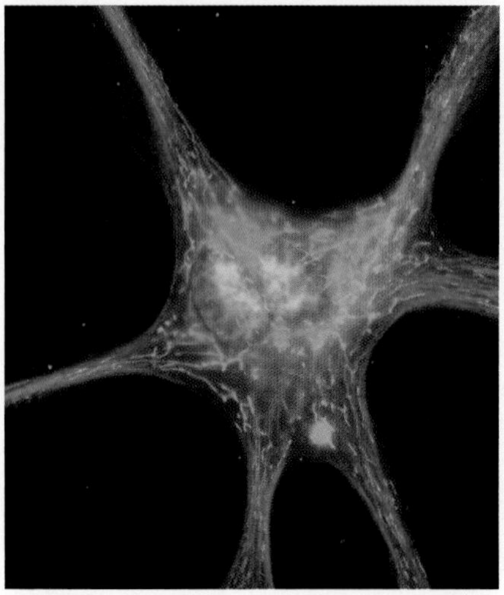

Figure 7.98 The cytoskeleton of a fixed and permeabilized bovine pulmonary artery endothelial cell detected using mouse monoclonal anti–α-tubulin antibody (A11126), visualized with Alexa Fluor® 647 goat anti–mouse IgG antibody (A21235) and pseudocolored magenta. Endogenous biotin in the mitochondria was labeled with green-fluorescent Alexa Fluor® 488 streptavidin (S11223) and DNA was stained with blue-fluorescent DAPI (D1306, D3571, D21490).

The high affinity of avidin for biotin was first exploited in histochemical applications in the mid-1970s.[1,2] This egg-white protein and its bacterial counterpart, streptavidin, have since become standard reagents for diverse detection schemes.[3–6] In their simplest form, such methods entail applying a biotinylated probe to a sample and then detecting the bound probe with a labeled avidin or streptavidin. These techniques are commonly used to localize antigens in cells and tissues[7,8] and to detect biomolecules in immunoassays and DNA hybridization procedures[6,9–11] (Section 8.5). In some applications, immobilized avidins are used to capture and release biotinylated targets. In addition to our important dye and enzyme conjugates of avidins and streptavidins, this section contains several products that can be used for the affinity isolation of biotin- and DSB-X™ biotin–conjugated molecules and their complexes with targets in cell and tissues. Our unique DSB-X™ biotin technology, which is described below, provides the most facile means available for reversing the strong interaction of biotin derivatives with avidins.[12] The product lists in Chapter 4 contain all of our biotin derivatives and biotin conjugates, including biotinylation reagents, biotin-based tracers and biotinylated site-selective probes, as well as our important DSB-X™ biotin reagents and conjugates.

Binding Characteristics of Biotin-Binding Proteins

Avidin, streptavidin and NeutrAvidin biotin-binding protein each bind four biotins per molecule with high affinity and selectivity. Dissociation of biotin from streptavidin (S888) is reported to be about 30 times faster than dissociation of biotin from avidin[13] (A887, A2667). Their multiple binding sites permit a number of techniques in which unlabeled avidin, streptavidin or NeutrAvidin biotin-binding protein can be used to bridge two biotinylated reagents. This bridging method, which is commonly used to link a biotinylated probe to a biotinylated enzyme in enzyme-linked immunohistochemical applications, often eliminates the background problems that can occur when using direct avidin– or streptavidin–enzyme conjugates. However, a few endogenously biotinylated proteins that have carboxylase activity are found in the mitochondria (Figure 7.98, Figure 12.27); therefore, sensitive detection of biotinylated targets in cells requires the use of biotin-blocking agents to reduce this background.[14,15] Our Endogenous Biotin-Blocking Kit (E21390, see below) provides the reagents and a protocol for this application. Nonspecific binding of avidin conjugates of enzymes to nitrocellulose can be blocked more effectively by adding extra salts to buffers rather than by adding protein-based blocking reagents.[16]

High-purity unlabeled avidin (A887), streptavidin (S888), NeutrAvidin biotin-binding protein (A2666) and CaptAvidin™ biotin-binding protein (C21385) are available in bulk from Molecular Probes at reasonable prices. We also offer avidin specially packaged in a smaller unit size for extra convenience (A2667). Our avidin, streptavidin and deglycosylated NeutrAvidin biotin-binding protein each bind greater than 12 µg of biotin per mg protein. See below for a description of reversible binding of biotinylated targets with our CaptAvidin™ biotin-binding protein and other affinity matrices.

Avidin

Avidin (A887, A2667; Table 7.22) is a highly cationic 66,000-dalton glycoprotein[17,18] with an isoelectric point of about 10.5. It is thought that avidin's positively charged residues and its oligosaccharide component (heterogeneous structures composed largely of mannose and

Table 7.22 — Molecular Probes' selection of avidin, streptavidin, NeutrAvidin and CaptAvidin™ conjugates

Label (Abs/Em Maxima) *	Streptavidin	NeutrAvidin	Avidin	CaptAvidin™
Fluorescent conjugates				
Alexa Fluor® 350 (346/442)	S11249	A11236		
Marina Blue® (365/460)	S11221	A11230		
Europium luminescent FluoSpheres® microspheres † (365/610)		F20883, F20885		
Platinum luminescent FluoSpheres® microspheres † (390/650)		F20889, F20890, F20891		

Table 7.22 — Molecular Probes' selection of avidin, streptavidin, NeutrAvidin and CaptAvidin™ conjugates — continued

Label (Abs/Em Maxima) *	Streptavidin	NeutrAvidin	Avidin	CaptAvidin™
Alexa Fluor® 405 (402/421)	S32351			
Cascade Yellow™ (402/545)	S11228			
Pacific Blue™ (410/455)	S11222			
Alexa Fluor® 430 (434/539)	S11237			
Fluorescein (494/518)	S869	A2662	A821	
Alexa Fluor® 488 (495/519)	S11223, S32354 ‡		A21370	
Oregon Green® 488 (496/524)	S6368	A6374		
R-Phycoerythrin (496/578) §	S866, S21388 **	A2660		
Alexa Fluor® 610–R-PE (496/628) §	S20982			
Alexa Fluor® 647–R-PE (496/668 §)	S20992			
Alexa Fluor® 680–R-PE (496/702) §	S20985			
Alexa Fluor® 750–R-PE (496/775) §	S32363			
DyeMer™ 488/605 (502/611)	S32385			
DyeMer™ 488/615 (502/617)	S32386			
DyeMer™ 488/630 (502/630)	S32387			
Alexa Fluor® 500 (503/525)	S32352			
Yellow-green–fluorescent FluoSpheres® microspheres † (505/515)	F8780	F8771, F8774, F8776		
Oregon Green® 514 (511/530)	S6369			
Alexa Fluor® 514 (518/540)	S32353			
Alexa Fluor® 532 (531/554)	S11224			
B-Phycoerythrin (546/575) §	S32350			
Tetramethylrhodamine (555/580)	S870	A6373		
Alexa Fluor® 546 (556/573)	S11225			
Alexa Fluor® 555 (555/565)	S21381, S32355 ‡			
Rhodamine B (570/590)	S871			
Rhodamine Red™-X (570/590)	S6366	A6378		
Alexa Fluor® 568 (578/603)	S11226			
Red-fluorescent FluoSpheres® microspheres † (580/605)		F8770, F8775		
Alexa Fluor® 594 (590/617)	S11227, S32356 ‡			
Texas Red® (595/615)	S872	A2665	A820	
Texas Red®-X (595/615)	S6370			
Alexa Fluor® 610 (612/628)	S32359			
Alexa Fluor® 633 (632/647)	S21375			
Alexa Fluor® 635 (633/647)	S32364			
Alexa Fluor® 647 (650/668)	S21374, S32357 ‡			
Allophycocyanin (650/660)	S868, S32362 **			
Alexa Fluor® 680–allophycocyanin (650/702)	S21002			
Alexa Fluor® 700–allophycocyanin (650/723)	S21005			
Alexa Fluor® 750–allophycocyanin (650/775)	S21008			
Alexa Fluor® 660 (663/690)	S21377			
Alexa Fluor® 680 (679/702)	S21378, S32358 ‡			
Alexa Fluor® 700 (702/723)	S21383			
Alexa Fluor® 750 (749/775)	S21384			
Other conjugates				
Acrylamide	S21379			C21387
Agarose	S951			C21386
Alkaline phosphatase	S921			
β-Galactosidase	S931			
Horseradish peroxidase	S911	A2664		
NANOGOLD	N24918			
Alexa Fluor® 488 FluoroNanogold (495/519)	A24926			
Alexa Fluor® 488 colloidal gold (495/519)	A32360 ††, A32361 ‡‡			
Alexa Fluor® 594 FluoroNanogold (590/617)	A24927			
Unlabeled avidins				
Unlabeled	S888	A2666	A887, A2667	C21385
Nonfluorescent FluoSpheres® microspheres †		F8772, F8777		

* Approximate absorption (Abs) and fluorescence emission (Em) maxima, in nm, for conjugates. † FluoSpheres® microspheres are available in different diameters, including 0.04 µm, 0.2 µm and 1.0 µm. ‡ These Alexa Fluor® streptavidin conjugates are supplied in 0.5 mL units of a 2 mg/mL solution. § Multiple absorption peaks. ** Premium grade. †† 5 nm colloidal gold conjugate. ‡‡ 10 nm colloidal gold conjugate.

N-acetylglucosamine) can interact nonspecifically with negatively charged cell surfaces and nucleic acids, sometimes causing background problems in some histochemical applications and flow cytometry. Methods have been developed to suppress this nonspecific avidin binding.[15] In some cases, avidin's nonspecific binding can also be exploited. For example, avidin and its conjugates selectively bind to a component in rodent and human mast cell granules in fixed-cell preparations and can be used to identify mast cells in normal and diseased human tissue without requiring a biotinylated probe.[19,20]

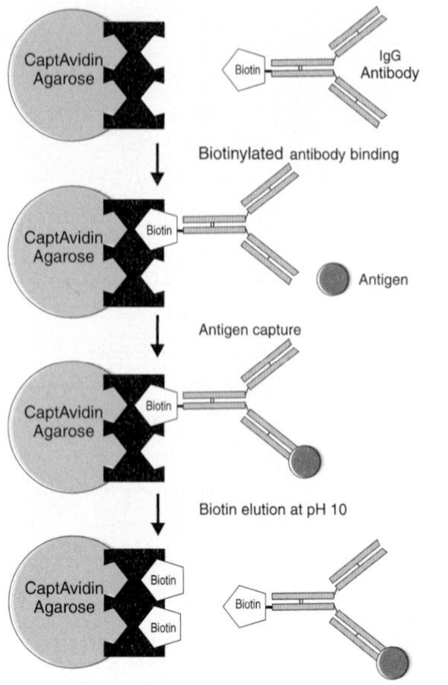

Figure 7.99 Diagram of the use of CaptAvidin™ agarose in affinity chromatography. A biotinylated IgG molecule and target antigen are used as an example.

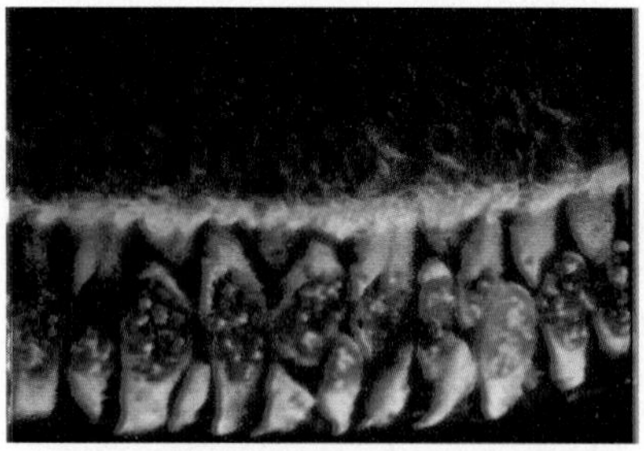

Figure 7.100 The cortical region of the developing follicle of the giant silkmoth *Antheraea polyphemus* stained with a monoclonal antibody against cytoskeletal actin. The primary antibody was visualized using biotin-XX goat anti-mouse IgG antibody (B2763), followed by incubation with Texas Red® streptavidin (S872). The orange to pink colors in this confocal laser-scanning micrograph show the distribution of cytoskeletal actin in the oocyte cortex and follicle cell cytoplasm. The blue color can be attributed to autofluorescence. The image was contributed by Ivo Sauman, Wesleyan University.

Streptavidin

Streptavidin (S888, Table 7.22), a nonglycosylated 52,800-dalton protein with a near-neutral isoelectric point, reportedly exhibits less nonspecific binding than avidin. However, streptavidin contains the tripeptide sequence Arg–Tyr–Asp (RYD) that apparently mimics the Arg–Gly–Asp (RGD) binding sequence of fibronectin, a component of the extracellular matrix that specifically promotes cellular adhesion.[21] This universal recognition sequence binds integrins and related cell-surface molecules.[22,23] Background problems sometimes associated with streptavidin may be attributable to this tripeptide. We have particularly observed binding of streptavidin and anti-biotin[24] conjugates to mitochondria in some cells (Figure 7.98, Figure 12.27) that can be blocked with the reagents in our Endogenous Biotin-Blocking Kit (E21390, see below).

NeutrAvidin Biotin-Binding Protein

Molecular Probes provides an alternative to the commonly used avidin and streptavidin. Our conjugates of NeutrAvidin biotin-binding protein (A2666, Table 7.22) — a protein that has been processed to remove the carbohydrate and lower its isoelectric point — can sometimes reduce background staining. The methods used to deglycosylate the avidin are reported to retain both its specific binding[25] and its complement of amine-conjugation sites. NeutrAvidin conjugates have been shown to provide improved detection of single-copy genes in metaphase chromosome spreads.[26]

CaptAvidin™ Biotin-Binding Protein: Reversible Binding of Biotinylated Molecules

CaptAvidin™ biotin-binding protein (C21385, Table 7.22) is an avidin derivative that provides reversible biotin binding. Selective nitration of tyrosine residues in the four biotin-binding sites of avidin considerably reduces the affinity of the protein for biotinylated molecules above pH 9.[27] Consequently, biotinylated probes can be adsorbed at neutral pH and released at pH ~10 (Figure 7.99). We use free biotin to block any remaining high-affinity biotin-binding sites that have not been nitrated. CaptAvidin™ agarose (C21386, see below) is particularly useful for separation and purification of biotin conjugates from complex mixtures. The biotin-binding capacity of CaptAvidin™ derivatives is at least 10 µg of free biotin per mg protein.

Secondary Detection with Avidins

Avidin, streptavidin and NeutrAvidin conjugates are extensively used as secondary detection reagents in histochemical applications (Figure 7.100, Figure 7.101), FISH (Section 8.5, Figure 8.92), flow cytometry,[28,29] microarrays (Section 8.5, Figure 6.42), blot analysis (Section 9.4, Figure 9.53) and immunoassays. These reagents can also be employed to localize biocytin, biotin ethylenediamine or any of our fluorescent biocytins — all of which are biotin derivatives commonly used as neuroanatomical tracers[30,31] (Section 14.3). DSB-X™ desthiobiocytin and DSB-X™ biotin ethylenediamine (D20652, D30752; Section 14.3) are similar polar tracers that reversibly bind to avidin derivatives.

The following are commonly used methods for employing avidin, streptavidin, NeutrAvidin biotin-binding protein and CaptAvidin™ biotin-binding protein as secondary detection reagents:

- Direct procedure. A biotinylated or desthiobiotinylated primary probe such as an antibody, single-stranded nucleic acid probe or lectin is bound to tissues, cells or other surfaces. Excess protein is removed by washing, and detection is mediated by reagents such as our fluorescent avidins, streptavidins or NeutrAvidin biotin-binding proteins or our enzyme-conjugated streptavidins plus a fluorogenic (Figure 7.102), chromogenic or chemiluminescent substrate. Enzyme conjugates of streptavidin are key reagents in some of our Tyramide Signal Amplification (TSA)

Kits (Section 6.2; Table 6.1; Figure 6.10, Figure 6.11, Figure 6.13) and in several of our kits for ultrasensitive detection of proteins on blots (Section 9.4, Table 9.7).

- Capture and release. Our unique DSB-X™ biotin technology permits the fully reversible labeling of DSB-X™ biotin derivatives by avidin and streptavidin conjugates [12] (Figure 7.103). Consequently, targets in cells and tissues or on blots labeled with DSB-X™ biotin conjugates of antibodies (Section 7.2, Table 7.10) or other DSB-X™ biotin reagents can initially be stained with fluorescent avidin or streptavidin conjugates, then the fluorescent staining can be reversed with D-biotin (B1595, B20656; Figure 7.103, Figure 7.104) and the sample restained with an enzyme-conjugated avidin or streptavidin derivative in conjunction with a permanent stain such as diaminobenzidine (DAB, D22187; Figure 7.105) or the combination of NBT and BCIP (N6495, B6492, N6547; Section 10.3).
- Bridging methods. A biotinylated antibody or oligonucleotide is used to probe a tissue, cell or other surface. This preparation is then treated with unlabeled avidin, streptavidin or NeutrAvidin biotin-binding protein. Excess reagents are removed by washing, and

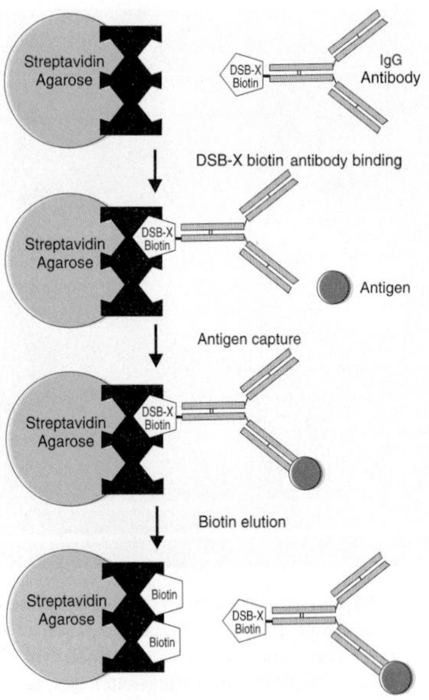

Figure 7.103 Diagram illustrating the use of streptavidin agarose and a DSB-X™ biotin bioconjugate in affinity chromatography. A DSB-X™ biotin–labeled IgG antibody and its target antigen are used as an example.

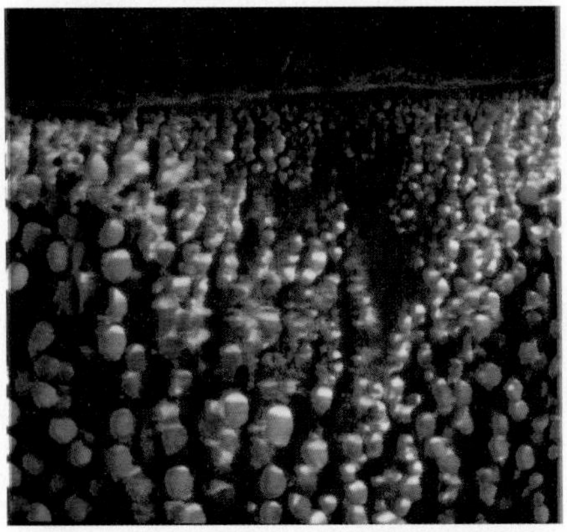
Figure 7.101 The "delta" region of a developing follicle of the giant silkmoth *Hyalophora cecropia* stained with an antibody against the largest subunit of the *Drosophila* RNA polymerase II (RNAp II). The primary antibody was visualized using a biotinylated secondary antibody followed by Texas Red® dye–conjugated streptavidin (S872). The distribution of the RNAp II appears violet because the Texas Red® staining colocalizes with the blue autofluorescence of the yolk granules. Image contributed by Ivo Sauman, Wesleyan University.

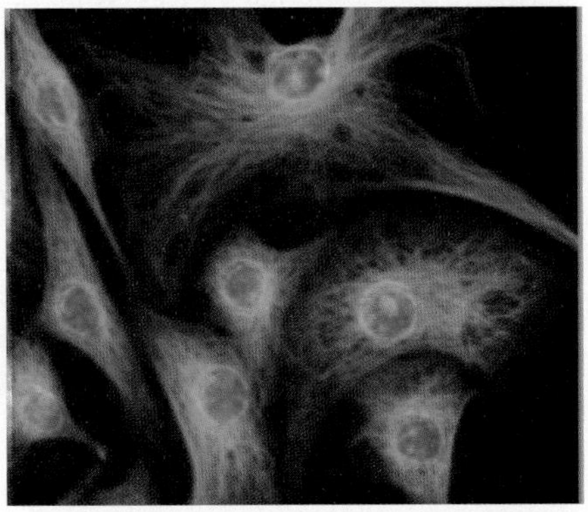
Figure 7.102 Microtubules of fixed bovine pulmonary artery endothelial cells (BPAEC) were localized with mouse monoclonal anti-α-tubulin antibody (A11126), followed by the biotin-XX–conjugated $F(ab')_2$ fragment of goat anti–mouse IgG antibody (B11027) and visualized with green-fluorescent Alexa Fluor® 488 streptavidin (S11223). The cell was counterstained with blue-fluorescent Hoechst 33342 (H1399, H3570, H21492) to image the DNA and red-fluorescent propidium iodide (P1304MP, P3566, P21493) to image nucleolar RNA. The multiple-exposure image was acquired using bandpass filter sets appropriate for Texas Red® dye, fluorescein and DAPI.

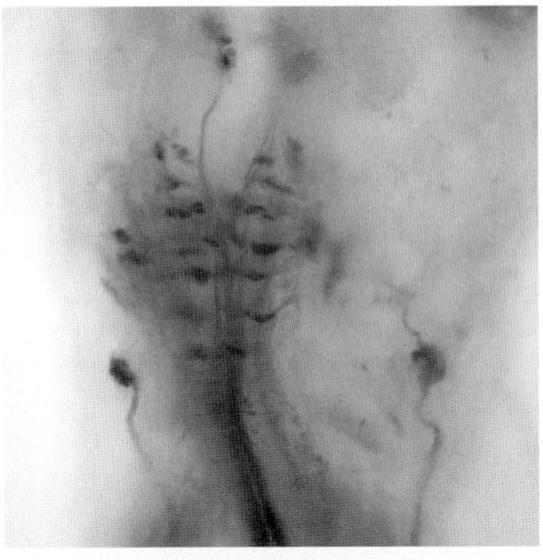
Figure 7.105 Zebrafish embryos were back-filled by incision with horseradish peroxidase (HRP) to trace the spinal neurons. The signal was then developed using diaminobenzidine (DAB) and hydrogen peroxide.

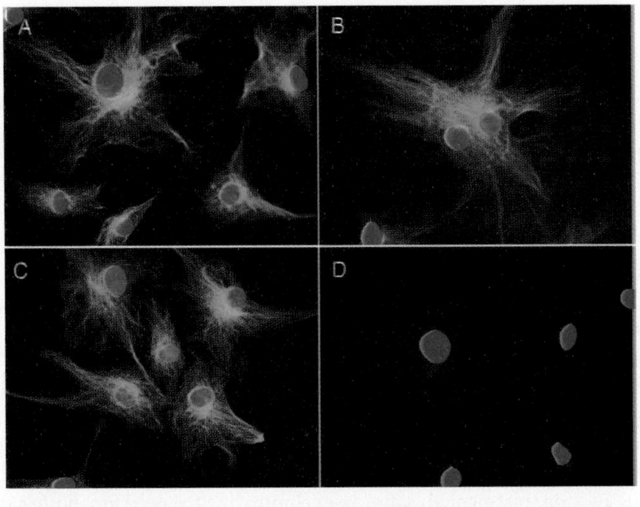

Figure 7.104 Reversible binding by DSB-X™ biotin. Microtubules of fixed bovine pulmonary artery endothelial cells were labeled with mouse monoclonal anti-α-tubulin antibody (A11126), detected with either biotin-XX goat anti-mouse IgG antibody (B2763, panel A) or DSB-X™ biotin goat anti-mouse IgG antibody (D20691, panel B) and visualized with green-fluorescent Alexa Fluor® 488 streptavidin (S11223). Nuclei were stained with blue-fluorescent DAPI (D1306, D3571, D21490). After incubating with 10 mM D-biotin (B1595, B20656), the binding between the biotinylated antibody is unaltered (panel C), whereas the streptavidin conjugate has been stripped from the DSB-X™ biotin–labeled antibody (panel D).

detection is mediated by a biotinylated detection reagent such as a fluorescent biotin or biocytin dye (Section 4.3), biotinylated R-phycoerythrin (P811, Section 6.4), biotinylated FluoSpheres® microspheres (Section 6.5) or biotinylated horseradish peroxidase (P917) plus a fluorogenic, chromogenic or chemiluminescent substrate.

- Indirect procedure. An unlabeled primary antibody is bound to a cell followed by a biotinylated species-specific secondary antibody. After washing, the complex is detected by one of the two procedures described above. Our Zenon® Biotin-XX and DSB-X™ Biotin Antibody Labeling Kits (Section 7.3, Table 7.13) permit the rapid and quantitative biotinylation of antibodies for combination with avidin–biotin detection methods.

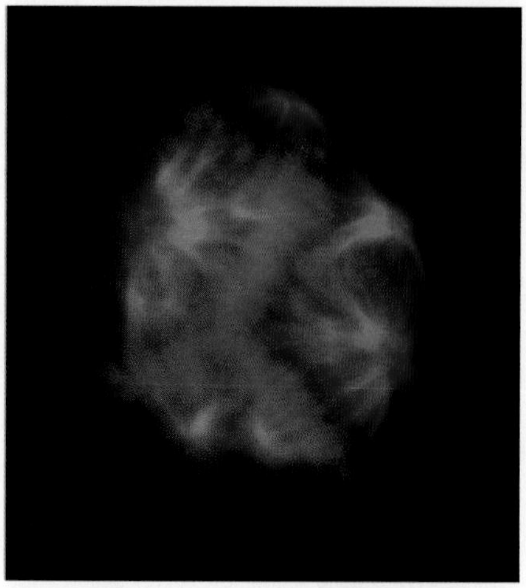

Figure 7.106 A multinucleate HeLa cell in metaphase that was fixed and then stained with a combination of fluorescent dyes. The chromosomes were stained with DAPI (D1306, D3571, D21490). The cytoskeleton was detected with the biotin-XX conjugate of mouse monoclonal anti–α-tubulin antibody (A21371), which was then visualized with red-fluorescent Alexa Fluor® 568 streptavidin (S11226). The multiple-exposure image was acquired using filter sets appropriate for rhodamine and DAPI.

Endogenous Biotin-Blocking Kit

Mammalian cells and tissues contain biotin-dependent carboxylases, which are required for a variety of metabolic functions. These biotin-containing enzymes sometimes produce substantial background signals when avidin–biotin detection systems are used to identify cellular targets[24] (Figure 7.98, Figure 12.27, Figure 12.29). Because biotin-based technologies can be so sensitive — particularly when using enzyme-amplified detection methods such as TSA — we recommend preblocking endogenous biotin present in cells with the reagents in our Endogenous Biotin-Blocking Kit (E21390). This kit provides streptavidin and biotin solutions in convenient dropper bottles and an easy-to-follow protocol. Sufficient material is provided for approximately one hundred 18 mm × 18 mm glass coverslips.

Image-iT™ FX Kits: All-in-One Kits for Fluorescence Imaging of Fixed Cells

Image-iT™ FX Kits

The Image-iT™ FX Kits (Table 7.6) provide some of our best secondary detection reagents and the supporting materials needed for optimal imaging of fixed cells and tissue sections:

- Alexa Fluor® conjugates of streptavidin, goat anti–mouse IgG antibody or goat anti–rabbit IgG antibody deliver superior photostability and brightness (Section 7.2, Table 7.7)
- ProLong® Gold antifade reagent reduces photobleaching (Figure 23.25, Figure 23.26, Figure 23.27; see Section 23.1 for more details)
- Image-iT™ FX signal enhancer improves the signal-to-noise ratio (Figure 7.47, Figure 7.48, Figure 23.32)
- A sample pack of two CultureWell chambered coverglasses makes sample processing more convenient (Figure 23.42, see Section 23.3 for more details)

Each Image-iT™ FX Kit provides sufficient materials to perform 50–100 assays. Furthermore, the components of each kit are available separately (Alexa Fluor® streptavidins, Table 7.22; Alexa Fluor® secondary antibodies, Table 7.1, Section 7.2; ProLong® Gold antifade reagent, P36930, Section 23.1; Image-iT™ FX signal enhancer, I36933, Section 7.2; CultureWell chambered coverglasses, C37000, C37005, Section 23.3) for flexibility in experimental design.

Image-iT™ FX Signal Enhancer

By efficiently blocking nonspecific interactions of a wide variety of fluorescent dyes with cell and tissue constituents, the Image-iT™ FX signal enhancer (I36933, Section 7.2) dramatically improves the signal-to-noise ratio of immunolabeled cells and tissues, allowing clear visualization of targets that would normally be indistinguishable due to background fluorescence (Figure 7.47, Figure 7.48, Figure 23.32). Background staining seen with fluorescent conjugates of streptavidin, goat anti–mouse IgG antibody or goat anti–rabbit IgG antibody is largely eliminated when Image-iT™ FX signal enhancer is applied to fixed and permeabilized cells prior to staining. Image-iT™ FX signal enhancer may also effectively prevent nonspecific staining that is typically blocked with 1–2% BSA or 10% serum treatment, in some cases eliminating the need for another step in the staining protocol.

Fluorescent Conjugates of Biotin-Binding Proteins

Fluorophore-Labeled Avidin, Streptavidin and NeutrAvidin Biotin-Binding Protein

Fluorescent avidin and streptavidin are extensively used in DNA hybridization techniques,[32,33] immunohistochemistry (Figure 7.106), MHC tetramer technology[34] (see Note 7.3 "Technical Focus: MHC Tetramer Technology") and multicolor flow cytometry.[35–37] Molecular Probes' selection of avidin, streptavidin and NeutrAvidin conjugates keeps growing as we introduce new and improved fluorophores and signal amplification technologies (Table 7.22). We continue to provide avidin, streptavidin and NeutrAvidin conjugates of fluorescein (A821, S869, A2662), tetramethylrhodamine (S870, A6373), rhodamine B (S871) and Texas Red® (A820, S872, A2665, S6370) dyes. However, we strongly recommend that researchers evaluate our many newer fluorescent conjugates:

- The green-fluorescent Alexa Fluor® 488 (Figure 7.5) and Oregon Green® (Figure 7.21) conjugates are not only brighter than fluorescein conjugates, but also much more photostable and less pH sensitive (Section 1.3; Figure 7.23, Figure 1.9, Figure 1.10, Figure 1.11) (see Note 1.1 "Product Highlight: The Alexa Fluor® Dye Series — Peak Performance across the Visible Spectrum" in Section 1.3).
- Like the Alexa Fluor® 488 conjugate, the green-fluorescent Alexa Fluor® 500 (Figure 7.6) and Alexa Fluor® 514 (Figure 7.7) streptavidin conjugates are far superior to fluorescein in both brightness and photostability, and they can be detected with standard fluorescein, Oregon Green® dye or Alexa Fluor® 488 dye filter sets. However, these Alexa Fluor® conjugates are specifically designed to be detected simultaneously with other green fluorophores using instruments with the capacity to differentiate between fluorescence emission maxima <5 nm apart. The Alexa Fluor® 500 dye can be optically separated from the Alexa Fluor® 514 dye, and the Alexa Fluor® 514 dye can be optically separated from both the Alexa Fluor® 488 and Alexa Fluor® 500 dyes. We also offer the yellow-green–fluorescent Alexa Fluor® 532 streptavidin (Figure 7.8).

Note 7.3 — Technical Focus

MHC Tetramer Technology

Cytotoxic T lymphocytes (CTLs) or "killer" T cells perform a crucial function in the vertebrate immune system — they serve to destroy cells that display foreign antigens on their surfaces. CTLs are distinguished from other types of T lymphocytes (such as "helper" T cells) by their expression of CD8, a transmembrane protein with immunoglobulin-like domains that interact with class I Major Histocompatibility Complexes[1] (MHCs). MHC molecules act in a dual role; their amino-terminal domains bind antigen for presentation to T cells, as well as serving as a marker identifying host cells to the immune system. Activation of CTLs to eliminate a target cell occurs only if the CD8 protein recognizes the proper MHC molecule and the α/β T-cell receptor binds the MHC-presented antigen.[2]

Historically, assaying for an antigen-specific T-cell response made use of the limiting dilution analysis (LDA) method, which requires that single clones survive, divide and differentiate before they can be detected. However, this method likely underestimates the number of CTLs that respond to a particular antigen because it will not detect cells that are part of the expanded effector population that can no longer divide.[3] Alternate approaches attempted to directly measure CTL response using an antigenic peptide and MHC. However, these experiments were hampered by the low affinity of the interaction between the MHC/antigen complex and the corresponding CTL receptors.[4]

Joining multiple copies of the MHC/antigen complex into a single probe — tetramer technology — resolved the difficulties presented by the low affinity of the class I MHC molecule for the CD8 receptor.[5] CTL-response assays using tetramer technology often detect a response rate that is 50–500 times higher than detected by the LDA method,[3] and have proven indispensable for the study of the CTL response to HIV,[6] cancers[7] and transplants.[8] Similar methods using class II MHC tetramers are also being employed to explore the response of helper (CD-4 expressing) T cells.[9]

MHC tetramers are formed by first refolding MHCs in the presence of high concentrations of the desired antigenic peptide, followed by biotinylation of the carboxy-terminus of one chain of the MHC molecule. This MHC/peptide complex can then be bound to streptavidin. Because the latter has four biotin-binding sites, four MHC molecules can be linked together in a single complex (Figure). The use of fluorophore-labeled streptavidin or streptavidin-coated magnetic beads for tetramer formation allows for efficient detection by flow cytometry or immunomagnetic methods.[10] It is crucial for MHC tetramer–based assays that the labeled streptavidin be free of unlabeled streptavidin because this lowers the apparent activity of the MHC complex by "blocking" the biotinylation site from binding to the labeled streptavidin.

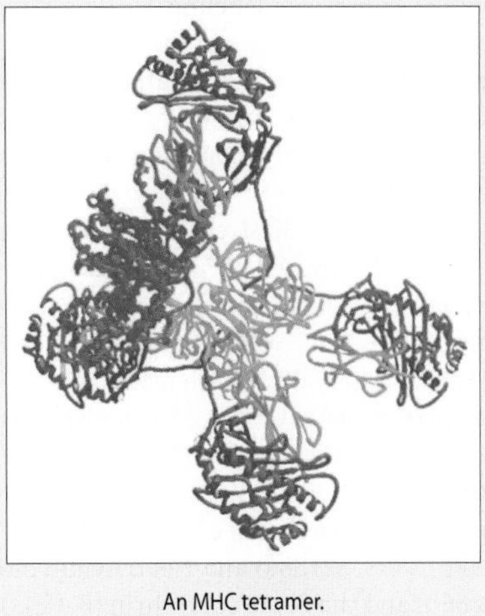

An MHC tetramer.

References

1. Annu Rev Immunol 10, 645 (1992); **2.** Adv Immunol 53, 59 (1993); **3.** J Exp Med 187, 1367 (1998); **4.** Proc Natl Acad Sci U S A 91, 12862 (1994); **5.** Immunol Rev 150, 5 (1996); **6.** Science 279, 2103 (1998); **7.** J Immunol 162, 2227 (1999); **8.** Nat Med 5, 839 (1999); **9.** J Clin Invest 104, 1669 (1999); **10.** Nat Med 6, 707 (2000).

- Other conjugates made with some of our brightest dyes include those labeled with our orange- and red-orange–fluorescent Alexa Fluor® 546 (Figure 7.9), Alexa Fluor® 555 (Figure 7.10), Alexa Fluor® 568 (Figure 7.11) and Rhodamine Red™-X (Figure 7.25) dyes, as well as those labeled with our red-fluorescent Alexa Fluor® 594 (Figure 7.12), Alexa Fluor® 610 (Figure 7.13) and Texas Red®-X (Figure 7.26) dyes. These conjugates are more fluorescent than traditional Lissamine rhodamine B and Texas Red® conjugates (Figure 1.76, Figure 1.84), yet have similar excitation and emission maxima (Figure 1.74).
- Our Alexa Fluor® 633 (Figure 7.14), Alexa Fluor® 635 (Figure 7.15), Alexa Fluor® 647 (Figure 7.16), Alexa Fluor® 660 (Figure 7.17), Alexa Fluor® 680 (Figure 7.18), Alexa Fluor® 700 (Figure 7.19) and Alexa Fluor® 750 (Figure 7.20) conjugates of streptavidin have fluorescence that is not visible to the eye, but their absorption occurs at wavelengths that are easily excited by laser and laser diode light sources (Figure 1.24) and their fluorescence is easily detected by infrared light–sensitive detectors. Conjugates of the Alexa Fluor® 555 and Alexa Fluor® 647 dyes, in particular, have fluorescence that is superior to that of the spectrally similar Cy3 and Cy5 dyes [38] (Figure 7.40, Figure 7.41), respectively, and their conjugates are more photostable than Cy3 and Cy5 conjugates (Figure 1.28). Furthermore, our Alexa Fluor® 635 dye produces brighter protein conjugates than does the Alexa Fluor® 633 dye because the absorption spectrum of the Alexa Fluor® 635 dye does not split into two peaks upon protein conjugation, as do the absorption spectra of the Alexa Fluor® 633, Cy5 and tetramethylrhodamine dyes (Figure 1.71).
- For blue-fluorescent labeling, we offer streptavidin and NeutrAvidin conjugates of the Alexa Fluor® 350, Alexa Fluor® 405, Marina Blue®, Cascade Blue® and Pacific Blue™ fluorophores. In side-by-side testing, our Alexa Fluor® 350 streptavidin (S11249) displays significantly more fluorescence than AMCA streptavidin (Figure 7.34).
- The Alexa Fluor® 430 streptavidin conjugate (S11237) absorbs maximally at ~434 nm, with bright yellow-green emission (Figure 7.4).
- Both our blue-fluorescent Alexa Fluor® 405 streptavidin (S32351, Figure 7.3) and our yellow-fluorescent Cascade Yellow™ streptavidin (S11228, Figure 7.38) absorb maximally at ~402 nm, making them near-perfect matches to the 405 nm spectral line of the blue diode laser recently developed for fluorescence microscopy and flow cytometry.
- R-phycoerythrin (R-PE) conjugates (Figure 7.28) of streptavidin (SAPE; S866, S21388) and NeutrAvidin biotin-binding protein (A2660) and the B-phycoerythrin (B-PE) conjugate of streptavidin (S32350) have the most intense fluorescence of all avidin conjugates. Our streptavidin conjugates of R-PE and B-PE have been purified to ensure that all unconjugated streptavidin has been removed (Figure 6.41), making them particularly important labels for multicolor flow cytometry (Section 6.4) and the detection of biotinylated probes on microarrays [39–46] (Section 8.5, Figure 6.42). Allophycocyanin streptavidin (S868, S32362; Figure 7.30) can be excited by the 633 nm spectral line of the He–Ne laser.[47] In imaging applications, allophycocyanin conjugates are both brighter and more photostable than Cy5 conjugates, with similar spectra (Figure 6.31). Our premium-grade R-PE and allophycocyanin conjugates of streptavidin (S21388, S32362) represent an even further fractionation of our R-PE and allophycocyanin conjugates of streptavidin (S866, S868), respectively.
- We have conjugated R-PE with four of our Alexa Fluor® dyes — the Alexa Fluor® 610, Alexa Fluor® 647, Alexa Fluor® 680 and Alexa Fluor® 750 dyes — then conjugated these fluorescent proteins to streptavidin to yield labeled conjugates that can be excited with the 488 nm spectral line of the argon-ion laser (Figure 6.34). The long-wavelength emission maxima are 630 nm for the Alexa Fluor® 610–R-PE conjugate (S20982), 667 nm for the Alexa Fluor® 647–R-PE conjugate (S20992), 702 nm for the Alexa Fluor® 680–R-PE conjugate (S20985) and 775 nm for the Alexa Fluor® 750–R-PE conjugate (S32363). Emission of the Alexa Fluor® 610–R-PE conjugates is shifted to longer wavelengths by about 13 nm relative to that of Texas Red® conjugates of R-PE (Figure 6.39). This slightly longer-wavelength emission maximum significantly improves the resolution that can be obtained when using the Alexa Fluor® 610–R-PE tandem conjugates in place of Texas Red®–R-PE tandem conjugates for multicolor flow cytometry. The Alexa Fluor® 647–R-PE tandem conjugates have spectra virtually identical to those of Cy5 conjugates of R-PE but are about three times more fluorescent (Figure 6.38). These tandem conjugates can potentially be used for simultaneous four-color labeling with a single excitation (Figure 6.34). In addition, we have reacted allophycocyanin (APC) with our Alexa Fluor® 680, Alexa Fluor® 700 and Alexa Fluor® 750 dyes and then conjugated these labels to streptavidin (S21002, S21005, S21008). The resulting probes can all be excited by the He–Ne laser at 633 nm or krypton-ion laser at 647 nm and have distinguishable emission spectra (Figure 6.37).
- Our DyeMer™ 488/605, DyeMer™ 488/615 and DyeMer™ 488/630 conjugates of streptavidin (S32385, S32386, S32387) are optimized for use in flow cytometry applications. The red-orange–fluorescent DyeMer™ 488/605, red-fluorescent DyeMer™ 488/615 and far-red–fluorescent DyeMer™ 488/630 conjugates are each labeled with a unique bifluorophore comprising two covalently linked fluorophores that act as a donor–acceptor pair for fluorescence resonance energy transfer (FRET). When the green-fluorescent donor dye is excited with the 488 nm spectral line of the argon-ion laser, efficient energy transfer produces fluorescence of the long-wavelength acceptor dye, which emits at 611, 617 or 630 nm (Figure 7.31, Figure 7.32, Figure 7.33). Any fluorescence from the donor dye due to incomplete FRET can easily be compensated for by setting up compensation circuits to remove unwanted signals. Although their total fluorescence is not as intense as that of the phycobiliprotein tandem conjugates, the DyeMer™ conjugates exhibit minimal lot-to-lot variation and less interference at the antigen- or biotin-binding site due to the relatively small size of the DyeMer™ bifluorophores. Moreover, their fluorescence can be excited either at 488 nm or at their longer-wavelength absorption maximum. Because there is some green fluorescence emitted from the donor dye, the DyeMer™ conjugates were not developed for imaging applications. By carefully choosing bandpass filters that block this green fluorescence or by using a green-fluorescent label for the most abundant target to keep exposure times short, these DyeMer™ conjugates can be successfully applied to multicolor fluorescence microscopy experiments.

A complete list of our current offerings of fluorophore-, enzyme- and gold-labeled avidins, streptavidins and NeutrAvidin biotin-binding proteins can be found in Table 7.22. To obtain the maximal fluorescence signal from some conjugates, free D-biotin (B1595, B20656) can be added (see Note 7.4 "Technical Focus: Add Free Biotin to Obtain Brighter Signals from Some Fluorescent Avidin Conjugates").

Streptavidin-, NeutrAvidin- and Biotin-Labeled Fluorescent Microspheres

Molecular Probes offers streptavidin, NeutrAvidin and biotin conjugates of the intensely fluorescent FluoSpheres® and TransFluoSpheres®

polystyrene microspheres in a variety of colors and sizes, including our europium and platinum luminescent beads labeled with the NeutrAvidin biotin-binding protein for time-resolved fluorometry (Figure 6.47, Figure 6.48; Table 14.8). Because single fluorescent microspheres can be detected, FluoSpheres® and TransFluoSpheres® beads have significant potential for ultrasensitive flow cytometry applications and immunodiagnostic assays.[48,49] They may also be useful as tracers that can be detected with standard enzyme-mediated histochemical methods (Section 14.6).

BlockAid™ blocking solution (B10710) is a protein-based reagent designed principally for use with our streptavidin-, NeutrAvidin- and biotin-labeled FluoSpheres® (Table 6.8) and our streptavidin- and NeutrAvidin-labeled TransFluoSpheres® microspheres (Table 6.9). Protein- and other macromolecule-labeled microspheres have hydrophobic regions that may cause them to bind to nontarget surfaces in some experimental systems. Although this nonspecific binding can often be relieved by the use of a blocking solution, we have found that microspheres require a stronger blocking solution than those in common use. In our tests, the BlockAid™ blocking solution was mixed with streptavidin-labeled FluoSpheres® microspheres, which were then used to stain several different cell types for subsequent analysis by flow cytometry. We found the BlockAid™ blocking solution to be superior to blocking solutions available from other companies, as well as to several standard blocking solutions described in the scientific literature for reducing nonspecific binding of labeled microspheres. BlockAid™ blocking solution has been found to be effective in flow cytometry applications involving NIH 3T3, A431, RAW and Jurkat cell lines. We expect that the BlockAid™ blocking solution will be useful for reducing the nonspecific binding of protein-coated or other macromolecule-coated microspheres in a variety of flow cytometry and microscopy applications. It may also be useful as a general blocking agent in a variety of other assays.

NANOGOLD and Alexa Fluor® FluoroNanogold Streptavidin

In collaboration with Nanoprobes, Inc.(www.nanoprobes.com), Molecular Probes offers NANOGOLD and Alexa Fluor® FluoroNanogold conjugates of streptavidin to facilitate immunoblotting, light microscopy and electron microscopy applications. NANOGOLD conjugates are covalently conjugated to the 1.4 nm NANOGOLD gold cluster label, whereas Alexa Fluor® FluoroNanogold conjugates are coupled to both a NANOGOLD label and either the Alexa Fluor® 488 or Alexa Fluor® 594 fluorophore, resulting in gold clusters with green or red fluorescence, respectively. Alexa Fluor® FluoroNanogold streptavidin conjugates have all the advantages of the NANOGOLD conjugates, with the additional benefit that they may be used for correlative fluorescence, light and electron microscopy[50,51] (Figure 7.55).

NANOGOLD gold clusters have several advantages over colloidal gold. They develop better with silver than do most gold colloids and, as a result, provide higher sensitivity. Additionally, NANOGOLD particles do not have as high affinity for proteins as do gold colloids, thereby reducing any background due to nonspecific binding. Several additional advantages of NANOGOLD and Alexa Fluor® FluoroNanogold streptavidin over colloidal gold conjugates include:

- The NANOGOLD gold clusters are an extremely uniform (1.4 nm ± 10% diameter) and stable compound, not a gold colloid.
- NANOGOLD gold clusters are smaller than a complete IgG (H+L) antibody — approximately 1/15 the size of an Fab fragment — and therefore will be able to better penetrate cells and tissues, reaching antigens that are inaccessible to conjugates of larger gold particles.
- NANOGOLD conjugates contain absolutely no aggregates, as they are chromatographically purified through gel filtration columns. This feature is in sharp contrast to colloidal gold conjugates, which are usually prepared by centrifugation to remove the largest aggregates and frequently contain significantly smaller aggregates.
- The ratio of NANOGOLD particle to streptavidin is nearly 1:1, making this product distinct from the 0.2–10 variable stoichiometry of most colloidal gold preparations.
- NANOGOLD cluster–stained targets develop better with silver than do most gold colloids, resulting in higher sensitivity.[52] Silver enhancement, such as the system provided in the LI Silver Enhancement Kit (L24919, Figure 7.57), can be used for light

Note 7.4 — Technical Focus

Add Free Biotin to Obtain Brighter Signals from Some Fluorescent Avidin Conjugates

Fluorophores conjugated to avidin and streptavidin may be quenched significantly, apparently because the dyes interact with amino acid residues in the biotin-binding pocket. Exceptions include at least the Cascade Blue® dye– and phycobiliprotein-labeled avidin and streptavidin; the dyes in these conjugates are not quenched because they do not interact with the biotin-binding site. A significant recovery of the avidin or streptavidin conjugate's fluorescence can be obtained if biotin (B1595, B20656; Section 4.2) is added as a final incubation step in the staining procedure (see Figure). Fluorescence enhancement of avidin conjugates by biotin has been shown to occur in <100 milliseconds.[1] Biotin apparently blocks the interaction of the fluorophore with residues in the biotin-binding pocket that quench the fluorescence, enhancing the fluorescence of the stained tissue, often multifold.

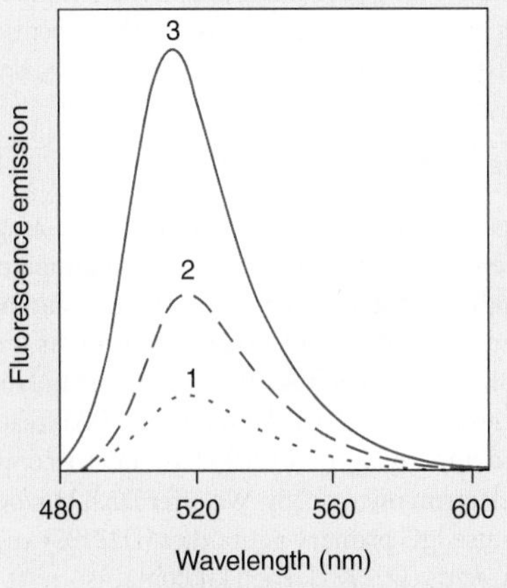

Spectra showing the fluorescence of 1) fluorescein-labeled avidin, 2) fluorescein-labeled avidin after addition of 10 µM biotin and 3) free fluorescein at the same concentration as the fluorescein label in the avidin conjugate.

Reference

1. Biophys J 69, 716 (1995).

microscopy and immunoblotting to provide improved results; see Section 7.2 for a complete description.

The sensitivity of NANOGOLD streptavidin, and presumably Alexa Fluor® FluoroNanogold streptavidin, in immunohistochemical applications can be further improved by first using one of our Tyramide Signal Amplification (TSA) Kits containing biotin tyramide (Section 6.2, Table 6.1) and then detecting the biotin tyramide conjugates with NANOGOLD streptavidin, enhanced by silver staining.[53,54]

Molecular Probes offers several other NANOGOLD and Alexa Fluor® FluoroNanogold reagents (Table 7.9), including the affinity-purified Fab fragments of the goat anti–mouse IgG, goat anti–rabbit IgG and rabbit anti–goat IgG antibodies covalently conjugated to the 1.4 nm NANOGOLD gold cluster label (Section 7.2). Also available are NANOGOLD mono(sulfosuccinimidyl ester) (N20130, Section 1.6, Figure 1.90) and NANOGOLD monomaleimide (N20345, Section 2.2, Figure 2.22), which can be conjugated to amines and thiols, respectively, in the same way that dyes are conjugated to proteins and nucleic acids.[55]

Colloidal Gold Complexes

Molecular Probes offers Alexa Fluor® 488 dye–labeled colloidal gold conjugates, including those of goat anti–mouse IgG (A31560, A31561; Section 7.2) and goat anti–rabbit IgG antibodies (A31565, A31566; Section 7.2) and streptavidin (A32360, A32361; Table 7.22). These conjugates, which have been adsorbed to 5 nm or 10 nm gold colloids, may be used as probes in immunoblotting, light microscopy, fluorescence microscopy or electron microscopy. The fluorescence of these conjugates can be easily detected by standard techniques, but visualization of colloidal gold can be greatly improved using silver-enhancement methods, such as those we provide in the LI Silver Enhancement Kit (L24919) described in Section 7.2.

Combining fluorescent secondary detection reagents with colloidal gold to form functional complexes is difficult because the fluorescence of fluorophores such as fluorescein is significantly quenched by proximity to the colloidal gold.[56] Molecular Probes makes fluorescent colloidal gold complexes with our Alexa Fluor® 488 dye, a dye that has superior brightness and photostability. Our Alexa Fluor® 488 dye–labeled colloidal gold complexes of anti-IgG antibody and of streptavidin can potentially be used to perform correlated immunofluorescence and electron microscopy in a two-step labeling procedure, rather than in the three-step indirect labeling procedure that is required with conventional nonfluorescent colloidal gold complexes of anti-IgG antibodies or streptavidin.[57]

DAB Histochemistry Kits

The use of horseradish peroxidase (HRP) for enzyme-amplified immunodetection, commonly referred to as immunoperoxidase labeling, is a well-established standard histochemical technique.[58,59] The most widely used HRP substrate for these applications is diaminobenzidine (DAB), which generates a brown-colored polymeric oxidation product localized at HRP-labeled sites. The DAB reaction product can be visualized directly by bright-field light microscopy or, following osmication, by electron microscopy. We offer DAB Histochemistry Kits for detecting mouse IgG primary antibodies (D22185) and biotinylated antibodies and tracers (D22187). Each kit contains:

- Diaminobenzidine (DAB)
- HRP-labeled goat anti–mouse IgG antibody (in Kit D22185) or streptavidin (in Kit D22187) conjugate
- H_2O_2 reaction additive
- Blocking reagent
- Staining buffer
- A detailed staining protocol

Each kit provides sufficient materials to stain approximately 200 slides.

Enzyme Conjugates of Biotin-Binding Proteins

Enzyme conjugates are extensively used in enzyme-linked immunosorbent assays (ELISAs),[60] blotting techniques,[61] *in situ* hybridization[62] and cytochemistry and histochemistry.[63] Enzyme-mediated *in situ* techniques using these conjugates provide better resolution and are safer, more sensitive and faster than radioactive methods. Most frequently, the enzymes of choice are horseradish peroxidase, alkaline phosphatase and *Escherichia coli* β-galactosidase because of their high turnover rate, stability, ease of conjugation and relatively low cost. Molecular Probes has prepared highly active streptavidin and NeutrAvidin biotin-binding protein conjugates of horseradish peroxidase (S911, A2664), alkaline phosphatase (S921) and β-galactosidase (S931), as well as biotin-XX horseradish peroxidase (P917). Fluorogenic substrates for ELISAs are often much more sensitive than chromogenic substrates in these important assays. Our fluorogenic, chromogenic and chemiluminescent substrates for these assays are described in Chapter 10.

Our enzyme conjugates of streptavidin and NeutrAvidin biotin-binding protein are prepared by techniques that yield an approximate 1:1 ratio of enzyme to avidin analog, thus ensuring maximum retention of activity of both enzyme and carrier protein. We offer streptavidin conjugates of alkaline phosphatase, horseradish peroxidase and β-galactosidase (S921, S911, S931) and the NeutrAvidin conjugate of horseradish peroxidase[64] (A2664). To decrease background problems, researchers often prefer to use the biotin-XX conjugate of horseradish peroxidase (P917) in conjunction with an avidin or streptavidin bridge for indirect detection of a wide array of biotinylated biomolecules. Our biotinylated horseradish peroxidase conjugate is prepared with a reactive biotin-XX derivative, which contains the longest available spacer and allows high avidin affinity.

A principal application of HRP and alkaline phosphatase conjugates of avidins and secondary antibodies is in enzyme-amplified histochemical staining of cells and tissues. Several of the Tyramide Signal Amplification (TSA) Kits (Table 6.1) in Section 6.2 and Enzyme-Labeled Fluorescence (ELF®) Kits in Section 6.3 utilize enzyme conjugates of streptavidin to yield intensely fluorescent staining of cellular targets (Figure 6.10, Figure 6.11, Figure 6.13, Figure 6.23). These kits are very useful for immunofluorescence, *in situ* hybridization and flow cytometry. Use of a combination of the TSA and ELF® technologies or double application of TSA methods promises to provide the highest sensitivity known for detection of low-abundance targets.[65]

Affinity Chromatography

Streptavidin Agarose

Molecular Probes prepares streptavidin conjugated to 4% beaded crosslinked agarose (S951) — a matrix that can be used to isolate biotinylated peptides, proteins, hybridization probes, haptens and other molecules.[66] In addition, biotinylated antibodies can be bound to streptavidin agarose to generate an affinity matrix for the large-scale isolation of antigens.[66] For instance, staurosporine-treated myotubules have been incubated with biotinylated α-bungarotoxin (B1196, Section 16.2) in order to isolate the acetylcholine receptors (AChRs) on streptavidin agarose and assess staurosporine's effect on the degree of phosphorylation of this receptor.[67] Streptavidin agarose has also been used to investigate the turnover of cell-surface proteins that had previously been derivatized with an amine-reactive biotin[68] (B1582, Section 4.2).

DSB-X™ Bioconjugate Isolation Kit #1

The DSB-X™ Bioconjugate Isolation Kit #1 (D20658) uses our unique DSB-X™ biotin technology for the easy affinity isolation of DSB-X™ biotin–labeled bioconjugates under extremely gentle conditions.[12] DSB-X™ biotin is a derivative of desthiobiotin (Figure 4.1), a stable biotin precursor.[69,70] DSB-X™ biotin utilizes a seven-atom spacer to increase the ability of the DSB-X™ biotin conjugate to bind in the deep biotin-binding pocket of streptavidin or avidin.[71,72] Whereas harsh chaotropic agents and low pH (6.0 M guanidine HCl, pH 1.5) are required to dissociate a biotin complex from avidin or streptavidin, streptavidin agarose has only a moderate affinity for conjugates of DSB-X™ biotin.[73] Therefore, binding can be rapidly reversed by adding excess D-desthiobiotin (D20657) or natural D-biotin[72] (B1595, B20656) to the matrix at neutral pH and at room temperature (or below).

Once bound to the streptavidin agarose matrix, the bioconjugate — an antibody, enzyme, oligonucleotide, nucleic acid, drug or other DSB-X™ biotin conjugate — can bind to its target, which may be from a variety of sources, including cell or tissue extracts (Figure 7.103). Gentle elution of the entire complex allows subsequent analysis of the affinity-isolated product by electrophoresis or other means. Elution with D-desthiobiotin rather than D-biotin may permit reuse of the matrix.

The DSB-X™ Bioconjugate Isolation Kit #1 (D20658) contains:

- Streptavidin agarose (5 mL of a sedimented bead suspension)
- Solutions of D-desthiobiotin and D-biotin
- Purification columns
- A suggested protocol for binding and release of DSB-X™ biotin conjugates

Molecular Probes provides a variety of antibody conjugates of DSB-X™ biotin (Section 7.2, Table 7.10) as well as DSB-X™ biotin hydrazide (D20653, Section 3.2) for selective labeling and capture of periodate-oxidized glycoproteins and polysaccharides. Labeling of amine residues of other proteins and other biomolecules is easily accomplished with the reagents in our DSB-X™ Biotin Protein Labeling Kit (D20655, Section 1.2).

CaptAvidin™ Agarose

CaptAvidin™ agarose (C21386) is another versatile form of a biotin-binding protein in that its affinity for biotinylated molecules can be completely reversed by raising the pH to 10, permitting the facile separation and isolation of biotin-labeled molecules from complex mixtures (Figure 7.99). This form of agarose-immobilized biotin-binding protein has been used to purify immunoglobulin from whole rabbit serum and to isolate anti-transferrin antibodies directly from rabbit antiserum.[27]

Captivate™ Ferrofluid Streptavidin

Captivate™ ferrofluid streptavidin (C21476) is a versatile product for rapid separation of biotinylated and DSB-X™ biotin–conjugated biomolecules and their targets from complex mixtures, including those in cell and tissue extracts and bodily fluids. Combination of Captivate™ ferrofluid streptavidin with DSB-X™ biotin (Figure 4.1) technology enables the selective capture and release of rare populations of viable cells by DSB-X™ biotin–conjugated antibodies to cell surface markers (Figure 7.107). A potentially important application of this technique is the detection of specific protein–protein and protein–nucleic acid interactions through selective isolation and release of their intact complexes.

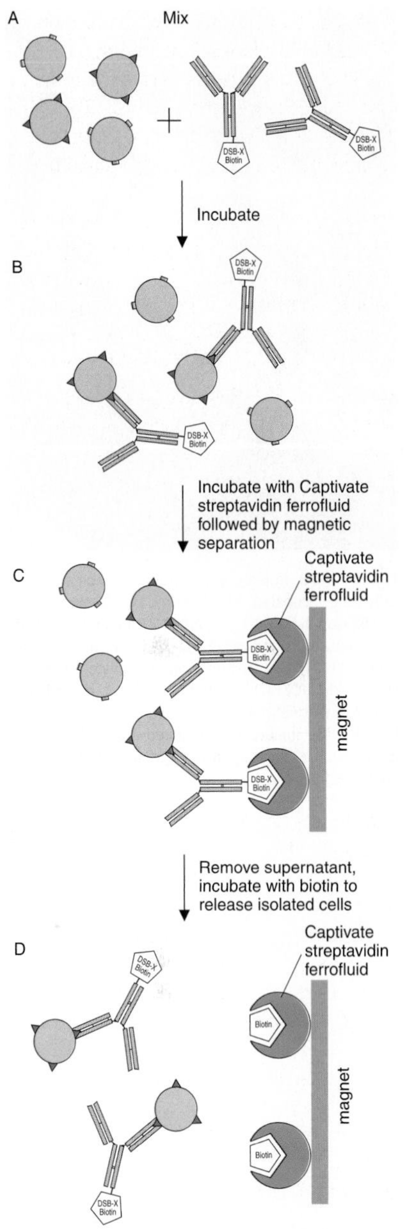

Figure 7.107 Cell separation using Captivate™ ferrofluid streptavidin and DSB-X™ biotin conjugates. A mixed population of cells is first mixed with a DSB-X™ biotin–labeled antibody against an appropriate surface antigen (panel A); subsequent incubation results in the labeling of a specific subpopulation (panel B). The sample is then incubated with Captivate™ ferrofluid streptavidin (C21476), which binds to the DSB-X™ biotin hapten, allowing the labeled cells to be isolated via a magnetic field (panel C). After the unlabeled cells have been washed away, the captured cells can be released by reversing the streptavidin linkage to DSB-X™ biotin with unlabeled biotin (panel D).

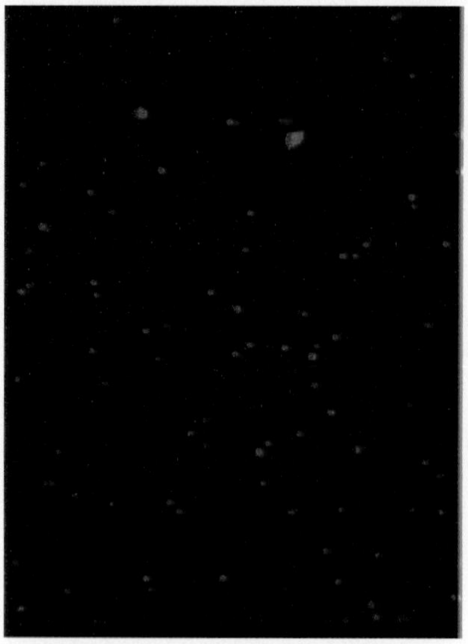

Figure 7.108 Human epidermoid carcinoma (A431) cells were incubated with 4 µg/mL EGF biotin (E3477), in PBS containing 0.1% BSA, for 15 minutes at room temperature, stained with 1 µM cell-permeant SYTO® 59 stain (S11341), and isolated using Captivate™ ferrofluid streptavidin (C21476) in the Captivate™ microscope-mounted magnetic yoke (C24700) and sample chamber (C24701). The images were acquired every 0.75 seconds for 1.5 min, at 10× magnification using a filter appropriate for TRITC.

The Captivate™ ferrofluid products are unique in that they represent the only superparamagnetic particles available that allow both cell sorting and cell-based imaging to be performed simultaneously by use of the Captivate™ microscope-mounted magnetic yoke assembly and associated Captivate™ disposable sample chambers (C24700, C24701; Section 23.3; Figure 7.58). The Captivate™ microscope-mounted magnetic yoke assembly includes one free set of 10 disposable sample chambers. Use of Captivate™ ferrofluid streptavidin in combination with biotin- or DSB-X™ biotin–conjugated probes permits the simultaneous isolation, visualization and counting of cells that are targets of the antibody by any researcher with access to a standard low-cost microscope with a 10× objective (Figure 7.108). Also, when used to capture DSB-X™ biotin–labeled antibodies to cell-surface antigens, the Captivate™ ferrofluid can be completely separated from the labeled cells by incubation with D-biotin (B1595, B20656; Section 4.2) or D-desthiobiotin (D20657, Section 4.2). In addition, the Captivate™ ferrofluid products should have advantages over other commercially available magnetic particles in liquid-handling robotic systems.

Molecular Probes also has available Captivate™ magnetic separators [74] for both microplates (C24702, Figure 23.58) and microtubes (C24703, Figure 23.59) that we find to be particularly useful with the Captivate™ ferrofluid products. The microplate separator is compatible with most 96-well microplates, whereas the microtube separator can accommodate six 1.5 mL microcentrifuge tubes. Both separators provide excellent separation efficiency and pull magnetic particles to one side, allowing easier removal of supernatants.

DSB-X™ Bioconjugate Isolation Kit #2

The DSB-X™ Bioconjugate Isolation Kit #2 (D20659) utilizes DSB-X™ biotin agarose for affinity isolation of any avidin or streptavidin conjugate [12] (Figure 7.109). DSB-X™ biotin agarose links desthiobiotin to agarose through a seven-atom spacer (Figure 4.1). Binding of the avidin or streptavidin conjugate can be fully reversed under extremely gentle conditions by addition of D-biotin or desthiobiotin. We have shown that when desthiobiotin (but not D-biotin) is used to reverse the binding, the avidin or streptavidin biotin-binding sites are fully saturated by the desthiobiotin; however, it is not necessary to remove the desthiobiotin before use of the affinity-purified avidin or streptavidin conjugate to label a biotin-conjugated probe. The reagents in this kit can be used to isolate streptavidin conjugates that are free from enzymes or other biomolecules when forming protein–protein or protein–nucleic acid conjugates. The DSB-X™ Bioconjugate Isolation Kit #2 (D20659) contains:

- DSB-X™ biotin agarose (5 mL of a sedimented bead suspension)
- Solutions of D-desthiobiotin and D-biotin
- Purification columns
- Suggested protocol for binding and release of DSB-X™ biotin conjugates

The DSB-X™ biotin agarose in this kit can potentially be reused several times.

Cell-Surface Biotinylation Kit

Biotin-XX sulfosuccinimidyl ester is a membrane-impermeant, amine-reactive compound that may be used to label proteins exposed on the surface of live cells [75] (Figure 4.5). The sulfosuccinimidyl ester forms an extremely stable conjugate with cell-surface proteins,[76] and the biotin provides a convenient hapten for subsequent isolation or analysis with an avidin-based protein such as streptavidin, NeutrAvidin or CaptAvidin™ biotin-binding protein or the Captivate™ ferrofluid streptavidin conjugate (C21476, Section 7.6). Cell-surface biotinylation techniques have been employed to differentially label proteins in the apical and basolateral plasma membranes of epithelial cells.[77,78] These techniques are also well suited for studying internalization of membrane proteins [79] and cell-surface targeting of proteins.[80–82] The FluoReporter® Cell-Surface Biotinylation Kit (F20650) provides a convenient method to label proteins exposed on the cell surface including, but not limited to, membrane proteins. This kit includes:

- Biotin-XX sulfosuccinimidyl ester
- Anhydrous DMSO for preparing stable stock solutions
- A detailed protocol for cell-surface biotinylation

The supplied protocol for cell-surface biotinylation is easy to perform and can be completed in less than one hour. Biotinylated proteins can be subsequently identified using the reagents in some of our Pro-Q®, Amplex® Gold and DyeChrome™ Western Blot Kits (Section 9.4).

Acrylamide Conjugates for Immobilization of Avidins in Polymers

Streptavidin acrylamide (S21379), which is prepared from the succinimidyl ester of 6-((*N*-acryloyl)amino)hexanoic acid (acryloyl-X, SE; A20770, Section 5.2), is a reagent that may be useful for preparing biosensors.[83] A similar streptavidin acrylamide has been shown to copolymerize with acrylamide on a polymeric surface to create a uniform monolayer of the immobilized protein. The streptavidin can then bind biotinylated ligands, including biotinylated hybridization probes, enzymes, antibodies and drugs. CaptAvidin™ acrylamide (C21387) is expected to have similar utility, but offers an advantage — the bond that it forms with biotinylated probes can be reversed at about pH 10.

Biotinylated Reagents for Use with Avidins

In addition to the direct conjugates of avidins, Molecular Probes offers an extensive selection of biotinylated products for use in conjunction with avidins; see Chapter 4 for a complete list of our biotinylation reagents and biotin conjugates. Molecular Probes offers a broad selection of biotinylating reagents, including FluoReporter® Biotin-XX and Biotin/DNP Protein Labeling Kits (F2610, F6347, F6348; Section 1.2). Reactive forms of DSB-X™ biotin and our unique DSB-X™ biotin bioconjugates are also described in Chapter 4.

Our diverse set of biotin and DSB-X™ biotin conjugates is described in Section 4.3. Combining one of our biotinylated or DSB-X™ biotin–labeled antibodies (Section 7.2, Table 7.1) with a fluorescent dye– or enzyme-labeled avidin provides an easy method for indirect detection of antibodies from various animal sources. Biotinylated R-phycoerythrin (P811, Section 6.4) can be used with an avidin or streptavidin bridge to detect biotinylated biomolecules;[84] this bridging technique may substantially reduce the nonspecific staining that is commonly seen when using phycobiliproteins for immunohistochemical applications.

Biotinylated liposomes can be prepared using Molecular Probes' biotin conjugates of phosphoethanolamine (B1550, B1616; Section 4.3). Avidin has been used to form a bridge between a biotinylated liposome loaded with fluorescent dyes and a target-specific biotinylated detection reagent. Biotinylated liposomes containing carboxyfluorescein have been employed in an immunoassay that was reported to be both faster and 100 times more sensitive than the comparable peroxidase-based ELISA.[85]

Anti-Biotin Antibody: An Alternative to Avidins

As an alternative to avidin-based reagents, Molecular Probes offers unlabeled, Alexa Fluor® 488 dye–labeled and Alexa Fluor® 594 dye–labeled versions of a high-affinity mouse monoclonal antibody to biotin (A11242, A31801, A31800). Our anti-biotin antibody can be used to detect biotinylated molecules in immunohistochemistry, *in situ* hybridization, ELISAs and Western blot applications. Somewhat unexpectedly, our anti-biotin antibody retains high affinity for desthiobiotin; consequently, its binding to DSB-X™ biotin bioconjugates cannot be easily reversed by addition of free D-biotin.[12]

It has been shown that certain monoclonal antibodies to biotin have biotin-binding motifs that are similar to those seen for avidin and streptavidin.[86] Anti-biotin antibody has been shown to selectively stain endogenous biotin-dependent carboxylase proteins used in fatty acid synthesis of the mitochondria.[24,87] Nonspecific staining of mitochondrial proteins by labeled avidins and by anti-biotin antibodies can be a complicating factor when using avidin–biotin techniques (Figure 7.98). This nonspecific binding can usually be blocked by pretreatment of the sample with the reagents in our Endogenous Biotin-Blocking Kit (E21390).

Especially useful for indirect immunofluorescence, the green-fluorescent Alexa Fluor® 488 conjugate exhibits excitation/emission maxima similar to fluorescein, but its fluorescence is brighter, more photostable and pH insensitive. Likewise, the red-fluorescent Alexa Fluor® 594 conjugate is spectrally similar to but much more fluorescent than Texas Red® conjugates, making it particularly useful for multilabeling experiments in combination with green-fluorescent probes. Because it is a mouse IgG_1 antibody, our anti-biotin antibody can be used with any of our Zenon® Mouse IgG_1 Labeling Kits (Section 7.3, Table 7.13) to create even more alternatives to avidin-based reagents for the detection of biotinylated probes.

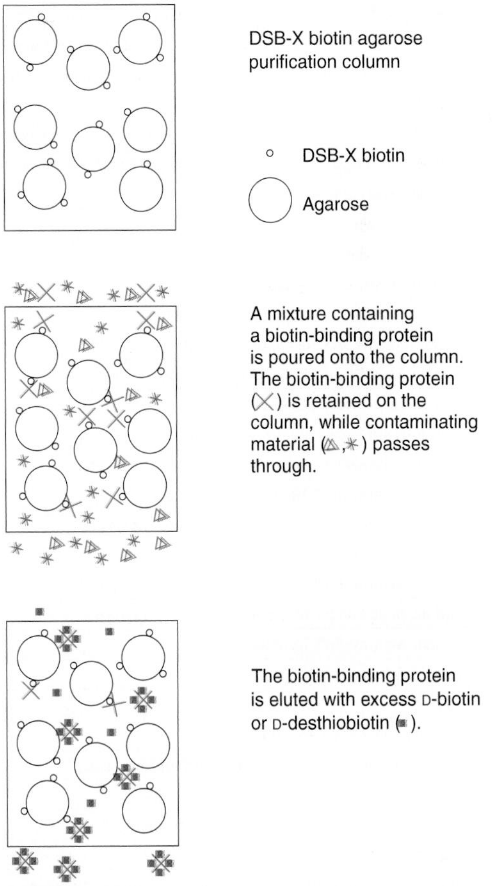

DSB-X biotin agarose purification column
DSB-X biotin
Agarose
A mixture containing a biotin-binding protein is poured onto the column. The biotin-binding protein (X) is retained on the column, while contaminating material (▲,✱) passes through.
The biotin-binding protein is eluted with excess D-biotin or D-desthiobiotin (■).

Figure 7.109 Diagram illustrating the use of DSB-X™ biotin agarose (D20659) for affinity chromatography.

References

1. Proc Natl Acad Sci U S A 71, 3537 (1974); **2.** Biochim Biophys Acta 264, 165 (1972); **3.** Clin Chem 37, 625 (1991); **4.** Methods Enzymol 184, (Complete Volume) (1990); **5.** Methods Biochem Anal 26, 1 (1980); **6.** Anal Biochem 171, 1 (1988); **7.** J Cell Biol 111, 1183 (1990); **8.** Physiol Plantarum 79, 231 (1990); **9.** Cytometry 11, 126 (1990); **10.** Proc Natl Acad Sci U S A 87, 6223 (1990); **11.** Science 249, 928 (1990); **12.** Anal Biochem 308, 343 (2002); **13.** J Immunol Methods 133, 141 (1990); **14.** Biochemistry 32, 8457 (1993); **15.** J Histochem Cytochem 29, 1196 (1981); **16.** J Histochem Cytochem 34, 1509 (1986); **17.** Adv Protein Chem 29, 85 (1975); **18.** Proc Natl Acad Sci U S A 90, 5076 (1993); **19.** J Histochem Cytochem 33, 27 (1985); **20.** J Invest Dermatol 83, 214 (1984); **21.** Biochem Biophys Res Commun 170, 1236 (1990); **22.** Eur J Cell Biol 58, 271 (1992); **23.** Eur J Cell Biol 60, 1 (1993); **24.** J Histochem Cytochem 45, 1053 (1997); **25.** Biochem J 248, 167 (1987); **26.** Trends Genet 9, 71 (1993); **27.** Anal Biochem 243, 257 (1996); **28.** J Microbiol Methods 12, 1 (1990); **29.** Biochemistry 16, 5150 (1977); **30.** J Neurosci 10, 3421 (1990); **31.** Brain Res 497, 361 (1989); **32.** Histochemistry 85, 4 (1986); **33.** Proc Natl Acad Sci U S A 83, 2934 (1986); **34.** Nat Med 6, 707 (2000); **35.** J Immunol 137, 1486 (1986); **36.** Methods Enzymol 108, 197 (1984); **37.** J Immunol 129, 532 (1982); **38.** J Histochem Cytochem 51, 1699 (2003); **39.** Biotechniques 31, 490 (2001); **40.** Proc Natl Acad Sci U S A 98, 8862 (2001); **41.** Proc Natl Acad Sci U S A 97, 3260 (2000); **42.** Proc Natl Acad Sci U S A 95, 3752 (1998); **43.** Proc Natl Acad Sci U S A 97, 2680 (2000); **44.** Anal Biochem 255, 188 (1998); **45.** J Biol Chem 275, 11181 (2000); **46.** Nat Biotechnol 14, 1675 (1996); **47.** Cytometry 15, 267 (1994); **48.** Flow Cytometry Sorting, 2nd Ed., Melamed MR, Lindmo T, Mendelsohn ML, Eds. pp. 367–380 (1990); **49.** J Immunol Methods 219, 57 (1998); **50.** J Histochem Cytochem 51, 707 (2003); **51.** Placenta 24, 557 (2003); **52.** J Microsc 199, 163 (2000); **53.** J Histochem Cytochem 48, 933 (2000); **54.** J Histochem Cytochem 45, 359 (1997); **55.** J Histochem Cytochem 48, 471 (2000); **56.** Colloidal Gold: Principles. Methods and Applications, Vol. 1, Hayat MA, Ed. pp.323–347 (1989); **57.** Proc Natl Acad Sci U S A 82, 109 (1985); **58.** J Histochem Cytochem 36, 317 (1988); **59.** Arch Pathol Lab Med 102, 113 (1978); **60.** Antibodies: A Laboratory Manual, Harlow E, Lane D pp. 553–612 (1988); **61.** Short Protocols in Molecular Biology, 2nd Ed., Ausubel FM, et al., Eds. (Complete Volume), (1992); **62.** (1988); **63.** J Histochem Cytochem 27, 1131 (1979); **64.** Histochemistry 84, 333 (1986); **65.** J Histochem Cytochem 48, 1593 (2000); **66.** J Chromatogr 510, 3 (1990); **67.** J Cell Biol 125, 661 (1994); **68.** Biochemistry 28, 574 (1989); **69.** Biochemistry 40, 8352 (2001); **70.** Biochemistry 40, 8343 (2001); **71.** Biochemistry 23, 2554 (1984); **72.** Biochemistry 21, 978 (1982); **73.** Langmuir 17, 1234 (2001); **74.** These products are not manufactured by Immunicon; **75.** Cell Biology: A Laboratory Handbook, 2nd Ed., Vol. 4, Celis JE, Ed. pp. 341–350 (1998); **76.** Bioconjug Chem 6, 447 (1995); **77.** J Neurochem 77, 1301 (2001); **78.** J Cell Sci 109, 3025 (1996); **79.** Cell Biology: A Laboratory Handbook, 2nd Ed., Vol. 1, Celis JE, Ed. pp. 341–350 (1998); **80.** J Cell Biol 153, 957 (2001); **81.** J Virol 75, 4744 (2001); **82.** J Biol Chem 274, 36801 (1999); **83.** Anal Biochem 282, 200 (2000); **84.** J Biol Chem 265, 15776 (1990); **85.** Anal Biochem 176, 420 (1989); **86.** FEBS Lett 322, 47 (1993); **87.** Histochemistry 100, 415 (1993).

Product List — 7.6 Avidin, Streptavidin, NeutrAvidin and CaptAvidin™ Biotin-Binding Proteins and Affinity Matrices

Cat #	Product Name	Unit Size
A24926	Alexa Fluor® 488 FluoroNanogold™ streptavidin *80 µg protein/mL*	1 mL
A24927	Alexa Fluor® 594 FluoroNanogold™ streptavidin *80 µg protein/mL*	1 mL
A32360	Alexa Fluor® 488 streptavidin, 5 nm colloidal gold conjugate *30 µg protein/mL*	0.5 mL
A32361	Alexa Fluor® 488 streptavidin, 10 nm colloidal gold conjugate *30 µg protein/mL*	0.5 mL
A11242	anti-biotin, mouse IgG_1, monoclonal 2F5	100 µg
A31801	anti-biotin, mouse IgG_1, monoclonal 2F5, Alexa Fluor® 488 conjugate *1 mg/mL*	100 µL
A31800	anti-biotin, mouse IgG_1, monoclonal 2F5, Alexa Fluor® 594 conjugate *1 mg/mL*	100 µL
A21370	avidin, Alexa Fluor® 488 conjugate	1 mg
A887	avidin, egg white	100 mg
A2667	avidin, egg white	5 mg
A821	avidin, fluorescein conjugate	5 mg
A11236	avidin, NeutrAvidin™, Alexa Fluor® 350 conjugate	1 mg
A2666	avidin, NeutrAvidin™ biotin-binding protein	5 mg
A2661	avidin, NeutrAvidin™, BODIPY® FL conjugate	1 mg
A2663	avidin, NeutrAvidin™, Cascade Blue® conjugate	1 mg
A2662	avidin, NeutrAvidin™, fluorescein conjugate	1 mg
A2664	avidin, NeutrAvidin™, horseradish peroxidase conjugate	1 mg
A11230	avidin, NeutrAvidin™, Marina Blue® conjugate	1 mg
A6374	avidin, NeutrAvidin™, Oregon Green® 488 conjugate	1 mg
A6378	avidin, NeutrAvidin™, Rhodamine Red™-X conjugate	1 mg
A2660	avidin, NeutrAvidin™, R-phycoerythrin conjugate *1 mg/mL*	1 mL
A6373	avidin, NeutrAvidin™, tetramethylrhodamine conjugate	1 mg
A2665	avidin, NeutrAvidin™, Texas Red® conjugate	1 mg
A820	avidin, Texas Red® conjugate	5 mg
B1595	D-biotin	1 g
B20656	D-biotin *50 mM aqueous solution*	10 mL
B10710	BlockAid™ blocking solution *for use with microspheres*	50 mL
C21387	CaptAvidin™ acrylamide	1 mg
C21386	CaptAvidin™ agarose *sedimented bead suspension*	5 mL
C21385	CaptAvidin™ biotin-binding protein	1 mg
C24701	Captivate™ disposable sample chamber *for Captivate™ magnetic yoke* *set of 10*	1 set

For current prices or to order online, visit probes.invitrogen.com

Cat #	Product Name	Unit Size
C21476	Captivate™ ferrofluid streptavidin (streptavidin, Captivate™ ferrofluid conjugate) *0.5 mg Fe/mL*	1 mL
C24702	Captivate™ magnetic separator for 96-well microplates	each
C24703	Captivate™ magnetic separator for six microtubes	each
C24700	Captivate™ microscope-mounted magnetic yoke assembly *includes 10 sample chambers*	each
D20657	D-desthiobiotin *50 mM aqueous solution*	10 mL
D22187	Diaminobenzidine (DAB) Histochemistry Kit #3 *with streptavidin–HRP*	1 kit
D20658	DSB-X™ Bioconjugate Isolation Kit #1 *with streptavidin agarose* *5 isolations*	1 kit
D20659	DSB-X™ Bioconjugate Isolation Kit #2 *with DSB-X™ biotin agarose* *5 isolations*	1 kit
E21390	Endogenous Biotin-Blocking Kit *100 assays*	1 kit
F20650	FluoReporter® Cell-Surface Biotinylation Kit	1 kit
F8766	FluoSpheres® biotin-labeled microspheres, 0.04 µm, yellow-green fluorescent (505/515) *1% solids*	0.4 mL
F8767	FluoSpheres® biotin-labeled microspheres, 0.2 µm, yellow-green fluorescent (505/515) *1% solids*	0.4 mL
F8769	FluoSpheres® biotin-labeled microspheres, 1.0 µm, nonfluorescent *1% solids*	0.4 mL
F8768	FluoSpheres® biotin-labeled microspheres, 1.0 µm, yellow-green fluorescent (505/515) *1% solids*	0.4 mL
F20883	FluoSpheres® NeutrAvidin™ labeled microspheres, 0.04 µm, europium luminescent (365/610) *0.5% solids*	0.4 mL
F20884	FluoSpheres® NeutrAvidin™ labeled microspheres, 0.2 µm, europium luminescent (365/610) *0.5% solids*	0.4 mL
F20885	FluoSpheres® NeutrAvidin™ labeled microspheres, 1.0 µm, europium luminescent (365/610) *0.5% solids*	0.4 mL
F20889	FluoSpheres® NeutrAvidin™ labeled microspheres, 0.04 µm, platinum luminescent (390/650) *0.5% solids*	0.4 mL
F20890	FluoSpheres® NeutrAvidin™ labeled microspheres, 0.2 µm, platinum luminescent (390/650) *0.5% solids*	0.4 mL
F20891	FluoSpheres® NeutrAvidin™ labeled microspheres, 1.0 µm, platinum luminescent (390/650) *0.5% solids*	0.4 mL
F8772	FluoSpheres® NeutrAvidin™ labeled microspheres, 0.04 µm, nonfluorescent *1% solids*	0.4 mL
F8777	FluoSpheres® NeutrAvidin™ labeled microspheres, 1.0 µm, nonfluorescent *1% solids*	0.4 mL
F8770	FluoSpheres® NeutrAvidin™ labeled microspheres, 0.04 µm, red fluorescent (580/605) *1% solids*	0.4 mL
F8775	FluoSpheres® NeutrAvidin™ labeled microspheres, 1.0 µm, red fluorescent (580/605) *1% solids*	0.4 mL
F8771	FluoSpheres® NeutrAvidin™ labeled microspheres, 0.04 µm, yellow-green fluorescent (505/515) *1% solids*	0.4 mL
F8774	FluoSpheres® NeutrAvidin™ labeled microspheres, 0.2 µm, yellow-green fluorescent (505/515) *1% solids*	0.4 mL
F8776	FluoSpheres® NeutrAvidin™ labeled microspheres, 1.0 µm, yellow-green fluorescent (505/515) *1% solids*	0.4 mL
F8780	FluoSpheres® streptavidin-labeled microspheres, 0.04 µm, yellow-green fluorescent (505/515) *0.5% solids*	0.4 mL
I37160	Image-iT™ FX Kit #11 *with Alexa Fluor® 350 streptavidin (S11249), ProLong® Gold antifade (P36930) and Image-iT™ FX signal enhancer (I36933)*	1 kit
I37161	Image-iT™ FX Kit #12 *with Alexa Fluor® 488 streptavidin (S11223), ProLong® Gold antifade (P36930) and Image-iT™ FX signal enhancer (I36933)*	1 kit
I37162	Image-iT™ FX Kit #13 *with Alexa Fluor® 555 streptavidin (S21381), ProLong® Gold antifade (P36930) and Image-iT™ FX signal enhancer (I36933)*	1 kit
I37163	Image-iT™ FX Kit #14 *with Alexa Fluor® 594 streptavidin (S11227), ProLong® Gold antifade (P36930) and Image-iT™ FX signal enhancer (I36933)*	1 kit
I37164	Image-iT™ FX Kit #15 *with Alexa Fluor® 647 streptavidin (S21374), ProLong® Gold antifade (P36930) and Image-iT™ FX signal enhancer (I36933)*	1 kit
L24919	LI Silver (LIS) Enhancement Kit	1 kit
N24918	NANOGOLD® streptavidin (streptavidin, NANOGOLD® conjugate) *80 µg protein/mL*	1 mL
P917	peroxidase from horseradish, biotin-XX conjugate	10 mg
S888	streptavidin	5 mg
S21379	streptavidin acrylamide	1 mg
S951	streptavidin agarose *sedimented bead suspension*	5 mL
S21002	streptavidin, Alexa Fluor® 680–allophycocyanin conjugate (Alexa Fluor® 680–allophycocyanin streptavidin) *1 mg/mL*	100 µL
S21005	streptavidin, Alexa Fluor® 700–allophycocyanin conjugate (Alexa Fluor® 700–allophycocyanin streptavidin) *1 mg/mL*	100 µL
S21008	streptavidin, Alexa Fluor® 750–allophycocyanin conjugate (Alexa Fluor® 750–allophycocyanin streptavidin) *1 mg/mL*	100 µL
S11249	streptavidin, Alexa Fluor® 350 conjugate	1 mg
S32351	streptavidin, Alexa Fluor® 405 conjugate	1 mg
S11237	streptavidin, Alexa Fluor® 430 conjugate	1 mg
S11223	streptavidin, Alexa Fluor® 488 conjugate	1 mg
S32354	streptavidin, Alexa Fluor® 488 conjugate *2 mg/mL*	0.5 mL
S32352	streptavidin, Alexa Fluor® 500 conjugate	1 mg
S32353	streptavidin, Alexa Fluor® 514 conjugate	1 mg
S11224	streptavidin, Alexa Fluor® 532 conjugate	1 mg
S11225	streptavidin, Alexa Fluor® 546 conjugate	1 mg
S21381	streptavidin, Alexa Fluor® 555 conjugate	1 mg
S32355	streptavidin, Alexa Fluor® 555 conjugate *2 mg/mL*	0.5 mL
S11226	streptavidin, Alexa Fluor® 568 conjugate	1 mg
S11227	streptavidin, Alexa Fluor® 594 conjugate	1 mg
S32356	streptavidin, Alexa Fluor® 594 conjugate *2 mg/mL*	0.5 mL
S32359	streptavidin, Alexa Fluor® 610 conjugate	1 mg

For current prices or to order online, visit probes.invitrogen.com

Product List — 7.6 Avidin, Streptavidin, NeutrAvidin and CaptAvidin™ Biotin-Binding Proteins and Affinity Matrices — continued

Cat #	Product Name	Unit Size
S21375	streptavidin, Alexa Fluor® 633 conjugate	1 mg
S32364	streptavidin, Alexa Fluor® 635 conjugate	1 mg
S21374	streptavidin, Alexa Fluor® 647 conjugate	1 mg
S32357	streptavidin, Alexa Fluor® 647 conjugate *2 mg/mL*	0.5 mL
S21377	streptavidin, Alexa Fluor® 660 conjugate	1 mg
S21378	streptavidin, Alexa Fluor® 680 conjugate	1 mg
S32358	streptavidin, Alexa Fluor® 680 conjugate *2 mg/mL*	0.5 mL
S21383	streptavidin, Alexa Fluor® 700 conjugate	1 mg
S21384	streptavidin, Alexa Fluor® 750 conjugate	1 mg
S20982	streptavidin, Alexa Fluor® 610–R-phycoerythrin conjugate (Alexa Fluor® 610–R-phycoerythrin streptavidin) *1 mg/mL*	100 µL
S20992	streptavidin, Alexa Fluor® 647–R-phycoerythrin conjugate (Alexa Fluor® 647–R-phycoerythrin streptavidin) *1 mg/mL*	100 µL
S20985	streptavidin, Alexa Fluor® 680–R-phycoerythrin conjugate (Alexa Fluor® 680–R-phycoerythrin streptavidin) *1 mg/mL*	100 µL
S32363	streptavidin, Alexa Fluor® 750–R-phycoerythrin conjugate (Alexa Fluor® 750–R-phycoerythrin streptavidin) *1 mg/mL*	100 µL
S921	streptavidin, alkaline phosphatase conjugate *2 mg/mL*	0.5 mL
S32362	streptavidin, allophycocyanin conjugate *premium grade* *1 mg/mL*	250 µL
S868	streptavidin, allophycocyanin, crosslinked, conjugate *1 mg/mL*	0.5 mL
S11228	streptavidin, Cascade Yellow™ conjugate	1 mg
S32385	streptavidin, DyeMer™ 488/605 conjugate	500 µg
S32386	streptavidin, DyeMer™ 488/615 conjugate	500 µg
S32387	streptavidin, DyeMer™ 488/630 conjugate	500 µg
S869	streptavidin, fluorescein conjugate	1 mg
S931	streptavidin, β-galactosidase conjugate	1 mg
S911	streptavidin, horseradish peroxidase conjugate	1 mg
S11221	streptavidin, Marina Blue® conjugate	1 mg
S6368	streptavidin, Oregon Green® 488 conjugate	1 mg
S6369	streptavidin, Oregon Green® 514 conjugate	1 mg
S11222	streptavidin, Pacific Blue™ conjugate	1 mg
S32350	streptavidin, B-phycoerythrin conjugate *1 mg/mL*	1 mL
S866	streptavidin, R-phycoerythrin conjugate (SAPE) *1 mg/mL*	1 mL
S871	streptavidin, rhodamine B conjugate	1 mg
S6366	streptavidin, Rhodamine Red™-X conjugate	1 mg
S21388	streptavidin, R-phycoerythrin conjugate (SAPE) *premium grade* *1 mg/mL*	1 mL
S870	streptavidin, tetramethylrhodamine conjugate	1 mg
S872	streptavidin, Texas Red® conjugate	1 mg
S6370	streptavidin, Texas Red®-X conjugate	1 mg
T8860	TransFluoSpheres® NeutrAvidin™ labeled microspheres, 0.04 µm (488/605) *1% solids*	0.4 mL
T8861	TransFluoSpheres® NeutrAvidin™ labeled microspheres, 0.1 µm (488/605) *1% solids*	0.4 mL
T10711	TransFluoSpheres® streptavidin-labeled microspheres, 0.04 µm (488/645) *0.5% solids*	0.4 mL

For current prices or to order online, visit probes.invitrogen.com

7.7 Lectins and Other Carbohydrate-Binding Proteins

Cellular proteoglycans, glycoproteins and glycolipids may contain any of a wide variety of oligosaccharides. Although most abundant on the cell surface, oligosaccharide residues are sometimes also found covalently attached to constituents within the cell.[1] Often, specific oligosaccharides are associated with a certain cell type or organelle. Lectins and certain other carbohydrate-binding proteins that bind to specific configurations of sugar molecules can thus serve to identify cell types or cellular components, making them versatile primary detection reagents in histochemical applications and flow cytometry[2] (Figure 7.110, Figure 7.111, Figure 7.112). Fluorescent derivatives of carbohydrate-binding proteins and other reagents have been used to detect cell-surface and intracellular glycoconjugates by microscopy[3,4] and flow cytometry,[5] to localize glycoproteins in gels and on protein blots[6–9] (Section 9.4), to precipitate glycoproteins from solution and to cause agglutination of specific cell types.[10,11] In addition, lectins are also useful markers of certain cancers, because these cells often display altered surface glycoproteins.[12,13] Molecular Probes has introduced some important reagents and kits for the selective detection of glycoproteins in gels and on blots, some of which involve lectin-based technology. These products are described in Section 9.4.

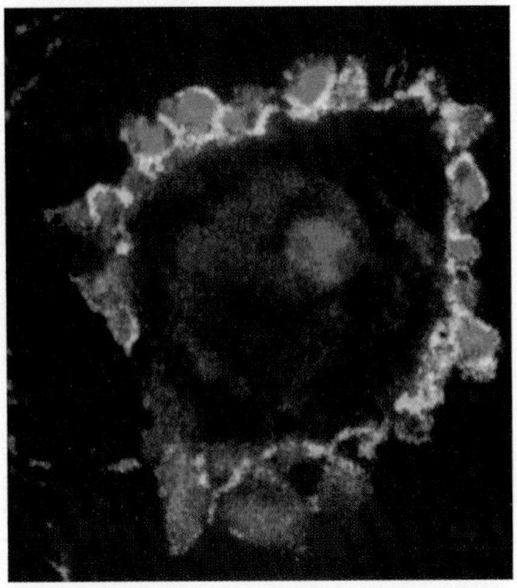

Figure 7.111 Apoptotic human keratinocytes that were fixed with paraformaldehyde and stained with fluorescein concanavalin A (C827). The cells were subsequently permeabilized with acetone, stained with propidium iodide (P1304MP, P3566, P21493) and visualized by confocal laser-scanning microscopy. This photomicrograph clearly shows that the green-fluorescent lectin staining outlines the apoptotic surface blebs, whereas the red-fluorescent propidium iodide stains the interior of the blebs. Image contributed by Livia Casciola-Rosen and Antony Rose, Johns Hopkins University. Reproduced from (J Exp Med 179, 1317 (1994)) by copyright permission of the Rockefeller University Press.

Carbohydrate-Binding Proteins and Their Conjugates

Concanavalin A and Wheat Germ Agglutinin

Molecular Probes offers several fluorescent conjugates of concanavalin A (Con A) and wheat germ agglutinin (WGA) — two of the most commonly used lectins in cell biology — as well as a biotin-XX conjugate of concanavalin A (C21420, Table 7.23). Con A selectively binds to α-mannopyranosyl and α-glucopyranosyl residues. In moderately acidic solutions (pH 4.5–5.6), Con A exists as a dimer with a molecular weight of approximately 52,000 daltons; above pH 7, it is primarily a tetramer with a molecular weight of 104,000 daltons. Con A is a metalloprotein that requires one Ca^{2+} and one Mn^{2+} per subunit for carbohydrate binding.[14,15] The 36,000-dalton dimeric WGA (normally cationic) binds to sialic acid and *N*-acetylglucosaminyl residues.

When Con A is succinylated with succinic anhydride, as in the Alexa Fluor® 488 conjugate of succinylated Con A (C21401), it is irreversibly converted to a dimer that retains the same sugar-binding specificity as the parent lectin. However, the succinylated Con A has a profile of biological activities quite different from that of the tetrameric form. In contrast to the tetramer, succinylated Con A does not induce capping of cell-surface glycoprotein receptors,

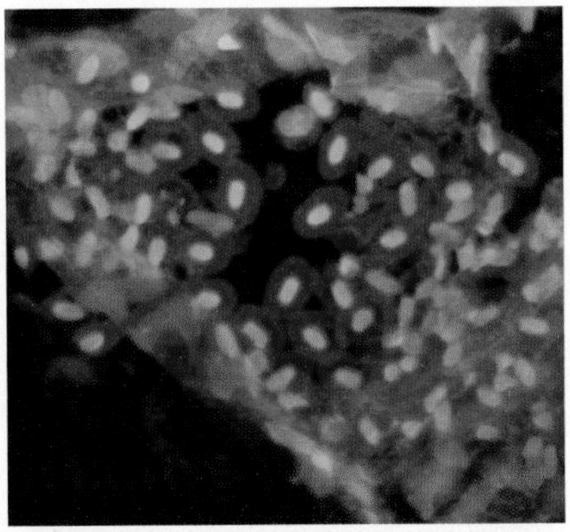

Figure 7.112 Zebrafish tissue section labeled with Texas Red®-X wheat germ agglutinin (W21405) and SYTOX® Green nucleic acid stain (S7020).

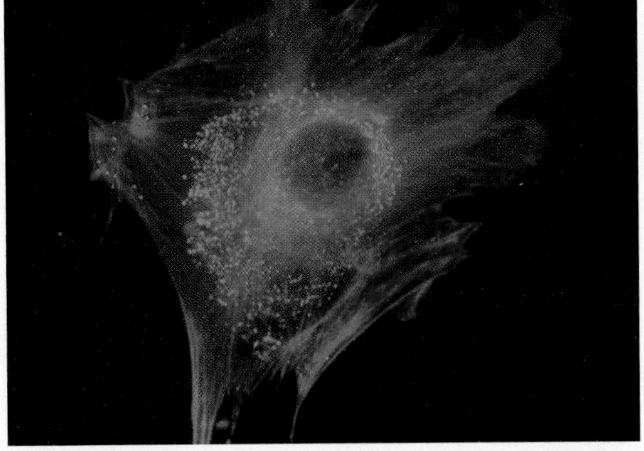

Figure 7.110 Microtubules of fixed bovine pulmonary artery endothelial cells localized with mouse monoclonal anti–α-tubulin antibody (A11126), which was subsequently visualized with Alexa Fluor® 350 goat anti–mouse IgG antibody (A11045). Next, the F-actin was labeled with Alexa Fluor® 594 phalloidin (A12381). Finally, the cells were incubated with Alexa Fluor® 488 wheat germ agglutinin (W11261) to stain components of endosomal pathways. The superimposed and pseudocolored images were acquired sequentially using bandpass filter sets appropriate for DAPI, the Texas Red® dye and fluorescein, respectively.

nor does it inhibit capping of cell-surface immunoglobulin receptors or strongly agglutinate erythrocytes or spleen cells. The mitogenic effect of succinylated Con A is similar to that of the native lectin, although it is mitogenic over a significantly wider range of concentrations than is the tetramer.[16,17]

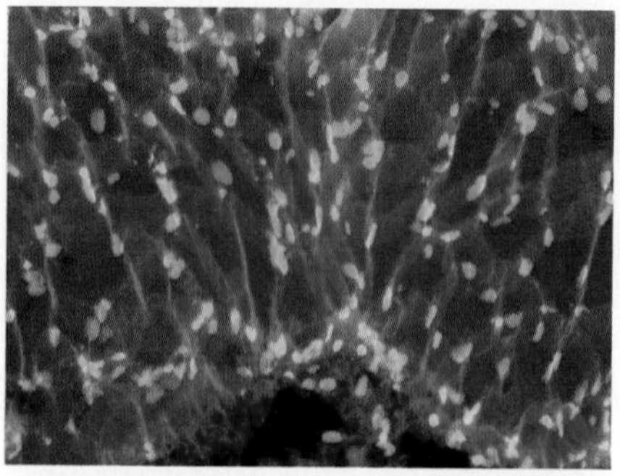

Figure 7.113 A zebrafish tissue section labeled with FRet 43 mouse monoclonal IgG in conjunction with Texas Red®-X goat anti–mouse IgG (T6390), Alexa Fluor® 350 wheat germ agglutinin (W11263) and SYTOX® Green nucleic acid stain (S7020). The multiple-exposure image was acquired using bandpass filter sets appropriate for DAPI, fluorescein and Texas Red® dye.

Concanavalin A and Wheat Germ Agglutinin Conjugates

Although we continue to provide fluorescein and tetramethylrhodamine conjugates of some lectins, we strongly recommend that researchers also evaluate our other fluorescent conjugates (Table 7.23), which exhibit excitation and emission maxima nearly identical to these traditional reagents but invariably show superior brightness. In particular, our green-fluorescent Alexa Fluor® 488 conjugate is not only brighter than fluorescein conjugates, but also much more photostable and pH insensitive in the physiological range (see Note 1.1 "Product Highlight: The Alexa Fluor® Dye Series — Peak Performance across the Visible Spectrum" in Section 1.3). Our Alexa Fluor® 488 conjugates of Con A (C11252) and succinylated Con A (C21401) should be the best green-fluorescent Con A derivatives available anywhere. Moreover, the red-fluorescent Alexa Fluor® 594 conjugate of Con A (C11252) is even more fluorescent than our Texas Red® conjugate of Con A. The Alexa Fluor® 633 and Alexa Fluor® 660 conjugates of Con A (C21402, C21403) and WGA (W21404, W21407) emit light at long wavelengths and are exceptionally useful for multicolor fluorescent labeling of cells and tissues, including those that have high intrinsic autofluorescence. For blue-fluorescent labeling, we recommend the Alexa Fluor® 350 conjugates of Con A and WGA (C11254, W11263; Figure 7.113) and the Marina Blue® conjugate of WGA (W11260). The blue-fluorescent Alexa Fluor® 350 Con A (C11254) is significantly more fluorescent than the corresponding AMCA conjugate. For researchers interested in testing our fluorescent WGA conjugates in their various applications, we offer a Wheat Germ Agglutinin Stain Sampler Kit (W7024), which contains 1 mg quantities each of WGA conjugates of the Alexa Fluor® 350, Oregon Green® 488, tetramethylrhodamine and Texas Red®-X dyes.

Applications for Fluorescent Con A

Although the distribution of oligosaccharides that may be bound by Con A and WGA varies widely among cell types, these two lectins have proven to be useful reagents for a number of applications, including immunolocalization of oncogene products,[18] specific intracellular enzymes,[19,20] viral proteins[21] and components of the cytoskeleton[22] (Figure 7.114, Figure 7.115). Con A also reportedly binds specifically to isolated Golgi fractions from rat liver, which enabled researchers to use fluorescein-labeled Con A to examine the effect of chronic ethanol

Table 7.23 — Molecular Probes' selection of lectin conjugates

Label (Abs/Em Maxima) *	Lectin Conjugate †							
	Con A	WGA	IB_4	GS-II	PHA-L	HPA	SBA	PNA
Alexa Fluor® 350 (346/442)	C11254	W11263						
Marina Blue® (365/460)		W11260						
Fluorescein (494/518)	C827	W834						
Alexa Fluor® 488 (495/519)	C11252 ‡	W11261	I21411	L21415	L11270	L11271	L11272	L21409
Oregon Green® 488 (496/524)	C6741	W6748						
Tetramethylrhodamine (555/580)	C860	W849						
Alexa Fluor® 568 (578/603)			I21412		L32455	L32452	L32461	L32458
Alexa Fluor® 594 (590/617)	C11253	W11262	I21413	L21416	L32456	L32453	L32462	L32459
Texas Red® (595/615)	C825							
Texas Red®-X (595/615)		W21405						
Alexa Fluor® 633 (632/347)	C21402	W21404						
Alexa Fluor® 647 (650/668)	C21421		I32450	L32451	L32457	L32454	L32463	L32460
Alexa Fluor® 660 (663/690)	C21403	W21407						
Biotin-XX (NA)	C21420		I21414					

* Approximate absorption (Abs) and fluorescence emission (Em) maxima, in nm, for conjugates. † Lectin sources: Concanavalin A (Con A) isolated from *Canavalia ensiformis* (jack bean); Wheat Germ Agglutinin (WGA) isolated from *Triticum vulgaris*; IB_4 isolated from *Griffonia simplicifolia* (an African legume); GS-II isolated from *Griffonia simplicifolia*; PHA-L isolated from *Phaseolus vulgaris* (red kidney bean); HPA isolated from *Helix pomatia* (edible snail); SBA isolated from *Glycine max* (soybean); PNA isolated from *Arachis hypogaea* (peanut). ‡ Succinylated Alexa Fluor® 488 concanavalin A is also available, C21401. NA = Not applicable. For researchers interested in testing our fluorescent WGA conjugates in their application, we also offer a Wheat Germ Agglutinin Stain Sampler Kit (W7024), which contains 1 mg quantities each of WGA conjugates of the Alexa Fluor® 350, Oregon Green® 488, tetramethylrhodamine and Texas Red®-X dyes.

intake on carbohydrate content in these organelles using flow cytometry.[23] Fluorescent Con A has also been used to:

- Determine if human sperm cells have undergone the progesterone-induced acrosome reaction[24]
- Investigate receptor capping in leukocytes[25]
- Measure lateral diffusion of glycoproteins, glycolipids and viruses in membranes[26,27]
- Show the redistribution of cell-surface glycoproteins in murine fibroblasts that had been induced to migrate by exposure to an electric field[28]

Applications for Fluorescent WGA

Nuclear core complexes have been found to contain several proteins with *O*-linked *N*-acetylglucosaminyl residues.[29–33] In a study of nuclear protein transport, nuclei isolated from monkey kidney epithelial cells were demonstrated to be intact by their bright staining with fluorescein WGA (W834); fluorescein Con A (C827), which binds to residues accessible only in nuclei with compromised membranes, was used as a negative control for intact nuclei.[34] Fluorescent WGA has also been employed to monitor reconstitution of the nuclear core complex in *Xenopus* egg extracts.[35] WGA conjugates undergo axonal transport[36,37] and have been shown to cross from axonal nerve endings into adjacent neurons.[38]

Fluorescent lectins are also useful in microbiology applications. Fluorescent WGA conjugates stain chitin in fungal cell walls[39] and have been reported to stain gram-positive but not gram-negative bacteria for subsequent analysis by either imaging[40] or flow cytometry.[41] Fluorescent WGA conjugates are utilized in our ViaGram™ Red⁺ Bacterial Gram Stain and Viability Kit (V7023, Section 15.3) to differentiate gram-positive and gram-negative bacteria. Fluorescent WGA also binds to sheathed microfilariae and has been used to detect filarial infection in blood smears.[42]

In addition to these nuclear core and microbiology studies, fluorescent WGA has been used to:

- Bind the sarcolemma of rat and dog cardiac myocytes, even within the intercalated discs and transverse tubules, allowing researchers to map the distribution of gap junctions in these cell types[43]
- Determine the intracellular distribution of altered lysosomal proteins, enabling the definition of the sequence requirements for proper cell sorting[44]
- Identify the differentiation state of Madin–Darby canine kidney (MDCK) cells[45]
- Investigate plant hemicelluloses[46]
- Measure cell membrane potential in combination with potential-sensitive membrane probes[47]

Lectins from *Griffonia simplicifolia*

Isolectin GS-IB_4 is a 114,000-dalton glycoprotein that is part of a family of five tetrameric type I isolectins (IA_4, IA_3B, IA_2B_2, IAB_3 and IB_4) isolated from the seeds of the tropical African legume *Griffonia simplicifolia* (formerly *Bandeiraea simplicifolia*). The A and B subunits are very similar, differing in amino acid sequence only at the N-terminus. However, the subunits display remarkably different binding specificities — the A subunit prefers *N*-acetyl-D-galactosamine end groups while the B subunit is selective for terminal α-D-galactosyl residues.[48]

Molecular Probes offers Alexa Fluor® 488, Alexa Fluor® 568, Alexa Fluor® 594 and Alexa Fluor® 647 dye conjugates of this versatile isolectin (I21411, I21412, I21413, I32450), as well as its biotinylated[49–51] (I21414) and unlabeled forms (I21410). Isolectin GS-IB_4 specifically agglutinates blood group B erythrocytes and was originally employed for this purpose.[52] Subsequent work has shown that isolectin GS-IB_4 is cytotoxic to several normal and tumor cell types[53] and has particularly strong affinity for brain microglial and perivascular cells[54] (Figure 7.116). Conjugates of isolectin GS-IB_4 have been particularly valuable as histochemical and flow cytometric probes for specifically labeling endothelial cells in a number of species.[55,56] They have also been used effectively for tracing central and peripheral neuronal pathways following local injections.[57–59]

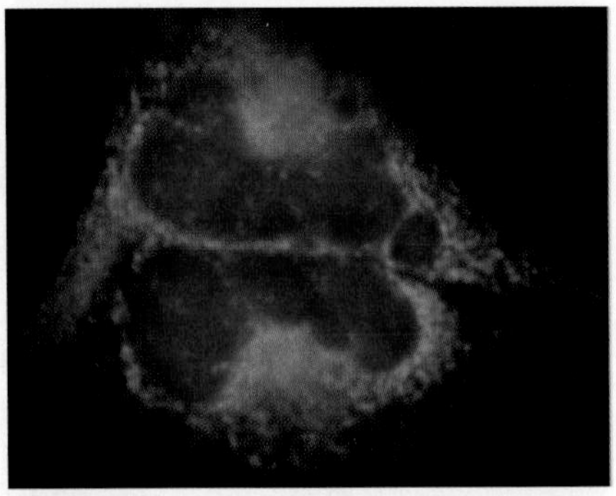

Figure 7.114 Fixed and permeabilized osteosarcoma cells simultaneously stained with the fluorescent lectins Alexa Fluor® 488 concanavalin A (Con A) (C11252) and Alexa Fluor® 594 wheat germ agglutinin (WGA) (W11262). Con A selectively binds α-glucopyranosyl residues, whereas WGA selectively binds sialic acid and *N*-acetylglucosaminyl residues. The nuclei were counterstained with blue-fluorescent Hoechst 33342 nucleic acid stain (H1399, H3570, H21492). The image was acquired using bandpass filter sets appropriate for the Texas Red® dye, fluorescein and AMCA.

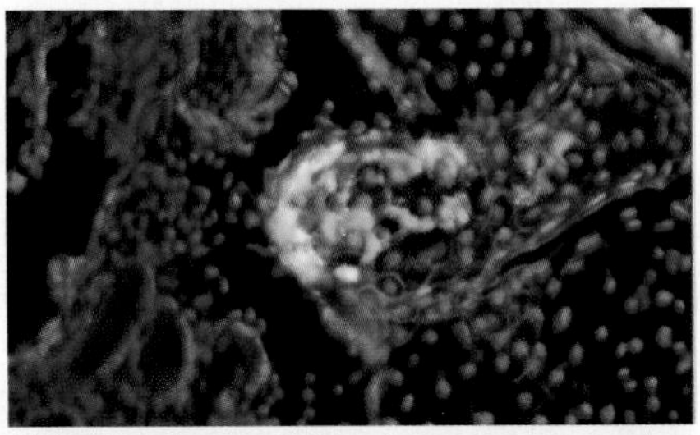

Figure 7.115 Endogenous alkaline phosphatase activity of osteoblast cells in a cartilaginous element of an adult zebrafish head cryosection. The activity was localized with the ELF® 97 Endogenous Phosphatase Detection Kit (E6601). In addition to the yellow-green fluorescence of the ELF® 97 precipitate, the section was stained with Texas Red®-X wheat germ agglutinin (W21405) and counterstained with the Hoechst 33342 nucleic acid stain (H1399, H3570, H21492). The triple-exposure image was acquired using bandpass filter sets appropriate for the ELF® precipitate, Texas Red® dye and AMCA.

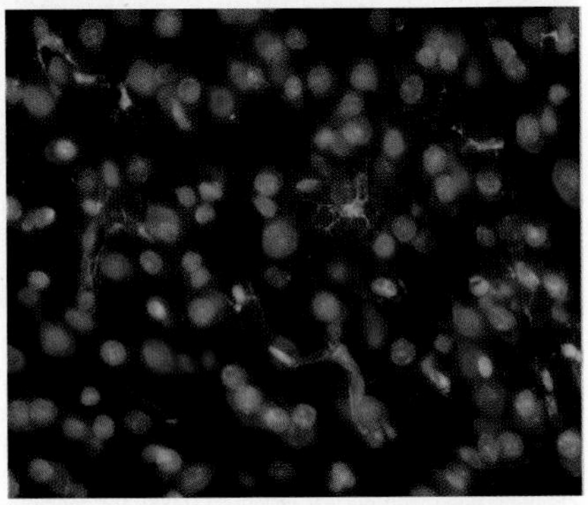

Figure 7.116 Capillary endothelial cells and microglia in a rat brain cryosection labeled with the green-fluorescent Alexa Fluor® 488 isolectin IB_4 (I21411). Neurons were identified using the NeuroTrace® 530/615 red-fluorescent Nissl stain (N21482) and nuclei were counterstained with blue-fluorescent DAPI (D1306, D3571, D21490). The digital image was obtained using filters appropriate for fluorescein, rhodamine and DAPI.

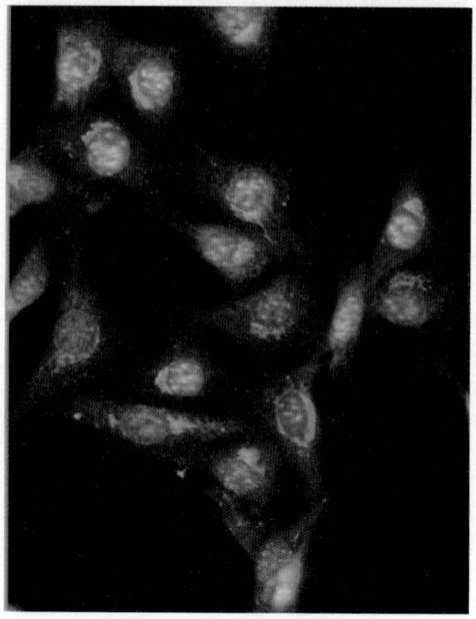

Figure 7.117 Fixed and permeabilized NIH 3T3 cells were labeled with the Alexa Fluor® 488 conjugate of lectin GS-II from *Griffonia simplicifolia* (L21415) and counterstained with DAPI (D1306, D3571, D21490). The fluorescent images are shown overlaid with the differential interference contrast (DIC) image.

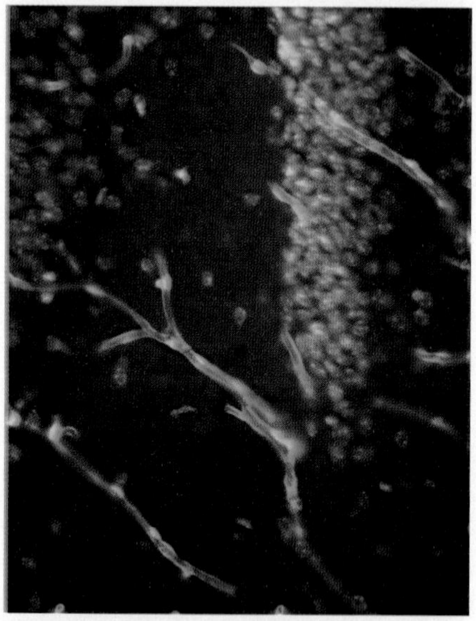

Figure 7.118 Capillaries in the hippocampal region of a mouse brain cryosection were visualized with the green-fluorescent Alexa Fluor® 488 conjugate of lectin HPA from *Helix pomatia* (L11271), which specifically binds to type A erythrocytes and α-*N*-acetylgalactosaminyl residues. The nuclei were counterstained with nuclear yellow (N21485). The multiple-exposure image was acquired using a DAPI longpass filter set and a filter set appropriate for fluorescein.

Lectin GS-II from *G. simplicifolia* differs from isolectin S-IB_4 in that it is the only known lectin that binds with high selectivity for terminal, nonreducing α- and β-*N*-acetyl-D-glucosaminyl (GlcNAc) residues of glycoproteins. Lectin GS-II is a tetrameric protein with an aggregate molecular weight of ~113,000 daltons, with each site binding a single carbohydrate. Because of its affinity for GlcNAc, lectin GS-II conjugates are useful for staining intermediate-to-trans Golgi — the site of *N*-acetylglucosaminyltransferase activity. The Golgi apparatus of oligodendrocytes and ganglion neurons are also stained by fluorescent GS-II conjugates. We have prepared the green-fluorescent Alexa Fluor® 488 (L21415, Figure 7.117), red-fluorescent Alexa Fluor® 594 (L21416) and far-red–fluorescent Alexa Fluor® 647 (L32451) conjugates of lectin GS-II for use in cell staining.

Phaseolus vulgaris *(Red Kidney Bean)* Lectin

Phaseolus vulgaris lectin (PHA-L) is a tetrameric protein with a molecular weight of 120,000 daltons. Its binding to glycoproteins is strongly inhibited by *N*-acetylglucosaminyl (1-2) mannopyranosyl residues.[11] Like WGA, PHA-L is widely used as an injectable neuronal tracer.[60] Iontophoretically injected PHA-L clearly demonstrates the morphological features of the filled neurons at the injection site and the labeled axons and axon terminals. Furthermore, PHA-L that has been transported is not degraded over long periods. PHA-L has been used in combination with our biotinylated lysine-fixable dextrans (BDA dextrans, Section 14.5, Table 14.4) and the fluorescent dextrans fluoro-ruby and mini-ruby (D1817, D3312; Section 14.5) to demonstrate their similar transport properties and to show the distribution of anterograde-labeled fibers.[61] We have prepared Alexa Fluor® 488, Alexa Fluor® 568, Alexa Fluor® 594 and Alexa Fluor® 647 conjugates of PHA-L (L11270, L32455, L32456, L32457).

Arachis hypogaea *(Peanut)* Lectin

Arachis hypogaea lectin (PNA) is a tetrameric protein with a molecular weight of ~110,000 daltons that has specificity for terminal β-galactose residues of glycoproteins. Lactose strongly inhibits binding of PNA to these glycoproteins, with D-galactose somewhat less effective. PNA binds to a broad range of receptors in human tissues, with some preference for glycoproteins that have been treated with neuraminidase (sialidase) to remove terminal sialic acids.[62] Molecular Probes offers Alexa Fluor® 488, Alexa Fluor® 568, Alexa Fluor® 594 and Alexa Fluor® 647 conjugates of PNA (L21409, L32458, L32459, L32460).

PNA-binding sites are widespread in human tissues, with staining patterns varying by tissue type.[63] Research has shown PNA to be selective for acrosomes in rat and human sperm,[64,65] and PNA serves as a marker for certain melanomas.[13,66] PNA has also been used to label the synaptic extracellular matrix in the study of developing neuromuscular junctions.[67]

Previous applications of fluorescent PNA conjugates include:

- Detecting the acrosome reaction of sperm[68]
- Labeling of photoreceptors in chick embryos and in intact retina and dissociated retinal cells[69]
- Binding to desialylated CD44, the PNA receptor in keratinocytes, as a marker of terminal differentiation[70]
- Staining colonic mucins in cultured human tumor cells, transitional cell carcinomas in the bladder and leukemic cells[71,72]

Helix pomatia *(Edible Snail)* Agglutinin

Helix pomatia agglutinin (HPA), a hexameric protein with a molecular weight of 70,000 daltons, selectively binds to type A erythrocytes and α-*N*-acetylgalactosaminyl residues[11] (Figure 7.118). In some cell types, HPA conjugates may be used as markers for the Golgi.[73,74] Furthermore, HPA conjugates have been shown to be as effective as monoclonal antibodies for the detection and differentiation of herpes simplex virus type 1 and type 2 (HSV-1 and HSV-2) in cultured cells.[73] Our Alexa Fluor® 488, Alexa Fluor® 568, Alexa Fluor® 594 and Alexa Fluor® 647 conjugates of HPA (L11271, L32452, L32453, L32454) should be particularly useful for cell staining.[75]

Glycine max *(Soybean) Agglutinin*

Soybean agglutinin (SBA) from *Glycine max* is a tetrameric protein that consists of a mixture of isolectins that have an aggregate molecular weight of ~120,000 daltons.[11] SBA has a stronger reaction with type A1 blood cells than with type A2 blood cells and is known to selectively bind to terminal α- and β-*N*-acetylgalactosaminyl and galactopyranosyl residues of glycoproteins. Neuraminidase-treated cells react more strongly with SBA conjugates than do untreated cells.[65] SBA has selective affinity for human $CD34^+$ hematopoietic stem cells and lymphocytes, and its immobilized conjugates are important reagents for the depletion of T cells in bone marrow transplantation.[76] In addition, a fluorescein conjugate of SBA was shown to be useful for assessing the stage of lymphoid cell differentiation in human leukemic–lymphoma cell lines.[77] Like many lectins, fluorescent SBA conjugates have been shown to bind with high affinity to several types of tumor cells.[78,79] SBA conjugates are also reported to be selective stains for glial cells[80] and the zona pellucida of the mammalian egg.[65] For detecting SBA-binding cells, we have prepared the Alexa Fluor® 488, Alexa Fluor® 568, Alexa Fluor® 594 and Alexa Fluor® 647 conjugates of SBA (L11272, L32461, L32462, L32463).

Cholera Toxin Subunit B

Fluorescent cholera toxins, which bind to galactosyl moieties, are markers of lipid rafts — regions of cell membranes high in ganglioside G_{M1} that are thought to be important in cell signaling[81–83] (see Note 7.5 "Technical Focus: Cholera Toxin Subunits A and B"). Lipid rafts are detergent-insoluble, sphingolipid- and cholesterol-rich membrane microdomains that form lateral assemblies in the plasma membrane.[84–90] Lipid rafts also sequester glycophosphatidylinositol (GPI)-linked proteins and other signaling proteins and receptors, which may be regulated by their selective interactions with these membrane microdomains.[81,91–95] Recent research has demonstrated that lipid rafts play a role in a variety of cellular processes — including the compartmentalization of cell-signaling events,[96–103] the regulation of apoptosis[104–106] and the intracellular trafficking of certain membrane proteins and lipids[107–109] — as well as in the infectious cycles of several viruses and bacterial pathogens.[110–115]

The Vybrant® Lipid Raft Labeling Kits (V34403, V34404, V34405; Section 17.4) provide the key reagents for fluorescently labeling lipid rafts *in vivo* with our bright and extremely photostable Alexa Fluor® dyes (Figure 13.33, Figure 17.41). Live cells are first labeled with the green-fluorescent Alexa Fluor® 488, orange-fluorescent Alexa Fluor® 555 or red-fluorescent Alexa Fluor® 594 conjugate of cholera toxin subunit B (CT-B). This CT-B conjugate binds to the pentasaccharide chain of plasma membrane ganglioside G_{M1}, which selectively partitions into lipid rafts.[81–83] An antibody that specifically recognizes CT-B is then used to crosslink the CT-B–labeled lipid rafts into distinct patches on the plasma membrane, which are easily visualized by fluorescence microscopy.[116,117] Each Vybrant® Lipid Raft Labeling Kit contains sufficient reagents to label 50 live-cell samples in a 2 mL assay, including:

- Recombinant cholera toxin subunit B (CT-B) labeled with the Alexa Fluor® 488 (in Kit V34403), Alexa Fluor® 555 (in Kit V34404) or Alexa Fluor® 594 (in Kit V34405) dye
- Anti–cholera toxin subunit B antibody (anti–CT-B)
- Concentrated phosphate-buffered saline (PBS)
- A detailed labeling protocol

Cholera toxin subunit B and its conjugates are also emerging as superior tracers for retrograde labeling of neurons.[118,119] Researchers have used cholera toxin subunit B in a variety of applications, including tracing of rat forebrain afferents,[120] projections of the parabrachial region[121] and neurons of the urinary bladder wall.[122] Cholera toxin subunit B conjugates bind to the pentasaccharide chain of ganglioside G_{M1} on neuronal cell surfaces and are actively taken up and transported; alternatively, they can be injected by iontophoresis. Unlike the carbocyanine-based neuronal tracers such as DiI (D282, D3911, V22885; Section 14.4), cholera toxin subunit B conjugates can be used on tissue sections that will be fixed and frozen.[123]

All of Molecular Probes' cholera toxin subunit B conjugates are prepared from recombinant cholera toxin subunit B, which is completely free of the toxic subunit A, thus eliminating any concern over toxicity or ADP-ribosylating activity. Our Alexa Fluor® 488 (C22841, C34775), Alexa Fluor® 555 (C22843, C34776), Alexa Fluor® 594 (C22842, C34777) and Alexa Fluor® 647 (C34778) conjugates of cholera toxin subunit B combine this versatile tracer with the superior brightness of our Alexa Fluor® dyes to provide sensitive and selective receptor labeling and neuronal tracing. We also offer biotin-XX (C34779) and horseradish peroxidase (C34780) conjugates of cholera toxin subunit B for use with sensitive secondary detection methods such as diaminobenzidine (DAB) and tyramide signal amplification (TSA, Section 6.2).

Note 7.5 — Technical Focus

Cholera Toxin Subunits A and B

Cholera toxin comprises two subunits, A and B, arranged in an AB_5 conformation. Subunit A is an ADP-ribosyltransferase, which disrupts the proper signaling of G proteins and eventually leads to dehydration of the cell.[1] The 12,000-dalton nontoxic subunit B ("choleragenoid"), which is assembled into a 60,000-dalton pentamer above pH 2,[2] allows the protein complex to bind to cellular surfaces via the pentasaccharide chain of ganglioside G_{M1}.[3]

References

1. J Biol Chem 255, 1252 (1980); **2.** Biochemistry 35, 16069 (1996); **3.** Mol Microbiol 13, 745 (1994).

Glycoprotein Detection on Blots and in Gels

Pro-Q® Glycoprotein Blot Stain Kit with Lectin-Based Detection

Our lectin-based Pro-Q® Glycoprotein Blot Stain Kit provides high-sensitivity detection of specific sugar residues in glycoproteins. Pro-Q® Glycoprotein Blot Stain Kit #5 (P21872, Section 9.4) is supplied with *Griffonia simplicifolia* lectin II (GS-II), which recognizes terminal nonreducing *N*-acetylglucosamine residues. This kit uses an alkaline phosphatase conjugate of the lectin as a convenient means of selectively detecting the corresponding glycoproteins on PVDF or nitrocellulose membranes, providing valuable information about the structure of glycoproteins in an experimental sample. The techniques in this Pro-Q® Glycoprotein Blot Stain Kit can also be applied to detect terminal α-mannopyranosyl and α-glucopyranosyl residues (that do not contain tri- or tetra-antennary structures) by using an alkaline phosphatase conjugate of Con A, as well as to detect *N*-acetylglucosamine and *N*-acetylneuraminic acid (sialic acid) residues by using an alkaline phosphatase conjugate of WGA.

The detection procedure in this kit is similar to that of Western blotting and uses a fluorogenic alkaline phosphatase substrate, DDAO phosphate, for the final detection step. After the proteins are separated on a polyacrylamide gel, they are blotted onto a membrane and incubated with the lectin–alkaline phosphatase conjugate. The alkaline phosphatase enzyme is then detected using DDAO phosphate, which is rapidly converted to the long-wavelength, red-fluorescent product DDAO (absorbance maxima ~275 nm and ~646 nm, emission maximum ~659 nm; Figure 10.7). The enzymatic reaction greatly amplifies the signal, making it possible to detect as little as 15 ng of a glycoprotein, depending on the degree and nature of glycosylation. Sensitivity of the DDAO phosphate–based detection technique rivals ECL chemiluminescence detection, but because DDAO phosphate–based detection produces a stable fluorescent product, there is no need to perform the reaction in a darkroom or to expose the blot to X-ray film. Additionally, unlike transient chemiluminescent signals, the red-fluorescent DDAO signal can be imaged several times and is stable indefinitely on dried blots.

For fluorescent detection of total proteins, this Pro-Q® Glycoprotein Blot Stain Kit can be used in conjunction with our highly sensitive SYPRO® Ruby protein blot stain (S11791, Section 9.3). When used prior to glycoprotein detection, SYPRO® Ruby protein blot stain makes it possible to assess the level of protein transfer to the blot, to compare stained proteins with molecular weight markers and to identify contaminating proteins in the sample. SYPRO® Ruby protein blot stain is particularly useful for blots of 2-D gels where total-protein staining makes it easier to localize stained glycoproteins in the complex protein pattern. Both the enzymatic hydrolysis product of DDAO phosphate (DDAO) and the SYPRO® Ruby blot stain can be easily visualized using either UV epi-illumination or a laser scanner. The Pro-Q® Glycoprotein Blot Stain Kit also provides a sample of our CandyCane™ glycoprotein molecular weight standards, which include eight glycoproteins, five of which are recognized by Con A or WGA (Figure 9.55).

Each Pro-Q® Glycoprotein Blot Stain Kit (P21872, Section 9.4) contains:

- Alkaline phosphatase conjugate of GS-II lectin
- DDAO phosphate
- Dimethylformamide to dissolve the DDAO phosphate
- CandyCane™ glycoprotein molecular weight standards
- Detailed protocols for staining and detection with GS-II

Each kit contains sufficient reagents for staining 10–20 minigel blots (8 cm × 10 cm). DDAO phosphate (D6487, Section 10.3), SYPRO® Ruby protein blot stain (S11791, Section 9.4) and CandyCane™ molecular weight standards (C21852, Section 9.4) are also available separately.

Other Glycoprotein and Lipopolysaccharide Stain Kits

Molecular Probes has developed some additional proprietary technology for the ultrasensitive detection of glycoproteins and lipopolysaccharides in gels and on blots that involves periodate oxidation of the carbohydrate moieties and subsequent detection with fluorescent or chromophoric dyes rather than lectin-based probes. These products, most of which are described in Section 9.4, include the:

- Pro-Q® Emerald 300 Glycoprotein Gel Stain Kit with SYPRO® Ruby protein gel stain (P21855)
- Pro-Q® Emerald 300 Glycoprotein Gel and Blot Stain Kit (P21857)
- Pro-Q® Emerald 488 Glycoprotein Gel and Blot Stain Kit (P21875)
- Pro-Q® Emerald 300 Lipopolysaccharide Gel Stain Kit (P20495, Section 3.2)

Each of these kits provides sufficient reagents for 10 minigels or minigel blots. The products yield both excellent sensitivity and linearity for selective detection of glycoproteins or lipopolysaccharides.

Metabolic Incorporation of Ketone-Containing Carbohydrate

N-Levulinoyl-D-mannosamine (ManLev, L20492, Figure 3.9) and ManLev tetraacetate (L20493) are ketone-containing monosaccharides that serve as substrates in the oligosaccharide synthesis pathway, resulting in ketone-tagged cell-surface oligosaccharides (Figure 3.11). These products are described in detail in Section 3.2.

References

1. J Biol Chem 275, 29179 (2000); **2.** Science 246, 227 (1989); **3.** J Parasitol 76, 130 (1990); **4.** Histochemistry 56, 265 (1978); **5.** Cytometry 19, 112 (1995); **6.** Electrophoresis 24, 588 (2003); **7.** The Protein Protocols Handbook, 2nd Ed., Walker JM, Ed. pp. 761–772 (2002); **8.** Proteomics 1, 841 (2001); **9.** Anal Biochem 96, 208 (1979); **10.** Mol Biochem Parasitol 23, 165 (1987); **11.** Adv Immunol 34, 213 (1983); **12.** J Histochem Cytochem 46, 793 (1998); **13.** Hum Pathol 30, 556 (1999); **14.** Biochemistry 4, 876 (1964); **15.** J Biol Chem 115, 583 (1936); **16.** Biochemistry 32, 5116 (1993); **17.** Proc Natl Acad Sci U S A 70, 1012 (1973); **18.** J Cell Biol 111, 3097 (1990); **19.** J Biol Chem 269, 1727 (1994); **20.** J Cell Biol 111, 2851 (1990); **21.** J Cell Biol 110, 625 (1990); **22.** J Cell Biol 111, 1929 (1990); **23.** Exp Cell Res 207, 136 (1993); **24.** Mol Cell Endocrinol 101, 221 (1994); **25.** J Virol Methods 29, 257 (1990); **26.** FEBS Lett 246, 65 (1989); **27.** Cell 23, 423 (1981); **28.** J Cell Biol 127, 117 (1994); **29.** Annu Rev Cell Biol 8, 495 (1992); **30.** Science 258, 942 (1992); **31.** Biochim Biophys Acta 1071, 83 (1991); **32.** Cell 64, 489 (1991); **33.** Physiol Rev 71, 909 (1991); **34.** J Biol Chem 269, 4910 (1994); **35.** J Biol Chem 269, 9289 (1994); **36.** J Neurosci Methods 9, 185 (1983); **37.** J Neurosci 2, 647 (1982); **38.** Brain Res 344, 41 (1985); **39.** Invest Ophthalmol Vis Sci 27, 500 (1986); **40.** Appl Environ Microbiol 56, 2245 (1990); **41.** Appl Environ Microbiol 69, 2857 (2003); **42.** Int J Parasitol 20, 1099 (1990); **43.** J Mol Cell Cardiol 24, 1443 (1992); **44.** J Cell Biol 111, 955 (1990); **45.** Cell Physiol Biochem 3, 42 (1993); **46.** Protoplasma 156, 67 (1990); **47.** Biophys J 69, 1272 (1995); **48.** J Biol Chem 252, 4739 (1977); **49.** J Immunol 164, 5446 (2000); **50.** Somatosens Mot Res 14, 17 (1997); **51.** Histochem Cell Biol 106, 331 (1996); **52.** Subcell Biochem 32, 127 (1999); **53.** Cancer Res 42, 2977 (1982); **54.** Histochemistry 102, 483 (1994); **55.** Histochem J 19, 225 (1987); **56.** Am J Pathol 134, 1227 (1989); **57.** Biol Bull 197, 115 (1999); **58.** Neurosci Lett 222, 53 (1997); **59.** Brain Res 811, 34 (1998); **60.** Cell Vision 2, 184 (1995); **61.** Histochem Cell Biol 107, 391 (1997); **62.** J Biol Chem 250, 8518 (1975); **63.** Hum Pathol 15, 904 (1984); **64.** Mol Reprod Dev 55, 289 (2000); **65.** Histochem J 29, 583 (1997); **66.** Oncol Res 5, 235 (1993); **67.** J Neurosci 14, 796 (1994); **68.** J Androl 19, 542 (1998); **69.** Invest Ophthalmol Vis Sci 25, 546 (1984); **70.** J Cell Sci 108, 1959 (1995); **71.** Cancer 53, 272 (1984); **72.** Immunology 49, 147 (1983); **73.** Proc Natl Acad Sci U S A 90, 2798 (1993); **74.** Histochemistry 94, 397 (1990); **75.** Curr Biol 11, 1847 (2001); **76.** Mol Biotechnol 11, 181 (1999); **77.** Leuk Res 11, 589 (1987); **78.** Surg Today 27, 293 (1997); **79.** Cancer Res 52, 5235 (1992); **80.** J Neurocytol 21, 211 (1992); **81.** J Cell Biol 147, 447 (1999); **82.** Biochemistry 35, 16069 (1996); **83.** Mol Microbiol 13, 745 (1994); **84.** J Cell Biol 162, 365 (2003); **85.** J Lipid Res 44, 655 (2003); **86.** Eur J Biochem 269, 737 (2002); **87.** Science 290, 1721 (2000); **88.** Mol Membr Biol 16, 145 (1999); **89.** Trends Cell Biol 9, 87 (1999); **90.** Annu Rev Cell Dev Biol 14, 111 (1998); **91.** Proc Natl Acad Sci U S A 100, 5813 (2003); **92.** J Immunol 170, 1329 (2003); **93.** J Membr Biol 189, 35 (2002); **94.** Proc Natl Acad Sci U S A 98, 9098 (2001); **95.** Mol Biol Cell 10, 3187 (1999); **96.** Biochim Biophys Acta 1610, 247 (2003); **97.** Annu Rev Immunol 21, 457 (2003); **98.** Mol Immunol 38, 1247 (2002); **99.** Nat Rev Immunol 2, 96 (2002); **100.** Biol Res 35, 127 (2002); **101.** Nat Rev Mol Cell Biol 1, 31 (2000); **102.** J Exp Med 190, 1549 (1999); **103.** J Cell Biol 143, 637 (1998); **104.** Immunity 18, 655 (2003); **105.** J Biol Chem 277, 39541 (2002); **106.** Biochem Biophys Res Commun 297, 876 (2002); **107.** Biol Chem 383, 1475 (2002); **108.** J Cell Biol 153, 529 (2001); **109.** J Cell Sci 114, 3957 (2001); **110.** J Virol 77, 9542 (2003); **111.** Exp Cell Res 287, 67 (2003); **112.** Traffic 3, 705 (2002); **113.** J Clin Virol 22, 217 (2001); **114.** Curr Biol 10, R823 (2000); **115.** J Virol 74, 3264 (2000); **116.** J Cell Biol 141, 929 (1998); **117.** J Biol Chem 269, 30745 (1994); **118.** Brain Res 243, 215 (1982); **119.** Brain Res 231, 33 (1982); **120.** Neuroscience 82, 443 (1998); **121.** Brain Res 816, 364 (1999); **122.** Neuroscience 87, 275 (1998); **123.** J Neurosci 22, 9419 (2002).

Product List — 7.7 Lectins and Other Carbohydrate-Binding Proteins

Cat #	Product Name	Unit Size
C22841	cholera toxin subunit B (recombinant), Alexa Fluor® 488 conjugate	500 µg
C34775	cholera toxin subunit B (recombinant), Alexa Fluor® 488 conjugate	100 µg
C22843	cholera toxin subunit B (recombinant), Alexa Fluor® 555 conjugate	500 µg
C34776	cholera toxin subunit B (recombinant), Alexa Fluor® 555 conjugate	100 µg
C22842	cholera toxin subunit B (recombinant), Alexa Fluor® 594 conjugate	500 µg
C34777	cholera toxin subunit B (recombinant), Alexa Fluor® 594 conjugate	100 µg
C34778	cholera toxin subunit B (recombinant), Alexa Fluor® 647 conjugate	100 µg
C34779	cholera toxin subunit B (recombinant), biotin-XX conjugate	100 µg
C34780	cholera toxin subunit B (recombinant), horseradish peroxidase conjugate	100 µg
C11254	concanavalin A, Alexa Fluor® 350 conjugate	5 mg
C11252	concanavalin A, Alexa Fluor® 488 conjugate	5 mg
C11253	concanavalin A, Alexa Fluor® 594 conjugate	5 mg
C21402	concanavalin A, Alexa Fluor® 633 conjugate	5 mg
C21421	concanavalin A, Alexa Fluor® 647 conjugate	5 mg
C21403	concanavalin A, Alexa Fluor® 660 conjugate	5 mg
C21420	concanavalin A, biotin-XX conjugate	10 mg
C827	concanavalin A, fluorescein conjugate	10 mg
C6741	concanavalin A, Oregon Green® 488 conjugate	5 mg
C21401	concanavalin A, succinylated, Alexa Fluor® 488 conjugate	5 mg
C860	concanavalin A, tetramethylrhodamine conjugate	10 mg
C825	concanavalin A, Texas Red® conjugate	10 mg
I21410	isolectin GS-IB$_4$ from *Griffonia simplicifolia*	1 mg
I21411	isolectin GS-IB$_4$ from *Griffonia simplicifolia*, Alexa Fluor® 488 conjugate	500 µg
I21412	isolectin GS-IB$_4$ from *Griffonia simplicifolia*, Alexa Fluor® 568 conjugate	500 µg
I21413	isolectin GS-IB$_4$ from *Griffonia simplicifolia*, Alexa Fluor® 594 conjugate	500 µg

For current prices or to order online, visit probes.invitrogen.com

Product List — 7.7 Lectins and Other Carbohydrate-Binding Proteins — continued

Cat #	Product Name	Unit Size
I32450	isolectin GS-IB_4 from *Griffonia simplicifolia*, Alexa Fluor® 647 conjugate	500 µg
I21414	isolectin GS-IB_4 from *Griffonia simplicifolia*, biotin-XX conjugate	500 µg
L21415	lectin GS-II from *Griffonia simplicifolia*, Alexa Fluor® 488 conjugate	500 µg
L21416	lectin GS-II from *Griffonia simplicifolia*, Alexa Fluor® 594 conjugate	500 µg
L32451	lectin GS-II from *Griffonia simplicifolia*, Alexa Fluor® 647 conjugate	500 µg
L11271	lectin HPA from *Helix pomatia* (edible snail), Alexa Fluor® 488 conjugate	1 mg
L32452	lectin HPA from *Helix pomatia* (edible snail), Alexa Fluor® 568 conjugate	1 mg
L32453	lectin HPA from *Helix pomatia* (edible snail), Alexa Fluor® 594 conjugate	1 mg
L32454	lectin HPA from *Helix pomatia* (edible snail), Alexa Fluor® 647 conjugate	1 mg
L11270	lectin PHA-L from *Phaseolus vulgaris* (red kidney bean), Alexa Fluor® 488 conjugate	1 mg
L32455	lectin PHA-L from *Phaseolus vulgaris* (red kidney bean), Alexa Fluor® 568 conjugate	1 mg
L32456	lectin PHA-L from *Phaseolus vulgaris* (red kidney bean), Alexa Fluor® 594 conjugate	1 mg
L32457	lectin PHA-L from *Phaseolus vulgaris* (red kidney bean), Alexa Fluor® 647 conjugate	1 mg
L21409	lectin PNA from *Arachis hypogaea* (peanut), Alexa Fluor® 488 conjugate	1 mg
L32458	lectin PNA from *Arachis hypogaea* (peanut), Alexa Fluor® 568 conjugate	1 mg
L32459	lectin PNA from *Arachis hypogaea* (peanut), Alexa Fluor® 594 conjugate	1 mg
L32460	lectin PNA from *Arachis hypogaea* (peanut), Alexa Fluor® 647 conjugate	1 mg
L11272	lectin SBA from *Glycine max* (soybean), Alexa Fluor® 488 conjugate	1 mg
L32461	lectin SBA from *Glycine max* (soybean), Alexa Fluor® 568 conjugate	1 mg
L32462	lectin SBA from *Glycine max* (soybean), Alexa Fluor® 594 conjugate	1 mg
L32463	lectin SBA from *Glycine max* (soybean), Alexa Fluor® 647 conjugate	1 mg
W11263	wheat germ agglutinin, Alexa Fluor® 350 conjugate	5 mg
W11261	wheat germ agglutinin, Alexa Fluor® 488 conjugate	5 mg
W11262	wheat germ agglutinin, Alexa Fluor® 594 conjugate	5 mg
W21404	wheat germ agglutinin, Alexa Fluor® 633 conjugate	5 mg
W21407	wheat germ agglutinin, Alexa Fluor® 660 conjugate	5 mg
W834	wheat germ agglutinin, fluorescein conjugate	5 mg
W11260	wheat germ agglutinin, Marina Blue® conjugate	5 mg
W6748	wheat germ agglutinin, Oregon Green® 488 conjugate	5 mg
W7024	Wheat Germ Agglutinin Sampler Kit *four fluorescent conjugates, 1 mg each*	1 kit
W849	wheat germ agglutinin, tetramethylrhodamine conjugate	5 mg
W21405	wheat germ agglutinin, Texas Red®-X conjugate	1 mg

For current prices or to order online, visit probes.invitrogen.com

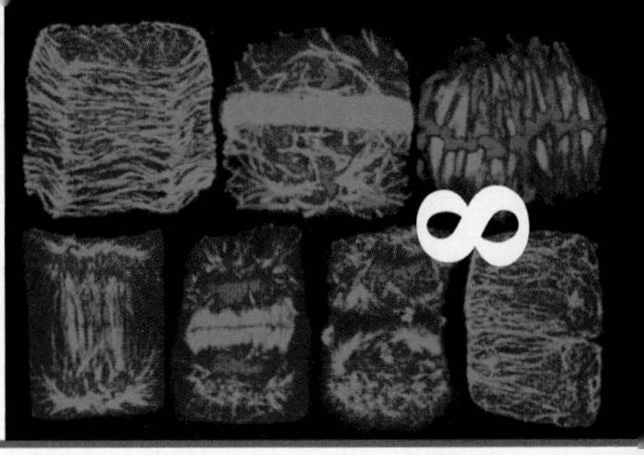

Chapter 8

Nucleic Acid Detection and Genomics Technology

8.1 Nucleic Acid Stains

Molecular Probes prepares the most extensive assortment of nucleic acid stains commercially available, many of which have been developed in our research laboratories. This section discusses the physical properties of the various classes of dyes listed below. The sections in Chapter 8 that follow discuss numerous applications of these dyes and our other reagents and technology for genomics research.

The four classes of Molecular Probes' proprietary cyanine dyes include:

- Premier dyes for ultrasensitive nucleic acid quantitation and gel staining (Table 8.1)
- The cell-impermeant TOTO®, TO-PRO® and SYTOX® families of dyes (Table 8.2)
- The cell-permeant SYTO® family of dyes (Table 8.3)
- Chemically reactive SYBR® dyes that can be used to form bioconjugates (see below)

The three classes of classic nucleic acid stains (Table 8.4) include:

- Intercalating dyes, such as ethidium bromide and propidium iodide
- Minor-groove binders, such as DAPI and the Hoechst dyes
- Miscellaneous nucleic acid stains, including acridine orange, 7-AAD, LDS 751 and hydroxystilbamidine, with special properties

Table 8.1 — Specialty nucleic acid reagents for molecular biology

Cat #	Dye Name	Ex/Em *	Application
Dyes for Ultrasensitive Solution Quantitation			
P7581, P11495, P7589, P11496, R21495	PicoGreen® Quantitation Reagent and Kits	502/523	Ultrasensitive reagent for solution quantitation of dsDNA
O7582, O11492	OliGreen® Quantitation Reagent and Kit	498/518	Ultrasensitive reagent for solution quantitation of ssDNA and oligonucleotides
R11491, R11490, R32700	RiboGreen® Quantitation Reagent and Kits	500/520	Ultrasensitive reagent for solution quantitation of RNA
Dyes for Sensitive Detection of Nucleic Acids in Gels and on Blots			
S11494	SYBR® Gold stain	495/537	Ultrasensitive gel stain for single- or double-stranded DNA or RNA post-electrophoresis
S7567, S7563, S7585	SYBR® Green I stain	494/521	Ultrasensitive gel stain for double-stranded DNA and oligonucleotides post-electrophoresis Also useful for real-time PCR assays
S7568, S7564, S7586	SYBR® Green II stain	492/513	Sensitive stain for RNA and single-stranded DNA post-electrophoresis
S33100, S33101, S33111, S33112	SYBR Safe™ stain	502/530	Sensitive DNA gel stain with significantly reduced mutagenicity
S7550	SYBR® DX DNA blot stain	475/499	Sensitive stain for DNA on blots (not recommended for staining RNA)

* All excitation (Ex) and emission (Em) maxima were determined for dyes bound to double-stranded calf thymus DNA in aqueous solution.

Table 8.2 — Cell membrane–impermeant cyanine nucleic acid stains

Cat #	Dye Name	Ex/Em *	Excitation Source †
SYTOX® Dyes — Ideal Dead-Cell Stains ‡			
S11348	SYTOX® Blue	445/470	Hg-arc lamp, 436 nm line
S7020	SYTOX® Green	504/523	Ar-ion laser, 488 nm line
S11368	SYTOX® Orange	547/570	Nd:YAG laser, 532 nm line
Cyanine Dimers — Very High Affinity Stains §			
P3580	POPO™-1	434/456	Hg-arc lamp, 436 nm line He–Cd laser, 442 nm line
B3582	BOBO™-1	462/481	Hg-arc lamp, 436 nm line He–Cd laser, 442 nm line
Y3601	YOYO®-1	491/509	Ar-ion laser, 488 nm line
T3600	TOTO®-1	514/533	Ar-ion laser, 514 nm line
J11372	JOJO™-1	529/545	Nd:YAG laser, 532 nm line
P3584	POPO™-3	534/570	Nd:YAG laser, 532 nm line
L11376	LOLO™-1	565/579	Kr-ion laser, 568 nm line
B3586	BOBO™-3	570/602	Hg-arc lamp, 578 nm line
Y3606	YOYO®-3	612/631	Orange He–Ne laser, 594 nm line
T3604	TOTO®-3	642/660	He–Ne laser, 633 nm line Kr-ion laser, 647 nm line 635 nm diode laser
N7565	Dimer Sampler Kit **	various	various
Cyanine Monomers — Ideal Counterstains ††			
P3581	PO-PRO™-1	435/455	Hg-arc lamp, 436 nm line He–Cd laser, 442 nm line
B3583	BO-PRO™-1	462/481	Hg-arc lamp, 436 nm line He–Cd laser, 442 nm line
Y3603	YO-PRO®-1	491/509	Ar-ion laser, 488 nm line
T3602	TO-PRO®-1	515/531	Ar-ion laser, 514 nm line
J11373	JO-PRO™-1	530/546	Nd:YAG laser, 532 nm line
P3585	PO-PRO™-3	539/567	Nd:YAG laser, 532 nm line He–Ne laser, 543 nm line
L11377	LO-PRO™-1	567/580	Kr-ion laser, 568 nm line
B3587	BO-PRO™-3	575/599	Hg-arc lamp, 578 nm line
Y3607	YO-PRO®-3	612/631	He–Ne laser, 594 nm line
T3605	TO-PRO®-3	642/661	He–Ne laser, 633 nm line Kr-ion laser, 647 nm line
T7596	TO-PRO®-5	747/770	Laser diodes

* Wavelengths of excitation (Ex) and emission (Em) maxima, in nm. All excitation and emission maxima were determined for dyes bound to double-stranded calf thymus DNA in aqueous solution. † Nearest major emission line of some common light sources. ‡ Products supplied as 250 µL of a 5 mM solution. § Products (except N7565) supplied as 200 µL of a 1 mM solution. ** Includes 10 µL each of a 1 mM solution of the TOTO®-1, TOTO®-3, YOYO®-1, YOYO®-3, BOBO™-1, BOBO™-3, POPO™-1 and POPO™-3 dyes. †† Products supplied as 1 mL of a 1 mM solution.

Table 8.3 — Cell-permeant cyanine nucleic acid stains

Cat #	Dye Name *	Ex/Em †
Blue-Fluorescent SYTO® Dyes		
S11351	SYTO® 40 blue-fluorescent nucleic acid stain	419/445
S11352	SYTO® 41 blue-fluorescent nucleic acid stain	426/455
S11353	SYTO® 42 blue-fluorescent nucleic acid stain	430/460
S11354	SYTO® 43 blue-fluorescent nucleic acid stain	437/464
S11355	SYTO® 44 blue-fluorescent nucleic acid stain	445/472
S11356	SYTO® 45 blue-fluorescent nucleic acid stain	452/484
S11350	SYTO® Blue-Fluorescent Nucleic Acid Stain Sampler Kit (SYTO® dyes 40–45) ‡	Various
Green-Fluorescent SYTO® Dyes		
S32703	SYTO® RNASelect™ green-fluorescent cell stain **	490/530 †
S34854	SYTO® 9 green-fluorescent nucleic acid stain **	483/503
S32704	SYTO® 10 green-fluorescent nucleic acid stain	484/505
S34855	SYTO® BC green-fluorescent nucleic acid stain **	485/500
S7575	SYTO® 13 green-fluorescent nucleic acid stain	488/509
S7578	SYTO® 16 green-fluorescent nucleic acid stain §	488/518
S7559	SYTO® 24 green-fluorescent nucleic acid stain	490/515
S7556	SYTO® 21 green-fluorescent nucleic acid stain	494/517
S32706	SYTO® 27 green-fluorescent nucleic acid stain	495/537
S32705	SYTO® 26 green-fluorescent nucleic acid stain	497/534
S7558	SYTO® 23 green-fluorescent nucleic acid stain	499/520
S7574	SYTO® 12 green-fluorescent nucleic acid stain	500/522
S7573	SYTO® 11 green-fluorescent nucleic acid stain	508/527
S7555	SYTO® 20 green-fluorescent nucleic acid stain §	512/530
S7557	SYTO® 22 green-fluorescent nucleic acid stain	515/535
S7577	SYTO® 15 green-fluorescent nucleic acid stain	516/546
S7576	SYTO® 14 green-fluorescent nucleic acid stain	517/549
S7560	SYTO® 25 green-fluorescent nucleic acid stain	521/556
S7572	SYTO® Green-Fluorescent Nucleic Acid Stain Sampler Kit #1 (SYTO® dyes 11–16) ‡	Various
S7554	SYTO® Green-Fluorescent Nucleic Acid Stain Sampler Kit #2 (SYTO® dyes 20–25) ‡	Various
Orange-Fluorescent SYTO® Dyes		
S32707	SYTO® 86 orange-fluorescent nucleic acid stain	528/556
S11362	SYTO® 81 orange-fluorescent nucleic acid stain	530/544
S11361	SYTO® 80 orange-fluorescent nucleic acid stain	531/545
S11363	SYTO® 82 orange-fluorescent nucleic acid stain	541/560
S11364	SYTO® 83 orange-fluorescent nucleic acid stain	543/559
S11365	SYTO® 84 orange-fluorescent nucleic acid stain	567/582
S11366	SYTO® 85 orange-fluorescent nucleic acid stain	567/583
S11360	SYTO® Orange-Fluorescent Nucleic Acid Stain Sampler Kit (SYTO® dyes 80–85) ‡	Various
Red-Fluorescent SYTO® Dyes		
S11346	SYTO® 64 red-fluorescent nucleic acid stain **	598/620
S11343	SYTO® 61 red-fluorescent nucleic acid stain	620/647
S7579	SYTO® 17 red-fluorescent nucleic acid stain **	621/634
S11341	SYTO® 59 red-fluorescent nucleic acid stain	622/645
S11344	SYTO® 62 red-fluorescent nucleic acid stain	649/680
S11342	SYTO® 60 red-fluorescent nucleic acid stain	652/678
S11345	SYTO® 63 red-fluorescent nucleic acid stain	654/675
S11340	SYTO® Red-Fluorescent Nucleic Acid Stain Sampler Kit (SYTO® dyes 17, 59–64) ‡	Various

* All products supplied as 250 µL of a 5 mM solution, with exceptions noted. † Wavelengths of excitation (Ex) and emission (Em) maxima, in nm. All excitation and emission maxima were determined for dyes bound to double-stranded calf thymus DNA in aqueous solution, except for the SYTO® RNASelect™ green-fluorescent cell stain, which was determined for the dye bound to *Escherichia coli* RNA. ‡ Supplied as six 50 µL vials. § Supplied as 250 µL of a 1 mM solution. ** Unit size = 100 µL.

Properties of Cyanine Dyes

Over the years, Molecular Probes researchers have invented many nucleic acid–binding cyanine dye derivatives that share several unique and outstanding properties:

- High molar absorptivity, with extinction coefficients typically greater than 50,000 $cm^{-1}M^{-1}$ at visible wavelengths
- Very low intrinsic fluorescence, with quantum yields usually less than 0.01 when not bound to nucleic acids
- Large fluorescence enhancements (often over 1000-fold) upon binding to nucleic acids, with increases in quantum yields to as high as 0.9
- Moderate to very high affinity for nucleic acids, with little or no staining of other biopolymers

Representatives of this class of nucleic acid stains have fluorescence excitations and emissions that span the visible-light spectrum from blue to near infrared (Figure 8.1) with additional absorption peaks in the UV, making them compatible with many different types of instrumentation. The cyanine dyes show differences in some physical characteristics — particularly differences in permeability to cell membranes and nucleic acid specificity — that allow their distribution into distinct classes. Those classes are discussed in detail in the following sections of this chapter.

Premier Cyanine Dyes for Ultrasensitive Nucleic Acid Detection and Quantitation

Several of our cyanine dyes give superior results in specific assays for the analysis of nucleic acids (Table 8.1). For these dyes, we have developed detailed and extensively tested protocols to facilitate reproducible, high-sensitivity results in these assays.

- The PicoGreen®, OliGreen® and RiboGreen® quantitation reagents in Section 8.3 set a benchmark for the detection and quantitation of DNA, RNA and oligonucleotides in solution. These reagents offer extremely simple and rapid protocols as well as linear ranges that span up to four orders of magnitude in nucleic acid concentration.

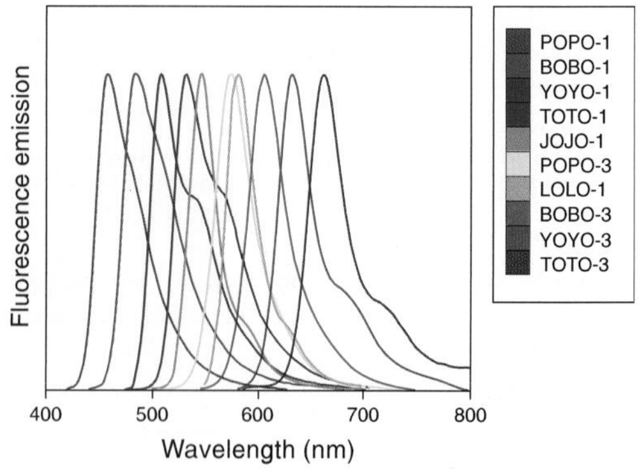

Figure 8.1 Normalized fluorescence emission spectra of DNA-bound cyanine dimers, identified by the color key on the sidebar.

Table 8.4 — Properties of classic nucleic acid stains

Cat #	Dye Name	Ex/Em *	Fluorescence Emission Color	Applications †
A666	Acridine homodimer	431/498	Green	• Impermeant • AT-selective • High-affinity DNA binding
A1301 A3568 ‡	Acridine orange	500/526 (DNA) 460/650 (RNA)	Green/Red	• Permeant • RNA/DNA discrimination measurements • Lysosome labeling • Flow cytometry • Cell-cycle studies
A1310	7-AAD (7-amino-actinomycin D)	546/647	Red	• Weakly permeant • GC-selective • Flow cytometry • Chromosome banding
A7592	Actinomycin D	442	None	• Chromosome banding
A1324	ACMA	419/483	Blue	• AT-selective • Alternative to quinacrine for chromosome Q banding • Membrane phenomena
D1306 D3571 D21490	DAPI	358/461	Blue	• Semi-permeant • AT-selective • Cell-cycle studies • Mycoplasma detection • Chromosome and nuclei counterstain • Chromosome banding
D1168 D11347 D23107	Dihydroethidium	518/605	Red §	• Permeant • Blue fluorescent until oxidized to ethidium
E1305 E3565 ‡	Ethidium bromide	518/605	Red	• Impermeant • dsDNA intercalator • Dead-cell stain • Chromosome counterstain • Electrophoresis • Flow cytometry • Argon-ion laser excitable
E1169	Ethidium homodimer-1 (EthD-1)	528/617	Red	• Impermeant • High-affinity DNA labeling • Dead-cell stain • Electrophoresis prestain • Argon-ion and green He–Ne laser excitable
E3599	Ethidium homodimer-2 (EthD-2)	535/624	Red	• Impermeant • Very high-affinity DNA labeling • Electrophoresis prestain
E1374	Ethidium monoazide	464/625 (unbound) **	Red	• Impermeant • Photocrosslinkable • Compatible with fixation procedures
H7593	Hexidium iodide	518/600	Red	• Permeant, except gram-negative bacteria • Stains nuclei and cytoplasm of eukaryotes and some bacteria
H1398 H3569 ‡ H21491	Hoechst 33258 (bis-benzimide)	352/461	Blue	• Permeant • AT-selective • Minor groove–binding • dsDNA-selective binding • Cell-cycle studies • Chromosome and nuclear counterstain
H1399 H3570 ‡ H21492	Hoechst 33342	350/461	Blue	• Permeant • AT-selective • Minor groove–binding • dsDNA-selective binding • Cell-cycle studies • Chromosome and nuclear counterstain
H21486	Hoechst 34580	392/498	Blue	• Permeant • AT-selective • Minor groove–binding • dsDNA-selective binding • Cell-cycle studies • Chromosome and nuclear counterstain

Table 8.4 — Properties of classic nucleic acid stains — continued

Cat #	Dye Name	Ex/Em *	Fluorescence Emission Color	Applications †
H22845	Hydroxystilbamidine	385/emission varies with nucleic acid	Varies	• AT-selective • Spectra dependent on secondary structure and sequence • RNA/DNA discrimination • Nuclear stain in tissue
L7595	LDS 751	543/712 (DNA) 590/607 (RNA)	Red/infrared	• Permeant • High Stokes shift • Long-wavelength spectra • Flow cytometry
N21485	Nuclear yellow	355/495	Yellow	• Impermeant • Nuclear counterstain
P1304MP P3566 ‡ P21493	Propidium iodide (PI)	530/625	Red	• Impermeant • Dead-cell stain • Chromosome and nuclear counterstain

* Excitation (Ex) and emission (Em) maxima in nm. All excitation and emission maxima were determined for dyes bound to double-stranded calf thymus DNA in aqueous solution, unless otherwise indicated. † Indication of dyes as "permeant" or "impermeant" are for the most common applications; permeability to cell membranes may vary considerably with the cell type, dye concentrations and other staining conditions. ‡ Available in aqueous solution for those wishing to avoid potentially hazardous and mutagenic powders. § After oxidation to ethidium. ** Prior to photolysis; after photolysis the spectra of the dye/DNA complexes are similar to those of ethidium bromide–DNA complexes.

- The SYBR® Gold, SYBR® Green I and SYBR® Green II nucleic acid gel stains in Section 8.4 are ultrasensitive gel stains that surpass the sensitivity of ethidium bromide by more than an order of magnitude in nucleic acid detection.
- The SYBR Safe™ DNA gel stain (Section 8.4) is not only significantly less mutagenic than ethidium bromide, but SYBR Safe™ stain's detection sensitivity is better than that of ethidium bromide. The SYBR Safe™ stain showed no or very low mutagenic activity when tested by an independent, licensed testing laboratory, and it is not classified as hazardous waste under U.S. Federal regulations (see Note 8.3 "Product Highlight: SYBR Safe™ DNA Gel Stain" in Section 8.4).
- SYBR® DX DNA blot stain (S7550, Section 8.5) allows the direct detection of DNA on filter membranes after Southern transfer, with sensitivity equivalent to that achieved with silver-enhanced gold staining.
- The CyQUANT® GR dye (C7026, Section 15.4) for quantitating cell proliferation can reliably detect the nucleic acids in as few as 50 cells.

Cell-Impermeant Cyanine Dimers: The TOTO® Family of Dyes

The patented cyanine dimer dyes listed in Table 8.2 are often referred to as the TOTO® family of dyes. These dyes are symmetric dimers of cyanine dyes with exceptional sensitivity for nucleic acids. This sensitivity is due to a high affinity for nucleic acids, in combination with a very high fluorescence enhancement and quantum yield upon binding. The unique physical characteristics of these dyes and some illustrative applications are discussed below. Specific applications are discussed in later sections of this chapter.

Each of the cyanine dimer dyes is available separately. For researchers designing new applications, the Nucleic Acid Stains Dimer Sampler Kit (N7565) provides samples of eight spectrally distinct analogs of the dimeric cyanine dyes for testing (Table 8.2).

High Affinity for Nucleic Acids

Appropriately designed dimers of nucleic acid–binding dyes have nucleic acid–binding affinities that are several orders of magnitude greater than those of their parent compounds.[1–3] For example, the intrinsic DNA binding affinity constants of ethidium bromide (E1305, E3565) and ethidium homodimer-1 (E1169) are reported to be 1.5×10^5 and 2×10^8 M^{-1}, respectively, in 0.2 M Na^+.[4] As a result, the dimeric cyanine dyes are among the highest-affinity fluorescent probes available for nucleic acid staining. For example, in the TOTO®-1 dimeric cyanine dye (T3600), the positively charged side chains of the TO-PRO®-1 monomeric cyanine dye (T3602, Figure 8.2) are covalently linked to form the TOTO®-1 molecule, with four positive charges (Figure 8.3). This linkage gives the TOTO®-1 dye a greatly enhanced affinity for nucleic acids — more than 100 times greater than that of the TO-PRO®-1 monomer. The TOTO®-1 dye exhibits a higher affinity for double-stranded DNA (dsDNA) than even the ethidium homodimers and also binds to both single-stranded DNA (ssDNA) and RNA. The extraordinary stability of TOTO®-1–nucleic acid complexes[2,5,6] ensures that the dye–DNA association remains stable, even during electrophoresis (Figure 8.4); thus, samples can be stained with nanomolar dye concentrations *prior to* electrophoresis,[7,8] thereby reducing the hazards inherent in handling large volumes of ethidium bromide staining solutions.[2,6,9] In contrast, the binding of thiazole orange — the parent compound of TOTO®-1 and TO-PRO®-1 — is rapidly reversible, limiting the dye's sensitivity and rendering its nucleic acid complex unstable to electrophoresis.[9]

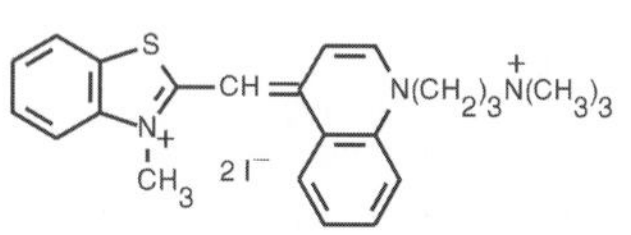

Figure 8.2 T3602 TO-PRO®-1 iodide (515/531).

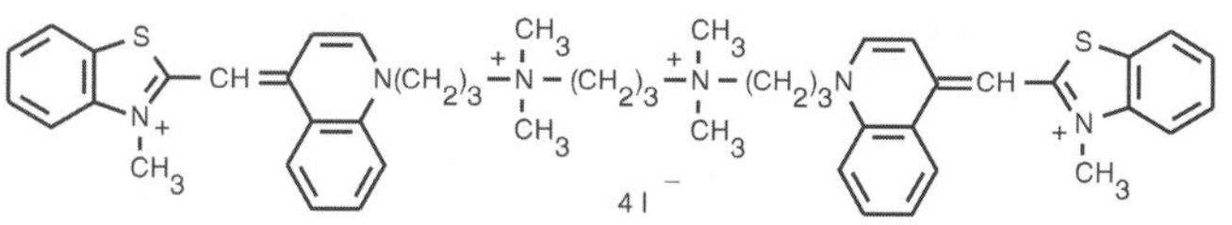

Figure 8.3 T3600 TOTO®-1 iodide (514/533).

High Fluorescence Enhancements and High Quantum Yields upon Binding to Nucleic Acids

In addition to their superior binding properties, TOTO®-1 dye and the other cyanine dimers are essentially nonfluorescent in the absence of nucleic acids and exhibit fluorescence enhancements upon DNA binding of 100- to 1000-fold,[5,10] which compares favorably with the fluorescence enhancement of thiazole orange upon DNA binding[11] (~3000-fold). Furthermore, the fluorescence quantum yields of the cyanine dimers bound to DNA are high (generally between 0.2 and 0.6), and their extinction coefficients are an order of magnitude greater than those of the ethidium homodimers.[5] This sensitivity is sufficient for detecting single molecules of labeled nucleic acids by optical imaging (Figure 8.5) and flow cytometry (Section 8.4) and for tracking dye-labeled virus particles in microbial communities and aquatic systems by fluorescence microscopy.[12,13] These dyes are generally considered to be cell impermeant, although their use to stain reticulocytes permeabilized by 5% DMSO has been reported.[14]

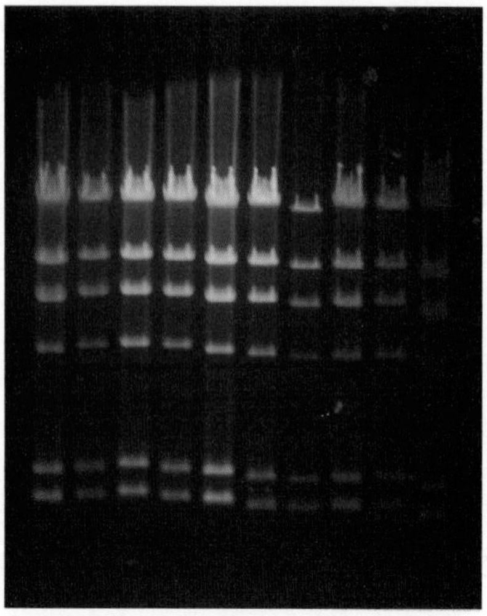

Figure 8.4 λ bacteriophage *Hin*dIII fragments were prestained with various nucleic acid dyes, run on a 0.7% agarose gel and visualized using a standard 300 nm UV transilluminator. From left to right, the dyes used were: POPO™-1 (P3580), BOBO™-1 (B3582), YOYO®-1 (Y3601), TOTO®-1 (T3600), JOJO™-1 (J11372), POPO™-3 (P3584), LOLO™-1 (L11376), BOBO™-3 (B3586), YOYO®-3 (Y3606) and TOTO®-3 (T3604) nucleic acid stains. The longest-wavelength stains are barely visible to the eye but can be detected with infrared-enhanced films and imaging equipment.

Modifying the Dimers Creates Compounds with Different Spectral Characteristics

Simply by changing the aromatic rings and the number of carbon atoms linking the cyanine monomers, we were able to synthesize an extended series of these dyes with different spectral characteristics (Table 8.2). Chemical modifications produce dramatic shifts in the absorption and emission spectra and reduce the quantum yields of the bound dyes but cause little or no change in their high affinity for DNA. The names of the dyes reflect their basic structure and spectral characteristics. For example, YOYO®-1 iodide (491/509) has one carbon atom bridging the aromatic rings of the oxacyanine dye and exhibits absorption/emission maxima of 491/509 nm when bound to dsDNA. The YOYO®-3 dye (612/631) — which differs from the YOYO®-1 dye only in the number of bridging carbon atoms — has absorption/emission maxima of 612/631 nm when bound to dsDNA. Fluorescence spectra for the POPO™, BOBO™, YOYO®, TOTO®, JOJO™ and LOLO™ dyes bound to dsDNA are shown in Figure 8.1. The spectra of these dyes at dye:base ratios of less than 1:1 are essentially the same for the corresponding dye–ssDNA and dye–RNA complexes. At higher dye:base ratios, however, ssDNA and RNA complexes of all of the monomethine ("-1") dyes of the TOTO® series and TO-PRO® series have red-shifted emissions, whereas corresponding complexes of the trimethine ("-3") analogs do not. Thus, the cyanine dimer family provides dyes with a broad range of spectral characteristics to match the output of almost any available excitation source. Some common light sources that match each dye are shown in Table 8.2.

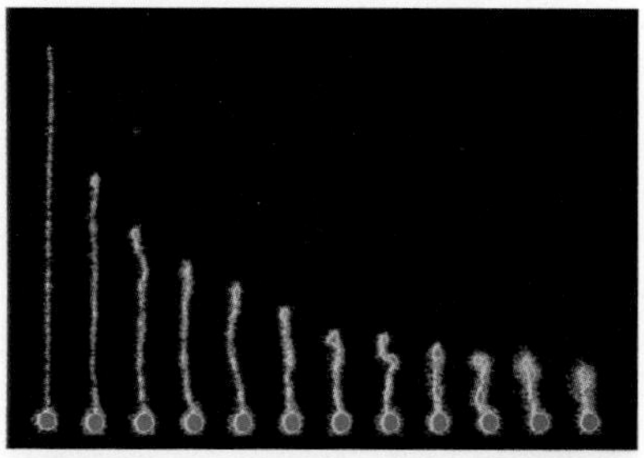

Figure 8.5 The relaxation of a single, 39 μm–long DNA molecule stained with YOYO®-1 iodide (Y3601) imaged at 4.5 second intervals. After the 1 μm polystyrene sphere was trapped with optical tweezers, the attached DNA was stretched to its full extension in a fluid flow and then allowed to relax upon stoppage of fluid flow due to its entropic elasticity (Science 264, 822 (1994)). The YOYO®-1 iodide–DNA complex is excited with the 488 nm spectral line of the argon-ion laser and visualized through a 515 nm longpass optical filter using a Hamamatsu SIT camera with image processing. Image contributed by Thomas Perkins, Stanford University.

Binding Modes of the Cyanine Dimers

The studies on cyanine dimer binding modes have focused on the YOYO®-1 and TOTO®-1 dyes. The YOYO®-1 dye was found to exhibit at least two distinct binding modes. At low dye:base pair ratios, the binding mode appears to consist primarily of bis-intercalation.[15–17] Each monomer unit intercalates between bases, with the benzazolium ring system sandwiched between the pyrimidines and the quinolinium ring between the purine rings, causing the helix to unwind.[17] The distortion in the local DNA structure caused by YOYO®-1 bis-intercalation has been observed by two-dimensional NMR spectroscopy.[18] At high dye:base pair ratios, a second, less well characterized mode of external binding begins to contribute.[15,16] Circular dichroism measurements also indicate a possible difference in the binding modes of the YOYO®-1 dye to ssDNA and dsDNA.[19] These data are consistent with our own results, including the observation that the fluorescence emission of the YOYO®-1 dye complex with nucleic acids shifts to longer wavelengths at high dye:base ratios upon binding to single-stranded nucleic acids and that the salt, ethanol and sodium dodecyl sulfate (SDS) sensitivity of YOYO®-1 dye binding to DNA is a function of the dye:base pair ratio.[20]

The TOTO®-1 dye is capable of bis-intercalation,[21] although it reportedly interacts with dsDNA and ssDNA with similarly high affinity.[1] NMR studies of TOTO®-1 dye interactions with a double-stranded 8-mer indicate that TOTO®-1 dye is a bis-intercalator, with the fluorophores intercalating between the bases and the linker region having interactions in the minor groove[22] (Figure 8.6). Binding of the dye partially unwinds the DNA,[22] distorting and elongating the helix.[23] However, another study using fluorescence polarization measurements suggests that an external binding mode, where the dipole of the dye molecule is aligned with the DNA grooves, may be more important.[24] The TOTO®-1 dye reportedly exhibits some sequence selectivity for the site 5′-CTAG-3′, although it will bind to almost any sequence in dsDNA.[25–28] The TOTO®-1 dye does not exhibit cooperative binding to DNA, suggesting that it may be a suitable dye for detecting nucleic acids in gels.[26]

The binding modes of the other members of the TOTO® dye series have also been partially characterized. Electrophoresis and fluorescence lifetime measurements have shown that the YOYO®-3 dye also appears to intercalate into DNA.[29] During application development, we have determined that staining of nucleic acids by the BOBO™-1 and POPO™-1 dyes is much faster (occurring within minutes) than staining by the YOYO®-1 or TOTO®-1 dyes (which can take several hours to reach equilibrium under the same experimental conditions),[21] indicating possible differences in their binding mechanisms. Fluorescence yield and lifetime measurements have been used to assess the base selectivity of an extensive series of these dyes.[10] Circular dichroism measurements have shown that bis-intercalation is the predominant binding mode for the POPO™-1 dye.[30]

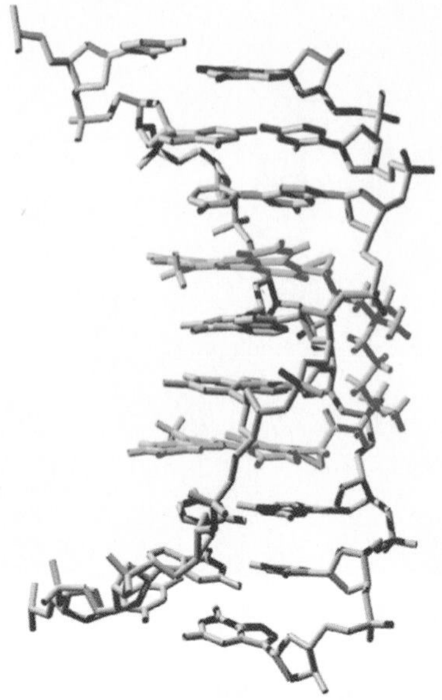

Figure 8.6 NMR solution structure of the TOTO®-1 dye (T3600) bound to DNA; the image was derived from data submitted to the Protein Data Bank (number PDB 108D, www.rcsb.org/pdb/, (Nucleic Acids Res 28, 235 (2000))). The NMR structure shows that TOTO®-1 binds to DNA through bis-intercalation (Biochemistry 34, 8542 (1995)).

Working with Cyanine Dimers

All of the dyes in the TOTO® series (Table 8.2) are supplied as 1 mM solutions in dimethylsulfoxide (DMSO), except for POPO™-3 (P3584), which is supplied as a 1 mM solution in dimethylformamide (DMF). These cationic dyes appear to be readily adsorbed out of aqueous solutions onto surfaces (particularly glass) but are very stable once complexed to nucleic acids. Several applications of these dyes for staining nucleic acids in solutions, gels, microarrays and cells are described in Section 8.3, Section 8.5, Section 8.6, Section 8.7 and Section 15.5.

Cell-Impermeant Cyanine Monomers: The TO-PRO® Family of Dyes

Our patented TO-PRO® family of dyes, all of which are listed in Table 8.2, each comprise a single cyanine dye and a cationic side chain (Figure 8.2). The eleven dyes in the TO-PRO® series are spectrally analogous to the corresponding dimeric cyanine dyes; however, with only two positive charges and one intercalating unit, the TO-PRO® dyes exhibit somewhat reduced affinity for nucleic acids relative to the dyes in the TOTO® series. Like their dimeric counterparts, these monomeric cyanine dyes are typically impermeant to cells,[31] although the YO-PRO®-1 (Y3603) dye has been shown to be permeant to apoptotic cells, providing a convenient indicator of apoptosis[32–35] (Section 15.5, Figure 15.81). YO-PRO®-1 has also been observed to pass through $P2X_7$ receptor channels of live cells.[36–38]

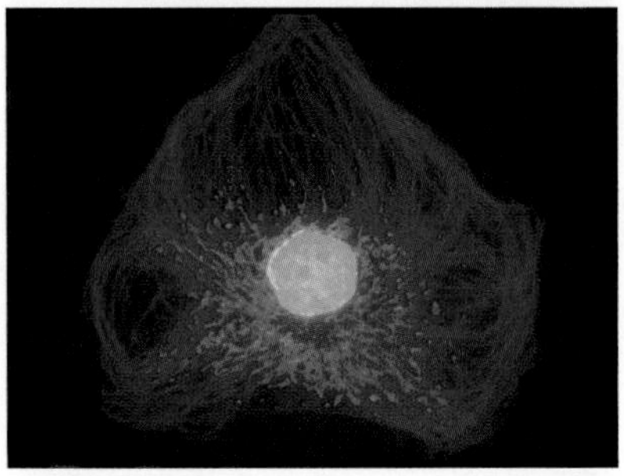

Figure 8.7 Bovine pulmonary artery endothelial cells (BPAEC) incubated with the fixable, mitochondrion-selective MitoTracker® Red CMXRos (M7512). After staining, the cells were formaldehyde-fixed, acetone-permeabilized, treated with DNase-free RNase and counterstained using SYTOX® Green nucleic acid stain (S7020) from our Cytological Nuclear Counterstain Kit (C7590). Microtubules were labeled with a mouse monoclonal anti–β-tubulin antibody, biotin-XX goat anti–mouse IgG antibody (B2763) and Cascade Blue® NeutrAvidin biotin-binding protein (A2663). This photograph was taken using multiple exposures through bandpass optical filters appropriate for Texas Red® dye, fluorescein and DAPI using a Nikon Labophot 2 microscope equipped with a Quadfluor epi-illumination system.

Spectral Characteristics of the Cyanine Dye Monomers

The TO-PRO® family of dyes retains all of the exceptional spectral properties of the dimeric cyanine dyes discussed above. The absorption and emission spectra of these monomeric cyanine dyes cover the visible and near-infrared spectrum (Table 8.2). They also have relatively narrow emission bandwidths, thus facilitating multicolor applications in imaging and flow cytometry. The YO-PRO®-1 (491/509) and TO-PRO®-1 (515/531) dyes are optimally excited by the 488 nm and 514 nm spectral lines of the argon-ion laser, respectively. In flow cytometric analysis, the TO-PRO®-3 (642/661) complex with nucleic acids has been excited directly by the red He–Ne laser[39] and indirectly by the argon-ion laser by using fluorescence resonance energy transfer (FRET) from co-bound propidium iodide[40] (see Note 1.2 "Technical Focus: Fluorescence Resonance Energy Transfer (FRET)" in Section 1.3). The TO-PRO®-3 complex with nucleic acids has also been detected in a flow cytometer equipped with an inexpensive 3 mW visible-wavelength diode laser that provides excitation at 635 nm.[41] Although the DNA-induced fluorescence enhancement of the TO-PRO®-5 dye (T7596) is not as large as that observed with our other cyanine dyes, its spectral characteristics (excitation/emission maxima ~745/770 nm) provide a unique alternative for multicolor applications.

Working with Cyanine Monomers

The binding affinity of the TO-PRO® series of dyes to dsDNA is lower than that of the TOTO® series of dyes but is still very high, with dissociation constants in the micromolar range.[42] TO-PRO® dyes also bind to RNA and ssDNA, although typically with somewhat lower fluorescence quantum yields. Fluorescence polarization studies indicate that the TO-PRO®-1 and PO-PRO™-1 dyes bind by intercalation, with unwinding angles of 2° and 31°, respectively.[30] Binding of these dyes to dsDNA is not sequence selective.[43] All dyes of the TO-PRO® series (Table 8.2) are supplied as 1 mM solutions in DMSO. Various applications of the TO-PRO® series of dyes for staining nucleic acids are described in Section 8.3, Section 8.5, Section 8.6 and Section 15.5.

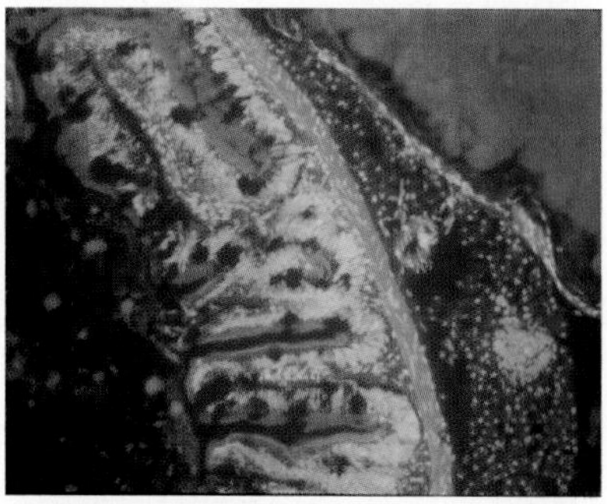

Figure 8.8 Adult zebrafish gut cryosections that have been incubated with BODIPY® TR-X phallacidin (B7464), followed by the SYTOX® Green nucleic acid stain (S7020), and then dehydrated and mounted. The image was obtained by taking multiple exposures through bandpass optical filter sets appropriate for fluorescein and the Texas Red® dye.

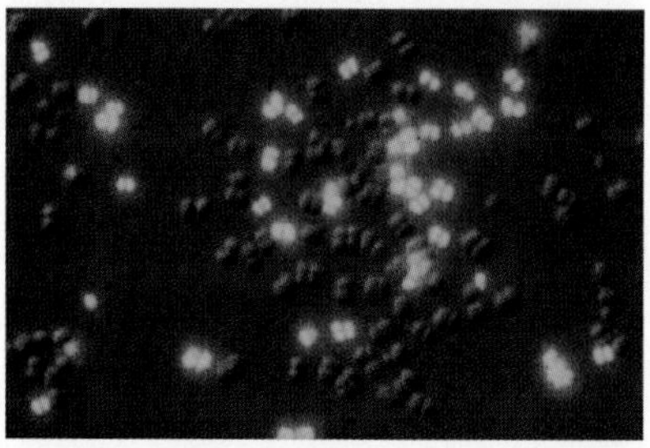

Figure 8.9 A mixed population of live and isopropyl alcohol–killed *Micrococcus luteus* stained with SYTOX® Blue nucleic acid stain (S11348), which does not penetrate intact plasma membranes. Dead cells exhibit bright blue-fluorescent staining. The image was acquired using a longpass optical filter set appropriate for the Cascade Blue® dye.

Cell-Impermeant SYTOX® Dyes for Dead-Cell Staining

Our three SYTOX® nucleic acid stains (Table 8.2) are cell-impermeant cyanine dyes that are particularly good dead-cell stains. These SYTOX® stains are included in our RediPlate™ 96 nucleic acid stain sampler microplate (R32715), which is described below.

SYTOX® Green Stain

The SYTOX® Green nucleic acid stain (S7020) is a high-affinity nucleic acid stain that easily penetrates cells with compromised plasma membranes and yet will not cross the membranes of live cells. It is especially useful for staining both gram-positive and gram-negative bacteria — and probably virus particles[13,44] — where an exceptionally bright signal is required. Following brief incubation with the SYTOX® Green stain, dead cells fluoresce bright green when excited with the 488 nm spectral line of the argon-ion laser or with any other 450–500 nm source. No wash steps are required, since all of the SYTOX® dyes are essentially nonfluorescent in aqueous medium. Unlike the DAPI or Hoechst dyes, the SYTOX® Green nucleic acid stain shows little base selectivity. These properties, combined with its ~1000-fold fluorescence enhancement upon nucleic acid binding and high quantum yield, make our SYTOX® Green stain a simple and quantitative single-step dead-cell indicator for use with epifluorescence and confocal laser-scanning microscopes, fluorometers, fluorescence microplate readers and flow cytometers (Figure 15.11). The SYTOX® Green dye is included as a dead-cell stain in our Vybrant® Apoptosis Assay Kits #1, #8, #9 and #10 (V13240, V35112, V35113, V35114; Section 15.5), in our ViaGram™ Red+ Bacterial Gram Stain and Viability Kit (V7023, Section 15.3) and in combination with C_{12}-resazurin in our LIVE/DEAD® Cell Vitality Assay Kit (L34951, Section 15.3).

The SYTOX® Green nucleic acid stain can be used with blue- and red-fluorescent labels for multiparameter analyses (Figure 8.7). It is also possible to combine the SYTOX® Green nucleic acid stain with the SYTO® 17 red-fluorescent nucleic acid stain (S7579) for two-color visualization of dead and live cells (Section 15.3). Because the SYTOX® Green nucleic acid stain is an excellent DNA counterstain for chromosome labeling and for fixed cells and tissues (Figure 8.8), we have incorporated it into our Cytological Nuclear Counterstain Kit (C7590), which is discussed in Section 8.6.

SYTOX® Blue Stain

Our SYTOX® Blue stain (S11348) is a high-affinity nucleic acid stain that typically penetrates only cells with compromised plasma membranes (Figure 8.9). The SYTOX® Blue stain labels both DNA and RNA with extremely bright fluorescence centered near 480 nm (Figure 8.119). The absorption maximum of the nucleic acid–bound SYTOX® Blue stain (~431 nm) permits very efficient fluorescence excitation by the 436 nm spectral line of the mercury-arc lamp. Unlike many blue-fluorescent dyes, the SYTOX® Blue stain is also efficiently excited by tungsten–halogen lamps and other sources that have relatively poor emission in the UV portion of the spectrum. The brightness of the SYTOX® Blue stain allows sensitive detection with fluorometers, microplate readers, arc-lamp–equipped flow cytometers and epifluorescence microscopes, including those not equipped with UV-pass optics.

In a side-by-side comparison with the SYTOX® Green stain, the SYTOX® Blue stain yielded identical results when quantitating membrane-compromised bacterial cells. Furthermore, like the SYTOX® Green stain, the SYTOX® Blue stain does not interfere with bacterial cell growth. Because their emission spectra overlap somewhat, we have found that it is not ideal to use the SYTOX® Blue stain and green-fluorescent dyes together; however, fluorescence emission of the SYTOX® Blue stain permits clear discrimination from orange- or red-fluorescent probes, facilitating the development of multicolor assays with minimal spectral overlap between signals.

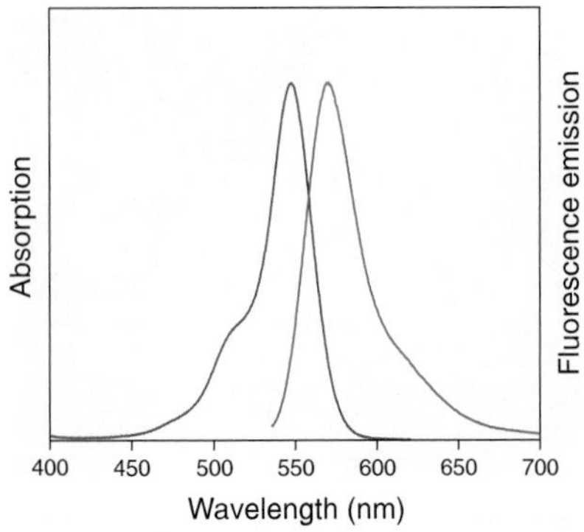

Figure 8.10 Absorption and fluorescence emission spectra of SYTOX® Orange nucleic acid stain bound to DNA.

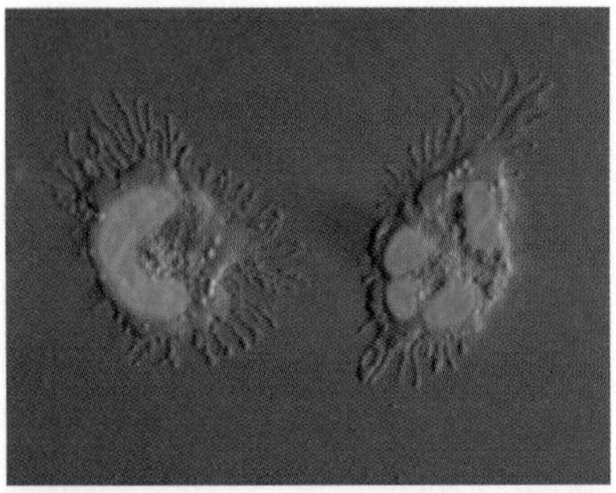

Figure 8.11 Human neutrophil nuclei stained with SYTO® 13 live-cell nucleic acid stain (S7575). The photo was acquired using an optical filter appropriate for fluorescein, and differential interference contrast (DIC) sequentially in a Nikon Eclipse E800 microscope.

SYTOX® Orange Stain

Our SYTOX® Orange nucleic acid stain (S11368) clearly distinguishes dead bacteria, yeast or mammalian cells. The SYTOX® Orange stain has shorter-wavelength emission, as compared with propidium iodide, and its spectra more closely match the rhodamine filter set (Figure 8.10). In addition, the SYTOX® Orange stain has a much higher molar absorptivity (extinction coefficient) than propidium iodide and a far greater fluorescence enhancement upon binding DNA, suggesting that it may have a higher sensitivity as a dead-cell stain or as a nuclear counterstain. The SYTOX® Orange stain was shown to be the best dye for DNA fragment sizing by single-molecule flow cytometry when using a Nd:YAG excitation source, with a 450-fold enhancement upon binding to dsDNA.[45]

Cell-Permeant Cyanine Dyes: The SYTO® Nucleic Acid Stains

SYTO® Nucleic Acid Stains for DNA and RNA

The numerous patented SYTO® dyes in Table 8.3 are somewhat lower-affinity nucleic acid stains that passively diffuse through the membranes of most cells. These UV- or visible light–excitable dyes can be used to stain RNA and DNA in both live and dead eukaryotic cells, as well as in gram-positive and gram-negative bacteria. Molecular Probes has synthesized a large number of SYTO® dyes (Table 8.3) that share several important characteristics:

- Permeability to virtually all cell membranes, including mammalian cells and bacteria (Chapter 15)
- High molar absorptivity, with extinction coefficients greater than 50,000 $cm^{-1}M^{-1}$ at visible absorption maxima
- Extremely low intrinsic fluorescence, with quantum yields typically less than 0.01 when not bound to nucleic acids
- Quantum yields typically greater than 0.4 when bound to nucleic acids

Available as blue-, green-, orange- or red-fluorescent dyes, these novel SYTO® stains provide researchers with visible light–excitable dyes for labeling DNA and RNA in live cells (Figure 8.11). The SYTO® dyes may also be useful for nucleic acid detection in solution, in electrophoretic gels, on blots, on microarrays and in several other assays. SYTO® dyes differ from each other in one or more characteristics, including cell permeability, fluorescence enhancement upon binding nucleic acids, excitation and emission spectra (Table 8.3), DNA/RNA selectivity and binding affinity. The SYTO® dyes are compatible with a variety of fluorescence-based instruments that use either laser excitation or a conventional broadband illumination source (e.g., mercury- and xenon-arc lamps).

The SYTO® dyes can stain both DNA and RNA. In most cases, the fluorescence wavelengths and emission intensities are similar for solution measurements of DNA or RNA binding. Exceptions that we know of include the SYTO® 12 and SYTO® 14 dyes, which are about twice as fluorescent when complexed with RNA as with DNA, and SYTO® 16, which is about twice as fluorescent on DNA than RNA. Consequently, the SYTO® dyes do not act exclusively as nuclear stains in live cells and should not be equated in this regard with DNA-selective compounds such as DAPI or the Hoechst 33258 and Hoechst 33342 dyes, which readily stain cell nuclei at low concentrations in most cells. SYTO® dye–stained eukaryotic cells will generally show diffuse cytoplasmic staining, as well as nuclear staining. The SYTO® 14 dye (S7576) has been used to visualize the translocation of endogenous RNA found in polyribosome complexes in living cells.[46,47] Particularly intense staining of intranuclear bodies is frequently observed. Because these dyes are generally cell permeant and most of the SYTO® dyes contain a net positive charge at neutral pH, they may also stain mitochondria. In addition, the SYTO® dyes will stain most gram-positive and gram-negative bacterial cells. Dead yeast cells are brightly stained with the SYTO® dyes, and live yeast cells typically exhibit staining of both the mitochondria and the nucleus. Some of the SYTO® dyes have been reported to be useful for detecting apoptosis[48,49] (Section 15.5), and dyes structurally similar to the SYTO® dyes have been used to detect multidrug-resistant cells[50] (Section 15.6). The red-fluorescent SYTO® dyes are proving useful as counterstains (Section 8.6) when combined with green-fluorescent antibodies (Section 7.2), lectins (Section 7.7) or the cell-impermeant SYTOX® Green nucleic acid stain (see above). Several of the green-fluorescent SYTO® dyes are excellent nuclear counterstains. We anticipate that many more applications will be found for these unique nucleic acid stains.

All of the patented SYTO® dyes are available separately (Table 8.3), and several SYTO® dyes are included in our LIVE/DEAD® Kits (Section 15.3, Table 15.2) and in our Bacteria Counting Kit (B7277, Section 15.4). The green-fluorescent SYBR® 14 dye, a component of our LIVE/DEAD® Sperm Viability Kit (L7011, Section 15.3), is also in the SYTO® family of dyes. To facilitate testing the SYTO® dyes in new applications, we offer several sampler kits containing sample sizes of SYTO® dyes in each color set (Table 8.3), as well as the RediPlate™ 96 nucleic acid stain sampler microplate (R32715, described below), which includes 36 different SYTO® dyes. With each purchase of a sampler kit or individual reagent we include a detailed product information sheet, describing the spectral properties of the dyes, to assist the researcher in designing staining protocols. The recommended dye concentration for cell staining depends on the assay and may vary widely but is typically 1–20 µM for bacteria, 1–100 µM for yeast and 10 nM–5 µM for other eukaryotes.

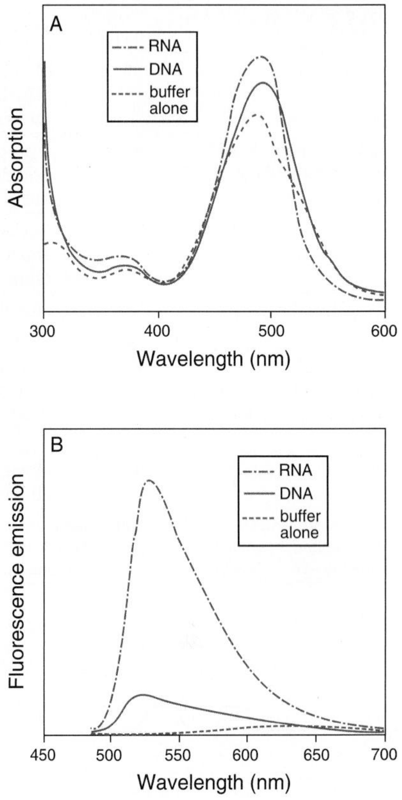

Figure 8.12 Relative absorption (A) and fluorescence emission (B) spectra of SYTO® RNASelect™ green-fluorescent cell stain (S32703) in the presence of *Escherichia coli* RNA or *E. coli* DNA, or in buffer alone.

SYTO® RNASelect™ Green-Fluorescent Cell Stain

SYTO® RNASelect™ green-fluorescent cell stain (S32703, Section 15.2) is a cell-permeant nucleic acid stain that selectively stains RNA (Figure 15.18). Although virtually nonfluorescent in the absence of nucleic acids, the SYTO® RNASelect™ stain exhibits bright green fluorescence when bound to RNA (absorption/emission maxima ~490/530 nm), but only a weak fluorescent signal when bound to DNA (Figure 8.12). Filter sets that are suitable for imaging cells labeled with fluorescein (FITC) will work well for imaging cells stained with SYTO® RNASelect™ stain (Figure 15.19, Figure 15.20).

Chemically Reactive Cyanine Dyes

The amine-reactive succinimidyl esters of the SYBR® 101, SYBR® 102 and SYBR® 103 dyes (S21500, S21501, S21502) can be conjugated to peptides, proteins, drugs, polymeric matrices and biomolecules with primary amine groups. The conjugates are expected to be essentially nonfluorescent until they are able to complex with nucleic acids, resulting in strong green fluorescence. Thus, they may be useful for studies of nucleic acid binding to various biomolecules, such as DNA-binding proteins. It is also possible that the fluorescence enhancement upon nucleic acid binding of reactive SYBR® dye conjugates will be useful for monitoring their transport into the nucleus. SYBR® dye conjugates of solid or semisolid matrices (such as microspheres, magnetic particles or various resins) may be useful for detection or affinity isolation of nucleic acids.

The reactive SYBR® dyes may also be conjugated to amine-modified nucleic acids. Although it is possible that the SYBR® dyes may show some fluorescence when conjugated to amine groups on nucleic acids, they may be useful for developing homogeneous hybridization assays in which a specific sequence can be quantitated in solution without the need to separate bound and free probes. For example, a similar reactive nucleic acid stain has been used to label peptide–nucleic acid conjugates (PNA) for use as probes in real-time PCR. The labeled PNA probes exhibited a fluorescence increase upon hybridization to their complementary sequence and have been used to identify a single-base mismatch in a 10-base target sequence.[51,52]

RediPlate™ 96 Nucleic Acid Stain Sampler Microplate

The SYTO® dyes are relatively low-affinity nucleic acid stains that passively diffuse through the membranes of most cells. Like the structurally similar SYBR® Gold, SYBR® Green and SYBR Safe™ nucleic acid stains (Section 8.4), these UV- or visible light–excitable dyes can be used to stain RNA and DNA in both live and dead eukaryotic cells, as well as in gram-positive and gram-negative bacteria.[53–56] The SYTO® dyes may also be useful for nucleic acid detection in solution, in electrophoretic gels, on blots, on microarrays and in many other applications.[57] Because of their relatively low nucleic acid–binding affinity, SYTO® dyes stain a wider variety of cellular targets than do dyes such as Hoechst 33342, YO-PRO®-1 and YOYO®-1, and the cellular staining behavior of SYTO® dyes can be variable and difficult to predict *a priori*. Consequently, extensive dye screening is beneficial in developing new applications for these dyes.

The RediPlate™ 96 nucleic acid stain sampler microplate (R32715) is designed to facilitate the screening of nucleic acid stains for new applications by providing samples of 36 different SYTO® dyes predispensed in a 96-well microplate. The plate also contains samples of the SYBR® Green I, SYBR® Green II and PicoGreen® dyes. Although these latter three dyes were primarily developed

Table 8.5 — General characteristics of the dyes provided in the RediPlate™ 96 nucleic acid stain sampler microplate (R32715)

Type of Nucleic Acid Stain	Number of Dyes *	Characteristics
SYTO® dyes	36	Membrane-permeant nucleic acid–binding dyes in a variety of fluorescent colors
SYBR® Green I, SYBR® Green II and PicoGreen® dyes	3	Dyes primarily used for nucleic acid detection in gels and for DNA quantitation in solution
SYBR® 101 and SYBR® 103 amine-reactive dyes	2	Nucleic acid–binding dyes with amine-reactive succinimidyl ester groups †
Hoechst 33342 dye	1	Blue-fluorescent, membrane-permeant nuclear stain
SYTOX® Blue, SYTOX® Green, SYTOX® Orange and propidium iodide dyes	4	Membrane-impermeant nucleic acid–binding dyes for detecting dead cells
Hexidium iodide dye	4	Membrane-permeant analog of ethidium bromide

* Duplicate samples of 47 dyes are provided, plus two empty wells for fluorescence background measurements, making up the total of 96 wells. † Amine reactivity of these dyes may diminish during prolonged storage of the microplate.

for detecting nucleic acids in electrophoretic gels or in solution, they have also proven useful in cellular staining applications.[58,59] Also included are samples of the amine-reactive SYBR® 101 and SYBR® 103 nucleic acid–binding dyes. Finally, samples of six other nucleic acid–binding dyes (Hoechst 33342, SYTOX® Green, SYTOX® Orange, SYTOX® Blue, propidium iodide and hexidium iodide) are provided for indicating cell viability and as references for the cellular staining behavior of the SYTO® dyes.

Each RediPlate™ 96 nucleic acid stain sampler microplate consists of one 96-well microplate containing duplicate samples of 47 different nucleic acid–binding dyes and two empty wells for fluorescence background measurements. The amount of dye in each well is calibrated to yield a concentration of 20 µM after solubilization in 100 µL of a suitable solvent, typically dimethylsulfoxide (DMSO) or aqueous buffer. The general characteristics of the dyes provided in the RediPlate™ 96 nucleic acid stain sampler microplate are summarized in Table 8.5 and described in detail in the accompanying product information sheet.

Phenanthridines and Acridines: Classic Intercalating Dyes

Cell-Impermeant Ethidium Bromide and Propidium Iodide

Ethidium bromide (EtBr, E1305; E3565; Figure 8.13) and propidium iodide (PI, P1304MP; P3566; FluoroPure™ Grade, P21493; Figure 8.14) are structurally similar phenanthridinium intercalators. PI is more soluble in water and less membrane permeant than EtBr, although both dyes are generally excluded from viable cells. EtBr and PI can be excited with mercury- or xenon-arc lamps or with the argon-ion laser, making them suitable for fluorescence microscopy, confocal laser-scanning microscopy (Figure 8.15), flow cytometry and fluorometry. These dyes bind with little or no sequence preference at a stoichiometry of one dye per 4–5 base pairs of DNA.[60] Excitation of the EtBr–DNA complex may result in photobleaching of the dye and single-strand breaks.[61] Both EtBr and PI also bind to RNA, necessitating treatment with nucleases to distinguish between RNA and DNA. Once these dyes are bound to nucleic acids, their fluorescence is enhanced ~10-fold, their excitation maxima are shifted ~30–40 nm to the red and their emission maxima are shifted ~15 nm to the blue[62] (Figure 8.16, Table 8.4). Although their molar absorptivities (extinction coefficients) are relatively low, EtBr and PI exhibit sufficiently large Stokes shifts to allow simultaneous detection of nuclear DNA and fluorescein-labeled antibodies, provided that the proper optical filters are used (Table 23.9).

PI is commonly used as a nuclear or chromosome counterstain (Section 8.6, Figure 8.15) and as a stain for dead cells (Section 15.2, Figure 15.17). EtBr currently is the most commonly used general nucleic acid gel stain (Section 8.4). However, our SYBR® Gold and SYBR® Green nucleic acid gel stains are far more sensitive than EtBr, and the SYBR® Green I stain has been shown to be significantly less mutagenic than EtBr by Ames testing[63] (Section 8.4). Furthermore, our SYBR Safe™ DNA gel stain (Section 8.4), which is about twice as sensitive as EtBr, is less mutagenic than EtBr in the standard Ames test, has tested negative in three mammalian cell–based assays for genotoxicity and is not classified as hazardous waste under U.S. Federal regulations (see Note 8.3 "Product Highlight: SYBR Safe™ DNA Gel Stain" in Section 8.4). EtBr and PI are potent mutagens and must be handled with extreme care. Solutions containing EtBr or PI can be decontaminated by filtration through activated charcoal, which is then incinerated, thus providing an economical decontamination procedure.[64] Alternatively, the dyes can be completely degraded in buffer by reaction with sodium nitrite and hypophosphorous acid.[65] EtBr and PI are offered as solids (E1305, P1304MP; FluoroPure™ Grade, P21493) as well as in aqueous solution (E3565, P3566), enabling researchers to avoid contact with the mutagenic powders.

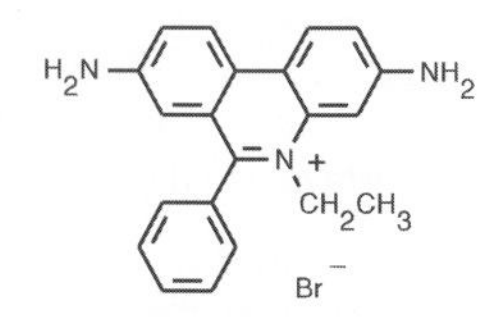

Figure 8.13 E1305 ethidium bromide.

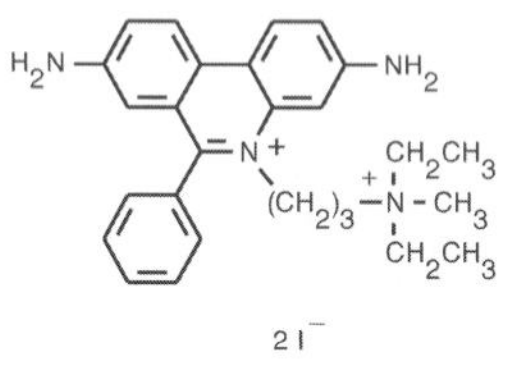

Figure 8.14 P1304MP propidium iodide.

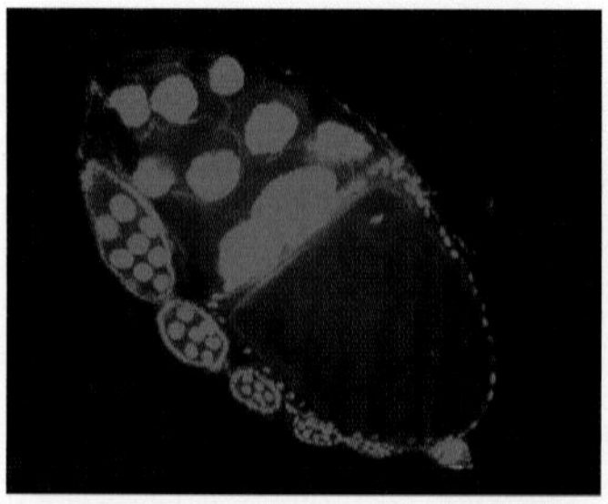

Figure 8.15 Day 10 of development of a *Drosophila* ovarian egg chamber assembly line. The nuclei of follicle and nurse cells were labeled with propidium iodide (P1304MP, P3566, P21493) and visualized by confocal laser-scanning microscopy using excitation by the 568 nm spectral line of an Ar–Kr laser. Image contributed by Sandra Orsulic, University of North Carolina at Chapel Hill.

Cell-Permeant Hexidium Iodide

Molecular Probes' patented hexidium iodide reagent (H7593) is a moderately lipophilic phenanthridinium dye (Figure 8.17) that is permeant to mammalian cells and selectively stains almost all gram-positive bacteria in the presence of gram-negative bacteria. Our LIVE *Bac*Light™ Bacterial Gram Stain Kit and ViaGram™ Red+ Bacterial Gram Stain and Viability Kit (L7005, V7023; Section 15.3) use hexidium iodide for the discrimination of bacterial gram sign (Figure 15.53). Hexidium iodide yields slightly shorter-wavelength spectra upon DNA binding than our ethidium or propidium dyes. Generally, both the cytoplasm and nuclei of eukaryotic cells show staining with hexidium iodide; however, mitochondria and nucleoli may also be stained.

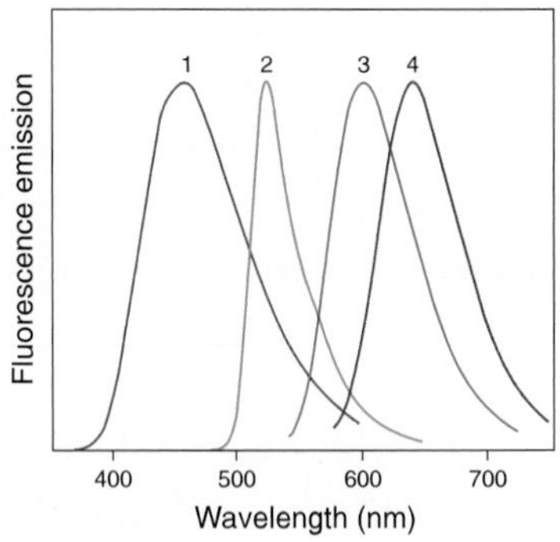

Figure 8.16 Normalized fluorescence emission spectra of DNA-bound **1)** Hoechst 33258 (H1398, H3569, H21491), **2)** acridine orange (A1301, A3568), **3)** ethidium bromide (E1305, E3565) and **4)** 7-aminoactinomycin D (A1310).

Cell-Permeant Dihydroethidium (Hydroethidine)

Dihydroethidium (also known as hydroethidine) is a chemically reduced ethidium derivative (Figure 15.23) that is permeant to live cells and exhibits blue fluorescence in the cytoplasm. Many viable cells oxidize the probe to ethidium, which then fluoresces red upon DNA intercalation[66–68] (Figure 18.14). Dihydroethidium, which is somewhat air sensitive, is available in a 25 mg vial (D1168) or specially packaged in 10 vials of 1 mg each (D11347); the special packaging is strongly recommended when small quantities of the dye will be used at a time. Dihydroethidium is also available as a 5 mM stabilized solution in dimethylsulfoxide (D23107).

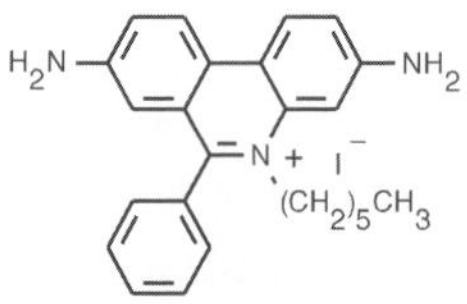

Figure 8.17 H7593 hexidium iodide.

High-Affinity Ethidium Homodimers

Ethidium homodimer-1 (EthD-1, E1169; Figure 8.18) and ethidium homodimer-2 (EthD-2, E3599; Figure 8.19) strongly bind to dsDNA, ssDNA, RNA and oligonucleotides with a significant fluorescence enhancement (>40-fold). EthD-1 also binds with high affinity to triplex nucleic acid structures.[69] One molecule of EthD-1 binds per four base pairs in dsDNA,[4] and the dye's intercalation is not sequence selective.[70] It was originally reported that only one of the two phenanthridinium rings of EthD-1 is bound at a time;[4] subsequent reports indicate that bis-intercalation appears to be involved in staining both double-stranded and triplex nucleic acids.[21,69]

The spectra and other properties of the EthD-1 and EthD-2 dimers are almost identical (Figure 8.20). However, the DNA affinity of EthD-2 is about twice that of EthD-1. EthD-2 is also about twice as fluorescent bound to dsDNA than to RNA. Because both EthD-1 and EthD-2 can be excited with UV light or by the 488 nm spectral line of the argon-ion laser, either dye can be used in combination with the TOTO®-1, YOYO®-1 or SYTOX® Green nucleic acid stains for multicolor experiments (Figure 8.21). The ethidium homodimer dyes are impermeant to cells with intact membranes, a property that makes EthD-1 useful as a dead-cell indicator in our LIVE/DEAD® Viability/Cytotoxicity Kit (L3224, Section 15.3, Figure 15.16) and EthD-2 (under our DEAD Red™ trademark name) a suitable dead-cell indicator in our LIVE/DEAD® Reduced Biohazard Cell Viability Kit #1 (L7013, Section 15.3, Figure 15.26, Figure 15.28). These dyes have also been

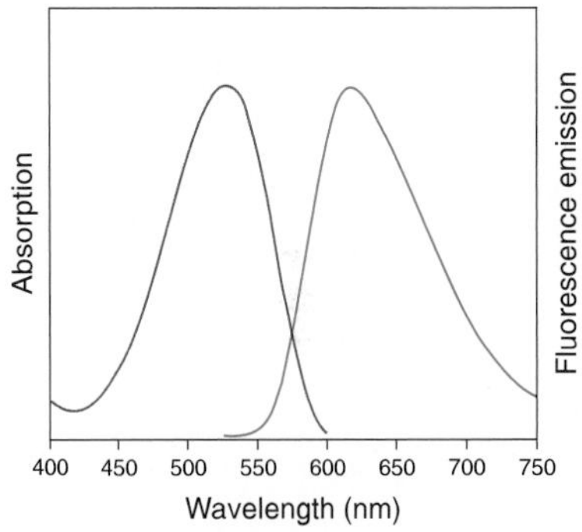

Figure 8.20 Absorption and fluorescence emission spectra of ethidium homodimer-1 bound to DNA.

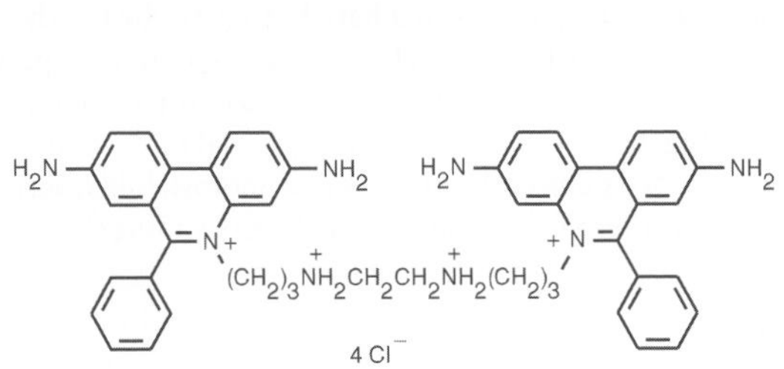

Figure 8.18 E1169 ethidium homodimer-1 (EthD-1).

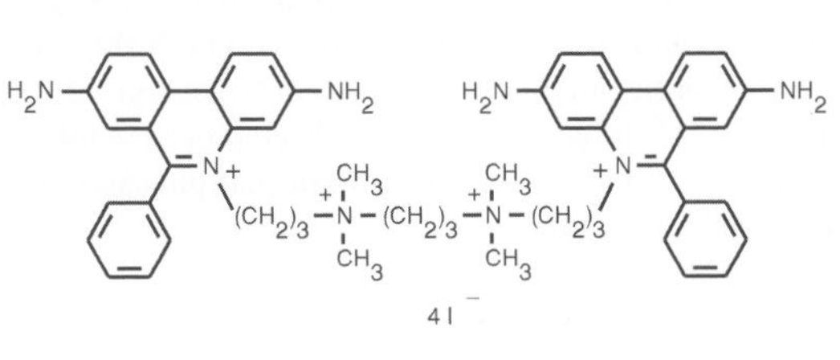

Figure 8.19 E3599 ethidium homodimer-2 (EthD-2).

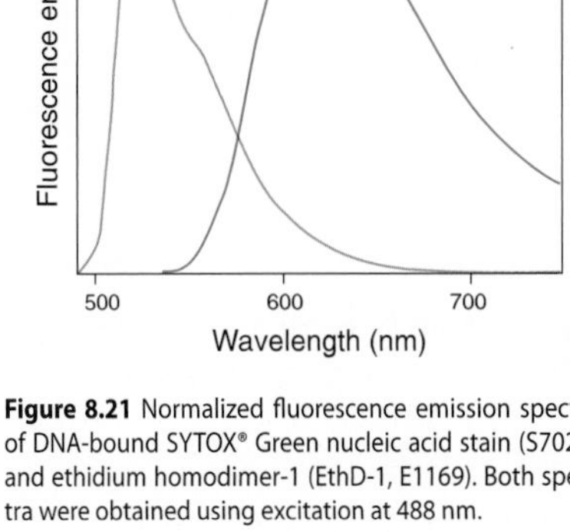

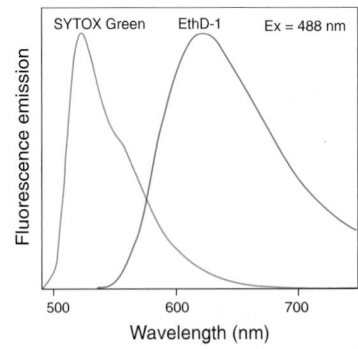

Figure 8.21 Normalized fluorescence emission spectra of DNA-bound SYTOX® Green nucleic acid stain (S7020) and ethidium homodimer-1 (EthD-1, E1169). Both spectra were obtained using excitation at 488 nm.

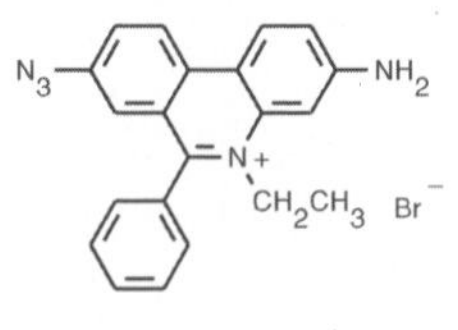

Figure 8.22 E1374 ethidium monoazide bromide (EMA).

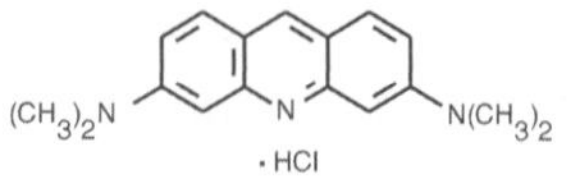

Figure 8.23 A1301 acridine orange.

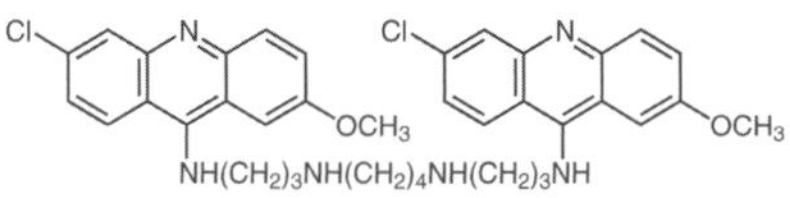

Figure 8.24 A666 acridine homodimer (bis-(6-chloro-2-methoxy-9-acridinyl)spermine).

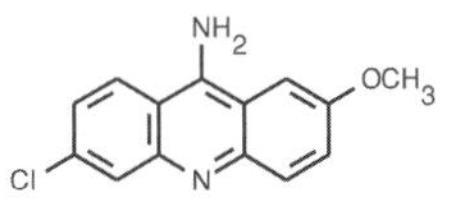

Figure 8.25 A1324 9-amino-6-chloro-2-methoxyacridine (ACMA).

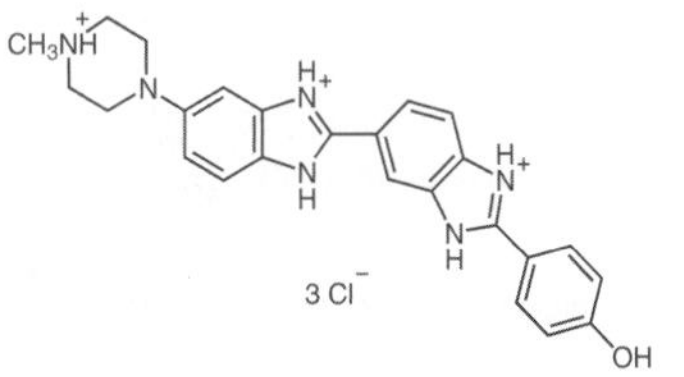

Figure 8.26 H1398 Hoechst 33258, pentahydrate (bis-benzimide).

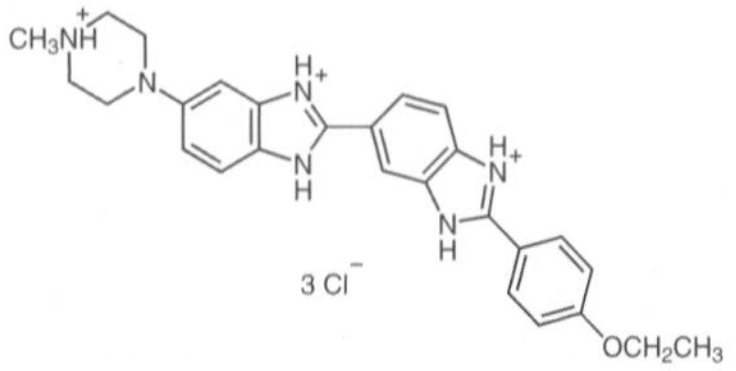

Figure 8.27 H1399 Hoechst 33342, trihydrochloride, trihydrate.

used to detect DNA in solution,[70] although they are not as sensitive or as easy to use as our PicoGreen® dsDNA quantitation reagent (Section 8.3).

Ethidium Monoazide: A Photocrosslinking Reagent

Nucleic acids can be covalently photolabeled by various DNA intercalators. Ethidium monoazide (E1374, Figure 8.22) is a fluorescent photoaffinity label that, after photolysis, binds covalently to nucleic acids both in solution and in cells that have compromised membranes.[71–75] The quantum yield for covalent photolabeling by ethidium monoazide is unusually high (>0.4).

The membrane-impermeant ethidium monoazide is reported to only label dead cells and is therefore particularly useful for assaying the viability of pathogenic cells (Section 15.2). A mixed population of live and dead cells incubated with this reagent can be illuminated with a visible-light source, washed, fixed and then analyzed in order to determine the viability of the cells at the time of photolysis.[76] This method not only reduces some of the hazards inherent in working with pathogenic cells, but also is compatible with immunocytochemical analyses requiring fixation. We have developed alternative assays for determining the original viability of fixed samples and provide these in four LIVE/DEAD® Reduced Biohazard Cell Viability Kits (L7013, L23101, L23102, L23105), which are described in Section 15.3.

In addition to its utility as a viability indicator, ethidium monoazide has been used to irreversibly label the DNA of *Candida albicans* in order to investigate phagocytic capacity of leukocytes.[77] Ethidium monoazide has also been employed to "footprint" drug-binding sites on DNA,[78] to probe for ethidium-binding sites in DNA[79] and transfer RNA (tRNA)[74] and to selectively photoinactivate the expression of genes in vertebrate cells.[80]

Acridine Orange: A Dual-Fluorescence Nucleic Acid Stain

Molecular Probes offers highly purified, flow cytometry–grade acridine orange, a dye that interacts with DNA and RNA by intercalation or electrostatic attractions. In condensed chromatin, however, the bulk of DNA is packed in a way that does not allow efficient acridine orange intercalation.[81] This cationic dye (Figure 8.23) has green fluorescence with an emission maximum at 525 nm when bound to DNA. Upon association with RNA, its emission is shifted to ~650 nm (red fluorescence).

Acridine orange is available as a solid (A1301) and, for ease of handling, as a 10 mg/mL aqueous solution (A3568).

AT-Selective Acridine Homodimer

The water-soluble acridine homodimer bis-(6-chloro-2-methoxy-9-acridinyl)spermine (A666, Figure 8.24) is one of several acridine dimers that have been described in the literature. This dye has extremely high affinity for AT-rich regions of nucleic acids, making it particularly useful for chromosome banding[82,83] (Section 8.6). Acridine homodimer emits a blue-green fluorescence when bound to DNA, yielding fluorescence that is proportional to the fourth power of the AT base-pair content.[84] Because of its greater brightness and photostability, acridine homodimer has been recommended as an alternative to quinacrine for Q banding.[82]

AT-Selective ACMA

ACMA (9-amino-6-chloro-2-methoxyacridine, A1324, Figure 8.25) is a DNA intercalator that selectively binds to poly(d(A-T)) with a binding affinity constant of 2×10^5 M^{-1} at pH 7.4.[85,86] Excitation of the ACMA–DNA complex (excitation/emission maxima ~419/483 nm) is possible with most UV-light sources, making it compatible for use with both shorter- and longer-wavelength dyes. ACMA also apparently binds to membranes in the energized state and becomes quenched if a pH gradient forms.[87] It has been extensively employed to follow cation and anion movement across membranes[87–90] and to study the proton-pumping activity of various membrane-bound ATPases[91,92] (Section 20.3).

Indoles and Imidazoles: Classic Minor Groove–Binding Dyes

DNA-Selective Hoechst Dyes

The bisbenzimide dyes — Hoechst 33258 (Figure 8.26), Hoechst 33342 (Figure 8.27) and Hoechst 34580 — are cell membrane–permeant, minor groove–binding DNA stains that fluoresce bright blue upon binding to DNA. Hoechst 33342 has slightly higher membrane permeability than Hoechst 33258,[62] but both dyes are quite soluble in water (up to 2% solutions can be prepared) and relatively nontoxic. Hoechst 34580[93] (H21486) has somewhat longer-wavelength spectra than the other Hoechst dyes when bound to nucleic acids. These Hoechst dyes, which can be excited with the UV spectral lines of the argon-ion laser and by most conventional fluorescence excitation sources, exhibit relatively large Stokes shifts (Figure 8.28) (excitation/emission maxima ~350/460 nm), making them suitable for multicolor labeling experiments. The Hoechst 33258 and Hoechst 33342 dyes have complex, pH-dependent spectra when not bound to nucleic acids, with a much higher fluorescence quantum yield at pH 5 than at pH 8. Their fluorescence is also enhanced by surfactants such as sodium dodecyl sulfate[94] (SDS). These dyes appear to show a wide spectrum of sequence-dependent DNA affinities and bind with sufficient strength to poly(d(A-T)) sequences that they can displace several known DNA intercalators.[95] They also exhibit multiple binding modes and distinct fluorescence emission spectra that are dependent on dye:base pair ratios.[96] Hoechst dyes are used in many cellular applications, including cell-cycle and apoptosis studies (Section 15.4, Section 15.5) and they are common nuclear counterstains (Section 8.6). Hoechst 33258, which is selectively toxic to malaria parasites,[97] is also useful for flow-cytometric screening of blood samples for malaria parasites and for assessing their susceptibility to drugs;[98–100] however, some of our SYTO® dyes are likely to provide superior performance in these assays.

The Hoechst 33258 and Hoechst 33342 dyes are available as solids (H1398, H1399), as guaranteed high-purity solids (FluoroPure™ Grade; H21491, H21492) and, for ease of handling, as 10 mg/mL aqueous solutions (H3569, H3570). The Hoechst 34580 dye is available as a solid (H21486).

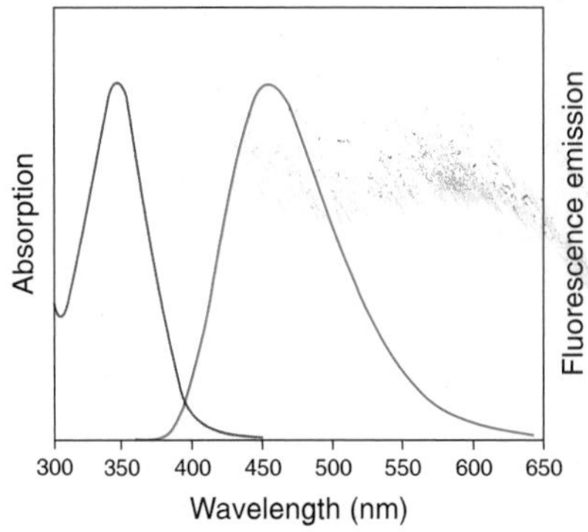

Figure 8.28 Absorption and fluorescence emission spectra of Hoechst 33258 bound to DNA.

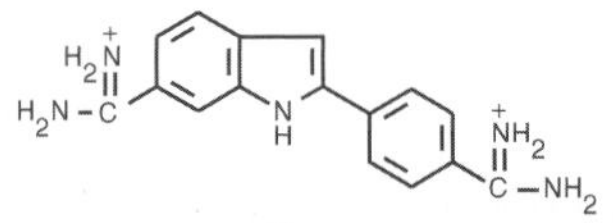

Figure 8.29 D1306 4′,6-diamidino-2-phenylindole, dihydrochloride (DAPI).

AT-Selective DAPI

DAPI (4′,6-diamidino-2-phenylindole; D1306, D3571; FluoroPure™ Grade, D21490; Figure 8.29) shows blue fluorescence (Figure 14.42) upon binding DNA and can be excited with a mercury-arc lamp or with the UV lines of the argon-ion laser. Like the Hoechst dyes, the blue-fluorescent DAPI stain apparently associates with the minor groove of dsDNA (Figure 8.30), preferentially binding to AT clusters;[101] there is evidence that DAPI also binds to DNA sequences that contain as few as two consecutive AT base pairs, perhaps employing a different binding mode.[102–104] DAPI is thought to employ an intercalating binding mode with RNA that is AU selective.[105]

The selectivity of DAPI for DNA over RNA is reported to be greater than that displayed by ethidium bromide and propidium iodide.[106] Furthermore, the DAPI–RNA complex exhibits a longer-wavelength fluorescence emission maximum than the DAPI–dsDNA complex (~500 nm versus ~460 nm) but a quantum yield that is only about 20% as high.[107]

Binding of DAPI to dsDNA produces an ~20-fold fluorescence enhancement, apparently due to the displacement of water molecules from both DAPI and the minor groove.[108] Although the Hoechst dyes may be somewhat brighter in some applications, their photostability when bound to dsDNA is less than that of DAPI. In the presence of appropriate salt concentrations, DAPI usually does not exhibit fluorescence enhancement upon binding to ssDNA or GC base pairs.[109] However, the fluorescence of DAPI does increase significantly upon binding to detergents,[110] dextran sulfate,[111] polyphosphates and other polyanions.[112] A review by Kapuscinski discusses the mechanisms of DAPI binding to nucleic acids, its spectral properties and its uses in flow cytometry and for chromosome staining.[113] DAPI is an excellent nuclear counterstain, showing a distinct banding pattern in chromosomes (Section 8.6, Figure 8.140), and we have included it in our Cytological Nuclear Counterstain Kit (C7590, Section 8.6). DAPI is quite soluble in water but has limited solubility in phosphate-buffered saline.

We also offer DAPI premixed with our *SlowFade*®, *SlowFade*® *Light* and ProLong® Gold antifade reagents (S24635, S24636, P36931, P36935). This combination of nucleic acid dye and antifade reagent permits simultaneous staining and protection of the stained sample from photobleaching.

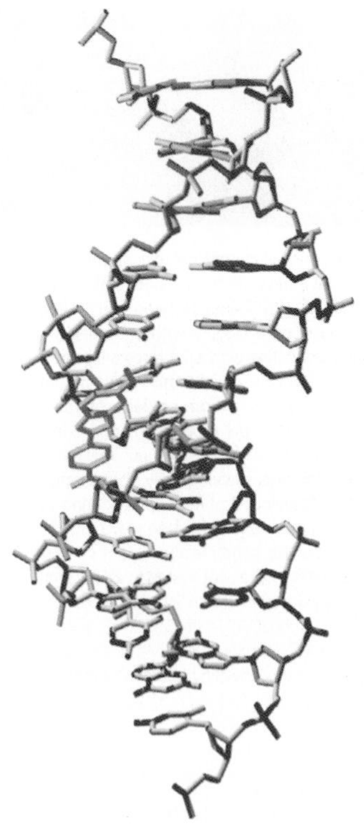

Figure 8.30 X-ray crystal structure of DAPI (D1306, D3571, D21490) bound to DNA; the image was derived from data submitted to the Protein Data Bank (number PDB 1D30, www.rcsb.org/pdb/, (Nucleic Acids Res 28, 235 (2000))). X-ray crystallography shows that DAPI binds to DNA in the minor groove (J Biomol Struct Dyn 7, 477 (1989)).

Other Nucleic Acid Stains

7-Aminoactinomycin D and Actinomycin D: Fluorescent Intercalators

7-AAD (7-aminoactinomycin D, A1310; Figure 8.31) is a fluorescent intercalator that undergoes a spectral shift upon association with DNA. 7-AAD/DNA complexes can be excited by the argon-ion laser and emit beyond 610 nm (Table 8.4, Figure 8.16, Figure 8.32), making this nucleic acid stain useful for multicolor fluorescence microscopy (Figure 8.33), confocal laser-scanning microscopy and immunophenotyping by flow cytometry.[114–119] 7-AAD appears to be generally excluded from live cells, although it has been reported to label the nuclear region of live cultured mouse L cells and salivary gland polytene chromosomes of *Chironomus thummi* larvae.[120] 7-AAD binds selectively to GC regions of DNA,[121] yielding a distinct banding pattern in polytene chromosomes and chromatin.[120,122] This sequence selectivity has been exploited for chromosome banding studies [123] (Section 8.6).

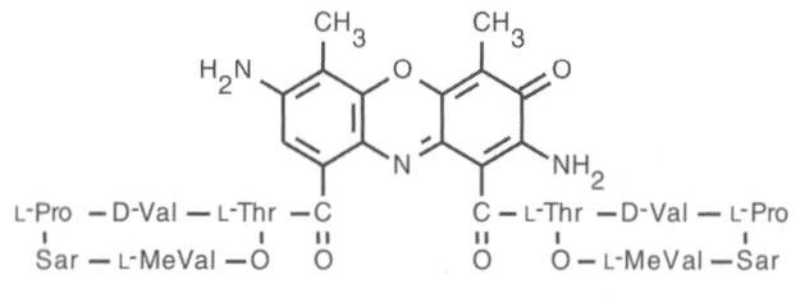

Figure 8.31 A1310 7-aminoactinomycin D (7-AAD).

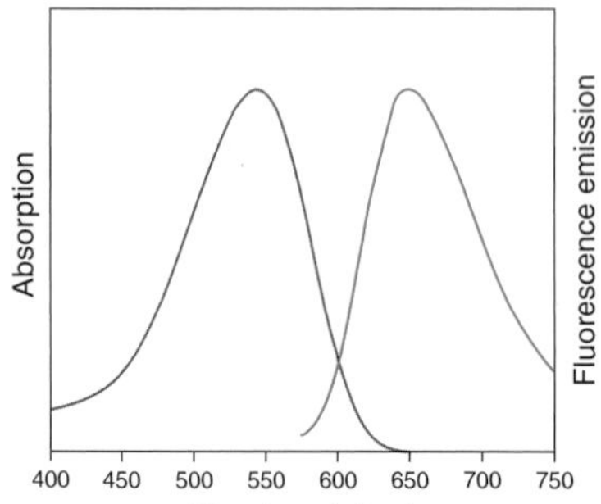

Figure 8.32 Absorption and fluorescence emission spectra of 7-aminoactinomycin D (7-AAD) bound to DNA.

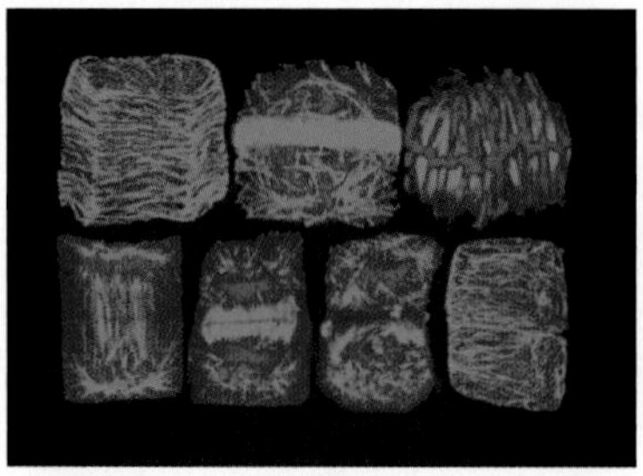

Figure 8.33 Panel of confocal micrographs showing cells from wheat root tips in seven stages of the cell cycle. DNA was stained with 7-aminoactinomycin D (A1310), and microtubules were labeled with an anti-β-tubulin antibody in conjunction with a fluorescein-labeled secondary antibody. Cells vary in width from about 15 µm to about 25 µm. The stages are (from top left): interphase cortical microtubule array; pre-prophase band of microtubules (predicts future plane of division); metaphase mitotic spindle; telophase, showing early phragmoplast and cell plate; fully developed phragmoplast during cytokinesis; late cytokinesis (plane of division matching plane of earlier pre-prophase band); restoration of cortical arrays in daughter cells. Image contributed by B.E.S. Gunning, Plant Cell Biology Group, Research School of Biological Sciences, Australian National University. Used with permission from Gunning, B.E.S. and Steer, M.W., *Plant Cell Biology - Structure and Function*, Jones and Bartlett Publishers (1995).

Actinomycin D (A7592) is a nonfluorescent intercalator that exhibits high GC selectivity and causes distortion at its binding site.[124] Binding of the nonfluorescent actinomycin D to nucleic acids changes the absorbance of the dye.[125] Like 7-AAD, actinomycin D has been used for chromosome banding studies.[126] Binding of actinomycin D to ssDNA is reported to inhibit reverse transcriptase and other polymerases.[127]

Multicolor Hydroxystilbamidine

Hydroxystilbamidine (H22845, Figure 8.34) — a trypanocidal drug that has previously been sold for research use as a neuronal tracer [128] under the trademark FluoroGold [129] (a trademark of FluoroChrome, Inc.) — is an interesting probe of nucleic acid conformation; its nucleic acid staining properties were first described in 1973.[130] Hydroxystilbamidine, a nonintercalating dye, exhibits AT-selective binding that is reported to favor regions of nucleic acids that have secondary structure. The interaction between hydroxystilbamidine and DNA has been investigated using binding isotherms [131] and temperature-jump relaxation studies.[132]

Hydroxystilbamidine has some unique spectral properties upon binding nucleic acids. At pH 5, the free dye exhibits UV excitation maxima at ~330 nm and ~390 nm, with dual emission at ~450 nm and ~600 nm (Figure 8.35). Although the red-fluorescent component remains present when bound to DNA, it is never observed when the dye is bound to RNA, permitting potential discrimination to be made between these two types of nucleic acids. The enhancement of its metachromatic fluorescence upon binding to DNA is proportional to the square of the AT base-pair content. Hydroxystilbamidine is reported to exhibit red fluorescence when bound to calf thymus DNA and T5 DNA, orange fluorescence with *Micrococcus lysodeikticus* DNA and blue-violet fluorescence on poly(d(A-T)).[130] It has been used for the treatment of myeloma, binding selectively to myeloma cells in the bone marrow.[133]

Because hydroxystilbamidine has been unavailable commercially, or its identity has been obscured by a trademark, its use as a nucleic acid stain in cellular applications has not been extensively tested. However, Murgatroyd described use of its metachromatic fluorescence properties for the selective permanent staining of DNA (with yellow fluorescence), mucosubstances and elastic fibers in paraffin sections.[134] He also reported that hydroxystilbamidine (as its isethionate salt, which is not available from Molecular Probes) is nonmutagenic in *Salmonella typhimurium* by the Ames test.[134]

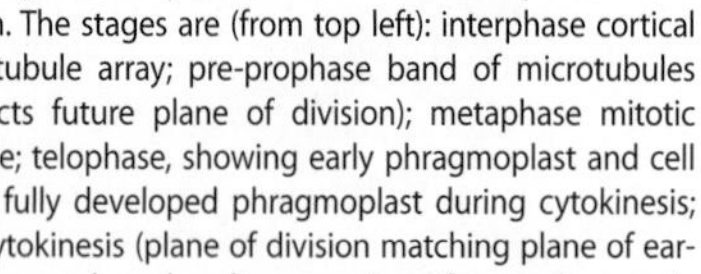

Figure 8.34 H22845 hydroxystilbamidine, methanesulfonate.

Long-Wavelength LDS 751

LDS 751 (L7595, Figure 8.36) is a cell-permeant nucleic acid stain that has been used to discriminate intact nucleated cells from nonnucleated and damaged nucleated cells,[135,136] as well as to identify distinct cell types in mixed populations of neutrophils, leukocytes and monocytes by flow cytometry.[137] LDS 751, which has its peak excitation at ~543 nm on dsDNA, can be excited by the argon-ion laser at 488 nm and is particularly useful in multicolor analyses due to its long-wavelength emission maximum (~712 nm). Binding of LDS 751 to dsDNA results in an ~20-fold fluorescence enhancement. When LDS 751 binds to RNA, we have observed a significant red shift in its excitation maximum to 590 nm and blue shift in its emission maxima to 607 nm, which may permit its use to discriminate DNA and RNA in cells. A report has ascribed the name LDS 751 to a dye called styryl 8;[138] however, their chemical structures are not the same.

NeuroTrace® Fluorescent Nissl Stains

The Nissl substance, described by Franz Nissl more than 100 years ago, is unique to neuronal cells.[139] Composed of an extraordinary amount of rough endoplasmic reticulum, the Nissl substance reflects the unusually high protein synthesis capacity of neuronal cells. Various fluorescent or chromophoric "Nissl stains" have been used for this counterstaining, including acridine orange,[140] ethidium bromide,[140] neutral red (N3246, Section 15.2), cresyl violet,[141] methylene blue, safranin-O and toluidine blue-O.[142] We have developed five fluorescent Nissl stains (Table 14.2) that not only provide a wide spectrum of fluorescent colors for staining neurons, but also are far more sensitive than the conventional dyes:

- NeuroTrace® 435/455 blue-fluorescent Nissl stain (N21479, Figure 8.125)
- NeuroTrace® 500/525 green-fluorescent Nissl stain (N21480; Figure 7.84, Figure 8.37, Figure 14.40, Figure 14.60)
- NeuroTrace® 515/535 yellow-fluorescent Nissl stain (N21481, Figure 8.142)
- NeuroTrace® 530/615 red-fluorescent Nissl stain (N21482; Figure 8.143, Figure 14.42)
- NeuroTrace® 640/660 deep red–fluorescent Nissl stain (N21483)

In addition, the Nissl substance redistributes within the cell body in injured or regenerating neurons. Therefore, these Nissl stains can also act as markers for the physiological state of the neuron. Staining by the Nissl stains is completely eliminated by pretreatment of tissue specimens with RNase; however, these dyes are not specific stains for RNA in solutions. The strong fluorescence (emission maximum ~515–520 nm) of NeuroTrace® 500/525 green-fluorescent Nissl stain (N21480) makes it the preferred dye for use as a counterstain in combination with orange- or red-fluorescent neuroanatomical tracers such as DiI[143] (D282, D3911, V22885; Section 14.4).

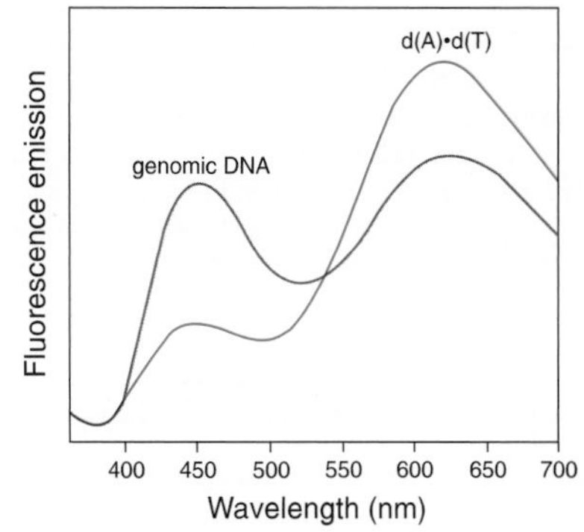

Figure 8.35 Fluorescence spectra of hydroxystilbamidine bound to different forms of DNA. Hydroxystilbamidine (H22845) was incubated with either calf thymus DNA (red) or a hybrid of poly(d(A)) and poly(d(T)) homopolymers (blue) in 50 mM sodium acetate, pH 5.0. The fluorescence emission spectra changes when the dye is bound to AT-rich DNA versus calf-thymus genomic DNA.

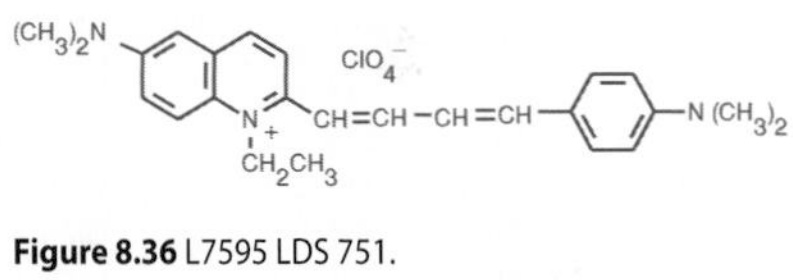

Figure 8.36 L7595 LDS 751.

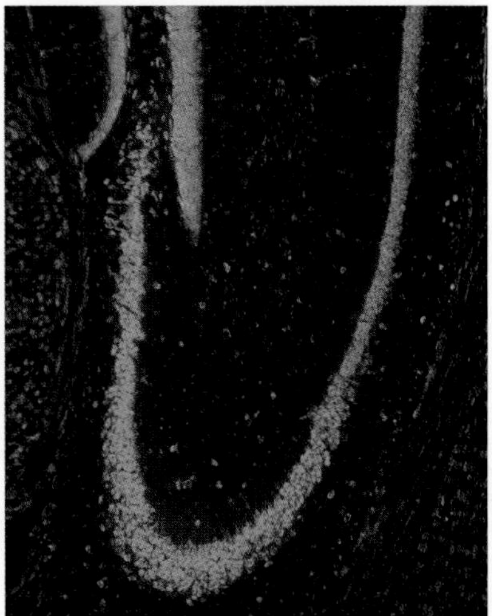

Figure 8.37 Pyramidal cells of the hippocampus and dentate gyrus in a transverse cryosection of paraformaldehyde-fixed mouse brain. NeuroTrace® green fluorescent Nissl stain (N21480) is localized to neuronal somata, while non-neuronal cells can be identified by the presence of DAPI-stained nuclei. This image is a composite of images taken using a 10× objective and filters appropriate for fluorescein and DAPI.

References

1. Nucleic Acids Res 23, 1215 (1995); **2.** Nucleic Acids Res 19, 327 (1991); **3.** Biochemistry 17, 5071 (1978); **4.** Biochemistry 17, 5078 (1978); **5.** Nucleic Acids Res 20, 2803 (1992); **6.** Proc Natl Acad Sci U S A 87, 3851 (1990); **7.** Nucleic Acids Res 21, 5720 (1993); **8.** Nature 359, 859 (1992); **9.** Biotechniques 10, 616 (1991); **10.** J Phys Chem 99, 17936 (1995); **11.** Cytometry 7, 508 (1986); **12.** Appl Environ Microbiol 66, 2283 (2000); **13.** Appl Environ Microbiol 61, 3623 (1995); **14.** Anal Biochem 221, 78 (1994); **15.** J Am Chem Soc 116, 8459 (1994); **16.** J Phys Chem 98, 10313 (1994); **17.** J Biomol Struct Dyn 16, 205 (1998); **18.** J Biomol Struct Dyn 16, 205 (1998); **19.** Anal Chem 67, 663A (1995); **20.** FASEB J 7, A1087, abstract #205 (1993); **21.** Nucleic Acids Res 23, 2413 (1995); **22.** Biochemistry 34, 8542 (1995); **23.** Biochemistry 37, 16863 (1998); **24.** Cytometry 37, 230 (1999); **25.** Bioconjug Chem 10, 824 (1999); **26.** Nucleic Acids Res 24, 859 (1996); **27.** Nucleic Acids Res 23, 753 (1995); **28.** Acta Chem Scand 52, 641 (1998); **29.** Biochem Mol Biol Int 34, 1189 (1994); **30.** Biopolymers 41, 481 (1997); **31.** Appl Environ Microbiol 60, 3284 (1994); **32.** Cancer Res 57, 3804 (1997); **33.** Blood 87, 4959 (1996); **34.** J Immunol Methods 185, 249 (1995); **35.** J Exp Med 182, 1759 (1995); **36.** Br J Pharmacol 130, 513 (2000); **37.** Br J Pharmacol 125, 1194 (1998); **38.** J Biol Chem 276, 125 (2001); **39.** Cytometry 17, 185 (1994); **40.** Cytometry 17, 310 (1994); **41.** Cytometry 15, 267 (1994); **42.** Handbook of Fluorescent Probes and Research Chemicals, 5th Ed., 1992-1994, Haugland RP (Complete Volume), (1992); **43.** J Phys Chem B 104, 7221 (2000); **44.** Limnol Oceanogr 40, 1050 (1995); **45.** Anal Biochem 286, 138 (2000); **46.** Proc Natl Acad Sci U S A 94, 14804 (1997); **47.** J Neurosci 16, 7812 (1996); **48.** Cytometry 21, 265 (1995); **49.** Neuron 15, 961 (1995); **50.** Cytometry 20, 218 (1995); **51.** Anal Biochem 287, 179 (2000); **52.** Anal Biochem 281, 26 (2000); **53.** Cytometry 50, 249 (2002); **54.** Methods 18, 222 (1999); **55.** Lett Appl Microbiol 34, 182 (2002); **56.** Cytometry 41, 223 (2000); **57.** Nucleic Acids Res 29, E34 (2001); **58.** Appl Environ Microbiol 66, 3790 (2000); **59.** Aquat Microbial Ecol 14, 113 (1998); **60.** J Mol Biol 13, 269 (1965); **61.** Biochemistry 29, 981 (1990); **62.** Methods Cell Biol 30, 417 (1989); **63.** Mutat Res 439, 37 (1999); **64.** Chromatographia 29, 167 (1990); **65.** Anal Biochem 162, 453 (1987); **66.** J Immunol Methods 170, 117 (1994); **67.** FEMS Microbiol Lett 101, 173 (1992); **68.** J Histochem Cytochem 34, 1109 (1986); **69.** Bioorg Med Chem 3, 701 (1995); **70.** Anal Biochem 94, 259 (1979); **71.** Biochemistry 30, 5644 (1991); **72.** Photochem Photobiol 43, 7 (1986); **73.** J Biol Chem 259, 11090 (1984); **74.** Photochem Photobiol 36, 31 (1982); **75.** J Mol Biol 92, 319 (1975); **76.** Cytometry 12, 133 (1991); **77.** Cytometry 11, 610 (1990); **78.** Eur J Biochem 182, 437 (1989); **79.** Biochemistry 19, 3221 (1980); **80.** Proc Natl Acad Sci U S A 97, 9504 (2000); **81.** Exp Cell Res 194, 147 (1991); **82.** Methods Mol Biol 29, 83 (1994); **83.** Biochemistry 18, 3354 (1979); **84.** Proc Natl Acad Sci U S A 72, 2915 (1975); **85.** Eur J Biochem 180, 359 (1989); **86.** J Biomol Struct Dyn 5, 361 (1987); **87.** Biochim Biophys Acta 722, 107 (1983); **88.** Biochim Biophys Acta 1143, 215 (1993); **89.** Eur Biophys J 19, 189 (1991); **90.** Biochemistry 19, 1922 (1980); **91.** J Biol Chem 269, 10221 (1994); **92.** Biochim Biophys Acta 1183, 161 (1993); **93.** Cytometry 44, 133 (2001); **94.** Photochem Photobiol 73, 339 (2001); **95.** Biochemistry 29, 9029 (1990); **96.** J Histochem Cytochem 33, 333 (1985); **97.** Mol Biochem Parasitol 58, 7 (1993); **98.** Am J Trop Med Hyg 43, 602 (1990); **99.** Cytometry 14, 276 (1993); **100.** Methods Cell Biol 42 Pt B, 295 (1994); **101.** Biochemistry 26, 4545 (1987); **102.** Biochemistry 32, 2987 (1993); **103.** J Biol Chem 268, 3944 (1993); **104.** Biochemistry 29, 8452 (1990); **105.** Biochemistry 31, 3103 (1992); **106.** Nucleic Acids Res 6, 3535 (1979); **107.** J Histochem Cytochem 38, 1323 (1990); **108.** Biochem Biophys Res Commun 170, 270 (1990); **109.** Nucleic Acids Res 6, 3519 (1979); **110.** Nucleic Acids

References — continued

Res 5, 3775 (1978); **111.** Can J Microbiol 26, 912 (1980); **112.** Biochim Biophys Acta 721, 394 (1982); **113.** Biotech Histochem 70, 220 (1995); **114.** Exp Parasitol 97, 141 (2001); **115.** Br J Haematol 104, 530 (1999); **116.** Cytometry 12, 221 (1991); **117.** Cytometry 12, 172 (1991); **118.** J Immunol 136, 2769 (1986); **119.** J Histochem Cytochem 23, 793 (1975); **120.** Histochem J 17, 131 (1985); **121.** Biopolymers 18, 1749 (1979); **122.** Cytometry 20, 296 (1995); **123.** Chromosoma 68, 287 (1978); **124.** J Mol Biol 225, 445 (1992); **125.** Biochemistry 32, 5554 (1993); **126.** Cancer Genet Cytogenet 1, 187 (1980); **127.** Biochemistry 35, 3525 (1996); **128.** J Neurocytol 18, 333 (1989); **129.** US 4,716,905; **130.** Biochemistry 12, 4827 (1973); **131.** Biochim Biophys Acta 407, 24 (1975); **132.** Biochim Biophys Acta 407, 43 (1975); **133.** J Lab Clin Med 37, 562 (1951); **134.** Histochemistry 74, 107 (1982); **135.** J Immunol Methods 123, 103 (1989); **136.** Cytometry 9, 477 (1988); **137.** J Immunol Methods 163, 155 (1993); **138.** J Photochem Photobiol A 84, 45 (1994); **139.** Neuroscience Protocols, Wouterlood FG, Ed. 93-050-12, pp. 01–07 (1993); **140.** Proc Natl Acad Sci U S A 77, 2260 (1980); **141.** J Neurosci Methods 33, 129 (1990); **142.** J Neurosci Methods 72, 49 (1997); **143.** Neurosci Lett 184, 169 (1995).

Data Table — 8.1 Nucleic Acid Stains

Cat #	MW	Storage	Soluble	Abs	EC	Em	Solvent	Notes
A666	685.69	L	DMSO, DMF	431	ND	498	H_2O/DNA	1, 2
A1301	301.82	L	H_2O, EtOH	500	53,000	526	H_2O/DNA	3, 4
A1310	1270.45	F,L	DMF, DMSO	546	25,000	647	H_2O/DNA	3
A1324	258.71	L	DMF, DMSO	412	8,200	471	MeOH	5
A3568	301.82	RR,L	H_2O	500	53,000	526	H_2O/DNA	3, 4, 6
A7592	1255.43	F,L	DMF, DMSO	442	23,000	none	MeOH	
B3582	1202.66	F,D,L	DMSO	462	114,000	481	H_2O/DNA	3, 6, 7, 8
B3583	595.32	F,D,L	DMSO	462	58,000	481	H_2O/DNA	3, 6, 7, 8
B3586	1254.73	F,D,L	DMSO	570	148,000	604	H_2O/DNA	3, 6, 7, 8
B3587	621.36	F,D,L	DMSO	575	81,000	599	H_2O/DNA	3, 6, 7, 8
D1168	315.42	FF,L,AA	DMF, DMSO	355	14,000	see Notes	MeCN	9, 10
D1306	350.25	L	H_2O, DMF	358	21,000	461	H_2O/DNA	3, 11
D3571	457.49	L	H_2O, MeOH	358	20,000	461	H_2O/DNA	3, 11
D11347	315.42	FF,L,AA	DMF, DMSO	355	14,000	see Notes	MeCN	9, 10
D21490	350.25	L	H_2O, DMF	358	21,000	461	H_2O/DNA	3, 11, 12
D23107	315.42	FF,D,L,AA	DMSO	355	14,000	see Notes	MeCN	10, 13
E1169	856.77	F,D,L	DMSO	528	7,000	617	H_2O/DNA	3, 7, 14
E1305	394.31	L	H_2O, DMSO	518	5,200	605	H_2O/DNA	3, 15
E1374	420.31	F,LL	DMF, EtOH	462	5,400	625	pH 7	16
E3561	401.86	F,LL	pH 3	432	5,700	496	pH 3	17
E3565	394.31	RR,L	H_2O	518	5,200	605	H_2O/DNA	3, 6, 15
E3599	1292.71	F,D,L	DMSO	535	8,000	624	H_2O/DNA	3, 6, 7, 14
H1398	623.96	L	H_2O, DMF	352	40,000	461	H_2O/DNA	3, 18
H1399	615.99	L	H_2O, DMF	350	45,000	461	H_2O/DNA	3, 18
H3569	623.96	RR,L	H_2O	352	40,000	461	H_2O/DNA	3, 6, 18
H3570	615.99	RR,L	H_2O	350	45,000	461	H_2O/DNA	3, 6, 18
H7593	497.42	L	DMSO	518	3,900	600	H_2O/DNA	3, 19
H21486	560.96	L	DMSO	392	47,000	440	H_2O/DNA	3
H21491	623.96	L	H_2O, DMF	352	40,000	461	H_2O/DNA	3, 12, 18
H21492	615.99	L	H_2O, DMF	350	45,000	461	H_2O/DNA	3, 12, 18
H22845	472.53	F,D,L	H2O, DMSO	360	27,000	625	H_2O/DNA	3, 20
J11372	1272.63	F,D,L	DMSO	530	171,000	545	H_2O/DNA	3, 6, 7, 8
J11373	630.31	F,D,L	DMSO	532	94,000	544	H_2O/DNA	3, 6, 7, 8
L7595	471.98	L	DMSO, EtOH	543	46,000	712	H_2O/DNA	3
L11376	1462.54	F,D,L	DMSO	566	108,000	580	H_2O/DNA	3, 6, 7, 8
L11377	725.27	F,D,L	DMSO	568	103,000	581	H_2O/DNA	3, 6, 7, 8
N21479	see Notes	F,D,L	DMSO	435	see Notes	457	H_2O/RNA	6, 8, 21
N21480	see Notes	F,D,L	DMSO	497	see Notes	524	H_2O/RNA	6, 8, 21
N21481	see Notes	F,D,L	DMSO	515	see Notes	535	H_2O/RNA	6, 8, 21
N21482	see Notes	F,D,L	DMSO	530	see Notes	619	H_2O/RNA	6, 8, 21
N21483	see Notes	F,D,L	DMSO	644	see Notes	663	H_2O/RNA	6, 8, 21
N21485	651.01	L	DMSO	355	36,000	495	H_2O/DNA	3
O7582	see Notes	F,D,L	DMSO	498	see Notes	518	H_2O/DNA	6, 8, 21
P1304MP	668.40	L	H_2O, DMSO	535	5,400	617	H_2O/DNA	3, 22
P3566	668.40	RR,L	H_2O	535	5,400	617	H_2O/DNA	3, 6, 22
P3580	1170.53	F,D,L	DMSO	434	92,000	456	H_2O/DNA	3, 6, 7, 8
P3581	579.26	F,D,L	DMSO	435	50,000	455	H_2O/DNA	3, 6, 7, 8
P3584	1222.61	F,D,L	DMF	534	146,000	570	H_2O/DNA	3, 6, 7, 8
P3585	605.30	F,D,L	DMSO	539	88,000	567	H_2O/DNA	3, 6, 7, 8
P7581	see Notes	F,D,L	DMSO	502	see Notes	523	H_2O/DNA	6, 8, 21
P11495	see Notes	F,D,L	DMSO	502	see Notes	523	H_2O/DNA	6, 8, 21
P21493	668.40	L	H_2O, DMSO	535	5,400	617	H_2O/DNA	3, 12, 22
R11491	see Notes	F,D,L	DMSO	500	see Notes	525	H_2O/RNA	6, 8, 21
S7020	~600	F,D,L	DMSO	504	67,000	523	H_2O/DNA	3, 6, 8, 23
S7555	~450	F,D,L	DMSO	512	64,000	530	H_2O/DNA	3, 6, 8, 23
S7556	~500	F,D,L	DMSO	494	43,000	517	H_2O/DNA	3, 6, 8, 23
S7557	~350	F,D,L	DMSO	515	43,000	535	H_2O/DNA	3, 6, 8, 23

Data Table — 8.1 Nucleic Acid Stains — continued

Cat #	MW	Storage	Soluble	Abs	EC	Em	Solvent	Notes
S7558	~400	F,D,L	DMSO	499	46,000	520	H_2O/DNA	3, 6, 8, 23
S7559	~550	F,D,L	DMSO	490	58,000	515	H_2O/DNA	3, 6, 8, 23
S7560	~450	F,D,L	DMSO	521	57,000	556	H_2O/DNA	3, 6, 8, 23
S7573	~400	F,D,L	DMSO	508	75,000	527	H_2O/DNA	3, 6, 8, 23
S7574	~300	F,D,L	DMSO	500	54,000	522	H_2O/DNA	3, 6, 8, 23
S7575	~400	F,D,L	DMSO	488	74,000	509	H_2O/DNA	3, 6, 8, 23
S7576	~500	F,D,L	DMSO	517	60,000	549	H_2O/DNA	3, 6, 8, 23
S7577	~400	F,D,L	DMSO	516	55,000	546	H_2O/DNA	3, 6, 8, 23
S7578	~450	F,D,L	DMSO	488	42,000	518	H_2O/DNA	3, 6, 8, 23
S7579	~650	F,D,L	DMSO	621	88,000	634	H_2O/DNA	3, 6, 8, 23
S11341	~550	F,D,L	DMSO	622	112,000	645	H_2O/DNA	3, 6, 8, 23
S11342	~500	F,D,L	DMSO	652	83,000	678	H_2O/DNA	3, 6, 8, 23
S11343	~500	F,D,L	DMSO	620	85,000	647	H_2O/DNA	3, 6, 8, 23
S11344	~550	F,D,L	DMSO	649	76,000	680	H_2O/DNA	3, 6, 8, 23
S11345	~550	F,D,L	DMSO	654	119,000	675	H_2O/DNA	3, 6, 8, 23
S11346	~400	F,D,L	DMSO	598	84,000	620	H_2O/DNA	3, 6, 8, 23
S11348	~400	F,D,L	DMSO	445	38,000	470	H_2O/DNA	3, 6, 8, 23
S11351	~250	F,D,L	DMSO	419	33,000	445	H_2O/DNA	3, 6, 8, 23
S11352	~450	F,D,L	DMSO	426	34,000	455	H_2O/DNA	3, 6, 8, 23
S11353	~350	F,D,L	DMSO	430	31,000	460	H_2O/DNA	3, 6, 8, 23
S11354	~400	F,D,L	DMSO	437	48,000	464	H_2O/DNA	3, 6, 8, 23
S11355	~300	F,D,L	DMSO	445	56,000	472	H_2O/DNA	3, 6, 8, 23
S11356	~300	F,D,L	DMSO	452	43,000	484	H_2O/DNA	3, 6, 8, 23
S11361	~400	F,D,L	DMSO	531	89,000	545	H_2O/DNA	3, 6, 8, 23
S11362	~300	F,D,L	DMSO	530	82,000	544	H_2O/DNA	3, 6, 8, 23
S11363	~350	F,D,L	DMSO	541	76,000	560	H_2O/DNA	3, 6, 8, 23
S11364	~350	F,D,L	DMSO	543	68,000	559	H_2O/DNA	3, 6, 8, 23
S11365	~500	F,D,L	DMSO	567	95,000	582	H_2O/DNA	3, 6, 8, 23
S11366	~350	F,D,L	DMSO	567	86,000	583	H_2O/DNA	3, 6, 8, 23
S11368	~500	F,D,L	DMSO	547	79,000	570	H_2O/DNA	3, 6, 8, 23
S21500	~600	F,D,L	DMSO	494	57,000	519	H_2O/DNA	3, 8, 23
S21501	~550	F,D,L	DMSO	484	39,000	520	H_2O/DNA	3, 8, 23
S21502	~600	F,D,L	DMSO	486	56,000	526	H_2O/DNA	3, 8, 23
S32703	~800	F,D,L	DMSO	491	107,000	532	H_2O/RNA	3, 6, 8, 23
S32704	~350	F,D,L	DMSO	484	67,000	505	H_2O/DNA	3, 6, 8, 23
S32705	~450	F,D,L	DMSO	497	53,000	534	H_2O/DNA	3, 6, 8, 23
S32706	~500	F,D,L	DMSO	495	61,000	537	H_2O/DNA	3, 6, 8, 23
S32707	~450	F,D,L	DMSO	528	48,000	556	H_2O/DNA	3, 6, 8, 23
S34854	~400	F,D,L	DMSO	483	65,000	503	H_2O/DNA	3, 6, 8, 23
S34855	~400	F,D,L	DMSO	480	66,000	502	H_2O/DNA	3, 6, 8, 23
T3600	1302.78	F,D,L	DMSO	514	117,000	533	H_2O/DNA	3, 6, 7, 8
T3602	645.38	F,D,L	DMSO	515	63,000	531	H_2O/DNA	3, 6, 7, 8
T3604	1354.85	F,D,L	DMSO	642	154,000	660	H_2O/DNA	3, 6, 7, 8
T3605	671.42	F,D,L	DMSO	642	102,000	661	H_2O/DNA	3, 6, 7, 8
T7596	697.46	F,D,L	DMSO	747	108,000	770	H_2O/DNA	3, 6, 7, 8
Y3601	1270.65	F,D,L	DMSO	491	99,000	509	H_2O/DNA	3, 6, 7, 8
Y3603	629.32	F,D,L	DMSO	491	52,000	509	H_2O/DNA	3, 6, 7, 8
Y3606	1322.73	F,D,L	DMSO	612	167,000	631	H_2O/DNA	3, 6, 7, 8
Y3607	655.36	F,D,L	DMSO	612	100,000	631	H_2O/DNA	3, 6, 7, 8

For definitions of the contents of this data table, see "Navigating *The Handbook*" in the introductory pages.

Notes

1. ND = not determined.
2. A666 in MeOH: Abs = 418 nm (EC = 12,000 $cm^{-1}M^{-1}$), Em = 500 nm.
3. Spectra represent aqueous solutions of nucleic acid-bound dye. EC values are derived by comparing the absorbance of the nucleic acid-bound dye with that of free dye in a reference solvent (H_2O or MeOH).
4. Acridine orange bound to RNA has Abs ~460 nm, Em ~650 nm (Methods Cell Biol 41, 401 (1994); Cytometry 2, 201 (1982)).
5. Spectra of this compound are in methanol acidified with a trace of HCl.
6. This product is supplied as a ready-made solution in the solvent indicated under "Soluble."
7. Although this compound is soluble in water, preparation of stock solutions in water is not recommended because of possible adsorption onto glass or plastic.
8. This product is essentially nonfluorescent except when bound to DNA or RNA.
9. This compound is susceptible to oxidation, especially in solution. Store solutions under argon or nitrogen. Oxidation may be induced by illumination.
10. Dihydroethidium has blue fluorescence (Em ~420 nm) until oxidized to ethidium (E1305). The reduced dye does not bind to nucleic acids (FEBS Lett 26, 169 (1972)).
11. DAPI in H_2O: Abs = 344 nm (EC = 23,000 $cm^{-1}M^{-1}$), Em = 450 nm. QY increases ~20-fold on binding to dsDNA (Ital J Biochem 31, 90 (1982)).
12. This product is specified to equal or exceed 98% analytical purity by HPLC.
13. This product is supplied as a ready-made solution in DMSO with sodium borohydride added to inhibit oxidation.
14. E1169 in H_2O: Abs = 493 nm (EC = 9100 $cm^{-1}M^{-1}$). E3599 in H_2O: Abs = 498 nm (EC = 10,800 $cm^{-1}M^{-1}$). Both compounds are very weakly fluorescent in H_2O. QY increases >40-fold on binding to dsDNA.
15. Ethidium bromide in H_2O: Abs = 480 nm (EC = 5600 $cm^{-1}M^{-1}$), Em = 620 nm (weakly fluorescent). Fluorescence is enhanced >10-fold on binding to dsDNA.
16. E1374 spectral data are for the free dye. Fluorescence is weak, but intensity increases ~15-fold on binding to DNA. After photocrosslinking to DNA, Abs = 504 nm (EC ~4000 $cm^{-1}M^{-1}$), Em = 600 nm (Nucleic Acids Res 5, 4891 (1978); Biochemistry 19, 3221 (1980)).

17. E3561 spectral data are for the free dye. Fluorescence is weak and decreases in intensity on binding to DNA (Biochemistry 19, 3221 (1980)).
18. MW is for the hydrated form of this product.
19. H7593 in H_2O: Abs = 482 nm (EC = 5500 $cm^{-1}M^{-1}$), Em = 625 nm (weakly fluorescent).
20. Nucleic acid–bound hydroxystilbamidine has a second fluorescence emission peak at ~450 nm. The relative amplitudes of the two emission peaks are dependent on the nucleotide content of the nucleic acid (Biochemistry 12, 4827 (1973)).
21. The active ingredient of this product is an organic dye with MW <1000. The exact MW and extinction coefficient values for this dye are proprietary.
22. Propidium iodide in H_2O: Abs = 493 nm (EC = 5900 $cm^{-1}M^{-1}$), Em = 636 nm (weakly fluorescent). Fluorescence is enhanced >10-fold on binding to dsDNA.
23. MW: The preceding ~ symbol indicates an approximate value, not including counterions.

Product List — 8.1 Nucleic Acid Stains

Cat #	Product Name	Unit Size
A666	acridine homodimer (bis-(6-chloro-2-methoxy-9-acridinyl)spermine)	10 mg
A1301	acridine orange	1 g
A3568	acridine orange *10 mg/mL solution in water*	10 mL
A7592	actinomycin D	10 mg
A1310	7-aminoactinomycin D (7-AAD)	1 mg
A1324	9-amino-6-chloro-2-methoxyacridine (ACMA)	100 mg
B3582	BOBO™-1 iodide (462/481) *1 mM solution in DMSO*	200 µL
B3586	BOBO™-3 iodide (570/602) *1 mM solution in DMSO*	200 µL
B3583	BO-PRO™-1 iodide (462/481) *1 mM solution in DMSO*	1 mL
B3587	BO-PRO™-3 iodide (575/599) *1 mM solution in DMSO*	1 mL
D1306	4',6-diamidino-2-phenylindole, dihydrochloride (DAPI)	10 mg
D21490	4',6-diamidino-2-phenylindole, dihydrochloride (DAPI) *FluoroPure™ grade*	10 mg
D3571	4',6-diamidino-2-phenylindole, dilactate (DAPI, dilactate)	10 mg
D1168	dihydroethidium (hydroethidine)	25 mg
D11347	dihydroethidium (hydroethidine) *special packaging*	10 x 1 mg
D23107	dihydroethidium (hydroethidine) *5 mM stabilized solution in DMSO*	1 mL
E1305	ethidium bromide	1 g
E3565	ethidium bromide *10 mg/mL solution in water*	10 mL
E3561	ethidium diazide chloride	5 mg
E1169	ethidium homodimer-1 (EthD-1)	1 mg
E3599	ethidium homodimer-2 (EthD-2) *1 mM solution in DMSO*	200 µL
E1374	ethidium monoazide bromide (EMA)	5 mg
H7593	hexidium iodide	5 mg
H1398	Hoechst 33258, pentahydrate (bis-benzimide)	100 mg
H3569	Hoechst 33258, pentahydrate (bis-benzimide) *10 mg/mL solution in water*	10 mL
H21491	Hoechst 33258, pentahydrate (bis-benzimide) *FluoroPure™ grade*	100 mg
H1399	Hoechst 33342, trihydrochloride, trihydrate	100 mg
H3570	Hoechst 33342, trihydrochloride, trihydrate *10 mg/mL solution in water*	10 mL
H21492	Hoechst 33342, trihydrochloride, trihydrate *FluoroPure™ grade*	100 mg
H21486	Hoechst 34580	5 mg
H22845	hydroxystilbamidine, methanesulfonate	10 mg
J11372	JOJO™-1 iodide (529/545) *1 mM solution in DMSO*	200 µL
J11373	JO-PRO™-1 iodide (530/546) *1 mM solution in DMSO*	1 mL
L7595	LDS 751	10 mg
L11376	LOLO™-1 iodide (565/579) *1 mM solution in DMSO*	200 µL
L11377	LO-PRO™-1 iodide (567/580) *1 mM solution in DMSO*	1 mL
N21479	NeuroTrace® 435/455 blue fluorescent Nissl stain *solution in DMSO*	1 mL
N21480	NeuroTrace® 500/525 green fluorescent Nissl stain *solution in DMSO*	1 mL
N21481	NeuroTrace® 515/535 yellow fluorescent Nissl stain *solution in DMSO*	1 mL
N21482	NeuroTrace® 530/615 red fluorescent Nissl stain *solution in DMSO*	1 mL
N21483	NeuroTrace® 640/660 deep-red fluorescent Nissl stain *solution in DMSO*	1 mL
N21485	nuclear yellow (Hoechst S769121, trihydrochloride, trihydrate)	10 mg
N7565	Nucleic Acid Stains Dimer Sampler Kit	1 kit
O11492	OliGreen® ssDNA Quantitation Kit *200-2000 assays*	1 kit
O7582	OliGreen® ssDNA quantitation reagent *200-2000 assays*	1 mL
P7589	PicoGreen® dsDNA Quantitation Kit *200-2000 assays*	1 kit
P11496	PicoGreen® dsDNA Quantitation Kit *200-2000 assays* *special packaging*	1 kit
P7581	PicoGreen® dsDNA quantitation reagent *200-2000 assays*	1 mL
P11495	PicoGreen® dsDNA quantitation reagent *200-2000 assays* *special packaging*	10 x 100 µL

For current prices or to order online, visit probes.invitrogen.com

Cat #	Product Name	Unit Size
P3580	POPO™-1 iodide (434/456) *1 mM solution in DMSO*	200 µL
P3584	POPO™-3 iodide (534/570) *1 mM solution in DMF*	200 µL
P3581	PO-PRO™-1 iodide (435/455) *1 mM solution in DMSO*	1 mL
P3585	PO-PRO™-3 iodide (539/567) *1 mM solution in DMSO*	1 mL
P1304MP	propidium iodide	100 mg
P21493	propidium iodide *FluoroPure™ grade*	100 mg
P3566	propidium iodide *1.0 mg/mL solution in water*	10 mL
R32715	RediPlate™ 96 nucleic acid stain sampler *one 96-well microplate*	each
R32716	RediPlate™ 96 PicoGreen® dsDNA Quantitation Kit *one 96-well microplate* *with separate DNA standard*	1 kit
R21495	RediPlate™ 96 PicoGreen® dsDNA Quantitation Kit *one 96-well microplate*	1 kit
R32701	RediPlate™ 96 PicoGreen® dsDNA quantitation microplate	each
R32700	RediPlate™ 96 RiboGreen® RNA Quantitation Kit *one 96-well microplate*	1 kit
R11490	RiboGreen® RNA Quantitation Kit *200-2000 assays*	1 kit
R11491	RiboGreen® RNA quantitation reagent *200-20,000 assays*	1 mL
R32702	RiboGreen® RNA-Specific Quantitation Kit *with DNase I* *2000 assays*	1 kit
S24635	*SlowFade®* Antifade Kit with DAPI	1 kit
S24636	*SlowFade® Light* Antifade Kit with DAPI	1 kit
S21500	SYBR® 101, succinimidyl ester	1 mg
S21501	SYBR® 102, succinimidyl ester	1 mg
S21502	SYBR® 103, succinimidyl ester	1 mg
S7550	SYBR® DX DNA blot stain *1000X concentrate in DMA*	1 mL
S11494	SYBR® Gold nucleic acid gel stain *10,000X concentrate in DMSO*	500 µL
S7563	SYBR® Green I nucleic acid gel stain *10,000X concentrate in DMSO*	500 µL
S7567	SYBR® Green I nucleic acid gel stain *10,000X concentrate in DMSO*	1 mL
S7585	SYBR® Green I nucleic acid gel stain *10,000X concentrate in DMSO* *special packaging*	20 x 50 µL
S7564	SYBR® Green II RNA gel stain *10,000X concentrate in DMSO*	500 µL
S7568	SYBR® Green II RNA gel stain *10,000X concentrate in DMSO*	1 mL
S7586	SYBR® Green II RNA gel stain *10,000X concentrate in DMSO* *special packaging*	20 x 50 µL
S7580	SYBR® Green Nucleic Acid Gel Stain Starter Kit	1 kit
S33101	SYBR Safe™ DNA gel stain in 0.5X TBE	4 L
S33102	SYBR Safe™ DNA gel stain *10,000X concentrate in DMSO*	400 µL
S33111	SYBR Safe™ DNA gel stain in 1X TAE	1 L
S33112	SYBR Safe™ DNA gel stain in 1X TAE	4 L
S33100	SYBR Safe™ DNA gel stain in 0.5X TBE	1 L
S33110	SYBR Safe™ DNA Gel Stain Starter Kit *with 1 L of SYBR Safe™ DNA gel stain in 0.5X TBE (S33100) and one photographic filter (S37100)*	1 kit
S11351	SYTO® 40 blue fluorescent nucleic acid stain *5 mM solution in DMSO*	250 µL
S11352	SYTO® 41 blue fluorescent nucleic acid stain *5 mM solution in DMSO*	250 µL
S11353	SYTO® 42 blue fluorescent nucleic acid stain *5 mM solution in DMSO*	250 µL
S11354	SYTO® 43 blue fluorescent nucleic acid stain *5 mM solution in DMSO*	250 µL
S11355	SYTO® 44 blue fluorescent nucleic acid stain *5 mM solution in DMSO*	250 µL
S11356	SYTO® 45 blue fluorescent nucleic acid stain *5 mM solution in DMSO*	250 µL
S11350	SYTO® Blue Fluorescent Nucleic Acid Stain Sampler Kit *SYTO® dyes 40-45* *50 µL each*	1 kit
S34854	SYTO® 9 green fluorescent nucleic acid stain *5 mM solution in DMSO*	100 µL
S32704	SYTO® 10 green fluorescent nucleic acid stain *5 mM solution in DMSO*	100 µL
S7573	SYTO® 11 green fluorescent nucleic acid stain *5 mM solution in DMSO*	250 µL
S7574	SYTO® 12 green fluorescent nucleic acid stain *5 mM solution in DMSO*	250 µL
S7575	SYTO® 13 green fluorescent nucleic acid stain *5 mM solution in DMSO*	250 µL
S7576	SYTO® 14 green fluorescent nucleic acid stain *5 mM solution in DMSO*	250 µL
S7577	SYTO® 15 green fluorescent nucleic acid stain *5 mM solution in DMSO*	250 µL
S7578	SYTO® 16 green fluorescent nucleic acid stain *1 mM solution in DMSO*	250 µL
S7555	SYTO® 20 green fluorescent nucleic acid stain *1 mM solution in DMSO*	250 µL
S7556	SYTO® 21 green fluorescent nucleic acid stain *5 mM solution in DMSO*	250 µL
S7557	SYTO® 22 green fluorescent nucleic acid stain *5 mM solution in DMSO*	250 µL
S7558	SYTO® 23 green fluorescent nucleic acid stain *5 mM solution in DMSO*	250 µL
S7559	SYTO® 24 green fluorescent nucleic acid stain *5 mM solution in DMSO*	250 µL
S7560	SYTO® 25 green fluorescent nucleic acid stain *5 mM solution in DMSO*	250 µL
S32705	SYTO® 26 green fluorescent nucleic acid stain *5 mM solution in DMSO*	100 µL
S32706	SYTO® 27 green fluorescent nucleic acid stain *5 mM solution in DMSO*	100 µL
S34855	SYTO® BC green fluorescent nucleic acid stain *5 mM solution in DMSO*	100 µL
S7572	SYTO® Green Fluorescent Nucleic Acid Stain Sampler Kit #1 *SYTO® dyes 11-16* *50 µL each*	1 kit

For current prices or to order online, visit probes.invitrogen.com

Product List — 8.1 Nucleic Acid Stains — continued

Cat #	Product Name	Unit Size
S7554	SYTO® Green Fluorescent Nucleic Acid Stain Sampler Kit #2 *SYTO® dyes 20-25* *50 µL each*	1 kit
S11361	SYTO® 80 orange fluorescent nucleic acid stain *5 mM solution in DMSO*	250 µL
S11362	SYTO® 81 orange fluorescent nucleic acid stain *5 mM solution in DMSO*	250 µL
S11363	SYTO® 82 orange fluorescent nucleic acid stain *5 mM solution in DMSO*	250 µL
S11364	SYTO® 83 orange fluorescent nucleic acid stain *5 mM solution in DMSO*	250 µL
S11365	SYTO® 84 orange fluorescent nucleic acid stain *5 mM solution in DMSO*	250 µL
S11366	SYTO® 85 orange fluorescent nucleic acid stain *5 mM solution in DMSO*	250 µL
S32707	SYTO® 86 orange fluorescent nucleic acid stain *5 mM solution in DMSO*	100 µL
S11360	SYTO® Orange Fluorescent Nucleic Acid Stain Sampler Kit *SYTO® dyes 80-85* *50 µL each*	1 kit
S7579	SYTO® 17 red fluorescent nucleic acid stain *5 mM solution in DMSO*	250 µL
S11341	SYTO® 59 red fluorescent nucleic acid stain *5 mM solution in DMSO*	100 µL
S11342	SYTO® 60 red fluorescent nucleic acid stain *5 mM solution in DMSO*	250 µL
S11343	SYTO® 61 red fluorescent nucleic acid stain *5 mM solution in DMSO*	250 µL
S11344	SYTO® 62 red fluorescent nucleic acid stain *5 mM solution in DMSO*	250 µL
S11345	SYTO® 63 red fluorescent nucleic acid stain *5 mM solution in DMSO*	250 µL
S11346	SYTO® 64 red fluorescent nucleic acid stain *5 mM solution in DMSO*	100 µL
S11340	SYTO® Red Fluorescent Nucleic Acid Stain Sampler Kit *SYTO® dyes 17 and 59-64* *50 µL each*	1 kit
S32703	SYTO® RNASelect™ green fluorescent cell stain *5 mM solution in DMSO*	100 µL
S11348	SYTOX® Blue nucleic acid stain *5 mM solution in DMSO*	250 µL
S7020	SYTOX® Green nucleic acid stain *5 mM solution in DMSO*	250 µL
S11368	SYTOX® Orange nucleic acid stain *5 mM solution in DMSO*	250 µL
T3602	TO-PRO®-1 iodide (515/531) *1 mM solution in DMSO*	1 mL
T3605	TO-PRO®-3 iodide (642/661) *1 mM solution in DMSO*	1 mL
T7596	TO-PRO®-5 iodide (745/770) *1 mM solution in DMSO*	1 mL
T3600	TOTO®-1 iodide (514/533) *1 mM solution in DMSO*	200 µL
T3604	TOTO®-3 iodide (642/660) *1 mM solution in DMSO*	200 µL
Y3603	YO-PRO®-1 iodide (491/509) *1 mM solution in DMSO*	1 mL
Y3607	YO-PRO®-3 iodide (612/631) *1 mM solution in DMSO*	1 mL
Y3601	YOYO®-1 iodide (491/509) *1 mM solution in DMSO*	200 µL
Y3606	YOYO®-3 iodide (612/631) *1 mM solution in DMSO*	200 µL

For current prices or to order online, visit probes.invitrogen.com

8.2 Labeling Oligonucleotides and Nucleic Acids

To facilitate the preparation of optimally labeled nucleic acids, Molecular Probes and its distributors exclusively supply many unique and important reagents and kits. The superior properties of our proprietary dyes ensure that the labeled nucleic acids are the best that can be prepared by each method. Our available technologies include:

- ChromaTide® dUTP, ChromaTide® OBEA-dCTP and ChromaTide® UTP nucleotides, which provide researchers with a large selection of fluorophore- and hapten-labeled nucleotides that can be enzymatically incorporated into DNA or RNA probes for FISH (fluorescence *in situ* hybridization), DNA arrays/microarrays and other hybridization techniques.
- Unlabeled aminoallyl derivatives of dUTP and UTP, as well as unlabeled and labeled aminohexylacrylamide (aha) derivatives of dUTP, that are easy to incorporate into nucleic acids for subsequent conjugation with any of our amine-reactive probes (Chapter 1).
- ULYSIS Nucleic Acid Labeling Kits, which employ a fast, simple and reliable chemical method for labeling nucleic acids without enzymatic incorporation of labeled nucleotides.
- ARES™ DNA Labeling Kits, which employ a versatile, two-step method for labeling DNA with fluorescent dyes to achieve a uniformity and consistency of labeling that is difficult to obtain with conventional enzymatic incorporation of labeled nucleotides.[1]
- Alexa Fluor® Oligonucleotide Amine Labeling Kits, which use familiar chemical labeling of amine-terminated oligonucleotides to prepare the best singly labeled fluorescent oligonucleotide conjugates.

Custom conjugations of most of our proprietary dyes to oligonucleotides for personal research use are available from several authorized sources. A variety of additional methods for preparing labeled oligonucleotides and nucleic acids and using them in nucleic acid sequencing are described in this section. Section 8.5 describes use of labeled nucleic acids as hybridization reagents for microarrays, FISH and real-time PCR assays. Section 8.5 also includes a discussion of our important ELF® and TSA technology for amplifying FISH signals.

Table 8.6 — Characteristics of ChromaTide® UTP nucleotides

Cat # *	Fluorescent UTP Nucleotide	Ex/Em † (nm/nm)	Applications ‡
Green Fluorescence			
C11403	Alexa Fluor® 488-5-UTP	490/520	SP6, T3, T7
C7603	Fluorescein-12-UTP	495/525	SP6, T3, T7
C7613	BODIPY® FL-14-UTP	505/515	SP6, T3, T7
Orange Fluorescence			
C7615	BODIPY® TMR-14-UTP	535/570	SP6, T3, T7
C7605MP	Tetramethylrhodamine-6-UTP	550/570	SP6, T3, T7
C11404	Alexa Fluor® 546-14-UTP	555/570	SP6, T3, T7
Red Fluorescence			
C7607MP	Texas Red®-5-UTP	595/615	SP6, T3, T7
C7617	BODIPY® TR-14-UTP	595/625	SP6, T3, T7

* ChromaTide® UTP nucleotides are supplied as 25 µL of a 1 mM solution in TE buffer. † Excitation (Ex) and emission (Em) maxima, in nm, for the labeled nucleotide. ‡ ChromaTide® UTP nucleotides were incorporated into RNA by standard transcription reactions using the indicated RNA polymerases.

ChromaTide® Nucleotides

Molecular Probes offers a series of uridine triphosphates (UTP, Table 8.6) and deoxyuridine or deoxycytidine triphosphates (dUTP, OBEA-dCTP; Table 8.7) conjugated to an extensive selection of fluorophores and haptens, including several that incorporate our superior Alexa

Table 8.7 — Characteristics of ChromaTide® dUTP, ChromaTide® OBEA-dCTP and aha-dUTP labeled nucleotides

Cat #	dUTP, aha-dUTP or OBEA-dCTP Nucleotide *	Ex/Em †	Applications ‡
Nonfluorescent			
C7610MP	Dinitrophenyl (DNP)-11-dUTP	NA	PCR, RP
B32766	Biotin-aha-dUTP	NA	RT
Blue Fluorescence			
C7612	Cascade Blue®-7-dUTP	400/420	PCR, TDT, RP
Green Fluorescence			
C11397	Alexa Fluor® 488-5-dUTP	490/520	PCR, TDT, RP, RT, NT
C21555	Alexa Fluor® 488-7-OBEA-dCTP	490/520	RT, NT
C7630	Oregon Green® 488-5-dUTP	495/520	PCR, TDT, RP
C7604	Fluorescein-12-dUTP	495/525	PCR, TDT, RP, NT
F32767	Fluorescein-aha-dUTP	495/525	RT
C7614	BODIPY® FL-14-dUTP	505/515	PCR, TDT, RP
C7629	Rhodamine Green™-5-dUTP	505/530	PCR, TDT, RP
Yellow Fluorescence			
C11398	Alexa Fluor® 532-5-dUTP	525/550	PCR, TDT, RP, RT, NT
Orange Fluorescence			
C7616	BODIPY® TMR-14-dUTP	535/570	PCR, TDT, RP
C7606MP	Tetramethylrhodamine-6-dUTP	550/570	PCR, TDT, RP
C11401	Alexa Fluor® 546-14-dUTP	555/570	PCR, TDT, RP, RT, NT
C21556	Alexa Fluor® 546-16-OBEA-dCTP	555/570	RT, NT
A32762	Alexa Fluor® 555-aha-dUTP	555/570	RT
Red Fluorescence			
C11399	Alexa Fluor® 568-5-dUTP	575/600	PCR, TDT, RP, NT
C7631	Texas Red®-12-dUTP	595/610	PCR, TDT, RP
C7608	Texas Red®-5-dUTP	595/615	PCR, TDT, RP
C7618	BODIPY® TR-14-dUTP	595/625	PCR, TDT, RP
C11400	Alexa Fluor® 594-5-dUTP	590/615	PCR, TDT, RP, NT
C21558	Alexa Fluor® 594-7-OBEA-dCTP	590/615	RT, NT
Far-Red Fluorescence			
C11395	BODIPY® 630/650-14-dUTP	630/650	§, TDT, RP, **
C11396	BODIPY® 650/665-14-dUTP	650/670	§, TDT, RP, **
C21559	Alexa Fluor® 647-12-OBEA-dCTP	650/670	RT, NT
A32763	Alexa Fluor® 647-aha-dUTP	650/670	RT

* All products are supplied as either 25 µL (dUTPs) or 50 µL (dCTPs) of a 1 mM solution in TE buffer. † Excitation (Ex) and emission (Em) maxima, in nm, for the labeled nucleotide. ‡ Except where otherwise noted, the following applications were tested: PCR, Taq polymerase for DNA amplification; TDT, terminal deoxynucleotidyl transferase for 3′-end labeling of dsDNA; RP, Klenow polymerase for labeling DNA by random hexamer priming; RT, murine leukemia virus (MLV) reverse transcriptase for synthesizing DNA from an RNA template; NT, nick translation using DNase I and DNA polymerase I. § Not recommended for PCR. ** Not recommended for RT.

Fluor® dyes (see Note 8.1 "Product Highlight: Alexa Fluor® Dyes for Labeling Nucleic Acids"). These ChromaTide® nucleotides are useful for generating labeled nucleic acids for molecular biology and molecular cytogenetics applications, including chromosome and mRNA FISH experiments [2–5] (Figure 8.85), gene expression studies and mutation detection on arrays and microarrays [6–16] (Figure 8.100), and *in situ* PCR and RT-PCR. The ChromaTide® dinitrophenyl (DNP)-11-dUTP (C7610MP) is useful for signal amplification in FISH and microarrays and for detecting probes hybridized to blots (Section 8.5). Our extensive selection of fluorescent labels provides the ideal tools for multicolor techniques such as spectral karyotyping, [17–23] multilocus FISH analysis, [24] "chromosome painting" [25] and comparative genome hybridization [26,27] (Section 8.5).

Structures of the ChromaTide® Nucleotides

The ChromaTide® UTP and dUTP nucleotides are modified at the *C*-5 position of UTP or dUTP via a unique aminoalkynyl linker (Figure 8.38). The *C*-5 position of UTP and dUTP is not involved in Watson–Crick base-pairing and so interferes little with probe hybridization. The aminoalkynyl linker [28] between the fluorophore and the nucleotide in the ChromaTide® UTP and dUTP nucleotides is designed to reduce the fluorophore's interaction with enzymes or target binding sites. In addition to this four-atom bridge, several of these nucleotides contain a seven- to 10-atom spacer that further separates the dye from the base. The number in the product's name (e.g., the "12" in ChromaTide® fluorescein-12-dUTP) indicates the net length of the spacer in atoms. Longer spacers typically result in brighter conjugates and increased hapten accessibility for secondary detection reagents.

The ChromaTide® OBEA-deoxycytidine triphosphates (OBEA-dCTP, Table 8.7) are modified at the *N*-4 position of cytosine using a patented 2-aminoethoxyethyl (OBEA) linker (Figure 8.39). The Alexa Fluor® 546 and Alexa Fluor® 647 OBEA-dCTP conjugates (C21555, C21559) also have a built-in spacer that reduces possible steric interference caused by the presence of the dye.

Fluorescent ChromaTide® Nucleotides

The spectral diversity of our ChromaTide® dUTP and ChromaTide® OBEA-dCTP nucleotides (Table 8.7) and of the ChromaTide® UTP nucleotides (Table 8.6) gives researchers significant flexibility in choosing a label that is compatible with a particular optical detection system or multicolor experiment. Probes made from the fluorescent ChromaTide® nucleotides can be imaged directly; alternatively, some fluorophores can be used as a hapten for signal amplification, as described in Section 8.5. In many cases, the TSA (Section 6.2) or ELF® technologies (Section 6.3) can be used to significantly amplify the signal of dye-labeled hybridization probes in cells and tissues and on microarrays (Section 8.5). Combination of the TSA and ELF® technologies promises to yield the most sensitive detection of *in situ* hybridization that is currently possible. [29] The Alexa Fluor® conjugates of UTP, OBEA-dCTP and dUTP provide fluorophore labels with demonstrably superior fluorescence properties, as compared with conventional dyes (see Note 8.1 "Product Highlight: Alexa Fluor® Dyes for Labeling Nucleic Acids"). The Alexa Fluor® 488, Alexa Fluor® 568 and Alexa Fluor® 594 nucleotides are spectrally similar to fluorescein, Lissamine rhodamine B and Texas Red® conjugates, respectively, but the Alexa Fluor® conjugates exhibit superior spectral and chemical properties. ChromaTide® OBEA-dCTP nucleotides have been prepared from four of our best dyes — the Alexa Fluor® 488, Alexa Fluor® 546, Alexa Fluor® 594 and Alexa Fluor® 647 dyes — with spectra virtually identical to those of fluorescein, Cy3, Texas Red® and Cy5 dyes, respectively (see Note 8.1 "Product Highlight: Alexa Fluor® Dyes for Labeling Nucleic Acids").

The ChromaTide® Alexa Fluor® dUTP and ChromaTide® Alexa Fluor® OBEA-dCTP nucleotides are highly water soluble, as are DNA probes that contain them. Thus, Alexa Fluor® dye–labeled DNA probes do not aggregate or precipitate, even in high-salt hybridization solutions. Fluorescence of the Alexa Fluor® conjugates is not pH sensitive in the range used for hybridization or microscopy mounting media. Additionally, the enhanced photostability of these conjugates makes them ideal for imaging applications.

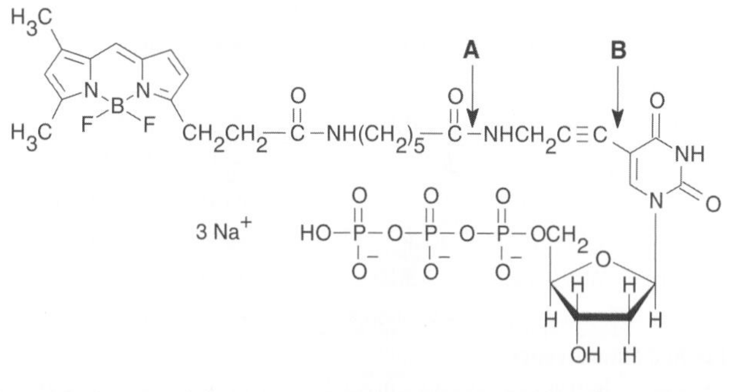

Figure 8.38 Structure of ChromaTide® BODIPY® FL-14-dUTP (C7614). This structure is representative of our other labeled ChromaTide® aminoalkynyl dUTP nucleotides. Fluorophore labels are attached via a four-atom aminoalkynyl spacer (between arrows A and B) to either deoxyuridine triphosphate (dUTP) or uridine triphosphate (UTP). Fluorophore labels for other ChromaTide® nucleotides, which also include OBEA-dCTP nucleotides, are indicated in Table 8.6 and Table 8.7.

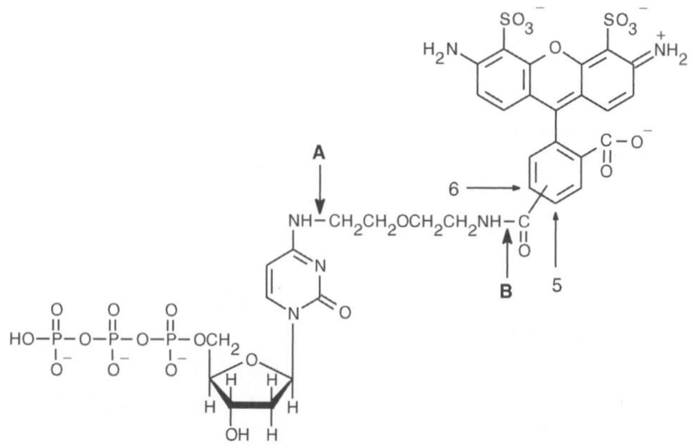

Figure 8.39 Structure of ChromaTide® Alexa Fluor® 488-7-OBEA-dCTP (C21555). This structure is representative of our labeled ChromaTide® OBEA-dCTP nucleotides. Fluorophore labels are attached via the OBEA spacer (between arrows A and B) to deoxycytidine triphosphate (dCTP). Fluorophore labels for other ChromaTide® nucleotides are indicated in Table 8.6 and Table 8.7.

Note 8.1 — Product Highlight

Alexa Fluor® Dyes for Labeling Nucleic Acids

Molecular Probes offers a variety of products for labeling nucleic acids with our family of superior Alexa Fluor® dyes (Section 8.2). The Alexa Fluor® dyes span the visible light spectrum and beyond (Figure 1.17, Figure 1.24, Figure 1.34) making them ideal tools for multicolor applications such as fluorescence *in situ* hybridization (FISH) and microarray experiments (Section 8.5). The spectral diversity provides an enormous amount of flexibility in choosing a label that is compatible with a particular optical detection system or multicolor experiment. The Alexa Fluor® dyes have several properties that make them superior to other fluorescent dyes:

- **High water solubility.** The Alexa Fluor® dyes are highly water soluble, making them ideal for hybridization experiments. Nucleic acids labeled with the Alexa Fluor® dyes do not aggregate or precipitate, even in high-salt conditions.
- **pH independence.** Fluorescence of the Alexa Fluor® conjugates is not pH sensitive in the ranges used for hybridization solutions and microscopy mounting media (Figure 1.12).
- **Resistance to photobleaching.** The enhanced photostability of Alexa Fluor® dyes makes them ideal for applications requiring imaging, such as FISH and microarrays (Figure 1.9, Figure 1.10, Figure 1.11, Figure 1.28).

Nucleic acids labeled with Alexa Fluor® dyes show brighter fluorescence than nucleic acids labeled with similar dyes. We have observed that nucleic acids labeled with the Cy3 dye exhibit abnormal quenching and absorption shifts to shorter wavelengths (Figure 1) that are correlated with a decrease in fluorescence emission (Figure 2).

Nucleic acids labeled with the spectrally similar Alexa Fluor® 546 dye do not show this absorption shift (Figure 1); therefore, they are far brighter than nucleic acids labeled with the Cy3 dye. Nucleic acids labeled with the Cy5 dye also show a similar absorption shift and accompanying loss of fluorescence, whereas nucleic acids labeled with the spectrally similar Alexa Fluor® 647 dye do not (Figure 1). Therefore, nucleic acids labeled with the Alexa Fluor® 647 dye exhibit much brighter fluorescence (Figure 2). The absorption shifts and fluorescence quenching phenomena appear to increase with the level of Cy dye labeling and are reversible upon treatment with nucleases. Thus, higher levels of labeling with Cy dyes do not result in appreciable increase in fluorescence, markedly limiting the brightness achievable with these dyes (Figure 3). Because Alexa Fluor® dyes do not show this absorption shift, nucleic acids can be very highly labeled to produce exceptionally bright and sensitive nucleic acid probes and labeled samples. Furthermore, the Alexa Fluor® 555/Alexa Fluor® 647 dye pair have been shown to display higher signal correlation coefficients than the Cy3/Cy5 dye pair when incorporated into hybridization probes for two-color DNA microarray assays.[1]

Reference

1. Anal Biochem 331, 243 (2004).

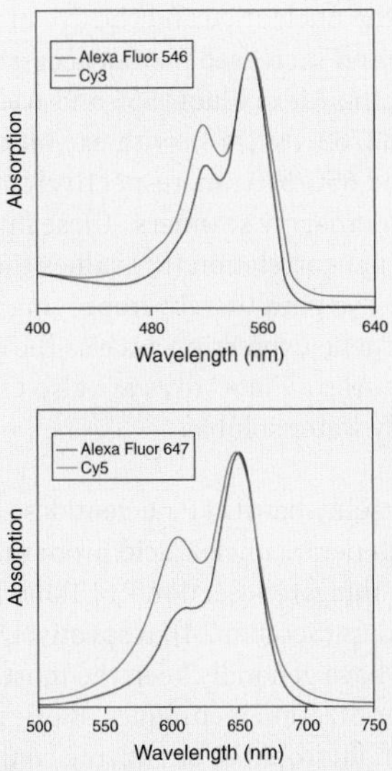

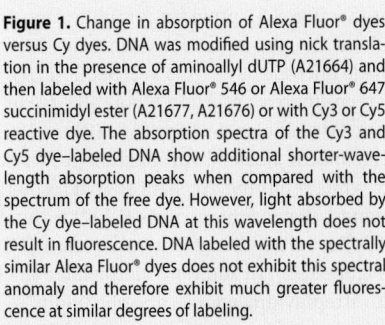

Figure 1. Change in absorption of Alexa Fluor® dyes versus Cy dyes. DNA was modified using nick translation in the presence of aminoallyl dUTP (A21664) and then labeled with Alexa Fluor® 546 or Alexa Fluor® 647 succinimidyl ester (A21677, A21676) or with Cy3 or Cy5 reactive dye. The absorption spectra of the Cy3 and Cy5 dye-labeled DNA show additional shorter-wavelength absorption peaks when compared with the spectrum of the free dye. However, light absorbed by the Cy dye–labeled DNA at this wavelength does not result in fluorescence. DNA labeled with the spectrally similar Alexa Fluor® dyes does not exhibit this spectral anomaly and therefore exhibit much greater fluorescence at similar degrees of labeling.

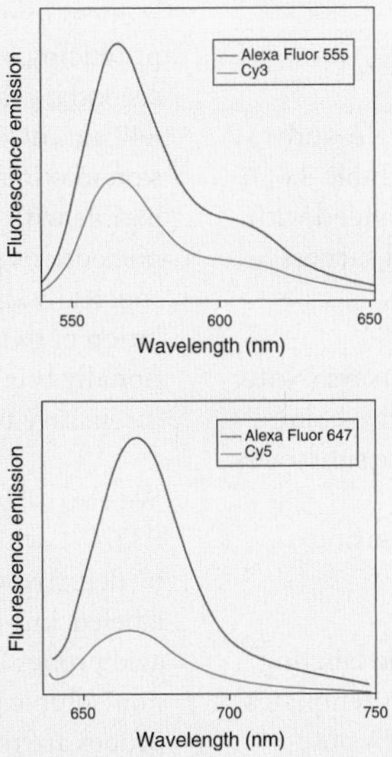

Figure 2. Fluorescence emission of DNA labeled with Alexa Fluor® dyes versus Cy dyes. DNA was amine modified by reverse transcription in the presence of aminoallyl dUTP (A21664). The modified DNA was then labeled with Alexa Fluor® 555 or Alexa Fluor® 647 succinimidyl ester (A21677, A21676) or with Cy3 or Cy5 reactive dye to a level optimal for hybridization. The fluorescence emission spectra for DNA samples labeled to the same degree show that the Alexa Fluor® dye–labeled DNA was consistently brighter than the spectrally similar Cy dye–labeled DNA.

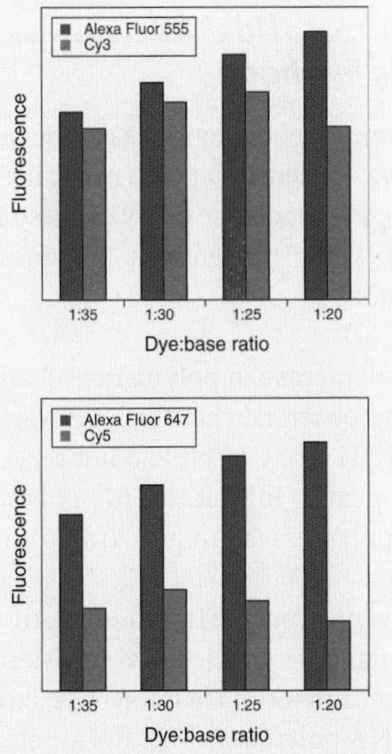

Figure 3. Change in signal brightness with level of labeling for Alexa Fluor® versus Cy dye–labeled DNA. Chromosome 17 α-satellite DNA was amine-modified by nick translation in the presence of varying ratios of aminoallyl dUTP (A21664) to dTTP. The pools of modified DNA were split into equal parts and labeled with Alexa Fluor® 555 or Alexa Fluor® 647 succinimidyl ester (A21677, A21676) or with Cy3 or Cy5 reactive dye. The degree of labeling was calculated for each reaction; each probe was then hybridized to human metaphase chromosomes and the brightness of each signal measured. The brightness of the signal was plotted against the degree of labeling for each dye. At higher levels of labeling, the Alexa Fluor® dyes become brighter, whereas the corresponding Cy dyes become quenched.

We also have available the Oregon Green® 488, Rhodamine Green™ and Texas Red® conjugates of dUTP (C7630, C7629, C7631, C7608). When compared with the corresponding fluorescein conjugates (C7603, C7604), the Oregon Green® 488 and Rhodamine Green™ conjugates have similar fluorescence spectra but superior photostability (Section 1.5). Texas Red®-12-dUTP (C7631) has an emission spectrum in solution that is narrower and about 25% more intense than that of Texas Red®-5-dUTP (C7608). For certain multicolor applications, we recommend conjugates of the BODIPY® dyes because they have narrow emission bandwidths with minimal spectral overlap. The BODIPY® 630/650-14-dUTP (C11395) and BODIPY® 650/665-14-dUTP (C11396) are well suited to excitation by the 633 nm spectral line of the He–Ne laser and the 647 nm spectral line of the Ar–Kr laser, respectively. Oregon Green® 488-5-dUTP has been microinjected into unfertilized oocytes to follow DNA synthesis in oocytes following fertilization.[30] Other microinjected fluorescent nucleotides have been utilized to follow the dynamics of chromosome formation and cell proliferation in live cells.[31,32]

ChromaTide® Dinitrophenyl (DNP)-11-dUTP

Our ChromaTide® dinitrophenyl-11-dUTP (DNP-11-dUTP, C7610MP) can be incorporated into DNA probes using a variety of enzymatic techniques (Table 8.7), providing a hapten that can be combined with fluorophores, biotin or other haptens in double-labeling experiments. The DNP hapten can be detected with our rabbit anti–DNP-KLH antibody, which is available unlabeled (A6430, Section 7.4) or labeled with the Alexa Fluor® 488 dye (A11097, Section 7.4) or fluorescein (A6423, Section 7.4).

Using ChromaTide® Nucleotides in Enzymatic Labeling Methods

The ChromaTide® nucleotides can be incorporated into DNA and RNA using conventional enzymatic labeling techniques (Table 8.6, Table 8.7). Protocols for many of these techniques are provided with the ChromaTide® nucleotides. Enzymes that we have used successfully include:

- *Taq* polymerase in polymerase chain reaction (PCR) assays (Note: we have observed that the long-wavelength BODIPY® dye conjugates (C11395, C11396) do not serve as *Taq* polymerase substrates and appear to inhibit the *Taq* polymerase reaction.)
- DNA polymerase I in nick-translation and primer-extension assays
- Klenow polymerase in random-primer labeling
- Terminal deoxynucleotidyl transferase (TdT) for 3′-end labeling
- Reverse transcriptase for synthesizing DNA from RNA templates
- SP6 RNA polymerase, T3 RNA polymerase and T7 RNA polymerase for *in vitro* transcription

Please note that not all ChromaTide® nucleotides have been tested in all applications. Refer to Table 8.6 and Table 8.7 for information on applications of individual ChromaTide® nucleotides.

ChromaTide® nucleotides have also been used in the TUNEL assay for detecting DNA fragmentation in apoptotic cells[33–36] (Section 15.5, Figure 15.84). Microinjected fluorescent nucleotides are incorporated into cellular nucleic acids where they assemble into chromosomes and persist through cell replication.[31]

Amine-Modified Nucleotides

Unlabeled and Labeled 5-Aminohexylacrylamido-dUTP (Aha-dUTP)

5-Aminohexylacrylamido-dUTP (aha-dUTP) can be used to produce amine-modified DNA by conventional enzymatic incorporation methods such as reverse transcription, nick translation, random-primed labeling or PCR, and it is incorporated more efficiently into DNA than is aminoallyl dUTP. The amine-modified DNA can then be labeled with any amine-reactive dye or hapten (described in Chapter 1). This two-step technique consistently results in a uniform and high degree of DNA labeling that is difficult to obtain by other methods. The protocols provided with the aha-dUTP yield a labeling efficiency of ~5–8 dyes per 100 bases, which we have found to be optimal for fluorescence *in situ* hybridization (FISH), dot blot hybridization and especially microarray applications, in which the consistency of labeling between samples is critical for accurate interpretation of results. The aha-dUTP nucleotide is available as 500 µL of a 2 mM solution (A32760) or as 50 µL of a 50 mM solution (A32761) in 10 mM Tris, 1 mM EDTA, pH 7.5 (TE). Molecular Probes also provides a wide variety of amine-reactive reagents for labeling amine-modified DNA, including succinimidyl esters of our Alexa Fluor® dyes, conventional fluorophores, biotin and dinitrophenyl (DNP) (Chapter 1).

The labeled aha-dUTP nucleotides can be used to generate labeled nucleic acid hybridization probes for many molecular biology and molecular cytogenetics applications, including multicolor techniques. These nucleotides are modified at the *C*-5 position of dUTP with a unique hexylacrylamide linker, which serves as a spacer between the nucleotide and the dye or hapten (Figure 8.40). This spacer reduces interactions between the nucleotide and the dye or hapten, producing brighter conjugates and increased hapten accessibility for secondary detection reagents. The Alexa Fluor® 555 and Alexa Fluor® 647 aha-dUTP nucleotides (A32762, A32763), with excitation/emission maxima of 555/570 nm and 650/670 nm, respectively, are compatible with commonly used microarray scanners. These fluorescent nucleotides provide greater signal correlation (R^2) values than do the spectrally similar Cy3 and Cy5 dye pair, thereby improving the resolution of two-color microarray gene expression assays. The exceptionally bright and photostable Alexa Fluor® dyes are also essentially insensitive to pH and are highly water soluble.

We also offer biotin and fluorescein aha-dUTP nucleotides (B32766, F32767), which can be used to generate nucleic acid probes that can be detected with streptavidin conjugates (Section 7.6, Table 7.22) or labeled anti-fluorescein antibodies (Section 7.4), respectively. Nucleic acid probes labeled with biotin have generally been the most common nonisotopic probes used in hybridization techniques. Biotinylated probes are readily detected with fluorophore or enzyme conjugates of avidins or streptavidins (Section 8.5), providing amplification of the signal (Figure 8.87). Biotin can also be detected with anti-biotin antibodies, which we provide unconjugated (A11242, Section 7.4), or conjugated to the bright green-fluorescent Alexa Fluor® 488 dye or the intensely red-fluorescent Alexa Fluor® 594 dye (A31801, A31800; Section 7.4). The signal from biotin-labeled hybridization probes can be considerably amplified, while retaining excellent spatial resolution, by combination with Enzyme-Labeled Fluorescence (ELF®) technology (Section 8.5, Figure 8.94) or tyramide signal amplification (TSA) technology (Section 8.5, Figure 8.92). In addition, biotinylated nucleic acids can be adsorbed onto streptavidin agarose or CaptAvidin™ agarose (S951, C21386; Section 7.6; Figure 7.99), bound to the streptavidin conjugate of Captivate™ ferrofluid superparamagnetic particles

(C21476, Section 7.6) or detected with NANOGOLD or Alexa Fluor® FluoroNanogold streptavidin [37–39] (N24918, A24926, A24927; Section 7.6).

The aha-dUTP nucleotides have been used in two-color microarray assays, Southern and Northern blots, colony and plaque hybridizations, DNA sequencing, primer extension, DNA and RNA amplification and bead-based separation techniques. In these applications, the labeled samples are generally detected with enzyme conjugates of streptavidin or anti-fluorescein antibody in conjunction with fluorescent, chemiluminescent or colorimetric substrates such as those employed in our Tyramide Signal Amplification (TSA) Kits (Section 6.2, Table 6.1).

Aminoallyl UTP and Aminoallyl dUTP

Aminoallyl UTP [40–42] (5-(3-aminoallyl)uridine 5′-triphosphate, A21663) and aminoallyl dUTP [43] (5-aminoallyl-2′-deoxyuridine 5′-triphosphate; 2 mM in TE, A21664; 50 mM in TE, A32764) can be incorporated into RNA and DNA, respectively, using conventional enzymatic incorporation techniques, as described above for the ChromaTide® UTP, OBEA-dCTP and dUTP nucleotides.[44] The resulting amine-modified nucleic acid can then be labeled using the amine-reactive dyes [1] and other reagents that are described in Chapter 1. Lacking bulky dye groups, the aminoallyl-modified nucleotides can be incorporated to extremely high and consistent levels. Subsequent reaction of the amine-modified nucleic acid with an excess of amine-reactive reagent achieves correspondingly high and consistent labeling efficiency, regardless of the labeling reagent chosen. We typically obtain labeling efficiencies of ~5–8 dyes per 100 bases. This two-step labeling method also eliminates the need to optimize an enzymatic reaction to accommodate different dye-modified nucleotides, which may incorporate at very different rates. This labeling method is ideal for both FISH probes (Figure 8.86, Figure 8.41) and microarray-based experiments (Figure 8.96). Aminoallyl dUTP labeling can be achieved easily using our convenient

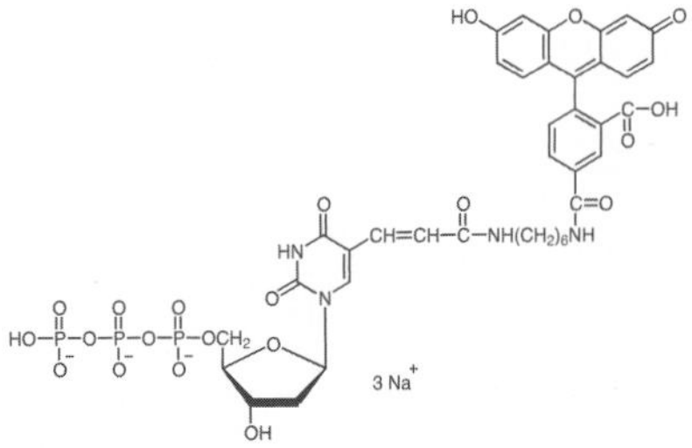

Figure 8.40 F32767 fluorescein-aha-dUTP.

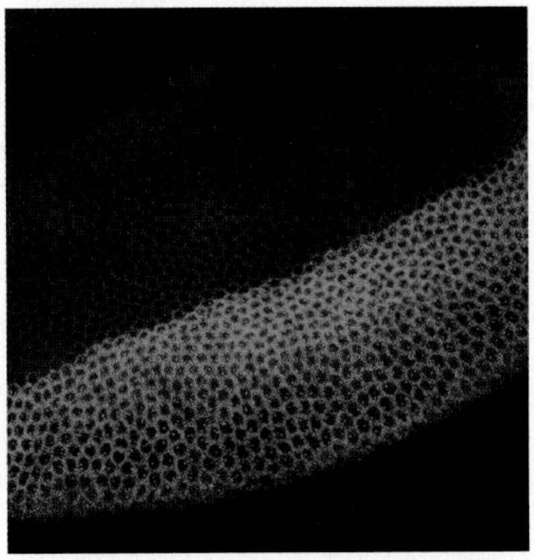

Figure 8.41 Expression of snail RNA in an early-stage fruit fly embryo visualized by FISH. A 1.7 kb RNA probe corresponding to the snail gene was labeled by *in vitro* transcription using aminoallyl UTP (A21663) followed by reaction with Alexa Fluor® 488 carboxylic acid, succinimidyl ester (A20000, A20100). The probe was hybridized to *Drosophila melanogaster* embryos and imaged using confocal laser-scanning microscopy. Image contributed by David Kosman and Ethan Bier, University of California, San Diego.

ARES™ DNA Labeling Kits (see below), which provide aminoallyl dUTP, premeasured aliquots of our best reactive dyes and carefully tested protocols.

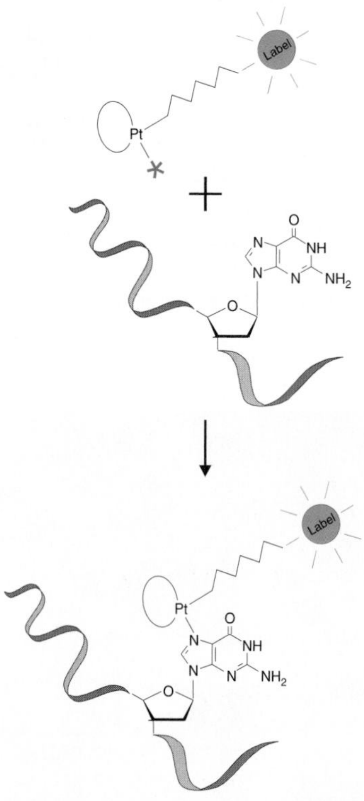

Figure 8.42 Schematic diagram of the labeling method provided in our ULYSIS Nucleic Acid Labeling Kits (Table 8.8). The ULS reagent in the ULYSIS Nucleic Acid Labeling Kits reacts with the *N*-7 position of guanine residues to provide a stable coordination complex between the nucleic acid and the fluorophore label.

Alexa Fluor® Amine-Reactive Dye Decapacks for Labeling Amine-Modified DNA and RNA

For labeling amine-modified DNA or RNA probes in microarray-based experiments, we offer three of our outstanding amine-reactive Alexa Fluor® dyes conveniently packaged in 10 single-use vials and rigorously tested for the ability to efficiently label aminoallyl-modified DNA — the Alexa Fluor® 555 reactive dye decapack (A32756), the Alexa Fluor® 594 reactive dye decapack (A32751), the Alexa Fluor® 647 reactive dye decapack (A32757) and also a set containing both the Alexa Fluor® 555 and Alexa Fluor® 647 reactive dye decapacks (A32755) for two-color experiments. These specially packaged amine-reactive dyes can be used in conjunction with our aminohexylacrylamido-dUTP (aha-dUTP, A32760), aminoallyl dUTP or aminoallyl UTP (A21664, A21663) nucleotides or with commercially available aminoallyl nucleotide–based nucleic acid labeling kits. With excitation/emission maxima of 555/565 nm, 590/617 nm and 650/668 nm, respectively, the Alexa Fluor® 555, Alexa Fluor® 594 and Alexa Fluor® 647 succinimidyl esters match the most popular wavelength channels used to scan microarrays. Furthermore, the Alexa Fluor® 555/Alexa Fluor® 647 dye pair have been shown to display higher signal correlation coefficients than the Cy3/Cy5 dye pair in two-color DNA microarray assays.[45]

5-Bromo-2′-Deoxyuridine, 5-Bromo-dUTP (BrdUTP) and 5-Bromo-UTP (BrUTP)

Cells can naturally incorporate the thymidine analog 5-bromo-2′-deoxyuridine (BrdU, B23151) into their DNA during cell division, making this nucleoside analog an excellent marker of both cell cycle and cell proliferation.[46] Analysis of incorporated BrdU can be either by direct detection with an antibody to BrdU-modified DNA or by modification of the fluorescence of a nucleic acid stain. For instance, the fluorescence of TO-PRO®-3 and LDS 751 is considerably enhanced by the presence of BrdU in DNA,[47] whereas that of the Hoechst dyes is specifically quenched.[48] 5-Bromo-2′-deoxyuridine 5′-triphosphate (BrdUTP, B21550) is commonly used in TUNEL-based methods to detect proliferating or apoptotic cells,[34,35] as in the ABSOLUTE-S SBIP Cell Proliferation Assay Kit (A23150, Section 15.4, Figure 15.63) and the Apo-BrdU TUNEL Assay Kit (A23210, Section 15.5). In addition, this nucleotide is a substrate for reverse transcriptase[49,50] and has been used in a sensitive nonisotopic assay for detection of HIV-1–associated reverse transcriptase activity.[49,51] Similarly, the corresponding brominated ribonucleotide, 5-bromouridine 5′-triphosphate (BrUTP, B21551), is an excellent substrate for RNA polymerase[52] and has been used to monitor nucleolar transcription *in situ*.[53,54]

BrdUTP, a component of the Apo-BrdU TUNEL Assay Kit (A23210, Section 15.5), is readily incorporated into apoptotic cells by terminal deoxynucleotidyl transferase (TdT), and is apparently metabolized in cells like thymidine 5′-triphosphate. Furthermore, UV light—induced photolysis of nucleic acids that have incorporated BrdU from either 5-bromo-2′-deoxyuridine or BrdUTP

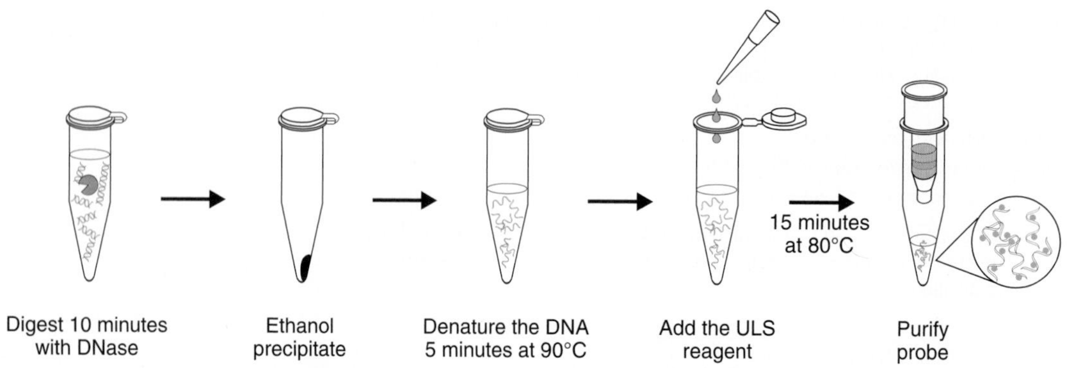

Figure 8.43 Nucleic acid labeling method provided in our ULYSIS Nucleic Acid Labeling Kits (Table 8.8).

are susceptible to photolytic cleavage, which is the basis for nucleic acid labeling and detection in the ABSOLUTE-S SBIP Cell Proliferation Assay Kit[34,35,55] (A23150, Section 15.4). BrdUTP can also be used to detect excision and repair of strand breaks in UV light–damaged DNA in cells.[56] BrdUTP is a substrate for reverse transcriptase[49,50] and Klenow polymerase,[57,58] and has been used in a sensitive nonisotopic assay for detecting HIV-1–associated reverse transcriptase activity.[49,51] Nucleic acids containing halogenated bases can be photocrosslinked to proteins with which they interact.[59,60] BrUTP and BrdUTP can serve as low-cost building blocks for nucleic acid probes, in the manner of the fluorescent ChromaTide® nucleotides (see below), with detection by labeled anti-BrdU antibodies (Section 15.4). BrUTP is reported to be a better substrate for RNA polymerase than is UTP itself.[52] BrUTP that has been microinjected into cells is incorporated into RNA of a nucleolar compartment.[53,54] For an especially efficient and low-cost method of producing large quantities of DNA probe, BrdUTP can be incorporated into DNA by cells or plasmid-containing bacteria grown in the presence of BrdU.[61]

Molecular Probes offers anti-BrdU mouse monoclonal antibodies conjugated with several of our superior Alexa Fluor® dyes (Section 15.4). Because incorporation of BrdU and the related BrdUTP into DNA is *specific*, use of the labeled anti-BrdU antibody permits unequivocal detection of DNA in cells. Also, our fluorescently labeled anti-BrdU antibody crossreacts with ribonucleic acids that have incorporated bromouridine or BrUTP, thus permitting the only method of *specifically* detecting transcribed RNA in cells with a fluorescent dye.

ULYSIS Nucleic Acid Labeling Kits

ULYSIS Nucleic Acid Labeling Kits (Table 8.8) combine some of Molecular Probes' best fluorescent dyes with the versatile, patented Universal Linkage System (ULS) platinum-based chemistry developed at KREATECH Diagnostics, resulting in a simple, fail-safe method for producing bright, fluorophore-labeled hybridization probes.[22,62,63] The ULS labeling technique directly labels nucleic acids without the need for enzymatic incorporation of modified nucleotides. The ULS method is based on the use of a platinum–dye complex, patented by KREATECH Biotechnology BV, that forms a stable adduct with the *N*-7 position of guanine and, to a lesser extent, adenine bases in DNA, RNA, PNA and oligonucleotides (Figure 8.42). The labeling reaction requires only 15 minutes, and separation of the labeled nucleic acids from the unreacted ULS complex can be accomplished through use of a simple spin-column procedure (Figure 8.43). DNA longer than ~1000 base pairs requires a 10-minute DNase digestion before labeling, which both optimizes labeling and fragments the probe for efficient hybridization.

The ULYSIS Kits allow researchers to label DNA with a wide variety of our exceptionally bright and photostable Alexa Fluor® dyes (see Note 8.1 "Product Highlight: Alexa Fluor® Dyes for Labeling Nucleic Acids") and the Oregon Green® 488 dye (Table 8.8). Probes labeled using the ULYSIS Kits are stable indefinitely and hybridize effectively to target DNA. The ULS method has been used to prepare labeled probes for dot, Southern, and Northern blot analysis, RNA and DNA *in situ* hybridization, multicolor fluorescence *in situ* hybridization (FISH, Section 8.5; Figure 8.44, Figure 8.83, Figure 8.84), comparative genome hybridization (CGH) and microarray analysis (Figure 8.99). We maintain a bibliography of references for the ULS technology that use our ULS reagents and those previously described (U24832). Combination of the Oregon Green® 488 dye or Alexa Fluor® 488 dye with antibodies to these dyes (Section 7.4) permits detection by chemiluminescent, chromogenic or fluorogenic enzyme-linked methods — including signal amplification schemes that use the TSA and ELF® technologies (Section 8.5) or the BOLD APB chemiluminescent substrate for alkaline phosphatase (B21901, Section 8.4).

Each ULYSIS Nucleic Acid Labeling Kit provides:

- ULS labeling reagent and an appropriate solvent
- Labeling buffer
- Deoxyribonuclease I (DNase I), for digesting DNA longer than 1000 base pairs prior to labeling
- DNase I storage buffer
- Concentrated DNase I reaction buffer
- Control DNA from calf thymus
- Nuclease-free H_2O
- A detailed procedure for preparing fluorescent DNA hybridization probes optimized for chromosome *in situ* hybridization and dot-blot hybridization

Sufficient materials are supplied in each kit for 20 labelings of 1 µg DNA each.

Table 8.8 — Spectral characteristics of the fluorescent dyes available in Molecular Probes' ULYSIS Nucleic Acid Labeling Kits

Cat #	Fluorophore	Ex/Em *	Similar Dyes
U21658	Pacific Blue™	410/455	SpectrumAqua
U21650	Alexa Fluor® 488	490/520	Fluorescein (FITC or FAM), SpectrumGreen
U21659	Oregon Green® 488	495/520	Fluorescein (FITC or FAM), SpectrumGreen
U21651	Alexa Fluor® 532	525/550	Rhodamine 6G
U21652	Alexa Fluor® 546	555/570	Cy3 dye, tetramethylrhodamine (TRITC), SpectrumOrange
U21653	Alexa Fluor® 568	575/600	Lissamine rhodamine B dye
U21654	Alexa Fluor® 594	590/615	Texas Red® dye, SpectrumRed
U21660	Alexa Fluor® 647	650/670	Cy5 dye
U21656	Alexa Fluor® 660	660/690	Cy5 dye, Cy5.5 dye
U21657	Alexa Fluor® 680	680/700	Cy5.5 dye

* Excitation (Ex) and Emission (Em) maxima, in nm.

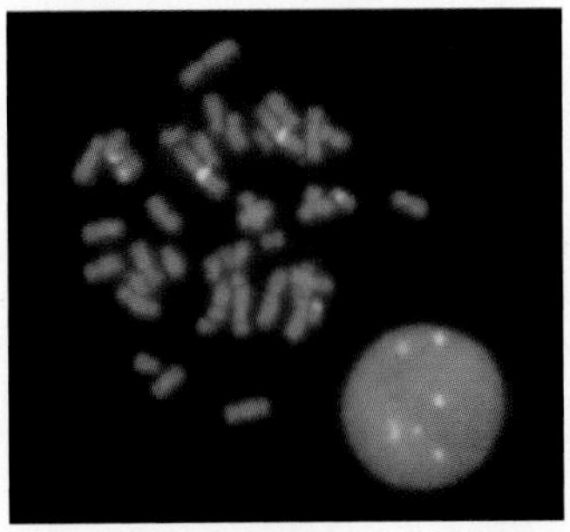

Figure 8.44 Centromere probes to chromosome 1, chromosome 15 and chromosome 17 were labeled with the ULYSIS Alexa Fluor® 546 (U21652), Alexa Fluor® 594 (U21654) and Oregon Green® 488 Nucleic Acid (U21659) Labeling Kits, respectively, and hybridized to human metaphase chromosomes. The chromosomes were then counterstained with Hoechst 33342 (H1399, H3570, H21492).

ARES™ DNA Labeling Kits

ARES™ DNA Labeling Kits (Table 8.9) provide a versatile two-step method for labeling DNA with fluorescent dyes [1] (Figure 8.45). This method achieves uniformity and consistency of labeling that is difficult to obtain with conventional enzymatic incorporation of labeled nucleotides. In the first step, an amine-modified nucleotide, 5-(3-aminoallyl)-dUTP, is enzymatically incorporated into DNA. This step ensures relatively uniform labeling of the probe with primary amine groups. The aminoallyl dUTP substrate used in this reaction is taken up efficiently by reverse transcription or nick translation, for which we provide the protocols; other enzymatic methods are also likely to be compatible. In the second step, the amine-modified DNA is chemically labeled using an amine-reactive fluorescent dye. This chemical reaction varies little in its efficiency from dye to dye, so that it is possible to use any combination of the ARES™ Kits, with their broad selection of the brightest and most photostable dyes, and obtain consistent labeling for every DNA sample. The labeling protocols provided generally result in about one dye per 12–20 bases, which we have determined to be optimal for FISH and dot-blot hybridization. Nucleic acids labeled using this method are ideal for FISH (Figure 8.46) or microarray experiments (Figure 8.96).

The ARES™ Kits are supplied with some of our best fluorescent dyes (Table 8.9). The Alexa Fluor® dyes (Section 1.3) have properties superior to conventional dyes for labeling nucleic acids (see Note 8.1 "Product Highlight: Alexa Fluor® Dyes for Labeling Nucleic Acids"). The Oregon Green® 488 dye is a modified fluorescein with reduced pH sensitivity and higher photostability (Figure 1.12, Figure 1.61). The signal of nucleic acids labeled with this dye can be amplified using our anti-fluorescein/Oregon Green® antibodies, as described in Section 8.5.

Each ARES™ DNA Labeling Kit provides:

- 5-(3-Aminoallyl)-dUTP
- Amine-reactive fluorescent dye and an appropriate solvent
- Sodium bicarbonate
- Nuclease-free H_2O
- A detailed protocol for labeling DNA using reverse transcriptase or nick translation

Sufficient materials are supplied for 5–10 labelings, each containing 1–5 µg DNA. The 5-(3-aminoallyl)-dUTP (A21664, Figure 8.47) and succinimidyl ester dyes are also available as stand-alone reagents. Enzymatic incorporation of 5-(3-aminoallyl)-dUTP permits incorporation of almost any amine-reactive dye in Chapter 1 into nucleic acids.[43]

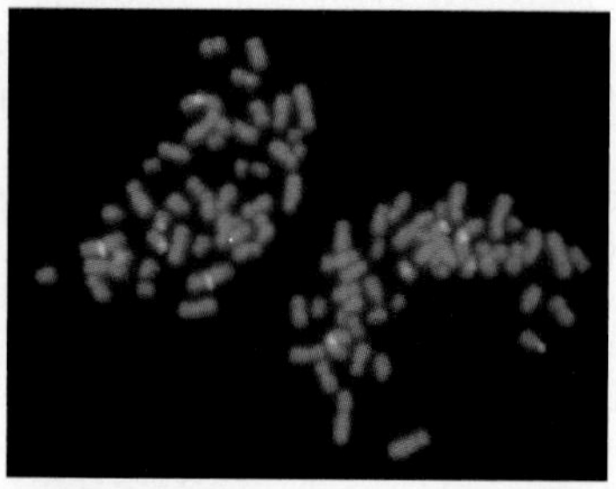

Figure 8.46 Fluorescent probes generated with ARES™ DNA Labeling Kits hybridized to human metaphase chromosome spreads. Centromere probes specific for chromosomes 17, 1 and 15 were prepared by nick translation and labeled with kits containing green-fluorescent Alexa Fluor® 488 (A21665), red-orange–fluorescent Alexa Fluor® 546 (A21667) and red-fluorescent Alexa Fluor® 594 (A21669) dyes. DNA was counterstained with the blue-fluorescent Hoechst 33342 dye (H1399, H3570, H21491), and the slides were mounted using the ProLong® Antifade Kit (P7481). This multiple-exposure image was obtained with bandpass filter sets appropriate for fluorescein, rhodamine, Texas Red® dye and DAPI.

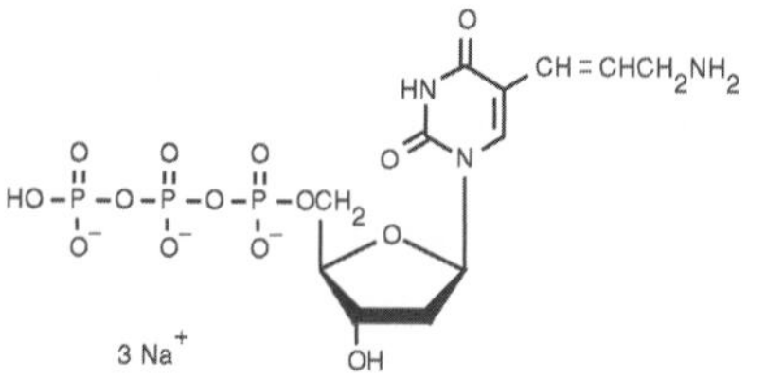

Figure 8.47 A21664 aminoallyl dUTP (5-(3-aminoallyl)-2′-deoxyuridine 5′-triphosphate, trisodium salt).

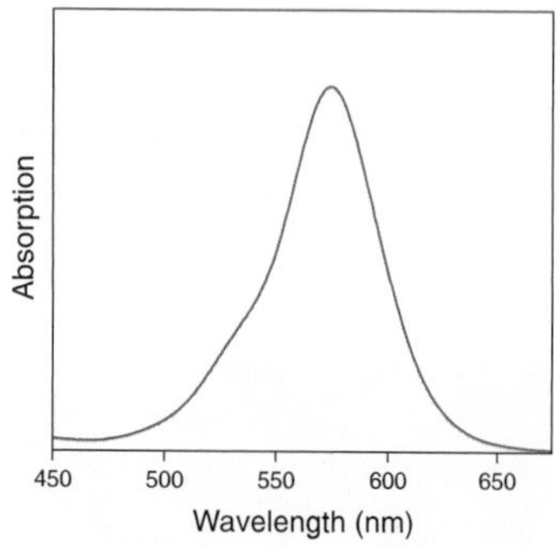

Figure 8.48 Absorption spectrum of 5′-QSY® 7–labeled M13 primer in pH 7.5 TE buffer.

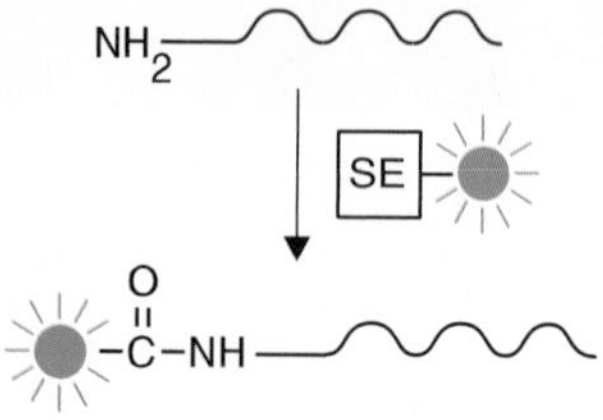

Figure 8.49 Schematic diagram of labeling amine-modified oligodeoxynucleotides with succinimidyl ester dyes.

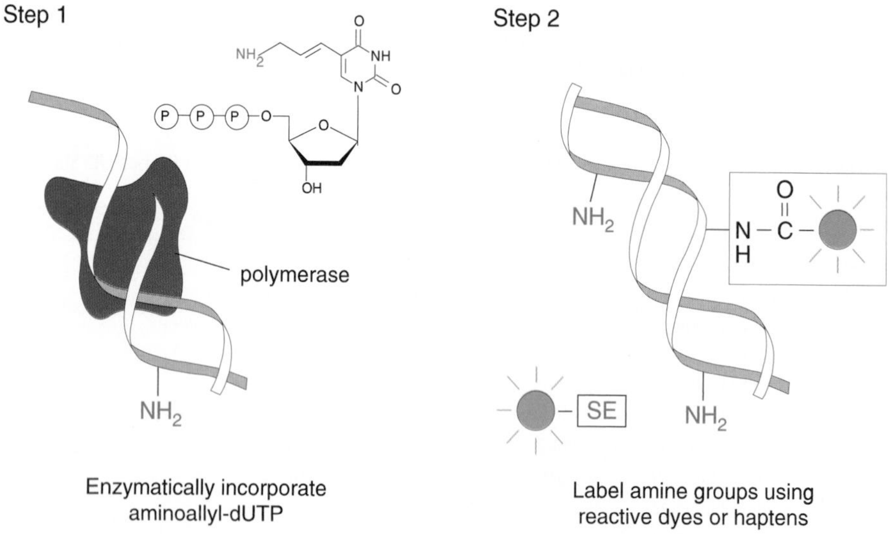

Figure 8.45 Schematic diagram of the labeling method provided in our ARES™ DNA Labeling Kits (Table 8.9). The ARES™ DNA Labeling Kits use a two-step method to label DNA. **Step 1)** The aminoallyl dUTP is enzymatically incorporated. **Step 2)** A reactive fluorophore is used to label the incorporated aminoallyl group.

Labeled Oligonucleotides

DNA can also be labeled from RNA templates by reverse transcription using fluorophore-labeled random oligonucleotide primers and unlabeled deoxynucleotide triphosphates. Molecular Probes provides two types of labeled oligodeoxynucleotides that can be used for this purpose. Our dT_{18} oligodeoxynucleotides (O21561, O21562, O21563) are labeled at the 5′-terminus with one of three of our popular Alexa Fluor® dyes (Table 8.18). The labeled dT_{18} oligodeoxynucleotides hybridize to poly(A) tails in RNA samples, providing primers for reverse transcription or hybridization probes for poly(A)-terminated mRNA in cell- and solution assays. Our Panomer™ 9 random-sequence oligodeoxynucleotides (Section 8.5) are covalently labeled on the 5′-terminus with one of our proprietary fluorescent dyes, with a nonfluorescent QSY® 7 quencher dye (Figure 8.48) or with biotin (Table 8.18). The Panomer™ 9 oligonucleotides are also useful as primers for synthesizing labeled DNA via Klenow DNA polymerase or reverse transcriptase. In these reactions, the primer provides the fluorescent label, whereas unlabeled nucleotides are incorporated by the enzyme. This labeling strategy ensures efficient and unbiased incorporation of nucleotides, because the bulky dye molecule does not interfere with nucleotide incorporation. However, because the synthesized probe contains only a single fluorophore, the labeling efficiency will typically be lower than that achieved by incorporating fluorophore-labeled nucleotides.

Labeling Amine- and Thiol-Modified Oligonucleotides

Amine or thiol groups can be incorporated into a chemically synthesized oligonucleotide. These groups can then be directly conjugated to an amine-reactive (Chapter 1) or thiol-reactive (Chapter 2) fluorophore or hapten (Figure 8.49). Fluorophore-labeled oligonucleotides are extensively used as primers for sequencing or PCR reactions (see below). Double-labeled oligonucleotides are used to produce fluorescence resonance energy transfer (FRET) (see Note 1.2 "Technical Focus: Fluorescence Resonance Energy Transfer (FRET)" in Section 1.3) or quenched reporters for real-time PCR assays (Section 8.5). Labeled oligonucleotides can also be used as probes for fluorescence *in situ* hybridization (Section 8.5).

Alexa Fluor® Oligonucleotide Amine Labeling Kits

The Alexa Fluor® Oligonucleotide Amine Labeling Kits (Table 8.10) provide the reagents required for labeling synthetic oligonucleotides that have amine groups incorporated at their 5′- or 3′-terminus. Our outstanding Alexa Fluor® dyes (Section 1.3) have properties superior to conventional dyes, including exceptionally high quantum yields, large extinction coefficients, excellent photostability, reduced pH sensitivity and improved water solubility (see Note 8.1 "Product Highlight: Alexa Fluor® Dyes for Labeling Nucleic Acids"). These dyes have excitation and emission wavelengths that span much of the visible-light spectrum (Figure 1.17, Figure 1.24, Figure 1.34). Following purification by standard chromatographic or electrophoretic procedures, these singly labeled oligonucleotides can serve as primers for a variety of applications. The dye-labeled oligonucleotides may also serve as FRET acceptors or donors in hybridization reactions (see Note 1.2 "Technical Focus: Fluorescence Resonance Energy Transfer (FRET)" in Section 1.3). Each Alexa Fluor® Oligonucleotide Amine Labeling Kit provides the reagents required for three labelings of 50 µg each, a detailed protocol and recommendations for methods to purify and characterize the conjugates.

Alexa Fluor® Amine-Reactive Dye Decapacks

For microarray users, we offer three of our outstanding amine-reactive Alexa Fluor® dyes conveniently packaged in 10 single-use vials and rigorously tested for the ability to efficiently label aminoallyl-modified DNA — the Alexa Fluor® 555 reactive dye decapack (A32756), the Alexa Fluor® 594 reactive dye decapack (A32751), the Alexa Fluor® 647 reactive dye decapack (A32757) and also a set containing both the Alexa Fluor® 555 and Alexa Fluor® 647 reactive dye decapacks (A32755) for two-color experiments. These specially packaged amine-reactive dyes can be used in conjunction with our aminohexylacrylamido-dUTP (aha-dUTP, A32760), aminoallyl dUTP or aminoallyl UTP (A21664, A21663) nucleotides or with commercially available aminoallyl nucleotide–based nucleic acid labeling kits.

The Alexa Fluor® 554 and Alexa Fluor® 647 succinimidyl esters produce high-efficiency labeling of aminoallyl-modified DNA or RNA — as high as one dye every 12 bases. With excitation/emission maxima of 555/565 nm and 650/670 nm, respectively, the Alexa Fluor® 555 and Alexa Fluor® 647 succinimidyl esters match the most popular wavelength channels used to scan microarrays. The Alexa Fluor® 555 and Alexa Fluor® 647 reactive dye decapacks contain 10 vials of each

Table 8.9 — Spectral characteristics of the fluorescent dyes available in Molecular Probes' ARES™ DNA Labeling Kits

Cat #	Fluorophore	Ex/Em *	Spectrally Similar Dyes
A21675	Alexa Fluor® 350	346/442	AMCA
A21665	Alexa Fluor® 488	490/520	Fluorescein (FITC), SpectrumGreen
A21666	Alexa Fluor® 532	525/550	Rhodamine 6G
A21667	Alexa Fluor® 546	555/570	Cy3 dye, tetramethylrhodamine (TRITC), SpectrumOrange
A21677	Alexa Fluor® 555	555/565	Cy3 dye, tetramethylrhodamine (TRITC), SpectrumOrange
A21668	Alexa Fluor® 568	575/600	Lissamine rhodamine B dye
A21669	Alexa Fluor® 594	590/615	Texas Red® dye, SpectrumRed
A21676	Alexa Fluor® 647	650/670	Cy5 dye
A21671	Alexa Fluor® 660	660/690	Cy5 dye, Cy5.5 dye
A21672	Alexa Fluor® 680	680/700	Cy5.5 dye

* Excitation (Ex) and Emission (Em) maxima, in nm.

Table 8.10 — Oligonucleotide Amine Labeling Kits

Cat #	Fluorophore	Ex/Em *
A20190	Alexa Fluor® 350	345/440
A20191	Alexa Fluor® 488	490/520
A20192	Alexa Fluor® 532	525/550
A20193	Alexa Fluor® 546	555/570
A20197	Alexa Fluor® 555	555/565
A20194	Alexa Fluor® 568	575/600
A20195	Alexa Fluor® 594	590/615
A20196	Alexa Fluor® 647	650/670

* Approximate excitation (Ex) and emission (Em) maxima, in nm.

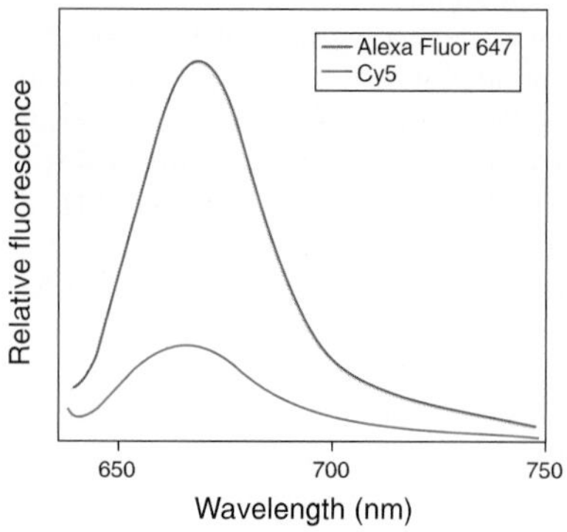

Figure 8.50 Fluorescence emission spectra of single-stranded DNA labeled with equivalent levels of the Alexa Fluor® 647 dye (blue curve) or Cy5 dye (red curve) using aminoallyl dUTP incorporation followed by incubation with a reactive dye. While the absorbance for the two samples is similar, the fluorescence emission from the Alexa Fluor® 647 dye–labeled DNA is several times more intense than that of the Cy5 dye–labeled DNA.

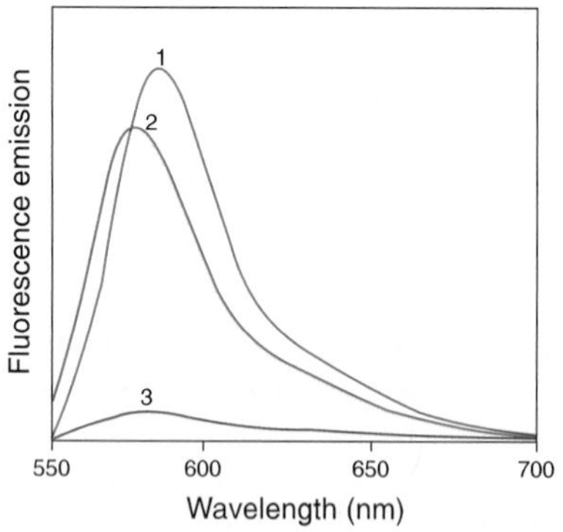

Figure 8.51 Fluorescence quenching of 5′-tetramethylrhodamine–labeled M13 primers by nonfluorescent dyes attached at the 3′-end. The comparison represents equal concentrations of oligonucleotides with (**1**) no 3′-quencher (control), (**2**) 3′-dabcyl quencher, (**3**) 3′-QSY® 7 quencher.

dye, which is enough dye for 10 standard two-color experiments. Each single-use vial contains sufficient dye to optimally label the amount of cDNA produced from reverse transcription of either 20 µg of total RNA or 1–5 µg of poly(A)+ RNA, in the presence of aminoallyl dUTP. For added convenience, we also offer the Alexa Fluor® 555 succinimidyl ester and the Alexa Fluor® 647 succinimidyl ester in separate packs of 10 vials each in the Alexa Fluor® 555 reactive dye decapack (A32756) and the Alexa Fluor® 647 reactive dye decapack (A32757).

Each decapack includes 10 single-use vial of amine-reactive Alexa Fluor® succinimidyl ester; sufficient dye is provided in each vial for optimally labeling the amount of cDNA produced from reverse transcription of either 20 µg of total RNA or 1–5 µg of poly(A)+ RNA in the presence of aminoallyl dUTP. With excitation/emission maxima of 555/565 nm, 590/617 nm and 650/668 nm, respectively, the Alexa Fluor® 555, Alexa Fluor® 594 and Alexa Fluor® 647 succinimidyl esters match the most popular wavelength channels used to scan microarrays. Furthermore, when single-stranded DNA is labeled with equivalent levels of Alexa Fluor® 647 dye or Cy5 dye using aminoallyl dUTP incorporation, the fluorescence emission from Alexa Fluor® 647–labeled DNA is several times more intense than that of Cy5 dye–labeled DNA (Figure 8.50).

Other Reactive Fluorescent Dyes and Quenchers

Several other dyes in Chapter 1 and Chapter 2, including the dyes for sequencing applications (see below), carboxydichlorofluorescein, carboxyrhodamine 6G, Rhodamine Green™ and Texas Red® derivatives, can be used to label primers, deoxynucleotides or dideoxynucleotides for nucleic acid sequencing and other applications. Oligonucleotides labeled with multiple dyes that form excited-state energy transfer pairs enhance the detection in sequencing applications that depend on the argon-ion laser for excitation and are particularly useful for the molecular beacon, TaqMan and related technologies [64] (Section 8.5). The Rhodamine Green™ and BODIPY® 505/515 dyes (see below) are useful for DNA sequencing using fluorescence decay lifetime measurements, a technique that uses the different lifetimes of the dyes to separate the fluorescence signals.[65] For optimal labeling of oligonucleotides that will be used with secondary detection reagents, we recommend amine-reactive haptens and fluorophores that contain aminohexanoyl spacers ("X") to reduce the label's interaction with the oligonucleotide and enhance its accessibility to secondary detection reagents. Oregon Green® 488-X, Rhodamine Green™-X, Rhodamine Red™-X, Texas Red®-X, fluorescein-X, tetramethylrhodamine-X, biotin-X, biotin-XX, DSB-X™ biotin and DNP-X succinimidyl esters (Table 4.2) are reactive forms of popular fluorescent dyes or haptens with aminohexanoyl spacer arms.

Our nonfluorescent QSY® 7, QSY® 9 and QSY® 21 dyes (Section 1.6) have absorption in the visible and near-infrared spectrum (Figure 1.70, Figure 8.48), making them excellent energy transfer acceptors from a wide variety of dyes that emit in the visible range, including fluoresceins, Oregon Green® dyes, rhodamines, Texas Red®, Cy3 and several of the Alexa Fluor® dyes [66] (Figure 8.51, Table 1.10) (see Note 1.2 "Technical Focus: Fluorescence Resonance Energy Transfer (FRET)" in Section 1.3). Conjugates of the QSY® 35 dye have somewhat shorter-wavelength absorption (Figure 1.70) and are useful as quenchers of UV light–excited fluorescent dyes. Oligonucleotide conjugates of the nonfluorescent dabcyl succinimidyl ester (D2245, Figure 1.122) have also been extensively used for FRET-based and quencher-based assays.[67–70] Several applications of QSY® and dabcyl conjugates of oligonucleotides are discussed in Section 8.5. A unique method that uses QSY® dye–conjugated oligonucleotides to reduce the background from "primer dimers" in real-time PCR assays is described in Section 8.3 (Figure 8.67).

The amine-reactive succinimidyl esters of the SYBR® 101, SYBR® 102 and SYBR® 103 dyes (S21500, S21501, S21502) can be coupled with amine-derivatized oligonucleotides. The conjugates may fluoresce green as the result of intramolecular or intermolecular association of the dye with the nucleic acid backbone; however, changes in intensity and fluorescence polarization may occur during hybridization reactions. Similar amine-reactive versions of the cyanine dyes have been utilized to label peptide–nucleic acid conjugates (PNA) and to detect their hybridization to target nucleic acids in solution.[71–74]

Dyes for Sequencing Applications

Molecular Probes is the primary manufacturer of several dyes that are used directly or indirectly in nucleic acid sequencing and provides these dyes in reactive forms for preparing conjugates (Table 8.11). Because the electrophoretic separation step during sequencing is highly sensitive to the chemical structure of the fragments, the use of single-isomer labels is essential. In addition to providing high-purity reactive succinimidyl esters of the common FAM, JOE, TET, HEX, TAMRA and ROX dyes, Molecular Probes also prepares amine-reactive single isomers of carboxyrhodamine 6G (CR 6G) (Table 8.11). The 6-isomer of the CR 6G dye has spectroscopic and electrophoretic properties that are superior to the JOE dye often used for automated DNA sequencing. Contact our Custom and Bulk Sales Department for information about availability of any of our reactive dyes in bulk.

Certain BODIPY® dyes (Section 1.4) have been shown to be very useful for DNA sequencing,[75–77] in part because the dyes have a minimal effect on the mobility of the fragment during electrophoresis and also exhibit well-resolved spectra with narrow bandwidths (Figure 1.41). Using BODIPY® dye energy transfer pairs further improves sensitivity. The patented BODIPY® dyes are all high-purity, pH-insensitive single isomers.

BODIPY® FL-X, BODIPY® TMR-X and BODIPY® TR-X succinimidyl esters (Section 1.4) are reactive versions of the BODIPY® fluorophores with emission properties similar to those of fluorescein, tetramethylrhodamine and Texas Red® dyes, respectively (Figure 1.43). The BODIPY® fluorophores exhibit high extinction coefficients, excellent quantum yields and a fluorescence emission that is quite photostable and insensitive to pH (Section 1.4). The narrow absorption and emission bandwidths of these BODIPY® fluorophores (Figure 1.41) make them particularly well suited to multicolor applications. The BODIPY® 630/650-X and BODIPY® 650/665-X succinimidyl esters provide long-wavelength amine-reactive fluorophores that match filter sets optimized for the Alexa Fluor® 647 and Cy5 dyes (Table 23.9). Oligonucleotide conjugates of the BODIPY® FL, BODIPY® R6G, BODIPY® 564/570 and BODIPY® FL, BODIPY® R6G, BODIPY® 564/570 and BODIPY® 581/591dyes have been found to be particularly useful for automated DNA sequencing.[75–77]

Labeling Phosphate-Modified Oligonucleotides

A fluorophore or hapten containing an aliphatic amine may be conjugated to the 3′- or 5′-phosphate group of an oligonucleotide by using the zero-length crosslinker EDAC (E2247, Section 3.3) in an *N*-methylimidazole buffer at pH 9. This reaction results in a phosphoramidate bond that is stable in most molecular biology assays. The method can be used in combination with T4 polynucleotide kinase to fluorescently label oligonucleotides lacking a 5′-phosphate, or to double-label radioactively labeled oligonucleotides. We have found that this reaction is very efficient — labeling over 90% of the oligonucleotides that contain a phosphate group — and much easier than conventional methods for modifying terminal phosphate groups, which typically require multistep synthesis.[78–80] For this reaction we recommend cadaverine-conjugated fluorophores (Section 3.3, Table 3.1) and biotins (Section 4.2).

It has also been reported that DNA can be reacted quantitatively with carbonyl diimidazole and a diamine (such as ethylenediamine) or a carbohydrazide to yield a phosphoramidate that has a free primary amine; the amine can then be modified with amine-reactive reagents[78–82] of the type described in Chapter 1. Fluorescent or biotinylated amines have been coupled to the 5′-phosphate of tRNA using dithiodipyridine and triphenylphosphine.[83] Wang and Giese[84] have reported a general method that employs an imidazole derivative prepared from our BODIPY® FL hydrazide (D2371, Section 3.2) to label phosphates, including nucleotides, for capillary electrophoresis applications.

Other Chemical Labeling Methods for Nucleic Acids

Labeling Cytidine Residues

DNA and RNA can be modified by reacting their cytidine residues with sodium bisulfite to form sulfonate intermediates that can then be directly coupled to hydrazides or aliphatic amines.[85–87] For example, biotin hydrazides (Section 4.2) have been used in a bisulfite-mediated reaction to couple biotin to cytidine residues in oligonucleotides.[88] The fluorescent, biotinylated and other hydrazides, hydroxylamines and aliphatic amines in Chapter 3 and Chapter 4,

Table 8.11 — Amine-reactive dyes for nucleic acid sequencing

Cat #	Reactive Dye *	Ex/Em §	Handbook Location
C2210	5-FAM, SE †	494/518	Section 1.5
C6164	6-FAM, SE	494/518	Section 1.5
C20092	6-TET, SE	521/536	Section 1.5
C6127	5-CR 6G, SE	525/555	Section 1.6
C6128	6-CR 6G, SE	525/555	Section 1.6
C6171MP	6-JOE, SE †	522/550	Section 1.5
C20091	6-HEX, SE	535/556	Section 1.5
C2211	5-TAMRA, SE	555/580	Section 1.6
C6123	6-TAMRA, SE †	555/580	Section 1.6
C6125	5-ROX, SE	580/605	Section 1.6
C6126	6-ROX, SE †	580/605	Section 1.6
D2184	BODIPY® FL, SE ‡	505/513	Section 1.4
D6140	BODIPY® FL, SSE	505/513	Section 1.4
D6102	BODIPY® FL-X, SE	505/513	Section 1.4
D6180	BODIPY® R6G, SE ‡	528/550	Section 1.4
D6117	BODIPY® TMR-X, SE	542/574	Section 1.4
D2222	BODIPY® 564/570, SE ‡	565/571	Section 1.4
D2228	BODIPY® 581/591, SE ‡	584/592	Section 1.4
D6116	BODIPY® TR-X, SE	589/617	Section 1.4

* FAM = carboxyfluorescein; TET = 6-carboxy-2′,4,7,7′-tetrachlorofluorescein; CR 6G = carboxyrhodamine 6G; JOE = 6-carboxy-4′,5′-dichloro-2′,7′-dimethoxyfluorescein; HEX = 6-carboxy-2′,4,4′,5′,7,7′-hexachlorofluorescein; TAMRA = carboxytetramethylrhodamine; ROX = carboxy-X-rhodamine; BODIPY® = a substituted 4,4-difluoro-4-bora-3a,4a-diaza-*s*-indacene derivative (Figure 1.42); SE = succinimidyl ester; SSE = water-soluble sulfosuccinimidyl ester. † These are the most widely used isomers for DNA sequencing.[1–4] ‡ These BODIPY® derivatives were reported to be useful for automated DNA sequencing, in part because the dyes have a minimal effect on the mobility of the fragment during electrophoresis and also exhibit well-resolved spectra with narrow bandwidths.[5] § Excitation (Ex) and emission (Em) maxima in nm. **1.** Anal Biochem 223, 39 (1994); **2.** Nucleic Acids Res 20, 2471 (1992); **3.** Proc Natl Acad Sci U S A 86, 9178 (1989); **4.** Genome Res 6, 995 (1996); **5.** Science 271, 1420 (1996).

except possibly the BODIPY® derivatives, might be useful in this reaction. The bisulfite-activated cytidylic acid can also be coupled to aliphatic diamines such as ethylenediamine.[89] The amine-modified DNA or RNA can then be modified with any of the amine-reactive dyes described in this section or in Chapter 1.

Labeling the 3′-Terminus of RNA

Selective oxidation of the 3′-terminus of RNA by sodium metaperiodate yields a dialdehyde. This dialdehyde can then be coupled with a fluorescent or biotin hydrazide or hydroxylamine reagent[82,90–95] (Section 3.2, Section 4.2).

Labeling Abasic Sites with ARP

The biotin hydroxylamine ARP (Aldehyde-Reactive Probe, A10550) has been used to modify abasic sites in DNA — apurinic sites and apyrimidinic lesions thought to be important intermediates in carcinogenesis[96–99] (Figure 8.147). Once the aldehyde group in an abasic site is modified with ARP, the resulting biotinylated DNA can be detected with the avidin and streptavidin conjugates described in Section 7.6 (Table 7.22). ARP is permeant to cell membranes, permitting detection of abasic sites in living cells.[100,101] Alexa Fluor® hydroxylamine derivatives (Section 3.2, Table 3.1) may have utility similar to that of ARP but will not be membrane permeant.

Specialized Methods for Nucleic Acid Modification

A few other specialized methods have been developed for nucleic acid modification. These include:

- Synthesis of DNA using fluorescent 2′- or 3′-acyl derivatives of uridine 5′-triphosphate and terminal deoxyribonucleotide transferase[102]
- Use of a fluorescent iodoacetamide or maleimide, along with T4 polynucleotide kinase and ATP-γ-*S* (ATP with a sulfur in the terminal phosphate), to introduce a thiophosphate at the 5′-terminus of 5′-dephosphorylated RNA[91] or DNA
- Introduction of 4-thiouridine at the 3′-terminus of DNA using calf thymus terminal deoxynucleotidyl transferase followed by treatment with ribonuclease and reaction with thiol-reactive probes[103,104]
- Direct reaction of thiol-reactive reagents with 4-thiouridine residues in nucleic acids[83,105–108]
- Direct reaction of amine- or thiol-reactive reagents with aminoacyl tRNA or thioacetylated aminoacyl tRNA[83,109,110]
- Reaction of the X-base of tRNA with isothiocyanates[93] or replacement of other uncommon bases in tRNA by fluorophores[111–113]
- Photolabeling of plasmid DNA with fluorescent 4-azido-2,3,5,6-tetrafluorobenzyl derivatives[114]
- Coupling of labeled diazonium salts to nucleic acids[115]

References

1. Biotechniques 36, 114 (2004); **2.** Trends Genet 13, 475 (1997); **3.** Bioessays 19, 75 (1997); **4.** Mol Pathol 51, 62 (1998); **5.** Cell Vis 5, 49 (1998); **6.** Nat Genet 21, 48 (1999); **7.** Nat Genet 21, 42 (1999); **8.** Nat Genet 21, 33 (1999); **9.** Nat Genet 21, 25 (1999); **10.** Nat Genet 21, 20 (1999); **11.** Nat Genet 21, 15 (1999); **12.** Nat Genet 21, 10 (1999); **13.** Nat Genet 21, 5 (1999); **14.** Mol Psychiatry 3, 483 (1998); **15.** Nat Biotechnol 16, 45 (1998); **16.** Biotechniques 19, 442 (1995); **17.** Nat Genet 14, 312 (1996); **18.** Histochem Cell Biol 108, 299 (1997); **19.** Genes Chromosomes Cancer 28, 318 (2000); **20.** Cytometry 35, 214 (1999); **21.** Genes Chromosomes Cancer 27, 418 (2000); **22.** Eur J Hum Genet 7, 2 (1999); **23.** Science 273, 494 (1996); **24.** Am J Hum Genet 61, 16 (1997); **25.** Cytobios 90, 7 (1997); **26.** J Mol Med 75, 801 (1997); **27.** J Cell Biochem Suppl 17G, 139 (1993); **28.** US 5,047,519; **29.** J Histochem Cytochem 48, 1593 (2000); **30.** Dev Biol 206, 232 (1999); **31.** J Cell Biol 144, 813 (1999); **32.** Biophys J 77, 2871 (1999); **33.** Cytometry 27, 1 (1997); **34.** Exp Cell Res 222, 28 (1996); **35.** Cell Prolif 28, 571 (1995); **36.** Cytometry 20, 172 (1995); **37.** Eur J Histochem 42, 111 (1998); **38.** Cell Vis 5, 83 (1998); **39.** Am J Pathol 150, 1553 (1997); **40.** J Clin Microbiol 29, 583 (1991); **41.** Histochemistry 93, 191 (1989); **42.** Biotechniques 5, 660 (1987); **43.** Biotechniques 28, 518 (2000); **44.** Proc Natl Acad Sci U S A 90, 4206 (1993); **45.** Anal Biochem 331, 243 (2004); **46.** Methods Cell Biol 41, 297 (1994); **47.** Cytometry 17, 310 (1994); **48.** Exp Cell Res 173, 256 (1987); **49.** Biotechnol Appl Biochem 29, 241 (1999); **50.** Biotechnol Appl Biochem 23, 95 (1996); **51.** J Virol Methods 31, 181 (1991); **52.** J Biochem (Tokyo) 96, 1501 (1984); **53.** Histochem Cell Biol 113, 181 (2000); **54.** Mol Biol Cell 10, 211 (1999); **55.** Cell Prolif 29, 539 (1996); **56.** Mutat Res 193, 167 (1988); **57.** Exp Cell Res 234, 498 (1997); **58.** Biochem J 253, 637 (1988); **59.** J Cell Biol 150, 797 (2000); **60.** Eur J Biochem 236, 389 (1996); **61.** Biotechniques 21, 82 (1996); **62.** Genes Chromosomes Cancer 25, 301 (1999); **63.** Cytogenet Cell Genet 87, 47 (1999); **64.** Molecular Probes' proprietary materials and methods have been found useful in the practice of a variety of patents. Although we indicate the usefulness of our materials and methods for the practice of third party technology, we emphasize that purchase of our products does not include a license to practice any third party patent, unless a license under such a patent is clearly indicated in our product literature; **65.** Anal Chem 69, 2392 (1997); **66.** J Forensic Sci 48, 282 (2003); **67.** Anal Biochem 276, 177 (1999); **68.** Biotechniques 27, 1116 (1999); **69.** Biotechniques 26, 552 (1999); **70.** J Am Chem Soc 121, 2921 (1999); **71.** Biochemistry 39, 4327 (2000); **72.** Anal Biochem 281, 26 (2000); **73.** Anal Biochem 287, 179 (2000); **74.** J Am Chem Soc 123, 803 (2001); **75.** Biotechniques 25, 446 (1998); **76.** Science 271, 1420 (1996); **77.** Nucleic Acids Res 20, 2471 (1992); **78.** Anal Biochem 218, 444 (1994); **79.** Biochem Biophys Res Commun 200, 1239 (1994); **80.** Methods Mol Biol 26, 145 (1994); **81.** J Chromatogr 608, 171 (1992); **82.** J Mol Biol 221, 441 (1991); **83.** Biochemistry 29, 10734 (1990); **84.** Anal Chem 65, 3518 (1993); **85.** J Clin Microbiol 23, 311 (1986); **86.** Biochemistry 19, 1774 (1980); **87.** Biochemistry 15, 2677 (1976); **88.** Biochem Biophys Res Commun 142, 519 (1987); **89.** Biochem J 108, 883 (1968); **90.** Bioconjug Chem 5, 436 (1994); **91.** Biochemistry 30, 4821 (1991); **92.** Biochemistry 19, 5947 (1980); **93.** Eur Biophys J 16, 45 (1988); **94.** Biochemistry 25, 5298 (1986); **95.** Eur J Biochem 142, 261 (1984); **96.** Anal Biochem 267, 331 (1999); **97.** Biochemistry 11, 3610 (1972); **98.** Biochemistry 31, 3703 (1992); **99.** Biochemistry 32, 8276 (1993); **100.** Proc Natl Acad Sci U S A 97, 686 (2000); **101.** J Biol Chem 275, 6741 (2000); **102.** Molekulyarnaya Biologiya 11, 598 (1977); **103.** Anal Biochem 170, 271 (1988); **104.** Nucleic Acids Res 7, 1485 (1979); **105.** Nucleic Acids Res 16, 2203 (1988); **106.** Anal Biochem 131, 419 (1983); **107.** Biochemistry 24, 692 (1985); **108.** J Mol Biol 156, 113 (1982); **109.** J Am Chem Soc 113, 2722 (1991); **110.** Eur J Biochem 172, 663 (1988); **111.** Eur J Biochem 98, 465 (1979); **112.** Methods Enzymol 29, 667 (1974); **113.** FEBS Lett 18, 214 (1971); **114.** Bioconjug Chem 11, 51 (2000); **115.** Nucleic Acids Res 16, 7197 (1988).

Product List — 8.2 Labeling Oligonucleotides and Nucleic Acids

Cat #	Product Name	Unit Size
A32760	aha-dUTP (5-aminohexylacrylamido-dUTP) *2 mM in TE buffer*	500 µL
A32761	aha-dUTP (5-aminohexylacrylamido-dUTP) *50 mM in TE buffer*	50 µL
A32762	Alexa Fluor® 555-aha-dUTP *1 mM in TE buffer*	50 µL
A32763	Alexa Fluor® 647-aha-dUTP *1 mM in TE buffer*	50 µL
A20190	Alexa Fluor® 350 Oligonucleotide Amine Labeling Kit *3 labelings*	1 kit
A20191	Alexa Fluor® 488 Oligonucleotide Amine Labeling Kit *3 labelings*	1 kit
A20192	Alexa Fluor® 532 Oligonucleotide Amine Labeling Kit *3 labelings*	1 kit
A20193	Alexa Fluor® 546 Oligonucleotide Amine Labeling Kit *3 labelings*	1 kit
A20197	Alexa Fluor® 555 Oligonucleotide Amine Labeling Kit *3 labelings*	1 kit
A20194	Alexa Fluor® 568 Oligonucleotide Amine Labeling Kit *3 labelings*	1 kit
A20195	Alexa Fluor® 594 Oligonucleotide Amine Labeling Kit *3 labelings*	1 kit
A20196	Alexa Fluor® 647 Oligonucleotide Amine Labeling Kit *3 labelings*	1 kit
A32756	Alexa Fluor® 555 reactive dye decapack *for microarrays* *set of 10 vials*	1 set
A32751	Alexa Fluor® 594 reactive dye decapack *for microarrays* *set of 10 vials*	1 set
A32757	Alexa Fluor® 647 reactive dye decapack *for microarrays* *set of 10 vials*	1 set
A32755	Alexa Fluor® 555 and Alexa Fluor® 647 reactive dye decapacks *for microarrays* *set of 2 x 10 vials* *includes A32756 and A32757 decapacks*	1 set
A21664	aminoallyl dUTP (5-(3-aminoallyl)-2′-deoxyuridine 5′-triphosphate, trisodium salt) *2 mM in TE buffer*	500 µL
A32764	aminoallyl dUTP (5-(3-aminoallyl)-2′-deoxyuridine 5′-triphosphate, trisodium salt) *50 mM in TE buffer*	50 µL
A21663	aminoallyl UTP (5-(3-aminoallyl)uridine 5′-triphosphate, trisodium salt) *2 mM in TE buffer*	500 µL
A32765	aminoallyl UTP (5-(3-aminoallyl)uridine 5′-triphosphate, trisodium salt) *50 mM in TE buffer*	50 µL
A10550	*N*-(aminooxyacetyl)-*N*′-(D-biotinoyl) hydrazine, trifluoroacetic acid salt (ARP)	10 mg
A21675	ARES™ Alexa Fluor® 350 DNA Labeling Kit *10 labelings*	1 kit
A21665	ARES™ Alexa Fluor® 488 DNA Labeling Kit *10 labelings*	1 kit
A21666	ARES™ Alexa Fluor® 532 DNA Labeling Kit *10 labelings*	1 kit
A21667	ARES™ Alexa Fluor® 546 DNA Labeling Kit *10 labelings*	1 kit
A21677	ARES™ Alexa Fluor® 555 DNA Labeling Kit *10 labelings*	1 kit
A21668	ARES™ Alexa Fluor® 568 DNA Labeling Kit *10 labelings*	1 kit
A21669	ARES™ Alexa Fluor® 594 DNA Labeling Kit *10 labelings*	1 kit
A21676	ARES™ Alexa Fluor® 647 DNA Labeling Kit *10 labelings*	1 kit
A21671	ARES™ Alexa Fluor® 660 DNA Labeling Kit *5-10 labelings*	1 kit
A21672	ARES™ Alexa Fluor® 680 DNA Labeling Kit *5-10 labelings*	1 kit
B32766	biotin-aha-dUTP *1 mM in TE buffer*	25 µL
B23151	5-bromo-2′-deoxyuridine (BrdU)	100 mg
B21550	5-bromo-2′-deoxyuridine 5′-triphosphate (BrdUTP) *10 mM in TE buffer*	25 µL
B21551	5-bromouridine 5′-triphosphate (BrUTP) *10 mM in TE buffer*	25 µL
C11397	ChromaTide® Alexa Fluor® 488-5-dUTP *1 mM in TE buffer*	25 µL
C11403	ChromaTide® Alexa Fluor® 488-5-UTP *1 mM in TE buffer*	25 µL
C11398	ChromaTide® Alexa Fluor® 532-5-dUTP *1 mM in TE buffer*	25 µL
C11401	ChromaTide® Alexa Fluor® 546-14-dUTP *1 mM in TE buffer*	25 µL
C11404	ChromaTide® Alexa Fluor® 546-14-UTP *1 mM in TE buffer*	25 µL
C11399	ChromaTide® Alexa Fluor® 568-5-dUTP *1 mM in TE buffer*	25 µL
C11400	ChromaTide® Alexa Fluor® 594-5-dUTP *1 mM in TE buffer*	25 µL
C21555	ChromaTide® Alexa Fluor® 488-7-OBEA-dCTP *1 mM in TE buffer*	50 µL
C21556	ChromaTide® Alexa Fluor® 546-16-OBEA-dCTP *1 mM in TE buffer*	50 µL
C21558	ChromaTide® Alexa Fluor® 594-7-OBEA-dCTP *1 mM in TE buffer*	50 µL
C21559	ChromaTide® Alexa Fluor® 647-12-OBEA-dCTP *1 mM in TE buffer*	50 µL
C11395	ChromaTide® BODIPY® 630/650-14-dUTP *1 mM in TE buffer*	25 µL
C11396	ChromaTide® BODIPY® 650/665-14-dUTP *1 mM in TE buffer*	25 µL
C7614	ChromaTide® BODIPY® FL-14-dUTP *1 mM in TE buffer*	25 µL
C7613	ChromaTide® BODIPY® FL-14-UTP *1 mM in TE buffer*	25 µL
C7616	ChromaTide® BODIPY® TMR-14-dUTP *1 mM in TE buffer*	25 µL
C7615	ChromaTide® BODIPY® TMR-14-UTP *1 mM in TE buffer*	25 µL
C7618	ChromaTide® BODIPY® TR-14-dUTP *1 mM in TE buffer*	25 µL
C7617	ChromaTide® BODIPY® TR-14-UTP *1 mM in TE buffer*	25 µL
C7612	ChromaTide® Cascade Blue®-7-dUTP *1 mM in TE buffer*	25 µL
C7610MP	ChromaTide® dinitrophenyl-11-dUTP (DNP-11-dUTP) *1 mM in TE buffer*	25 µL
C7604	ChromaTide® fluorescein-12-dUTP *1 mM in TE buffer*	25 µL

For current prices or to order online, visit probes.invitrogen.com

Important Licensing Information
These products may be covered by one or more Limited Use Label Licenses (See the Invitrogen Web site, www.invitrogen.com, or the Molecular Probes Web site, probes.invitrogen.com). By the use of these products you accept the terms and conditions of all applicable Limited Use Label Licenses. All products are for research use only. CAUTION: Not intended for human or animal diagnostic or therapeutic uses.

Product List — 8.2 Labeling Oligonucleotides and Nucleic Acids — continued

Cat #	Product Name	Unit Size
C7603	ChromaTide® fluorescein-12-UTP *1 mM in TE buffer*	25 µL
C7630	ChromaTide® Oregon Green® 488-5-dUTP *1 mM in TE buffer*	25 µL
C7629	ChromaTide® Rhodamine Green™-5-dUTP *1 mM in TE buffer*	25 µL
C7628	ChromaTide® Rhodamine Green™-5-UTP *1 mM in TE buffer*	25 µL
C7606MP	ChromaTide® tetramethylrhodamine-6-dUTP *1 mM in TE buffer*	25 µL
C7605MP	ChromaTide® tetramethylrhodamine-6-UTP *1 mM in TE buffer*	25 µL
C7608	ChromaTide® Texas Red®-5-dUTP *1 mM in TE buffer*	25 µL
C7607MP	ChromaTide® Texas Red®-5-UTP *1 mM in TE buffer*	25 µL
C7631	ChromaTide® Texas Red®-12-dUTP *1 mM in TE buffer*	25 µL
F32767	fluorescein-aha-dUTP *1 mM in TE buffer*	25 µL
O21561	oligodeoxythymidine-18, Alexa Fluor® 555 conjugate (Alexa Fluor® 555 dT_{18})	10 nmol
O21562	oligodeoxythymidine-18, Alexa Fluor® 594 conjugate (Alexa Fluor® 594 dT_{18})	10 nmol
O21563	oligodeoxythymidine-18, Alexa Fluor® 647 conjugate (Alexa Fluor® 647 dT_{18})	10 nmol
S21500	SYBR® 101, succinimidyl ester	1 mg
S21501	SYBR® 102, succinimidyl ester	1 mg
S21502	SYBR® 103, succinimidyl ester	1 mg
U21650	ULYSIS® Alexa Fluor® 488 Nucleic Acid Labeling Kit *20 labelings*	1 kit
U21651	ULYSIS® Alexa Fluor® 532 Nucleic Acid Labeling Kit *20 labelings*	1 kit
U21652	ULYSIS® Alexa Fluor® 546 Nucleic Acid Labeling Kit *20 labelings*	1 kit
U21653	ULYSIS® Alexa Fluor® 568 Nucleic Acid Labeling Kit *20 labelings*	1 kit
U21654	ULYSIS® Alexa Fluor® 594 Nucleic Acid Labeling Kit *20 labelings*	1 kit
U21660	ULYSIS® Alexa Fluor® 647 Nucleic Acid Labeling Kit *20 labelings*	1 kit
U21656	ULYSIS® Alexa Fluor® 660 Nucleic Acid Labeling Kit *20 labelings*	1 kit
U21657	ULYSIS® Alexa Fluor® 680 Nucleic Acid Labeling Kit *20 labelings*	1 kit
U21659	ULYSIS® Oregon Green® 488 Nucleic Acid Labeling Kit *20 labelings*	1 kit
U21658	ULYSIS® Pacific Blue™ Nucleic Acid Labeling Kit *20 labelings*	1 kit

For current prices or to order online, visit probes.invitrogen.com

8.3 Nucleic Acid Detection and Quantitation in Solution

Nucleic Acid Detection and Quantitation in Solution

Through intensive research efforts in both chemical synthesis and bioassay development, Molecular Probes scientists have developed rapid and exceptionally sensitive fluorescence-based assays for quantitation of nucleic acids in solution. The Quant-iT™ Assay Kits represent the most advanced quantitation systems for DNA, RNA or protein samples. Described in detail below, these state-of-the-art assays deliver high sensitivity and specificity together with a streamlined protocol, prediluted standards and a ready-to-use buffer.

In addition, the PicoGreen® dsDNA quantitation reagent, OliGreen® ssDNA quantitation reagent and RiboGreen® RNA quantitation reagent — optimized for double-stranded DNA, oligonucleotides and RNA, respectively — have a high affinity for nucleic acids and an extremely large fluorescence enhancement upon binding, making possible the direct detection of minute amounts of nucleic acids in complex solutions within minutes, usually without interference from other biomolecules. These patented reagents and quantitation assays provide the following advantages:

- **Sensitivity.** The PicoGreen® dye–, OliGreen® dye– and RiboGreen® dye–based fluorescence assays are up to 10,000-fold more sensitive than UV absorbance measurements and at least 400-fold more sensitive than assays that use the Hoechst 33258 dye [1] (H1398, H3569; FluoroPure™ Grade, H21491), requiring much less sample for quantitation.
- **Accuracy.** Unlike measurements of UV absorbance, these assays are not affected by the presence of proteins, free nucleotides or very short oligonucleotides, making quantitation of intact oligonucleotides and nucleic acids much more accurate in complex mixtures such as serum or whole blood.
- **Precision.** The average standard deviations of triplicate assays using these reagents are typically less than 5%.
- **Simplicity.** These assays have a very simple protocol that requires no separation steps, making them ideal for automated, high-throughput measurements.
- **Broad dynamic range.** Quantitation is accurate over four orders of magnitude for the PicoGreen® and OliGreen® assays, with a single dye concentration. The RiboGreen® assay is accurate over three orders of magnitude.
- **Instrument compatibility.** Quantitation assays can be performed using a fluorescence microplate reader with standard filters optimized for fluorescein-like dyes, a relatively inexpensive filter-based spectrofluorometer or a standard spectrofluorometer.
- **Convenience.** Each reagent is available separately or in a kit that additionally contains a nuclease-free buffer and standards. The PicoGreen® dsDNA and the RiboGreen® RNA quantitation assays are also available in the RediPlate™ 96 format — a prepared 96-well microplate with standards included — for high-throughput applications.

Quant-iT™ Assay Kits for DNA and RNA

The Quant-iT™ family of assay kits provides state-of-the-art reagents for sensitive and selective quantitation of DNA, RNA or protein samples using a standard fluorescence microplate reader (Table 8.12). These kits have been specially formulated with ready-to-use buffers, prediluted standards and easy-to-follow instructions, making quantitation both accurate and extremely easy (Figure 8.52). Each Quant-iT™ assay is:

- **Ready to use.** Only the dye is diluted in the supplied buffer; dilution of standards or buffer is not required.
- **Easy to perform.** Just add the sample to the diluted dye and read the fluorescence.
- **Highly sensitive.** The Quant-iT™ protein assay is orders of magnitude more sensitive than UV absorbance measurements.

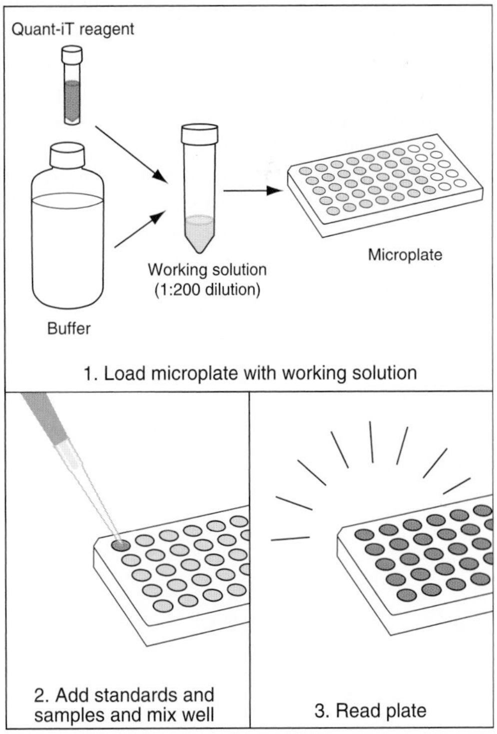
Quant-iT reagent
Buffer
Working solution
(1:200 dilution)
Microplate
1. Load microplate with working solution
2. Add standards and samples and mix well
3. Read plate

Figure 8.52 DNA, RNA or protein quantitation with the Quant-iT™ Assay Kits (Q33120, Q33130, Q33140 described in Section 8.3; Q33210 described in Section 9.2).

Table 8.12 — Selection Guide for the Quant-iT™ Assay Kits

Cat #	Kit Name	Target	Useful Range *	Ex/Em †
Q33120	Quant-iT™ DNA Assay Kit, High Sensitivity	dsDNA	0.2–100 ng	502/523
Q33130	Quant-iT™ DNA Assay Kit, Broad Range	dsDNA	2–1000 ng	510/527
Q33140	Quant-iT™ RNA Assay Kit	RNA	5–100 ng	644/673
Q33210	Quant-iT™ Protein Assay Kit	Protein	0.25–5 µg	470/570

* The useful range assumes a 1–20 µL sample volume in a 96-well microplate assay.
† Excitation (Ex) and emission (Em) maxima of the Quant-iT™ reagents bound to their corresponding targets, in nm.

- **Highly selective.** Separate kits are available for quantitating DNA, RNA (see below) or protein (Section 9.2), with minimal interference from common contaminants.
- **Precise.** CVs are generally less than 5%.

Because the fluorescent dye in each Quant-iT™ Kit matches common fluorescence excitation and emission filter sets in microplate readers, these assay kits are ideal for high-throughput environments, as well as for small numbers of samples.

Quant-iT™ DNA Assay Kits

The Quant-iT™ DNA Assay Kits simplify DNA quantitation without sacrificing sensitivity. The Quant-iT™ DNA High-Sensitivity DNA Assay Kit (Q33120) provides a linear detection range between 0.2 ng and 100 ng double-stranded DNA (dsDNA) (Figure 8.53), corresponding to initial experimental sample concentrations between 10 pg/µL and 100 ng/µL. This high-sensitivity DNA assay is ideal for quantitating PCR products, viral DNA, DNA fragments for subcloning and other applications requiring small amounts of DNA. The Quant-iT™ DNA Broad-Range DNA Assay Kit (Q33130) provides a linear detection range between 2 ng and 1000 ng double-stranded DNA (dsDNA) (Figure 8.54), corresponding to initial experimental sample concentrations between 100 pg/µL and 1000 ng/µL. This broad-range DNA assay eliminates the need to dilute concentrated samples, such as genomic DNA and miniprep DNA, prior to high-throughput procedures. Both Quant-iT™ DNA assays are highly selective for dsDNA over RNA, and have proven to be accurate even in the presence of an equal mass of RNA. Moreover, their fluorescence signals are unaffected by many common contaminants, including free nucleotides, salts, solvents and proteins. Each Quant-iT™ DNA Assay Kit contains:

- Quant-iT™ DNA HS reagent (in Kit Q33120) or Quant-iT™ DNA BR reagent (in Kit Q33130)
- Quant-iT™ DNA HS buffer (in Kit Q33120) or Quant-iT™ DNA BR buffer (in Kit Q33130)
- A set of eight prediluted λ DNA standards between 0 and 10 ng/µL (in Kit Q33120) or between 0 and 100 ng/µL (in Kit Q33130)
- Easy-to-follow instructions for the high-sensitivity DNA assay or the broad-range DNA assay

Sufficient reagents are provided to perform 1000 assays, based on a 200 µL assay volume in a 96-well microplate format; this assay can also be adapted for use in cuvettes or 384-well microplates. Both the high-sensitivity assay and the broad-range assay can be detected using standard fluorescein filters, and the fluorescence signal is stable for three hours at room temperature. The Quant-iT™ HS reagent is a new formulation of Molecular Probes' PicoGreen® reagent, which is described below.

Quant-iT™ RNA Assay Kit

The Quant-iT™ RNA Assay Kit (Q33140) provides the first homogeneous assay ever developed for quantitating RNA in the presence of DNA. This RNA assay exhibits a linear detection range between 5 ng and 100 ng RNA (Figure 8.55), corresponding to initial experimental sample concentrations between 250 pg/µL and 100 ng/µL. Because of the high selectivity of the Quant-iT™ RNA reagent for RNA over dsDNA, this assay provides accurate RNA quantitation even in the presence of an equal mass of DNA. The fluorescence signal is unaffected by many common contaminants, including free nucleotides, salts, solvents and proteins, making this assay ideal for measuring samples for microarray, RT-PCR and Northern blot procedures. Each Quant-iT™ RNA Assay Kit contains:

- Quant-iT™ RNA reagent
- Quant-iT™ RNA buffer
- A set of eight prediluted *Escherichia coli* rRNA standards between 0 and 10 ng/µL
- Easy-to-follow instructions

Sufficient reagents are provided to perform 1000 assays, based on a 200 µL assay volume in a 96-well microplate format; this assay can

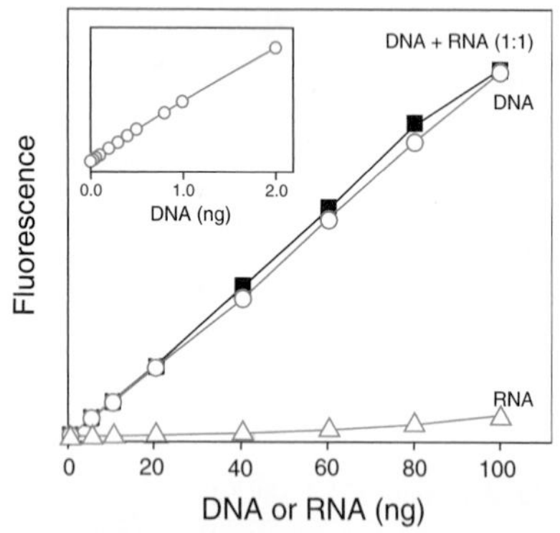

Figure 8.53 DNA selectivity and sensitivity of the Quant-iT™ DNA High-Sensitivity assay. Triplicate 10 µL samples of DNA (○), *Escherichia coli* rRNA (△) or a 1:1 mixture of DNA and RNA (■) were assayed with the Quant-iT™ DNA High-Sensitivity Assay Kit (Q33120). Fluorescence was measured at 485/530 nm and plotted versus the mass of nucleic acid for the DNA alone, the mass of nucleic acid for the RNA alone or the mass of the DNA component in the 1:1 mixture. The coefficient of variation (CV) of replicate DNA determinations was ≤2%. The inset, a separate experiment with octuplicate determinations, shows the extreme sensitivity of the assay for DNA. Background fluorescence has not been subtracted.

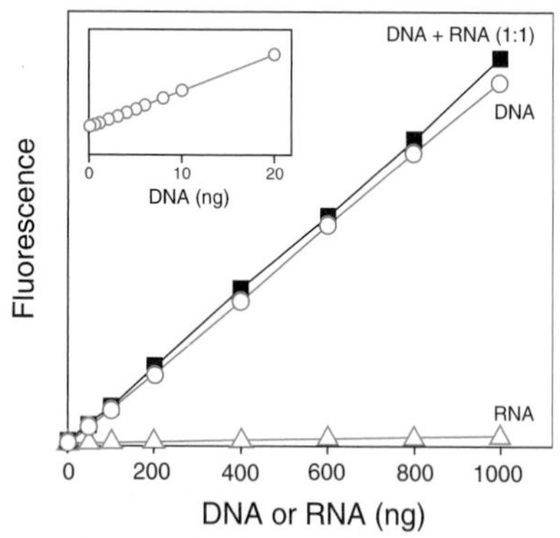

Figure 8.54 DNA selectivity and sensitivity of the Quant-iT™ DNA Broad-Range assay. Triplicate 10 µL samples of DNA (○), *Escherichia coli* rRNA (△) or a 1:1 mixture of DNA and RNA (■) were assayed with the Quant-iT™ DNA Broad-Range Assay Kit (Q33130). Fluorescence was measured at 485/530 nm and plotted versus the mass of nucleic acid for the DNA alone, the mass of nucleic acid for the RNA alone or the mass of the DNA component in the 1:1 mixture. The coefficient of variation (CV) of replicate DNA determinations was ≤3%. The inset, a separate experiment with octuplicate determinations, shows the sensitivity of the assay for DNA. Background fluorescence has not been subtracted.

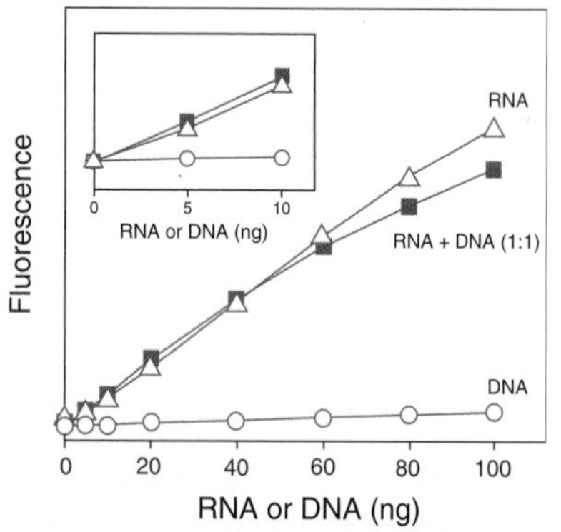

Figure 8.55 RNA selectivity and sensitivity of the Quant-iT™ RNA assay. Triplicate 10 µL samples of *Escherichia coli* rRNA (△), DNA (○) or a 1:1 mixture of RNA and DNA (■) were assayed with the Quant-iT™ RNA Assay Kit (Q33140). Fluorescence was measured at 630/680 nm and plotted versus the mass of nucleic acid for the RNA alone, the mass of nucleic acid for the DNA alone or the mass of the RNA component in the 1:1 mixture. The coefficient of variation (CV) of replicate RNA determinations was ≤10%. The inset is an enlargement of the graph to show the sensitivity of the assay for RNA. Background fluorescence has not been subtracted.

also be adapted for use in cuvettes or 384-well microplates. The fluorescence signal exhibits excitation/emission maxima of 644/673 nm and is stable for three hours at room temperature.

PicoGreen® dsDNA Quantitation Assay

PicoGreen® dsDNA Quantitation Reagent and Kits

The patented PicoGreen® reagent[2] (P7581, P11495) and Kits (P7589, P11496) can accurately quantitate as little as 25 pg/mL of dsDNA in a fluorometer or 250 pg/mL (typically 50 pg in a 200 µL volume) in a fluorescence microplate reader. The PicoGreen® assay is more than 10,000 times as sensitive as conventional UV absorbance measurements at 260 nm (an A_{260} of 0.1 corresponds to an ~5 µg/mL dsDNA solution) and at least 400 times more sensitive than the Hoechst 33258 dye–based assay. It is even more sensitive than assays based on our YO-PRO®-1 and YOYO®-1 dyes, which have reported detection limits of approximately 2.5 ng/mL[3] and 0.5 ng/mL,[4] respectively. Although the PicoGreen® reagent is not specific for dsDNA, it shows a >1000-fold fluorescence enhancement upon binding to dsDNA, and much less fluorescence enhancement upon binding to single-stranded DNA (ssDNA) or RNA, making it possible to quantitate dsDNA in the presence of equimolar amounts of ssDNA, RNA or proteins[5] (Figure 8.56). The PicoGreen® reagent also selectively detects DNA–RNA hybrids in the presence of ssDNA and RNA.[6] Differences in the emission lifetimes of the PicoGreen® complexes with dsDNA and ssDNA make it possible to quantitate the relative amounts of each species in solution by time-resolved measurements.[7] By contrast, UV absorbance measurements cannot distinguish between dsDNA, ssDNA and RNA or proteins. Thus, the PicoGreen® reagent allows direct quantitation of PCR amplicons without purification from the reaction mixture and makes it possible to detect low levels of DNA contamination in recombinant protein products.[8] In comparison to the Hoechst 33258 dye, which shows significant AT selectivity, the PicoGreen® reagent shows little if any AT- or GC-selectivity and is thus accurate for quantitating DNA from almost any source. The PicoGreen® reagent can be excited at 488 nm with an argon-ion laser, and is reported to be the best nucleic acid stain for analysis of single DNA molecules in a flow cytometer.[9] A method that utilizes the PicoGreen® reagent for the absolute quantitation of cDNA using real-time PCR has been reported.[10]

The protocol for the PicoGreen® assay is easy to conduct and requires very few steps — the dye is simply added to the sample and incubated for five minutes, then the fluorescence is measured (Figure 8.57). In addition, the fluorescence signal from binding of the PicoGreen® reagent to dsDNA is linear over at least four orders of magnitude (Figure 8.58) with a single dye concen-

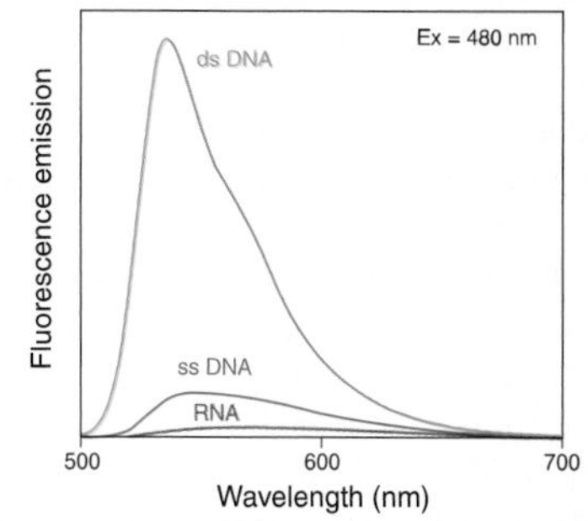

Figure 8.56 Fluorescence enhancement of the PicoGreen® reagent upon to binding dsDNA, ssDNA and RNA. Samples containing 500 ng/mL calf thymus DNA, M13 ssDNA or *Escherichia coli* ribosomal RNA were added to cuvettes containing PicoGreen® reagent (P7581, P7589, P11495, P11496) in TE buffer. Samples were excited at 480 nm, and the fluorescence emission spectra were collected using a spectrofluorometer. Emission spectra for samples containing dye and nucleic acids, as well as for dye alone (baseline), are shown.

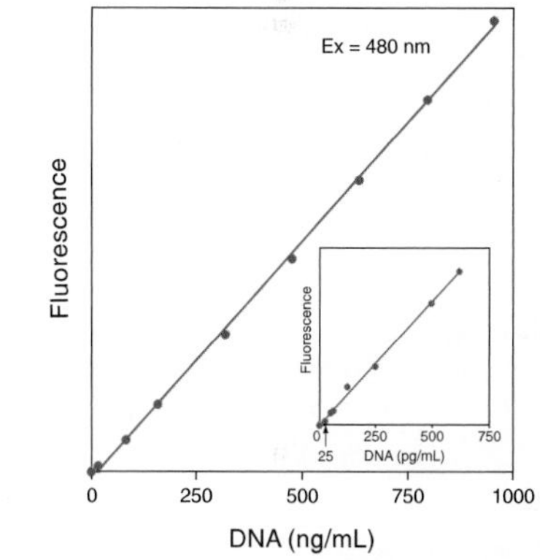

Figure 8.58 Linear quantitation of calf thymus DNA from 25 pg/mL to 1000 ng/mL using the PicoGreen® dsDNA quantitation reagent (P7581, P7589, P11495, P11496). Samples in 10 mm × 10 mm cuvettes were excited at 480 nm. The fluorescence emission intensity was measured at 520 nm using a spectrofluorometer and plotted as a function of DNA concentration. The inset shows an enlargement of the results obtained with DNA concentrations between 0 and 750 pg/mL.

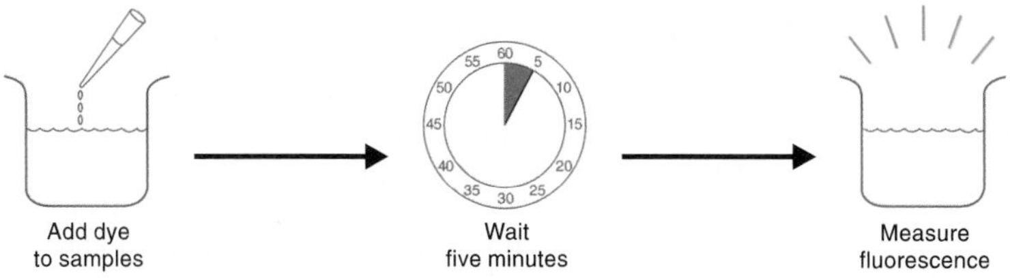

Figure 8.57 All of our nucleic acid quantitation assays are quick and easy.

tration, whereas assays using ethidium bromide, Hoechst 33258 or the YOYO®-1 dye exhibit a much more limited linear range.[4,11,12] We have found that this linearity is maintained in the presence of several compounds commonly found in nucleic acid preparations, including salts, urea, ethanol, chloroform, detergents, proteins and agarose[5] (Table 8.13). The PicoGreen® assay is faster, more precise and much less expensive than dipstick or blot assays.

The PicoGreen® assay is useful for quantitating DNA templates for PCR,[13] labeling reactions, electrophoretic mobility-shift (bandshift) assays, DNA-footprinting assays and filter-binding assays, and for measuring yields from PCR reactions,[14] DNA minipreps and maxi-preps, cDNA synthesis and nuclease protection assays. The simplicity and selectivity of the assay also make it ideal for high-throughput automated quantitation assays used in forensic and genomics research. Furthermore, the PicoGreen® reagent has been used for:

- Genotyping by allele-specific PCR [15]
- Quantitating dsDNA samples before and after PCR amplification or after agarose gel electrophoresis [8,16]
- Determining PCR amplification yields before sequencing [14]
- Automating quantitation of DNA isolated from biological samples or obtained from PCR reactions, prior to running DNA typing gels for high-throughput genotyping [17]
- Quantitating DNA from buccal scrapes prior to DNA profiling by short tandem repeat (STR) analysis [18]
- Identifying contaminating DNA in recombinant protein products [19] or purified monoclonal antibody preparations [20,21]
- Monitoring DNA strand breaks in plasmids and bacterial artificial chromosomes [22]

Table 8.13 — Effects of Contaminants on the PicoGreen® Assay
Effects of several compounds that commonly contaminate nucleic acid preparations on the signal intensity of the PicoGreen® dsDNA quantitation assay.

Compound	Concentration	% Signal Change *
Salts		
Ammonium acetate	50 mM	3% decrease
Sodium acetate	30 mM	3% increase
Sodium chloride	200 mM	30% decrease
Zinc chloride	5 mM	8% decrease
Magnesium chloride	50 mM	33% decrease
Urea	2 M	9% increase
Organic Solvents		
Phenol	0.1%	13% increase
Ethanol	10%	12% increase
Chloroform	2%	14% increase
Detergents		
Sodium dodecyl sulfate (SDS)	0.01%	1% decrease
Triton X-100	0.1%	7% increase
Proteins		
Bovine serum albumin (BSA)	2%	16% decrease
IgG	0.1%	19% increase
Other Compounds		
Poly(ethylene glycol)	2%	8% increase
Agarose	0.1%	4% increase

* The compounds were incubated at the indicated concentrations with PicoGreen® reagent in the presence of 500 ng/mL calf thymus DNA. All samples were assayed in a final volume of 200 µL in 96-well microplates using a CytoFluor microplate reader. Samples were excited at 485 nm, and the fluorescence intensity was measured at 520 nm.

- Quantitating the efficiency of DNA extraction from frozen and formalin-fixed tissue sections [23]
- Detecting mammalian telomerase activity in tumor cells using the PCR-based TRAP assay [24–26]
- Developing assays for DNA polymerase [6]
- Measuring the activity of reverse transcriptase [6] or DNase I [27]
- Measuring supercoiled DNA forms in solution, based on their renaturation properties [28]
- Monitoring plasmid production during fermentation and downstream processing [29]
- Quantitating DNA denaturation as a measure for DNA damage in purified DNA preparations, cell lysates or homogenized solid tissues [30–32]

Each vial of the PicoGreen® dsDNA quantitation reagent (P7581) contains a sufficient amount of dye for at least 200 assays using a 2 mL assay volume and a standard fluorometer, or 2000 assays using a 200 µL assay volume and a fluorescence microplate reader. The product is accompanied by a simple protocol that ensures linear and reproducible quantitation of dsDNA. We also provide the PicoGreen® reagent in a kit (P7589) that contains:

- PicoGreen® dsDNA quantitation reagent
- Low-fluorescence, nucleic acid– and nuclease-free assay buffer concentrate, essential for the accurate measurement of dsDNA
- dsDNA standard solution for assay calibration
- A detailed protocol for dsDNA quantitation

This kit provides sufficient reagents for 200 assays using a 2 mL assay volume and a standard fluorometer or 2000 assays using a 200 µL assay volume and a fluorescence microplate reader. Both the stand-alone reagent and the kit are also available in special packaging, in which the PicoGreen® reagent is supplied as 10 vials of 100 µL aliquots for added convenience (P11495; Kit, P11496). The special packaging reduces thawing times, provides individual aliquots for each person performing the assay, and allows smaller amounts of dye to be taken into the field for analysis of water or other samples.

RediPlate™ 96 PicoGreen® dsDNA Quantitation Kits and Microplate

The PicoGreen® assay is also available as the convenient RediPlate™ 96 PicoGreen® dsDNA Quantitation Kits and microplate (R21495, R32716, R32701), in which the reagent is predispensed into a 96-well microplate. Nuclease-free buffer and the sample are simply added to the microplate wells — there is no need to handle the PicoGreen® reagent. After a five-minute incubation, the microplate is ready to read in a fluorescence microplate reader. The RediPlate™ PicoGreen® assay has sensitivity and linearity identical to that of the PicoGreen® reagents and kits described above (Figure 8.59).

We offer two different RediPlate™ 96 PicoGreen® dsDNA Quantitation Kits, as well as a RediPlate™ 96 PicoGreen® dsDNA quantitation microplate:

- In the RediPlate™ 96 PicoGreen® dsDNA Quantitation Kit (R21495), the microplate is provided in a resealable foil packet, and it snaps apart into twelve strips to permit assays in any multiple of eight (Figure 8.60). Eleven of the strips are preloaded with the PicoGreen® reagent; the remaining strip, marked with blackened tabs, contains a series of DNA standards for generating a standard curve. This kit also includes nuclease-free buffer and detailed instructions.

- In the RediPlate™ 96 PicoGreen® dsDNA Quantitation Kit (R32716), the microplate is provided in a resealable foil packet and snaps apart into twelve strips, but in this microplate all twelve strips are preloaded with the PicoGreen® reagent; the DNA standards are not predispensed into any of the microplate wells. Instead, a λ DNA standard is provided in a separate vial for generating a standard curve in the appropriate experimental range. Nuclease-free buffer and detailed instructions are also provided.
- The RediPlate™ 96 PicoGreen® dsDNA quantitation microplate (R32701) is the same microplate provided in the RediPlate™ 96 PicoGreen® dsDNA Quantitation Kit (R32716) with all wells preloaded with PicoGreen® reagent, for those who wish to prepare their own nuclease-free buffer and DNA standard curve. Multiple plates are available at significant discounts.

OliGreen® ssDNA Quantitation Reagent and Kit

For researchers working with ssDNA and oligonucleotides, as well as for companies that synthesize oligonucleotides, Molecular Probes offers our patented OliGreen® ssDNA quantitation reagent (O7582) and Kit (O11492). Short, synthetic oligonucleotides are used in a number of molecular biology techniques, including DNA sequencing, site-directed mutagenesis, DNA amplification, antisense gene suppression and *in situ* and blot hybridization. The conventional methods for quantitating oligonucleotides are not very sensitive, often requiring highly concentrated samples, and are quite subject to interference from sample contaminants. The most commonly used technique for measuring oligonucleotide and ssDNA concentrations is the determination of absorbance at 260 nm (an A_{260} of 0.1 corresponds to an ~3 µg/mL solution of a synthetic 24-mer M13 sequencing primer).

The OliGreen® ssDNA quantitation reagent enables researchers to routinely quantitate as little as 100 pg/mL of ssDNA or oligonucleotide (200 pg in a 2 mL assay volume with a standard fluorometer) or 200 pg in a 200 µL assay volume using a fluorescence microplate reader (Figure 8.61). Thus, quantitation with the OliGreen® reagent is about 10,000 times more sensitive than quantitation with UV absorbance methods and at least 500 times more sensitive (and far faster, with a greater throughput) than detecting oligonucleotides on electrophoretic gels stained with ethidium bromide. Using an easy-to-follow protocol (Figure 8.57) and fluorescein excitation and emission wavelengths, we have quantitated oligonucleotides that range from 10 to 50 nucleotides in length, as well as several sources of ssDNA, such as M13 and ϕX174 viral DNA and denatured calf thymus DNA, and obtained similar sensitivity. The OliGreen® reagent has also been used to detect phosphodiester and phosphorothioate oligonucleotides.[33]

Significant disadvantages of the UV absorbance method for oligonucleotide quantitation include the large relative contribution of free nucleotides to the signal and the interference caused by contaminants commonly found in nucleic acid preparations. By contrast, nucleotides and short oligonucleotides of six bases or less do not interfere with the OliGreen® ssDNA quantitation assay. However, the OliGreen® ssDNA quantitation reagent does exhibit fluorescence enhancement when bound to dsDNA and RNA. Like the PicoGreen® assay, the linear detection range of the OliGreen® assay in a standard fluorometer extends over four orders of magnitude — from 100 pg/mL to 1 µg/mL — with a single dye concentration (Figure 8.61). The linearity of the OliGreen® assay is maintained in the presence of several compounds commonly found to contaminate nucleic acid preparations, including salts, urea, ethanol, chloroform, detergents, proteins, ATP and agarose; however, many of these compounds do affect the signal intensity to some extent, so standard curves should be generated using solutions that closely mimic those of the samples (Table 8.14). The OliGreen® assay can even be performed using samples as complex as whole blood or serum.[33]

Our experiments with homopolymers have demonstrated that the OliGreen® reagent may exhibit significant base selectivity. The OliGreen® reagent shows a large fluorescence enhancement when bound to poly(dT) but only a relatively small fluorescence enhancement when bound to poly(dG) and little signal with poly(dA) and poly(dC). Thus, it is important to use an oligonucleotide with similar base composition when generating the standard curve.

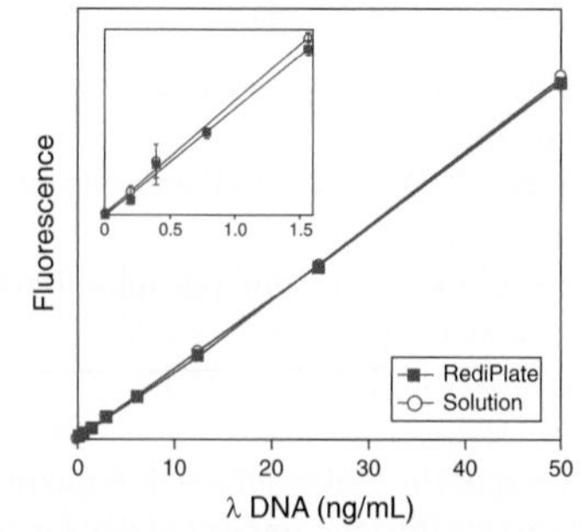

Figure 8.59 Linear quantitation of DNA from 0 to 50 ng/mL using the PicoGreen® dsDNA quantitation reagent in the standard microplate assay (open circles; P7581, P7589, P11495, P11496) or in the RediPlate™ 96 format assay (closed squares; R21495). The fluorescence emission intensity was measured using a fluorescence microplate reader and plotted as a function of DNA concentration. The inset shows an enlargement of the results obtained with DNA concentrations between 0 and 1.5 ng/mL. The assay shows consistently reproducible results, regardless of the format.

Figure 8.60 A RediPlate™ 96 microplate.

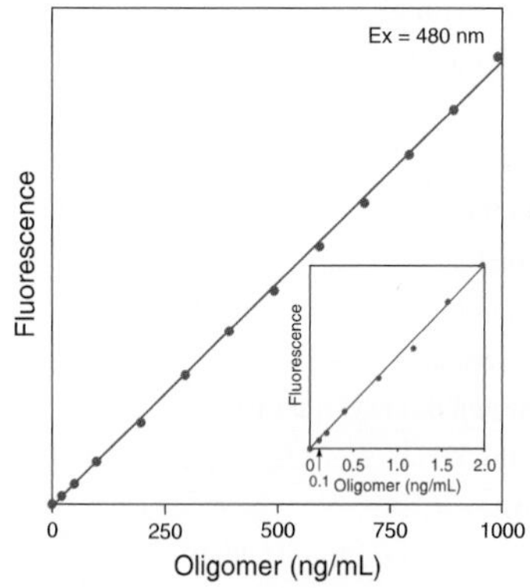

Figure 8.61 Linear quantitation of a synthetic 24-mer (an M13 sequencing primer) from 0.1 to 1000 ng/mL using the OliGreen® ssDNA quantitation reagent (O7582, O11492). Samples in 10 mm × 10 mm cuvettes were excited at 480 nm. The fluorescence emission intensity was measured at 520 nm using a spectrofluorometer and plotted as a function of oligonucleotide concentration. The inset shows an enlargement of the results obtained with oligonucleotide concentrations between zero and 2.0 ng/mL.

The remarkable properties of our OliGreen® ssDNA quantitation reagent make it ideal for the fast and accurate detection and quantitation of:

- Antisense oligonucleotides
- Aptamers
- Genomic DNA isolated under denaturing conditions
- PCR primers
- Phosphorothioate and phosphodiester oligodeoxynucleotides[33]
- Sequencing primers
- Single-stranded phage DNA

Each vial of the OliGreen® ssDNA quantitation reagent (O7582) contains a sufficient amount of dye for at least 200 assays using a 2 mL assay volume and a standard fluorometer, or 2000 assays using a 200 µL assay volume and a fluorescence microplate reader. The product is accompanied by a simple protocol that ensures linear and reproducible quantitation of ssDNA. We also provide the OliGreen® reagent in a kit form — the OliGreen® ssDNA Quantitation Kit (O11492) — that contains:

- The OliGreen® ssDNA quantitation reagent
- A low-fluorescence, nucleic acid– and nuclease-free assay buffer concentrate, essential for the accurate measurement of ssDNA
- An oligonucleotide standard (M13 sequencing primer) solution for assay calibration
- A detailed protocol for ssDNA quantitation

This kit provides sufficient reagents for 200 assays using a 2 mL assay volume and a standard fluorometer or 2000 assays using a 200 µL assay volume and a fluorescence microplate reader.

Table 8.14 — Effects of Contaminants on the OliGreen® Assay
Effects of several compounds that commonly contaminate nucleic acid preparations on the signal intensity of the OliGreen® ssDNA quantitation assay.

Compound	Concentration	% Signal Change *
Salts		
Ammonium acetate	50 mM	13% decrease
Sodium acetate	30 mM	3% decrease
Sodium chloride	100 mM	25% decrease
Zinc chloride	1 mM	43% decrease
Magnesium chloride	5 mM	34% decrease
Urea	2 M	47% increase
Organic Solvents		
Phenol	0.2%	19% decrease
Ethanol	10%	19% increase
Chloroform	2%	2% increase
Detergents		
Sodium dodecyl sulfate (SDS)	0.01%	73% increase
Triton X-100	0.1%	11% increase
Proteins		
Bovine serum albumin (BSA)	2%	20% increase
IgG	0.1%	37% increase
Other Compounds		
Poly(ethylene glycol)	1%	29% increase
Agarose	0.1%	8% increase
ATP	0.1%	30% increase

* The compounds were incubated at the indicated concentrations with OliGreen® reagent in the presence of 660 ng/mL of a 24-mer M13 sequencing primer. All samples were assayed in a final volume of 200 µL in 96-well microplates. Samples were excited at 485 nm, and the fluorescence intensity was measured at 520 nm.

RiboGreen® RNA Quantitation Assay

RiboGreen® RNA Quantitation Reagent and Kit

The patented RiboGreen® RNA quantitation reagent (R11491) is our premier stain for quantitating RNA in solution. Like the PicoGreen® dsDNA and OliGreen® ssDNA quantitation assays, the RiboGreen® RNA quantitation assay relies on a proprietary dye that exhibits a large fluorescence enhancement upon binding to nucleic acids. The extinction coefficient of the RiboGreen® reagent, as well as its quantum yield and fluorescence enhancement upon binding RNA, are all significantly greater than those of ethidium bromide (Table 8.15).

The RiboGreen® assay allows detection of as little as 1 ng/mL RNA in a standard fluorometer, fluorescence microplate reader or filter-based fluorometer using standard fluorescein excitation and emission settings (Figure 8.62). This sensitivity is at least 200-fold better than that achieved with ethidium bromide[34] and at least 1000-fold better than that achieved using conventional absorbance measurements at 260 nm (an A_{260} of 0.1 corresponds to an ~4 µg/mL RNA solution). Unlike UV absorbance measurements at 260 nm, the RiboGreen® reagent does not detect significant sample contamination by free nucleotides.[35] Thus, the RiboGreen® reagent more accurately measures the amount of intact RNA polymers in potentially degraded samples.

Using two different dye concentrations to cover its full dynamic range of three orders of magnitude, we have observed a linear correlation between the RNA concentration and fluorescence for 1.0 ng/mL to 50 ng/mL RNA using a 4000-fold dilution of the RiboGreen® dye, and for 20 ng/mL to 1 µg/mL using a 400-fold dilution of the dye (Figure 8.62). Assay linearity is maintained in the presence of several compounds commonly found in nucleic acid preparations, including salts, urea, ethanol, chloroform, detergents, proteins and agarose[35] (Table 8.16).

The RiboGreen® RNA reagent is not appreciably selective for RNA — the dye also shows significant fluorescence enhancement upon binding to DNA. However, a simple DNase pretreatment of samples removes the contribution of DNA to the signal; see below for a description of our RiboGreen® RNA-Specific Quantitation Kit with DNase I (R32702). The RiboGreen® reagent may also have some base selectivity; it exhibits about 60% less fluorescence when bound to poly(G) homopolymers and virtually no fluorescence when bound to

Table 8.15 — Comparison of the RiboGreen® RNA quantitation reagent and ethidium bromide

Nucleic Acid Stain	Extinction Coefficient ($cm^{-1}M^{-1}$) *	Quantum Yield †	Fluorescence Enhancement ‡
RiboGreen® reagent (R11490, R11491)	67,000	0.65	>1000-fold
Ethidium bromide (E1305, E3565)	5,500	<0.3	<30-fold

* Extinction coefficients were determined at 482 nm. † Quantum yield for the dye bound to RNA. ‡ Fluorescence enhancement upon binding RNA or DNA.

poly(U) or poly(C) homopolymers compared with the fluorescence when bound to poly(A) homopolymers or to rRNA.[35]

Using the RiboGreen® RNA quantitation reagent, we have reproducibly quantitated RNA from a wide variety of sources, including ribosomal RNA (rRNA), transfer RNA (tRNA), viral RNA, polyA+ fractions and total cellular RNA.[35] The RiboGreen® reagent is ideal for:

- Fast and accurate measurements of RNA yields before generating cDNA
- Determination of RNA yields from *in vitro* transcription
- Accurate measurements of RNA before performing Northern blot analysis,[36] S1 nuclease assays, RNase-protection assays, reverse-transcription PCR and differential-display PCR
- Assay of DNA-dependent RNA polymerase activity[37]
- Detection of capillary electrophoresis–separated viral RNA that has been stained *in vitro*[38]

Each vial of the RiboGreen® RNA quantitation reagent (R11491) contains a sufficient amount of dye for at least 200 high-range assays or 2000 low-range assays using a 2 mL assay volume and a standard fluorometer. With a fluorescence microplate reader and a 96-well microplate, the assay volume is reduced to 200 µL, allowing 2000 high-range assays or 20,000 low-range assays. Included with each vial of the RiboGreen® reagent is a simple protocol (Figure 8.57) that ensures linear and reproducible quantitation of RNA. We also provide the RiboGreen® reagent in a kit — the RiboGreen® RNA Quantitation Kit (R11490) — that contains:

- The RiboGreen® RNA quantitation reagent
- A low-fluorescence, nucleic acid– and nuclease-free assay buffer concentrate, essential for the accurate measurement of RNA
- A ribosomal RNA standard (16S and 23S rRNA from *Escherichia coli*) solution for assay calibration
- A detailed protocol

This kit provides sufficient reagents for at least 200 assays using a 2 mL assay volume and a standard fluorometer or at least 2000 assays using a 200 µL assay volume and a fluorescence microplate reader. The RNase-free TE buffer concentrate, which is essential to the success of the assay, is also available separately (T11493) and can be used to extend the number of low-concentration assays possible with the kit.

Table 8.16 — Effects of Contaminants on the RiboGreen® Assay.

Compound	Maximum Acceptable Concentration	% Signal Change *
Salts		
Ammonium acetate	20 mM	4% decrease
Sodium acetate	20 mM	11% decrease
Sodium chloride	20 mM	15% decrease
Zinc chloride	1 mM	9% decrease
Magnesium chloride	0.5 mM	9% decrease
Calcium chloride	0.1 mM	2% increase
Cesium chloride	10 mM	8% decrease
Guanidinium thiocyanate	10 mM	9% decrease
Urea	3 M	13% decrease
Organic Solvents		
Phenol	0.5%	5% decrease
Ethanol	20%	10% decrease
Chloroform	2%	15% increase
Detergents		
Sodium dodecyl sulfate (SDS)	0.05%	10% decrease
Triton X-100	0.5%	8% decrease
Proteins		
Bovine serum albumin (BSA)	0.2%	11% decrease
IgG	0.02%	4% decrease
Other Compounds		
Formamide	10%	12% decrease
Sucrose	>500 mM	4% decrease
Boric acid	100 mM	15% decrease
Poly(ethylene glycol)	10%	10% decrease
Agarose	0.2%	3% increase

* The compounds were incubated at the indicated concentrations with RiboGreen® reagent in the presence of 1.0 mg/mL ribosomal RNA. All samples were assayed in a final volume of 200 µL in 96-well microplates using a fluorescence microplate reader. Samples were excited at 485 ± 10 nm, and the fluorescence intensity was measured at 530 ± 12.5 nm.

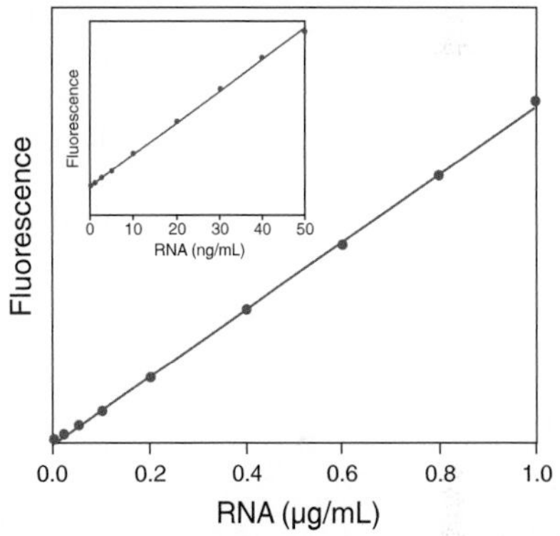

Figure 8.62 Linear quantitation of ribosomal RNA using the RiboGreen® RNA quantitation reagent (R11491, R11490). For the high-range assay, the RiboGreen® reagent was diluted 200-fold into 10 mM Tris-HCl, 1 mM EDTA, pH 7.5 (TE), and 100 µL of the reagent solution was added to microplate wells containing 100 µL ribosomal RNA in TE. For the low-range assay (see inset), the RiboGreen® reagent was diluted 2000-fold into TE, and 100 µL of the reagent solution was added to 100 µL of ribosomal RNA in TE. Samples were excited at 485 ± 10 nm, and the fluorescence emission intensity was measured at 530 ± 12.5 nm using a fluorescence microplate reader. Background fluorescence was not subtracted.

RediPlate™ 96 RiboGreen® RNA Quantitation Kit

The RiboGreen® assay is also available in a convenient RediPlate™ 96 RiboGreen® RNA Quantitation Kit in which the RiboGreen® reagent is predispensed into a 96-well microplate (R32700). The buffer and sample are simply added to the microplate wells — there is no need to handle the RiboGreen® reagent. After a 10-minute incubation, the microplate is ready to read in a fluorescence microplate reader. The RediPlate™ RiboGreen® assay has a linear range of ~15–1000 ng/mL (~3–200 ng in a 200 µL assay volume) with a single dye concentration (Figure 8.63). The microplate used in the RediPlate™ 96 RiboGreen® RNA Quantitation Kit is provided in a resealable foil packet, and it snaps apart into twelve strips to permit assays in any multiple of eight (Figure 8.60). Eleven of the strips are preloaded with the RiboGreen® reagent; the remaining strip, marked with blackened tabs, contains a series of RNA standards for generating a standard curve. In addition to the 96-well microplate, each RediPlate™ RiboGreen® 96 RNA Quantitation Kit includes RNase-free reaction buffer and detailed instructions. Multiple plates are available at significant discounts.

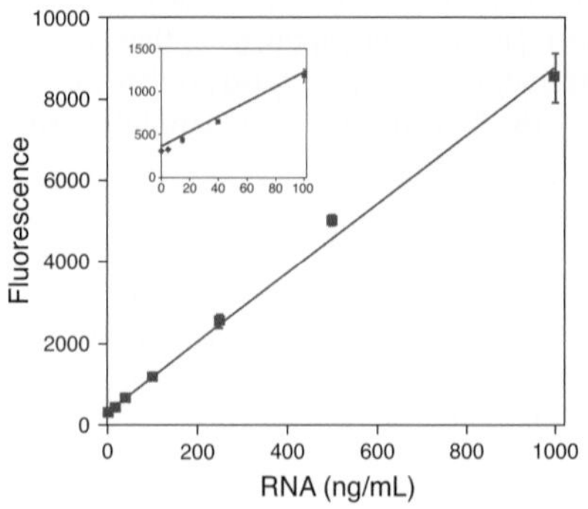

Figure 8.63 Dynamic range and sensitivity of the RediPlate™ 96 RiboGreen® RNA quantitation assay. The RNA standards provided in the RediPlate™ 96 RiboGreen® RNA Quantitation Kit (R32700) were added in quadruplicate to assay wells as described in the accompanying protocol, and fluorescence was measured in a fluorescence microplate reader using excitation at 485 ± 12.5 nm and fluorescence detection at 530 ± 15 nm. Fluorescence was plotted against the RNA concentration with no background subtraction. The inset shows the sensitivity of the assay at very low levels of RNA.

RiboGreen® RNA-Specific Quantitation Kit with DNase I

Although the RiboGreen® RNA quantitation reagent is insensitive to proteins, detergents, salts and other common contaminants, it is sensitive to both RNA and DNA. The presence of DNA in experimental samples will therefore elicit substantial errors in quantitative determinations of RNA. The RiboGreen® RNA-Specific Quantitation Kit (R32702) is designed to circumvent this problem. The DNase I provided in this kit is used to reduce DNA concentrations from as high as 1 µg/mL to minimally detectable levels prior to fluorescence quantitation of RNA using the RiboGreen® reagent. Because DNase I digestion and the RiboGreen® fluorescence quantitation assay have quite different buffer-composition requirements, the two reactions must be carried out sequentially. The linear range for RNA quantitation with the RiboGreen® RNA-Specific Quantitation Kit extends over almost three orders of magnitude in concentration — from 5 to 1000 ng/mL RNA (Figure 8.64). The lower limit of detection is about 40 times lower than that achieved with ethidium bromide–based fluorescence assays,[34] and about 250 times lower than that achieved with A_{260} measurements. The original RiboGreen® assay described above attains a slightly greater sensitivity due to the absence of DNase I and its attendant divalent cations. The

Note 8.2 — Product Highlight

SYBR® Green I and SYBR® Green II Dyes for Quantitating Nucleic Acids on Plastic Wrap or Paraffin Sheets

Molecular biologists frequently need a quick estimate of nucleic acid concentration of solutions. We have found that the SYBR® Green dyes make excellent detection reagents for DNA and RNA spotted onto plastic wrap or paraffin sheets (e.g., Parafilm brand). Extremely small quantities of the dyes are required for this assay. Using the following simple procedure, we have obtained 10- to 25-fold better sensitivity with SYBR® Green dyes than with 1 µM ethidium bromide, depending on the nucleic acid tested. The procedure is as follows:

Step 1. Dilute an aliquot of the SYBR® Green I (S7563, S7567, S7585) or SYBR® Green II (S7564, S7568, S7586) DMSO stock solution 1:5000 in TE (10 mM Tris-HCl, 1 mM EDTA, pH 8).

Step 2. Mix 5 µL of a nucleic acid–containing sample with 5 µL of the 1:5000 dilution of SYBR® Green I dye or SYBR® Green II dye prepared in step 1.

Step 3. Spot the mixture onto plastic wrap or a paraffin sheet that is directly placed on a transilluminator.

Step 4. Illuminate with 300 nm transillumination and photograph through a SYBR® gel stain photographic filter (S7569) using Polaroid 667 black-and-white print film. Photography is essential for obtaining the highest sensitivity.

Step 5. For a semiquantitative assay, repeat steps 2 through 4 with known amounts of nucleic acid and compare the signals with those from experimental samples.

Detection limits per spot of phage λ DNA are approximately 3 ng and 30 ng with SYBR® Green I dye and ethidium bromide, respectively. Visual detection limits for ribosomal RNA under the same conditions are approximately 3 ng, 9 ng and 80 ng with SYBR® Green II dye, SYBR® Green I dye and ethidium bromide, respectively.

RiboGreen® RNA-Specific Quantitation Kit with DNase I is configured for use with a fluorescence microplate reader and contains:

- The RiboGreen® RNA quantitation reagent
- A low-fluorescence, nucleic acid– and nuclease-free assay buffer concentrate, essential for the accurate measurement of RNA
- DNase I from bovine pancreas
- Concentrated DNase I buffer
- A ribosomal RNA standard (16S and 23S rRNA from *Escherichia coli*) solution for assay calibration
- A detailed protocol

Sufficient reagents are provided for at least 2000 assays using 200 µL assay volumes in a 96-well microplate format.

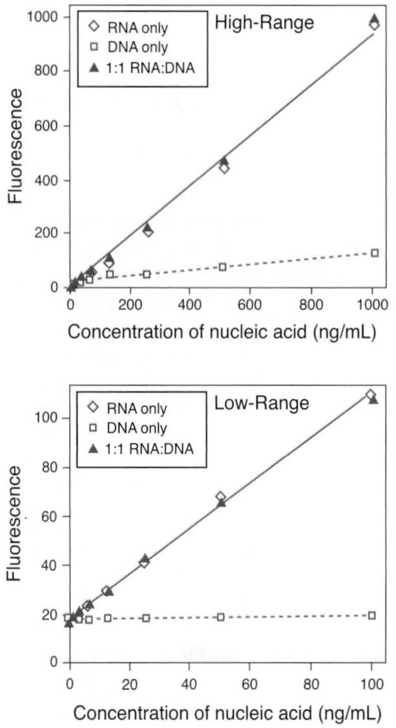

Figure 8.64 Linear range and sensitivity of the RiboGreen® RNA-specific quantitation assay. The high-range RNA quantitation assay (upper panel) and the low-range RNA quantitation assay (lower panel) were performed with DNase I treatment, as described in the protocol for the RiboGreen® RNA-Specific Quantitation Kit (R32702). The nucleic acids assayed were: RNA only, DNA only and a 1:1 mixture of RNA and DNA. Samples were excited at 485 ± 10 nm, and the fluorescence emission intensity was measured at 530 ± 12.5 nm using a fluorescence microplate reader. Fluorescence emission intensity was then plotted versus nucleic acid concentration. Note that the nucleic acid concentration plotted in the case of the RNA:DNA mixture is that of the RNA component only, rather than that of the RNA plus the DNA components. If the DNase I treatment is omitted (data not shown), the DNA-only samples produce a curve comparable (slightly steeper) to that of the RNA-only samples, and the RNA:DNA mixture–samples produce a curve with about twice the slope as that of the RNA-only or DNA-only samples. Background fluorescence has not been subtracted.

Other Stains for Nucleic Acid Quantitation in Solution

Cyanine Dyes and Phenanthridine Dyes for Nucleic Acid Quantitation in Solution

The dimeric cyanine dyes TOTO®-1 and YOYO®-1 are useful for sensitive fluorometric measurement of dsDNA, ssDNA and RNA in solution,[4] although the PicoGreen®, OliGreen® and RiboGreen® reagents generally are faster, have greater sensitivity and show a linear response over a broader range of nucleic acid concentrations. The linear range of assays that use the TOTO®-1 and YOYO®-1 dyes for DNA quantitation encompasses about two orders of magnitude, with a sensitivity limit of about 0.5 ng/mL. The TOTO®-1, YOYO®-1 and YO-PRO®-1 nucleic acid stains have been used to quantitate PCR amplification products in a homogeneous human leukocyte antigen (HLA) typing method that requires no transfer or washing steps, thus minimizing the risk of sample contamination.[39,40] Other dyes for nucleic acid quantitation in solution and their applications include:

- YOYO®-1 dye (Y3601, Section 8.1) for solution quantitation of oligonucleotides,[41] PCR products[42] and nuclear run-on assays[43]
- YO-PRO®-1 dye (Y3603, Section 8.1) for quantitating dsDNA in a fluorescence microplate reader, with a reported sensitivity limit of about 2.5 ng/mL[3]
- YO-PRO®-1 dye for quantitating RNA isolated from *Xenopus* embryos[44]
- YO-PRO®-1 dye and SYBR® Green I dye for direct counting of viruses in marine and freshwater environments[45–50] (Figure 8.65)
- PO-PRO™-3 dye (P3585, Section 8.1) for quantitating DNA in a fluorescence microplate reader,[51] with fluorescence measurements reported to be independent of base-pair composition
- Ethidium bromide (E1305, E3565; Section 8.1) for measuring the yield of PCR products[52]
- Ethidium bromide and acridine homodimer (A666, Section 8.1) for quantitating covalently closed, circular DNA and for measuring the activity of polymerases, deoxynucleotidyl transferases, ligases, gyrases, topoisomerases and nucleases[11,53,54]
- YOYO®-1 dye for measuring the activity of DNases[55]
- SYBR® Gold dye (S11494, Section 8.4) for detecting DNA mutations in a simple PCR-based assay[56]
- SYBR® Green I dye for quantitation of nucleic acids on plastic wrap or paraffin (see Note 8.2 "Product Highlight: SYBR® Green I and SYBR® Green II Dyes for Quantitating Nucleic Acids on Plastic Wrap or Paraffin Sheets")

Dyes such as the ethidium homodimers and our dimeric cyanine dyes — the TOTO®, YOYO®, BOBO™, POPO™, JOJO™ and LOLO™ dyes (Table 8.2) — exhibit a high affinity for double-stranded nucleic acids but label small single-stranded oligonucleotides less well. This characteristic of ethidium homodimer-1 (E1169, Section 8.1) was exploited to analyze short self-annealing oligonucleotides for their ability to hybridize.[57] Because our dimeric cyanine dyes and the PicoGreen® dsDNA quantitation reagent have extremely low intrinsic fluorescence in the absence of DNA, high fluorescence enhancements upon binding, higher quantum yields and much larger extinction coefficients than ethidium homodimer-1,[3,58] they should prove superior in this application.

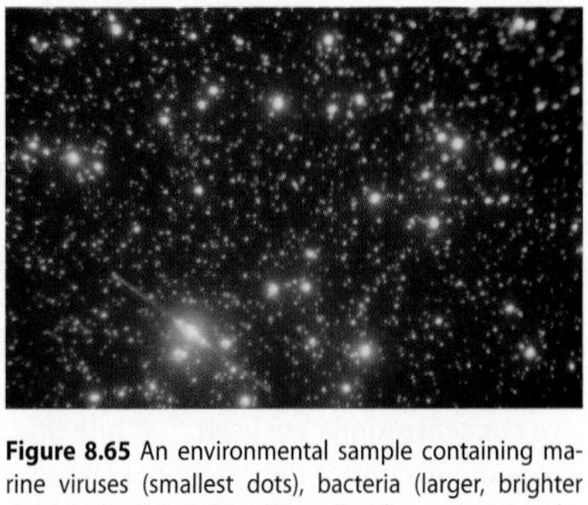

Figure 8.65 An environmental sample containing marine viruses (smallest dots), bacteria (larger, brighter dots), and a diatom (long thin cell with prominent nucleus) stained with SYBR® Green I nucleic acid stain (S7563, S7567, S7585). Image contributed by Jed Fuhrman, University of Southern California.

Hoechst 33258 Dye for Quantitating DNA in Solution

The Hoechst 33258 dye (H1398, H3569; FluoroPure™ Grade, H21491) has been extensively used to quantitate dsDNA in solution. Hoechst 33258 shows a fluorescence increase upon binding nucleic acids and a preference for binding to AT regions. Hoechst 33258 is selective (but not specific) for dsDNA over RNA in high-salt buffers and for dsDNA over ssDNA in low-salt buffers. The Hoechst 33258 dye can quantitatively detect from 10 ng/mL to ~10 µg/mL dsDNA when two different dye concentrations are used.[12] While this assay uses principles that are similar to other fluorescent assays, newer dyes such as the PicoGreen® reagent provide much higher sensitivity, better selectivity and a much broader dynamic range with a single dye concentration.

The FluoReporter® Blue Fluorometric dsDNA Quantitation Kit (F2962) provides the protocols developed by Rago and colleagues[1] for analyzing cellular DNA with the blue-fluorescent Hoechst 33258 nucleic acid stain. The kit enables researchers to detect ~10 ng of isolated calf thymus DNA or ~1000 mouse NIH 3T3 cells in a 200 µL sample (substantially lower levels are detectable using our CyQUANT® Cell Proliferation Assay Kit described in Section 15.4). With this kit, quantitation of cellular DNA is rapid, and all manipulations can be carried out in microplate wells. The cells are lysed by freezing them in distilled water, which circumvents the requirement for extraction procedures used in other Hoechst 33258 dye–based protocols.[12,59–62] The diluted dye solution is then added to lysed cells and the fluorescence is measured. Kit components include:

- Hoechst 33258 in dimethylsulfoxide (DMSO)/H_2O
- TNE buffer
- A detailed protocol

Each kit provides sufficient reagents for assaying 2000 samples using a fluorescence microplate reader.

Real-Time Quantitative PCR Using the SYBR® Green I Nucleic Acid Gel Stain

Measurements of PCR products can be taken during the linear portion of the amplification reactions, allowing accurate quantitation of templates. Several methods exist for real-time quantitation of PCR products, including fluorescence resonance energy transfer techniques using fluorescently labeled primers or molecular beacons (Section 8.5). Identification of PCR products during the reaction can also be monitored using the SYBR® Green I nucleic acid gel stain (S7563, S7567, S7585); this method has been shown to be more precise than TaqMan assays using labeled oligonucleotide probes.[63] In addition, individual DNA molecules have been detected with on-line capillary PCR coupled with laser-induced fluorescence detection by adding the SYBR® Green I stain to the reaction mixture.[64] Our patented SYBR® Green I stain binds preferentially to dsDNA and thus can accurately quantitate the amount of double-stranded product in the presence of single-stranded oligonucleotide primers[65] (Figure 8.66). SYBR® Green I stain is stable to the extremes of temperature required for PCR reactions and does not interfere with *Taq* polymerase. Improved specificity for quantitating desired products can be achieved by using the SYBR® Green I stain after the assay to measure the melting temperature of the products.[66–74] Double-stranded DNA with no base mismatches will show a higher melting temperature than the nonspecific templates that contain mismatches. Further specificity may possibly be obtained using PNA probes labeled with one of our reactive SYBR® dyes (S21500, S21501, S21502; Section 8.2). Real-time quantitative PCR experiments can be carried out using instruments specialized for the application[75,76] or by quantitating amplification products manually at different time points.[77] Real-time quantitative PCR with the SYBR® Green I dye has been used to develop reliable and simple diagnostic assays for detecting genetic mutations, including duplications and deletions in mosquito drug-resistance genes,[78] chromosomal translocations in human disease genes[70,79] and base substitutions.[67,80,81] It has also been used for the unequivocal identification of viral, bacterial or fungal pathogens.[66,68,69,71,72,82–84] In addition, this method has been used successfully for quantitative reverse-transcription PCR.[63,75]

A Useful Technique to Reduce Background Fluorescence in Nucleic Acid Detection

Researchers commonly use SYBR® Green I nucleic acid gel stain to detect polymerase chain reaction (PCR) or other nucleic acid amplification products in real time.[65,69,70,73,74,76,79,83,85] The PicoGreen® reagent (P7581, P11495) can also be used to detect such products after amplification[8,14] and to detect products of chain elongation by telomerase,[26] reverse transcriptase and DNA polymerase[6] (Section 8.7). One drawback of these methods, however, is that both primers and primer dimers can contribute to the fluorescence signal, limiting sensitivity. To solve this problem, we have developed a patented technique that reduces the contribution of primers and primer dimers to the fluorescence signal. A QSY® 7 or QSY® 9 dye attached to the 5′-terminus of an oligonucleotide primer effectively quenches the fluorescence of nucleic acid stain molecules that bind to the primer or its dimers. As the chain elongates, the nucleic acid stain molecules that bind at sites sufficiently remote from the quencher exhibit fluorescence (Figure 8.67). Thus, the signal in PCR measurements more accurately indicates initial target numbers, and the background fluorescence in reverse transcription, telomerase or DNA polymerization assays is reduced. The preferred QSY® dyes for these conjugations are the succinimidyl esters of QSY® 7 carboxylic acid (Q10193) or more water-soluble QSY® 9 carboxylic acid (Q20131), which are readily conjugated to amine-derivatized oligonucleotides. The QSY® 7 and QSY® 9 dyes have broad visible absorption similar to that of tetramethylrhodamine (Figure 8.48). Our QSY® 21 carboxylic acid succinimidyl ester (Q20132) has even longer wavelength absorption (near 660 nm, Figure 1.70) and is a highly efficient quencher for red-fluorescent dyes such as the Alexa Fluor® 633, Alexa Fluor® 647, TOTO®-3 and TO-PRO®-3 dyes (Table 1.10). QSY® 35 acetic acid, succinimidyl ester (Q20133) is an excellent fluorescence acceptor from blue-fluorescent dyes such as the Hoechst and DAPI nucleic acid stains (Figure 1.70).

References

1. Anal Biochem 191, 31 (1990); **2.** Nucleic Acids Res 32, e103 (2004); **3.** Biophys J 61, A314, abstract #1806 (1992); **4.** Anal Biochem 208, 144 (1993); **5.** Anal Biochem 249, 228 (1997); **6.** Biotechniques 21, 664 (1996); **7.** Chem Commun 689 (2000); **8.** Anal Biochem 279, 111 (2000); **9.** Anal Chem 71, 5470 (1999); **10.** J Immunol Methods 278, 261 (2003); **11.** Anal Biochem 230, 353 (1995); **12.** Anal Biochem 102, 344 (1980); **13.** Mol Cell Probes 9, 145 (1995); **14.** Biotechniques 20, 676 (1996); **15.** Biotechniques 24, 206 (1998); **16.** Biotechniques 21, 372 (1996); **17.** Genome Res 6, 781 (1996); **18.** Biotechniques 23, 18 (1997); **19.** Biotechniques 23, 532 (1997); **20.** Biotechol Tech 13, 681 (1999); **21.** Bioseparation 8, 281 (1999); **22.** Nucleic Acids Res 31, e65 (2003); **23.** Am J Pathol 156, 1189 (2000); **24.** Anal Biochem 323, 65 (2003); **25.** Clin Chem 44, 2133 (1998); **26.** Proc Natl Acad Sci U S A 93, 6091 (1996); **27.** Anal Biochem 281, 95 (2000); **28.** Nucleic Acids Res 28, E57 (2000); **29.** Biotechnol Bioeng 66, 195 (1999); **30.** Anal Biochem 270, 195 (1999); **31.** Anal Chem 71, 4423 (1999); **32.** Eur J Biochem 153, 105 (1985); **33.** Antisense Nucleic Acid Drug Dev 7, 133 (1997); **34.** Anal Biochem 17, 100 (1966); **35.** Anal Biochem 265, 368 (1998); **36.** J Immunol 161, 4332 (1998); **37.** Anal Biochem 324, 183 (2004); **38.** Anal Chem 76, 882 (2004); **39.** Hum Immunol 39, 1 (1994); **40.** Anal Biochem 221, 340 (1994); **41.** Biotechniques 16, 1032 (1994); **42.** Anal Biochem 218, 458 (1994); **43.** Anal Biochem 221, 202 (1994); **44.** Neuron 14, 865 (1995); **45.** Nature 399, 541 (1999); **46.** Aquat Microbial Ecol 14, 113 (1998); **47.** Appl Environ Microbiol 65, 45 (1999); **48.** Appl Environ Microbiol 64, 1725 (1998); **49.** Appl Environ Microbiol 63, 186 (1997); **50.** Limnol Oceanogr 40, 1050 (1995); **51.** Biotechniques 18, 136 (1995); **52.** Biotechniques 9, 310 (1990); **53.** Nucleic Acids Res 7, 571 (1979); **54.** Nucleic Acids Res 7, 547 (1979); **55.** Biotechniques 18, 231 (1995); **56.** Nucleic Acids Res 28, E36 (2000); **57.** Biotechniques 15, 1060 (1993); **58.** Nucleic Acids Res 20, 2803 (1992); **59.** In Vitro Toxicol 3, 219 (1990); **60.** J Immunol Methods 162, 41 (1993); **61.** Cancer Res 49, 565 (1989); **62.** Anal Biochem 131, 538 (1983); **63.** Anal Biochem 285, 194 (2000); **64.** Anal Chem 73, 1537 (2001); **65.** Biotechniques 22, 130 (1997); **66.** J Clin Microbiol 38, 2756 (2000); **67.** Clin Chem 46, 1540 (2000); **68.** J Clin Microbiol 38, 795 (2000); **69.** J Microbiol Methods 35, 23 (1999); **70.** Lab Invest 79, 337 (1999); **71.** Syst Appl Microbiol 21, 89 (1998); **72.** Anal Biochem 259, 112 (1998); **73.** Biotechniques 24, 954 (1998); **74.** Anal Biochem 245, 154 (1997); **75.** Mol Vis 6, 178 (2000); **76.** Biotechniques 22, 176 (1997); **77.** PCR Methods Appl 4, 234 (1995); **78.** Biochem J 346 Pt 1, 17 (2000); **79.** Am J Pathol 154, 97 (1999); **80.** Mol Genet Metab 68, 357 (1999); **81.** Anal Biochem 260, 142 (1998); **82.** Biotechniques 31, 278 (2001); **83.** J Clin Microbiol 37, 987 (1999); **84.** J Clin Microbiol 38, 586 (2000); **85.** Mol Diagn 3, 3 (1998).

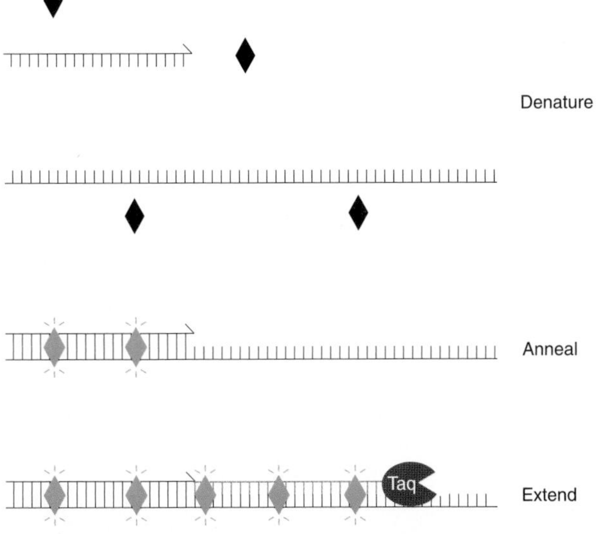

Figure 8.66 Schematic representation of real-time PCR with the SYBR® Green I dye. SYBR® Green I dye (black diamonds) becomes fluorescent (green diamonds) upon binding to double-stranded DNA, providing a direct method for quantitating PCR products in real time.

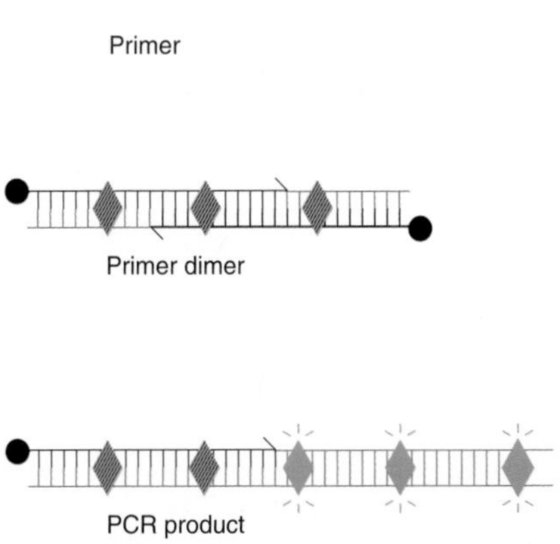

Figure 8.67 Schematic representation of real-time PCR with quencher-labeled primers and the SYBR® Green I dye. The SYBR® Green I dye (diamonds) becomes fluorescent (sparkling green diamonds) upon binding to double-stranded DNA. However, a quencher (black circles) bound to a primer suppresses the fluorescence of nearby SYBR® Green I dye molecules (dark green diamonds). In this way, the fluorescence signal of the dye bound to PCR products is maintained while background fluorescence from the dye bound to primer dimers is minimized.

Product List — 8.3 Nucleic Acid Detection and Quantitation in Solution

Cat #	Product Name	Unit Size
F2962	FluoReporter® Blue Fluorometric dsDNA Quantitation Kit *200-2000 assays*	1 kit
H1398	Hoechst 33258, pentahydrate (bis-benzimide)	100 mg
H3569	Hoechst 33258, pentahydrate (bis-benzimide) *10 mg/mL solution in water*	10 mL
H21491	Hoechst 33258, pentahydrate (bis-benzimide) *FluoroPure™ grade*	100 mg
O11492	OliGreen® ssDNA Quantitation Kit *200-2000 assays*	1 kit
O7582	OliGreen® ssDNA quantitation reagent *200-2000 assays*	1 mL
P7589	PicoGreen® dsDNA Quantitation Kit *200-2000 assays*	1 kit
P11496	PicoGreen® dsDNA Quantitation Kit *200-2000 assays* *special packaging*	1 kit
P7581	PicoGreen® dsDNA quantitation reagent *200-2000 assays*	1 mL
P11495	PicoGreen® dsDNA quantitation reagent *200-2000 assays* *special packaging*	10 x 100 µL
Q10193	QSY® 7 carboxylic acid, succinimidyl ester	5 mg
Q20131	QSY® 9 carboxylic acid, succinimidyl ester	5 mg
Q20132	QSY® 21 carboxylic acid, succinimidyl ester	5 mg
Q20133	QSY® 35 acetic acid, succinimidyl ester	5 mg
Q33130	Quant-iT™ DNA Assay Kit, Broad Range *1000 assays*	1 kit
Q33135	Quant-iT™ DNA Assay Kit, Broad Range *introductory kit, 200 assays*	1 kit
Q33120	Quant-iT™ DNA Assay Kit, High Sensitivity *1000 assays*	1 kit
Q33125	Quant-iT™ DNA Assay Kit, High Sensitivity *introductory kit, 200 assays*	1 kit
Q33155	Quant-iT™ DNA Assay Kits *includes introductory kits Q33125 and Q33135, 200 assays each*	1 kit
Q33139	Quant-iT™ DNA Broad Range Assay Kit product info sheet MP33130	each
Q33129	Quant-iT™ DNA High Sensitivity Assay Kit product info sheet MP33120	each
Q33140	Quant-iT™ RNA Assay Kit *1000 assays*	1 kit
Q33145	Quant-iT™ RNA Assay Kit *introductory kit, 200 assays*	1 kit
R32716	RediPlate™ 96 PicoGreen® dsDNA Quantitation Kit *one 96-well microplate* *with separate DNA standard*	1 kit
R21495	RediPlate™ 96 PicoGreen® dsDNA Quantitation Kit *one 96-well microplate*	1 kit
R32701	RediPlate™ 96 PicoGreen® dsDNA quantitation microplate	each
R32700	RediPlate™ 96 RiboGreen® RNA Quantitation Kit *one 96-well microplate*	1 kit
R11490	RiboGreen® RNA Quantitation Kit *200-2000 assays*	1 kit
R11491	RiboGreen® RNA quantitation reagent *200-20,000 assays*	1 mL
R32702	RiboGreen® RNA-Specific Quantitation Kit *with DNase I* *2000 assays*	1 kit
S7563	SYBR® Green I nucleic acid gel stain *10,000X concentrate in DMSO*	500 µL
S7567	SYBR® Green I nucleic acid gel stain *10,000X concentrate in DMSO*	1 mL
S7585	SYBR® Green I nucleic acid gel stain *10,000X concentrate in DMSO* *special packaging*	20 x 50 µL
T11493	20X TE buffer *RNase free*	100 mL

For current prices or to order online, visit probes.invitrogen.com

8.4 Nucleic Acid Detection and Quantitation in Electrophoretic Gels and Capillaries

Nucleic Acid Detection in Gels

The new generation of fluorescent nucleic acid gel stains from Molecular Probes — the SYBR® Gold, SYBR® Green I and SYBR® Green II dyes — are by far the best high-sensitivity reagents for staining DNA (Figure 8.68) and RNA (Figure 8.69) in electrophoretic gels.[1] These gel stains provide greater sensitivity with lower background fluorescence than the conventional gel stain, ethidium bromide. In addition, the SYBR Safe™ DNA gel stain showed very low mutagenic activity when tested by an independent, licensed testing laboratory, and it is not classified as hazardous waste or as a pollutant under U.S. Federal regulations (see Note 8.3 "Product Highlight: SYBR Safe™ DNA Gel Stain").

SYBR® Gold Nucleic Acid Gel Stain

Our patented SYBR® Gold nucleic acid gel stain (S11494) is simply the most sensitive stain available for detecting DNA or RNA in gels using a standard 300 nm UV transilluminator and Polaroid 667 black-and-white print film. Although the SYBR® Green I and SYBR® Green II gel stains are still the standard by which gel stains are judged and are preferred for specific applications, certain characteristics of the SYBR® Gold stain represent a further improvement over our SYBR® Green I and SYBR® Green II gel stains for routine gel analysis. The SYBR® Gold nucleic acid gel stain provides:

- **Maximum sensitivity.** Upon binding to nucleic acids, the SYBR® Gold stain exhibits a >1000-fold fluorescence enhancement and a quantum yield of ~0.6.[2] By comparison, ethidium bromide exhibits <30-fold fluorescence enhancement upon binding nucleic acids[3] and a quantum yield of ~0.15.[4] Because of its superior fluorescence characteristics, the SYBR® Gold stain is greater than 10-fold more sensitive than ethidium bromide for detecting DNA and RNA in gels using a 300 nm UV transilluminator and black-and-white photography. We routinely detect as little as 25 pg of dsDNA or 1 ng of RNA per band using a 300 nm UV transilluminator or a blue-light transilluminator — sensitivity levels even higher than those of silver staining.[2] For detecting glyoxalated RNA with 300 nm transillumination, the SYBR® Gold stain is 25–100 times more sensitive than ethidium bromide (Figure 8.70) and thus represents a significant advance for protocols requiring sensitive RNA detection. The SYBR® Gold stain has also proven to be more sensitive than our SYBR® Green II stain for detecting single-strand conformation polymorphism (SSCP) products.[5]
- **Rapid gel penetration.** Staining gels with the SYBR® Gold stain after electrophoresis followed by gel photography provides the optimal sensitivity. The SYBR® Gold stain penetrates agarose gels faster, and stains thick and high-percentage gels better than any other post-electrophoresis stain.
- **Versatility.** The SYBR® Gold stain is a universal nucleic acid gel stain that provides the highest sensitivity for dsDNA, ssDNA

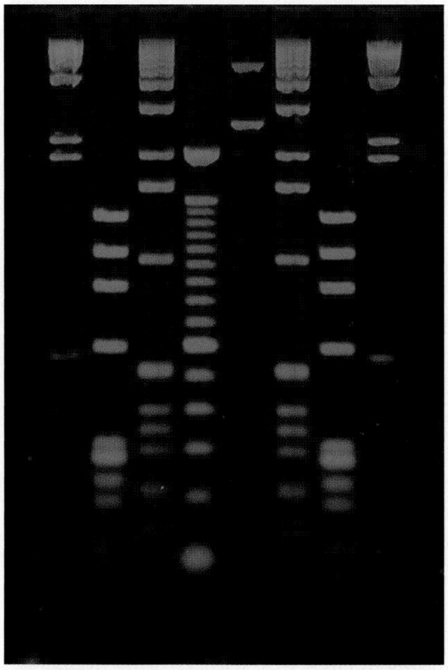

Figure 8.68 DNA molecular weight ladders that have been electrophoresed on a 1% agarose gel and then stained for 30 minutes with a 1:10,000 dilution of SYBR® Green I nucleic acid gel stain (S7563, S7567, S7585). Lanes 1 and 8 contain *Hin*dIII–cut λ DNA; lanes 2 and 7, *Hae*III–cut φX174 RF DNA; lanes 3 and 6, 1 kilobase pair DNA ladder; lane 4, 100 base pair DNA ladder; lane 5, *Eco*RI–cut pUC19 DNA mixed with *Pst*I–cut φX174 RF DNA. Gel staining was visualized using 254 nm epi-illumination.

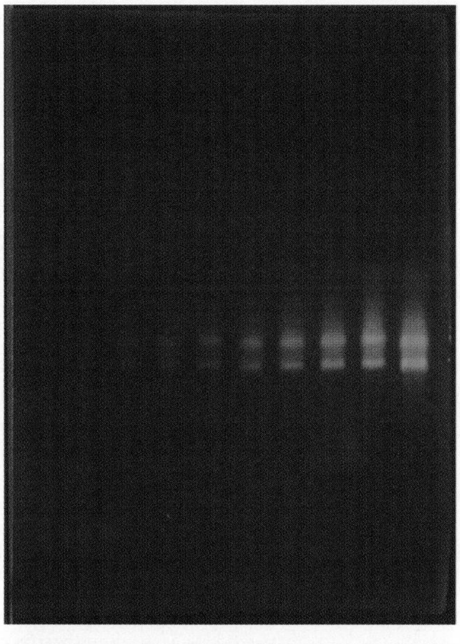

Figure 8.69 A twofold dilution series of *Escherichia coli* 16S and 23S ribosomal RNA (rRNA) that has been electrophoresed on a nondenaturing 1% agarose gel and then stained with our SYBR® Green II RNA gel stain (S7564, S7568, S7586). Gel staining was visualized with 254 nm epi-illumination.

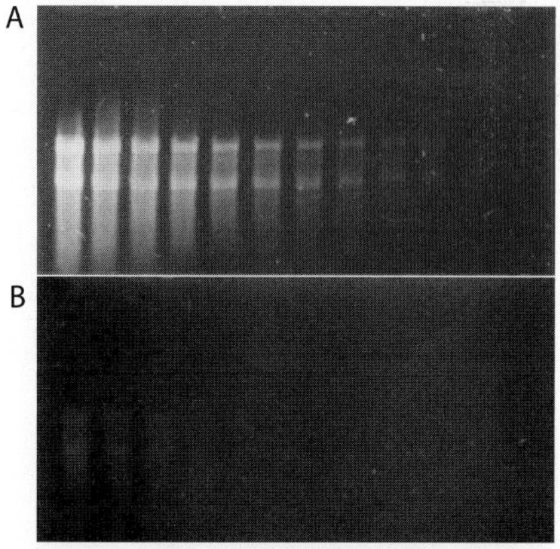

Figure 8.70 Comparison of glyoxalated RNA stained with ethidium bromide and with the SYBR® Gold nucleic acid gel stain (S11494). Identical twofold dilutions of glyoxalated *Escherichia coli* 16S and 23S ribosomal RNA were separated on 1% agarose minigels using standard methods and stained for 30 minutes with SYBR® Gold stain in TBE buffer (panel A) or 0.5 µg/mL ethidium bromide in 0.1 M ammonium acetate (panel B). Both gels were subjected to 300 nm transillumination and photographed using Polaroid 667 black-and-white print film and a SYBR® photographic filter (S7569, panel A) or an ethidium bromide photographic filter (panel B).

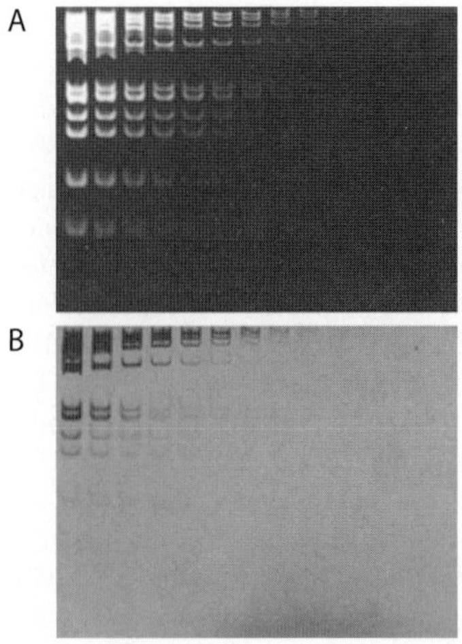

Figure 8.71 Comparison of the sensitivity achieved using SYBR® Gold stain (S11494) with 300 nm transillumination (panel A) and silver stain to detect double-stranded DNA separated on native polyacrylamide gels (panel B).

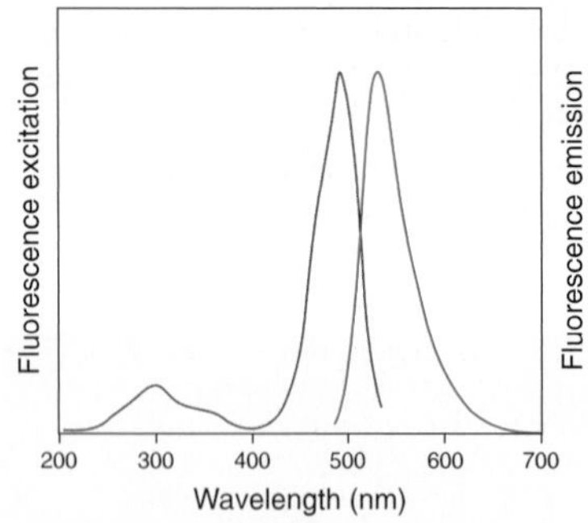

Figure 8.72 Fluorescence excitation and emission spectra of SYBR® Gold nucleic acid gel stain (S11494) bound to double-stranded DNA.

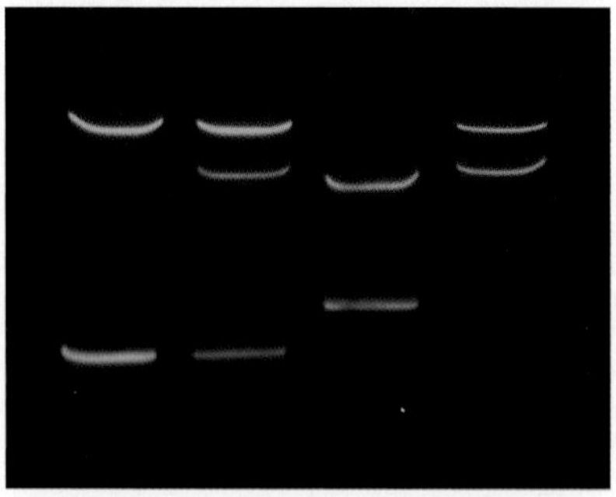

Figure 8.73 Sensitive and direct visualization of single-strand conformation polymorphism (SSCP) in exon 1 of human K-*ras* using SYBR® Gold nucleic acid gel stain (S11494). Lane 1 contains wild-type DNA and lanes 2–4 contain DNA from various adenocarcinoma samples with mutant alleles. Image contributed by Valerie DeGroff and Chris Weghorst, Ohio State University.

and RNA detection in many gel types, including high-percentage agarose, glyoxal/agarose, formaldehyde/agarose, native polyacrylamide and urea–polyacrylamide gels. No wash step is required in order to achieve maximal sensitivities.[2]

- **Ease of use.** As a result of the low intrinsic fluorescence of the unbound dye, gel staining with the SYBR® Gold dye shows extremely low background fluorescence and does not require a destaining step, even when staining agarose/formaldehyde gels. After incubating the gel in the SYBR® Gold staining solution for 10–40 minutes (depending on the thickness and percentage of the agarose or polyacrylamide gel) the golden-yellow–fluorescent DNA or RNA bands are ready to be photographed.
- **Economy.** The SYBR® Gold stain is at least as sensitive as silver staining for detecting dsDNA in polyacrylamide gels[2] (Figure 8.71). Also, the SYBR® Gold stain is very competitively priced, making it an affordable alternative to labor-intensive silver staining.
- **Compatibility with other molecular biology techniques.** The presence of unbound SYBR® Gold dye in stained gels at standard staining concentrations does not interfere with restriction endonuclease or ligase activity or with subsequent PCR reactions. SYBR® Gold nucleic acid staining is compatible with both Northern and Southern blotting — the stain transfers with the DNA or RNA to the blot and is washed off during incubation in the prehybridization mix.[2] The SYBR® Gold stain is also easily removed from dsDNA by simple ethanol precipitation, leaving templates ready for subsequent manipulation or analysis.
- **Instrument compatibility.** Because the nucleic acid–bound SYBR® Gold dye exhibits excitation maxima at both ~495 nm and ~300 nm (the emission maximum is ~537 nm) (Figure 8.72), it is compatible with a wide variety of instrumentation, ranging from UV epi- and transilluminators and blue-light transilluminators, to mercury-arc lamp and argon-ion laser–based gel scanners. Short-wavelength (254 nm) epi-illumination is not required to obtain high sensitivity with the SYBR® Gold stain. For optimal sensitivity with black-and-white print film and UV illumination, SYBR® Gold dye–stained gels should be photographed through the SYBR® photographic filter (S7569).

The SYBR® Gold dye should prove invaluable in applications such as agarose/formaldehyde gel electrophoresis prior to Northern blot analysis, denaturing gradient gel electrophoresis (DGGE) and single-strand conformation polymorphism (SSCP) studies (Figure 8.73), as well as routine gel analysis. The high signals of the dye–DNA complex and the remarkable photostability observed with 300 nm transilluminators will make it easier to cut out low-abundance bands for subsequent manipulation, including subcloning, bandshift assays or other dsDNA template–based reactions.

SYBR® Gold is the dye of choice for methylation-sensitive single-strand conformation analysis[6] (MS-SSCA). It is also reportedly more sensitive and easier to use than silver staining in the telomeric repeat amplification protocol[7] (TRAP). In the electrophoretic analysis of DNA forms in liposomes, the dye showed 40-fold greater sensitivity and more consistent staining between different isoforms of DNA compared with ethidium bromide.[8] It has also been used to monitor the formation of crosslinked peptide–DNA complexes.[9]

Each 500 µL vial of the SYBR® Gold nucleic acid gel stain (S11494) contains sufficient reagent to stain at least 100 agarose or polyacrylamide minigels. The SYBR® Gold nucleic acid stain is accompanied by detailed instructions for use of the dye in staining nucleic acids; answers to frequently asked questions about all our SYBR® dyes are available in a separate information sheet.

SYBR® Green I Nucleic Acid Gel Stain

Molecular Probes' patented SYBR® Green I nucleic acid gel stain[10] (S7563, S7567, S7585) is an extremely sensitive fluorescent stain for detecting nucleic acids in agarose and polyacrylamide gels. As with the SYBR® Gold stain, this remarkable sensitivity can be attributed to a combination of unique dye characteristics. Our SYBR® Green I stain exhibits exceptional affinity for DNA and a large fluorescence enhancement upon binding to DNA — at least an order of magnitude greater than that of ethidium bromide when detected by photography. Also, the fluorescence quantum yield of the SYBR® Green I dye–DNA complex (~0.8) is over five times greater than that of the ethidium complex of DNA (~0.15). Furthermore, the SYBR® Green I stain has been shown to be significantly less mutagenic than EtBr by Ames testing.[11] The SYBR® Green I stain is somewhat less sensitive than our SYBR® Gold stain, but has some important characteristics that make it the preferred reagent for certain applications:

- **Preferential DNA staining.** The SYBR® Green I nucleic acid stain has a much greater fluorescence enhancement when bound to dsDNA and oligonucleotides than when bound to RNA. With a standard 300 nm UV transilluminator and photographic detection, as little as 60 pg dsDNA per band can be detected with the SYBR® Green I stain [12–14] (Figure 8.74), whereas the SYBR® Green I stain is not much more sensitive than ethidium bromide for staining RNA. This quality makes the SYBR® Green I dye the ideal gel stain for applications in which RNA in the sample may obscure the results, such as when visualizing DNA fragmentation ladders from apoptotic cells [15,16] (Figure 8.75). Fluorescence of nucleic acid–bound SYBR® Green I dye is also of sufficient sensitivity to allow detection and discrimination of viruses by flow cytometry.[17]
- **Sensitivity for oligonucleotide detection.** We have determined that the SYBR® Green I nucleic acid gel stain is nearly two orders of magnitude more sensitive than ethidium bromide for staining oligonucleotides in gels, provided that the gel is photographed according to instructions. Using 254 nm epi-illumination, it is possible to detect 1–2 ng of a synthetic 24-mer on 5% polyacrylamide gels (Figure 8.76).
- **Exceptionally low background.** The SYBR® Green I stain shows very low background fluorescence in the gel, making it the preferred dye for some laser-scanning instruments, where background fluorescence can produce unacceptable noise levels.
- **Spectral compatibility with lasers and filter sets.** The SYBR® Green I stain has a UV-excitation peak of ~250 nm (Figure 8.77). Thus, higher sensitivity can be achieved with the SYBR® Green I stain using 254 nm transillumination, as compared with the more common 300 nm transillumination. However, the visible excitation peak of SYBR® Green I dye–stained nucleic acids near 497 nm is very close to the principal emission lines of many laser-scanning instruments. Because nucleic acid–bound SYBR® Green I dye exhibits spectral characteristics (excitation/emission maxima ~497/520 nm) very similar to those of fluorescein (Figure 1.52), it is compatible with the most common filter sets used in laser scanners.

Like the SYBR® Gold stain, the SYBR® Green I dye is very easy to use — the staining procedure can be completed in 10–40 minutes (somewhat longer for thicker gels), with no destaining step required prior to photography. Presence of typical staining concentrations of the SYBR® Green I dye does not significantly inhibit the ability of several restriction endonucleases to cleave DNA.[12] This property makes staining with the SYBR® Green I dye potentially compatible with in-gel subcloning protocols.[18] The SYBR® Green I stain is also easily removed from dsDNA by simple ethanol precipitation. Answers to frequently asked questions about all our SYBR® dyes are available in a separate information sheet. For optimal sensitivity with black-and-white print film and UV illumination, gels stained with the SYBR® Green dye should be photographed through the SYBR® photographic filter (S7569). Very good sensitivity is also achieved using a CCD camera.

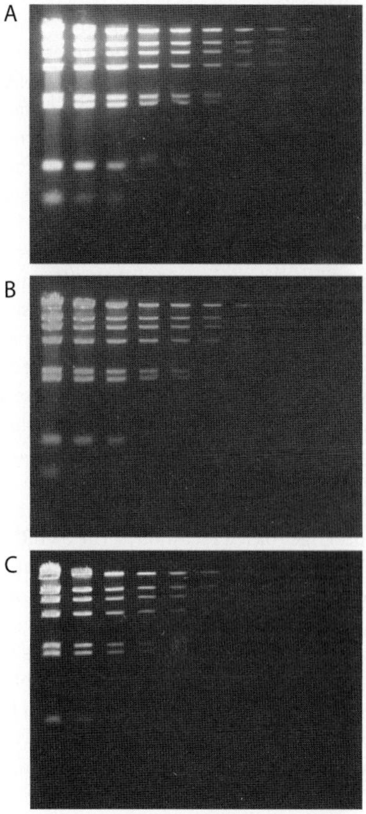

Figure 8.74 Comparison of dsDNA detection in native gels using SYBR® Green I nucleic acid gel stain and ethidium bromide. Identical threefold dilutions of bacteriophage λ DNA digested with *Hin*dIII restriction endonuclease were electrophoresed on 1% agarose gels. Gels were stained for 30 minutes with a 1:10,000 dilution of the SYBR® Green I nucleic acid gel stain (S7563, S7567, S7585) and not destained (panels A and B) or with 5 µg/mL ethidium bromide (E1305, E3565) for 30 minutes and destained for a further 30 minutes in water (panel C). Gel staining was visualized using 254 nm epi-illumination (panel A) or 300 nm transillumination (panels B and C) and then photographed using Polaroid 667 black-and-white print film and a SYBR® photographic filter (panels A and B, S7569) or an ethidium bromide gel stain photographic filter (panel C).

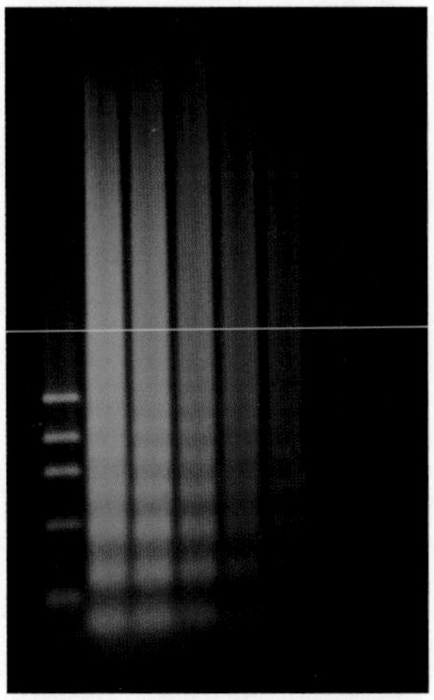

Figure 8.75 DNA extracts from camptothecin-treated HL-60 cells separated on an agarose gel and stained with SYBR® Green I nucleic acid gel stain (S7563, S7567, S7585). The 200 to 5000 bp DNA fragments characteristic of apoptotic cells (which appear as "ladders") are clearly visualized with this sensitive nucleic acid stain. Cell preparations were gifts of Zbigniew Darzynkiewicz, Cancer Research Institute, New York Medical College.

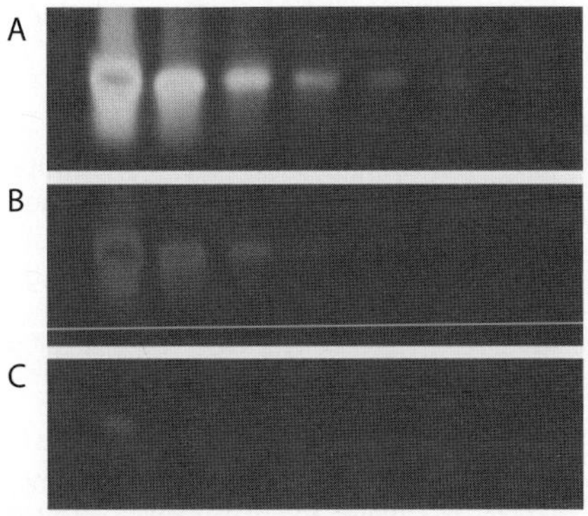

Figure 8.76 Comparison of single-stranded oligonucleotide detection using SYBR® Green I nucleic acid gel stain and ethidium bromide. Identical threefold dilutions of a synthetic, single-stranded 24-mer were electrophoresed on 10% polyacrylamide gels. Gels were stained for 30 minutes with a 1:10,000 dilution of SYBR® Green I nucleic acid gel stain (S7563, S7567, S7585) and not destained (panels A and B) or with 5 µg/mL ethidium bromide (E1305, E3565) for 30 minutes and destained for a further 30 minutes in water (panel C). Gel staining was visualized using 254 nm epi-illumination (panel A) or 300 nm transillumination (panels B and C) and then photographed using Polaroid 667 black-and-white print film and a SYBR® photographic filter (S7569, panels A and B) or an ethidium bromide gel stain photographic filter (panel C).

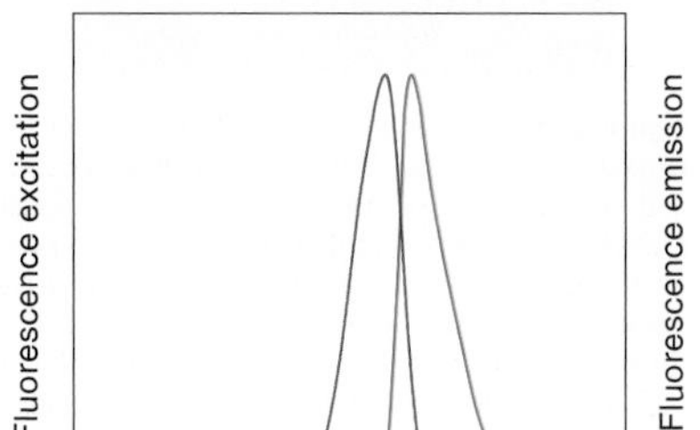

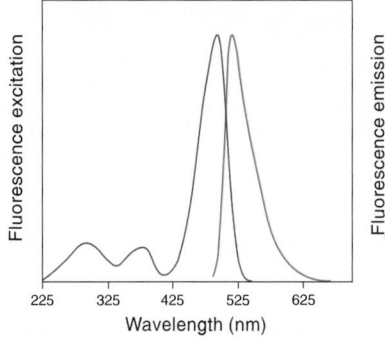

Figure 8.77 Fluorescence excitation and emission spectra of dsDNA-bound SYBR® Green I nucleic acid gel stain (S7563, S7567, S7585).

The ultrasensitivity of the SYBR® Green I dye makes it useful for detecting the products of DNA and RNA amplification reactions by gel electrophoresis,[19] restriction mapping small amounts of DNA and detecting the products of bandshift[20] and nuclease-protection assays. At least two independent laboratories found that use of the SYBR® Green I stain allows the detection of DNA amplification products from low–target number PCR.[21] Amplification products that are at the limit of detection using ethidium bromide are easily detected using the SYBR® Green I dye. Reverse-transcription PCR (RT-PCR) products have been detected with high sensitivity following gel electrophoresis and staining with the SYBR® Green I dye, allowing the cycle number to be lowered, which reduces heteroduplex formation during amplification.[22] The SYBR® Green I stain was used to detect RT-PCR products amplified from B cells,[23] *Xenopus laevis* embryos[24] and smooth muscle cells.[25] Using a laser scanner and the SYBR® Green I stain, researchers have developed a high-throughput RT-PCR DNA profiling assay in multiwell agarose gels.[26] The SYBR® Green I dye was used to stain DNA in high-resolution gels capable of resolving 100–200 base-pair DNA fragments and differing by as few as two base pairs.[27]

In other gel-based techniques, the SYBR® Green I nucleic acid gel stain has enabled researchers to eliminate silver staining and frequently even radioactivity from their protocols. SYBR® Green I dye staining was shown to be as sensitive as silver staining — as well as being more rapid, less laborious and less expensive — in a nonradioactive method for detecting hypervariable simple sequence repeats in electrophoretic gels.[28] The SYBR® Green I dye staining has completely replaced conventional silver staining techniques for routine identity testing in some forensics laboratories. In addition, the SYBR® Green I stain is as sensitive as silver staining, but less expensive, for detecting STR (short tandem repeat) polymorphisms,[29,30] and mitochondrial DNA deletions.[31]

Use of the SYBR® Green I stain also eliminates the need to label PCR products with radioisotopes in a kinetic PCR assay.[32–34] Likewise, in a gel assay for detection of telomerase activity (telomeric repeat amplification protocol or TRAP) in human cells and tumors, SYBR® Green I dye staining was found to be more sensitive than silver staining and gave results comparable to those achieved with a radioisotope-based TRAP assay.[35,36] Moreover, unlike silver stains, the SYBR® Green I stain does not label proteins carried over from the reaction mixture. SYBR® Green I dye staining has also been shown to be as sensitive as ^{3}H-labeled thymidine for detecting double-strand breaks in mammalian cells.[37] It may be possible to further increase the sensitivity of some of these reported applications of the SYBR® Green I stain by using the SYBR® Gold nucleic acid gel stain (see above).

The high chemical stability of the SYBR® Green I nucleic acid stain and the dye's selective sensitivity for detecting double-stranded products made in the presence of single-stranded oligonucleotide primers make the SYBR® Green I stain the preferred dye for real-time quantitative analysis of PCR products in a solution assay (Section 8.3).

Each milliliter of our concentrated SYBR® Green I nucleic acid gel stain (S7563, S7567, S7585) contains a sufficient amount of the reagent to stain at least 100 agarose or polyacrylamide minigels. Reuse of the staining solution can significantly increase the number of gels stained per vial. In some applications, such as preparative agarose gel electrophoresis, the amount of SYBR® Green I dye used per gel can also be significantly reduced if the dye is added directly to the loading buffer. However, because the dye affects DNA mobility and dissociates from the smaller DNA fragments during electrophoresis, this method should not be used for size determination or for DNA fragments less than ~100 base pairs in length.[38]

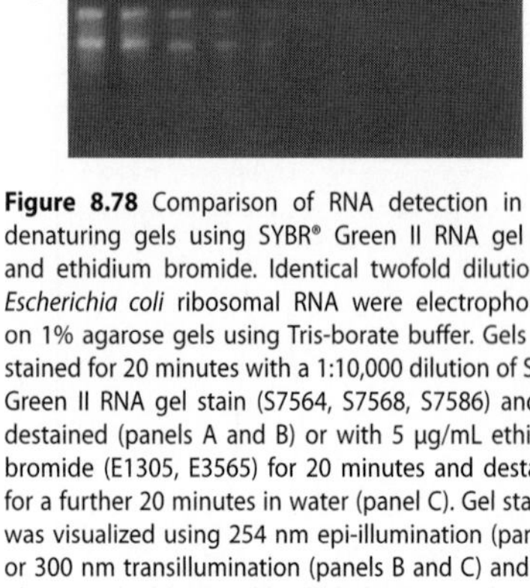

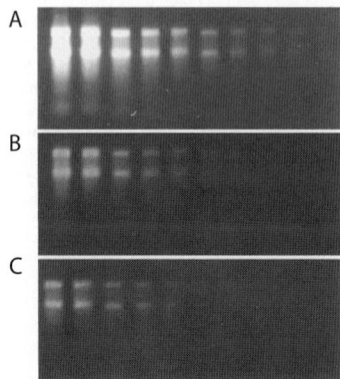

Figure 8.78 Comparison of RNA detection in nondenaturing gels using SYBR® Green II RNA gel stain and ethidium bromide. Identical twofold dilutions of *Escherichia coli* ribosomal RNA were electrophoresed on 1% agarose gels using Tris-borate buffer. Gels were stained for 20 minutes with a 1:10,000 dilution of SYBR® Green II RNA gel stain (S7564, S7568, S7586) and not destained (panels A and B) or with 5 µg/mL ethidium bromide (E1305, E3565) for 20 minutes and destained for a further 20 minutes in water (panel C). Gel staining was visualized using 254 nm epi-illumination (panel A) or 300 nm transillumination (panels B and C) and then photographed using Polaroid 667 black-and-white print film and a SYBR® photographic filter (panels A and B, S7569) or an ethidium bromide gel stain photographic filter (panel C).

SYBR® Green II RNA Gel Stain

Our patented SYBR® Green II RNA gel stain (S7564, S7568, S7586) is a highly sensitive dye for detecting RNA or ssDNA in agarose or polyacrylamide gels (Figure 8.78). Some outstanding features of the SYBR® Green II RNA gel stain include its high binding affinity for RNA and its large fluorescence enhancement and exceptionally high quantum yield upon binding to RNA. Although it is not a specific stain for RNA, SYBR® Green II dye exhibits a larger fluorescence quantum yield when bound to RNA (~0.54) than to dsDNA (~0.36). This property is unusual among nucleic acid stains; most show far greater quantum yields and fluorescence enhancements when bound to double-stranded nucleic acids. Moreover, the fluorescence quantum yield of the SYBR® Green II complex of RNA is over seven times greater than that of the ethidium bromide–RNA complex[39] (~0.07). The affinity of SYBR® Green II RNA gel stain for RNA is also higher than that of ethidium bromide, and its fluorescence enhancement upon binding to RNA is well over an order of magnitude greater. Like the SYBR® Green I stain, our SYBR® Green II stain gives the greatest sensitivity on 254 nm transillumination or laser scanners. However, the best sensitivity for RNA detection using 300 nm transillumination is achieved with the SYBR® Gold dye (see above). Other important properties of SYBR® Green II RNA gel stain include:

- **Sensitivity.** Using 254 nm epi-illumination, Polaroid 667 black-and-white print film and a SYBR® photographic filter (S7569), we have been able to detect as little as 100 pg of ribosomal RNA (rRNA) per band on native 1% agarose gels and <1 ng rRNA per band on 5% polyacrylamide gels stained with SYBR® Green II RNA gel stain. The detection limit of SYBR® Green II dye–stained native gels excited with 300 nm transillumination is approximately 500 pg per band, as compared with about 1.5 ng for ethidium bromide–stained gels[14] (Figure 8.78).
- **Ease of use.** Like the SYBR® Green I and SYBR® Gold stains, SYBR® Green II RNA gel stain has a very low intrinsic fluorescence, eliminating the need to destain gels.
- **Compatibility with urea and formaldehyde gels.** Fluorescence of the SYBR® Green II dye–RNA complexes does not appear to be quenched in the presence of urea or formaldehyde, so that denaturing gels do not have to be washed free of the denaturant prior to staining.
- **Broad linear dynamic range.** When used on a laser scanner, the SYBR® Green II stain shows a dynamic range of over five orders of magnitude — far greater than the linear dynamic range of ethidium bromide — allowing more accurate quantitation of bands in the gel.[40]
- **Compatibility with Northern blots.** Research at Molecular Probes has shown that SYBR® Green II dye staining is also compatible with agarose/formaldehyde gels. The formaldehyde does not have to be removed prior to staining, and the sensitivity of SYBR® Green II dye staining is 5–10 times better than that of ethidium bromide on these gels. In addition, staining agarose/formaldehyde gels with the SYBR® Green II dye does not interfere with transfer of the RNA to filters or subsequent hybridization in Northern blot analysis, provided that 0.1% to 0.3% SDS is included in the prehybridization and hybridization buffers.[41] Thus, SYBR® Green II stain can be used to normalize the hybridization signal to the amount of RNA loaded on the gel.[40,42,43]

SYBR® Green II RNA gel stain facilitates the detection of viroid RNAs and other multicopy cellular RNA species. This gel stain has been used to visualize the migration behavior of 5S rRNA species after electrophoresis through a denaturing gradient gel, a method that was used to discriminate among different acidophile species in a mixed culture.[44] SYBR® Green II RNA gel stain should also improve the analysis of small aliquots from an RNA preparation, leaving the researcher with more material to carry out the primary experiment, be it Northern blotting, start-site mapping or cDNA preparation.

In addition to its use for detecting RNA, the SYBR® Green II RNA gel stain is useful for single-strand conformation polymorphism (SSCP) analysis,[45,46] which demands extremely sensitive detection techniques.[47] Many of the nonradioisotopic SSCP methods currently in use, such as silver staining or chemiluminescence-mediated signal amplification, require long, complex procedures.[48–51] An SSCP assay using precast polyacrylamide minigels and the SYBR® Green II stain not only provides the precise temperature control required for the assay,[52] but it is more rapid, less expensive and less labor-intensive than assays that use silver staining for detection.[53] In another report, the SYBR® Green II RNA gel stain was used to detect Ki-*ras* mutants by SSCP analysis and was reported to yield 10-fold better sensitivity than standard silver-staining techniques.[46] The SYBR® Green II stain is compatible with amplification by PCR — after SSCP analysis, the SYBR® Green II dye–stained bands can be excised out of the gel and used in cycle-sequencing.[54] The SYBR® Green II nucleic acid stain also provides high-sensitivity staining for rRNA separated by high-resolution denaturing gradient electrophoresis (DGGE), making it possible to discriminate between closely related species of bacteria.[44]

SYBR® Green Nucleic Acid Gel Stains: Special Packaging and a Starter Kit

In addition to providing the SYBR® Green nucleic acid gel stains packaged as 500 µL or 1 mL stock solutions in DMSO (S7563, S7564, S7567, S7568), we make both SYBR® Green I and SYBR® Green II available as a set of 20 individual vials, each containing 50 µL of the DMSO stock solution (S7585, S7586). This convenient packaging makes it easy to supply members of the laboratory with an aliquot of stock solution, or to share stock with other laboratories. Special packaging also minimizes potential losses due to contamination, spills and light exposure. Each milliliter of the concentrated gel stain provides sufficient reagent to prepare 10 liters of a staining solution. Although best results are obtained with freshly diluted dye, properly prepared staining solution can be stored for up to a week, if kept refrigerated and protected from light, and can be reused 2–3 times with little loss of signal. The SYBR® Green nucleic acid stains are accompanied by detailed instructions for their use in staining gels; answers to frequently asked questions about all the SYBR® dyes are available in a separate information sheet.

Our SYBR® Green Nucleic Acid Gel Stain Starter Kit (S7580) is designed for laboratories that want to sample these products. The kit includes single 50 µL vials of both the SYBR® Green I and SYBR® Green II stains and a SYBR® gel stain photographic filter, along with complete directions for their use.

Our SYBR® dyes are covered by patents issued to Molecular Probes. These products are offered for research purposes only. Molecular Probes welcomes inquiries about licensing these products for resale or other commercial uses, including fee-for-service activities.

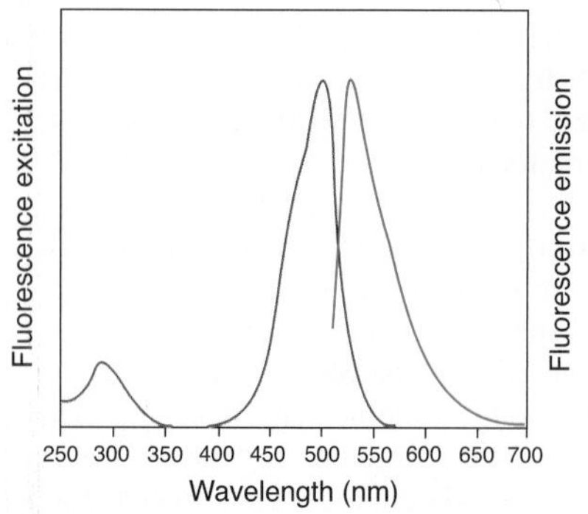

Figure 8.79 Normalized fluorescence excitation and emission spectra of the SYBR Safe™ DNA gel stain (S33100, S33101, S33110), determined in the presence of double-stranded DNA.

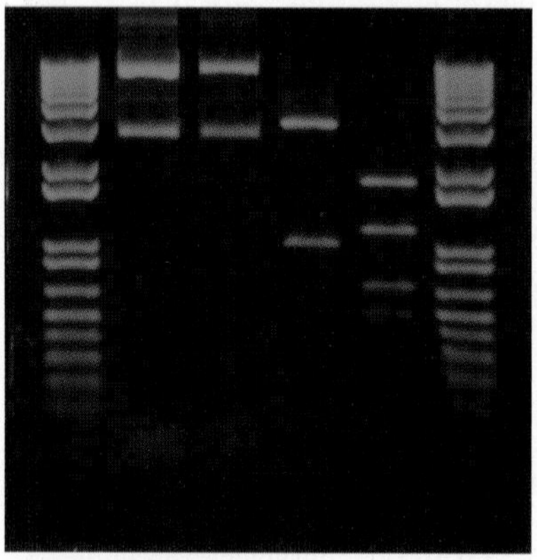

Figure 8.80 DNA fragments were electrophoresed through an agarose gel, then stained with SYBR Safe™ DNA gel stain (S33100, S33101, S33110).

SYBR Safe™ DNA Gel Stain

The SYBR Safe™ DNA gel stain provides sensitive DNA detection with significantly reduced mutagenicity, making it safer than ethidium bromide for staining DNA in agarose or acrylamide gels. Not only is the SYBR Safe™ stain less mutagenic than ethidium bromide, but it is up to twice as sensitive as ethidium bromide and 400 times as sensitive as colorimetric stains for detecting DNA in electrophoretic gels. The SYBR Safe™ stain is provided as a premixed solution that can directly replace ethidium bromide in standard protocols; the SYBR Safe™ stain can either be cast into the gel or be used as a post-electrophoresis stain. DNA bands stained with the SYBR Safe™ DNA gel stain can be detected using a standard UV transilluminator, a visible-light transilluminator or a laser scanner. The SYBR Safe™ stain is also suitable for detecting RNA in gels. Bound to nucleic acids, the SYBR Safe™ stain has fluorescence excitation maxima at 280 and 502 nm, and an emission maximum at 530 nm (Figure 8.79). The SYBR Safe™ DNA gel stain offers:

- **Increased safety.** The SYBR Safe™ DNA gel stain has tested negative in three mammalian cell–based assays for genotoxicity, is less mutagenic than ethidium bromide in standard Ames tests and is not classified as hazardous waste under U.S. Federal regulations (see Note 8.3 "Product Highlight: SYBR Safe™ DNA Gel Stain").
- **Better performance.** The SYBR Safe™ DNA gel stain is twice as sensitive as ethidium bromide and 400 times as sensitive as colorimetric stains.
- **Convenience.** The SYBR Safe™ stain is provided as a ready-to-use solution in 0.5X TBE or 1X TAE; it can be cast directly in the gel or used as a post-electrophoresis stain (Figure 8.80).
- **A quick staining protocol.** Simply incubate the gel in staining solution for 30 minutes; no destaining is required.

The SYBR Safe™ DNA gel stain is supplied ready-to-use in two different sizes and in two different buffers. The 1 L unit size in 0.5X TBE or 1X TAE (S33100, S33111) provides sufficient reagent to stain ~20 minigels; the 4 L unit size in 0.5X TBE or 1X TAE (S33101, S33112) provides sufficient reagent to stain ~80 minigels and is supplied in a cube-shaped container with a removable spigot. We also offer a 400 µL volume of 10,000X concentrate (S33102). The SYBR Safe™ DNA Gel Stain Starter Kit (S33110) is a convenient packaging of the 1 L unit size of SYBR Safe™ stain in 0.5X TBE plus one SYBR Safe™ photographic filter (S37100).

Ethidium Bromide

Ethidium bromide (EtBr, E1305, E3565, Figure 8.13) is the most commonly used dye for DNA and RNA detection in gels.[3] It binds to single-, double- and triple-stranded DNA.[55–57] Ethidium bromide has also been used to detect protein–DNA complex formation in bandshift assays[58] and to observe single DNA molecules undergoing gel electrophoresis.[59,60] In addition to the solid form (E1305), we supply ethidium bromide in a 10 mg/mL concentrated stock solution (E3565) for those wishing to avoid contact with the mutagenic powder.

Cyanine Monomers for Staining DNA in Electrophoretic Gels

Although the SYBR® dyes are now the preferred gel stains, at least six of the monomeric cyanine dyes — TO-PRO®-1, YO-PRO®-1, BO-PRO™-1, PO-PRO™-1, JO-PRO™-1 and LO-PRO™-1 (Section 8.1, Table 8.2) — are also sensitive reagents for staining gels after electrophoresis and are compatible with UV trans- or epi-illumination or with laser-excited gel scanners. Their range of absorption maxima may make them superior to the SYBR® dyes when using some lasers as excitation sources. We have determined that the limit of detection of dsDNA with some of these dyes is about 60 pg/band, using 254 nm epi-illumination and Polaroid 667 black-and-white print film photography.

Our TO-PRO®-3 dye (T3605) can detect less than 0.1 ng/band DNA in an ultrathin-layer agarose gel–based electrophoretogram when excited by an inexpensive 640 nm red diode laser.[61] Preloading of the gel buffer with the TO-PRO®-3 dye has been recommended for this application when analyzing migrating allele-specific PCR fragments.[62,63]

Cyanine and Ethidium Dimers for Staining DNA Prior to Electrophoresis

The extraordinary stability of our dimeric cyanine– and ethidium homodimer–nucleic acid complexes[64–66] (Table 8.2) ensures that the dye–DNA association remains stable during electrophoresis. Thus, samples can be prestained with subsaturating nanomolar dye concentrations before electrophoresis[67,68] (Figure 8.4), thereby reducing the hazards inherent in handling large

Note 8.3 — Product Highlight

SYBR Safe™ DNA Gel Stain

SYBR Safe™ stain tests negative in standardized mammalian cell tests for genotoxicity.

Certified testing (Table 1) has shown that SYBR Safe™ DNA gel stain does not induce transformations in primary cultures of Syrian hamster embryo (SHE) cells when compared with solvent alone. This test has a high concordance (>80%) with rodent carcinogenesis assays;[1] thus, a negative test strongly indicates that the SYBR Safe™ stain is noncarcinogenic. In contrast, ethidium bromide tests positive in the SHE cell assay,[2] consistent with its known activity as a strong mutagen.

In addition, SYBR Safe™ stain does not cause mutations in mouse lymphoma cells at the TK locus, nor does it induce chromosomal aberrations in cultured human peripheral blood lymphocytes, with or without S9 metabolic activation, using standardized tests against appropriate controls (Table 1).

SYBR Safe™ stain is less mutagenic than ethidium bromide in the standard Ames test.

Compared with ethidium bromide, SYBR Safe™ DNA gel stain causes fewer mutations in the Ames test, as measured in several different strains of *Salmonella typhimurium*. Weakly positive results for SYBR Safe™ stain in this test occurred in four out of seven strains and only with activation by a mammalian S9 fraction (Figure 1).

SYBR Safe™ stain is not classified as hazardous waste.

SYBR Safe™ DNA gel stain has been extensively tested for environmental safety. According to the test results (Table 2), this stain is not classified as hazardous waste under U.S. Federal regulations (Resource Conservation and Recovery Act (RCRA)). Contact your safety officer for proper disposal procedures.

Table 1 — Summary of mammalian cell test results for SYBR Safe™ DNA gel stain

Test *	Cell Type	With S9 Activation †	Without S9 Activation
Transformation	Syrian hamster embryo (SHE) cells	NA	Negative
Chromosomal Aberrations	Cultured human peripheral blood lymphocytes	Negative	Negative
Forward Mutation	L5178YTK+/- mouse lymphoma cells	Negative	Negative

* All tests were performed by Covance Laboratories Inc., Vienna, VA, an independent testing laboratory.
† Mammalian S9 fraction obtained from Aroclor 1254–induced rat liver. NA = Not applicable.

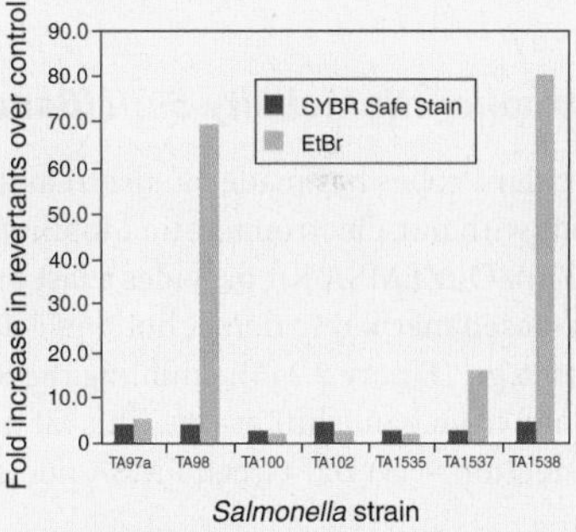

Figure 1. Summary of Ames test results for mutagenicity of SYBR Safe™ DNA gel stain and ethidium bromide. Samples were pretreated with a mammalian S9 fraction and then tested using the indicated test strain. With strains TA97a, TA98, TA100 and TA102, a fold increase in revertants of more than twofold over background is a positive result for mutagenicity in this test. With strains TA1535, TA1537 and TA1538, a fold increase in revertants of more than threefold over background is a positive result. All tests were performed by Covance Laboratories, Inc., Vienna, VA, an independent testing laboratory.

Table 2 — Environmental safety test results

Analysis *	Method	Results
Ignitability	EPA 1010	Not ignitable (>212°F)
Corrosivity	EPA 150.1	Not corrosive (pH = 8.25)
Reactivity	EPA 9010B/9030A	No reactivity detected
Corrosivity (by Corrositex)	DOT-E 10904	Category 2 noncorrosive
Aquatic toxicity	Fathead minnow CA Title 22 acute screening	Not classified as hazardous or toxic to aquatic life

* All tests were independently confirmed by AMEC Earth and Environmental San Diego Bioassay Laboratory, San Diego, CA.

References

1. Toxicol Sci 60, 28 (2001); **2.** Mutat Res 439, 37 (1999).

volumes of ethidium bromide staining solutions.[65,66,69] The fluorescence intensities of both the EthD-1–DNA and TOTO®-1–DNA complexes are directly proportional to the amount of DNA in a band; however, TOTO®-1 dye staining has less effect on the electrophoretic mobility of DNA fragments than does EthD-1. Furthermore, unlike EthD-1–labeled DNA, in which up to two-thirds of the bound dye can be transferred to excess unlabeled DNA, the extent of transfer of TOTO®-1 dye to unlabeled DNA is reported to be only about 15–20%, even when the TOTO®-1–DNA complexes are incubated for up to 10 hours with a 100-fold excess of uncomplexed dsDNA.[64,70,71] This property is valuable for multiplexed electrophoretic separations,[64] particularly since our cyanine nucleic acid stains are available in so many visually distinct colors. If two DNA populations are stained with spectrally distinct cyanine dimer dyes and run in the same lane, simultaneous two-color detection can potentially eliminate errors caused by lane-to-lane variations in electrophoretic mobility. Binding of the TOTO®-1 dye (T3600), YOYO®-1 dye (Y3601) and ethidium homodimer-1 (E1169) to DNA initially results in inhomogeneous binding that yields double bands in DNA gel electrophoresis.[72] These double bands can be avoided by incubating complexes for times long enough to allow binding to come to equilibrium or by heating samples to 50°C for at least two hours. Binding of our other dimeric nucleic acid stains (Table 8.2) does not seem to give this problem.

An extremely sensitive confocal laser–based gel scanner has been exploited in multiplexed electrophoretic separations to detect as little as 4 pg per band of TOTO®-1 dye– and YOYO®-1 dye–stained dsDNA;[64,68,71,73] although sophisticated equipment is required for achieving these low detection limits, such equipment is not essential for detecting somewhat larger quantities of these nucleic acid–dye complexes. Our TOTO®-1 dye has been used to label DNA prior to electrophoresis in order to detect cystic fibrosis mutant alleles with a laser-excited fluorescence gel scanner,[74] as well as to detect DNA amplification products on agarose gels with standard UV transillumination.[75] The TOTO®-1 dye has also been used to label nine DNA fragments of the dystrophin gene that were simultaneously generated using the polymerase chain reaction.[76] The resolution obtained by gel electrophoresis of these labeled fragments compared favorably to that observed using fluorophore-labeled primers. The TOTO®-3 and POPO™-1 dyes (T3604, P3580; Section 8.1) have been similarly used to analyze DNA with a xenon lamp–based luminescence analyzer.[77]

Ethidium homodimer-1 (EthD-1, E1169) has been used for fluorescence detection of 30–60 pg DNA per band on polyacrylamide gels using a confocal laser–based scanning system.[65,66,69] Ethidium homodimer-2 (EthD-2, E3599; Section 8.1), which has a higher affinity for nucleic acids than does ethidium homodimer-1, may also be useful for this application.

Electrophoretic Mobility-Shift (Bandshift) Assay (EMSA) Kit

Molecular Probes has made bandshift assays easy and more convenient with our Electrophoretic Mobility-Shift Assay (EMSA) Kit (E33075). Our EMSA Kit provides a fast and quantitative fluorescence-based method to detect both nucleic acids and proteins in the same gel (Figure 8.145), doubling the information that can be obtained from bandshift assays. This kit uses two fluorescent dyes for detection — SYBR® Green EMSA nucleic acid gel stain for RNA or DNA and SYPRO® Ruby EMSA protein gel stain for proteins. Because the nucleic acids and proteins are stained in the gel after electrophoresis, there is no need to prelabel the DNA or RNA with a radioisotope, biotin or a fluorescent dye before the binding reaction, and therefore there is no possibility that the label will interfere with protein binding. Staining takes only about 20 minutes for the nucleic acid stain, and about 4 hours for the subsequent protein stain, yielding results much faster than radioisotope labeling (which may require multiple exposure times) or chemiluminescence-based detection (which requires blotting and multiple incubation steps). This kit also makes it possible to perform ratiometric measurements of nucleic acid and protein in the same band, providing more detailed information on the binding interaction. The signals from the two stains are linear over a broad range, allowing accurate determination of the amount of nucleic acid and protein, even in a single band, with detection limits of ~1 ng for nucleic acids and ~20 ng for proteins. Both stains can be detected using a standard 300 nm UV illuminator, a 254 nm epi-illuminator or a laser scanner (Figure 8.145). Digital images can easily be overlaid for a two-color representation of nucleic acid and protein in the gel. The EMSA Kit contains sufficient reagents for 10 nondenaturing polyacrylamide minigel assays, including:

- SYBR® Green EMSA nucleic acid gel stain
- SYPRO® Ruby EMSA protein gel stain
- Trichloroacetic acid for preparing the working solution of SYPRO® Ruby EMSA protein gel stain
- Concentrated EMSA gel-loading solution
- *lac* repressor, a DNA-binding protein to be used as a control
- *lac* operator, control DNA
- Concentrated buffer for the *lac* repressor:operator controls
- A detailed protocol

Section 8.7 describes several other probes and reagents for analyzing DNA structure, DNA binding and DNA damage.

Other Nucleic Acid Stains for Gel-Staining Applications

DAPI (D1306, D3571; FluoroPure™ Grade, D21490; Section 8.1) reportedly provides a significantly more sensitive means of detecting dsDNA in agarose gels than ethidium bromide.[78] Selective detection of dsDNA in the presence of dsRNA in gels with DAPI has been reported.[79] Likewise, the Hoechst 33258 and Hoechst 33342 dyes (Section 8.1) have been used to detect DNA in the presence of RNA in agarose gels.[80] DNA conformational changes during gel electrophoresis have been investigated with acridine orange [81,82] (A1301, A3568; Section 8.1).

Capillary Electrophoresis and Channel Electrophoresis

Capillary Electrophoresis

Capillary gel electrophoresis (CGE) performs separations of nucleic acids in a manner analogous to standard slab-gel electrophoresis, but with the advantages of faster run times, higher resolution and greater sensitivity. The use of on-line detection by laser-induced fluorescence (LIF) increases the sensitivity by several orders of magnitude over UV detection, eliminates the time spent staining and photographing the gel and allows for the possibility of automated sample processing. CGE-LIF is now widely used for the separation and identification of DNA fragments and has increased the efficiency of genomics, DNA typing and forensics laboratories.[83,84] Researchers are using several of our high-sensitivity nucleic acid stains in capillary electrophoresis, a rapid and sensitive technique that is superior to slab-gel electrophoresis for resolving similar-length DNA fragments.[85] Dyes for nucleic acid sequencing by electrophoresis are discussed in Section 8.2.

- Our SYBR® Green I nucleic acid gel stain exhibits a large linear detection range and high resolution of DNA fragments from 100 to 1000 base pairs in length. A clinically applicable high-throughput screen was developed using the SYBR® Green I stain to detect mutations in the methylenetetrahydrofolate reductase gene.[86,87]
- The SYBR® Gold stain has sufficient sensitivity to detect electrophoretically separated nucleic acids from single cells.[88]
- The OliGreen® ssDNA quantitation reagent (O7582, O11492; Section 8.3) has been employed to detect short single-stranded oligonucleotides using capillary gel electrophoresis with laser-induced fluorescence detection; formation of the fluorescent oligonucleotide complexes is accomplished on the column.[89] The specificity of the OliGreen® reagent enabled researchers to detect oligonucleotides in plasma without prior sample handling.[90]
- Both our TOTO®-1 dye (T3600) and ethidium bromide (E1305, E3565) have been used with capillary-array electrophoresis for high-speed, high-throughput parallel separation of DNA fragments.[91,92] This technique may prove useful for DNA sequencing or for analysis of DNA amplification products.
- Capillary electrophoresis has been used to quantitate DNA complexes with the YOYO®-1 dye (Y3601) in polymerase chain reaction (PCR) mixtures.[93,94]
- Hepatitis B viral fragments have been detected by incorporation of submicromolar concentrations of either our POPO™-3 dye (P3584) or ethidium homodimer-2 (E3599) in the detection buffer.[95] Sensitivity was as great as 3.9×10^{-16} M (390 attomolar), with low background, and increased with fragment length.
- Our green-fluorescent YO-PRO®-1 dye (Y3603) has been used to develop a more rapid screening technique for identifying hypervariable regions in mitochondrial DNA. RFLP fragments were generated after PCR amplification and detected in CGE-LIF.[96] Automated CGE-LIF with the YO-PRO®-1 dye made it possible to replace time-consuming slab gel methods of analyzing variable number of tandem repeats (VNTR) in DNA typing labs.[97–99] The red-fluorescent YO-PRO®-3 dye (T3605) has proven useful for identifying single-sequence-repeat polymorphisms with high accuracy, using as little as 80 zeptomoles of sample DNA.[100]
- Capillary electrophoresis using ethidium bromide, SYBR® Green I or SYBR® Gold stain has been used in single-nucleotide polymorphism (SNP) analysis, making it possible to analyze as many as 96 samples in parallel.[101,102]
- CGE-LIF has been used for short tandem repeat (STR) genotyping using nucleic acids stained by an on-column labeling technique with either TO-PRO®-1, YO-PRO®-1, TOTO®-1 or YOYO®-1.[103]
- YO-PRO®-1 dye and ethidium bromide have both been used in heteroduplex analysis (HDA) by capillary electrophoresis.[104]
- The use of CGE-LIF with the YO-PRO®-1 dye makes it possible to accurately quantitate RNA transcripts from competitive RT-PCR.[105] CGE-LIF with the YO-PRO®-1 dye can also detect fragmented DNA from apoptotic cells, making it possible to use 1000–2000-fold fewer cells than are needed for ladder detection on conventional slab gels.[106]
- Using POPO™-3 dye (P3584) or ethidium homodimer-2, researchers have been able to detect as little as 3.9×10^{-13} M duck hepatitis B virus.[107]
- Our dimeric cyanine dyes (Table 8.2, Section 8.1) may also prove useful with a high-speed sequencing method developed for use with capillary electrophoresis.[108]

In these capillary electrophoresis applications, the dye can be chosen to match available laser excitation sources.[94,109–113] Multiple dyes can be used to prestain samples, which can then be used for multiplexed capillary electrophoresis.[114]

As an alternative labeling method, pre- or post-separation chemical derivatization of thiol- or amine-containing oligonucleotides is possible with many of the dyes described in Chapter 1 and Chapter 2. The thiol-reactive Alexa Fluor®, BODIPY®, fluorescein and Oregon Green® dyes are particularly suitable for labeling thiolated oligonucleotides and for applications that use ultrasensitive laser-scanning techniques.[115] Several papers have been published on separation of fluorescent oligonucleotides by capillary electrophoresis.[116–119] The technique has even been used to study DNA–protein interactions [120] (Section 8.7).

Channel Electrophoresis

Similar in concept to capillary electrophoresis, channel electrophoresis on microchips promises even higher throughput by using completely automated nucleic acid analysis. Our intensely fluorescent nucleic acid dyes make sensitive on-line detection possible. Our SYBR® Green I dye was used to detect amplified DNA on a nanoliter device that mixes DNA samples, amplifies DNA fragments and separates the products in a channel for on-line detection.[121] The TO-PRO®-1 dye (T3602) detected DNA fragments from bacterial DNA that had been extracted, amplified and separated in channels on the same microchip.[122] Our YOYO®-1 dye (Y3601) has been used to detect as little as a few zeptomoles (10^{-21} mole) of DNA fragments on a chip device[123] and YO-PRO®-1 dye (Y3603) made it possible to distinguish triplet repeat DNA fragments in a 6 mm channel in only 12 seconds.[124] A novel radial microchip device simultaneously separates 96 DNA samples prestained with YOYO®-1 dye.[125] The TO-PRO®-3 dye has been used to detect DNA in a polycarbonate channel electrophoresis device.[126] Fluorescence-based sequencing using dye-labeled primers (see above) in capillary electrophoresis chips allowed sequencing of ~200 bases in only 10 minutes.[127]

References

1. Fluorescent and Luminescent Probes for Biological Activity, 2nd Ed., Mason WT, Ed., pp. 51-62 (1999); **2.** Anal Biochem 268, 278 (1999); **3.** Anal Biochem 17, 100 (1966); **4.** Methods Biochem Anal 20, 41 (1971); **5.** Chris Weghorst, Ohio State University, personal communication; **6.** Hum Mutat 14, 289 (1999); **7.** Mol Pathol 51, 342 (1998); **8.** Biochim Biophys Acta 1509, 176 (2000); **9.** J Biol Chem 275, 9970 (2000); **10.** Nucleic Acids Res 32, e103 (2004); **11.** Mutat Res 439, 37 (1999); **12.** Biomed Products 19, 68 (1994); **13.** Biophys J 66, A159, abstract #Tu (1994); **14.** FASEB J 8, A1266, abstract #44 (1994); **15.** J Biol Chem 275, 288 (2000); **16.** Proc Natl Acad Sci U S A 94, 12419 (1997); **17.** J Virol Methods 85, 175 (2000); **18.** Biotechniques 3, 452 (1985); **19.** Mol Cell Probes 9, 145 (1995); **20.** FASEB J 10, A1128, abstract #751 (1996); **21.** Felix Baker, Stanford University, personal communication; Andreas Oberhauser, Mayo Clinic, personal communication; **22.** PCR Methods Appl 4, 234 (1995); **23.** Immunity 5, 377 (1996); **24.** Cell 88, 757 (1997); **25.** J Biol Chem 273, 7643 (1998); **26.** Biotechniques 22, 1107 (1997); **27.** Anal Biochem 275, 116 (1999); **28.** Biotechniques 19, 223 (1995); **29.** Biotechniques 22, 976 (1997); **30.** Nat Biotechnol 16, 91 (1998); **31.** Biochim Biophys Acta 1360, 193 (1997); **32.** Anal Biochem 237, 204 (1996); **33.** J Microbiol Methods 35, 23 (1999); **34.** J Clin Microbiol 37, 987 (1999); **35.** Cell Res 10, 71 (2000); **36.** Methods Cell Sci 17, 1 (1995); **37.** Nucleic Acids Res 25, 2945 (1997); **38.** Biotechniques 27, 34 (1999); **39.** Cytometry 7, 508 (1986); **40.** Biotechniques 26, 46 (1999); **41.** J Chinese Biochem Soc 32, 1 (1995); **42.** J Biol Chem 275, 6945 (2000); **43.** J Biol Chem 275, 32846 (2000); **44.** Appl Environ Microbiol 62, 1969 (1996); **45.** Cancer Res 58, 4227 (1998); **46.** Diagnostic Mol Pathol 5, 260 (1996); **47.** Genomics 5, 874 (1989); **48.** Trends Genet 8, 49 (1992); **49.** Nucleic Acids Res 19, 3154 (1991); **50.** Nucleic Acids Res 19, 2500 (1991); **51.** Nucleic Acids Res 19, 405 (1991); **52.** Nucleic Acids Res 21, 3637 (1993); **53.** Anal Biochem 236, 373 (1996); **54.** Proc Natl Acad Sci U S A 94, 10745 (1997); **55.** J Biol Chem 266, 5417 (1991); **56.** Nucleic Acids Res 19, 1521 (1991); **57.** J Mol Biol 13, 269 (1965); **58.** Anal Biochem 190, 331 (1990); **59.** Biopolymers 28, 1491 (1989); **60.** Science 243, 203 (1989); **61.** J Chromatogr A 871, 289 (2000); **62.** J Chromatogr A 828, 481 (1998); **63.** Electrophoresis 20, 497 (1999); **64.** Nucleic Acids Res 20, 2803 (1992); **65.** Nucleic Acids Res 19, 327 (1991); **66.** Proc Natl Acad Sci U S A 87, 3851 (1990); **67.** Nucleic Acids Res 21, 5720 (1993); **68.** Nature 359, 859 (1992); **69.** Biotechniques 10, 616 (1991); **70.** Nucleic Acids Res 23, 1215 (1995); **71.** Methods Enzymol 217, 414 (1993); **72.** Nucleic Acids Res 23, 2413 (1995); **73.** Rev Sci Instrum 65, 807 (1994); **74.** Mol Cell Probes 8, 245 (1994); **75.** Mod Pathol 7, 385 (1994); **76.** Biotechniques 15, 274 (1993); **77.** Biotechniques 20, 708 (1996); **78.** J Biochem Biophys Methods 6, 95 (1982); **79.** Nucleic Acids Res 6, 3535 (1979); **80.** Nucleic Acids Res 15, 10589 (1987); **81.** Annu Rev Biophys Biophys Chem 20, 415 (1991); **82.** Biochemistry 29, 3396 (1990); **83.** Forensic Sci Int 92, 89 (1998); **84.** Electrophoresis 19, 2695 (1998); **85.** Anal Chem 64, 1737 (1992); **86.** Clin Chem 43, 267 (1997); **87.** Biotechniques 23, 58 (1997); **88.** J Chromatogr A 911, 269 (2001); **89.** J Chromatogr A 755, 271 (1996); **90.** L. Reyderman and S. Stavchansky, University of Texas at Austin, personal communication; **91.** Anal Chem 66, 1424 (1994); **92.** Anal Biochem 215, 163 (1993); **93.** Anal Biochem 224, 140 (1995); **94.** J Chromatogr B Biomed Appl 658, 271 (1994); **95.** Vis Neurosci 8, 295 (1992); **96.** Electrophoresis 19, 119 (1998); **97.** Electrophoresis 19, 80 (1998); **98.** Chem Pharm Bull (Tokyo) 46, 294 (1998); **99.** Electrophoresis 16, 974 (1995); **100.** Genome Res 6, 893 (1996); **101.** Biotechniques 30, 334 (2001); **102.** Anal Chem 72, 2499 (2000); **103.** J Chromatogr B Biomed Sci Appl 732, 365 (1999); **104.** Anal Chem 72, 5483 (2000); **105.** Biotechniques 25, 130 (1998); **106.** J Chromatogr A 700, 151 (1995); **107.** J Chromatogr A 853, 309 (1999); **108.** Anal Chem 67, 1913 (1995); **109.** Anal Biochem 231, 359 (1995); **110.** FASEB J 9, A1423, abstract #965 (1995); **111.** J Chromatogr A 669, 205 (1994); **112.** Appl Theor Electrophor 3, 235 (1993); **113.** J Microcolumn Separation 5, 275 (1993); **114.** Anal Chem 69, 1355 (1997); **115.** J Am Chem Soc 116, 7801 (1994); **116.** Anal Chem 66, 1941 (1994); **117.** Anal Chem 65, 3518 (1993); **118.** J Chromatogr A 652, 83 (1993); **119.** J Chromatogr A 652, 75 (1993); **120.** Anal Chem 72, 5583 (2000); **121.** Science 282, 484 (1998); **122.** Anal Chem 70, 5172 (1998); **123.** Anal Chem 69, 3451 (1997); **124.** Electrophoresis 21, 176 (2000); **125.** Anal Chem 71, 5354 (1999); **126.** Anal Chem 73, 4196 (2001); **127.** Anal Chem 67, 3676 (1995).

Product List — 8.4 Nucleic Acid Detection in Electrophoretic Gels and Capillaries

Cat #	Product Name	Unit Size
E33075	Electrophoretic Mobility-Shift Assay (EMSA) Kit *with SYBR® Green and SYPRO® Ruby EMSA stains* *10 minigel assays*	1 kit
E1305	ethidium bromide	1 g
E3565	ethidium bromide *10 mg/mL solution in water*	10 mL
E1169	ethidium homodimer-1 (EthD-1)	1 mg
E3599	ethidium homodimer-2 (EthD-2) *1 mM solution in DMSO*	200 µL
O11492	OliGreen® ssDNA Quantitation Kit *200-2000 assays*	1 kit
O7582	OliGreen® ssDNA quantitation reagent *200-2000 assays*	1 mL
P3584	POPO™-3 iodide (534/570) *1 mM solution in DMF*	200 µL
S11494	SYBR® Gold nucleic acid gel stain *10,000X concentrate in DMSO*	500 µL
S7563	SYBR® Green I nucleic acid gel stain *10,000X concentrate in DMSO*	500 µL
S7567	SYBR® Green I nucleic acid gel stain *10,000X concentrate in DMSO*	1 mL
S7585	SYBR® Green I nucleic acid gel stain *10,000X concentrate in DMSO* *special packaging*	20 x 50 µL
S7564	SYBR® Green II RNA gel stain *10,000X concentrate in DMSO*	500 µL
S7568	SYBR® Green II RNA gel stain *10,000X concentrate in DMSO*	1 mL
S7586	SYBR® Green II RNA gel stain *10,000X concentrate in DMSO* *special packaging*	20 x 50 µL
S7580	SYBR® Green Nucleic Acid Gel Stain Starter Kit	1 kit
S7569	SYBR® photographic filter	each
S33101	SYBR Safe™ DNA gel stain in 0.5X TBE	4 L
S33100	SYBR Safe™ DNA gel stain in 0.5X TBE	1 L
S33110	SYBR Safe™ DNA Gel Stain Starter Kit *with 1 L of SYBR Safe™ DNA gel stain in 0.5X TBE (S33100) and one photographic filter (S37100)*	1 kit

For current prices or to order online, visit probes.invitrogen.com

Cat #	Product Name	Unit Size
S37100	SYBR Safe™ photographic filter	each
T3602	TO-PRO®-1 iodide (515/531) *1 mM solution in DMSO*	1 mL
T3605	TO-PRO®-3 iodide (642/661) *1 mM solution in DMSO*	1 mL
T3600	TOTO®-1 iodide (514/533) *1 mM solution in DMSO*	200 µL
T3604	TOTO®-3 iodide (642/660) *1 mM solution in DMSO*	200 µL
Y3603	YO-PRO®-1 iodide (491/509) *1 mM solution in DMSO*	1 mL
Y3601	YOYO®-1 iodide (491/509) *1 mM solution in DMSO*	200 µL

For current prices or to order online, visit probes.invitrogen.com

8.5 Detecting Nucleic Acid Hybridization

The double-helical structure of nucleic acids, in which one strand binds specifically to its exact complement, is a fortuitous design for the study of biology. The ease of constructing assays based on this feature is responsible for the incredibly fast pace that has characterized molecular biology research since its inception. With the incorporation of fluorescence technologies, the ability to design multiplexed and high-throughput assays has increased the pace still further, to the point in which sophisticated bioinformatics are required to analyze the huge outpouring of data. From nucleic acid sequencing to real-time polymerase chain reaction (PCR) assays to microarrays, the new genomics era owes its development in large part to the development of fluorescence methodologies. This section discusses the use of fluorescence- and luminescence-based detection technologies in assays based on hybridization of a nucleic acid fragment to its complement.

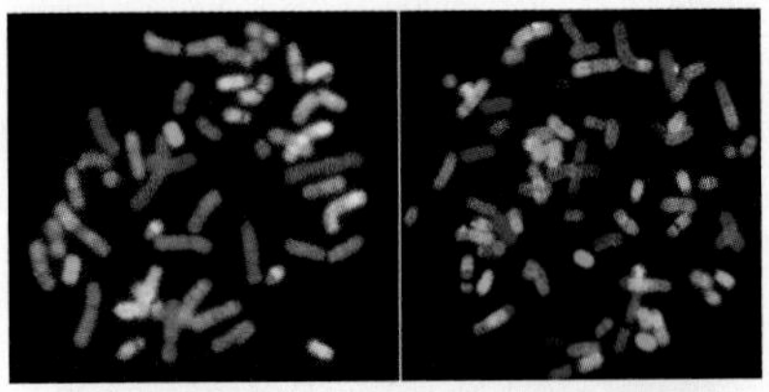

Figure 8.81 Human metaphase chromosomes hybridized to chromosome paints. Human metaphase chromosomes from normal human blood cells (left) or a cancerous cell line (right) were hybridized to human chromosome paint probes using SkyPaint (Applied Spectra Imaging). In this method, a combination of dyes is used to label the probes, the spectrum of each pixel is measured and a color assigned based on the spectral signature. Numerous chromosomes with more than one color reveal the large number of chromosomal translocations and other aberrations in the cancerous cell line (right). Image contributed by Applied Spectral Imaging (used with permission).

Principles of Fluorescence *In Situ* Hybridization (FISH)

Fluorescence *in situ* hybridization (FISH) offers many advantages over radioactive and chromogenic methods for localizing and determining the relative abundance of specific nucleic acid sequences in cells, tissue, interphase nuclei and metaphase chromosomes. Not only are fluorescence techniques fast and precise, they allow the simultaneous analysis of multiple probes that may be spatially or even spectrally overlapping.[1–7] It is possible to distinguish at least four to five different fluorescent signals in a single sample using their excitation and emission properties alone and the appropriate optical filters, and even more signals using an interferometer and linear unmixing software.[8] Using defined ratios of two fluorescent labels per probe (called COBRA, for combined binary ratio labeling) in conjunction with highly discriminating optical filters or an interferometer and appropriate software, researchers can distinguish over 40 signals on the same sample[9–13] (Figure 8.81). In cases where optical hardware or image analysis software is less sophisticated, up to 18 chromosome pairs can be distinguished using sequential FISH, in which several rounds of hybridization are performed on the same sample.[14] Chromosome FISH has become extremely important for:

- Gene mapping[7]
- Identification of mutations correlated with inherited or somatic genetic diseases[15–18] (Figure 8.81, Figure 8.82)
- Clinical diagnostics[19–21]
- Studies of chromosome and nuclear architecture[22,23]
- Identification of viruses and microorganisms within their natural environment[24–27]

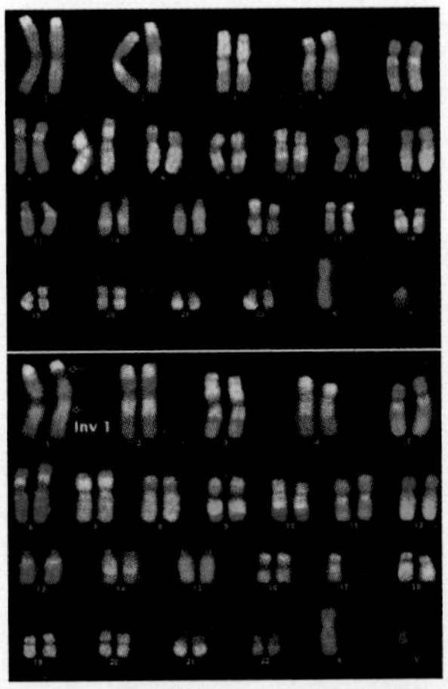

Figure 8.82 Karyotype of human metaphase chromosomes using RxFISH. RxFISH painted chromosomes were visualized using Applied Imaging CytoVision. In this method, human metaphase chromosomes are hybridized with paint probes made from gibbon chromosomes. The fact that there are virtually no unpainted regions demonstrates that, while significantly rearranged (over 30 translocations), gibbon and human chromosomal DNA is well conserved from a common ancestor. The top panel shows a normal human karyotype, whereas the bottom panel shows a human karotype with an inversion in chromosome 1. Image contributed by Applied Imaging Corporation (used with permission).

Chromosome paint probes (Figure 8.81, Figure 8.83) and multicolor banding with microdissection probes[28] (Figure 8.84) provide landmarks for specific chromosomes or parts of chromosomes and are used to study a specific region of the genome. Multicolor chromosome FISH techniques that cover the entire genome are even more powerful, because they allow identification of chromosomal lesions without any prior knowledge about their possible location. Entire genome techniques include:

- Spectral karyotyping (SKY) and multiplexed FISH (M-FISH), in which every chromosome is painted with a different color or mixture of colors[9,16,18,29–33] (Figure 8.81)
- Cross-species color segmenting, in which chromosome paint probes from other primates are hybridized to human chromosomes to produce multicolor banding patterns[34] (Figure 8.82)
- Comparative genome hybridization (CGH), in which differentially labeled genomic DNA from a test sample and reference sample are simultaneously hybridized to normal human chromosomes to facilitate detection of deletions and duplications[35,36]

FISH in metaphase chromosomes has a resolution of about 1 Mbase, but fiber FISH, using stretched chromosomes, has resolution that can be measured in the hundreds of base pairs.[37,38] A discussion of FISH methodology can be found in the literature.[39,40]

Molecular Probes offers a wide variety of reagents for the detection of *in situ* hybridization signals. These include reagents and kits for preparing labeled hybridization probes (Section 8.2), secondary detection reagents for detecting labeled probes (Chapter 6, Chapter 7), kits and reagents for amplifying signals (Section 6.2, Section 6.3) and dyes for counterstaining nuclei or chromosome spreads (Section 8.6). Molecular Probes' proprietary fluorescent dyes are brighter and more photostable than conventional dyes — including the Cy3 and Cy5 dyes (see the Alexa Fluor® 546, Alexa Fluor® 555 and Alexa Fluor® 647 dyes in Section 1.3) — and provide the brightest labels for DNA or RNA probes (see Note 8.1 "Product Highlight: Alexa Fluor® Dyes for Labeling Nucleic Acids" in Section 8.2). Our extensive dye selection spans the visible spectrum and certain combinations of dyes are ideal for multicolor labeling techniques.

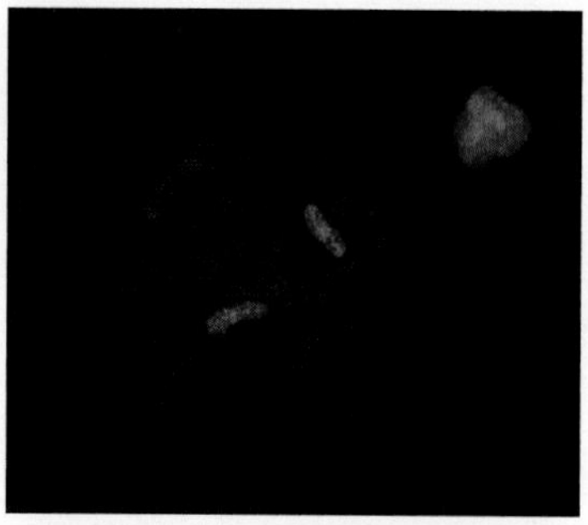

Figure 8.83 A paint probe for chromosome 2 was labeled with the ULYSIS Alexa Fluor® 546 Nucleic Acid Labeling Kit (U21652) and hybridized to human metaphase chromosomes. Image contributed by Joop Wiegant, Leiden University Medical Center, Leiden, The Netherlands.

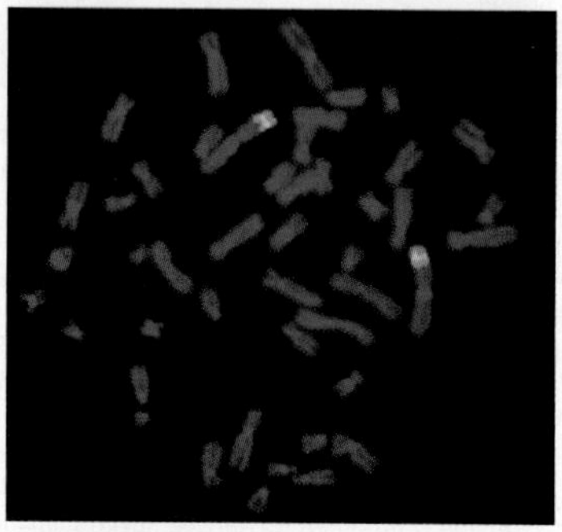

Figure 8.84 Human metaphase chromosomes hybridized to fluorescent probes from two overlapping microdissection libraries. Probes specific to chromosome regions 1p34–35 and 1p36 were labeled using the ULYSIS Oregon Green® 488 (U21659) and Alexa Fluor® 594 (U21654) Nucleic Acid Labeling Kits, respectively. The chromosomes were counterstained with DAPI (D1306, D3571, D21490). Image contributed by Jingwei Yu, Colorado Genetics Laboratory.

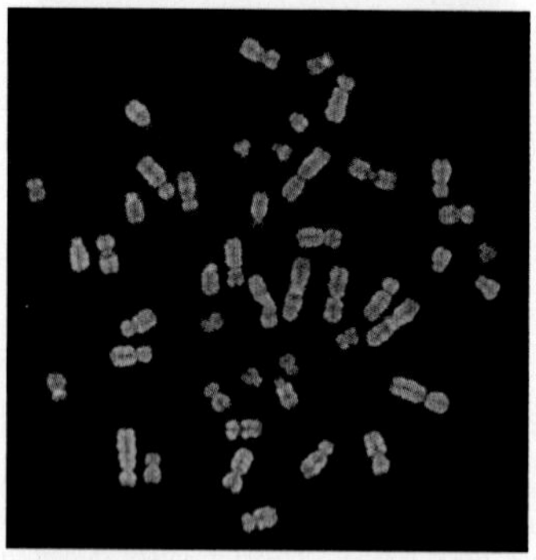

Figure 8.85 Human metaphase chromosomes hybridized to centromere probes labeled with ChromaTide® OBEA-dCTP nucleotides. Probes specific to the α-satellite sequences from human chromosome 17, chromosome 15 and chromosome 1 were labeled using nick translation with ChromaTide® Alexa Fluor® 488-7-OBEA-dCTP (green; C21555), ChromaTide® Alexa Fluor® 594-7-OBEA-dCTP (red; C21558) and ChromaTide® Alexa Fluor® 647-12-OBEA-dCTP (pink; C21559), respectively. The probes were hybridized to metaphase spreads from peripheral blood lymphocyte cultures. The chromosomes were counterstained with Hoechst 33342 (blue) (H1399, H3570, H21492).

Probe Preparation for FISH

Enzymatic Incorporation of ChromaTide® Labeled Nucleotides

The conventional method for labeling FISH probes involves the enzymatic incorporation of a modified nucleotide using a DNA template and an RNA or DNA polymerase (Figure 8.85). Our ChromaTide® dUTP, ChromaTide® OBEA-dCTP and ChromaTide® UTP nucleotides (Section 8.2; Table 8.6, Table 8.7) are modified with either a fluorophore, a dinitrophenyl group (DNP) or biotin attached on the base (Figure 8.38, Figure 8.39). DNP and biotin, as well as some fluorophores, permit signal amplification through secondary detection techniques (see below). The ChromaTide® dUTP nucleotide can be incorporated using a DNA template and standard nick translation, random-primer labeling or PCR techniques.[15,33] Some of the ChromaTide® dUTPs can also be incorporated by reverse transcriptase. Additionally, oligonucleotides can be end-labeled with a ChromaTide® dUTP using terminal deoxynucleotidyl transferase. The ChromaTide® OBEA-dCTP nucleotides can be incorporated into a DNA probe using nick translation and reverse transcription and will most likely be incorporated by other common enzymatic methods as well. The ChromaTide® UTP nucleotides can be incorporated into riboprobes using SP6, T3 or T7 RNA polymerase. Detailed labeling protocols are available in our product literature.

Aminoallyl dUTP Labeling Using the ARES™ Kits

Labeling with fluorophore-modified nucleotides (as described above) is straightforward but does have some drawbacks. The presence of a bulky dye molecule on the nucleotide may make it difficult for the enzyme to incorporate it into DNA or RNA. A protocol optimized for one fluorophore may not be optimal for a chemically different fluorophore. To circumvent these problems, it is possible to enzymatically incorporate a less bulky, amine-modified nucleotide and then label the amine-modified DNA afterwards using an amine-reactive reagent.[41] This two-step labeling method (Figure 8.45) is employed in the ARES™ DNA Labeling Kits (Section 8.2, Table 8.9). Because there is no bulky dye on the nucleotide, the aminoallyl-modified dUTP is incorporated very efficiently. In the second step, an excess of an amine-reactive dye is used, which results in very consistent labeling levels, regardless of the dye used in the reaction. The dyes available in our ARES™ kits include our bright and photostable Alexa Fluor® dyes (see Note 8.1 "Product Highlight: Alexa Fluor® Dyes for Labeling Nucleic Acids" in Section 8.2). Although it is possible to label DNA to extremely high levels using this technique, we have optimized the kits to label the DNA to about one dye molecule for every 12–20 bases, which we have determined to be optimal for hybridization to metaphase chromosomes (Figure 8.86). The 5-(3-aminoallyl)-2′-deoxyuridine 5′-triphosphate (aminoallyl dUTP; A21664, A32764; Section 8.2) used in the ARES™

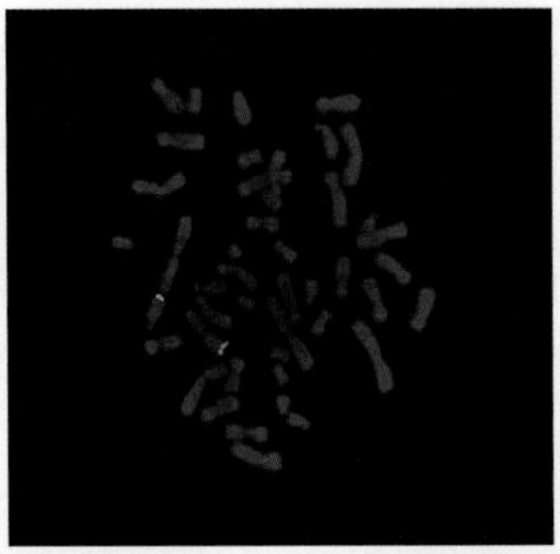

Figure 8.86 Fluorescence *in situ* hybridization (FISH) mapping of a BAC clone on human metaphase chromosomes. FISH was performed using a BAC clone labeled using the ARES™ Alexa Fluor® 488 DNA Labeling Kit (A21665). The chromosomes were counterstained with DAPI (D1306, D3571, D21490). Image contributed by Nallasivam Palanisamy, Cancer Genetics Inc.

Kits to generate amine-modified DNA is also available separately, as is 5-aminohexylacrylamido-dUTP (aha-dUTP; A32760, A32761; Section 8.2), which is incorporated into DNA more efficiently than is aminoallyl dUTP. In addition, we offer 5-(3-aminoallyl)uridine 5′-triphosphate [42] (aminoallyl UTP, A21663, Section 8.2), which can be used in combination with our many amine-reactive dyes (Chapter 1) to synthesize dye-labeled RNA probes [43] (Figure 8.41).

Direct Chemical Labeling of Nucleic Acids Using the ULYSIS Kits

The ULYSIS Nucleic Acid Labeling Kits (Section 8.2, Table 8.8) offer an alternative labeling strategy that eliminates complex enzymatic incorporation protocols altogether. These kits employ a platinum compound that labels the *N*-7 position of guanine bases directly (Figure 8.42) using patented ULS technology developed by KREATECH Biotechnology BV. The reaction is complete in just 15 minutes (Figure 8.43). The method in the ULYSIS labeling kits can be used to reliably achieve a labeling ratio of about one dye for every 30–50 bases, which we have found to be optimal for hybridization of ULS platinum complex–labeled probes to metaphase chromosomes, and results in strong staining of hybridization targets (Figure 8.44, Figure 8.83). The optimal labeling ratio is somewhat lower than that for probes labeled on the uridine base. The ULS chemistry has been employed to label probes for metaphase and interphase chromosome FISH,[44] multicolor whole genome FISH,[10] and CGH.[45] The ULYSIS Kits have been used for labeling overlapping microdissection probes for use in multicolor chromosome-banding techniques (Figure 8.84).

Labeling Oligonucleotides

Short oligonucleotide probes can also be used for FISH,[27,46] although a secondary detection method is often required to amplify the signal [47] (see below). However, by using a series of multiply labeled oligos to adjacent sequences, oligonucleotide probes can be sufficiently sensitive to detect a single RNA transcript *in situ*.[48] Molecular beacons that are labeled with a fluorophore and a quencher (see below) provide the sensitivity required to detect 10 molecules of RNA in a single cell *in situ* without the need for amplification by PCR.[49] A related technique uses a "UniPrimer" universal primer (see below) to detect a single target sequence after amplification by *in situ* PCR or RT-PCR.[50]

Multiple labels can be added to the 3′-terminus of a probe by using the enzyme terminal deoxynucleotidyl transferase (TdT) in combination with a labeled ChromaTide® dUTP nucleotide (Table 8.7). Alternatively, TdT can be used to add an amine-modified dUTP such as aminoallyl dUTP (A21664, A32764) or aminohexylacrylamido-dUTP (A32760, A32761) to the 3′-terminus, with subsequent labeling of the amine with a dye, hapten or enzyme.

Single or multiple labels can also be added chemically to oligonucleotides or peptide–nucleic acid conjugates (PNA) that have been modified with an amine or thiol group during synthesis. Our amine-reactive succinimidyl esters (Chapter 1) provide a simple and reliable method for labeling amine-modified oligonucleotides. The reaction results in a stable amide bond that links the fluorophore to the oligonucleotide (Figure 1.2). The Alexa Fluor® Oligonucleotide Amine Labeling Kits (Section 8.2, Table 8.10) make it easy to label amine-modified oligonucleotides with our superior Alexa Fluor® dyes (see Note 8.1 "Product Highlight: Alexa Fluor® Dyes for Labeling Nucleic Acids" in Section 8.2). These kits include:

- Three vials of the reactive dye
- Buffers
- A detailed protocol for labeling 5′-amine-modified oligonucleotides and recommendations for conjugate purification

Each kit provides sufficient reagents for three labelings of at least 50 µg each.

Chemical labeling of thiolated oligonucleotides can be accomplished using fluorescent iodoacetamides [51–58] (Chapter 2).

Signal Amplification for FISH Using Secondary Detection Reagents

For very low-abundance targets, it may be necessary to use a secondary detection strategy to amplify the signal. A common secondary detection method uses a dye- or enzyme-labeled streptavidin to detect a biotinylated probe, such as a biotinylated nucleic acid generated using biotin-aha-dUTP (B32766). It is also possible to use dyes as haptens and amplify the signal using anti-dye antibodies. For the highest level of amplification, however, an enzyme label in combination with a fluorogenic or chemiluminescent substrate can be employed. Because each enzyme label acts upon many substrate molecules, the resultant signal is greatly amplified.

Biotin and Streptavidin

Table 7.1 and Table 7.22 in Chapter 7 list a wide variety of antibodies, avidin, streptavidin, NeutrAvidin and CaptAvidin™ biotin-binding proteins labeled with fluorophores, haptens, enzymes, NANOGOLD and Alexa Fluor® FluoroNanogold 1.4 nm gold clusters or Captivate™ ferrofluid magnetic particles. The fluorescent streptavidin derivatives are important for multicolor fluorescence *in situ* hybridization applications using biotinylated probes (Figure 8.87). Because there are several fluorophores conjugated to each biotin-binding protein, the signal is potentially amplified severalfold over the signal from DNA, RNA or PNA probes that are directly labeled with fluorophores (Figure 8.88). NeutrAvidin conjugates have been shown to provide improved detection of single-copy genes in metaphase chromosome spreads.[59]

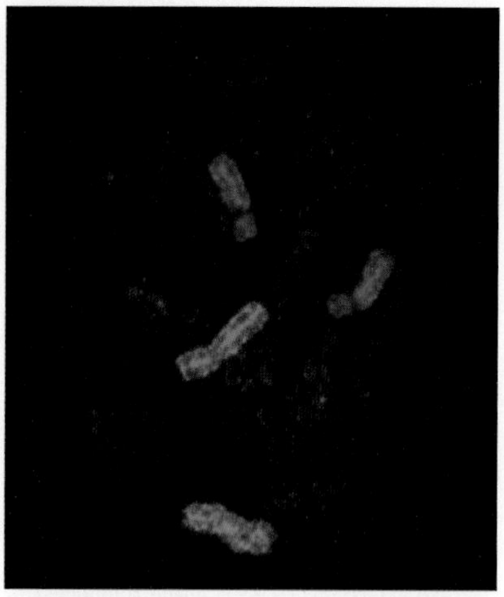

Figure 8.87 Labeled paint probes hybridized to human metaphase chromosomes. A biotinylated chromosome 5 probe was detected with Alexa Fluor® 594 streptavidin (S11227), and a digoxigenin-labeled chromosome 2 probe detected with mouse anti-digoxigenin in combination with Alexa Fluor® 488 goat anti–mouse IgG antibody (A11001). Image contributed by Joop Wiegant, Leiden University Medical Center, Leiden, The Netherlands.

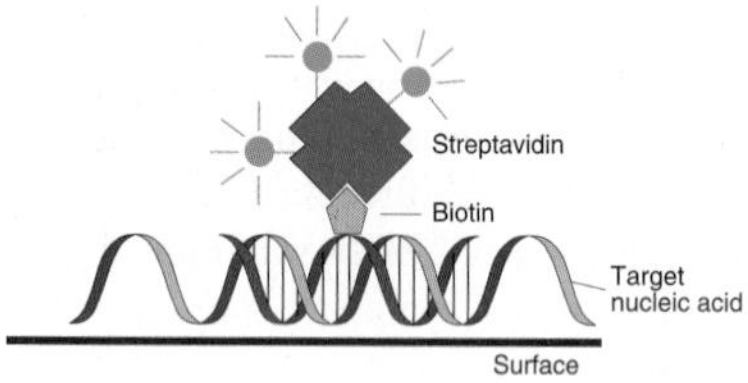

Figure 8.88 Schematic representation of *in situ* hybridization detection using amplification with biotin and a labeled streptavidin.

Signal Amplification Using Anti-Dye Antibodies

Signal amplification can also be accomplished using a fluorophore or chromophore as a hapten for an anti-dye antibody (Section 7.4; Table 7.18; Figure 8.89, Figure 8.90). We offer various labeled and unlabeled rabbit antibodies to:

- Fluorescein (and Oregon Green® dyes)
- Alexa Fluor® 488 dye
- Tetramethylrhodamine
- Texas Red® dye
- BODIPY® FL dye
- Alexa Fluor® 405 and Cascade Blue® dyes
- Lucifer yellow
- Dansyl
- The dinitrophenyl (DNP) and nitrotyrosine haptens

When used in combination with a signal-generating method — for instance, a secondary antibody to the primary anti-dye antibody, a streptavidin conjugate or an enzyme conjugate in combination with a fluorogenic or chromogenic substrate — anti-dye or anti-hapten antibodies can be used to amplify signals from probes containing those labels, to restore fluorescence of partially bleached samples and to discriminate among probes labeled with different haptens, including those prepared from several of our ChromaTide® nucleotides (Section 8.2; Table 8.6, Table 8.7). The anti-fluorescein antibodies also strongly crossreact with our Oregon Green® dyes. In addition, we supply the Alexa Fluor® 488 Signal Amplification Kit for easy amplification of

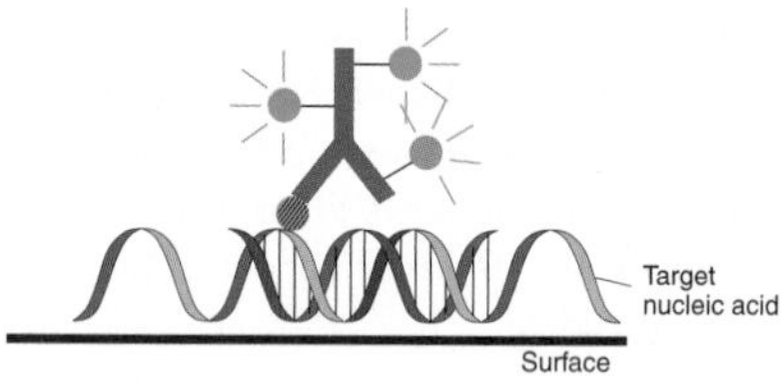

Figure 8.89 Schematic representation of *in situ* hybridization detection using amplification with a dye-labeled anti-dye antibody.

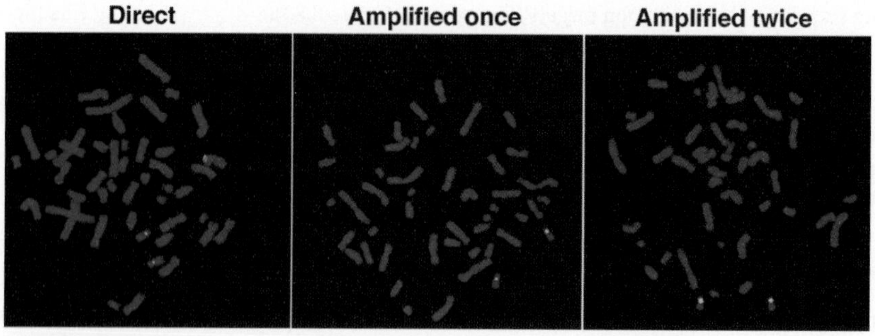

Figure 8.90 Amplification of FISH signals using the Alexa Fluor® 488 Signal-Amplification Kit for Fluorescein- and Oregon Green® Dye–Conjugated Probes (A11053). Chromosome spreads were prepared from the cultured fibroblast cell line MRC-5 and hybridized with an α-satellite probe labeled with the Oregon Green® 488 dye and specific for chromosome 17. The probe was labeled using the ULYSIS Alexa Fluor® 488 Nucleic Acid Labeling Kit (U21659) (left panel). The signal was amplified using the Alexa Fluor® 488 conjugate of rabbit anti-fluorescein/Oregon Green® antibody (A11090; also available in A11053) (middle panel) and amplified once again using Alexa Fluor® 488 goat anti–rabbit IgG antibody (A11008; also available in A11053) (right panel). Note the significant signal enhancement with each amplification step.

fluorescein or Oregon Green® signals with an Alexa Fluor® 488 dye–conjugated anti-fluorescein/Oregon Green® antibody (A11053, Section 7.4, Figure 8.90). Preferred haptenylation reagents and their corresponding anti-hapten antibodies are listed in Table 4.2. Our fluorescent goat anti–rabbit IgG antibody conjugates and the avidin and streptavidin conjugates (Table 7.1, Table 7.22) can be used to further amplify signals from our anti-dye antibodies.

Rabbit and goat polyclonal antibodies and mouse monoclonal antibodies to fluorescein have been employed to simultaneously detect two different mRNA sequences in double *in situ* hybridizations using fluorescein-, Oregon Green® dye– or biotin-labeled oligonucleotides.[5] The high affinity and specificity of anti-fluorescein/Oregon Green® antibodies makes these dyes excellent haptens for *in situ* hybridizations and other secondary detection methods.[5,60] Researchers have found fluorescein–anti-fluorescein ELISA techniques to display low nonspecific binding and to be similar in sensitivity to biotin–streptavidin methods.[61] Our anti–BODIPY® FL preparation has been shown to bind specifically to BODIPY® FL dye–labeled oligonucleotides, where it has been detected with an alkaline phosphatase–conjugated anti–rabbit IgG[62] (G21079, Section 7.2).

Our biotin-XX and fluorescein conjugates of anti-DNP antibodies (A6435, A6423; Section 7.4) are especially suitable for detecting hybridization probes labeled with the DNP hapten.[7,63] These anti-DNP antibodies are prepared against the DNP–keyhole limpet hemocyanin (KLH) conjugate and thus do not crossreact with bovine serum albumin (BSA), which is commonly used as a blocking or carrier molecule in hybridization applications. Anti-DNP antibodies have been used to localize a DNP-labeled DNA probe in HIV-infected cells.[64] It has also been reported that human chromosomes can be probed with equal sensitivities by biotinylated, DNP-modified and digoxigenin-modified cosmid probes.[7] DNP-labeled DNA probes are readily prepared using ChromaTide® dinitrophenyl-11-dUTP (C7610MP, Section 8.2). In addition, the anti-DNP antibodies can be used in tyramide signal amplification schemes that use our TSA Kits containing DNP-X tyramide (Section 6.2, Table 6.1).

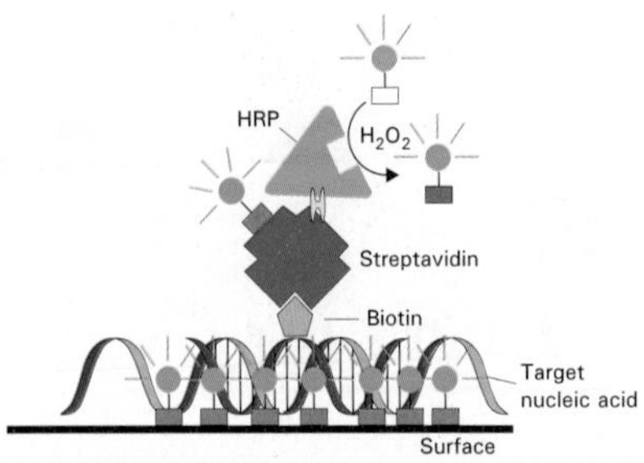

Figure 8.91 Schematic representation of mRNA *in situ* hybridization detection using tyramide signal amplification (TSA). In the presence of horseradish peroxidase (HRP) and hydrogen peroxide, tyramide radicals are formed (red box) that can covalently react with nearby residues.

Tyramide Signal Amplification (TSA)

The tyramide signal amplification technology — originally referred to as catalyzed reporter deposition (CARD) — is an enzyme-mediated detection method that uses the catalytic activity of horseradish peroxidase (HRP) to generate high-density labeling of a target protein or nucleic acid sequence *in situ* while preserving high spatial resolution of the staining pattern.[65–68] In this technique, which is described in detail in Section 6.2, a probe is directly or indirectly labeled with HRP. The HRP enzyme then converts a fluorescent or biotinylated tyramide derivative to a highly reactive form that binds covalently to nearby residues in proteins and other biomolecules (Figure 8.91). The turnover of multiple dye- or hapten-labeled tyramide substrates per peroxidase label results in strong signal amplification (Figure 6.14, Figure 8.92). The increased sensitivity afforded by this technique can be critically important for detecting low abundance DNA or mRNA targets in FISH.[68–72] The amplification also makes it possible to use relatively short oligonucleotide probes, which can minimize background from nonspecific binding that is sometimes seen with longer probes.[73] TSA methodology has been used for identifying:

- Bacterial species in environmental samples[26,47]
- Loss of heterozygosity in fixed, paraffin-embedded tissue sections[74–76]
- Chromosome FISH probes less than 1 kilobase[77]

The use of TSA produces fluorescent signals that are sufficiently bright to be seen in the presence of considerable tissue autofluorescence.[47,74] In addition, the optimal probe concentrations are usually 2- to 10-fold lower for TSA-detected FISH than for conventional detection procedures, which can lead to considerable savings on expensive hybridization probes.[69]

Hybridization probes can be labeled either directly or indirectly with HRP. Most commonly, probes are labeled with biotin or a hapten, which is then detected using an HRP conjugate of streptavidin or of an anti-hapten antibody, respectively[77–79] (Figure 8.91). Alternatively, oligonucleotides can be directly conjugated to HRP using a bifunctional crosslinker[80] (Section 5.2). Direct labeling of nucleic acid probes by HRP can reduce background signals caused by nonspecific binding of HRP conjugates.[67,73,80,81] Several probes can be hybridized simultaneously to identify multiple targets. However, signal development using multicolored fluorescent tyramides must be carried out sequentially, with a peroxidase inactivation step by dilute acid used between each TSA reaction to prevent crosslabeling.[69,78]

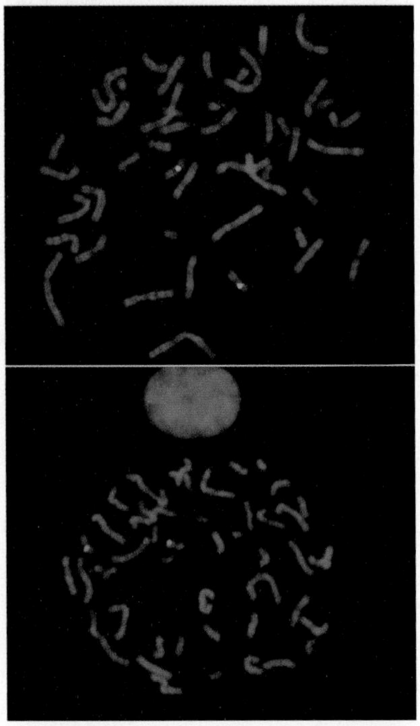

Figure 8.92 Fluorescence *in situ* hybridization detected by tyramide signal amplification. Chromosome spreads were prepared from the cultured fibroblast cell line MRC-5 and hybridized with a biotinylated α-satellite probe specific for chromosome 17. The probe was generated by nick translation in the presence of biotinyl-ated dUTP. For detection by TSA, hybridized chromosome spreads were labeled using TSA Kit #22 (T20932) with HRP-conjugated streptavidin and Alexa Fluor® 488 tyramide (upper panel) or using TSA Kit #23 (T20933) with HRP-conjugated streptavidin and Alexa Fluor® 546 tyramide (lower panel). After counterstaining with DAPI (D1306, D3571, D21490), images were obtained using filters appropriate for DAPI, FITC or TRITC.

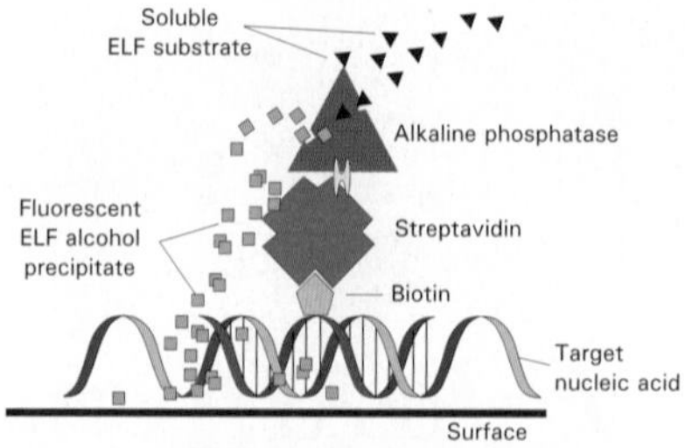

Figure 8.93 Schematic representation of mRNA *in situ* hybridization detection using the Enzyme-Labeled Fluorescence (ELF®) technology (Section 6.3). Alkaline phosphatase converts ELF® 97 phosphate (black triangles) to a brilliant green-fluorescent precipitate (green squares).

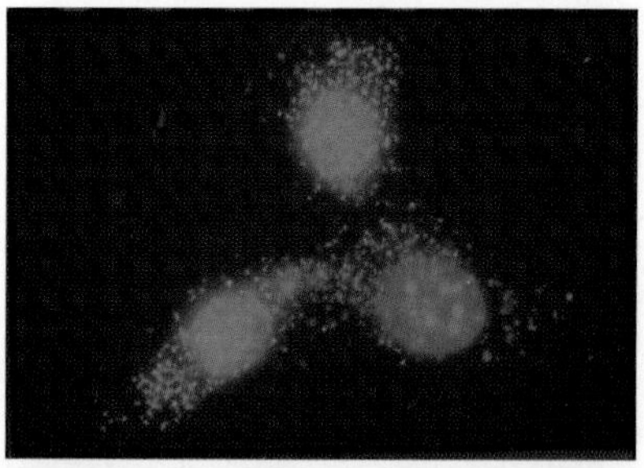

Figure 8.94 *lacZ* mRNA in transformed mouse fibroblasts (CRE BAG 2 cells) hybridized with a singly biotinylated, complementary oligonucleotide. Hybrids were then detected by incubation with a streptavidin–alkaline phosphatase conjugate in combination with the ELF® 97 alkaline phosphatase substrate, both of which are provided in our ELF® 97 mRNA *In Situ* Hybridization Kit (E6604, E6605). Cells were counterstained with DAPI (D1306, D3571, D21490) and photographed using a longpass optical filter appropriate for DAPI.

Molecular Probes' TSA Kits (Section 6.2, Table 6.1) offer 27 different combinations of a fluorescent tyramide and an HRP conjugate of either streptavidin or the goat anti–mouse IgG or goat anti–rabbit IgG antibodies. The Alexa Fluor® 350, Alexa Fluor® 488, Alexa Fluor® 532, Alexa Fluor® 546, Alexa Fluor® 568, Alexa Fluor® 594, Alexa Fluor® 647, Pacific Blue™ and Oregon Green® 488 tyramides are nine of our best dyes, with spectra that cover the entire UV, visible and near-infrared spectrum. Additionally, biotin-XX tyramide and DSB-X™ biotin are used in six TSA Kits in combination with streptavidin HRP, and three TSA Kits use a 2,4-dinitrophenyl tyramide (DNP-X tyramide) as the hapten. The TSA Kits that include DSB-X™ biotin tyramide permit fully reversible staining of targets by fluorescent dye– or enzyme-conjugated biotin-binding proteins (Section 7.6). Our extensive bibliography of TSA applications (T24831), which contains over 250 references, should be consulted for detailed information on applications of TSA; continuously updated copies are available upon request from our Technical Assistance Department or through our web site (probes.invitrogen.com). Each TSA Kit provides sufficient materials to stain at least 100 slide preparations and includes the following components:

- A fluorescent tyramide, biotin-XX tyramide, DSB-X™ biotin tyramide or DNP-X tyramide (Table 6.1)
- A horseradish peroxidase conjugate of goat anti–mouse IgG antibody, goat anti–rabbit IgG antibody or streptavidin
- A hydrogen peroxide stock solution
- An optimized staining buffer
- Blocking reagents
- A staining protocol

The biotin-XX tyramide that we use in our TSA Kits has an extra 14-atom spacer that makes the hapten more accessible (Figure 4.3) than the biotin tyramide used in earlier publications, many of which are included in our bibliography for TSA Kit #21 (T20931). DSB-X™ biotin tyramide and DNP-X tyramide contain a seven-atom spacer between the hapten and the tyramide.

Signal Amplification Using Enzyme-Labeled Fluorescence (ELF®) Technology

Our Enzyme-Labeled Fluorescence (ELF®) technology, which is discussed in detail in Section 6.3, uses our proprietary ELF® 97 phosphatase substrate in combination with alkaline phosphatase conjugates to amplify signals. Upon enzymatic cleavage, the weakly blue-fluorescent ELF® 97 phosphatase substrate yields a yellow-green–fluorescent precipitate (Figure 8.93) that is significantly brighter than signals achieved either with directly labeled fluorescent nucleic acid probes or with hapten-labeled probes in combination with fluorophore-labeled secondary detection reagents.[82–85] Development of the fluorescent signal is very rapid, occurring in seconds to minutes. The ELF® 97 phosphatase substrate has been used for detecting *in situ* hybridization signals in whole-mount zebrafish embryos,[85–87] sectioned mouse embryo hindlimbs[88] and cultured fibroblasts.[85] The substrate was also used to detect the products of reverse-transcription PCR in fixed frozen sections to show reversion of a point mutation in the dystrophin gene by gene therapy.[89]

We have developed and optimized procedures for using the ELF® 97 phosphatase substrate to detect mRNA *in situ* hybridization in cells and tissue sections (Figure 8.94). We provide the key reagents for this application in our ELF® 97 mRNA *In Situ* Hybridization Kits (E6604, E6605). The ELF® 97 phosphatase substrate can also be used in combination with other labeled probes and anti-dye, anti-hapten or secondary antibodies.[86–88]

The ELF® 97 mRNA *In Situ* Hybridization Kits include:

- Alkaline phosphatase streptavidin (in Kit #2, E6605, only)
- ELF® wash, blocking and developing buffers
- Application-specific ELF® 97 phosphatase substrate solution
- Hoechst 33342 nucleic acid counterstain
- ELF® mounting medium
- 50 plastic coverslips
- A detailed protocol

The ELF® 97 mRNA *In Situ* Hybridization Kit #2 (E6605) contains alkaline phosphatase streptavidin and can be used to detect biotinylated DNA or RNA probes. The ELF® 97 mRNA *In Situ* Hybridization Kit #1 (E6604), which does not include alkaline phosphatase streptavidin, is de-

Table 8.17 — Tools for hybridization experiments

Cat #	Chamber Dimensions	Depth	Usable Volume	Quantity per Package
HybriWell hybridization sealing system				
H24720	13 mm diameter	0.25 mm	30 µL	100
H24721	20 mm diameter	0.15 mm	30 µL	100
H24723	22 mm × 22 mm	0.15 mm	30–50 µL	100
H18210	40 mm × 21 mm	0.15 mm	50–100 µL	100
H24722	40 mm × 22 mm	0.25 mm	180–200 µL	100
Secure-Seal hybridization chambers				
S24734	22 mm × 22 mm	0.8 mm	250 µL	50
S24730	20 mm diameter	0.8 mm	200 µL	40
S24731	20 mm diameter	1.3 mm	280 µL	40
S24732	9 mm diameter	0.8 mm	20 µL	20
S24733	9 mm diameter	1.3 mm	40 µL	20
HybriSlip hybridization covers				
H18200	22 mm × 22 mm	NA	NA	500
H18201	40 mm × 22 mm	NA	NA	500
H18202	60 mm × 22 mm	NA	NA	500
Seal tabs				
A18211	Adhesive seal tab	NA	NA	400

NA = Not applicable.

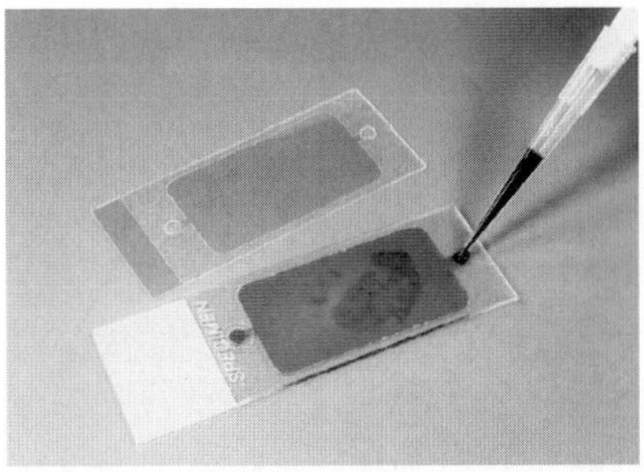

Figure 8.95 HybriWell hybridization sealing system.

signed for use with other alkaline phosphatase conjugates that have been applied to detect DNA or RNA probes labeled with haptens other than biotin. Each kit contains sufficient reagents for 50 slides or coverslips.

Signal Amplification Using Two Rounds of Amplification

Although TSA and ELF® amplification technologies enhance FISH signals to a great degree, very low abundance signals can still elude detection. A strategy using two sequential amplifications has been shown to be useful for visualizing signals that could not be seen with only one round of amplification. Sequential TSA and ELF® amplification has been used to visualize very low abundance mRNA species that could not be seen using either technology separately.[90] In this strategy, a biotinylated probe was amplified first by HRP streptavidin in conjunction with biotin tyramide. The second step used alkaline phosphatase streptavidin, followed by ELF® 97 phosphate (both components of the ELF® 97 mRNA *In Situ* Hybridization Kit (E6605)). In another variation, two rounds of TSA amplification — the first with a dinitrophenyl tyramide and the second with an HRP–anti-DNP antibody followed by fluorescein tyramide — made it possible to detect a FISH signal from as few as 50–60 HRP-labeled oligonucleotide molecules.[73] A particularly useful combination uses a first step TSA procedure that lays down biotin-XX tyramide at the site of the target, followed by a second TSA step that uses HRP-labeled streptavidin to deposit a fluorescent tyramide (Figure 6.5).

Colorimetric Signal Amplification

The colorimetric enzyme substrates NBT/BCIP (N6495, B6492, N6547; Section 10.3) can be used to detect hapten-labeled probes with conjugates of alkaline phosphatase. The combination of NBT and BCIP yields a dark blue, nonfluorescent precipitate at the site of enzymatic activity.

Counterstaining Chromosomes for FISH

Counterstains are used to locate the chromosomes or nuclei in FISH experiments. Molecular Probes provides a spectrum of dyes for staining hybridized metaphase or interphase chromosomes in FISH assays. For best results, we generally recommend using the less bright blue- or far-red–fluorescent dyes as counterstains and the brighter green- or red-fluorescent dyes to label the probes. The blue-fluorescent nuclear stain DAPI (D1306, D3571; FluoroPure™ Grade, D21490; Section 8.6) is commonly used for multicolor chromosome FISH techniques. DAPI provides an excellent counterstain for green-fluorescent, red-fluorescent and far-red–fluorescent probes and also shows a unique banding pattern that helps to identify the chromosomes in metaphase preparations (Figure 8.84). TO-PRO®-3 dye (T3605, Section 8.6) provides a far-red–fluorescent counterstain whose spectra are well separated from those of the common green- and red-fluorescent dyes and from tissue autofluorescence. Although staining by the TO-PRO®-3 dye can be detected using film or a CCD camera, its fluorescence cannot be seen with the naked eye, and it is thus best for applications in which direct visualization of the chromosomes or nuclei is not required to position the slide for analysis.

Gaskets for *In Situ* Hybridization Experiments

Precut, ready-to-use adhesive gaskets provide low-volume hybridization chambers for *in situ* hybridization studies. Designed especially for hybridization experiments, the HybriWell hybridization sealing systems (Figure 8.95) and the higher-volume Secure-Seal hybridization chambers (Figure 23.50) isolate single or multiple specimens on a slide. These hybridization gaskets (Table 8.17) have a special adhesive that bonds to glass slides in seconds, creating a watertight seal that holds at high temperatures, but can also be removed cleanly and easily after hybridization. The hydrophobic surfaces are RNase free and will not trap or bind probes like glass surfaces can. Access ports in the chamber surface permit the addition or removal of hybridization solutions and are easily sealed using seal tabs to create leak-proof chambers that eliminate evaporation. Seal tabs are provided with the HybriWell hybridization sealing system and are also available separately (A18211) for use with the Secure-Seal chambers. We also provide ready-to-use, RNase-free HybriSlip hybridization covers (Figure 23.48), which are hydrophobic plastic coverslips that do not bind to labeled nucleic acids. These covers remain flat, even at high temperatures, to facilitate uniform reagent distribution.

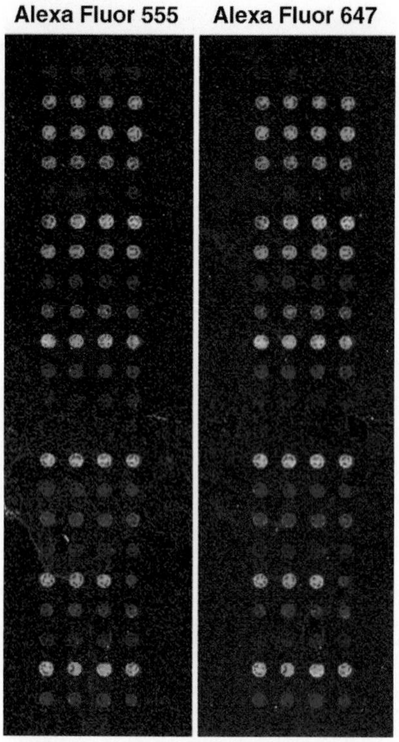

Figure 8.96 DNA microarray hybridized to DNA labeled using the ARES™ DNA Labeling Kits. Total human RNA was labeled by reverse transcription using either ARES™ Alexa Fluor® 555 DNA Labeling Kit (A21677) or ARES™ Alexa Fluor® 647 DNA Labeling Kit (A21676). Labeled DNA was hybridized to a microarray containing human housekeeping genes. After hybridization, the array was imaged using a ScanArray 5000XL microarray scanner (Packard BioScience) using the appropriate lasers and filter sets. The image was pseudocolored so that red and white areas show the most intense signal and green and blue areas show the least intense signal.

Nucleic Acid Hybridization on Blots and Microarrays

Experiments in which labeled sample nucleic acids are hybridized to nucleic acids on solid supports, most notably Southern and Northern blots, have been core technologies in the field of molecular biology. Conventionally, samples were labeled with radioisotopes, hybridized to nucleic acids on the membrane and imaged for long periods with X-ray film. With the advent of genomics and the desire for higher-throughput methods of analysis, solid-surface hybridization technologies have developed a very high level of sophistication, culminating in the DNA microarray, in which hundreds of thousands of sequences are spotted in an area of just a few square centimeters on a glass support.[91–94] Although some users still employ radioactive labeling for microarray experiments, fluorescent labeling and detection now dominate the field. Fluorescence provides an important advantage because the majority of microarray experiments rely on comparison of hybridization signals between two or more samples, and fluorescence detection allows the analysis of multiple samples on the same array, minimizing artifactual variation in signals.

Multicolor fluorescence hybridization on microarrays is especially useful for expression profiling, which compares the mRNA levels between two or more samples.[95–98] Hybridization on arrays has been used to identify groups of genes that may be involved in:

- Tumorigenesis and tumor suppression [99–101]
- Apoptosis [102]
- Leptin-induced changes in metabolism [103]
- Klinefelter's syndrome [104]
- Yeast cell cycle [105]
- *Drosophila* metamorphosis [106]
- Drug sensitivity of *Mycobacterium* tuberculosis [107]
- Development of *Plasmodium falciparum* [108]

Microarray-based experiments promise to be useful for drug discovery processes [109,110] and toxicogenomics.[111] Microarray technology can also be used for sequencing,[112] genotyping,[113,114] detecting DNA copy number changes [115] and gene mapping.[116,117]

The interpretation of microarray-based experiments relies on the comparison of signals from the labeled samples that have hybridized to the spots of the array. Many variables can contribute

Invitrogen Product Highlight

Random Primers

Random Primers are oligodeoxyribonucleotides (mostly hexamers) used to prepare labeled DNA probes from templates for filter hybridization or *in situ* hybridization and to prime mRNAs with or without poly(A) for cDNA synthesis. These primers are truly random and are suitable for DNA synthesis using Klenow fragment with DNA templates or for cDNA synthesis using reverse transcriptase with mRNA templates. To avoid storage buffer interference, Random Primers are supplied in a low-salt buffer.

48190-011	Random Primers	9 A_{260} units

to the level of signal detected and, as in any experiment, it is important to identify and minimize the variables that are artifacts of the experimental process. This section describes Molecular Probes' products that can help to minimize experimental artifacts so that it is possible to identify and quantitate meaningful signal changes.

Labeling Nucleic Acid Samples for Microarray Experiments

Consistent, Uniform Sample Labeling with ARES™ DNA Labeling Kits

The use of fluorophore labels rather than radioactive labels makes it possible to measure several samples on the same array, thereby eliminating variability that can be introduced by comparing hybridization results from different arrays. However, labeling DNA with fluorescent dyes introduces several variables that can make quantitative measurements of hybridization efficiency difficult. A large, relatively hydrophobic dye attached to a nucleotide alters the efficiency of enzymatic incorporation. Thus, samples prepared from labeled nucleotides may have different levels of labeling, making it difficult to compare levels of hybridization between samples. Furthermore, variation of the fluorescence yield with degree of dye conjugation to the nucleic acid probe — as is observed with Cy3 dye– and Cy5 dye–labeled probes — can significantly reduce the reliability of quantitative measures of hybridization assays (see Note 8.1 "Product Highlight: Alexa Fluor® Dyes for Labeling Nucleic Acids" in Section 8.2). To minimize this variability, an alternative two-step labeling technique (Table 8.9, Figure 8.45) uses conventional enzymatic incorporation of an amine-modified nucleotide followed by labeling with a reactive fluorescent dye[41] (Section 8.2). The ARES™ DNA Labeling Kits use this technique to provide reliable and consistent labeling with our state-of-the-art fluorescent dyes, including our Alexa Fluor® 546, Alexa Fluor® 555 and Alexa Fluor® 647 dyes (Figure 8.96), whose nucleic acid conjugates are likely to perform better than the widely used Cy3 and Cy5 dye conjugates in quantitative microarray assays. Uniform labeling of the sample is possible because in the first step of the ARES™ procedure, there are no bulky dye molecules on the nucleotide to restrict the enzymatic incorporation. In the second step, the fluorescent labeling is performed with an excess of a reactive dye to ensure consistent labeling of the amine-modified DNA. The result is a consistent labeling ratio of approximately one dye molecule per 12–20 bases, which is higher than we can obtain with alternative labeling technologies. The ARES™ DNA Labeling Kits (Section 8.2) are available with many of our best fluorophores (Table 8.9), including dyes in the Alexa Fluor® series (see Note 8.1 "Product Highlight: Alexa Fluor® Dyes for Labeling Nucleic Acids" in Section 8.2). Both the Alexa Fluor® 546 and Alexa Fluor® 555 dyes match the Cy3 filter set (Figure 8.97) and the Alexa Fluor® 647 dye exactly matches the Cy5 filter set (Figure 8.98), while the other dyes in the Alexa Fluor® family provide choices matched to other lasers and filter sets. Aminoallyl dUTP (A21664, A32764; Section 8.2) and aha-dUTP (A32760, A32761; Section 8.2), both of which can be used to generate amine-modified DNA, as well as amine-reactive fluorescent dyes (Chapter 1) are also available separately.

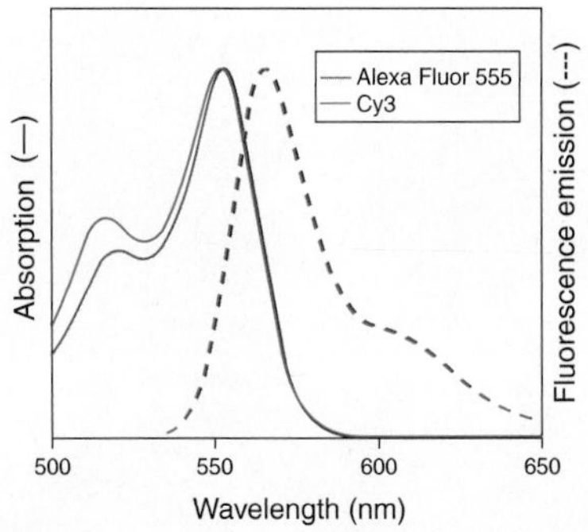

Figure 8.97 Comparison of the absorption and fluorescence emission spectra of the Alexa Fluor® 555 and Cy3 dyes. Spectra have been normalized to the same intensity for comparison purposes.

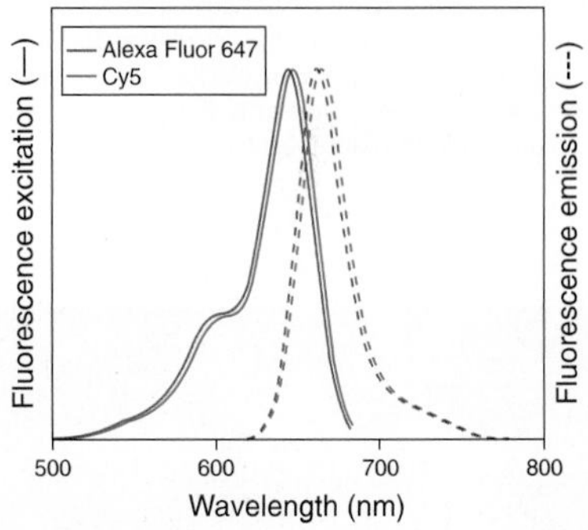

Figure 8.98 Comparison of the fluorescence spectra of the Alexa Fluor® 647 and Cy5 dyes. Spectra have been normalized to the same intensity for comparison purposes.

Alexa Fluor® Reactive Dye Decapacks for Microarray Applications

For labeling amine-modified DNA or RNA probes in microarray-based experiments, we also offer three of our outstanding amine-reactive Alexa Fluor® dyes conveniently packaged in 10 single-use vials and rigorously tested for the ability to efficiently label aminoallyl-modified DNA — the Alexa Fluor® 555 reactive dye decapack (A32756), the Alexa Fluor® 594 reactive dye decapack (A32751), the Alexa Fluor® 647 reactive dye decapack (A32757) and a set containing both the Alexa Fluor® 555 and Alexa Fluor® 647 reactive dye decapacks (A32755) for two-color experiments. These specially packaged amine-reactive dyes can be used in conjunction with our aminohexylacrylamido-dUTP (aha-dUTP, A32760, Section 8.2), aminoallyl dUTP or aminoallyl UTP (A21664, A21663; Section 8.2) nucleotides or with commercially available aminoallyl nucleotide–based nucleic acid labeling kits. A two-step labeling method achieves extremely high and consistent labeling efficiencies, which is especially important for microarray applications in which the consistency of labeling is critical for accurate interpretation of results.[118] In the first step, the amine-modified dUTP or UTP is easily and efficiently incorporated by the enzyme, without interference from bulky dyes. In the second step, the amine-reactive Alexa Fluor® succinimidyl ester reacts to form a covalent bond with the introduced amine groups on the DNA or RNA. This method is highly efficient, resulting in fluorescent labeling of up to one dye every 12 bases.

Each decapack includes 10 single-use vials of amine-reactive Alexa Fluor® succinimidyl ester. Sufficient dye is provided in each vial for optimally labeling the amount of cDNA produced from reverse transcription of either 20 µg of total RNA or 1–5 µg of poly(A)+ RNA in the presence of aminoallyl dUTP. With excitation/emission maxima of 555/565 nm, 590/617 nm and 650/668 nm, respectively, the Alexa Fluor® 555, Alexa Fluor® 594 and Alexa Fluor® 647 succinimidyl esters match the most popular wavelength channels used to scan microarrays. When single-stranded DNA is labeled with equivalent levels of Alexa Fluor® 647 dye or Cy5 dye using aminoallyl dUTP incorporation, the fluorescence emission from the Alexa Fluor® 647–labeled DNA is several times more intense than that of the Cy5 dye–labeled DNA (Figure 8.50). Furthermore, the Alexa Fluor® 555/Alexa Fluor® 647 dye pair has been shown to display higher signal correlation coefficients than the Cy3/Cy5 dye pair in two-color DNA microarray assays.[119]

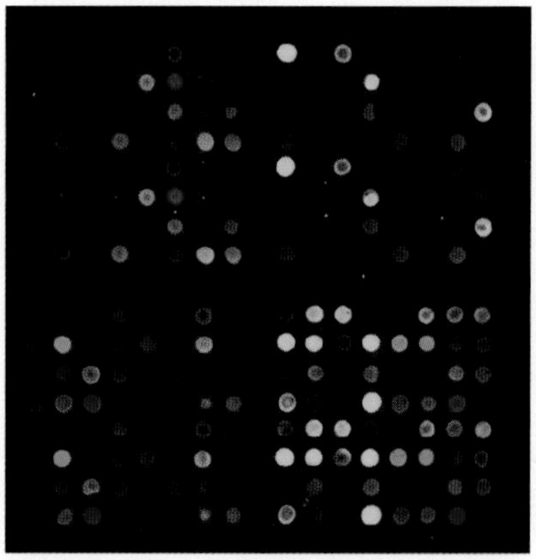

Figure 8.99 ULYSIS reagent–labeled RNA hybridized to a microarray. Poly(A)+ RNA samples from the spleen of an irradiated or unirradiated mouse were labeled using the Alexa Fluor® 594 ULS reagent or Alexa Fluor® 546 ULS reagent, respectively. The labeled samples were mixed and hybridized to a cDNA microarray. The image was contributed by Rahul Mitra (Baylor College of Medicine) and Mini Kapoor, Thomas H. Burrows, and Rachel Grier (MD Anderson Cancer Center).

Fast and Easy Direct Labeling with ULYSIS Nucleic Acid Labeling Kits

The ULYSIS kits use a direct chemical labeling method that vastly simplifies nucleic acid labeling with fluorescent dyes (Section 8.2, Table 8.8), including our Alexa Fluor® dyes. These kits use the platinum-based ULS chemistry developed at KREATECH Biotechnology BV to directly label the *N*-7 position of guanine residues without using enzymatic incorporation. ULS chemistry has also been used to label RNA directly, obviating the need to make cDNA from mRNA samples (Figure 8.99). These kits can be used reliably to achieve a labeling efficiency of about one dye for every 30–50 bases, which we have determined is the optimal level for hybridization to dot blots.

Fluorophore-Labeled Nucleotides

It is possible to label nucleic acid samples for microarray-based experiments using standard enzymatic incorporation of fluorescent ChromaTide® nucleotides or aha-nucleotides via reverse transcription, PCR, nick translation or random-hexamer labeling (Figure 8.100). The ChromaTide® dUTP, ChromaTide® OBEA-dCTP, aha-dUTP and ChromaTide® UTP nucleotides (Section 8.2; Table 8.6, Table 8.7) are available labeled with Alexa Fluor® dyes, DNP, biotin and other conventional fluorophores. A careful study of parameters affecting the quality of microarray data has shown that the incorporation of Alexa Fluor® 546-14-dUTP (C11401) into a DNA probe by reverse transcription of total RNA results in a threefold higher signal on microarrays when compared with the signal obtained from reverse transcription of the same RNA sample using a Cy3 dye–labeled dUTP.[120] Detailed protocols for enzymatic labeling are available in our product literature.

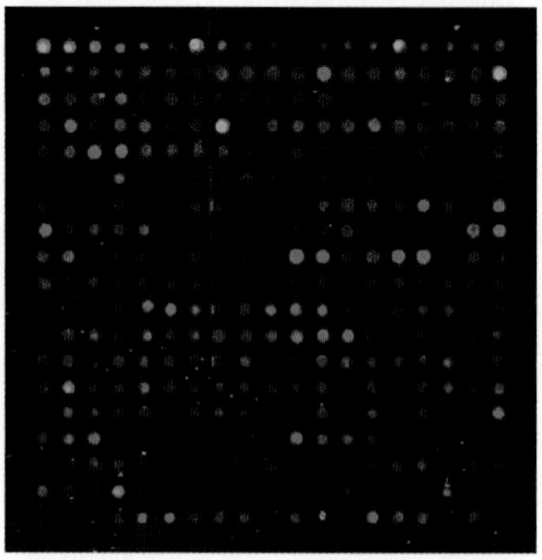

Figure 8.100 A microarray hybridized to Alexa Fluor® 546 dye–labeled cDNA. cDNA was labeled by reverse transcription from *Vibrio cholerae* total RNA using ChromaTide® Alexa Fluor® 546-14-dUTP (C11404). Labeled cDNA was then hybridized to a *V. cholerae* O1 El Tor microarray. The array was imaged with a ScanArray 5000XL scanner (Packard BioScience). The image was contributed by Kimberly Chong and Gary Schoolnik, Stanford University.

Labeled dT_{18} and Random Oligodeoxynucleotides

RNA samples can also be labeled by reverse transcription using fluorophore-labeled random oligonucleotides as primers in combination with unlabeled deoxynucleotide triphosphates. Molecular Probes provides two types of labeled oligodeoxynucleotides that can be used for this purpose. Our dT_{18} oligodeoxynucleotides are labeled at the 5′-terminus with one of three of our Alexa Fluor® dyes (Table 8.18). The labeled dT_{18} oligodeoxynucleotides hybridize to poly(A) tails in RNA samples, providing primers for reverse transcription. Our Panomer™ 9 random-sequence oligodeoxynucleotides are covalently labeled on the 5′-terminus with one of our proprietary fluorescent dyes, with a nonfluorescent QSY® 7 quencher dye or with biotin (Table 8.18). The Panomer™ 9 oligonucleotides are also useful as primers for synthesizing labeled DNA via Klenow DNA polymerase or reverse transcriptase. In these reactions, the primer provides the detectable label, whereas unlabeled nucleotides are incorporated by the enzyme. This labeling strategy ensures efficient and unbiased incorporation of nucleotides because the bulky dye molecule does not interfere with nucleotide incorporation. However, because the resulting DNA fragments contain only a single label, the labeling efficiency will typically be lower than that achieved by incorporating fluorophore- or hapten-labeled nucleotides.

Using Labeled Oligonucleotides as Biosensors on Solid Supports

Molecular beacons[121] are dual-labeled oligonucleotides that become fluorescent upon binding to their complementary sequence (Figure 8.113, see below). These probes were originally employed for solution-based hybridization assays, such as real-time PCR, but they can also be used on solid supports. By linking a biotin molecule to the oligonucleotide, the molecular beacon can be attached to a streptavidin-coated surface, such as a glass slide or optical fiber surface.[122,123] Multiple molecular beacons attached to a surface at defined locations provide an array that can identify specific sequences in complex samples without the need to label the samples.

Secondary Detection for Signal Amplification

Detecting Biotin Labels with Fluorescent Streptavidin Conjugates

For very low amounts of sample or low-abundance sequences, it may be necessary to use a secondary detection strategy to amplify the signal. A common secondary detection method uses streptavidin to amplify a sample labeled with a biotinylated dUTP,[102] such as biotin-aha-dUTP (B32766). Labeled streptavidins are available conjugated to Alexa Fluor® dyes, fluorescent phycobiliproteins and many other fluorescent dyes (Section 7.6, Table 7.22). The phycobiliproteins, phycoerythrin and allophycocyanin (Section 6.4) are extremely bright fluorescent proteins that can be visualized with filter sets standard on most microarray readers [102] and are commonly used for signal amplification in microarray experiments (Figure 6.42).

Alternative secondary detection methods include detection of DNP with a labeled anti-DNP antibody (Section 7.4) or detection of dyes, such as fluorescein or the Oregon Green® 488 dye, with a labeled anti-dye antibody (Section 7.4). Although they were optimized for staining cells or tissues, our Alexa Fluor® Signal Amplification Kits (Section 7.2, Table 7.8) may potentially be adapted for amplification of microarray signals.

Signal Amplification with the ELF® 97 Phosphatase Substrate

Our Enzyme-Labeled Fluorescence (ELF®) technology, which is discussed in Section 6.3, uses our patented ELF® 97 phosphatase substrate to amplify alkaline phosphatase–generated signals. Upon enzymatic cleavage, the weakly blue-fluorescent ELF® 97 phosphatase substrate yields a bright yellow-green–fluorescent precipitate (Figure 8.93). Because one phosphatase enzyme can act upon many substrate molecules, the signal is greatly amplified. The ELF® 97 mRNA *In Situ* Hybridization Kits (E6604, E6605), which include the ELF® 97 phosphatase substrate, have been used to detect hybridization signals on oligonucleotide arrays.[124] Samples labeled with biotin were incubated with alkaline phosphatase streptavidin and then detected with the ELF® 97 phosphatase substrate.

Table 8.18 — Spectral characteristics of labeled oligonucleotides

Fluorophore	Ex/Em *	Panomer™ 9 Random Oligos	Oligo $(dT)_{18}$
Alexa Fluor® 350	345/440	P21679	
Pacific Blue™	410/455	P21678	
Alexa Fluor® 488	490/520	P21680	
Alexa Fluor® 532	525/550	P32925	
Alexa Fluor® 546	555/570	P21681	
Alexa Fluor® 555	555/565	P21687	O21561
Alexa Fluor® 594	590/615	P21682	O21562
Alexa Fluor® 633	630/650	P21683	
Alexa Fluor® 647	650/670	P21686	O21563
Alexa Fluor® 660	660/690	P21684	
Alexa Fluor® 680	680/700	P21685	
Biotin	NA	P21689	
QSY® 7	560 †	P21688	

* Approximate excitation (Ex) and fluorescence emission (Em) maxima in nm.
† Approximate absorption maximum, in nm. NA = Not applicable.

Chemiluminescent Detection on Blots

Chemiluminescent enzyme substrates provide a sensitive alternative to radioactive labeling for Southern and Northern blots and for macroarrays on nitrocellulose or nylon membranes. Molecular Probes offers the BOLD APB chemiluminescent substrate (B21901), an alkaline phosphatase substrate developed for applications on nitrocellulose or nylon. To use this detection method, the nucleic acid probe is first labeled with biotin using biotinylated dUTP. After hybridization of the biotinylated probe to the blot, the blot is incubated with an alkaline phosphatase conjugate of streptavidin (S921), followed by the BOLD APB substrate. Alternatively, the probe can be labeled with a dye, such as fluorescein or the DNP hapten, and then detected with an anti-dye antibody conjugated to alkaline phosphatase (Table 7.18). Many other combinations of haptens and antibodies can also be used (Section 7.4).

The BOLD APB substrate is based on a 1,2-dioxetane molecule that emits bright chemiluminescence upon reaction with alkaline phosphatase. The substrate is provided as a ready-to-use solution that requires no mixing, making it extremely easy to use — there is no need for special blockers or enhancers that are required for use of other chemiluminescent substrates. The signal-to-noise ratio is exceptionally high, permitting sensitivity that is potentially several times that of fluorescence techniques. The BOLD APB chemiluminescent substrate emits a signal that increases in intensity for two hours and then remains constant for at least six more hours, allowing plenty of time for the multiple exposures that may be necessary for optimal detection sensitivity. In contrast to fluorescent reagents, chemiluminescent reagents do not require an excitation light source; the energy from the chemical reaction generates light. Consequently, the detection of chemiluminescence is essentially background free. The chemiluminescent signal can be detected by directly exposing the blot to X-ray film or by using a scanning instrument designed for chemiluminescence. The BOLD APB chemiluminescent substrate is available as 25 mL of ready-to-use solution, sufficient for staining 25 minigel blots.

Other Types of Signal Amplification

Dendrimers [121] are complexes of labeled oligonucleotides built up from several layers of overlapping oligonucleotide sequences.[125] The outer layer comprises two types of oligonucleotides, one that contains a capture sequence complementary to the sequence of interest, and another that is labeled with a fluorescent dye. Because there are so many labeled oligonucleotides in this layer (about 250), the dendrimer exhibits a greatly amplified fluorescent signal compared with a single fluorescent dye. For microarray applications, labeled samples are generated by reverse transcription using primers tailed with the complement to the capture sequence.[126] The cDNA samples are then labeled by hybridization of the dendrimer capture sequence to the complementary sequence on the primer. This amplification technique makes it possible to use very small amounts of sample in the hybridization reaction[126] (Figure 8.101).

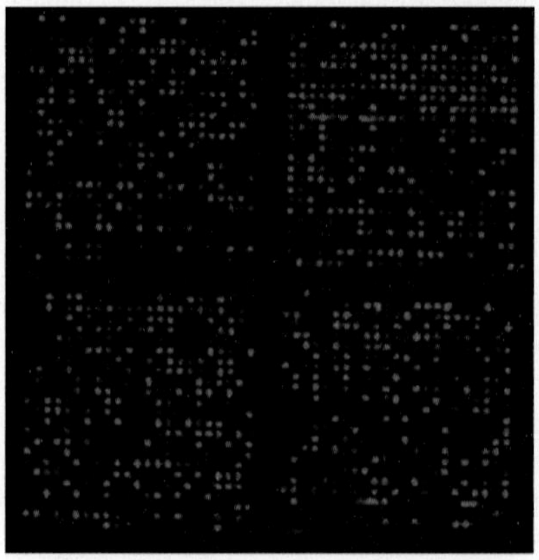

Figure 8.101 Microarray expression analysis using an Alexa Fluor® 546 dye–labeled dendrimer. Complementary DNA (cDNA) from 500 ng of total mouse liver RNA was prepared by reverse transcription using specially designed primers. The primers were designed such that a dendrimer capture sequence was attached to the 5′-end of an oligo(dT) sequence. The cDNA was then hybridized to three DNA dendrimers labeled with the Alexa Fluor® 546 dye such that approximately 125 Alexa Fluor® 546 dyes were coupled to the dendrimers. The labeled cDNA was then hybridized to a microarray. The arrays were scanned using a ScanArray 3000 scanner (Packard BioScience). The image was contributed by Robert Getts, Genisphere.

Tools and Techniques for Quality Control Testing and Normalization on Microarrays and Blots

Whether using Northern blots, macroarrays on membranes or microarrays on glass slides, it is important to normalize the signal to the amount of nucleic acid on the solid support. Differences in purification, loading and transfer may create differences in RNA levels on blots, and even with sophisticated robotics, direct spotting techniques for creating arrays of nucleic acids on solid supports vary widely in reproducibility (Figure 8.102, Figure 8.103). Our experience is that the uniformity of nucleic acid arrays depends to a significant extent on its production; some commercially available arrays have poor uniformity (Figure 8.103). At the very least, a method to qualitatively determine the amount of nucleic acid on a support is desirable for quality control purposes. Quantitative data that can be used for signal normalization are even more useful, making it possible to validate perceived changes in RNA expression between samples, despite differences in the nucleic acid levels on the solid support. Often, hybridization of a "constitutively expressed" RNA sequence is used for normalization on Northern blots. However, it is sometimes discovered that the level of such RNA sequences is not constant through changing physiological states of a cell or tissue. Direct measurement of the levels of nucleic acid spotted on the slide provides a reliable method for normalization and can also be used to assess the amount of nucleic acid remaining on a support after stripping off a probe and before reusing the blot or array.

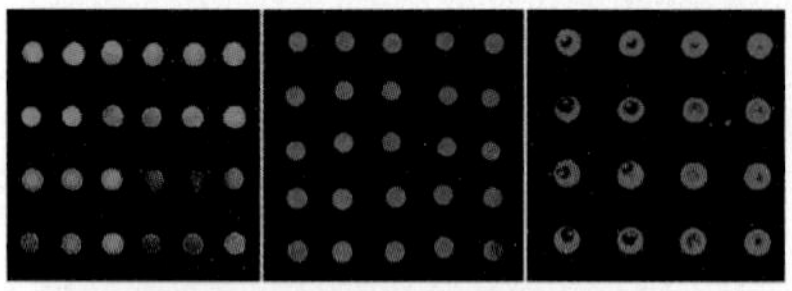

Figure 8.102 DNA microarrays stained with nucleic acid stains for quality control. DNA microarrays were stained with dilutions of SYBR® Green II dye (green; S7568, S7564, S7586), POPO™-3 dye (orange, P3584) or SYTO® 59 dye (magenta, S11341) in aqueous buffer. The microarrays were imaged on a ScanArray 5000XL microarray scanner (Packard BioScience) using the appropriate lasers and filters. Staining reveals the variable amounts of DNA spotted onto the different microarrays.

PARAGON™ DNA Microarray QC Stain Kit

The quality and consistency of microarray slides directly affects the outcome of microarray experiments. The PARAGON™ DNA Microarray QC Stain Kit (P32930) is expressly designed to meet the growing demand for quality-control testing of DNA microarray slides, providing a method for routine quality-control testing of both cDNA and oligonucleotide microarrays that is complete in as little as 10 minutes (Figure 8.104). This kit contains SYBR® 555 nucleic acid stain, which exhibits a large fluorescence enhancement upon nucleic acid binding while display-

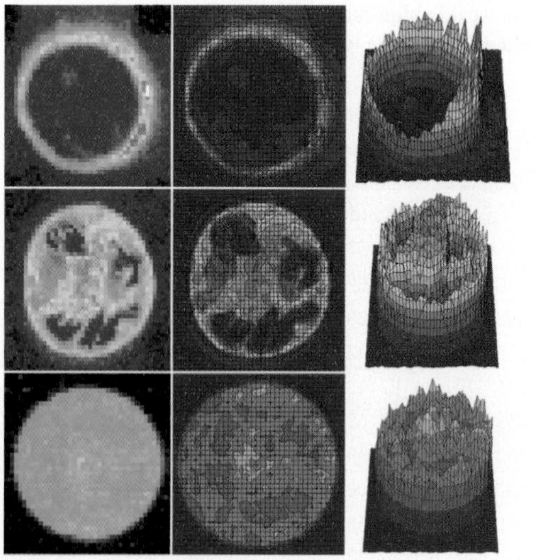

Figure 8.103 Panomer™ 9 oligodeoxynucleotides for quality control of microarray spotting. Three microarrays were made using three different spotting protocols. Each microarray was then hybridized to a Panomer™ 9 oligonucleotide, conjugated with either the Alexa Fluor® 488 dye (top) or the Alexa Fluor® 546 dye (middle and bottom), washed and imaged using a ScanArray 5000XL microarray scanner (Packard BioScience). One representative spot from each slide was selected for comparison purposes. The spots were analyzed using Metamorph software (Universal Imaging, Inc.), and the data is presented as a three-dimensional graph with high-intensity areas as peaks and low-intensity areas as valleys. For further clarification, the graphs are color coded so that the highest intensity areas are red and the lowest intensity areas are blue. The comparison shows that the Panomer™ 9 oligodeoxynucleotides are ideal for microanalysis of spot morphology on DNA microarrays.

ing a low affinity for the glass substrate. The high sensitivity and low background staining displayed by the SYBR® 555 stain make it ideal for routine quality-control testing of both cDNA and oligonucleotide microarrays. With a sensitivity of 1 pg of DNA per spot and a linear range of detection from 10 to 100 pg of DNA per spot, the SYBR® 555 nucleic acid stain is also useful for comparing the relative amount of DNA in spots on microarray slides.

The SYBR® 555 nucleic acid stain provides remarkably consistent slide-to-slide staining with low background and no streaking. This stain is compatible with all types of slide surfaces tested, as well as with nucleic acids spotted out of 50% dimethylsulfoxide (DMSO), 3X SSC (1X SSC = 150 mM NaCl and 15 mM sodium citrate, pH 7.0), phosphate-buffered saline (PBS) and commercially available spotting buffers such as ArrayIt Micro Spotting Plus Solution (TeleChem International, Inc.) and OmniGrid 2X Spotting Buffer (GeneMachines). DNA stained with the SYBR® 555 dye can be efficiently scanned using the Alexa Fluor® 546 or Alexa Fluor® 555 dye channel (also known as the green or Cy3 channel) of standard microarray scanners.

Each PARAGON™ DNA Microarray QC Stain Kit contains:

- SYBR® 555 stain concentrate
- Staining tubes
- Stain buffer concentrate
- Wash buffer concentrate
- PARAGON™ DNA microarray QC slide, containing three identical dilution series of a 1 kb double-stranded DNA fragment (from approximately 1 pg to 160 pg DNA per spot), spotted and crosslinked onto an amine-coated cDNA microarray slide (Figure 8.105)
- A detailed protocol

The PARAGON™ DNA microarray QC slide is useful for determining whether the staining technique is working. However, because the quantity of DNA in the spots can be somewhat variable, this slide should not be used as a quantitation standard.

PARAGON™ DNA Microarray QC Hybridization Kits

The PARAGON™ DNA Microarray QC Hybridization Kits #1 and #2 (P32934, P32937) can be used to determine the relative amount of printed DNA that is single stranded and therefore available for hybridization, providing a valuable method for protocol optimization and improved analysis of hybridization results. With these kits, analysis takes less than 30 minutes from the start of the protocol to when the slides are ready to be scanned. The procedure is carried out at room temperature, and the hybridization is reversible. The PARAGON™ DNA Microarray QC Hybridization Kits are particularly useful for assessing the effectiveness of slide preparation protocols.

The primary component of these kits is a labeled Panomer™ 9 random oligodeoxynucleotide, a nine-base, random-sequence oligonucleotide mix that is covalently labeled on the 5′ end with the Alexa Fluor® 555 (in Kit #1, P32934) or the Alexa Fluor® 647 (in Kit #2, P32937) dye. These state-of-the-art Alexa Fluor® dyes exhibit exceptionally bright and photostable orange (excitation/emission maxima ~555/565 nm) and far-red (excitation/emission maxima ~650/670 nm) fluorescence, respectively, and are generally compatible with commonly used filter sets. Also included in this kit are buffers that have been optimized to achieve efficient hybridization and a high signal-to-noise ratio, and a control slide for confirming that the kit protocol has been performed successfully. Specifically, each PARAGON™ DNA Microarray QC Hybridization Kit provides:

- Alexa Fluor® 555 (in Kit #1, P32934) or Alexa Fluor® 647 (in Kit #2, P32937) Panomer™ 9 random oligodeoxynucleotide conjugate
- DNA microarray control slide in a separate slide tube (Figure 8.105)
- Resuspension, hybridization and wash buffers
- Four wash tubes, accommodating four slides each
- Two coverslips
- A detailed protocol

Sufficient materials are supplied for treating 16 slides.

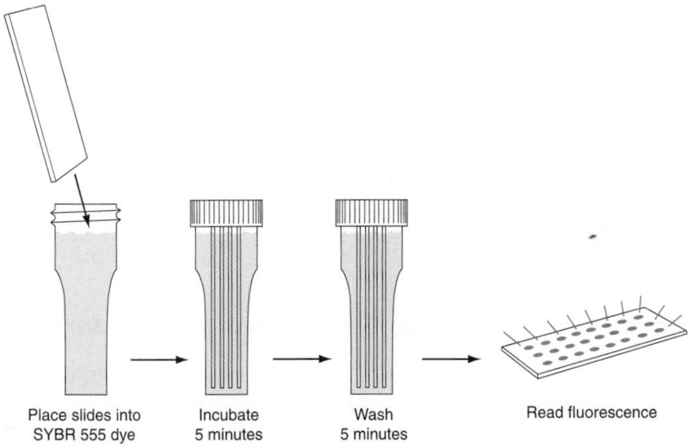

Figure 8.104 Schematic diagram of method used in the PARAGON™ DNA Microarray QC Stain Kit (P32930). The quality of microarray slides can be determined in just 10 minutes.

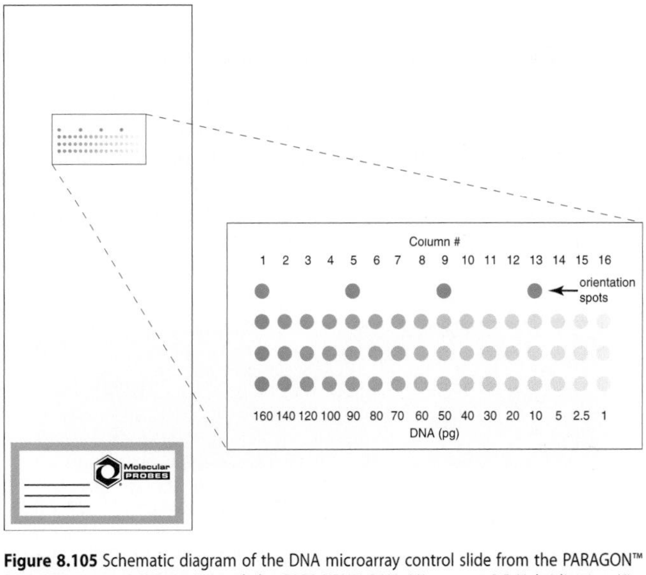

Figure 8.105 Schematic diagram of the DNA microarray control slide from the PARAGON™ DNA Microarray QC Stain Kit and the PARAGON™ DNA Microarray QC Hybridization Kits (P32930, P32934, P32937). This slide contains three identical dilution series of a 1 kb double-stranded DNA fragment, from 1 pg to 160 pg of DNA per spot.

PARAGON™ Genomic DNA Hybridization Test Kits

Prepared genomic DNA is a useful standard for microarray experiments — it provides comprehensive coverage for all human genes, including those encoded on the X and Y chromosomes, it does not vary by tissue or developmental state and it will target mRNA-derived cDNA libraries as well. Labeled genomic DNA has been suggested as a substitute for reference RNA because it may be a more consistent, stable and universal control, particularly when microarray studies require large, complex sample sets.[127] The Alexa Fluor® dye–labeled human genomic DNA included in the PARAGON™ Genomic DNA Hybridization Test Kits #1 and #2 (P32938, P32942) can be used in several ways to improve microarray experiments:

- For judging the print quality and spot morphology of human expression arrays
- For optimizing hybridization and wash conditions without using valuable experimental samples
- As a substitute for reference RNA

Each PARAGON™ Genomic DNA Hybridization Test Kit provides:

- Alexa Fluor® 555 (in Kit #1, P32938) or Alexa Fluor® 647 (in Kit #2, P32942) dye–labeled genomic DNA
- Genomic DNA microarray control slide (Figure 8.106)
- A detailed protocol

Sufficient labeled DNA is provided for up to 16 array tests. The genomic DNA microarray control slide contains a dilution series of male human genomic DNA printed in triplicate rows, with rows and columns spaced 500 µm apart. Spots contain known masses of DNA, ranging from 10 pg to 2.5 fg. Fluorescently labeled spots mark columns 1, 5, 9 and 13, allowing easy orientation of the array (Figure 8.106). This control slide can be used to confirm the efficacy of the provided labeled DNA solution and to test hybridization and wash conditions. When the labeled DNA is used to check the quality of an experimental printed array, the control slide (if hybridized under identical conditions) can also be used to estimate the amount of DNA in the spots of the array.

PARAGON™ Microarray Scanner Calibration Slide

The PARAGON™ microarray scanner calibration slide (P32927) is ideal for evaluating and calibrating microarray scanner performance. This four-color slide is printed with an array of Panomer™ 9 oligodeoxynucleotides, which are random-sequence oligonucleotides (9-mers) labeled with one of four Alexa Fluor® dyes. These four Alexa Fluor® dyes — the green-fluorescent Alexa Fluor® 488, orange-fluorescent Alexa Fluor® 555, red-fluorescent Alexa Fluor® 594 and far-red–fluorescent Alexa Fluor® 647 dyes — were chosen for their superior performance in multicolor microarray experiments[118,128,129] and their compatibility with available microarray scanners. The dilution series represented on each PARAGON™ microarray scanner calibration slide covers a range of seven orders of magnitude, allowing accurate determination of the linear dynamic range of the instrument for each dye. This versatile microarray slide can be used to:

- Determine the linear dynamic range of the instrument for each dye
- Identify the ideal lasers and filters sets to use for each dye
- Determine the spectral overlap of each dye
- Facilitate the application of linear-unmixing, data-processing algorithms to spectrally resolve multiple fluorophores
- Test the effects of environmental conditions, such as ozone and antifade reagents, on dye stability

Each PARAGON™ microarray scanner calibration slide is provided in a slide case that is sealed in a moisture- and light-proof foil pouch.

PARAGON™ Dye Ratio Calibration Slide

The PARAGON™ dye ratio calibration slide (P32944) provides a method for qualitatively judging expression levels in two-color microarray experiments, establishing a baseline normalization factor for the fluorescent signals produced by the differentially labeled targets, assaying emission bleedthrough between fluorescent dyes and evaluating drift in the performance of a microarray scanner.

Most experiments with microarrays involve investigating differential expression of treated and untreated sample genes. The array printed on the PARAGON™ dye ratio calibration slide comprises a twofold dilution series of known ratios of differentially labeled male human genomic DNA. These ratios are independent of the DNA mass printed; the ratios are based on the calculated total numbers of Alexa Fluor® 555 or Alexa Fluor® 647 fluorescent dyes covalently attached to the genomic DNA. The array includes dilution series representing DNA labeled solely with either the Alexa Fluor® 555 dye or the Alexa Fluor® 647 dye, allowing the researcher to look at channel bleedthrough and false contribution of fluorescence.

Stored properly, this slide can be used for microarray analysis as many as thirty times for up to six months; signal loss under these conditions has been observed to be 0.9% for the Alexa Fluor® 555 dye and 1.3% for the Alexa Fluor® 647 dye. Total dye numbers from 97,656 to 100,000,000 are represented by the printed labeled DNA in an average spot size of 160 µm, or approximately 4–40,000 dyes/µm^2. Rows and columns use a 500 µm spacing arrangement; the layout of the PARAGON™ dye ratio calibration slide is shown in Figure 8.107.

Other Nucleic Acid Stains for Standardizing Microarrays

The simplest technique for comparing the amounts of DNA spotted onto arrays is to use a fluorescent nucleic acid stain (see Note 8.4 "Product Highlight: Procedure for Staining Microarrays with SYBR® Green II Dye"). Molecular Probes' proprietary nucleic acid stains exhibit a strong fluorescence signal when bound to nucleic acids, providing an easy and effective method for measuring the amount of nucleic acids on solid supports (Figure 8.102). Several nucleic acid stains that have been used effectively for microarrays are listed in Table 8.19. Other dyes in these families (Section 8.1) should also

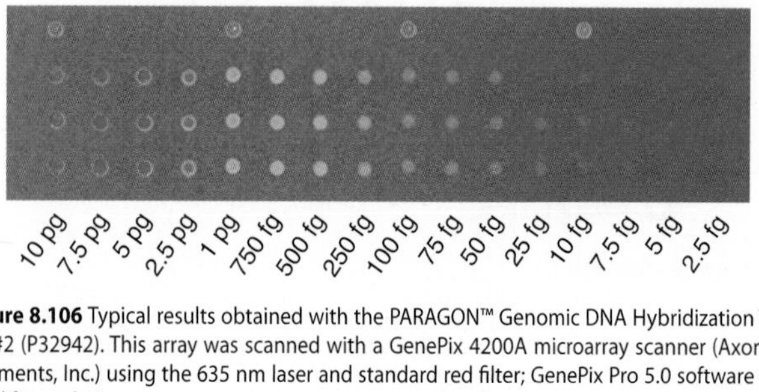

Figure 8.106 Typical results obtained with the PARAGON™ Genomic DNA Hybridization Test Kit #2 (P32942). This array was scanned with a GenePix 4200A microarray scanner (Axon Instruments, Inc.) using the 635 nm laser and standard red filter; GenePix Pro 5.0 software was used for analysis.

Note 8.4 — Product Highlight

Procedure for Staining Microarrays with SYBR® Green II Dye

Procedure for staining microarrays with nucleic acid stains. SYBR® Green II RNA gel stain (S7564, S7568, S7586) provides a quick and easy test to determine whether DNA has been uniformly spotted onto a microarray.[1]

- Dilute the SYBR® Green II stain 10,000-fold in TBE buffer (45 mM Tris-borate, 1 mM EDTA, pH 8.0).
- Cover the microarray with the diluted stain and incubate at room temperature for 2–3 minutes.
- Wash the microarray 3–4 times with TBE buffer.
- Spin-dry the microarray for 1–2 minutes.
- Scan the microarray using filter sets appropriate for the Alexa Fluor® 488 dye or fluorescein (FITC). SYBR® Green II dye has a fluorescence excitation maximum at 494 nm and a fluorescence emission maximum at 521 nm.

Excess stain can be removed from the slide by a 1-hour incubation at room temperature with a solution of 1% SDS, 10 mM Tris, 1 mM EDTA, pH 7.5. After drying the slides, they can be used in hybridization experiments.

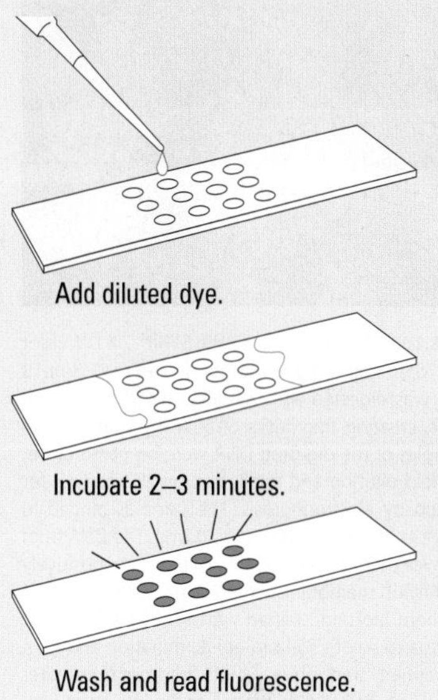

Reference

1. Biotechniques 29, 78 (2000).

prove useful in this application. When staining nucleic acids on solid supports with nucleic acid stains, it is important to choose a dye that matches the light sources and filter sets available in the image analysis system or the array reader. For example, the POPO™-3 dye has a maximum fluorescence excitation at 534 nm and a maximum fluorescence emission at 570 nm, which reasonably match the filter sets for the Alexa Fluor® 546 dye, Alexa Fluor® 555 dye or Cy3 dyes. In one case in which POPO™-3 staining was used to determine the number of spots on the microarray that contained PCR products, 1281 spots of 9216 spots did not display a significant POPO™-3 signal due to poor growth of the bacterial clones, failure of the PCR amplification or improper printing of the spots due to irregularities on the array.[130] When testing dyes to use for normalization of signals, it is important to carefully test several dilutions of the dye to determine the one that gives the best linear response over the range of DNA in the spot. It is also important to determine any effects of the dye on subsequent hybridization.

SYBR® DX DNA Blot Stain

In addition to providing a means of normalizing hybridization signals, staining denatured DNA or RNA directly on filter membranes after blotting protocols provides for more accurate comparison of the sample to molecular weight markers and eliminates guesswork about transfer efficiency. However, direct staining on blotting membranes has not been widely used because the most common methods for detecting denatured DNA or RNA — ethidium bromide[131] or methylene blue staining — give rise to high background fluorescence. Silver staining or gold staining followed by silver enhancement provides 10- to 100-fold better sensitivity than ethidium bromide but is expensive, time-consuming and tedious. Also, because of the affinity of gold for suitable for use with gold staining; higher amounts of sulfate invariably result in unacceptably high background signals.

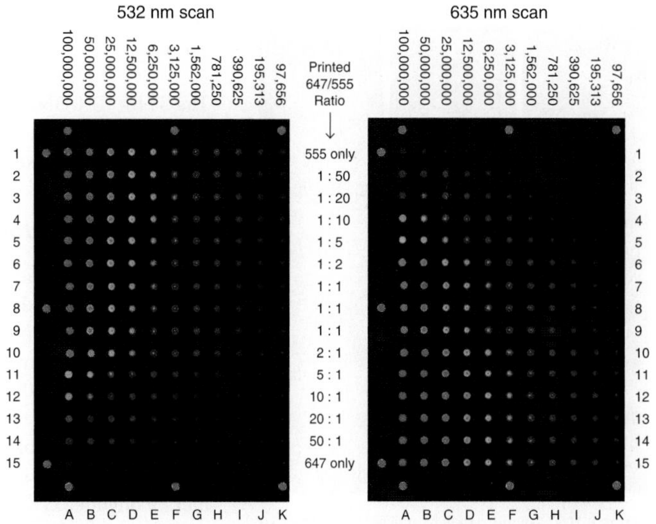

Figure 8.107 Typical results obtained with the PARAGON™ dye ratio calibration slide (P32944). This array was scanned with a GenePix 4200A microarray scanner (Axon Instruments, Inc.) using the 532 nm laser and the 635 nm laser and standard green and red filters; GenePix Pro 5.0 software was used for analysis.

Table 8.19 — Nucleic acid stains used for microarray quality control

Nucleic Acid Stain	Ex/Em *	Cat #
SYBR® Green II stain	492/513	S7564, S7568, S7586
SYBR® 555 dye	531/544	P32930
POPO™-3 dye	534/570	P3584
SYTO® 59 dye	622/645	S11341
SYTO® 61 dye	628/645	S11343

* Approximate excitation (Ex) and emission (Em) maxima, in nm.

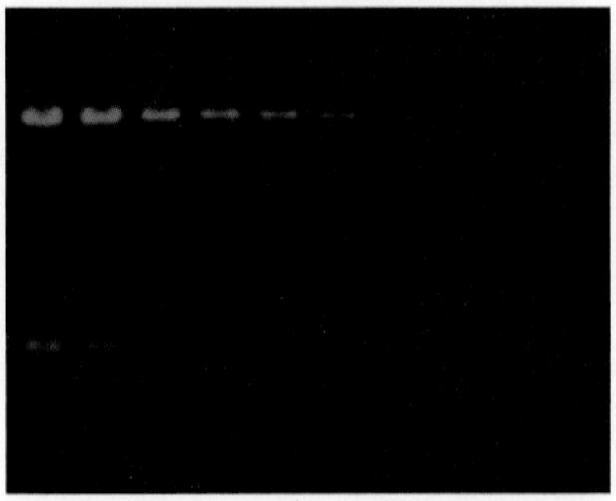

Figure 8.108 DNA stained with the SYBR® DX DNA blot stain (S7550) following Southern transfer. M13mp19 RF DNA was digested with *Hin*dIII and *Bgl*II restriction enzymes, creating fragments of 6548 bp and 701 bp. Ten samples of the digested DNA were prepared by serial twofold dilution and applied to an agarose gel for separation by electrophoresis. The samples ranged in total DNA content from 100 ng to 0.2 ng. The DNA from the gel was then transferred to a Hybond-N+ positively charged nylon membrane (Amersham Life Science, Inc.) by Southern blotting, stained with SYBR® DX DNA blot stain, visualized with 254 nm epi-illumination and then photographed through a SYBR® photographic filter (S7569) using Polaroid 667 black-and-white print film. Not all of the bands visible in the original photograph are visible in this reproduction.

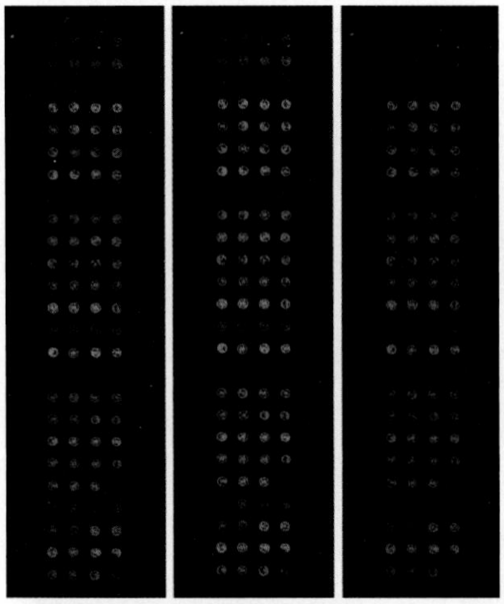

Figure 8.109 DNA microarray hybridized to Panomer™ 9 random oligodeoxynucleotides. A DNA microarray slide was hybridized sequentially with one of three different Panomer™ 9 random oligodeoxynucleotides at room temperature for two minutes. After each hybridization, the slide was washed first in 2X SSC and 0.2% SDS and then in 1X SSC. After drying, the slide was imaged on a ScanArray 5000XL microarray reader (Packard BioScience), using appropriate lasers and filter sets. After imaging, the Panomer™ 9 oligodeoxynucleotide was stripped from the microarray by incubation in deionized water for one minute at room temperature and the microarray was hybridized to another Panomer™ 9 oligodeoxynucleotide. From left to right, the images show the array hybridized to Panomer™ 9 oligodeoxynucleotides labeled with the Alexa Fluor® 488 dye (P21680), Alexa Fluor® 546 dye (P21681) and Alexa Fluor® 647 dye (P21686). Each image has been pseudocolored to indicate the different dyes. The hybridization results reveal the variable amounts of DNA spotted onto this microarray.

By contrast, our patented SYBR® DX DNA blot stain (S7550) provides a rapid and easy method for fluorescent staining of denatured DNA and RNA on blotting membranes, with sensitivity superior to that of any other nucleic acid stain we have tested. Direct staining of immobilized nucleic acids following blotting gives an indication of the efficiency of transfer from the gel to the membrane; thus, there is no need to re-examine the gel for residual DNA. After transfer, DNA is fixed to the membrane by UV crosslinking or baking in a vacuum oven, in the usual fashion. The fixed blot is then incubated with the diluted SYBR® DX stain for as little as 10 minutes and photographed. Unlike silver-enhanced gold labeling, no blocking steps are required. We have found that it is possible to detect 200 pg/band of denatured M13 RF DNA following Southern transfer to a nylon membrane using the SYBR® DX DNA blot stain with 254 nm epi-illumination, a SYBR® gel stain photographic filter (S7569) and Polaroid 667 black-and-white print film (Figure 8.108). The sensitivity is reduced somewhat when using 300 nm transillumination due to light scattering through the nylon membrane. However, in both cases, the sensitivity is at least 10-fold better than that obtained with ethidium bromide in parallel experiments. Blot staining with the SYBR® DX dye can also be analyzed with commercially available CCD documentation systems and laser scanners equipped with appropriate filters.

Both neutral and positively charged nylon membranes can be used with the SYBR® DX DNA blot stain, and staining is fully compatible with subsequent hybridization and colorimetric detection of alkaline phosphatase–coupled probes using the chromogenic enzyme substrates nitro blue tetrazolium (NBT) and 5-bromo-4-chloro-3-indolyl phosphate (BCIP) (N6495, B6492, N6547; Section 10.3). Blots that have been hybridized and detected by radioactive, chemiluminescent or colorimetric reagents can also be stained with the SYBR® DX dye, provided that the membrane is not blocked with ssDNA.

The SYBR® DX DNA blot stain has been employed to measure trace amounts of contaminant DNA in drinking water.[132] In a broad-spectrum assay for bacterial contamination, samples were simply spotted or vacuum-blotted onto nylon membranes and stained with the SYBR® DX dye. Detection of DNA was quantitative down to about 50 ng when a fluorescence microplate reader was used.

The SYBR® DX DNA blot stain (S7550) is provided as a 1000-fold concentrate in dimethylacetamide (DMA). This amount of dye is sufficient for staining about 50–100 blots, and the staining solution can be reused at least three times with little loss of staining intensity.

Panomer™ Random-Sequence Oligonucleotides

Fluorescently labeled random-sequence oligonucleotides — such as the Panomer™ 9 random oligodeoxynucleotides (Table 8.18) — provide an alternative method for assessing the level of nucleic acids immobilized on solid supports. This method assays the capability of spotted DNA to hybridize, making it possible to determine if hybridization efficiency varies across the array[133] (Figure 8.109). These nine-base, random-sequence Panomer™ oligodeoxynucleotides are covalently labeled on the 5′-end with a fluorescent dye. The variety of available fluorescent dyes makes it possible to use any fluorescence channel of interest and to compare relative signal intensities per spot in several different channels (Figure 8.110). It is also possible to use Panomer™ 9 oligodeoxynucleotides for quality control of spotting techniques or to assay the stability of DNA spots after the array is subjected to washing, boiling, hybridization or other conditions (Figure 8.109).

Sample Quantitation

Measuring the amount of nucleic acid in the sample helps to ensure success and consistency in microarray printing or sample labeling. The Quant-iT™ DNA and RNA Assay Kits (Q33120, Q33130, Q33140; Section 8.3), PicoGreen® dsDNA Quantitation Kit and reagent (P7581, P7589, P11495, P11496; Section 8.3) and RiboGreen® RNA Quantitation Kit and reagent (R11490, R11491; Section 8.3) make it easy to quantitate large numbers of samples of dsDNA or RNA. These one-step procedures for quantitating nucleic acids are both sensitive and easily adaptable to high-throughput automation. The assays are orders of magnitude more sensitive than UV absorbance (A_{260}) measurements, so only minimal amounts of sample are required. Furthermore, in contrast to UV absorbance measurements, where proteins and free ribonucleotides in the mixture interfere with accurate quantitation, the Quant-iT™, PicoGreen® and RiboGreen® reagents measure only polymeric nucleic acids. These assays can be used to quantitate yields from PCR amplification, RNA purification or cDNA synthesis reactions.

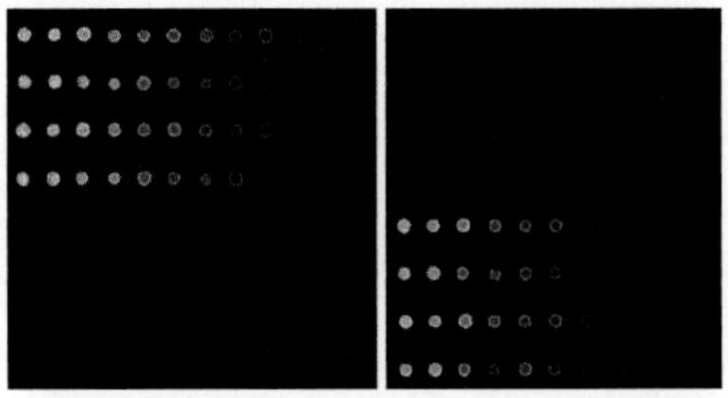

Figure 8.110 Microarray spotted with the Alexa Fluor® 546 (P21681) and Alexa Fluor® 647 (P21686) Panomer™ 9 random oligodeoxyribonucleotides. Equal amounts of two Panomer™ 9 random oligodeoxyribonucleotides were spotted directly onto microscope slides and the fluorescence documented using two different channels of a ScanArray 5000XL microarray reader (Packard BioScience). The Alexa Fluor® 546 Panomer™ 9 random oligodeoxyribonucleotide signal was completely separated from the Alexa Fluor® 647 Panomer™ 9 random oligodeoxyribonucleotide signal.

Hybridization Chambers for Microarrays

Uniform distribution of the labeled sample is essential for efficient and even hybridization across the array. Precut, ready-to-use adhesive gaskets help to optimize fluid dynamics in the hybridization reaction. The 22 mm × 22 mm Secure-Seal hybridization chambers (Figure 8.111) are ideal for microarray-based hybridization experiments. When the chambers are partially filled and placed on a rocker, they provide a surface-to-volume ratio that facilitates uniform hybridization. They adhere directly to glass slides, creating a watertight seal that is temperature resistant, but can also be removed cleanly and easily after the hybridization. The hydrophobic surfaces are RNase free and will not trap or bind probes like glass surfaces can. Access ports in the chamber surface permit the addition or removal of solutions and are easily sealed using adhesive seal-tabs (A18211) to create leak-proof chambers that eliminate evaporation. For very small volume samples, the lower-volume HybriWell Sealing Systems can be used (Table 8.17, Figure 8.95). As an alternative, we also provide HybriSlip hybridization covers, which are hydrophobic plastic coverslips that do not bind to labeled nucleic acids (Table 8.17, Figure 8.112). The covers remain flat, even at high temperatures, to facilitate uniform reagent distribution.

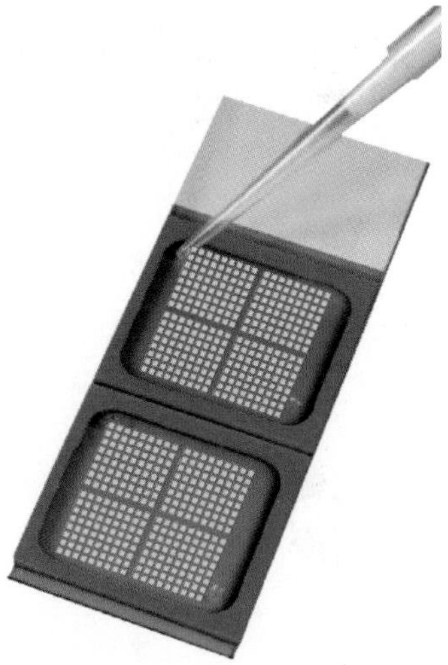

Figure 8.111 Secure-Seal gasket for use with microarray hybridizations.

Solution-Based Hybridization Assays

Assays based on measurement of a specific hybridization product formed in solution become very powerful if the hybridization product can be measured directly in the reaction tube, without any separation steps. Fluorescence technology using dyes selective for dsDNA or using fluorescence resonance energy transfer (FRET) methods (see Note 1.2 "Technical Focus: Fluorescence Resonance Energy Transfer (FRET)" in Section 1.3) make it possible to perform such homogeneous assays with very high sensitivity and very high throughput, making them valuable screening tools. This type of methodology is particularly useful for real-time PCR assays but can be used in other solution-based hybridization assays as well.

Real-Time Quantitative PCR Using FRET and Quenching Techniques

PCR products can be quantitated during the linear portion of the amplification reactions, allowing accurate quantitation of templates. Several fluorescence-based methods exist for real-time quantitation of PCR products, including assays based on fluorescent nucleic acid stains and FRET techniques that use fluorescently labeled primers or molecular beacons. In addition to providing a more streamlined assay, single-tube methods minimize the possibility for cross-contamination between PCR reactions.

Figure 8.112 HybriSlip covers for hybridization.

Fluorescence resonance energy transfer (FRET) refers to a process by which energy is transferred from one dye molecule (the donor) to another (the acceptor) without the emission of a photon (see Note 1.2 "Technical Focus: Fluorescence Resonance Energy Transfer (FRET)" in Section 1.3). If the acceptor dye is a fluorophore, the energy may be emitted as fluorescence that is characteristic of the acceptor dye; otherwise, the energy is dissipated and the fluorescence quenched. FRET technology has been used in several ways to develop homogeneous and real-time hybridization assays.

A molecular beacon [121] is made up of an oligonucleotide with a fluorescent dye attached to one end and a quencher (nonfluorescent acceptor dye, such as our QSY® 7 or QSY® 9 dye) attached to the other. The sequence is designed so that the oligonucleotide forms a hairpin loop, which

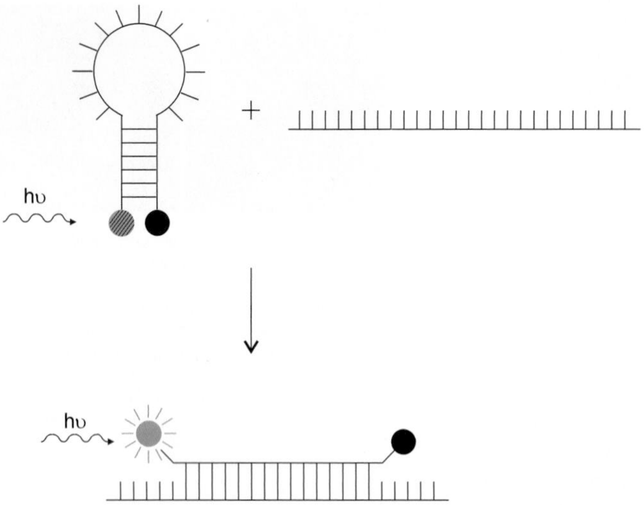

Figure 8.113 Schematic representation of molecular beacons. In the hairpin loop structure, the quencher (black circle) forms a nonfluorescent complex with the fluorophore (green circle). Upon hybridization of the molecular beacon to a complementary sequence, the fluorophore and quencher are separated, restoring the fluorescence.

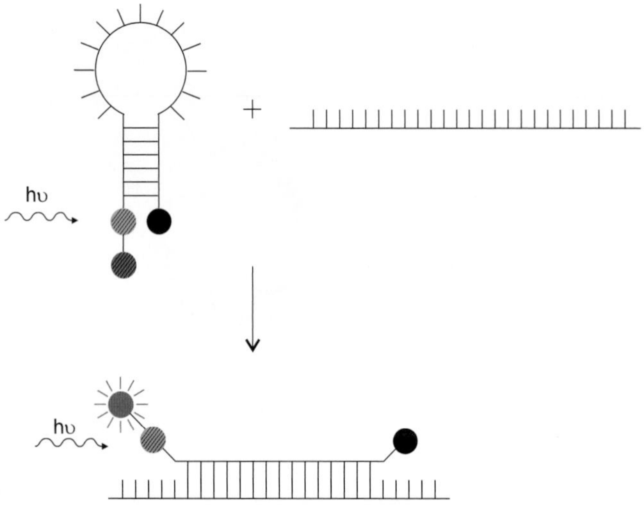

Figure 8.114 Schematic representation of wavelength-shifting molecular beacons. The molecular beacon has two fluorophores on one end — a "harvester" (green circle) and an "emitter" (red circle) — and a quencher on the other end (black circle). In the hairpin loop structure, the quencher forms a nonfluorescent complex with the harvester. Upon hybridization of the molecular beacon to a complementary sequence, quenching of the harvester fluorophore is relieved, and it transfers energy (via FRET) to the emitter, which emits fluorescence.

brings the fluorescent dye and quencher together [134] (Figure 8.113). In this configuration, the fluorescence is nearly completely quenched. The loop portion of the hairpin is complementary to the sequence of interest in the assay. Upon hybridization to the sequence, the hairpin unfolds, separating the fluorescent dye from the quencher (Figure 8.113). Thus, a fluorescent signal indicates hybridization of the molecular beacon to the sequence of interest.

Molecular beacons can be constructed by using an oligonucleotide modified with an amine group on one end and a thiol group on the other end. Amine-reactive (Chapter 1) and thiol-reactive (Chapter 2) dyes can be covalently bound to the amine and thiol modifications, respectively. Dabcyl (D2245, Section 1.8) is a very efficient quencher, reducing the fluorescence emission of most fluorophores by over 99%,[135] making it possible to detect as few as 10 complementary sequences out of 100,000 available molecules.[136] Dabcyl has been reported to act as a universal quencher, dissipating the fluorescence emission of any fluorophore, regardless of its fluorescence emission profile.[135] In addition, the quenching efficiencies are much higher than usually reported for FRET. Because this pattern does not follow the rules of classical FRET, it has been suggested that the quenching by the dabcyl dye occurs by another mechanism, possibly by the formation of a nonfluorescent complex comprising both dyes.[135] The QSY® 7, QSY® 9, QSY® 22 and QSY® 35 quenchers (Section 1.6, Section 1.8, Section 2.2, Section 3.3) have much stronger absorbance than the dabcyl quencher at visible wavelengths (Figure 1.70) and they efficiently quench a broad assortment of fluorescent donors, including fluoresceins, the Oregon Green® 488 and Oregon Green® 514 dyes, the Alexa Fluor® 488 and Alexa Fluor® 532 dyes and other similar fluorophores (Table 1.10). FRET efficiencies from several donor dyes to the QSY® 7 quencher in molecular beacon hybridization probes have been calculated.[137]

NANOGOLD 1.4 nm gold clusters can be attached to appropriately derivatized oligonucleotides by using NANOGOLD mono-(sulfosuccinimidyl ester) (N20130, Section 1.6, Figure 1.90) or NANOGOLD monomaleimide (N20345, Section 2.2, Figure 2.22). These probes have been shown to be particularly efficient quenchers in molecular beacon applications, with reported sensitivity enhancements up to 100-fold over the dabcyl-labeled quencher and eightfold greater sensitivity in detection of single-base mismatches.[138]

Molecular beacons can be used in either end-point or real-time PCR to detect the synthesis of a specific amplicon. Because the fluorescence signal is based on hybridization to a complementary sequence, molecular beacons provide much greater specificity than gel-based analysis. Depending on the design, a molecular beacon is capable of distinguishing differences of a single base pair,[135,139] short tandem repeat markers [140] or specific single-nucleotide polymorphisms in a complex sample.[141] Furthermore, the difference in stability between the stem–loop structure and the structure of the oligonucleotide bound to the target ensures that the molecular beacons bind their targets more specifically than do conventional FRET probes.[142] Multiple molecular beacons, bearing different fluorophores, can be used simultaneously in the same PCR reaction for multiplexed analysis.[136,140,143–145]

The use of "wavelength-shifting" molecular beacons [121] makes multiplexed analysis even more versatile. In this design, there are two fluorophores on one end — a "harvester" that can transfer energy to the "emitter" at the same end via FRET and a quencher at the other end of the probe [146] (Figure 8.114). In the hairpin formation, the "harvester" is quenched; upon hybridization to the target, the "harvester" transfers energy to the "emitter." By using different FRET pairs with the same "harvester" fluorophore and varying "emitter" fluorophores, one can design multiple molecular beacons that have different fluorescence emissions when excited by the same wavelength.

Molecular beacon–based PCR assays have been used for many applications, including to:

- Distinguish CC chemokine receptor genotypes [143,147]
- Detect and quantitate the levels of multiple viruses in clinical samples [136]
- Detect specific alleles of *c-Ki-Ras* in stool samples [141]
- Identify human papillomavirus (HPV) particles in tissue specimens [148]
- Identify drug-resistant variants of *Mycobacterium tuberculosis* [149,150]
- Discriminate between different species of *Candida* [151]
- Identify different bacterial species in environmental or food samples [152,153]

Reverse transcription followed by real-time PCR with molecular beacons can be used to measure RNA transcript levels.[154,155] Molecular beacons have also been used for real-time monitoring of RNA amplification reactions using an RNA polymerase.[156] Our SYBR® Green I nucleic acid stain has also been extensively used to follow real-time PCR (Section 8.3).

The TaqMan assay [121] uses FRET to monitor PCR reactions in real time.[157] A non-extendable oligonucleotide probe (the detection probe) complementary to the sequence of interest is labeled with a donor fluorophore at one end and an acceptor fluorophore at the other (Figure 8.115). FRET between the two fluorophores results in quenching of the donor's fluorescence. During the hybridization steps, this quenched probe, along with flanking PCR primers, hybridizes to the sequence of interest. When *Taq* polymerase encounters the detection probe during the extension steps, it uses its 5′-endonuclease activity to cleave it, separating the fluorophores and relieving the quenching of the donor. Real-time measurement of donor fluorescence allows accurate quantitation of the amplicon. Multiplex measurements of as many as seven colors have been achieved through the use of multiple detection probes.[158,159] The TaqMan assay can provide similar discrimination to molecular beacon–based assays, with each assay exhibiting superior characteristics in particular situations.[160] The TaqMan assay has been used for SNP detection [159] and quantitation of enterovirus RNA in urban sludge samples,[161] and it has been adapted for quantitative detection of nucleic acid methylation [162] and for detection of reverse transcriptase activity.[163]

In a modification to the molecular beacon design, Scorpions [121] primers incorporate the hairpin directly into the primer.[164,165] The hairpin loop is complementary to the amplicon and performs a "flip" as it releases from the hairpin to hybridize to the newly formed amplicon (Figure 8.116). The faster kinetics of this intramolecular hybridization, as compared with the bimolecular reaction with molecular beacons, allow identification of the amplicon using fewer cycle numbers.

UniPrimer [121] technology (also called Sunrise or Amplifluor) also uses a hairpin quencher design, but one that can be used to detect any sequence of interest amplified in a PCR reaction.[166] In the PCR

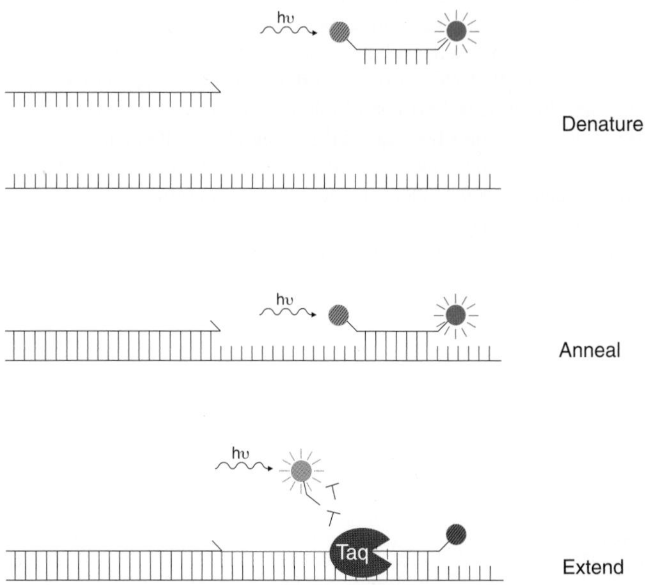

Figure 8.115 Schematic representation of real-time PCR with TaqMan primers. In the intact TaqMan probe, energy is transferred (via FRET) from the short-wavelength fluorophore on one end (green circle) to the long-wavelength fluorophore on the other end (red circle), quenching the short-wavelength fluorescence. After hybridization, the probe is susceptible to degradation by the endonuclease activity of a processing *Taq* polymerase. Upon degradation, FRET is interrupted, increasing the fluorescence from the short-wavelength fluorophore and decreasing the fluorescence from the long-wavelength fluorophore.

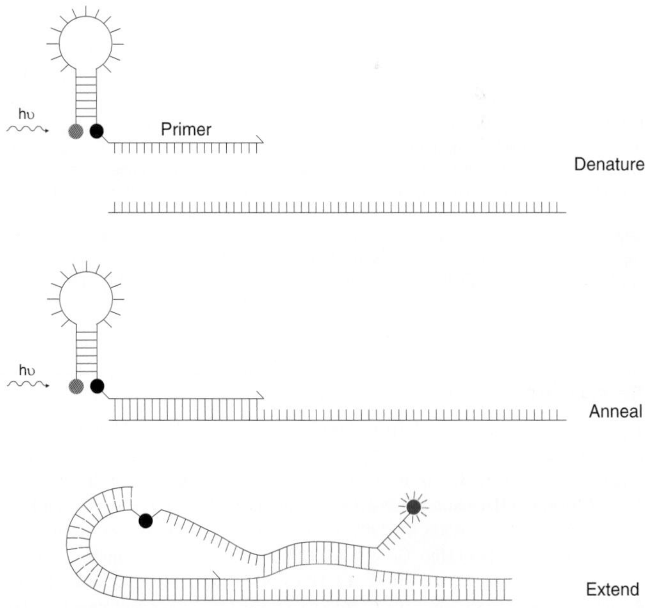

Figure 8.116 Schematic representation of real-time PCR with Scorpions primers. In the hairpin loop structure, the quencher (black circle) forms a nonfluorescent complex with the fluorophore (green circle). Upon extension of the amplicon, the Scorpions probe hybridizes to the newly formed complementary sequence, separating the fluorophore from the quencher and restoring the fluorescence.

reaction, one of the primers is designed with a 5′-tail identical to a 3′-tail on the "universal" labeled hairpin primer (Figure 8.117). After the second cycle, the tail on the PCR primer and its complement are both part of the amplicon sequence. Thus, in the third cycle, the universal primer can hybridize to the amplicon to start DNA synthesis. By the fourth cycle, synthesis in the opposite direction extends through the universal primer, unfolding the hairpin and relieving the quenching. The advantage of this design is that it can be used to detect any desired sequence. UniPrimer technology has been used for SNP genotyping,[167] identification of point mutations,[168] detection of prostate-specific antigen cDNA,[166] a closed-tube telomeric repeat amplification protocol (TRAP) [169] and *in situ* PCR and RT-PCR.[50]

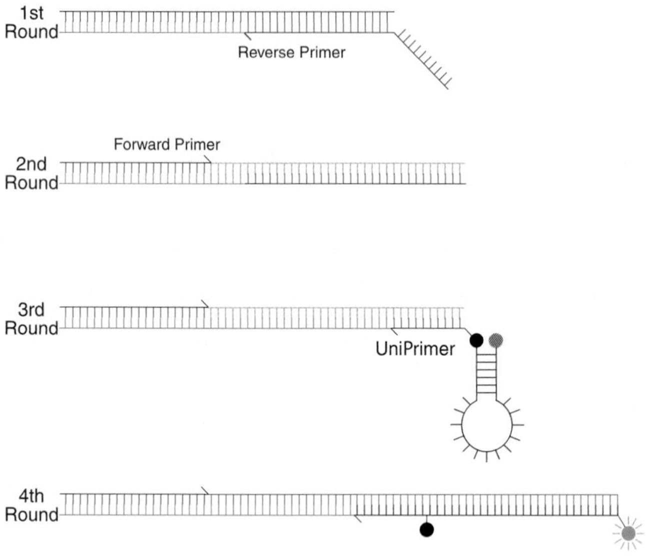

Figure 8.117 Schematic representation of real-time PCR with UniPrimer technology. In the first round of amplification, the reverse primer, containing a special sequence tag, primes synthesis along the template. In the second round, the forward primer primes synthesis that extends through the special sequence tag, forming a complementary sequence to the tag. In the third round, the UniPrimer hybridizes to this complementary sequence via the special sequence tag. The hairpin structure of the UniPrimer ensures that the quencher (black circle) suppresses the fluorescence of the fluorophore (green circle). Finally, in the fourth round, synthesis extends through the hairpin loop, relieving the quenching of the fluorophore.

Other Solution-Based Hybridization Assays Using FRET and Quenching Techniques

Specific DNA or RNA molecules have been quantitated in solution by measuring the degree of quenching observed upon hybridization with a BODIPY® FL dye–labeled oligonucleotide.[170] The oligonucleotide contained a BODIPY® FL dye–modified cytosine at its 5′-end, and its fluorescence was quenched upon binding to the complementary guanine in the target DNA. The rate of quenching was reportedly proportional to the amount of target DNA. This technique can be applied to quantitative DNA detection in solution, as well as to real-time quantitative PCR.

Single-stranded RNA molecules from a plant viral genome have been detected using FRET techniques in conjunction with a set of fluorescently labeled DNA probes that hybridize next to each other on the target RNA.[171] In this study, the BODIPY® 493/503 dye was chosen as the donor fluorophore because of its narrow excitation and emission spectra, which minimize background fluorescence. When hybridized near Cy5 dye–labeled acceptor oligonucleotides on target RNA, donor oligonucleotides that were double-labeled with the BODIPY® 493/503 dye showed an unexpected enhancement of FRET signals, as compared with single-labeled donor probes. These double-labeled donor probes also exhibited less fluorescence when not hybridized on the target RNA, probably due to self-quenching of the BODIPY® 493/503 fluorophores.

Other Solution-Based Hybridization Assays Using Fluorescent Nucleic Acid Stains

The use of melting curve analysis with the SYBR® Green I nucleic acid stain has proven to be an ideal method for characterizing amplicons in a PCR reaction, as described in Section 8.3. This method can also be used to streamline restriction-length fragment polymorphism (RFLP) analysis, where SNPs and other mutations are detected based on changes in fragment sizes produced by restriction endonucleases. Conventionally, fragment size is determined by agarose gel electrophoresis. However, because melting temperature depends on fragment length, the fragment size can also be detected by measuring the melting temperature. In this way, this simple and accurate assay can be performed in a single tube, greatly increasing throughput possibilities.[172]

References

1. J Cell Sci 116, 2833 (2003); **2.** Histochem J 27, 4 (1995); **3.** Exp Cell Res 194, 310 (1991); **4.** Nucleic Acids Res 19, 3237 (1991); **5.** J Histochem Cytochem 38, 467 (1990); **6.** Br J Haematol 107, 844 (1999); **7.** Science 247, 64 (1990); **8.** Science 305, 846 (2004); **9.** Science 273, 494 (1996); **10.** Eur J Hum Genet 7, 2 (1999); **11.** J Histochem Cytochem 41, 1755 (1993); **12.** Proc Natl Acad Sci U S A 89, 1388 (1992); **13.** Cytometry 11, 126 (1990); **14.** Cancer Genet Cytogenet 100, 111 (1998); **15.** Cancer Res 60, 2775 (2000); **16.** Cytogenet Cell Genet 87, 225 (1999); **17.** Cytogenet Cell Genet 90, 219 (2000); **18.** Nat Genet 15, 406 (1997); **19.** Hum Genet 103, 619 (1998); **20.** Histochem Cell Biol 108, 381 (1997); **21.** Science 250, 559 (1990); **22.** Trends Genet 16, 143 (2000); **23.** Genes Dev 14, 212 (2000); **24.** J Virol Methods 72, 15 (1998); **25.** J Microbiol Methods 41, 85 (2000); **26.** Mol Cell Probes 13, 261 (1999); **27.** Appl Environ Microbiol 65, 4077 (1999); **28.** Genomics 14, 769 (1992); **29.** Trends Genet 13, 475 (1997); **30.** Hum Genet 101, 255 (1997); **31.** Nat Genet 12, 368 (1996); **32.** Blood 96, 1297 (2000); **33.** Genes Chromosomes Cancer 27, 418 (2000); **34.** Cytometry 33, 445 (1998); **35.** Hum Genet 90, 590 (1993); **36.** Science 258, 818 (1992); **37.** Curr Opin Biotechnol 9, 19 (1998); **38.** Trends Genet 12, 379 (1996); **39.** Biotech Histochem 73, 6 (1998); **40.** Introduction to Fluorescence in Situ Hybridization, Pinkel D, Andreeff M, Eds. (Complete Volume), pp. 472 (1999); **41.** Biotechniques 36, 114 (2004); **42.** J Clin Microbiol 29, 583 (1991); **43.** Proc Natl Acad Sci U S A 90, 4206 (1993); **44.** Cytogenet Cell Genet 87, 47 (1999); **45.** Genes Chromosomes Cancer 25, 301 (1999); **46.** EMBO J 17, 6020 (1998); **47.** Appl Environ Microbiol 65, 1259 (1999); **48.** Science 280, 585 (1998); **49.** Proc Natl Acad Sci U S A 95, 11538 (1998); **50.** J Histochem Cytochem 47, 273 (1999); **51.** Biochemistry 30, 4821 (1991); **52.** Anal Biochem 170, 271 (1988); **53.** Nucleic Acids Res 7, 1485 (1979); **54.** Biochemistry 29, 10734 (1990); **55.** Nucleic Acids Res 16, 2203 (1988); **56.** Biochemistry 24, 692 (1985); **57.** Anal Biochem 131, 419 (1983); **58.** J Mol Biol 156, 113 (1982); **59.** Trends Genet 9, 71 (1993); **60.** Fluorescein Hapten: An Immunological Probe, Voss EW, Ed. (Complete Volume) (1984); **61.** J Immunol Methods 122, 115 (1989); **62.** G.S. Schneider, Tropix, Inc., personal communication; **63.** Nucleic Acids Res 18, 3175 (1990); **64.** Biotechniques 9, 186 (1990); **65.** J Immunol Methods 125, 279 (1989); **66.** Cytometry 23, 48 (1996); **67.** J Histochem Cytochem 45, 375 (1997); **68.** J Histochem Cytochem 47, 281 (1999); **69.** Current Protocols in Cytometry, JP Robinson, Ed. Suppl 11,

References — continued

8.9.1 (2000); **70.** Mutat Res 400, 287 (1998); **71.** J Histochem Cytochem 47, 431 (1999); **72.** Histochem Cell Biol 111, 435 (1999); **73.** Histochem Cell Biol 110, 431 (1998); **74.** J Clin Pathol 50, 322 (1997); **75.** Diagnostic Mol Pathol 7, 76 (1998); **76.** Vet Pathol 37, 47 (2000); **77.** Biotechniques 27, 608 (1999); **78.** J Histochem Cytochem 45, 1439 (1997); **79.** Eur J Histochem 43, 185 (1999); **80.** Histochem Cell Biol 113, 175 (2000); **81.** J Histochem Cytochem 46, 1249 (1998); **82.** Am J Hum Genet 55 (Suppl), A271, abstract #1585 (1994); **83.** FASEB J 8, A1444, abstract #1081 (1994); **84.** Mol Biol Cell (Suppl 4), 226a, abstract #1312 (1993); **85.** J Histochem Cytochem 45, 345 (1997); **86.** Trends Genet 12, 387 (1996); **87.** A Laboratory Guide to RNA: Isolation, Analysis, and Synthesis, Krieg PA, Ed. pp. 381–409 (1996); **88.** Trends Genet 12, 385 (1996); **89.** Am J Hum Genet 63, A397, abstract #2305 (1998); **90.** J Histochem Cytochem 48, 1593 (2000); **91.** Science 277, 393 (1997); **92.** Nat Genet 21, 20 (1999); **93.** Genome Res 6, 639 (1996); **94.** Microarray Biochip Technology, Schena M, Ed. pp. 149–166 (2000); **95.** Nat Genet 21, 10 (1999); **96.** Science 270, 467 (1995); **97.** Proc Natl Acad Sci U S A 93, 10614 (1996); **98.** Nat Genet 21, 25 (1999); **99.** Nat Genet 14, 457 (1996); **100.** Cancer Res 58, 5009 (1998); **101.** Electrophoresis 20, 223 (1999); **102.** Proc Natl Acad Sci U S A 97, 2680 (2000); **103.** Genes Dev 14, 963 (2000); **104.** Dev Genet 23, 215 (1998); **105.** Mol Biol Cell 9, 3273 (1998); **106.** Science 286, 2179 (1999); **107.** Proc Natl Acad Sci U S A 96, 12833 (1999); **108.** Mol Microbiol 39, 26 (2001); **109.** Nat Genet 21, 48 (1999); **110.** Curr Opin Biotechnol 9, 643 (1998); **111.** Mol Carcinog 24, 153 (1999); **112.** Science 274, 610 (1996); **113.** Nat Genet 21, 42 (1999); **114.** Nucleic Acids Res 29, E25 (2001); **115.** Nat Genet 23, 41 (1999); **116.** Mol Psychiatry 3, 483 (1998); **117.** Nat Genet 18, 225 (1998); **118.** J Bacteriol 183, 7027 (2001); **119.** Anal Biochem 331, 243 (2004); **120.** Biotechniques 30, 202 (2001); **121.** Molecular Probes' proprietary materials and methods have been found useful in the practice of a variety of patents. Although we indicate the usefulness of our materials and methods for the practice of third party technology, we emphasize that purchase of our products does not include a license to practice any third party patent, unless a license under such a patent is clearly indicated in our product literature; **122.** Anal Biochem 283, 56 (2000); **123.** Chem Eur J 6, 1107 (2000); **124.** Biotechniques 30, 368 (2001); **125.** J Theor Biol 187, 273 (1997); **126.** Physiol Genomics 3, 93 (2000); **127.** Biotechniques 33, 924 (2002); **128.** BMC Genomics 5, 13 (2004); **129.** Toxicology 178, 135 (2002); **130.** Nucleic Acids Res 30, e116 (2002); **131.** J Neurosci Methods 42, 211 (1992); **132.** J Environ Health 60, 14 (1997); **133.** Nucleic Acids Res 31, e18 (2003); **134.** Nat Biotechnol 14, 303 (1996); **135.** Nat Biotechnol 16, 49 (1998); **136.** Proc Natl Acad Sci U S A 96, 6394 (1999); **137.** Nucleic Acids Res 30, e122 (2002); **138.** Nat Biotechnol 19, 365 (2001); **139.** Clin Chem 44, 482 (1998); **140.** Biotechniques 29, 1296 (2000); **141.** Proc Natl Acad Sci U S A 96, 9236 (1999); **142.** Proc Natl Acad Sci U S A 96, 6171 (1999); **143.** Proc Natl Acad Sci U S A 96, 12004 (1999); **144.** Genet Anal 14, 151 (1999); **145.** Science 279, 1228 (1998); **146.** Nat Biotechnol 18, 1191 (2000); **147.** AIDS 14, 483 (2000); **148.** J Virol Methods 89, 29 (2000); **149.** Antimicrob Agents Chemother 44, 103 (2000); **150.** Nat Biotechnol 16, 359 (1998); **151.** J Clin Microbiol 38, 2829 (2000); **152.** Appl Environ Microbiol 63, 1143 (1997); **153.** J Food Prot 63, 855 (2000); **154.** Cancer Res 60, 1711 (2000); **155.** Cytokine 11, 1031 (1999); **156.** Nucleic Acids Res 26, 2150 (1998); **157.** Genome Res 6, 986 (1996); **158.** Biotechniques 27, 1116 (1999); **159.** Biotechniques 27, 342 (1999); **160.** Biotechniques 28, 732 (2000); **161.** Biotechniques 29, 88 (2000); **162.** Nucleic Acids Res 28, E32 (2000); **163.** Biotechniques 25, 972 (1998); **164.** Nat Biotechnol 17, 804 (1999); **165.** Nucleic Acids Res 28, 3752 (2000); **166.** Nucleic Acids Res 25, 2516 (1997); **167.** Genome Res 11, 163 (2001); **168.** Mol Diagn 3, 217 (1998); **169.** Biotechniques 26, 552 (1999); **170.** Nucleic Acids Res 29, E34 (2001); **171.** Nucleic Acids Res 28, E107 (2000); **172.** Biotechniques 30, 358 (2001).

Product List — 8.5 Detecting Nucleic Acid Hybridization

Cat #	Product Name	Unit Size
A18211	Adhesive seal-tab, for HybriWell™ hybridization sealing system *set of 400*	1 set
A32760	aha-dUTP (5-aminohexylacrylamido-dUTP) *2 mM in TE buffer*	500 µL
A32761	aha-dUTP (5-aminohexylacrylamido-dUTP) *50 mM in TE buffer*	50 µL
A32762	Alexa Fluor® 555-aha-dUTP *1 mM in TE buffer*	50 µL
A32763	Alexa Fluor® 647-aha-dUTP *1 mM in TE buffer*	50 µL
A32756	Alexa Fluor® 555 reactive dye decapack *for microarrays* *set of 10 vials*	1 set
A32751	Alexa Fluor® 594 reactive dye decapack *for microarrays* *set of 10 vials*	1 set
A32757	Alexa Fluor® 647 reactive dye decapack *for microarrays* *set of 10 vials*	1 set
A32755	Alexa Fluor® 555 and Alexa Fluor® 647 reactive dye decapacks *for microarrays* *set of 2 x 10 vials* *includes A32756 and A32757 decapacks*	1 set
A21664	aminoallyl dUTP (5-(3-aminoallyl)-2′-deoxyuridine 5′-triphosphate, trisodium salt) *2 mM in TE buffer*	500 µL
A32764	aminoallyl dUTP (5-(3-aminoallyl)-2′-deoxyuridine 5′-triphosphate, trisodium salt) *50 mM in TE buffer*	50 µL
A21663	aminoallyl UTP (5-(3-aminoallyl)uridine 5′-triphosphate, trisodium salt) *2 mM in TE buffer*	500 µL
A32765	aminoallyl UTP (5-(3-aminoallyl)uridine 5′-triphosphate, trisodium salt) *50 mM in TE buffer*	50 µL
B32766	biotin-aha-dUTP *1 mM in TE buffer*	25 µL
B21901	BOLD™ APB chemiluminescent substrate *for membrane-based alkaline phosphatase detection* *25 minigel blots*	25 mL
E6604	ELF® 97 mRNA *In Situ* Hybridization Kit #1 *50 assays*	1 kit
E6605	ELF® 97 mRNA *In Situ* Hybridization Kit #2 *with streptavidin, alkaline phosphatase conjugate* *50 assays*	1 kit
F32767	fluorescein-aha-dUTP *1 mM in TE buffer*	25 µL
H18200	HybriSlip™ hybridization cover, 22 mm x 22 mm *RNase free* *set of 500*	1 set
H18201	HybriSlip™ hybridization cover, 40 mm x 22 mm *RNase free* *set of 500*	1 set
H18202	HybriSlip™ hybridization cover, 60 mm x 22 mm *RNase free* *set of 500*	1 set
H24720	HybriWell™ hybridization sealing system, 13 mm diameter chamber, 0.25 mm deep *set of 100*	1 set
H24721	HybriWell™ hybridization sealing system, 20 mm diameter chamber, 0.15 mm deep *set of 100*	1 set
H24723	HybriWell™ hybridization sealing system, 22 mm x 22 mm chamber, 0.15 mm deep *set of 100*	1 set
H18210	HybriWell™ hybridization sealing system, 40 mm x 21 mm chamber, 0.15 mm deep *set of 100*	1 set
H24722	HybriWell™ hybridization sealing system, 40 mm x 22 mm chamber, 0.25 mm deep *set of 100*	1 set
L8455	luminol (3-aminophthalhydrazide)	25 g
P21679	Panomer™ 9 random oligodeoxynucleotide, Alexa Fluor® 350 conjugate	10 nmol
P21680	Panomer™ 9 random oligodeoxynucleotide, Alexa Fluor® 488 conjugate	10 nmol

For current prices or to order online, visit probes.invitrogen.com

Product List — 8.5 Detecting Nucleic Acid Hybridization — continued

Cat #	Product Name	Unit Size
P32925	Panomer™ 9 random oligodeoxynucleotide, Alexa Fluor® 532 conjugate	10 nmol
P21681	Panomer™ 9 random oligodeoxynucleotide, Alexa Fluor® 546 conjugate	10 nmol
P21687	Panomer™ 9 random oligodeoxynucleotide, Alexa Fluor® 555 conjugate	10 nmol
P21682	Panomer™ 9 random oligodeoxynucleotide, Alexa Fluor® 594 conjugate	10 nmol
P21683	Panomer™ 9 random oligodeoxynucleotide, Alexa Fluor® 633 conjugate	10 nmol
P21686	Panomer™ 9 random oligodeoxynucleotide, Alexa Fluor® 647 conjugate	10 nmol
P21684	Panomer™ 9 random oligodeoxynucleotide, Alexa Fluor® 660 conjugate	10 nmol
P21685	Panomer™ 9 random oligodeoxynucleotide, Alexa Fluor® 680 conjugate	10 nmol
P21689	Panomer™ 9 random oligodeoxynucleotide, biotin-XX conjugate	10 nmol
P21678	Panomer™ 9 random oligodeoxynucleotide, Pacific Blue™ conjugate	10 nmol
P21688	Panomer™ 9 random oligodeoxynucleotide, QSY® 7 conjugate	10 nmol
P32934	PARAGON™ DNA Microarray QC Hybridization Kit #1 *with Alexa Fluor® 555 dye*	1 kit
P32937	PARAGON™ DNA Microarray QC Hybridization Kit #2 *with Alexa Fluor® 647 dye*	1 kit
P32930	PARAGON™ DNA Microarray QC Stain Kit *with SYBR® 555 stain and control slide*	1 kit
P32944	PARAGON™ dye ratio calibration slide	each
P32938	PARAGON™ Genomic DNA Hybridization Test Kit #1 *with Alexa Fluor® 555 labeled genomic DNA*	1 kit
P32942	PARAGON™ Genomic DNA Hybridization Test Kit #2 *with Alexa Fluor® 647 labeled genomic DNA*	1 kit
P32927	PARAGON™ microarray scanner calibration slide *with intensity arrays of four Alexa Fluor® dyes*	each
S24732	Secure-Seal™ hybridization chamber gasket, eight chambers, 9 mm diameter, 0.8 mm deep *set of 20*	1 set
S24733	Secure-Seal™ hybridization chamber gasket, eight chambers, 9 mm diameter, 1.3 mm deep *set of 20*	1 set
S24730	Secure-Seal™ hybridization chamber gasket, one chamber, 20 mm diameter, 0.8 mm deep *set of 40*	1 set
S24731	Secure-Seal™ hybridization chamber gasket, one chamber, 20 mm diameter, 1.3 mm deep *set of 40*	1 set
S24734	Secure-Seal™ hybridization chamber gasket, one chamber, 22 mm x 22 mm, 0.8 mm deep *set of 50*	1 set
S24737	Secure-Seal™ spacer, eight wells, 9 mm diameter, 0.12 mm deep *set of 100*	1 set
S24735	Secure-Seal™ spacer, one well, 13 mm diameter, 0.12 mm deep *set of 100*	1 set
S24736	Secure-Seal™ spacer, one well, 20 mm diameter, 0.12 mm deep *set of 100*	1 set
S7550	SYBR® DX DNA blot stain *1000X concentrate in DMA*	1 mL

For current prices or to order online, visit probes.invitrogen.com

8.6 Nuclear and Chromosome Counterstaining and Nissl Stains

The use of nucleic acid stains to visualize nuclei and chromosomes and for chromosome banding is discussed in this section. Nucleic acid stains and related products for analyzing cell cycle, measuring cell proliferation and detecting apoptotic and dead cells are discussed in Chapter 15. The counterstains described in this section are compatible with a wide range of cytological labeling techniques, including direct or indirect antibody-based detection methods, *in situ* hybridization and detection of specific cellular structures with fluorescent probes such as our mitochondrion-selective MitoTracker® (Section 12.2, Table 12.2) and F-actin–selective phalloidin (Section 11.1, Table 11.1) probes. These counterstains can also serve to fluorescently label cells for analysis in multicolor imaging experiments, and several of these stains find specific application as Nissl stains in neuronal cells. Although particularly known for its unique nucleic acid stains, Molecular Probes is also the world's primary manufacturer of high-quality DAPI, propidium iodide and the "Hoechst" dyes.

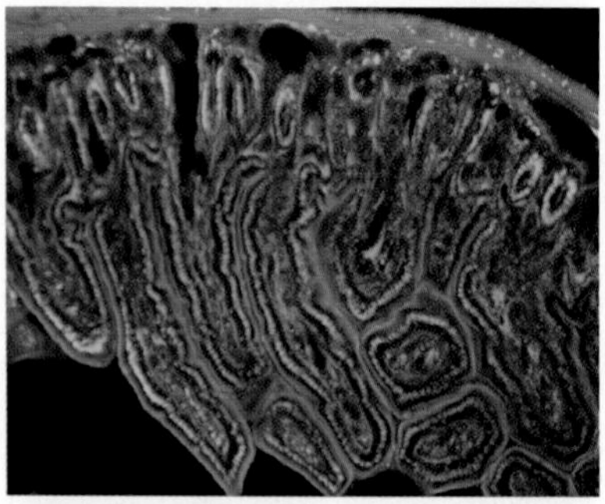

Figure 8.118 Mouse intestine cryosection showing basement membranes labeled with our chicken IgY anti-fibronectin antibody (A21316) and the Alexa Fluor® 488 goat anti-chicken IgG (A11039, green). Goblet cells and crypt cells were labeled with Alexa Fluor® 594 wheat germ agglutinin (W11262, red). The microvillar brush border and smooth muscle layers were visualized with Alexa Fluor® 680 phalloidin (A22286, pseudocolored purple). The section was counterstained with DAPI (D1306, D3571, D21490, blue).

Nuclear Counterstaining of Fixed Cells and Tissues

Blue-Fluorescent Counterstains

DAPI (D1306, D3571; FluoroPure™ Grade, D21490) is the classic nuclear and chromosome counterstain, used for years to identify nuclei and show chromosome-banding patterns. DAPI binds selectively to dsDNA and thus shows little to no background staining of the cytoplasm. Its relatively low-level fluorescence emission does not overwhelm signals from green- or red-fluorescent secondary antibodies or FISH probes. DAPI is semipermeant to live cells and can be used on unfixed cells or tissue sections (Figure 23.19, Figure 8.118). We also offer DAPI premixed with our *SlowFade®*, *SlowFade® Light* and ProLong® Gold antifade reagents (S24635, S24636, P36931, P36935) for simultaneous nuclear staining and antifade protection.

The Hoechst 33342 dye (H1399, H3570; FluoroPure™ Grade, H21492) has been used widely for staining the nuclei of living cells. Hoechst dyes preferentially bind to AT regions, making them quite selective (but not specific) for DNA; Hoechst dye–stained cells and tissues show virtually no cytoplasmic staining (Figure 6.29). The Hoechst 33342 dye is commonly used in combination with labeling by 5-bromo-2′-deoxyuridine (BrdU, B23151) to distinguish the compact chromatin of apoptotic nuclei, to identify replicating cells and to sort cells based on their DNA content (Section 15.4, Section 15.5).

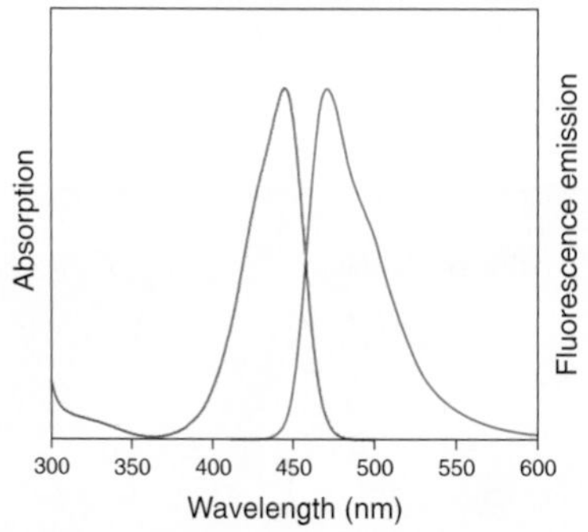

Figure 8.119 Absorption and fluorescence emission spectra of SYTOX® Blue nucleic acid stain bound to DNA.

Our patented blue-fluorescent BOBO™-1 nucleic acid stain (B3582) emits a brighter fluorescent signal than does DAPI. BOBO™-1 has been used effectively as a counterstain for *Drosophila* chromosomes in combination with Cy3 dye– or fluorescein-labeled antibodies.[1] The SYTOX® Blue nucleic acid stain (S11348) also emits bright blue fluorescence upon binding to nucleic acids and is a very good nuclear counterstain. Fluorescence emission of the SYTOX® Blue complex with nucleic acids (Figure 8.119) somewhat overlaps the emission of fluorescein (Figure 1.52) and our Alexa Fluor® 488 and Oregon Green® 488 dyes and thus we recommend SYTOX® Blue dye only as a counterstain for orange- or red-fluorescent dyes.

Green-Fluorescent Counterstains

Some of our proprietary cyanine dyes (Section 8.1; Table 8.1, Table 8.2, Table 8.3) provide the only green-fluorescent nuclear counterstains available. Our YO-PRO®-1 dye (Y3603) and SYTOX® Green stain (S7020) are excellent nuclear counterstains for cells in culture or for whole-mount tissues[2–4] (Figure 8.120, Figure 8.121, Figure 8.122, Figure 8.123) and will most likely be useful counterstains for tissue sections as well. The SYTOX® Green dye shows highly selective nuclear staining; the YO-PRO®-1 dye shows more intense staining but also weakly stains the cytoplasm and nucleolus.[2,3] The SYTOX® Green dye has been used to follow changes in nuclear morphology in apoptotic cells (Figure 8.124) and is a component in our Vybrant® Apoptosis Assay Kits #1, #8, #9 and #10 (V13240, V35112, V35113, V35114; Section 15.5). The SYTOX® Green stain has been used as a specific nuclear counterstain for multicolor labeling in *Drosophila* imaginal disc cells.[5] Nuclear staining by the YO-PRO®-1 dye has provided a method

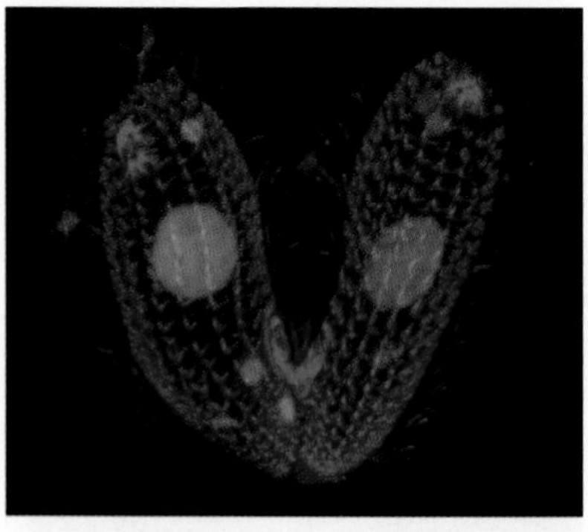

Figure 8.120 Confocal micrograph illustrating sexual reproduction of the ciliate protist, *Tetrahymena thermophila*, six hours after mating. After fixation and permeabilization, the cytoskeleton was labeled with an anti-tubulin antibody and subsequently visualized with Texas Red®-X goat anti-mouse IgG antibody (T6390). The macro- and micronuclei were stained with SYTOX® Green nucleic acid stain (S7020). Image contributed by David Asai and Amy Walanski, Purdue University.

to identify individual cells within single living, perfused mesentery microvessels.[6] YO-PRO®-1, which is a component of our Vybrant® Apoptosis Assay Kits #4 and #7 (V13243, V23201; Section 15.5), and several of our other "cyanine monomer" series of nucleic acid stains (Section 8.1, Table 8.2) are selectively permeant to apoptotic cells, enabling facile identification of this cell population by flow cytometry[7,8] (Section 15.5, Figure 15.81). Our YOYO®-1 dye (Y3601) has been used as a counterstain for immunofluorescent staining of chromatin in the nuclei of developing *Drosophila* embryos.[1] The high sensitivity of YOYO®-1 dye staining permitted the detection of discrete ribosome-containing domains within the cytoplasm of mature cell axons, which were traditionally thought to contain no transcriptional activity.[9]

Staining with the TOTO®-1 (T3600) and YOYO®-1 (Y3601) nucleic acid stains enables extremely sensitive flow cytometric analysis of nuclei and isolated human chromosomes.[10] In this study, YOYO®-1 dye staining produced more than 1000 times the fluorescence signal obtained with mithramycin; furthermore, histograms of both TOTO®-1 and YOYO®-1 on RNase-treated nuclei provided coefficients of variation that were at least as low as those found with propidium iodide or mithramycin. These researchers also found that when nuclei were simultaneously stained with the YOYO®-1 and Hoechst 33258 (H1398, H3569, H21491) dyes, the ratio of the fluorescence of these two dyes varied as a function of cell cycle. This observation suggests that our cyanine dyes might be useful for examining cell cycle–dependent changes that occur in chromatin structure.

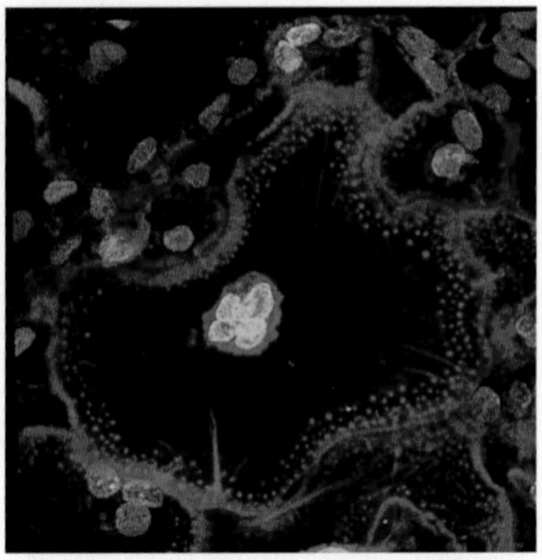

Figure 8.121 Macrophages cultured on a polymer surface that have fused to form a foreign-body giant cell following treatment with interleukin-4. Cells were fixed with 3.7% formaldehyde, treated with RNase A and stained with rhodamine phalloidin (R415) to visualize F-actin, and with YO-PRO®-1 iodide (Y3603) to visualize cell nuclei. Cells were imaged with a Bio-Rad MRC600 confocal laser-scanning microscope. The image is a composite of optical sections taken through the Z-axis of the cell. F-actin (red) is restricted to the periphery of the multinucleated cell and surrounds a cluster of nuclei (green). Image contributed by Kristin DeFife and James M. Anderson, Institute of Pathology, Case Western Reserve University.

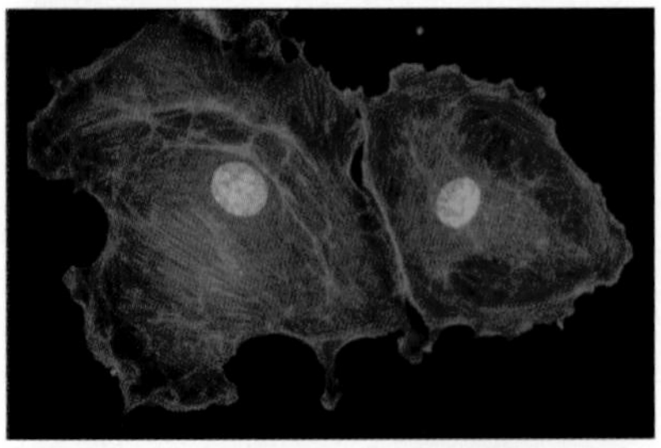

Figure 8.122 Permeabilized bovine pulmonary artery endothelial cells stained with SYTOX® Green nucleic acid stain (S7020) to label the nuclei and with BODIPY® TR-X phallacidin (B7464) to label the F-actin. The image was acquired by taking sequential exposures through bandpass optical filter sets appropriate for fluorescein and the Texas Red® dye.

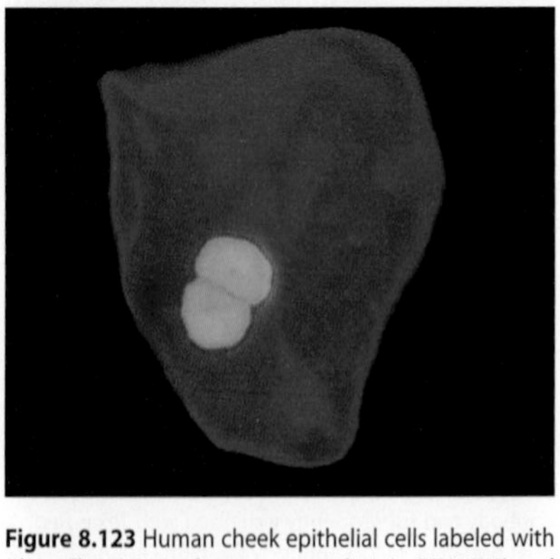

Figure 8.123 Human cheek epithelial cells labeled with Alexa Fluor® 350 wheat germ agglutinin (W11263) and stained with SYTOX® Green nucleic acid stain (S7020). This multiple-exposure image was acquired using bandpass filter sets appropriate for DAPI and fluorescein.

Yellow-Fluorescent Counterstain

The long-wavelength tracer nuclear yellow (Hoechst S769121, N21485; Figure 8.125, Figure 8.126) is often combined with the popular retrograde tracer true blue (T1323, Section 14.3) for two-color neuronal mapping. In neuronal cells, nuclear yellow primarily stains the nucleus with yellow fluorescence,[11–14] whereas true blue is a UV light–excitable, divalent cationic dye (Figure 8.127) that stains the cytoplasm with blue fluorescence.[11,15–18] Both nuclear yellow and true blue are stable when subjected to immunohistochemical processing and can be used to photoconvert DAB into an insoluble, electron-dense reaction product[19–22] (see Note 14.2 "Product Highlight: Fluorescent Probes for Photoconversion of Diaminobenzidine Reagents" in Section 14.3).

Orange- and Red-Fluorescent Counterstains

Propidium iodide (PI; P1304MP, P3566; FluoroPure™ Grade, P21493) has long been the preferred dye for red-fluorescent counterstaining of nuclei and chromosomes (Figure 8.15). Under some fixation conditions, PI shows highly selective nuclear staining. Other preparations of cells and tissues require a simple treatment with a ribonuclease (RNase) to achieve specific nuclear staining.

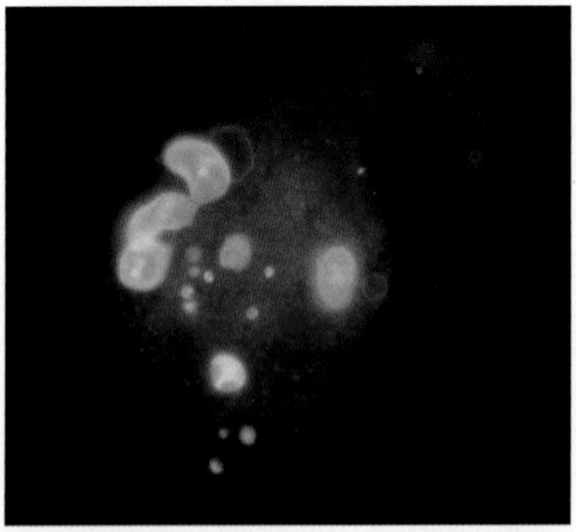

Figure 8.124 Nuclear deformation of an apoptotic cell visualized with the SYTOX® Green dye (S7020). Bovine pulmonary artery endothelial cells were treated with camptothecin for 24 hours, stained with the SYTOX® Green nucleic acid stain and photographed using a fluorescence microscope equipped with a bandpass filter set designed for fluorescein-like dyes.

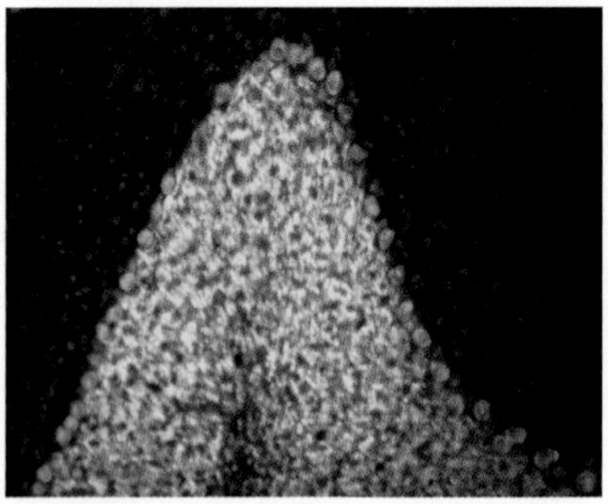

Figure 8.125 Mouse brain section stained with NeuroTrace® 435/455 blue-fluorescent Nissl stain (N21479) and counterstained with nuclear yellow (N21485).

PI provides an excellent counterstain for cells stained with green-fluorescent probes or secondary antibodies conjugated to Alexa Fluor® 488, Oregon Green®, BODIPY® FL or fluorescein dyes.

The BOBO™-3 (B3586) and SYTOX® Orange (S11368) cyanine dyes have fluorescence emission that is similar to that of PI, but show greater fluorescence enhancement upon binding to DNA and so should provide brighter nuclear staining. The BOBO™-3 dye has been used as a nuclear stain in whole-mount *Xenopus laevis* embryos.[23] Our YOYO®-3 (Y3606) and YO-PRO®-3 (Y3607) dyes show strong and specific staining of the nucleus in most cultured cells.[2]

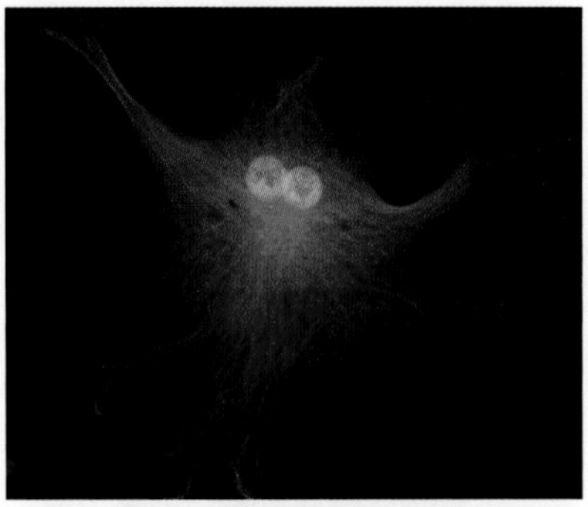

Figure 8.126 A binucleate bovine pulmonary artery endothelial cell labeled with the biotin-XX conjugate of anti-α-tubulin antibody (A21371) and Alexa Fluor® 568 streptavidin (S11226), then counterstained with nuclear yellow (N21485).

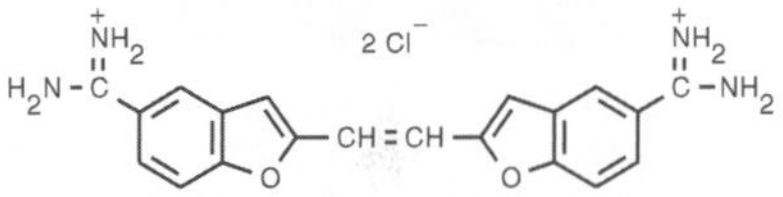

Figure 8.127 T1323 true blue chloride.

Long-Wavelength Nuclear Counterstains

The long-wavelength TOTO®-3 (T3604) and TO-PRO®-3 (T3605) dyes provide nuclear counterstains whose fluorescence is well separated from that of commonly used fluorophores, such as our popular Alexa Fluor® dyes, Oregon Green®, fluorescein (FITC), rhodamine (TRITC), Texas Red®, coumarin (AMCA), Marina Blue® and Pacific Blue™ dyes. Their long-wavelength spectra make these red-fluorescent nucleic acid stains particularly useful for three- or even four-color labeling using confocal laser-scanning or standard epifluorescence microscopes (Figure 8.128, Figure 11.25). The absorbance peaks of the TOTO®-3 (Figure 8.129) and TO-PRO®-3 (Figure 8.130) dyes closely match the 633 nm and 647 nm laser line of many confocal laser-scanning microscopes, and the spectra match filter sets typically used for the Alexa Fluor® 647 and Cy5 dyes (Table 23.9). The high absorptivity of TO-PRO®-3 is sufficient to make it a good chromosome stain, even when excited at 488 nm.

Long-wavelength light–absorbing dyes have the advantage that their fluorescence is usually not obscured by the autofluorescence of tissues. For example, analysis of fluorescently stained whole-mount *Xenopus laevis* embryos has traditionally been difficult due to the large amount of autofluorescence from the yolk. Two reports have shown that the TO-PRO®-3 dye can be used as a fluorescent nuclear stain in these embryos, allowing them to be analyzed by confocal laser-scanning microscopy. When either the 633 nm or 647 nm spectral line of a confocal laser-scanning microscope is used with long-wavelength filter sets, the autofluorescence from the yolk is almost completely eliminated.[23,24]

The TOTO®-3 and TO-PRO®-3 dyes were tested as counterstains for aldehyde-fixed frozen rat tissue sections. The TO-PRO®-3 dye showed less cytoplasmic staining and little overlap with signals from fluorescein- or tetramethylrhodamine-labeled secondary antibodies in the same section.[25] The TO-PRO®-3 dye gives strong and selective staining of the nucleus in cultured cells.[2] A high selectivity for nuclear staining over cytoplasmic staining made TO-PRO®-3 the preferred dye for detecting amplification of the *Her-2/neu* gene by dual-color FISH in paraffin sections.[26] Although its nucleic acid complex reportedly bleaches relatively rapidly,[2] photobleaching can be slowed with antifade reagents such as are provided in our *SlowFade®*, *SlowFade® Light*, ProLong® and ProLong® Gold antifade reagents (S2828, S7461, P7481, P36930, P36934; Section 23.1). Nuclear staining by the TO-PRO®-3 dye has been used to study the structure of the nucleus in interphase cells[27] and to demonstrate segregation of chromosomes during meiosis in mouse oocytes.[28] The TO-PRO®-3 dye was also used to counterstain the chromatin

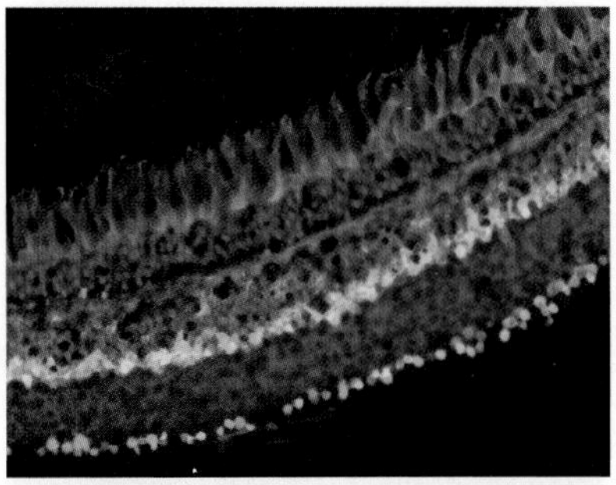

Figure 8.128 Immunohistochemical detection using tyramide signal amplification. A transverse section of fixed zebrafish retina was probed with mouse monoclonal FRet 34 antibody and subsequently developed for visualization using HRP-conjugated goat anti-mouse IgG antibody and Alexa Fluor® 488 tyramide, which are supplied in the TSA Kit #2 (T20912). The section was counterstained with the blue-fluorescent Alexa Fluor® 350 wheat germ agglutinin (W11263) and the far red–fluorescent TOTO®-3 nuclear stain (T3604).

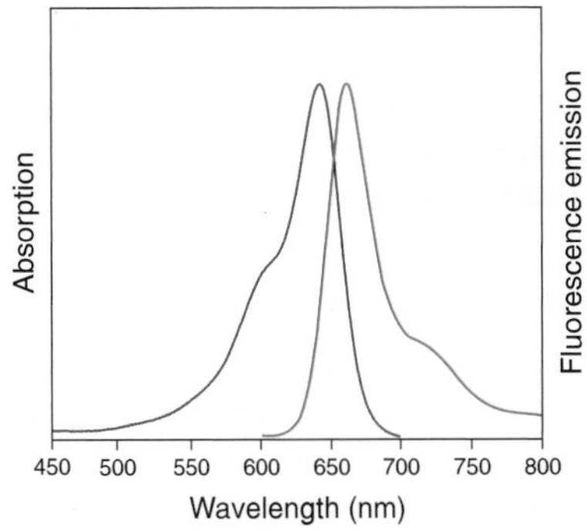

Figure 8.129 Absorption and fluorescence emission spectra of TOTO®-3 bound to DNA.

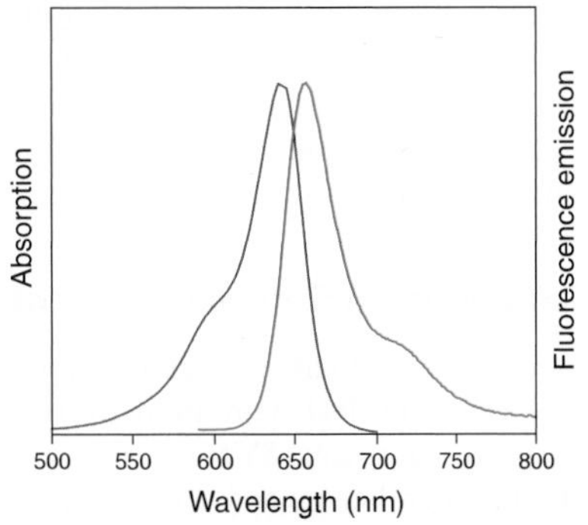

Figure 8.130 Absorption and fluorescence emission spectra of TO-PRO®-3 bound to DNA.

in nuclei of developing *Drosophila* embryos that were immunostained with Cy3 dye– or fluorescein-labeled antibodies.[1] Our TOTO®-3 dye has been used as a counterstain for TUNEL assays[29] and for annexin V–based apoptosis assays[30] (Section 15.5). The TOTO®-3 dye has also been used in combination with Cy3 dye–labeled anti-BrdU antibody staining to show that replicons labeled with BrdU form clusters in the nucleus that are stable through several cell cycles.[31] Molecular Probes provides monoclonal anti-BrdU antibody labeled with the spectrally similar Alexa Fluor® 546 dye (A21308, Section 15.4) and with several other Alexa Fluor® dyes for cell proliferation and apoptosis studies (Section 15.4).

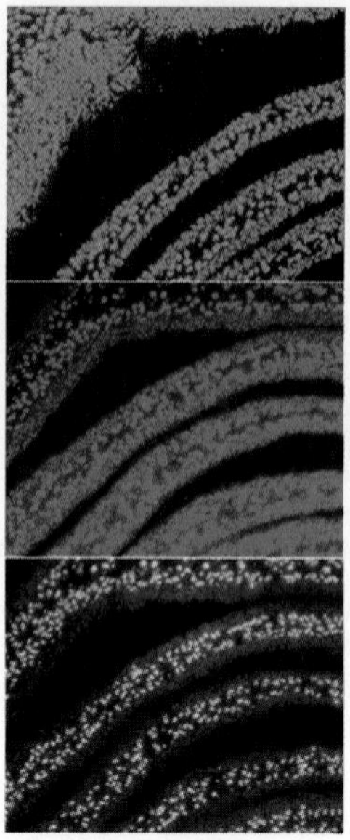

Figure 8.131 Gill filaments from *Solemya reidi* — a gutless mollusk inhabiting the highly sulfidic sediments characteristic of pulpmill effluents and sewage outfall sites along the western coast of North America — stained with either the SYTOX® Green nucleic acid stain (S7020, top), propidium iodide (P1304MP, P3566, P21493; middle) or DAPI (D1306, D3571, D21490; bottom). The ribbon-like bands of the gill lamella are composed of two cell types — granular cells, which harbor sulfur-oxidizing cells; endosymbiotic bacteria; and symbiont-free intercalary cells. The three images were acquired using a fluorescein bandpass optical filter set, a propidium iodide longpass optical filter set and a DAPI longpass optical filter set, respectively. The images were contributed by K. Warren and S. C. Cary, College of Marine Studies, University of Delaware.

Cytological Nuclear Counterstain Kit

For RNA *in situ* hybridization with tissue culture cells, we recommend our Cytological Nuclear Counterstain Kit (C7590), which contains three spectrally distinct fluorescent dyes for staining nuclei in fixed-cell preparations:

- Concentrated SYTOX® Green nucleic acid stain in DMSO
- Concentrated propidium iodide in water
- Concentrated DAPI in water
- Detailed protocols for fixation and staining

Each of the nucleic acid stains is provided as a convenient 300X solution, ready for dilution and staining. This kit provides sufficient reagents for staining 300 slides with each counterstain.

The reagents in the Cytological Nuclear Counterstain Kit are especially valuable for multicolor applications, in which an appropriate counterstain can be selected to contrast spectrally with other fluorescent probes in the sample. When used according to our protocols, the counterstains in this kit selectively stain nuclei, with little or no cytoplasmic labeling. Observed by fluorescence microscopy, the nuclei stand out in vivid contrast to fluorescent probes of other cell structures (Figure 8.131).

Nuclear Counterstains for Live Cells and Unfixed Tissues

Cell-permeant nuclear stains make it possible to stain live cells or tissues that have been minimally processed. Nuclear staining can reveal the natural location of cells in tissues and can provide a means to follow nuclear changes throughout processes such as meiosis and apoptosis (Section 15.5). Most of these dyes have little effect on cell function, allowing live cells to be traced as they move during development or as they infect other cells. In particular, some of our SYTO® dyes have greatly facilitated the studies of live cells.

Cell-Permeant Blue-Fluorescent Counterstains

The membrane-permeant Hoechst 33342 dye (H1399, H3570, H21492) has been extensively used for staining the nuclei of living cells. The Hoechst 33342 dye shows AT-selective staining — Hoechst dye–stained cells and tissues show virtually no cytoplasmic staining. Hoechst 33342 is commonly used to distinguish the compact chromatin of apoptotic nuclei, in combination with BrdU labeling to identify replicating cells and to sort cells based on DNA content (Section 15.5). While not all of the blue-fluorescent SYTO® dyes in Section 8.1 show specific nuclear staining, SYTO® 40 (S11351) shows excellent staining of the nuclei in a freshwater snail embryo (Figure 8.132). All of the blue-fluorescent SYTO® dyes listed in Table 8.3 are available individually or in a sampler kit (S11350) to facilitate finding the best counterstain for a particular cell or tissue type.

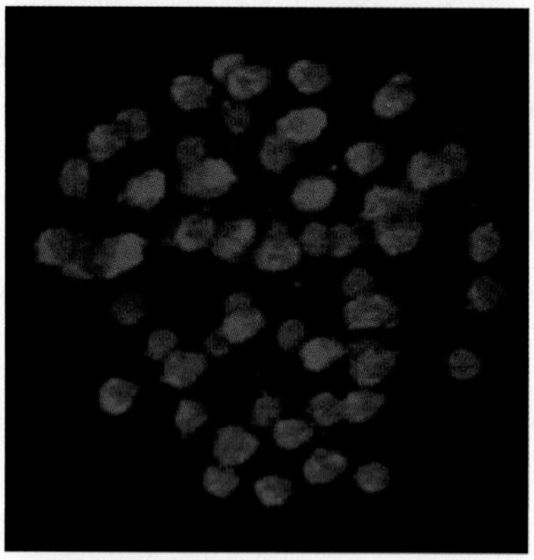

Figure 8.132 The developing embryo of a freshwater snail stained with SYTO® 40 blue-fluorescent nucleic acid stain (S11351), a component of the SYTO® Blue Fluorescent Stain Sampler Kit (S11350). A series of Z-plane images was acquired with a wide-field optical sectioning confocal microscope. A three-dimensional volume rendering was generated from the deconvolved image series. Image contributed by Bruce Roth and Paul Millard, Molecular Probes, Inc., and Hillary MacDonald, Applied Precision, Inc.

Cell-Permeant Green-Fluorescent Counterstains

Some of our predominantly green-fluorescent cell-permeant SYTO® dyes (Section 8.1, Table 8.3) are excellent nuclear stains for live cells in culture (Figure 8.133) and for unfixed tissue sections. The green-fluorescent SYTO® 11 dye (S7573) has shown selective nuclear staining in heart tissue, vascular endothelium and cultured myocytes[32] and in cultured aortic vascular smooth muscle cells,[33] showing promise for broad use in noninvasive confocal laser-scanning microscope investigations. For instance, use of the SYTO® 11 and SYTO® 13 (S7573, S7575; Section 8.1) dyes facilitated counting cells in brain slices without disrupting the three-dimensional environment.[34]

Staining with the SYTO® 11 dye was used to follow the movement of cells during development in whole-mount zebrafish embryos.[35] The SYTO® 11 dye has also been used to identify meiotic cells in developing brain tissue.[36] *Trypanosoma cruzi* whose nuclei have been stained with the SYTO® 11 dye can easily be detected in cells they have infected.[37] Our SYTO® 16 dye (S7578) is also an effective nuclear counterstain in cultured cells[38] and has been used to stain nuclei in whole maize roots.[39]

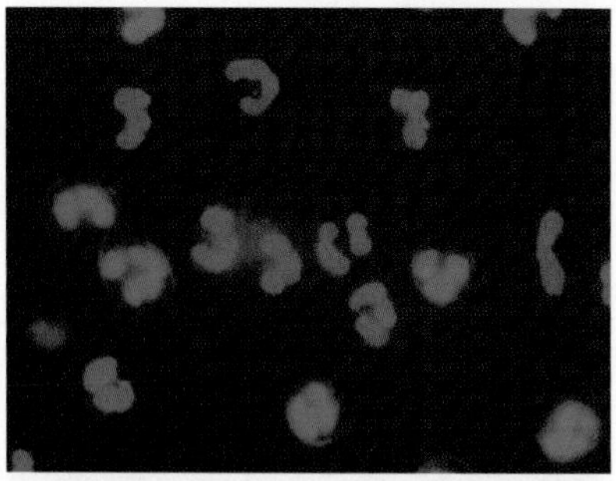

Figure 8.133 Adherent cells from human peripheral blood stained with the SYTO® 13 dye (S7575), one of the six visible light–excitable cell-permeant nucleic acid stains in our SYTO® Green Fluorescent Nucleic Acid Stain Sampler Kit #1 (S7572). The multilobed nuclei of these polymorphonuclear leukocytes are particularly striking in this field of view.

The green-fluorescent SYTO® dyes have also been used to investigate changes in the nucleus in live cells. For example, the SYTO® 13 dye was used in a double-labeling experiment with BODIPY® 558/568 phalloidin (B3475, Section 11.1) to stain actin fibers, making it possible to look at nuclear changes and cytoskeletal changes concurrently in apoptotic cells.[40] The SYTO® 12 dye (S7574) was used to follow chromosome movement during meiosis in live maize myocytes,[41] and the SYTO® 14 dye (S7576) allowed researchers to follow RNA localization within living cells.[42,43]

The green-fluorescent SYTO® dyes listed in Table 8.3 are available individually dissolved in either 100 µL or 250 µL of DMSO, as components in one of two SYTO® Green-Fluorescent Nucleic Acid Stain Sampler Kits (S7554, S7572) or in the RediPlate™ 96 nucleic acid stain sampler microplate (R32715, Section 8.1). These SYTO® Stain Sampler Kits contain 50 µL each of six different green-fluorescent SYTO® dyes to facilitate finding the best counterstain for a particular cell or tissue type. The RediPlate™ 96 nucleic acid stain sampler microplate facilitates the screening of a wide array of nucleic acid–binding dyes — including 36 different SYTO® dyes, SYBR® Green I, SYBR® Green II and PicoGreen® dyes, amine-reactive SYBR® 101 and SYBR® 103 dyes, SYTOX® Green, SYTOX® Orange and SYTOX® Blue dyes, Hoechst 33342, propidium iodide and hexidium iodide — that have been predispensed into a 96-well microplate.

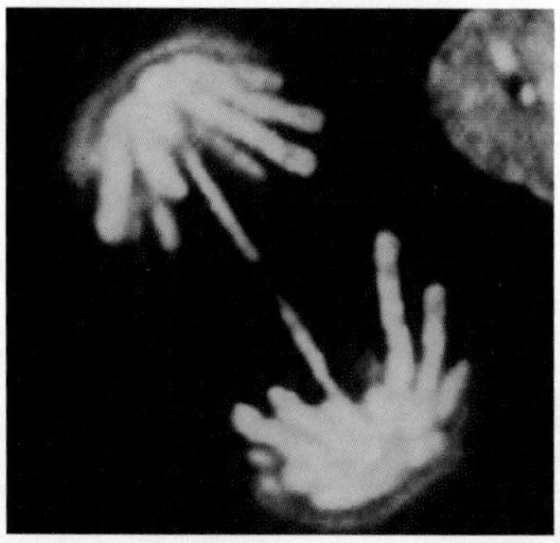

Figure 8.134 DAPI-stained condensed chromatin in PtK2 cells during the later stages of mitosis. DAPI (D1306, D3571, D21490) binds to the minor groove of DNA with significant fluorescence enhancement.

Cell-Permeant Orange- and Red-Fluorescent Counterstains

The red-fluorescent SYTO® 17 dye (S7579) was used as a nuclear counterstain for the green-fluorescent membrane stain $DiOC_6(3)$ (D273, Section 12.2), with fluorescein immunostaining, and with the TUNEL apoptosis assay using ChromaTide® fluorescein-12-dUTP (C7604, Section 8.2) to investigate chromatin degradation and denucleation of lens tissue.[44,45] *Leishmania* cells stained with the SYTO® 17 dye could later be identified in cells they had infected.[46] Our SYTO® 59 dye (S11341) has been used as a red-fluorescent nuclear counterstain in combination with the green-fluorescent protein (GFP) expressed in lymphoid cells[47] and human embryonic kidney cells[48] (see Note 12.1 "Product Highlight: Fluorescent Probes for Use with GFP" in Section 12.1). SYTO® 59 dye has also proven very useful in the study of *Cryptosporidium* oocytes; the intensity of staining appears to be related to the infectivity of the oocytes, providing a valuable research tool.[49]

The orange- and red-fluorescent SYTO® nucleic acid stains listed in Table 8.3 may also prove useful as nuclear counterstains for live cells. All of these orange- or red-fluorescent SYTO® dyes are available individually as solutions in DMSO or as components in the SYTO® Orange Fluorescent Stain Sampler Kit (S11360) or the SYTO® Red Fluorescent Stain Sampler Kit S11340), which contain 50 µL each of six different orange-fluorescent or red-fluorescent SYTO® dyes to facilitate finding the best counterstain for a particular cell or tissue type.

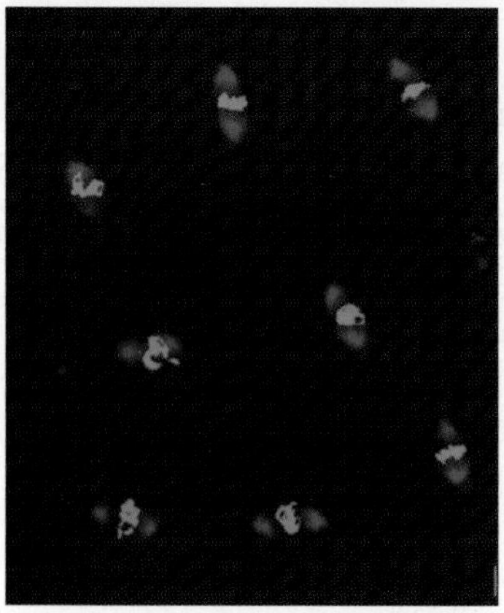

Figure 8.135 Mitotic divisions in early *Drosophila* embryos. The spindles were labeled with an anti–α-tubulin primary antibody and probed with a secondary antibody labeled with Lissamine rhodamine B sulfonyl chloride (L20, L1908). After a brief RNase treatment to reduce background fluorescence, the chromosomes were counterstained with SYTOX® Green nucleic acid stain (S7020). The image was contributed by Tulle Hazelrigg and Amy MacQueen, Columbia University.

Tracking Chromosomes through Mitosis

Many nucleic acid stains can be used to observe chromosomes caught in the act of cell division in fixed cells and tissues (Figure 8.134, Figure 8.135, Figure 8.136, Figure 8.137). Dimeric cyanine dyes (Table 8.2) have also been used to observe mitotic chromosome movement in live cells. For example, YOYO®-1 dye (Y3601) has been microinjected into cells in order to follow mitotic chromosomes through at least six cell cycles in fertilized sea urchin eggs[50] (Figure 8.138). Another useful technique for tracking chromosomes through mitosis involves metabolic incorporation of microinjected fluorescent nucleotides, including our fluorescein-12-dUTP, Oregon Green® 488-5-dUTP and BODIPY® TR-14-dUTP (C7604, C7630, C7618; Section 8.2) by endogenous cellular enzymes into DNA. Incorporation of the fluorescent tracer does not interfere with subsequent progress through the cell cycle, and fluorescent strands of DNA can be followed as they assemble into chromosomes and segregate into daughters and granddaughters.[51–53] Presumably, injection of 5′-bromo-2′-deoxyuridine triphosphate (BrdUTP, B21550; Section 8.2), followed by detection of the incorporated BrdU with one of our Alexa Fluor® conjugates of the anti-BrdU antibody (Section 15.4), would also be suitable for studying mitosis.

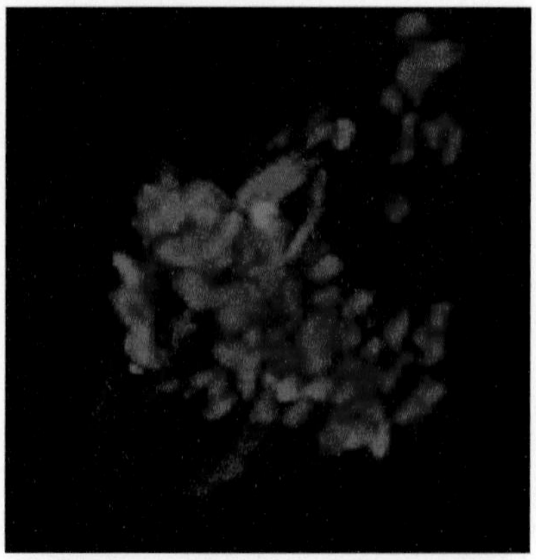

Figure 8.136 Microtubules of bovine pulmonary artery endothelial cells that have been labeled with mouse monoclonal anti–α-tubulin antibody (A11126), followed by biotin-XX goat anti–mouse IgG antibody (B2763), and then visualized with Marina Blue® streptavidin (S11221). The cells were next treated with RNase, and the chromosomes were labeled with TO-PRO®-3 iodide (T3605). A series of Z-plane images was acquired with a wide-field optical sectioning confocal laser-scanning microscope. A three-dimensional volume rendering was generated from the deconvolved image series.

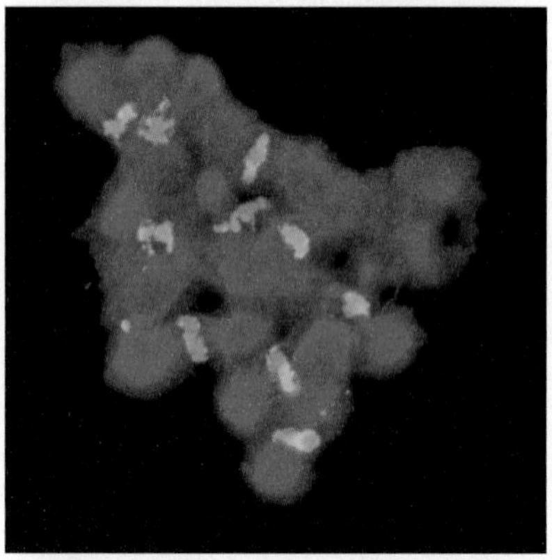

Figure 8.137 Mitotic spindles isolated from sea urchin eggs that are labeled with YOYO®-1 iodide (Y3601) and a monoclonal anti–β-tubulin antibody in conjunction with Texas Red® goat anti–rat IgG antibody (T6392). This image was generated by epifluorescence microscopy. Image contributed by John Murray, University of Pennsylvania.

Chromosome Counterstaining

Molecular Probes provides a spectrum of dyes for counterstaining hybridized metaphase or interphase chromosomes in fluorescence *in situ* hybridization (FISH) assays (Section 8.5). Our extensive selection of counterstains in colors spanning the spectrum makes it easy to find the ideal counterstain.

Red-Fluorescent Counterstaining for Green-Fluorescent Probes

The best contrast provided for one-color staining with green-fluorescent antibodies or probes is a red-fluorescent counterstain. Green-fluorescent signals appear yellow when overlapping the red counterstaining (Figure 8.139). Propidium iodide (PI; P1304MP, P3566; FluoroPure™ Grade, P21493) is a preferred red-fluorescent nuclear counterstain that can be excited using excitation filters appropriate for green-fluorescent dyes (Table 23.9). Staining by PI also yields relatively low background fluorescence from RNA staining.[54] Some of our longer-wavelength cyanine dyes, including the YO-PRO®-3, TO-PRO®-3, YOYO®-3 and TOTO®-3 dyes (see below) yield red-fluorescent nuclear staining that can be excited without exciting the fluorescence of green-fluorescent dyes.

The Best Green-Fluorescent Counterstains

The SYTOX® Green (S7020) and YOYO®-1 (Y3601) nucleic acid stains are the premier dyes for green-fluorescent nuclear counterstains because of their bright nuclear signal and low cytoplasmic background staining. Both dyes show bright green fluorescence upon binding to nucleic acids, and a wash step is not required because the dyes are essentially nonfluorescent in aqueous medium. Researchers at Molecular Probes have found that both the YOYO®-1 and SYTOX® Green dyes provide simple and reliable green-fluorescent counterstains for FISH analysis (Section 8.5), though they differ somewhat in their properties and applications. Optimal staining by the YOYO®-1 dye requires RNase treatment for background reduction, whereas SYTOX® Green

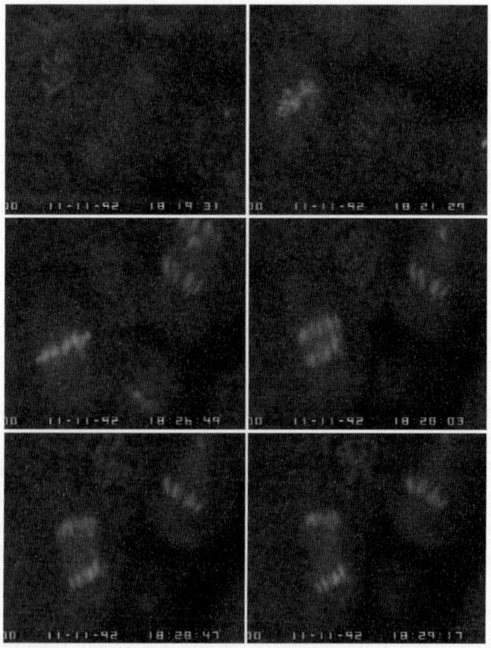

Figure 8.138 Using the YOYO®-1 dye to follow cell division in a sea urchin egg. The YOYO®-1 dye (Y3601) was injected into an unfertilized sea urchin egg. The egg was fertilized and then observed by confocal laser-scanning microscopy. Images were obtained every 15 sec in this sequence. Every fourth image is shown in the first part, then every image is shown during chromosome separation. The image was contributed by Mark Terasaki, University of Connecticut Health Center.

dye staining does not. In addition, counterstaining with the SYTOX® Green dye is more rapid than YOYO®-1 dye counterstaining. Although the spectral properties of the two green-fluorescent dyes differ slightly, nucleic acids counterstained with either of these green-fluorescent dyes can be efficiently excited with the mercury-arc lamp or argon-ion laser and can be visualized using standard fluorescein optical filter sets (Table 23.9). Dual-wavelength excitation of either TOTO®-1 dye– or YOYO®-1 dye–stained chromosomes reportedly permits specific chromosomes to be identified and sorted.[55]

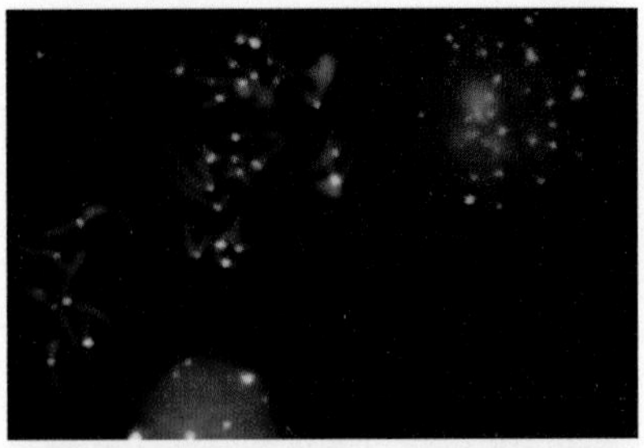

Figure 8.139 Centromeres in a human metaphase chromosome spread probed with a biotinylated human centromere-specific probe and detected by sequential labeling with fluorescein streptavidin (S869), biotinylated anti-fluorescein/Oregon Green® antibody (A982) and again with fluorescein streptavidin (S869). Labeled centromeres are clearly visible on these metaphase chromosomes and interphase cell nuclei, both of which are counterstained with propidium iodide (P1304MP, P3566, P21493).

Blue-Fluorescent Counterstaining for Multicolor Labeling

DAPI (D1306, D3571; FluoroPure™ Grade, D21490) is the classic nuclear and chromosome counterstain, used for years to identify nuclei and show chromosome-banding patterns (Figure 8.140). DAPI binds selectively to dsDNA and thus shows little to no cytoplasmic background staining.[56–58] DAPI's relatively low-level fluorescence emission does not overwhelm signals from green- or red-fluorescent secondary antibodies or FISH probes (Figure 8.86, Figure 8.84). We also offer DAPI premixed with our *SlowFade*®, *SlowFade*® *Light* and ProLong® Gold antifade reagents (S24635, S24636, P36931, P36935). The Hoechst 33342 dye (H1399, H3570, H21492) is also commonly used for chromosome counterstaining. Our SYTOX® Blue nucleic acid stain (S11348), which is essentially nonfluorescent except when bound to nucleic acids, may be similarly useful.

Very Long-Wavelength Counterstains for Multicolor Labeling

Our patented TO-PRO®-3 (T3605) and TOTO®-3 (T3604) dyes are excellent chromosomal counterstains that are particularly useful for multicolor labeling. These dyes have very long–wavelength fluorescence emissions (maxima at ~660 nm, Figure 8.129) that are well separated from the emissions of other commonly used fluorophores, such as Texas Red® dye, fluorescein or the Alexa Fluor® family of dyes that absorb maximally below 600 nm (Section 1.3), making three- or even four-color labeling possible. *Drosophila* polytene chromosomes and nuclei of cultured mammalian cells stained with the TO-PRO®-3 dye have also been detected with two-photon scanning near-field optical microscopy.[59]

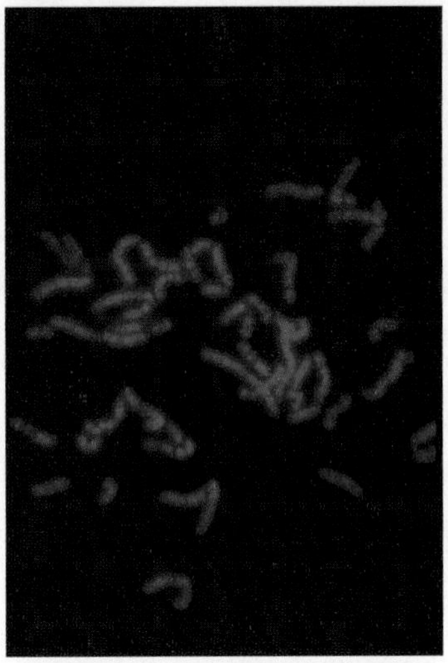

Figure 8.140 Human metaphase chromosomes stained with DAPI (D1306, D3571, D21490).

Chromosome Banding

SYTOX® Green

When chromosomes are stained with the SYTOX® Green dye in combination with methyl green — a major-groove–binding dye that binds selectively to AT sequences along the chromosome — a banding pattern arises that indicates the location of AT-rich regions (Figure 8.141). This phenomenon has been exploited to examine metaphase chromatin structure[60] and represents an extremely simple, rapid, fluorescence-based banding method that may prove useful for general karyotype analysis. The green-fluorescent SYTOX® Green dye is efficiently excited by the argon-ion laser, permitting analysis of chromosome structure by confocal laser-scanning microscopy. In addition, use of the SYTOX® Green dye eliminates the need for RNase treatment of slides.

Acridine Homodimer

The water-soluble acridine homodimer (A666) has extremely high affinity for AT-rich regions of nucleic acids, making it particularly useful for chromosome banding.[61,62] Acridine homodimer emits a blue-green fluorescence when bound to DNA, yielding fluorescence that is proportional to the fourth power of the AT base-pair content.[63] Acridine homodimer has been recommended as an alternative to quinacrine for Q banding because of its greater brightness and higher photostability.[61]

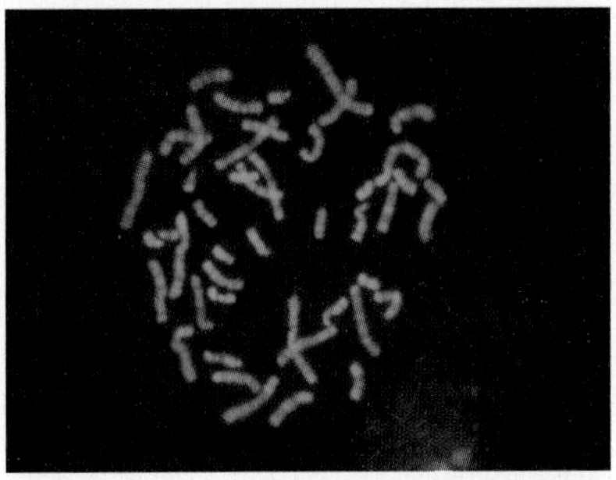

Figure 8.141 Human metaphase chromosomes stained with SYTOX® Green nucleic acid stain (S7020) and methyl green, and then mounted in Cytoseal 60 mounting medium.

Other Dyes and Chromosome Banding Reagents

A wide variety of fluorescent nucleic acid stains have been used for chromosome banding:[61,64–66]

- Hoechst 33342 dye (H1399, H3570, H21492) has been used in chromosome sorting, multivariate analysis and karyotyping.[67]

- High-resolution flow karyotyping has also been carried out with DAPI[68,69] (D1306, D3571, D21490).
- DAPI (Figure 8.140) or combinations of DAPI or Hoechst 33258 (H1398, H3569, H21491) with nonfluorescent DNA-binding drugs have been used for chromosome-banding studies.[70]
- The Hoechst dyes have been employed in combination with chromomycin and a high-resolution, dual-laser method to sort 21 unique human chromosome types onto nitrocellulose filters, followed by hybridization to gene-specific probes.[71]
- 7-Aminoactinomycin D (7-AAD, A1310) binds selectively to GC regions of DNA,[72] yielding a distinct banding pattern in polytene chromosomes and chromatin.[73,74]
- 9-Amino-6-chloro-2-methoxyacridine (ACMA, A1324) fluoresces with greater intensity in AT-rich regions on chromosomes,[75] yielding a staining pattern similar to the Q-banding pattern produced with quinacrine.

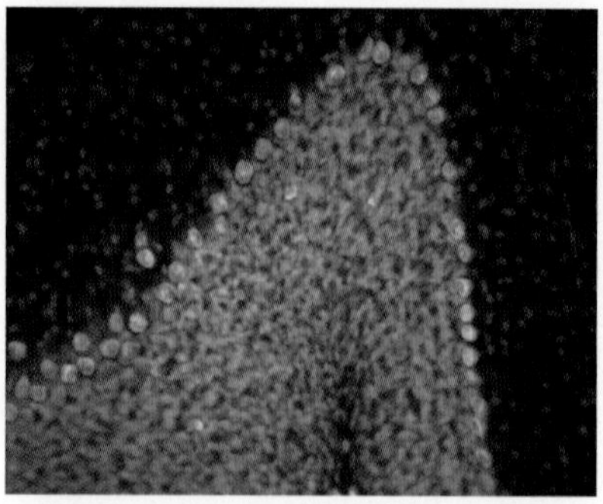

Figure 8.142 Mouse brain section stained with NeuroTrace® 515/535 yellow-fluorescent Nissl stain (N21481) and counterstained with nuclear yellow (N21485).

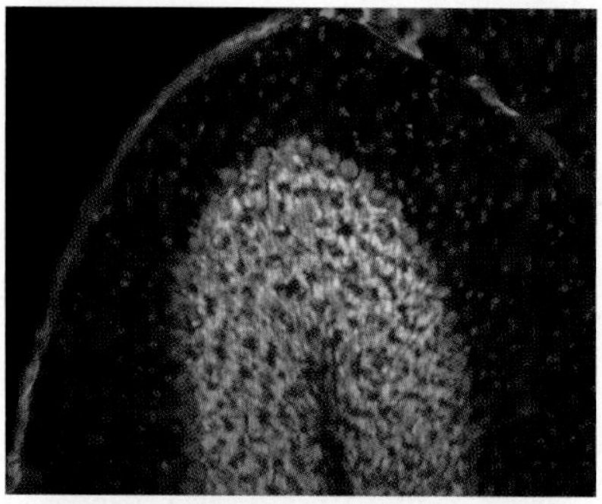

Figure 8.143 Neurons in a mouse cerebellum section labeled with NeuroTrace® 530/615 red-fluorescent Nissl stain (N21482). The Nissl substance, ribosomal RNA associated with the rough endoplasmic reticulum, is specific to neuronal cells. Other cells in the sample are identified with the contrasting nuclear counterstain nuclear yellow (N21485). Smaller neurons appear to be labeled primarily with the nuclear yellow stain. This image is a composite of two micrographs acquired using a DAPI longpass filter set and a filter set appropriate for tetramethylrhodamine.

NeuroTrace® Fluorescent Nissl Stains

The Nissl substance, described by Franz Nissl more than 100 years ago, is unique to neuronal cells.[76] Composed of an extraordinary amount of rough endoplasmic reticulum, the Nissl substance reflects the unusually high protein synthesis capacity of neurons. Various fluorescent or chromophoric "Nissl stains" have been used for this counterstaining, including acridine orange,[77] ethidium bromide,[77] neutral red (N3246, Section 15.2), cresyl violet,[78] methylene blue, safranin-O and toluidine blue-O.[79] We have developed five fluorescent Nissl stains (Table 14.2) that not only provide a wide spectrum of fluorescent colors for staining neurons, but also are far more sensitive than the conventional dyes:

- NeuroTrace® 435/455 blue-fluorescent Nissl stain (N21479, Figure 8.125)
- NeuroTrace® 500/525 green-fluorescent Nissl stain (N21480; Figure 7.84, Figure 8.37, Figure 14.40, Figure 14.60)
- NeuroTrace® 515/535 yellow-fluorescent Nissl stain (N21481, Figure 8.142)
- NeuroTrace® 530/615 red-fluorescent Nissl stain (N21482; Figure 8.143, Figure 14.42)
- NeuroTrace® 640/660 deep red–fluorescent Nissl stain (N21483)

In addition, the Nissl substance redistributes within the cell body in injured or regenerating neurons. Therefore, these Nissl stains can also act as markers for the physiological state of the neuron. Staining by the Nissl stains is completely eliminated by pretreatment of tissue specimens with RNase; however, these dyes are not specific stains for RNA in solutions. The strong fluorescence (emission maximum ~515–520 nm) of NeuroTrace® 500/525 green-fluorescent Nissl stain (N21480) makes it the preferred dye for use as a counterstain in combination with orange- or red-fluorescent neuroanatomical tracers such as DiI[80] (D282, D3911, V22885; Section 14.4).

References

1. J Cell Biol 141, 469 (1998); **2.** Acta Histochem Cytochem 30, 309 (1997); **3.** Acta Histochem Cytochem 31, 297 (1998); **4.** J Cell Biol 143, 1329 (1998); **5.** Genes Dev 12, 435 (1998); **6.** Microcirculation 2, 267 (1995); **7.** Cancer Res 57, 3804 (1997); **8.** J Immunol Methods 185, 249 (1995); **9.** J Neurosci 16, 1400 (1996); **10.** Cytometry 15, 129 (1994); **11.** Neuroscience 60, 125 (1994); **12.** Neuroscience 28, 725 (1989); **13.** Acta Anat (Basel) 122, 158 (1985); **14.** Neurosci Lett 18, 25 (1980); **15.** Neurosci Lett 128, 137 (1991); **16.** J Neurosci Methods 35, 175 (1990); **17.** J Neurosci Methods 32, 15 (1990); **18.** Meth Neurosci 3, 275 (1990); **19.** Neuroscience Protocols, Wouterlood FG, Ed. 93-050-06, pp. 01–13 (1993); **20.** Microsc Res Tech 24, 2 (1993); **21.** J Comp Neurol 258, 230 (1987); **22.** J Neurosci Methods 14, 273 (1985); **23.** J Histochem Cytochem 44, 399 (1996); **24.** Trends Genet 11, 9 (1995); **25.** J Histochem Cytochem 45, 49 (1997); **26.** Histochem Cell Biol 115, 293 (2001); **27.** J Cell Biol 136, 531 (1997); **28.** Science 270, 1595 (1995); **29.** Nat Med 2, 1361 (1996); **30.** J Biomol Screen 4, 193 (1999); **31.** J Cell Biol 140, 1285 (1998); **32.** Mol Cell Biochem 172, 171 (1997); **33.** Can J Physiol Pharmacol 75, 652 (1997); **34.** Cytometry 32, 66 (1998); **35.** Dev Biol 180, 184 (1996); **36.** Cell 82, 631 (1995); **37.** J Biol Chem 272, 12482 (1997); **38.** J Neurochem 67, 2484 (1996); **39.** Protoplasma 192, 70 (1996); **40.** J Immunol 160, 2626 (1998); **41.** J Cell Biol 139, 831 (1997); **42.** J Neurosci 16, 7812 (1996); **43.** Proc Natl Acad Sci U S A 94, 14804 (1997); **44.** Invest Ophthalmol Vis Sci 38, 301 (1997); **45.** Invest Ophthalmol Vis Sci 38, 1678 (1997); **46.** Am J Trop Med Hyg 59, 182 (1998); **47.** J Biol Chem 273, 28040 (1998); **48.** Invest Ophthalmol Vis Sci 41, 2849 (2000); **49.** Int J Parasitol 27, 787 (1997); **50.** M. Terasaki and L. Jaffe, personal communication; **51.** J Cell Biol 144, 813 (1999); **52.** Biophys J 77, 2871 (1999); **53.** Dev Biol 206, 232 (1999); **54.** Biotechniques 16, 441 (1994); **55.** US 5,418,169; **56.** J Microsc 157, 73 (1990); **57.** Proc Natl Acad Sci U S A 87, 9358 (1990); **58.** Proc Natl Acad Sci U S A 87, 6634 (1990); **59.** Biophys J 75, 1513 (1998); **60.** Cell 76, 609 (1994); **61.** Methods Mol Biol 29, 83 (1994); **62.** Biochemistry 18, 3354 (1979); **63.** Proc Natl Acad Sci U S A 72, 2915 (1975); **64.** Hum Genet 57, 1 (1981); **65.** Bioessays 15, 349 (1993); **66.** Am J Hum Genet 51, 17 (1992); **67.** Cytometry 11, 80 (1990); **68.** Cytometry 11, 184 (1990); **69.** Stain Technol 60, 7 (1985); **70.** Eur J Cell Biol 20, 290 (1980); **71.** Science 225, 57 (1984); **72.** Biopolymers 18, 1749 (1979); **73.** Cytometry 20, 296 (1995); **74.** Histochem J 17, 131 (1985); **75.** Exp Cell Res 117, 451 (1978); **76.** Neuroscience Protocols, Wouterlood FG, Ed. 93-050-12, pp. 01–07 (1993); **77.** Proc Natl Acad Sci U S A 77, 2260 (1980); **78.** J Neurosci Methods 33, 129 (1990); **79.** J Neurosci Methods 72, 49 (1997); **80.** Neurosci Lett 184, 169 (1995).

Product List — 8.6 Nuclear and Chromosome Counterstaining and Nissl Stains

Cat #	Product Name	Unit Size
A1310	7-aminoactinomycin D (7-AAD)	1 mg
A1324	9-amino-6-chloro-2-methoxyacridine (ACMA)	100 mg
B3582	BOBO™-1 iodide (462/481) *1 mM solution in DMSO*	200 µL
C7587	Chromosome Banding Kit #2 *SYTOX® Green/Methyl Green* *200 slides*	1 kit
C7590	Cytological Nuclear Counterstain Kit *DAPI/SYTOX® Green/PI* *300 slides*	1 kit
D1306	4',6-diamidino-2-phenylindole, dihydrochloride (DAPI)	10 mg
D21490	4',6-diamidino-2-phenylindole, dihydrochloride (DAPI) *FluoroPure™ grade*	10 mg
D3571	4',6-diamidino-2-phenylindole, dilactate (DAPI, dilactate)	10 mg
H1398	Hoechst 33258, pentahydrate (bis-benzimide)	100 mg
H3569	Hoechst 33258, pentahydrate (bis-benzimide) *10 mg/mL solution in water*	10 mL
H21491	Hoechst 33258, pentahydrate (bis-benzimide) *FluoroPure™ grade*	100 mg
H1399	Hoechst 33342, trihydrochloride, trihydrate	100 mg
H3570	Hoechst 33342, trihydrochloride, trihydrate *10 mg/mL solution in water*	10 mL
H21492	Hoechst 33342, trihydrochloride, trihydrate *FluoroPure™ grade*	100 mg
N21479	NeuroTrace® 435/455 blue fluorescent Nissl stain *solution in DMSO*	1 mL
N21480	NeuroTrace® 500/525 green fluorescent Nissl stain *solution in DMSO*	1 mL
N21481	NeuroTrace® 515/535 yellow fluorescent Nissl stain *solution in DMSO*	1 mL
N21482	NeuroTrace® 530/615 red fluorescent Nissl stain *solution in DMSO*	1 mL
N21483	NeuroTrace® 640/660 deep-red fluorescent Nissl stain *solution in DMSO*	1 mL
N21485	nuclear yellow (Hoechst S769121, trihydrochloride, trihydrate)	10 mg
P36931	ProLong® Gold antifade reagent with DAPI	10 mL
P36935	ProLong® Gold antifade reagent with DAPI *special packaging*	5 x 2 mL
P1304MP	propidium iodide	100 mg
P21493	propidium iodide *FluoroPure™ grade*	100 mg
P3566	propidium iodide *1.0 mg/mL solution in water*	10 mL
S24635	*SlowFade®* Antifade Kit with DAPI	1 kit
S24636	*SlowFade® Light* Antifade Kit with DAPI	1 kit
S7573	SYTO® 11 green fluorescent nucleic acid stain *5 mM solution in DMSO*	250 µL
S7574	SYTO® 12 green fluorescent nucleic acid stain *5 mM solution in DMSO*	250 µL
S7576	SYTO® 14 green fluorescent nucleic acid stain *5 mM solution in DMSO*	250 µL
S7578	SYTO® 16 green fluorescent nucleic acid stain *1 mM solution in DMSO*	250 µL
S7572	SYTO® Green Fluorescent Nucleic Acid Stain Sampler Kit #1 *SYTO® dyes 11-16* *50 µL each*	1 kit
S7554	SYTO® Green Fluorescent Nucleic Acid Stain Sampler Kit #2 *SYTO® dyes 20-25* *50 µL each*	1 kit
S11360	SYTO® Orange Fluorescent Nucleic Acid Stain Sampler Kit *SYTO® dyes 80-85* *50 µL each*	1 kit
S7579	SYTO® 17 red fluorescent nucleic acid stain *5 mM solution in DMSO*	250 µL
S11341	SYTO® 59 red fluorescent nucleic acid stain *5 mM solution in DMSO*	100 µL
S11340	SYTO® Red Fluorescent Nucleic Acid Stain Sampler Kit *SYTO® dyes 17 and 59-64* *50 µL each*	1 kit
S11348	SYTOX® Blue nucleic acid stain *5 mM solution in DMSO*	250 µL
S7020	SYTOX® Green nucleic acid stain *5 mM solution in DMSO*	250 µL
T3605	TO-PRO®-3 iodide (642/661) *1 mM solution in DMSO*	1 mL
T3600	TOTO®-1 iodide (514/533) *1 mM solution in DMSO*	200 µL
T3604	TOTO®-3 iodide (642/660) *1 mM solution in DMSO*	200 µL
Y3601	YOYO®-1 iodide (491/509) *1 mM solution in DMSO*	200 µL

For current prices or to order online, visit probes.invitrogen.com

8.7 Analysis of DNA Structure, DNA Binding and DNA Damage

Nucleic Acid Conformational Analysis

A number of conventional dyes have been used to analyze nucleic acid conformation *in vitro* and *in vivo*:

- Acridine orange (A1301, A3568; Section 8.1) is one of the most popular and versatile fluorescent stains for histochemistry and cytochemistry and can provide a wide variety of information about the *in situ* content, molecular structure, conformation and environment of many nucleic acid–containing cell constituents.[1]
- Fluorescence photobleaching of DNA that has been photolytically labeled with ethidium monoazide (E1374, Section 8.1) permits measurement of slow reorientational motions.[2]
- The fluorescence intensity and binding affinity of the Hoechst dyes appear to be highly dependent on the sequence and conformation of the DNA base pairs.[3–5] For example, staining by Hoechst 33258 (H1398, H3569; FluoroPure™ Grade, H21491; Section 8.1) can discriminate parallel and antiparallel stem regions in hairpin DNA conformations.[6]
- The fluorescence lifetime of the PicoGreen® dye (P7581, P11495; Section 8.3) bound to single-stranded DNA is reported to be different when bound to double-stranded DNA.[7]

We also anticipate that several of our cyanine dyes (Section 8.1) — in particular the SYTO® dyes (Table 8.3) — may be useful in these applications because many of these stains appear to yield environment-sensitive metachromatic shifts upon binding to nucleic acids. Fluorescence of the TOTO®-1, YOYO®-1, BOBO™-1 and POPO™-1 dyes (Table 8.2) is dependent on nucleic acid secondary structure; a shift to longer-wavelength emission and a concomitant drop in quantum yield are observed upon binding of these dyes to single-stranded nucleic acids at high dye:base ratios.[8] Most of our unsymmetrical cyanine dyes show this spectral shift, and some show sequence selectivity in their fluorescence intensity as well.

Examining the Behavior of Single Nucleic Acid Molecules

Once bound to nucleic acids, several of the cyanine dyes in Section 8.1 are so bright that they can be used to directly visualize single nucleic acid molecules in the fluorescence microscope (Figure 8.5, Figure 8.150). The YOYO®-1 and POPO™-3 dyes (Y3601, P3584) have also been used to follow the making and breaking of single chemical bonds.[9,10] A number of laboratories have taken advantage of the high sensitivity of these dyes to detect single nucleic acid molecules and to study biopolymer behavior:

- Video microscopy has been used to observe relaxation of YOYO®-1 dye–stained phage λ DNA multimers, after stretching in a fluid flow,[11] on a surface[12] or with optical tweezers.[13] TOTO®-1 dye (T3600) has also been used in this application.[14]
- Individual YOYO®-1 dye–ssDNA molecular complexes have been imaged in solution by fluorescence video microscopy.[15]
- Molecular combing, a technique that uses a receding fluid interface to elongate DNA molecules for optical mapping of genetic loci, was developed using the YOYO®-1 dye.[16]
- Adsorption and desorption of single molecules of YOYO®-1 dye–stained phage λ DNA have been observed on fused-silica and C_{18} chromatographic surfaces.[17]
- The activity of a single RecBCD enzyme, which unwinds and separates the strands of dsDNA, has been studied using YOYO®-1 dye–stained dsDNA in conjunction with optical tweezers and epifluorescence microscopy.[18,19]
- Our YOYO®-1 dye (Y3601) has been used to stain DNA manipulated in solution by changing electronic fields, a technique that could prove valuable in miniaturizing and automating the analysis of DNA fragments.[20]
- Staining with the YOYO®-1 dye (Y3601) was used to observe the interaction of DNA with various liposomes[21] and to size plasmids in a flowing stream.[22]

- The YOYO®-1 dye was also used to detect radiation-induced double-strand breaks in individual electrostretched bacterial DNA molecules.[23]
- Single-molecule imaging of nucleic acids stained with either YOYO®-1 or POPO™-3 or a combination of the two dyes through collection of the entire fluorescence spectrum of their complex has been reported.[24]
- Highly sensitive sheath-flow techniques have also been developed for detecting and discriminating the size of single TOTO®-1 dye–DNA molecular complexes.[25–27]
- Large fragments of DNA stained with our TOTO®-1 dye (T3600) have been sorted by flow cytometry. This extremely rapid analytical method yields a linear relationship between the fluorescence intensity and the fragment size over a 10–50 kb pair range.[28]
- The POPO™-1 and POPO™-3 stains (P3580, P3584) have been used to sensitively detect single DNA fragments by flow cytometry using two-photon fluorescence excitation.[29]
- The POPO™-3 dye (P3584) has been used to study a single chemical reaction with an individual DNA molecule. POPO™-3 dye–stained DNA molecules stretched taut on a glass surface relax when a focused laser beam causes fluorescence-related breakage of the DNA backbone, forming a gap that is visible by fluorescence microscopy.[9]
- The TOTO®-1 (T3600), YOYO®-1 (Y3601), POPO™-3 (P3584) and SYBR® Green I (S7563, S7567, S7585) dyes have been used to visualize λ DNA that has been stretched between beads with optical tweezers.[11,30–32]
- Fragment sizing on single molecules of dsDNA stained with our PicoGreen® reagent has also been reported.[33,34]
- The SYTOX® Orange dye (S11368) is the preferred dye for single-molecule sizing of DNA fragments by flow cytometry in an instrument equipped with a Nd:YAG laser.[35]
- DAPI (D1306, D3571; FluoroPure™ Grade, D21490) has also been employed to detect a single DNA molecule in solution[36] and by fluorescence microscopy[37] and to detect femtograms of DNA in single cells and chloroplasts.[38]

The high affinity and bright fluorescence of other cyanine dimers has allowed researchers to follow stained and transfected plasmids or stained virus particles within a cell.[39–43]

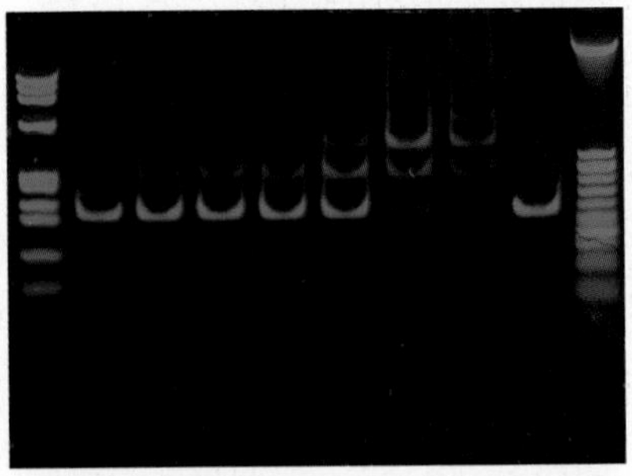

Figure 8.144 Electrophoretic bandshift assays using SYBR® Green I nucleic acid gel stain (S7563, S7567, S7585). The association between a 208-bp fragment purified from *Ava*I–digested plasmid p5S208-12 and a mutant restriction endonuclease (*Eco*RI/*Gln*111) was analyzed on a 4% native polyacrylamide gel. Samples containing approximately 50 ng total fragments and various amounts of the mutant enzyme were subjected to electrophoresis and stained with SYBR® Green I nucleic acid gel stain. Gel staining was visualized using 254 nm epi-illumination and then photographed using Polaroid 667 black-and-white print film and a SYBR® photographic filter (S7569). Lane 1 contains *Hae*III-digested φX174 RF DNA markers; lanes 2 through 9 contain 0, 0.05, 0.1, 0.2, 0.4, 0.6, 0.8 and 0 µM *Eco*RI/*Gln*111; lane 10 contains *Hha*I-digested plasmid p5S208-12 as a size standard.

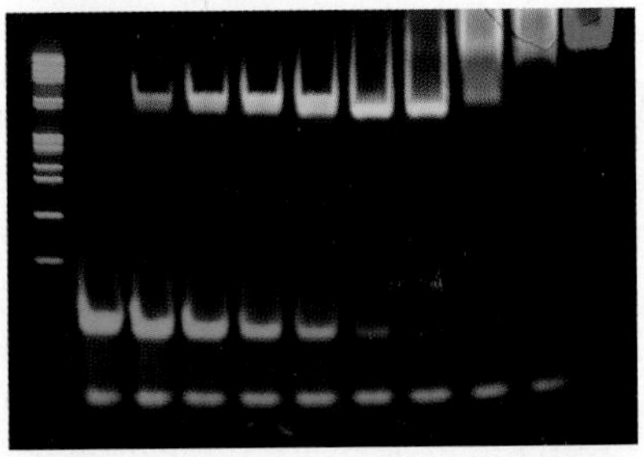

Figure 8.145 Titration of *lac* operator DNA with *lac* repressor protein. Increasing amounts of *lac* repressor protein were mixed with 40 ng of *lac* operator DNA, incubated for 20 minutes and then separated on a 6% nondenaturing polyacrylamide gel. The gel was stained with SYBR® Green EMSA stain (green) followed by SYPRO® Ruby EMSA stain (red), components of the Electrophoretic Mobility-Shift Assay Kit (E33075). After each staining, the image was documented using an FLA-3000 laser-based scanner (Fuji) and the digital images pseudocolored and overlaid. Yellow bands indicate areas stained with both stains.

DNA Binding Assays

Electrophoretic Mobility-Shift (Bandshift) Assays

Bandshift assays to analyze DNA–protein interactions are conventionally performed using radioactively labeled DNA fragments. However, use of our high-sensitivity fluorescent dyes makes these assays much simpler to perform and eliminates radioactive waste issues. For example, SYBR® Green I nucleic acid gel stain (S7567, S7563, S7585) has been used to stain gels after electrophoresis and can detect bound and unbound DNA fragments with high sensitivity[44] (Figure 8.144). The SYBR® Gold nucleic acid gel stain (S11494) is potentially even more useful in bandshift experiments because of its higher sensitivity.

Molecular Probes has made bandshift assays easy and more convenient with the Electrophoretic Mobility-Shift Assay (EMSA) Kit (E33075). Our EMSA Kit provides a fast and quantitative fluorescence-based method to detect both nucleic acid and protein in the same gel (Figure 8.145), doubling the information that can be obtained from bandshift assays. This kit uses two fluorescent dyes for detection — SYBR® Green EMSA nucleic acid gel stain for RNA or DNA and SYPRO® Ruby EMSA protein gel stain for proteins. Because the nucleic acids and proteins are stained in the gel after electrophoresis, there is no need to prelabel the DNA or RNA with a radioisotope, biotin or a fluorescent dye before the binding reaction, and therefore there is no possibility that the label will interfere with protein binding. Staining takes only about 20 minutes for the nucleic acid stain, and about 4 hours for the subsequent protein stain, yielding results much faster than radioisotope labeling (which may require multiple exposure times) or chemiluminescence-based detection (which requires blotting and multiple incubation steps). This kit also makes it possible to perform ratiometric measurements of nucleic acid and protein in the same band, providing more detailed information on the binding interaction. The signals from the two stains are linear over a broad range, allowing accurate determination of the amount of nucleic acid and protein, even in a single band, with detection limits of ~1 ng for nucleic acids and ~20 ng for protein. Both stains can be detected using a standard 300 nm UV illuminator, a 254 nm epi-illuminator or a laser scanner (Figure 8.145). Digital images can easily be overlaid for a two-color representation of nucleic acid and protein in the gel. The EMSA Kit contains sufficient reagents for 10 nondenaturing polyacrylamide minigel assays, including:

- SYBR® Green EMSA nucleic acid gel stain
- SYPRO® Ruby EMSA protein gel stain
- Trichloroacetic acid, for preparing the working solution of SYPRO® Ruby EMSA protein gel stain
- Concentrated EMSA gel-loading solution
- *lac* repressor, a DNA-binding protein to be used as a control
- *lac* operator, control DNA
- Concentrated buffer for the *lac* repressor:operator controls
- A detailed protocol

Fluorescent dyes have also been used to stain the DNA fragments or proteins before electrophoresis. For instance, proteins or DNA labeled covalently with a reactive fluorescent dye (Chapter 1, Section 8.2) can be easily tracked during capillary electrophoresis to monitor DNA–protein interactions.[45] High-affinity nucleic acid stains have also been used prior to electrophoresis, although they can potentially interfere with protein binding and alter mobility on the gel. The ethidium homodimer-1 (EthD-1, E1169; Section 8.1), YOYO®-1 and TOTO®-1 dyes have been shown by several laboratories to be useful tools for labeling DNA prior to electrophoresis in bandshift assays. EthD-1 and TOTO®-1 were used to examine interactions between the binding domain of the *Kluyveromyces lactis* heat shock transcription factor and its specific binding site.[46] YOYO®-1 dye has been used to study the association of *E. coli* RNA polymerase with DNA templates[47] and the binding of a heat-shock transcription factor to its promoter.[48] All 10 of our spectrally distinct (Figure 8.1), high-affinity dimeric cyanine dyes (Table 8.2) and the ethidium homodimers are potentially useful for multicomponent analysis in this application.

DNA Binding Assays in Solution

Molecular beacons exploit fluorescence resonance energy transfer (FRET) to simplify detection of nucleic acid hybridization in solution (Section 8.5, Figure 8.113). This method has also proven useful for studying DNA–protein interactions in solution. Binding of a molecular beacon to lactic dehydrogenase separated the fluorophore from the quencher on the two ends of the labeled oligonucleotide, resulting in an increase in fluorescence.[49] The assay is sufficiently accurate to measure binding constants. A molecular beacon was also used to develop a solution-based binding assay for α-CP_2, which is part of an RNA-binding complex.[50]

Selective Cleavage of Nucleic Acids with a Chemical Nuclease

The thiol-reactive iodoacetamide of 1,10-phenanthroline (P6879, Section 2.3) is a useful adjunct reagent for bandshift assays. Conjugation to thiol-containing ligands confers the metal-binding properties of this important complexing agent on the ligand. For example, the covalent copper–phenanthroline complex of oligonucleotides or nucleic acid–binding molecules in combination with hydrogen peroxide acts as a chemical nuclease to selectively cleave DNA or RNA.[51–57] This reagent can also be conjugated to proteins to detect nucleic acid binding and targeted cleavage.[58]

Assessing DNA Damage

Comet (Single-Cell Gel Electrophoresis) Assay to Detect Damaged DNA

The comet assay, or single-cell gel electrophoresis assay, is used for rapid detection and quantitation of DNA damage from single cells.[59–61] The comet assay is based on the alkaline lysis of labile DNA at sites of damage. Cells are immobilized in a thin agarose matrix on slides and gently lysed. When subjected to electrophoresis, the unwound, relaxed DNA migrates out of the cells. After staining with a nucleic acid stain, cells that have accumulated DNA damage exhibit brightly fluorescent comets, with tails of DNA fragmentation or unwinding (Figure 8.146). In contrast, cells with normal, undamaged DNA appear as round dots, because their intact DNA does not migrate out of the cell. The ease and sensitivity of the comet assay has provided a fast and convenient way to measure damage to human sperm DNA,[62] monitor the sensitivity of tumor cells to radiation damage[63] and assess the sensitivity of molluscan cells to toxins in the environment.[64] The comet assay can also be used in combination with FISH to identify specific sequences of damaged DNA.[63]

Comet assays have traditionally been performed using ethidium bromide (E1305, E3565) to stain the DNA;[60] however, our YOYO®-1 dye (Y3601) increases the sensitivity of the assay approximately eightfold as compared with ethidium bromide, and the fluorescence background from unbound YOYO®-1 dye is negligible.[61] Use of the SYBR® Gold and SYBR® Green I stains (Section 8.4) further improves the sensitivity of this assay.[65,66]

TUNEL Assay for In Situ Detection of Fragmented DNA

To detect fragmented DNA in labeled cells, terminal deoxynucleotidyl transferase (TdT) along with a fluorophore-, biotin-, or hapten-labeled dUTP can be added to cells. TdT adds the labeled nucleotide to all available 3′-ends — the more fragmented the DNA, the more 3′-ends are available and the brighter the fluorescent signal. Direct TUNEL assays using ChromaTide® BODIPY® FL-14-dUTP (C7614) to visualize DNA fragment ends are four times more sensitive than TUNEL assays using fluorescein-labeled dUTP[67–70] (Figure 15.84). Terminal deoxynucleotidyl transferase (TdT)–catalyzed incorporation of bromo dUTP into nucleic acids of apoptotic cells and detection of the incorporated BrdU with an antibody conjugate is the basis of the APO-BrdU TUNEL Assay Kit (A23210, Section 15.5). Indirect TUNEL assays using probes such as biotin-aha-dUTP or ChromaTide® DNP-11-dUTP (B32766, C7610MP; Section 8.2) allow for amplification of the signal with our fluorophore- or enzyme-conjugated streptavidin conjugates (Section 7.6, Table 7.22) or with anti-DNP antibody (Section 7.4). Several additional assays for apoptosis can be found in Section 15.5.

Microplate Assays for DNA Damage

Abasic sites in DNA can be generated spontaneously or through the action of free radicals, ionizing radiation or mutagens like MMS (methyl methanesulfonate). They are one of the most common lesions in DNA and are thought to be important intermediates in mutagenesis. A quick and sensitive microplate assay for abasic sites can be performed using ARP (A10550, Figure 8.147), a biotin hydroxylamine that reacts with the exposed aldehyde group at abasic sites. Biotins bound to the abasic sites can be quantitated with our fluorescent or enzyme-conjugated streptavidin complexes[71–74] (Section 7.6, Table

7.22). ARP is permeant to cell membranes, permitting detection of abasic sites in living cells.[75,76] Alexa Fluor® hydroxylamine derivatives (Section 3.2, Table 3.1) may have utility similar to that of ARP but will not be membrane permeant.

The PicoGreen® reagent has also been used to simplify denaturation assays for DNA damage. Strand breaks in dsDNA that result from DNA damage can be quantified by measuring the relative amounts of ssDNA and dsDNA in a damaged sample. The relative amounts of dsDNA to ssDNA can be assessed by measuring the increase in absorbance at 260 nm or by separating the two forms of DNA by alkaline sucrose gradient centrifugation,[77] filters[78] or hydroxyapatite chromatography.[79] However, the absorption-based technique suffers from low sensitivity and thus requires relatively large sample sizes,[80] and separation of ssDNA from dsDNA is laborious. This assay becomes much simpler and more sensitive using the PicoGreen® dsDNA quantitation reagent (P7581, P7589, P11495, P11496, R21495; Section 8.3), which preferentially detects dsDNA in the presence of ssDNA.[81–83] The dye can be added directly to the sample and the fluorescence read on a fluorescence microplate reader. This method makes it possible to screen large numbers of very small samples in a high-throughput setting. The PicoGreen® reagent was also used to develop a homogeneous PCR-based genotyping assay.[84] Because the products do not need to be run on a gel, the assay can be easily adapted for high throughput, particularly using the RediPlate™ 96 version of the PicoGreen® dsDNA quantitation assay (R21495, Section 8.3).

Assays for Enzymes that Modify Nucleic Acids

Gel Assays for DNase Detection

Our SYBR® Green I stain (S7563, S7567, S7585) has been used to develop DNase assays that show up to a 64-fold increase in sensitivity over similar ethidium bromide–based assays and up to 10,000-fold higher sensitivity than the traditional UV hyperchromicity assay. In a fast and simple assay, a single-length fragment of DNA can be incubated with the sample, followed by a short gel electrophoresis. Staining the gel with the SYBR® Green I dye permits easy detection of less than 10^{-5} Kunitz units (~5 pg) of DNase activity.[85] Even greater sensitivity can be achieved using the single radial enzyme diffusion (SRED) method,[86] in which the SYBR® Green I stain is mixed with DNA in melted agarose and the mixture is poured into a 2 mm thick slab. The sample to be tested is poured into 1.5 mm circular wells punched out of the solidified agarose slab. As the sample diffuses through the agarose, the DNase degrades the DNA, creating dark circles around the sample wells that do not show staining with the SYBR® Green I dye when illuminated with UV light. The radius of these dark circles is proportional to the level of DNase activity. This method allows detection of as little as 2×10^{-7} units (~0.1 pg) of DNase I or 2×10^{-6} (~0.9 pg) of DNase II. A third DNase assay — called the dried agarose film overlay (DAFO) method — uses the SYBR® Green I stain to detect the presence of DNase activity in a polyacrylamide gel, allowing the identification of DNase heterogeneity.[87] This method allows the detection of 4×10^{-6} units (~2 pg) DNase I or DNase II.

Solution Assays for Nuclease Detection

Contaminating DNases are often responsible for poor resolution of DNA fragments, degradation of samples and nicking of supercoiled

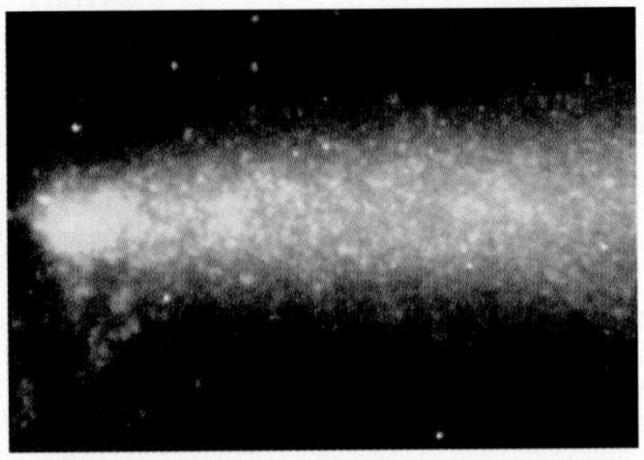

Figure 8.146 Comet assay with SYBR® Green I nucleic acid gel stain (S7563, S7567, S7585). DNA fragmentation associated with oxidative DNA damage was visualized using Trevigen's CometAssay kit. HL-60 cells were treated with H_2O_2 and immobilized onto a Trevigen CometSlide for analysis. The cells were gently lysed, washed and treated with endonuclease. Slides were subjected to electrophoresis in alkaline electrophoresis buffer and stained with SYBR® Green I stain.

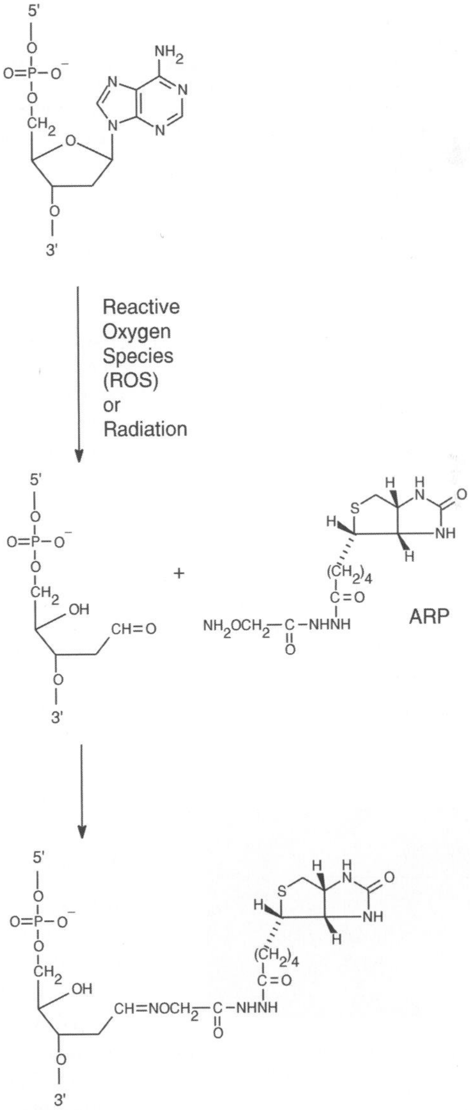

Figure 8.147 Aldehyde-reactive probe (ARP) used to detect DNA damage. The biotin hydroxylamine ARP (A10550) reacts with aldehyde groups formed when reactive oxygen species depurinate DNA. This reaction forms a covalent bond linking the DNA to biotin. The biotin can then be detected using a fluorophore- or enzyme-linked streptavidin.

Important Licensing Information

plasmids. Conventional DNase assays detect DNase activity by monitoring the increase in UV absorbance that occurs when the base pairs unstack as the DNA is degraded. This absorbance method, however, is intrinsically insensitive, as it requires large sample volumes and relies on small changes in absorbance. In contrast, our dyes for nucleic acid detection show a tremendous fluorescence increase upon binding to nucleic acids, but their fluorescence is not affected by the presence of a large excess of a nucleotide or very short oligonucleotides. Thus, nuclease activity can be easily and accurately measured by the decrease in fluorescence of the complex in the presence of one of these dyes. For example, the YOYO®-1 nucleic acid stain (Y3601) has been used in a fluorescence-based microplate assay for nuclease activity.[88] This assay takes advantage of the large fluorescence enhancement of the YOYO®-1 dye upon binding to nucleic acids and corresponding lack of fluorescence in the presence of released nucleotides and very small nucleic acid fragments. Other dyes — in particular our PicoGreen® dsDNA quantitation reagent (P7581, P11495; Section 8.3) — are likely to be more suitable for this assay. Similarly, use of the RiboGreen® RNA quantitation reagent (R11490, R11491; Section 8.3) should allow ultrasensitive detection of ribonuclease (RNase) activity.

Using a design similar to that of molecular beacons (Section 8.5), the stem sequence in an oligonucleotide hairpin loop can be modified to be a substrate for specific DNA cleavage agents, including nucleases. Dubbed a "break light," this substrate shows increased fluorescence as the cleavage agent breaks the DNA strand, separating the fluorophore from the quencher.[89,90]

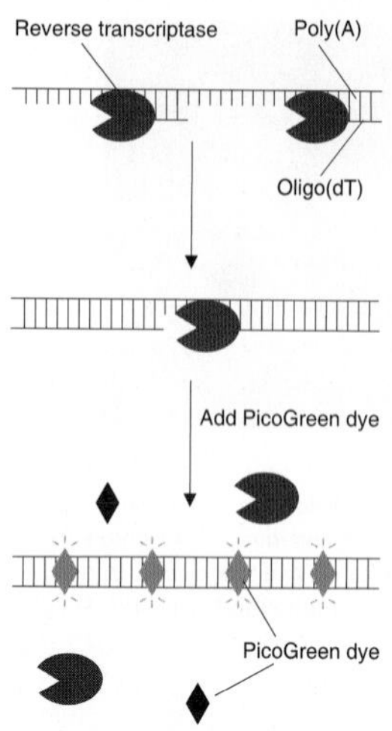

Figure 8.148 Schematic diagram of the mechanism used in the EnzChek® Reverse Transcriptase Assay Kit (E22064). A poly(A) substrate and oligo(dT) primers are provided in the EnzChek® Reverse Transcriptase Assay Kit; after hybridization, the primers can be elongated in the presence of reverse transcriptase and dTTP. The resulting DNA–RNA hybrid is detected using the PicoGreen® dsDNA detection reagent, which becomes fluorescent upon binding to DNA–RNA hybrids.

An Assay for Reverse Transcriptase Activity

The EnzChek® Reverse Transcriptase Assay Kit (E22064) is a convenient, efficient and inexpensive assay for measuring reverse transcriptase activity (Figure 8.148). The key to this method is our PicoGreen® dsDNA quantitation reagent, which preferentially detects dsDNA or RNA–DNA heteroduplexes over single-stranded nucleic acids or free nucleotides. In the assay, the sample to be measured is added to a mixture of a long poly(A) template, an oligo(dT) primer and dTTP. Reverse transcriptase activity in the sample results in the formation of long RNA–DNA heteroduplexes, which are detected by the PicoGreen® reagent at the end of the assay. In less than an hour, samples can be read in a fluorometer or microplate reader with filter sets appropriate for fluorescein (FITC). The assay is sensitive, detecting as little as 0.02 units of HIV reverse transcriptase, and has about a 50-fold linear range (Figure 8.149). Because it is much more rapid and less expensive than standard isotopic assays or immunoassays, it is suitable for testing large numbers of biological samples. The assay's simplicity also makes it useful for automated high-throughput screening of reverse transcriptase inhibitors.

The EnzChek® Reverse Transcriptase Assay Kit (E22064) contains:

- The PicoGreen® dsDNA quantitation reagent
- A λ DNA standard
- A poly(A) ribonucleotide template
- An oligo dT_{16} primer
- TE buffer, polymerization buffer and an EDTA solution
- A detailed protocol

Each kit provides sufficient reagents for approximately 1000 assays using a fluorescence microplate reader.

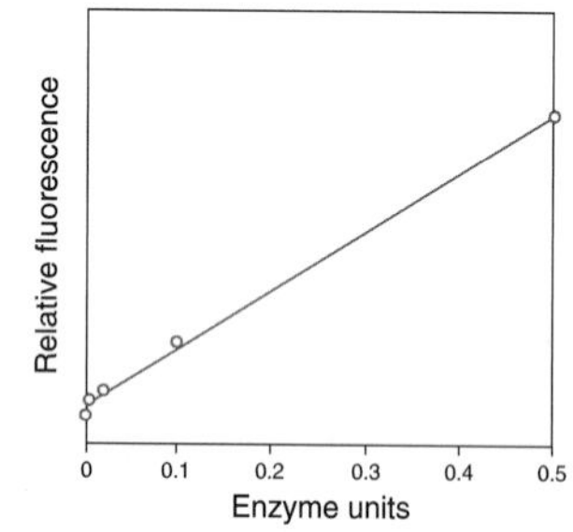

Figure 8.149 Detection of HIV reverse transcription using the EnzChek® Reverse Transcriptase Assay Kit (E22064), showing detection of 0.02 to 0.5 units of the enzyme. One unit of activity is defined as incorporation of 1 nanomole of dTTP in 10 minutes at 37°C, using poly(A) and oligo(dT) as the template and primer, respectively.

Telomerase

In a gel assay for detection of telomerase activity (the telomeric repeat amplification protocol, or TRAP) in human cells and tumors, SYBR® Green I dye staining was found to be more sensitive than silver staining and gave results comparable to those achieved with a radioisotope-based TRAP assay.[91–93] Moreover, unlike the silver stains, the SYBR® Green I stain did not label proteins carried over from the reaction mixture. The SYBR® Gold stain was also shown to be more sensitive than silver staining in the TRAP assay, and much easier to use.[94] The SYBR® Green I stain (S7567, S7563, S7585) has also been used to develop high-sensitivity assays to detect topoisomerase activity.[95]

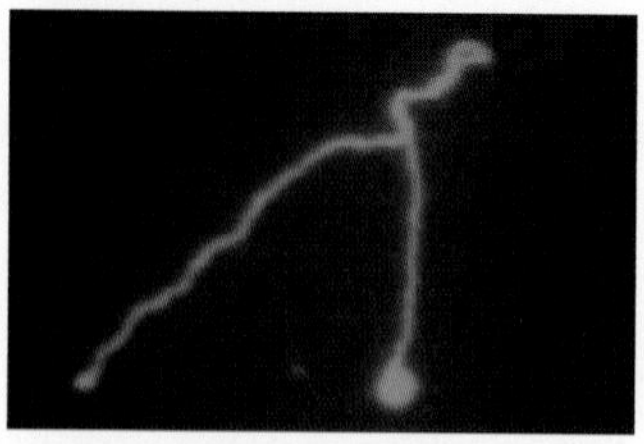

Figure 8.150 T2 phage genomic DNA stained with YOYO®-1 (Y3601), our high-affinity nucleic acid stain. This single 164-kilobase molecule, which appears to be supercoiling, was imaged under rigorously deoxygenated conditions with a cooled CCD camera. This work was performed in collaboration with Sergio Gurrieri and Carlos Bustamante, Institute of Molecular Biology, University of Oregon.

References

1. Flow Cytometry Sorting, 2nd Ed., Melamed MR, Lindmo T, Mendelsohn ML, Eds. pp. 291–314 (1990); **2.** Biophys J 53, 215 (1988); **3.** Biochemistry 30, 182 (1991); **4.** Biochemistry 29, 10181 (1990); **5.** Nucleic Acids Res 18, 3753 (1990); **6.** Science 241, 551 (1988); **7.** Chem Commun 689 (2000); **8.** FASEB J 7, A1087, abstract #205 (1993); **9.** Anal Chem 70, 1743 (1998); **10.** Proc Natl Acad Sci U S A 92, 2278 (1995); **11.** Science 264, 822 (1994); **12.** Biophys J 75, 513 (1998); **13.** Science 264, 819 (1994); **14.** Science 268, 83 (1995); **15.** C R Acad Sci III 316, 459 (1993); **16.** Science 265, 2096 (1994); **17.** Anal Chem 73, 1091 (2001); **18.** Biophotonics Int 48 (2001); **19.** Nature 409, 374 (2001); **20.** Biophys J 74, 1024 (1998); **21.** Science 281, 78 (1998); **22.** Cytometry 32, 132 (1998); **23.** Mutat Res 429, 159 (1999); **24.** Anal Chem 72, 4640 (2000); **25.** Anal Chem 67, 1755 (1995); **26.** Anal Chem 65, 849 (1993); **27.** Ber Bunsenges Phys Chem 97, 1535 (1993); **28.** Nucleic Acids Res 21, 803 (1993); **29.** Anal Chem 71, 2108 (1999); **30.** Cytometry 36, 200 (1999); **31.** Nature 399, 446 (1999); **32.** Paul Matsudaira, MIT Whitehead Institute, personal communication; **33.** Cytometry 41, 203 (2000); **34.** Anal Chem 71, 5470 (1999); **35.** Anal Biochem 286, 138 (2000); **36.** J Biochem (Tokyo) 89, 693 (1981); **37.** J Mol Biol 152, 501 (1981); **38.** J Histochem Cytochem 34, 761 (1986); **39.** J Neurosci 16, 7812 (1996); **40.** Proc Natl Acad Sci U S A 93, 12643 (1996); **41.** Virology 207, 345 (1995); **42.** Cell 76, 925 (1994); **43.** Plant Cell 5, 1783 (1993); **44.** J Biol Chem 274, 27287 (1999); **45.** Anal Chem 72, 5583 (2000); **46.** J Biol Chem 268, 25229 (1993); **47.** Proc Natl Acad Sci U S A 91, 6870 (1994); **48.** J Biol Chem 271, 32168 (1996); **49.** Anal Chem 72, 3280 (2000); **50.** Nucleic Acids Res 28, 4306 (2000); **51.** Nucleic Acids Res 22, 4789 (1994); **52.** Proc Natl Acad Sci U S A 91, 1721 (1994); **53.** Biochemistry 33, 3848 (1994); **54.** Bioconjug Chem 4, 69 (1993); **55.** Methods Enzymol 208, 414 (1991); **56.** J Am Chem Soc 111, 4941 (1989); **57.** Proc Natl Acad Sci U S A 86, 9702 (1989); **58.** Science 265, 959 (1994); **59.** Methods Mol Biol 100, 301 (1998); **60.** Exp Cell Res 175, 184 (1988); **61.** Int J Radiat Biol 66, 23 (1994); **62.** Mol Hum Reprod 2, 613 (1996); **63.** Mutagenesis 13, 1 (1998); **64.** Mutat Res 399, 87 (1998); **65.** Mutat Res 466, 63 (2000); **66.** Biotechniques 27, 846 (1999); **67.** Cytometry 27, 1 (1997); **68.** Exp Cell Res 222, 28 (1996); **69.** Cell Prolif 28, 571 (1995); **70.** Cytometry 20, 172 (1995); **71.** Anal Biochem 267, 331 (1999); **72.** Biochemistry 11, 3610 (1972); **73.** Biochemistry 31, 3703 (1992); **74.** Biochemistry 32, 8276 (1993); **75.** Proc Natl Acad Sci U S A 97, 686 (2000); **76.** J Biol Chem 275, 6741 (2000); **77.** Nature 209, 49 (1966); **78.** Biochemistry 15, 4629 (1976); **79.** DNA Repair. A Laboratory Manual of Research Procedures, Vol. 1, Part B, Friedberg EC, Hanawalt PC, E pp. 403–418 (1973); **80.** Chemical Basis of Radiation Biology pp. 194–220 (1989); **81.** Anal Biochem 270, 195 (1999); **82.** Anal Chem 71, 4423 (1999); **83.** Cell Mol Biol (Noisy-le-grand) 45, 211 (1999); **84.** Biotechniques 24, 206 (1998); **85.** FASEB J 9, A1400, abstract #836 (1995); **86.** Anal Biochem 255, 274 (1998); **87.** Electrophoresis 19, 2416 (1998); **88.** Biotechniques 18, 231 (1995); **89.** Proc Natl Acad Sci U S A 97, 13537 (2000); **90.** Nucleic Acids Res 28, E32 (2000); **91.** J Biol Chem 274, 7264 (1999); **92.** Biotechniques 25, 660 (1998); **93.** Methods Cell Sci 17, 1 (1995); **94.** Mol Pathol 51, 342 (1998); **95.** J Biol Chem 272, 21927 (1997).

Product List — 8.7 Analysis of DNA Structure, DNA Binding and DNA Damage

Cat #	Product Name	Unit Size
A10550	*N*-(aminooxyacetyl)-*N'*-(D-biotinoyl) hydrazine, trifluoroacetic acid salt (ARP)	10 mg
C7614	ChromaTide® BODIPY® FL-14-dUTP *1 mM in TE buffer*	25 µL
D1306	4',6-diamidino-2-phenylindole, dihydrochloride (DAPI)	10 mg
D21490	4',6-diamidino-2-phenylindole, dihydrochloride (DAPI) *FluoroPure™ grade*	10 mg
D3571	4',6-diamidino-2-phenylindole, dilactate (DAPI, dilactate)	10 mg
E33075	Electrophoretic Mobility-Shift Assay (EMSA) Kit *with SYBR® Green and SYPRO® Ruby EMSA stains* *10 minigel assays*	1 kit
E22064	EnzChek® Reverse Transcriptase Assay Kit *1000 assays*	1 kit
E1305	ethidium bromide	1 g
E3565	ethidium bromide *10 mg/mL solution in water*	10 mL
P3580	POPO™-1 iodide (434/456) *1 mM solution in DMSO*	200 µL
P3584	POPO™-3 iodide (534/570) *1 mM solution in DMF*	200 µL
S11494	SYBR® Gold nucleic acid gel stain *10,000X concentrate in DMSO*	500 µL
S7563	SYBR® Green I nucleic acid gel stain *10,000X concentrate in DMSO*	500 µL
S7567	SYBR® Green I nucleic acid gel stain *10,000X concentrate in DMSO*	1 mL
S7585	SYBR® Green I nucleic acid gel stain *10,000X concentrate in DMSO* *special packaging*	20 x 50 µL
S11368	SYTOX® Orange nucleic acid stain *5 mM solution in DMSO*	250 µL
T3600	TOTO®-1 iodide (514/533) *1 mM solution in DMSO*	200 µL
Y3601	YOYO®-1 iodide (491/509) *1 mM solution in DMSO*	200 µL

For current prices or to order online, visit probes.invitrogen.com

ELF 97 Endogenous Phosphatase Detection Kit

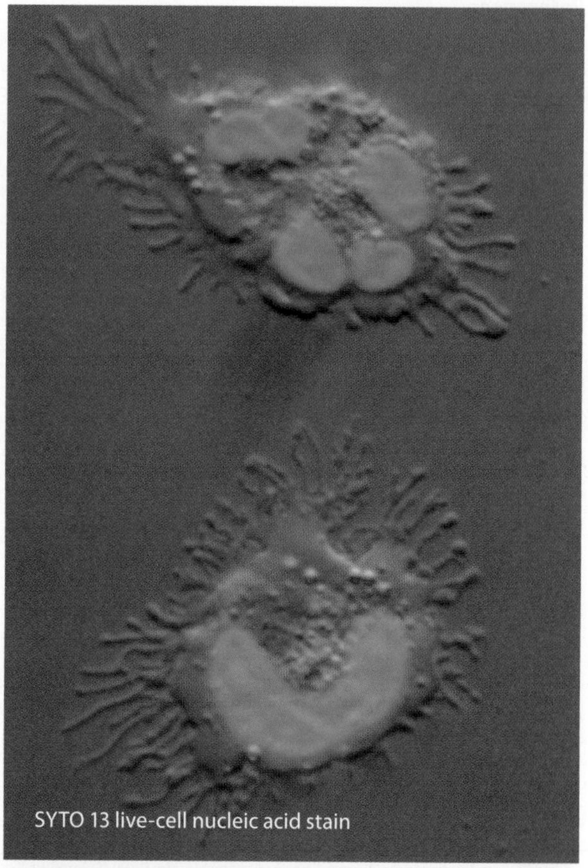

SYTO 13 live-cell nucleic acid stain

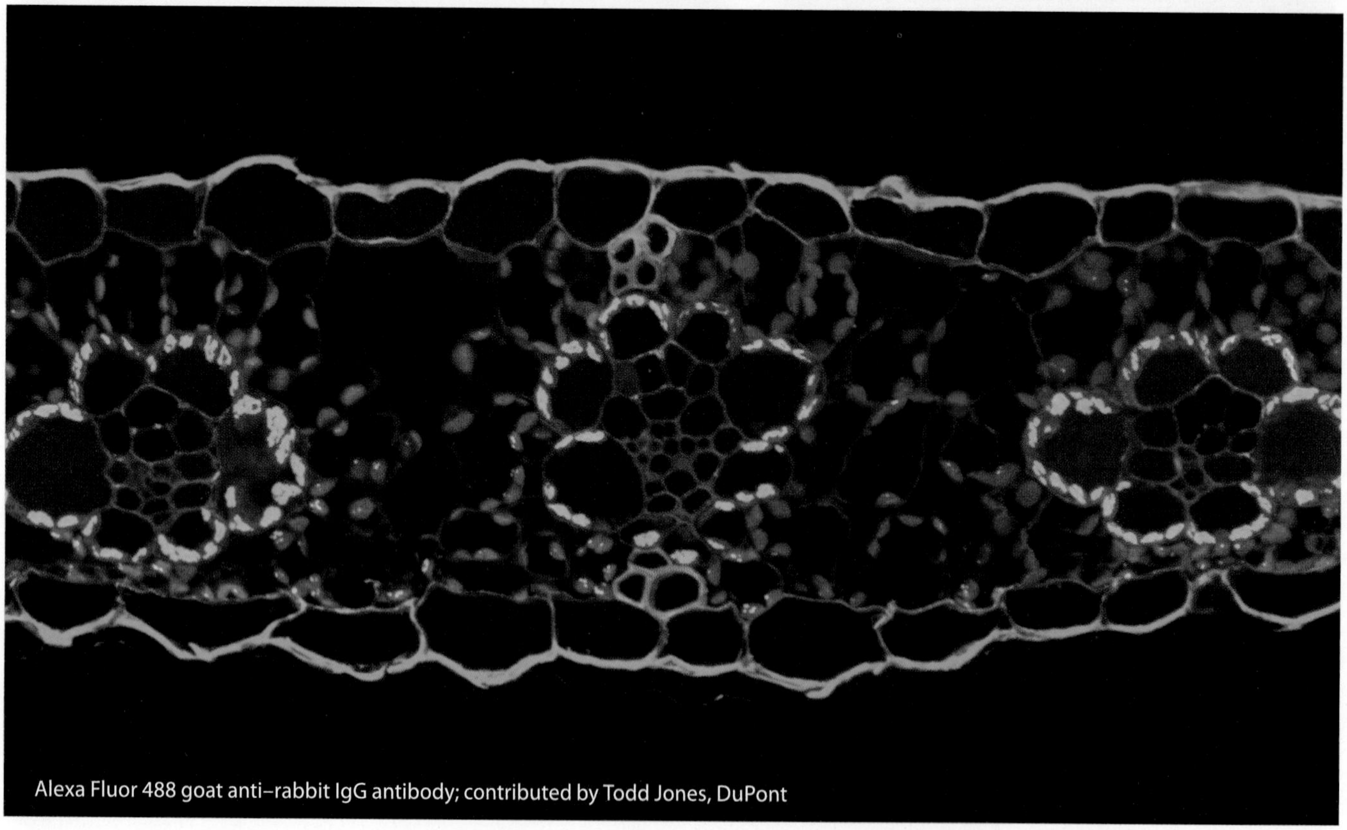

Alexa Fluor 488 goat anti–rabbit IgG antibody; contributed by Todd Jones, DuPont

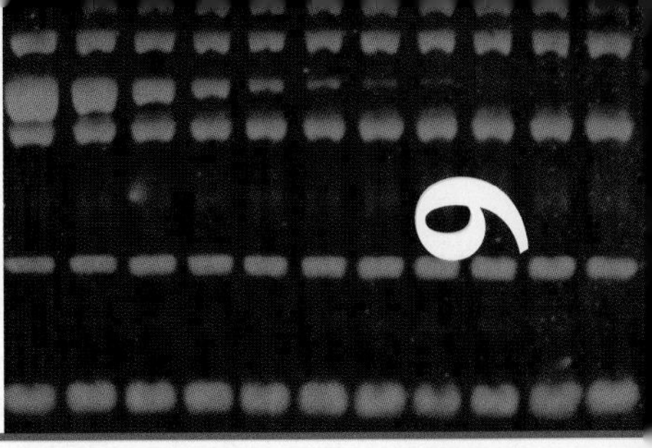

Chapter 9

Protein Detection and Proteomics Technology

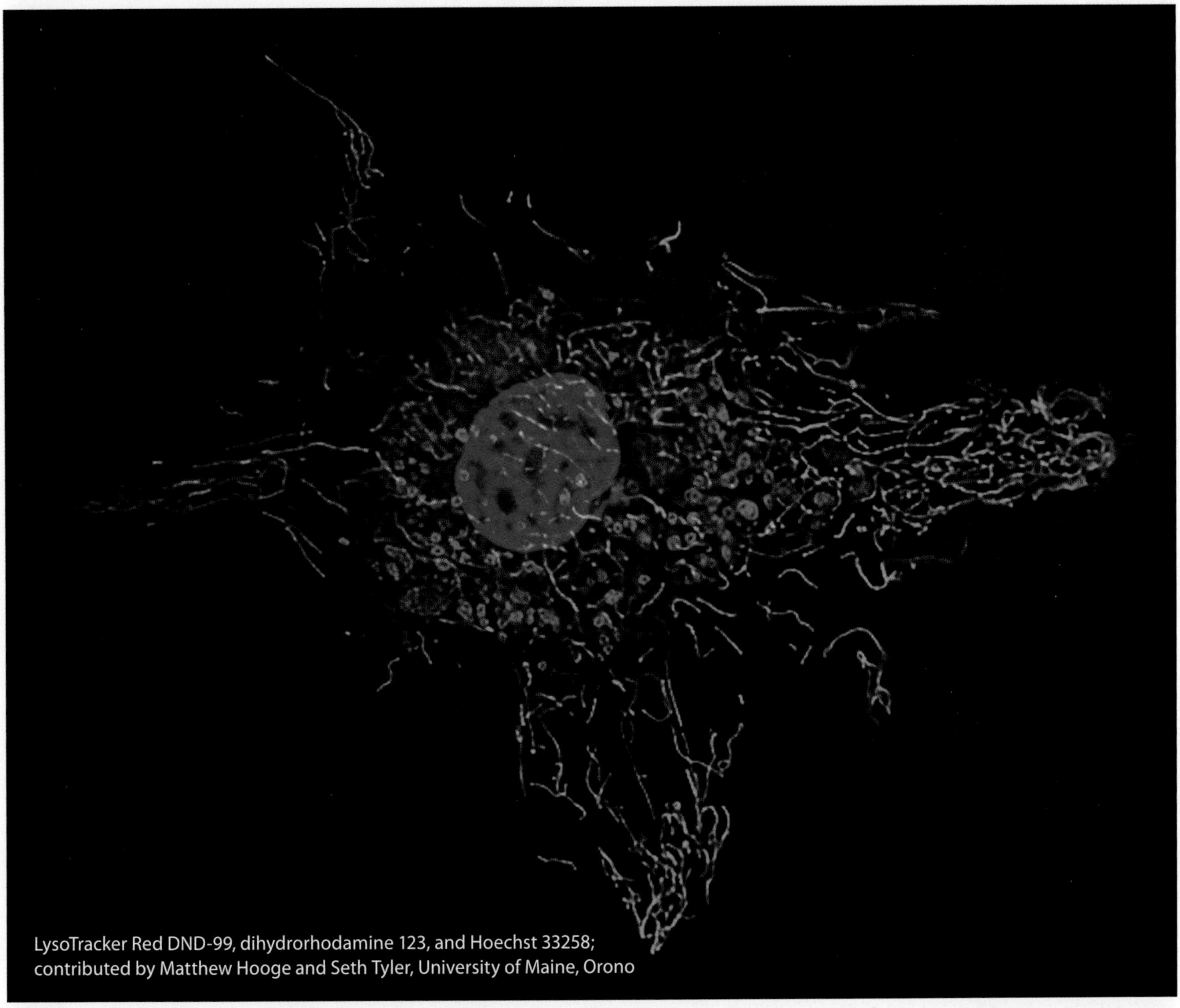

LysoTracker Red DND-99, dihydrorhodamine 123, and Hoechst 33258; contributed by Matthew Hooge and Seth Tyler, University of Maine, Orono

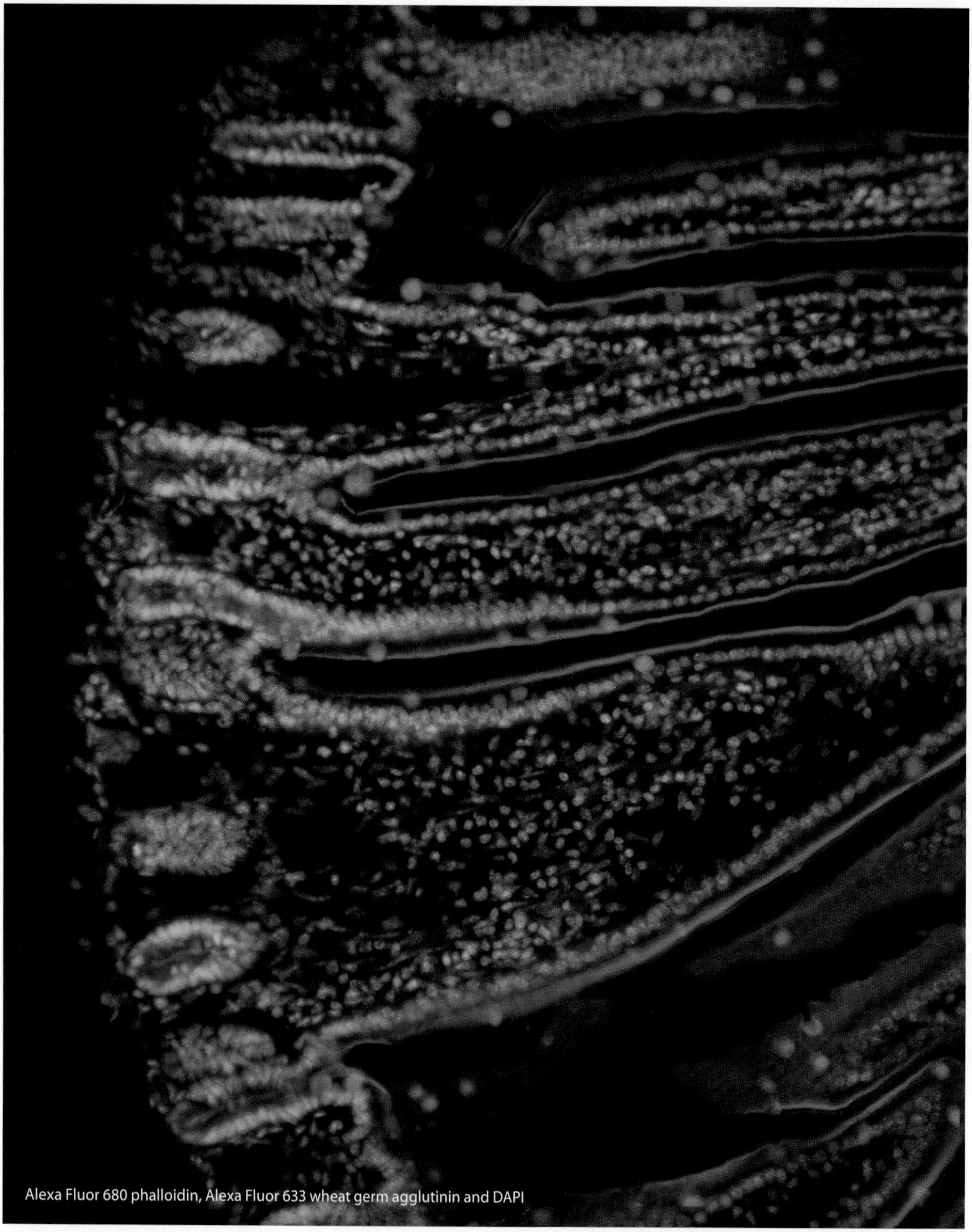
Alexa Fluor 680 phalloidin, Alexa Fluor 633 wheat germ agglutinin and DAPI

9.1 Introduction to Protein Detection

Proteomics: A Rapidly Developing Field

For decades, polyacrylamide gel electrophoresis and related blotting techniques have formed the core technologies for protein analysis. Traditionally, these technologies have been paired with chromogenic dye–based protein detection techniques, such as silver or Coomassie brilliant blue staining. However, with the rapid growth of proteomics[1] (Figure 9.1), the limitations and experimental disadvantages of absorption-based detection technologies and labor-intensive silver staining techniques have become glaringly apparent. The field of proteomics requires new, highly quantitative electrophoresis and blotting techniques that can interface seamlessly with improved microanalysis methods and that can perform in an increasingly high-throughput environment. These requirements are particularly important for quantitative proteomics and our Multiplexed Proteomics® technology.

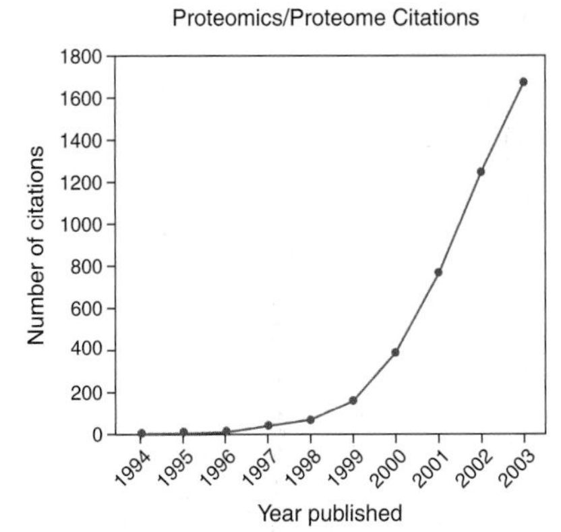

Figure 9.1 Growth of proteomics. Using the search parameter "proteome*" the NCBI database was queried for citations. The number of citations in each year plotted against the year shows the tremendous increase in research and interest in the proteomics field.

Molecular Probes' Detection Technology for Proteomics

Molecular Probes is meeting the demands of the rapidly expanding field of proteomics through the development of fluorescence- and luminescence-based detection methods for proteins in solutions, in gels and on blots and microarrays. Several seminal papers describe our novel technologies and their applications (see Note 9.1 "Technical Focus: Seminal Articles Using Molecular Probes' Luminescence-Based Protein Detection Technologies"). We are continuing to develop new reagents and detection methods for proteins and their modifications, such as phosphorylation, glycosylation and epitope tags, as well as improved methods of separating and analyzing peptides and proteins. Our advanced technologies are compatible with modern needs for sensitivity, specificity, sequencing compatibility, automatability and accurate quantitation capabilities. Application of our unique detection reagents requires minimal investment in labor, as compared with older technologies, while significantly increasing throughput, reducing total cost and accelerating discovery. Furthermore, the greater sensitivity and linearity of most of our premier reagents makes it possible to do quantitative proteomics and perform comparative protein expression measurements on very small samples.

Note 9.1 — Technical Focus

Seminal Articles Using Molecular Probes' Luminescence-Based Protein Detection Technologies

Reviews

"Detection technologies in proteome analysis." W.F. Patton, J Chromatogr B Analyt Technol Biomed Life Sci 771, 3 (2002).

"Making blind robots see: The synergy between fluorescent dyes and imaging devices in automated proteomics." W.F. Patton, Biotechniques 28, 944 (2000).

"A thousand points of light: The application of fluorescence detection technologies to two-dimensional gel electrophoresis and proteomics." W.F. Patton, Electrophoresis 21, 1123 (2000).

"Better approaches to finding the needle in a haystack: Optimizing proteome analysis through automation." M.F. Lopez, Electrophoresis 21, 1082 (2000).

NanoOrange® Protein Quantitation Assay

"Development and characterization of the NanoOrange® protein quantitation assay: A fluorescence-based assay of proteins in solution." L.J. Jones, R.P. Haugland, V.L Singer, Biotechniques 34, 850 (2003).

Pro-Q® Diamond Phosphoprotein Gel and Blot Stains

"Strategies and solid-phase formats for the analysis of protein and peptide phosphorylation employing a novel fluorescent phosphorylation sensor dye." K. Martin et al., Comb Chem High Throughput Screen 6, 331 (2003).

"Analysis of steady-state protein phosphorylation in mitochondria using a novel fluorescent phosphosensor dye." B. Schulenberg et al., J Biol Chem 278, 27251 (2003).

"Quantitative analysis of protein phosphorylation status and protein kinase activity on microarrays using a novel fluorescent phosphorylation sensor dye." K. Martin et al., Proteomics 3, 1244 (2003).

"Global quantitative phosphoprotein analysis using multiplexed proteomics technology." T.H. Steinberg et al., Proteomics 3, 1128 (2003).

Pro-Q® Emerald Glycoprotein Gel and Blot Stains

"Rapid and simple single nanogram detection of glycoproteins in polyacrylamide gels and on electroblots." T.H. Steinberg et al., Proteomics 1, 841 (2001).

continued on next page

Multiplexed Proteomics® Technology

Fluorescence- or luminescence-based detection technologies also offer the opportunity for multicolor labeling, making multiplexed analysis possible (Figure 9.2). In particular, Molecular Probes' Multiplexed Proteomics® technology creates the ability to identify specific proteins within the context of the entire protein profile. This multiparameter staining capability uses our luminescence-based total-protein stains together with our novel fluorescence-based technologies for detection of specific proteins and protein modifications (for example, phosphorylation, glycosylation and epitope tags). Simultaneous measurement of several variables greatly increases the amount of data that can be collected in a single experiment. In addition, directly comparing multiple measurements leads to more controlled experiments, more accurate data and fewer ambiguities. The detection characteristics of our Multiplexed Proteomics® portfolio of products greatly streamline protocols for whole-proteome analysis and promise to bring to proteomics the same capability for rapid, large-scale data acquisition that fluorescence has brought to genomics and other fields.

Molecular Probes' Reagents and Kits for Proteomics

In this chapter, Section 9.2 includes our reagents and kits (including the Quant-iT™, NanoOrange®, CBQCA and EZQ® protein quantitation reagents) for quantitating proteins and certain protein modifications in solution. Section 9.3 includes our important SYPRO® stains for detecting and quantitating total proteins in gels and on blots. The unique reagents for our Multiplexed Proteomics® technology in Section 9.4 include several important products that permit qualita-

continued from previous page

Pro-Q® Sapphire Oligohistidine Gel Stains

"Fluorescence detection and quantitation of recombinant proteins containing oligohistidine tag sequences directly in sodium dodecyl sulfate–polyacrylamide gels." C. Hart et al., Electrophoresis 24, 599 (2003).

SYPRO® Ruby Protein Gel Stain

"Quantitative evaluation of proteins in one- and two-dimensional polyacrylamide gels using a fluorescent stain." J.C. Nishihara and K.M Champion, Electrophoresis 23, 2203 (2002).

"A novel subfractionation approach for mitochondrial proteins, a three-dimensional mitochondrial proteome map." B.J. Hanson et al., Electrophoresis 22, 950 (2001).

"Mass spectrometry compatibility of two-dimensional gel protein stains." W.M. Lauber et al., Electrophoresis 22, 906 (2001).

"Comparison of three different fluorescent visualization strategies for detecting *Escherichia coli* ATP synthase subunits after sodium dodecyl sulfate-polyacrylamide gel electrophoresis." K.N. Berggren et al., Proteomics 1, 54 (2001).

"A comparison of silver stain and SYPRO® Ruby protein gel stain with respect to protein detection in two-dimensional gels and identification by peptide mass profiling." M.F. Lopez et al., Electrophoresis 21, 3673 (2000).

"Postelectrophoretic staining of proteins separated by two-dimensional gel electrophoresis using SYPRO® dyes." J.X. Yan et al., Electrophoresis 21, 3657 (2000).

"Background-free, high sensitivity staining of proteins in one- and two-dimensional sodium dodecyl sulfate-polyacrylamide gels using a luminescent ruthenium complex." K. Berggren et al., Electrophoresis 21, 2509 (2000).

"The current state of two-dimensional electrophoresis with immobilized pH gradients." A. Görg et al., Electrophoresis 21, 1037 (2000).

SYPRO® Ruby and SYPRO® Rose Plus Protein Blot Stains

"A luminescent ruthenium complex for ultrasensitive detection of proteins immobilized on membrane supports." K. Berggren et al., Anal Biochem 276, 129 (1999).

"Herp, a new ubiquitin-like membrane protein induced by endoplasmic reticulum stress." K. Kokame et al., J Biol Chem 275, 32846 (2000).

"An improved, luminescent europium-based stain for detection of electroblotted proteins on nitrocellulose or polyvinylidene difluoride membranes." C. Kemper et al., Electrophoresis 22, 881 (2001).

SYPRO® Orange and SYPRO® Red Protein Gel Stains

"Analysis of tear protein patterns of dry-eye patients using fluorescent staining dyes and two-dimensional quantification algorithms." F.H. Grus, P. Sabuncuo, A.J. Augustin, Electrophoresis 22, 1845 (2001).

"Green-light transilluminator for the detection without photodamage of proteins and DNA labeled with different fluorescent dyes." F.J. Alba, A. Bermudez, J.R. Daban, Electrophoresis 22, 399 (2001).

"Optimal filter combinations for photographing SYPRO® Orange or SYPRO® Red dye-stained gels." T.H. Steinberg, H.M. White, V.L. Singer, Anal Biochem 248, 168 (1997).

"Applications of SYPRO® Orange and SYPRO® Red protein gel stains." T.H. Steinberg, R.P. Haugland, V.L. Singer, Anal Biochem 239, 238 (1996).

"SYPRO® Orange and SYPRO® Red protein gel stains: One-step fluorescent staining of denaturing gels for detection of nanogram levels of protein." T.H. Steinberg et al., Anal Biochem 239, 223 (1996).

SYPRO® Tangerine Protein Gel Stain

"Simultaneous, two-color fluorescence detection of total protein profiles and β-glucuronidase activity in polyacrylamide gel." C. Kemper et al., Electrophoresis 22, 970 (2001).

"Fluorescence detection of proteins in sodium dodecyl sulfate-polyacrylamide gels using environmentally benign, nonfixative, saline solution." T.H. Steinberg et al., Electrophoresis 21, 497 (2000).

DyeChrome™ Western Blot Stain Kits

"A novel subfractionation approach for mitochondrial proteins: A three-dimensional mitochondrial proteome map." B.J. Hanson et al., Electrophoresis 22, 950 (2001).

"Green/red dual fluorescence detection of total protein and alkaline phosphate-conjugated probes on blotting membranes." K.P. Top et al., Electrophoresis 22, 896 (2001).

Rhinohide™ Polyacrylamide Gel Strengthener

"An improved mechanically durable electrophoresis gel matrix that is fully compatible with fluorescence-based protein detection technologies." B. Schulenberg, B. Arnold, W.F. Patton. Proteomics 3, 1196 (2003).

tive and quantitative detection of specific proteins or modifications of proteins, including protein phosphorylation and glycosylation. Among these are the following products:

- Pro-Q® Diamond phosphoprotein gel stain (P33300, P33301, P33302) — a breakthrough technology for selectively detecting phosphoproteins in polyacrylamide gels
- Pro-Q® Emerald 300 and Pro-Q® Emerald 488 glycoprotein gel and blot stains — the world's best and easiest stains for detecting periodate-oxidized glycoproteins in gels and on blots
- Pro-Q® Sapphire 365 and Pro-Q® Sapphire 488 oligohistidine gel stains for fast and easy detection of oligohistidine fusion proteins in gels
- Amplex® Gold Western Blot Stain Kits for staining horseradish peroxidase–labeled targets on Western blots
- Pro-Q® Western Blot Stain Kits for staining alkaline phosphatase–labeled targets on Western blots
- DyeChrome™ Western Blot Stain Kits for simultaneous dichromatic staining of total proteins and specific proteins on blots (and probably microarrays)
- DyeChrome™ Double Western Blot Stain Kit (D21887) — the first technology that permits simultaneous trichromatic detection of total proteins and two different specific proteins or protein modifications on a single Western blot
- The BOLD APB chemiluminescent substrate (B21901) for ultrasensitive detection of alkaline phosphatase conjugates on PVDF or nitrocellulose membranes

Section 9.5 describes reagents used in the synthesis of fluorescent dye– or hapten-labeled peptides and fluorogenic protease substrates, as well as in peptide analysis and sequencing.

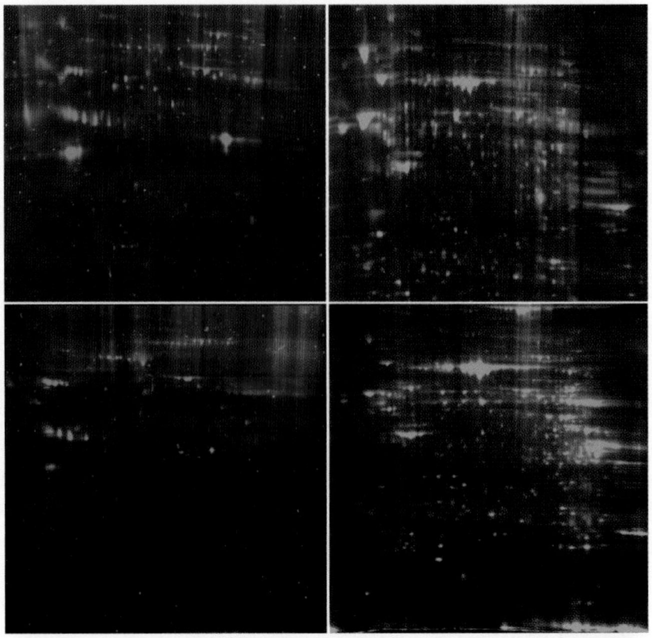

Figure 9.2 2-D protein gels of tumor vs. normal cells stained for glycoproteins and total proteins. Lysates from rat liver tumor cells (top panels) or rat normal liver cells (bottom panels) were run on identical 2-D gels. Following electrophoresis, the gels were stained with the Pro-Q® Emerald 300 glycoprotein detection reagent (left panels) (available in the Pro-Q® Emerald 300 Kits P21855 and P21857). After documentation of the fluorescence signal, the gel was stained with the SYPRO® Ruby protein gel stain (right panels) (S12000, S12001, S21900).

Reference

1. Proteomics 1, 169 (2001).

9.2 Quantitation and Selective Purification of Proteins in Solution

Several colorimetric methods have been described for quantitating proteins in solution, including the widely used Bradford[1] and Lowry[2] assays, as well as an assay described by Smith[3] that uses bicinchoninic acid (BCA). However, because they rely on absorption-based measurements, these methods are inherently limited in both sensitivity and effective range. Molecular Probes has developed four unique fluorometric methods for quantitating proteins in solution — the Quant-iT™ Protein Assay Kit (Q33210), the NanoOrange® Protein Quantitation Kit (N6666), the CBQCA Protein Quantitation Kit (C6667) and the EZQ® Protein Quantitation Kit (R33200) — that outperform *all* existing methods (Table 9.1). We also offer several other fluorescent reagents useful for protein detection in solution.

Quant-iT™ Protein Assay Kit

The Quant-iT™ family of assay kits provides state-of-the-art reagents for sensitive and selective quantitation of protein (Table 9.1), DNA or RNA (Table 8.12) samples using a standard fluorescence microplate reader. These kits have been specially formulated with ready-to-use buffers, prediluted standards and easy-to-follow instructions, making quantitation both accurate and extremely easy (Figure 8.52). Each Quant-iT™ assay is:

- **Ready to use.** Only the dye is diluted in the supplied buffer; no dilution of standards or buffer required.
- **Easy to perform.** Just add the sample to the diluted dye and read the fluorescence.
- **Highly sensitive.** The Quant-iT™ protein assay is orders of magnitude more sensitive than UV absorbance measurements.
- **Highly selective.** Separate kits are available for quantitating DNA, RNA (Section 8.3) or protein (see below), with minimal interference from common contaminants.
- **Precise.** CVs are generally less than 5% for typical users.

Because the fluorescent dye in each Quant-iT™ Kit matches common fluorescence excitation and emission filter sets in microplate readers, these assay kits are ideal for high-throughput environments, as well as for small numbers of samples.

The Quant-iT™ Protein Assay Kit (Q33210) simplifies protein quantitation without sacrificing sensitivity. This protein assay exhibits a detection range between 0.25 and 5 µg protein (Figure 9.3), and the response curve is sigmoidal (pseudolinear from 0.5 to 4 µg) with little protein-to-protein difference in signal intensity. Common contaminants, including salts, solvents, 2-mercaptoethanol, amino acids and DNA, are well tolerated in this assay; however, it is not compatible with detergents. Each Quant-iT™ Protein Assay Kit contains:

- Quant-iT™ protein reagent
- Quant-iT™ protein buffer
- A set of eight prediluted bovine serum albumin (BSA) standards between 0 and 500 ng/µL
- Easy-to-follow instructions

Sufficient reagents are provided to perform 1000 assays, based on a 200 µL assay volume in a 96-well microplate format; this assay can

Table 9.1 — A comparison of reagents for detecting and quantitating proteins in solution

Assay	Detection Wavelength(s) (nm) *	Sensitivity and Effective Range	Mechanism of Action	Notes
Quant-iT™ protein quantitation assay (Q33210)	470/570	Pseudolinear from 0.5 to 4 µg in a 200 µL assay volume, with a sample volume of 1–20 µL	Binds to detergent coating on proteins and hydrophobic regions of proteins; the unbound dye is nonfluorescent	• Extremely fast and easy — just add sample to diluted dye and read fluorescence • High sensitivity • Little protein-to-protein variation • Compatible with salts, solvents, 2-mercapto-ethanol, amino acids and DNA, but not detergents
NanoOrange® protein quantitation assay (N6666)	470/570	10 ng/mL to 10 µg/mL	Binds to detergent coating on proteins and hydrophobic regions of proteins; the unbound dye is nonfluorescent	• High sensitivity • Little protein-to-protein variation • Rapid and accurate assay with a simple procedure • Compatible with reducing agents, but not detergents
CBQCA protein quantitation assay (C6667)	450/550	10 ng/mL to 150 µg/mL	Reacts with primary amine groups on proteins in the presence of cyanide or thiols; the unreacted dye is nonfluorescent	• High sensitivity • Sensitivity depends on the number of amines present • Linear over an extended range of protein concentration • Compatible with detergents and lipophilic proteins • Not compatible with buffers containing amines or thiols
EZQ® protein quantitation assay (R33200)	280 and 450/618	50 µg/mL to 5 mg/mL, with a sample volume of 1 µL	Binds to detergent coating on proteins and hydrophobic regions of proteins; the unbound dye is nonfluorescent	• Ideal for determining protein concentration prior to electrophoresis • Solid-phase format designed for high-throughput analysis • Little protein-to-protein variation • Compatible with detergents, reducing agents, urea and tracking dyes
Bradford assay [1] (Coomassie brilliant blue)	595	1 µg/mL to 1.5 mg/mL	Directly binds specific amino acids and protein tertiary structures; the dye's color changes from brown to blue	• High protein-to-protein variation • Not compatible with detergents • Rapid assay • Useful when accuracy is not crucial
BCA method [2] (bicinchoninic acid)	562	0.5 µg/mL to 1.2 mg/mL	Cu^{2+} is reduced to Cu^{+} in the presence of proteins at high pH; the BCA reagent chelates Cu^{+} ions, forming purple-colored complexes	• Compatible with detergents, chaotropes and organic solvents • Not compatible with reducing agents • The sample must be read within 10 minutes
Lowry assay [3] (biuret reagent plus Folin–Ciocalteu reagent)	750	1 µg/mL to 1.5 mg/mL	Cu^{2+} is reduced to Cu^{+} in the presence of proteins at high pH; the biuret reagent chelates the Cu^{+} ion, then the Folin–Ciocalteu reagent enhances the blue color	• Lengthy procedure with carefully timed steps • Not compatible with detergents or reducing agents
Fluorescamine [4–7] (F2332, F20261)	390/475	0.3 µg/mL to 13 µg/mL	Reacts with primary amine groups on proteins; unbound dye is nonfluorescent	• Sensitivity depends on the number of amines present • Reagent is unstable • Not compatible with amine-containing buffers
OPA [8–10] (o-phthaldialdehyde) (P2331MP)	340/455	0.2 µg/mL to 25 µg/mL	Reacts with primary amine groups on proteins in the presence of 2-mercaptoethanol; unbound dye is nonfluorescent	• Sensitivity depends on the number of amines present • Not compatible with amine-containing buffers • Low cost
UV absorption [11]	205/280	10 µg/mL to 50 µg/mL or 50 µg/mL to 2 mg/mL	Peptide bond absorption; tryptophan and tyrosine absorption	• Sensitivity depends on the number of aromatic amino acid residues present • Nondestructive • Low cost

* Excitation and emission wavelength maxima or absorbance wavelength maximum, in nm. **1.** Anal Biochem 72, 248 (1976); **2.** Anal Biochem 150, 76 (1985); **3.** J Biol Chem 193, 265 (1951); **4.** Science 178, 871 (1972); **5.** Clin Chim Acta 157, 73 (1986); **6.** J Lipid Res 27, 792 (1986); **7.** Anal Biochem 214, 346 (1993); **8.** Anal Biochem 115, 203 (1981); **9.** Biotechniques 4, 130 (1986); **10.** J Immunol Methods 172, 141 (1994); **11.** Protein Purification: Principles and Practice, 2nd Ed., Scopes RK pp. 253–283 (1987).

also be adapted for use in cuvettes or 384-well microplates. The fluorescence signal exhibits excitation/emission maxima of 470/570 nm and is stable for three hours at room temperature. The Quant-iT™ protein reagent is a new formulation of Molecular Probes' NanoOrange® reagent, which is described below.

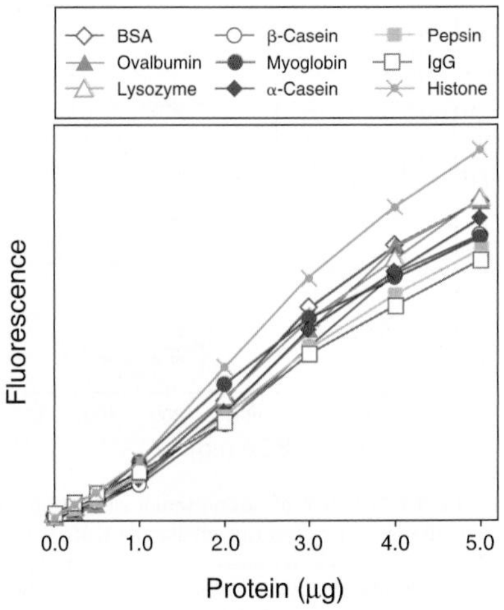

Figure 9.3 Low protein-to-protein variation in the Quant-iT™ protein assay. Solutions of the following proteins were prepared, diluted and assayed with the Quant-iT™ Protein Assay Kit (Q33210): bovine serum albumin (BSA), chicken-egg ovalbumin, chicken-egg lysozyme, bovine-milk β-casein, equine myoglobin, bovine-milk α-casein, porcine pepsin, mouse immunoglobulin (IgG) and calf-thymus histone. Fluorescence was measured at 485/590 nm and plotted versus the mass of protein sample. At 3 μg, the fluorescence variation was 12.4%, or 8.7% excluding the highly basic histone protein. Background fluorescence has not been subtracted.

NanoOrange® Protein Quantitation Kit

Our patented NanoOrange® Protein Quantitation Kit (N6666) provides an ultrasensitive assay for measuring the concentration of proteins in solution.[4] The NanoOrange® Protein Quantitation Kit has several important features:

- **Ease of use.** The NanoOrange® assay protocol is much easier to perform than the Lowry method (Figure 9.4). Protein samples are simply added to the diluted NanoOrange® reagent in a lipid-containing medium, and the mixtures are heated at 95°C for 10 minutes. After cooling the mixtures to room temperature, their fluorescence emissions are measured directly. The interaction of the lipid-coated proteins with the NanoOrange® reagent produces a large fluorescence enhancement that can be used to generate a standard curve for protein determination; fluorescence of the reagent in aqueous solutions in the absence of proteins is negligible.
- **Sensitivity and effective range.** The NanoOrange® assay can detect proteins at a final concentration as low as 10 ng/mL when a standard spectrofluorometer or minifluorometer is used. A single protocol is suitable for quantitating protein concentrations between 10 ng/mL and 10 μg/mL — an effective range of three orders of magnitude (Figure 9.5).
- **Stability.** The NanoOrange® reagent and its protein complex have high chemical stability. In contrast to the Bradford and BCA assays, readings can be taken for up to six hours after sample preparation with no loss in signal, provided that samples are protected from light.
- **Little protein-to-protein variability** (Figure 9.6). The NanoOrange® assay is not only more sensitive, but shows less protein-to-protein variability than Bradford assays.
- **Insensitivity to sample contaminants.** Unlike the Lowry and BCA assays, the NanoOrange® assay is compatible with the presence of reducing agents. Furthermore, the high sensitivity of the assay and stability of the protein–dye complex make it possible to dilute out most poten-

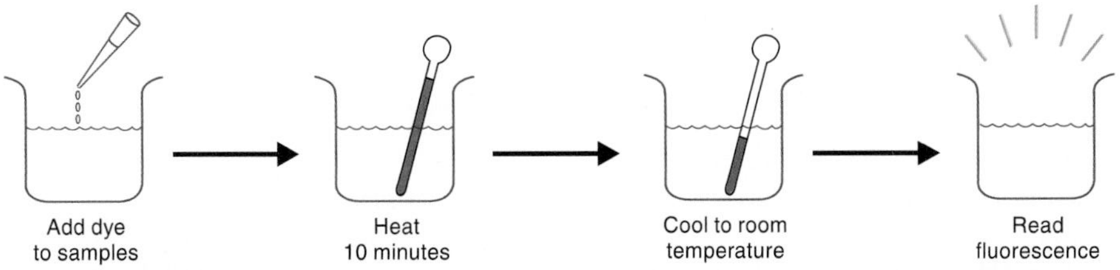

Figure 9.4 Protein quantitation with the NanoOrange® Protein Quantitation Kit. The NanoOrange® assay (N6666) is simple to perform: after adding diluted dye, the samples are heated to denature the proteins, cooled to room temperature and the fluorescence read in either a microplate reader or a fluorometer.

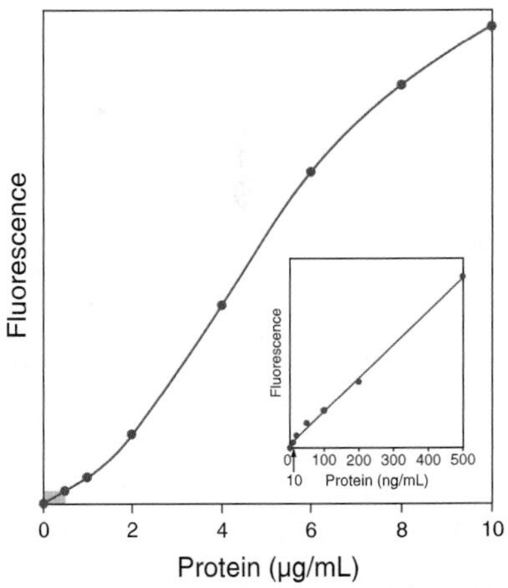

Figure 9.5 Quantitative analysis of bovine serum albumin (BSA) using the NanoOrange® Protein Quantitation Kit (N6666). Fluorescence measurements were carried out on an SLM SPF-500C fluorometer using excitation/emission wavelengths of 485/590 nm. The inset shows an enlargement of the results obtained (0–500 ng protein per mL) and illustrates the detection limit of ~10 ng/mL.

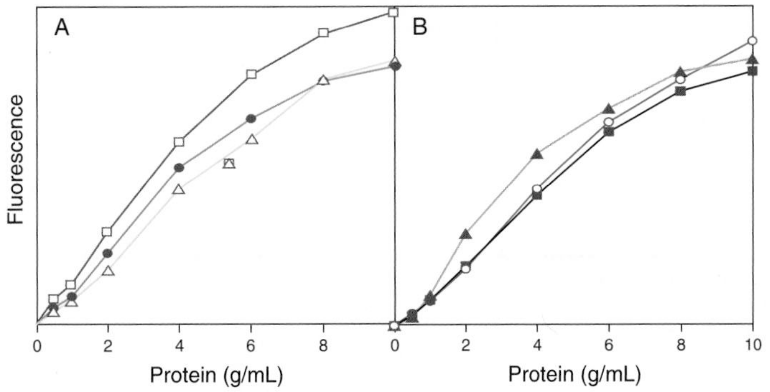

Figure 9.6 Quantitative analysis of six different proteins using the NanoOrange® Protein Quantitation Kit (N6666): Panel A) bovine serum albumin (BSA, □), trypsin (●) and carbonic anhydrase (△); Panel B) IgG (■), streptavidin (○) and RNase A (▲). The y-axis fluorescence intensity scale is the same in both panels, illustrating the minimal protein-to-protein staining variation of the NanoOrange® assay. Data were collected using a microplate reader with excitation/emission wavelengths set at 485 ± 20 nm/590 ± 35 nm.

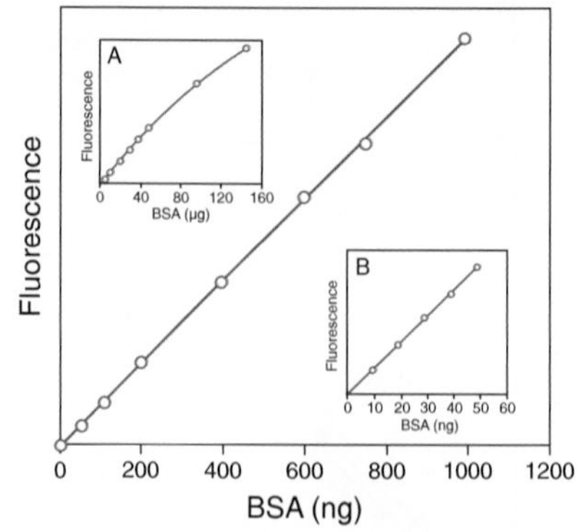

Figure 9.7 Detection of bovine serum albumin (BSA) using the CBQCA Protein Quantitation Kit (C6667). The primary plot shows detection of BSA from 50 ng to 1000 ng. Inset A shows that the detection range can extend up to 150 µg. Inset B shows that the lower detection limit can extend down to 10 ng. Each point is the average of four determinations.

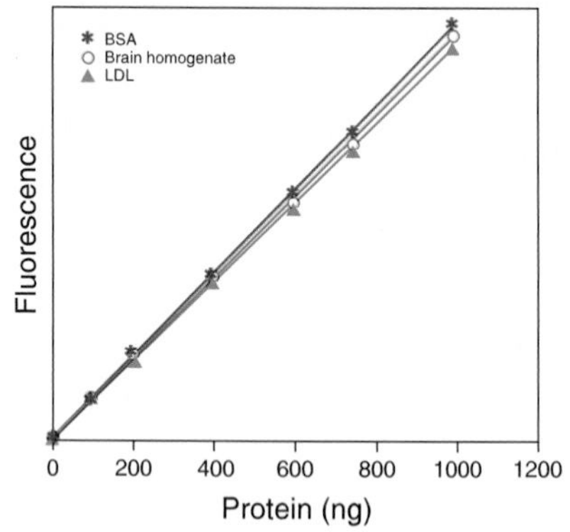

Figure 9.9 Quantitation of proteins in a lipid environment using the CBQCA Protein Quantitation Kit (C6667). The protein concentrations of an LDL preparation and a bovine brain homogenate were first determined by the modified Lowry method using BSA as a standard. Assays were then performed using the CBQCA Protein Quantitation Kit on samples containing from 100 ng to 1000 ng protein in 0.1 M sodium borate buffer, pH 9.3, containing 0.1% Triton X-100. Similar results were obtained without the addition of detergent (data not shown). Fluorescence was measured using a fluorescence microplate reader with excitation at 485 ± 10 nm and emission detection at 530 ± 12.5 nm. Each point is the average of three determinations.

tial contaminants, including detergents and salts (Table 9.2). Nucleic acids do not interfere with protein quantitation using the NanoOrange® reagent. Although unusually high concentrations of lipids in the sample can interfere with the NanoOrange® assay, this interference can be eliminated by acetone precipitation of the protein, followed by delipidation with diethyl ether.[5]

Our NanoOrange® protein quantitation reagent, with an excitation/emission maxima of 470/570 when bound to proteins, is suitable for use with a variety of instrumentation. Fluorescence is typically measured using instrument settings or filters that provide excitation/emission at ~485/590 nm, which are commonly available for both spectrofluorometers and microplate readers. A spectrofluorometer — either a standard fluorometer or a minifluorometer — offers the greatest effective range and lowest detection limits for this assay. With fluorescence microplate readers, the NanoOrange® assay is useful over a somewhat narrower range — from 100 ng/mL to 10 µg/mL in final protein concentration.

The NanoOrange® Protein Quantitation Kit (N6666) supplies:

- Concentrated NanoOrange® reagent in dimethylsulfoxide (DMSO)
- Concentrated NanoOrange® diluent
- Bovine serum albumin (BSA) as a protein reference standard
- A detailed protocol for protein quantitation

The amount of dye supplied in this kit is sufficient for ~200 assays using a 2 mL assay volume and a standard fluorometer or minifluorometer, or ~2000 assays using a 200 µL assay volume and a fluorescence microplate reader.

The NanoOrange® reagent is ideal for quantitating protein samples before gel electrophoresis[5] and Western blot analysis.[6] It has also been used to measure bound versus free protein levels in

Table 9.2 — Tolerance levels for contaminants in the NanoOrange® protein quantitation assay

Contaminating Compound	Maximum Tolerable Concentration *
Glycerol	10% by volume
Poly(ethylene glycol) (PEG)	1% by volume
Urea	1 M
Dithiothreitol (DTT), 2-mercaptoethanol	100 mM
KCl, NaCl, sodium acetate, sodium phosphate	20 mM
Ammonium sulfate, ascorbic acid, HEPES buffer, HCl, NaOH, sodium azide, sucrose	10 mM
EDTA	5 mM
Calcium chloride, magnesium chloride	1 mM
Amino acids	100 µg/mL
DNA	100 ng/mL
Sodium dodecyl sulfate (SDS)	0.01%
Tween 20, Triton X-100	0.001%

* Compounds present in the final assay solution at or below the indicated concentrations do not appreciably interfere with the NanoOrange® protein quantitation assay. Whenever feasible, the blank and protein standards should be prepared in a solution closely matching that of the experimental samples.

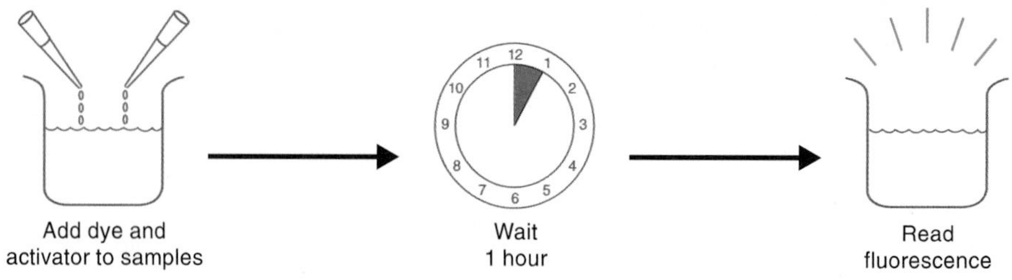

Figure 9.8 Protein quantitation with the CBQCA Protein Quantitation Kit. The CBQCA assay (C6667) is simple to perform: after the dye and an activator are added, the sample is incubated for an hour and the fluorescence is read in either a microplate reader or a fluorometer.

protein binding assays, and was even able to detect protein trapped in filters during a separation step.[7] The NanoOrange® reagent is also an optimal reagent for detecting proteins that have been separated by microchip capillary electrophoresis.[8,9] A high-throughput assay that may be suitable for clinical samples has been developed for quantitating human serum albumin using a fluorescence microplate reader and using capillary electrophoresis laser-induced fluorescence[10] (CE-LIF). Additionally, the NanoOrange® reagent has been shown to be useful in cell-based assays, including an assay designed to measure total protein content of cell cultures[11] and a rapid method for demonstrating flagellar movement of bacteria.[12]

CBQCA Protein Quantitation Kit

The ATTO-TAG™ CBQCA reagent was originally developed as a chromatographic derivatization reagent for amines[13–15] (Section 1.8), but this reagent is also useful for quantitating proteins (Figure 9.7) by virtue of its rapid and quantitative reaction with their accessible amines. Molecular Probes has developed the CBQCA Protein Quantitation Kit (C6667, Figure 9.8), which employs the ATTO-TAG™ CBQCA reagent for rapid and sensitive protein quantitation in solution[16] (Table 9.1). The CBQCA protein quantitation assay functions well in the presence of lipids and detergents,[16,17] substances that interfere with many other protein determination methods.[16] For example, the CBQCA-based assay can be used directly to determine the protein content of lipoprotein samples or lipid–protein mixtures (Figure 9.9). The CBQCA assay has been shown to give faster and more sensitive detection of both free amino acids in human plasma[18] and both low and high molecular weight primary amines in clinical samples from hemodialysis.[19] ATTO-TAG™ CBQCA is more water soluble than either fluorescamine or *o*-phthaldialdehyde and much more stable in aqueous solution than fluorescamine. Moreover, ATTO-TAG™ CBQCA provides greater sensitivity for protein quantitation in solution than either fluorescamine or *o*-phthaldialdehyde (Figure 9.10). As little as 10 ng of BSA can be detected in a 100–200 µL assay volume using a fluorescence microplate reader, and the effective range extends up to 150 µg (Figure 9.7). Alternatively, the reaction mixtures can be diluted to 1–2 mL for fluorescence measurement in a standard fluorometer or minifluorometer.

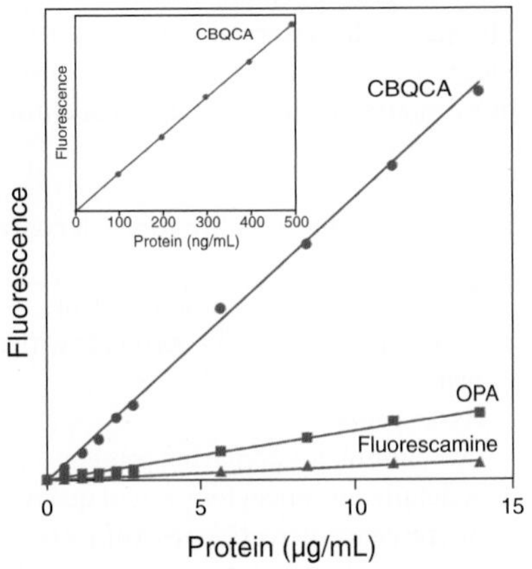

Figure 9.10 Comparison of the fluorometric quantitation of bovine serum albumin (BSA) using ATTO-TAG™ CBQCA (which is supplied in the CBQCA Protein Quantitation Kit, C6667), OPA (P2331MP) or fluorescamine (F2332, F20261). BSA samples were derivatized using large molar excesses of the fluorogenic reagents and were analyzed using a fluorescence microplate reader. Excitation/emission wavelengths were 360/460 nm for OPA and fluorescamine and 485/530 nm for ATTO-TAG™ CBQCA. The inset shows an enlargement of the results obtained using CBQCA to assay protein concentrations between 0 and 500 ng/mL.

Each CBQCA Protein Quantitation Kit (C6667) contains:

- ATTO-TAG™ CBQCA detection reagent
- Potassium cyanide
- Dimethylsulfoxide (DMSO)
- Bovine serum albumin (BSA) protein reference standard
- A detailed protocol for protein quantitation

The CBQCA Protein Quantitation Kit provides sufficient reagents for 300–800 assays using a standard fluorometer, minifluorometer or fluorescence microplate reader.

EZQ® Protein Quantitation Kit

The EZQ® Protein Quantitation Kit (R33200) provides a fast and easy high-throughput assay for proteins in solution. Because detergents, reducing agents, urea and tracking dyes do not interfere, this fluorescence-based protein quantitation assay is ideal for determining the protein concentration of samples prior to polyacrylamide gel electrophoresis. This convenient kit can also provide a quick assessment of protein content during protein purification schemes and fractionation procedures.

The EZQ® assay requires only 1 µL of a sample per spot, and up to 96 samples, including standards, can be assayed in one session. The protein samples are simply spotted onto one of the provided assay papers, fixed with methanol and then stained with our proprietary EZQ® protein quantitation reagent. This assay paper is then clamped into the specially designed 96-well microplate for quick analysis in a top- or bottom-reading fluorescence microplate reader (Figure 9.11). For added versatility, the solid-phase assay format and provided 96-well microplate are also compatible with laser scanners equipped with 450, 473 or 488 nm lasers and with UV illuminators in combination with photographic or CCD cameras for image documentation and analysis. Once the samples are spotted, the assay protocol can be completed in about 1 hour. The protein concentration is determined from a standard curve, and the effective range for the assay is generally 0.05–5 mg/mL or 0.05–5 µg per spot (Figure 9.12). Protein-to-protein sensitivity differences in the assay are minimal — the observed coefficient of variation is typically ~16% (Figure 9.13). The EZQ® Protein Quantitation Kit is extremely useful for estimating the concentration of chromatographically separated protein fractions.

Each EZQ® Protein Quantitation Kit contains:

- EZQ® protein quantitation reagent
- A bottomless 96-well microplate with a stainless steel backing plate
- Assay paper
- Ovalbumin, for preparing protein standards
- A detailed protocol for protein quantitation using a variety of fluorescence-detection instruments

Sufficient reagent and assay paper are provided for ~2000 protein quantitation assays.

Other Reagents for Protein Quantitation in Solution

Other than our premier protein quantitation products described above, most other fluorogenic reagents for general protein quantitation in solution detect accessible primary amines. The sensitivity of assays based on these reagents therefore depends on the number of amines available — a function of both the protein's three-dimensional structure and its amino acid composition. For example, horseradish peroxidase (MW ~40,000 daltons), which has only six lysine residues,[20] will be detected less efficiently than egg white avidin (MW ~66,000 daltons), which has 36 lysine residues,[21,22] and bovine serum albumin (MW ~66,000 daltons), which has 59 lysine residues.[23] However, the assays are generally rapid and easy to conduct, particularly in minifluorometer and fluorescence microplate reader formats.

Certain dyes that detect primary aliphatic amines, including ATTO-TAG™ CBQCA (A6222), fluorescamine (F2332; FluoroPure™ Grade, F20261) and *o*-phthaldialdehyde (OPA, P2331MP), have been the predominant reagents for fluorometric determination of proteins in solution (Table 9.1). These same reagents, and others such as naphthalene-2,3-dicarboxaldehyde[24,25] (NDA, N1138; Section 1.8), have frequently been used for amino acid analysis of hydrolyzed proteins.

Fluorescamine

Fluorescamine (F2332; FluoroPure™ Grade, F20261) is intrinsically nonfluorescent but reacts in milliseconds with primary aliphatic amines, including peptides and proteins, to yield a fluorescent derivative[26] (Figure 1.116). This amine-reactive reagent has been shown to be useful for determining protein concentrations of aqueous solutions[27–29] and for measuring the number of accessible lysine residues in proteins.[23] Protein quantitation with fluorescamine is particularly well suited to a minifluorometer or fluorescence microplate reader.[30] Fluorescamine can also be used to detect proteins in gels and to analyze low molecular weight amines by TLC, HPLC and capillary electrophoresis.[31]

o-Phthaldialdehyde

The combination of *o*-phthaldialdehyde (OPA, P2331MP) and 2-mercaptoethanol provides a rapid and simple method of determining protein concentrations in the range of 0.2 µg/mL to 25 µg/mL[32] (Figure 1.117). As compared with fluorescamine, OPA is both more soluble and stable in aqueous buffers and its sensitivity for detection of peptides is reported to be 5–10 times better.[33] The OPA assay for lysine content is reasonably reliable over a broad range of proteins.[23] OPA (and likely the ATTO-TAG™ CBQCA reagent) can also be used to detect *increases* in the concentration of free amines that result from protease-catalyzed protein hydrolysis.[34]

SYPRO® Red and SYPRO® Orange Protein Gel Stains

An assay has been reported that uses the SYPRO® Red protein gel stain (S6653, S6654; Section 9.3) for quantitating total protein content of bacterial cells by flow cytometry.[35] This assay provides an accurate measure of planktonic bacterial biomass in marine samples. Fluorescence of the SYPRO® Orange protein gel stain (S6650, S6651; Section 9.3) has been used to follow isothermal protein denaturation[36] and to selectivly stain proteins in biofilms prior to two-photon laser-scanning microscopy.[37]

Selective Protein Quantitation in Solution

EZQ® Phosphoprotein Quantitation Kit

The EZQ® Phosphoprotein Quantitation Kit (E33201) provides a fast and simple assay for phosphoproteins in solution. No radioactivity or antibodies are required, and sample analysis can typically

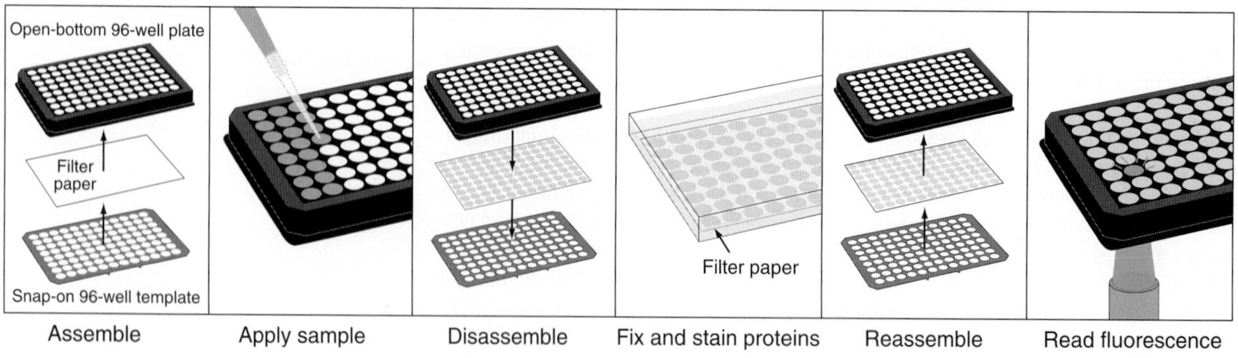

Figure 9.11 Schematic diagram of method used in the EZQ® Protein Quantitation Kit (R33200).

be completed within 60 minutes. The EZQ® phosphoprotein quantitation assay shows high selectivity for phosphoproteins over nonphosphorylated proteins (Figure 9.14) and is compatible with samples containing detergents, reducing agents and urea buffers with up to 1% carrier ampholytes. Furthermore, this assay requires only 1 µL of sample, and up to 96 samples, including standards, can be assayed simultaneously. This kit is ideal for analyzing protein kinase or phosphatase activities, as well as for monitoring relative phosphoprotein concentrations during chromatography or after IEF fractionation of protein samples.

In this assay, the phosphoprotein samples are spotted onto specially prepared assay paper, fixed onto the paper with methanol and then stained with our proprietary EZQ® phosphoprotein quantitation reagent. Relative phosphate content is determined from a standard curve of ovalbumin or any standard phosphoprotein of interest. As little as 20 ng of ovalbumin that contains 2 phosphate residues per ovalbumin can be selectively detected, and the ovalbumin standard curve has an overall dynamic range of 250-fold, from 0.4 to 120 picomoles. The Z-factor for this assay is in the "excellent" range at greater than 0.8, with N = 8. For normalizing the phosphoprotein signal to the total protein levels, total protein quantitation can be easily performed after phosphoprotein analysis on the same paper using the EZQ® Protein Quantitation Kit (R33200) described above. Each EZQ® Phosphoprotein Quantitation Kit contains:

- EZQ® phosphoprotein quantitation reagent
- EZQ® phosphoprotein destain reagent
- EZQ® 96-well microplate cassette
- Assay paper
- Ovalbumin standard
- A detailed protocol for phosphoprotein quantitation

Sufficient materials are provided for 2000 microplate-well assays. The EZQ® Phosphoprotein Quantitation Kit is designed for high-throughput analysis. The solid-phase format and special 96-well microplate can be used with readily available fluorescence-based detection instruments, including either top- or bottom-reading microplate readers and laser scanners equipped with 532–560 nm lasers, as well as UV illuminators in combination with photographic or CCD cameras for image documentation and analysis (with lower sensitivity).

EZQ® Phosphopeptide Quantitation Kit

The EZQ® Phosphopeptide Quantitation Kit (E33202) permits accurate quantitation of phosphopeptides in solution, in the presence of standard buffer components. As with the EZQ® Phosphoprotein Quantitation Kit described above, no radioactivity or antibodies are required, and sample analysis can typically be completed within 60 minutes. This phosphopeptide assay requires only 1 µL of sample, and up to 96 samples, including standards, can be assayed simulta-

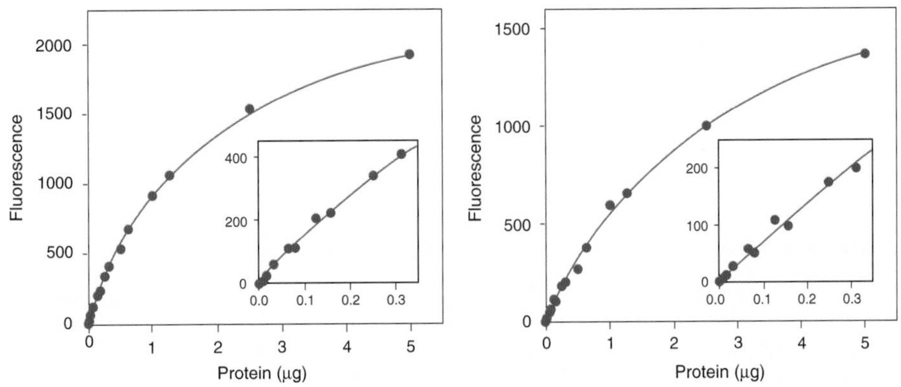

Figure 9.12 EZQ® protein quantitation assay of ovalbumin. A dilution series of ovalbumin was prepared, assayed with the EZQ® Protein Quantitation Kit (R33200) and then quantitated using both a 473 nm laser–based scanning instrument (left panel) and a fluorescence microplate reader (right panel). The assays were performed over a broad range; the insets show the low range in greater detail. The assays were performed in triplicate, and the mean values, in arbitrary fluorescence units, were plotted after subtracting background values of 86 (left panel) or 18 (right panel).

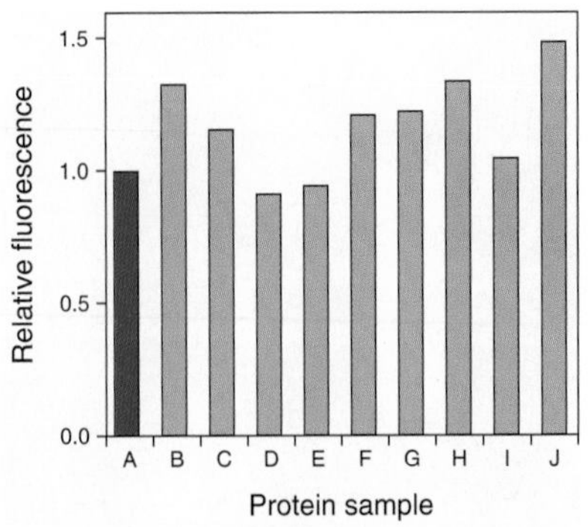

Figure 9.13 Protein-to-protein variation in the EZQ® protein quantitation assay. Triplicate 1 µg samples of various proteins were assayed using the EZQ® Protein Quantitation Kit (R33200) and a fluorescence microplate reader. The mean fluorescence values, after correcting for background fluorescence, are expressed relative to that of ovalbumin. The coefficient of variation is ~16%. The protein samples are: A, ovalbumin; B, bovine serum albumin (BSA); C, myoglobin; D, soybean trypsin inhibitor; E, β-casein; F, carbonic anhydrase; G, transferrin; H, mouse IgG; I, lysozyme; and J, histones.

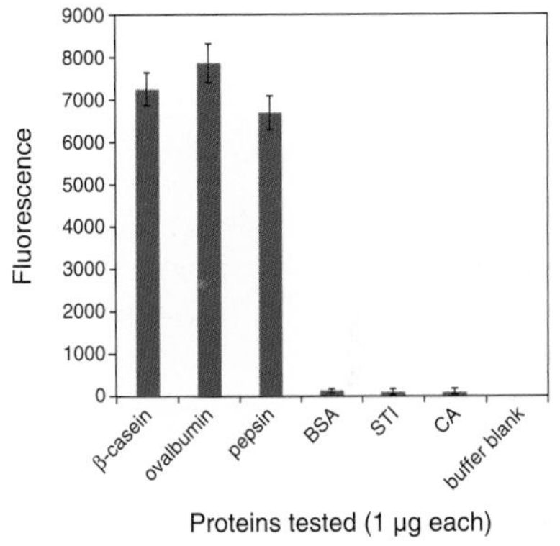

Figure 9.14 Highly selective staining of phosphoproteins using the EZQ® Phosphoprotein Quantitation Kit (E33201). For each of the proteins assayed, a solution of 1 µg/µL was prepared. One microliter of each solution was spotted onto the assay paper, and the proteins were stained using the kit protocol. Only the phosphorylated proteins (β-casein, ovalbumin and pepsin) show a significant level of staining with respect to the buffer blank. (For the proteins tested, BSA, STI and CA stand for bovine serum albumin, soybean trypsin inhibitor and carbonic anhydrase, respectively.)

neously. This kit is ideal for analyzing phosphatase and kinase activities, as well as for monitoring relative phosphopeptide concentrations before and after analysis by liquid chromatography, mass spectrometry or other separation technique.

Figure 9.15 Fluorescence enhancement of 1,8-ANS (1-anilinonaphthalene-8-sulfonic acid, A47) upon binding to protein. The image shows aqueous solutions of 1,8-ANS excited by ultraviolet light. The addition of protein (bovine serum albumin) to the solution in the cuvette on the left results in intense blue fluorescence. In comparison, the fluorescence of uncomplexed free dye in the cuvette on the right is negligible.

In the EZQ® phosphopeptide quantitation assay, the phosphopeptide samples are spotted onto specially prepared assay paper, fixed onto the paper with methanol and then stained with our proprietary EZQ® phosphopeptide quantitation reagent. Relative phosphate content is determined from a standard curve of control phosphopeptide pT1721 or any standard phosphopeptide of interest. Subpicomole amounts of most monophosphorylated peptides can be detected; for peptides that we have tested, the overall dynamic range of detection is over 500-fold, from 0.2–0.8 picomole at the lower end to about 400 picomoles, depending on the peptide. The Z-factor for this assay is in the "excellent" range at greater than 0.8, with N = 8. Each EZQ® Phosphopeptide Quantitation Kit contains:

- EZQ® phosphopeptide quantitation reagent
- EZQ® phosphopeptide destain reagent
- EZQ® 96-well microplate cassette
- Assay paper
- Positive control phosphopeptide pT1721
- Kemptide, a negative control peptide
- A detailed protocol for phosphopeptide quantitation

Sufficient materials are provided for 1000 microplate-well assays. The EZQ® Phosphopeptide Quantitation Kit is designed for high-throughput analysis. The solid-phase format and special 96-well microplate can be used with readily available fluorescence-based detection instruments, including either top- or bottom-reading microplate readers and laser scanners equipped with 532–560 nm lasers, as well as UV illuminators in combination with photographic or CCD cameras for image documentation and analysis (with somewhat lower sensitivity).

Pro-Q® Diamond LC Phosphopeptide Detection Kit

The Pro-Q® Diamond LC Phosphopeptide Detection Kit (P33203) provides sensitive and selective fluorescence-based detection of phosphorylated peptides during liquid chromatography separations. The Pro-Q® Diamond LC phosphopeptide detection reagent interacts selectively with phosphoserine-, phosphothreonine- and phosphotyrosine-containing peptides to form unique, highly fluorescent dye–phosphopeptide complexes that elute from an HPLC column with altered retention times, allowing identification and purification of phosphopeptides prior to analysis by mass spectrometry. This kit is ideal for isolating phosphopeptides from chromatographic fractions of semi-complex peptide mixtures or from complex peptide mixtures such as the tryptic digest of a phosphoprotein. The Pro-Q® Diamond LC Phosphopeptide Detection Kit provides:

- Pro-Q® Diamond LC phosphopeptide detection reagent
- Concentrated activation buffer
- Positive control phosphopeptide RII
- Kemptide, a negative control peptide
- A detailed protocol

Sufficient reagents are provided for 20 HPLC separations; a single separation will selectively detect 20 picomoles or less of a monophosphorylated peptide using a standard microbore C_{18} HPLC column.

MBDS: A Fluorogenic Reagent for Serum Albumins

4-Amino-4′-benzamidostilbene-2,2′-disulfonic acid (MBDS, A11760) is a reagent with properties similar to a commonly used probe for hydrophobic sites in proteins, 1-anilinonaphthalene-8-sulfonic acid (1,8-ANS, A47; Section 13.5; Figure 9.15). Like 1,8-ANS (see Note 13.3 "Product Highlight: Monitoring Protein-Folding Processes with Anilinonaphthalenesulfonate Dyes" in Section 13.5), MBDS is virtually nonfluorescent in water (quantum yield <0.01); however, upon binding to the hydrophobic pocket of serum albumins and some other proteins, it undergoes an almost 100-fold increase in its fluorescence.[38,39]

Anti-Dinitrophenyl Antibody: A Reagent for Measuring Protein Carbonyls

Oxidative injury can be monitored by following the formation of protein-derived aldehydes and ketones. Traditionally, protein-derived aldehydes and ketones have been quantitated using a colorimetric assay based on their reaction with 2,4-dinitrophenylhydrazine to yield protein-bound dinitrophenyl moieties (DNP). A much more sensitive ELISA method has been developed that detects the protein-bound DNP using unlabeled or biotin-labeled anti-DNP antibodies[40,41] (A6430, A6435; Section 7.4). The bound anti-DNP antibody is subsequently detected with horseradish peroxidase–conjugated secondary detection reagents (Section 7.2). Our Alexa Fluor® 488 and fluorescein conjugates of the anti-DNP antibody (A11097, A6423; Section 7.2) may potentially also be applied to this detection scheme. Our polyclonal antibody to nitrotyrosine (A21285, Section 7.4) can be used similarly to separate and detect proteins of cell extracts that have been naturally nitrated by nitric oxide (Section 18.3, Figure 18.23). Use of these rabbit polyclonal antibodies in combination with Captivate™ ferrofluid goat anti–rabbit IgG antibody (C21474) permits selective isolation of modified proteins and their targets from solutions (Figure 7.58, Figure 7.107).

EnzChek® and Amplex® Red Assay Kits

Molecular Probes prepares numerous chromogenic and fluorogenic substrates that are useful for quantitating enzymes and enzymatic activity in experimental samples. In addition, we have developed several EnzChek® Assay Kits, DQ™ Assay Kits and Amplex® Red Assay Kits especially designed for detecting a wide variety of enzymes and their substrates. Most of these products are described in Chapter 10.

Selective Protein Purification

Glutathione Agarose and Anti–Glutathione S-Transferase Antibody for GST Fusion Protein Identification and Purification

In protein fusion techniques, the coding sequence of one protein is fused in-frame with another so that the expressed hybrid protein possesses desirable properties of both parent proteins. One common partner in these engineered products is glutathione *S*-transferase (GST), a protein with natural binding specificity that can be exploited to facilitate its purification.[42] Because the GST portion of the fusion protein retains its affinity and selectivity for glutathione, the fusion protein can be conveniently purified from the cell lysate in a single step by affinity chromatography on glutathione agarose[43–48] (Figure 9.16). For purification of GST fusion proteins, Molecular Probes offers glutathione linked via the sulfur atom to crosslinked beaded agarose (10 mL of sedimented bead suspension, G2879). This reagent is also available from Molecular Probes in bulk quantities (100 mL of sedimented bead suspension, G21800). Each milliliter of gel can bind approximately 5–6 mg of bovine-liver GST. Adding excess free glutathione liberates the GST fragment from the matrix, which can then be regenerated by washing with a high-salt buffer.

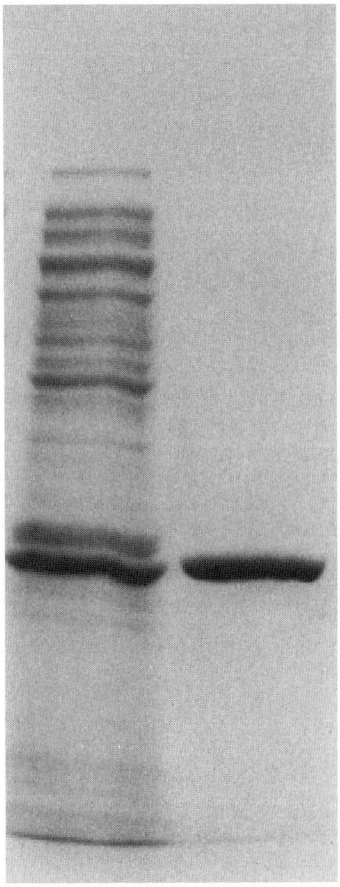

Figure 9.16 Coomassie brilliant blue–stained SDS-polyacrylamide gel, demonstrating the purification of a glutathione *S*-transferase (GST) fusion protein using glutathione agarose (G2879, G21800). Lane 1 contains crude supernatant from an *Escherichia coli* lysate and lane 2 contains the affinity-purified GST fusion protein.

Molecular Probes also offers a highly purified rabbit polyclonal anti-GST antibody (A5800) that can be used to purify GST fusion proteins by immunoprecipitation.[49] This highly specific antibody, which was generated against a 260–amino acid N-terminal fragment of the *Schistosoma japonica* enzyme expressed in *Escherichia coli*, is also useful for detecting GST fusion proteins on Western blots (Section 9.4) and for detecting GST distribution in cells (Section 7.5). The intensely green-fluorescent Alexa Fluor® 488 conjugate of anti–glutathione *S*-transferase (A11131) is also available for direct detection of GST fusion proteins.

Our Glutathione Transferase Fusion Protein Purification Kit (G21801) facilitates isolation and characterization of GST fusion proteins. This kit, which contains sufficient materials for five isolations, contains:

- Glutathione agarose
- Anti–glutathione *S*-transferase antibody
- Purification columns
- A detailed protocol

Following purification, the fusion protein can serve as an immunogen for antibody production [50,51] or its properties can be compared with those of the native polypeptide to provide insights on the normal function of the polypeptide of interest. Such methods have been used to investigate biological properties of many proteins. Examples include cleavage of the capsid assembly protein ICP35 by the herpes simplex virus type 1 protease,[52] the role of the Rho GTP-binding protein in *lbc* oncogene function [53] and the association of v-Src with cortactin in Rous sarcoma virus–transformed cells.[54] In fact, the Ca^{2+}-binding properties of a protein kinase C–GST fusion protein were examined while the GST fusion protein was still bound to the glutathione agarose.[55] Likewise, interactions of a DNA-binding protein–GST fusion protein have been assessed using an affinity column consisting of the fusion protein bound to glutathione agarose.[43] Alternatively, the GST fusion expression vector can be engineered to encode a recognition sequence for a site-specific protease, such as thrombin or factor Xa, between the GST structural gene and gene of interest.[56–59] Once the fusion protein is bound to the affinity matrix, the site-specific enzyme can be added to release the protein.

Streptavidin Agarose and CaptAvidin™ Agarose

Molecular Probes prepares both streptavidin and CaptAvidin™ biotin-binding protein conjugated to 4% beaded crosslinked agarose (S951, C21386) — matrices that can be used to isolate biotinylated peptides, proteins, hybridization probes, haptens and other molecules.[60] In addition, biotinylated antibodies can be bound to streptavidin agarose or CaptAvidin™ agarose to generate affinity matrices for the large-scale isolation of antigens.[60] For instance, streptavidin agarose has been used to isolate acetylcholine receptors from cultured myotubules after labeling the receptors with biotinylated α-bungarotoxin [61] (B1196, Section 16.2). Streptavidin agarose has also been used to investigate the turnover of cell-surface proteins that had previously been derivatized with an amine-reactive biotin [62] (B1582, Section 4.2). The binding capacity of our streptavidin agarose is measured in an assay using fluorescein biotin (B1370, Section 4.3, Figure 4.9). Typically, the conjugate binds 15–20 µg (18–24 nanomoles) of fluorescein biotin per milliliter of sedimented gel. Our DSB-X™ biotin technology (see below) makes the capture and release of antigens and receptors from solutions even easier.

CaptAvidin™ agarose has been specially designed to allow easier dissociation of the avidin–biotin complex (Figure 7.99). Avidin and biotin form a very strong noncovalent bond with a K_a of ~10^{15} M^{-1}. Although this high affinity is advantageous for many histochemical applications, it is a major drawback for affinity chromatography. The conditions needed to dissociate the avidin–biotin complex (8 M guanidine hydrochloride, pH 1.5) are usually too harsh for proteins and prevent the use of avidin for purifying biotinylated molecules. To address this problem, the tyrosine residues in the four biotin-binding sites of CaptAvidin™ biotin-binding protein (C21385) are nitrated, considerably reducing its affinity for biotinylated molecules above pH 9. At pH 4.0, CaptAvidin™ biotin-binding protein binds biotin tightly, with a K_a of 10^9 M^{-1}. At pH 10, however, this association is reversed, allowing complete dissociation of the avidin–biotin complex.

Researchers have used CaptAvidin™ agarose affinity chromatography to purify immunoglobulins from whole rabbit serum and to isolate anti-transferrin antibody directly from rabbit IgG fractions.[63] CaptAvidin™ agarose can be used to isolate cellular proteins that are selectively biotinylated with the reagents in our FluoReporter® Cell-Surface Biotinylation Kit (F20650, Section 4.2) and to selectively isolate glycoproteins bound to the biotin-XX conjugate of concanavalin A (C21420, Section 7.7). The biotin-binding capacity of CaptAvidin™ derivatives is at least 10 µg of biotin per mg protein.

Streptavidin Acrylamide, CaptAvidin™ Acrylamide and Reactive Acrylamide Derivatives

Streptavidin acrylamide (S21379), which is prepared from the succinimidyl ester of 6-((acryloyl)amino)hexanoic acid (acryloyl-X, SE, A20770), may be useful for the preparation of biosensors.[64] A similar streptavidin acrylamide has been shown to copolymerize with acrylamide on a polymeric surface to create a uniform monolayer of the immobilized protein. The streptavidin can then bind biotinylated ligands, including biotinylated hybridization probes, enzymes, antibodies and drugs. CaptAvidin™ acrylamide (C21387) is expected to have similar utility, but offers an advantage — the bond that it forms with biotinylated probes is reversible at about pH 10.

Like streptavidin and CaptAvidin™ biotin-binding protein, other amine-containing biomolecules can be crosslinked to acrylamides using acryloyl-X, SE. Acryloyl-X, SE reacts with amines of proteins, amine-modified nucleic acids and other biomolecules to yield acrylamides that can be copolymerized into polyacrylamide matrices or on surfaces, such as in microarrays and in biosensors.

DSB-X™ Biotin: Easily Reversible Binding to Streptavidin Agarose

Our exclusive DSB-X™ biotin technology,[65] which is described in greater detail in Section 7.6, permits the selective binding and release of proteins that are labeled with DSB-X™ biotin succinimidyl ester, a component of our DSB-X™ Biotin Protein Labeling Kit (D20655, Section 1.2). Temporary immobilization of a DSB-X™ biotin–conjugated macromolecule, such as an antibody, on streptavidin agarose permits the antibody to selectively capture antigens from solutions (Figure 7.103). Following gentle elution at neutral pH with either D-biotin or D-desthiobiotin (Figure 4.1), the DSB-X™ biotin–conjugated protein and its targets are completely released, permitting further analysis of the released proteins (or nucleic acids) in gels or on blots.

The DSB-X™ Bioconjugate Isolation Kit #1 (D20658) provides:

- Streptavidin agarose (5 mL of a sedimented bead suspension)
- Solutions of D-biotin or D-desthiobiotin
- Purification columns
- A recommended protocol for binding and release of DSB-X™ biotin conjugates

DSB-X™ biotin–labeled proteins can be prepared with the DSB-X™ Biotin Protein Labeling Kit (D20655, Section 1.2).

Captivate™ Ferrofluid Conjugates

The Captivate™ ferrofluid conjugates of streptavidin (C21476), goat anti–mouse IgG antibody (C21473) and goat anti–rabbit IgG antibody (C21474), which have been developed in cooperation with Immunicon Corporation (www.immunicon.com), permit the facile isolation of biotinylated, DSB-X™ biotin–labeled or antibody-complexed proteins — including antibodies and their haptens, as well as receptors and their receptor ligands — using magnetic separation technology (Section 7.2, Section 7.6). Cells that have been selectively separated by the Captivate™ ferrofluid conjugates (Figure 7.107) can be lysed and analyzed for their proteins by standard gel electrophoresis (Section 9.3) or blotting techniques (Section 9.4). The Captivate™ ferrofluid streptavidin conjugate can also bind biotinylated lectins and DSB-X™ biotin–labeled lectins for selective isolation of glycoproteins from solutions.

The Captivate™ ferrofluid products are unique in that they represent the only superparamagnetic particles available that allow both cell sorting and cell-based imaging to be performed simultaneously by use of the Captivate™ microscope-mounted magnetic yoke assembly and associated Captivate™ disposable sample chambers (C24701, C24700; Section 23.3; Figure 23.57). The Captivate™ microscope-mounted magnetic yoke assembly includes one free set of 10 disposable sample chambers. Use of Captivate™ ferrofluid streptavidin in combination with biotin- or DSB-X™ biotin–conjugated probes permits the simultaneous isolation, visualization and counting of cells that are targets of the antibody by any researcher with access to a standard low-cost microscope with a 10× objective (Figure 7.108). Also, when used to capture DSB-X™ biotin–labeled antibodies to cell-surface antigens the Captivate™ ferrofluid can be completely separated from the labeled cells by incubation with D-biotin (B1595, B20656; Section 4.2) or D-desthiobiotin (D20657, Section 4.2). The extremely fast capture rate and small particle size of Captivate™ ferrofluid means that these products should also have significant advantages over other commercially available magnetic particles in liquid-handling robotic systems.

Captivate™ Microscale Phosphopeptide Isolation Kit

The Captivate™ Microscale Phosphopeptide Isolation Kit (C33355) provides a highly selective and sensitive method for isolating phosphopeptides from complex solutions. This technology is ideal for isolating phosphorylated peptides as a front-end fractionation step prior to liquid chromatography– and mass spectrometry–based proteomics systems.

The Captivate™ Microscale Phosphopeptide Isolation Kit uses modified superparamagnetic particles (suspended as a ferrofluid) that bind rapidly and selectively to phosphate groups in a reversible, noncovalent manner. In conjunction with magnetic separation devices (such as the Captivate™ magnetic separator for six microcentrifuge tubes or the Captivate™ magnetic separator for 96-well microplates (C24703, C24702; Section 23.3), these particles provide a simple and straightforward method for isolating phosphopeptides from small sample volumes. For example, 1 picomole or less of a monophosphorylated peptide can be isolated from a volume of 5 µL. Subjecting the samples to selective β-elimination/addition modification prior to mass spectroscopy analysis allows one to distinguish between phosphorylated serine, threonine and tyrosine residues. The binding capacity of the ferrofluid is approximately 1–2 picomoles of phosphate per microgram of ferrofluid. Phosphopeptide binding is highly pH dependent, with the optimum phosphopeptide capture occurring at ~pH 4.

Nonspecific binding tends to increase with increasing pH, and phosphopeptide capture efficiency tends to decrease below pH 3.5.

Each Captivate™ Microscale Phosphopeptide Isolation Kit provides:

- Captivate™ ferrofluid phosphopeptide-binding reagent
- Binding/wash buffer
- Elution buffer
- Barium hydroxide and methylamine for a β-elimination reaction and alkylation reaction, respectively, to distinguish among the three different types of peptide phosphorylation
- Phosphopeptide control mixture containing four different phosphopeptides and three peptides that are not phosphorylated

The Captivate™ ferrofluid phosphate-binding reagent can also be used for other applications. This ferrofluid reagent selectively binds inorganic phosphate, phosphoamino acids, phosphopeptides, ATP/GTP compounds and phosphoinositol compounds.

References

1. Anal Biochem 72, 248 (1976); **2.** J Biol Chem 193, 265 (1951); **3.** Anal Biochem 150, 76 (1985); **4.** Biotechniques 34, 850 (2003); **5.** J Biol Chem 272, 12762 (1997); **6.** J Biol Chem 275, 3256 (2000); **7.** J Biol Chem 274, 35367 (1999); **8.** Anal Chem 73, 4994 (2001); **9.** Anal Chem 72, 4608 (2000); **10.** J Chromatogr B Biomed Sci Appl 754, 345 (2001); **11.** J Cell Biol 142, 1313 (1998); **12.** Appl Environ Microbiol 66, 3632 (2000); **13.** Anal Chem 63, 408 (1991); **14.** Anal Chem 63, 413 (1991); **15.** J Chromatogr 499, 579 (1990); **16.** Anal Biochem 244, 277 (1997); **17.** J Biol Chem 274, 25461 (1999); **18.** J Chromatogr B Biomed Sci Appl 754, 217 (2001); **19.** Clin Chim Acta 308, 147 (2001); **20.** Eur J Biochem 96, 483 (1979); **21.** Adv Protein Chem 29, 85 (1975); **22.** J Biol Chem 246, 698 (1971); **23.** Anal Biochem 115, 203 (1981); **24.** Anal Chem 62, 1580 (1990); **25.** Anal Chem 62, 1577 (1990); **26.** Science 178, 871 (1972); **27.** Clin Chim Acta 157, 73 (1986); **28.** J Lipid Res 27, 792 (1986); **29.** Anal Biochem 248, 195 (1997); **30.** Anal Biochem 214, 346 (1993); **31.** J Chromatogr 502, 247 (1990); **32.** J Immunol Methods 172, 141 (1994); **33.** Proc Natl Acad Sci U S A 72, 619 (1975); **34.** Anal Biochem 123, 41 (1982); **35.** Appl Environ Microbiol 65, 3251 (1999); **36.** Anal Biochem 292, 40 (2001); **37.** Appl Environ Microbiol 68, 901 (2002); **38.** J Biochem (Tokyo) 101, 89 (1987); **39.** Biochim Biophys Acta 229, 547 (1971); **40.** Free Radic Biol Med 23, 361 (1997); **41.** Methods Enzymol 300, 106 (1999); **42.** Proc Natl Acad Sci U S A 83, 8703 (1986); **43.** Meth Mol Genet 1, 267 (1993); **44.** Biotechniques 13, 856 (1992); **45.** Biotechniques 10, 178 (1991); **46.** Nucleic Acids Res 19, 4005 (1991); **47.** Science 252, 712 (1991); **48.** Gene 67, 31 (1988); **49.** J Biol Chem 272, 8133 (1997); **50.** J Cell Biol 131, 1003 (1995); **51.** J Cell Biol 130, 651 (1995); **52.** J Biol Chem 270, 30168 (1995); **53.** J Biol Chem 270, 9031 (1995); **54.** J Biol Chem 270, 26613 (1995); **55.** J Biol Chem 268, 3715 (1993); **56.** J Biol Chem 270, 24525 (1995); **57.** J Cell Biol 129, 189 (1995); **58.** Mol Biol Cell 6, 247 (1995); **59.** Biochemistry 31, 5841 (1992); **60.** J Chromatogr 510, 3 (1990); **61.** J Cell Biol 125, 661 (1994); **62.** Biochemistry 28, 574 (1989); **63.** Anal Biochem 243, 257 (1996); **64.** Anal Biochem 282, 200 (2000); **65.** Anal Biochem 308, 343 (2002).

Data Table — 9.2 Quantitation and Selective Purification of Proteins in Solution

Cat #	MW	Storage	Soluble	Abs	EC	Em	Solvent	Notes
A6222	305.29	F,D,L	MeOH	465	ND	560	MeOH	1, 2, 3
A11760	518.47	L	H_2O	342	37,000	450	pH 7	
A20770	282.30	F,D,L	DMSO	<300		none		
D20657	214.26	RO	pH >6	<300		none		4
F2332	278.26	F,D,L	MeCN	380	7,800	464	MeCN	5
F20261	278.26	F,D,L	MeCN	380	8,400	464	MeCN	5, 6
P2331MP	134.13	L	EtOH	334	5,700	455	pH 9	7

For definitions of the contents of this data table, see "Navigating *The Handbook*" in the introductory pages.

Notes

1. Spectral data are for the reaction product with glycine in the presence of cyanide. Unreacted reagent in MeOH: Abs = 254 nm (EC = 46,000 $cm^{-1}M^{-1}$), nonfluorescent.
2. ND = not determined.
3. Solubility in methanol is improved by addition of base (e.g., 1–5% (v/v) 0.2 M KOH).
4. This product is supplied as a ready-made solution in the solvent indicated under "Soluble."
5. Fluorescamine spectra are for the reaction product with butylamine. The fluorescence quantum yield and lifetime of the butylamine adduct in EtOH are 0.23 and 7.5 nanoseconds, respectively (Arch Biochem Biophys 163, 390 (1974)). The unreacted reagent is nonfluorescent (Abs = 234 nm, EC = 28,000 $cm^{-1}M^{-1}$ in MeCN).
6. This product is specified to equal or exceed 98% analytical purity by HPLC.
7. Spectral data are for the reaction product of P2331MP with alanine and 2-mercaptoethanol. The spectra and stability of the adduct depend on the amine and thiol reactants (Biochim Biophys Acta 576, 440 (1979)). Unreacted reagent in H_2O: Abs = 257 nm (EC = 1000 $cm^{-1}M^{-1}$).

Product List — 9.2 Quantitation and Selective Purification of Proteins in Solution

Cat #	Product Name	Unit Size
A20770	6-((acryloyl)amino)hexanoic acid, succinimidyl ester (acryloyl-X, SE)	5 mg
A11760	4-amino-4′-benzamidostilbene-2,2′-disulfonic acid, disodium salt (MBDS)	100 mg
A5800	anti-glutathione *S*-transferase, rabbit IgG fraction *3 mg/mL*	0.5 mL
A11131	anti-glutathione *S*-transferase, rabbit IgG fraction, Alexa Fluor® 488 conjugate *2 mg/mL*	0.5 mL
A6222	ATTO-TAG™ CBQCA derivatization reagent (CBQCA; 3-(4-carboxybenzoyl)quinoline-2-carboxaldehyde)	10 mg
C21387	CaptAvidin™ acrylamide	1 mg
C21386	CaptAvidin™ agarose *sedimented bead suspension*	5 mL
C21385	CaptAvidin™ biotin-binding protein	1 mg
C21473	Captivate™ ferrofluid goat anti-mouse IgG (H+L) *0.5 mg Fe/mL*	1 mL
C21474	Captivate™ ferrofluid goat anti-rabbit IgG (H+L) *0.5 mg Fe/mL*	1 mL
C21476	Captivate™ ferrofluid streptavidin (streptavidin, Captivate™ ferrofluid conjugate) *0.5 mg Fe/mL*	1 mL
C33355	Captivate™ Microscale Phosphopeptide Isolation Kit *for magnetic separation* *50 isolations of 10 µmol each*	1 kit
C6667	CBQCA Protein Quantitation Kit *300-800 assays*	1 kit
D20657	D-desthiobiotin *50 mM aqueous solution*	10 mL
D20658	DSB-X™ Bioconjugate Isolation Kit #1 *with streptavidin agarose* *5 isolations*	1 kit
E33202	EZQ® Phosphopeptide Quantitation Kit *1000 assays*	1 kit
E33201	EZQ® Phosphoprotein Quantitation Kit *2000 assays*	1 kit
R33200	EZQ® Protein Quantitation Kit *2000 assays*	1 kit
F2332	fluorescamine	100 mg
F20261	fluorescamine *FluoroPure™ grade*	100 mg
G2879	glutathione agarose, linked through sulfur *sedimented bead suspension*	10 mL
G21800	glutathione agarose, linked through sulfur *sedimented bead suspension* *bulk packaging*	100 mL
G21801	Glutathione Transferase Fusion Protein Purification Kit *5 purifications*	1 kit
N6666	NanoOrange® Protein Quantitation Kit *200-2000 assays*	1 kit
P2331MP	*o*-phthaldialdehyde (OPA) *high purity*	1 g
P33203	Pro-Q® Diamond LC Phosphopeptide Detection Kit	1 kit
Q33210	Quant-iT™ Protein Assay Kit *1000 assays*	1 kit
Q33215	Quant-iT™ Protein Assay Kit *introductory kit, 200 assays*	1 kit
S21379	streptavidin acrylamide	1 mg
S951	streptavidin agarose *sedimented bead suspension*	5 mL

For current prices or to order online, visit probes.invitrogen.com

9.3 Detection of the Total-Protein Profile in Gels, on Blots, on Microarrays and in Capillary Electrophoresis

SYPRO® Protein Gel Stains

The luminescent SYPRO® protein gel stains are revolutionizing the detection of the total-protein profile in polyacrylamide gels. These novel protein detection reagents combine several characteristics that together make them far superior to traditional staining methods, including:

- **High sensitivity**, making it possible to detect even minimally expressed proteins
- **Fast and easy staining protocols**, simplifying the processing of multiple gels or blots
- **Minimal protein-to-protein variation in staining**, allowing quantitative comparisons between proteins [1–3]
- **Broad linear quantitation range**, an essential property for performing comparative protein expression studies
- **Compatibility with subsequent microanalysis**, streamlining techniques such as immunostaining, microsequencing and mass spectrometry [4]
- **No nucleic acid staining or polysaccharide staining**, allowing analysis of relatively impure or contaminated samples
- **Instrument compatibility**, making the dyes suitable for research labs with either simple UV transilluminators or laser scanners

Currently the most common methods for universal profiling of proteins in gels are Coomassie brilliant blue staining [5] and silver staining.[6] Although Coomassie brilliant blue is an inexpensive reagent, its staining is relatively insensitive and, because it requires destaining, time consuming. Silver staining may be up to 100 times more sensitive than Coomassie brilliant blue staining, but it is relatively expensive and entails several labor-intensive and time-sensitive steps. Silver staining also exhibits a high degree of protein-to-protein variability; staining intensity and color are very dependent on each polypeptide's sequence and degree of glycosylation, and some proteins are detectable only as negatively stained patches. Moreover, silver staining shows very poor linearity with protein concentration (Figure 9.17) and poor reproducibility in staining from gel to gel, making it inadequate for comparative studies of protein expression in cells. The drawbacks of these traditional stains can all be overcome by using one of the SYPRO® stains, without sacrificing detection sensitivity.[7] We have developed a SYPRO® dye optimized for protein profiling in nearly every type of gel (Table 9.3) or blot application (Table 9.4). The characteristics and applications

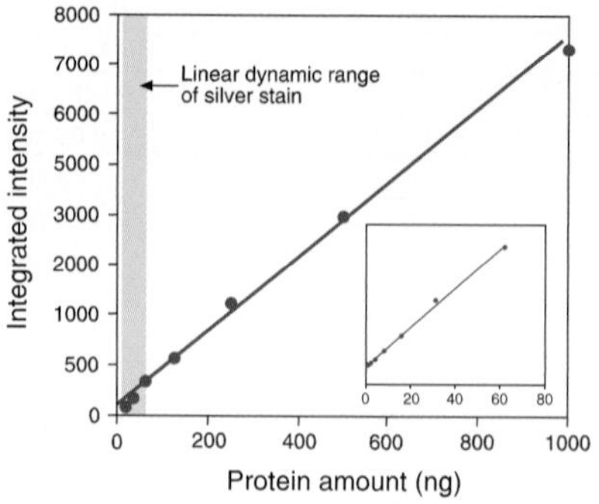

Figure 9.18 Amounts of carbonic anhydrase ranging from 1 ng to 1000 ng were separated on an SDS-polyacrylamide gel and stained with the SYPRO® Ruby protein gel stain (S12000, S12001, S21900). The inset shows the excellent linearity in the lower part of the range from 1 ng to 60 ng protein. Staining intensities were quantitated using the Molecular Imager FX documentation system (Bio-Rad Laboratories). For comparison, the gray band shows the linear range for the same protein detected with silver staining.

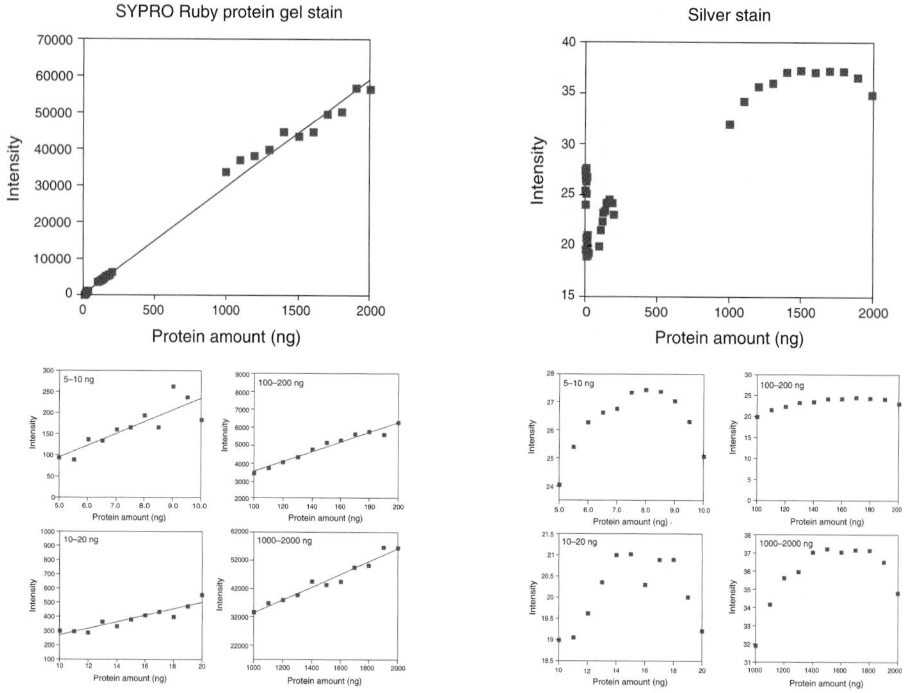

Figure 9.17 Quantitation of proteins in gels using SYPRO® Ruby protein gel stain versus silver stain. Dilutions of proteins were electrophoresed on eight different SDS-polyacrylamide gels, two gels for each of four dilution ranges. The gels were stained with either SYPRO® Ruby protein gel stain (S12000, S12001, S21900) or a silver stain. Staining intensities were quantitated using either the Fluor-S MAX MultiImager documentation system (Bio-Rad Laboratories) or the FLA3000G laser scanner (Fuji Photo Film Co.) and plotted against the protein amount for bovine serum albumin. SYPRO® Ruby protein gel stain shows a linear quantitation range over three orders of magnitude, as well as consistent staining intensities from gel to gel. In contrast, the silver stain shows linear quantitation over only a small range, a very shallow slope and inconsistent staining intensities from gel to gel, even when corrected for background differences.

Table 9.3 — Summary of SYPRO® and Coomassie Fluor™ luminescent and fluorescent protein gel stains

Dye Name	Ex/Em *	Major Applications	Features
SYPRO® Ruby protein gel stain	280, 450/610	2-D gels, IEF gels, 1-D SDS-PAGE	• Highest sensitivity (1–2 ng/band; comparable to silver staining) • Linear quantitation range over three orders of magnitude
SYPRO® Orange protein gel stain	300, 470/570	1-D SDS-PAGE	• Very good sensitivity (4–8 ng/band; higher than Coomassie brilliant blue staining) • Little protein-to-protein variability • Linear quantitation range over three orders of magnitude
SYPRO® Red protein gel stain	300, 550/630	1-D SDS-PAGE	• Very good sensitivity (4–8 ng/band; higher than Coomassie brilliant blue staining) • Little protein-to-protein variability • Linear quantitation range over three orders of magnitude
SYPRO® Tangerine protein gel stain	300, 490/640	1-D SDS-PAGE, blotting applications, zymography, electroelution	• Very good sensitivity (4–8 ng/band; higher than Coomassie brilliant blue staining) • Little protein-to-protein variability • Linear quantitation range over three orders of magnitude • No fixation required
Coomassie Fluor™ Orange protein gel stain	300, 470/570	1-D SDS-PAGE	• Premixed and ready-to-use solution • Very good sensitivity (8 ng/band; higher than Coomassie brilliant blue staining) • Little protein-to-protein variability • Linear quantitation range over at least two orders of magnitude

All SYPRO® gel and blot stains are compatible with Edman sequencing and mass spectrometry. * Excitation (Ex) and emission (Em) maxima, in nm. For maximum sensitivity, use excitation sources and optical filters matched to these values.

of the individual SYPRO® protein gel and blot stains for detecting the total-protein profile of a sample are described in this section. Section 9.4 discusses combining these SYPRO® stains with selective protein detection reagents for multiparameter staining with our Multiplexed Proteomics® technology.

SYPRO® Ruby Protein Gel Stain: Ultrasensitive Protein Detection in 1-D, 2-D and IEF Gels

Our patented SYPRO® Ruby protein gel stain[4,7–20] (S12000, S12001, S21900) is a ready-to-use protein stain that has sensitivity equal to or exceeding that of the best silver staining techniques,[8,10,11,14–16] is compatible with Edman sequencing and mass spectrometry[4] and can be visualized with a simple UV transilluminator or a laser scanner. SYPRO® Ruby protein gel stain has characteristics that make it far superior to conventional staining techniques:

- **High-sensitivity staining.** SYPRO® Ruby protein gel stain provides at least the same subnanogram sensitivity as the best silver staining techniques in 1-D, 2-D[14,16] or IEF gels (Figure 9.18).
- **Simple protocol.** After fixation, the gel is incubated in the staining solution (Figure 9.19). No stop solutions or destaining steps are required and, unlike silver staining, gels can be left in the dye solution for indefinite periods without overstaining, vastly simplifying the simultaneous processing of multiple gels and making it possible to perform high-throughput staining without investing in robotic staining devices.
- **Accurate peptide and protein detection.** SYPRO® Ruby protein gel stain shows little protein-to-protein variability in staining[3] and detects some proteins that are completely missed by silver staining (Figure 9.20), such as heavily glycosylated proteins. Unlike silver staining, SYPRO® Ruby dye does not stain extraneous nucleic acids, lipids or carbohydrates in the sample.[16]
- **Excellent performance in comparative protein expression studies.** SYPRO® Ruby stain shows a greater linear quantitation range than either silver or Coomassie brilliant blue

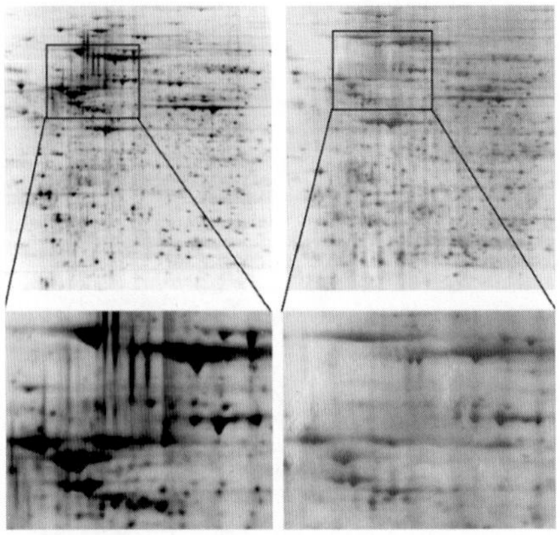

Figure 9.20 SYPRO® Ruby protein gel stain (S12000, S12001, S21900) shows less protein-to-protein variation than silver staining. Proteins from a cell lysate were run on a 2-D gel and stained with SYPRO® Ruby protein gel stain (left) or silver stain (right). The grayscale values of the SYPRO® Ruby dye–stained gel have been inverted for easier comparison with the silver-stained gel.

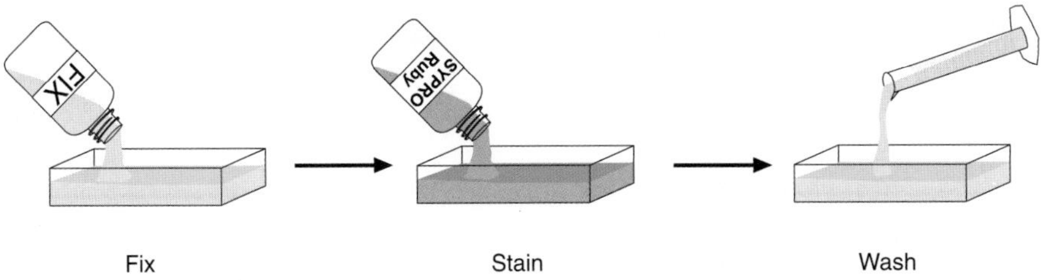

Figure 9.19 Staining gels with SYPRO® Ruby protein gel stain (S12000, S12001, S21900) is simple: just fix, stain and wash.

Table 9.4 — Summary of fluorescent and luminescent protein blot stains

Dye Name	Ex/Em *	Major Applications	Features
SYPRO® Ruby protein blot stain	280, 450/618	Mass spectrometry, microsequencing, counterstain for blot-based detection techniques (nitrocellulose or PVDF membranes)	• Highest sensitivity (1–2 ng/band; comparable to colloidal gold staining) • Reversible
SYPRO® Rose Plus protein blot stain	350/610	Mass spectrometry, microsequencing, counterstain for blot-based detection techniques (nitrocellulose or PVDF membranes), reversible staining of proteins on surfaces	• Highest sensitivity (1–2 ng/band; comparable to colloidal gold staining) • Readily reversible
BODIPY® FL-X †	365, 505/575	Counterstain for blot-based detection techniques (PVDF membranes)	• Very good sensitivity (4–8 ng/band) • Permanent, covalent staining for multicolor techniques
BODIPY® TR-X ‡	300, 590/615	Counterstain for blot-based detection techniques (PVDF membranes)	• Very good sensitivity (4–8 ng/band) • Permanent, covalent staining for multicolor techniques

* Excitation (Ex) and emission (Em) maxima, in nm. For maximum sensitivity, use excitation sources and optical filters matched to these values. † Available in DyeChrome™ Western Blot Stain Kits #1, #2 and #3 (D21881, D21882, D21883; Section 9.4) or as a stand-alone reagent (D6102). ‡ Available in DyeChrome™ Western Blot Stain Kits #4, #5 and #6 (D21884, D21885, D21886; Section 9.4) or as a stand-alone reagent (D6116).

Figure 9.21 Comparison of two protein samples run on 2-D gels. Proteins from either a normal liver tissue sample or a liver tumor sample were run on two 2-D gels and stained with SYPRO® Ruby protein gel stain (S12000, S12001, S21900). Images of the gels were captured using the FLA-3000 scanner (Fuji). Images from a portion of the two gels were then pseudocolored either pink or green, overlaid and matched spot-for-spot using Z3 software (Compugen). Green spots represent proteins expressed in the liver tumor samples; pink spots represent proteins expressed in the normal liver tissue sample. Black spots represent proteins expressed in both tissues.

staining — extending over three orders of magnitude — making it possible to accurately compare protein expression levels [16] (Figure 9.17, Figure 9.18). Gel-to-gel staining is extremely consistent; same-spot intensity comparisons between identical 2-D gels show a correlation coefficient of 0.9.[15] Multiple gels can easily be compared using available software (Figure 9.21). No other protein quantitation method, including running multiple prestained samples on the same gel, gives results that approach this level of discrimination.[21]

- **Compatibility with microsequencing and mass spectrometry.**[4] Unlike silver staining techniques, which use glutaraldehyde- or formaldehyde-based fixatives, SYPRO® Ruby dye is a gentle stain that interacts noncovalently with proteins. Thus, high-quality Edman sequencing or mass spectrometry data [4,15,16,22] (Figure 9.22) can be obtained immediately after staining, without modification steps that may compromise sensitivity. Automated in-gel digestion methods have been used in the analysis of femtomole levels of SYPRO® Ruby dye–stained proteins.[23]
- **Utility for isoelectric focusing (IEF).** SYPRO® Ruby protein gel stain also provides reliable, high-sensitivity staining for isoelectric focusing (IEF) gels (Figure 9.23) without the problems typically encountered with silver staining, such as ampholyte staining or mirroring effects on the plastic gel backing.
- **Easily visualized signal.** SYPRO® Ruby protein gel stain comprises the transition metal ruthenium, which shows an extremely bright and photostable red-orange luminescence when excited with either UV or blue light (Figure 9.24). Stained proteins can be visualized using a UV transilluminator, a blue-light transilluminator or a laser-scanning instrument. Gels can then be documented using Polaroid 667 black-and-white print film, a CCD camera with an image documentation system or a laser-scanning instrument [16] (Table 9.5). For optimal sensitivity using a UV transilluminator and Polaroid 667 black-and-white print film, the SYPRO® photographic filter (S6656, Figure 23.62) is recommended.

Table 9.5 — Imaging platforms validated as suitable for visualization of SYPRO® Ruby protein stains

Manufacturer *	Instrument	Excitation Source	Emission Filter
Alpha Innotech Corp.	AlphaImager	300 nm UV transillumination	620 nm bandpass
Bio-Rad Laboratories	Fluor-S MultiImager	300 nm UV light box	610 nm longpass
Bio-Rad Laboratories	Molecular Imager FX	488 or 532 nm laser	640 ± 35 nm
Clare Chemical Research	Dark Reader	490 nm blue light box	600 ± 35 nm (or the system's amber lid)
Fotodyne Inc.	FOTO/Analyst Archiver CCD system	300 nm UV transillumination	618 nm bandpass
Fotodyne Inc.	FOTO/UV 450 transilluminator with Polaroid camera	300 nm UV transillumination	490 nm longpass (SYPRO® photographic filter, S6656)
Fuji Photo Film Co.	FLA3000G	473 or 532 nm laser	580 nm longpass
Fuji Photo Film Co.	LAS-1000 plus	470 nm blue LED	515 nm longpass
Genomic Solutions	BioImage 2-D Analyzer Camera System	300 nm UV light box	600 ± 35 nm
Hitachi Genetic Systems	FMBIO II	532 nm laser	625 ± 7.5 nm
Kodak/NEN	Image Station 440CF	300 or 365 nm UV epi-illumination	590 nm longpass
Molecular Devices	SPECTRAmax GEMINI Microplate Reader	485 ± 4.5 nm †	595 ± 4.5 nm †
Molecular Dynamics	Storm 860	450 ± 15 nm	520 nm longpass
Molecular Dynamics	FluorImager	488 nm laser	610 ± 35 nm
Nucleotech Corp.	Nucleovision 920	300 nm UV transillumination	Texas Red® (~630 nm bandpass)
PerkinElmer Life Sciences, Inc.	Wallac 1442 Arthur multi-wavelength fluoroimager	480 nm excitation interference filter, epi-illumination	625 ± 15 nm
Roche/Boehringer-Mannheim	Lumi-Imager F1	300 nm UV light box	600 ± 20 nm
Scanalytics Inc.	Docugel gel documentation system	300 nm UV transillumination	600 nm bandpass
Stratagene	Eagle-Eye II	300 nm UV transillumination	ethidium bromide (~600 nm bandpass) or Coomassie Blue (~570 nm bandpass)
Ultra-Lum Inc.	TUI-6000	300 nm UV transillumination	600 nm bandpass
UVP Laboratory Products	UV transilluminator, Visi-Blue plate and Polaroid system	300 nm UV light or 480 nm blue light (using Visi-Blue plate)	600 ± 35 nm or 490 nm longpass (SYPRO® photographic filter, S6656)

* These instruments were available in 2002; their availability and specifications are subject to change. † Monochromator.

- **Minimal hazardous waste.** The amount of hazardous waste generated with the SYPRO® Ruby protein gel stain is greatly reduced as compared with that of silver staining, minimizing the hassles and expense associated with waste disposal.

SYPRO® Ruby protein gel stain is supplied as 200 mL of a 1X staining solution (S12001), sufficient for staining about four minigels, or 1 L of a 1X staining solution (S12000), sufficient for staining about 20 minigels or two standard 2-D gels. Additionally, we offer SYPRO® Ruby protein gel stain in a 5 L box (S21900), sufficient for staining about 100 minigels or 10 standard 2-D gels. These boxes are easy to stack and store, and the convenient spigot makes it easy to dispense just the right amount of stain (Figure 9.25). Significant discounts are available for multiple-unit purchases of the SYPRO® Ruby products. All of the SYPRO® Ruby protein gel stains are accompanied by detailed instructions for staining and photography of gels.

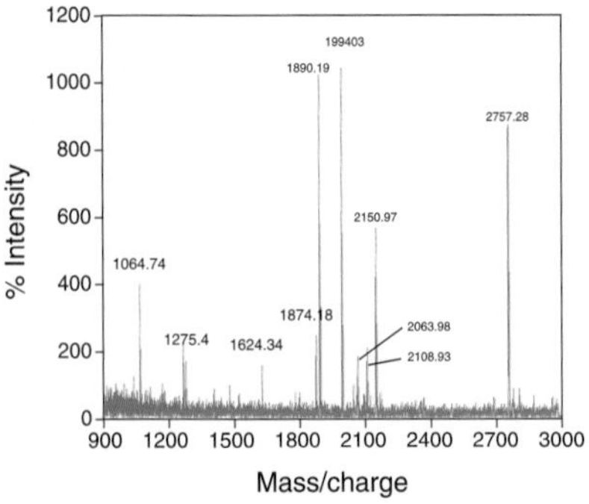

Figure 9.22 Mass spectrum profile of NADH:ubiquinone reductase precursor (75,000-dalton subunit) obtained after 2-D gel electrophoresis of bovine heart mitochondria and staining with SYPRO® Ruby protein gel stain (S12000, S12001, S21900). Bovine heart mitochondria were a gift of Roderick Capaldi, University of Oregon.

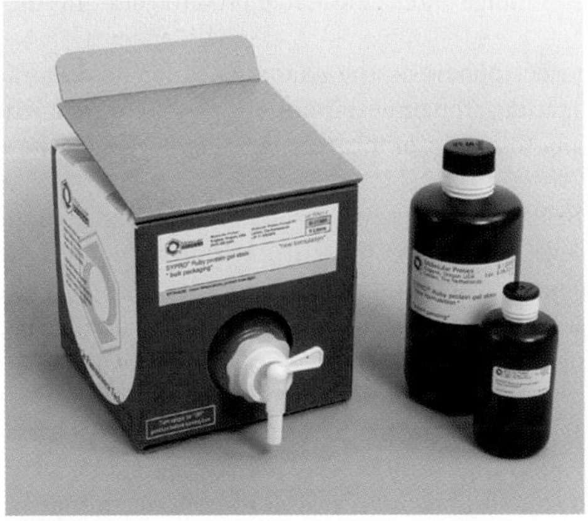

Figure 9.25 SYPRO® Ruby protein gel stain is available in 200 mL, 1 L or 5 L sizes (S12000, S12001, S21900). Generous bulk discounts are available for multiple-unit purchases of these products.

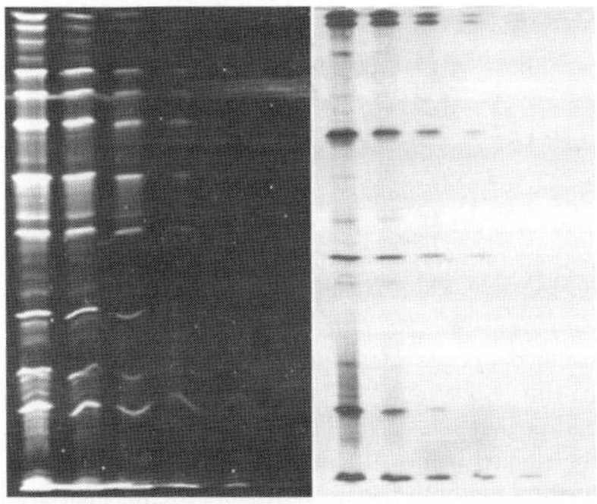

Figure 9.23 SYPRO® Ruby protein gel stain versus silver stain for IEF gels. Serial dilutions of isoelectric focusing protein standards were electrophoresed on two identical polyacrylamide gels. One gel was stained with SYPRO® Ruby protein gel stain (S12000, S12001, S21900) (left) and the other with silver stain (right). Both stains show a similar limit of sensitivity for all proteins.

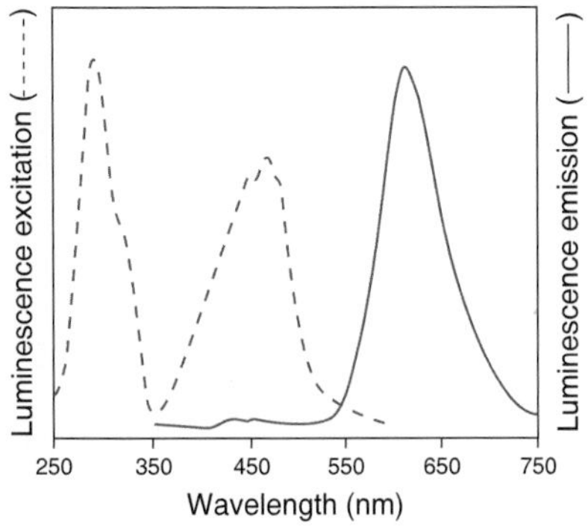

Figure 9.24 Luminescence excitation (dashed line) and emission (solid line) spectra of the SYPRO® Ruby protein gel and blot stains (S11791, S12000, S12001, S21900).

SYPRO® Orange and SYPRO® Red Protein Gel Stains: For Routine Detection of Proteins in 1-D SDS-Polyacrylamide Gels

Molecular Probes' patented SYPRO® Orange (S6650, S6651) and SYPRO® Red (S6653, S6654) protein gel stains provide a fluorescence-based alternative for protein detection in SDS-polyacrylamide gels that is not only faster and more sensitive than Coomassie brilliant blue staining, but can be as sensitive as short-protocol silver staining methods (Figure 9.26) at a fraction of the time, effort and cost of silver staining.[1,24–27] In the presence of excess SDS, nonpolar regions of polypeptides are coated with detergent molecules, forming a micelle-like structure with a nearly constant SDS/protein ratio (1.4 g SDS:1.0 g protein); this constant charge-per-mass ratio is the basis of molecular weight determination by SDS-polyacrylamide gel electrophoresis.[28] The SYPRO® Orange and SYPRO® Red dyes appear to bind to the SDS coat that surrounds proteins in SDS-polyacrylamide gels. Thus, the staining observed with these dyes exhibits relatively little protein-to-protein variation and is linearly related to protein mass (Figure 9.27). Some important features of the SYPRO® Orange and SYPRO® Red protein gel stains include:

- **Ease of use.** Following electrophoresis, the gel is stained for 10–60 minutes and then briefly rinsed — no separate fixation, stop or destaining steps are required. After staining, the gel is immediately ready for photography, or it can be stored, in or out of the staining solution, for days.
- **High sensitivity.** The SYPRO® Orange and SYPRO® Red protein gel stains routinely provide a sensitivity level of at least 8–16 ng per band in SDS-polyacrylamide minigels when visualized with standard 300 nm transillumination (Figure 9.26). Photography using Polaroid 667 black-and-white print film and a SYPRO® photographic filter (S6656, Figure 23.62) enhances the detection of staining with SYPRO® Orange or SYPRO® Red dye by several-fold over visible detection because the film integrates the signal throughout the duration of the exposure. Laser scanners also detect nanogram quantities of SYPRO® dye–stained proteins in gels.
- **Broad linear quantitation range.** Protein detection in gels stained with either the SYPRO® Orange or SYPRO® Red stain is linear over three orders of magnitude in protein quantity[27] (Figure 9.27).
- **Uniform protein staining.** Unlike silver staining,[29] the SYPRO® Orange and SYPRO® Red dyes exhibit relatively low protein-to-protein variability in SDS-polyacrylamide gels[1] (Figure 9.27) and do not stain nucleic acids, which are sometimes found in protein mixtures from cell or tissue extracts.[27] In addition, the SYPRO® Orange and SYPRO® Red dyes only weakly stain

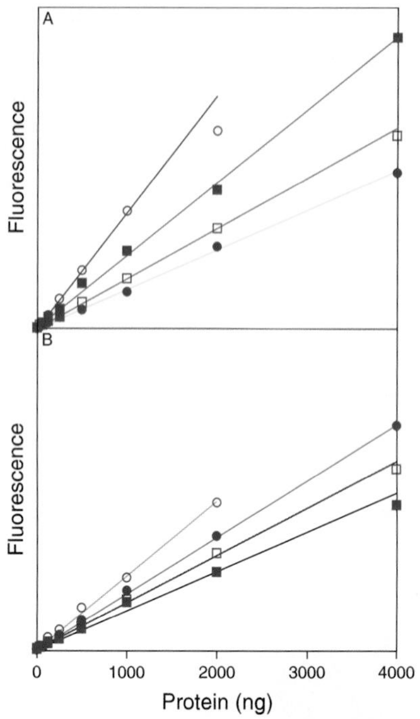

Figure 9.27 Quantitation of proteins in a gel using SYPRO® Orange protein gel stain (S6650, S6651). A protein mixture was serially diluted and electrophoresed on a 15% SDS-polyacrylamide gel and then stained with SYPRO® Orange protein gel stain. The gel was then scanned using a Molecular Dynamics Storm gel and blot analysis system (excitation/emission 488/>520 nm) and analyzed to yield the fluorescence intensities of the stained bands. The fluorescence intensity scale is the same in both panels, illustrating the minimal protein-to-protein staining variation of the SYPRO® Orange gel stain. Detection limits are between 2 and 16 ng of protein; the linear detection ranges are approximately 1000-fold. Proteins represented are: Panel A) β-galactosidase (○), lysozyme (■), bovine serum albumin (BSA,□) and phosphorylase B (●); Panel B) myosin (○), soybean trypsin inhibitor (■), ovalbumin (□) and carbonic anhydrase (●).

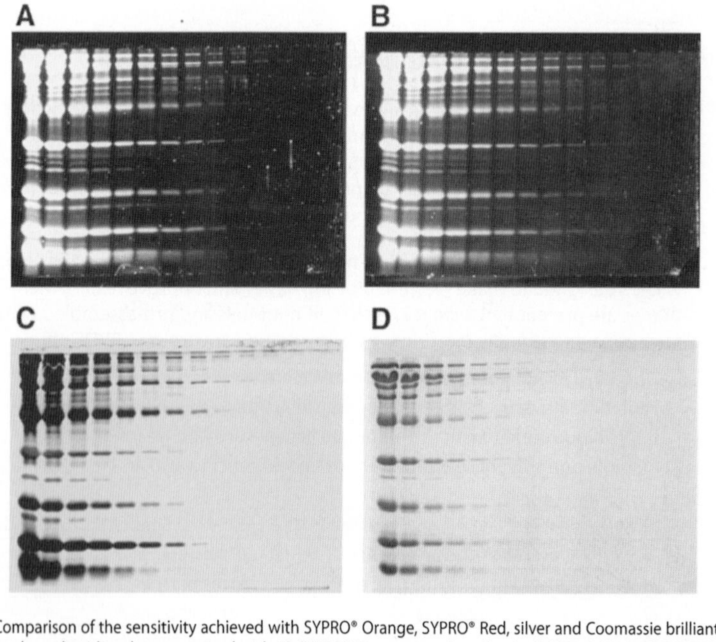

Figure 9.26 Comparison of the sensitivity achieved with SYPRO® Orange, SYPRO® Red, silver and Coomassie brilliant blue stains. Identical SDS-polyacrylamide gels were stained with **A)** SYPRO® Orange protein gel stain (S6650, S6651), **B)** SYPRO® Red protein gel stain (S6653, S6654), **C)** silver stain and **D)** Coomassie brilliant blue stain, according to standard protocols. The SYPRO® Orange and SYPRO® Red dye–stained gels were photographed using 300 nm transillumination, a SYPRO® photographic filter (S6656) and Polaroid 667 black-and-white print film. The silver- and Coomassie brilliant blue–stained gels were photographed with transmitted white light and Polaroid 667 black-and-white print film; no photographic filter was used to photograph these gels.

lipopolysaccharides in bacterial lysates, whereas these biopolymers are strongly detected by some types of silver staining.[27] Glycoproteins (such as the IgG variable subunit) and proteins with prosthetic groups (such as bovine cytochrome oxidase) are also efficiently stained with the SYPRO® Orange and SYPRO® Red dyes.[1]

- **Photostability.** Proteins stained with the SYPRO® Orange or SYPRO® Red dye are relatively photostable, enabling the researcher to acquire multiple photographic images and to use long film-exposure times (2–8 seconds). Gels that are illuminated for long periods of time may partially photobleach but can be restained with little loss of sensitivity.[30]
- **Compatibility with many types of instruments.** Although their excitation maxima are in the visible range (Figure 9.28), SYPRO® dye–stained gels are readily visualized using standard 300 nm transilluminators.[24] SYPRO® Orange protein gel stain also exhibits good sensitivity when viewed with a blue-light transilluminator, and both SYPRO® Orange and SYPRO® Red protein gel stains are suitable for use with many laser-scanning instruments.[1]
- **Chemical stability.** The SYPRO® Orange and SYPRO® Red gel stains are chemically stable; if protected from light, fluorescence of the stained gel is stable for several days, and staining solutions can be stored for months.
- **Economy.** The SYPRO® Orange and SYPRO® Red gel stains are not only less expensive than silver-staining kits but faster and less laborious to use. Additionally, use of the SYPRO® Orange or SYPRO® Red dye avoids the costs of purchase and disposal of large amounts of organic solvents that are required for Coomassie brilliant blue staining. Significant discounts are available on multiple-unit purchases of all of the SYPRO® dyes for high-throughput research applications.
- **Compatibility with mass spectroscopy.** Unlike silver staining, the SYPRO® Orange and SYPRO® Red dyes do not covalently bind to proteins, allowing subsequent analysis of stained proteins by microsequencing[26] or mass spectrometry.[4,31]

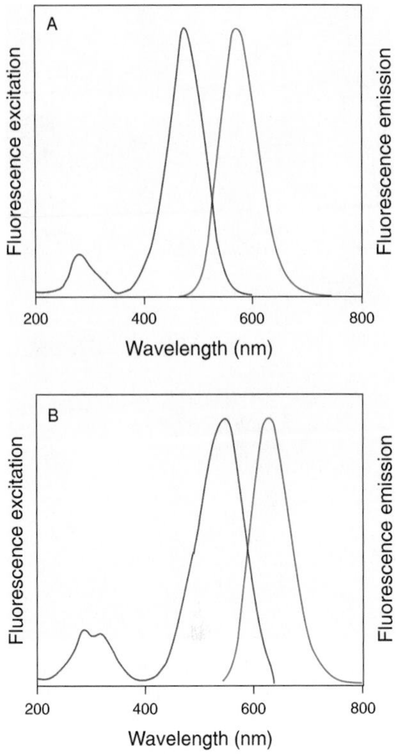

Figure 9.28 Luminescence excitation and emission spectra of **A)** SYPRO® Orange (S6650, S6651) and **B)** SYPRO® Red (S6653, S6654) protein gel stains diluted 1:10,000 in water containing 0.05% SDS and 150 µg/mL bovine serum albumin (BSA).

The SYPRO® Orange and SYPRO® Red stains have very similar staining properties, though we have observed that proteins stained with the SYPRO® Orange dye are slightly brighter, whereas gels stained with the SYPRO® Red dye tend to have lower background fluorescence. For maximum sensitivity with UV transilluminators, we recommend documenting the signal using Polaroid 667 black-and-white print film and the SYPRO® photographic filter (S6656, Figure 23.62). For maximum sensitivity with laser scanners, we recommend matching the appropriate SYPRO® dye with the excitation light source of the instrument. For instance, SYPRO® Orange protein gel stain is most suitable for gel scanners that employ argon-ion lasers with output at 488 nm, whereas SYPRO® Red protein gel stain is best matched to laser-scanning instruments that employ Nd:YAG lasers with output at 532 nm. Interestingly, the SYPRO® Red dye is also compatible with scanners using excitation by the 633 nm spectral line of the He–Ne laser. The SYPRO® Red protein gel stain has been used as a prestain for protein analysis in an automated ultrathin-layer gel electrophoretic technique.[32,33] The SYPRO® Orange protein gel stain has been used for protein sizing on a microchip[34] and for analyzing the kinetics of isothermal protein denaturation.[35]

The SYPRO® Orange and SYPRO® Red protein gel stains are compatible with SDS or urea/SDS gels. Staining native proteins in gels in the absence of SDS results in more protein-to-protein variation and lower sensitivity than staining SDS-denatured proteins, due to variations in hydrophobicity of the target polypeptides. However, sensitivity of SYPRO® dye staining in native gels can be improved if gels are soaked in 0.05% SDS solution after electrophoresis but prior to staining. For optimal staining of proteins in 2-D gels and IEF gels, we recommend the SYPRO® Ruby protein gel stain (S12000, S12001, S21900; see above).

Because the SYPRO® Orange and SYPRO® Red dyes do not covalently bind to proteins, stained proteins can be subsequently analyzed by microsequencing[26] or mass spectrometry.[4,31] However, these dyes are not recommended for staining gels prior to blotting, as there is a significant loss of sensitivity when proteins are stained with the SYPRO® Orange or SYPRO® Red dyes in typical Western blotting buffers. For maximum sensitivity and ease of use in staining proteins on blots, we recommend the use of SYPRO® Tangerine protein gel stain (S12010, see below) to stain proteins on the gel before blotting, or SYPRO® Ruby or SYPRO® Rose Plus protein blot stains (S11791, S12011; see below) for staining proteins on nitrocellulose or PVDF membranes after blotting.

The patented SYPRO® Orange and SYPRO® Red protein gel stains are available as 500 µL stock solutions in dimethylsulfoxide (DMSO), either in a single vial (S6650, S6653) or specially packaged as a set of 10 vials, each containing 50 µL (S6651, S6654). The reagents are supplied as 5000X concentrates; thus, 500 µL of either stain yields 2.5 L of staining solution. Significant discounts are available on multiple-unit purchases of all of the SYPRO® dyes for high-throughput research applications. Photography of proteins in gels, which is essential for obtaining the maximum sensitivity, requires use of the SYPRO® photographic filter (S6656).

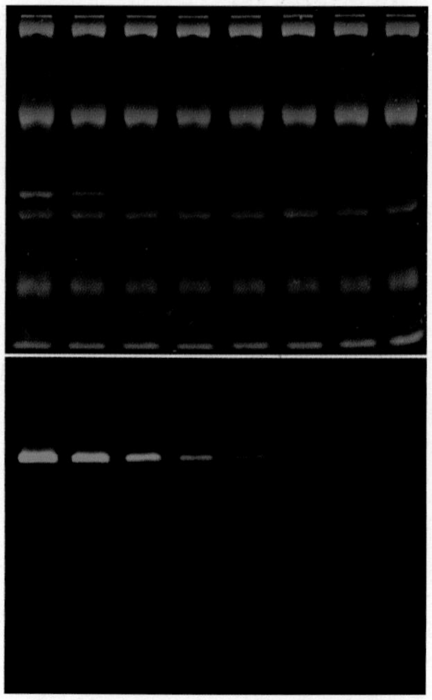

Figure 9.29 SYPRO® Tangerine protein gel stain and ELF® β-D-glucuronide for zymography. Molecular weight standards containing decreasing amounts of *Escherichia coli* β-glucuronidase were run on an SDS-polyacrylamide gel and stained with SYPRO® Tangerine protein gel stain (orange, S12010) followed by incubation with the ELF® 97 β-D-glucuronidase substrate (green, E6587) to detect the activity of β-glucuronidase.

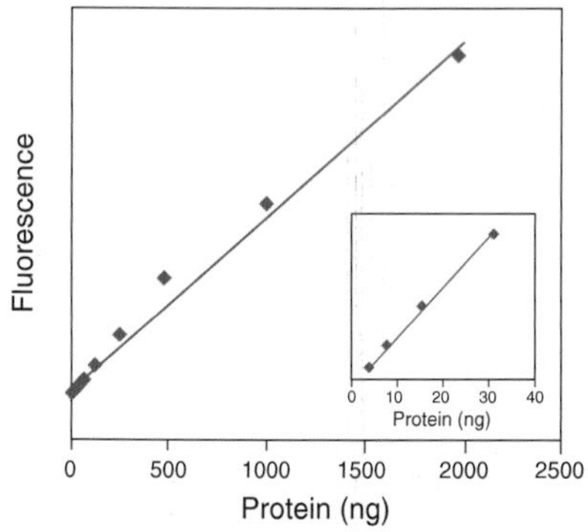

Figure 9.30 Linearity of SYPRO® Tangerine protein gel stain (S12010). A dilution series of carbonic anhydrase was electrophoresed through a 13% SDS-polyacrylamide gel and stained with SYPRO® Tangerine protein gel stain in 7% acetic acid. The fluorescence signal was quantified and plotted versus the protein amount, revealing a sensitivity limit of about 4 ng/band and a linear quantitation range over at least three orders of magnitude.

SYPRO® Tangerine Protein Gel Stain: Sensitive Protein Staining without Fixation for Electroelution, Zymography and Classroom Use

Our SYPRO® Tangerine protein gel stain [2,7] (S12010) stains proteins in gels without the need for either acids or organic solvents and thus serves as an alternative to conventional protein stains that fix proteins in the gel.[2] Whereas the SYPRO® Orange and SYPRO® Red stains require a staining solution containing acetic acid for maximum performance, staining with the SYPRO® Tangerine protein gel stain is possible in almost any buffer that contains NaCl. Because proteins are not fixed during the staining procedure, they can be readily eluted from gels, used for zymography (in-gel enzyme activity assays, Figure 9.29) or analyzed by mass spectrometry.[2] The SYPRO® Tangerine stain can also be used to stain gels before transferring the proteins to nitrocellulose or PVDF membranes for immunostaining [2] (Western blotting). Like the SYPRO® Orange and SYPRO® Red protein gel stains, the SYPRO® Tangerine protein gel stain shows high sensitivity (down to ~4 ng/band) and a broad linear quantitation range (Figure 9.30). Environmentally friendly and easy to use, the SYPRO® Tangerine protein gel stain is also ideal for use in educational settings, especially when used with UV-free blue-light transilluminators.

The SYPRO® Tangerine stain is compatible with conventional SDS-polyacrylamide gel electrophoresis, but it is not recommended for 2-D or IEF gels. Stained proteins can be visualized using a UV transilluminator, a blue-light transilluminator or a laser scanner. Photography of stained gels using Polaroid 667 black-and-white print film requires use of the SYPRO® photographic filter (S6656) for optimal sensitivity.

The SYPRO® Tangerine protein gel stain [2,7] (S12010) is available as 500 µL of a 5000X concentrate in dimethylsulfoxide (DMSO), an amount sufficient to stain about 100 minigels. Significant discounts are available on multiple unit purchases.

SYPRO® Protein Gel Stain Starter Kit

Our SYPRO® Orange, SYPRO® Red and SYPRO® Tangerine protein gel stains are available in a SYPRO® Protein Gel Stain Starter Kit (S12012) for first-time users. Each kit includes:

- 50 µL of SYPRO® Orange protein gel stain, sufficient for 5–20 minigels
- 50 µL of SYPRO® Red protein gel stain, sufficient for 5–20 minigels
- 50 µL of SYPRO® Tangerine protein gel stain, sufficient for 5–20 minigels
- A SYPRO® protein gel stain photographic filter
- Detailed protocols

Protein Molecular Weight Standards

Molecular Probes offers a protein mixture for use as molecular weight markers in SDS-polyacrylamide gel electrophoresis (Figure 9.31). This broad-range marker mixture (P6649) contains a balanced formulation of 11 polypeptides with molecular weights from 6500 to 205,000 daltons. These protein molecular weight standards give rise to sharp, well-separated bands when the gel is stained with any of our protein gel or blot stains. The mixture provides amounts of marker proteins sufficient for loading about 200 gel lanes.

Molecular Probes also has available PeppermintStick™ phosphoprotein molecular weight standards (P33350), CandyCane™ glycoprotein molecular weight standards (C21852) and human heart mitochondrial proteins for SDS-polyacrylamide gel electrophoresis (M22430), all of which are described in Section 9.4.

Electrophoretic Mobility-Shift (Bandshift) Assay (EMSA) Kit

Molecular Probes has made bandshift assays easy and more convenient with our Electrophoretic Mobility-Shift Assay (EMSA) Kit (E33075). Our EMSA Kit provides a fast and quantitative fluorescence-based method to detect both nucleic acid and protein in the same gel (Figure

8.145), doubling the information that can be obtained from bandshift assays. This kit uses two fluorescent dyes for detection — SYBR® Green EMSA nucleic acid gel stain for RNA or DNA and SYPRO® Ruby EMSA protein gel stain for proteins. Because the nucleic acids and proteins are stained in the gel after electrophoresis, there is no need to prelabel the DNA or RNA with a radioisotope, biotin or a fluorescent dye before the binding reaction, and therefore there is no possibility that the label will interfere with protein binding. Staining takes only about 20 minutes for the nucleic acid stain, and about 4 hours for the subsequent protein stain, yielding results much faster than radioisotope labeling (which may require multiple exposure times) or chemiluminescence-based detection (which requires blotting and multiple incubation steps). This kit also makes it possible to perform ratiometric measurements of nucleic acid and protein in the same band, providing more detailed information on the binding interaction. The signals from the two stains are linear over a broad range, allowing accurate determination of the amount of nucleic acid and protein, even in a single band, with detection limits of ~1 ng for nucleic acids and ~20 ng for protein. Both stains can be detected using a standard 300 nm UV illuminator, a 254 nm epi-illuminator or a laser scanner (Figure 8.145). Digital images can easily be overlaid for a two-color representation of nucleic acid and protein in the gel. The EMSA Kit contains sufficient reagents for 10 nondenaturing polyacrylamide minigel assays, including:

- SYBR® Green EMSA nucleic acid gel stain
- SYPRO® Ruby EMSA protein gel stain
- Trichloroacetic acid, for preparing the working solution of SYPRO® Ruby EMSA protein gel stain
- Concentrated EMSA gel-loading solution
- *lac* repressor, a DNA-binding protein to be used as a control
- *lac* operator, control DNA
- Concentrated buffer for the *lac* repressor:operator controls
- A detailed protocol

Section 8.7 describes several other probes and reagents for analyzing DNA structure, DNA binding and DNA damage.

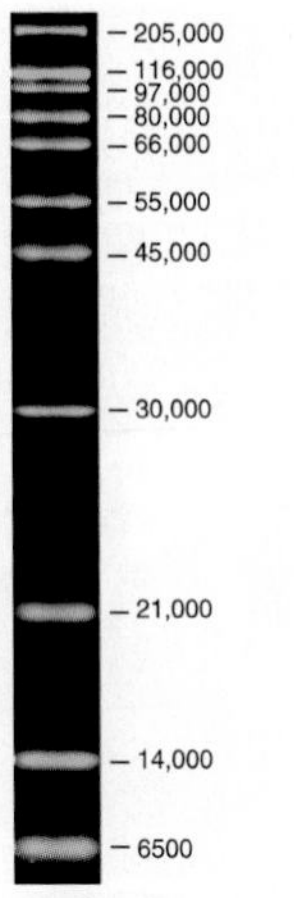

Figure 9.31 Protein molecular weight standards (P6649) separated on a 15% SDS-polyacrylamide gel and stained with SYPRO® Orange protein gel stain (S6650, S6651).

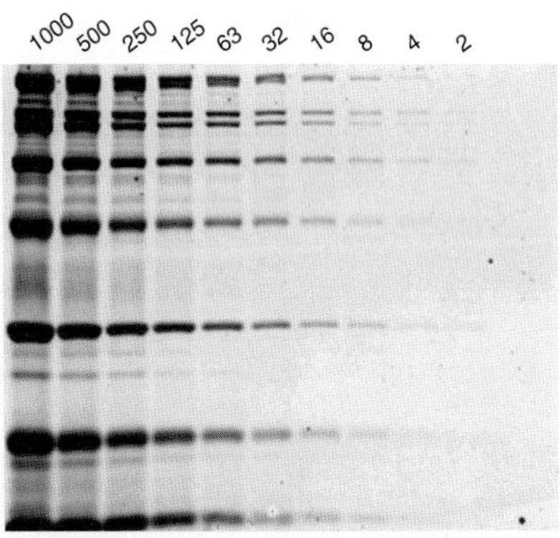

Figure 9.32 Protein molecular weight standards (in nanograms) were separated on a 12% SDS-polyacrylamide gel and then stained with Coomassie Fluor™ Orange protein gel stain (C33250, C33251). The colors have been digitally reversed.

Coomassie Fluor™ Orange Protein Gel Stain

Molecular Probes' proprietary Coomassie Fluor™ Orange protein gel stain (C33250, C33251) provides fast, simple and sensitive staining of proteins in SDS-polyacrylamide electrophoretic gels. Gels do not need to be washed before staining with the Coomassie Fluor™ Orange dye or destained after staining — after electrophoresis, the gel is simply stained, rinsed and photographed on a standard UV transilluminator. Our premixed and ready-to-use Coomassie Fluor™ Orange protein gel stain offers the following advantages over conventional colorimetric stains:

- **High sensitivity.** Coomassie Fluor™ Orange protein gel stain detects as little as 8 ng of protein per minigel band (Figure 9.32). This sensitivity matches the best colloidal Coomassie stains and handily beats standard Coomassie brilliant blue stains.
- **Broad linear range of detection.** The fluorescence intensity of Coomassie Fluor™ Orange dye–stained bands is linear with protein quantity over at least two orders of magnitude, providing accurate quantitation.
- **Rapid staining.** Staining is complete in less than an hour, and there is no risk of overstaining the gel.
- **Compatibility with standard laboratory equipment.** Stained proteins can be visualized using a standard 300 nm UV transilluminator or a laser scanner (Figure 9.33). For optimal sensitivity using a UV transilluminator and Polaroid 667 black-and-white print film, the SYPRO® photographic filter (S6656, Figure 23.62) is recommended.
- **Low protein-to-protein variability.** Because Coomassie Fluor™ Orange dye interacts with the SDS coat around proteins in the gel, it gives more consistent staining between different types of proteins, as compared with Coomassie brilliant blue staining, and it never exhibits negative staining. Coomassie Fluor™ Orange dye also stains glycoproteins.
- **High selectivity for proteins.** Coomassie Fluor™ Orange protein gel stain detects a variety of proteins down to ~6500 daltons without staining nucleic acid or lipopolysaccharide contaminants that are sometimes found in protein preparations derived from cell or tissue extracts.

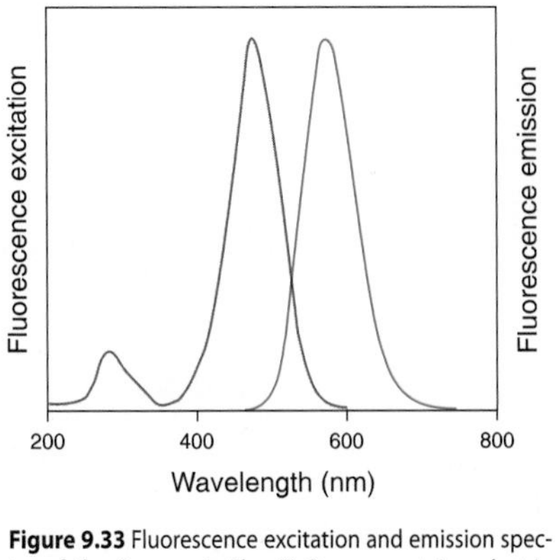

Figure 9.33 Fluorescence excitation and emission spectra of the Coomassie Fluor™ Orange protein gel stain (C33250) in a solution of 150 µg/mL bovine serum albumin (BSA) with 0.05% SDS.

Coomassie Fluor™ Orange protein gel stain is not recommended for staining proteins in 2-D, IEF or nondenaturing gels; for these applications we recommend our SYPRO® Ruby protein gel stain (see above; S12000, S12001, S21900).

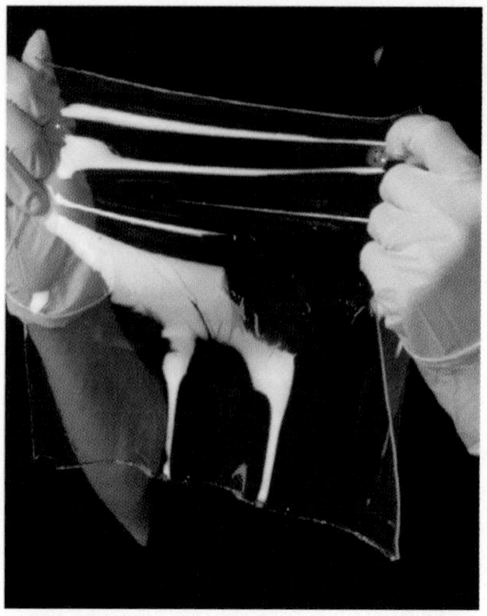

Figure 9.34 Demonstration of the strength and durability of gels made with the Rhinohide™ polyacrylamide gel strengthener (R33400, R33410).

Rhinohide™ Polyacrylamide Gel Strengthener

Our Rhinohide™ polyacrylamide gel strengthener improves upon classic polyacrylamide gel technology by making gels much stronger, providing easier handling and much greater resistance to tearing without adverse side effects (Figure 9.34). Rhinohide™ polyacrylamide gel strengthener is highly recommended for low-percentage gels, large-format gels and gels subject to multiple staining and handling steps.

SDS-polyacrylamide gels supplemented with Rhinohide™ polyacrylamide gel strengthener exhibit resolution capabilities comparable to traditional SDS-polyacrylamide gels, with clear, focused bands and without the undesirable side effects common with other gel strengtheners.[36] For example, film-backed gels and polyester fabric–reinforced gels interfere with blotting techniques and can negatively affect protein staining. Alternatively, strengthening gels by the addition of pre-formed polymers causes turbidity and can produce serious spot-morphology artifacts, such as the distortion of high molecular weight bands or doubling of protein spots in the molecular weight dimension of 2-D gels.[3]

Rhinohide™ polyacrylamide gel strengthener produces gels with excellent transparency, providing exceptional image viewing and scanning of fluorescently stained gels with minimal background staining. Compatible with silver and Coomassie staining, it is also the perfect companion to our Multiplexed Proteomics® technology, which is described in Section 9.4. Our Rhinohide™ Polyacrylamide Gel Strengthener Kit (R33410) includes:

- Rhinohide™ polyacrylamide gel strengthener
- Premeasured acrylamide/bis-acrylamide mixture (37.5:1 ratio)
- A protocol for casting gels from 5% to 20%

This kit provides sufficient materials for making 1 L of a 30% acrylamide/bis-acrylamide stock solution containing the Rhinohide™ gel strengthener. We also offer a concentrated form of the Rhinohide™ polyacrylamide gel strengthener (R33400) for adding to existing stock solutions of acrylamide/bis-acrylamide (37.5:1), as well as the acrylamide/bis-acrylamide mixture (A33405) for making these stock solutions. Because prestained proteins, such as prestained molecular weight markers, will not migrate correctly in acrylamide gels containing the Rhinohide™ polyacrylamide gel strengthener, we recommend using only unstained proteins as markers.

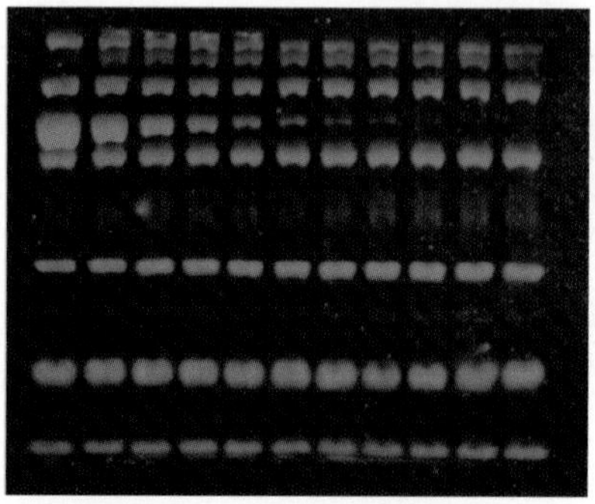

Figure 9.35 Protein detection with SYPRO® Ruby protein blot stain (S11791). Samples of protein molecular weight standards containing a twofold dilution series of α-tubulin, starting with 1 µg of tubulin in the left-most lane, were run on an SDS-polyacrylamide gel, blotted onto a PVDF membrane and stained with the SYPRO® Ruby protein blot stain.

Fluorescent and Luminescent Total-Protein Blot Stains

To characterize specific proteins in complex mixtures, proteins are frequently separated by electrophoresis, then blotted onto nitrocellulose or PVDF (poly(vinylidene difluoride)) membranes (blots) for immunostaining[37] (referred to as Western blotting), glycoprotein staining, sequencing or mass spectrometry. Universal protein stains provide valuable information about the protein samples on blots, making it possible to assess the efficiency of protein transfer to the blot, detect contaminating proteins in the sample and compare the sample with molecular weight standards. For blots of 2-D gels, staining of the entire protein profile makes it easier to localize a protein to a particular spot in the complex protein pattern. The superior properties of our fluorescent and luminescent protein stains, compared with conventional colorimetric stains, makes it possible to quickly and easily obtain this information without running duplicate gels. Combining our luminescent and fluorescent protein staining technology with our fluorescent reagents for selective protein detection, which are described in detail in Section 9.4, creates the capability of multiparameter staining with our Multiplexed Proteomics® technology.

SYPRO® Ruby Protein Blot Stain: A Versatile Blot Stain

The SYPRO® Ruby protein blot stain[7,19,38,39] (Table 9.4) provides fast and highly sensitive detection of proteins blotted onto membranes, making it easy to assess the efficiency of protein transfer to the blot and to determine if lanes are loaded equally[40] (Figure 9.35). Because the stain does not covalently alter the proteins, it can be used to locate proteins on blots before sequencing or mass spectrometry.[4,38] It can also be used before chromogenic, fluorogenic or chemiluminescent immunostaining procedures to locate molecular weight markers and visualize the total-protein profile in the sample.[38] Furthermore, the stain does not interfere with subsequent identification techniques, eliminating the need to run duplicate gels, vastly simplifying the comparison of total protein and target protein on Western blots, and allowing precise localization of the target protein relative to other proteins on electroblots of 2-D gels. The SYPRO® Ruby protein blot stain for general protein detection is also compatible with our Pro-Q® Emerald glycoprotein blot stains for glycoproteins (Section 9.4, Figure 9.53). The superior properties of the SYPRO® Ruby protein blot stain, as compared with conventional protein blot stains, make it possible to routinely stain blots for total protein before continuing with specific protein detection techniques.

The SYPRO® Ruby protein blot stain[7,13,19,38,39] (S11791) combines the following superior staining characteristics:

- **High sensitivity.** SYPRO® Ruby protein blot stain can detect as little as 0.25–1 ng protein/mm^2 (~2–8 ng/band) blotted onto PVDF or nitrocellulose membranes after only 15 minutes of staining[38] (Figure 9.35). This sensitivity on blots is far better than that of colorimetric stains, such as Ponceau S, amido black or Coomassie brilliant blue, and rivals the best colloidal gold blot-staining techniques (Figure 9.36).
- **Rapid total-protein staining procedure.** The SYPRO® Ruby protein blot-staining protocol takes less than an hour — including fixation and wash steps — and maximum sensitivity is achieved after only 15 minutes of dye staining, even for some peptides as small as seven amino acids. In contrast, gold or silver staining procedures may require overnight incubations to achieve maximum sensitivity and usually include extensive wash procedures that must be carefully timed.
- **Compatibility with Western blot protocols.** Staining the total-protein profile on the blot eliminates guesswork about transfer efficiency and removes the need to run two gels for comparison of total and target protein.[40] The SYPRO® Ruby protein blot stain is gentle and, unlike colorimetric or colloidal gold blot stains, does not interfere with subsequent colorimetric or chemiluminescent immunodetection of proteins on Western blots[38] (Figure 9.59, Figure 9.68). The SYPRO® Ruby protein blot stain is available as a component of the Pro-Q® Glycoprotein Blot Stain Kits and Pro-Q® Western Blot Stain Kits (Table 9.7). These products are described in detail in Section 9.4.
- **Compatibility with standard microsequencing and mass spectrometry protocols.** Whereas colloidal gold, Coomassie brilliant blue and amido black staining can interfere with post-staining

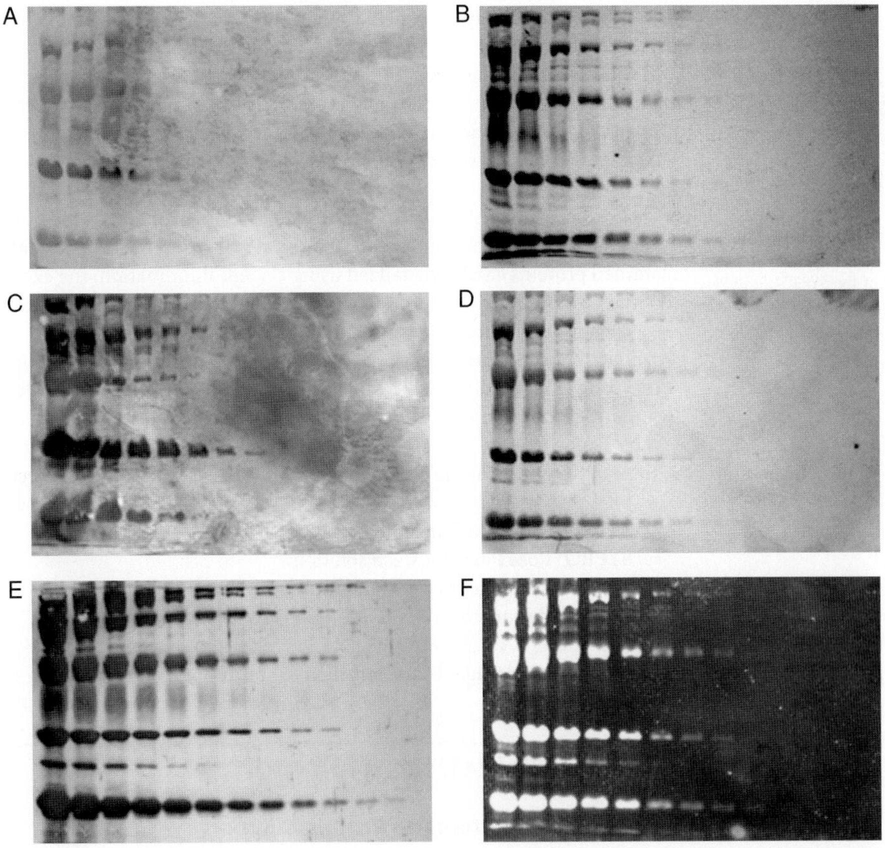

Figure 9.36 Comparison of commonly used stains for proteins on blots. Twofold serial dilutions of protein molecular weight standards ranging from 2000 to 1 ng/band were run on six identical SDS-polyacrylamide gels and blotted to PVDF membrane. The membranes were then stained with A) Ponceau S stain, B) Coomassie brilliant blue stain, C) colloidal silver stain, D) amido black stain, E) colloidal gold stain or F) SYPRO® Ruby protein blot stain (S11791).

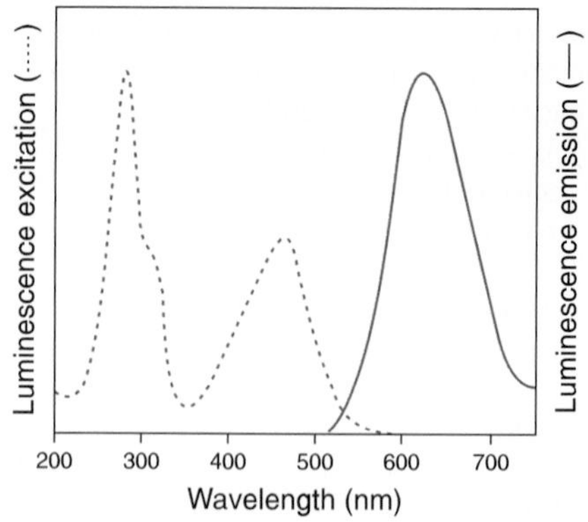

Figure 9.37 Luminescence excitation and emission spectra of the SYPRO® Ruby protein blot stain (S11791).

analysis,[41] SYPRO® Ruby protein blot stain binds noncovalently to proteins and is thus fully compatible with Edman sequencing or mass spectrometry.[4,38]

- **Easily visualized signal.** The SYPRO® Ruby protein blot stain comprises ruthenium complexed with an organic chelator. Because the ruthenium complex has dual-excitation maxima (Figure 9.37), the dye exhibits luminescence upon excitation with either UV or visible light. This property makes it possible to visualize the luminescence with many types of instruments, including UV epi-illumination sources, UV or blue-light transilluminators and a variety of laser-scanning instruments, including those with excitation light at 450 nm, 473 nm, 488 nm or 532 nm. Also, SYPRO® Ruby dye–stained proteins can be indirectly excited by the chemiluminescence of the high-energy intermediate produced in the reaction of bis-(2,4,6-trichlorophenyl) oxalate (TCPO) with H_2O_2.[42] The red luminescence of the ruthenium complex has a peak at ~618 nm that is well separated from these excitation peaks, minimizing the amount of background signal seen from the excitation source. The staining signal can be documented using Polaroid 667 black-and-white print film and a SYPRO® photographic filter (S6656), using a CCD-based imaging system equipped with a 600 nm bandpass or 490 nm longpass filter, or by using the appropriate filter set and software in a laser scanner (Table 9.5). The SYPRO® Ruby protein blot stain has exceptional photostability, allowing long exposure times for maximum sensitivity.

The patented SYPRO® Ruby protein blot stain (S11791) is supplied as a 1X staining solution, which is sufficient for staining ~1600 cm^2 of blotting membrane, and is accompanied by a detailed protocol for its use.

Figure 9.38 After application to a PVDF membrane, a fingerprint was stained for five minutes with the SYPRO® Rose Plus protein blot stain (a component of the SYPRO® Rose Plus Protein Blot Stain Kit, S12011), washed, and imaged under UV epi-illumination.

SYPRO® Rose Plus Protein Blot Stain: A Readily Reversible Protein Blot Stain

Our patented SYPRO® Rose Plus protein blot stain (S12011) has the same high-sensitivity detection capability as the SYPRO® Ruby blot stain — about 0.25–1 ng protein/mm^2 (~2–8 ng/band)[7,19,43] — and is fully compatible with subsequent immunostaining, lectin staining, mass spectrometry and Edman sequencing. However, unlike the SYPRO® Ruby dye, the SYPRO® Rose Plus dye produces protein staining that can be completely reversed by washing the blot. Because the staining can be so easily reversed, SYPRO® Rose Plus protein blot stain may be useful for the temporary detection of proteins on other surfaces, like protein arrays, where it would be useful for signal normalization or quality control. It has been used to detect fingerprints on surfaces (Figure 9.38) and may be useful for detecting cells and proteins on contact lenses, electronic components and other surfaces for quality control purposes.

The SYPRO® Rose Plus protein blot stain contains europium as the luminophore.[19,43] The stain has an excitation maximum at ~350 nm and a narrow emission peak at ~610 nm (Figure 9.39). Stained proteins can be visualized using UV epi-illumination; the excitation characteristics of the SYPRO® Rose Plus protein blot stain preclude it from being visualized using visible-wavelength excitation sources. Like the SYPRO® Ruby protein blot stain, the SYPRO® Rose Plus protein blot stain has exceptional photostability. In addition, the europium luminescence has a very long emission lifetime (20–50 µsec), which may allow time-resolved luminescence measurements that would greatly minimize background fluorescence.

The SYPRO® Rose Plus protein blot stain (S12011) is provided as a kit containing:

- SYPRO® Rose Plus blot stain solution
- SYPRO® Rose Plus blot wash solution
- SYPRO® Rose Plus blot destain solution
- A detailed protocol

The quantities of reagents are sufficient to stain ~1600 cm^2 of blotting membrane.

Protein Detection in Microarrays

Detection of Proteins on Protein Microarrays

We have found that our protein blot stains perform particularly well when staining proteins on PVDF microarrays for quality control and normalization purposes. SYPRO® Ruby protein blot stain (S11791) shows good sensitivity on protein microarrays (Figure 9.40) and should be very useful for staining proteins before exposing the microarray to the sample. The stain washes off PVDF membranes very easily under conditions used with typical Western blot blocking buffers. SYPRO® Rose Plus protein blot stain (S12011) may also be useful for the temporary detection and normalization of proteins on microarrays because the staining is so easily reversed. BODIPY® FL-X succinimidyl ester (D6102) shows even greater sensitivity in this application, as described below, and should be useful for quality control or as an internal normalization standard.

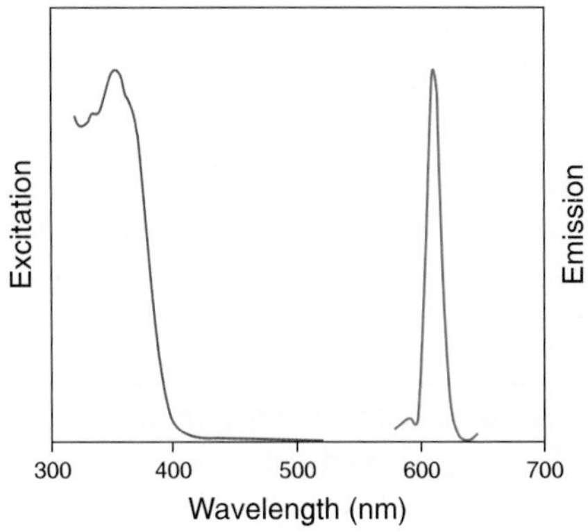

Figure 9.39 Luminescence excitation and emission spectra of the SYPRO® Rose Plus protein blot stain, a component of the SYPRO® Rose Plus Protein Blot Stain Kit (S12011).

Reactive Fluorescent Dyes for Permanent Protein Blot and Microarray Staining

Our patented BODIPY® reactive dyes in Section 1.4 label amine groups (predominantly lysine residues) on proteins, and we have found the BODIPY® FL-X succinimidyl ester and BODIPY® TR-X succinimidyl ester (D6102, D6116) to be particularly effective general stains for proteins on PVDF membranes [13,44] (Table 9.4). This unique method of staining for total protein on blots with the reactive BODIPY® dyes has an approximately 30-fold linear dynamic range (Figure 9.64), although the absolute intensity between proteins may vary somewhat with the nature of the protein. Reactive BODIPY® dye–based staining is rapid, simple and highly sensitive, permitting detection of as little as 4 ng of a protein per band in about an hour. Because the reactive dyes form a covalent bond with the protein, the staining is permanent and lasts through any subsequent conventional blot manipulations. The covalent modification appears to minimally interfere with subsequent immunostaining, as we have successfully performed simultaneous two-color labeling with reactive BODIPY® dyes and either fluorogenic immunostains or fluorogenic glycoprotein stains and found both stains to be visible at the same time on the same blot (Figure 9.62, Figure 9.63). Simultaneous dual labeling of a sample enormously simplifies localization of a specific protein with respect to other proteins in the sample, particularly on electroblots of 2-D gels, pairs of which are difficult to align.

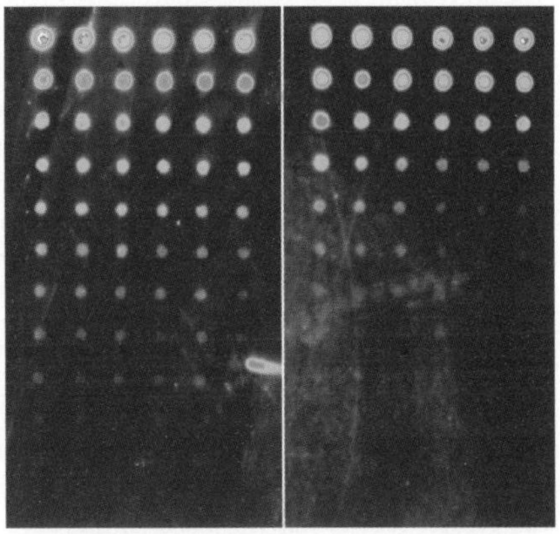

Figure 9.40 Protein detection on microarrays using BODIPY® FL-X SE or SYPRO® Ruby protein blot stain. Bovine serum albumin was arrayed onto a PVDF membrane using a Packard BioScience PiezoTip dispenser. The array contains 72 spots with 12 dilutions of the dye, in replicates of 6, ranging from 666–0.325 pg per spot. The proteins were stained with either BODIPY® FL-X SE (D6102, left) in sodium borate buffer, pH 9.5, or with SYPRO® Ruby protein blot stain (S11791). Arrays were imaged on a ScanArray 5000XL microarray analysis system (Packard BioScience) and pseudocolored such that the different colors indicate different signal intensities. The sensitivity limit was 1.3–2.6 pg of protein in a 175 µm spot for the BODIPY® FL-X SE detection technique and 104 pg of protein per 175 µm spot for the SYPRO® Ruby protein blot stain technique.

The optimal BODIPY® dyes and procedures for use with our fluorogenic Western blot detection reagents are included in our DyeChrome™ Western Blot Stain Kits (Section 9.4, Table 9.7). The green-fluorescent BODIPY® FL-X succinimidyl ester is used in combination with DDAO phosphate (Figure 9.63, Figure 9.66), which produces a red-fluorescent product in the presence of alkaline phosphatase; the red-fluorescent BODIPY® TR-X succinimidyl ester is used in combination with ELF® 39 phosphate (Figure 9.62, Figure 9.67), which produces a green-fluorescent product in the presence of alkaline phosphatase. The fluorescent staining can be visualized using UV illumination or a laser scanner. The stains can be documented simultaneously using color photography or — using the appropriate filters, such as those in the DyeChrome™ Red/Green Photographic Filter Set (D24771; Section 23.4; Figure 23.63, Figure 23.64) — can be documented separately. Note that because reaction of the dye covalently modifies the protein at random locations, staining by the amine-reactive BODIPY® dye may complicate or preclude subsequent analysis by mass spectrometry or microsequencing.

Our DyeChrome™ Double Western Blot Stain Kit (D21887, Section 9.4) uses another fluorescent reactive dye, MDPF (2-methoxy-2,4-diphenyl-3(2*H*)-furanone), to stain the total-protein profile on PVDF membranes. This blue-fluorescent dye is visible using UV epi-illumination and can be used with two (or possibly more) different fluorogenic Western blot stains. In the DyeChrome™ Double Western Blot Stain Kit, MDPF is used together with DDAO phosphate, which produces the red-fluorescent DDAO dye (Figure 10.7, Figure 10.12) in the presence of alkaline phosphatase, and our proprietary Amplex® Gold reagent, which produces a yellow-fluorescent compound in the presence of horseradish peroxidase, for detection of two different specific proteins and the total-protein profile, all on the same blot (Section 9.4, Figure 9.70).

Pro-Q® Diamond Phosphoprotein/Phosphopeptide Microarray Stain Kit

The Pro-Q® Diamond Phosphoprotein/Phosphopeptide Microarray Stain Kit (P33706) provides a method for selective staining of phosphoproteins or phosphopeptides on microarrays, without the use of antibodies or radioactivity. This kit permits direct detection of phosphate groups attached to tyrosine, serine or threonine residues in a microarray environment and has been optimized for microarrays with acrylamide gel surfaces. Each Pro-Q® Diamond Phosphoprotein/Phosphopeptide Microarray Stain Kit provides:

- Pro-Q® Diamond phosphoprotein/phosphopeptide microarray stain
- Pro-Q® Diamond microarray destain solution
- Microarray staining gasket with seal tabs, 10 chambers
- Slide holder tube, 20 tubes
- Detailed protocols

The Pro-Q® Diamond Phosphoprotein/Phosphopeptide Microarray Stain Kit is ideal for identifying kinase targets in signal transduction pathways and for phosphoproteomics studies.

Protein Detection in Capillary Electrophoresis

Capillary electrophoresis (CE) is an exceptionally powerful tool for the resolution of biomolecules.[45,46] Fluorescent detection of proteins that are separated by capillary electrophoresis can occur either during the run — the more common procedure — or subsequent to the separation on isolated fractions. When detected during the electrophoretic separation, the protein is either derivatized with a fluorescent reagent prior to the separation or labeled with a fluorescent dye that is incorporated into the running medium. In general, the same reagents may be useful for fluorometric detection of peptides and proteins that are separated by high-performance liquid chromatography (HPLC). In addition the total-protein staining techniques described below, many selective staining techniques, such as the use of BODIPY® FL GTP-γ-*S* to detect GTP-binding proteins,[47] can be applied to proteins separated by capillary electrophoresis.

Use of SYPRO® Dyes for Capillary Electrophoresis

SDS–capillary gel electrophoresis (SDS-CGE) separates proteins based on principles similar to those of standard slab-gel electrophoresis, but with the advantages of faster run times, higher resolution and greater sensitivity. The use of online detection by laser-induced fluorescence (LIF) increases the sensitivity several orders of magnitude over UV detection, eliminates the time spent staining and photographing the gel and allows for the possibility of automated sample processing. SDS-CGE analyzed by LIF is already being widely used for the separation and identification of DNA fragments and has increased the efficiency of genomics, DNA typing and forensics laboratories.[45,46] SDS-CGE promises to be just as useful for proteomics laboratories and other laboratories that require characterization of a large number of protein samples.

For SDS-CGE of protein samples, the amine groups of lysine residues and the N-terminus of the proteins are typically derivatized with a fluorescent or fluorogenic dye such as the ATTO-TAG™ CBQCA[48,49] (A2333, A6222) or ATTO-TAG™ FQ[50–53] (A2334, A10192) reagents before separation in the capillary. The derivatized proteins are then coated with SDS and travel through the capillary gel towards the positive electrode based on their size, with smaller proteins traveling faster. The derivatized proteins are detected by fluorescence emitted as they pass a laser that excites the fluorophores. One disadvantage of this technique is that the proteins generally contain multiple amine groups, each of which can react with the derivatization reagent. Typically, only a few of the amine groups on each protein molecule react, and the result is an enormous number of different derivatives, creating broad peaks that may be difficult to correlate with the original protein's structure or abundance.[53] In addition, variations between runs make it difficult to reproducibly estimate molecular weights. In contrast, use of SYPRO® Red protein gel stain (S6653, S6654) to prestain SDS-coated proteins allows more accurate determination of molecular weights because the proteins are relatively uniformly coated with SDS and the dye. This method leads to molecular weight determinations similar in accuracy to those achieved with polyacrylamide slab gels, with a limit of detection estimated to exceed the detection limit of silver staining in slab gels.[54]

Use of SYTO®, SYBR® and NanoOrange® Dyes for Capillary Electrophoresis

Our SYTO® and SYBR® dyes — which are extremely useful stains for nucleic acids (Chapter 8) — are essentially nonfluorescent in aqueous medium unless they are bound to nucleic acids. However, we have found that these same dyes may become highly fluorescent once bound to lipid-complexed proteins. Although we are not aware of any published description of the use of these dyes for detecting proteins in capillary electrophoresis, we anticipate that they can be used in the same manner as the SYPRO® dyes for these applications. The broad spectral range of available SYTO® (Table 8.3) and SYBR® dyes (Table 8.1) should permit their use with a wide variety of excitation sources. Several of the SYTO® and SYBR® dyes also stain proteins in SDS-polyacrylamide gels, but usually with lower sensitivity than do the SYPRO® dyes. The NanoOrange® reagent (N6666, Section 9.2) is reported to be an optimal reagent for detecting proteins that have been separated by microchip capillary electrophoresis.[55–57]

Derivatization Reagents for Proteins

Several of the same reagents that were described in Section 9.2 for protein quantitation in solution are also useful for peptide and protein derivatization, either prior to or following separation by capillary electrophoresis. However, chemical derivatization prior to separation is likely to change the electronic charge and always changes the mass of the protein. Furthermore, incomplete derivatization of amines or thiols on the protein can lead to a pure protein resolving into multiple species in the electrophoretogram.

In an improved procedure for fluorescent analysis of peptides by capillary electrophoresis, Zhou and colleagues[58] modified all α- and ε-amino groups of the peptide with phenyl isothiocyanate. Following one cycle of Edman degradation, the single free α-amino group was modified with fluorescent reagents to give a homogeneous, dye-labeled peptide.

The preferred reagents for derivatizing amine residues in proteins either prior to or following electrophoretic separation are those that are essentially nonfluorescent until reacted with the protein. Derivatization reagents that react with thiols or other functional groups have also been used. These preferred reagents include:

- ATTO-TAG™ CBQCA, which is available in our ATTO-TAG™ CBQCA Amine-Derivatization Kit (A2333) and as a standalone reagent (A6222). ATTO-TAG™ CBQCA reacts with primary amines to form highly fluorescent isoindoles[48,49,59–67] and has been extensively used for the derivatization of amino acids,[49,59,68–70] peptides[61,71–74] and carbohydrates[60,62,63,65,66,75–79] prior to capillary electrophoretic separation. ATTO-TAG™ CBQCA has been used to derivatize a fusion protein expressed in the bacterium *Escherichia coli* before purification by capillary zone electrophoresis. After purification, the fluorescent isoindole can be removed by acid treatment to allow sequencing of the purified protein.[48]

- ATTO-TAG™ FQ (3-(2-furoyl)quinoline-2-carboxaldehyde), which is available in our ATTO-TAG™ FQ Amine-Derivatization Kit (A2334) and as a stand-alone reagent (A10192). ATTO-TAG™ FQ has been used as a protein detection reagent in capillary electrophoresis.[80–83] It has been reported that ATTO-TAG™ FQ can detect as little as 200 attomoles of a protein by capillary electrophoresis.[82] Excitation of amine derivatives of ATTO-TAG™ FQ by the 488 nm spectral line of the argon-ion laser is more efficient than that of ATTO-TAG™ CBQCA derivatives. A report[83] describes the solid-phase derivatization of dilute peptide solutions (10^{-8} M) that have been immobilized on Immobilon CD membranes. This technique permits the quantitative derivatization and analysis by capillary electrophoresis of only a few picomoles of the analyte.
- Fluorescamine (F2332; FluoroPure™ Grade, F20261), a nonfluorescent reagent that rapidly reacts with amines to give a fluorescent product. Fluorescamine has been used for solution quantitation of proteins and peptides (Section 9.2). It is also useful as a peptide and protein detection reagent for capillary electrophoresis.[74,84,85] Use of fluorescamine to derivatize a standard protein of known molecular weight together with use of the ATTO-TAG™ FQ reagent to derivatize the sample protein allows the sample to be run simultaneously with the standard, improving the accuracy of molecular weight determination.[81] Chiral separation of fluorescamine-labeled amino acids has been optimized using capillary electrophoresis in the presence of hydroxypropyl-β-cyclodextran, a method designed for use in extraterrestrial exploration on Mars.[86]
- Dialdehydes OPA and NDA (P2331MP, N1138), which react with amines in the presence of a nucleophile (Figure 1.117, Figure 1.118) to give fluorescent products. These inexpensive reagents have been used for capillary electrophoresis of peptides and proteins.[87–94]
- Other amine-reactive reagents. Chapter 1 describes a variety of other amine-reactive reagents, including our numerous succinimidyl esters, isothiocyanates and sulfonyl chlorides, that have been used or may be useful for peptide and protein detection in capillary electrophoresis, including dansyl chloride[95] (D21), NBD chloride (FluoroPure™ Grade, C20260), NBD fluoride (F486), FITC[58,96] (F143) and other common reagents described in Section 1.8. After reaction with Alexa Fluor® succinimidyl esters (Section 1.3), proteins in bacteriophage T7 capsid have been separated and detected in gels by their intrinsic fluorescence;[97] analyzing protein accessibility with the water-soluble Alexa Fluor® dyes can also be applied to the localization of proteins in cells and tissues.
- Reactive reagents for other groups on proteins. Thiol-reactive probes such as maleimides and iodoacetamides can be used for the selective detection of natural or engineered proteins that contain a free thiol group (cysteine). Most of the fluorescent derivatization reagents for thiols (Chapter 2) could potentially be used for detection of thiolated proteins in capillary electrophoresis. Thiol-reactive reagents that are essentially nonfluorescent until conjugated to thiols, such as the coumarin maleimides CPM and DACM (D346, D10251; Section 2.3), monobromobimane (M1378; FluoroPure™ Grade, M20381; Section 2.3) and *N*-(1-pyrene)maleimide (P28, Section 2.3), should work well in this application. Although intrinsically fluorescent, BODIPY® iodoacetamides and maleimides (Section 2.2) have been used to detect thiol-containing proteins in SDS gels and by reverse-phase HPLC.[98] Proteins that have been labeled with 5-iodoacetamidofluorescein (I30451, Section 2.2) have been analyzed by capillary electrophoresis.[99] A particularly unique derivatization scheme using 6-iodoacetamidofluorescein (I30452, Section 2.2) has been applied to selective detection of peptides and proteins containing phosphoserine residues by capillary electrophoresis[95,100] (Figure 9.41). Although the original procedure[95] used 6-iodoacetamidofluorescein, almost any of the thiol-reactive reagents in Chapter 2 may be useful for this method. To identify glycoproteins in capillary electrophoresis, reagents derived from hydrazine derivatives and hydroxylamine derivatives such as those described in Section 3.2 may be useful for indirectly labeling the hydroxyl groups subsequent to their oxidation to aldehydes. Dansyl hydrazine (D100, Section 3.2) labeling has been used to detect periodate-oxidized proteins separated by HPLC.[101]

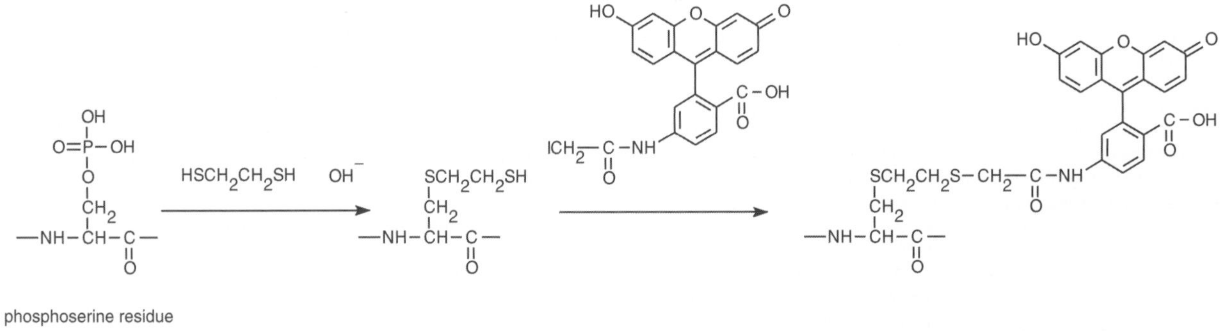

Figure 9.41 Selective detection of phosphoserine residues in proteins via derivatization by 1,2-ethanedithiol, followed by 6-iodoacetamidofluorescein (I30452).

References

1. Anal Biochem 239, 223 (1996); **2.** Electrophoresis 21, 497 (2000); **3.** Electrophoresis 21, 486 (2000); **4.** Electrophoresis 22, 906 (2001); **5.** Biochim Biophys Acta 71, 377 (1963); **6.** Methods Enzymol 182, 477 (1990); **7.** Biotechniques 28, 944 (2000); **8.** Electrophoresis 23, 2203 (2002); **9.** Proteomics 1, 54 (2001); **10.** Biotechniques 31, 146 (2001); **11.** Electrophoresis 22, 829 (2001); **12.** Electrophoresis 22, 919 (2001); **13.** Electrophoresis 22, 950 (2001); **14.** Electrophoresis 21, 3657 (2000); **15.** Electrophoresis 21, 3673 (2000); **16.** Electrophoresis 21, 2509 (2000); **17.** Electrophoresis 21, 1082 (2000); **18.** Electrophoresis 21, 1037 (2000); **19.** Electrophoresis 21, 1123 (2000); **20.** Scientist 14, 26 (2000); **21.** Proteomics 1, 377 (2001); **22.** Mol Cell Proteomics (in press) (2001); **23.** Electrophoresis 24, 3508 (2003); **24.** Anal Biochem 248, 168 (1997); **25.** Biotechnol Intl 1, 339 (1997); **26.** Am Biotechnol Lab 14, 12 (1996); **27.** Anal Biochem 239, 238 (1996); **28.** Electrophoresis: Theory, Techniques, and Biochemical and Clinical Applications, 2nd Ed., Andr AT pp. 117–147 (1986); **29.** Anal Biochem 165, 33 (1987); **30.** J NIH Res 7, 82 (1995); **31.** IDrugs 1, 299 (1998); **32.** J Chromatogr A 894, 329 (2000); **33.** Anal Chem 72, 2519 (2000); **34.** Anal Chem 73, 1207 (2001); **35.** Anal Biochem 292, 40 (2001); **36.** Anal Biochem 148, 384 (1985); **37.** Proc Natl Acad Sci U S A 76, 4350 (1979); **38.** Anal Biochem 276, 129 (1999); **39.** Electrophoresis 21, 2196 (2000); **40.** J Biol Chem 275, 32846 (2000); **41.** Electrophoresis 19, 752 (1998); **42.** J Chromatogr B Analyt Technol Biomed Life Sci 793, 75 (2003); **43.** Electrophoresis 22, 881 (2001); **44.** Electrophoresis 22, 896 (2001); **45.** Forensic Sci Int 92, 89 (1998); **46.** Electrophoresis 19, 2695 (1998); **47.** Anal Chem 75, 4297 (2003); **48.** J Chromatogr B Biomed Sci Appl 695, 67 (1997); **49.** Anal Chem 66, 3512 (1994); **50.** Anal Chem 75, 3163 (2003); **51.** Anal Chem 75, 3170 (2003); **52.** Mol Cell Proteomics 1, 69 (2002); **53.** Anal Chem 70, 2493 (1998); **54.** Electrophoresis 19, 2169 (1998); **55.** Biotechniques 34, 850 (2003); **56.** Anal Chem 73, 4994 (2001); **57.** Anal Chem 72, 4608 (2000); **58.** J Chromatogr 608, 239 (1992); **59.** J Neurosci Methods 65, 33 (1996); **60.** Anal Chem 66, 3477 (1994); **61.** Anal Chem 65, 563 (1993); **62.** Electrophoresis 14, 373 (1993); **63.** Anal Chem 63, 413 (1991); **64.** Anal Chem 63, 408 (1991); **65.** J Chromatogr 559, 223 (1991); **66.** Proc Natl Acad Sci U S A 88, 2302 (1991); **67.** J Chromatogr 499, 579 (1990); **68.** Anal Chim Acta 299, 319 (1995); **69.** Chromatographia 39, 7 (1994); **70.** J Chromatogr B Biomed Appl 659, 185 (1994); **71.** J Chromatogr A 716, 389 (1995); **72.** Biopolymers 33, 1299 (1993); **73.** Chem Eng News November, 35 (1990); **74.** J Chromatogr 519, 189 (1990); **75.** J Chromatogr A 716, 221 (1995); **76.** Anal Chem 66, 3466 (1994); **77.** Glycobiology 4, 397 (1994); **78.** Proc Natl Acad Sci U S A 90, 9451 (1993); **79.** Anal Chem 64, 973 (1992); **80.** J Chromatogr B Analyt Technol Biomed Life Sci 793, 141 (2003); **81.** Electrophoresis 19, 2175 (1998); **82.** Anal Chem 69, 3015 (1997); **83.** Electrophoresis 16, 534 (1995); **84.** J Chromatogr A 814, 213 (1998); **85.** Trends Anal Chem 11, 114 (1992); **86.** J Chromatogr A 1021, 191 (2003); **87.** Anal Chem 67, 4261 (1995); **88.** Anal Chem 63, 417 (1991); **89.** J Chromatogr 540, 343 (1991); **90.** Anal Chem 62, 2189 (1990); **91.** Science 242, 224 (1988); **92.** Anal Chem 67, 58 (1995); **93.** Science 246, 57 (1989); **94.** Anal Chem 71, 28 (1999); **95.** Anal Biochem 258, 38 (1998); **96.** Bioconjug Chem 6, 447 (1995); **97.** Electrophoresis 25, 779 (2004); **98.** Electrophoresis 24, 2348 (2003); **99.** Electrophoresis 24, 2796 (2003); **100.** Anal Biochem 225, 81 (1995); **101.** Chem Pharm Bull 34, 4887 (1986).

Data Table — 9.3 Detection of the Total-Protein Profile in Gels, on Blots, on Microarrays and in Capillary Electrophoresis

Cat #	MW	Storage	Soluble	Abs	EC	Em	Solvent	Notes
A2333	305.29	F,D,L	MeOH	465	ND	560	MeOH	1, 2, 3, 4
A2334	251.24	F,D,L	EtOH	486	ND	591	MeOH	2, 4, 5
A6222	305.29	F,D,L	MeOH	465	ND	560	MeOH	1, 2, 3
A10192	251.24	F,L	EtOH	486	ND	591	MeOH	2, 5
D6102	502.32	F,D,L	DMSO, MeCN	504	85,000	510	MeOH	
D6116	634.46	F,D,L	DMSO, MeCN	588	68,000	616	MeOH	
F2332	278.26	F,D,L	MeCN	380	7,800	464	MeCN	6
F20261	278.26	F,D,L	MeCN	380	8,400	464	MeCN	6, 7
N1138	184.19	L	DMF, MeCN	419	9,400	493	see Notes	8
P2331MP	134.13	L	EtOH	334	5,700	455	pH 9	9
S6650	see Notes	D,L	DMSO	467	see Notes	570	H_2O/BSA	10, 11, 12
S6653	see Notes	D,L	DMSO	542	see Notes	630	H_2O/BSA	10, 11, 12
S12000	see Notes	L	see Notes	462	see Notes	610	MeOH	13, 14, 15
S12010	see Notes	D,L	DMSO	492	see Notes	639	H_2O/BSA	10, 11, 12

For definitions of the contents of this data table, see "Navigating *The Handbook*" in the introductory pages.

Notes

1. Spectral data are for the reaction product with glycine in the presence of cyanide. Unreacted reagent in MeOH: Abs = 254 nm (EC = 46,000 $cm^{-1}M^{-1}$), nonfluorescent.
2. ND = not determined.
3. Solubility in methanol is improved by addition of base (e.g., 1–5% (v/v) 0.2 M KOH).
4. Data represent the reactive dye component of this labeling kit.
5. Spectral data are for the reaction product with glycine in the presence of cyanide. Unreacted reagent in MeOH: Abs = 282 nm (EC = 21,000 $cm^{-1}M^{-1}$), nonfluorescent.
6. Fluorescamine spectra are for the reaction product with butylamine. The fluorescence quantum yield and lifetime of the butylamine adduct in EtOH are 0.23 and 7.5 nanoseconds, respectively (Arch Biochem Biophys 163, 390 (1974)). The unreacted reagent is nonfluorescent (Abs = 234 nm, EC = 28,000 $cm^{-1}M^{-1}$ in MeCN).
7. This product is specified to equal or exceed 98% analytical purity by HPLC.
8. Spectral data are for the reaction product with glycine in the presence of cyanide, measured in pH 7.0 buffer/MeCN (40:60) (Anal Chem 59, 1102 (1987)). Unreacted reagent in MeOH: Abs = 279 nm (EC = 5500 $cm^{-1}M^{-1}$), Em = 330 nm.
9. Spectral data are for the reaction product of P2331MP with alanine and 2-mercaptoethanol. The spectra and stability of the adduct depend on the amine and thiol reactants (Biochim Biophys Acta 576, 440 (1979)). Unreacted reagent in H_2O: Abs = 257 nm (EC = 1000 $cm^{-1}M^{-1}$).
10. This product is supplied as a ready-made solution in the solvent indicated under "Soluble."
11. The active ingredient of this product is an organic dye with MW <1000. The exact MW and extinction coefficient values for this dye are proprietary.
12. Abs and Em values are for the dye complexed with bovine serum albumin (H_2O/BSA).
13. This product is supplied as a ready-made staining solution.
14. The active ingredient of this product is an organometallic complex with MW <1500. The exact MW value and extinction coefficient of the complex are proprietary.
15. SYPRO® Ruby protein gel stain also has an absorption peak at 278 nm with about 4-fold higher EC than the 462 nm peak.

Invitrogen Product Highlight

BenchMark™ Fluorescent Protein Standard

The BenchMark™ Fluorescent Protein Standard consists of fluorescent dye–conjugated proteins, ranging in size from ~11–155 kilodaltons. The standard proteins can be resolved into sharp bands in SDS-PAGE and visualized using a UV transilluminator or commonly used laser scanner systems. The BenchMark™ Fluorescent Protein Standard offers:

- Seven tight, clear bands that resolve well in NuPAGE® Bis-Tris Gels and Novex® Tris-Glycine Gels
- Visualization directly under the UV light box along with the proteins labeled with the Lumio™ Green Detection Reagent
- Easy molecular weight estimation of fluorescent dye–conjugated proteins in SDS-PAGE and Western blots
- Detection with Coomassie Brilliant Blue R-250

LC5928	BenchMark™ Fluorescent Protein Standard	125 µl

Product List — 9.3 Detection of the Total-Protein Profile in Gels, on Blots, on Microarrays and in Capillary Electrophoresis

Cat #	Product Name	Unit Size
A33405	acrylamide/bis-acrylamide mixture (37.5:1 ratio) *electrophoresis grade*	300 g
A2333	ATTO-TAG™ CBQCA Amine-Derivatization Kit	1 kit
A6222	ATTO-TAG™ CBQCA derivatization reagent (CBQCA; 3-(4-carboxybenzoyl)quinoline-2-carboxaldehyde)	10 mg
A2334	ATTO-TAG™ FQ Amine-Derivatization Kit	1 kit
A10192	ATTO-TAG™ FQ derivatization reagent (FQ; 3-(2-furoyl)quinoline-2-carboxaldehyde)	10 mg
C33250	Coomassie Fluor™ Orange protein gel stain *ready-to-use solution*	1 L
C33251	Coomassie Fluor™ Orange protein gel stain *ready-to-use solution* *bulk packaging*	5 L
D6102	6-((4,4-difluoro-5,7-dimethyl-4-bora-3a,4a-diaza-*s*-indacene-3-propionyl)amino)hexanoic acid, succinimidyl ester (BODIPY® FL-X, SE)	5 mg
D6116	6-(((4-(4,4-difluoro-5-(2-thienyl)-4-bora-3a,4a-diaza-*s*-indacene-3-yl)phenoxy)acetyl)amino)hexanoic acid, succinimidyl ester (BODIPY® TR-X, SE)	5 mg
E33075	Electrophoretic Mobility-Shift Assay (EMSA) Kit *with SYBR® Green and SYPRO® Ruby EMSA stains* *10 minigel assays*	1 kit
F2332	fluorescamine	100 mg
F20261	fluorescamine *FluoroPure™ grade*	100 mg
N1138	naphthalene-2,3-dicarboxaldehyde (NDA)	100 mg
P2331MP	*o*-phthaldialdehyde (OPA) *high purity*	1 g
P33706	Pro-Q® Diamond Phosphoprotein/Phosphopeptide Microarray Stain Kit	1 kit
P6649	protein molecular weight standards *broad range* *200 gel lanes*	400 µL
R33400	Rhinohide™ polyacrylamide gel strengthener concentrate *sufficient additive for 1 L of 30% acrylamide/bis-acrylamide (37.5:1)*	200 mL
R33410	Rhinohide™ Polyacrylamide Gel Strengthener Kit *makes 1 L of Rhinohide™ 30% acrylamide/bis-acrylamide (37.5:1)*	1 kit
S6650	SYPRO® Orange protein gel stain *5000X concentrate in DMSO*	500 µL
S6651	SYPRO® Orange protein gel stain *5000X concentrate in DMSO* *special packaging*	10 x 50 µL
S6656	SYPRO® photographic filter	each
S12012	SYPRO® Protein Gel Stain Starter Kit	1 kit
S6653	SYPRO® Red protein gel stain *5000X concentrate in DMSO*	500 µL
S6654	SYPRO® Red protein gel stain *5000X concentrate in DMSO* *special packaging*	10 x 50 µL
S12011	SYPRO® Rose Plus Protein Blot Stain Kit *10-40 blots*	1 kit
S11791	SYPRO® Ruby protein blot stain *10-40 blots*	200 mL
S12000	SYPRO® Ruby protein gel stain	1 L
S12001	SYPRO® Ruby protein gel stain	200 mL
S21900	SYPRO® Ruby protein gel stain *bulk packaging*	5 L
S12010	SYPRO® Tangerine protein gel stain *5000X concentrate in DMSO*	500 µL

For current prices or to order online, visit probes.invitrogen.com

9.4 Multiplexed Proteomics® Technology for Detecting Specific Proteins in Gels and on Blots

Multiplexed Proteomics® Technology

Molecular Probes is the leader in the growing field of Multiplexed Proteomics® technology — the simultaneous detection of multiple protein targets in a single sample. We have developed a suite of compatible methodologies for the differential staining of specific proteins and the total-protein profile in two or more visually distinguishable colors, producing a more complete picture of the proteome than has ever before been possible. Our state-of-the-art Multiplexed Proteomics® technology not only offers the capacity for multicolor staining, but also provides a combination of high sensitivity and simplicity that can streamline protocols and accelerate the pace of research.

Our Multiplexed Proteomics® technology relies on a set of protein stains that enable the global detection of differences both in specific protein expression (phosphoproteins, glycoproteins or membrane proteins) and in total-protein expression in 1-D and 2-D polyacrylamide gels or on blots. Our fluorescent and luminescent protein gel stains include:

- Pro-Q® Diamond phosphoprotein gel stain (P33300, P33301, P33302, M33305, M33306, MPP33300, MPP33301, MPP33302, MPM33305, MPM33306; Table 9.6)
- Pro-Q® Emerald glycoprotein gel stains (P21855, P21857, P21875, M33307)
- Pro-Q® Amber transmembrane protein gel stain (M33308)
- SYPRO® Ruby protein gel stain (S12000, S12001, S21900)

The Pro-Q® Diamond phosphoprotein gel stain, Pro-Q® Emerald glycoprotein gel stains and SYPRO® Ruby protein gel stain — which we have optimized to complement each other in selectivity, sensitivity and staining protocols — are used in serial detection of phosphoproteins, glycoproteins and total proteins on a single protein sample separated by 1-D or 2-D gel electrophoresis (Figure 9.42). Our Rhinohide™ polyacrylamide gel strengthener (R33400, R33410; described at the end of this section) greatly improves the strength of any polyacrylamide gel, making it easy to perform these multiple staining procedures without special gel handling. After each staining step, an image of the gel is collected. Once collected, the three images can be overlaid in any combination for analysis of phosphorylation, glycosylation and total-protein expression. Because all three stains are used on the same gel, unambiguous spot matching of phosphoproteins and glycoproteins is made simple by direct comparison with the total-protein profile provided by the SYPRO® Ruby protein gel stain. This simultaneous measurement of several variables ensures perfect spatial registration of signals and increases the amount of data that can be collected in a single experiment, leading to more controlled experiments, more accurate data comparisons and fewer ambiguities. When used in combination with the SYPRO® Ruby protein gel stain, the Pro-Q® Amber transmembrane protein gel stain extends the power of our Multiplexed Proteomics® technology to allow selective identification of transmembrane proteins.

For multiplexed protein blot staining, we have developed fluorescent phosphoprotein and glycoprotein stains, as well as several different Western blot stains for detecting specific antibody-tagged proteins or protein modifications (Table 9.7):

Table 9.6 — Pro-Q® Diamond gel stain reagents and kits

Product	Cat #	Includes			Number of Gels Stained
		Pro-Q® Diamond Phosphoprotein Gel Stain	SYPRO® Ruby Protein Gel Stain	Phosphoprotein MW Standard	
Pro-Q® Diamond phosphoprotein gel stain	P33300	1 L			~20 minigels or two large-format gels (e.g., 2-D gels)
Pro-Q® Diamond phosphoprotein gel stain	P33301	200 mL			~4 minigels
Pro-Q® Diamond phosphoprotein gel stain	P33302	5 L			~100 minigels or 10 large-format gels
Multiplexed Proteomics® Phosphoprotein Gel Stain Kit #1	M33305	1 L	1 L		~20 minigels or two large-format gels
Multiplexed Proteomics® Phosphoprotein Gel Stain Kit #2	M33306	200 mL	200 mL		~4 minigels
Pro-Q® Diamond Phosphoprotein Gel Staining Kit	MPP33300	1 L		40 µL	~20 minigels or two large-format gels
Pro-Q® Diamond Phosphoprotein Gel Staining Kit	MPP33301	200 mL		40 µL	~4 minigels
Pro-Q® Diamond Phosphoprotein Gel Staining Kit	MPP33302	5 L		40 µL	~100 minigels or 10 large-format gels
Multiplexed Proteomics® Phosphoprotein Gel Stain Kit	MPM33305	1 L	1 L	40 µL	~20 minigels or two large-format gels
Multiplexed Proteomics® Phosphoprotein Gel Stain Kit	MPM33306	200 mL	200 mL	40 µL	~4 minigels

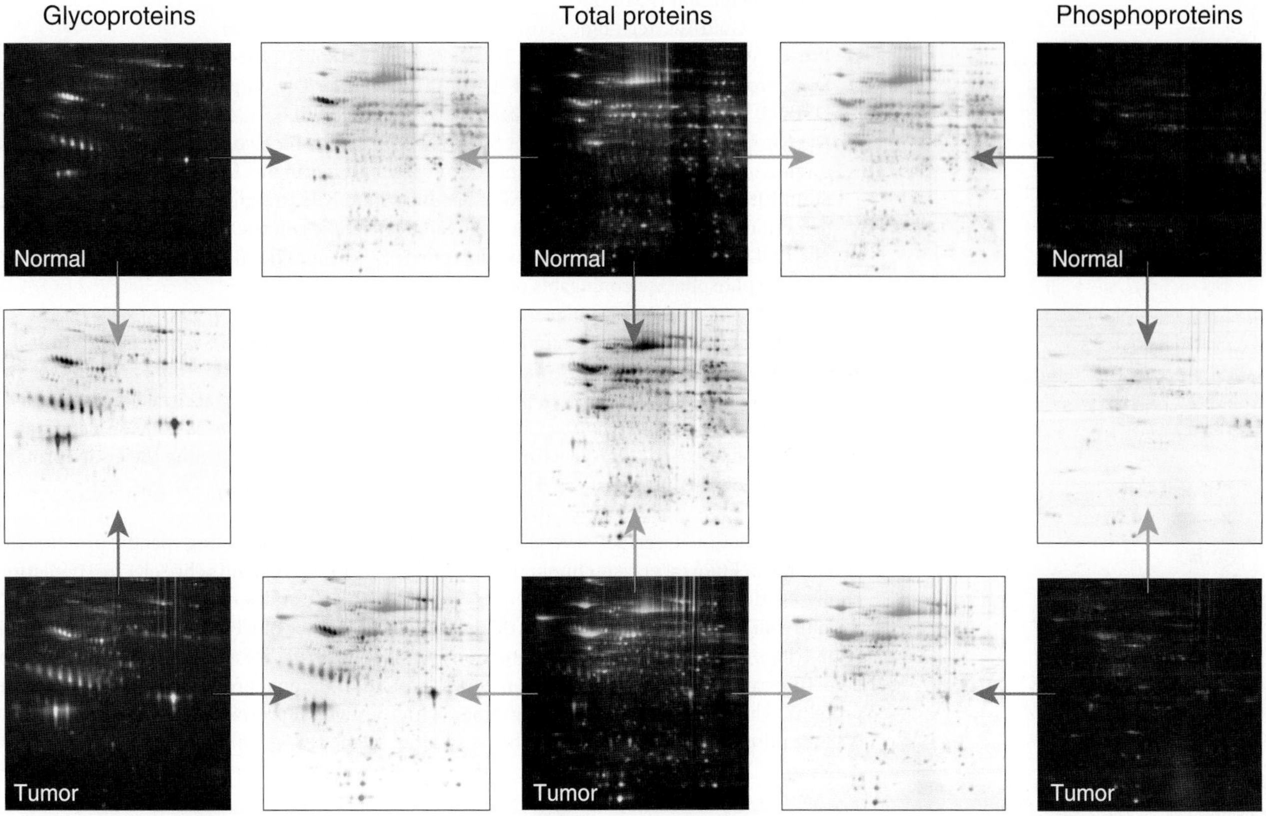

Figure 9.42 An overview of the Multiplexed Proteomics® approach. Images collected after each staining step can be overlaid in any combination for analysis of protein expression, phosphorylation and glycosylation between samples.

Table 9.7 — Fluorescence-based Western blot stain kits

Kit	Immunostaining Technique *	Total-Protein Detection Technique *	Secondary Detection Conjugate	Cat # of Kit
DyeChrome™ Western Blot Stain Kits #1, #2 and #3	DDAO phosphate (far-red fluorescence, Abs/Em = 275, 645/660)	BODIPY® FL, SE † (green fluorescence, Abs/Em = 365, 505/515)	AP goat anti–mouse IgG	D21881
			AP goat anti–rabbit IgG	D21882
			AP streptavidin	D21883
DyeChrome™ Western Blot Stain Kits #4, #5 and #6	ELF® 39 phosphate (green fluorescence, Abs/Em = 345/495)	BODIPY® TR, SE (red-orange fluorescence, Abs/Em = 300, 590/615)	AP goat anti–mouse IgG	D21884
			AP goat anti–rabbit IgG	D21885
			AP streptavidin	D21886
DyeChrome™ Double Western Blot Stain Kit	Amplex® Gold reagent (yellow fluorescence, Abs/Em = 515/535) DDAO phosphate (far-red fluorescence, Abs/Em = 275, 645/660)	MDPF (blue fluorescence, Abs/Em = 385/480)	AP goat anti–mouse IgG HRP goat anti–mouse IgG	D21887
Amplex® Gold Western Blot Stain Kits #1, #2 and #3	Amplex® Gold reagent (yellow fluorescence, Abs/Em = 515/535)	none	HRP goat anti–mouse IgG	A21890
			HRP goat anti–rabbit IgG	A21891
			HRP streptavidin	A21892
Pro-Q® Western Blot Stain Kits #2, #4 and #6	DDAO phosphate (far-red fluorescence, Abs/Em = 275, 645/660)	SYPRO® Ruby protein blot stain (red-orange fluorescence, Abs/Em = 280, 450/618)	AP goat anti–mouse IgG	P21860
			AP goat anti–rabbit IgG	P21861
			AP streptavidin	P21862
Pro-Q® Western Blot Stain Kits #3 and #5	DDAO phosphate (far-red fluorescence, Abs/Em = 275, 645/660)	none	AP goat anti–rabbit IgG	P21864
			AP streptavidin	P21865

* Absorption (Abs) and emission (Em) maxima, in nm. SE = Succinimidyl ester. AP = Alkaline phosphatase. HRP = Horseradish peroxidase.

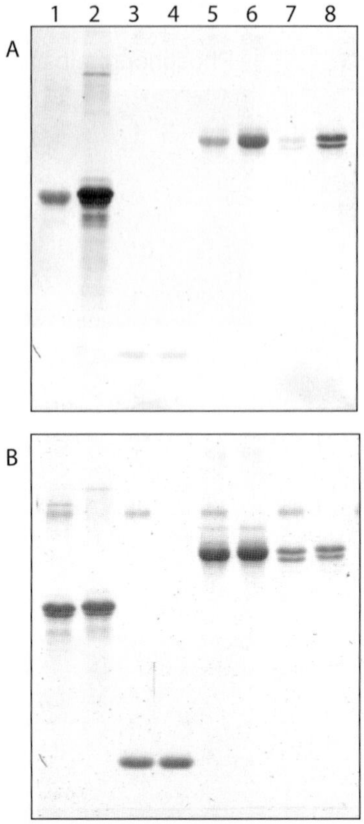

Figure 9.43 Selectivity of the Pro-Q® Diamond phosphoprotein gel stain (P33300, P33301, P33302) for phosphoproteins. A polyacrylamide gel containing various proteins was stained with Pro-Q® Diamond phosphoprotein gel stain (panel A) followed by SYPRO® Ruby protein gel stain (panel B). This gel shows a nonphosphorylated protein, lysozyme (lanes 3 and 4), as well as several phosphoproteins, α-casein (lanes 1 and 2), ovalbumin (lanes 5 and 6) and pepsin (lanes 7 and 8), before (even lanes) and after (odd lanes) treatment with phosphatases. Loss of Pro-Q® Diamond staining indicates loss of all phosphates from pepsin, partial loss of phosphates from α-casein and ovalbumin and no change in the nonphosphorylated protein lysozyme.

- Pro-Q® Diamond Phosphoprotein Blot Stain Kit (P33356)
- Pro-Q® Glycoprotein Blot Stain Kits containing Pro-Q® Emerald stains (P21857, P21875)
- Pro-Q® Glycoprotein Blot Stain Kit with *Griffonia simplicifolia* lectin II (GS-II)–based glycoprotein detection (P21872)
- Amplex® Gold Western Blot Stain Kits (A21890, A21891, A21892)
- Pro-Q® Western Blot Stain Kits (P21860, P21861, P21862, P21864, P21865)
- DyeChrome™ Western Blot Stain Kits containing either DDAO phosphate (D21881, D21882, D21883) or ELF® 39 phosphate (D21884, D21885, D21886)
- DyeChrome™ Double Western Blot Stain Kit (D21887), which combines a blue-fluorescent total-protein stain with the immunostaining techniques in our DyeChrome™ Western Blot Stain Kits and our Amplex® Gold Western Blot Stain Kits to yield simultaneous trichromatic detection of two different enzyme-conjugated antibodies on the same blot
- The BOLD APB chemiluminescent substrate (B21901) for chemiluminescent detection of alkaline phosphatase conjugates on Western blots

The Pro-Q® Glycoprotein Blot Stain Kits, Amplex® Gold Western Blot Stain Kits and Pro-Q® Western Blot Stain Kits can all be paired with our luminescent SYPRO® Ruby protein blot stain (S11791) to detect the total-protein profile on the same blot, ensuring accurate registration of protein bands or spots. The DyeChrome™ Western Blot Stain Kits each provide a compatible fluorescence-based total-protein detection method for counterstaining the entire protein complement on the blot.

Lastly, this section describes several specialized techniques for detecting specific proteins in gels and on blots. Fluorescence technology from Molecular Probes permits the selective detection of oligohistidine fusion proteins in gels or on blots with ease and sensitivity using our Pro-Q® Sapphire oligohistidine gel stains (P21876, P21877, P33354) or our Pro-Q® Oligohistidine Blot Stain Kits with biotin NTA–based detection (P21878, P21879). We also describe methods for detecting calcium-binding proteins, enzymes, protein functional groups and penicillin-binding proteins, which can potentially be combined with the general protein stains described in Section 9.3 for multiplexed protein staining that is tailored to answer specific research questions.

Pro-Q® Diamond Phosphoprotein Stain for Gels and Blots

Pro-Q® Diamond Phosphoprotein Gel Stain and Destain

Molecular Probes' Pro-Q® Diamond phosphoprotein gel stain [1–4] is a breakthrough technology that provides a simple, direct method for selectively staining *O*-linked phosphoproteins in polyacrylamide gels (Figure 9.43). It is ideal for the identification of kinase targets in signal transduction pathways and for phosphoproteomic studies. This proprietary fluorescent stain allows direct, in-gel detection of phosphate groups attached to tyrosine, serine or threonine residues. The Pro-Q® Diamond phosphoprotein gel stain can be used with standard SDS-polyacrylamide gels (Figure 9.43) or with 2-D gels (Figure 9.44) — blotting is not required and there is no need for radioisotopes, phosphoprotein-specific antibodies or Western blot detection reagents. The simple and reliable staining protocol delivers results in as little as 4 to 5 hours. The stain is also compatible with mass spectrometry, allowing meaningful analysis of the phosphorylation state of entire proteomes for the first time. The Pro-Q® Diamond phosphoprotein gel stain provides:

- **Simple in-gel detection.** Proteins containing phosphate groups attached to tyrosine, serine or threonine residues can be detected directly in either 1-D or 2-D polyacrylamide gels after the gel is fixed, stained and destained; no antibodies are required and no blotting is necessary.
- **Selectivity without radioactivity.** The Pro-Q® Diamond phosphoprotein gel stain is a fluorescent stain that selectively detects phosphoproteins; radioisotopes are not used and therefore no radioactive waste is generated.
- **Sensitivity.** The Pro-Q® Diamond phosphoprotein gel stain allows the detection of as little as 1–16 ng of phosphoprotein per band, depending on the phosphorylation level of the protein.
- **Quantitation.** The Pro-Q® Diamond signal for individual phosphoproteins is linear over three orders of magnitude and correlates with the number of phosphate groups (Figure 9.45).
- **Compatibility.** Pro-Q® Diamond gel stain (excitation/emission maxima ~555/580 nm) is compatible with a visible-light–scanning instrument, a visible-light transilluminator or (with

reduced sensitivity) a 300 nm transilluminator, as well as with mass spectrometry analysis (Figure 9.46).

- **Multiplexing capability.** Pro-Q® Diamond gel stain can be used with SYPRO® Ruby protein gel stain (Figure 9.43) and Pro-Q® Emerald glycoprotein gel stain on the same gel for multiparameter staining.

The Pro-Q® Diamond phosphoprotein gel stain (Table 9.6) is supplied ready-to-use in three different sizes: a 200 mL size (P33301) suitable for staining approximately four minigels; a 1 L size (P33300) suitable for staining approximately 20 minigels or two large-format gels, e.g., 2-D gels; and a 5 L bulk-packaging size (P33302). In addition, we offer Pro-Q® Diamond Phosphoprotein Gel Staining Kits (MPP33300, MPP33301, MPP33302) that include both the Pro-Q® Diamond gel stain and the PeppermintStick™ phosphoprotein molecular weight standards (see below). All products are accompanied by a simple and reliable staining and destaining protocol that delivers results in as little as four to five hours. For convenient destaining, we also offer the Pro-Q® Diamond phosphoprotein gel destaining solution as a ready-to-use solution in either a 1 L (P33310) or 5 L (P33311) size.

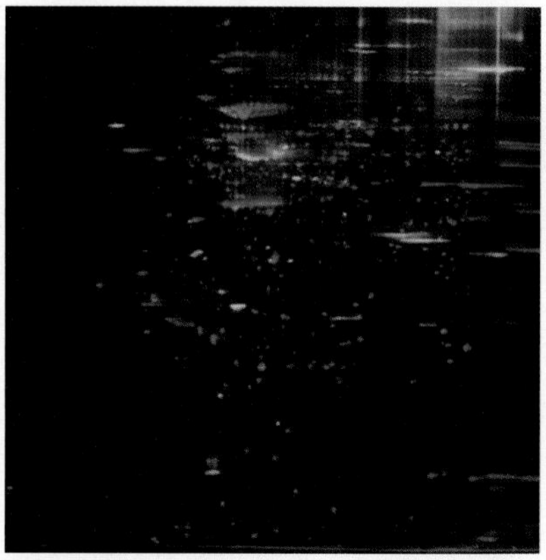

Figure 9.44 Visualization of total protein and phosphoproteins in a 2-D gel. Proteins from a Jurkat T-cell lymphoma line cell lysate were separated by 2-D gel electrophoresis and stained with Pro-Q® Diamond phosphoprotein gel stain (P33300, P33301, P33302, blue) followed by SYPRO® Ruby protein gel stain (S12000, S12001, S21900, red). After each dye staining, the gel was imaged on an FLA-3000 scanner (Fuji). The digital images were acquired using Z3 software (Compugen), and the resulting composite image was digitally pseudocolored and overlaid.

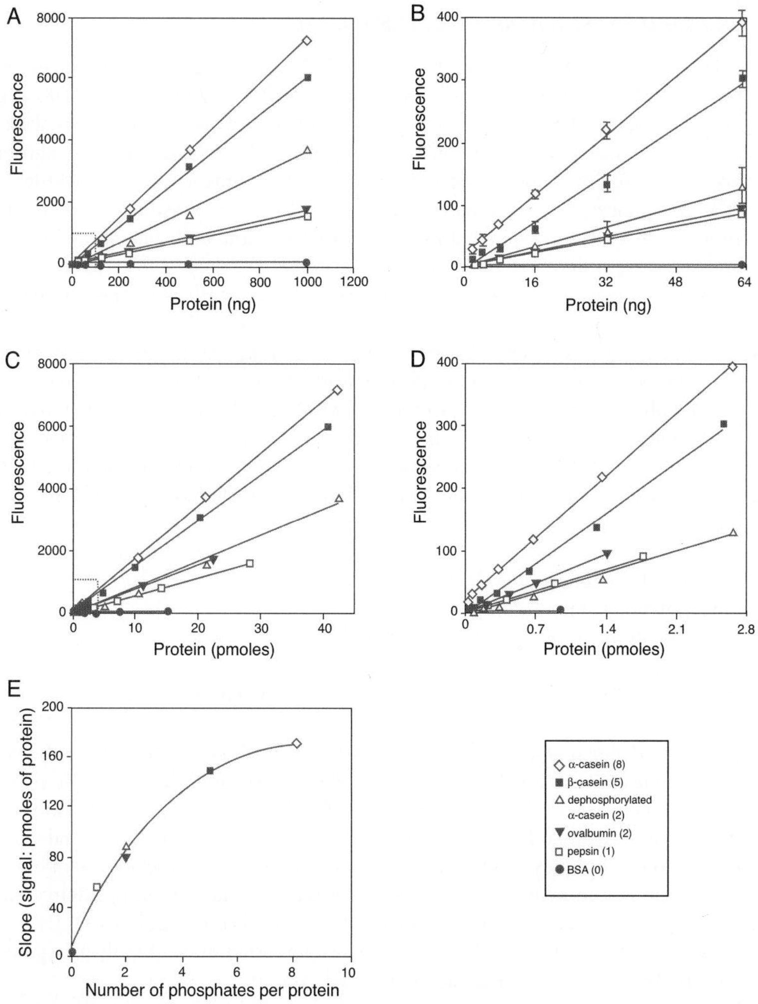

Figure 9.45 Sensitivity and linear range of Pro-Q® Diamond phosphoprotein gel stain (P33300, P33301, P33302). Six different proteins were serially diluted and run on separate SDS-polyacrylamide gels, which were then stained with Pro-Q® Diamond phosphoprotein gel stain. The images were documented on a fluorescence imager, and the fluorescence emission from each band was quantitated. The number of known phosphate groups on each protein is indicated in the figure legend. A) Fluorescence emission of the band, plotted as a function of protein amount, in nanograms. B) Magnification of data points in the highlighted box in panel A. C) The fluorescence emission of the band, plotted as a function of picomoles of protein. D) Magnification of the data points in the highlighted box in panel C. E) The slope of the line for each protein in panel C, plotted against the known number of phosphates per protein.

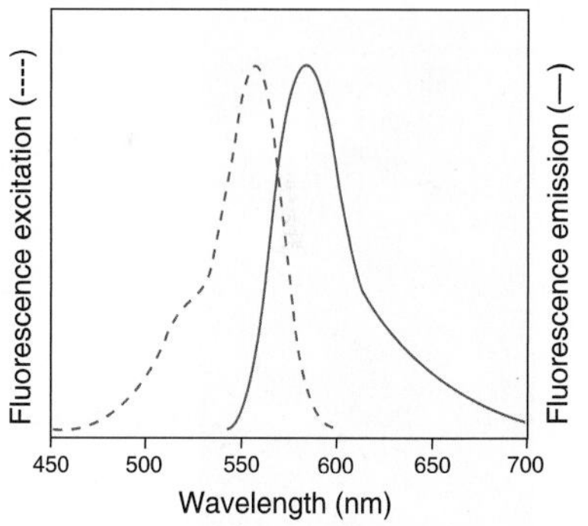

Figure 9.46 Fluorescence excitation and emission spectra of the Pro-Q® Diamond phosphoprotein gel stain (P33300, P33301, P33302).

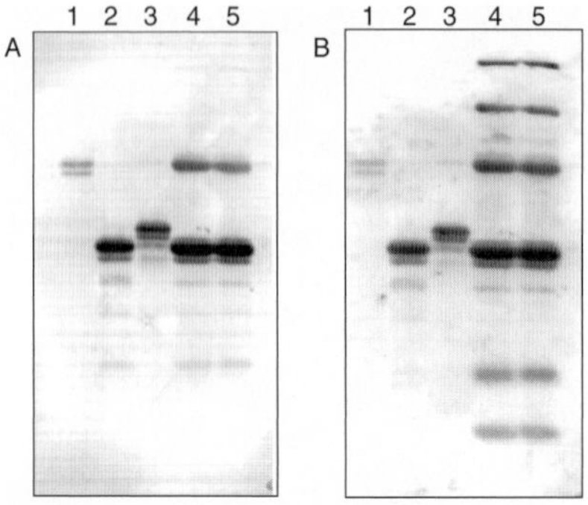

Figure 9.47 Selectivity of the Pro-Q® Diamond phosphoprotein blot stain. A polyacrylamide gel containing various proteins was electroblotted to a PVDF membrane, stained with Pro-Q® Diamond phosphoprotein blot stain (P33356) (Panel A) and subsequently stained with SYPRO® Ruby protein blot stain (S11791) (Panel B). Lane 1, pepsin (one phosphate residue/protein); lane 2, β-casein (five phosphate residues/protein); lane 3, α-casein (eight phosphate residues/protein); lanes 4 and 5, PeppermintStick™ phosphoprotein molecular weight standards (P27167, P33350), a set of molecular weight standards containing β-galactosidase, bovine serum albumin (BSA), ovalbumin (two phosphate residues/protein), β-casein (five phosphate residues/protein), avidin and lysozyme.

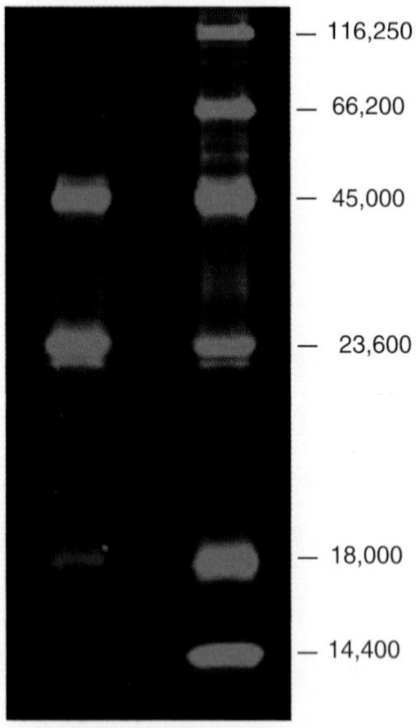

Figure 9.48 PeppermintStick™ phosphoprotein molecular weight standards (P33350, P27167) separated on a 13% SDS polyacrylamide gel. The markers contain (from largest to smallest) β-galactosidase, bovine serum albumin (BSA), ovalbumin, α-casein, avidin and lysozyme. Ovalbumin and α-casein are phosphorylated. The gel was stained with Pro-Q® Diamond phosphoprotein gel stain (blue) followed by SYPRO® Ruby protein gel stain (red). The digital images were pseudocolored.

Multiplexed Proteomics® Kits for Phosphoprotein and Total-Protein Gel Staining

When used together, the Pro-Q® Diamond phosphoprotein gel stain and the SYPRO® Ruby protein gel stain (S12000, S12001, S21900; Section 9.3) make a powerful combination for proteome analysis. The SYPRO® Ruby dye is a total-protein stain that, like the Pro-Q® Diamond gel stain, is quantitative over three orders of magnitude. Determining the ratio of the Pro-Q® Diamond dye to SYPRO® Ruby dye signal intensities for each band or spot thus provides a measure of the phosphorylation level normalized to the total amount of protein. Using both stains in combination makes it possible to distinguish a low amount of a highly phosphorylated protein from a higher amount of a less phosphorylated protein. To make this staining more convenient and economical, we offer the Multiplexed Proteomics® Kit #1 with 200 mL of the Pro-Q® Diamond phosphoprotein gel stain and 200 mL of the SYPRO® Ruby protein gel stain (M33306), the Multiplexed Proteomics® Kit #2 with 1 L of each stain (M33305) and the Multiplexed Proteomics® Phosphoprotein Gel Stain Kits (MPM33305, MPM33306), which include the Pro-Q® Diamond phosphoprotein gel stain, SYPRO® Ruby protein gel stain and PeppermintStick™ phosphoprotein molecular weight standards (see below); Table 9.6 summarizes all of our Pro-Q® Diamond gel stain reagents and kits.

Pro-Q® Diamond Phosphoprotein Blot Stain Kit

The Pro-Q® Diamond Phosphoprotein Blot Stain Kit (P33356) provides a simple and quick method for directly detecting phosphoproteins on poly(vinylidene difluoride) (PVDF) (Figure 9.47) or nitrocellulose membranes without the use of radioactivity or antibodies. As with the gel stain described above, the Pro-Q® Diamond phosphoprotein blot stain detects phosphoserine-, phosphothreonine- and phosphotyrosine-containing proteins, independent of the sequence context of the phosphorylated amino acid residue. Thus, the native phosphorylation levels of proteins from a variety of sources, including tissue specimens and body fluids, can be analyzed. Protein samples are separated by 1-D or 2-D gel electrophoresis, electroblotted to the membrane, stained and destained using a protocol similar to that typically performed with amido black or Ponceau S staining of total-protein profiles on membranes. After staining, gels are simply imaged using any of a variety of laser scanners, xenon-arc lamp–based scanners or CCD-based imaging devices employing UV transilluminators; the excitation/emission maxima of the Pro-Q® Diamond phosphoprotein blot stain are ~555/580 nm. The limits of detection for the stain on PVDF membrane blots are typically 8–16 ng of phosphoprotein, with a linear dynamic range of approximately 15-fold. The sensitivity of the Pro-Q® Diamond phosphoprotein blot stain is decreased when using nitrocellulose blots. Each Pro-Q® Diamond Phosphoprotein Blot Stain Kit provides:

- Pro-Q® Diamond phosphoprotein blot stain reagent
- Pro-Q® Diamond blot stain buffer
- Detailed protocols for staining and photographing the blot

Sufficient reagents are provided for staining ~20 minigel electroblots.

The Pro-Q® Diamond phosphoprotein blot stain binds noncovalently to phosphoproteins and is thus fully compatible with matrix-assisted laser desorption ionization time-of-flight mass spectrometry (MALDI-TOF MS) and Edman sequencing. Furthermore, the Pro-Q® Diamond phosphoprotein blot stain is compatible with the standard colorimetric, fluorometric and chemiluminescent detection techniques employed in immunoblotting. This phosphoprotein blot stain may be used in conjunction with the SYPRO® Ruby protein blot stain, a total-protein stain that is quantitative over two orders of magnitude on blots. Using the SYPRO® and Pro-Q® Diamond blot stains in combination makes it possible to distinguish a low amount of a highly phosphorylated protein from a higher amount of a less phosphorylated protein.

PeppermintStick™ Phosphoprotein Molecular Weight Standards

PeppermintStick™ phosphoprotein molecular weight standards are a mixture of phosphorylated and nonphosphorylated proteins with molecular weights from 14,400 to 116,250 daltons. Separation by polyacrylamide gel electrophoresis resolves this mixture into two phosphorylated and four nonphosphorylated protein bands (Figure 9.48). These standards serve both as molecular weight markers and as positive and negative controls for our Pro-Q® Diamond phosphoprotein gel stain and other methods that detect phosphorylated proteins. We offer two different unit sizes of the PeppermintStick™ phosphoprotein molecular weight standards: a 40 µL unit size sufficient for 20–40 gel lanes (P27167) and a 400 µL unit size sufficient for 200–400 gel lanes (P33350).

Other Reagents for Phosphoproteomics

The Captivate™ Microscale Phosphopeptide Isolation Kit (C33355), described in detail in Section 9.2, provides a highly selective and sensitive method for isolating phosphopeptides from complex solutions. This technology is ideal for isolating phosphorylated peptides as a front-end fractionation step prior to liquid chromatography– and mass spectrometry–based proteomics systems.

The Antibody Beacon™ Tyrosine Kinase Assay Kit (A35725), described in detail in Section 10.3, provides a simple yet robust solution assay for real-time monitoring of tyrosine kinase activity and the effectiveness of potential inhibitors and modulators. The key to this tyrosine kinase assay is a small-molecule tracer ligand labeled with our bright green-fluorescent Oregon Green® 488 dye. When an anti-phosphotyrosine antibody binds this tracer ligand to form the Antibody Beacon™ detection complex, the fluorescence of the Oregon Green® 488 dye is efficiently quenched. In the presence of a phosphotyrosine-containing peptide, however, this Antibody Beacon™ detection complex is rapidly disrupted, releasing the tracer ligand and relieving its antibody-induced quenching. Upon its displacement by a phosphotyrosine residue, the Oregon Green® 488 dye-labeled tracer ligand exhibits an approximately fourfold enhancement in its fluorescence, enabling the detection of as little as 50 nM phosphotyrosine-containing peptide with excellent signal-to-background discrimination.

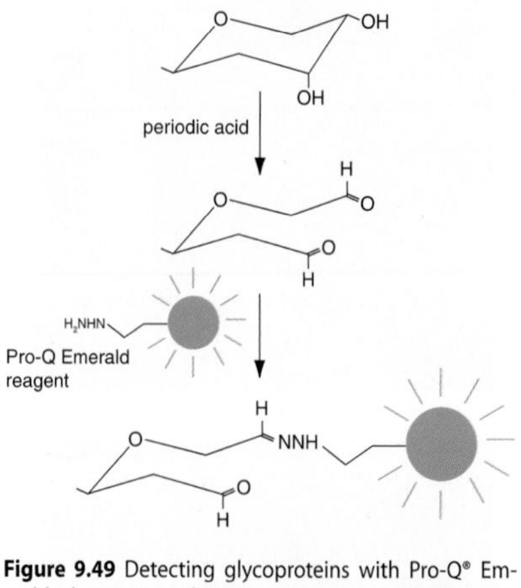

Figure 9.49 Detecting glycoproteins with Pro-Q® Emerald glycoprotein detection reagents. Oxidation with periodic acid converts *cis*-glycols to dialdehydes, which can then react with the hydrazide-based Pro-Q® Emerald reagents to form a covalent bond.

Pro-Q® Glycoprotein Stain Kits for Gels and for Blots

Glycoproteins play important roles as cell-surface markers and in cell adhesion, immune recognition and inflammation reactions.[5] To facilitate research on glycoproteins, Molecular Probes has introduced the Pro-Q® Glycoprotein Stain Kits for Gels and for Blots, which provide unsurpassed sensitivity, linearity and ease of use for selective detection of glycoproteins.

Pro-Q® Emerald Glycoprotein Stain Kits for Gels and for Blots

Our Pro-Q® Emerald 300 and Pro-Q® Emerald 488 Glycoprotein Stain Kits (Table 9.8) provide the most advanced reagents known for detecting glycoproteins in gels and on blots. These stains are easier to use and more sensitive than any other glycoprotein staining technique (Table 9.9). The Pro-Q® Emerald glycoprotein stains react with periodate-oxidized carbohydrate groups, creating a bright green-fluorescent signal on glycoproteins (Figure 9.49). The staining procedure requires only three steps: fixation, oxidation and staining — no reduction step is required (Figure 9.50). Depending on the nature and degree of glycosylation, the Pro-Q® Emerald 300 stain allows the detection of as little as 1 ng of a glycoprotein per band in gels (4 ng/band with the Pro-Q® Emerald 488 stain), making these stains about 50 times more sensitive than the standard periodic acid–Schiff base method using acidic fuchsin dye. Blot staining is not quite as sensitive (2–18 ng of a glycoprotein per band can be detected) and is more time consuming, but provides an opportunity to combine glycoprotein staining with immunostaining or other blot-based detection techniques. The Pro-Q® Emerald 300 stain is best visualized using 300 nm UV illumination, whereas the Pro-Q® Emerald 488 stain is best visualized using visible light with

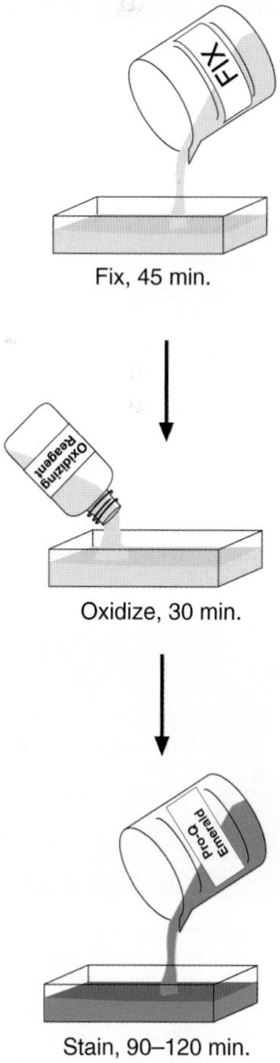

Figure 9.50 Detecting glycoproteins with the Pro-Q® Emerald 300 glycoprotein detection reagents requires only three steps: fixation, periodate oxidation of the *cis*-glycols to dialdehydes, and incubation with the Pro-Q® Emerald 300 glycoprotein detection reagent (P21855, P21857). No destaining step is required.

Table 9.8 — Pro-Q® Emerald glycoprotein stain kits for gels and for blots

Product	Glycoprotein Stain	Kit Type	Cat #
Pro-Q® Emerald 300 Glycoprotein Stain Kits	Pro-Q® Emerald 300 stain, Ex/Em = 280/530 nm	Gel Stain Kit (includes SYPRO® Ruby protein gel stain *)	P21855
		Gel and Blot Stain Kit (does not include a total-protein stain)	P21857
Pro-Q® Emerald 488 Glycoprotein Stain Kits	Pro-Q® Emerald 488 stain, Ex/Em = 510/520 nm	Gel and Blot Stain Kit (does not include a total-protein gel stain)	P21875

* See Section 9.3 for a description of the SYPRO® Ruby protein stains.

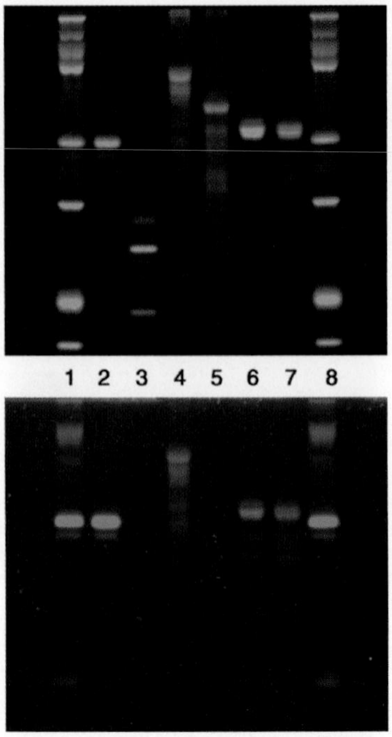

Figure 9.52 Mobility-shift gel assay using deglycosylating enzymes, stained with the SYPRO® Ruby protein gel stain (top, S12000, S12001, S21900) and Pro-Q® Emerald 300 glycoprotein stain (bottom). The glycoproteins α1-acidic glycoprotein, fetuin and horseradish peroxidase (HRP) are shown before (lanes 2, 4 and 6, respectively) and after (lanes 3, 5 and 7, respectively) glycosidase treatment. Glycosidase treatment resulted in a mobility shift and loss of green-fluorescent Pro-Q® Emerald 300 staining for α1-acidic glycoprotein and fetuin, indicating that the carbohydrate groups had been cleaved off. HRP, which contains an α-(1,3)-fucosylated asparagine GlcNac-linkage that is resistant to many glycosidases, showed neither a mobility shift nor a loss of green-fluorescent Pro-Q® Emerald 300 staining. Thus, use of the Pro-Q® Emerald 300 Glycoprotein Stain Kits (P21855, P21857, M33307) identifies glycoproteins that are not susceptible to the glycosidases used in the assay, providing important structural information about the glycoprotein's carbohydrate moiety.

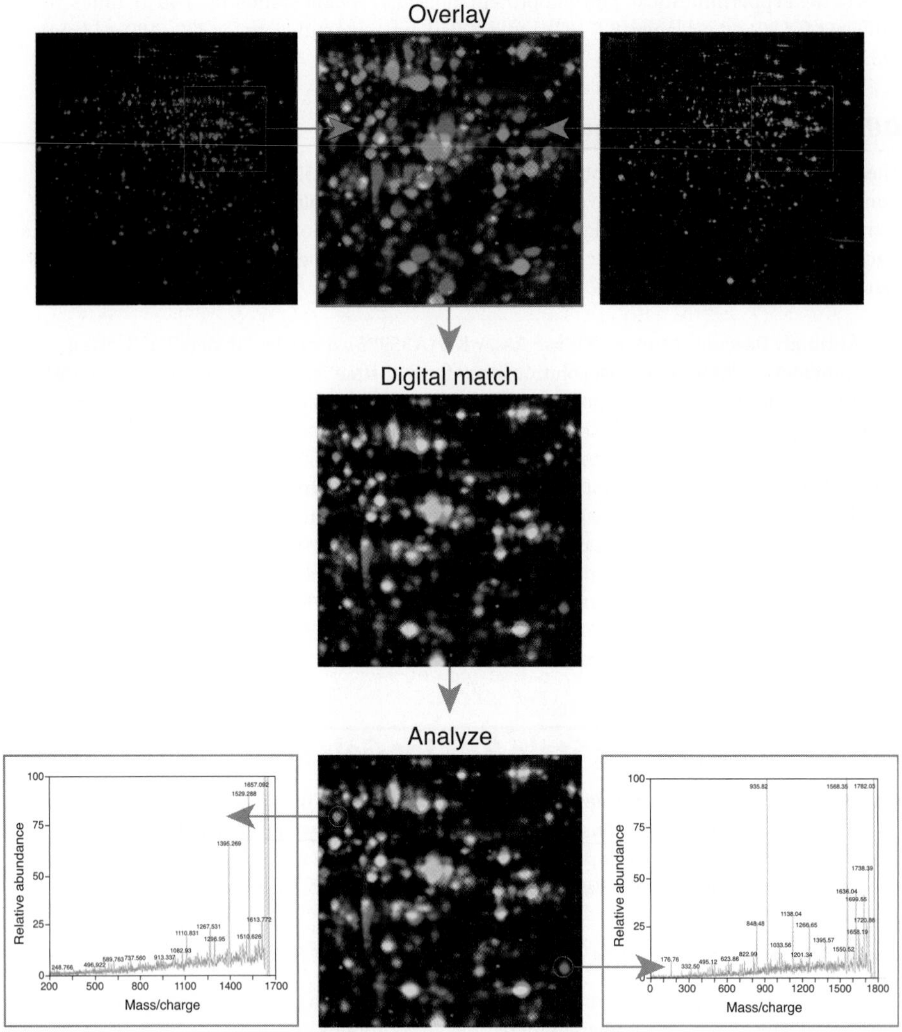

Figure 9.51 Multiplexed analysis of normal liver cells (left) and liver tumor cells (right). Gels are stained for total protein and glycoproteins using SYPRO® Ruby protein gel stain (S12000, S12001, S21900) and a Pro-Q® Emerald glycoprotein stain (P21855, P21857, P21875), respectively. Individual gel images can then be digitally overlaid, matched and analyzed for changes in protein expression and glycosylation.

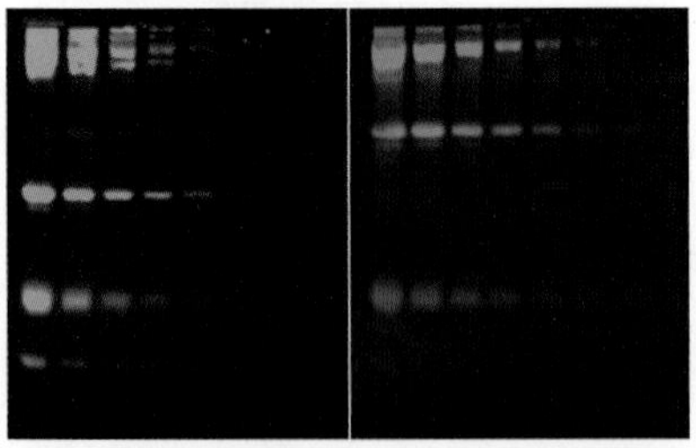

Figure 9.53 Staining glycoproteins and the total protein profile on blots using the Pro-Q® Emerald 300 Glycoprotein Gel and Blot Stain Kit (P21857). A twofold dilution series of the CandyCane™ glycoprotein molecular weight standards (C21852) was run an SDS-polyacrylamide gel and blotted onto a PVDF membrane. The blot was first stained with the SYPRO® Ruby protein blot stain (S11791) to detect the total protein profile (left). After documentation of the signal, the blot was stained with the Pro-Q® Emerald 300 glycoprotein stain (right) provided in the Pro-Q® Emerald 300 Glycoprotein Gel and Blot Stain Kit.

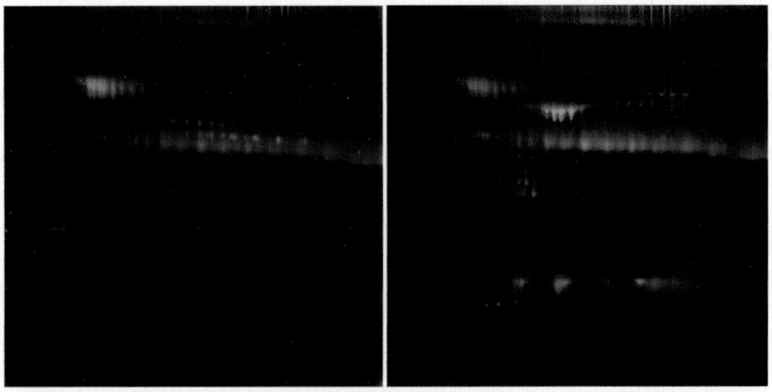

Figure 9.54 2-D gel stained with the SYPRO® Ruby protein gel stain and the Pro-Q® Emerald 300 reagent. Combined Cohn fractions II and III from cow plasma, containing primarily β- and γ-globulins, were run on a 2-D gel and stained first with the Pro-Q® Emerald 300 reagent (P21855, P21857; left) and then with the SYPRO® Ruby protein gel stain (S12000, S12001, S21900, and in P21855; right).

wavelengths near its 510 nm excitation maximum. The Pro-Q® Emerald dye is also used as the detection reagent in our Pro-Q® Emerald 300 Lipopolysaccharide Gel Stain Kit (P20495), which is described in Section 3.2 (Figure 3.19, Figure 3.20, Figure 3.21).

The Pro-Q® Emerald glycoprotein stains can be combined with general protein stains for dichromatic detection of glycoproteins and total proteins in gels and on blots, making it much easier to identify the location of the glycoproteins in the total-protein profile (Figure 9.51, Figure 9.52, Figure 9.53, Figure 9.54). The easy-to-use patented SYPRO® Ruby protein gel and blot stains (described in Section 9.3) provide the same sensitivity as silver staining (gels) or colloidal gold staining (blots) but, unlike these chromogenic techniques, do not require formaldehyde or glutaraldehyde, which can produce false positive responses when glycoproteins are stained. These total-protein stains make it possible to visualize the entire protein complement of a sample and to thus identify contaminating proteins, to compare stained proteins to molecular weight standards and to provide a control for protease contamination in glycosidase mobility-shift experiments. The SYPRO® Ruby protein blot stain is additionally useful for assessing the efficiency of protein transfer to a blot (Figure 9.53), which is especially important when working with glycoproteins, because they often transfer poorly to blotting membranes. Proteins labeled with the SYPRO® Ruby total-protein stains exhibit red-orange fluorescence when excited with either a 300 nm UV light source or a laser scanner with a 473, 488 or 532 nm laser light source.

The Pro-Q® Emerald Glycoprotein Stain Kits also include our exclusive CandyCane™ molecular weight standards, a mixture of glycosylated and nonglycosylated proteins that, when separated by electrophoresis, provide alternating positive and negative controls (Figure 9.55). The CandyCane™ molecular weight standards are also available separately (C21852). In addition, we offer a Pro-Q® Emerald 300 Glycoprotein Gel Stain Kit (P21855) that includes our SYPRO® Ruby protein gel stain for detecting total proteins. The Pro-Q® Emerald Glycoprotein Stain Kits for gels and blots contain:

- Pro-Q® Emerald 300 glycoprotein stain (in Kits P21855 and P21857) or Pro-Q® Emerald 488 glycoprotein stain (in Kit P21875)
- Pro-Q® Emerald 300 staining buffer (in Kits P21855 and P21857 or Pro-Q® Emerald 488 staining buffer (in Kit P21875)
- Oxidizing reagent (periodic acid)
- SYPRO® Ruby protein gel stain (in Kit P21855 only)
- CandyCane™ glycoprotein molecular weight standards
- Detailed protocols

Each kit provides sufficient materials to stain approximately ten 8 cm × 10 cm gels or blots.

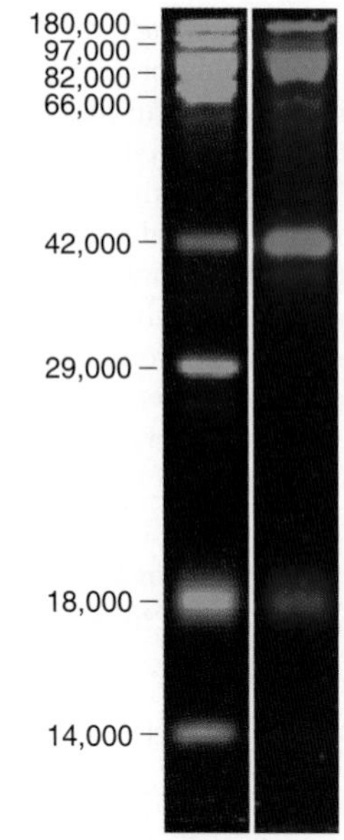

Figure 9.55 Glycosylated and nonglycosylated proteins in the CandyCane™ glycoprotein molecular weight standards (C21852). The standards were electrophoresed through two identical 13% polyacrylamide gels. Both lanes contain ~0.5 µg of protein in each band. The left lane was stained with our SYPRO® Ruby protein gel stain (S12000, S12001, S21900) to detect all eight marker proteins. The right lane was stained using the reagents in the Pro-Q® Emerald 300 Glycoprotein Gel Stain Kit (P21855).

Table 9.9 — Comparison of various commercially available glycoprotein stain kits

Product	Detection Technology *	Staining Time †	Sensitivity Limits ‡	Remarks
Pro-Q® Emerald 300 Glycoprotein Stain Kits (Molecular Probes)	Pro-Q® Emerald 300 stain	2.5 hours 6 steps	1–2 ng/band (gel kit) 2–18 ng/band (blot kit)	• Signal stable indefinitely § • View with 300 nm illumination
Pro-Q® Emerald 488 Glycoprotein Stain Kits (Molecular Probes)	Pro-Q® Emerald 488 stain	2.5 hours 6 steps	4 ng/band (gel kit) 4 ng/band (blot kit)	• Signal stable indefinitely § • View with visible light (450–510 nm)
ECL Glycoprotein Detection (Amersham-Pharmacia)	Biotin hydrazide reaction followed by HRP streptavidin followed by ECL detection reagents	6 hours 11 steps	18–150 ng/band (blots)	• Transient signal fades quickly
DIG Glycan Detection Kit (Roche)	Digoxigenin hydrazide reaction followed by AP anti-digoxigenin antibody followed by NBT/BCIP	6 hours 11 steps	2–37 ng/band (blots)	• Permanent signal • Crossreaction with carbonic anhydrase
GlycoTrack Detection Kit (Glyko)	Biotin hydrazide reaction followed by AP streptavidin followed by NBT/BCIP	6 hours 11 steps	2–37 ng/band (blots)	• Permanent signal • Crossreaction with carbonic anhydrase

* All detection procedures begin with periodate oxidation of carbohydrates. † Includes all staining and wash steps, but does not include time for blotting required in the blot detection kits. ‡ Sensitivities were measured for three glycoproteins of differing carbohydrate components: α1-acidic glycoprotein (40% carbohydrate), glucose oxidase (12% carbohydrate) and avidin (7% carbohydrate). The ranges reported represent differences in detection sensitivity for the different glycoproteins. § If stored protected from light. HRP = Horseradish peroxidase conjugate. AP = Alkaline phosphatase conjugate. NBT/BCIP = Colorimetric detection of alkaline phosphatase using nitro blue tetrazolium chloride and 5-bromo-4-chloro-Aphosphate.

Multiplexed Proteomics® Kit for Glycoprotein and Total-Protein Gel Staining

When used together, the Pro-Q® Emerald 300 glycoprotein gel stain and the SYPRO® Ruby protein gel stain (S12000, S12001, S21900; Section 9.3) make a powerful combination for proteome analysis (Figure 9.51). Determining the ratio of the Pro-Q® Emerald dye to SYPRO® Ruby dye signal intensities for each band or spot provides a measure of the glycosylation level normalized to the total amount of protein. Using both stains in combination makes it possible to distinguish a lightly glycosylated, high-abundance protein from a heavily glycosylated, low-abundance protein. To make this staining more convenient and economical, we offer the Multiplexed Proteomics® Glycoprotein Gel Stain Kit with 1 L of our Pro-Q® Emerald 300 glycoprotein gel stain and 1 L of our SYPRO® Ruby protein gel stain (M33307).

Pro-Q® Glycoprotein Blot Stain Kit with Lectin-Based Detection

Our lectin-based Pro-Q® Glycoprotein Blot Stain Kit provides high-sensitivity detection of specific sugar residues in glycoproteins. Pro-Q® Glycoprotein Blot Stain Kit #5 (P21872) is supplied with *Griffonia simplicifolia* lectin II (GS-II), which recognizes terminal nonreducing *N*-acetylglucosamine residues. This kit uses an alkaline phosphatase conjugate of the lectin as a convenient means of selectively detecting the corresponding glycoproteins on PVDF or nitrocellulose membranes, providing valuable information about the structure of glycoproteins in an experimental sample. The techniques in this Pro-Q® Glycoprotein Kit can also be applied to detect terminal α-mannopyranosyl and α-glucopyranosyl residues (that do not contain tri- or tetra-antennary structures) by using an alkaline phosphatase conjugate of concanavalin A (Con A), as well as to detect *N*-acetylglucosamine and *N*-acetylneuraminic acid (sialic acid) residues by using an alkaline phosphatase conjugate of wheat germ agglutinin (WGA).

The detection procedure in this kit is similar to that of Western blotting and uses a fluorogenic alkaline phosphatase substrate, DDAO phosphate, for the final detection step. After the proteins are separated on a polyacrylamide gel, they are blotted onto a membrane and incubated with the lectin–alkaline phosphatase conjugate. The alkaline phosphatase enzyme is then detected using DDAO phosphate, which is rapidly converted to the long-wavelength, red-fluorescent product DDAO (absorbance maxima ~275 nm and ~646 nm, emission maximum ~659 nm) (Figure 10.7). The enzymatic reaction greatly amplifies the signal, making it possible to detect as little as 15 ng of a glycoprotein, depending on the degree and nature of glycosylation. Sensitivity of the DDAO phosphate–based detection technique rivals ECL chemiluminescence detection, but because DDAO phosphate–based detection produces a stable fluorescent product, there is no need to perform the reaction in a darkroom or to expose the blot to X-ray film. Additionally, unlike transient chemiluminescent signals, the red-fluorescent DDAO signal can be imaged several times and is stable indefinitely on dried blots.

For fluorescent detection of total proteins, this Pro-Q® Glycoprotein Blot Stain Kit can be used in conjunction with our highly sensitive SYPRO® Ruby protein blot stain (S11791). When used prior to glycoprotein detection, SYPRO® Ruby protein blot stain makes it possible to assess the level of protein transfer to the blot, to compare stained proteins with molecular weight markers and to identify contaminating proteins in the sample. SYPRO® Ruby protein blot stain is particularly useful for blots of 2-D gels where total-protein staining makes it easier to localize stained glycoproteins in the complex protein pattern. Both the enzymatic hydrolysis product of DDAO phosphate (DDAO) and the SYPRO® Ruby blot stain can be easily visualized using either UV epi-illumination or a laser scanner. Pro-Q® Glycoprotein Blot Stain Kit #5 also provides a sample of our CandyCane™ glycoprotein molecular weight standards, which include eight glycoproteins, five of which are recognized by Con A or WGA (Figure 9.55).

Each Pro-Q® Glycoprotein Blot Stain Kit (P21872) contains:

- An alkaline phosphatase conjugate of GS-II lectin
- DDAO phosphate
- Dimethylformamide to dissolve the DDAO phosphate
- CandyCane™ glycoprotein molecular weight standards
- Detailed protocols for staining and detection with GS-II

Each kit contains sufficient reagents for staining 10–20 minigel blots (8 cm × 10 cm). DDAO phosphate (D6487, Section 10.3), SYPRO® Ruby protein blot stain (S11791) and CandyCane™ molecular weight standards (C21852) are also available separately.

CandyCane™ Glycoprotein Molecular Weight Standards

CandyCane™ glycoprotein molecular weight standards (C21852) contain a mixture of glycosylated and nonglycosylated proteins with molecular weights from 14,000 to 180,000 daltons. When separated by polyacrylamide gel electrophoresis, the standards appear as alternating bands corresponding to glycosylated and nonglycosylated proteins (Figure 9.55). Thus, these standards serve both as molecular weight markers and as positive and negative controls for methods that detect glycosylated proteins, such as those provided in our Pro-Q® Emerald Glycoprotein Stain Kits (see above).

Pro-Q® Amber Transmembrane Protein Gel Stain

The Multiplexed Proteomics® Transmembrane Protein Gel Stain Kit (M33308) provides two fluorescent gel stains — the Pro-Q® Amber transmembrane protein gel stain (excitation/emission maxima ~470/570 nm), which is selective for transmembrane proteins in gels, and the SYPRO® Ruby protein gel stain (excitation/emission maxima ~280, 450/610 nm), which stains all proteins. Once proteins are separated by SDS-polyacrylamide gel electrophoresis, the gel is simply fixed, stained with the Pro-Q® Amber reagent, washed and imaged using a laser scanner. Once the transmembrane proteins are visualized, the gel is then stained with SYPRO® Ruby dye to detect the total-protein profile and normalize the Pro-Q® Amber signals. Thus, after sequentially staining and imaging a gel, transmembrane proteins can be discriminated from nontransmembrane proteins. With the Pro-Q® Amber stain, as little as 10 ng of bacteriorhodopsin, a seven-domain transmembrane protein, can be detected. Moreover, the staining intensity is linear over more than two orders of magnitude, and the staining intensity of bacteriorhodopsin is at least 20 times greater than that of carbonic anhydrase, a nontransmembrane protein (Figure 9.56). The Pro-Q® Amber stain has been tested with a number of proteins, including those known to have hydrophobic transmembrane α-helices and those with none, and has been found to preferentially stain proteins with two or more transmembrane domains (Figure 9.57). Each Multiplexed Proteomics® Transmembrane Protein Gel Stain Kit contains:

- Pro-Q® Amber transmembrane protein gel stain
- SYPRO® Ruby protein gel stain
- Transmembrane protein standards, which include bacteriorhodopsin (seven-domain transmembrane protein) and carbonic anhydrase (nontransmembrane protein)
- Detailed protocols

Each kit provides sufficient materials to stain approximately ten 0.5–1 mm thick, 8 cm × 10 cm minigels. The Pro-Q® Amber stain is not recommended for staining proteins in 2-D, IEF or nondenaturing gels and is not suitable for staining proteins on blots.

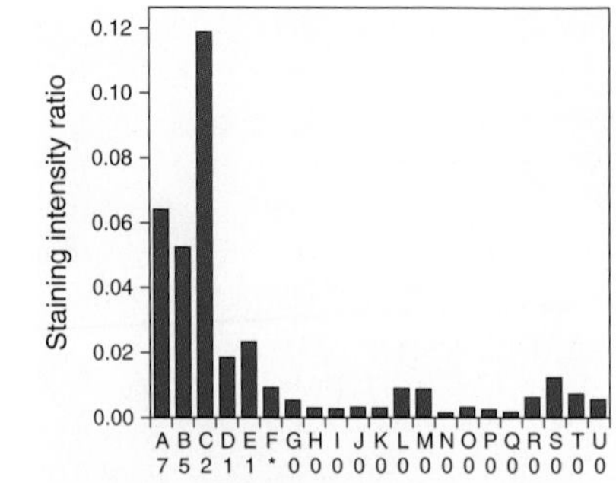

Figure 9.57 Ratio of the Pro-Q® Amber transmembrane gel stain signal to the SYPRO® Ruby gel stain signal for various transmembrane and nontransmembrane proteins. Proteins were separated by SDS-PAGE, stained with the Pro-Q® Amber transmembrane protein gel stain (provided in the Multiplexed Proteomics® Transmembrane Protein Gel Stain Kit, M33308) and imaged. The gel was then stained with the SYPRO® Ruby protein gel stain (also provided in the kit) and imaged again. The intensity of each band was measured, and the ratio of the two signals was plotted as a bar graph. Proteins tested were as follows: A, bacteriorhodopsin; B, ATP synthase F_0 a subunit; C, ATP synthase F_0 c subunit; D, ATP synthase F_0 b subunit; E, glycophorin; F, porin; G, zein; H, carbonic anhydrase; I, ATP synthase F_1 α subunit; J, ATP synthase F_1 β subunit; K, ATP synthase F_1 γ subunit; L, ATP synthase F_1 δ subunit; M, ATP synthase F_1 ε subunit; N, myosin; O, β-galactosidase; P, phosphorylase b; Q, bovine serum albumin (BSA); R, ovalbumin; S, soybean trypsin inhibitor; T, lysozyme; and U, aprotinin. The numbers along the x-axis indicate the number of α-helical transmembrane domains present in the corresponding protein; the asterisk denotes a 16-strand anti-parallel β-sheet transmembrane domain.

Western Blot Stain Kits and Reagents

The Western blot immunodetection technique provides a powerful method for detecting a protein or proteins of interest on a PVDF or nitrocellulose membrane. The proteins on the blot are typically incubated with a primary antibody against the protein of interest, followed by either an enzyme-labeled secondary antibody or a biotinylated secondary antibody in conjunction with an enzyme-labeled streptavidin. Finally, presence of the enzyme is detected using chromogenic, fluorogenic or chemiluminescent enzyme substrates. Specific proteins and total proteins are difficult to detect on the same blot using conventional chromogenic stains, which has complicated the assessment of protein transfer efficiency, the identification of contaminating proteins and the localization of an immunostained protein in electroblots of 2-D gels. The development of fluorogenic enzyme substrates and luminescent protein stains solves this problem by making it possible to visualize total proteins and specific proteins on the same blot. The Amplex® Gold, Pro-Q® and DyeChrome™ Western Blot Stain Kits use fluorogenic immunostains that can be combined with our proprietary luminescent total-protein detection technologies to make it easy to routinely obtain this valuable information without running duplicate gels. Fluorescent protein detection methods offer high sensitivity, streamlined procedures and the opportunity for multicolor labeling. In the development of these products, we have emphasized reagents that provide a combination of selective and general detection of multiple protein targets by well-resolved dichromatic or polychromatic staining technology.

Amplex® Gold Western Blot Stain Kits

Amplex® Gold reagent is a fluorogenic horseradish peroxidase (HRP) substrate that provides a sensitive fluorescence-based detection method for Western blots. In the presence of the enzyme, this nonfluorescent substrate is converted to a golden-yellow–fluorescent product

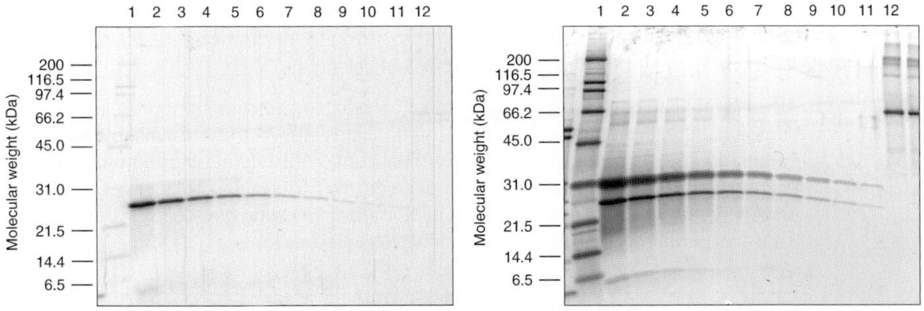

Figure 9.56 Sensitivity of the Pro-Q® Amber transmembrane protein gel stain. An SDS-polyacrylamide gel containing a twofold dilution series of the transmembrane protein standards was stained with the Pro-Q® Amber transmembrane protein gel stain (left) and subsequently with the SYPRO® Ruby protein gel stain (right), both of which are provided in the Multiplexed Proteomics® Transmembrane Protein Gel Stain Kit (M33308). Lane 1 contains 250 ng of each marker in the broad-range molecular weight markers; lanes 2–11, twofold dilution series of the protein standards provided in the kit, starting with 2 µg carbonic anhydrase and 1.4 µg bacteriorhodopsin in lane 2; lane 12, 250 ng bovine serum albumin (BSA). Carbonic anhydrase (upper band) is a nontransmembrane protein, and bacteriorhodopsin (lower band) is a seven-domain transmembrane protein. The numbers at the left indicate the molecular weights of the markers. The images were acquired using a 473 nm laser–based gel scanner with a 520 nm bandpass filter for the detection of Pro-Q® Amber signal and a 580 nm bandpass filter for detection of the SYPRO® Ruby signal.

(Figure 9.58). The Amplex® Gold reagent is simple to use, producing a fluorescent signal at the reaction site within minutes. The reaction does not require addition of hydrogen peroxide. The signal amplification of the enzymatic reaction allows detection of as little as 1–3 ng of a protein per band, depending on the antibodies used. The signal is stable indefinitely and can be documented using UV epi-illumination and a Polaroid camera; use of the inexpensive Amplex® Gold photographic filter (A24772, Section 23.3) produces optimal sensitivity. The signal can also be documented using a laser scanner. Scanners using light sources near the excitation maxima for the Amplex® Gold peroxidation product (~515 nm) provide the highest sensitivity. The Amplex® Gold Western Blot Stain Kits provide the Amplex® Gold reagent in combination with either goat anti–mouse IgG antibody, goat anti–rabbit IgG antibody or streptavidin (see Table 9.7). These kits can be used in combination with the SYPRO® Ruby protein blot stain (S11791, Section 9.3) for detecting the total-protein profile on the same blot.

Each Amplex® Gold Western Blot Stain Kit contains the following reagents, which are sufficient to stain ~20 minigel blots (6 cm × 9 cm):

- Amplex® Gold reagent (10 vials)
- Solvent for Amplex® Gold reagent
- Reaction buffer
- Horseradish peroxidase conjugate of goat anti–mouse IgG antibody (in Kit #1, A21890), goat anti–rabbit IgG antibody (in Kit #2, A21891) or streptavidin (in Kit #3, A21892)
- A detailed protocol

Pro-Q® Western Blot Stain Kits

Our Pro-Q® Western Blot Stain Kits (Table 9.7) use the fluorogenic substrate DDAO phosphate for simple and rapid detection of an antibody or streptavidin conjugated to alkaline phosphatase (Figure 9.59). DDAO phosphate is a remarkable reagent that provides very rapid and highly sensitive fluorescence detection of alkaline phosphatase conjugates. Alkaline phosphatase rapidly converts DDAO phosphate to the long-wavelength, red-fluorescent product, DDAO (Figure 9.60,

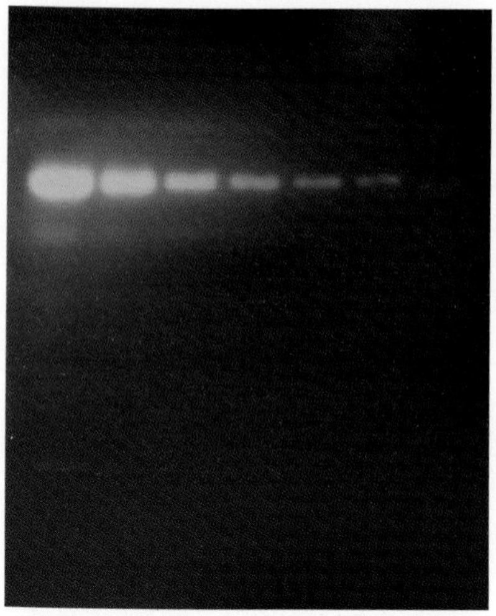

Figure 9.58 Immunodetection using the Amplex® Gold Western Blot Stain Kit #1 (A21890). Samples of protein molecular weight standards (P6649) containing decreasing amounts of α-tubulin were run on an SDS-polyacrylamide gel and blotted onto a PVDF membrane. The blot was incubated with a mouse monoclonal anti-α-tubulin antibody (A11126), followed by a horseradish peroxidase conjugate of goat anti–mouse IgG antibody, which is included in the kit. Finally, the blot was stained with the Amplex® Gold reagent and photographed.

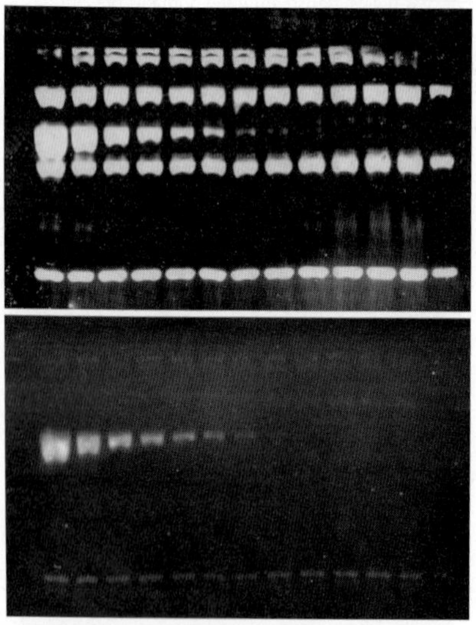

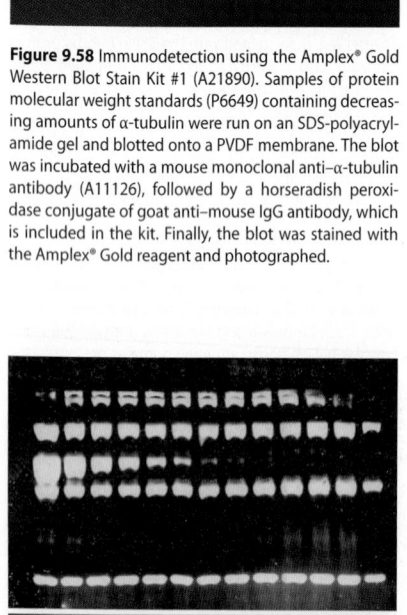

Figure 9.59 Protein detection with the Pro-Q® Western Blot Stain Kit #2 (P21860). Samples of protein molecular weight standards containing decreasing amounts of α-tubulin were run on an SDS-polyacrylamide gel, blotted onto a PVDF membrane and stained with the SYPRO® Ruby protein blot stain (top). After staining, the blot was incubated with a mouse monoclonal anti–α-tubulin antibody (not included in the kit, A11126), followed by the alkaline phosphatase conjugate of goat anti–mouse IgG antibody. The enzymatic activity was detected using DDAO phosphate and imaged under UV epi-illumination using the Fluor-S MAX MultiImager documentation system (Bio-Rad Laboratories) (bottom).

Figure 10.7). The signal amplification of the enzymatic reaction allows detection of as little as 1–3 ng of a protein per band, depending on the antibodies used. The sensitivity rivals that of chemiluminescence-based techniques, but because it results in a stable fluorescent product, there is no need to perform the reactions in a darkroom or to incubate the blots with X-ray film. Furthermore, the fluorescent signals, unlike transient chemiluminescent signals, can be imaged several times and are stable indefinitely on dried blots.

Our Pro-Q® Western Blot Stain Kits include:

- DDAO phosphate substrate with an appropriate solvent
- Alkaline phosphatase conjugate of either goat anti–mouse IgG antibody (in Kit #2, P21860), goat anti–rabbit IgG antibody (in Kit #3, P21864 and Kit #4, P21861) or streptavidin (in Kit #5, P21865 and Kit #6, P21862)
- SYPRO® Ruby protein blot stain (only in Kits #2, #4 and #6; P21860, P21861, P21862)
- Detailed protocols for total and specific protein detection

Kits #2, #4 and #6 also include the SYPRO® Ruby protein blot stain for highly sensitive detection of total protein on the blot before immunostaining, as described in detail in Section 9.3. Much more sensitive than Ponceau S, amido black or Coomassie brilliant blue, and fully compatible with immunodetection techniques, this brilliant red-orange–luminescent stain makes it easy to routinely obtain valuable information about the total-protein complement of the sample. The DDAO and SYPRO® Ruby signals can both be visualized using either UV epi-illumination or a laser scanner.

Each Pro-Q® Western Blot Stain Kit contains sufficient materials to stain approximately 10–20 minigel blots (8 cm × 10 cm).

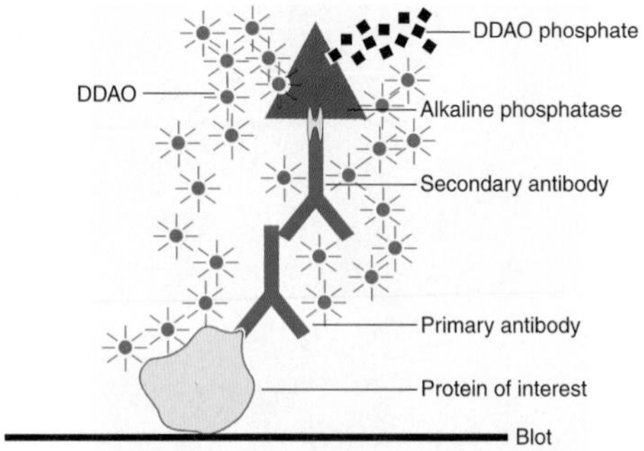

Figure 9.60 Schematic diagram of Western blot immunodetection with DDAO phosphate (D6487), a component of the DyeChrome™ Western Blot Stain Kits #1, #2 and #3 (D21881, D21882, D21883; Table 9.7).

DyeChrome™ Western Blot Stain Kits

Our DyeChrome™ Western Blot Stain Kits (Table 9.7) use a fluorogenic alkaline phosphatase conjugate of a secondary antibody or streptavidin and a fluorogenic alkaline phosphatase substrate for immunodetection of specific proteins in combination with an amine-reactive BODIPY® dye to detect all proteins on a blot in a contrasting fluorescent color[6,7] (Figure 9.61).

The DyeChrome™ Western Blot Stain Kits include a novel method of staining total proteins on blots using two of our proprietary amine-reactive BODIPY® dyes. The reactive dye forms a permanent covalent bond with proteins that lasts through subsequent immunostaining.[6,7] This staining technique makes it possible to perform simultaneous two-color labeling, with both total protein and immunostained proteins visible at the same time on the same blot (Figure 9.62, Figure 9.63). BODIPY® dye–based staining of the total-protein profile is rapid, simple and highly sensitive — a combination of traits not found in con-

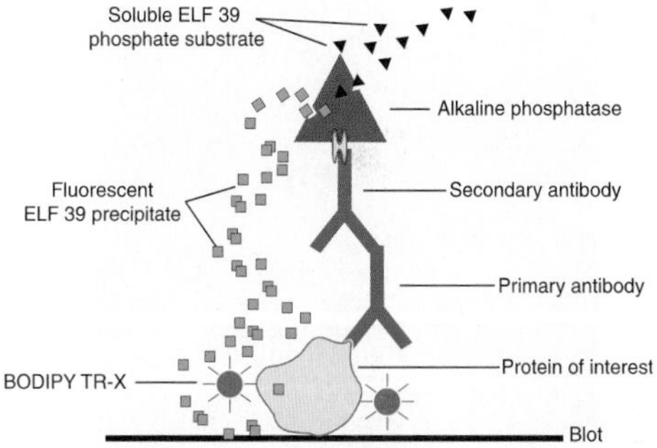

Figure 9.61 Schematic diagram of Western blot immunodetection with BODIPY® TR-X succinimidyl ester and ELF® 39 phosphate, which are components of our DyeChrome™ Western Blot Stain Kits #4, #5 and #6 (D21884, D21885, D21886; Table 9.7).

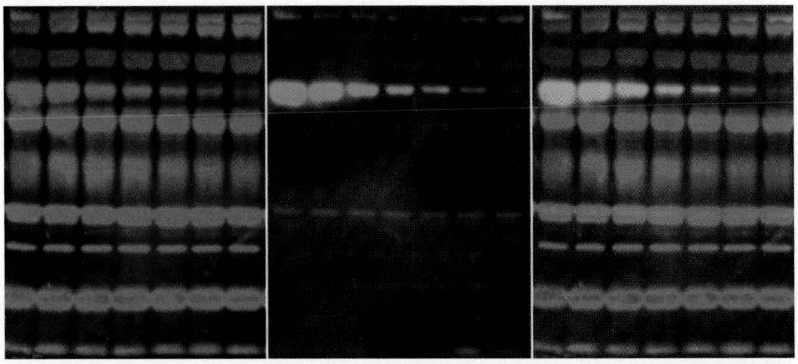

Figure 9.62 Protein detection with the DyeChrome™ Western Blot Stain Kit #4 (D21884). Samples of protein molecular weight standards (P6649) containing decreasing amounts of α-tubulin were run on an SDS-polyacrylamide gel and blotted onto a PVDF membrane. After electrophoresis, the blot was stained with BODIPY® TR-X, succinimidyl ester (red signal), to detect total protein. After staining, the blot was incubated with a mouse monoclonal anti–α-tubulin antibody (A11126), followed by an alkaline phosphatase conjugate of goat anti-mouse IgG antibody, which is included in the kit. Finally, the blot was stained with ELF® 39 phosphate (green signal) to detect the alkaline phosphatase enzyme. The signal was visualized under UV epi-illumination. The two fluorescent signals were captured separately, using the DyeChrome™ Red/Green Photographic Filter Set (D24771), and the two resulting digital images were overlaid using Adobe Photoshop software.

ventional chromophoric dye–based protein stains. Staining with the amine-reactive BODIPY® dyes allows the detection of as little as 4 ng of a protein per band in about an hour, with a linear dynamic range of almost two orders of magnitude (Figure 9.64). We offer two colors of BODIPY® total-protein blot stains: the green-fluorescent BODIPY® FL-X dye, used in combination with DDAO phosphate (Figure 9.63), which produces a red-fluorescent hydrolysis product, and the red-fluorescent BODIPY® TR-X dye, used in combination with ELF® 39 phosphate (Figure 9.62, Figure 9.65), which produces a green-fluorescent hydrolysis product. The BODIPY® dyes can be visualized using either UV illumination or a laser scanner. The fluorescence signals from the two stains in each kit show very little spectral overlap (Figure 9.66, Figure 9.67) and can be viewed simultaneously and documented separately using the DyeChrome™ Red/Green Photographic Filter Set (D24771, Section 23.4). Note that because reaction of the BODIPY® succinimidyl ester covalently modifies the protein at random locations, total-protein staining by either of the amine-reactive BODIPY® dyes may complicate or preclude subsequent analysis by mass spectrometry or microsequencing.

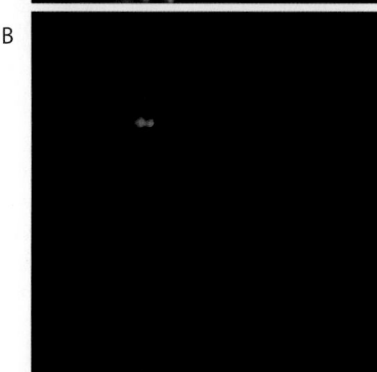

DyeChrome™ Kits #1, #2 and #3 use the fluorogenic alkaline phosphatase substrate DDAO phosphate, which is rapidly converted to the red-fluorescent product DDAO in the presence of alkaline phosphatase. As little as 1–3 ng of protein per band can be detected with this substrate, depending on the primary antibodies used. To counterstain the entire protein complement on the blot, the kits use BODIPY® FL-X succinimidyl ester to stain the proteins with a bright green fluorescence. The fluorescence signals from both stains can be visualized using either UV epi-illumination or visible excitation with a laser scanner.

DyeChrome™ Kits #1, #2 and #3 include:

- DDAO phosphate, with an appropriate solvent
- Alkaline phosphatase conjugate of goat anti–mouse IgG antibody (in Kit #1, D21881), goat anti–rabbit IgG antibody (in Kit #2, D21882) or streptavidin (in Kit #3, D21883)
- BODIPY® FL-X succinimidyl ester (10 vials) and an appropriate solvent
- A detailed protocol

DyeChrome™ Kits #4, #5 and #6 use our proprietary ELF® 39 phosphate (Figure 9.65), a novel fluorogenic substrate for alkaline phosphatase that rapidly forms a bright green-fluorescent precipitate at the site of enzyme activity. Sensitive and simple to use, this dye permits the detection of as little as 4–8 ng of a protein per band, depending on the primary antibodies used. The fluorescent signal can be visualized using UV epi-illumination and can be easily separated from

A

B

C

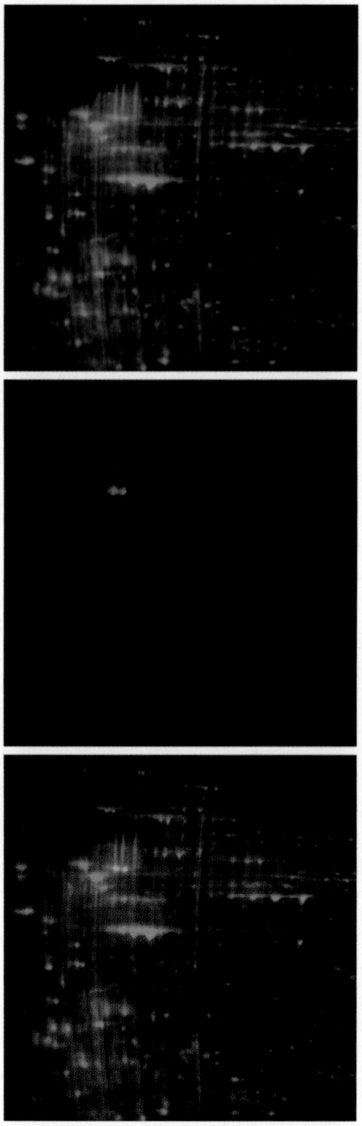

Figure 9.63 Protein detection with the DyeChrome™ Western Blot Stain Kit #1 (D21881). Proteins from a rat fibroblast lysate were separated by 2-D gel electrophoresis and blotted onto a PVDF membrane. The proteins are acidic to basic (left to right) and high to low molecular weight (top to bottom). After electrophoresis, the blot was stained with BODIPY® FL-X succinimidyl ester (green) to detect total protein. The blot was then incubated with an anti-α-tubulin antibody (A11126), followed by the alkaline phosphatase conjugate of goat anti-mouse IgG antibody, which is included in the kit. Finally, the blot was stained with DDAO phosphate (red). The fluorescent signals were visualized using UV epi-illumination. The signals were documented separately, using the DyeChrome™ Red/Green Photographic Filter Set (D24771) (**A** and **B**), and the resulting images overlaid (**C**).

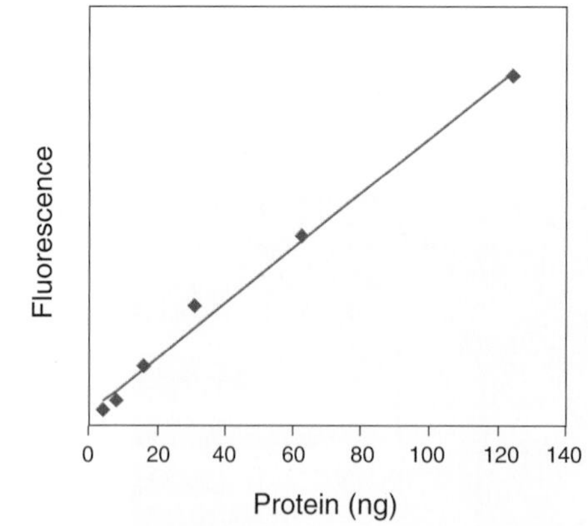

Figure 9.64 Linear dynamic range of detection for BODIPY® FL-X succinimidyl ester, used as a blot stain. A twofold dilution series of molecular weight markers (P6649) was loaded onto a gel, electrophoresed and electroblotted to a PVDF membrane. The proteins on the blot were then stained with BODIPY® FL-X succinimidyl ester, as described for the DyeChrome™ Western Blot Stain Kits #1, #2 and #3 (D21881, D21882, D21883). The fluorescence intensity for one of the proteins (carbonic anhydrase) was measured and plotted against the amount of protein loaded in the lane. The result shows an approximately linear dynamic range from 4 ng to 125 ng.

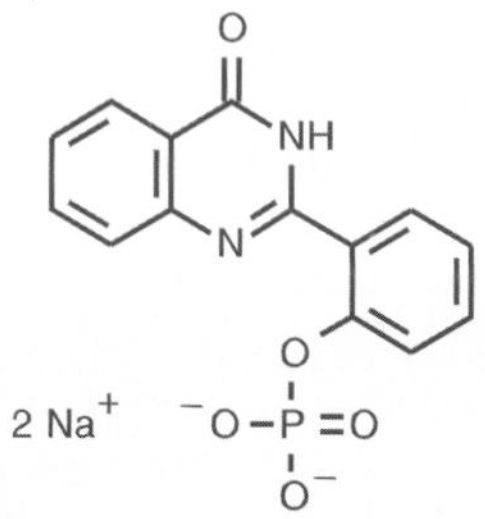

Figure 9.65 Structure of ELF® 39 phosphate, a component of DyeChrome™ Western Blot Stain Kits #4, #5 and #6 (D21884, D21885, D21886).

that of the red-fluorescent BODIPY® TR-X total-protein stain included in the kits as a contrasting stain. BODIPY® TR-X staining can be visualized using either UV epi-illumination or visible excitation with a laser scanner. Our DyeChrome™ Red/Green Photographic Filter Set (D24771, Section 23.4), which contains two specially selected gelatin filters, is recommended for photography of the dichromatic staining using Polaroid 667 black-and-white print film.

DyeChrome™ Kits #4, #5 and #6 include:

- ELF® 39 phosphate, with an appropriate solvent
- Alkaline phosphatase conjugate of goat anti–mouse IgG antibody (in Kit #4, D21884), goat anti–rabbit IgG antibody (in Kit #5, D21885) or streptavidin (in Kit #6, D21886)
- BODIPY® TR-X succinimidyl ester (10 vials) and an appropriate solvent
- A detailed protocol

Chemiluminescent Protein Detection on Western Blots

Chemiluminescent enzyme substrates generally provide the most sensitive and background-free method for detecting specific proteins on Western blots. Molecular Probes offers the BOLD APB chemiluminescent substrate (B21901) for detecting alkaline phosphatase conjugates on PVDF or nitrocellulose membranes. Developed at Serologicals Corp., this substrate is based on a 1,2-dioxetane molecule that emits bright chemiluminescence upon reaction with alkaline phosphatase. The BOLD APB chemiluminescent substrate is provided as a 25 mL ready-to-use solution (sufficient for staining 25 minigel blots), making it extremely easy to use — there is no need to worry about special blockers or enhancers that are required for other chemiluminescent substrates. The BOLD APB chemiluminescent substrate has several important features:

- The sensitivity of the BOLD APB substrate is up to 10 times greater than the sensitivity offered by alternative chemiluminescent alkaline phosphatase substrates on PVDF membranes and twofold higher on nitrocellulose membranes.
- The signal-to-noise ratio of chemiluminescence is exceptionally high, allowing for sensitivity potentially several times that of most fluorescence techniques.
- The BOLD APB chemiluminescent substrate emits a strong signal that increases in intensity for two hours and remains approximately constant for at least six more hours, allowing plenty of time for the multiple exposures for optimizing detection sensitivity.
- The BOLD APB chemiluminescent substrate has a five-log dynamic range standard curve.
- The BOLD APB chemiluminescent substrate is provided as a ready-to-use solution, with a shelf life of at least one year when stored at 4°C.

Although the nature of chemiluminescence precludes the *simultaneous* detection of multiple colors on the same blot, immunodetection by the BOLD APB chemiluminescent substrate can be paired with *sequential* staining by the SYPRO® Ruby protein blot stain (S11791) for detection of the entire protein profile on the blot (Figure 9.68). In contrast to fluorescent reagents, chemiluminescent reagents do not require an excitation light source; the energy from a chemical reaction generates light. The chemiluminescent signal can be de-

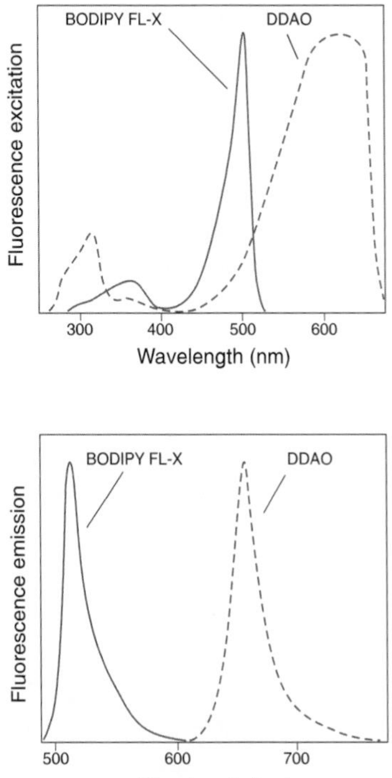

Figure 9.66 Fluorescence excitation and emission spectra for the BODIPY® FL-X dye and DDAO, products generated in the application of DyeChrome™ Western Blot Stain Kits #1, #2 and #3 (D21881, D21882, D21883).

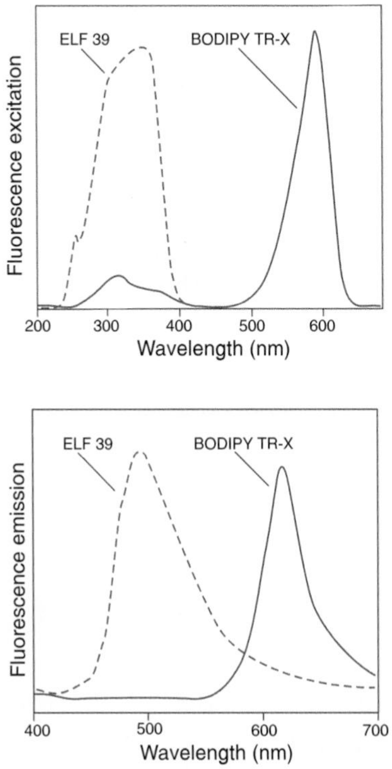

Figure 9.67 Fluorescence excitation and emission spectra for the BODIPY® TR-X dye and ELF® 39 dye, products generated in the application of DyeChrome™ Western Blot Stain Kits #4, #5 and #6 (D21884, D21885, D21886).

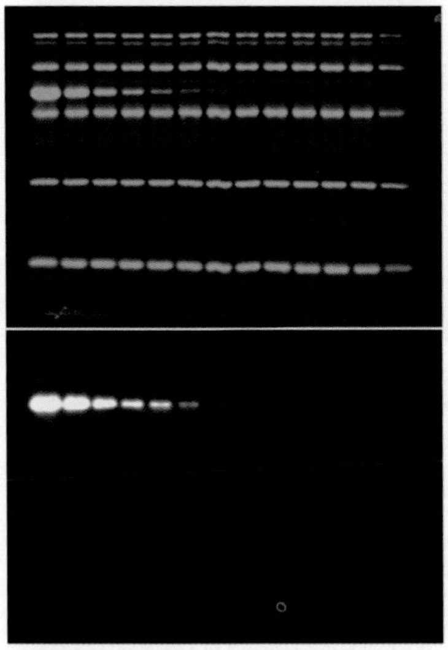

Figure 9.68 Immunodetection on a Western blot with the BOLD APB chemiluminescent substrate. Samples of protein molecular weight standards (P6649) containing decreasing amounts of α-tubulin were run on an SDS-polyacrylamide gel and blotted onto a PVDF membrane. After electrophoresis, the blot was stained with SYPRO® Ruby protein blot stain (S11791) to detect total protein. After documentation of the total protein stain (top), the blot was incubated with a mouse monoclonal anti–α-tubulin antibody (A11126), followed by an alkaline phosphatase conjugate of goat anti–mouse IgG antibody (G21060). Finally, the blot was stained with the BOLD APB chemiluminescent substrate (B21901) to detect the alkaline phosphatase enzyme. The chemiluminescent signal was visualized using a scanner in chemiluminescence detection mode.

tected by directly exposing the blot to X-ray film or by using a scanning instrument designed for chemiluminescence.

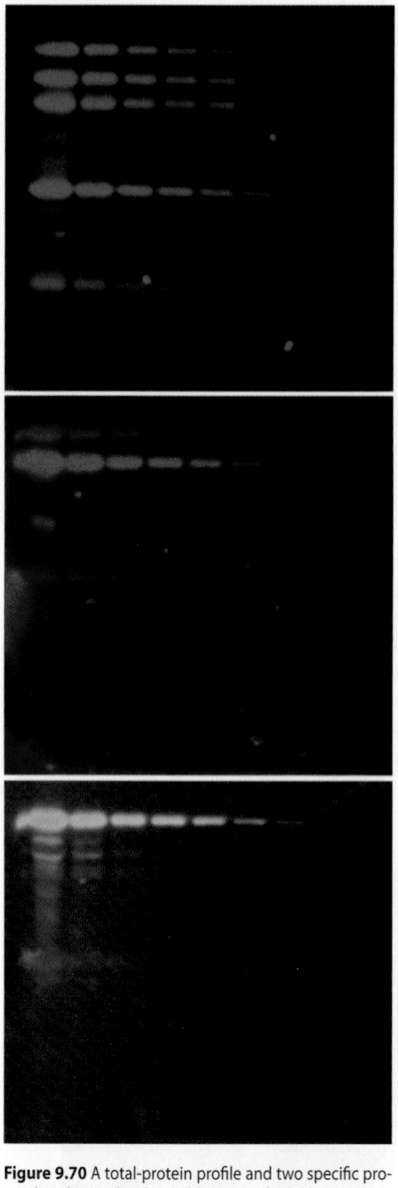

Figure 9.70 A total-protein profile and two specific protein bands visualized on a blot. A twofold dilution series of a protein mixture containing bovine serum albumin (BSA), tubulin, ovalbumin, carbonic anhydrase and soybean trypsin inhibitor (from 1 µg to 0.24 ng each) was separated by electrophoresis through a 13% SDS-polyacrylamide gel and blotted onto a PVDF membrane. The DyeChrome™ Double Western Blot Stain Kit (D21887) components were used, together with two antibodies, to stain all proteins and to visualize two specific proteins. The total-protein profile was stained with the blue-fluorescent dye MDPF. Tubulin was detected using mouse monoclonal anti-α-tubulin antibody (A11126) followed by an alkaline phosphatase conjugate of goat anti-mouse IgG antibody, along with DDAO phosphate (red fluorescence). BSA was detected using an antibody against BSA followed by a horseradish peroxidase conjugate of goat anti-rabbit IgG antibody, along with the Amplex® Gold reagent (yellow fluorescence). The fluorescent signals were detected separately using appropriate excitation light and emission filters on either the Fluor-S MAX MultiImager documentation system (Bio-Rad Laboratories) or the FLA3000G laser scanner (Fuji Photo Film Co.).

Chromogenic Protein Detection on Western Blots

Western blotting techniques have conventionally used chromogenic enzyme substrates to detect specific proteins. Substrates for alkaline phosphatase (AP), horseradish peroxidase (HRP) or β-galactosidase have all been used. Conventional chromogenic substrates include:

- For alkaline phosphatase conjugates: the combination of NBT (nitro blue tetrazolium, N6495) and BCIP (5-bromo-4-chloro-3-indolyl phosphate, B6492), also available in our NBT/BCIP Reagent Kit (N6547, Section 10.3), yields a dark blue precipitate at the site of enzyme activity (Figure 9.69).
- For horseradish peroxidase conjugates: diaminobenzidine, available in the Diaminobenzidine Histochemistry Kits (D22185, D22187; Section 10.5), generates a brown-colored polymeric oxidation product localized at HRP-labeled sites (Figure 4.12).
- For β-galactosidase conjugates: 5-bromo-4-chloro-3-indolyl galactoside (X-Gal; B1690, B22015; Section 10.2) yields a turquoise-colored precipitate at the site of enzyme activity.

Multiplexed Western Blots: Detecting Multiple Protein Targets Simultaneously

DyeChrome™ Double Western Blot Stain Kit

The DyeChrome™ Double Western Blot Stain Kit (D21887) is the first detection kit for multiplexed protein blot staining that permits the use of two different enzyme-conjugated antibodies and a general protein stain for the simultaneous *trichromatic* detection of multiple targets on the same blot (Figure 9.70). The components of this kit are:

- A horseradish peroxidase (HRP) conjugate of goat anti–rabbit IgG antibody and the Amplex® Gold reagent, for yellow-fluorescent detection of a rabbit antibody to a specific protein or proteins
- An alkaline phosphatase conjugate of goat anti–mouse IgG antibody and DDAO phosphate, for far-red–fluorescent detection of a mouse antibody to a specific protein or proteins
- MDPF (2-methoxy-2,4-diphenyl-3(2*H*)-furanone) for blue-fluorescent detection of the total-protein profile
- Appropriate solvents and buffers for the enzymatic reactions
- A detailed protocol

Each DyeChrome™ Double Western Blot Stain Kit contains sufficient materials to stain ~20 mini-gel blots (6 cm × 9 cm). The two antigens are developed and detected simultaneously; staining is stable indefinitely on dried blots.

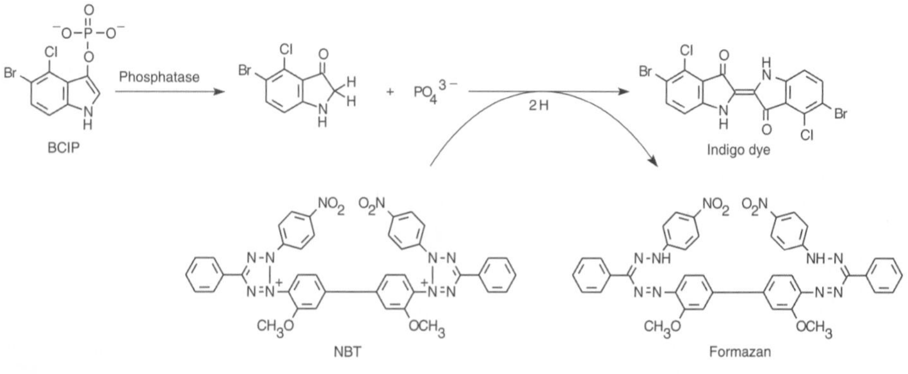

Figure 9.69 Principle of enzyme-linked detection using the reagents in our NBT/BCIP Reagent Kit (N6547). Phosphatase hydrolysis of BCIP is coupled to reduction of NBT, yielding a formazan and an indigo dye that together form a black-purple-colored precipitate.

Staining with Two Different Labeled Primary Antibodies

To use multiple antibodies on the same blot, the secondary or primary antibodies may also be labeled directly with amine-reactive dyes, such as the succinimidyl esters described in Chapter 1. Direct labeling usually provides somewhat lower sensitivity than indirect labeling using enzymatic substrates because the enzymatic substrates can greatly amplify the signal. However, for abundant proteins, direct labeling provides a more streamlined method for staining the blot with multiple antibodies. The limit on the number of colors that can be used together depends only on the compatibility of the antibodies used and the ability of the instrumentation to separate the signals from the fluorescent dyes used (Figure 9.71).

As an alternative to directly labeling primary antibodies with an amine-reactive dye, our exceptional Zenon® immunolabeling technology (Section 7.3) provides an easy, versatile and truly unique method of labeling antibodies with Molecular Probes' premier dyes, haptens and enzymes. This enabling technology not only eliminates the need for secondary detection reagents in many applications, but also simplifies immunolabeling applications that previously were time consuming or impractical, including the use of multiple antibodies derived from the same species in the same protocol, as well as the detection of antibody binding in tissue samples when both the antibody and the tissue are derived from the same species. Moreover, Zenon® immunolabeling technology permits the rapid and quantitative preparation of antibody complexes from a purified antibody fraction or from a crude antibody preparation such as serum, ascites fluid or a hybridoma supernatant. Our Zenon® reagents may eventually be the only antibody-based detection reagents needed in the laboratory for many high-throughput applications, replacing both direct conjugates of primary antibodies and dye- and enzyme-labeled secondary antibodies in a wide variety of procedures.

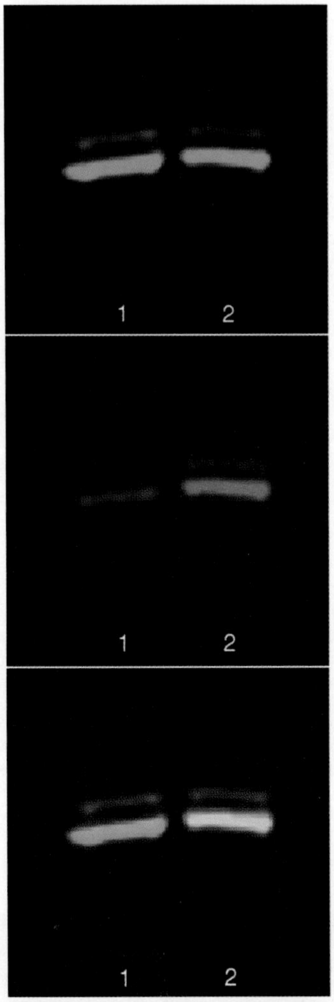

Figure 9.71 Multiplexed detection of two different antibodies on the same blot using fluorophore-labeled secondary antibodies. Cell lysates from nonstimulated (left band) or EGF-stimulated (right band) A431 cells were electrophoresed in an SDS-polyacrylamide gel and blotted. The blot was incubated with primary antibodies against ERK1 and ERK2, p44/42 MAP kinases. Total ERK protein was detected using rabbit anti–ERK IgG antibody followed by anti–rabbit IgG antibody labeled with IRDye 800 (green, Licor). Tyrosine-phosphorylated ERK was detected using mouse anti-phospho-ERK IgG antibody, followed by Alexa Fluor® 680 anti–mouse IgG antibody (red, A21057). The blots were imaged using the Odyssey Infrared Imaging System (Licor). Each signal is shown separately (top and middle) and viewed simultaneously on digitally overlaid images (bottom).

Immunoreagents and Labeled Avidins for Use in Western Blot Detection

Fluorescent Avidin Conjugates

Molecular Probes prepares NeutrAvidin biotin-binding protein and streptavidin labeled with a vast assortment of fluorescent dyes (Section 7.6, Table 7.22), as well as fluorescent microspheres conjugated to streptavidin (Section 6.5). All of these reagents can be used in combination with biotinylated probes for detection of proteins. Although typically not as sensitive as enzyme-amplified techniques, fluorescent avidin conjugates are easy to use and permit multicolor detection of targets.

Primary Antibodies

Western blotting relies on immunostaining with antibodies to specific proteins. Molecular Probes has available a variety of primary antibodies that are useful for detecting specific proteins on blotting membranes. These include antibodies directed against:

- Cytochrome oxidase (COX) subunits (Section 12.2)
- Other mitochondrial proteins (Section 12.2)
- Intermediate filament proteins (Section 11.2)
- β-Tubulin (Section 11.2)
- T-cell differentiation markers (Section 7.5)
- Cell-cycle proteins (Section 15.4)
- Matrix metalloproteinases (Section 10.4)
- 5-Bromo-2′-deoxyuridine (BrdU) (Section 15.4)
- Second messenger compounds (Section 17.4)
- Neuronal markers (Section 7.5)
- Human transferrin receptor (Section 7.5)
- NMDA receptor subunits (Section 16.2)
- Synapsin I (Section 17.3)
- Yeast proteins (Section 12.2, Section 12.4)

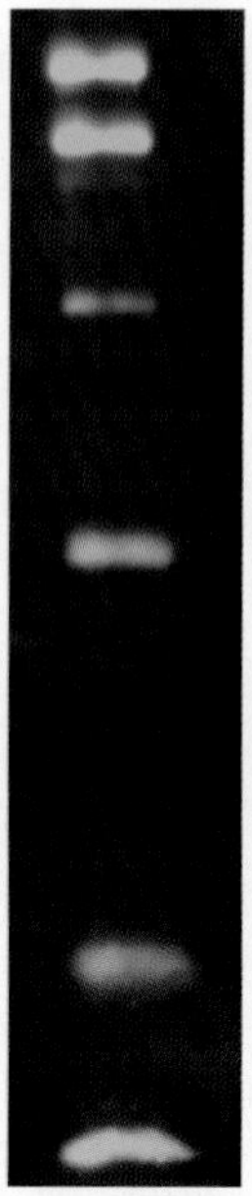

Figure 9.72 Detection of HA-fusion proteins using anti-HA antibody. Six proteins, each fused to the HA domain, were electrophoresed through a 13% polyacrylamide gel and blotted onto a PVDF membrane. The blot was incubated with the Alexa Fluor® 488 conjugate of anti-HA antibody (A21287), followed by rabbit anti–Alexa Fluor® 488 antibody (A11094). The antibody complex was then detected using the Amplex® Gold Western Blot Stain Kit #2 (A21891).

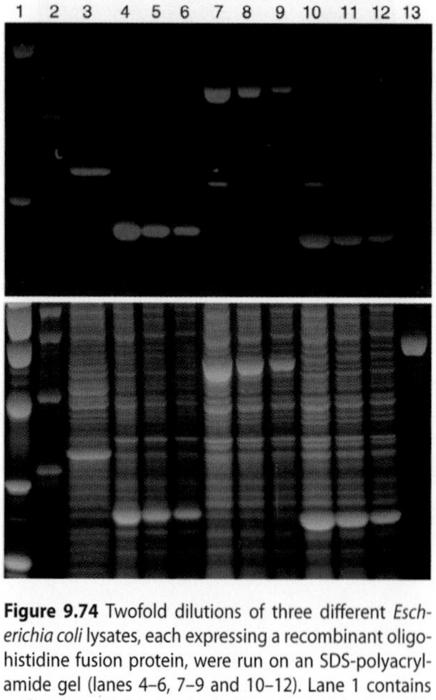

Figure 9.74 Twofold dilutions of three different *Escherichia coli* lysates, each expressing a recombinant oligohistidine fusion protein, were run on an SDS-polyacrylamide gel (lanes 4–6, 7–9 and 10–12). Lane 1 contains molecular weight standards, lane 2 contains a 6xHis protein ladder (QIAGEN), lane 3 contains a control lysate with hexahistidine-tagged urate oxidase (Pierce), and lane 13 contains purified BSA. After electrophoresis, the gel was stained using the Pro-Q® Sapphire 365 oligohistidine gel stain (P21876, top). After documentation of the signal, the gel was stained with the SYPRO® Ruby protein gel stain (S12000, S12001, S21900; bottom).

Molecular Probes also provides antibodies against epitope and protein tags for detecting appropriately tagged recombinant proteins:

- Green-fluorescent protein (GFP) (A6455, A11120, A11121, A11122, A21311, A21312; Section 7.5)
- c-myc tag (A21280, A21281; Section 7.5)
- Glutathione *S*-transferase (GST) (A5800, A11131; Section 7.5)
- β-Galactosidase (A11132; Section 10.2)
- β-Glucuronidase (GUS) (A5790; Section 10.2)
- Oligohistidine fusion proteins (P21315; see the description later in this section)
- Hemagglutinin (HA)-tag (A21287, A21288; Section 7.5; Figure 9.72)

Finally, our anti-dye, anti-biotin, anti-DNP and anti-nitrotyrosine (Figure 18.23) antibodies can be employed for the selective detection of primary or secondary proteins labeled with fluorescent dyes, biotin, DSB-X™ biotin or the DNP or *o*-nitrophenol haptens (Section 7.4, Table 7.18). Section 4.2 describes our recommended reagents for labeling proteins and nucleic acids with biotin (Table 4.1) and haptens (Table 4.2).

Fluorescence-Based Detection of Oligohistidine Fusion Proteins

The oligohistidine domain is a Ni^{2+}-binding peptide sequence comprising a string of four to six histidine residues. When the DNA sequence corresponding to the oligohistidine domain is fused in frame with a gene of interest, the resulting recombinant protein can be easily purified using a nickel-chelating resin.[8,9] Molecular Probes has developed technologies that make it possible to quickly and easily identify oligohistidine fusion proteins in gels or on blots.

Pro-Q® Sapphire 532 Oligohistidine Gel Stain

Traditional analysis of fusion proteins containing an oligohistidine domain has generally required purification using a nickel-chelating resin followed by protein separation with SDS-polyacrylamide gel electrophoresis and Western blot analysis. With the Pro-Q® Sapphire 532 oligohistidine gel stain (P33354), oligohistidine fusion proteins can be detected directly in an SDS-polyacrylamide gel (Figure 9.73), eliminating the need to blot the protein to a membrane. The Pro-Q® Sapphire 532 oligohistidine gel stain consists of a proprietary fluorescent dye selective for oligohistidine domains. Staining is complete within hours, and as little as 15 ng of a hexahistidine fusion protein can be detected. The fluorescence intensity of the stained protein varies somewhat with the fusion protein, indicating that the dye binding may be dependent on protein context. Typically, a band containing 30–50 ng of oligohistidine fusion protein can be detected in a minigel. Samples run in a standard-size gel may be more difficult to detect because the protein is more dispersed in the larger well and thicker gel. Note that with highly basic proteins, weak crossreactivity with the reagent may occur. For weakly expressed proteins requiring higher sensitivity, the Pro-Q® Oligohistidine Blot Stain Kits (P21878, P21879) are recommended.

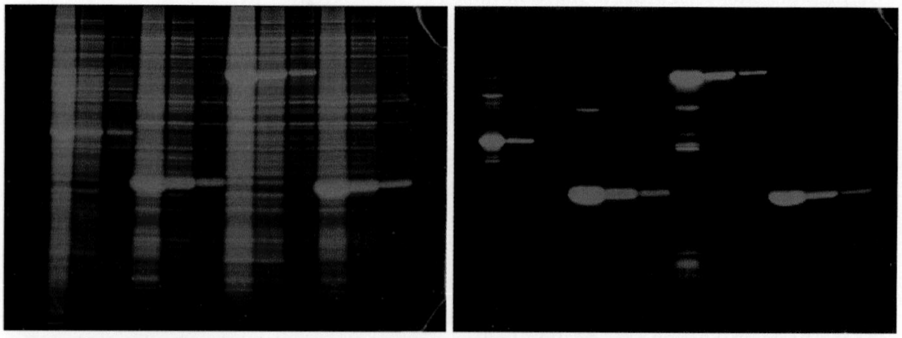

Figure 9.73 SDS-polyacrylamide gels stained with SYPRO® Ruby protein gel stain (S12000, S12001, S21900; left, pseudocolored red) and Pro-Q® Sapphire 532 oligohistidine gel stain (P33354; right, pseudocolored blue) to detect oligohistidine fusion protein expression.

Pro-Q® Sapphire 532 stain has excitation/emission maxima of approximately 535/572 nm, so it is optimally excited with 532 nm laser scanners. However, because the excitation spectrum is broad, the stain can also be detected after excitation by 473 nm or 488 nm blue lasers or by UV illumination. After documenting the oligohistidine signal, the gel can be stained for total protein using SYPRO® Ruby protein gel stain.

Pro-Q® Sapphire 365 and Pro-Q® Sapphire 488 Oligohistidine Gel Stains

The Pro-Q® Sapphire 365 and Pro-Q® Sapphire 488 oligohistidine gel stains (P21876, P21877) provide a simple method for detecting oligohistidine fusion proteins directly in an SDS-polyacrylamide gel (Figure 9.74, Figure 9.75), eliminating the need to blot the protein to a membrane.[10] These proprietary reagents each comprise a state-of-the-art fluorescent dye conjugated to a nitrilotriacetic acid (NTA) moiety. The staining procedure is very simple — simply fix the gel and incubate it with the stain. The NTA moiety chelates Ni^{2+} bound by the oligohistidine domain, resulting in optimal staining in just 45 minutes. Note that because the NTA is negatively charged, there may also be some weak crossreactivity with highly basic proteins. The Pro-Q® Sapphire 365 oligohistidine gel stain (P21876) can be viewed using 365 nm UV illumination and the SYPRO® photographic filter (S6656, Section 23.4, Figure 23.62); it has a sensitivity limit of ~30 ng/band of an oligohistidine fusion protein. The Pro-Q® Sapphire 488 oligohistidine gel stain (P21877) can be viewed using visible light with wavelengths near its 510 nm excitation maximum and has a sensitivity limit of ~30 ng/band. These limits of sensitivity were determined using a hexahistidine–urate oxidase fusion protein; other fusion proteins we have tested show levels of sensitivity between 60 and 100 ng per band, suggesting that the protein environment may have an effect on the ability of NTA-based compounds to bind to oligohistidine domains. After documenting the oligohistidine signal, the total-protein profile can be visualized using the SYPRO® Ruby protein gel stain (Section 9.3, Figure 9.74).

Pro-Q® Oligohistidine Blot Stain Kits

The Pro-Q® Oligohistidine Blot Stain Kits provide a simple, fast and sensitive method for the detection of oligohistidine fusion proteins on PVDF membranes. The staining technique uses biotin-X nitrilotriacetic acid (biotin-X NTA, Figure 4.6), which chelates Ni^{2+}. The blot is incubated with a complex of biotin-X NTA, Ni^{2+} and alkaline phosphatase streptavidin. Within 20 minutes, the complex binds to oligohistidine fusion proteins. The complex is then detected using a fluorogenic alkaline phosphatase substrate — either DDAO phosphate (in Kit #1, P21878; Figure 9.76), which produces a red-fluorescent product, or ELF® 39 phosphate (in Kit #2, P21879; Figure 9.65), which produces a green-fluorescent product. Both substrates (described in Section 10.3 and above under the heading "Western Blot Stain Kits and Reagents" provide very rapid and sensitive detection of the alkaline phosphatase conjugates, making it possible to detect as little as ~16 ng/band in less than 90 minutes after blotting, depending on the particular fusion

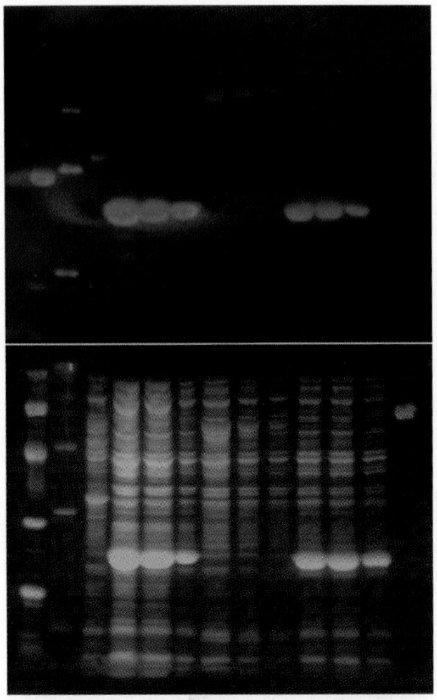

Figure 9.76 Staining hexahistidine fusion proteins with Pro-Q® Oligohistidine Blot Stain Kit #1. Twofold dilutions of three different *Escherichia coli* lysates, each expressing a recombinant oligohistidine fusion protein, were analyzed (lanes 4–6, 7–9 and 10–12). Also shown are molecular weight standards (lane 1), a 6xHis protein ladder (QIAGEN, lane 2), a control lysate with a hexahistidine fusion protein of urate oxidase (Pierce, lane 3) and purified BSA (lane 13). Identical blots were stained with either the Pro-Q® Oligohistidine Blot Stain Kit #1 (P21878, top) or the SYPRO® Ruby protein gel stain (S12000, S12001, S21900; bottom).

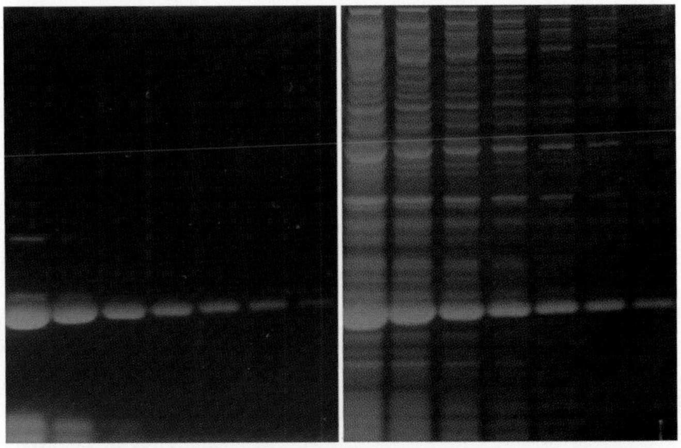

Figure 9.75 Staining of an oligohistidine fusion protein with the Pro-Q® Sapphire 488 oligohistidine gel stain (P21877). Twofold dilutions of an *Escherichia coli* lysate containing overexpressed oligomycin sensitivity–conferring protein (OSCP) fused with an oligohistidine domain were run on an SDS-polyacrylamide gel. After electrophoresis, the gel was stained using the Pro-Q® Sapphire 488 oligohistidine gel stain (left). After documentation of the oligohistidine signal, the gel was stained for total protein (right) using the SYPRO® Ruby protein gel stain (S12000, S12001, S21900).

protein. The sensitivity of these fluorogenic substrates rivals that of chemiluminescence detection. However, because the fluorescent products are chemically stable, there is no need to perform the reaction in a darkroom or to incubate the blot with X-ray film. Furthermore, the fluorescent signal, unlike transient chemiluminescent signals, can be imaged several times and is stable indefinitely on dried blots. The biotin-X NTA and DDAO can be removed from the blot for restaining with another detection method; the ELF® 39 stain, however, is permanent. Biotin-X NTA is also available separately (B11790).

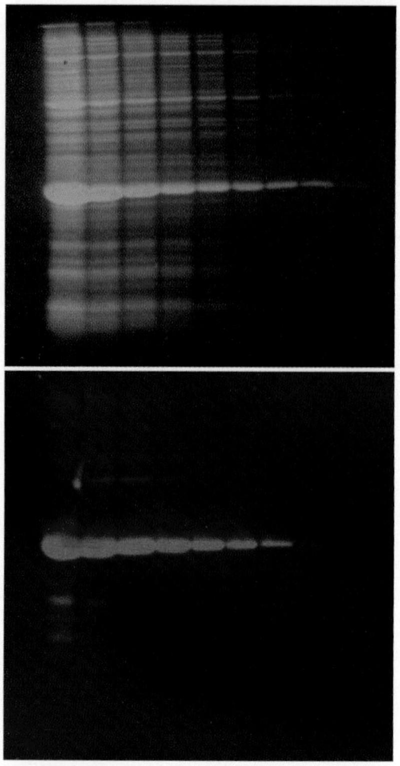

Figure 9.77 Detection of an oligohistidine fusion protein with the Penta·His mouse monoclonal antibody. Twofold serial dilutions of an *Escherichia coli* lysate containing overexpressed oligomycin sensitivity–conferring protein (OSCP) fused with a hexahistidine domain were run an SDS-polyacrylamide gel and blotted onto a PVDF membrane. The blot was stained with the SYPRO® Ruby protein blot stain (S11791) to detect the entire protein profile (top). After imaging, the blot was incubated with Penta·His mouse IgG_1 monoclonal antibody (P21315), followed by immunodetection using the Pro-Q® Western Blot Stain Kit #2 (P21860; bottom).

Penta·His Antibody

Developed by QIAGEN, the Penta·His mouse IgG_1 monoclonal antibody (P21315) provides a sensitive method for specific detection of fusion proteins that have an oligohistidine domain comprising five or six consecutive histidine residues. The antibody does not recognize tetrahistidine domains or domains in which the histidine string is interrupted by another amino acid. The Penta·His antibody binds to the oligohistidine domain regardless of the surrounding amino acid context and even when the group is partially hidden, although subtle differences in the amino acid context may change the sensitivity limit for a particular fusion protein. The antibody is ideal for detecting oligohistidine fusion proteins on blots in combination with our Western Blot Stain Kits (Figure 9.77; see the description of our Amplex® Gold, Pro-Q® and DyeChrome™ Western Blot Stain Kits above). The Penta·His antibody is also useful for immunoprecipitation, ELISA assays, and immunohistochemistry.

Other Specialized Techniques for Detecting Specific Proteins in Gels and on Blots

Detecting Calcium-Binding Proteins in Gels

The luminescent lanthanide terbium, which is available from Molecular Probes as its chloride salt (Tb^{3+} from $TbCl_3$, T1247), selectively stains calcium-binding proteins in SDS-polyacrylamide gels.[11] With some modifications to the staining protocol, these lanthanides can also be used to detect all protein bands.[11] Terbium chloride has also been used as a rapid negative stain for proteins in SDS-polyacrylamide gels, in which the background is green fluorescent and the proteins are unstained.[12]

Detecting Glutathiolation

Biotinylated glutathione ethyl ester (BioGEE, G36000) is a cell-permeant, biotinylated glutathione analog for detecting glutathiolation. Under conditions of oxidative stress, cells may transiently incorporate glutathione into proteins. Stressed cells incubated with BioGEE will also incorporate this biotinylated glutathione derivative into proteins, facilitating the identification of oxidation-sensitive proteins.[13] Once these cells are fixed and permeabilized, glutathiolation levels can be detected with a fluorescent streptavidin conjugate (Section 7.6, Table 7.22) using either flow cytometry or fluorescence microscopy. Proteins glutathiolated with BioGEE can also be extracted and analyzed by mass spectrometry or by Western blotting methods in conjunction with fluorophore- or enzyme-labeled streptavidin conjugates.

Detecting Penicillin-Binding Proteins

BOCILLIN™ FL penicillin and BOCILLIN™ 650/665 penicillin (B13233, B13234) are green- and infrared-fluorescent penicillin analogs, respectively, that bind selectively and with high affinity to penicillin-binding proteins present on the cytoplasmic membranes of eubacteria.[14,15] When electrophoresed under nonreducing conditions, the dye-labeled penicillin-binding proteins are easily visible in the gel with sensitivity in the low nanogram range [16] (Figure 9.78). BOCILLIN™ FL penicillin, synthesized from penicillin V and the BODIPY® FL dye (spectrally similar to fluorescein), has been used to determine the penicillin-binding protein profiles of *Escherichia coli, Pseudomonas aeruginosa* and *Streptococcus pneumoniae,* and these binding profiles are found to be similar to those reported by researchers using radioactively labeled penicillin V.[14]

Fluorescently labeled penicillin has also been used for direct labeling and rapid detection of whole *E. coli* and *Bacillus licheniformis*[17] and of *Enterobacter pneumoniae*.[18] The β-lactam sensor-transducer (BlaR), an integral membrane protein from *Staphylococcus aureus*, covalently and stoichiometrically reacts with β-lactam antibiotics, including BOCILLIN™ FL penicillin, by acylation of its active-site serine residue.[19]

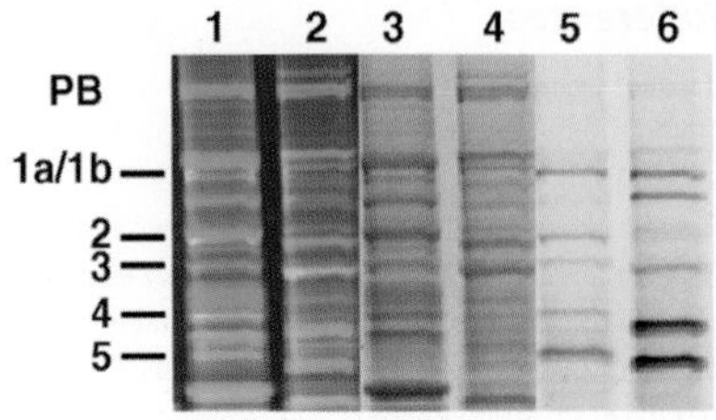

Figure 9.78 Detection of penicillin-binding proteins (PBPs) from *Escherichia coli* and *Pseudomonas aeruginosa* (Electrophoresis 22, 960 (2001)). The membrane fractions from *E. coli* and *P. aeruginosa* were prepared as previously described (Antimicrob Agents Chemother 43, 1124 (1999)) and labeled with BOCILLIN™ 650/665 penicillin (B13234). The labeled membranes were separated on an SDS-polyacrylamide gel, stained with SYPRO® Ruby and visualized using a Typhoon imager (Molecular Dynamics). The location of PBPs from *E. coli* are labeled to the left of the gels. Lanes 1, 3, and 5 are *E. coli* membrane preparations; lanes 2, 4, and 6 are *P. aeruginosa* membrane preparations; lanes 1 and 2 are overlays of images obtained from total protein (green) and PBP (red) scans; lanes 3 and 4 are total protein visualized with the SYPRO® Ruby protein gel stain; lanes 5 and 6 are PBPs as detected by BOCILLIN™ 650/665. Image used with permission from Wiley VCH publishers.

Detecting Enzymes in Nondenaturing Gels

Many different enzymes have been detected in nondenaturing gels by using various chromogenic substrates, including X-Gal (B1690, B22015; Section 10.2), X-GlcU (B1691, Section 10.2) and NBT/BCIP[20] (N6495, B6492; Section 10.3). In unpublished experiments, we have shown that our ELF® 97 phosphatase substrate (E6589, Section 10.3) forms a highly fluorescent precipitate at the site of enzymatic activity (either acid or alkaline phosphatase activity) in nondenaturing polyacrylamide gels. In addition, we have demonstrated that our ELF® 97 β-D-glucuronidase substrate (E6587, Section 10.2) has similar utility for detecting β-glucuronidase in native or SDS-polyacrylamide gels, with a detection limit of less than 5 ng of the enzyme[21] (Figure 10.24). The ELF® 97 β-D-glucuronidase substrate can also be used in combination with our SYPRO® Tangerine protein gel stain (S12010, Section 9.3) for detecting the total-protein profile in the gel (Figure 9.29). Fluorogenic protease substrates based on the rhodamine 110 dye (Section 10.4, Table 10.2) have been applied by overlaying filter paper impregnated with the substrates on SDS-polyacrylamide gels to detect protease activity.[22]

Detecting Protein Functional Groups in Gels and on Blots

Several of the low molecular weight, thiol-reactive reagents described in Chapter 2 can potentially be used to selectively detect thiol-containing proteins in gels without appreciable staining of proteins that do not contain thiols. Compounds that may be particularly useful include BODIPY® 493/503 methyl bromide and BODIPY® 630/650 methyl bromide (B2103, B22802; Section 2.2), IANBD amide (D2004, Section 2.2), monochlorobimane and monobromobimane[23] (M1381MP, M1378; FluoroPure™ Grade, M20381; Section 2.3), the coumarin iodoacetamide IDCC (D20382, Section 2.3) and CellTracker™ Blue CMAC (C2110, Section 14.2). These selected compounds are all electrically neutral reagents and thus do not appreciably change the charge or mass of the protein, a feature that may make them useful for derivatizing the thiolated protein prior to separation by isoelectric focusing. Monobromobimane has been used to derivatize thiol-containing proteins prior to separation by isoelectric focusing without the modification having an appreciable effect on the protein's electrophoretic mobility.[24–27] 8-Aminonaphthalene-1,3,6-trisulfonic acid (A350, Section 3.2) has been used to directly stain periodate-oxidized glycoproteins on PVDF membranes.[28] Glycoprotein binding to PVDF membranes was selectively enhanced by pre-coating the membrane with wheat germ agglutinin (WGA). Alexa Fluor® 350 hydrazide (A10439, Section 3.2) has been used similarly for glycoprotein detection both in gels and on blots.[29]

Chemical Labeling of Nascent Proteins

The relatively compact BODIPY® FL fluorophore (D6140, Section 1.4) has been used as a fluorescent reporter group in nascent proteins. This dye was incorporated at the *N*-terminus of nascent proteins using an *Escherichia coli* tRNA(fmet) misaminoacylated with a methionine containing a BODIPY® FL fluorophore at its amino group.[30] Under optimal conditions, subnanogram quantities of green-fluorescent bands from *in vitro*–produced fluorescent proteins can be detected by gel electrophoresis using a laser scanner.

Mitochondrial Protein Extracts

For researchers seeking a source of mitochondrial protein standards, Molecular Probes offers human heart mitochondrial proteins for SDS-polyacrylamide gel electrophoresis (M22430). This complete mitochondrial lysate has tested negative for hepatitis B and C, as well as HIV 1 and 2 in serology tests. Mitochondrial protein extracts are useful for comparing new mitochondrial protein preparations in SDS-polyacrylamide gels and for testing mitochondrial antibodies.

Rhinohide™ Polyacrylamide Gel Strengthener

Our Rhinohide™ polyacrylamide gel strengthener improves upon classic polyacrylamide gel technology by making gels much stronger, providing easier handling and much greater resistance to tearing without adverse side effects (Figure 9.34). Rhinohide™ polyacrylamide gel strengthener is highly recommended for low-percentage gels, large-format gels and gels subject to multiple staining and handling steps.

SDS-polyacrylamide gels supplemented with Rhinohide™ polyacrylamide gel strengthener exhibit resolution capabilities comparable to traditional SDS-polyacrylamide gels, with clear, focused bands and without the undesirable side effects common for other gel strengtheners.[31] For example, film-backed gels and polyester fabric–reinforced gels interfere with blotting techniques and can negatively affect protein staining. Alternatively, strengthening gels by the addition of pre-formed polymers causes turbidity and can produce serious spot-morphology artifacts, such as the distortion of high molecular weight bands or doubling of protein spots in the molecular weight dimension of 2-D gels.[32]

Rhinohide™ polyacrylamide gel strengthener produces gels with excellent transparency, providing exceptional image viewing and scanning of fluorescently stained gels with minimal background staining. Compatible with silver and Coomassie staining, it is also the perfect companion to our Multiplexed Proteomics® technology described earlier in this section. Our Rhinohide™ Polyacrylamide Gel Strengthener Kit (R33410) includes:

- Rhinohide™ polyacrylamide gel strengthener
- Premeasured acrylamide/bis-acrylamide mixture (37.5:1 ratio)
- A protocol for casting gels from 5% to 20%

This kit provides sufficient materials for making 1 L of a 30% acrylamide/bis-acrylamide stock solution containing the Rhinohide™ gel strengthener. We also offer a concentrated form of the Rhinohide™ polyacrylamide gel strengthener (R33400) for adding to existing stock solutions of acrylamide/bis-acrylamide (37.5:1), as well as the acrylamide/bis-acrylamide mixture (A33405) for making these stock solutions. Because prestained proteins, such as prestained molecular weight markers, will not migrate correctly in acrylamide gels containing the Rhinohide™ polyacrylamide gel strengthener, we recommend using only unstained proteins as markers.

References

1. J Biol Chem 278, 27251 (2003); **2.** Proteomics 3, 1244 (2003); **3.** Proteomics 3, 1128 (2003); **4.** Comb Chem High Throughput Screen 6, 331 (2003); **5.** Laboratory Techniques in Biochemistry and Molecular Biology, Vol. 16, Burdon R, van Knippenberg P, (Complete Volume), (1985); **6.** Electrophoresis 22, 950 (2001); **7.** Electrophoresis 22, 896 (2001); **8.** J Chromatogr 411, 117 (1987); **9.** J Chromatogr 411, 177 (1987); **10.** Electrophoresis 24, 599 (2003); **11.** Anal Biochem 216, 439 (1994); **12.** Anal Biochem 220, 218 (1994); **13.** Biochemistry 39, 11121 (2000); **14.** Antimicrob Agents Chemother 43, 1124 (1999); **15.** J Biol Chem 275, 17693 (2000); **16.** Electrophoresis 22, 960 (2001); **17.** Biochem J 291, 19 (1993); **18.** Biochem J 300, 141 (1994); **19.** J Biol Chem 278, 18419 (2003); **20.** Anal Biochem 203, 1 (1992); **21.** J Biochem Biophys Methods 33, 197 (1996); **22.** Biotechniques 29, 1108 (2000); **23.** Anal Biochem 265, 8 (1998); **24.** Biotechniques 31, 146 (2001); **25.** Proteomics 1, 54 (2001); **26.** Biotechniques 28, 944 (2000); **27.** Electrophoresis 21, 1123 (2000); **28.** Biotechniques 30, 1272 (2001); **29.** Proteomics 1, 841 (2001); **30.** Anal Biochem 279, 218 (2000); **31.** Anal Biochem 148, 384 (1985); **32.** Electrophoresis 21, 486 (2000).

Product List — 9.4 Multiplexed Proteomics Technology for Detecting Specific Proteins in Gels and on Blots

Cat #	Product Name	Unit Size
A33405	acrylamide/bis-acrylamide mixture (37.5:1 ratio) *electrophoresis grade*	300 g
A24772	Amplex® Gold photographic filter	each
A21890	Amplex® Gold Western Blot Stain Kit #1 *with goat anti-mouse IgG* *20 minigel blots*	1 kit
A21891	Amplex® Gold Western Blot Stain Kit #2 *with goat anti-rabbit IgG* *20 minigel blots*	1 kit
A21892	Amplex® Gold Western Blot Stain Kit #3 *with streptavidin* *20 minigel blots*	1 kit
B11790	biotin-X nitrilotriacetic acid, tripotassium salt (biotin-X NTA)	5 mg
B13233	BOCILLIN™ FL penicillin, sodium salt	1 mg
B13234	BOCILLIN™ 650/665 penicillin, sodium salt	1 mg
B21901	BOLD™ APB chemiluminescent substrate *for membrane-based alkaline phosphatase detection* *25 minigel blots*	25 mL
C21852	CandyCane™ glycoprotein molecular weight standards *200 gel lanes*	400 µL
D21887	DyeChrome™ Double Western Blot Stain Kit *for mouse IgG, rabbit IgG and total protein detection* *20 minigel blots*	1 kit
D21881	DyeChrome™ Western Blot Stain Kit #1 *with goat anti-mouse IgG, DDAO phosphate and BODIPY® FL-X, SE* *20 minigel blots*	1 kit
D21882	DyeChrome™ Western Blot Stain Kit #2 *with goat anti-rabbit IgG, DDAO phosphate and BODIPY® FL-X, SE* *20 minigel blots*	1 kit
D21883	DyeChrome™ Western Blot Stain Kit #3 *with streptavidin, DDAO phosphate and BODIPY® FL-X, SE* *20 minigel blots*	1 kit
D21884	DyeChrome™ Western Blot Stain Kit #4 *with goat anti-mouse IgG, ELF® 39 phosphate and BODIPY® TR-X, SE* *20 minigel blots*	1 kit
D21885	DyeChrome™ Western Blot Stain Kit #5 *with goat anti-rabbit IgG, ELF® 39 phosphate and BODIPY® TR-X, SE* *20 minigel blots*	1 kit
D21886	DyeChrome™ Western Blot Stain Kit #6 *with streptavidin, ELF® 39 phosphate and BODIPY® TR-X, SE* *20 minigel blots*	1 kit
E33202	EZQ® Phosphopeptide Quantitation Kit *1000 assays*	1 kit
G36000	glutathione ethyl ester, biotin amide (BioGEE) *glutathiolation detection reagent* *special packaging*	10 x 100 µg
M22430	mitochondrial proteins (human heart) for SDS-polyacrylamide gel electrophoresis *2 mg/mL*	100 µL
M33307	Multiplexed Proteomics® Glycoprotein Gel Stain Kit *with 1 L each of Pro-Q® Emerald 300 and SYPRO® Ruby (S12000) gel stains*	1 kit
MPM33305	Multiplexed Proteomics® Phosphoprotein Gel Stain Kit *includes MPP33300 and S12000*	1 kit
MPM33306	Multiplexed Proteomics® Phosphoprotein Gel Stain Kit *includes MPP33301 and S12001*	1 kit
M33305	Multiplexed Proteomics® Phosphoprotein Gel Stain Kit #1 *with 1 L each of Pro-Q® Diamond (P33300) and SYPRO® Ruby (S12000) gel stains*	1 set
M33306	Multiplexed Proteomics® Phosphoprotein Gel Stain Kit #2 *with 200 mL each of Pro-Q® Diamond (P33301) and SYPRO® Ruby (S12001) gel stains*	1 set
M33308	Multiplexed Proteomics® Transmembrane Protein Gel Stain Kit *with 500 mL each of Pro-Q® Amber and SYPRO® Ruby gel stains*	1 kit
P21315	Penta·His™ mouse IgG_1, monoclonal antibody (anti-pentahistidine) *BSA free*	100 µg
P27167	PeppermintStick™ phosphoprotein molecular weight standards	40 µL
P33350	PeppermintStick™ phosphoprotein molecular weight standards *200 gel lanes*	400 µL
P33356	Pro-Q® Diamond Phosphoprotein Blot Stain Kit *20 minigel blots*	1 kit
P33310	Pro-Q® Diamond phosphoprotein gel destaining solution	1 L
P33311	Pro-Q® Diamond phosphoprotein gel destaining solution *bulk packaging*	5 L
P33300	Pro-Q® Diamond phosphoprotein gel stain	1 L
P33301	Pro-Q® Diamond phosphoprotein gel stain	200 mL
P33302	Pro-Q® Diamond phosphoprotein gel stain *bulk packaging*	5 L
MPP33301	Pro-Q® Diamond Phosphoprotein Gel Staining Kit *includes 200 mL stain and 40 µL standard*	1 kit
MPP33300	Pro-Q® Diamond Phosphoprotein Gel Staining Kit *includes 1 L stain and 40 µL standard*	1 kit
MPP33302	Pro-Q® Diamond Phosphoprotein Gel Staining Kit *includes 5 L stain and 400 µL standard*	1 kit
P21857	Pro-Q® Emerald 300 Glycoprotein Gel and Blot Stain Kit *10 minigels or minigel blots*	1 kit
P21855	Pro-Q® Emerald 300 Glycoprotein Gel Stain Kit *with SYPRO® Ruby protein gel stain* *10 minigels*	1 kit
P21875	Pro-Q® Emerald 488 Glycoprotein Gel and Blot Stain Kit *10 minigels or minigel blots*	1 kit
P21872	Pro-Q® Glycoprotein Blot Stain Kit #5 *with *Griffonia simplicifolia* lectin II (GS-II) and DDAO phosphate* *>20 minigel blots*	1 kit
P21861	Pro-Q® Western Blot Stain Kit #4 *with goat anti-rabbit IgG, DDAO phosphate and SYPRO® Ruby protein blot stain* *10-20 minigel blots*	1 kit
P21878	Pro-Q® Oligohistidine Blot Stain Kit #1 *with biotin NTA, streptavidin and DDAO phosphate* *20 minigel blots*	1 kit
P21879	Pro-Q® Oligohistidine Blot Stain Kit #2 *with biotin NTA, streptavidin and ELF® 39 phosphate* *20 minigel blots*	1 kit
P21876	Pro-Q® Sapphire 365 oligohistidine gel stain *20 minigels*	500 mL
P21877	Pro-Q® Sapphire 488 oligohistidine gel stain *20 minigels*	500 mL
P33354	Pro-Q® Sapphire 532 oligohistidine gel stain *20 minigels*	500 mL
P21860	Pro-Q® Western Blot Stain Kit #2 *with goat anti-mouse IgG, DDAO phosphate and SYPRO® Ruby protein blot stain* *10-20 minigel blots*	1 kit
P21864	Pro-Q® Western Blot Stain Kit #3 *with goat anti-rabbit IgG and DDAO phosphate* *>20 minigel blots*	1 kit
P21865	Pro-Q® Western Blot Stain Kit #5 *with streptavidin and DDAO phosphate* *>20 minigel blots*	1 kit
P21862	Pro-Q® Western Blot Stain Kit #6 *with streptavidin, DDAO phosphate and SYPRO® Ruby protein blot stain* *10-20 minigel blots*	1 kit
R33400	Rhinohide™ polyacrylamide gel strengthener concentrate *sufficient additive for 1 L of 30% acrylamide/bis-acrylamide (37.5:1)*	200 mL
R33410	Rhinohide™ Polyacrylamide Gel Strengthener Kit *makes 1 L of Rhinohide™ 30% acrylamide/bis-acrylamide (37.5:1)*	1 kit
S6656	SYPRO® photographic filter	each
S11791	SYPRO® Ruby protein blot stain *10-40 blots*	200 mL
S12000	SYPRO® Ruby protein gel stain	1 L
S12001	SYPRO® Ruby protein gel stain	200 mL
S21900	SYPRO® Ruby protein gel stain *bulk packaging*	5 L

For current prices or to order online, visit probes.invitrogen.com

9.5 Reagents for Peptide Analysis, Sequencing and Synthesis

This section describes Molecular Probes' reagents used in the synthesis of fluorescent dye– or hapten-labeled peptides and fluorogenic protease substrates, as well as in peptide and protein sequencing. The dominant chemistry for sequencing peptides employs the nonfluorescent reagent phenyl isothiocyanate, which forms phenylthiohydantoins (PTH) in the sequencing reaction. Some of our fluorescent probes and research chemicals have been used for N-terminal amino acid analysis and peptide sequencing, as well as for protein fragment modification prior to PTH sequencing.

N-Terminal Amino Acid Analysis

Except when it is already blocked by formylation, acetylation, pyroglutamic acid formation or other chemistry, the N-terminal amino acid of proteins can be labeled with a variety of fluorescent and chromophoric reagents from Chapter 1. However, only those functional groups that survive complete protein hydrolysis, such as sulfonamides, are useful for N-terminal amino acid analysis. Dansyl chloride (D21) and dabsyl chloride (D1537) are the most commonly employed reagents for such analyses.[1–3]

Nonacylated N-terminal serine and threonine residues of proteins can be periodate-oxidized to aldehydes[4–6] (Figure 3.1) that can then be modified by a variety of hydrazine derivatives and hydroxylamine derivatives listed in Section 3.2. Only peptides and proteins that contain these two terminal amino acids become fluorescent, although oxidation of the carbohydrate portion of glycoproteins to aldehydes may cause interference in this analysis.

N-Acetylated or *N*-formylated proteins have been detected by transfer of the acyl group to dansyl hydrazine (D100) and subsequent chromatographic separation of the fluorescent product.[7,8] The sensitivity of this method can likely be improved by the use of other fluorescent hydrazine derivatives and hydroxylamine derivatives described in Section 3.2.

Peptide Sequencing

As analogs of phenyl isothiocyanate, the peptide conjugates of fluorescein-5-isothiocyanate (FITC; F143, F1906, F1907; Section 1.5) and other fluorescent isothiocyanates are susceptible to Edman degradation via their thiohydantoins. Thus, these fluorescent reagents are potentially useful for ultrasensitive amino acid sequencing.[9–12]

Peptide Synthesis

Peptides specifically labeled with fluorescent dyes, haptens, photoactive groups or radioisotopes are important both as probes for receptors and as substrates for enzymes (Section 10.4). Labeled peptides can be prepared by modifying isolated peptides or by incorporating the label during solid-phase synthesis. Molecular Probes offers some fluorescent neuropeptides, most of which are described in Section 16.2.

Labeling Peptides in Solution

Appropriately substituted synthetic peptides can be labeled in solution by almost any of the reactive probes in Chapters 1–5 (see Note 9.2 "Technical Focus: Labeling Small Peptides with Amine-Reactive Dyes in Organic Solvents"). Many peptides contain multiple residues that can be modified, potentially leading to complex mixtures of products, some of which may be biologically inactive. Modification of a peptide's thiol group by one of the thiol-reactive reagents described in Chapter 2 is usually easy, selective and very efficient. If the peptide is synthetic, or can be modified by site-directed mutagenesis, incorporation of a cysteine residue at the desired site of labeling is recommended. The N-terminus of peptides, which has a lower pK_a than the ε-amino group of lysine residues, can sometimes be labeled in the presence of other amines if the pH is kept near neutral. Conversion of tyrosine residues to *o*-aminotyrosines (Section 3.1, Figure 3.3) can be used to provide selective sites for peptide modification, unless the tyrosine residues are essential for the biological activity of the peptide.

Solid-Phase Synthesis of Labeled Peptides

Because specific labeling of peptides in solution is problematic, it may be more convenient to conjugate the fluorophore to the N-terminus of a resin-bound peptide *before* removal of other protecting groups and release of the labeled peptide from the resin. About five equivalents of an amine-reactive fluorophore are usually used per amine of the immobilized peptide. The fluorescein, eosin, Alexa Fluor®, Oregon Green®, Rhodamine Green™, tetramethylrhodamine, Rhodamine Red™, Texas Red®, coumarin and NBD fluorophores, the QSY®, dabcyl and dabsyl chromophores and biotin are all expected to be reasonably stable to hydrogen fluoride (HF) as well as to most other acids.[13–18] These fluorophores, chromophores and biotin are also expected to be stable to reagents used for deprotection of peptides synthesized using FMOC chemistry.[19] The BODIPY® fluorophore may be unstable to the conditions used to remove some protecting groups.

Molecular Probes has prepared some unique reagents for automated synthesis of peptides that are specifically labeled with fluorophores, chromophores and haptens. Use of these precursors permits the incorporation of these groups at specific sites in the peptide's sequence. The α-FMOC derivative of ε-dabcyl-L-lysine (D6216) can be used to incorporate the dabcyl chromophore at selected sites in the peptide sequence. The dabcyl chromophore, which has broad visible absorption (Figure 10.55), has been extensively used as a quenching group in the automated synthesis of HIV protease (H2930, Section 10.4), renin (R2931, Section 10.4) and other fluorogenic peptidase substrates.[20–23] The dabcyl group can also be incorporated at the N-terminus by using dabcyl succinimidyl ester[18,24] (D2245). The aminonaphthalene derivative EDANS (A91) has been the most common fluorophore for pairing with the dabcyl quencher in fluorescence resonance energy transfer (FRET) experiments because its fluorescence emission spectrum overlaps the absorption spectrum of dabcyl (Figure 10.55) (see Note 1.2 "Technical Focus: Fluorescence Resonance Energy Transfer (FRET)" in Section 1.3). This fluorophore is conveniently introduced during automated synthesis of peptides by using γ-EDANS-α-FMOC-L-glutamic acid (F11831) or the corresponding *t*-BOC derivative[18,20] (B6215). The tetramethylrhodamine fluorophores can be incorporated during automated FMOC synthesis of peptides using our single-isomer α-(FMOC)-ε-TMR-L-lysine building block (F11830). Site-selective biotinylation of peptides can be achieved using the FMOC derivative of biocytin (B20651) during automated synthesis. This reagent can also be attached to the synthesis resin as the first residue to provide automated synthesis of C-terminal biotinylated peptides.

Our QSY® dyes (Section 1.6, Section 1.8) have broad visible to near-infrared absorption (Table 1.9, Figure 1.70). These dyes, which are essentially nonfluorescent, are particularly useful as energy acceptors from blue-, green-, orange- or red-fluorescent donor dyes (Table 1.10). The QSY® 7, QSY® 9, QSY® 21 and QSY® 35 chromophores can be conjugated to amines via their succinimidyl esters (Q10193, Q20131, Q20132, Q20133). The QSY® 7 dye can also be conjugated to thiols of peptides or to thiol-modified oligonucleotides via its maleimide[25] (Q10257) and the QSY® 35 dye coupled via its iodoacetamide (Q20348). Additionally, peptide amides can be prepared from the QSY® 7 and QSY® 35 aliphatic amines (Q10464, Q20540). We have also prepared α-(FMOC)-ε-QSY® 7-L-lysine and α-FMOC-β-QSY® 35-L-alanine (Q21930, Q21931), which can be used in the automated synthesis of QSY® 7 quencher– or QSY® 35 quencher–containing peptides.

References

1. J Chromatogr 553, 123 (1991); **2.** Anal Biochem 174, 38 (1988); **3.** Anal Biochem 170, 542 (1988); **4.** Biochem J 108, 883 (1968); **5.** Biochem J 95, 180 (1965); **6.** Biochem J 94, 17 (1965); **7.** J Cell Biol 106, 1607 (1988); **8.** Anal Biochem 29, 186 (1969); **9.** Biosci Biotechnol Biochem 58, 300 (1994); **10.** Biol Chem Hoppe Seyler 367, 1259 (1986); **11.** FEBS Lett 198, 150 (1986); **12.** Anal Biochem 141, 446 (1984); **13.** Biochemistry 33, 7211 (1994); **14.** Biochemistry 33, 6966 (1994); **15.** J Biol Chem 269, 15124 (1994); **16.** Techniques in Protein Chemistry V, Crabb JW, Ed. pp. 493–500 (1994); **17.** Anal Biochem 202, 68 (1992); **18.** J Med Chem 35, 3727 (1992); **19.** Biochemistry 33, 10951 (1994); **20.** Bioorg Med Chem Lett 2, 1665 (1992); **21.** J Protein Chem 9, 663 (1990); **22.** Science 247, 954 (1990); **23.** Tetrahedron Lett 31, 6493 (1990); **24.** FEBS Lett 297, 100 (1992); **25.** Proc Natl Acad Sci U S A 100, 13308 (2003).

Note 9.2 — Technical Focus

Labeling Small Peptides with Amine-Reactive Dyes in Organic Solvents

Most of the product literature associated with our amine-reactive dyes provides protocols for labeling proteins, typically IgG antibodies in aqueous buffers. The following protocol is a starting point for labeling peptides in organic solvents. Please note that the reaction conditions, including concentrations of the reactants and the reaction times, may require optimization. Furthermore, many peptides are not soluble in a 100% organic solution. It is very important to test the solubility of the peptide in DMSO or DMF before attempting this procedure.

1. Dissolve the peptide to be labeled in DMSO or DMF at 0.1–1 mM.
2. Add 100 mM triethylamine to the reaction solution. This will ensure that the amines to be derivatized are deprotonated.
3. Add the amine-reactive dye to the reaction solution. The reactive dye should be in a 1:1 to 3:1 molar ratio to the peptide.
4. React at room temperature or at 4°C for at least 4 hours with continuous stirring, protected from light. The reaction can proceed overnight. Thin-layer chromatography may be useful for monitoring the reaction's progress.
5. Purify the conjugate by an appropriate method, such as HPLC-based separation.

Data Table — 9.5 Reagents for Peptide Analysis, Sequencing and Synthesis

Cat #	MW	Storage	Soluble	Abs	EC	Em	Solvent	Notes
A91	288.30	L	pH >10, DMF	335	5,900	493	pH 8	
B6215	495.55	F,D,L	DMF	341	5,400	470	MeOH	
B6217	497.59	F,D,L	DMF, MeCN	428	30,000	none	MeOH	
B20651	594.72	F,D	DMF, MeCN	<300		none		
D21	269.75	F,DD,L	DMF, MeCN	372	3,900	none	$CHCl_3$	1, 2
D100	265.33	L	EtOH	336	4,400	534	MeOH	
D1537	323.80	F,DD,L	DMF, MeCN	466	33,000	none	MeOH	2, 3
D2245	366.38	F,D,L	DMF, DMSO	453	32,000	none	MeOH	4
D6216	619.72	F,D,L	DMF, MeCN	427	30,000	none	MeOH	
F11830	780.88	F,D,L	DMF, MeCN	543	92,000	570	MeOH	
F11831	617.67	F,D,L	DMF, MeCN	341	5,200	471	MeOH	
Q10193	791.32	F,D,L	DMSO	560	90,000	none	MeOH	
Q10257	858.45	F,D,L	DMSO	560	92,000	none	MeOH	
Q10464	814.87	L	DMSO	560	92,000	none	MeOH	
Q20131	951.43	F,D,L	H_2O, DMSO	562	88,000	none	MeOH	5
Q20132	815.34	F,D,L	DMSO	661	90,000	none	MeOH	
Q20133	411.33	F,D,L	DMSO	475	23,000	none	MeOH	
Q20348	453.20	F,D,L	DMSO	475	24,000	none	MeOH	6
Q20540	399.29	L	DMSO, DMF	472	24,000	none	MeOH	
Q21930	1044.66	F,D,L	DMF, MeCN	560	90,000	none	MeOH	
Q21931	565.54	F,D,L	DMF, MeCN	475	23,000	none	MeOH	

For definitions of the contents of this data table, see "Navigating *The Handbook*" in the introductory pages.

Notes

1. D21 butylamine derivative has Abs = 337 nm (EC = 5300 $cm^{-1}M^{-1}$), Em = 492 nm in $CHCl_3$. Em and QY are highly solvent dependent: Em = 496 nm (QY = 0.45) in dioxane, 536 nm (QY = 0.28) in MeOH and 557 nm (QY = 0.03) in H_2O (Biochemistry 6, 3408 (1967)). EC typically decreases upon conjugation to proteins (EC = 3400 $cm^{-1}M^{-1}$ at 340 nm) (Biochemistry 25, 513 (1986)). Fluorescence lifetimes (τ) of protein conjugates are typically 12–20 nanoseconds (Arch Biochem Biophys 133, 263 (1969); Arch Biochem Biophys 128, 163 (1968)).
2. Do NOT dissolve in DMSO.
3. D1537 is nonfluorescent both before and after reaction with amines. Reation product with butylamine has Abs = 435 nm (EC = 31,000 $cm^{-1}M^{-1}$) in MeOH.
4. D2245 is nonfluorescent both before and after reaction with amines. Reaction product with butylamine has Abs = 428 nm (EC = 32,000 $cm^{-1}M^{-1}$) in MeOH.
5. This sulfonated succinimidyl ester derivative is water-soluble and may be dissolved in buffer at ~pH 8 for reaction with amines. Long-term storage in water is NOT recommended due to hydrolysis.
6. Iodoacetamides in solution undergo rapid photodecomposition to unreactive products. Minimize exposure to light prior to reaction.

Product List — 9.5 Reagents for Peptide Analysis, Sequencing and Synthesis

Cat #	Product Name	Unit Size
A91	5-((2-aminoethyl)amino)naphthalene-1-sulfonic acid, sodium salt (EDANS)	1 g
B20651	ε-biotinoyl-α-(9-fluorenylmethoxycarbonyl)-L-lysine (FMOC biocytin)	25 mg
B6217	α-(*t*-BOC)-ε-(4-dimethylaminophenylazobenzoyl)-L-lysine (α-(*t*-BOC)-ε-dabcyl-L-lysine)	100 mg
B6215	5-((2-(*t*-BOC)-γ-L-glutamylaminoethyl)amino)naphthalene-1-sulfonic acid (γ-EDANS-α-(*t*-BOC)-L-glutamic acid)	100 mg
D1537	4-dimethylaminoazobenzene-4′-sulfonyl chloride (dabsyl chloride)	100 mg
D21	5-dimethylaminonaphthalene-1-sulfonyl chloride (dansyl chloride)	1 g
D100	5-dimethylaminonaphthalene-1-sulfonyl hydrazine (dansyl hydrazine)	100 mg
D2245	4-((4-(dimethylamino)phenyl)azo)benzoic acid, succinimidyl ester (dabcyl, SE)	100 mg
D6216	ε-(4-((4-(dimethylamino)phenyl)azo)benzoyl)-α-9-fluorenylmethoxycarbonyl-L-lysine (ε-dabcyl-α-FMOC-L-lysine)	100 mg
F11830	N^{α}-(9-fluorenylmethoxycarbonyl)-N^{ε}-tetramethylrhodamine-(5-carbonyl)-L-lysine (α-FMOC-ε-TMR-L-lysine)	25 mg
F11831	5-((2-(FMOC)-γ-L-glutamylaminoethyl)amino)naphthalene-1-sulfonic acid (γ-EDANS-α-FMOC-L-glutamic acid)	100 mg
Q10464	QSY® 7 amine, hydrochloride	5 mg
Q10193	QSY® 7 carboxylic acid, succinimidyl ester	5 mg
Q10257	QSY® 7 C_5-maleimide	5 mg
Q21930	N^{ε}-(QSY® 7)-N^{α}-(9-fluorenylmethoxycarbonyl)-L-lysine (α-FMOC-ε-QSY® 7-L-lysine)	5 mg
Q20131	QSY® 9 carboxylic acid, succinimidyl ester	5 mg
Q20132	QSY® 21 carboxylic acid, succinimidyl ester	5 mg
Q20133	QSY® 35 acetic acid, succinimidyl ester	5 mg
Q21931	N^{β}-(QSY® 35)-N^{α}-(9-fluorenylmethoxycarbonyl)-L-alanine (α-FMOC-β-QSY® 35-L-alanine)	5 mg
Q20348	QSY® 35 iodoacetamide	5 mg
Q20540	QSY® 35 methylamine	5 mg

For current prices or to order online, visit probes.invitrogen.com

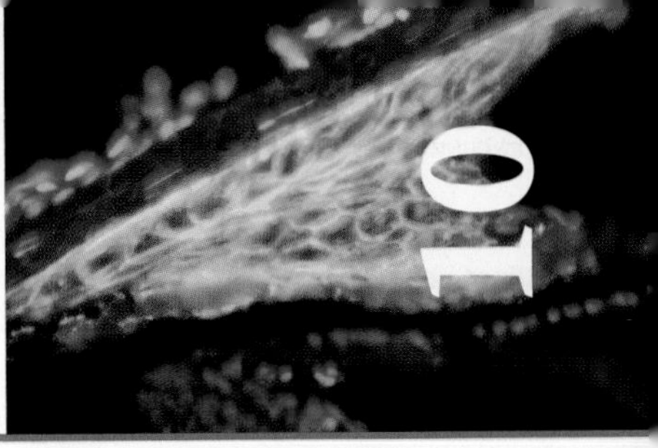

Chapter 10

Enzyme Substrates

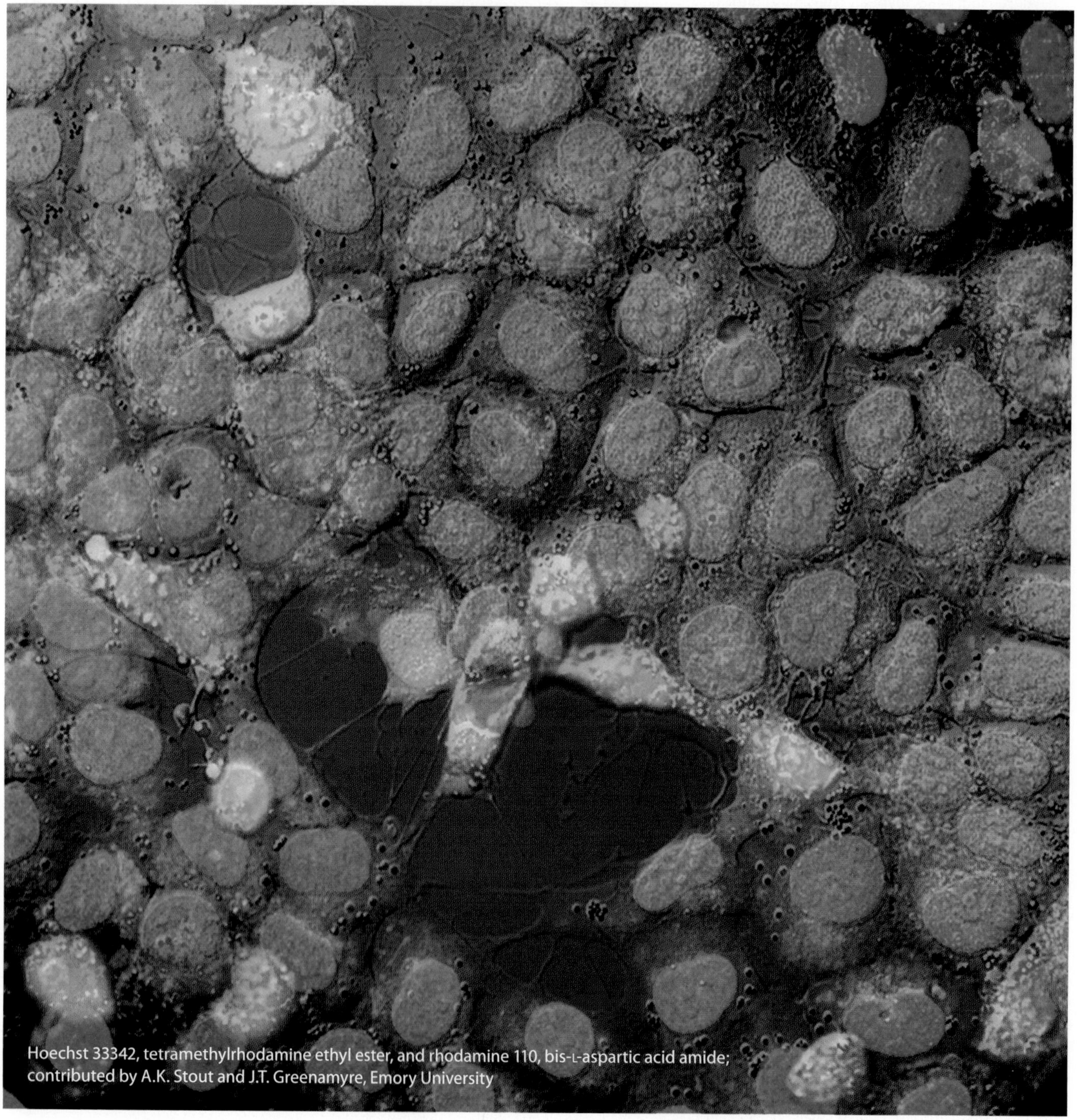

Hoechst 33342, tetramethylrhodamine ethyl ester, and rhodamine 110, bis-L-aspartic acid amide; contributed by A.K. Stout and J.T. Greenamyre, Emory University

10.1 Introduction to Enzyme Substrates and Their Reference Standards

Molecular Probes offers a large assortment of common and uncommon fluorogenic and chromogenic enzyme substrates. We prepare substrates for enzyme-linked immunosorbent assays (ELISAs), as well as substrates for detecting very low levels of enzymatic activity in fixed cells, tissues, cell extracts and purified preparations. Our RediPlate™ product line includes enzyme substrates predispensed in 96-well or 384-well plates for high-throughput applications, along with the appropriate reference standards and other reaction components. We have also developed effective methods for detecting some enzymes in live cells. In this section, we describe the characteristics of our enzyme substrates and the fluorophores and chromophores from which they are derived, focusing primarily on the suitability of these substrates for different types of enzyme assays. The fluorophores that are available as reference standards — including a NIST-traceable fluorescein standard — can be found in the data table and product list associated with this section. Substrates for specific enzymes are described in subsequent sections of this chapter.

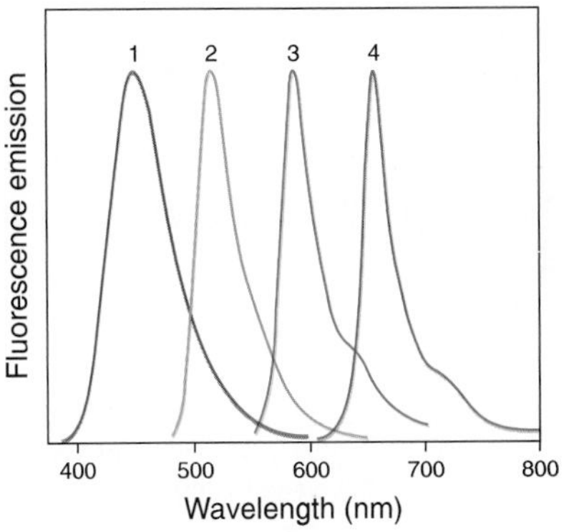

Figure 10.1 Normalized emission spectra of 1) 7-hydroxy-4-methylcoumarin (H189) and 6,8-difluoro-7-hydroxy-4-methylcoumarin (DiFMU, D6566), 2) fluorescein (F1300, F36915), 3) resorufin (R363) and 4) DDAO (H6482) in aqueous solution at pH 9. These fluorophores correspond to the hydrolysis, oxidation or reduction products of several of our fluorogenic enzyme substrates.

Substrates Yielding Soluble Fluorescent Products

Solution assays designed to quantitate enzymatic activity in cell extracts or other biological fluids typically employ substrates that yield highly fluorescent or intensely absorbing water-soluble products. ELISAs also rely on these substrates for indirect quantitation of analytes.[1–3] An ideal fluorogenic substrate for fluorescence-based solution assays yields a highly fluorescent, water-soluble product with optical properties significantly different from those of the substrate. If the fluorescence spectra of the substrate and product overlap significantly, analysis will likely require a separation step, especially when using excess substrate to obtain pseudo–first-order kinetics. Fortunately, many substrates have low intrinsic fluorescence or are metabolized to products that have longer-wavelength excitation or emission spectra (Figure 10.1). These fluorescent products can typically be quantitated in the presence of the unreacted substrate using a fluorometer or a fluorescence microplate reader. Microplate readers facilitate high-throughput analysis and require relatively small assay volumes, which usually reduces reagent costs. Moreover, the front-face optics in many microplate readers allows researchers to use more concentrated solutions, which may both improve the linearity of the kinetics and reduce inner-filter effects.

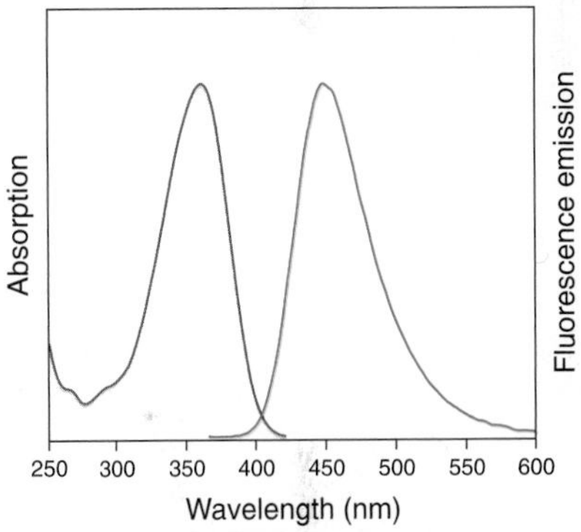

Figure 10.2 Absorption and fluorescence emission spectra of 7-hydroxy-4-methylcoumarin (H189) in pH 9.0 buffer. The spectra of 6,8-difluoro-7-hydroxy-4-methylcoumarin (D6566) are essentially identical.

When the spectral characteristics of the substrate and its metabolic product are similar, techniques such as thin-layer chromatography (TLC), high-performance liquid chromatography (HPLC), capillary electrophoresis, solvent extraction or ion exchange can be used to separate the product from unconsumed substrate prior to analysis. For example, our *FAST* CAT® Chloramphenicol Acetyltransferase Assay Kits (F2900, F6616, F6617; Section 10.6) utilize chromatography to separate the intrinsically fluorescent substrates from their fluorescent products.

Substrates Derived from Water-Soluble Coumarins

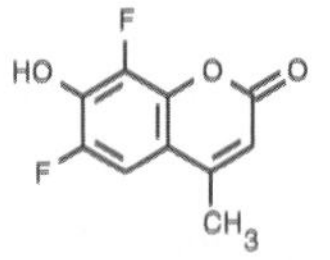

Figure 10.3 D6566 6,8-difluoro-7-hydroxy-4-methylcoumarin (DiFMU).

Hydroxy- and amino-substituted coumarins have been the most widely used fluorophores for preparing fluorogenic substrates. Coumarin-based substrates produce highly soluble, intensely blue-fluorescent products. Phenolic dyes with high pK_as, such as 7-hydroxycoumarin (often called umbelliferone) and the more common 7-hydroxy-4-methylcoumarin (β-methylumbelliferone, H189; Figure 10.2), are not fully deprotonated and therefore not fully fluorescent unless the pH of the reaction mixture is raised to above pH ~10. Thus, substrates derived from these fluorophores are seldom used for continuous measurement of enzymatic activity in solution or live cells. The similar 3-cyano-7-hydroxycoumarin (C183) and 6,8-difluoro-7-hydroxy-4-methylcoumarin (DiFMU, D6566; Figure 10.2, Figure 10.3) have lower pK_as[4] (Figure 1.96), making them suitable for a broader range of applications. Ether, ester and phosphate substrates derived from these phenolic dyes may be fluorescent but invariably exhibit shorter-wavelength absorption and emission spectra that can be easily distinguished from those of their metabolic product. The phosphate ester of 6,8-difluoro-7-hydroxy-4-methylcoumarin (DiFMUP, D6567, D22065, E12020; Section 10.3) exhibits extraordinary spectral properties, making it one of the most sensitive fluorogenic substrates for continuous high-throughput assay of alkaline phosphatase and its bioconjugates.

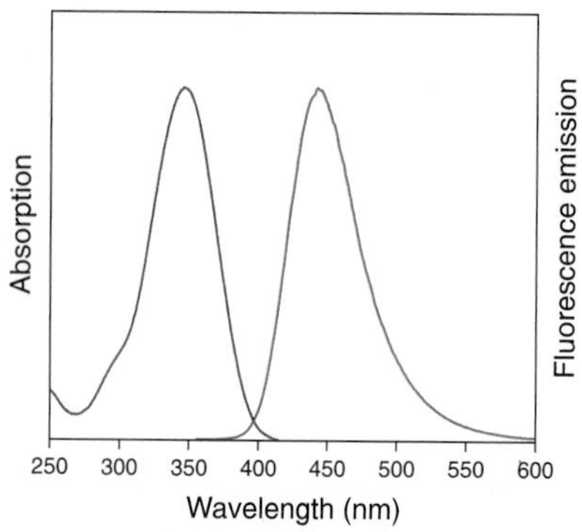

Figure 10.4 Absorption and fluorescence emission spectra of 7-amino-4-methylcoumarin in pH 7.0 buffer.

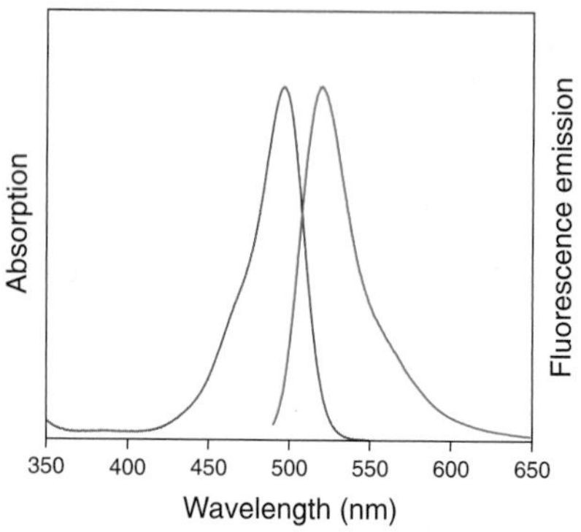

Figure 10.5 Absorption and fluorescence emission spectra of rhodamine 110 in pH 7.0 buffer.

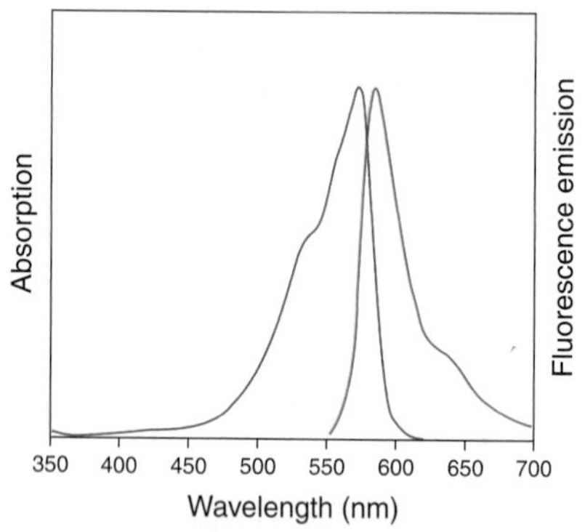

Figure 10.6 Absorption and fluorescence emission spectra of resorufin in pH 9.0 buffer.

Aromatic amines, including the commonly used 7-amino-4-methylcoumarin (AMC, A191; Figure 10.4), are partially protonated at low pH (less than ~5) but fully deprotonated at physiological pH. Thus, their fluorescence spectra are not subject to variability due to pH-dependent protonation/deprotonation when assayed near or above physiological pH. AMC is widely used to prepare peptidase substrates in which the amide has shorter-wavelength absorption and emission spectra than the amine hydrolysis product.

Substrates Derived from Water-Soluble Green to Yellow Fluorophores

As compared with coumarin-based substrates, substrates derived from fluoresceins, rhodamines, resorufins and some other dyes often provide significantly greater sensitivity in fluorescence-based enzyme assays. In addition, most of these longer-wavelength dyes have extinction coefficients that are five to 25 times that of coumarins, nitrophenols or nitroanilines, making them additionally useful as sensitive chromogenic substrates.

Hydrolytic substrates based on the derivatives of fluorescein (fluorescein reference standard, F1300; fluorescein NIST-traceable standard, F36915; Figure 1.52) or rhodamine 110 (R110, R6479; Figure 10.5) usually incorporate two moieties, each of which serves as a substrate for the enzyme. Consequently, they are cleaved first to the monosubstituted analog and then to the free fluorophore. Because the monosubstituted analog often absorbs and emits light at the same wavelengths as the ultimate hydrolysis product, this initial hydrolysis complicates the interpretation of hydrolysis kinetics.[5] However, when highly purified, the disubstituted fluorescein- and rhodamine 110–based substrates have virtually no visible-wavelength absorbance or background fluorescence, making them extremely sensitive detection reagents. For example, researchers have reported that the activity of as few as 1.6 *molecules* of β-galactosidase can be detected with fluorescein di-β-D-galactopyranoside (FDG) and capillary electrophoresis.[6] Fluorogenic substrates based on either the AMC and R110 fluorophore are used in our EnzChek® Caspase Assay Kits (Section 15.5) to detect apoptotic cells.

Chemical reduction of fluorescein- and rhodamine-based dyes yields colorless and nonfluorescent dihydrofluoresceins (Figure 18.7) and dihydrorhodamines (Figure 12.25). Although extremely useful for detection of reactive oxygen species (ROS) in phagocytic and other cells (Section 18.2), these dyes tend to be insufficiently stable for solution assays. An exception is our patented Amplex® Gold reagent, which is utilized in our Amplex® Gold and DyeChrome™ Double Western Blot Stain Kits (Figure 9.70). These kits are described in Section 9.4.

Substrates Derived from Water-Soluble Red Fluorophores

Long-wavelength fluorophores are often preferred because background absorbance and autofluorescence are generally lower when longer excitation wavelengths are used. Substrates derived from the red-fluorescent resorufin (R363, Figure 10.6) and the dimethylacridinone derivative 7-hydroxy-9*H*-(1,3-dichloro-9,9-dimethylacridin-2-one) (DDAO, H6482; Figure 10.7, Figure 10.12) contain only a single hydrolysis-sensitive moiety (Figure 10.29), thereby avoiding the biphasic kinetics of both fluorescein- and rhodamine-based substrates.[7]

Resorufin is used to prepare several substrates for glycosidases, hydrolytic enzymes and dealkylases. In most cases, the relatively low pK_a of resorufin (~6.0) permits continuous measurement of enzymatic activity. Thiols such as DTT or 2-mercaptoethanol should be avoided in assays utilizing resorufin-based substrates. Our Amplex® Red peroxidase substrate (A12222, A22177; Section 10.5) is a chemically reduced, colorless form of resorufin (Figure 10.58) that is oxidized to resorufin by HRP in combination with hydrogen peroxide. Resorufin is also the product of enzyme-catalyzed reduction of resazurin (R12204; Section 10.6, Section 15.2) — also known as alamarBlue, a trademark of AccuMed International, Inc. Our Amplex® UltraRed reagent (A36006, Section 10.5) improves upon the performance of the Amplex® Red reagent, offering brighter fluorescence and enhanced sensitivity on a per-mole basis in peroxidase or peroxidase-coupled enzyme assays.

Substrates derived from DDAO, a red He–Ne laser–excitable fluorophore, generally exhibit good water solubility, low K_ms and high turnover rates. In addition, the difference between the excitation maximum of the DDAO-based substrates and that of the phenolic DDAO product is greater than 150 nm (Figure 10.7), which allows the two species to be easily distinguished. We have utilized DDAO phosphate (D6487, Section 10.3) in several of our Pro-Q® Glycoprotein Blot

Stain Kits, as well as in some of our DyeChrome™ and Pro-Q® Western Blot Stain Kits (Section 9.4) for the sensitive detection of proteins. In our unique DyeChrome™ Double Western Blot Kit (D21887, Section 9.4), we have combined the DDAO phosphate substrate with both the Amplex® Gold HRP substrate and MPDF, a total-protein stain, for simultaneous trichromatic detection of two specific proteins and total proteins on Western blots (Figure 9.70).

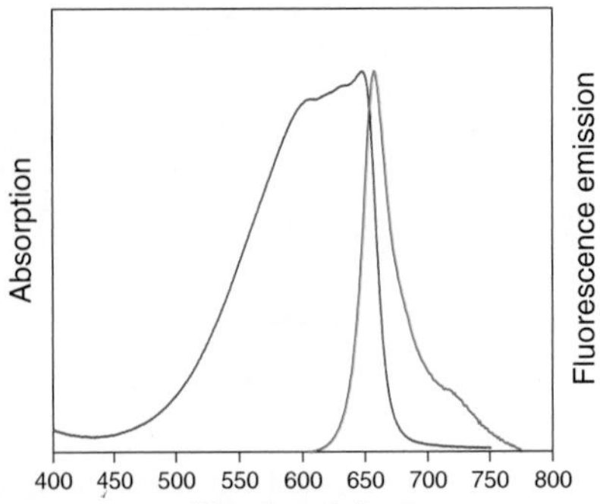

Figure 10.7 Normalized absorption and fluorescence emission spectra of DDAO, which is formed by alkaline phosphatase–mediated hydrolysis of DDAO phosphate (D6487).

Substrates for Live-Cell Enzyme Assays

Molecular Probes has developed a number of innovative strategies for investigating enzymatic activity in live cells.[8,9] For example, we offer a diverse set of probes that can passively enter the cell; once inside, they are processed by intracellular enzymes to generate products with improved cellular retention. We also offer kits and reagents for detecting the expression of several common reporter genes in cells and cell extracts. These include substrates for β-galactosidase (Section 10.2), β-glucuronidase (Section 10.2), secreted alkaline phosphatase (SEAP, Section 10.3), chloramphenicol acetyltransferase (CAT, Section 10.6) and luciferase (Section 10.6). Some of our EnzChek® and DQ™ Kits are useful for study of the uptake and metabolism of proteins during phagocytosis (Section 16.1), as well as for the general screening of certain glycosidases (Section 10.2) and proteases (Section 10.4). Substrates for specific proteases are also useful for the detection of apoptosis (Section 15.5).

Thiol-Reactive Fluorogenic Substrates

Molecular Probes prepares a number of enzyme substrates for live-cell assays that incorporate a mildly thiol-reactive chloromethyl moiety. Once inside the cell, this chloromethyl group undergoes what is believed to be a glutathione *S*-transferase–mediated reaction to produce a membrane-impermeant, glutathione–fluorescent dye adduct, although our experiments suggest that they may also react with other intracellular components. Regardless of the mechanism, many cell types loaded with these chloromethylated substrates are both fluorescent and viable for at least 24 hours after loading and often through several cell divisions. Furthermore, unlike the free dye, the peptide–fluorescent dye adducts contain amino groups and can therefore be covalently linked to surrounding biomolecules by fixation with formaldehyde or glutaraldehyde. This property permits long-term storage of the labeled cells or tissue and, in cases where the anti-dye antibody is available (Section 7.4), amplification of the conjugate by standard immunochemical techniques, including the tyramide signal amplification (TSA, Section 6.2) and Enzyme-Labeled Fluorescence (ELF®, Section 6.3) technologies. Chloromethyl analogs of fluorogenic substrates for glycosidases (for example, our DetectaGene™ Green CMFDG Kit, (D2920); Section 10.2), peptidases, dealkylases, peroxidases and esterases are available. Our CellTracker™ Blue CMAC and CellTracker™ Blue CMF_2HC dyes (C2110, Figure 14.7; C12881, Figure 14.9) are precursors to peptidase and glycosidase substrates, respectively. They are also used for long-term cell tracing (Section 14.2). The improved retention of the MitoTracker® (Section 12.2) and CellTracker™ (Section 14.2) probes in fixed cells is also based on this principle.

Lipophilic Fluorophores

Lipophilic analogs of fluorescein and resorufin exhibit many of the same properties as the water-soluble fluorophores, including relatively high extinction coefficients and good quantum yields. In most cases, however, substrates based on these lipophilic analogs load more readily into cells, permitting use of much lower substrate concentrations in the loading medium, and their fluorescent products are better retained after cleavage than their water-soluble counterparts. Lipophilic substrates and their products probably also distribute differently in cells and likely associate with lipid regions of the cell. When passive cell loading or enhanced dye retention are critical parameters of the experiment, we recommend using our lipophilic substrates for glycosidases (such as our ImaGene Green™ and ImaGene Red™ products, Section 10.2) and dealkylases (Section 10.6). Like resazurin (R12204, Section 15.2), dodecylresazurin — the substrate in our LIVE/DEAD® Cell Vitality Assay Kit, Vybrant® Cell Metabolic Assay Kit and Vybrant® Apoptosis Assay Kit #10 (V23110, L34951, V35114; Section 15.3, Section 15.5) — is reduced to dodecylresorufin by metabolically active cells; however, this lipophilic substrate is more useful than resazurin for microplate assays of all metabolic activity and permits single-cell analysis of cell metabolism by flow cytometry and cell counting (Figure 15.32, Figure 15.33, Figure 15.34, Figure 15.91). Dodecylresorufin is also the product produced by hydrolysis of the β-galactosidase substrate (Figure 10.22) used in our ImaGene Red™ $C_{12}RG$ *lacZ* Gene Expression Kit (I2906, Section 10.2).

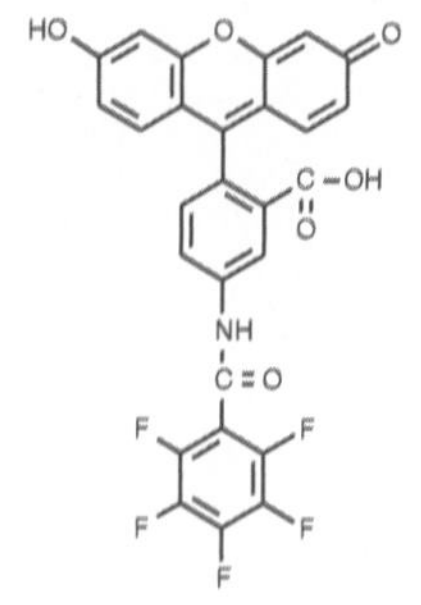

Figure 10.8 P12925 5-(pentafluorobenzoylamino)fluorescein (PFB-F).

Pentafluorobenzoyl Fluorogenic Enzyme Substrates

Detecting enzyme activity in live cells with fluorogenic substrates has been difficult both because the cell membrane is often a barrier to substrate penetration and because, once formed, the fluorescent product tends to leak from viable cells. We have found that our pentafluorobenzoyl (PFB) fluorogenic substrates address both of these difficulties. First, when compared with conventional fluorescein-based substrates, several of our PFB substrates exhibit improved penetration through the cell membrane, permitting cell loading directly from culture medium. Second, the green-fluorescent PFB aminofluorescein (PFB-F, P12925; Figure 10.8) released upon hydrolysis of the PFB-F substrates exhibits better cell retention than does fluorescein, the hydrolysis product of the fluorescein-based substrates. The hydrolysis products of the PFB substrates appear to be retained in viable cells by two mechanisms: 1) retention of the relatively lipophilic PFB group of the hydrolysis products in the cell membrane, and 2) glutathione *S*-transferase–catalyzed reaction of the nonfluorescent substrate and its fluorescent hydrolysis products with intracellular glutathione.

Substrates Yielding Insoluble Fluorescent Products

Alkaline phosphatase, β-galactosidase and horseradish peroxidase (HRP) conjugates are widely used as secondary detection reagents for immunohistochemical analysis and *in situ* hybridization, as well as for protein and nucleic acid detection by Western, Southern and Northern blots. Also, various methods such as chromatography, isoelectric focusing and gel electrophoresis are commonly employed to separate enzymes preceding their detection. A review by Weder and Kaiser discusses the use of a wide variety of fluorogenic substrates for the detection of electrophoretically separated hydrolases.[10]

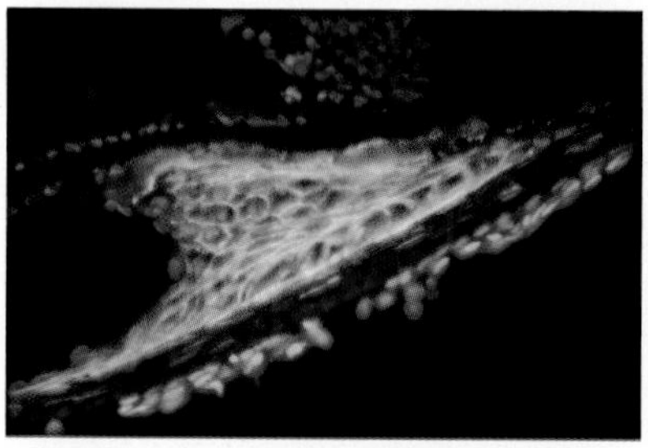

Figure 10.9 The yellow-green fluorescence of the ELF® 97 alcohol precipitate, demonstrating localization of endogenous alkaline phosphatase activity in the ciliary body of the zebrafish eye. Adult zebrafish cryosections were first stained with Texas Red®-X wheat germ agglutinin (W21405) followed by the ELF® 97 phosphate substrate in the ELF® 97 Endogenous Phosphatase Detection Kit (E6601), and finally the nuclei were counterstained with the blue-fluorescent Hoechst 33342 nucleic acid stain (H1399, H3570, H21492). The triple-exposure image was acquired using bandpass filters appropriate for the Texas Red® dye, ELF® 97 alcohol precipitate and AMCA.

In order to precisely localize enzymatic activity in a tissue or cell, on a blot or in a gel, the substrate must yield a product that immediately precipitates or reacts at the site of enzymatic activity. In addition to the commonly used chromogenic substrates, including X-Gal, BCIP and NBT, Molecular Probes has developed fluorogenic ELF® substrates for alkaline phosphatase and several other hydrolytic enzymes (Section 6.3). Our ELF® substrates fluoresce only weakly in the blue range. However, upon enzymatic cleavage, these substrates form the intensely yellow-green–fluorescent ELF® 97 alcohol (E6578), which precipitates immediately at the site of enzymatic activity (Figure 6.23, Figure 7.115, Figure 10.9). The fluorescent ELF® alcohol precipitate is exceptionally photostable (Figure 6.16) and has a high Stokes shift (Figure 6.17). We offer several ELF® kits based on our ELF® 97 phosphatase substrate; see Section 6.3 for a complete discussion of our ELF® technology. The similar ELF® 39 phosphate (Figure 9.65) is used for detection of specific proteins in some of our DyeChrome™ Western Blot Stain Kits (Section 9.4, Figure 9.62). DDAO phosphate is very useful for solution assays but we have also been able to adapt it to yield a fluorescent precipitate that can detect proteins in Western blots; several kits containing DDAO phosphate are described in Section 9.4.

Tyramide signal amplification (TSA) technology (Section 6.2) utilizes a unique concept in fluorescent substrates. Tyramide derivatives labeled with detectable moieties such as biotin or fluorophores are activated by HRP to a phenoxyl radical that is trapped near the site of its formation by reaction with nearby tyrosine residues (Figure 6.5). The covalent bond formed results in detection of HRP-labeled targets with high spatial resolution.

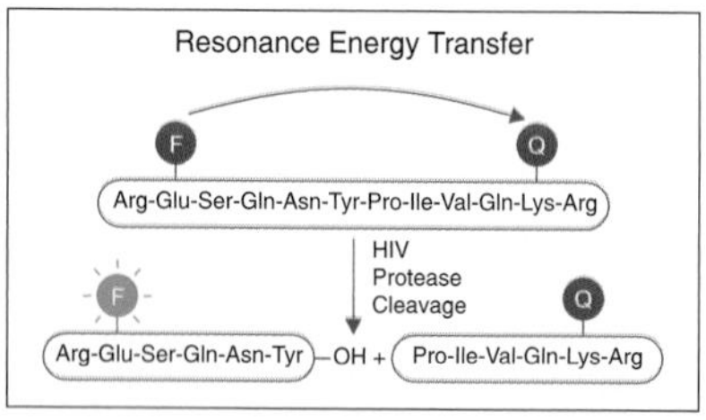

Figure 10.10 Principle of the fluorogenic response to protease cleavage exhibited by HIV protease substrate 1 (H2930). Quenching of the EDANS fluorophore (F) by distance-dependent resonance energy transfer to the dabcyl quencher (Q) is eliminated upon cleavage of the intervening peptide linker.

Substrates Based on Excited-State Energy Transfer

The principle of excited-state energy transfer can also be used to generate fluorogenic substrates (see Note 1.2 "Technical Focus: Fluorescence Resonance Energy Transfer (FRET)" in Section 1.3). For example, the EDANS fluorophore in our HIV protease and renin substrates is effectively quenched by a nearby dabcyl acceptor chromophore (Figure 10.10). This chromophore has been carefully chosen for maximal overlap of its absorbance with the fluorophore's fluorescence, thus ensuring that the fluorescence is quenched through excited-state energy transfer. Proteolytic cleavage of the substrate results in spatial separation of the fluorophore and the acceptor chromophore, thereby restoring the fluorophore's fluorescence.[11–14] Many of the dyes described in Chapter 1 have been used to form energy-transfer pairs, some of which can be introduced during automated synthesis of peptides using modified amino acids described in Section 9.5. Table 1.9 lists our nonfluorescent quenching dyes and their spectral properties. Our QSY® dyes

(Section 1.6, Section 1.8, Section 2.2) have spectral properties that are superior to those of the dabcyl chromophore (Table 1.10, Figure 1.70), making the QSY® dyes useful as nonfluorescent quenchers for a broad range of fluorescent donor dyes (Figure 8.51).

The protease substrates in two of our EnzChek® Protease Assay Kits and their RediPlate™ 96 and RediPlate™ 384 versions (Section 10.4) are heavily labeled casein conjugates; the close proximity of dye molecules results in considerable self-quenching. Hydrolysis of the protein to smaller fragments is accompanied by a dramatic increase in fluorescence, which forms the basis of a simple and sensitive continuous assay for a variety of proteases. In addition, we offer a phospholipase A substrate (bis-BODIPY® FL C_{11}-PC, B7701; Section 17.4) that contains a BODIPY® FL fluorophore on each phospholipid acyl chain. Proximity of the BODIPY® FL fluorophores on adjacent phospholipid acyl chains causes fluorescence self-quenching that is relieved only when the fluorophores are separated by phospholipase A–mediated cleavage. PED6, a phospholipid with a green-fluorescent BODIPY® fatty acid on the lipid portion of the molecule and a 2,4-dinitrophenyl quencher on the polar head group (PED6, D23739; Section 17.4; Figure 17.24) is useful as a specific phospholipase-A_2 substrate.[15]

Fluorescent Derivatization Reagents for Discontinuous Enzyme Assays

The mechanism of some enzymes makes it difficult to obtain a continuous optical change during reaction with an enzyme substrate. However, a discontinuous assay can often be developed by derivatizing the reaction products with one of the reagents described in Chapter 1, Chapter 2 and Chapter 3, usually followed by a separation step in order to generate a product-specific fluorescent signal. For example, fluorescamine (F2332, F20261; Section 1.8) or *o*-phthaldialdehyde (OPA, P2331MP; Section 1.8) can detect the rate of *any* peptidase reaction by measuring the increase in the concentration of free amines in solution.[16,17] The activity of enzymes that produce free coenzyme A from its esters can be detected using thiol-reactive reagents such as 5,5′-dithiobis-(2-nitrobenzoic acid) (DTNB, D8451; Section 5.2) or 7-fluorobenz-2-oxa-1,3-diazole-4-sulfonamide [18] (ABD-F, F6053; Section 2.2). The products of enzymes that metabolize low molecular weight substrates can frequently be detected by chromatographic or electrophoretic analysis. HPLC or capillary zone electrophoresis can also be used to enhance the sensitivity of reactions that yield fluorescent products.[19] Measuring the activity of phospholipases, in particular, often requires chromatographic means to separate the detectable hydrolysis products (Section 17.4).

Substrates that Yield Insoluble Chromophoric Products

A number of chromogenic substrates for hydrolytic enzymes are derived from indolyl chromophores. These initially form a colorless — and sometimes blue-fluorescent — 3-hydroxyindole ("indoxyl"), which spontaneously, or through mediation of an oxidizing agent such as nitro blue tetrazolium (NBT, N6495; Section 10.3) or potassium ferricyanide,[20] is converted to an intensely colored indigo dye that typically precipitates from the medium (Figure 9.69). Halogenated indolyl derivatives, including 5-bromo-4-chloro-3-indolyl β-D-galactopyranoside (X-Gal, B1690, B22015; Section 10.2) and 5-bromo-4-chloro-3-indolyl phosphate (BCIP, B6492, Section 10.3) are generally preferred because they produce finer precipitates that are less likely to diffuse from the site of formation, making them especially useful for detecting enzymatic activity in cells and tissues, on blots and in gels.

References

1. Methods Mol Biol 32, 461 (1994); **2.** J Immunol Methods 150, 5 (1992); **3.** Methods Enzymol 70, 419 (1980); **4.** Bioorg Med Chem Lett 8, 3107 (1998); **5.** Biochemistry 30, 8535 (1991); **6.** Anal Biochem 226, 147 (1995); **7.** Angew Chem Int Ed Engl 30, 1646 (1991); **8.** Biotech Histochem 70, 243 (1995); **9.** J Fluorescence 3, 119 (1993); **10.** J Chromatogr A 698, 181 (1995); **11.** Bioorg Med Chem Lett 2, 1665 (1992); **12.** J Protein Chem 9, 663 (1990); **13.** Science 247, 954 (1990); **14.** Tetrahedron Lett 31, 6493 (1990); **15.** Anal Biochem 276, 27 (1999); **16.** Biochemistry 29, 6670 (1990); **17.** Anal Biochem 123, 41 (1982); **18.** Chem Pharm Bull (Tokyo) 38, 2290 (1990); **19.** Anal Biochem 115, 177 (1981); **20.** Histochemie 23, 266 (1970).

Data Table — 10.1 Introduction to Enzyme Substrates and Their Reference Standards

Cat #	MW	Storage	Soluble	Abs	EC	Em	Solvent	Notes
A191	175.19	L	DMF, DMSO	351	18,000	430	MeOH	1
C183	187.15	L	pH >8, DMF	408	43,000	450	pH 9	
C2110	209.63	F,D,L	DMSO	353	14,000	466	pH 9	2
C12881	246.60	F,D,L	DMSO	371	16,000	464	pH 9	3
D6566	212.15	L	DMSO, DMF	358	18,000	452	pH 9	3, 4
E6578	307.14	L	DMSO	345	ND	530	pH 8	5, 6, 7
F1300	332.31	L	pH >6, DMF	490	93,000	514	pH 9	8
F36915	332.31	RO,L	see Notes	490	93,000	514	pH 9.5	8, 9
H189	176.17	L	DMSO, MeOH	360	19,000	449	pH 9	3
H6482	308.16	L	DMF	646	41,000	659	pH 10	
P12925	541.39	F,D,L	DMSO, EtOH	492	80,000	516	pH 10	8
R363	235.17	L	pH >7, DMF	571	58,000	585	pH 9	10, 11
R6479	366.80	L	DMSO	499	92,000	521	MeOH	12
T659	230.14	L	MeOH	385	16,000	502	pH 10	3

For definitions of the contents of this data table, see "Navigating *The Handbook*" in the introductory pages.

Notes

1. A191 in aqueous solution (pH 7.0): Abs = 342 nm (EC = 16,000 $cm^{-1}M^{-1}$), Em = 441 nm.
2. C2110 in MeOH: Abs = 364 nm (EC = 16,000 $cm^{-1}M^{-1}$), Em = 454 nm.
3. Spectra of hydroxycoumarins are pH-dependent. Below the pK_a, Abs shifts to shorter wavelengths (325–340 nm) and fluorescence intensity decreases. Approximate pK_a values are 7.8 (H189, C2111), 7.5 (H185), 7.3 (T659) and 4.9 (D6566, C12881).
4. The fluorescence quantum yield of DiFMU (D6566) is 0.89 measured in 0.1 M phosphate buffer, pH 10 (Bioorg Med Chem Lett 8, 3107 (1998)).
5. ND = not determined.
6. This product is supplied as a ready-made solution in the solvent indicated under "Soluble."
7. ELF® 97 alcohol is insoluble in water. Spectral maxima listed are for an aqueous suspension; for this reason, the value of EC cannot be determined.
8. Absorption and fluorescence of fluorescein derivatives are pH-dependent. Extinction coefficients and fluorescence quantum yields decrease markedly at pH <7.
9. F36915 consists of a fluorescein solution in 100 mM sodium borate buffer pH 9.5. The concentration of fluorescein is set spectrophotometrically to be equivalent to that of NIST Standard Reference Material (SRM) 1932.
10. Absorption and fluorescence of resorufin are pH-dependent. Below the pK_a (~6.0), Abs shifts to ~480 nm and both EC and the fluorescence quantum yield are markedly lower.
11. R363 is unstable in the presence of thiols such as dithiothreitol (DTT) and 2-mercaptoethanol.
12. R6479 in aqueous solution (pH 7.0): Abs = 496 nm (EC = 83,000 $cm^{-1}M^{-1}$), Em = 520 nm.

Product List — 10.1 Introduction to Enzyme Substrates and Their Reference Standards

Cat #	Product Name	Unit Size
A191	7-amino-4-methylcoumarin *reference standard*	100 mg
C2110	CellTracker™ Blue CMAC (7-amino-4-chloromethylcoumarin)	5 mg
C12881	CellTracker™ Blue CMF_2HC (4-chloromethyl-6,8-difluoro-7-hydroxycoumarin)	5 mg
C183	3-cyano-7-hydroxycoumarin	100 mg
D6566	6,8-difluoro-7-hydroxy-4-methylcoumarin (DiFMU) *reference standard*	10 mg
E6578	ELF® 97 alcohol *1 mM solution in DMSO*	1 mL
F1300	fluorescein *reference standard*	1 g
F36915	fluorescein *NIST-traceable standard* *nominal concentration 50 µM* *special packaging*	5 x 1 mL
H6482	7-hydroxy-9*H*-(1,3-dichloro-9,9-dimethylacridin-2-one) (DDAO) *reference standard*	10 mg
H189	7-hydroxy-4-methylcoumarin *reference standard*	1 g
P12925	5-(pentafluorobenzoylamino)fluorescein (PFB-F)	5 mg
R363	resorufin, sodium salt *reference standard*	100 mg
R6479	rhodamine 110 (R110) *reference standard*	25 mg
T659	β-trifluoromethylumbelliferone (7-hydroxy-4-trifluoromethylcoumarin) *reference standard*	100 mg

For current prices or to order online, visit probes.invitrogen.com

10.2 Detecting Glycosidases

Glycosidase enzymes exhibit very high selectivity for hydrolysis of their preferred sugars. For example, β-galactosidase rapidly hydrolyzes β-D-galactopyranosides but usually does not hydrolyze either the anomeric α-D-galactopyranosides or the isomeric β-D-glucopyranosides. Endogenous glycosidase activity is frequently used to characterize strains of microorganisms[1–3] and to selectively label organelles of mammalian cells;[4–6] defects in glycosidase activity are characteristic of several diseases.[7–9]

In addition, glycosidases are important reporter gene markers. Specifically, *lacZ*, which encodes β-galactosidase, is extensively used as a reporter gene in animals and yeast, whereas the β-glucuronidase (GUS) gene is a popular reporter gene in plants.[10–13] Glycosidase substrates are also used in conjunction with glycosidase-conjugated secondary detection reagents in immunohistochemical techniques and enzyme-linked immunosorbent assays[14] (ELISAs). Molecular Probes' complete line of fluorogenic and chromogenic glycosidase substrates is listed in Table 10.1.

Table 10.1 — Glycosidase enzymes and their fluorogenic and chromogenic substrates

Carbohydrate (Enzyme)	Notes on Enzyme Activity	Labeled Substrate (Abs/Em of the products) *		Cat #
β-D-Galactopyranoside (β-Galactosidase, E.C. 3.2.1.23)	• Useful as a reporter gene marker[1–4] • Useful for ELISAs[5–8] • Useful for enumerating coliforms from the family *Enterobacteriaceae*[9–11] • Useful for classifying mycobacteria[12]	Blue-fluorescent products	3-Carboxyumbelliferyl (386/448)	C1488[5,13]
			4-Chloromethyl-6,8-difluoroumbelliferyl (371/464)	C11946
			6,8-Difluoro-4-methylumbelliferyl (358/452)	D11945[14]
			6,8-Difluoro-4-heptadecylumbelliferyl (366/454)	D11950
			4-Methylumbelliferyl (360/449)	M1489MP[15,16]
		Green-fluorescent products	Fluorescein (490/514)	F1179[1–3]
			5-(Pentafluorobenzoylamino)-fluorescein (490/514)	P11948
			C_2-Fluorescein (490/514)	A22010[17]
			C_8-Fluorescein (490/514)	O2892[18]
			C_{12}-Fluorescein (490/514)	D2893, I2904 ‡[19–21]
			5-Chloromethylfluorescein (490/514)	D2920 †[22]
		Red-fluorescent products	C_{12}-Resorufin (571/585)	I2906 ‡[23,24]
			DDAO (646/659)	D6488
			Resorufin (571/585)	R1159[25]
		Chromogenic substrates	5-Bromo-4-chloro-3-indoyl (615/NA)	X-Gal; B1690, B22015[26]
β-D-Glucopyranoside (β-Glucosidase, E.C. 3.2.1.31)	• Deficiency in acid β-glucosidase, which leads to abnormal lysosomal storage, characterizes Gaucher's disease[27] • Useful as a marker for the endoplasmic reticulum[28]	Green-fluorescent products	Fluorescein (490/514)	F2881[27,29]
			5-(Pentafluorobenzoylamino)fluorescein (490/514)	P11947[30]
β-D-Glucuronide (β-Glucuronidase, GUS; E.C. 3.2.1.31)	• Useful as a reporter gene marker[31] • Useful as a lysosomal marker[32,33] • Useful for detecting *E. coli*; 94–96% of *E. coli* contain this enzyme, but it is less common in *Shigella* (44–58%), *Salmonella* (20–29%) and *Yersinia* strains[9,34–36]	Blue-fluorescent products	6,8-Difluoro-4-methylumbelliferyl (358/452)	D11951
			4-Methylumbelliferyl (360/449)	M1490[15,32,33,37–39]
			4-Trifluoromethylumbelliferyl (385/502)	T658[40]
		Green-fluorescent products	Fluorescein (490/514)	F2915[41]
			5-(Pentafluorobenzoylamino)fluorescein (490/514)	P11949[41]
			C_{12}-Fluorescein (490/514)	I2908 ‡[42,43]
			ELF® 97 (345/530)	E6587[44,45]
		Chromogenic substrates	5-Bromo-4-chloro-3-indoyl (615/NA)	X-GlcU, B1691[33,37]
			5-Bromo-6-chloro-3-indoyl (565/NA)	B8408[46]

* Approximate absorption (Abs) and fluorescence emission (Em) maxima of enzymatic hydrolysis product, in nm. † DetectaGene™ Green Gene Expression Kit. ‡ ImaGene Green™ or ImaGene Red™ Gene Expression Kit. NA = Not applicable. **1.** Cytometry 17, 216 (1994); **2.** Dev Biol 161, 77 (1994); **3.** Proc Natl Acad Sci U S A 85, 2603 (1988); **4.** Biophys J 74, 11 (1998); **5.** Anal Biochem 146, 211 (1985); **6.** Exp Parasitol 73, 440 (1991); **7.** J Immunol Methods 54, 297 (1982); **8.** J Virol Methods 3, 155 (1981); **9.** Microbiol Rev 55, 335 (1991); **10.** J Appl Bacteriol 64, 65 (1988); **11.** Appl Environ Microbiol 35, 136 (1978); **12.** Zentralbl Bakteriol 280, 476 (1994); **13.** Infect Immun 61, 5231 (1993); **14.** Anal Biochem 273, 41 (1999); **15.** Anal Biochem 104, 182 (1980); **16.** Anal Biochem 215, 24 (1993); **17.** FEMS Microbiol Lett 179, 317 (1999); **18.** Cytometry 20, 324 (1995); **19.** Appl Environ Microbiol 60, 4638 (1994); **20.** Proc Natl Acad Sci U S A 89, 10681 (1992); **21.** FASEB J 5, 3108 (1991); **22.** J Neurosci 15, 1025 (1995); **23.** Biotechnol Bioeng 42, 1113 (1993); **24.** US Patent No. 5,242,805 (1993); **25.** Anal Chim Acta 163, 67 (1984); **26.** Biotechniques 7, 576 (1989); **27.** Cell Biochem Funct 11, 167 (1993); **28.** Nature 369, 113 (1994); **29.** Anal Biochem 247, 268 (1997); **30.** Blood 89, 3412 (1997); **31.** Plant Mol Biol Rep 5, 387 (1988); **32.** Cell Signal 3, 625 (1991); **33.** J Immunol Methods 100, 211 (1987); **34.** Appl Environ Microbiol 59, 3534 (1993); **35.** Appl Environ Microbiol 50, 1383 (1985); **36.** J Clin Microbiol 13, 483 (1981); **37.** J Appl Bacteriol 74, 223 (1993); **38.** Arch Biochem Biophys 286, 394 (1991); **39.** Plant Sci 78, 73 (1991); **40.** Biochem Int 24, 1135 (1991); **41.** J Biol Chem 274, 657 (1999); **42.** Microbiology 143, 267 (1997); **43.** Plant J 10, 745 (1996); **44.** Electrophoresis 21, 497 (2000); **45.** Tetrahedron 53, 7159 (1997); **46.** Biotechniques 19, 352 (1995).

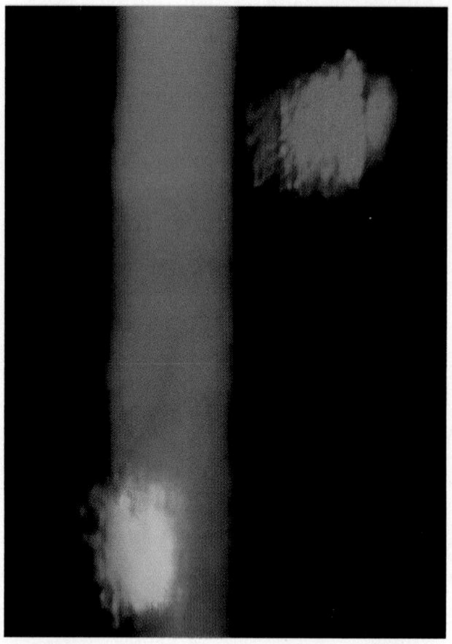

Figure 10.11 Sternomastoid muscle fibers of a living mouse that have been transfected with YOYO®-1 dye–stained DNA (red) containing the *lacZ* reporter gene and then stained with the β-galactosidase substrate fluorescein di-β-D-galactopyranoside (FDG, F1179). DNA stained with YOYO®-1 (Y3601) prior to implantation could still be localized five days after application. Fluorescence signals were visualized *in situ* by epifluorescence microscopy with a low–light level SIT camera and a computer imaging system. Image contributed by Peter van Mier, Washington University School of Medicine.

Some General Fluorogenic β-Galactosidase Substrates

Fluorescein Digalactoside

Probably the most sensitive fluorogenic substrate for detecting β-galactosidase is fluorescein di-β-D-galactopyranoside[15] (FDG, F1179; Figure 10.11). Nonfluorescent FDG is sequentially hydrolyzed by β-galactosidase, first to fluorescein monogalactoside (FMG) and then to highly fluorescent fluorescein (F1300, F36915; Section 10.1; Figure 1.52). Enzyme-mediated hydrolysis of FDG can be followed by the increase in either absorbance or fluorescence. Although the turnover rates of FDG and its analogs are considerably slower than that of the common spectrophotometric galactosidase substrate, *o*-nitrophenyl β-D-galactopyranoside (ONPG),[16,17] the absorbance of fluorescein is about fivefold greater than that of *o*-nitrophenol. Moreover, fluorescence-based measurements can be several orders of magnitude more sensitive than absorption-based measurements. Fluorescence-based assays employing FDG are also reported to be 100- to 1000-fold more sensitive than radioisotope-based ELISAs.[18]

In addition to its use in ELISAs, the FDG substrate has proven very effective for identifying *lacZ*-positive cells with fluorescence microscopy[19–22] and flow cytometry.[23–28] FDG has been employed to identify cells infected with recombinant herpesvirus,[29] to detect unique patterns of β-galactosidase expression in live transgenic zebrafish embryos[19] and to monitor β-galactosidase expression in bacteria.[20,30,31] The purity of FDG and its analogs is very important because a reagent with extremely low fluorescence background is essential for most applications. Our stringent quality control ensures that the fluorescent contamination of FDG is less than 50 ppm.

The FluoReporter® *lacZ* Flow Cytometry Kits (50-test kit, F1930; 250-test kit, F1931) provide materials and protocols for quantitating β-galactosidase activity with FDG in single cells using flow cytometry. These kits are accompanied by a license to practice patented techniques for loading FDG by hypotonic shock and improving retention of fluorescein in *lacZ*-positive cells. In addition to a detailed protocol, each FluoReporter® *lacZ* Flow Cytometry Kit contains convenient premixed solutions of:

- FDG
- Phenylethyl β-D-thiogalactopyranoside (PETG; also available separately as a solid, P1692), a broad-spectrum β-galactosidase inhibitor for stopping the reaction[32]
- Chloroquine diphosphate for inhibiting hydrolysis of the substrate in acidic organelles by endogenous galactosidase enzymes
- Propidium iodide for detecting dead cells

Each kit provides sufficient reagents for 50 (in Kit F1930) or 250 (in Kit F1931) flow cytometry assays. This assay enables researchers to detect heterogeneous expression patterns and to sort and clone individual cells expressing known quantities of β-galactosidase. Practical reviews on using FDG for flow cytometric analysis and sorting of *lacZ*-positive cells are available.[33,34]

The fluorescent hydrolysis product of FDG is fluorescein (F1300, F36915; Section 10.1; Figure 15.3), which rapidly leaks from cells under physiological conditions, making the use of FDG problematic for prolonged studies. Our DetectaGene™ Green, ImaGene Green™ and ImaGene Red™ substrates (see below) have been specifically designed to improve retention of the fluorescent hydrolysis products in cells.

Resorufin Galactoside

Unlike FDG, resorufin β-D-galactopyranoside (R1159) requires only a single-step hydrolysis reaction to attain full fluorescence.[35] This substrate is especially useful for sensitive enzyme measurements in ELISAs.[14,36] The relatively low pK_a (~6.0) of its hydrolysis product, resorufin (R363, Section 10.1, Figure 10.6), permits its use for continuous measurement of enzymatic activity at physiological pH. Resorufin galactoside has also been used to quantitate β-galactosidase activity in single yeast cells by flow cytometry[37] and to detect immobilized β-galactosidase activity in bioreactors.[38,39]

DDAO Galactoside

Although substrates based on DDAO (7-hydroxy-9*H*-(1,3-dichloro-9,9-dimethylacridin-2-one)) are intrinsically fluorescent (excitation/emission ~460/610 nm), β-galactosidase–catalyzed hydrolysis of DDAO galactoside (D6488) liberates the DDAO fluorophore (Figure 10.12), which absorbs and emits light at much longer wavelengths (excitation/emission ~645/660 nm) (Figure 10.13). Not only can DDAO (H6482, Section 10.1) be excited without interference from the unhydrolyzed substrate, but its fluorescence emission is detected at wavelengths that are well beyond the autofluorescence exhibited by most biological samples. The relatively low pK_a of DDAO (~5.5) permits continuous monitoring of β-galactosidase activity at physiological pH.

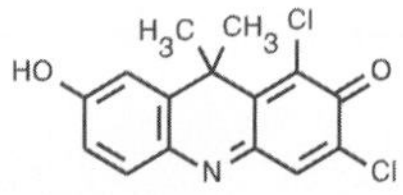

Figure 10.12 H6482 7-hydroxy-9*H*-(1,3-dichloro-9,9-dimethylacridin-2-one) (DDAO).

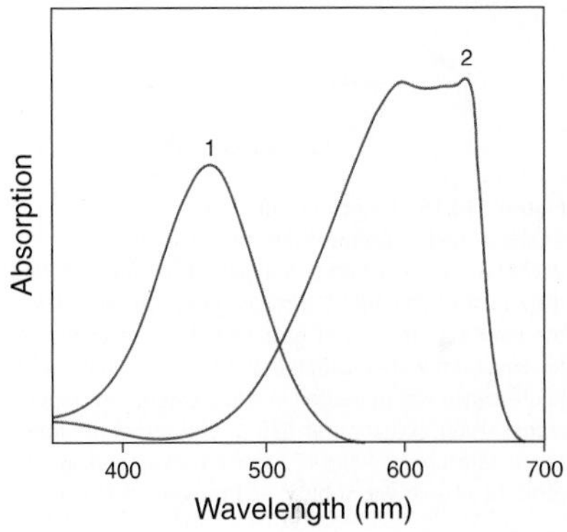

Figure 10.13 Absorption spectra of **1)** DDAO galactoside (D6488) and **2)** DDAO (H6482) at equal concentrations in pH 9 aqueous buffer. These spectra show the large spectral shift accompanying enzymatic cleavage of DDAO-based substrates. DDAO phosphate (D6487) has very similar spectra.

Methylumbelliferyl Galactoside and Its Difluorinated Analog

The fluorogenic β-galactosidase substrate β-methylumbelliferyl β-D-galactopyranoside (MUG, M1489MP) is commonly used to detect β-galactosidase activity in cell extracts,[40–42] lysosomes[43] and human blood serum.[44] However, the hydrolysis product, 7-hydroxy-4-methylcoumarin (β-methylumbelliferone, H189; Section 10.1; Figure 10.2), has a relatively high pK_a (~7.8), precluding its use for continuous measurement of enzymatic activity. 6,8-Difluoro-4-methylumbelliferyl β-D-galactopyranoside (DiFMUG, D11945) yields a hydrolysis product — 6,8-difluoro-7-hydroxy-4-methylcoumarin (D6566, Section 10.1, Figure 10.2) — with a much lower pK_a (4.9),[45] allowing its detection at physiological pH.[46,47] Given the low pK_a of its hydrolysis product, DiFMUG should be especially useful for the continuous *in vitro* assay of β-D-galactosidase activity at any pH >6. The fluorinated coumarin glycosides are patented by Molecular Probes.

Carboxyumbelliferyl Galactoside and the FluoReporter® lacZ/Galactosidase Quantitation Kit

Hydrolysis of 3-carboxyumbelliferyl β-D-galactopyranoside (CUG, C1488) by β-galactosidase yields 7-hydroxycoumarin-3-carboxylic acid (H185, Section 10.1). 7-Hydroxycoumarin has a pK_a below the pH at which the turnover rate is optimal, facilitating the use of CUG for continuous measurements of β-galactosidase activity. Unlike most substrates for β-galactosidase, CUG is quite water-soluble and can be used over a wide range of concentrations in enzymatic activity measurements.[48–50] Our FluoReporter® *lacZ*/Galactosidase Quantitation Kit (F2905) provides a CUG-based method for quantitating β-galactosidase activity in ELISAs or *lacZ*-positive cell extracts. Each kit contains:

- CUG
- 7-Hydroxycoumarin-3-carboxylic acid, a reference standard
- A detailed protocol suitable for use with any fluorescence microplate reader

Sufficient reagents are provided for approximately 1000 β-galactosidase assays. We have demonstrated a practical detection limit of ~0.5 pg of β-galactosidase using this kit and a fluorescence microplate reader.

Fluorescent Glycosphingolipids

β-Galactosidase enzymes that act on the lipophilic sphingosyl galactosides, including galactosylceramidase (EC 3.2.1.46) and G_{M1} ganglioside β-galactosidase (EC 3.2.1.23), are particularly important in neurochemistry. The preferred substrates for these enzymes are sphingolipids derived from galactose (Section 13.3). Galactosylceramidase converts substrates such as our BODIPY® FL C_{12}-galactosylceramide (D7519) back to the ceramide. Purified G_{M1} ganglioside galactosidase removes the terminal galactose residue from lactosylceramides such as our BODIPY® FL C_5-lactosylceramide[51] (D13951), yielding the corresponding glucosylceramide.[52] BODIPY® FL C_5-lactosylceramide complexed with bovine serum albumin (BSA) (B34402) may also be useful for assaying G_{M1} ganglioside galactosidase. Complexing fluorescent lipids with BSA facilitates the preparation of aqueous solutions by eliminating the need for organic solvents to dissolve the lipophilic probe. The lack of a spectral shift between the substrates and the hydrolysis products in these reactions means that extraction and chromatographic separation of the products is necessary for assessment of enzyme activity.

Amplex® Red Galactose/Galactose Oxidase Assay Kit

Our Amplex® Red reagent (10-acetyl-3,7-dihydroxyphenoxazine, A12222, A22177; Section 10.5; Figure 10.58) is an unusually stable peroxidase substrate that we have used in coupled reactions to detect a wide variety of analytes, including both enzymes and their substrates (see Section 10.5 for a list of all of our Amplex® Red Kits and reagents). Most of the assays can be performed as continuous assays at neutral or slightly acidic pH and are particularly suitable for automation and high-throughput screening using either an absorption- or fluorescence-based microplate reader.

Rather than requiring an unnatural fluorogenic or chromogenic substrate for β-galactosidase (or α-galactosidase), our Amplex® Red reagent–based technology permits the direct quantitation of free galactose, which is produced by a wide variety of enzymes. Even enzymes that act on polysaccharides and glycolipids but are difficult to assay using known chromogenic substrates can, in some cases, be detected and their activity quantitated using the Amplex® Red reagent in combination with galactose oxidase and horseradish peroxidase. Unlike glucose oxidase, galactose oxidase produces H_2O_2 from either free galactose or from polysaccharides — including glycoproteins in solution and on cell surfaces — and from certain glycolipids in which galactose is the terminal residue (Figure 10.14). Because the galactose oxidase–catalyzed reaction does not require prior cleavage of the glycoside to free galactose by a galactosidase, appropriate control reactions must be used to ascertain whether the rate-limiting step is the galactosidase- or galactose oxidase–mediated reaction.

The Amplex® Red Galactose/Galactose Oxidase Assay Kit (A22179) provides an ultrasensitive method for detecting galactose (Figure 10.15) and galactose oxidase (Figure 10.16) activity. This assay utilizes the Amplex® Red reagent (Figure 10.58) to detect H_2O_2 generated by galactose oxidase–mediated oxidation of desialated galactose moieties. In the presence of horseradish peroxidase (HRP), the H_2O_2 thus produced reacts with the Amplex® Red reagent in a 1:1 stoichiometry to generate the red-fluorescent oxidation product resorufin.[53] Resorufin has absorption and fluorescence emission maxima of approximately 571 nm and 585 nm, respectively (Figure 10.6), and because its extinction coefficient is high (54,000 $cm^{-1}M^{-1}$), the assay can be performed either fluorometrically or spectrophotometrically. The Amplex® Red Galactose/Galactose Oxidase Assay Kit provides all the reagents and a general protocol for the assay of galactose-producing enzymes or for the assay of galactose oxidase, including:

- Amplex® Red reagent
- Dimethylsulfoxide (DMSO)
- Horseradish peroxidase (HRP)
- Hydrogen peroxide (H_2O_2)

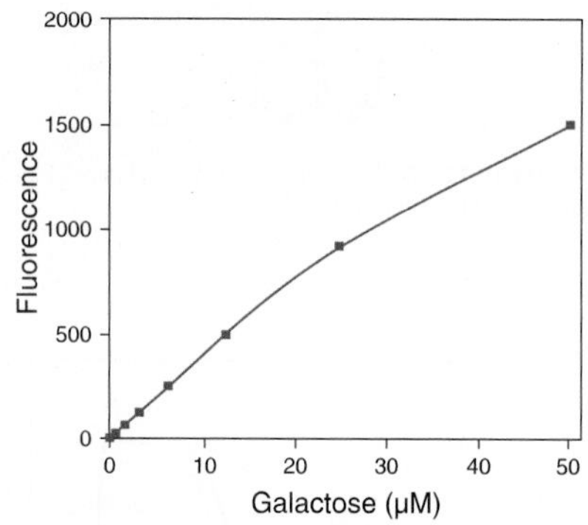

Figure 10.15 Detection of galactose using the Amplex® Red Galactose/Galactose Oxidase Assay Kit (A22179). Each reaction contained 50 µM Amplex® Red reagent, 0.1 U/mL HRP, 2 U/mL of galactose oxidase and the indicated amount of galactose in 1X reaction buffer. Reactions were incubated at 37°C. After 30 minutes, fluorescence was measured in a fluorescence microplate reader using excitation at 530 ± 12.5 nm and fluorescence detection at 590 ± 17.5 nm. A background fluorescence of 93 units was subtracted from each data point.

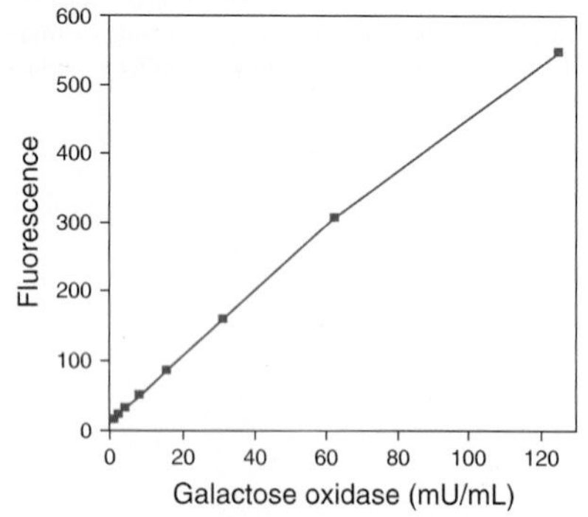

Figure 10.16 Detection of galactose oxidase activity using the Amplex® Red Galactose/Galactose Oxidase Assay Kit (A22179). Each reaction contained 50 µM Amplex® Red reagent, 0.1 U/mL HRP, 100 µM galactose and the indicated amount of galactose oxidase in 1X reaction buffer. Reactions were incubated at 37°C. After 20 minutes, fluorescence was measured in a fluorescence microplate reader using excitation at 530 ± 12.5 nm with fluorescence detection at 590 ± 17.5 nm.

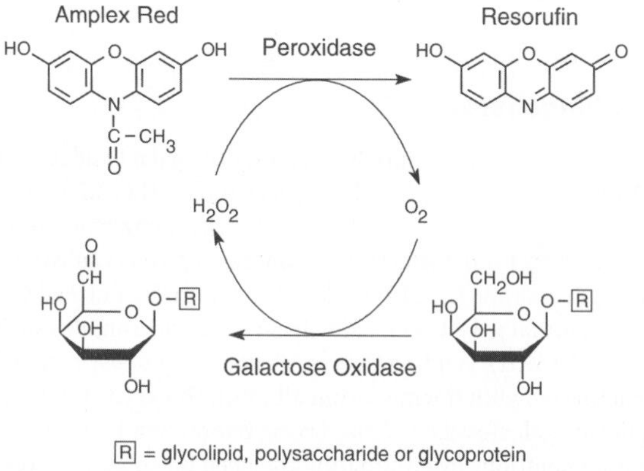

Figure 10.14 Detection scheme utilized in the Amplex® Red Galactose/Galactose Oxidase Assay Kit (A22179). Oxidation of the terminal galactose residue of a glycoprotein, glycolipid or polysaccharide results in the generation of H_2O_2, which, in the presence of horseradish peroxidase (HRP), reacts stoichiometrically with the Amplex® Red reagent to generate the red-fluorescent oxidation product, resorufin.

- Concentrated reaction buffer
- Galactose oxidase from *Dactylium dendroides*
- D-Galactose
- A detailed protocol

Sufficient reagents are provided for approximately 400 assays using either a fluorescence- or absorption-based microplate reader and reaction volumes of 100 µL per assay. The Amplex® Red galactose/galactose oxidase assay accurately measures as low as 4 µM galactose and 2 mU/mL galactose oxidase activity (Figure 10.15, Figure 10.16). Because of the high absorbance of resorufin, the absorptimetric assay has only slightly lower sensitivity than the fluorometric assay.

Modified Fluorogenic β-Galactosidase Substrates with Improved Cellular Retention

The primary problems associated with detecting *lacZ* expression in live cells using fluorogenic substrates are:

- Difficulty in loading the substrates under physiological conditions
- Leakage of the fluorescent product from live cells
- High levels of endogenous β-galactosidase activity in many cells

Our DetectaGene™ Green, ImaGene Green™ and ImaGene Red™ Kits are designed to improve the sensitivity of β-galactosidase assays by yielding products that are better retained in viable cells and, in the case of the ImaGene Green™ and ImaGene Red™ Kits, by providing substrates that can be passively loaded into live cells. The high level of endogenous β-galactosidase activity remains an obstacle when detecting low levels of *lacZ* expression.

DetectaGene™ Green lacZ *Gene Expression Kit*

The patented substrate in our DetectaGene™ Green *lacZ* Gene Expression Kit (D2920) — 5-chloromethylfluorescein di-β-D-galactopyranoside (CMFDG) — is a galactose derivative that has been chemically modified to include a mildly thiol-reactive chloromethyl group (Figure 10.17). Once loaded into the cell using the Influx™ pinocytic cell-loading reagent (I14402, included in Kit D2920; Figure 10.18) or by microinjection, hypotonic shock or another technique (Table 14.1), the DetectaGene™ substrate undergoes two reactions: 1) its two galactose moieties are cleaved by intracellular β-galactosidase and 2) either simultaneously or sequentially, its chloromethyl moiety reacts with glutathione and possibly other intracellular thiols to form a membrane-impermeant, peptide–fluorescent dye adduct[54] (Figure 10.17). Because peptides do not readily cross the plasma membrane, the resulting fluorescent adduct is much better retained than is the free dye, even in cells that have been kept at 37°C. We have found that *lacZ*-positive cells loaded from medium containing 1 mM CMFDG are as fluorescent as cells loaded with 40-fold higher concentrations of FDG. Furthermore, unlike the free dye, the peptide–fluorescent dye adducts contain amine groups and can therefore be covalently linked to surrounding biomolecules by fixation with formaldehyde or glutaraldehyde. This property permits long-term storage of the labeled cells or tissue, as well as amplification of the conjugate by standard immunohistochemical techniques using our anti-fluorescein/Oregon Green® antibody (Section 7.4, Table 7.18).

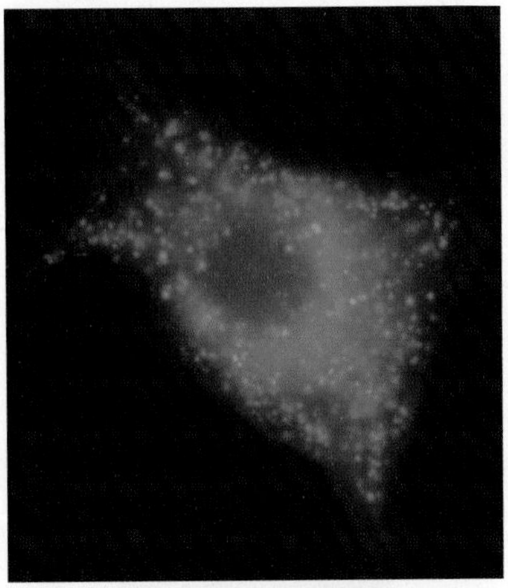

Figure 10.18 Live CRE BAG 2 cells loaded with the β-galactosidase substrate from the DetectaGene™ Green CMFDG *lacZ* Gene Expression Kit (D2920). The substrate was loaded into cells with the aid of the Influx™ pinocytic cell-loading reagent (I14402), a component of the DetectaGene™ Green Kit. The cells were then stained with LysoTracker® Red DND-99 (L7528) to differentiate lysosomal from cytoplasmic localization of the green-fluorescent CMFDG product, as well as to illustrate the selective rupture of only the Influx™ reagent-induced pinocytic vesicles. The double-exposure image was acquired using bandpass filters appropriate for fluorescein and Texas Red® dye.

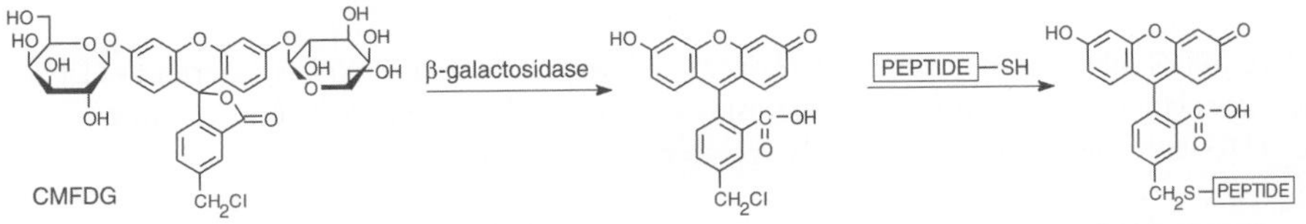

Figure 10.17 Sequential β-galactosidase hydrolysis and peptide conjugate formation of CMFDG, a component of the DetectaGene™ Green CMFDG *lacZ* Gene Expression Kit (D2920).

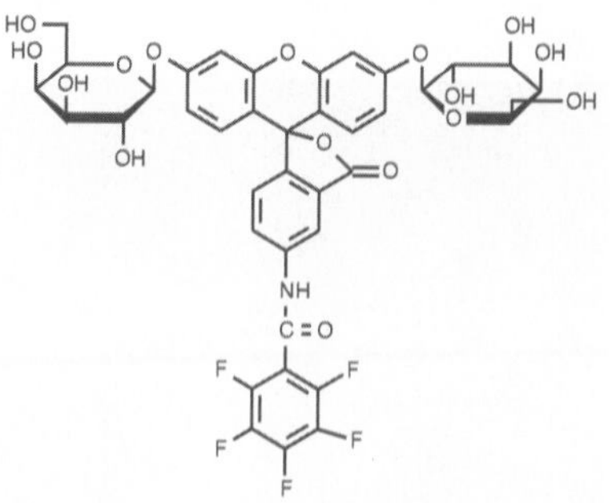

Figure 10.19 P11948 5-(pentafluorobenzoylamino)-fluorescein di-β-D-galactopyranoside (PFB-FDG).

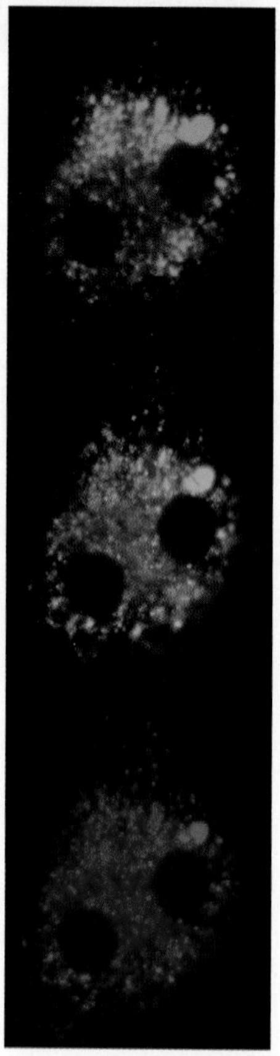

Figure 10.20 Bovine pulmonary artery endothelial cells simultaneously stained with LysoTracker® Red DND-99 (L7528), a cell-permeant, fixable lysosomal stain, and with 5-(pentafluorobenzoylamino)fluorescein di-β-D-galactopyranoside (PFB-FDG, P11948), a fluorogenic substrate for β-galactosidase. PFB-FDG is nonfluorescent until enzymatically hydrolyzed to green-fluorescent PFB-F. The center image demonstrates colocalization of the LysoTracker® Red DND-99 dye and PFB-F to the lysosomes. The top image was acquired with a bandpass filter set appropriate for fluorescein, the bottom image was acquired with a bandpass filter set appropriate for Texas Red® dye, and the center image was acquired with a double bandpass optical filter set appropriate for fluorescein and the Texas Red® dye.

The CMFDG substrate in our DetectaGene™ Green *lacZ* Gene Expression Kit was used to stain *lacZ*-expressing floor plate cells in tissue dissected from a developing mouse embryo,[55] to identify *lacZ*-enhancer–trapped *Drosophila* neurons in culture and to detect β-galactosidase activity in hippocampus slices.[56] In the latter study, the fluorescence of the neurons could still be visualized 24 hours after dye loading, and the fluorescent CMFDG-loaded neurons exhibited a normal pattern and time course of axonal outgrowth and branching.[57] CMFDG also has been microinjected into primary hepatocytes, fibroblasts and glioma cells to detect β-galactosidase activity[58] and has been incorporated into an electrophysiological recording pipette to confirm the identity of neurons cotransfected with the *lacZ* gene and a second gene encoding Ca^{2+}/calmodulin-dependent protein kinase II[59] (CaM kinase II).

The DetectaGene™ Green CMFDG *lacZ* Gene Expression Kit (D2920) contains:

- DetectaGene™ Green CMFDG substrate (Figure 10.17)
- Phenylethyl β-D-thiogalactopyranoside (PETG; also available separately as a solid, P1692), a broad-spectrum β-galactosidase inhibitor for stopping the reaction[32]
- Verapamil for inhibiting product efflux[60,61]
- Chloroquine diphosphate for inhibiting acidic hydrolysis of the substrate
- Propidium iodide for detecting dead cells
- Influx™ pinocytic cell-loading reagent for introducing CMFDG into cells
- A detailed protocol for detecting β-galactosidase activity

When used at the recommended dilutions, sufficient reagents are provided for approximately 200 flow cytometry tests with the DetectaGene™ Green CMFDG Kit. Verapamil has been added to the DetectaGene™ Green CMFDG *lacZ* Gene Expression Kit because we have observed that cell retention of the fluorescent dye–peptide adduct can be considerably improved in many cell types by adding verapamil to the medium.[60]

PFB Aminofluorescein Digalactoside

Our patented 5-(pentafluorobenzoylamino)fluorescein di-β-D-galactopyranoside (PFB-FDG, P11948; Figure 10.19) yields the green-fluorescent PFB-F dye (P12925, Section 10.1), which appears to localize to endosomal and lysosomal compartments when loaded into cells by pinocytosis (Figure 10.20), similar to our PFB aminofluorescein diglucoside (PFB-FDGlu, P11947; see below). Thus, PFB-FDG is potentially useful for studying lysosomal storage diseases, including Krabbe's disease, G_{M1} gangliosidosis, galactosialidosis and Morquio syndrome, which are all associated with deficient lysosomal β-galactosidase activity.[62]

ImaGene Green™ and ImaGene Red™ lacZ Reagents and Gene Expression Kits

The patented fluorescein- and resorufin-based galactosidase substrates in our ImaGene Green™ and ImaGene Red™ *lacZ* Gene Expression Kits (I2904, I2906) have been covalently modified to include a 12-carbon lipophilic moiety. Unlike FDG or CMFDG (Figure 10.17), these lipophilic fluorescein- and resorufin-based substrates — abbreviated C_{12}FDG (Figure 10.21) and C_{12}RG (Figure 10.22) for the ImaGene Green™ and ImaGene Red™ substrates, respectively — can be loaded simply by adding the substrate to the aqueous medium in which the cells or organisms are growing, either at ambient temperatures or at 37°C. Once inside the cell, the substrates are cleaved by β-galactosidase, producing fluorescent products that are well retained by the cells, probably by incorporation of their lipophilic tails within the cellular membranes. Mammalian NIH 3T3 *lacZ*-positive cells grown for several days in medium containing 60 µM C_{12}FDG appear morphologically normal, continue to undergo cell division and remain fluorescent for up to three cell divisions after replacement with substrate-free medium.[54,63]

The C_{12}FDG substrate in our ImaGene Green™ *lacZ* Expression Kit (I2904) is superior to FDG for flow cytometric detection of β-galactosidase activity in live mammalian cells.[64] Using C_{12}FDG with flow cytometric methods, researchers have:

- Assessed levels of *lacZ* gene expression in recombinant Chinese hamster ovary (CHO) cells throughout the cell cycle, which was monitored with Hoechst 33342[65] (H1399; H3570; FluoroPure™ Grade, H21492; Section 8.1)
- Identified endocrine cell precursors in dissociated fetal pancreatic tissue based on their high levels of endogenous acid β-galactosidase[66]

- Measured β-galactosidase activity in single recombinant *E. coli* bacteria [67]
- Detected the activity of β-galactosidase fusion proteins in yeast [68]
- Sorted β-galactosidase–expressing mouse sperm cells [69] and insect cells that harbor recombinant baculovirus [70,71]

The C_{12}FDG substrate was also useful in a fluorescence microscopy study of zebrafish expressing a *lacZ* reporter gene that was under the control of a mammalian homeobox gene promoter.[72] In some cell types, C_{12}FDG produces high levels of background fluorescence that may prohibit its use in assaying low β-galactosidase expression.[21]

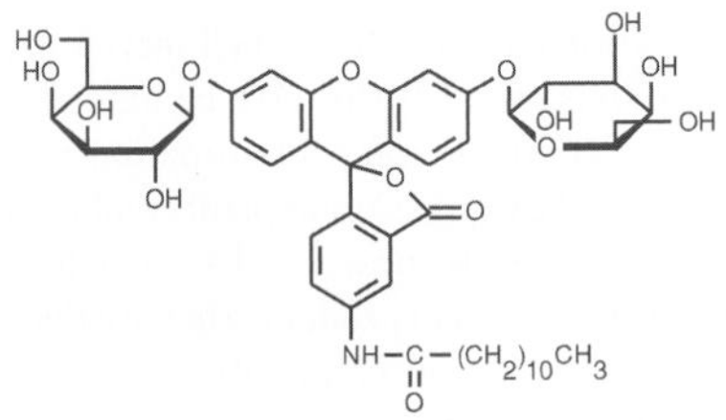

Figure 10.21 I2904 ImaGene™ Green C_{12}FDG.

Molecular Probes' ImaGene Green™ C_{12}FDG or ImaGene Red™ C_{12}RG *lacZ* Gene Expression Kits contain:

- ImaGene Green™ C_{12}FDG (in Kit I2904) or ImaGene Red™ C_{12}RG (in Kit I2906)
- Phenylethyl β-D-thiogalactopyranoside (PETG; also available separately as a solid, P1692), a broad-spectrum β-galactosidase inhibitor for stopping the reaction [32]
- Chloroquine diphosphate for inhibiting acidic hydrolysis of the substrate
- A detailed protocol for detecting β-galactosidase activity

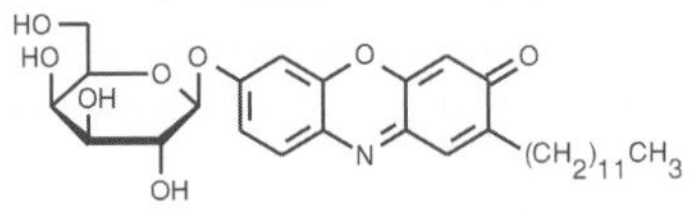

Figure 10.22 I2906 ImaGene™ Red C_{12}RG.

Each kit provides sufficient reagents for 100–200 assays, depending on the volume used for each experiment.

5-Dodecanoylaminofluorescein di-β-D-galactopyranoside (C_{12}FDG) is available separately (D2893) and we also offer the somewhat less lipophilic 5-octanoylaminofluorescein di-β-D-galactopyranoside (C_8FDG, O2892). The C_8FDG analog is optimal for investigating the expression of *lacZ* fusion genes in sporulating cultures of *Bacillus subtilis* [73] and is a better substrate than C_{12}FDG for the detection of β-galactosidase activity in sperm containing the *lacZ* gene.[74] 5-Acetylaminofluorescein di-β-D-galactopyranoside (C_2FDG, A22010) is particularly useful for detecting *lacZ* reporter gene expression in slow-growing mycobacteria, including *Mycobacterium tuberculosis*, using a fluorescence microplate reader or a flow cytometer.[75]

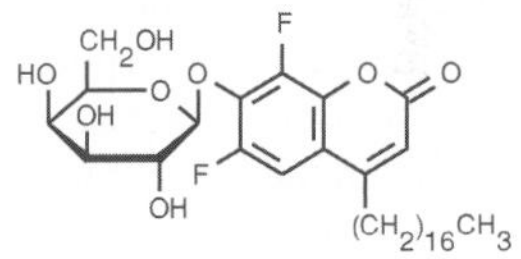

Figure 10.23 D11950 6,8-difluoro-4-heptadecylumbelliferyl β-D-galactopyranoside (C_{17}DiFUG).

Chloromethyl and Lipophilic Derivatives of DiFMUG

The relatively low pK_a of our 6,8-difluoro-7-hydroxycoumarin derivatives (Figure 1.96) has also allowed us to develop some useful probes for detecting enzymatic activity *in vivo*. Although the β-galactosidase DiFMUG (D11945) readily enters many live eukaryotic cells, its hydrolysis product (6,8-difluoro-7-hydroxy-4-methylcoumarin, DiFMU; D6566; Section 10.1; Figure 10.3) is not well retained. To address this limitation, we have developed two modified galactosidase substrates using product-retention strategies that have proven useful for our patented DetectaGene™ Green, ImaGene Green™ and ImaGene Red™ glycosidase substrates.

As with our DetectaGene™ products, we have replaced the methyl group of DiFMUG with a mildly thiol-reactive chloromethyl group, yielding the β-galactosidase substrate CMDiFUG (C11946), which is the 6,8-difluorinated analog of 4-chloromethylcoumarin-7-yl β-D-galactopyranoside (CMCG). We have previously shown that incorporating a chloromethyl group into dyes, as in our CellTracker™ and MitoTracker® probes,[61,76] considerably improves the retention of fluorescent products in live cells. This enhanced cell retention is at least partially attributable to the formation of dye conjugates with intracellular thiols, including glutathione.[77] Our results indicate that CMDiFUG discriminates *lacZ*-positive and *lacZ*-negative live cells better than all the other fluorogenic β-galactosidase substrates we have tested, including our DetectaGene™ Green, ImaGene Green™ and ImaGene Red™ substrates.

Similar to our ImaGene Green™ and ImaGene Red™ products, 6,8-difluoro-4-heptadecylumbelliferyl β-D-galactopyranoside (C_{17}DiFUG, D11950) contains a lipophilic moiety in place of the methyl group of DiFMUG (Figure 10.23). This modification improves the penetration of this substrate through cell membranes, as well as the retention of the fluorescent product of β-galactosidase activity in live cells. The fluorinated coumarin glycosides are patented by Molecular Probes.

Fluorogenic β-Glucuronidase Substrates

The substrate 4-methylumbelliferyl β-D-glucuronide (MUGlcU, M1490) is probably the most commonly used fluorogenic reagent for identifying *E. coli* contamination and for detecting GUS reporter gene expression in plants and plant extracts.[78,79] However, β-glucuronidase substrates based on fluorescein may be much more sensitive and yield products that are fluorescent at physiological pH, making them useful for continuous monitoring of enzymatic activity. In addition, we offer a fluorogenic ELF® 97 β-D-glucuronidase substrate (E6587), which produces an intensely green-fluorescent precipitate at the site of enzymatic activity that can be clearly distinguished from most autofluorescence.[80] This substrate has been used for in-gel zymography to detect β-glucuronidase activity[81–83] (Figure 9.29, Figure 10.24), immunoassays on protein microarrays[84] and for the flow cytometric analysis and separation of *E. coli* that had been transfected with *gusA* expression vectors.[85]

Fluorescein Diglucuronide

Fluorescein di-β-D-glucuronide (FDGlcU, F2915) is colorless and nonfluorescent until it is hydrolyzed to the monoglucuronide and then to highly fluorescent fluorescein (F1300, F36915; Section 10.1). FDGlcU has been used to detect β-glucuronidase activity in plant extracts containing the GUS reporter gene[79] and may also be useful for assaying lysosomal enzyme release from neutrophils.[86,87] FDGlcU has also been used in the flow cytometric assay of individual mammalian cells expressing the *E. coli* β-glucuronidase gene.[88]

PFB Aminofluorescein Diglucuronide

Our patented 5-(pentafluorobenzoylamino)fluorescein di-β-D-glucuronide (PFB-FDGlcU, P11949) yields the green-fluorescent PFB-F (P12925, Section 10.1), which appears to localize to endosomal and lysosomal compartments when loaded into cells by pinocytosis, similar to our PFB aminofluorescein diglucoside (PFB-FDGlu, P11947). PFB-FDGlcU has been used for the quantitative analysis of β-glucuronidase activity in viable cells and for sorting high-expressing cells by flow cytometry.[89] Enzyme enrichment has promise as a tool for gene therapy.

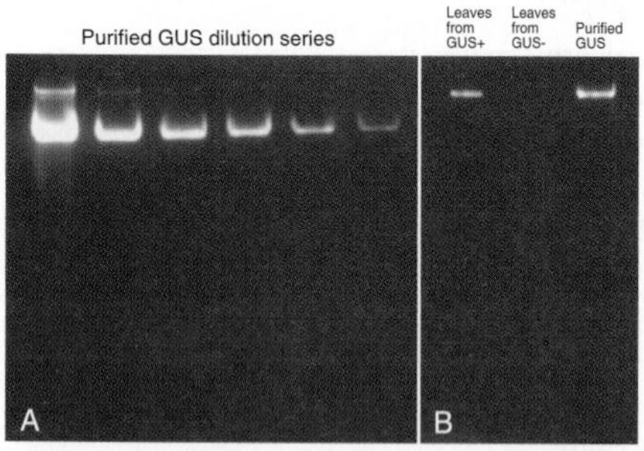

Figure 10.24 *In situ* gel assay of β-D-glucuronidase (GUS) activity with ELF® 97 β-D-glucuronide (E6587). A) Twofold dilutions of the purified GUS enzyme or B) cell extracts from single leaves from GUS-positive and -negative *Arabidopsis* plants were electrophoresed through a native 7.5% polyacrylamide gel. Following electrophoresis, the gel was washed with 0.1 M sodium phosphate, pH 7.0, containing 0.2% Triton X-100, at room temperature for 60 minutes and then incubated with 15 µM ELF® 97 β-D-glucuronide in 0.1 M sodium phosphate, pH 7.0, at 37°C, for 30–60 minutes. The gel was photographed using 300 nm transillumination, a SYBR® photographic filter (S7569, Section 23.4) and Polaroid 667 black-and-white print film.

Coumarin Glucuronides

4-Methylumbelliferyl β-D-glucuronide (MUGlcU, M1490) has been used extensively to detect *E. coli* in food,[90,91] water,[92] urine[93] and environmental samples.[94] MUGlcU is stable to the conditions required for sterilization of media. A fluorogenic bioassay using MUGlcU has been developed to assess the detrimental effects of Li^+, Al^{3+}, Cr^{6+} and Hg^{2+} on the proliferation of *E. coli*.[95]

MUGlcU is also commonly used to identify plant tissue expressing the GUS reporter gene,[96–98] including nondestructive assays that allow propagation of the transformed plant lines.[83,99] In addition, MUGlcU has served as a sensitive substrate for lysosomal enzyme release from neutrophils.[86,87]

Enzyme-mediated hydrolysis of 6,8-difluoro-4-methylumbelliferyl β-D-glucuronide (DiFMUGlcU, D11951) yields a highly fluorescent product (6,8-difluoro-7-hydroxy-4-methylcoumarin, DiFMU; D6566; Section 10.1; Figure 10.3) that has a very low pK_a, which should make DiFMUGlcU especially useful for the continuous *in vitro* assay of β-D-glucuronidase activity at pH 6 or greater. The hydrolysis product of β-trifluoromethylumbelliferyl β-D-glucuronide (T658) exhibits longer-wavelength excitation and emission spectra than those of either MUGlcU or DiFMUGlcU, which can be advantageous for cells that have high levels of endogenous fluorescence, such as plant cells.

ImaGene Green™ β-D-Glucuronidase Substrate

Molecular Probes also offers a lipophilic analog of fluorescein di-β-D-glucuronide in our ImaGene Green™ C_{12}FDGlcU GUS Gene Expression Kit (I2908). As with our similar ImaGene Green™ and ImaGene Red™ substrates for β-galactosidase (see above), we have shown that this lipophilic β-glucuronidase substrate freely diffuses across the membranes of viable cultured tobacco leaf cells or protoplasts under physiological conditions. Furthermore, the fluorescent cleavage product is retained in the plant cell for hours to days, facilitating long-term measurements of GUS gene expression. In thin sections of transgenic tomato leaf, the ImaGene Green™ C_{12}FDGlcU GUS Gene Expression Kit provided a simple and reliable GUS assay that, coupled with confocal laser-scanning microscopy, yielded good cellular resolution.[100] The substrate has also been used to detect β-glucuronidase activity in an *Acremonium* transformant containing the GUS reporter gene.[101]

Molecular Probes' ImaGene Green™ C_{12}FDGlcU GUS Gene Expression Kit contains:

- ImaGene Green™ C_{12}FDGlcU
- D-Glucaric acid-1,4-lactone, a β-glucuronidase inhibitor for stopping the reaction
- A detailed protocol for detecting β-glucuronidase activity

Each kit provides sufficient reagents for approximately 100 tests, depending on the volume used for each experiment.

ELF® 97 β-D-Glucuronide

Molecular Probes' ELF® 97 β-D-glucuronidase substrate[102] (ELF® 97 β-D-glucuronide, E6587) may be the ideal substrate for analyzing GUS enzyme activity in transgenic plants and in fixed cells and tissues. Upon hydrolysis, this fluorogenic substrate produces a bright yellow-green–fluorescent precipitate at the site of enzymatic activity.

This fluorescent precipitate has some unique spectral characteristics, including an extremely large Stokes shift (Figure 6.17), that make it easily distinguishable from the endogenous fluorescent components commonly found in plants (see Section 6.3 for a description of our patented ELF® technology). We have used this substrate to detect the GUS enzyme in *Arabidopsis* and have found that, after only 4 hours incubation, the signal can be detected in whole-leaf cuttings from GUS-positive plants.[83] Homogenization of a small portion of a leaf from a GUS-positive *Arabidopsis* plant followed by separation on a nondenaturing gel yields a discrete band corresponding to the glucuronidase enzyme (Figure 10.24). We have also used the ELF® 97 glucuronidase substrate for in-gel zymography in one aspect of our Multiplexed Proteomics® technology (Section 9.4, Figure 9.29). It is possible to detect as little as 0.5 ng of purified β-glucuronidase in a nondenaturing gel incubated with ELF® 97 glucuronide. This substrate may also be useful for detecting GUS fusion proteins in gels, for identifying *E. coli* in agarose-containing medium [103] and for assaying lysosomal enzyme release from neutrophils.[86,87] The ELF® substrates are patented by Molecular Probes.

Fluorogenic β-Glucosidase Substrates

β-Glucosidase, which is a marker for the endoplasmic reticulum (Section 12.4), is present in nearly all species. Its natural substrate is a glucosylceramide (Section 13.3). People with Gaucher's disease have mutations in the acid β-glucosidase gene that result in abnormal lysosomal storage.[9,104] Enzyme replacement therapy in Gaucher's disease patients [105] requires sensitive and selective methods for measuring β-glucosidase activity (Table 10.1). Plant β-glucosidases are implicated in a variety of key metabolic events and growth-related responses.[106]

Fluorescein Diglucoside

As with the other fluorescein diglycosides, Molecular Probes' fluorogenic fluorescein di-β-D-glucopyranoside (FDGlu, F2881) is likely to yield the greatest sensitivity for detecting β-glucosidase activity in both cells [104] and cell extracts. This substrate has been used to demonstrate the utility of *Saccharomyces cerevisiae* and *Candida albicans* exo-1,3-β-glucanase genes as reporter genes.[107] Because these reporter genes encode secreted proteins, assays for reporter gene expression do not require cell permeabilization. FDGlu has been reported to be a selective substrate for the flow cytometric assay of lysosomal glucocerebrosidase activity in a variety of cells.[108] The assay demonstrated the inordinately low glucocerebrosidase activity present in fibroblasts of Gaucher's disease patients.

PFB Aminofluorescein Diglucoside

Through a collaboration with Matthew Lorincz and Leonard A. Herzenberg at Stanford University Medical School,[109] our patented PFB aminofluorescein diglucoside (PFB-FDGlu, P11947) has proven to be an excellent substrate for the flow cytometric discrimination of normal peripheral blood mononuclear cells (PBMC) from the PBMC of patients with Gaucher's disease, a genetic deficiency in lysosomal β-glucocerebrosidase activity. These researchers loaded the nonfluorescent PFB-FDGlu substrates into cells by pinocytosis, and then observed the green-fluorescent hydrolysis products in endosomal and lysosomal compartments. Under similar loading conditions, we have shown that the hydrolysis products of PFB aminofluorescein digalactoside (PFB-FDG, P11948; Figure 10.20) and of PFB aminofluorescein diglucuronide (PFB-FDGlcU, P11949) are similarly localized to endosomes and lysosomes.

Fluorescent Glucocerebrosides

The natural substrates for glucocerebrosidase are sphingosyl β-D-glucopyranosides. Our BODIPY® FL analogs of this molecule — BODIPY® FL C_5-glucocerebroside [110,111] (D7548) and BODIPY® FL C_{12}-glucocerebroside (D7547) — are likely to be substrates for this lysosomal enzyme, which is lacking in Gaucher's disease patients. However, the lack of spectral shift of the hydrolysis products — BODIPY® FL C_5-ceramide (D3521, Section 13.2) and BODIPY® FL C_{12}-ceramide — means that extraction and chromatographic separation of the products is necessary for assessment of the activity.

Detection of Glucose and Glucose-Producing Enzymes

Amplex® Red Reagent for Glucose

The Amplex® Red reagent (10-acetyl-3,7-dihydroxyphenoxazine, A12222, A22177; Section 10.5; Figure 10.58) is a colorless, stable and extremely versatile peroxidase substrate.[112] In an application similar to our use of the Amplex® Red reagent to detect galactose-producing enzymes (see above), we have shown that it is practical to detect free glucose with high specificity at levels as low as 0.5 µg/mL using the Amplex® Red reagent in combination with excess glucose oxidase (Figure 10.25). Because the peroxidase- and glucose oxidase–mediated reactions can be coupled, it is potentially possible to measure the release of glucose by *any* glucosidase enzyme — for instance, α-glucosidase, β-glucosidase and glucocerebrosidase — in either a continuous or discontinuous assay (Figure 10.59). This assay should also be very useful for quantitation of glucose levels in foods, fermentation media and bodily fluids. The long-wavelength spectral properties of resorufin (Figure 10.6) and high sensitivity of the assay result in little interference from colored components in the samples.

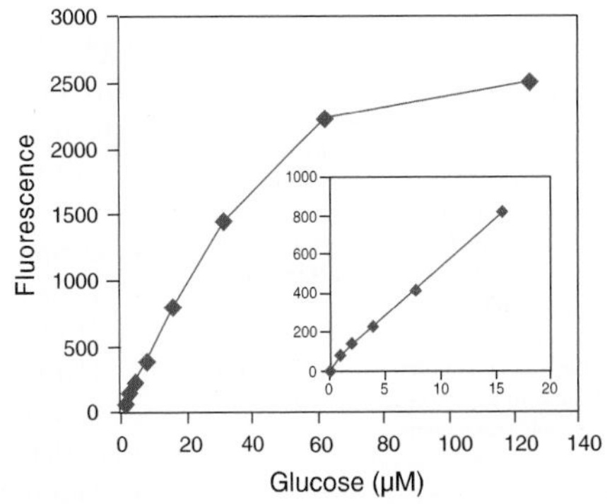

Figure 10.25 Detection of glucose using the Amplex® Red Glucose/Glucose Oxidase Assay Kit (A22189). Reactions containing 50 µM Amplex® Red reagent, 0.1 U/mL HRP, 1 U/mL glucose oxidase and the indicated amount of glucose in 50 mM sodium phosphate buffer, pH 7.4, were incubated for one hour at room temperature. Fluorescence was then measured with a fluorescence microplate reader using excitation at 530 ± 12.5 nm and fluorescence detection at 590 ± 17.5 nm. Background fluorescence (arbitrary units), determined for a no-glucose control reaction, has been subtracted from each value. The inset shows the sensitivity and linearity of the assay at low levels of glucose (0–15 µM).

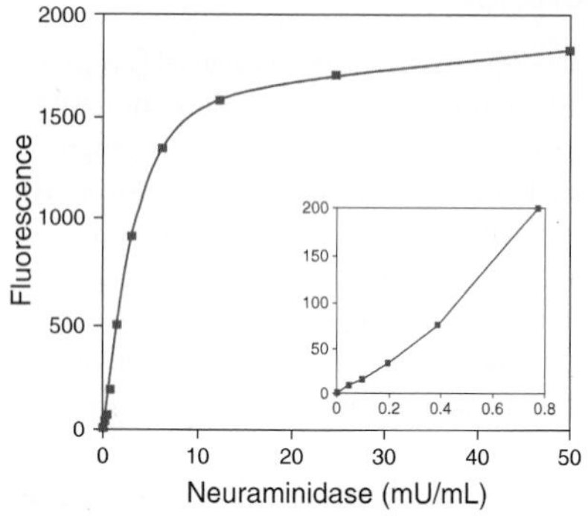

Figure 10.26 Detection of neuraminidase activity using the Amplex® Red Neuraminidase (Sialidase) Assay Kit (A22178). Each reaction contained 50 µM Amplex® Red reagent, 0.1 U/mL HRP, 2 U/mL galactose oxidase, 250 µg/mL fetuin and the indicated amount of neuraminidase in 1X reaction buffer. Reactions were incubated at 37°C. After 30 minutes, fluorescence was measured in a fluorescence microplate reader using excitation at 530 ± 12.5 nm and fluorescence detection at 590 ± 17.5 nm. A background fluorescence of 70 fluorescence units was subtracted from each data point. The inset shows the sensitivity and linearity of the assay at low levels of neuraminidase (0–0.8 mU/mL).

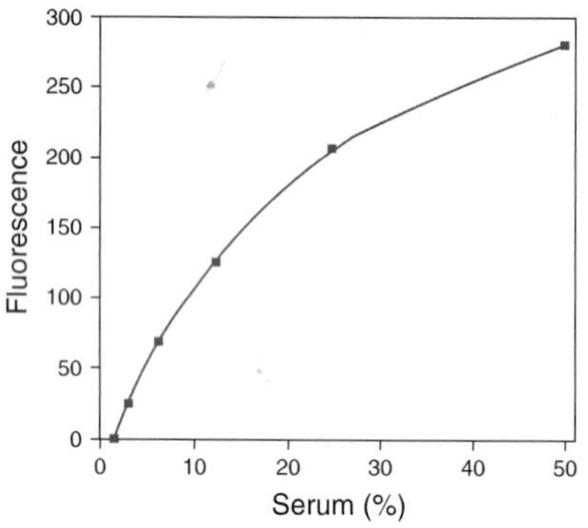

Figure 10.27 Detection of neuraminidase activity in serum using the Amplex® Red Neuraminidase (Sialidase) Assay Kit (A22178). Each reaction contained 50 µM Amplex® Red reagent, 0.1 U/mL HRP, 2 U/mL galactose oxidase, 250 µg/mL fetuin and the indicated amount of serum in 1X reaction buffer. Reactions were incubated at 37°C. After 60 minutes, fluorescence was measured in a fluorescence microplate reader using excitation at 530 ± 12.5 nm and fluorescence detection at 590 ± 17.5 nm. A background fluorescence of 112 units was subtracted from each data point.

Amplex® Red Glucose/Glucose Oxidase Assay Kit

Our Amplex® Red Glucose/Glucose Oxidase Assay Kit (A22189) provides all the reagents required for the assay of glucose and enzymes that produce glucose. This kit is also useful for the assay of glucose oxidase activity from cell extracts. We have even shown that the Amplex® Red reagent can detect glucose liberated from native dextrans by dextranase [113] and from carboxymethylcellulose. The Amplex® Red Glucose/Glucose Oxidase Assay Kit contains:

- Amplex® Red reagent
- DMSO
- Horseradish peroxidase (HRP)
- Hydrogen peroxide (H_2O_2) for use as a positive control
- Concentrated reaction buffer
- Glucose oxidase
- D-glucose
- A detailed protocol

The kit provides sufficient reagents for approximately 500 assays using either a fluorescence- or absorption-based microplate reader and a reaction volume of 100 µL per assay.

Amplex® Red Neuraminidase/Sialidase Assay Kit

Neuraminidase (NA, also known as sialidase) is a very common enzyme that hydrolyzes terminal sialic acid residues on polysaccharide chains, most often exposing a galactose residue. Although NA is found in mammals, it is predominantly expressed in microorganisms such as bacteria and viruses,[114] including the negative-stranded RNA influenza virus. NA located on the surface of the influenza virus is thought to play a key role in its invasion of target cells and subsequent replication through cleavage of target cell receptor sialic acid moieties. Anti-influenza drug design has therefore focused on the inhibition of NA.[115] Various methods using chemiluminescence, absorption and fluorescence have been developed to quantitate NA in biological fluids for detecting influenza virus [116,117] and for screening inhibitors of NA activity in drug development.[117,118] The ultimate goal has been to develop a rapid, single-step assay that is sensitive and adaptable for a high-throughput screening format.

Designed to meet these needs, the Amplex® Red Neuraminidase (Sialidase) Assay Kit (A22178) provides an ultrasensitive method for detecting NA activity. This assay utilizes the Amplex® Red reagent to detect H_2O_2 generated by galactose oxidase–mediated oxidation of desialated galactose, the end result of NA action. In the presence of HRP, the H_2O_2 thus produced reacts with a 1:1 stoichiometry with the Amplex® Red reagent to generate the red-fluorescent oxidation product, resorufin.[53] Resorufin has absorption and fluorescence emission maxima of approximately 571 nm and 585 nm, respectively (Figure 10.6), and because the extinction coefficient is high (54,000 $cm^{-1}M^{-1}$), the assay can be performed either fluorometrically or spectrophotometrically. In a purified system with fetuin as the substrate, NA levels as low as 0.2 mU/mL have been detected with the Amplex® Red Neuraminidase (Sialidase) Assay Kit (Figure 10.26). NA activity can also be detected in biological samples such as serum (Figure 10.27). Kit contents include:

- Amplex® Red reagent
- Dimethylsulfoxide (DMSO)
- Horseradish peroxidase (HRP)
- Hydrogen peroxide (H_2O_2)
- Concentrated reaction buffer
- Galactose oxidase from *Dactylium dendroides*
- Fetuin from fetal calf serum
- Neuraminidase from *Clostridium perfringens*
- A detailed protocol

Each kit provides sufficient reagents for approximately 400 assays using either a fluorescence- or absorption-based microplate reader and reaction volumes of 100 µL per assay.

Fluorogenic Chitinase/*N*-Acetylglucosaminidase Substrate

Chitin is the second most abundant organic compound in nature [119] and various chitinases and *N*-acetylglucosaminidases are widely distributed in bacteria, plants and eukaryotic cells. We have utilized our proprietary ELF® technology (Section 6.3) to prepare the ELF® 97 chitinase/*N*-acetylglucosaminidase substrate (ELF® 97 *N*-acetylglucosaminide, ELF® 97 NAG; E22011), which is designed to allow spatially resolved detection of enzyme activity on colony indicator plates and histochemical analysis specimens. Other fluorogenic substrates for these enzymes [120,121] generate diffusible products and are therefore unsuitable for applications of this type. In addition to the capacity for localized precipitation at sites of enzymatic activity, the ELF® 97 alcohol product that is generated upon hydrolysis of ELF® 97 NAG is extremely photostable (Figure 6.18) and has widely separated fluorescence excitation and emission peaks (~360/520 nm, Figure 6.17). These properties make the signal easy to discriminate from any background fluorescence. ELF® 97 NAG has been utilized to differentiate chitinase-active and non-chitinase–active subpopulations of a marine bacterium during chitin degradation.[122–124]

EnzChek® Amylase Assay Kit

α-Amylase is a hydrolytic enzyme that catalyzes the conversion of starch to a mixture of glucose, maltose, maltotriose and dextrins. The levels of α-amylase in various fluids of the human body are of clinical importance,[125–127] while plant and microbial α-amylases are important enzymes for industry.[128]

Our patented EnzChek® Amylase Assay Kit (E11954) provides the speed, high sensitivity and convenience required for measuring α-amylase activity or for screening inhibitors in a high-throughput format. This EnzChek® kit contains a starch derivative that is labeled with the BODIPY® FL dye to such a degree that the fluorescence is quenched (Figure 10.56). α-Amylase–catalyzed hydrolysis relieves this quenching, yielding brightly fluorescent BODIPY® FL dye–labeled fragments. The accompanying increase in fluorescence is proportional to amylase activity and can be monitored with a fluorescence microplate reader, minifluorometer or standard fluorometer. Each EnzChek® Amylase Assay Kit includes:

- A heavily labeled BODIPY® FL conjugate of starch from corn (DQ™ starch)
- Concentrated reaction buffer
- α-Amylase from *Bacillus* sp., for use as a positive control
- A detailed protocol

Each kit provides sufficient reagents for ~1000 assays using 200 µL assay volumes and 96-well microplates or ~100 assays using 2 mL assay volumes and standard fluorescence cuvettes.

Using 12.5 µg/mL of the DQ™ starch substrate and a 60-minute incubation period at room temperature, the assay can detect the activity of this enzyme down to a final concentration of 1×10^{-4} U/mL (~0.3 µg protein/mL), where one unit is defined as the amount of enzyme required to liberate 1 mg of maltose from starch in 3 minutes at 20°C, at pH 6.9.

EnzChek® Lysozyme Assay Kit

Lysozyme (muramidase) is an important but difficult enzyme to assay. Lysozyme hydrolyzes β-1-4-glycosidic linkages between *N*-acetylmuramic acid and *N*-acetyl-D-glucosamine residues present in the mucopolysaccharide cell wall of a variety of microorganisms. Lysozyme is present in human serum, urine, tears, seminal fluid and milk. Serum and urine lysozyme levels may be elevated in acute myelomonocytic leukemia (FAB-M4), chronic myelomonocytic leukemia (CMML) and chronic myelocytic leukemia [129] (CML). Increased serum lysozyme activity is also present in tuberculosis,[130] sarcoidosis, megaloblastic anemias,[131] acute bacterial infections, ulcerative colitis [132] and Crohn's disease.[130,132] Elevated levels of urine and serum lysozyme occur during severe renal insufficiency, renal transplant rejection,[133] urinary tract infections,[134] glomerulonephritis and nephrosis.[135]

Molecular Probes has developed a simple and sensitive assay that can continuously measure the activity of lysozyme in solution. Our fluorescence-based EnzChek® Lysozyme Assay Kit (E22013) permits the detection of as little as 30 U/mL of lysozyme (Figure 10.28). One unit of lysozyme is the quantity of enzyme that produces a decrease in turbidity of 0.001 optical density units per minute at 450 nm measured at pH 7.0 (25°C) using a 0.3 mg/mL suspension of *Micrococcus lysodeikticus* cells as substrate.[136] Our EnzChek lysozyme assay measures lysozyme activity on *M. lysodeikticus* cell walls that are labeled with fluorescein to such a degree that fluorescence is quenched. Lysozyme action can relieve the quenching, yielding a dramatic increase in fluorescence that is proportional to lysozyme activity. This increase in fluorescence can be measured with any spectrofluorometer, mini-fluorometer or fluorescence microplate reader that can detect fluorescein (excitation/emission maxima ~490/525 nm).

The EnzChek® Lysozyme Assay Kit (E22013) contains:

- DQ™ lysozyme substrate
- Reaction buffer
- Lysozyme from chicken egg white, for use as a positive control
- A detailed protocol

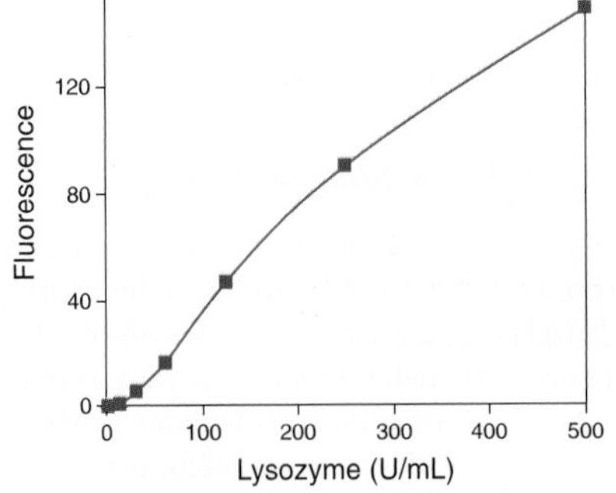

Figure 10.28 Detection of lysozyme activity using the EnzChek® Lysozyme Assay Kit (E22013). Increasing amounts of lysozyme were incubated with the DQ™ lysozyme substrate for 60 minutes at 37°C. The fluorescence was measured in a fluorescence microplate reader using excitation/emission wavelengths of ~485/530 nm. Background fluorescence, determined for a no-enzyme control, was subtracted from each value.

Each kit contains sufficient materials for approximately 400 assays of 100 µL in a fluorescence microplate reader.

Chromogenic Glycosidase Substrates

The widely used β-galactosidase substrate — 5-bromo-4-chloro-3-indolyl β-D-galactopyranoside (X-Gal, B1690, B22015) — yields a dark blue precipitate at the site of enzymatic activity. X-Gal is useful for numerous histochemical and molecular biology applications, including detection of *lacZ* activity in cells and tissues. In contrast to β-glucuronidase as a gene marker, β-galactosidase can be fixed in cells and tissues with glutaraldehyde without loss of activity and detected with high resolution with X-Gal.[137]

The chromogenic substrate 5-bromo-4-chloro-3-indolyl β-D-glucuronic acid (X-GlcU, B1691) forms a dark blue precipitate. X-GlcU is routinely used to detect GUS expression in transformed plant cells and tissues.[138–144] However, because it is relatively difficult to differentiate the blue color of the product of X-GlcU against the dark green chloroplasts,[145] we also offer the isomeric 5-bromo-6-chloro-3-indolyl β-D-glucuronide[146] (B8408), which forms a magenta-colored precipitate. X-GlcU can also be used to detect *E. coli* contamination in food and water.[103,147]

Auxiliary Products for Glycosidase Research

Phenylethyl β-D-Thiogalactopyranoside (PETG)

Phenylethyl β-D-thiogalactopyranoside (PETG, P1692) is a cell-permeant inhibitor of β-galactosidase activity.[32,148] We provide PETG in our FluoReporter®, DetectaGene™ Green, ImaGene Green™ and ImaGene Red™ *lacZ* Gene Expression Kits for stopping the enzymatic reaction.

Streptavidin Conjugate of β-Galactosidase

Molecular Probes also offers the streptavidin conjugate of β-galactosidase (S931), a reagent used in a variety of ELISAs.[149] β-D-Galactosidase streptavidin reportedly provided enhanced sensitivity over that obtained with the avidin conjugate of HRP in the detection of a variety of mammalian interleukins and their receptors by ELISA.[150] This reagent has also been used in fluorometric-reverse (IgE-capture)[151] and fluorescence-sandwich[152] ELISAs.

Rabbit Anti–β-Galactosidase Antibody

Molecular Probes offers a polyclonal antibody to the widely used reporter gene product, β-galactosidase. Our rabbit anti–β-galactosidase antibody (A11132) is raised against *E. coli*–derived β-galactosidase and demonstrates high selectivity for the enzyme. Whether it is being used as a reporter gene or to generate fusion proteins, anti–β-galactosidase provides an easy tool for detecting the enzyme. The antibody is suited to a variety of techniques, including immunoblotting, ELISA, immunoprecipitation and most immunological methods. β-Galactosidase has been used as a tag for quantitative detection of molecules expressed on a cell surface in unfixed, live cells, using anti–β-galactosidase and a β-galactosidase substrate for detection.[153] This novel "cell-ELISA" technique is reported to be applicable to adherent cells and nonadherent cells and to have utility for large-scale screening for expression of cell-surface molecules and of hybridomas for production of antibodies to cell-surface epitopes. This rabbit polyclonal antibody can be used in combination with any of our Zenon® Rabbit IgG Labeling Kits (Section 7.3, Table 7.13).

Rabbit Anti–β-Glucuronidase Antibody

In combination with a fluorophore- or enzyme-labeled anti–rabbit IgG secondary antibody (Section 7.2, Table 7.1) or any of our Zenon Rabbit IgG Labeling Kits (Section 7.3, Table 7.13), our anti–β-glucuronidase antibody (A5790) can be used to detect the GUS enzyme in transformed plant tissue[154,155] and in transfected animal cells[156] using Western blotting or immunohistochemical techniques. Furthermore, this antibody, which is raised in rabbits against *E. coli*–type X-A β-glucuronidase, can be immobilized in microplate wells in order to capture the GUS enzyme from cell lysates.[157] The enzymatic activity can subsequently be determined using any of our fluorogenic or chromogenic β-glucuronidase substrates[158] (see above).

ManLev: A Metabolically Active Carbohydrate Analog

N-Levulinoyl-D-mannosamine (ManLev, L20492; Section 3.2, Figure 3.9) and *N*-levulinoyl-D-mannosamine, tetraacetate (ManLev tetraacetate, L20493; Section 3.2) are ketone-containing monosaccharides that serve as substrates in the oligosaccharide synthesis pathway, resulting in ketone-tagged cell-surface oligosaccharides.[159–162] Because ketones are rare in cells, reaction with 2 µM biotinylated aldehyde-reactive probe (ARP, A10550; Section 3.2; Figure 3.10) followed by a fluorescent avidin or streptavidin conjugate (Section 7.6) provides a means of identifying and tracing tagged cells by either imaging (Figure 3.11) or flow cytometry.

Related Products for Carbohydrate Research

Molecular Probes offers an extensive assortment of reagents for detection and analysis of carbohydrates that are described in other sections of *The Handbook*. These products include:

- Hydrazine, hydroxylamine and aromatic amine reagents for derivatization and analysis of reducing sugars and periodate-oxidized carbohydrates by electrophoretic methods (Section 3.2, Table 3.1)
- Lectins and fluorescent lectin conjugates (Section 7.7, Table 7.23)
- Pro-Q® Glycoprotein Blot and Gel Stain Kits (Section 9.4)
- Pro-Q® Emerald 300 Lipopolysaccharide Gel Stain Kit (P20495, Section 3.2)
- Fluorescent lipopolysaccharides (Section 13.3, Section 16.1; Table 16.1)
- Fluorescent glycolipids, including phosphatidylinositol derivatives (Section 13.2, Section 13.3)
- BODIPY® FL C_5-ganglioside G_{M1} (B13950, Section 13.3)
- Fluorescent and biotinylated dextrans (Section 14.5, Table 14.4)
- NBD-glucosamine derivatives for glucose-transport studies (N13195, N23106; Section 15.2)
- Fluorescein insulin (I13269, Section 16.1)
- Fluorescent phosphatidylinositol phosphate derivatives (Table 17.3) and antibodies to phosphatidylinositol phosphates (Section 17.4)

References

1. J Clin Microbiol 30, 1402 (1992); **2.** Microbiol Rev 55, 335 (1991); **3.** Meth Microbiol 19, 105 (1987); **4.** Nature 369, 113 (1994); **5.** J Cell Biol 110, 309 (1990); **6.** Anal Biochem 148, 50 (1985); **7.** Traffic 1, 836 (2000); **8.** Clin Chim Acta 205, 87 (1992); **9.** Crit Rev Biochem Mol Biol 25, 385 (1990); **10.** Mol Gen Genet 216, 321 (1989); **11.** Mol Gen Genet 215, 38 (1988); **12.** Plant Mol Biol 10, 387 (1988); **13.** Proc Natl Acad Sci U S A 83, 8447 (1986); **14.** J Immunol Methods 150, 5 (1992); **15.** Anal Biochem 257, 234 (1998); **16.** J Immunol Methods 150, 23 (1992); **17.** J Immunol Methods 48, 133 (1982); **18.** Exp Parasitol 73, 440 (1991); **19.** Dev Biol 161, 77 (1994); **20.** Mol Microbiol 13, 655 (1994); **21.** J Neurosci 13, 1418 (1993); **22.** Eur J Immunol 19, 1619 (1989); **23.** Cytometry 17, 216 (1994); **24.** Eur J Cell Biol 62, 324 (1993); **25.** J Biol Chem 268, 9762 (1993); **26.** Neuron 9, 1117 (1992); **27.** Science 251, 81 (1991); **28.** Proc Natl Acad Sci U S A 85, 2603 (1988); **29.** J Virol Methods 44, 99 (1993); **30.** Proc Natl Acad Sci U S A 90, 8194 (1993); **31.** Appl Environ Microbiol 56, 3861 (1990); **32.** Carbohydr Res 56, 153 (1977); **33.** Methods 2, 261 (1991); **34.** Methods 2, 248 (1991); **35.** Anal Chim Acta 163, 67 (1984); **36.** Oncogene 10, 2323 (1995); **37.** Cytometry 9, 394 (1988); **38.** Ann N Y Acad Sci 613, 333 (1990); **39.** Anal Chim Acta 213, 245 (1988); **40.** Anal Biochem 215, 24 (1993); **41.** Neuron 10, 427 (1993); **42.** Proc Natl Acad Sci U S A 84, 156 (1987); **43.** J Histochem Cytochem 33, 965 (1985); **44.** Clin Chim Acta 12, 647 (1965); **45.** Bioorg Med Chem Lett 8, 3107 (1998); **46.** Anal Lett 21, 193 (1988); **47.** J Histochem Cytochem 34, 585 (1986); **48.** Biotechniques 30, 776 (2001); **49.** Infect Immun 61, 5231 (1993); **50.** Anal Biochem 146, 211 (1985); **51.** Proc Natl Acad Sci U S A 95, 6373 (1998); **52.** J Biochem (Tokyo) 100, 707 (1986); **53.** J Immunol Methods 202, 133 (1997); **54.** J Fluorescence 3, 119 (1993); **55.** Development 119, 1217 (1993); **56.** Neuron 14, 685 (1995); **57.** J Neurosci 15, 1025 (1995); **58.** Exp Cell Res 219, 372 (1995); **59.** Science 266, 1881 (1994); **60.** Cytometry 28, 36 (1997); **61.** J Histochem Cytochem 44, 1363 (1996); **62.** Lysosomes, Holtzman E pp. 319–361 (1989); **63.** FASEB J 5, 3108 (1991); **64.** Appl Environ Microbiol 60, 4638 (1994); **65.** Biotechnol Bioeng 42, 1113 (1993); **66.** J Clin Endocrinol Metab 78, 1232 (1994); **67.** Biotechnol Bioeng 42, 708 (1993); **68.** J Biol Chem 271, 29312 (1996); **69.** Proc Natl Acad Sci U S A 89, 10681 (1992); **70.** Methods Cell Biol 42 Pt B, 563 (1994); **71.** Biotechniques 14, 274 (1993); **72.** Genes Dev 6, 591 (1992); **73.** Cytometry 20, 324 (1995); **74.** Hum Mol Genet 5, 875 (1996); **75.** FEMS Microbiol Lett 179, 317 (1999); **76.** Cytometry 12, 184 (1991); **77.** Cytometry 15, 349 (1994); **78.** Biotechniques 8, 37 (1990); **79.** Plant Mol Biol Rep 5, 387 (1988); **80.** Tetrahedron 53, 7159 (1997); **81.** Electrophoresis 22, 970 (2001); **82.** Electrophoresis 21, 497 (2000); **83.** J Biochem Biophys Methods 33, 197 (1996); **84.** Anal Biochem 278, 123 (2000); **85.** Biotechniques 30, 474 (2001); **86.** Cell Signal 3, 625 (1991); **87.** J Immunol Methods 100, 211 (1987); **88.** Cytometry 24, 321 (1996); **89.** J Biol Chem 274, 657 (1999); **90.** J Assoc Off Anal Chem 71, 589 (1988); **91.** Appl Environ Microbiol 50, 1383 (1985); **92.** Can J Microbiol 39, 1066 (1993); **93.** J Microbiol Methods 12, 51 (1990); **94.** J Microbiol Methods 12, 235 (1990); **95.** Biotechniques 16, 888 (1994); **96.** GUS Protocols: Using the GUS Gene as a Reporter of Gene Expression, Gallapher SR, Ed. pp. 61–76 (1992); **97.** Plant Sci 78, 73 (1991); **98.** Plant Mol Biol 15, 527 (1990); **99.** Plant Mol Biol Rep 10, 37 (1992); **100.** Plant J 10, 745 (1996); **101.** Microbiology 143, 267 (1997); **102.** Ann N Y Acad Sci 346, 419 (1980); **103.** J Appl Bacteriol 74, 223 (1993); **104.** Cell Biochem Funct 11, 167 (1993); **105.** Neurochem Res 24, 301 (1999); **106.** 533 (1993); **107.** Yeast 10, 747 (1994); **108.** Anal Biochem 247, 268 (1997); **109.** Blood 89, 3412 (1997); **110.** Frontiers in Bioactive Lipids, Vanderhoek JV, Ed. pp. 203–213 (1996); **111.** J Cell Biol 125, 769 (1994); **112.** Anal Biochem 253, 162 (1997); **113.** Anal Biochem 260, 257 (1998); **114.** J Biochem Biophys Methods 22, 23 (1991); **115.** Nat Biotechnol 18, 835 (2000); **116.** Antiviral Res 47, 1 (2000); **117.** J Med Chem 13, 697 (1970); **118.** Anal Biochem 280, 291 (2000); **119.** Trends Biotechnol 16, 301 (1998); **120.** Appl Environ Microbiol 64, 613 (1998); **121.** Anal Biochem 208, 74 (1993); **122.** Methods Enzymol 336, 279 (2001); **123.** Appl Environ Microbiol 66, 3566 (2000); **124.** Appl Environ Microbiol 66, 3574 (2000); **125.** Medicine (Baltimore) 55, 269 (1976); **126.** Clin Chem 21, 57 (1976); **127.** Clin Chem 30, 387 (1984); **128.** Starch/Starke 35, 169 (1983); **129.** Mod Pathol 7, 771 (1994); **130.** Acta Pathol Jpn 28, 689 (1978); **131.** N Engl J Med 277, 10 (1967); **132.** J Clin Pathol 36, 1312 (1983); **133.** Clin Chem 32, 1807 (1986); **134.** Toxicology 28, 347 (1983); **135.** Nephron 63, 423 (1993); **136.** Biochim Biophys Acta 8, 302 (1952); **137.** EMBO J 8, 343 (1989); **138.** Biotechniques 19, 106 (1995); **139.** Biotechnology (N Y) 8, 833 (1990); **140.** Plant Cell Physiol 31, 805 (1990); **141.** Science 249, 1285 (1990); **142.** Science 248, 471 (1990); **143.** Nature 342, 837 (1989); **144.** EMBO J 6, 3901 (1987); **145.** Biotechniques 7, 922 (1989); **146.** Biotechniques 19, 352 (1995); **147.** Lett Appl Microbiol 13, 212 (1991); **148.** Anal Biochem 199, 119 (1991); **149.** J Immunol Methods 125, 279 (1989); **150.** Biochemistry 26, 4922 (1987); **151.** J Immunol Methods 116, 181 (1989); **152.** J Immunol Methods 110, 129 (1988); **153.** J Immunol Methods 234, P153 (2000); **154.** J Biol Chem 269, 17635 (1994); **155.** Plant Mol Biol 15, 821 (1990); **156.** Biotechniques 27, 896 (1999); **157.** J Clin Microbiol 32, 1444 (1994); **158.** Appl Environ Microbiol 53, 1073 (1987); **159.** Glycobiology 11, 11R (2001); **160.** Nat Biotechnol 19, 553 (2001); **161.** Methods Enzymol 327, 260 (2000); **162.** Glycobiology 10, 1049 (2000).

Data Table — 10.2 Detecting Glycosidases

Cat #	MW	Storage	Soluble	Abs	EC	Em	Solvent	Product	Notes
A12222	257.25	FF,D,A	DMSO	280	6,000	none	pH 8	R363	1
A22010	713.65	F,D	DMSO	289	5,500	none	MeOH	see Notes	2
B1689	408.63	F,D	DMSO	290	4,900	none	H_2O	see Notes	3
B1690	408.63	F,D	DMSO	290	4,900	none	H_2O	see Notes	3
B1691	521.79	F,D	pH >6	292	4,800	none	MeOH	see Notes	3
B8408	521.79	F,D	pH >6	294	4,600	none	pH 7	see Notes	4
B22015	408.63	F,D	DMSO	290	4,900	none	H_2O	see Notes	3
B34402	~66,000	F,D,L	H_2O	505	80,000	511	MeOH	see Notes	5, 6, 7
C1488	368.30	F,D	pH >6, DMSO	330	16,000	396	pH 8	H185	8
C1492	458.46	F,D	pH >6	329	18,000	395	pH 7	H185	8
C6541MP	700.52	F,D	pH >5, DMSO	282	8,700	none	MeOH	see Notes	9
C11946	408.74	F,D,L	DMSO, H_2O	284	8,000	none	pH 9	C12881	
D2893	853.92	F,D	DMSO	289	6,000	none	MeOH	D109	
D2920	705.07	F,L	see Notes	273	4,800	none	MeOH	see Notes	10, 11, 12
D6486	484.29	F,D,L	DMSO	463	26,000	607	MeOH	H6482	
D6488	470.31	F,D,L	DMSO	465	24,000	608	pH 7	H6482	
D7519	861.96	FF,D,L	DMSO, EtOH	505	85,000	511	MeOH	see Notes	5, 6
D7547	861.96	FF,D,L	DMSO, EtOH	505	85,000	511	MeOH	see Notes	5, 6
D7548	763.77	FF,D,L	DMSO, EtOH	505	85,000	511	MeOH	see Notes	5, 6
D11945	374.29	F,D	DMSO, H_2O	313	6,900	see Notes	pH 9	D6566	8
D11950	598.72	F,D	DMSO	314	6,400	none	MeCN	D12760	
D11951	394.21	F,D	H_2O	313	6,200	see Notes	pH 9	D6566	8
D11953	598.72	F,D	DMSO	314	7,000	none	MeCN	D12760	
D13951	925.91	FF,D,L	DMSO, EtOH	505	80,000	511	MeOH	see Notes	5, 6
E6587	483.26	F,D,L	DMSO, H_2O	302	14,000	see Notes	MeOH	E6578	8
E22011	511.34	F,D,L	DMSO	290	11,000	see Notes	DMSO	E6578	8

Data Table — 10.2 Detecting Glycosidases — continued

Cat #	MW	Storage	Soluble	Abs	EC	Em	Solvent	Product	Notes
F1179	656.60	F,D	DMSO	273	6,500	none	MeOH	F1300	13
F2881	656.60	F,D	DMSO	272	6,200	none	MeOH	F1300	
F2905	368.30	F,D,L	pH 7	330	16,000	396	pH 8	H185	8, 12, 14
F2915	684.56	F,D	pH >6, DMSO	272	5,700	none	MeOH	F1300	
I2904	853.92	F,D,L	DMSO	289	6,000	none	MeOH	D109	12, 14
I2906	543.66	F,D,L	see Notes	448	20,000	none	MeOH	see Notes	12, 15, 16
I2908	881.88	F,D	see Notes	290	5,400	none	MeOH	D109	10, 12
I6621	238.30	D	DMSO, H_2O	<300		none			
M1489MP	338.31	D	DMSO, H_2O	316	14,000	376	pH 9	H189	8
M1490	352.30	F,D	pH >6	316	12,000	375	pH 9	H189	8
O2892	797.81	F,D	DMSO	289	5,500	none	MeOH	see Notes	2
P1692	300.37	F,D	DMSO, H_2O	<300		none			
P11947	865.67	F,D	DMSO	260	26,000	none	MeOH	P12925	
P11948	865.67	F,D	DMSO	260	25,000	none	MeOH	P12925	
P11949	893.64	F,D	pH >6, DMSO	260	21,000	none	MeOH	P12925	
R1159	375.33	F,D,L	DMSO	469	19,000	none	pH 9	R363	
R1161	427.41	F,D,L	pH >6	479	17,000	none	pH 8	R363	
T657	392.28	F,D	DMSO	325	13,000	410	pH 9	T659	8
T658	406.27	F,D	pH >6	325	11,000	410	pH 8	T659	8

For definitions of the contents of this data table, see "Navigating *The Handbook*" in the introductory pages.

Notes

1. This substrate is used for peroxidase-coupled detection in our Amplex® Red Assay Kits.
2. Enzymatic cleavage of this substrate yields a 5-acylaminofluorescein derivative with spectroscopic properties similar to D109.
3. Enzymatic cleavage of this substrate yields a water-insoluble, blue-colored indigo dye (Abs ~615 nm).
4. Enzymatic cleavage of this substrate yields a water-insoluble, magenta-colored indigo dye (Abs ~565 nm).
5. Em for BODIPY® FL sphingolipids shifts to ~620 nm when high concentrations of the probe (>5 mol %) are incorporated in lipid mixtures (J Cell Biol 113, 1267 (1991)).
6. Enzymatic cleavage of this product yields a fluorescent ceramide or glycosylceramide with unchanged spectral properties.
7. This product is a lipid complexed with bovine serum albumin (BSA). Spectroscopic data are for the free lipid in MeOH.
8. Fluorescence of the unhydrolyzed substrate is very weak.
9. Product of *N*-acetyl-β-D-glucosaminidase hydrolysis is 6′-(*O*-carboxymethyl)-2′,7′-dichlorofluorescein. Abs = 489 nm (EC = 5,600 $cm^{-1}M^{-1}$) in MeOH (Chem Pharm Bull 41, 1513 (1993)).
10. This product is packaged as a solution in 1:1 (v/v) DMSO/H_2O.
11. Enzymatic cleavage of this substrate yields 5-chloromethylfluorescein, with spectroscopic properties similar to C1904.
12. Data represent the substrate component of this kit.
13. F1179 is soluble at 1 mM in water, but it is best to prepare a stock solution in DMSO.
14. This product is supplied as a ready-made solution in the solvent indicated under "Soluble."
15. This product is packaged as a solution in 7:3 (v/v) DMSO/EtOH.
16. Enzymatic cleavage of this substrate yields 2-dodecylresorufin, Abs = 578 nm (EC = 69,000 $cm^{-1}M^{-1}$), Em = 597 nm in MeOH.

Product List — 10.2 Detecting Glycosidases

Cat #	Product Name	Unit Size
A22010	5-acetylaminofluorescein di-β-D-galactopyranoside (C_2FDG)	5 mg
A22179	Amplex® Red Galactose/Galactose Oxidase Assay Kit *400 assays*	1 kit
A22189	Amplex® Red Glucose/Glucose Oxidase Assay Kit *500 assays*	1 kit
A22178	Amplex® Red Neuraminidase (Sialidase) Assay Kit *400 assays*	1 kit
A12222	Amplex® Red reagent (10-acetyl-3,7-dihydroxyphenoxazine)	5 mg
A11132	anti-β-galactosidase, rabbit IgG fraction *2 mg/mL*	0.5 mL
A5790	anti-β-glucuronidase, rabbit IgG fraction *2 mg/mL*	0.5 mL
B34402	BODIPY® FL C_5-lactosylceramide complexed to BSA	1 mg
B1690	5-bromo-4-chloro-3-indolyl β-D-galactopyranoside (X-Gal)	1 g
B22015	5-bromo-4-chloro-3-indolyl β-D-galactopyranoside (X-Gal) *bulk packaging*	25 g
B1689	5-bromo-4-chloro-3-indolyl β-D-glucopyranoside (X-Glu)	100 mg
B1691	5-bromo-4-chloro-3-indolyl β-D-glucuronide, cyclohexylammonium salt (X-GlcU, CHA)	100 mg
B8408	5-bromo-6-chloro-3-indolyl β-D-glucuronide, cyclohexylammonium salt	25 mg
C6541MP	6′-(*O*-(carboxymethyl))-2′,7′-dichlorofluorescein 3′-(*O*-(*N*-acetyl-β-D-glucosaminide)) (CM-DCF-NAG)	5 mg
C1488	3-carboxyumbelliferyl β-D-galactopyranoside (CUG)	10 mg
C1492	3-carboxyumbelliferyl β-D-glucuronide (CUGlcU)	10 mg
C11946	4-chloromethyl-6,8-difluoroumbelliferyl β-D-galactopyranoside (CMDiFUG)	5 mg
D2920	DetectaGene™ Green CMFDG *lacZ* Gene Expression Kit	1 kit
D6488	9*H*-(1,3-dichloro-9,9-dimethylacridin-2-one-7-yl) β-D-galactopyranoside (DDAO galactoside)	5 mg

For current prices or to order online, visit probes.invitrogen.com

Cat #	Product Name	Unit Size
D6486	9*H*-(1,3-dichloro-9,9-dimethylacridin-2-one-7-yl) β-D-glucuronide (DDAO GlcU)	5 mg
D7519	*N*-(4,4-difluoro-5,7-dimethyl-4-bora-3a,4a-diaza-*s*-indacene-3-dodecanoyl)sphingosyl 1-β-D-galactopyranoside (BODIPY® FL C_{12}-galactocerebroside)	25 µg
D7547	*N*-(4,4-difluoro-5,7-dimethyl-4-bora-3a,4a-diaza-*s*-indacene-3-dodecanoyl)sphingosyl 1-β-D-glucopyranoside (BODIPY® FL C_{12}-glucocerebroside)	250 µg
D7548	*N*-(4,4-difluoro-5,7-dimethyl-4-bora-3a,4a-diaza-*s*-indacene-3-pentanoyl)sphingosyl 1-β-D-glucopyranoside (BODIPY® FL C_5-glucocerebroside)	250 µg
D13951	*N*-(4,4-difluoro-5,7-dimethyl-4-bora-3a,4a-diaza-*s*-indacene-3-pentanoyl)sphingosyl 1-β-D-lactoside (BODIPY® FL C_5-lactosylceramide)	25 µg
D11950	6,8-difluoro-4-heptadecylumbelliferyl β-D-galactopyranoside (C_{17}DiFUG)	5 mg
D11953	6,8-difluoro-4-heptadecylumbelliferyl β-D-glucopyranoside (C_{17}DiFUGlu)	5 mg
D11945	6,8-difluoro-4-methylumbelliferyl β-D-galactopyranoside (DiFMUG)	10 mg
D11951	6,8-difluoro-4-methylumbelliferyl β-D-glucuronide, lithium salt (DiFMUGlcU)	5 mg
D2893	5-dodecanoylaminofluorescein di-β-D-galactopyranoside (C_{12}FDG)	5 mg
E22011	ELF® 97 chitinase/*N*-acetylglucosaminidase substrate (ELF® 97 *N*-acetylglucosaminide; ELF® 97 NAG)	5 mg
E6587	ELF® 97 β-D-glucuronidase substrate (ELF® 97 β-D-glucuronide)	5 mg
E11954	EnzChek® Amylase Assay Kit *1000 assays*	1 kit
E22013	EnzChek® Lysozyme Assay Kit *400 assays*	1 kit
F1930	FluoReporter® *lacZ* Flow Cytometry Kit *50 assays*	1 kit
F1931	FluoReporter® *lacZ* Flow Cytometry Kit *250 assays*	1 kit
F2905	FluoReporter® *lacZ*/Galactosidase Quantitation Kit *1000 assays*	1 kit
F1179	fluorescein di-β-D-galactopyranoside (FDG)	5 mg
F2881	fluorescein di-β-D-glucopyranoside (FDGlu)	5 mg
F2915	fluorescein di-β-D-glucuronide (FDGlcU)	5 mg
I2904	ImaGene Green™ C_{12}FDG *lacZ* Gene Expression Kit	1 kit
I2908	ImaGene Green™ C_{12}FDGlcU GUS Gene Expression Kit	1 kit
I2906	ImaGene Red™ C_{12}RG *lacZ* Gene Expression Kit	1 kit
I14402	Influx™ pinocytic cell-loading reagent *makes 10 x 5 mL*	1 set
I6621	isopropyl β-D-thiogalactopyranoside (IPTG) *dioxane free*	1 g
M1489MP	4-methylumbelliferyl β-D-galactopyranoside (MUG)	1 g
M1490	4-methylumbelliferyl β-D-glucuronide (MUGlcU)	100 mg
O2892	5-octanoylaminofluorescein di-β-D-galactopyranoside (C_8FDG)	5 mg
P11948	5-(pentafluorobenzoylamino)fluorescein di-β-D-galactopyranoside (PFB-FDG)	5 mg
P11947	5-(pentafluorobenzoylamino)fluorescein di-β-D-glucopyranoside (PFB-FDGlu)	5 mg
P11949	5-(pentafluorobenzoylamino)fluorescein di-β-D-glucuronide (PFB-FDGlcU)	5 mg
P1692	phenylethyl β-D-thiogalactopyranoside (PETG)	10 mg
R1159	resorufin β-D-galactopyranoside	25 mg
R1161	resorufin β-D-glucuronide, potassium salt	5 mg
S931	streptavidin, β-galactosidase conjugate	1 mg
T657	β-trifluoromethylumbelliferyl β-D-galactopyranoside	100 mg
T658	β-trifluoromethylumbelliferyl β-D-glucuronide	25 mg

For current prices or to order online, visit probes.invitrogen.com

10.3 Detecting Enzymes That Metabolize Phosphates and Polyphosphates

Cells utilize a wide variety of phosphate and polyphosphate esters as enzyme substrates, second messengers, membrane structural components and vital energy reservoirs. This section includes an assortment of reagents and methods for detecting the metabolism of phosphate esters. Our diverse array of fluorogenic and chromogenic substrates include substrates for phosphatases, as well as reagents to measure the activity of enzymes such as ATPases, GTPases and DNA and RNA polymerases. Unlike phosphatases, which hydrolyze phosphate esters, kinases use ATP to phosphorylate their target. Our Antibody Beacon™ Tyrosine Kinase Assay Kit (A35725, described below) provides a general and high-throughput solution assay for measuring the activity of tyrosine kinases using unlabeled peptides. In addition to these reagents, we offer several nucleotide analogs and substrates for phosphodiesterases and phospholipases that are described in Section 17.3 and Section 17.4, respectively.

By far the largest group of chromogenic and fluorogenic substrates for phosphate-ester metabolizing enzymes are those for simple phosphatases such as alkaline and acid phosphatase, both of which hydrolyze phosphate monoesters to an alcohol and inorganic phosphate. Conjugates of calf intestinal alkaline phosphatase are extensively used as secondary detection reagents in ELISAs,[1] immunohistochemical techniques[2] and Northern, Southern and Western blot analyses (Section 8.5, Section 9.4). In addition, phosphatases serve as enzyme markers, allowing researchers to identify primordial germ cells,[3] to distinguish subpopulations of bone marrow stromal cells[4] and to investigate *in vitro* differentiation in carcinoma cell lines.[5–7] *P ALP-1*, the gene for human placental alkaline phosphatase, has been used as a eukaryotic reporter gene that is superior to *lacZ* for lineage studies in murine retina.[8,9] This gene has also been engineered to produce a secreted alkaline phosphatase (SEAP), allowing quantitation of gene expression without disrupting the cells.[10]

Molecular Probes supplies the best phosphatase substrates and assay kits for a wide variety of applications:

- Fluorescein diphosphate (F2999) — probably the most sensitive substrate available for alkaline phosphatase activity measurements.
- DDAO phosphate, a long-wavelength, dual-purpose phosphatase substrate for both solution assays and amplified detection of specific targets in blot assays (Section 9.4).
- ELF® 97 phosphate, an acid and alkaline phosphatase substrate whose hydrolysis immediately yields a green-fluorescent precipitate at the sites of endogenous phosphatase activity in cells and tissues. ELF® 97 phosphate is also utilized in our Enzyme-Labeled Fluorescence technology for immunostaining and fluorescence *in situ* hybridization applications (Section 6.3).
- DiFMUP, which is available as a stand-alone reagent (D6567, D22065) and as a component of our EnzChek® Phosphatase Assay Kit (E12020). The RediPlate™ 96 and RediPlate™ 384 EnzChek® Tyrosine Phosphatase Assay Kits (R22067, R22068) and the RediPlate™ 96 EnzChek® Serine/Threonine Phosphatase Assay Kit (R33700) utilize the DiFMUP substrate for assaying tyrosine phosphatase activity and serine/threonine phosphatase activity, respectively, and for screening phosphatase inhibitors in a convenient high-throughput format.
- 5-Bromo-4-chloro-3-indolyl phosphate (BCIP, B6492), a chromogenic phosphatase substrate that is extensively used in various histological and molecular biology techniques.
- BODIPY® FL ATP-γ-*S* (A22184) and BODIPY® FL GTP-γ-*S* (G22183) thioesters, which are important substrates for Fhit, a member of the histidine triad superfamily of nucleotide-binding proteins.[11–13]
- The P_iPer™ and EnzChek® Phosphate and EnzChek® Pyrophosphate Assay Kits — unique products that can assay a wide variety of phosphatases, including ATPases and GTPases, that cannot be assayed with the typical fluorogenic or chromogenic phosphatase substrates.
- The BOLD APB chemiluminescent substrate (B21901), whose sensitivity for detection of alkaline phosphatase–labeled probes on blots we find to be superior to that of other commercially available chemiluminescent phosphatase substrates (Section 9.4, Figure 9.68).

Phosphatase Substrates Yielding Soluble Fluorescent Products

Fluorescein Diphosphate

First described in 1963,[14] fluorescein diphosphate (FDP, F2999) is perhaps the most sensitive fluorogenic phosphatase substrate available. The colorless and nonfluorescent FDP reagent is hydrolyzed to fluorescein (F1300, F36915; Section 10.1), which exhibits superior spectral properties (ε ~90,000 $cm^{-1}M^{-1}$, quantum yield ~0.92; Figure 1.52). We have succeeded in preparing a highly purified FDP and find it to be an excellent substrate for alkaline phosphatase in ELISAs, providing detection limits at least 50 times lower than those obtained with the chromogenic 4-nitrophenyl phosphate.[15] The relatively high pH required to monitor alkaline phosphatase activity is advantageous because it also enhances fluorescein's fluorescence. FDP has been used for a diverse set of applications, including:

- Measuring endogenous phosphatase in an assay for cell adhesion and migration that is reported to be as sensitive as ^{51}Cr-release assays[16]
- Quantitating the effect of inhibitors on tyrosine phosphatases[17–19]
- Detecting alkaline phosphatase immobilized on microspheres in an optical sensor array[20]
- Assaying diarrheic shellfish toxins in a microplate assay[21]
- Assaying alkaline phosphatase in a microfluidic device[22]

Dimethylacridinone (DDAO) Phosphate

Our 7-hydroxy-9*H*-(1,3-dichloro-9,9-dimethylacridin-2-one (DDAO phosphate, D6487; Figure 10.29) phosphatase substrate yields a hydrolysis product that is efficiently excited by the 633 nm spectral line of the He–Ne laser to produce bright red fluorescence with absorption/emission maxima of ~646/659 nm (Figure 10.7). Although the substrate itself is fluorescent, the difference between the substrate's excitation maximum and that of the phenolic hydrolysis product is over 200 nm (Figure 10.13), allowing the two species to be easily distinguished. Like other DDAO-based substrates, DDAO phosphate has good water solubility, a low K_M and a high turnover rate, making it particularly useful for both fluorescence- and absorption-based microplate assays.[23] Our Pro-Q® Western Blot Stain Kits, Pro-Q® Glycoprotein Blot Stain Kits and some of our DyeChrome™ Western Blot Stain Kits (Table 9.7) utilize DDAO phosphate in combination with alkaline phosphatase conjugates for the ultrasensitive detection of proteins on blots. Unlike chemiluminescent assays, the Pro-Q® and DyeChrome™ Blot Stain Kits give permanent staining of the blots. DDAO phosphate and the Amplex® Gold peroxidase substrate are used in combination with the SYPRO® Ruby Blot Stain in the Dye-Chrome™ Double Western Blot Stain Kit (D21887) for the simultaneous detection of two specific proteins and total proteins on Western blots. These kits are described in detail in Section 9.4.

Methylumbelliferyl Phosphate (MUP) and Difluorinated Methylumbelliferyl Phosphate (DiFMUP)

We offer 4-methylumbelliferyl phosphate (MUP), a widely used fluorogenic substrate for alkaline phosphatase detection, as either its free acid (M6491) or dicyclohexylammonium salt (M8425). MUP has been used for a variety of ELISA protocols[24] in which the relatively high pH optimum of alkaline phosphatase permits continuous detection of the rate of formation of 4-methylumbelliferone (7-hydroxy-4-methylcoumarin, H189, Section 10.1). MUP has also been used to count cells based on their alkaline phosphatase activity,[25] to detect PCR amplification products[26,27] and to identify and characterize bacteria.[28,29]

Our patented 6,8-difluoro-4-methylumbelliferyl phosphate (DiFMUP, D6567, D22065; Figure 10.30) exhibits extraordinary spectral properties that are advantageous for the assay of both acid and alkaline phosphatase activity and is probably the best general substrate available for measuring the activity of the protein phosphatases that are important for high-throughput screening applications under physiological conditions.[30] The hydrolysis product of DiFMUP — 6,8-difluoro-4-methylumbelliferone (6,8-difluoro-7-hydroxy-4-methylcoumarin, D6566; Section 10.1; Figure 10.3) — exhibits both a lower pK_a (4.9 versus 7.8, Figure 1.96) and a higher fluorescence quantum yield (0.89 versus 0.63) than the hydrolysis product of MUP.[31] The low pK_a of its hydrolysis product makes DiFMUP a sensitive substrate for the continuous assay of acid phosphatases (Figure 10.31, Figure 10.32), which is not possible with MUP because its fluorescence must be measured at alkaline pH (pH >9). Furthermore, with its high fluorescence quantum yield, DiFMUP increases the sensitivity of both acid and alkaline phosphatase measurements. As with our fluorinated fluorescein derivatives (Oregon Green® dyes, Section 1.5), fluorination renders the methylumbelliferone fluorophore much less susceptible to photobleaching, yet does not significantly affect the extinction coefficient or excitation/emission maxima. DiFMUP is available as a single 5 mg vial (D6567) or as a set of 10 vials, each containing 10 mg of the substrate (D22065) for high-throughput screening applications. DiFMUP is also used in our EnzChek® Phosphatase Detection Kit (E12020), our RediPlate™ 96 and RediPlate™ 384 EnzChek® Tyrosine Phosphatase Assay Kits (R22067, R22068) and our RediPlate™ 96 EnzChek® Serine/Threonine Phosphatase Assay Kit (R33700), which are described below with our other phosphatase assay kits.

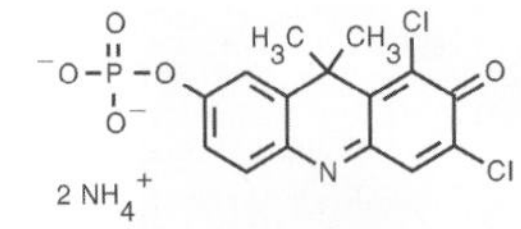

Figure 10.29 D6487 9*H*-(1,3-dichloro-9,9-dimethylacridin-2-one-7-yl) phosphate, diammonium salt (DDAO phosphate).

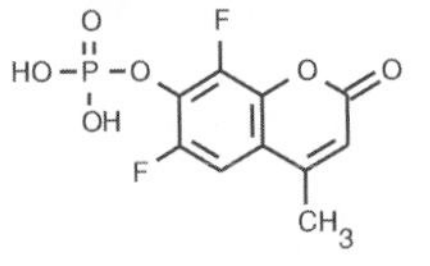

Figure 10.30 D6567 6,8-difluoro-4-methylumbelliferyl phosphate (DiFMUP).

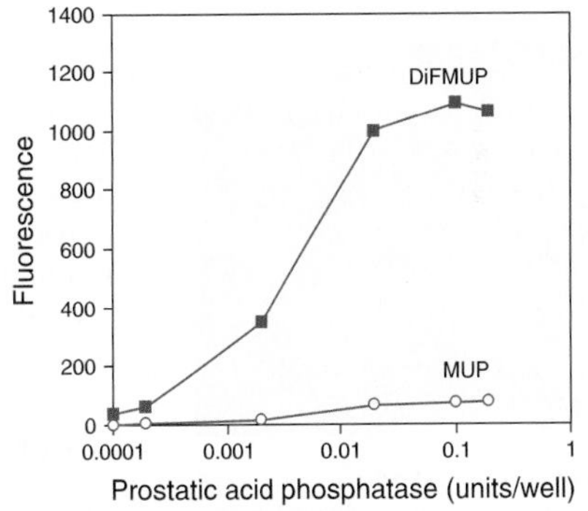

Figure 10.31 Comparison of DiFMUP (D6567, D22065) with MUP (M6491) for the detection of acid phosphatase activity at pH 5.5. Increasing amounts of prostatic acid phosphatase from human semen were reacted with 100 µM DiFMUP, the substrate in the EnzChek® Acid Phosphatase Assay Kit (E12020), or 100 µM MUP, in 100 mM sodium acetate, pH 5.5, at room temperature. Fluorescence was measured after 60 minutes in a fluorescence microplate reader using excitation at 360 ± 20 nm and emission detection at 460 ± 20 nm.

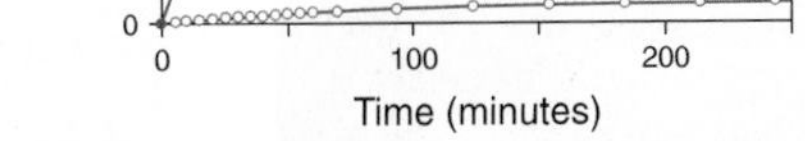

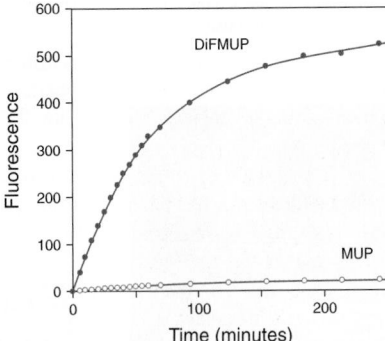

Figure 10.32 Time course of the reaction of prostatic acid phosphatase with DiFMUP (D6567, D22065) and MUP (M6491). Prostatic acid phosphatase from human semen (0.002 units) was reacted with 100 µM DiFMUP or 100 µM MUP in 100 mM sodium acetate, pH 5.5, at room temperature. Fluorescence was measured at the indicated times in a fluorescence microplate reader using excitation at 360 ± 20 nm and emission detection at 460 ± 20 nm.

ELF® 97 Phosphate: A Phosphatase Substrate That Yields a Fluorescent Precipitate

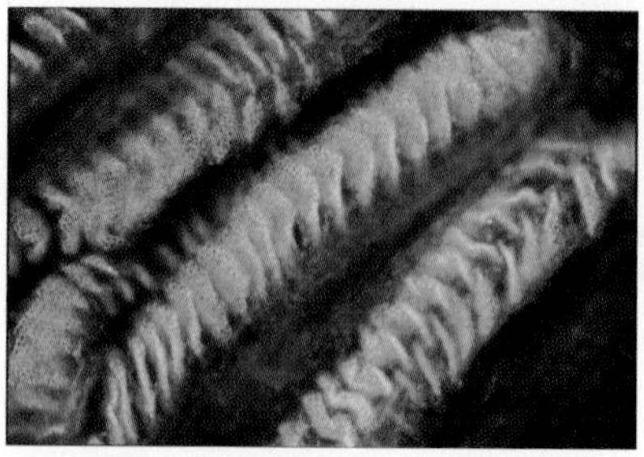

Figure 10.33 A cryostat section of lightly fixed adult zebrafish gills that have been incubated with the ELF® 97 substrate in our ELF® 97 Endogenous Phosphatase Detection Kit (E6601). This kit's novel ELF® 97 phosphatase substrate yields a yellow-green–fluorescent precipitate at the site of endogenous phosphatase activity. This staining pattern is identical to that seen when employing the conventional Gomori method for detecting phosphatase activity.

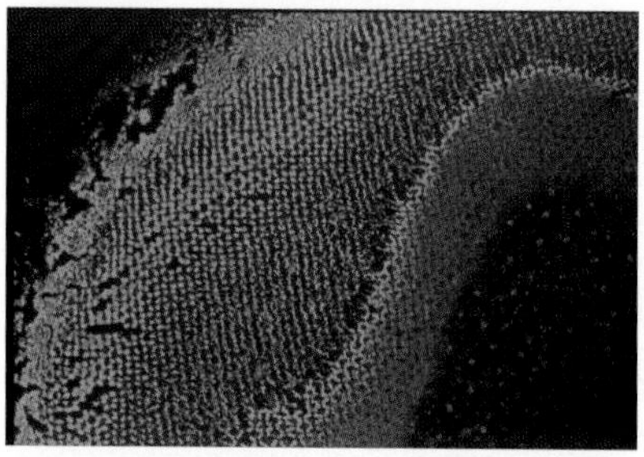

Figure 10.34 Fixed zebrafish retinal sections stained with FRet 43, an antibody that labels both double cone cells and a subset of bipolar interneurons. The antibody has been developed for visualization with standard enzyme-mediated immunohistochemical techniques using our ELF® 97 Immunohistochemistry Kit (E6600). The ELF® 97 phosphatase substrate in this kit produces an intense yellow-green–fluorescent precipitate at the site of enzymatic activity. The tissue has been sectioned tangentially to reveal the mosaic nature of the zebrafish retina. In this section, the lightly stained round profiles in the lower right are bipolars, whereas the adjacent stained configurations are the double cones, beginning with the synaptic pedicles and progressing through the nuclei, inner segments and outer segments.

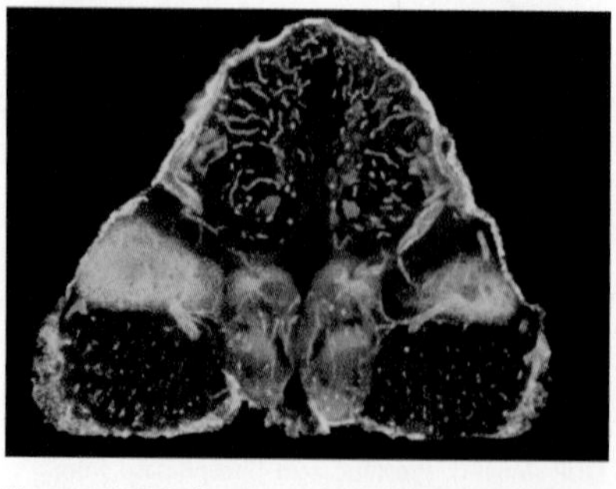

Figure 10.35 Endogenous phosphatase activity in the zebrafish brain, localized with the ELF® 97 Endogenous Phosphatase Detection Kit (E6601). Enzymatic cleavage of the ELF® 97 phosphatase substrate yields a bright yellow-green–fluorescent precipitate at the site of enzyme activity. The image was acquired with a bandpass filter set appropriate for the ELF® alcohol precipitate.

Scientists at Molecular Probes have developed substrates that yield fluorescent precipitates at the site of enzymatic activity — a patented process we call Enzyme-Labeled Fluorescence (ELF®) (Figure 10.33, Figure 10.34). Our first product in this line was the ELF® 97 phosphatase substrate (ELF® 97 phosphate, E6588, E6589). Upon enzymatic cleavage (Figure 6.15), this weakly blue-fluorescent substrate yields an extremely photostable (Figure 6.18) green-fluorescent precipitate that is up to 40 times brighter than the signal achieved when using either directly labeled fluorescent hybridization probes or fluorescent secondary detection methods in comparable applications.[32–34] ELF® 97 phosphate can be used over a wide pH range to selectively detect either acid- or alkaline-phosphatase activity. Although optimally excited with UV light (Figure 6.17), the ELF® 97 alcohol precipitate can also reportedly be excited with the 488 nm spectral line of the argon-ion laser, making it compatible with flow cytometry and confocal laser-scanning microscopy.[35] Using ELF® 97 phosphate and confocal laser-scanning microscopy, researchers have developed a semiautomated method for analyzing the position within a regenerating newt limb of transfected cells expressing the secreted alkaline phosphatase reporter gene.[35] Kits based on our ELF® 97 phosphate include:

- ELF® 97 mRNA *In Situ* Hybridization Kits[36] (E6604, E6605; Figure 6.21, Figure 8.94)
- ELF® 97 Cytological Labeling Kit (E6603, Figure 6.23, Figure 6.26)
- ELF® 97 Immunohistochemistry Kit (E6600, Figure 6.2)
- ELF® 97 Endogenous Phosphatase Detection Kit (E6601, Figure 6.29, Figure 10.35)

These kits and their contents are described in detail in Section 6.3. ELF® 97 phosphate is also available separately as a 5 mM solution in water containing sodium azide (E6589) or in a 0.2 µm–filtered solution (E6588). Filtration of ELF® 97 phosphate through an ELF® spin filter (E6606) is recommended before use. We have found that enzyme-catalyzed precipitation is often improved by incorporating a trace amount of the hydrolysis product — the yellow-green–fluorescent ELF® 97 alcohol — in the detection buffer. The ELF® 97 alcohol is available as a concentrated solution in DMSO (E6578, Section 10.1).

The ELF® 97 phosphate substrate can be used to detect endogenous phosphatase activity (Figure 10.36) or in combination with alkaline phosphatase conjugates of secondary antibodies (Section 7.2), streptavidin (Section 7.6), concanavalin A (Section 7.7) or other alkaline phosphatase conjugates for signal amplification. A particularly easy means of preparing alkaline phosphatase–labeled antibodies utilizes our exclusive Zenon® Alkaline Phosphatase Antibody Labeling Kits (Section 7.3, Table 7.13). With these kits, it is possible to rapidly and quantitatively label even extremely small (submicrogram) quantities of an antibody. Following labeling of the target, the alkaline phosphatase activity of the complex can be detected with the ELF® 97 phosphatase substrate or any of the other phosphatase substrates in this section. We have directly detected the alkaline phosphatase enzyme with an antibody to the protein (Figure 10.37).

A different ELF® phosphatase substrate — ELF® 39 phosphate — is used to detect alkaline phosphatase–conjugated secondary antibodies or streptavidin in three of our DyeChrome™ Western Blot Stain Kits (Section 9.4, Table 9.7).

Our patented ELF® technology and products are offered for research purposes only. Molecular Probes welcomes inquiries about licensing these products for resale or other commercial uses.

BODIPY® FL ATP-γ-*S* and BODIPY® FL GTP-γ-*S* Thioesters: Substrates for the Fhit Nucleotide-Binding Protein

The patented BODIPY® FL ATP-γ-*S* (A22184) and BODIPY® FL GTP-γ-*S* (G22183) thioesters are important substrates for Fhit (Figure 17.18), a member of the histidine triad superfamily of nucleotide-binding proteins that binds and cleaves diadenosine polyphosphates.[11–13] Fhit, one of the most frequently inactivated proteins in lung cancer, functions as a tumor suppressor by inducing apoptosis.[12,37,38] In addition to their use for screening potential Fhit inhibitors, these BODIPY® FL nucleotides should also be important for studying other nucleotide-binding proteins because they bind to ATP- or GTP-binding sites but are not metabolized (Section 17.3). As with other fluorescent nucleotides, the fluorescence polarization properties of the bound nucleotide should differ from that of the free nucleotide. The fluorescence of BODIPY® FL GTP-γ-*S* thioester is quenched ~90% relative to that of the free dye (Figure 17.16) but is recovered upon binding to at least some G-proteins.[39,40]

Chromogenic Phosphatase Substrate

BCIP

5-Bromo-4-chloro-3-indolyl phosphate (BCIP, B6492) is commonly used with a number of different chromogens in various histological and molecular biology techniques (Section 8.4, Section 9.4). Hydrolysis of this indolyl phosphate, followed by oxidation, produces a blue-colored precipitate at the site of enzymatic activity.

NBT: A Co-Precipitant for the BCIP Reaction

Nitro blue tetrazolium (NBT, N6495) is the most commonly used electron-transfer agent and co-precipitant for the BCIP (B6492) reaction, forming a dark blue, precisely localized precipitate in the presence of alkaline phosphatase[41,42] (Figure 9.69, Figure 10.38). For added convenience, we offer the NBT/BCIP Reagent Kit (N6547), which provides 1 g samples of both NBT and BCIP.

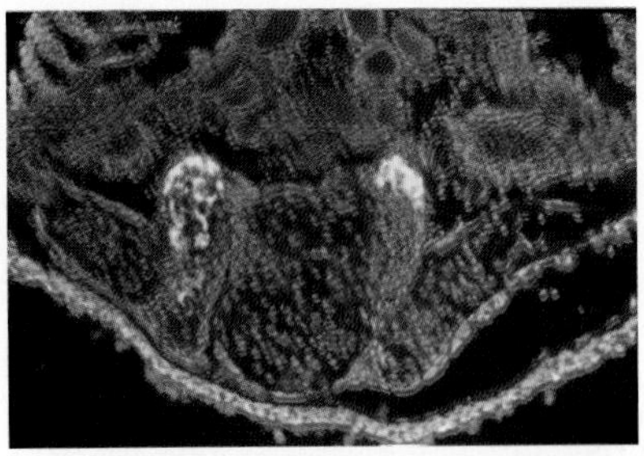

Figure 10.36 Endogenous phosphatase activity of osteoblast cells in a cartilaginous element of an adult zebrafish head localized using the ELF® 97 Endogenous Phosphatase Detection Kit (E6601) to stain a cryosection. In addition to the yellow-green fluorescence of the ELF® 97 alcohol precipitate, the section was stained with red-fluorescent Texas Red®-X wheat germ agglutinin (W21405) and with the blue-fluorescent Hoechst 33342 nucleic acid stain (H1399, H3570, H21492). The triple-exposure image was acquired using bandpass filter sets appropriate for ELF® 97 alcohol, Texas Red® dye and DAPI.

Kits for Detecting Phosphatases, Polymerases and Nucleases

Molecular Probes has developed some unique products for following the activity of phosphatases, polymerases and nucleases. Our patented P_iPer™ Phosphate and P_iPer™ Pyrophosphate Assay Kits provide ultrasensitive assays for free phosphate and pyrophosphate, respectively, through the formation of resorufin, which can be detected either fluorometrically or spectrophotometrically. Our EnzChek® Phosphate and EnzChek® Pyrophosphate Assay Kits provide colorimetric assays for inorganic phosphate and pyrophosphate, respectively. Both the P_iPer™ and the EnzChek® Phosphate Assay Kits permit continuous measurement of the activity of ATPases, GTPases, phosphatases, nucleotidases and a number of enzymes that produce or consume inorganic phosphate. Moreover, these enzyme assay kits utilize the natural substrate for the enzyme rather than a synthetic analog and detect the inorganic phosphate produced using enzyme-coupled reactions. The P_iPer™ Kit is more sensitive and better suited for high-throughput studies in microplates, but requires an additional enzymatic step, whereas the EnzChek® Kit is less sensitive but has a simpler protocol. In both the P_iPer™ and the EnzChek® Pyrophosphate Assay Kits, the phosphate assay is coupled with the enzyme, pyrophosphatase, in order to monitor the activity of pyrophosphate-producing enzymes such as DNA- and RNA-polymerases, adenylate cyclase and guanylate cyclase.[43,44] In addition to these kits, our EnzChek® Acid Phosphatase Detection Kit employs the fluorogenic substrate DiFMUP for the continuous assay of all phosphatases, including acid phosphatases, which are not compatible with assays based on MUP because its fluorescence must be measured at alkaline pH. The RediPlate™ 96 and RediPlate™ 384 EnzChek® Tyrosine Phosphatase Assay Kits (R22067, R22068, see below) and the RediPlate™ 96 EnzChek® Serine/Threonine Phosphatase Assay Kit (R33700) utilize DiFMUP for assaying tyrosine phosphatase activity and serine/threonine phosphatase activity, respectively, and for screening phosphatase inhibitors in a convenient high-throughput format.

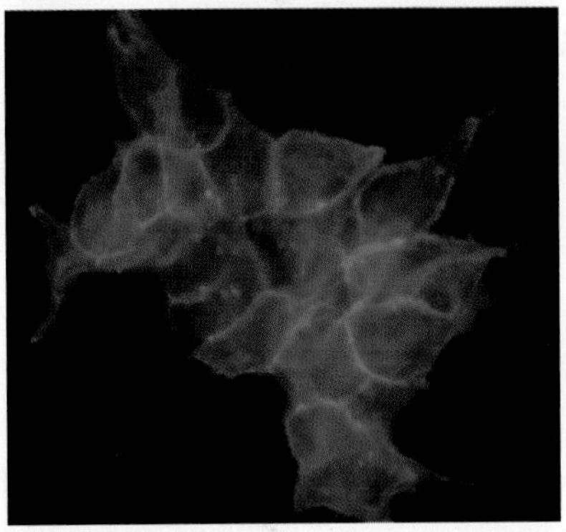

Figure 10.37 The endogenous alkaline phosphatase enzyme of osteosarcoma cells localized with a mouse anti-rat alkaline phosphatase monoclonal antibody, RBM 211.13, which was visualized with Alexa Fluor® 594 goat anti-mouse IgG, $F(ab')_2$ fragments (A11020). The blue-fluorescent Hoechst 33342 (H1399, H3570, H21492) nucleic acid stain was used as a counterstain to the red fluorescence of the Alexa Fluor® 594 secondary antibody. The primary antibody was a gift from Dr. Jane Aubin, University of Toronto. The double-exposure image was acquired using longpass filter sets appropriate for the Texas Red® dye and DAPI.

P_iPer™ Phosphate Assay Kit

Molecular Probes' patented P_iPer™ Phosphate Assay Kit (P22061) provides an ultrasensitive assay that detects free phosphate in solution through the formation of the fluorescent product resorufin. Because resorufin also has strong absorption, the assay can be performed either fluorometrically or spectrophotometrically. This kit can be used to detect inorganic phosphate (P_i) in a variety of samples or to monitor the kinetics of phosphate release by a variety of enzymes, including ATPases, GTPases, 5′-nucleotidase, protein phosphatases, acid and alkaline phosphatases and phosphorylase kinase. Furthermore, the assay can be modified to detect virtually any naturally occurring organic phosphate molecule by including an enzyme that can specifically digest the organic phosphate to liberate inorganic phosphate.

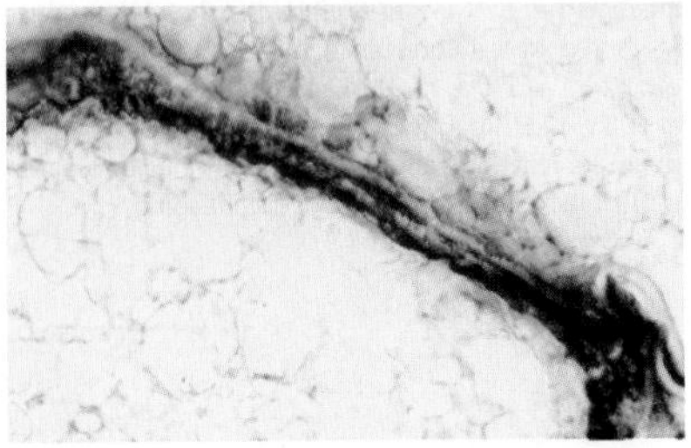

Figure 10.38 Endogenous phosphatase activity in a zebrafish ovary cross-section, stained with the BCIP (B6492) and NBT (N6495) reagents. These reagents are also available in the NBT/BCIP Reagent Kit (N6547).

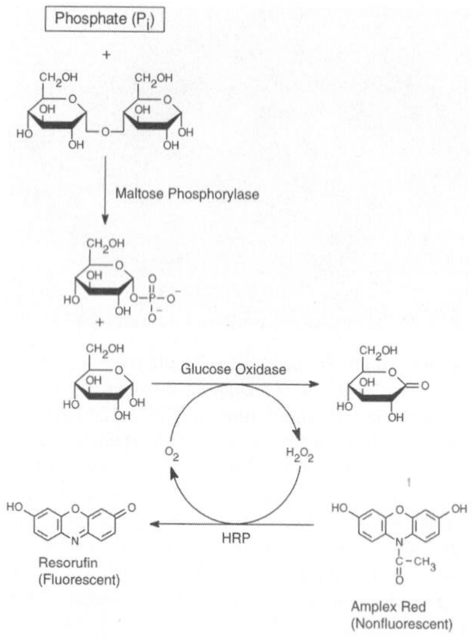

Figure 10.39 Principle of the P_iPer™ Phosphate Assay Kit (P22061). In the presence of inorganic phosphate, maltose phosphorylase converts maltose to glucose 1-phosphate and glucose. Then, glucose oxidase converts the glucose to gluconolactone and H_2O_2. Finally, with horseradish peroxidase (HRP) as a catalyst, the H_2O_2 reacts with the Amplex® Red reagent to generate the highly fluorescent resorufin. The resulting increase in fluorescence or absorption is proportional to the amount of P_i in the sample.

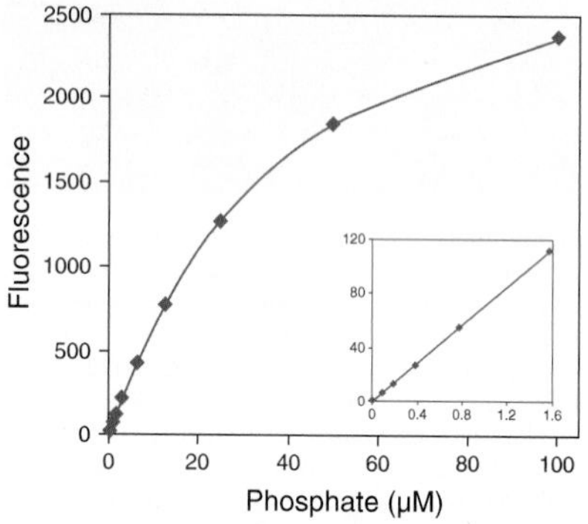

Figure 10.40 Detection of inorganic phosphate using the P_iPer™ Phosphate Assay Kit (P22061). Each reaction contained 50 μM Amplex® Red reagent, 2 U/mL maltose phosphorylase, 1 mM maltose, 1 U/mL glucose oxidase and 0.2 U/mL HRP in 1X reaction buffer. Reactions were incubated at 37°C. After 60 minutes, fluorescence was measured in a fluorescence microplate reader using excitation at 530 ± 12.5 nm and fluorescence detection at 590 ± 17.5 nm. Data points represent the average of duplicate reactions, and a background value of 43 (arbitrary units) was subtracted from each reading.

In the P_iPer™ phosphate assay (Figure 10.39), maltose phosphorylase converts maltose (in the presence of P_i) to glucose 1-phosphate and glucose. Then glucose oxidase converts the glucose to gluconolactone and H_2O_2. Finally, with horseradish peroxidase (HRP) as a catalyst, the H_2O_2 reacts with the Amplex® Red reagent (10-acetyl-3,7-dihydroxyphenoxazine) to generate resorufin, which has absorption/emission maxima of ~571/585 nm [45,46] (Figure 10.6). The resulting increase in fluorescence or absorption is proportional to the amount of P_i in the sample. This kit can be used to detect as little as 0.2 μM P_i by fluorescence (Figure 10.40) or 0.4 μM P_i by absorption.

Each P_iPer™ Phosphate Assay Kit contains:

- Amplex® Red reagent
- Dimethylsulfoxide (DMSO) and a concentrated reaction buffer
- Recombinant maltose phosphorylase from *Escherichia coli*
- Maltose
- Glucose oxidase from *Aspergillus niger*
- Horseradish peroxidase (HRP)
- Phosphate standard
- Hydrogen peroxide
- A detailed protocol for detecting phosphatase activity

Each kit provides sufficient reagents for approximately 1000 assays using a reaction volume of 100 μL per assay and either a fluorescence or absorbance microplate reader.

P_iPer™ Pyrophosphate Assay Kit

Our P_iPer™ Pyrophosphate Assay Kit (P22062) provides a sensitive fluorometric or colorimetric method for measuring the inorganic pyrophosphate (PP_i) in experimental samples or for monitoring the kinetics of PP_i release by a variety of enzymes, including DNA and RNA polymerases, adenylate cyclase and *S*-acetyl coenzyme A synthetase. In the P_iPer™ pyrophosphate assay, inorganic pyrophosphatase hydrolyzes PP_i to two molecules of inorganic phosphate (P_i). The PP_i then enters into the same cascade of reactions as it does in the P_iPer™ Phosphate Assay Kit (Figure 10.39). In this case, the resulting increase in fluorescence or absorption is proportional to the amount of PP_i in the sample. This kit can be used to detect as little as 0.1 μM PP_i by fluorescence or 0.2 μM PP_i by absorption (Figure 10.41).

Each P_iPer™ Pyrophosphate Assay Kit contains:

- Amplex® Red reagent
- Dimethylsulfoxide (DMSO) and a concentrated reaction buffer
- Recombinant maltose phosphorylase from *Escherichia coli*
- Maltose
- Glucose oxidase from *Aspergillus niger*
- Horseradish peroxidase (HRP)
- Inorganic pyrophosphatase from baker's yeast
- Pyrophosphate standard
- A detailed protocol for detecting phosphatase activity

Each kit provides sufficient reagents for approximately 1000 assays using a reaction volume of 100 μL per assay and either a fluorescence or absorbance microplate reader.

EnzChek® Phosphate Assay Kit

Continuous assay of many phosphate ester–metabolizing enzymes is difficult because suitable substrates are not available. It usually has been necessary to determine inorganic phosphate release using tedious colorimetric assays or radioisotope-based methods. The EnzChek® Phosphate Assay Kit (E6646), which is based on a method originally described by Webb,[47,48] provides a rapid and highly sensitive enzymatic assay for detecting inorganic phosphate through the formation of a chromophoric product (Figure 10.42). This unique spectrophotometric technique permits the continuous assay of ATPase activity, and potentially the activity of many other enzymes such as GTPases and phosphatases that produce inorganic phosphate. Each EnzChek® Phosphate Assay Kit contains:

- 2-Amino-6-mercapto-7-methylpurine riboside (MESG)
- Purine nucleoside phosphorylase (PNP)
- Concentrated reaction buffer
- KH_2PO_4 standard
- A detailed protocol for detecting and quantitating phosphate

In the presence of inorganic phosphate, MESG is enzymatically converted by PNP to ribose 1-phosphate and the chromophoric product 2-amino-6-mercapto-7-methylpurine (Figure 10.42). Although the MESG reagent is somewhat unstable above pH 7, the reaction can be performed over the pH range of 6.5 to 8.5 with the proper controls.[48] This kit contains sufficient reagents for about 100 phosphate assays using 1 mL assay volumes and standard cuvettes.

The substrate MESG and the enzyme PNP included in our EnzChek® Phosphate Assay Kit have already been adapted for monitoring the kinetics of phosphate release by:

- Actin-activated myosin ATPase[48,49]
- Actin polymerization[50]
- Aminoacyl-tRNA synthetase[51]
- Aspartate transcarbamylase[47,52]
- ArsA ATPase, the catalytic subunit of the arsenite pump[53]
- Dethiobiotin synthetase[54]
- Glycerol kinase[48]
- Glycogen phosphorylase[55]
- GTPases[56–61]
- ATPases[52,62,63]
- *myo*-Inositol monophosphatase[64]
- Phospholysine and phosphohistidine phosphatases[65,66]
- Phosphorylase *a* phosphatase[67]
- Phosphorylase kinase[68]
- Serine phosphatase[69]
- Self-assembly of actin and tubulin[70]
- Autodephosphorylation of CheY, a response regulator that mediates bacterial chemotaxis[71]

Moreover, the EnzChek® phosphate assay is sufficiently fast and quantitative to permit stopped-flow kinetic experiments on enzymes that produce phosphate, an important development for mechanistic enzyme studies.[48]

Although this kit is usually used to determine the inorganic phosphate produced by enzymes such as ATPases and GTPases, it can also be used to specifically quantitate inorganic phosphate contamination of reagents and solution, with a detection limit of ~2 µM P_i (~0.2 µg/mL) and an effective range between 2 and 150 µM inorganic phosphate (between 2 and 150 nanomoles phosphate in a 1 mL volume). For example, the assay has been used for the rapid assay of inorganic phosphate in the presence of high concentrations of acid-labile phosphates using a microplate reader.[72] The reagents in this kit can also be used as a phosphate "mop" to remove almost all inorganic phosphate from a protein solution.[73]

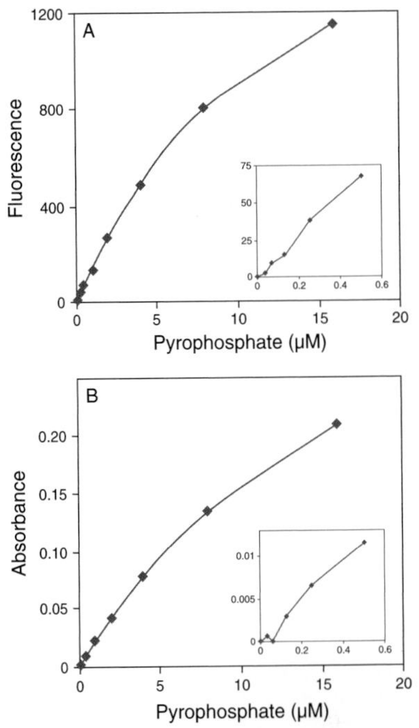

Figure 10.41 Detection of pyrophosphate using the PiPer™ Pyrophosphate Assay Kit (P22062). Each reaction contained 50 µM Amplex® Red reagent, 0.01 U/mL inorganic pyrophosphatase, 2 U/mL maltose phosphorylase, 0.2 mM maltose, 1 U/mL glucose oxidase and 0.2 U/mL HRP in 1X reaction buffer. Reactions were incubated at 37°C. After 60 minutes, fluorescence was measured in a fluorescence-based microplate reader using excitation at 530 ± 12.5 nm and fluorescence detection at 590 ± 17.5 nm (A) or absorbance was measured in an absorption-based microplate reader at 576 ± 5 nm (B). Data points represent the average of duplicate reactions. In panel A, a background value of 78 (arbitrary units) was subtracted from each reading; in panel B, a background absorbance of 0.011 was subtracted from each reading.

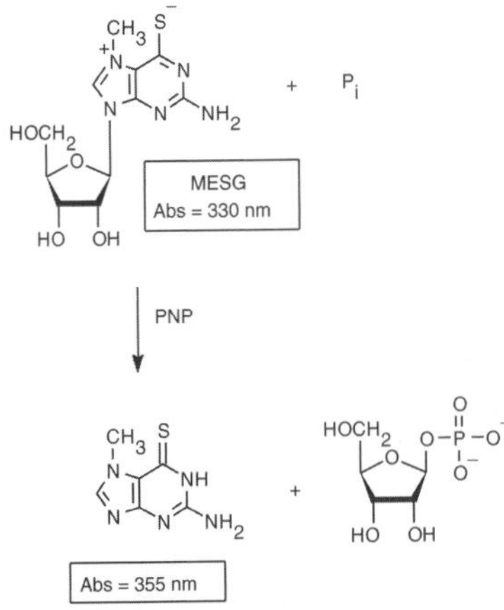

Figure 10.42 Enzymatic conversion of 2-amino-6-mercapto-7-methylpurine riboside (MESG) to ribose 1-phosphate and 2-amino-6-mercapto-7-methylpurine by purine nucleoside phosphorylase (PNP), reagents supplied in our EnzChek® Phosphate Assay Kit (E6646). The accompanying change in the absorption maximum (Abs) allows quantitation of inorganic phosphate (P_i) consumed in the reaction.

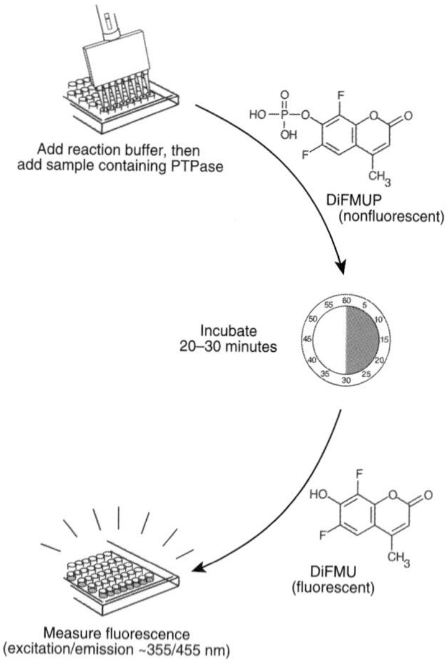

Figure 10.43 Schematic diagram of the method used in the RediPlate™ EnzChek® Phosphatase Assay Kits (R22067, R22068, R33700).

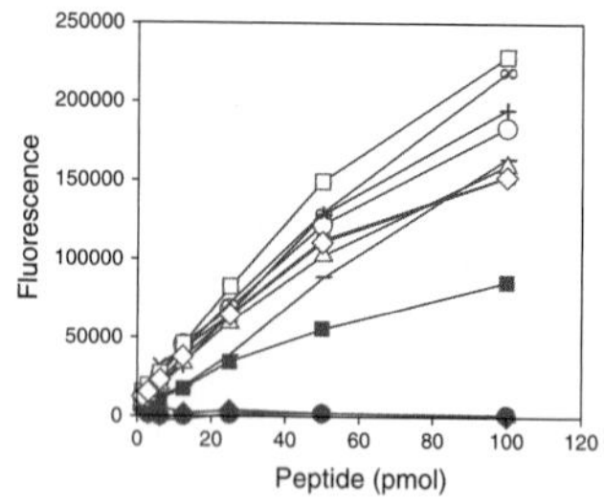

Symbol (in graph above)	Peptide Name	Sequence	# of Phos-phates
◇	3pY	TRDIpYETDpYpYRK	3
□	pTpY	DHTGFLpTEpYVATR	2
△	pTpY-A	DHTGFLpTGYVATR	1
×	1pY	TRDIpYETDYYRK	1
∞	pT	KRpTIRR	1
○	pDSIP	WAGGNApSGE	1
+	Promega peptide	RRApTVA	1
–	RII	DLDVPIPGRFDRRVpSVAAE	1
■	pp60c-src	TSTEPQPpYQPGENL	1
NA	pT1721	VPIPGRFDRRVpTVE	1
◆	p60c-src	TSTEPQPYQPGENL	0
●	AT	DRVYIHPFHL	0
▲	A8186	RKRARKE	0
NA	Kemptide	LRRASLG	0

NA = Not applicable.

Figure 10.44 Specificity of the RediPlate™ 96 and RediPlate™ 384 EnzChek® Tyrosine Phosphatase Assay Kits (R22067, R22068) for tyrosine phosphatase. The phosphatases listed in the tables were applied to a RediPlate™ 96 EnzChek® tyrosine phosphatase assay microplate. At the indicated time points, the fluorescence was measured in a fluorescence microplate reader using excitation at 355 ± 20 nm and emission at 460 ± 12.5 nm.

EnzChek® Pyrophosphate Assay Kit

We have adapted the method provided in our EnzChek® Phosphate Assay Kit to permit the sensitive spectrophotometric detection of pyrophosphate, which is converted by the enzyme pyrophosphatase to inorganic phosphate.[44] Because two moles of phosphate are released per mole of pyrophosphate consumed, the sensitivity limit of the EnzChek® Pyrophosphatase Assay Kit is 1 µM PP_i (~0.2 µg/mL). This assay has been modified to continuously detect several enzymes that liberate pyrophosphate[74–77] such as aminoacyl-tRNA synthetase,[51] luciferase, cytidylyl transferase[78] and *S*-acetyl coenzyme A synthetase[44] and potentially DNA and RNA polymerases, adenylate cyclase and guanylyl cyclase.[43] Each EnzChek® Pyrophosphate Assay Kit (E6645) contains:

- Inorganic pyrophosphatase
- 2-Amino-6-mercapto-7-methylpurine riboside (MESG)
- Purine nucleoside phosphorylase (PNP)
- Concentrated reaction buffer
- $Na_2P_2O_7$ standard
- A detailed protocol for detecting and quantitating pyrophosphate

This kit contains sufficient reagents for about 100 pyrophosphate assays using 1 mL assay volumes and standard cuvettes.

Coumarin-Based Probes for Detection of Inorganic Phosphate

We offer 7-diethylamino-3-((((2-maleimidyl)ethyl)amino)carbonyl)coumarin (MDCC, D10253; Section 2.3; Figure 2.25) and the corresponding iodoacetamide (IDCC, D20382, Section 2.3). When conjugated to a mutant phosphate-binding protein,[79] MDCC has proven useful for direct, real-time measurement of inorganic phosphate release during enzymatic reactions.[73,80–83] An IDCC conjugate of a mutant nucleoside diphosphate kinase has been used as a fluorescent sensor of the phosphorylation state of the kinase and to monitor purine nucleoside diphosphate concentrations in real time.[84] MDCC and IDCC are also useful reagents for general labeling of thiols, exhibiting bright blue fluorescence.

EnzChek® Phosphatase Assay Kit

The EnzChek® Phosphatase Assay Kit[85] (E12020), which includes our patented DiFMUP substrate, can be used to continuously detect phosphatase activity at neutral, basic or moderately acidic pH. Using the assay outlined in the kit protocol, we have found that DiFMUP is about 100 times more sensitive than MUP for the detection of prostatic acid phosphatase at pH 5.5 (Figure 10.31) and can measure this activity at a pH that is optimal for the enzyme (Figure 10.32). The EnzChek® Phosphatase Assay Kit is perfect for the continuous assay of prostatic acid phosphatase, protein phosphatase 1 or almost any other phosphatase that can be assayed with nonprotein-based substrates such as MUP or 4-nitrophenyl phosphate (PNPP). Each EnzChek® Phosphatase Assay Kit contains:

- DiFMUP substrate
- Concentrated reaction buffer
- Acid phosphatase from potato for use as a positive control
- 6,8-Difluoro-7-hydroxy-4-methylcoumarin for use as a reference standard
- A detailed protocol for detecting phosphatase activity

The kit provides sufficient reagents for performing approximately 1000 assays, using a reaction volume of 100 µL per assay.

RediPlate™ 96 and RediPlate™ 384 EnzChek® Tyrosine Phosphatase Assay Kits

Protein tyrosine phosphatases (PTP) represent a large family of enzymes that play a very important role in intra- and intercellular signaling. PTPs work antagonistically with protein tyrosine kinases to regulate signal transduction pathways in response to a variety of signals, including hormones and mitogens.[86–88] Our RediPlate™ 96 and RediPlate™ 384 EnzChek® Tyrosine Phosphatase Assay Kits (R22067, R22068) provide researchers with a sensitive and convenient means to monitor PTP and screen PTP inhibitors for a variety of research areas (Figure 10.43), including:

- Insulin regulation [89–91]
- Cell proliferation and differentiation [92]
- Axonal outgrowth [93,94]
- Immune response and inflammation [95]
- Angiogenesis [96]

Our tyrosine phosphatase assay is based on our patented 6,8-difluoro-4-methylumbelliferyl phosphate (DiFMUP, D6567, D22065), an acid and alkaline phosphatase substrate whose hydrolysis product (6,8-difluoro-7-hydroxy-4-methylcoumarin, DiFMU; D6566, Section 10.1, Figure 10.3) exhibits excitation/emission maxima of ~358/455 nm (Figure 10.2), a low pK_a (~4.9, Figure 1.96) and a high quantum yield (~0.89). Unlike other end-point tyrosine phosphatase assay kits, the RediPlate™ 96 and RediPlate™ 384 EnzChek® tyrosine phosphatase assay is continuous, allowing researchers to easily measure fluorescence at various time points in order to follow the kinetics of the reaction. Furthermore, the assay is not affected by free phosphate and is compatible with most nonionic detergents, resulting in minimal sample processing before analysis. Most importantly, each assay well contains inhibitors to ensure that the assay is selective for tyrosine phosphatases; other phosphatases, including serine/threonine phosphatases, will not hydrolyze DiFMUP under our assay conditions (Figure 10.44). Unlike phosphopeptide-based assays, this DiFMUP-based assay can be used to monitor a variety of tyrosine phosphatases, including PTP-1B and CD-45. Tyrosine phosphatase inhibitors can be evaluated quantitatively in the assay for their effect on tyrosine phosphatase activity.

Each RediPlate™ 96 EnzChek® Tyrosine Phosphatase Assay Kit (R22067) or RediPlate™ 384 EnzChek® Tyrosine Phosphatase Assay Kit (R22068) includes one microplate of either 96 or 384 wells, respectively, contained in a resealable foil packet to ensure the integrity of the fluorogenic components, plus a vial of reaction buffer. The first row of wells in the microplate contains a dilution series of the 6,8-difluoro-7-hydroxy-4-methylcoumarin (DiFMU) reference standard for generating a standard curve, and the remaining wells are preloaded with the DiFMUP substrate. Additionally, each RediPlate™ 96 assay plate has removable lanes that allow researchers to perform only as many assays as required for the experiment (Figure 8.60). The RediPlate™ 384 EnzChek® Tyrosine Phosphatase Assay Kit includes a single 384-well plate for high-throughput screening of tyrosine phosphatase activity. Table 10.3 summarizes our other RediPlate™ 96 and RediPlate™ 384 Assay Kits for serine/threonine phosphatase activity (see below), dsDNA quantitation (Section 8.3) and protease activity (Section 10.4). Significant discounts apply to purchases of multiple units of all of our RediPlate™ products.

RediPlate™ 96 EnzChek® Serine/Threonine Phosphatase Assay Kit

The majority of protein phosphorylation occurs on serine and threonine residues, with <0.01–0.05% on tyrosine residues.[86] Serine/threonine phosphatases represent a large family of enzymes that have been implicated in the regulation of metabolism,[97] transcription,[98] translation,[99] differentiation,[100] cell cycle,[86] cytoskeletal dynamics,[101] oncogenesis [102,103] and signal transduction.[104,105] Our RediPlate™ 96 EnzChek® Serine/Threonine Phosphatase Assay Kit (R33700) provides a fast, simple and direct fluorescence-based assay for detecting serine/threonine phosphatases and their corresponding modulators and inhibitors (Figure 10.43).

As with the RediPlate™ EnzChek® Tyrosine Phosphatase Kits, the substrate incorporated in the RediPlate™ 96 EnzChek® Serine/Threonine Phosphatase Assay Kit is our patented DiFMUP, which upon hydrolysis generates DiFMU (D6566, Section 10.1, Figure 10.3) with excitation/emission maxima of 358/452 nm, a low pK_a (~4.9) and a high quantum yield (~0.89). Inhibitors are included in each assay well to ensure that the assay is selective for serine/threonine phosphatases; under the prescribed assay conditions, other phosphatases, including tyrosine phosphatases, do not significantly react with the substrate (Figure 10.45). Furthermore, unlike phosphopeptide-based assays, this DiFMUP-based assay can be used to monitor a variety of serine/threonine phosphatases including PP-1, PP-2A and PP-2B (Figure 10.45). Serine/threonine phosphatase inhibitors can be evaluated quantitatively in the assay for their effect on serine/threonine phosphatase activity (Figure 10.46). Additional advantages of this RediPlate™ assay include compatibility with nonionic detergents and insensitivity to free phosphate, resulting in minimal sample processing before analysis.

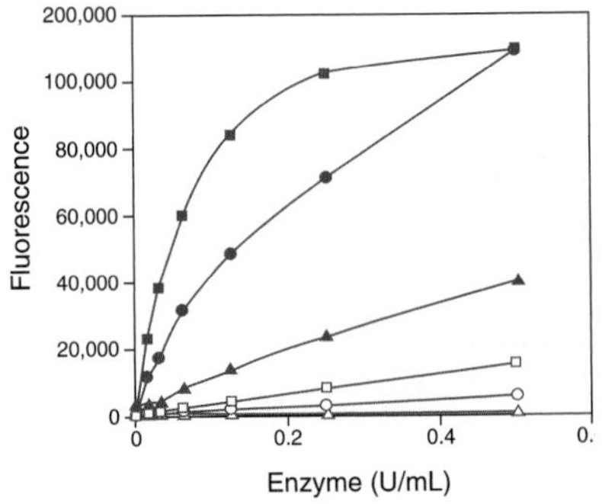

Symbol	Enzyme (Class
■	PP-2A (Ser/Thr phosphatase)
●	PP-1 (Ser/Thr phosphatase)
▲	PP-2B (Ser/Thr phosphatase)
□	Alkaline phosphatase
○	Acid phosphatase
△	LAR (tyrosine phosphatase)

Figure 10.45 Specificity of the RediPlate™ 96 EnzChek® Serine/Threonine Phosphatase Assay Kit (R33700) for serine/threonine phosphatases. The phosphatases listed in the tables were applied at the indicated concentrations to a RediPlate™ 96 EnzChek® serine/threonine phosphatase assay microplate. Reactions were incubated at 37°C. After 1 hour, fluorescence was measured in a fluorescence microplate reader using excitation at 355 ± 20 nm and emission at 460 ± 12.5 nm.

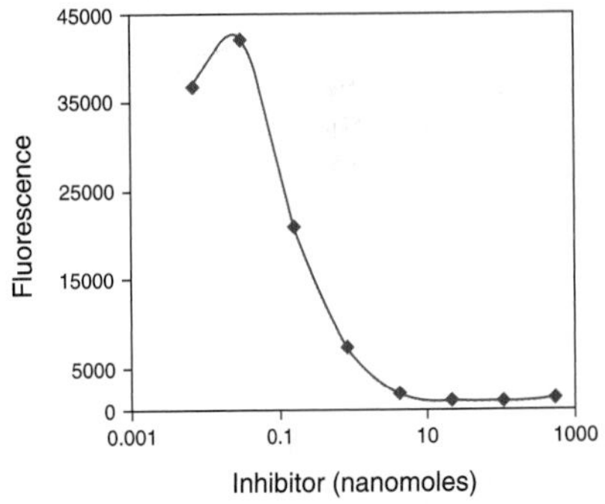

Figure 10.46 Detection of PP-2A inhibition by okadaic acid using the RediPlate™ 96 EnzChek® Serine/Threonine Phosphatase Assay Kit (R33700). Each reaction contained 50 µM DiFMUP, 10 mU/mL PP-2A and the indicated concentration (log scale) of okadaic acid in reaction buffer containing 50 mM Tris-HCl, 0.1 mM $CaCl_2$, 1 mM $NiCl_2$, 125 µg/mL bovine serum albumin (BSA) and 0.05% Tween 20. Reactions were incubated at 37°C. After 30 minutes, fluorescence was measured in a fluorescence microplate reader using excitation at 355 ± 20 nm and emission at 460 ± 12.5 nm.

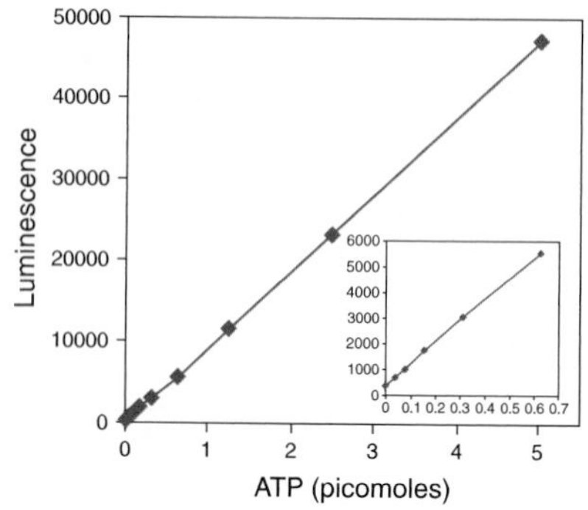

Figure 10.47 Detection of ATP using the ATP Determination Kit (A22066). Each reaction contained 1.25 µg/mL of firefly luciferase, 50 µM D-luciferin and 1 mM DTT in 1X reaction buffer. Luminescence was measured after a 15-minute incubation.

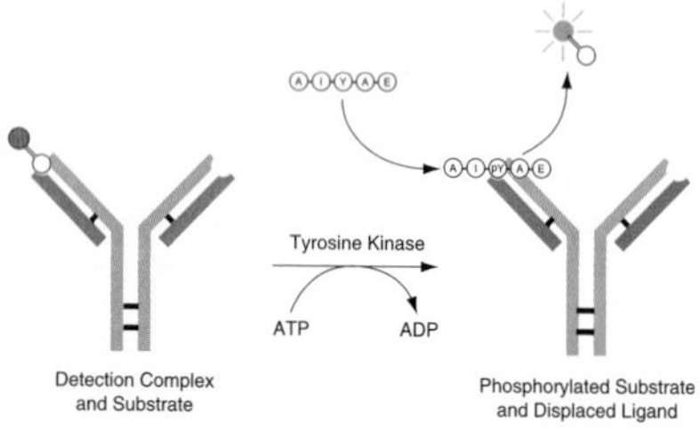

Figure 10.48 Reaction scheme for the tyrosine kinase assay used in the Antibody Beacon™ Tyrosine Kinase Assay Kit (A35725). The unlabeled natural substrate (AIYAE) is phosphorylated by the tyrosine kinase to AIY(P)AE, which displaces the quenched Oregon Green® 488 dye–labeled peptide from the anti-phosphotyrosine antibody, resulting in a large increase in its fluorescence that is proportional to the amount of AIY(P)AE formed in the reaction.

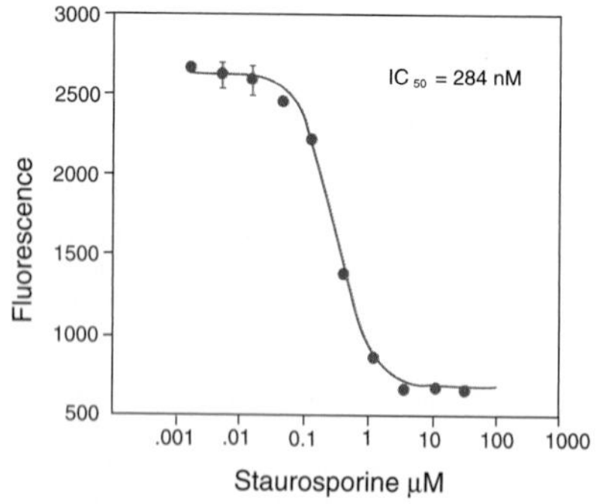

Figure 10.49 Detection of the src kinase by staurosporine using the Antibody Beacon™ Tyrosine Kinase Assay Kit (A35725). Varying concentrations of staurosporine were incubated with src kinase (25 U/mL in reaction buffer) for 20 minutes at 37°C. The Antibody Beacon™ tyrosine kinase detection complex, kinase substrate (poly(Glu:Tyr), 4:1) and ATP were then added to each well, and the reactions were incubated at 37°C. After 1 hour, fluorescence was measured in a fluorescence microplate reader using excitation at 485 nm and emission at 535 nm.

Each RediPlate™ 96 EnzChek® Serine/Threonine Phosphatase Assay Kit includes:

- One RediPlate™ 96 EnzChek® serine/threonine phosphatase assay 96-well microplate
- Concentrated reaction buffer
- $NiCl_2$
- $MnCl_2$
- Dithiothreitol
- A detailed assay protocol

To ensure the integrity of the fluorogenic components, the 96-well microplate is contained in a resealable foil packet and consists of twelve removable strips, each with eight wells (Figure 8.60). Eleven of the strips (88 wells) are preloaded with the fluorogenic substrate DiFMUP. The remaining strip, marked with blackened tabs, contains a dilution series of the DiFMU reference standard for generating a standard curve. We also offer RediPlate™ 96 and RediPlate™ 384 Assay Kits for tyrosine phosphatase activity (see above), dsDNA quantitation (Section 8.3) and protease activity (Section 10.4), which are summarized in Table 10.3. Significant discounts apply to purchases of multiple units of all of our RediPlate™ products.

ATP Determination Kit

Molecular Probes has a convenient ATP Determination Kit (A22066) for the sensitive bioluminescence-based detection of ATP with recombinant firefly luciferase and its substrate, luciferin. This assay is based on luciferase's absolute requirement for ATP to produce light. In the presence of Mg^{2+}, luciferase catalyzes the reaction of luciferin, ATP and O_2 to form oxyluciferin, AMP, CO_2, pyrophosphate and ~560 nm light (Figure 15.57). The ATP Determination Kit can also be used in an assay of cell viability and cytotoxicity (Section 15.3).

The luciferin–luciferase bioluminescence assay is extremely sensitive; most luminometers can detect as little as 1 picomole of pre-existing ATP or ATP as it is generated in kinetic systems (Figure 10.47). This sensitivity has led to its widespread use for detecting ATP in various enzymatic reactions, as well as for measuring viable cell number [106] (Section 15.2, Section 15.3) and for detecting low-level bacterial contamination in samples such as blood, milk, urine, soil and sludge.[107–111] The luciferin–luciferase bioluminescence assay has also been used to determine cell proliferation and cytotoxicity in both bacterial [112,113] and mammalian cells,[114,115] and to distinguish cytostatic versus cytocidal potential of anticancer drugs on malignant cell growth.[116]

Each ATP Determination Kit (A22066) contains:

- Luciferin (5 vials, each containing 3.0 mg)
- Luciferase
- Dithiothreitol (DTT)
- ATP
- Concentrated reaction buffer
- A detailed protocol for ATP quantitation

Unlike most other commercially available ATP detection kits, our ATP Determination Kit provides the luciferase and luciferin packaged separately, which enables researchers to optimize the reaction conditions for their particular instruments and samples. The ATP Determination Kit provides sufficient reagents for performing 200 ATP assays using 0.5 mL sample volumes or 500 ATP assays using 0.2 mL sample volumes.

Antibody Beacon™ Tyrosine Kinase Assay Kit: Real-Time Measurement of Tyrosine Kinase Activity

Tyrosine kinases are critical players in signal transduction pathways; however, the fluorometric assay of all kinases has been difficult because phosphorylation of the target by the combination of ATP and a fluorescent peptide target does not lead to appreciable changes in the fluorescence of any product. Previous attempts to develop fluorometric assays for kinases have typically utilized synthetic peptides labeled with an environment-sensitive fluorescent dye, which, after considerable trial and error in substrate selection, may exhibit an adventitious but small fluorescence change (either up or down) results upon phosphorylation. Molecular Probes has discovered a unique and general method for the continuous assay of most or all tyrosine kinases that promises to be very useful for both routine laboratory use and high-throughput screening applications. Moreover, this method utilizes the natural, unlabeled target peptide or protein, which yields results that may be more relevant to the researcher.

The Antibody Beacon™ Tyrosine Kinase Assay Kit (A35725) provides a simple yet robust solution assay for measuring the activity of tyrosine kinases (Figure 10.48) and the effectiveness of potential inhibitors and modulators (Figure 10.49). The key to this tyrosine kinase assay is a small-molecule tracer ligand labeled with our bright green-fluorescent Oregon Green® 488 dye. When an anti-phosphotyrosine antibody binds this tracer ligand to form the Antibody Beacon™ detection complex, the fluorescence of the Oregon Green® 488 dye is efficiently quenched. In the presence of a phosphotyrosine-containing peptide, however, this Antibody Beacon™ detection complex is rapidly disrupted, releasing the tracer ligand and relieving its antibody-induced quenching. Upon its displacement by a phosphotyrosine residue, the Oregon Green® 488 dye–labeled tracer ligand exhibits an approximately fourfold enhancement in its fluorescence, enabling the detection of as little as 50 nM phosphotyrosine-containing peptide with excellent signal-to-background discrimination (Figure 10.50).

We have optimized each component of this kit in order to provide minimal background fluorescence, maximal displacement of the tracer ligand and a large fluorescence enhancement upon the ligand's release. Key benefits of the Antibody Beacon™ Tyrosine Kinase Assay Kit include:

- **Real-time measurements.** Unlike many other commercially available tyrosine kinase assays, the Antibody Beacon™ Tyrosine Kinase Assay Kit permits real-time monitoring of kinase activity (Figure 10.51). Not only is the Antibody Beacon™ detection complex rapidly dissociated in the presence of phosphotyrosine residues, but the assay components have been designed to be simultaneously combined, eliminating any delay in the measurements.
- **Simple detection protocol.** Tyrosine kinase activity is measured by a simple increase in fluorescence intensity; no special equipment, additional reagents, or extra steps are required. The absorption and emission spectra of the Oregon Green® 488 dye perfectly match those of fluorescein, making this assay readily compatible with any fluorescence microplate reader.
- **Use of natural substrates.** The Antibody Beacon™ tyrosine kinase assay utilizes unlabeled peptides or proteins (provided by the user) and is applicable to the assay of a wide variety of kinases.
- **Compatibility.** The anti-phosphotyrosine antibody provided in the Antibody Beacon™ Tyrosine Kinase Assay Kit is specific for phosphotyrosine residues; coexisting assay components such as ATP (up to 1 mM) and reducing agents such as dithiothreitol (DTT, up to 1 mm) do not interfere with this assay. This anti-phosphotyrosine antibody was selected from among several clones to produce the greatest fluorescence enhancement by the kinase-phosphorylated product.
- **Reliability.** This tyrosine kinase assay has a broad signal window, indicated by a Z′ factor [117] of >0.85.

The Antibody Beacon™ Tyrosine Kinase Assay Kit comes with all the reagents needed to perform this assay right out of the box, including:

- Oregon Green® 488 dye–labeled tracer ligand
- Anti-phosphotyrosine antibody
- Concentrated tyrosine kinase reaction buffer
- Two generic tyrosine kinase substrate solutions: a poly(Glu:Tyr) solution and a poly(Glu:Ala:Tyr) solution
- Dithiothreitol (DTT)
- Adenosine triphosphate (ATP)
- Phosphotyrosine-containing peptide, phospho-pp60 c-src (521–533), for use as a reference

Each kit provides sufficient reagents to perform ~400 assays using a 50 µL assay volume in a fluorescence microplate reader.

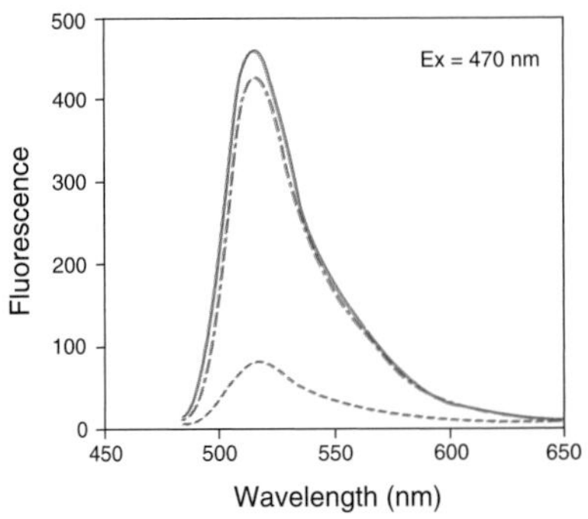

Figure 10.50 Fluorescence response of the Antibody Beacon™ detection complex in the presence of a phosphotyrosine-containing peptide. The fluorescence of the free Oregon Green® 488 peptide ligand (solid line), Antibody Beacon™ detection complex of the Oregon Green® 488 peptide ligand (dashed line) and Antibody Beacon™ detection complex plus phosphorylated Abl substrate peptide (EAIpYAAPFAKKK; dot-dash line) was measured in tyrosine kinase assay buffer using the Antibody Beacon™ Tyrosine Kinase Assay Kit (A35725). In the presence of the phosphopeptide, the Oregon Green® 488 peptide ligand was displaced from the Antibody Beacon™ complex and exhibited a fourfold enhancement over the fluorescence of the Antibody Beacon™ complex in buffer alone.

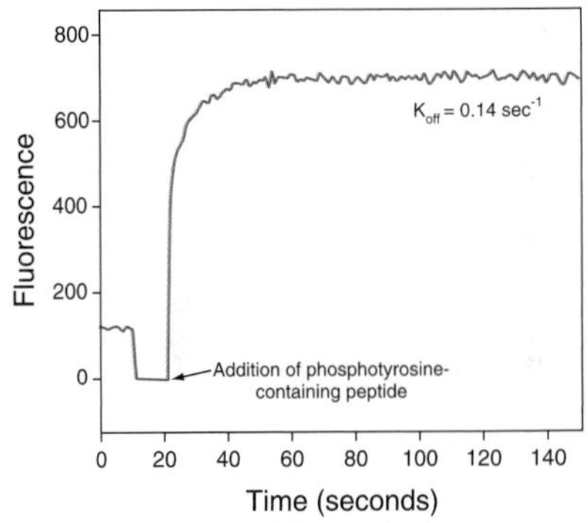

Figure 10.51 Real-time detection capability of the Antibody Beacon™ Tyrosine Kinase Assay Kit (A35725). Fluorescence of the Antibody Beacon™ detection complex in tyrosine kinase assay buffer was monitored over time. After ~15 seconds, an excess of phosphotyrosine-containing peptide was added to the Antibody Beacon™ detection complex and the off-rate was calculated.

Pro-Q® Diamond Phosphoprotein/Phosphopeptide Microarray Stain Kit

The Pro-Q® Diamond Phosphoprotein/Phosphopeptide Microarray Stain Kit (P33706) provides a method for selective staining of phosphoproteins or phosphopeptides on microarrays, without the use of antibodies or radioactivity. This kit permits direct detection of phosphate groups attached to tyrosine, serine or threonine residues in a microarray environment and has been optimized for microarrays with acrylamide gel surfaces. Each Pro-Q® Diamond Phosphoprotein/ Phosphopeptide Microarray Stain Kit provides:

- Pro-Q® Diamond phosphoprotein/phosphopeptide microarray stain
- Pro-Q® Diamond microarray destain solution
- Microarray staining gasket with seal tabs, 10 chambers
- Slide holder tube, 20 tubes
- Detailed protocols

The Pro-Q® Diamond Phosphoprotein/Phosphopeptide Microarray Stain Kit is ideal for identifying kinase targets in signal transduction pathways and for phosphoproteomics studies.

References

1. Methods Mol Biol 32, 461 (1994); **2.** J Clin Microbiol 19, 230 (1984); **3.** Anatomical Record 118, 135 (1954); **4.** J Histochem Cytochem 40, 1059 (1992); **5.** Dev Biol 88, 279 (1981); **6.** Cell 5, 229 (1975); **7.** Proc Natl Acad Sci U S A 70, 3899 (1973); **8.** Biotechniques 14, 818 (1993); **9.** Proc Natl Acad Sci U S A 89, 693 (1992); **10.** Methods Enzymol 216, 362 (1992); **11.** Proc Natl Acad Sci U S A 100, 1592 (2003); **12.** Curr Biol 10, 907 (2000); **13.** J Biol Chem 275, 4555 (2000); **14.** Proc Natl Acad Sci USA 50, 1 (1963); **15.** J Immunol Methods 149, 261 (1992); **16.** J Immunol Methods 192, 165 (1996); **17.** J Biol Chem 272, 22472 (1997); **18.** Biochem Pharmacol 54, 721 (1997); **19.** Biochem Pharmacol 54, 703 (1997); **20.** Anal Chem 70, 1242 (1998); **21.** Anal Biochem 248, 258 (1997); **22.** Drug Discov Today HTS Suppl 1, 33 (2000); **23.** Toxicon 38, 1833 (2000); **24.** J Immunol Methods 150, 23 (1992); **25.** In Vitro Cell Dev Biol 25, 105 (1989); **26.** Anal Biochem 205, 1 (1992); **27.** Mol Cell Probes 6, 489 (1992); **28.** Zentralbl Bakteriol 280, 476 (1994); **29.** Microbiol Rev 55, 335 (1991); **30.** Anal Biochem 273, 41 (1999); **31.** Bioorg Med Chem Lett 8, 3107 (1998); **32.** Am J Hum Genet 55 (Suppl), A271, abstract #1585 (1994); **33.** FASEB J 8, A1444, abstract #1081 (1994); **34.** J Histochem Cytochem 47, 1443 (1999); **35.** J Histochem Cytochem 44, 559 (1996); **36.** J Histochem Cytochem 45, 345 (1997); **37.** Am J Pathol 156, 419 (2000); **38.** J Natl Cancer Inst 92, 338 (2000); **39.** J Biol Chem 276, 29275 (2001); **40.** Anal Biochem 291, 109 (2001); **41.** Biotechniques 12, 656 (1992); **42.** Histochemistry 58, 203 (1978); **43.** Biochemistry 35, 11013 (1996); **44.** Anal Biochem 243, 41 (1996); **45.** Anal Biochem 253, 162 (1997); **46.** J Immunol Methods 202, 133 (1997); **47.** Anal Biochem 218, 449 (1994); **48.** Proc Natl Acad Sci U S A 89, 4884 (1992); **49.** Biochemistry 36, 11837 (1997); **50.** Biosci Rep 14, 309 (1994); **51.** Nucleic Acids Res 23, 2886 (1995); **52.** Anal Biochem 246, 86 (1997); **53.** J Biol Chem 274, 16153 (1999); **54.** Biochemistry 34, 10976 (1995); **55.** Anal Biochem 221, 348 (1994); **56.** J Biol Chem 275, 25299 (2000); **57.** Biochemistry 37, 5249 (1998); **58.** J Biol Chem 272, 32830 (1997); **59.** Biochemistry 34, 15592 (1995); **60.** Biochem J 287, 555 (1992); **61.** J Biol Chem 272, 21999 (1997); **62.** Biochemistry 35, 10922 (1996); **63.** Biochemistry 37, 17209 (1998); **64.** Biochem J 307, 585 (1995); **65.** Anal Biochem 222, 14 (1994); **66.** Biochem J 296, 293 (1993); **67.** Anal Biochem 226, 68 (1995); **68.** Anal Biochem 230, 55 (1995); **69.** Biochemistry 33, 2380 (1994); **70.** Biochemistry 35, 12038 (1996); **71.** J Biol Chem 276, 18478 (2001); **72.** Anal Biochem 230, 173 (1995); **73.** Biochemistry 33, 8262 (1994); **74.** J Biol Chem 275, 17962 (2000); **75.** Biochemistry 39, 2297 (2000); **76.** J Biol Chem 273, 16555 (1998); **77.** J Biol Chem 273, 22151 (1998); **78.** Biochemistry 40, 5041 (2001); **79.** The bacterial clone for expressing the mutant phosphate-binding protein is available from Martin Webb, National Institute for Medical Research, London, UK; **80.** Biochemistry 37, 10381 (1998); **81.** Biophys J 74, 3120 (1998); **82.** J Physiol 501, 125 (1997); **83.** FEBS Lett 364, 59 (1995); **84.** Biochemistry 40, 5087 (2001); **85.** J Virol 76, 11505 (2002); **86.** Oncogene 19, 6607 (2000); **87.** Trends Cell Biol 11, 258 (2001); **88.** Curr Opin Cell Biol 13, 182 (2001); **89.** Curr Opin Chem Biol 5, 416 (2001); **90.** J Mol Med 78, 473 (2000); **91.** Biochem Pharmacol 60, 877 (2000); **92.** Cell Res 10, 279 (2000); **93.** Curr Opin Neurobiol 11, 95 (2001); **94.** Neuroreport 11, R5 (2000); **95.** Biochem Biophys Res Commun 286, 721 (2001); **96.** Adv Exp Med Biol 476, 35 (2000); **97.** Proc Natl Acad Sci U S A 98, 13710 (2001); **98.** Biochem Biophys Res Commun 285, 1192 (2001); **99.** J Biol Chem 276, 14829 (2001); **100.** J Neurosci Methods 105, 87 (2001); **101.** Eur J Immunol 30, 3422 (2000); **102.** Proc Natl Acad Sci U S A 97, 3207 (2000); **103.** Eur J Biochem 263, 605 (1999); **104.** Eur J Biochem 269, 1060 (2002); **105.** Proc Natl Acad Sci U S A 98, 13613 (2001); **106.** J Biolumin Chemilumin 10, 29 (1995); **107.** Anal Biochem 175, 14 (1988); **108.** Bio/Technology 6, 634 (1988); **109.** J Clin Microbiol 20, 644 (1984); **110.** J Clin Microbiol 18, 521 (1983); **111.** Methods Enzymol 57, 3 (1978); **112.** Biotechnol Bioeng 42, 30 (1993); **113.** J Biolumin Chemilumin 6, 193 (1991); **114.** Biochem J 295, 165 (1993); **115.** J Immunol Methods 160, 81 (1993); **116.** J Natl Cancer Inst 77, 1039 (1986); **117.** J Biomol Screen 4, 67 (1999).

Data Table — 10.3 Detecting Enzymes That Metabolize Phosphates and Polyphosphates

Cat #	MW	Storage	Soluble	Abs	EC	Em	Solvent	Product	Notes
A22184	878.28	FF,L	H_2O	504	68,000	514	pH 7	see Notes	1, 2, 3
B6492	370.43	F,D	DMSO, H_2O	292	3,800	none	H_2O	see Notes	4
D6487	422.20	F,D,L	DMSO, H_2O	478	26,000	628	pH 7	H6482	
D6567	292.13	F,D	DMSO, H_2O	320	14,000	385	pH 9	D6566	5
D22065	292.13	F,D	DMSO, H_2O	320	14,000	385	pH 9	D6566	5
E6588	431.08	F,L	H_2O	289	12,000	see Notes	pH 10	E6578	2, 5
E6589	431.08	F,L	H_2O	289	12,000	see Notes	pH 10	E6578	2, 5
E6645	313.33	FF,D	H_2O	332	16,000	none	pH 7	see Notes	6, 7
E6646	313.33	F,D	H_2O	332	16,000	none	pH 7	see Notes	6, 7
F2999	560.39	F,D	H_2O	272	5,300	none	MeOH	F1300	8
G22183	894.28	FF,L	H_2O	504	68,000	510	pH 7	see Notes	1, 2, 3, 9
M6491	256.15	F,D	DMSO, H_2O	319	15,000	383	pH 9	H189	5
M8425	508.55	F,D	H_2O	318	14,000	385	pH 9	H189	5, 10
N6495	817.65	D,L	H_2O, DMSO	256	64,000	none	MeOH	see Notes	4
N6613	371.15	F,D,L	H_2O	310	11,000	none	pH 7	see Notes	10, 11

For definitions of the contents of this data table, see "Navigating *The Handbook*" in the introductory pages.

Notes

1. The molecular weight (MW) of this product is approximate because the degree of hydration and/or salt form has not been conclusively established.
2. This product is supplied as a ready-made solution in the solvent indicated under "Soluble."
3. This compound is a nonhydrolyzable substrate analog.
4. Phosphatase hydrolysis of BCIP (B6492) is coupled to reduction of NBT (N6495), yielding a water-insoluble indigo dye (Abs ~615 nm) and a water-insoluble formazan (Abs ~605 nm) respectively.
5. Fluorescence of the unhydrolyzed substrate is very weak.
6. Data represent the substrate component of this kit.
7. Enzymatic phosphorylation of this substrate yields 2-amino-6-mercapto-7-methylpurine (Abs = 355 nm) (Proc Natl Acad Sci U S A 89, 4884 (1992)).
8. Unstable in water. Use immediately.
9. Fluorescence of BODIPY® dye–labeled guanosine derivatives is generally weak due to base-specific intramolecular quenching (Anal Biochem 291, 109 (2001)).
10. MW is for the hydrated form of this product.
11. Enzymatic cleavage of this substrate yields 4-nitrophenol, Abs = 399 nm (EC = 18,000 $cm^{-1}M^{-1}$) in pH 9 buffer.

Product List — 10.3 Detecting Enzymes That Metabolize Phosphates and Polyphosphates

Cat #	Product Name	Unit Size
A22184	adenosine 5′-*O*-(3-thiotriphosphate), BODIPY® FL thioester, sodium salt (BODIPY® FL ATP-γ-S, thioester) *5 mM in buffer*	50 µL
A35725	Antibody Beacon™ Tyrosine Kinase Assay Kit *400 assays*	1 kit
A22066	ATP Determination Kit *special packaging* *200-1000 assays*	1 kit
B21901	BOLD™ APB chemiluminescent substrate *for membrane-based alkaline phosphatase detection* *25 minigel blots*	25 mL
B6492	5-bromo-4-chloro-3-indolyl phosphate, disodium salt (BCIP, Na)	1 g
D6487	9*H*-(1,3-dichloro-9,9-dimethylacridin-2-one-7-yl) phosphate, diammonium salt (DDAO phosphate)	5 mg
D6567	6,8-difluoro-4-methylumbelliferyl phosphate (DiFMUP)	5 mg
D22065	6,8-difluoro-4-methylumbelliferyl phosphate (DiFMUP) *packaged for high-throughput screening*	10 x 10 mg
E6603	ELF® 97 Cytological Labeling Kit *with streptavidin, alkaline phosphatase conjugate* *50 assays*	1 kit
E6601	ELF® 97 Endogenous Phosphatase Detection Kit	1 kit
E6600	ELF® 97 Immunohistochemistry Kit	1 kit
E6604	ELF® 97 mRNA *In Situ* Hybridization Kit #1 *50 assays*	1 kit
E6605	ELF® 97 mRNA *In Situ* Hybridization Kit #2 *with streptavidin, alkaline phosphatase conjugate* *50 assays*	1 kit
E6589	ELF® 97 phosphatase substrate (ELF® 97 phosphate) *5 mM in water* *contains 2 mM azide*	1 mL
E6588	ELF® 97 phosphatase substrate (ELF® 97 phosphate) *5 mM in water* *0.2 µm filtered*	1 mL
E6606	ELF® spin filters *20 filters*	1 box
E12020	EnzChek® Phosphatase Assay Kit *1000 assays*	1 kit
E6646	EnzChek® Phosphate Assay Kit *100 assays*	1 kit
E6645	EnzChek® Pyrophosphate Assay Kit *100 assays*	1 kit
F2999	fluorescein diphosphate, tetraammonium salt (FDP)	5 mg
G22183	guanosine 5′-*O*-(3-thiotriphosphate), BODIPY® FL thioester, sodium salt (BODIPY® FL GTP-γ-S, thioester) *5 mM in buffer*	50 µL
M8425	4-methylumbelliferyl phosphate, dicyclohexylammonium salt, trihydrate (MUP DCA salt)	1 g
M6491	4-methylumbelliferyl phosphate, free acid (MUP)	1 g
N6547	NBT/BCIP Reagent Kit	1 kit
N6495	nitro blue tetrazolium chloride (NBT)	1 g
N6613	4-nitrophenyl phosphate, disodium salt, hexahydrate (PNPP)	5 g
P22061	P_iPer™ Phosphate Assay Kit *1000 assays*	1 kit
P22062	P_iPer™ Pyrophosphate Assay Kit *1000 assays*	1 kit
P33706	Pro-Q® Diamond Phosphoprotein/Phosphopeptide Microarray Stain Kit	1 kit
R33700	RediPlate™ 96 EnzChek® Serine/Threonine Phosphatase Assay Kit *one 96-well microplate*	1 kit
R22067	RediPlate™ 96 EnzChek® Tyrosine Phosphatase Assay Kit *one 96-well microplate*	1 kit
R22068	RediPlate™ 384 EnzChek® Tyrosine Phosphatase Assay Kit *one 384-well microplate*	1 kit

For current prices or to order online, visit probes.invitrogen.com

10.4 Detecting Peptidases and Proteases

Peptidases and proteases play essential roles in protein activation, cell regulation and signaling, as well as in the generation of amino acids for protein synthesis or utilization in other metabolic pathways. In general, peptidases cleave shorter peptides, and proteases cleave longer peptides and proteins. A great deal of useful information on proteases and protease inhibitors, including an image gallery, is available at the Prolysis web site (http://delphi.phys.univ-tours.fr/Prolysis/).

Depending on their site of cleavage, peptidases can be classified as exopeptidases if they preferentially hydrolyze amino acid residues from the terminus of a peptide, or endopeptidases if they cleave internal peptide bonds.[1] Exopeptidases are further divided into aminopeptidases and carboxypeptidases depending on whether they hydrolyze residues from the amine or the carboxy terminus.

Although the spectral properties of fluorogenic peptidase and protease substrates and their hydrolysis products are easily predictable, the utility of a given substrate for an enzyme depends on the kinetics of hydrolysis by the enzyme, which, in turn, depends on the substrate's concentration and amino acid sequence, as well as on the pH, temperature and presence of cofactors in the medium. For measurements in live cells, the suitability of a particular substrate also hinges on its accessibility to the enzyme and the cellular retention of the hydrolysis product.[2] In addition to these factors, the chromophore or fluorophore conjugated to the substrate can influence its hydrolysis rate and specificity, as well as the permeability of the substrate and its hydrolysis product.

Molecular Probes prepares a variety of protease substrates, including selective protease substrates for caspase-3 and caspase-8 — enzymes that are activated during apoptosis (Section 15.5) — HIV protease and renin. Our patented EnzChek® and DQ™ protease substrates include:

- The green-fluorescent and red-fluorescent EnzChek® Protease Assay Kits (E6638, E6639), which use a heavily BODIPY® dye–labeled DQ™ casein derivative for the assay of a wide variety of proteases (Table 10.4, Figure 10.56). These products are also available in a RediPlate™ 96 and RediPlate™ 384 format for the convenient, high-throughput screening of protease inhibitors in either 96-well or 384-well microplates (R22130, R22132, R22131, R22133).
- The EnzChek® Polarization Assay Kit for Proteases (E6658), which uses a green-fluorescent BODIPY® FL casein conjugate with an optimal degree of labeling for fluorescence polarization-based general protease assays (see Note 1.5 "Technical Focus: Fluorescence Polarization (FP)" in Section 1.4).
- The EnzChek® Gelatinase/Collagenase Assay Kit (E12055) and EnzChek® Elastase Assay Kit (E12056), which use DQ™ gelatin or DQ™ elastin as substrates, provide the speed, high sensitivity and convenience required for measuring gelatinase (collagenase) or elastase activity[3] and for screening of protease inhibitors in a high-throughput format.
- DQ™ collagen (D12052, D12060), DQ™ BSA (D12050, D12051) and DQ™ ovalbumin (D12053), which are useful for the general screening of protease activity and matrix metalloproteinase (MMP) inhibitors (including *in situ* zymography in gels[4]) and for the study of antigen processing.

Additionally, we provide some antibodies to matrix metalloproteinases and fluorescent protease inhibitors, which are described below.

Peptidase Substrates

The carboxy terminus of single amino acids and short peptides can be conjugated to certain amine-containing fluorophores to create fluorogenic peptidase substrates. The dyes used to make these substrates are fluorescent at physiological pH; however, when the dyes are coupled in an amide linkage to peptides, their absorption maxima are usually shortened significantly. The resulting substrates are sometimes fluorescent but with relatively short-wavelength emission spectra. In an extreme case such as that of rhodamine 110–based substrates, detectable long-wavelength absorbance and fluorescence are completely eliminated by amide formation. Peptidase activity releases the fluorophore, restoring its free-dye fluorescence.

UV Light–Excitable Substrates Based on 7-Aminocoumarins

7-Amino-4-methylcoumarin (AMC, A191; Section 10.1) is a blue-fluorescent dye (Figure 10.4) whose peptide amides are used extensively as substrates for detecting enzymatic activity in cells, homogenates and solutions. The CBZ-L-phenylalanyl-L-arginine amide of AMC (A6521) is a substrate for a variety of serine proteases, including cathepsins, kallikrein and plasmin.[5–14] AMC and 7-amino-4-trifluoromethylcoumarin (AFC) — a dye with somewhat longer-wavelength spectra than AMC (excitation/emission maxima of ~380/500 nm) at pH 7 — are released from the caspase-3, caspase-7 and caspase-8 substrates listed in Table 15.5. These caspases are activated during early stages of apoptosis (Section 15.5). The Z-DEVD-AMC substrate is also a component of the EnzChek® Caspase-3 Assay Kit #1 (E13183, see below).

7-Amino-4-chloromethylcoumarin (CMAC, C2110; Section 10.1) is a mildly thiol-reactive analog of AMC; CMAC-based substrates yield fluorescent peptidase products with improved retention in live cells. The fluorogenic *t*-BOC-Leu-Met-CMAC substrate[15,16] (A6520) has been used to measure calpain activity in hepatocytes following the addition of extracellular ATP.[17,18]

Visible Light–Excitable Substrates Based on Rhodamine 110

Rhodamine 110 (R110, R6479; Section 10.1) is a visible light–excitable dye with much stronger absorption than AMC; R110-based substrates usually comprise two identical amino acids or peptides attached to a single fluorophore. Molecular Probes' bisamide derivatives of rhodamine 110 are sensitive and selective substrates for assaying protease activity in solution or inside live cells. Originally developed by Walter Mangel and colleagues, these substrates comprise an amino acid or peptide covalently linked to each of R110's amino groups, thereby suppressing both its visible absorption and fluorescence.[19,20] Upon enzymatic cleavage, the nonfluorescent bisamide substrate is converted in a two-step process first to the fluorescent monoamide and then to the even more fluorescent R110 (Figure 10.52). The fluorescence intensities of the monoamide and of R110 are constant from pH 3–9. Both of these hydrolysis products exhibit spectral properties similar to those of fluorescein, with peak excitation and emission wavelengths of 496 nm and 520 nm (Figure 10.5), respectively, making them compatible with flow cytometers[21] and other instrumentation based on the argon-ion laser. Substrates based on R110 may also be useful for sensitive absorptimetric assays because the R110 dye has intense visible absorption ($\varepsilon_{496\ nm}$ = ~80,000 $cm^{-1}M^{-1}$ in pH 6 solution).

Molecular Probes prepares a variety of substrates based on the rhodamine 110 fluorophore (Table 10.2). Bis-(CBZ-Arg)-R110 (BZAR, R6501) is a general substrate for serine proteases that has proven to be 50- to 300-fold more sensitive than the analogous AMC-based substrate.[19,20,22] This enhanced sensitivity can be attributed both to the greater fluorescence of the enzymatic product and to the enhanced reactivity of the cleavage site. In addition, BZAR inhibits guanidinobenzoatase activity in tumor cells.[22,23] The tripeptide derivative bis-(CBZ-Ile-Pro-Arg)-R110 (BZiPAR, R6505) allows direct and continuous monitoring of enzyme turnover, making it useful for determining individual kinetic constants of fast-acting, irreversible trypsin inhibitors.[24] BZiPAR has been shown to enter intact cells where it is cleaved by lysosomal proteases.[25] Simultaneous measurement of enzymatic activity with BZiPAR and Ca^{2+} transients with fura-2 (F1201, F1221, F14185; Section 19.2) has been reported.[26] Bis-(CBZ-Phe-Arg)-R110 (R6502) has been employed for flow cytometric analysis of the cysteine proteases cathepsin B and L in human monocytes and rat macrophages.[27–29] Bis-(CBZ-Ala-Ala)-R110 amide[30] (R6504) is a long-wavelength calpain substrate. Bis-(CBZ-Ala-Ala-Ala-Ala)-R110 (R6506), an elastase substrate, has been used in a novel DNA detection assay.[31] Bis-(CBZ-Ala-Arg)-R110 (R6508) is a fluorogenic substrate for both elastase and trypsin.[19,28] The bis-(tosyl-Gly-Pro-Arg) amide of rhodamine 110 (R22124) is a selective substrate for thrombin.[32] Turnover of this substrate by thrombin on a membrane in the presence of thromboplastin produces both color and fluorescence that has been reported to model coagulation and blood clot formation. We also offer the human renin substrate 1 (R2931, see below) for measuring the activity of this important blood-pressure-regulating enzyme.

EnzChek® Caspase-3 Assay Kits and Caspase Substrates

Members of the caspase (CED-3/ICE) family of proteases have been identified as crucial mediators of the complex biochemical events associated with apoptosis.[33–35] Caspase-3 (CPP32/apopain) is a key effector in the apoptotic pathway, amplifying the signal from initiator caspases (such as caspase-8) and signifying full commitment to cellular disassembly. The active caspase-3 protease recognizes the amino acid sequence Asp-Glu-Val-Asp (DEVD) and has been shown to cleave other caspases in the enzyme cascade, as well as poly(ADP-ribose) polymerase (PARP), DNA-dependent protein kinase, protein kinase Cδ and actin.[35,36]

EnzChek® Caspase-3 Assay Kits #1 and #2

Molecular Probes' EnzChek® Caspase-3 Assay Kits #1 and #2 (E13183, E13184), which contain AMC- and R110-labeled peptidase substrates, respectively, permit the detection of apoptosis by assay-

Table 10.2 — Rhodamine 110–based bis-peptide substrates

Cat #	Proteinase Substrate *	Enzymes †
R22122	$(Asp)_2$-R110	caspase-3 and other apoptosis-related proteases [1]
R6504	$(CBZ\text{-}Ala\text{-}Ala)_2$-R110	elastase [2]
R6506	$(CBZ\text{-}Ala\text{-}Ala\text{-}Ala\text{-}Ala)_2$-R110	elastase [3]
R33752	$(CBZ\text{-}Ala\text{-}Ala\text{-}Asp)_2$-R110	granzyme B
R6508	$(CBZ\text{-}Ala\text{-}Arg)_2$-R110	trypsin [4]
R6501	$(CBZ\text{-}Arg)_2$-R110	trypsin [4,5]
R22120	$(CBZ\text{-}Asp\text{-}Glu\text{-}Val\text{-}Asp)_2$-R110	caspase-3, -6, -7, -8, -10 [1]
R6505	$(CBZ\text{-}Ile\text{-}Pro\text{-}Arg)_2$-R110	trypsin [6,7]
R33753	$(CBZ\text{-}Leu\text{-}Glu\text{-}Glu\text{-}Asp)_2$-R110	caspase-13
R33751	$(CBZ\text{-}Leu\text{-}Glu\text{-}His\text{-}Asp)_2$-R110	caspase-9, -4, -5
R6502	$(CBZ\text{-}Phe\text{-}Arg)_2$-R110	plasmin, cathepsin L [2,8,9]
R33750	$(CBZ\text{-}Tyr\text{-}Val\text{-}Ala\text{-}Asp)_2$-R110	caspase-1, -4
R33755	$(CBZ\text{-}Val\text{-}Asp\text{-}Val\text{-}Ala\text{-}Asp)_2$-R110	caspase-2
R33754	$(CBZ\text{-}Val\text{-}Glu\text{-}Ile\text{-}Asp)_2$-R110	caspase-6
R22124	$(p\text{-}tosyl\text{-}Gly\text{-}Pro\text{-}Arg)_2$-R110	thrombin [10]

* CBZ = benzyloxycarbonyl; R110 = rhodamine 110; SC = succinoyl; *p*-tosyl = *p*-toluenesulfonyl. † Caspase substrates can often be cleaved by multiple enzymes. The caspase most often associated with the given peptide sequence is listed first.
1. Biochemistry 38, 13906 (1999); **2.** Biol Chem Hoppe Seyler 373, 547 (1992); **3.** Anal Chem 65, 2352 (1993); **4.** Biochem J 215, 253 (1983); **5.** Biochem J 209, 299 (1983); **6.** Biochim Biophys Acta 788, 74 (1984); **7.** Photochem Photobiol 44, 461 (1986); **8.** Glia 7, 183 (1993); **9.** Biol Chem Hoppe Seyler 373, 433 (1992); **10.** Biomed Instrum Technol 30, 245 (1996).

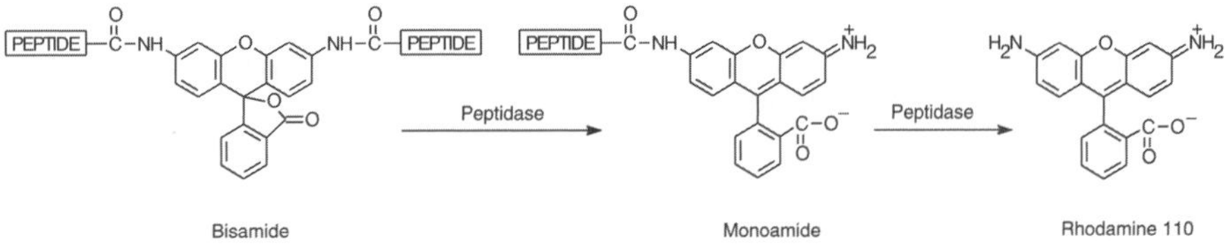

Figure 10.52 Sequential peptidase cleavage of a rhodamine 110–based substrate. The nonfluorescent bisamide substrate is first converted to the fluorescent monoamide and then to the highly fluorescent rhodamine 110.

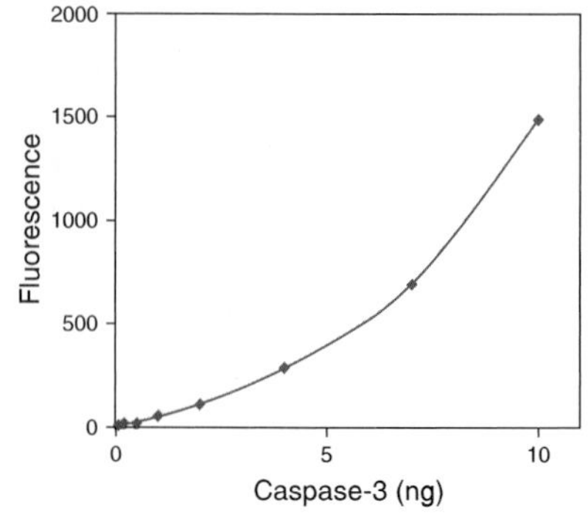

Figure 10.53 Detection of caspase-3 activity using the EnzChek® Caspase-3 Assay Kit #1 (E13183). Increasing amounts of purified active human (recombinant) caspase-3 (PharMingen) were allowed to react with 100 µM Z-DEVD–AMC in 1X reaction buffer for ~45 minutes at room temperature. Fluorescence was measured in a fluorescence microplate reader using excitation at 360 ± 17.5 nm and emission detection at 465 ± 17.5 nm. Background fluorescence (386 arbitrary units), determined for a no-enzyme control, was subtracted from each value.

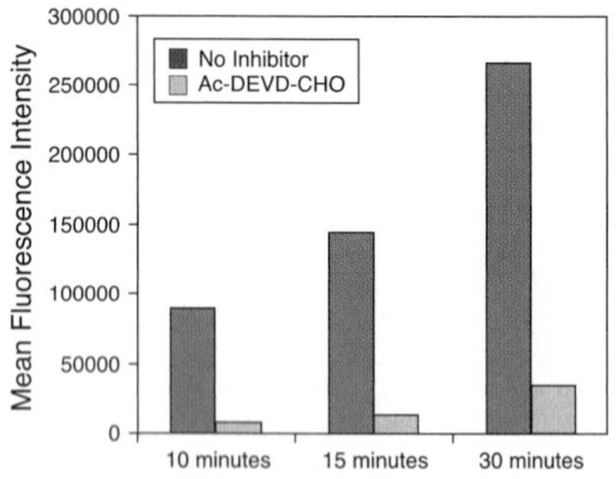

Figure 10.54 Detection of protease activity in Jurkat cells using the RediPlate™ 96 EnzChek® Caspase-3 Assay Kit (R35100). Jurkat human T-cell leukemia cells were first exposed to 10 µM camptothecin at 37°C to induce apoptosis, and then harvested and lysed according to the kit protocol. The cell lysate was separated into two samples, one of which was treated with the Ac-DEVD-CHO inhibitor (provided in the RediPlate™ 96 EnzChek® Caspase-3 Assay Kit). Assay reactions on both the inhibited and the uninhibited samples were carried out at 37°C, and fluorescence was measured in a fluorescence microplate reader (excitation/emission = 485/535 nm).

ing for increases in caspase-3 and caspase-3–like protease activities (Figure 10.53, Figure 15.94). The activation of caspase-3 (CPP32/apopain), which has a substrate selectivity for the amino acid sequence Asp-Glu-Val-Asp (DEVD) and cleaves a number of different proteins, including poly(ADP-ribose) polymerase (PARP), DNA-dependent protein kinase, protein kinase Cδ and actin, is important for the initiation of apoptosis.[35,36] Both kits can be used to continuously measure the activity of caspase-3 and closely related proteases in cell extracts and purified enzyme preparations using a fluorescence microplate reader or fluorometer. AMC-based DEVD substrates, which yield blue fluorescence upon proteolytic cleavage, are widely used to monitor caspase-3 activity.[36,37] The longer-wavelength spectra and higher extinction coefficient of the green-fluorescent products of the R110-based substrate in Kit #2 (E13184) should provide even greater sensitivity.[38,39] Each kit contains:

- Z-DEVD-AMC substrate (in Kit #1, E13183) or Z-DEVD-R110 substrate (in Kit #2, E13184)
- Concentrated cell-lysis buffer
- Concentrated reaction buffer
- Ac-DEVD-CHO inhibitor, for confirming that the observed fluorescence signal is due to the activity of caspase-3–like proteases[36]
- AMC in Kit #1 (E13183) or R110 in Kit #2 (E13184) as a reference standard
- A detailed protocol

Each kit provides sufficient reagents for performing ~500 assays using a volume of 100 µL per assay. For information about additional kits and reagents for studying apoptosis, see Section 15.5.

RediPlate™ 96 EnzChek® Caspase-3 Assay Kit

Our EnzChek® Caspase-3 Assay Kit #2 is also available as a convenient RediPlate™ 96 EnzChek® Caspase-3 Assay Kit (R35100), which includes one 96-well microplate, contained in a resealable foil packet to ensure the integrity of the fluorogenic components, plus all necessary buffers and reagents for performing the assay (Figure 10.54). The enzyme sample to be assayed is added to the microplate in a suitable buffer, along with any compounds to be tested. Then, after incubation, the resultant fluorescence is quantitated on a fluorescence microplate reader equipped with filters appropriate for the green-fluorescent R110, with excitation/emission maxima of 496/520 nm. The microplate consists of twelve removable strips, each with eight wells, allowing researchers to perform only as many assay as required for the experiment (Figure 8.60). Eleven of the strips (88 wells) are preloaded with the Z-DEVD-R110 substrate. The remaining strip, marked with blackened tabs, contains a dilution series of free R110 that may be used as a fluorescence reference standard. The reversible aldehyde-based inhibitor Ac-DEVD-CHO, which is supplied in a separate vial, can be used to confirm that the observed fluorescence signal in both induced and control cell populations is due to the activity of caspase-3–like proteases.[36] Table 10.3 summarizes our other RediPlate™ 96 and RediPlate™ 384 Assay Kits for protease activity (see below), phosphatase activity (Section 10.3) and dsDNA quantitation (Section 8.3). Significant discounts apply to purchases of multiple units of all of our RediPlate™ products.

Caspase-3 Substrates

The Z-DEVD-R110 substrate,[38,39] a component of our EnzChek® Caspase-3 Assay Kit #2 (E13184) and RediPlate™ 96 EnzChek® Caspase-3 Assay Kit (R35100), is also available separately in a 20 mg unit size for high-throughput screening applications (R22120, Table 10.2). This nonfluorescent bisamide is first converted by caspase-3 (or a closely related protease) to the fluorescent monoamide and then to the even more fluorescent rhodamine 110 (excitation/emission maxima ~496/520 nm). The bis-L-aspartic acid amide of R110 (R22122, Table 10.2) contains the rhodamine 110 fluorophore flanked by only aspartic acid residues. This compound does not appear to require any invasive techniques like osmotic shock to gain entrance into the cytoplasm, and may serve as a substrate for a variety of apoptosis related proteases, including caspases-3 and -7[38] (Figure 15.93).

Caspase-8 Substrates

Caspase-8 plays a critical role in the early cascade of apoptosis, acting as an initiator of the caspase activation pathways. Activation of the enzyme itself is accomplished through direct interaction with the death domains of cell surface receptors for apoptosis inducing ligands.[40,41]

The activated protease has been shown to be involved in a pathway that mediates the release of cytochrome *c* from the mitochondria[42] and is also known to activate downstream caspases, such as caspase-3.[43] Three fluorogenic substrates containing the caspase-8 recognition sequence Ile-Glu-Thr-Asp (IETD) are available (Table 15.5): (A22127; blue fluorescent after cleavage), (A22128; blue-green fluorescent after cleavage) and Z-IETD-R110 (R22125, R22126; green fluorescent after cleavage).

Other Caspase and Granzyme B Substrates

In addition to our R110-derived caspase-3 and -8 substrates, we offer R110-based substrates for caspase-1, -2, -6, -9 and -13, as well as substrates for granzyme B (Table 15.5). Granzyme B, a serine protease contained within cytotoxic T lymphocytes and natural killer cells, is thought to induce apoptosis in target cells by activating caspases and causing mitochondrial cytochrome *c* release.[44]

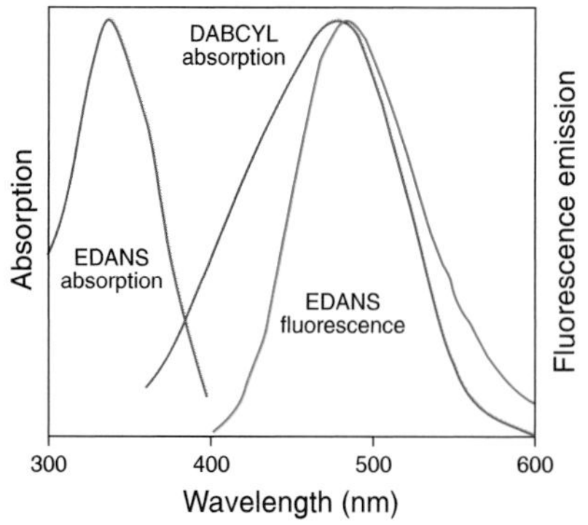

Figure 10.55 Spectral overlap between EDANS fluorescence and dabcyl absorption, which is required for efficient quenching of EDANS fluorescence by resonance energy transfer to the nonfluorescent dabcyl chromophore. Spectra are normalized to the same intensities.

Substrates for HIV Protease and Renin

Alternative strategies have been employed to create substrates specifically for some endopeptidases. Our HIV protease and renin substrates (H2930, R2931) utilize fluorescence resonance energy transfer (FRET) to generate a spectroscopic response to protease cleavage (see Note 1.2 "Technical Focus: Fluorescence Resonance Energy Transfer (FRET)" in Section 1.3). In this type of substrate, both an acceptor molecule and a fluorescent molecule are attached to the peptide or protein. The acceptor molecule is carefully chosen so that its absorbance overlaps with the fluorophore's excited-state fluorescence (Figure 10.55), thus ensuring that the fluorescence is quenched through resonance energy transfer.[45] Enzyme hydrolysis of the substrate results in spatial separation of the fluorophore and the acceptor molecule, thereby restoring the fluorophore's fluorescence (Figure 10.10). See Section 9.5 for a discussion of our reagents for synthesizing labeled peptides and peptidase substrates, including our QSY® series of nonfluorescent dyes (Figure 1.70), which have broad visible or near-infrared absorption spectra and serve as almost universal quenchers of most fluorescent donors that emit in the visible, with unusually high efficiency (Table 1.10).

Table 10.3 — RediPlate™ Assay Kits — One-step Fluorescent Microplate Assays

RediPlate™ Assay Kit *	Cat #		Assay Details
	96-well	384-well	
EnzChek® Caspase-3 Assay Kit	R35100	Inquire	A direct fluorescence-based assay for detecting caspase-3 and other DEVD-selective protease activities (e.g., caspase-7) in cell extracts and purified enzyme preparations. Caspase activity is indicated by increasing green fluorescence (excitation/emission maxima ~496/520 nm).
EnzChek® Protease Assay Kit *green fluorescence*	R22130	R22131	A direct fluorescence-based assay for detecting metallo-, serine, acid and sulfhydryl proteases and their inhibitors. Protease activity is indicated by increasing green fluorescence (excitation/emission maxima ~503/513 nm).
EnzChek® Protease Assay Kit *red fluorescence*	R22132	R22133	A direct fluorescence-based assay for detecting metallo-, serine, acid and sulfhydryl proteases and their inhibitors. Protease activity is indicated by increasing red fluorescence (excitation/emission maxima ~589/617 nm).
EnzChek® Tyrosine Phosphatase Assay Kit (Section 10.3)	R22067	R22068	An assay for monitoring protein tyrosine phosphatases (PTP) and for screening PTP inhibitors and modulators. PTP activity is indicated by increasing blue fluorescence (excitation/emission maxima ~358/452 nm).
EnzChek® Serine/Threonine Phosphatase Assay Kit (Section 10.3)	R33700	Inquire	An assay for monitoring serine/threonine (Ser/Thr) phosphatases and for screening Ser/Thr inhibitors and modulators. Ser/Thr phosphatase activity is indicated by increasing blue fluorescence (excitation/emission maxima ~358/452 nm).
PicoGreen® dsDNA Quantitation Kit (Section 8.3)	R21495, R32701, R32716	Inquire	An assay for accurately quantitating low levels of dsDNA (250 pg/mL) with a broad dynamic range — over four orders of magnitude. When bound to nucleic acids, the PicoGreen® reagent exhibits excitation/emission maxima of ~502/523 nm.
RiboGreen® RNA Quantitation Kit (Section 8.3)	R32700	Inquire	An assay for accurately quantitating low levels of RNA (1 ng/mL) with a broad dynamic range — over three orders of magnitude using two different dye concentrations. When bound to RNA, the RiboGreen® reagent exhibits excitation/emission maxima of ~500/520 nm.

* We also offer the RediPlate™ 96 microplate intensity standards (R36901, R36902, R36903, R36904, R36910; Section 23.1), which provide stable and consistent reference materials for standardizing fluorescence measurements in 96-well microplates.

Substrate for Detecting HIV Protease Activity

HIV protease substrate 1 (H2930) is a peptide that includes the HIV protease cleavage site, along with two covalently modified amino acid residues — one that has been linked to EDANS and the other to dabcyl.[46–48] Proteolytic cleavage releases a fragment containing only the EDANS fluorophore, thus liberating it from the quenching effect of the nearby dabcyl chromophore (Figure 10.10). HIV protease activity can be measured by exciting the sample at ~340 nm and measuring the resulting fluorescence at 490 nm. HIV protease substrate 1 has been used to analyze the effects of solvent composition, incubation time and enzyme concentration on HIV-1 protease activity[49] and to investigate a newly designed inhibitor of the enzyme.[50] HIV protease substrate 1 has also been employed to follow the inhibition of HIV-1 protease activity after the enzyme's two cysteine residues are reversibly modified by nitric oxide.[51] One milligram of HIV protease substrate 1 is sufficient for approximately 120 enzyme assays using 2 mL assay volumes and standard fluorescence cuvettes or ~1600 assays using 150 µL assay volumes and microcuvettes.

Human Renin Substrate 1

Assaying renin activity with human renin substrate 1 (R2931) is analogous to assaying HIV protease activity with the HIV protease substrate described above. Renin, an aspartic protease, plays an important role in blood-pressure regulation and is therefore a target for anti-hypertension therapeutics. Using renin substrate 1, researchers have discovered a stable, partially active conformational variant of recombinant human prorenin.[52] This substrate has also been used to investigate the kinetics and pH stability of recombinant human renin.[53] A fluorogenic substrate similar to our renin substrate 1 was used to develop a microplate assay for screening renin inhibitors.[54] One milligram of the renin substrate 1 is sufficient for approximately 100 enzyme assays using 2 mL volumes and standard fluorescence cuvettes or ~1400 assays using 150 µL assay volumes and microcuvettes. The short-wavelength excitation maximum (335 nm) of the EDANS fluorophore precludes use of this substrate in most fluorescence microplate readers. Molecular Probes also has a fluorogenic substrate for thrombin (rhodamine 110, bis-(tosyl-Gly-Pro-Arg) amide, R22124; see above) that is useful for measuring the activity of this enzyme, which is important for coagulation and blood clot formation.[32]

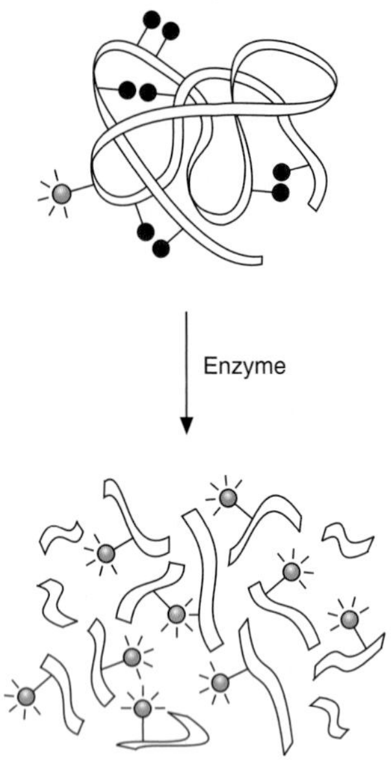

Figure 10.56 Principle of enzyme detection via the disruption of intramolecular self-quenching. Enzyme-catalyzed hydrolysis of the heavily labeled and almost totally quenched substrates provided in our EnzChek® Protease Assay Kits (E6638, E6639), EnzChek® Amylase Assay Kit (E11954), EnzChek® Gelatinase/Collagenase Assay Kit (E12055), EnzChek® Elastase Kit (E12056), EnzChek® Lysozyme Assay Kit (E22013) — as well as the stand-alone quenched substrates DQ™ BSA (D12050, D12051), DQ™ collagen (D12052, D12060), DQ™ ovalbumin (D12053) and DQ™ gelatin (D12054) — relieves the intramolecular self-quenching, yielding brightly fluorescent reaction products.

EnzChek® Protease Assay Kits and Fluorescein Casein

Often it is necessary to have fluorogenic substrates for the assay of purified enzymes with unknown specificity or for which there are no known useful substrates. Assay for contamination of biological preparations by unknown proteases requires substrates that can detect a variety of enzymes. Our patented method of relieving the fluorescence quenching of BODIPY® dye–labeled biopolymers by enzymatic hydrolysis (Figure 10.56) has been used in several of the general or selective protease assay kits and DQ™ reagents described in this section. We have also described the method's use in an assay for dextranase,[55] and others have applied it to the assay of *O*-sialoglycoprotein endopeptidase[56] and enzymes that process vesicular stomatitis virus[57] (VSV). The DQ™ and EnzChek® protease assay reagents may have significant potential for detecting matrix metalloproteinase (MMP) activity in living tissues by simple incubation of the tissue with the protein-based fluorogenic substrates.[2] Fluorescent products have been shown to accumulate on the cell's surface where proteases are active, including in living human breast cancer cells.[58] These quenched protease substrates are particularly useful for following cell migration through matrices[59–61] (Figure 10.57).

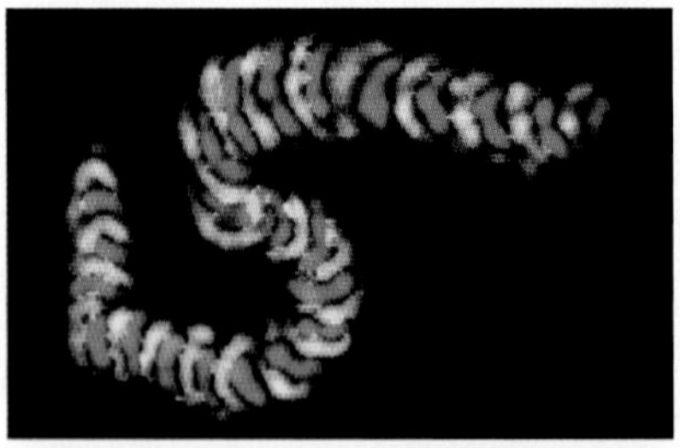

Figure 10.57 Unlabeled neutrophils that have been allowed to migrate spontaneously in gelatin matrices containing a prototype of DQ™ Green BSA (D12050) and dihydrotetramethylrosamine. Extracellular release of reactive oxygen metabolites oxidizes dihydrotetramethylrosamine to tetramethylrosamine, yielding orange fluorescence. Extracellular protease activity cleaves highly quenched DQ™ Green BSA, yielding green-fluorescent peptides. The micrograph illustrates an alternating pattern of orange and green fluorescence and shows that extracellular release of oxidants and proteolytic activity oscillate 180° out of phase during cell locomotion. Image contributed by Howard R. Petty, Wayne State University.

The EnzChek® Protease Assay Kits provide exceptionally fast, simple and direct fluorescence assays for detecting metallo-, serine, acid and thiol proteases. Our two EnzChek® Protease Assay Kits (E6638, E6639) measure the increase in fluorescence intensity that results from protease hydrolysis of a heavily labeled casein derivative, whereas our EnzChek® Polarization Assay Kit for Proteases (E6658) monitors fluorescence polarization changes that occur during protease hydrolysis of a lightly labeled fluorescent casein derivative. Although the detection principles of these protease assays are quite different, no separation steps are required for either, and both assays are rapid, sensitive and versatile.

EnzChek® Protease Assay Kits for Fluorescence Intensity Measurements

Our patented EnzChek® Protease Assay Kits contain a casein derivative that is heavily labeled with either the green-fluorescent BODIPY® FL or red-fluorescent BODIPY® TR-X dye, resulting in almost total quenching of the conjugate's fluorescence; they typically exhibit <3% of the fluorescence of the corresponding free dyes.[62–64] Protease-catalyzed hydrolysis relieves this quenching, yielding brightly fluorescent BODIPY® FL dye– or BODIPY® TR-X dye–labeled peptides[63,64] (Figure 10.56). The increase in fluorescence, which can be measured with a spectrofluorometer, minifluorometer or fluorescence microplate reader, is directly proportional to protease activity.

In contrast to the conventional fluorescein thiocarbamoyl (FTC)–casein protease assay, these EnzChek® assays do not involve any separation steps and, consequently, can be used to continuously measure the kinetics of a variety of exopeptidases and endopeptidases over a wide pH range. They can also be used to measure the total substrate turnover at a fixed time following addition of the enzyme. We have found that these protease assays are over 100-times more sensitive and much easier to perform than the labor-intensive FTC–casein assay. Detection limits for fluorescence intensity measurements with these kits are given in Table 10.4.

Hydrolysis of the fluorogenic substrates by proteases provides a sensitive assay of cell proliferation and a means of detecting the sterility of a sample. In addition to their utility for detecting protease contamination in culture medium and other experimental samples, BODIPY® FL casein and BODIPY® TR-X casein have significant potential as general, nontoxic, pH-insensitive markers for phagocytic cells in culture (Section 16.1). We have shown that uptake of these quenched conjugates by neutrophils is accompanied by hydrolysis of the labeled proteins by intracellular proteases and generation of fluorescent products that are well retained in cells. This phagocytosis assay is readily performed in a fluorescence microplate reader or a flow cytometer; localization of the fluorescent products can be determined by fluorescence microscopy. The same substrates can readily detect secretion of proteases from live cells.

BODIPY® FL casein and BODIPY® TR-X casein can be used interchangeably, depending on whether green or red fluorescence is desired. The peptide hydrolysis products of BODIPY® FL casein exhibit green fluorescence that is optimally excited by the argon-ion laser, permitting flow sorting of the cells. The red-fluorescent BODIPY® TR-X–labeled peptides, with excitation and emission spectra similar to those of the Texas Red® fluorophore, should be useful for multilabeling experiments or measurements in the presence of green autofluorescence. Each EnzChek® Protease Assay Kit includes:

- BODIPY® FL casein (in Kit E6638) or BODIPY® TR-X casein (in Kit E6639)
- Concentrated digestion buffer
- A detailed protocol

Each kit provides sufficient reagents for ~100 assays using 2 mL assay volumes and standard fluorescence cuvettes or ~1000 assays using 200 µL assay volumes and 96-well microplates.

Our EnzChek® Protease Assay Kits are also available as convenient RediPlate™ 96 and RediPlate™ 384 EnzChek® Protease Assay Kits (R22130, R22132). Each RediPlate™ 96 EnzChek® Protease Assay Kit includes one 96-well microplate, with all of the necessary reagents predispensed into the wells, where 88 wells (11 lanes) are intended for assays and 8 wells (1 lane) include a dilution series of an appropriate reference standard for generation of standard curves. The enzyme sample to be assayed is added to the microplate in a suitable buffer, along with any compounds to be tested. Then, after incubation, the resultant fluorescence is quantitated on a fluorescence microplate reader equipped with filters appropriate for the green- or red-fluorescent dye. Each RediPlate™ 96 microplate has removable lanes that allow researchers to perform only as many assays as required for the experiment (Figure 8.60). Resealable packaging ensures plate and well integrity between experiments.

The RediPlate™ 384 EnzChek® Protease Assay Kits (R22131, R22133) provide a single 384-well plate for high-throughput screening of protease activity. These standard 384-well microplates include 368 wells (23 lanes) for activity measurements and 16 wells (1 lane) containing a dilution series of an appropriate reference dye for generation of standard curves.

Table 10.3 summarizes our other RediPlate™ 96 and RediPlate™ 384 Assay Kits for caspase-3 activity (see above), phosphatase activity (Section 10.3) and dsDNA quantitation (Section 8.3). Significant discounts apply to purchases of multiple units of all of our RediPlate™ products.

Table 10.4 — Detection limits of the EnzChek® Protease Assay Kits (E6638, E6639)

Enzyme (Source)	Class	Detection Limit (Units) *	Buffer Conditions
Elastase, Type IV (porcine pancreas)	Serine protease	2.2×10^{-3}	10 mM Tris-HCl, pH 8.8
Chymotrypsin, Type II (bovine pancreas)	Serine protease	5.0×10^{-5}	10 mM Tris-HCl, pH 7.8
Thermolysin (*Bacillus thermoproteolyticus* Rokko)	Acid protease	4.4×10^{-5}	10 mM Tris-HCl, pH 7.8
Trypsin, Type IX (porcine pancreas)	Serine protease	1.3×10^{-2}	10 mM Tris-HCl, pH 7.8
Papain (papaya latex)	Cysteine protease	2.1×10^{-4}	10 mM MES, pH 6.2
Pepsin (porcine stomach mucosa)	Acid protease	2.1×10^{-3}	10 mM HCl, pH 2.0
Elastase (*Pseudomonas aeruginosa*)	Metallo-protease	1.0×10^{-3}	20 mM sodium phosphate, pH 8.0
Cathepsin D	Acid protease	2.0×10^{-4}	20 mM sodium citrate, pH 5.0
Elastase (human leukocyte)	Serine protease	1.0×10^{-3}	10 mM Tris-HCl, pH 7.5

* The detection limit is defined as the amount of enzyme required to cause a 10–20% change in fluorescence compared with the control sample at 22°C. Enzyme unit definitions are standard definitions for each individual enzyme. Detection limits were determined with BODIPY® FL casein and with BODIPY® TR-X casein; both substrates yielded similar results. Detection limits may vary with instrumentation.

EnzChek® Protease Assay Kit for Fluorescence Polarization Measurements

When a fluorescent molecule tethered to a protein is excited by polarized fluorescent light, the polarization of fluorescence emission is dependent on the rate of molecular tumbling. Upon proteolytic cleavage of the fluorescently labeled protein, the resultant smaller peptides tumble faster, and the emitted light is depolarized relative to the light measured from the intact conjugate. The EnzChek® Polarization Assay Kit for Proteases[65] (E6658) contains green-fluorescent BODIPY® FL casein with an optimal degree of labeling for fluorescence polarization–based protease assays.[66,67] Fluorescence polarization technology is more sensitive than many nonradioactive protease assays and allows measurements to be taken in real time, permitting the collection of kinetics data (see Note 1.5 "Technical Focus: Fluorescence Polarization (FP)" in Section 1.4). Our BODIPY® FL dye has an adequate fluorescence lifetime and pH-insensitive fluorescence — two prerequisites for successful measurement of protease activity by fluorescence polarization. The EnzChek® Polarization Assay Kit for Proteases contains:

- BODIPY® FL casein
- Concentrated digestion buffer
- A detailed protocol

Each kit provides sufficient reagents for ~100 assays using 2 mL assay volumes and standard fluorescence cuvettes or ~1000 assays using 200 µL assay volumes and 96-well microplates. With the advent of high-capacity automated instrumentation, this kit provides an important tool for high-throughput screening of proteases and their inhibitors in research laboratories.

Fluorescein Casein

We also offer fluorescein casein (C2990) for assaying protease activity. In this assay, unhydrolyzed fluorescein casein must be precipitated with trichloroacetic acid, separated by centrifugation, transferred for measurement and then pH-adjusted for fluorescein signal enhancement.[68–72] Fluorescein casein may be useful for a continuous assay if monitored by fluorescence polarization.[67] Fluorescein casein is rapidly degraded by *Bacteroides gingivalis* but only slowly by streptococci.[73]

EnzChek® Gelatinase/Collagenase Assay Kit

Collagen is a major component of the extracellular matrix, which not only serves as scaffolding to stabilize tissue structure, but also influences the development, migration, proliferation and metabolism of cells that contact it. Gelatinases and collagenases — matrix metalloproteinases (MMPs) that digest collagen or gelatin (denatured collagen) — are increasingly important to our understanding of both normal development and carcinogenesis.[74] For example, gelatinase A (20,000-dalton MMP-2) is primarily responsible for degrading the helical domains of type IV collagen, the principal collagen of basement membranes.[75] Thus, gelatinase A likely plays a major role in the turnover of basement membrane during fetal tissue development, wound healing, angiogenesis and tumor invasion.

The EnzChek® Gelatinase/Collagenase Assay Kit (E12055) provides the speed, high sensitivity and convenience required for measuring gelatinase or collagenase activity or for screening inhibitors[76] in a high-throughput format. This kit contains:

- DQ™ gelatin substrate
- 1,10-Phenanthroline, a general metalloproteinase inhibitor
- Type IV collagenase from *Clostridium histolyticum* for use as a positive control
- Concentrated reaction buffer
- A detailed protocol

DQ™ gelatin, the highly quenched gelatinase/collagenase substrate provided, is efficiently digested by most, if not all, gelatinases and collagenases, releasing brightly fluorescent peptides (Figure 10.56). The increase in fluorescence upon digestion is proportional to proteolytic activity and can be monitored with a fluorescence microplate reader, minifluorometer or spectrofluorometer. Depending on the substrate concentration used in each reaction, sufficient reagents are supplied for 250–1000 assays using 200 µL assay volumes and 96-well microplates. Using 100 µg/mL DQ™ gelatin and a two-hour incubation period, we have detected as little as 2×10^{-3} U/mL (7 ng protein/mL) of *C. histolyticum* collagenase, where one unit is defined as the amount of enzyme required to liberate 1 µmole L-leucine equivalents from collagen in 5 hours at 37°C, pH 7.5. Longer incubation times increase the sensitivity, whereas higher enzyme concentrations decrease the incubation times. Using human gelatinase A (not provided), 100 µg/mL DQ™ gelatin and a 24-hour incubation period, we have detected concentrations of gelatinase as low as 3×10^{-4} U/mL, where one unit is defined as the amount of enzyme that can hydrolyze 1 mg of type IV collagen in one hour at 37°C, pH 7.5. DQ™ gelatin and some of our other highly quenched protease substrates have been utilized for *in situ* detection of matrix metalloproteinase and other protease activity in cell preparations, tissue sections and SDS gels.[3,77–80]

EnzChek® Elastase Assay Kit

Molecular Probes' EnzChek® Elastase Assay Kit (E12056) provides the speed, high sensitivity and convenience required for measuring elastase activity or for screening inhibitors in a high-throughput format. This kit contains DQ™ elastin — soluble bovine neck ligament elastin that has been labeled with our BODIPY® FL dye such that the conjugate's fluorescence is quenched. Upon digestion by elastase or other proteases, the fluorescence is revealed (Figure 10.56). The resulting increase in fluorescence can be monitored with a fluorescence microplate reader, minifluorometer or spectrofluorometer. Digestion products from the DQ™ elastin substrate have absorption maxima at ~505 nm and fluorescence emission maxima at ~515 nm. Because the assay is continuous, kinetics data can be obtained easily. Furthermore, because fluorescence of the BODIPY® FL dye is pH insensitive between pH 3 and 9, the assay can be performed under a variety of buffer conditions. Please note that DQ™ elastin is also digested by proteases other than elastase. Each EnzChek® Elastase Assay Kit (A10256) contains:

- DQ™ elastin substrate
- Concentrated reaction buffer
- Elastase from pig pancreas for use as a positive control

- *N*-Methoxysuccinyl-Ala-Ala-Pro-Val-chloromethyl ketone, a selective elastase inhibitor
- A detailed protocol

Each kit provides sufficient reagents for approximately 600 assays using a fluorescence microplate reader and reaction volumes of 200 µL. The *N*-methoxysuccinyl-Ala-Ala-Pro-Val-chloromethyl ketone inhibitor can be used to confirm the identity of the protease responsible for substrate digestion or, alternatively, as a control inhibitor for use when screening for elastase inhibitors.

DQ™ Substrates

DQ™ Collagens

Our DQ™ collagens, type I (D12060) and type IV (D12052), are complementary reagents to the DQ™ gelatin provided in the EnzChek® Gelatinase/Collagenase Assay Kit. Like DQ™ gelatin, these highly quenched substrates are heavily labeled with fluorescein and release fluorescent peptides when enzymatically cleaved. DQ™ collagen, type I should be useful in assays detecting matrix metalloproteases (MMP-1) activity.[81] DQ™ collagen, type IV may prove particularly useful in the development of assays for gelatinase A (MMP-2) and gelatinase A inhibitors, as well as for other gelatinases and collagenases that specifically degrade type IV collagen. DQ™ collagens may be used with the EnzChek® Gelatinase/Collagenase Assay Kit, and a sample protocol is included. Because of its more complex structure, DQ™ collagens generally require either greater amounts of the enzyme or longer incubation periods than does DQ™ gelatin. Please note that both the DQ™ collagens and DQ™ gelatin can be digested by proteases other than gelatinases and collagenases. The fluorescence generated by hydrolysis of DQ™ collagen (D12052) by cellular collagenase has been used to visualize the migratory pathway followed by tumor cells during invasion of a gelatin matrix and to image proteolysis by living breast cancer cells.[58,59]

In addition to the DQ™ substrates, we have prepared gelatin and collagen conjugates that have been labeled to maximize probe fluorescence and minimize dye quenching. We offer two green-fluorescent conjugates of gelatin, one in which gelatin is coupled to our photostable Oregon Green® 488 dye (G13186, Section 15.6) and the other to fluorescein (G13187, Section 15.6).

DQ™ BSA

DQ™ Green BSA (D12050, excitation/emission maxima 500/506 nm) and DQ™ Red BSA (D12051, excitation/emission maxima 589/617 nm) are bovine serum albumin (BSA) conjugates that have been labeled to such a high degree that the BODIPY® dyes used to label them are strongly self-quenched. Proteolysis of the DQ™ BSA can easily be monitored as proteolytic fragments containing the fluorophores are released from the larger conjugate and become brightly fluorescent[82] (Figure 10.56). An unlabeled neutrophil making its way through a gelatin matrix containing a DQ™ Green BSA prototype, as well as dihydrotetramethylrosamine, a nonfluorescent probe that fluoresces bright orange upon oxidation, leaves behind a fluorescent trail[61] (Figure 10.57). The alternating green- and orange-fluorescent bands dramatically demonstrate that the proteolytic and oxidative activities of the migrating neutrophil are oscillatory and are 180° out of phase with each other. Intracellular processing of a similar BODIPY® BSA conjugate by J774 macrophages can be completely inhibited by protease inhibitors.[82] DQ™ Green BSA has been embedded in a gelatin matrix and used to image both extracellular and intracellular proteolysis in living cells. DQ™ BSA can be complexed with our rabbit IgG fraction anti-BSA (A11133, Section 7.5) to form an immune complex that is internalized through the Fc receptor and processed in the phagovacuole to highly fluorescent peptides (Section 16.1). DQ™ Green BSA has been used for imaging proteolysis in living breast cancer cells.[58]

DQ™ Ovalbumin

DQ™ ovalbumin[83,84] (D12053) is a self-quenched ovalbumin conjugate designed specifically for the study of antigen processing. Ovalbumin is efficiently processed through mannose receptor–mediated endocytosis by antigen-presenting cells and is widely used for studying antigen processing.[85–87] DQ™ ovalbumin is labeled with our pH-insensitive, green-fluorescent BODIPY® FL dye such that the fluorescence is almost completely quenched. Upon endocytosis and proteolysis, highly fluorescent peptides are released. DQ™ ovalbumin appears to be an excellent indicator of macrophage-mediated antigen processing in flow cytometry and microscopy assays.

Matrix Metalloproteinases

The matrix metalloproteinases (MMPs) constitute a family of zinc-dependent endopeptidases that function within the extracellular matrix. These enzymes are responsible for the breakdown of connective tissues and are important in bone remodeling, the menstrual cycle and repair of tissue damage. While the exact contribution of MMPs to certain pathological processes is difficult to assess, MMPs appear to have a key role in the development of arthritis and the invasion and metastasis of cancer.[88,89]

MMPs tend to have multiple substrates, with most family members having the ability to degrade several different types of collagen along with elastin, gelatin and fibronectin.[90] Most MMPs contain three major domains: a regulatory domain (which must be removed before the enzyme can be active), a catalytic domain and a hemopexin domain. The hemopexin domain aids in enzyme binding to certain substrates, although it is not necessary for the catalytic function of the enzyme.[91]

To assist researchers in the study of these important enzymes, Molecular Probes offers high activity rabbit antibodies against MMP-1, MMP-2, MMP-3 and MMP-9 (Table 7.21). In each case, the antibody is directed at the stretch of amino acids that form the small hinge region between the catalytic and hemopexin domain (Figure 7.97). The hinge region is highly variable among MMPs;[90] therefore, antibodies raised against this peptide sequence have very little crossreactivity with other MMPs. All of these antibodies recognize both the pro (inactive) and active forms of their respective MMP target, and are suitable for Western blotting, immunoprecipitation and immunohistochemistry applications.

Alternative Methods for Detecting Protease Activity

Peptidases typically liberate a free amine for each hydrolysis step. Thus, fluorogenic amine detection reagents such as fluorescamine (F2332; FluoroPure™ Grade, F20261; Section 1.8) and *o*-phthaldialdehyde (P2331MP, Section 1.8) have been used to detect the rate of amine production by peptidases.[92–95]

Peptidases that liberate single free amino acids for which specific oxidases exist can be analyzed by coupling the hydrolytic reaction to oxidation of our Amplex® Red reagent (Section 10.5) to the red-fluorescent dye resorufin (Figure 10.6). For example, glutamic acid production can be monitored using glutamate oxidase[96] and D-amino acid liberation monitored using a D-amino acid oxidase.

Protease assays conducted in highly autofluorescent or strongly light-scattering solutions (such as crude cell and tissue extracts) often can be improved by extracting the fluorescent hydrolysis product from the assay mixture with an organic solvent such as toluene, chloroform or ethyl acetate.[97] Most unhydrolyzed peptidase substrates will remain in the aqueous layer.

Endopeptidase substrates that are singly labeled at the amine terminus with a fluorophore usually do not undergo a fluorescence change upon hydrolysis of internal peptide bonds; however, fluorescence (or absorbance) of the fluorophore that remains attached to the cleaved peptide can be used to detect the hydrolysis product following separation by TLC, HPLC or capillary electrophoresis.

Fluorescent Protease Inhibitors

Alexa Fluor® 488 Soybean Trypsin Inhibitor

Trypsin inhibitor from soybean (SBTI) is a 21,000-dalton protein that inhibits the catalytic activity of serine proteases.[98–100] SBTI binds to acrosin, an acrosomal serine protease that is associated with binding of spermatozoa and penetration of the zona pellucida,[101,102] and SBTI binding patterns in non-fixed human sperm have demonstrated its usefulness for detecting acrosome-reacted sperm.[103] In particular, an Alexa Fluor® 488 conjugate of the protein has been used to measure the acrosomal status of macaque sperm and to determine the localization of acrosin during the reaction.[104] Molecular Probes provides a fluorescent SBTI conjugate with one of our best fluorophores, the Alexa Fluor® 488 dye (T23011). The Alexa Fluor® 488 dye (Section 1.3) has spectral characteristics similar to fluorescein (excitation at 495 nm and emission at 519 nm) but produces conjugates that are brighter and more photostable. Furthermore, the fluorescence of Alexa Fluor® 488 conjugates is insensitive to pH from 4 to 10 (Figure 1.12).

BODIPY® FL Pepstatin

Pepstatin A is an inhibitor of carboxyl (acid) proteases that contain aspartate residues at their active sites, including cathepsin D, pepsin and renin.[105–107] Molecular Probes has prepared the green-fluorescent BODIPY® FL pepstatin A analog (P12271), which we have shown binds to cathepsin D in live cells[108] (Section 15.5).

References

1. Methods Enzymol 244, 1 (1994); **2.** J Histochem Cytochem 49, 1473 (2001); **3.** Am J Physiol Lung Cell Mol Physiol 287, L184 (2004); **4.** Exp Cell Res 283, 206 (2003); **5.** J Biol Chem 270, 558 (1995); **6.** Arch Biochem Biophys 314, 171 (1994); **7.** FEBS Lett 341, 197 (1994); **8.** J Biochem (Tokyo) 113, 441 (1993); **9.** FEBS Lett 257, 388 (1989); **10.** Arch Biochem Biophys 259, 131 (1987); **11.** Biochem J 201, 367 (1982); **12.** Biochem J 193, 187 (1981); **13.** Methods Enzymol 80 Pt C, 341 (1981); **14.** J Biochem (Tokyo) 82, 1495 (1977); **15.** J Biol Chem 275, 2390 (2000); **16.** J Biol Chem 275, 9452 (2000); **17.** J Biol Chem 268, 23593 (1993); **18.** J Biol Chem 274, 787 (1999); **19.** Biochem J 215, 253 (1983); **20.** Biochem J 209, 299 (1983); **21.** Cytometry 20, 334 (1995); **22.** Anticancer Res 8, 1179 (1988); **23.** J Enzyme Inhib 2, 209 (1988); **24.** Biochim Biophys Acta 788, 74 (1984); **25.** Photochem Photobiol 44, 461 (1986); **26.** Proc Natl Acad Sci U S A 97, 13126 (2000); **27.** Glia 7, 183 (1993); **28.** Biol Chem Hoppe Seyler 373, 547 (1992); **29.** Biol Chem Hoppe Seyler 373, 433 (1992); **30.** Neuron 20, 1123 (1998); **31.** Anal Chem 65, 2352 (1993); **32.** Biomed Instrum Technol 30, 245 (1996); **33.** Immunol Cell Biol 76, 1 (1998); **34.** Science 281, 1312 (1998); **35.** Trends Biochem Sci 22, 388 (1997); **36.** Nature 376, 37 (1995); **37.** J Neurosci Res 52, 334 (1998); **38.** Biochemistry 38, 13906 (1999); **39.** Bioorg Med Chem Lett 9, 3231 (1999); **40.** Cell Death Differ 6, 821 (1999); **41.** Science 281, 1305 (1998); **42.** J Biol Chem 274, 17484 (1999); **43.** Exp Cell Res 250, 203 (1999); **44.** J Biol Chem 276, 6974 (2001); **45.** J Biochem Biophys Methods 33, 135 (1996); **46.** Science 247, 954 (1990); **47.** Tetrahedron Lett 31, 6493 (1990); **48.** J Biol Chem 272, 15603 (1997); **49.** J Biol Chem 267, 20028 (1992); **50.** Science 249, 527 (1990); **51.** Biochemistry 38, 13407 (1999); **52.** J Protein Chem 9, 663 (1990); **53.** J Protein Chem 10, 553 (1991); **54.** Anal Biochem 210, 351 (1993); **55.** Anal Biochem 260, 257 (1998); **56.** Anal Biochem 259, 8 (1998); **57.** J Virol Methods 70, 45 (1998); **58.** Neoplasia 2, 496 (2000); **59.** FASEB J 15, 932 (2001); **60.** Exp Cell Res 260, 292 (2000); **61.** Biophys J 74, 90 (1998); **62.** Anal Biochem 279, 170 (2000); **63.** Anal Biochem 251, 144 (1997); **64.** Anal Biochem 254, 144 (1997); **65.** Anal Biochem 243, 1 (1996); **66.** J Biomol Screen 1, 33 (1996); **67.** Biotechniques 17, 585 (1994); **68.** Cytometry 15, 213 (1994); **69.** Anal Biochem 197, 347 (1991); **70.** Anal Biochem 191, 133 (1990); **71.** Anal Biochem 143, 30 (1984); **72.** Anal Biochem 121, 290 (1982); **73.** FEMS Microbiol Lett 55, 257 (1990); **74.** Chem Biol 3, 895 (1996); **75.** J Biol Chem 270, 5872 (1995); **76.** J Biol Chem 276, 11347 (2001); **77.** J Histochem Cytochem 52, 711 (2004); **78.** Biol Reprod 66, 685 (2002); **79.** Biol Reprod 66, 1083 (2002); **80.** J Neurosci 19, 8464 (1999); **81.** Lab Invest 78, 687 (1998); **82.** Eur J Cell Biol 75, 192 (1998); **83.** J Immunol 165, 49 (2000); **84.** Proc Natl Acad Sci U S A 96, 15056 (1999); **85.** Eur J Immunol 25, 1823 (1995); **86.** J Immunol 149, 2894 (1992); **87.** J Immunol 145, 417 (1990); **88.** Int J Oncol 12, 1343 (1998); **89.** Mol Med Today 4, 130 (1998); **90.** Matrix Metalloproteinases and TIMPs, Woessner JF 11 (2000); **91.** Matrix Biol 15, 511 (1997); **92.** Biochemistry 29, 6670 (1990); **93.** Anal Biochem 123, 41 (1982); **94.** Anal Biochem 87, 556 (1978); **95.** Biochem Biophys Res Commun 53, 75 (1973); **96.** Anal Biochem 284, 382 (2000); **97.** Anal Biochem 87, 257 (1978); **98.** J Cell Biol 161, 79 (2003); **99.** J Biol Chem 241, 3955 (1966); **100.** Methods Enzymol 45, 700 (1976); **101.** Development 109, 41 (1990); **102.** Zygote 7, 143 (1999); **103.** Fertil Steril 62, 1044 (1994); **104.** Zygote 8, 127 (2000); **105.** J Biol Chem 267, 24725 (1992); **106.** Biochemistry 24, 3165 (1985); **107.** J Antibiot (Tokyo) 29, 97 (1976); **108.** J Biochem Biophys Methods 42, 137 (2000).

Data Table — 10.4 Detecting Peptidases and Proteases

Cat #	MW	Storage	Soluble	Abs	EC	Em	Solvent	Product	Notes
A6520	554.10	F,D	DMSO	330	13,000	403	MeOH	C2110	1
A6521	649.14	F,D	DMSO	326	19,000	384	MeOH	A191	1
A6575	536.41	F,D	DMSO	330	15,000	403	MeOH	C2110	1
A22121	821.72	F,D	DMSO	339	7,900	435	MeOH	see Notes	1, 2
A22127	767.79	F,D	DMSO	326	17,000	392	MeOH	A191	1
A22128	821.76	F,D	DMSO	340	8,200	434	MeOH	see Notes	1, 2
E13183	767.74	F,D,L	DMSO	325	16,000	395	pH 7	A191	1, 3
E13184	1515.46	F,D,L	DMSO	232	52,000	none	MeOH	R6479	3
H2930	~2016	F,D,L	DMF, H_2O	430	23,000	none	MeOH	see Notes	4
L6543	~475	F,D	H_2O	<300		none			
P12271	1044.14	F,D,L	DMSO	504	86,000	511	MeOH		
R2931	~2281	F,D,L	DMF, H_2O	460	13,000	none	H_2O	see Notes	4
R6501	983.91	F,D	DMSO, DMF	232	55,000	none	MeOH	R6479	
R6502	1278.26	F,D	DMSO, DMF	232	60,000	none	MeOH	R6479	
R6504	882.92	F,D	DMSO, DMF	232	57,000	none	MeOH	R6479	
R6505	1404.46	F,D	DMSO, DMF	231	44,000	none	MeOH	R6479	
R6506	1167.24	F,D	DMSO, DMF	232	56,000	none	MeOH	R6479	
R6507	1178.14	F,D	DMSO, DMF	232	58,000	none	MeOH	R6479	
R6508	1126.06	F,D	DMSO, DMF	232	57,000	none	MeOH	R6479	
R6513	1047.33	F,D	DMSO, DMF	232	60,000	none	MeOH	R6479	
R6560	809.70	F,D	DMSO, DMF	232	54,000	none	MeOH	see Notes	5
R6577	852.74	F,D	DMSO, DMF	232	56,000	none	MeOH	R6479	
R22120	1515.46	F,D	DMSO, DMF	232	52,000	none	MeOH	R6479	
R22122	788.57	F,D	DMSO, DMF	232	55,000	none	MeOH	R6479	
R22124	1259.42	F,D	DMSO, DMF	232	54,000	none	MeOH	R6479	
R22125	1515.55	F,D	DMSO, DMF	232	52,000	none	MeOH	R6479	
R22126	1515.55	F,D	DMSO, DMF	232	52,000	none	MeOH	R6479	
R33750	1495.56	F,D	DMSO, DMF	230	76,000	none	MeOH	R6479	
R33751	1587.62	F,D	DMSO, DMF	232	57,000	none	MeOH	R6479	
R33752	1113.10	F,D	DMSO, DMF	232	57,000	none	MeOH	R6479	
R33753	1571.57	F,D	DMSO, DMF	232	57,000	none	MeOH	R6479	
R33754	1511.60	F,D	DMSO, DMF	232	57,000	none	MeOH	R6479	
R33755	1597.65	F,D	DMSO, DMF	232	57,000	none	MeOH	R6479	

For definitions of the contents of this data table, see "Navigating *The Handbook*" in the introductory pages.

Notes

1. Fluorescence of the unhydrolyzed substrate is very weak.
2. Enzymatic cleavage of this substrate yields 7-amino-4-trifluoromethylcoumarin: Abs = 380 nm (EC = 13,000 $cm^{-1}M^{-1}$), Em = 500 nm in pH 7 buffer.
3. Data represent the substrate component of this kit.
4. Fluorescence of this substrate is >99% quenched. The proteolytic cleavage products fluoresce at 500 nm (excitation at 335 nm).
5. Peptidase cleavage product is a 4-(chloromethyl)benzoyl amide derivative of rhodamine 110, Abs = 492 nm (EC = 24,000 $cm^{-1}M^{-1}$), Em = 529 nm in MeOH (based on reported data) (Biochem J 209, 299 (1983)).

Product List — 10.4 Detecting Peptidases and Proteases

Cat #	Product Name	Unit Size
A6520	7-amino-4-chloromethylcoumarin, *t*-BOC-L-leucyl-L-methionine amide (CMAC, *t*-BOC-Leu-Met)	5 mg
A6575	7-amino-4-chloromethylcoumarin, CBZ-L-arginine amide, hydrochloride (CMAC, CBZ-Arg)	5 mg
A22127	7-amino-4-methylcoumarin, *N*-CBZ-L-isoleucyl-L-glutamyl-L-threonyl-L-aspartic acid amide (Z-IETD-AMC)	5 mg
A6521	7-amino-4-methylcoumarin, CBZ-L-phenylalanyl-L-arginine amide, hydrochloride	25 mg
A22121	7-amino-4-trifluoromethylcoumarin, *N*-CBZ-L-aspartyl-L-glutamyl-L-valyl-L-aspartic acid amide (Z-DEVD-AFC)	5 mg
A22128	7-amino-4-trifluoromethylcoumarin, *N*-CBZ-L-isoleucyl-L-glutamyl-L-threonyl-L-aspartic acid amide (Z-IETD-AFC)	5 mg
A21290	anti-matrix metalloproteinase-1 (hinge region), affinity-purified rabbit antibody (anti-MMP-1) *1 mg/mL*	100 µL
A21291	anti-matrix metalloproteinase-2 (hinge region), affinity-purified rabbit antibody (anti-MMP-2) *1 mg/mL*	100 µL
A21292	anti-matrix metalloproteinase-3 (hinge region), affinity-purified rabbit antibody (anti-MMP-3) *1 mg/mL*	100 µL
A21293	anti-matrix metalloproteinase-9 (hinge region), affinity-purified rabbit antibody (anti-MMP-9) *1 mg/mL*	100 µL
C2990	casein, fluorescein conjugate	25 mg
D12060	DQ™ collagen, type I from bovine skin, fluorescein conjugate	1 mg
D12052	DQ™ collagen, type IV from human placenta, fluorescein conjugate	1 mg
D12054	DQ™ gelatin from pig skin, fluorescein conjugate *special packaging*	5 x 1 mg
D12050	DQ™ Green BSA *special packaging*	5 x 1 mg
D12053	DQ™ ovalbumin *special packaging*	5 x 1 mg
D12051	DQ™ Red BSA *special packaging*	5 x 1 mg
E13183	EnzChek® Caspase-3 Assay Kit #1 *Z-DEVD-AMC substrate* *500 assays*	1 kit

For current prices or to order online, visit probes.invitrogen.com

Product List — 10.4 Detecting Peptidases and Proteases — continued

Cat #	Product Name	Unit Size
E13184	EnzChek® Caspase-3 Assay Kit #2 *Z-DEVD-R110 substrate* *500 assays*	1 kit
E12056	EnzChek® Elastase Assay Kit *600 assays*	1 kit
E12055	EnzChek® Gelatinase/Collagenase Assay Kit *250-2000 assays*	1 kit
E6658	EnzChek® Polarization Assay Kit for Proteases *green fluorescence* *100-1000 assays*	1 kit
E6638	EnzChek® Protease Assay Kit *green fluorescence* *100-1000 assays*	1 kit
E6639	EnzChek® Protease Assay Kit *red fluorescence* *100-1000 assays*	1 kit
H2930	HIV Protease Substrate 1 (Arg-Glu(EDANS)-Ser-Gln-Asn-Tyr-Pro-Ile-Val-Gln-Lys(dabcyl)-Arg)	1 mg
L6543	leupeptin hemisulfate	10 mg
P12271	pepstatin A, BODIPY® FL conjugate	25 µg
R35100	RediPlate™ 96 EnzChek® Caspase-3 Assay Kit *Z-DEVD-R110 substrate* *one 96-well microplate*	1 kit
R22130	RediPlate™ 96 EnzChek® Protease Assay Kit *green fluorescence* *one 96-well microplate*	1 kit
R22131	RediPlate™ 384 EnzChek® Protease Assay Kit *green fluorescence* *one 384-well microplate*	1 kit
R22132	RediPlate™ 96 EnzChek® Protease Assay Kit *red fluorescence* *one 96-well microplate*	1 kit
R22133	RediPlate™ 384 EnzChek® Protease Assay Kit *red fluorescence* *one 384-well microplate*	1 kit
R2931	Renin Substrate 1 (Arg-Glu(EDANS)-Ile-His-Pro-Phe-His-Leu-Val-Ile-His-Thr-Lys(dabcyl)-Arg)	1 mg
R22122	rhodamine 110, bis-(L-aspartic acid amide), trifluoroacetic acid salt	1 mg
R6513	rhodamine 110, bis-(*t*-BOC-L-leucyl-L-methionine amide)	5 mg
R6504	rhodamine 110, bis-(CBZ-L-alanyl-L-alanine amide)	5 mg
R6506	rhodamine 110, bis-(CBZ-L-alanyl-L-alanyl-L-alanyl-L-alanine amide)	5 mg
R6508	rhodamine 110, bis-(CBZ-L-alanyl-L-arginine amide), dihydrochloride	5 mg
R6501	rhodamine 110, bis-(CBZ-L-arginine amide), dihydrochloride (BZAR)	5 mg
R22120	rhodamine 110, bis-(*N*-CBZ-L-aspartyl-L-glutamyl-L-valyl-L-aspartic acid amide) (Z-DEVD-R110) *bulk packaging*	20 mg
R22125	rhodamine 110, bis-(*N*-CBZ-L-isoleucyl-L-glutamyl-L-threonyl-L-aspartic acid amide) (Z-IETD-R110)	2 mg
R22126	rhodamine 110, bis-(*N*-CBZ-L-isoleucyl-L-glutamyl-L-threonyl-L-aspartic acid amide) (Z-IETD-R110) *bulk packaging*	20 mg
R6505	rhodamine 110, bis-(CBZ-L-isoleucyl-L-prolyl-L-arginine amide), dihydrochloride (BZiPAR)	5 mg
R6502	rhodamine 110, bis-(CBZ-L-phenylalanyl-L-arginine amide), dihydrochloride	5 mg
R6507	rhodamine 110, bis-(CBZ-L-prolyl-L-arginine amide), dihydrochloride	5 mg
R6577	rhodamine 110, bis-(L-phenylalanine amide), di(trifluoroacetic acid) salt	5 mg
R33752	rhodamine 110, bis-(*N*-CBZ-L-alanyl-L-alanyl-L-aspartic acid amide) (Z-AAD-R110)	2 mg
R33753	rhodamine 110, bis-(*N*-CBZ-L-leucyl-L-glutamyl-L-glutamyl-L-aspartic acid amide) (Z-LEED-R110)	2 mg
R33751	rhodamine 110, bis-(*N*-CBZ-L-leucyl-L-glutamyl-L-histidinyl-L-aspartic acid amide) (Z-LEHD-R110)	2 mg
R33750	rhodamine 110, bis-(*N*-CBZ-L-tyrosinyl-L-valyl-L-alanyl-L-aspartic acid amide) (Z-YVAD-R110)	2 mg
R33755	rhodamine 110, bis-(*N*-CBZ-L-valyl-L-aspartyl-L-valyl-L-alanyl-L-aspartic acid amide) (Z-VDVAD-R110)	2 mg
R33754	rhodamine 110, bis-(*N*-CBZ-L-valyl-L-glutamyl-L-isoleucyl-L-aspartic acid amide) (Z-VEID-R110)	2 mg
R22124	rhodamine 110, bis-(p-tosyl-L-glycyl-L-prolyl-L-arginine amide)	2 mg
R6560	rhodamine 110, 4-(chloromethyl)benzoyl amide, CBZ-L-arginine amide, hydrochloride (CMB-R110, CBZ-Arg)	1 mg
T23011	trypsin inhibitor from soybean, Alexa Fluor® 488 conjugate	1 mg

For current prices or to order online, visit probes.invitrogen.com

10.5 Substrates for Oxidases, Including Amplex® Red Kits

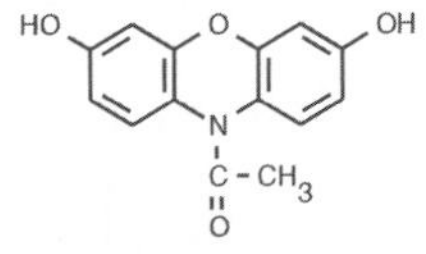

Figure 10.58 A12222 Amplex® Red reagent (10-acetyl-3,7-dihydroxyphenoxazine).

Oxidases, the most useful of which is undoubtedly horseradish peroxidase (HRP), are important enzymes that are used in a wide variety of bioassays. Peroxidase activity is also present in many cells. Reagents for quantitating peroxidase and the activity of a variety of other oxidases are described in this section; reagents for detecting the activity of cellular peroxidases and the oxygen radicals produced by these peroxidases are described in Section 16.1 and Section 18.2. Antibody, protein G, avidin and streptavidin conjugates of horseradish peroxidase are listed in the product list for this section and described in Section 7.2 and Section 7.6. Tyramide signal amplification (TSA) technology (Section 6.2) makes extensive use of peroxidase-conjugated reagents and fluorescent dye– or hapten-labeled tyramides to deposit a detectable product at the site of enzymatic activity (Figure 6.5). Our exclusive Zenon® technology (Section 7.3) includes the Zenon® Horseradish Peroxidase Antibody Labeling Kits (Table 7.13), which permit the rapid and quantitative formation of HRP-labeled antibody complexes; the Zenon® Antibody Labeling Kits are described in detail in Section 7.3.

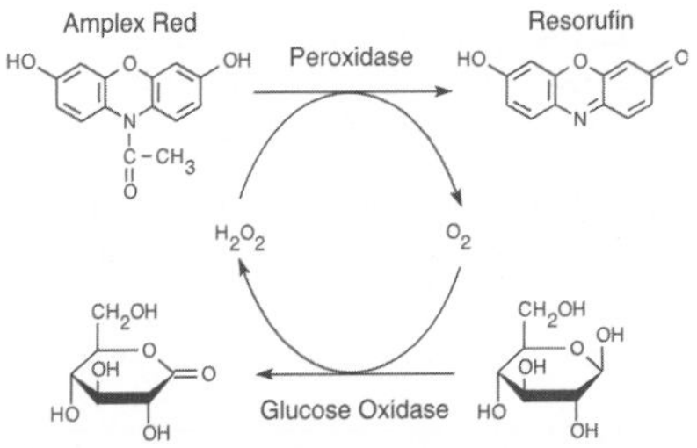

Figure 10.59 Principle of coupled enzymatic assays using our Amplex® Red reagent. Oxidation of glucose by glucose oxidase results in generation of H_2O_2, which is coupled to conversion of the Amplex® Red reagent to fluorescent resorufin by HRP. The detection scheme shown here is used in our Amplex® Red Glucose/Glucose Oxidase Assay Kit (A22189).

We have used our extremely versatile Amplex® Red reagent — the most stable and sensitive fluorogenic substrate known for horseradish peroxidase — to develop a variety of novel fluorogenic and chromogenic assays for enzymes that produce hydrogen peroxide. Furthermore, these coupled assays permit the ultrasensitive quantitation of a diverse assortment of analytes, including glucose, galactose, cholesterol, glutamic acid, xanthine (or hypoxanthine), uric acid, choline and acetylcholine, as well as hydrogen peroxide. Our patented P_iPer™ Phosphate Assay Kit and P_iPer™ Pyrophosphate Assay Kit (P22061, P22062; Section 10.3) also utilize our exclusive Amplex® Red technology for the continuous assays of enzymes that produce either inorganic phosphate or pyrophosphate.

Peroxidases

Amplex® Red Reagent: Stable Substrate for Peroxidase Detection

In the presence of horseradish peroxidase (HRP), the Amplex® Red reagent (10-acetyl-3,7-dihydroxyphenoxazine, A12222, A22177; Figure 10.58) reacts with H_2O_2 with a 1:1 stoichiometry to produce highly fluorescent resorufin [1] (R363, Section 10.1, Figure 10.59). The Amplex® Red reagent has greater stability, yields less background and produces a red-fluorescent product that is more readily detected than the similar reduced methylene blue derivatives commonly used for colorimetric determination of lipid peroxides in plasma, sera, cell extracts and a variety of membrane systems.[2–4] Using the Amplex® Red reagent in conjunction with HRP, we have found that release of hydrogen peroxide to the medium by as few as 2000 phorbol ester–stimulated neutrophils can be detected in a fluorescence microplate reader.

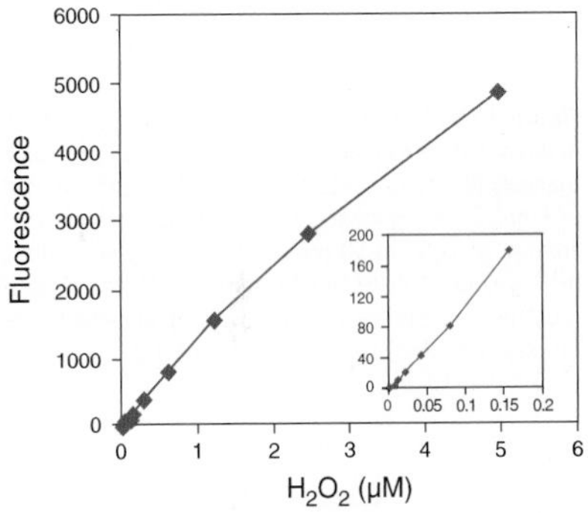

Figure 10.60 Detection of H_2O_2 using the Amplex® Red Hydrogen Peroxide/Peroxidase Assay Kit (A22188). Reactions containing 50 µM Amplex® Red reagent, 1 U/mL HRP and the indicated amount of H_2O_2 in 50 mM sodium phosphate buffer, pH 7.4, were incubated for 30 minutes at room temperature. Fluorescence was measured with a fluorescence microplate reader using excitation at 530 ± 12.5 nm and fluorescence detection at 580 ± 25 nm. Background fluorescence (24 units), determined for a no-H_2O_2 control reaction, was subtracted from each value. The inset shows the sensitivity and linearity of the assay at low levels of H_2O_2.

The Amplex® Red reagent has been used to detect the release of H_2O_2 from activated human leukocytes,[1,5] to measure the activity of monoamine oxidase in cow brain tissue,[6] to demonstrate the extracellular production of H_2O_2 produced by UV light stimulation of human keratinocytes [7–9] and to measure L-glutamate in food samples.[10] Using the Amplex® Red reagent, researchers have discovered that antibodies can convert molecular oxygen to H_2O_2, which may be important in understanding a new chemical arm of the immune system, as well as the evolution of antibodies and the role they may play in human diseases.[11,12] The sensitivity of the Amplex® Red reagent in detecting the activity of D-amino acid oxidase has been reported to be 5- to 25-times better than that of the QuantaBlu fluorogenic peroxidase substrate,[13] with a lower limit for detection of D-alanine of 2 picomoles.[13] The Amplex® Red reaction can be used to routinely detect as little as 10 picomoles of H_2O_2 in a 100 µL volume (50 nM, Figure 10.60), at least a 10-fold greater sensitivity than that attained with the commonly used scopoletin assay for H_2O_2.[1,5] In the scopoletin assay, HRP catalyzes conversion of the fluorescent scopoletin to a nonfluorescent product. Unlike scopoletin, the Amplex® Red reagent is a fluorogenic substrate with very low background fluorescence. Consequently, assays using Amplex® Red as the substrate result in an increase in fluorescence, not a decrease — an inherently superior method for enzymatic assays. Other advantages of the Amplex® Red reaction over scopoletin-based H_2O_2 assays include high chemical stability of the Amplex® Red reagent and its fluorescent product, resorufin, and the

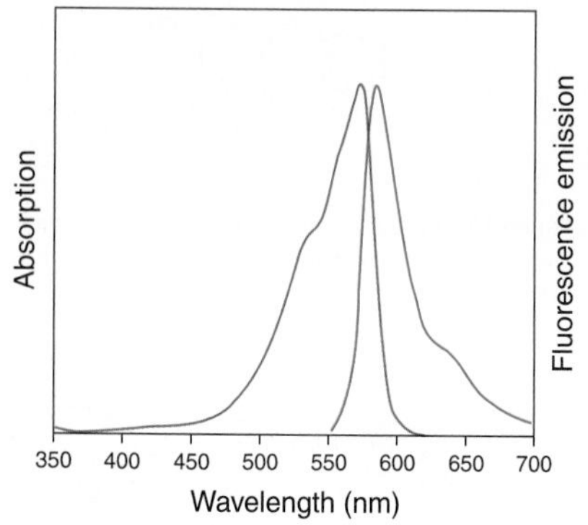

Figure 10.61 Absorption and fluorescence emission spectra of resorufin in pH 9.0 buffer.

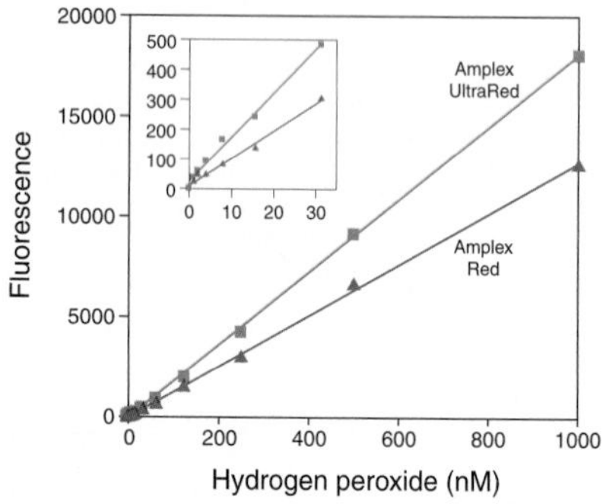

Figure 10.62 Detection of H_2O_2 using Amplex® UltraRed reagent (red square) or Amplex® Red reagent (blue triangle). Reactions containing 50 µM Amplex® UltraRed or Amplex® Red reagent, 1 U/mL HRP and the indicated amount of H_2O_2 in 50 mM sodium phosphate buffer, pH 7.4, were incubated for 30 minutes at room temperature. The inset shows the sensitivity and linearity of the Amplex® UltraRed assay at low levels of H_2O_2.

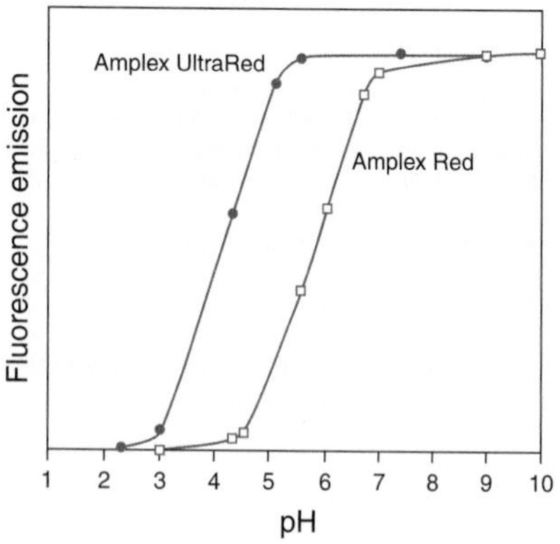

Figure 10.63 Comparison of pH-dependent fluorescence of Amplex® UltraRed reagent (●) and Amplex® Red reagent (□). Fluorescence intensities were measured using excitation/emission of ~570/585 nm.

long-wavelength spectra of resorufin. Because resorufin has excitation/emission maxima (Figure 10.61) of ~570/585 nm (versus 360/460 nm for scopoletin), there is much less interference from autofluorescence in most biological samples. The Amplex® Red reagent can be purchased separately in a single 5 mg vial (A12222) or packaged as a set of 10 vials, each containing 10 mg of the substrate, for high-throughput screening applications (A22177).

Amplex® UltraRed Reagent: Brighter and More Sensitive than the Amplex® Red Reagent

Our Amplex® UltraRed reagent (A36006) improves upon the performance of the Amplex® Red reagent, offering brighter fluorescence and enhanced sensitivity on a per-mole basis in horseradish peroxidase or horseradish peroxidase-coupled enzyme assays (Figure 10.62). Fluorescence of the oxidized Amplex® UltraRed reagent is also less sensitive to pH (Figure 10.63), and the substrate and its oxidation product exhibit greater stability that the Amplex® Red reagent in the presence of hydrogen peroxide (H_2O_2) or thiols such as dithiothreitol (DTT). Like the Amplex® Red reagent, the nonfluorescent Amplex® UltraRed reagent reacts with H_2O_2 in a 1:1 stoichiometric ratio to produce a brightly fluorescent and strongly absorbing reaction product (excitation/emission maxima ~568/581 nm) (Figure 10.64). Because the reaction product has long-wavelength spectra, there is little interference from the blue or green autofluorescence found in most biological samples.

The Amplex® UltraRed reagent can provide increased sensitivity in peroxidase-based enzyme-linked immunosorbent assays (ELISAs). With a high extinction coefficient and good quantum efficiency, the fluorescence-based Amplex® UltraRed reagent is more sensitive than standard colorimetric reagents and provides a broader measurement range for ELISAs. In contrast to commonly used ELISA reagents such as ABTS and TMB, the Amplex® UltraRed reagent is exceptionally resistant to autooxidation, making it a superior alternative for peroxidase detection (Table 10.5). Like the Amplex® Red reagent, the versatile Amplex® UltraRed reagent can be detected using either fluorescence- or absorption-based instrumentation. The Amplex® UltraRed reagent, which should be suitable for any of the applications described for the Amplex® Red reagent (Section 10.5), is available as a set of five vials, each containing 1 mg of the substrate (A36006).

Coupled Enzymatic Reactions with the Amplex® Red and Amplex® UltraRed Reagents

Because H_2O_2 is produced in many different enzymatic reactions, the Amplex® Red and Amplex® UltraRed reagents can be used in coupled enzymatic reactions to detect the activity of many different enzymes such as NADPH oxidase [14] and lysyl oxidase,[15] or, when the substrate concentration is limited, to assay solutions for metabolically active constituents such as glucose, acetylcholine and cholesterol (Figure 10.65). Advantages of Amplex® Red reagent–and Amplex® UltraRed reagent–based assays include the following:

- The Amplex® Red and Amplex® UltraRed reagents are fluorogenic substrates with extremely low background color or fluorescence.
- Stock solutions of the Amplex® Red and Amplex® UltraRed reagents are chemically stable.
- The fluorescent peroxidase reaction products are also stable.
- The long-wavelength spectra of the peroxidase reaction products (Figure 10.6, Figure 10.64) result in little interference from blue or green autofluorescence in biological samples.
- Detection can be by either absorption or fluorescence.
- The peroxidase reaction products can be detected by either fluorescence- or absorption-based methods.
- In most cases, Amplex® Red and Amplex® UltraRed assays can detect either unlabeled natural biomolecules, including amino acids, sugars or lipids, or the activity of enzymes that metabolize these substrates.

The Amplex® Red reagent is also utilized as the detection reagent in our many Amplex® Red Assay Kits. Substituting the Amplex® UltraRed reagent in these kits should offer even greater sensitivity. The Amplex® Red Assay Kits include:

- Amplex® Red Hydrogen Peroxide/Peroxidase Assay Kit (A22188)
- Amplex® Red Catalase Assay Kit (A22180)

- Amplex® Red Monoamine Oxidase Assay Kit (A12214)
- Amplex® Red Glutamic Acid/Glutamate Oxidase Assay Kit [10] (A12221)
- Amplex® Red Glucose/Glucose Oxidase Assay Kit (A22189)
- Amplex® Red Galactose/Galactose Oxidase Assay Kit (A22179)
- Amplex® Red Neuraminidase (Sialidase) Assay Kit (A22178)
- Amplex® Red Cholesterol Assay Kit (A12216)
- Amplex® Red Acetylcholine/Acetylcholinesterase Assay Kit (A12217)
- Amplex® Red Phosphatidylcholine-Specific Phospholipase C Assay Kit [16] (A12218, Section 17.4)
- Amplex® Red Phospholipase D Assay Kit [16,17] (A12219, Section 17.4)
- Amplex® Red Sphingomyelinase Assay Kit (A12220, Section 13.3)
- Amplex® Red Uric Acid/Uricase Assay Kit (A22181)
- Amplex® Red Xanthine/Xanthine Oxidase Assay Kit (A22182)
- Amplex® Red ELISA Kits #1 and #2 (A22170, A22171)

Most of the Amplex® Red Kits are further discussed in this section; however, some are only presented in the sections listed above. The Amplex® Red and Amplex® UltraRed Kits and reagents are sold for noncommercial use and for high-throughput screening applications only.

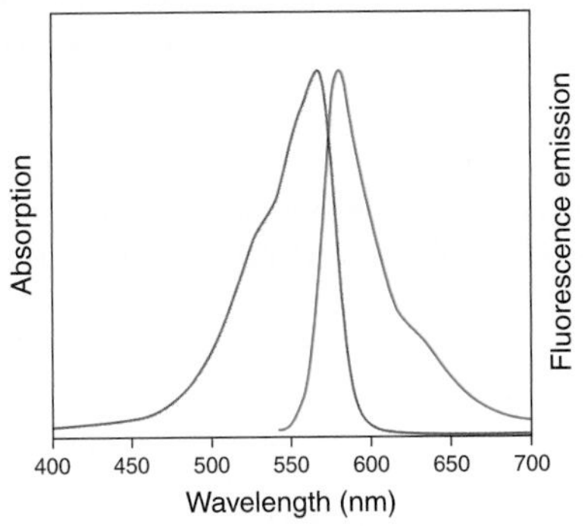

Figure 10.64 Absorption and fluorescence emission spectra of the product generated by horseradish peroxidase–mediated oxidation of the Amplex® UltraRed reagent in pH 7.5 buffer.

Table 10.5 — Advantages of the Amplex® UltraRed reagent over chromogenic reagents

Peroxidase Detection Reagent	Abs *	Em *	Notes
Amplex® UltraRed reagent	568	581	• More resistant to oxidation • More sensitive • Fast fluorescence (and color) development
Amplex® Red reagent	570	585	• Resistant to oxidation • Sensitive • Fast fluorescence (and color) development
ABTS (2′-azino-*bis*-(3-ethylbenzothiazoline-6-sulfonic acid))	405	NA	• Readily oxidized • Slow color development
OPD (*o*-phenylenediamine)	492	NA	• Light sensitive
TMB (3,3′,5,5′-tetramethylbenzidine)	450 (stopped reaction) 653 (kinetic assay)	NA	• Readily oxidizes • Precipitates easily due to low water solubility

* Absorption (Abs) and fluorescence emission (Em) maxima, in nm. NA = Not applicable.

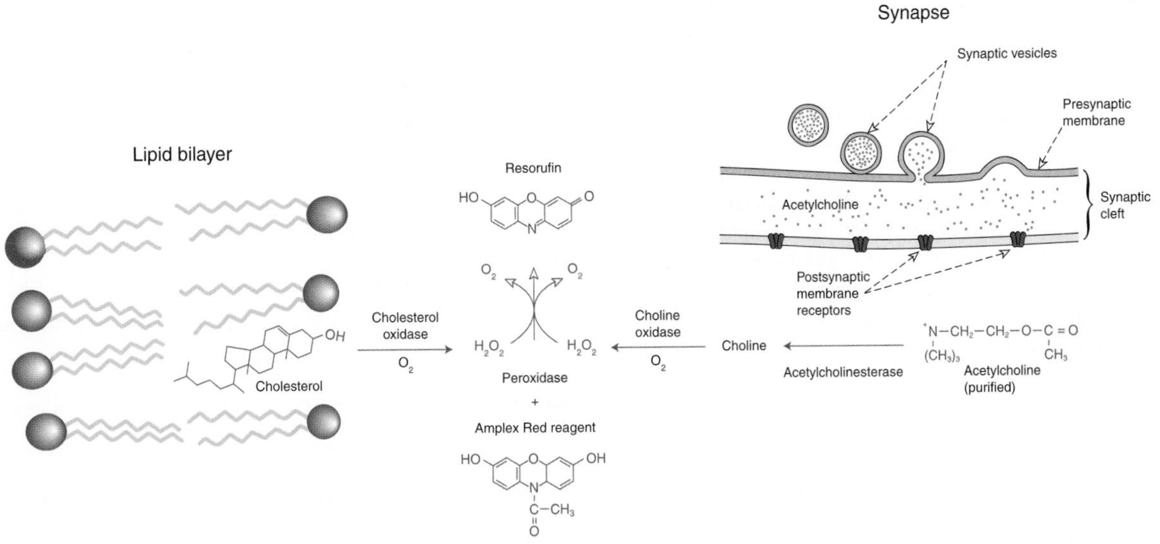

Figure 10.65 Enzyme-coupled Amplex® Red assays. Enzyme reactions that produce H_2O_2 can be made into Amplex® Red assays. The Amplex® Red Cholesterol Assay Kit (A12216) uses cholesterol oxidase to produce H_2O_2, which is then detected by the Amplex® Red reagent in the presence of horseradish peroxidase (HRP). Similarly, the Amplex® Red Acetylcholine/Acetylcholinesterase Assay Kit (A12217) uses choline oxidase to produce H_2O_2.

Amplex® Red Hydrogen Peroxide/Peroxidase Assay Kit

The Amplex® Red Hydrogen Peroxide/Peroxidase Assay Kit (A22188) provides a simple, sensitive, one-step assay for detecting H_2O_2 or the activity of horseradish peroxidase either by measuring fluorescence with a fluorescence-based microplate reader or a fluorometer (Figure 10.66) or by measuring absorption with an absorption-based microplate reader or a spectrophotometer. The Amplex® Red peroxidase substrate can detect the presence of active peroxidases and the release of H_2O_2 from biological samples, including cells and cell extracts [1,5,18–20] and is also useful for detecting H_2O_2 that is produced as a product of enzyme-coupled reactions.[7,14,15,21] The Amplex® Red Hydrogen Peroxide/Peroxidase Assay Kit contains:

- Amplex® Red reagent
- Dimethylsulfoxide (DMSO)
- Horseradish peroxide (HRP)
- H_2O_2 for use as a positive control
- Concentrated reaction buffer
- A detailed protocol

Each kit provides sufficient reagents for approximately 500 assays using a fluorescence- or absorption-based microplate reader and a reaction volume of 100 µL per assay.

Amplex® Red ELISA Kits

Molecular Probes' Amplex® Red ELISA Kits offer an extremely sensitive fluorometric or colorimetric detection method for horseradish peroxidase (HRP)–amplified enzyme-linked immunosorbent assays (ELISAs). The Amplex® Red ELISA Kit #1 (A22170) contains an HRP goat anti–mouse IgG antibody conjugate, which can be used for the ELISA detection of any mouse IgG antibody. The Amplex® Red ELISA Kit #2 (A22171) contains the versatile protein G conjugate of HRP, which can be used for the ELISA detection of IgGs from most commonly used species, including human, mouse, rabbit, goat, sheep, bovine and horse. The Amplex® Red reagent (10-acetyl-3,7-dihydroxyphenoxazine, Figure 10.58) provided in these kits is a highly sensitive and stable probe for the detection of HRP activity. In the presence of HRP, the Amplex® Red reagent reacts with hydrogen peroxide with a 1:1 stoichiometry to form the fluorescent product resorufin [1,5] (R363, Section 10.1; absorption/emission maxima ~571/ 585 nm, Figure 10.59). Because resorufin also has strong absorption, the assay can be performed either fluorometrically or spectrophotometrically. The Amplex® Red ELISA Kit #1 with the HRP–goat anti–mouse IgG antibody conjugate has detection limits of as little as 10 pg/microplate well of a mouse IgG by fluorometry or 50 pg/microplate well by colorimetry (Figure 7.53). The Amplex® Red ELISA Kit #2 with HRP–protein G has detection limits of as little as 1 ng/microplate well of a mouse IgG by fluorometry or 3 ng/microplate well by colorimetry (Figure 7.54) in 96-well plates.

Each Amplex® Red ELISA Kit contains:

- Amplex® Red reagent
- Dimethylsulfoxide (DMSO)
- Concentrated reaction buffer
- Hydrogen peroxide
- Horseradish peroxidase (HRP) conjugate of goat anti–mouse IgG antibody (in Kit #1, A22170) or of protein G (in Kit #2, A22171)
- Detailed ELISA protocols

Each kit provides sufficient reagents for approximately 1000 ELISAs using either a fluorescence- or absorption-based microplate reader and a reaction volume of 100 µL per assay. Our HRP conjugates of the goat anti–mouse IgG antibody (G21040), goat anti–rabbit IgG antibody (G21234) and protein G (P21041) are available separately. HRP conjugates of additional antibodies that can be used with the Amplex® Red reagent (A12222, A22177; Section 10.5) are listed in Table 7.4.

Other Substrates for Peroxidase Assays

Although HRP is an important enzyme for both histochemistry and ELISAs, fluorogenic peroxidase substrates have not been extensively used for its detection. Fluorogenic peroxidase substrates such as the dihydrofluoresceins (also known as fluorescins) (D399, C400, C13293), dihydrocalcein AM (D23805, Figure 15.4), dihydrorhodamines (D632, D633, D23806; Section 18.3) and dihydroethidium (hydroethidine; D1168, D11347, D23107; Section 18.2) are converted to highly fluorescent products in the presence of the enzyme and hydrogen peroxide. Because these substrates are insufficiently stable for routine use in ELISA assays, Molecular Probes has converted the dihydrofluoresceins to diacetates. When used in intracellular applications, the acetates are cleaved by endogenous esterases, releasing the intact substrate. However, when used for *in vitro* assays, an esterase or a mild base must first be added to cleave the acetates, releasing the substrate. The dihydrofluoresceins have been used to measure peroxidase activity [22] and to detect hydroperoxide formation.[23–26] In addition to being a reagent for derivatization of aldehydes and ketones (Section 3.2) and detection of nitric oxide (Section 18.3), NBD methylhydrazine (*N*-methyl-4-hydrazino-7-nitrobenzofurazan, M20490) has been reported to be useful as a fluorogenic peroxidase substrate, with a sensitivity limit for detection of H_2O_2 of about 75 nM.[27]

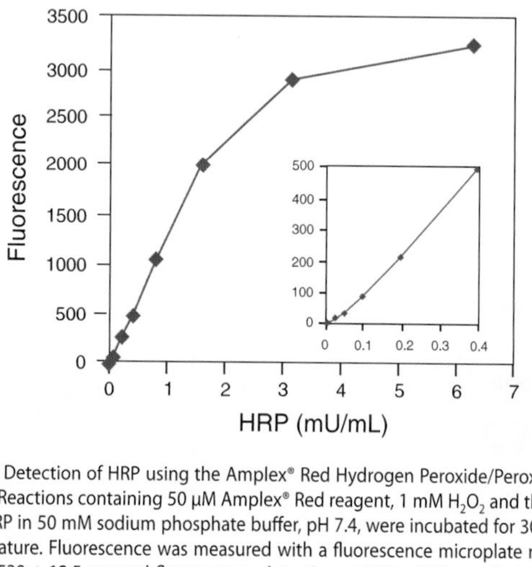

Figure 10.66 Detection of HRP using the Amplex® Red Hydrogen Peroxide/Peroxidase Assay Kit (A22188). Reactions containing 50 µM Amplex® Red reagent, 1 mM H_2O_2 and the indicated amount of HRP in 50 mM sodium phosphate buffer, pH 7.4, were incubated for 30 minutes at room temperature. Fluorescence was measured with a fluorescence microplate reader using excitation at 530 ± 12.5 nm and fluorescence detection at 590 ± 17.5 nm. Background fluorescence (3 units), determined for a no-HRP control reaction, was subtracted from each value. The inset shows the sensitivity of the assay at very low levels of HRP.

Luminol and MCLA: Chemiluminescent Peroxidase Substrates

Nonisotopic immunoassays utilizing peroxidase conjugates and the chemiluminescent horseradish peroxidase substrate luminol (L8455) have provided a rapid and sensitive method for quantitating a wide variety of analytes, including cholesterol,[28] digoxin[29] and acetylcholine.[30] Addition of trace amounts of luciferin (L2911, L2912, L2916; Section 10.6) has been shown to considerably enhance the sensitivity in the assay of thyroxine, digoxin, α-fetoprotein and other analytes.[31] A method that employs luminol has been developed for the quantitation of very limiting samples of human DNA from single hairs, saliva, small blood stains and paraffin-embedded and fixed tissue sections. Using a biotinylated oligodeoxynucleotide probe to membrane-immobilized DNA, horseradish peroxidase streptavidin and luminol, researchers have detected 150 pg of human DNA.[32]

MCLA (M23800) is principally utilized as a superoxide-sensitive chemiluminescent probe (Section 18.2). MCLA has also been utilized for the determination of both horseradish peroxidase[33] and myeloperoxidase.[34–36]

DAB Histochemistry Kits

The use of horseradish peroxidase (HRP) for enzyme-amplified immunodetection — commonly referred to as immunoperoxidase labeling — is a well-established standard histochemical technique.[37,38] The most widely used HRP substrate for these applications is diaminobenzidine (DAB), which generates a brown-colored polymeric oxidation product localized at HRP-labeled sites. The DAB reaction product can be visualized directly by bright-field light microscopy or, following osmication, by electron microscopy. We offer DAB Histochemistry Kits for detecting mouse IgG primary antibodies (D22185) and biotinylated antibodies and tracers (D22187). Each kit contains:

- Diaminobenzidine (DAB)
- HRP-labeled goat anti–mouse IgG (in Kit D22185) or streptavidin (in Kit D22187) conjugate
- H_2O_2 reaction additive
- Blocking reagent
- Staining buffer
- A detailed staining protocol

Each kit provides sufficient materials to stain approximately 200 slides.

Catalase

The Amplex® Red Catalase Assay Kit (A22180) provides an ultrasensitive, yet simple, assay for measuring catalase activity. Catalase is a heme-containing redox protein found in nearly all animal and plant cells, as well as in aerobic microorganisms. In eukaryotic cells, it is concentrated in the peroxisomes. Catalase is an important enzyme because H_2O_2 is a powerful oxidizing agent that is potentially damaging to cells. By preventing excessive buildup of H_2O_2, catalase allows important cellular processes that produce H_2O_2 as a by-product to take place safely.

In the assay, catalase first reacts with H_2O_2 to produce water and oxygen (O_2). Next, the Amplex® Red reagent reacts with a 1:1 stoichiometry with any unreacted H_2O_2 in the presence of horseradish peroxidase to produce the highly fluorescent oxidation product, resorufin. Therefore, as catalase activity increases, the signal from resorufin decreases (Figure 10.67). The results are typically plotted by subtracting the observed fluorescence from that of a no-catalase control. Using this kit, it is possible to detect catalase activity in a purified system at levels as low as 50 mU/mL.

Resorufin has absorption and fluorescence emission maxima of approximately 571 nm and 585 nm, respectively (Figure 10.6). Because the absorption is strong, the assay can be performed either fluorometrically or spectrophotometrically. The Amplex® Red Catalase Assay Kit contains:

- Amplex® Red reagent
- Dimethylsulfoxide (DMSO)
- Horseradish peroxidase (HRP)

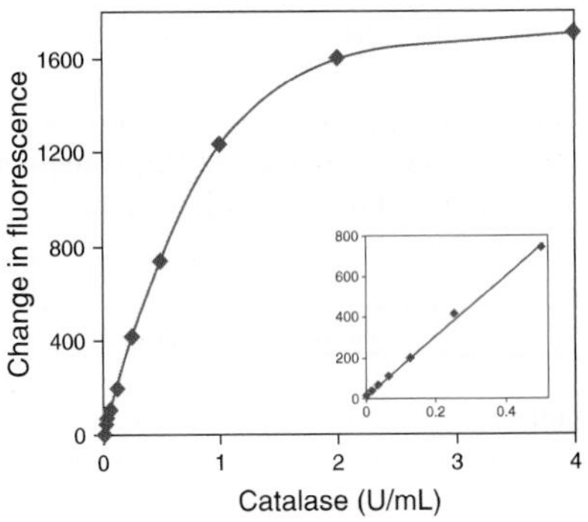

Figure 10.67 Detection of catalase using the Amplex® Red Catalase Assay Kit (A22180). Reactions contained the indicated amount of catalase and 20 µM H_2O_2 in 1X reaction buffer and was incubated for 30 minutes. The final reaction containing 50 µM Amplex® Red reagent and 0.2 U/mL HRP and was incubated at 37°C. After 30 minutes, fluorescence was measured in a fluorescence microplate reader using excitation at 530 ± 12.5 nm and fluorescence detection at 590 ± 17.5 nm. The change in fluorescence is reported as the observed fluorescence intensity subtracted from that of a no-catalase control.

- Hydrogen peroxide (H_2O_2)
- Concentrated reaction buffer
- Catalase
- A detailed protocol

Each kit provides sufficient reagents for approximately 400 assays using either a fluorescence- or absorption-based microplate reader and a reaction volume of 100 µL per assay.

Glucose and Glucose Oxidase

Glucose oxidase is widely used for glucose determination and, when conjugated to antibodies, for use in enzyme immunoassays (EIAs). Molecular Probes has found that the Amplex® Red reagent can be utilized for the ultrasensitive detection of both glucose and glucose oxidase. In this enzyme-coupled assay, glucose oxidase reacts with glucose to form gluconolactone and H_2O_2. The H_2O_2 is then detected using the Amplex® Red reagent peroxidase substrate (Figure 10.59). The Amplex® Red Glucose/Glucose Oxidase Assay Kit (A22189) can be used to detect glucose levels as low as 3 µM or 0.5 µg/mL (Figure 10.25) and is at least 10-fold more sensitive than assays using *o*-dianisidine as the peroxidase substrate. This kit can also be used to detect glucose oxidase levels as low as 0.05 mU/mL (Figure 10.68). We have even shown that the Amplex® Red reagent can detect glucose liberated from native dextrans by dextranase[39] and from carboxymethylcellulose. The Amplex® Red Glucose/Glucose Oxidase Assay Kit contains:

- Amplex® Red reagent
- Dimethylsulfoxide (DMSO)
- Horseradish peroxidase (HRP)
- H_2O_2 for use as a positive control
- Concentrated reaction buffer
- Glucose oxidase
- D-Glucose
- A detailed protocol

The kit provides sufficient reagents for approximately 500 assays using either a fluorescence- or absorption-based microplate reader and a reaction volume of 100 µL per assay.

Galactose and Galactose Oxidase

The Amplex® Red Galactose/Galactose Oxidase Assay Kit (A22179) provides the reagents and a general protocol for the assay of terminal galactosylated proteins, galactose-producing enzymes and for the assay of galactose oxidase. Unlike glucose oxidase, galactose oxidase can produce H_2O_2 from either free galactose or from polysaccharides — including glycoproteins in solution or on cell surfaces — in which galactose is the terminal residue, producing an aldehyde moiety on the 6-position of the galactose (Figure 10.14). We have used our Amplex® Red galactose oxidase assay for the quantitative assay of mucin-type glycoproteins by using a method similar to one described by Kinosita and collaborators.[40] The Amplex® Red Galactose/Galactose Oxidase Assay Kit (A22179) contains:

- Amplex® Red reagent
- Dimethylsulfoxide (DMSO)
- Horseradish peroxidase (HRP)
- Hydrogen peroxide (H_2O_2)
- Concentrated reaction buffer
- Galactose oxidase from *Dactylium dendroides*
- D-Galactose
- A detailed protocol

Sufficient reagents are provided for approximately 400 assays using either a fluorescence- or absorption-based microplate reader and a reaction volume of 100 µL per assay. The Amplex® Red galactose/galactose oxidase assay accurately measures as low as 4 µM galactose and 2 mU/mL galactose oxidase activity (Figure 10.15, Figure 10.16). Because of the high absorption of resorufin, the absorptimetric assay has only slightly lower sensitivity than the fluorometric assay. The Amplex® Red Neuraminidase (Sialidase) Assay Kit (A22178) utilizes this galactose oxidase–coupled chemistry for continuous assay of neuraminidase-catalyzed hydrolysis of fetuin, a sialoglyconjugate. This product is described in detail in Section 10.2.

Cholesterol and Cholesterol Oxidase

The Amplex® Red Cholesterol Assay Kit (A12216) provides an exceptionally sensitive assay for both cholesterol and cholesteryl esters in complex mixtures that is suitable for use with either fluorescence microplate readers or fluorometers. The assay provided in this kit can detect as little as 5 ng/mL (5×10^{-4} mg/dL) cholesterol (Figure 13.38) and can accurately measure the cholesterol or cholesteryl ester content in the equivalent of 0.01 µL of human serum.[41] The assay uses an enzyme-coupled reaction scheme in which cholesteryl esters are hydrolyzed by cholesterol esterase into cholesterol, which is then oxidized by cholesterol oxidase to yield H_2O_2 and the corresponding ketone steroidal product (Figure 10.65). The H_2O_2 is then detected using the Amplex® Red reagent in combination with HRP. The Amplex® Red cholesterol assay is continuous and requires no separation or wash steps. These characteristics make the assay particularly

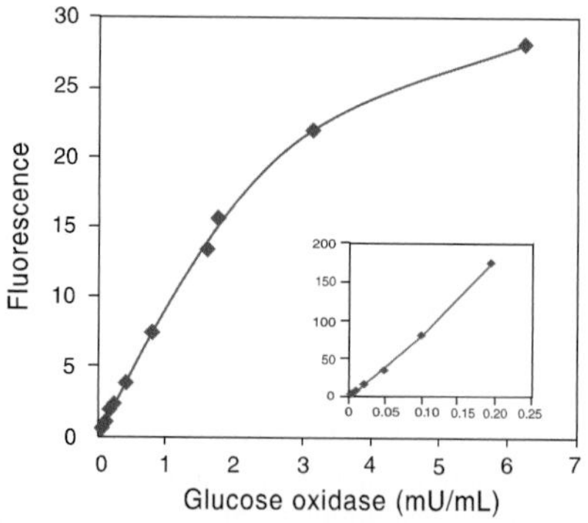

Figure 10.68 Detection of glucose oxidase using the Amplex® Red Glucose/Glucose Oxidase Assay Kit (A22189). Reactions containing 50 µM Amplex® Red reagent, 1 U/mL HRP, 50 mM glucose and the indicated amount of glucose oxidase in 50 mM sodium phosphate buffer, pH 7.4, were incubated for 30 minutes at room temperature. Fluorescence was measured with a fluorescence microplate reader using excitation at 530 ± 12.5 nm and fluorescence detection at 590 ± 17.5 nm. Background fluorescence (19 units) determined for a no-glucose oxidase control reaction was subtracted from each value. The inset shows the assay's sensitivity at low levels of glucose oxidase (0–0.2 mU/mL).

well suited for the rapid and direct analysis of cholesterol in blood and food samples using automated instruments. By performing two separate measurements in the presence and absence of cholesterol esterase, this assay is also useful for determining the fraction of cholesterol that is in the form of cholesteryl esters within a sample.[42] In addition, by adding an excess of cholesterol to the reaction, this assay can be used to sensitively detect the activity of cholesterol oxidase. The Amplex® Red Cholesterol Assay Kit contains:

- Amplex® Red reagent
- Dimethylsulfoxide (DMSO)
- Horseradish peroxidase (HRP)
- H_2O_2 for use as a positive control
- Concentrated reaction buffer
- Cholesterol oxidase from *Streptomyces*
- Cholesterol esterase from *Pseudomonas*
- Cholesterol for preparation of a standard curve
- A detailed protocol

Each kit provides sufficient reagents for approximately 500 assays using a fluorescence microplate reader and a reaction volume of 100 µL per assay

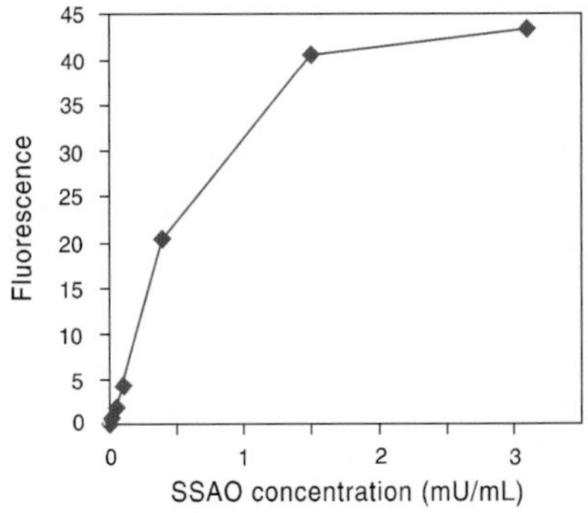

Figure 10.69 Detection of plasma amine oxidase (an SSAO) activity using the Amplex® Red Monoamine Oxidase Assay Kit (A12214) and benzylamine as the substrate. Each reaction contained 1 mM benzylamine, 1 U/mL HRP, 200 µM Amplex® Red reagent and the indicated amount of SSAO in 50 mM potassium phosphate, pH 7.4. Reactions were incubated at room temperature for 15 minutes. Fluorescence was measured with a fluorescence microplate reader using excitation at 560 ± 10 nm and fluorescence detection at 590 ± 10 nm.

Monoamine Oxidase

Monoamine oxidase, which inactivates several primary, secondary and tertiary amines via oxidative transamination, serves to regulate tissue levels of amine neurotransmitters and dietary amines. The Amplex® Red Monoamine Oxidase Assay Kit (A12214) provides a simple fluorometric method for the continuous measurement of amine oxidase activity in tissue homogenates or purified preparations. We have found that the assay is able to sensitively detect both monoamine oxidase (MAO) activity and semicarbazide-sensitive amine oxidase (SSAO) activity and is useful for performing both end-point and continuous measurements of amine oxidase activity. The assay is able to detect both MAO-A and MAO-B from cow brain tissue using as little as 200 µg of total protein per sample[6] and has been used to measure plasma amine oxidase (an SSAO) activity levels as low as 1.2×10^{-5} U/mL using a commercially available enzyme (Figure 10.69).

To facilitate discrimination of MAO-A and MAO-B activity, two MAO substrates and two MAO inhibitors are included in the kit. *p*-Tyramine is a substrate for both MAO-A and MAO-B, whereas benzylamine is a substrate for MAO-B.[43] Both *p*-tyramine and benzylamine are also substrates for SSAO enzymes. Clorgyline is a specific inhibitor of MAO-A activity, and pargyline is a specific inhibitor of MAO-B activity.[44,45] The potential applications of this kit include the measurement of amine oxidase activity in normal and diseased tissues, blood samples and other biological fluids, the screening of drugs as possible MAO inhibitors or substrates and the determination of kinetic constants for different amine oxidase substrates. Each kit contains:

- Amplex® Red reagent
- Dimethylsulfoxide (DMSO)
- Horseradish peroxidase (HRP)
- H_2O_2 for use as a positive control
- Concentrated reaction buffer
- Benzylamine, a substrate for MAO-B and SSAO enzymes
- *p*-Tyramine, a substrate for MAO-A, MAO-B and SSAO enzymes
- Clorgyline, a specific inhibitor of MAO-A activity
- Pargyline, a specific inhibitor of MAO-B activity
- Resorufin for use as a reference standard (Figure 10.6)
- A detailed protocol

Each kit provides sufficient reagents for approximately 500 assays using a reaction volume of 200 µL per assay.

Glutamic Acid and Glutamate Oxidase

The Amplex® Red Glutamic Acid/Glutamate Oxidase Assay Kit (A12221) provides an ultrasensitive method for continuously detecting glutamic acid [46] or for monitoring glutamate oxidase activity in a fluorescence microplate reader or a fluorometer.[10] In this assay, L-glutamic acid is oxidized by glutamate oxidase to produce α-ketoglutarate, NH_3 and H_2O_2. L-Alanine and L-glutamate–pyruvate transaminase are also included in the reaction. Thus, the L-glutamic acid is regenerated by transamination of α-ketoglutarate, resulting in multiple cycles of the initial reaction and a significant amplification of the H_2O_2 produced. Hydrogen peroxide reacts with the Amplex® Red reagent in a 1:1 stoichiometry in a reaction catalyzed by horseradish peroxidase (HRP) to generate the highly fluorescent product resorufin [1,5] (R363, Section 10.1). Because resorufin has absorption/emission maxima of ~571/ 585 nm (Figure 10.6), there is little interference from autofluorescence in most biological samples.

If the concentration of L-glutamic acid is limiting in this assay, then the fluorescence increase is proportional to the initial L-glutamic acid concentration. The Amplex® Red Glutamic Acid/Glutamate Oxidase Assay Kit allows detection of as little as 10 nM L-glutamic acid in purified systems using a 30-minute reaction time (Figure 16.34). If the reaction is modified to include an excess of L-glutamic acid, then this kit can be used to continuously monitor glutamate oxidase activity. For example, purified L-glutamate oxidase from *Streptomyces* can be detected at levels as low as 40 μU/mL (Figure 16.35). The Amplex® Red reagent has been used to quantitate the activity of glutamate-producing enzymes in a high-throughput assay for drug discovery.[46] Each Amplex® Red Glutamic Acid/Glutamate Oxidase Assay Kit contains:

- Amplex® Red reagent
- Dimethylsulfoxide (DMSO)
- Horseradish peroxidase (HRP)
- Hydrogen peroxide (H_2O_2)
- Concentrated reaction buffer
- L-Glutamate oxidase from *Streptomyces* sp.
- L-Glutamate–pyruvate transaminase from pig heart
- L-Glutamic acid
- L-Alanine
- A detailed protocol

Each kit provides sufficient reagents for approximately 200 assays using a fluorescence microplate reader and a reaction volume of 100 μL per assay.

Acetylcholine, Acetylcholinesterase and Choline Oxidase

Acetylcholine, the neurotransmitter released from the nerve terminal at neuromuscular junctions, binds to the acetylcholine receptor and opens its transmitter-gated ion channel (Section 16.3). The action of acetylcholine (ACh) is regulated by acetylcholinesterase (AChE), which hydrolyzes ACh to choline and acetate. The Amplex® Red Acetylcholine/Acetylcholinesterase Assay Kit (A12217) provides an ultrasensitive method for continuously monitoring AChE activity or for detecting ACh in a fluorescence microplate reader or a fluorometer. Other potential uses for this kit include screening for AChE inhibitors and measuring the release of ACh from synaptosomes. The Amplex® Red Acetylcholine/Acetylcholinesterase Assay Kit can also be used for the ultrasensitive and specific assay of free choline, an "essential nutrient," in foods.[47]

In the assay, AChE activity is monitored indirectly using the Amplex® Red reagent (Figure 10.65). First, AChE converts the acetylcholine substrate to choline. Choline is in turn oxidized by choline oxidase to betaine and H_2O_2, the latter of which, in the presence of HRP, reacts with the Amplex® Red reagent to generate the red-fluorescent product resorufin (Figure 10.6). Experiments with purified AChE from electric eel indicate that the Amplex® Red Acetylcholine/Acetylcholinesterase Assay Kit can detect AChE levels as low as 0.002 U/mL using a reaction time of one hour (Figure 16.27). We have been able to detect acetylcholinesterase activity from a tissue sample with total protein content as low as 200 ng/mL or 20 ng/well in a microplate assay.[48] By providing an excess of AChE in the assay, the kit can also be used to detect acetylcholine levels as low as 0.3 μM, with a range of detection from 0.3 μM to ~100 μM acetylcholine (Figure 16.28). The Amplex® Red Acetylcholine/Acetylcholinesterase Assay Kit contains:

- Amplex® Red reagent
- Dimethylsulfoxide (DMSO)
- Horseradish peroxidase (HRP)
- H_2O_2 for use as a positive control
- Concentrated reaction buffer
- Choline oxidase from *Alcaligenes* sp.
- Acetylcholine (ACh)
- Acetylcholinesterase (AChE) from electric eel
- A detailed protocol

Each kit provides sufficient reagents for approximately 500 assays using a fluorescence microplate reader and a reaction volume of 200 μL per assay.

Xanthine and Xanthine Oxidase

The Amplex® Red Xanthine/Xanthine Oxidase Assay Kit (A22182) provides an ultrasensitive method for detecting xanthine or hypoxanthine or for monitoring xanthine oxidase activity. In the assay, xanthine oxidase catalyzes the oxidation of purine nucleotides, hypoxanthine or xanthine, to uric acid and superoxide. In the reaction mixture, the superoxide spontaneously degrades to H_2O_2, which in the presence of HRP reacts stoichiometrically with the Amplex® Red reagent to generate the red-fluorescent oxidation product, resorufin. Resorufin has absorption and fluorescence emission maxima of approximately 571 nm and 585 nm, respectively, and because the extinction coefficient is high (54,000 $cm^{-1}M^{-1}$), the assay can be performed either fluorometrically or spectrophotometrically.

In healthy individuals, xanthine oxidase is present in appreciable amounts only in the liver and jejunum. However, in various liver disorders the enzyme is released into circulation. Therefore, determination of serum xanthine oxidase level serves as a sensitive indicator of acute liver damage such as jaundice. The Amplex® Red xanthine/xanthine oxidase assay has been used as a marker of recovery from exercise stress.[49] Previously, researchers have utilized chemiluminescence or absorption to monitor xanthine oxidase activity. The Amplex® Red Xanthine/Xanthine Oxidase Assay Kit permits the detection of xanthine oxidase in a purified system at levels as low as

0.1 mU/mL by fluorescence (Figure 18.4). This kit can also be used to detect as little as 200 nM hypoxanthine or xanthine (Figure 18.5), and, when coupled to the purine nucleotide phosphorylase enzyme, to detect inorganic phosphate.[50]

The Amplex® Red Xanthine/Xanthine Oxidase Assay Kit (A22182) contains:

- Amplex® Red reagent
- Dimethylsulfoxide (DMSO)
- Horseradish peroxidase (HRP)
- Hydrogen peroxide (H_2O_2)
- Concentrated reaction buffer
- Xanthine oxidase from buttermilk
- Hypoxanthine
- Xanthine
- A detailed protocol

Each kit provides sufficient reagents for approximately 400 assays using either a fluorescence- or absorption-based microplate reader and a reaction volume of 100 µL per assay.

Uric Acid and Uricase

Serum uric acid is the end product of purine metabolism in the body tissues and is cleared through the kidneys by glomerular filtration. Most animals can metabolize uric acid to more readily excreted products, but humans lack the necessary enzyme, urate oxidase (uricase), as a result of the presence of two "nonsense mutations" in the human gene for uricase. Increased uric acid levels may result from leukemia, polycythemia, ingestion of foods high in nucleoproteins (e.g., liver and kidney) or impaired renal function. Gout results from the deposit of uric acid in body joints.

The Amplex® Red Uric Acid/Uricase Assay Kit (A22181) provides an ultrasensitive method for detecting uric acid or for monitoring uricase activity.[51] In the assay, uricase catalyzes the conversion of uric acid to allantoin, H_2O_2 and carbon dioxide. In the presence of HRP, the H_2O_2 reacts stoichiometrically with Amplex® Red reagent to generate the red-fluorescent oxidation product, resorufin. Resorufin has absorption and fluorescence emission maxima of approximately 571 nm and 585 nm, respectively, and because the extinction coefficient is high (54,000 $cm^{-1}M^{-1}$), the assay can be performed either fluorometrically or spectrophotometrically. Previous literature reports colorimetric detection limits at 3.6 µM, whereas the Amplex® Red Uric Acid/Uricase Assay Kit can be used to detect as little as 100 nM uric acid in a purified system. A biosensor containing an encapsulated uricase–peroxidase system and the Amplex® Red reagent exhibits a high specificity for uric acid in the presence of interfering species and a linear response from 20 nM to 1 µM uric acid.[51] The Amplex® Red Uric Acid/Uricase Assay Kit can also be used to detect as little as 0.2 mU/mL uricase in a purified system.

The Amplex® Red Uric Acid/Uricase Assay Kit (A22181) contains:

- Amplex® Red reagent
- Dimethylsulfoxide (DMSO)
- Horseradish peroxidase (HRP)
- Hydrogen peroxide (H_2O_2)
- Concentrated reaction buffer
- Uricase
- Uric acid
- A detailed protocol

Each kit provides sufficient reagents for approximately 400 assays using either a fluorescence- or absorption-based microplate reader and a reaction volume of 100 µL per assay.

References

1. Anal Biochem 253, 162 (1997); **2.** Proc Soc Exp Biol Med 206, 53 (1994); **3.** Free Radic Biol Med 12, 389 (1992); **4.** Biochem Int 10, 205 (1985); **5.** J Immunol Methods 202, 133 (1997); **6.** Anal Biochem 253, 169 (1997); **7.** J Invest Dermatol 112, 751 (1999); **8.** Free Radic Biol Med 27, 1197 (1999); **9.** J Invest Dermatol 110, 966 (1998); **10.** Anal Chim Acta 402, 47 (1999); **11.** Proc Natl Acad Sci U S A 97, 10930 (2000); **12.** Science 293, 1806 (2001); **13.** Anal Biochem 287, 196 (2000); **14.** J Biol Chem 275, 15749 (2000); **15.** Anal Biochem 300, 245 (2002); **16.** Proc Natl Acad Sci U S A 101, 9745 (2004); **17.** J Biol Chem 277, 45592 (2002); **18.** Theriogenology 57, 1025 (2002); **19.** J Neurochem 79, 266 (2001); **20.** Am J Physiol Lung Cell Mol Physiol 281, L993 (2001); **21.** Mol Hum Reprod 7, 237 (2001); **22.** Anal Biochem 11, 6 (1965); **23.** J Clin Invest 87, 711 (1991); **24.** J Lab Clin Med 117, 291 (1991); **25.** Anal Biochem 187, 129 (1990); **26.** Anal Biochem 134, 111 (1983); **27.** Angew Chem Int Ed Engl 39, 1453 (2000); **28.** Biochim Biophys Acta 1210, 151 (1994); **29.** Clin Chem 31, 1335 (1985); **30.** J Neurochem 39, 248 (1982); **31.** Nature 305, 158 (1983); **32.** Nucleic Acids Res 20, 5061 (1992); **33.** J Biolumin Chemilumin 9, 355 (1994); **34.** Cell Mol Neurobiol 18, 565 (1998); **35.** Methods Enzymol 233, 495 (1994); **36.** Anal Biochem 199, 191 (1991); **37.** J Histochem Cytochem 36, 317 (1988); **38.** Arch Pathol Lab Med 102, 113 (1978); **39.** Anal Biochem 260, 257 (1998); **40.** Anal Biochem 284, 87 (2000); **41.** J Biochem Biophys Methods 38, 43 (1999); **42.** J Lipid Res 45, 396 (2004); **43.** Methods Enzymol 142, 617 (1987); **44.** Anal Biochem 244, 384 (1997); **45.** Biochem Pharmacol 18, 1447 (1969); **46.** Anal Biochem 284, 382 (2000); **47.** Science 281, 794 (1998); **48.** Proc SPIE-Int Soc Opt Eng 3926, 166 (2000); **49.** Am J Physiol Endocrinol Metab 282, E474 (2002); **50.** Anal Biochem 320, 292 (2003); **51.** Anal Biochem 322, 238 (2003).

Data Table — 10.5 Substrates for Oxidases, Including Amplex Red Kits

Cat #	MW	Storage	Soluble	Abs	EC	Em	Solvent	Product	Notes
A6551	425.57	FF,D,AA	DMSO	286	8,000	none	MeOH	see Notes	1
A12222	257.25	FF,D,A	DMSO	280	6,000	none	pH 8	R363	2
A22177	257.25	FF,D,A	DMSO	280	6,000	none	pH 8	R363	2
A36006	~300	FF,D,A	DMSO	293	11,000	none	pH 8	see Notes	3
C400	531.30	F,D	DMSO, EtOH	290	5,600	none	MeCN	see Notes	4
C13293	498.39	F,D	DMSO, EtOH	290	5,500	none	MeCN	see Notes	5
D399	487.29	F,D	DMSO, EtOH	258	11,000	none	MeOH	see Notes	4
D23805	1068.95	F,D	DMSO	285	5,800	none	MeCN	C481	
L8455	177.16	D,L	DMF	355	7,500	411	MeOH	see Notes	6
M20490	209.16	F,L	MeCN	487	24,000	none	MeOH	see Notes	7
M23800	291.74	FF,D,LL,AA	DMSO	430	8,400	546	MeOH	see Notes	8

For definitions of the contents of this data table, see "Navigating *The Handbook*" in the introductory pages.

Notes

1. Peroxidase-catalyzed reaction of A6551 with H_2O_2 produces fluorescent 2-dodecylresorufin (Abs = 578 nm (EC = 69,000 $cm^{-1}M^{-1}$), Em = 597 nm in MeOH).
2. This substrate is used for peroxidase-coupled detection in our Amplex® Red Assay Kits.
3. Peroxidase-catalyzed reaction of the Amplex® UltraRed reagent (A36006) with H_2O_2 yields a fluorescent product with Abs = 568 nm (EC = 57,000 $cm^{-1}M^{-1}$), Em = 581 nm in pH 7.5 buffer.
4. Dihydrofluorescein diacetates are colorless and nonfluorescent until both of the acetate groups are hydrolyzed and the products are subsequently oxidized to fluorescein derivatives. The materials contain less than 0.1% of oxidized derivative when initially prepared. The oxidation products of C400, C2938, C6827, D399 and D2935 are 2′,7′-dichlorofluorescein derivatives with spectra similar to C368.
5. Difluorodihydrofluorescein diacetates are colorless and nonfluorescent. Acetate hydrolysis and subsequent oxidation generate a fluorescent 2′,7′-difluorofluorescein derivative with spectra similar to O6146.
6. This compound emits chemiluminescence upon oxidation in basic aqueous solutions. Emission peaks are at 425 nm (L8455) and 470 nm (L6868).
7. Peroxidase-catalyzed oxidation of NBD methylhydrazine generates fluorescent *N*-methyl-4-amino-7-nitrobenzofurazan, Abs = 470 nm, Em = 547 nm in aqueous buffer (pH 5.8) (Angew Chem Int Ed Engl 39, 1453 (2000)).
8. Generates chemiluminescence (Em = 455 nm) upon reaction with superoxide.

Product List — 10.5 Substrates for Oxidases, Including Amplex Red Kits

Cat #	Product Name	Unit Size
A6551	10-acetyl-3,7-dihydroxy-2-dodecylphenoxazine *special packaging*	10 x 100 µg
A12217	Amplex® Red Acetylcholine/Acetylcholinesterase Assay Kit *500 assays*	1 kit
A22180	Amplex® Red Catalase Assay Kit *400 assays*	1 kit
A12216	Amplex® Red Cholesterol Assay Kit *500 assays*	1 kit
A22170	Amplex® Red ELISA Kit #1 *with goat anti-mouse IgG, horseradish peroxidase conjugate* *1000 assays*	1 kit
A22171	Amplex® Red ELISA Kit #2 *with protein G, horseradish peroxidase conjugate* *1000 assays*	1 kit
A22179	Amplex® Red Galactose/Galactose Oxidase Assay Kit *400 assays*	1 kit
A22189	Amplex® Red Glucose/Glucose Oxidase Assay Kit *500 assays*	1 kit
A12221	Amplex® Red Glutamic Acid/Glutamate Oxidase Assay Kit *200 assays*	1 kit
A22188	Amplex® Red Hydrogen Peroxide/Peroxidase Assay Kit *500 assays*	1 kit
A12214	Amplex® Red Monoamine Oxidase Assay Kit *500 assays*	1 kit
A22178	Amplex® Red Neuraminidase (Sialidase) Assay Kit *400 assays*	1 kit
A12218	Amplex® Red Phosphatidylcholine-Specific Phospholipase C Assay Kit *500 assays*	1 kit
A12219	Amplex® Red Phospholipase D Assay Kit *500 assays*	1 kit
A12222	Amplex® Red reagent (10-acetyl-3,7-dihydroxyphenoxazine)	5 mg
A22177	Amplex® Red reagent *packaged for high-throughput screening*	10 x 10 mg
A12220	Amplex® Red Sphingomyelinase Assay Kit *500 assays*	1 kit
A22181	Amplex® Red Uric Acid/Uricase Assay Kit *400 assays*	1 kit
A22182	Amplex® Red Xanthine/Xanthine Oxidase Assay Kit *400 assays*	1 kit
A36006	Amplex® UltraRed reagent	5 x 1 mg
C400	5-(and-6)-carboxy-2′,7′-dichlorodihydrofluorescein diacetate (carboxy-H_2DCFDA) *mixed isomers*	25 mg
C13293	5-(and-6)-carboxy-2′,7′-difluorodihydrofluorescein diacetate (carboxy-H_2DFFDA) *mixed isomers*	5 mg
D22185	Diaminobenzidine (DAB) Histochemistry Kit #1 *with goat anti-mouse IgG–HRP*	1 kit
D22187	Diaminobenzidine (DAB) Histochemistry Kit #3 *with streptavidin–HRP*	1 kit
D399	2′,7′-dichlorodihydrofluorescein diacetate (2′,7′-dichlorofluorescin diacetate; H_2DCFDA)	100 mg
D23805	dihydrocalcein, AM *special packaging*	20 x 50 µg
G21040	goat anti-mouse IgG (H+L), horseradish peroxidase conjugate	1 mg
L8455	luminol (3-aminophthalhydrazide)	25 g
M20490	*N*-methyl-4-hydrazino-7-nitrobenzofurazan (NBD methylhydrazine)	25 mg
M23800	2-methyl-6-(4-methoxyphenyl)-3,7-dihydroimidazo[1,2-a]pyrazin-3-one, hydrochloride (MCLA)	5 mg
P22061	P_iPer™ Phosphate Assay Kit *1000 assays*	1 kit
P22062	PP_iPer™ Pyrophosphate Assay Kit *1000 assays*	1 kit
P21041	protein G, horseradish peroxidase conjugate	1 mg

For current prices or to order online, visit probes.invitrogen.com

10.6 Substrates for Microsomal Dealkylases, Acetyltransferases, Luciferases and Other Enzymes

Fluorogenic substrates that detect glycosidases (Section 10.2) and phosphatases (Section 10.3) have been by far the dominant probes for measuring enzymatic activity. Exactly the same fluorophores and chromophores — fluoresceins, resorufins and umbelliferones (7-hydroxycoumarins) — can be used to prepare substrates for other hydrolytic enzymes and ether-metabolizing microsomal dealkylase (cytochrome) enzymes or peroxidases. In addition, we offer substrates for chloramphenicol acetyltransferase (CAT) and luciferase, which are usually not widely expressed in cells. These substrates are important tools for detecting cells transfected with reporter genes that encode these enzymes. We also have available several reagents that are substrates for detecting enzyme-catalyzed chemical reduction associated with cells, including the tetrazolium salts MTT and XTT [1] (M6494, X6493; Section 15.2) and resazurin (R12204), which is useful for quantitatively measuring cell-mediated cytotoxicity,[2] cell proliferation [3,4] and mitochondrial metabolic activity in isolated neural tissue.[5]

Microsomal Dealkylases

Metabolic oxidation of chemical compounds, including many pollutants, is the function of the cytochrome-mediated monooxygenase or mixed-function oxidase system. Several enzymes are involved, including cytochrome P448 monooxygenase (aryl hydrocarbon hydroxylase), which is induced by carcinogenic polyaromatic hydrocarbons. Cytochrome P450 is a useful marker of endoplasmic reticulum membranes.[6] The very low turnover rate of these enzymes can be followed using various fluorogenic alkyl ether derivatives of coumarin,[7] resorufin [8] and fluorescein,[9] all of which yield cleavage products with longer-wavelength spectral properties than the parent substrates.

Resorufin-Based Microsomal Dealkylase Substrates

The four resorufin ether–based substrates (R351, R352, R441, R1147), which all yield fluorescent resorufin (R363, Section 10.1; excitation/emission maxima ~571/585 nm, Figure 10.6), have been extensively used to differentiate isozymes of cytochrome P450.[8,10–16] Ethoxyresorufin *O*-deethylase and total protein concentration have been simultaneously assayed in a fluorescence microplate reader using resorufin ethyl ether (ethoxyresorufin, R352) and fluorescamine [17] (F2332; FluoroPure™ Grade, F20261; Section 9.2).

Coumarin-Based Microsomal Dealkylase Substrates

Fluorescence detection of the deethylation of 3-cyano-7-ethoxycoumarin [10,18] (C684) is reported to be 50–100 times more sensitive than that of ethoxyresorufin, primarily because of the faster turnover rate of 3-cyano-7-ethoxycoumarin;[19,20] however, ethoxyresorufin exhibits lower fluorescence background due to its more favorable spectral shifts. The deethylase product of 3-cyano-7-ethoxycoumarin, 3-cyano-7-hydroxycoumarin (C183, Section 10.1), has a lower pK_a than that of 7-ethoxycoumarin,[21,22] allowing continuous measurements of enzyme activity at pH 7.

The cytochrome P450 substrate 7-ethoxy-4-trifluoromethylcoumarin (E2882) yields a product with a fluorescence emission that is distinct from that of the substrate and of NADPH, making this substrate useful for the direct measurement of enzymatic activity.[23–26] Researchers have shown that this substrate is cleaved by at least the 1A2, 2E1 and 2B1 isozymes of cytochrome P450.[24,27]

Other Microsomal Dealkylase Substrates

The fluorescent products of most microsomal dealkylase substrates rapidly leak from live cells, making them ineffective for measuring intracellular enzymatic activity by imaging or flow cytometric analysis. Using techniques for product retention that proved successful for our patented DetectaGene™ Green, ImaGene Green™ and ImaGene Red™ glycosidase substrates, we have developed unique substrates that can potentially be used to detect dealkylase activity in single cells.

Like the DetectaGene™ CMFDG β-galactosidase substrate (D2920, Section 10.2), the mildly thiol-reactive chloromethyl moiety of 5-chloromethylfluorescein diethyl ether (C6533) reacts with glutathione or other intracellular thiols to produce a product that is retained in cells through cell division. Adding a chloromethyl moiety to our glycosidase and peptidase substrates (Section 10.2, Section 10.4; Figure 10.17) has enabled researchers to identify cells with enzymatic activity 24 hours after loading the substrate.[28] Fluorescein ethers are known microsomal dealkylase substrates.[20] Chloromethylfluorescein diethyl ether was used to monitor cytochrome P450–dependent mixed function oxidase activity in cultured hepatocytes.[29]

Lipases

Lipases generally include glycerol ester hydrolases and cholesterol esterases. Phospholipase A selectively hydrolyzes lipophilic esters of phospholipids. Because of their importance to the process of signal transduction in cells, our extensive selection of substrates and other probes for phospholipases is discussed in Section 17.4.

Coumarin-Based Lipase Substrates

The fluorogenic lipase substrate *O*-pivaloyloxymethyl umbelliferone (C-POM, P35901) was developed to deliver optimal performance in assays of lipase activity. Standard lipase substrates may exhibit high levels of undesirable nonspecific reactivity, either through spontaneous hydrolysis or direct reaction of the substrate with noncatalytic proteins such as BSA.[30] C-POM is much less prone to these unwanted side reactions, and the resulting low level of background fluorescence yields a better signal-to-noise ratio, providing a more accurate measure of lipase catalysis. Enzymatic conversion of the essentially nonfluorescent C-POM yields a bright blue-fluorescent reaction product (excitation/emission ~360/460 nm). C-POM has been shown to serve as a substrate for a variety of lipases and displays excellent stability in solution, making it an ideal substrate for specific lipases or for general or high-throughput screening.

Unlike lipase substrates that are esters of 7-hydroxy-4-methylcoumarin (β-methylumbelliferone, H189; Section 10.1) — a dye that is not appreciably fluorescent at neutral pH — 6,8-difluoro-4-methylumbelliferyl octanoate (DiFMU octanoate, D12200) can be used for the continuous *in vitro* assay of lipases at a pH greater than or equal to 6;[31] the blue-fluorescent hydrolysis product of DiFMU octanoate, 6,8-difluoro-7-hydroxy-4-methylcoumarin (DiFMU, D6566; Section 10.1; Figure 10.3), has a pK_a of 4.9.[32]

Cholesterol Esterase Assay

The cholesterol produced by cholesterol esterases is readily quantitated using the Amplex® Red Cholesterol Assay Kit (A12216), which is discussed in Section 10.5 and Section 13.3. It should be possible to modify the Amplex® Red cholesterol assay to continuously measure the activity of cholesterol esterases.

Acetylcholinesterase and Histone Acetyltransferase

The Amplex® Red Acetylcholine/Acetylcholinesterase Assay Kit (A12217), which is discussed in Section 10.5 and Section 16.2, provides an ultrasensitive method for continuously monitoring acetylcholinesterase activity or for detecting acetylcholine in a fluorescence microplate reader or fluorometer (Figure 16.27, Figure 16.28).

Acetylcholinesterase has also been assayed using the acetylcholinesterase-catalyzed release of thiocholine from acetylthiocholine, followed by detection of the thiol with the essentially nonfluorescent 7-diethylamino-3-(4′-maleimidylphenyl)-4-methylcoumarin[33] (CPM, D346; Section 2.3) dye or Ellman's reagent[34] (DTNB, D8451; Section 2.3).

In a similar assay, the activity of histone acetyltransferase, which transfers an acetyl group from acetyl coenzyme A to lysine residues in the N-terminal tail of histones, was measured by using CPM to derivatize the thiol-containing coenzyme A (CoASH) product.[35]

Chloramphenicol Acetyltransferase (CAT)

Because of the close correlation between its transcript levels and enzymatic activity and the excellent sensitivity of the enzyme assay, the chloramphenicol acetyltransferase (CAT) reporter gene system has proven to be a powerful tool for investigating transcriptional elements in animal[36,37] and plant cells.[38,39] Most conventional CAT assays require incubation of cell extracts with radioactive substrates, typically ^{14}C chloramphenicol or ^{14}C acetyl CoA, followed by organic extraction and autoradiography or scintillation counting.[40–42] Molecular Probes' patented *FAST* CAT® Chloramphenicol Acetyltransferase Assay Kits contain unique BODIPY® chloramphenicol fluorescent substrates that take advantage of the exquisite sensitivity of fluorescence techniques, thus eliminating the need for hazardous radiochemicals, film, fluors, scintillation counters and expensive radioactive waste disposal.[43,44] The original *FAST* CAT® Kit and our *FAST* CAT® Green and Yellow (deoxy) Kits provide detection limits similar to those achieved with conventional radioactive methods and yield results that are easily visualized using a hand-held UV lamp.

FAST CAT® Chloramphenicol Acetyltransferase Assay Kit

The green-fluorescent BODIPY® FL chloramphenicol substrate in our original *FAST* CAT® Chloramphenicol Acetyltransferase Assay Kit (F2900) has a K_M for purified CAT of 7.4 µM and a V_{max} of 375 picomoles/unit/minute, values that are similar to those of ^{14}C-labeled chloramphenicol[44,45] (K_M = 12 µM and V_{max} = 120 picomole/unit/minute). To perform the assay, cell extracts are simply incubated with BODIPY® FL chloramphenicol and acetyl coenzyme A. After a suitable incubation period, the products and remaining substrate are extracted and separated by thin-layer chromatography (TLC). The brightly fluorescent, well-resolved spots can be immediately visualized with a hand-held UV lamp or quantitated with a laser scanner or CCD camera (Figure 10.70). Alternatively, quantitation can be accomplished using a fluorometer or spectrophotometer after a simple extraction. HPLC analysis of the fluorescent products has also been used to further enhance the assay's sensitivity.[46,47]

These attributes have enabled researchers to use this *FAST* CAT® substrate to measure CAT activity in crude cellular extracts of transfected ovarian granulosa cells.[45] Our *FAST* CAT® Kit has also been employed to study hormonal regulation of prodynorphin gene expression[48,49] and to measure the rate of hair growth in single follicles of transgenic mice.[47]

Each *FAST* CAT® Chloramphenicol Acetyltransferase Assay Kit (F2900) is available in a 100-test size and includes:

- BODIPY® FL chloramphenicol substrate
- A mixture of the 1- and 3-acetyl and 1,3-diacetyl BODIPY® FL derivatives, which serve as a reference standard for the fluorescent products
- A detailed protocol

FAST CAT® (Deoxy) Chloramphenicol Acetyltransferase Assay Kits

Molecular Probes' two *FAST* CAT® (deoxy) Chloramphenicol Acetyltransferase Assay Kits (F6616, F6617) contain substrates that greatly simplify the quantitation of chloramphenicol acetyltransferase (CAT) activity and extend the linear detection range of Molecular Probes' original *FAST* CAT® assay.[50] The BODIPY® FL chloramphenicol substrate in our original *FAST* CAT® kit contains two acetylation sites, only one of which is acetylated by the CAT enzyme. Once the CAT enzyme adds an acetyl group to this position, the acetyl group can be nonenzymatically transferred to the second site, leaving the original position open for another enzymatic acetylation.[51–53] Therefore, enzyme acetylation of our original BODIPY® FL *FAST* CAT® substrate produces three products — one diacetylated and two monoacetylated chloramphenicols — thus complicating the quantitative analysis of CAT gene activity. More importantly, because the nonenzymatic transacetylation is the rate-limiting step, the rate of product accumulation may not accurately reflect CAT activity.[51,54,55]

To overcome this limitation, we have modified the original *FAST* CAT® substrate, producing reagents that undergo a single acetylation reaction (Figure 10.71). The green-fluorescent BODIPY® FL *deoxy*chloramphenicol and yellow-fluorescent BODIPY® 543/569 *deoxy*chloramphenicol substrates in our *FAST* CAT® Green and *FAST* CAT® Yellow (deoxy) Chloramphenicol Acetyltransferase Assay Kits (F6616, F6617) are acetylated at a single position, yielding only one fluorescent product[50,55] (Figure 10.71). This simplified reaction scheme provides a straightforward and reliable measure of CAT activity and extends the linear detection range of our original *FAST* CAT® assay.

The *FAST* CAT® Green and *FAST* CAT® Yellow (deoxy) Chloramphenicol Acetyltransferase Assay Kits are available in a 100-test size and include:

- BODIPY® FL 1-deoxychloramphenicol substrate (in Kit F6616) or BODIPY® TMR 1-deoxychloramphenicol substrate (in Kit F6617)
- 3-Acetyl BODIPY® FL derivative (in Kit F6616) or BODIPY® TMR derivative (in Kit F6617), which serves as a reference standard for the fluorescent product
- A detailed protocol

The CAT substrate in our *FAST* CAT® Green (deoxy) Chloramphenicol Acetyltransferase Assay Kit (F6616) is spectrally identical to the green-fluorescent BODIPY® FL chloramphenicol substrate in our original *FAST* CAT® Kit. The *FAST* CAT® Yellow (deoxy) Chloramphenicol Acetyltransferase Assay Kit (F6617) contains a red-orange–fluorescent BODIPY® TMR derivative. The availability of two spectrally distinct CAT substrates allows researchers to choose the optimal fluorophore for a particular excitation source or multicolor labeling experiment.

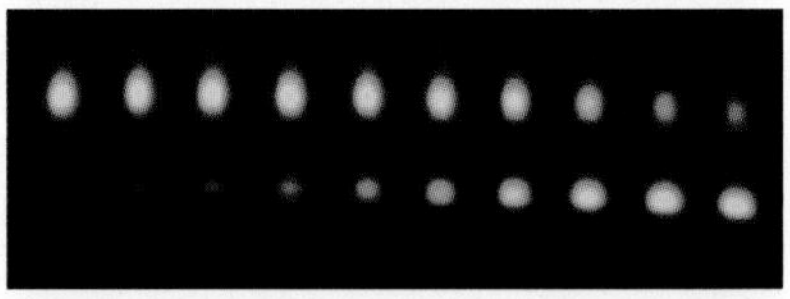

Figure 10.70 Chloramphenicol acetyltransferase (CAT) assays using our *FAST* CAT® Yellow (deoxy) Chloramphenicol Acetyltransferase Assay Kit (F6617). Decreasing amounts of purified CAT enzyme (twofold dilutions) were incubated with the corresponding deoxy substrate in the presence of acetyl CoA; the reaction mixture was then separated with standard thin-layer chromatography (TLC) methods and visualized with 366 nm epi-illumination. The bottom row of fluorescent spots in each TLC represents the substrate; the top, the monoacetylated reaction product.

Luciferase

Firefly luciferase (*Photinus*-luciferin:oxygen 4-oxidoreductase or luciferin 4-monooxygenase, EC 1.13.12.7) produces light by the ATP-dependent oxidation of luciferin (Figure 15.57). The 560 nm chemiluminescence from this reaction peaks within seconds, with light output that is proportional to luciferase concentration when substrates are present in excess.[56] The *luc* gene, which encodes the 62,000-dalton firefly luciferase, is a popular reporter gene for plants,[38,39,57–60] bacteria[61,62] and mammalian cells[63,64] and for monitoring baculovirus gene expression in insects.[65,66] Chemiluminescent techniques are virtually background-free, making the *luc* reporter gene ideal for detecting low-level gene expression.[67]

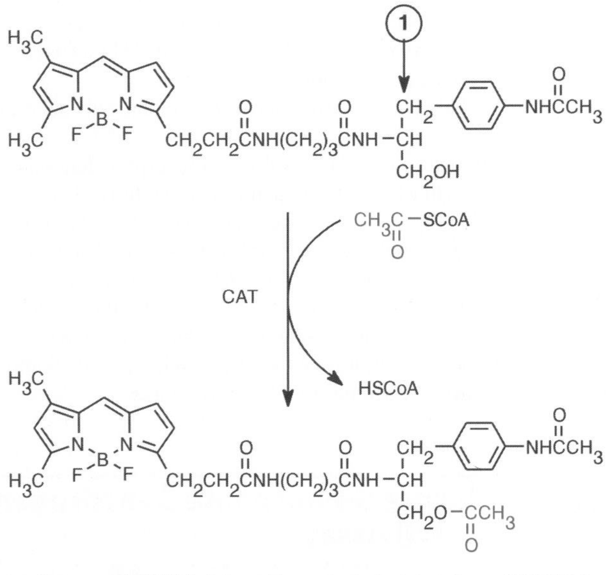

Figure 10.71 The green-fluorescent BODIPY® FL 1-deoxychloramphenicol substrate in our *FAST* CAT® Green (deoxy) Chloramphenicol Acetyltransferase Assay Kit (F6616). CAT-mediated acetylation of this substrate and of the BODIPY® TMR 1-deoxychloramphenicol in our *FAST* CAT® Yellow (deoxy) Chloramphenicol Acetyltransferase Assay Kit (F6617) results in single fluorescent products because these substrates contain only one hydroxyl group that can be acetylated. In contrast, the BODIPY® FL chloramphenicol substrate in our original *FAST* CAT® Kit (F2900) contains a second hydroxyl group at the 1-position (indicated by the labeled arrow). This hydroxyl group undergoes a nonenzymatic transacetylation step, restoring the original hydroxyl for a second acetylation. CAT-mediated acetylation of this chloramphenicol substrate produces three fluorescent products, thus complicating the analysis.

Luciferin

The substrate for firefly luciferase, D-(-)-2-(6′-hydroxy-2′-benzothiazolyl)thiazoline-4-carboxylic acid, commonly known as luciferin, was first isolated by Bitler and McElroy[68] (9 mg from approximately 15,000 fireflies!). In the firefly, spent luciferin (oxyluciferin) is recycled back to luciferin.[69] Molecular Probes is a primary manufacturer of synthetic luciferin (L2911) and its water-soluble sodium (L2912; FluoroPure™ Grade, L22172) and potassium (L2916) salts. The physical properties of these derivatives are identical to those of the natural compound. Our prices for luciferin are significantly lower than those of other suppliers; additional discounts are available for bulk purchases or standing orders.

Typically, luciferase expression is measured by adding the substrates ATP and luciferin to cell lysates and then analyzing light production with a luminometer. As little as 0.02 pg (250,000 molecules) of luciferase can be reliably measured using a standard scintillation counter.[70] Moreover, a CCD-based imaging method of detecting *luc* gene expression in single cells has been developed.[71]

Caged Luciferin

Although luciferase activity is sometimes measured in living cells,[71,72] *in vivo* quantitation appears to be limited by the difficulty in delivering luciferin into intact cells.[73] Molecular Probes' DMNPE-caged luciferin (L7085) readily crosses cell membranes. Once the caged luciferin is inside the cell, active luciferin can be released either instantaneously by a flash of UV light or continuously by the action of endogenous intracellular esterases, which are found in many cell types. This probe should facilitate *in vivo* luciferase assays in two important ways. First, caged luciferin improves the sensitivity and quantitative analysis of these assays by allowing more efficient delivery of luciferin into intact cells. Second, hydrolysis by intracellular esterases provides a continuous supply of active luciferin, permitting long-term measurements and reducing the need for rapid mixing protocols and costly injection devices. Moreover, DMNPE-caged luciferin may make it easier to follow dynamic changes in gene expression in live cells. Molecular Probes also offers DMNPE-caged ATP (A1049, Section 5.3), which can be used in conjunction with DMNPE-caged luciferin (L7085) for this *in vivo* luciferase assay.[74]

Luciferin–Luciferase Assays for ATP, Anesthetics and Hormones

Luciferin has been used in an exquisitely sensitive and specific ATP assay,[75,76] which allows the detection of femtomolar quantities of ATP.[77] This bioluminescent ATP assay has been employed to determine cell proliferation and cytotoxicity in both bacteria[78,79] and mammalian cells.[80,81] Molecular Probes provides all the reagents needed for this important assay in its ATP Determination Kit (A22066, Section 10.3).

Researchers have also adapted the luciferin–luciferase ATP assay system for detecting single base changes in a solid-phase DNA sequencing method.[82] In addition, amphipathic and hydrophobic substances, including certain anesthetics and hormones, compete with luciferin for the hydrophobic site on the luciferase molecule, providing a convenient method to assay subnanomolar concentrations of these substances.[83] A protein A–luciferase fusion protein has been developed that can be used in bioluminescence-based immunoassays.[84,85]

Coelenterazines for Renilla *Luciferase*

Coelenterazine and its analogs are substrates for the bioluminescent *Renilla* luciferase.[86,87] Molecular Probes offers coelenterazine (C2944) and several synthetic coelenterazine analogs, including coelenterazine *cp*, *f*, *h*, *hcp* and *n* (C14260, C6779, C6780, C14261, C6776; Section 19.5; Table 19.4). Luciferin and coelenterazine have been used together for dual detection of firefly and *Renilla* luciferases in live mice.[88] Coelenterazine analogs have been characterized for their effectiveness in measuring *Renilla* luciferase in both live cells and live animals.[89] Our Coelenterazine Sampler Kit (C6777) contains 25 µg samples of each of our coelenterazine analogs, as well as 25 µg of native coelenterazine. Coelenterazine is readily solubilized in aqueous solutions containing 50 mM hydroxypropyl-β-cyclodextrin.[90]

Resazurin Derivatives for Dehydrogenase Assays

Resazurin (R12204), which under the name alamarBlue (a trademark of AccuMed International, Inc.) has been reported to be useful for quantitatively measuring cell-mediated cytotoxicity,[2] cell proliferation[3,4] and mitochondrial metabolic activity in isolated neural tissue, is also a useful substrate for measuring the dehydrogenase activity or a wide variety of dehydrogenase enzymes *in vitro*. Among the assays reported are the use of resazurin to detect:

- Serum formate using formate dehydrogenase and NAD^+[91]
- Bile acids in human urine, feces and serum using NAD^+ 3α-hydroxysteroid dehydrogenase[92–96]
- Glucose 6-phosphate dehydrogenase (G6PD) activity[97]
- NADH and bile acids with NADH oxidoreductase[98,99]
- Triacylglycerols with glycerol dehydrogenase[100]
- Argininosuccinate lyase and NAPDH by a coupled diaphorase–resazurin reaction sequence[101]
- Urinary acylcarnitines in an immobilized enzyme reactor[102,103]

Our extensive bibliography on resazurin includes numerous references in which this reagent has been referred to as alamarBlue. The dehydrogenase substrate in our Vybrant® Cell Metabolic Assay Kit and LIVE/DEAD® Cell Vitality Assay Kit (V23110, L34951; Section 15.3) is dodecylresazurin, a more lipophilic version of resazurin. Because this substrate readily penetrates the membranes of live cells and its fluorescent reduction product (dodecylresorufin) is better retained in cells, it is preferred for both microscopy and flow cytometry assays. See Section 15.3 for more details.

Glucose 6-Phosphate Dehydrogenase (G6PD) Assay

Glucose 6-phosphate dehydrogenase (G6PD) is a ubiquitous enzyme that is part of the pentose phosphate pathway, and is crucial for cellular antioxidant defenses via its production of NADPH.[104,105] Our Vybrant® Cytotoxicity Assay Kit (V23111) was designed to monitor the release of this cytosolic enzyme from damaged cells into the surrounding medium. However, our method also provides an extremely sensitive and specific assay for G6PD in cell-free extracts. Detection of G6PD is via a two-step enzymatic process that leads to the reduction of resazurin into the red-fluorescent resorufin (Figure 15.35).

The resulting signal is proportional to the amount of G6PD released into the cell media, which correlates with the number of dead cells in the sample (Figure 15.36).

The Vybrant® Cytotoxicity Assay Kit contains all enzymes and substrates needed to measure the activity of G6PD and to detect the release of G6PD from damaged and dying cells. The assay can be completed in less than an hour and is effective with as few as 500 cells per sample. Resorufin, the end product of the G6PD cytotoxicity assay, has absorption and emission maxima at ~571 nm and 585 nm, respectively, placing the fluorescent signal beyond the autofluorescence of most biological samples. In addition, the levels of G6PD in serum commonly used for cell culture are much lower than those of lactate dehydrogenase (LDH), an enzyme often used in similar assays, thus resulting in lower background signals (Figure 15.37). The Vybrant® Cytotoxicity Assay Kit (V23111) contains:

- Resazurin (5 vials)
- DMSO
- Reaction mixture (diaphorase, glucose 6-phosphate and $NADP^+$)
- Reaction buffer
- Cell lysis buffer
- A detailed protocol

Sufficient reagents are provided for about 1000 assays in a fluorescence microplate reader.

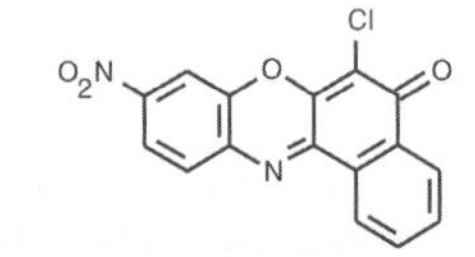

Figure 10.72 C22220 6-chloro-9-nitro-5-oxo-5*H*-benzo[a]phenoxazine (CNOB).

Nitroreductase/Nitrate Reductase

We have developed a unique fluorogenic substrate that can detect the enzymatic activity of certain enzymes that reduce nitro compounds to amines or inorganic nitrate to nitrite. 6-Chloro-9-nitro-5-oxo-5*H*-benzo[a]phenoxazine (CNOB, C22220; Figure 10.72) is reduced to an aminophenoxazine dye that absorbs maximally at ~620 nm and has an emission maximum near 630 nm. We have shown that CNOB is a good substrate for at least some bacterial nitroreductases but apparently is not a good substrate for a mammalian nitroreductase. The utility of CNOB for detection of nitroreductase activity or detection of hypoxia in tumor cells has not yet been tested; however, it is known that some nitroimidazoles and other nitroaromatic compounds are reduced to amines under highly reducing conditions.[106]

References

1. J Immunol Methods 142, 257 (1991); **2.** J Immunol Methods 213, 157 (1998); **3.** J Clin Lab Anal 9, 89 (1995); **4.** J Immunol Methods 175, 181 (1994); **5.** J Neurosci Res 45, 216 (1996); **6.** J Biol Chem 270, 24327 (1995); **7.** Anal Biochem 191, 354 (1990); **8.** Biochem J 240, 27 (1986); **9.** Anal Biochem 133, 46 (1983); **10.** Anal Biochem 248, 188 (1997); **11.** Biochem Pharmacol 47, 893 (1994); **12.** Biochem Pharmacol 46, 933 (1993); **13.** Anal Biochem 188, 317 (1990); **14.** Biochem Pharmacol 40, 2145 (1990); **15.** Eur J Immunol 16, 829 (1986); **16.** Biochem Pharmacol 34, 3337 (1985); **17.** Anal Biochem 222, 217 (1994); **18.** Biopharm Drug Dispos 24, 375 (2003); **19.** Anal Biochem 172, 304 (1988); **20.** Biochem J 247, 23 (1987); **21.** Anal Biochem 115, 177 (1981); **22.** Hoppe Seylers Z Physiol Chem 353, 1171 (1972); **23.** Biochemistry 37, 13184 (1998); **24.** Biochem Pharmacol 46, 1577 (1993); **25.** Biochem Pharmacol 37, 1731 (1988); **26.** Biochemistry 36, 11707 (1997); **27.** Arch Biochem Biophys 323, 303 (1995); **28.** J Neurosci 15, 1025 (1995); **29.** Int J Artif Organs 21, 360 (1998); **30.** Bioorg Med Chem Lett 13, 2105 (2003); **31.** Microbiology 150, 1947 (2004); **32.** Bioorg Med Chem Lett 8, 3107 (1998); **33.** Anal Biochem 133, 450 (1983); **34.** Biochem Pharmacol 7, 88 (1961); **35.** Anal Biochem 287, 319 (2000); **36.** Development 109, 577 (1990); **37.** Proc Natl Acad Sci U S A 87, 6848 (1990); **38.** Methods Cell Biol 50, 425 (1995); **39.** Methods Mol Biol 55, 147 (1995); **40.** Gene 67, 271 (1988); **41.** J Virol 62, 297 (1988); **42.** Anal Biochem 156, 251 (1986); **43.** Methods Enzymol 216, 369 (1992); **44.** Biotechniques 8, 170 (1990); **45.** Anal Biochem 197, 401 (1991); **46.** J Biol Chem 270, 28392 (1995); **47.** Eur J Clin Chem Clin Biochem 31, 41 (1993); **48.** Mol Cell Neurosci 3, 278 (1992); **49.** Mol Endocrinol 6, 2244 (1992); **50.** Biotechniques 19, 488 (1995); **51.** Biochemistry 30, 3763 (1991); **52.** Biochemistry 30, 3758 (1991); **53.** Biochemistry 29, 2075 (1990); **54.** Annu Rev Biophys Biophys Chem 20, 363 (1991); **55.** Nucleic Acids Res 19, 6648 (1991); **56.** Mol Cell Biol 7, 725 (1987); **57.** J Biolumin Chemilumin 8, 267 (1993); **58.** Methods Enzymol 216, 397 (1992); **59.** Dev Genet 11, 224 (1990); **60.** J Biolumin Chemilumin 5, 141 (1990); **61.** J Gen Microbiol 138, 1289 (1992); **62.** Methods Mol Cell Biol 1, 107 (1989); **63.** Methods Mol Biol 7, 237 (1991); **64.** Biotechniques 7, 1116 (1989); **65.** FEBS Lett 274, 23 (1990); **66.** Gene 91, 135 (1990); **67.** Anal Biochem 176, 28 (1989); **68.** Arch Biochem Biophys 72, 358 (1957); **69.** J Biol Chem 276, 36508 (2001); **70.** Anal Biochem 171, 404 (1988); **71.** J Biolumin Chemilumin 5, 123 (1990); **72.** Biotechnology (N Y) 10, 565 (1992); **73.** Biochem J 276, 637 (1991); **74.** Biotechniques 15, 848 (1993); **75.** J Appl Biochem 3, 473 (1981); **76.** Anal Biochem 29, 381 (1969); **77.** Lett Appl Microbiol 1, 208 (1990); **78.** Biotechnol Bioeng 42, 30 (1993); **79.** J Biolumin Chemilumin 6, 193 (1991); **80.** Biochem J 295, 165 (1993); **81.** J Immunol Methods 160, 81 (1993); **82.** Anal Biochem 208, 171 (1993); **83.** Anal Biochem 190, 304 (1990); **84.** Anal Biochem 208, 300 (1993); **85.** J Immunol Methods 137, 199 (1991); **86.** Biotechniques 24, 185 (1998); **87.** Biochem Biophys Res Commun 233, 349 (1997); **88.** Proc Natl Acad Sci U S A 99, 377 (2002); **89.** Mol Imaging 3, 43 (2004); **90.** Biosci Biotechnol Biochem 61, 1219 (1997); **91.** J Anal Toxicol 8, 273 (1984); **92.** Clin Chem 29, 171 (1983); **93.** Arch Biochem Biophys 337, 121 (1997); **94.** J Membr Biol 159, 197 (1997); **95.** Clin Chim Acta 70, 79 (1976); **96.** Clin Chem 24, 1150 (1978); **97.** Biochim Biophys Acta 484, 249 (1977); **98.** Clin Chim Acta 107, 149 (1980); **99.** Clin Chim Acta 102, 241 (1980); **100.** Clin Chem 26, 613 (1980); **101.** Anal Biochem 164, 482 (1987); **102.** Clin Chim Acta 216, 135 (1993); **103.** Clin Chem 36, 2072 (1990); **104.** J Biol Chem 275, 40042 (2000); **105.** Nucleic Acids Res 14, 2511 (1986); **106.** Anticancer Drug Des 13, 687 (1998).

Data Table — 10.6 Substrates for Microsomal Dealkylases, Acetyltransferases, Luciferases and Other Enzymes

Cat #	MW	Storage	Soluble	Abs	EC	Em	Solvent	Product	Notes
C684	215.21	L	DMSO	356	20,000	411	pH 7	C183	
C2944	423.47	FF,D,LL,AA	MeOH	429	7,500	see Notes	pH 7		
C6533	436.89	F,D	DMSO	275	8,200	none	MeOH	see Notes	1
C6776	457.53	FF,D,LL,AA	MeOH	431	9,000	see Notes	MeOH		
C6779	425.46	FF,D,LL,AA	MeOH	437	8,700	see Notes	MeOH		
C6780	407.47	FF,D,LL,AA	MeOH	437	9,500	see Notes	MeOH		
C7933	287.23	F,D,L	DMSO	299	16,000	431	MeOH	see Notes	2
C12202	274.65	F,D	MeCN	288	8,600	none	MeOH	C12881	
C14260	415.49	FF,D,LL,AA	MeOH	430	7,000	see Notes	MeOH		
C14261	399.49	FF,D,LL,AA	MeOH	433	10,000	see Notes	MeOH		
C22220	326.70	F,D,L	DMSO	448	13,000	none	MeOH	see Notes	3
D12200	338.35	F,D	MeCN	312	5,000	none	MeCN	D6566	
D12203	240.21	D	MeCN	315	8,500	none	MeCN	D6566	
E2882	258.20	L	DMSO, DMF	333	14,000	415	MeOH	T659	
E6580	349.17	F,D,L	DMSO, DMF	289	16,000	ND	MeOH	E6578	4, 5
E6583	545.55	F,D,L	DMSO, DMF	288	14,000	ND	MeOH	E6578	4, 5
F2900	583.44	F,D,L	MeOH	504	80,000	511	MeOH	see Notes	6, 7
F6489	529.94	F,D,L	DMF	452	15,000	519	pH 7	F1300	
F6616	567.44	F,D,L	MeOH	504	81,000	510	MeOH	see Notes	7, 8
F6617	673.57	F,D,L	MeOH	545	60,000	570	MeOH	see Notes	7, 8
G7702	903.08	FF,D,L	$CHCl_3$	341	107,000	473	MeOH	P1903MP	
L2911	280.32	F,D,L,A	pH >6, DMSO	328	18,000	532	pH 7	see Notes	9
L2912	302.30	F,D,L,A	pH >6	328	17,000	533	pH 7	see Notes	9
L2916	318.41	F,D,L,A	pH >6	328	18,000	533	pH 7	see Notes	9
L7085	489.52	FF,D,LL	DMSO, DMF	334	22,000	none	MeOH	see Notes	10, 11
L22172	302.30	F,D,L,A	pH >6	328	17,000	533	pH 7	see Notes	9, 12
P35901	276.29	F,D,L	DMSO	316	14,000	380	MeOH	see Notes	13
R351	227.22	L	DMSO	463	23,000	none	MeOH	R363	
R352	241.25	L	DMSO	464	23,000	none	MeOH	R363	
R441	303.32	L	DMSO	463	21,000	none	MeOH	R363	
R1147	283.33	L	DMSO	465	21,000	none	MeOH	R363	
R12204	251.17	L	H_2O, MeOH	604	60,000	none	MeOH	R363	

For definitions of the contents of this data table, see "Navigating *The Handbook*" in the introductory pages.

Notes

1. Enzymatic cleavage of this substrate yields 5-chloromethylfluorescein, with spectroscopic properties similar to C1904.
2. Enzymatic hydroxylation yields a 7-hydroxycoumarin derivative with spectroscopic properties similar to H185.
3. Enzymatic reduction of C22220 yields a fluorescent aminobenzophenoxazine derivative (Abs = 617 nm, Em = 625 nm).
4. ND = not determined.

5. Fluorescence of the unhydrolyzed substrate is very weak.
6. Acetylation by chloramphenicol acetyltransferase (CAT) yields a mixture of 1-acetyl, 3-acetyl and 1,3-diacetyl chloramphenicol derivatives. Spectroscopic properties of these products are similar to the substrate.
7. Data represent the substrate component of this kit.
8. Acetylation by chloramphenicol acetyltransferase (CAT) yields a 3-acetyl-1-deoxychloramphenicol derivative with similar spectroscopic properties to the substrate.
9. ATP-dependent oxidation of luciferin by luciferase results in bioluminescence (Em = 560 nm) at neutral and alkaline pH. Bioluminescence is red-shifted (Em = 617 nm) under acidic conditions (J Am Chem Soc 88, 2015 (1966)).
10. All photoactivatable probes are sensitive to light. They should be protected from illumination except when photolysis is intended.
11. L7085 is converted to bioluminescent luciferin (L2911) upon ultraviolet photoactivation.
12. This product is specified to equal or exceed 98% analytical purity by HPLC.
13. Enzymatic cleavage of this substrate yields 7-hydroxycoumarin (umbelliferone), which has similar spectroscopic properties to H189.

Product List — 10.6 Substrates for Microsomal Dealkylases, Acetyltransferases, Luciferases and Other Enzymes

Cat #	Product Name	Unit Size
C12202	4-chloromethyl-6,8-difluoro-7-ethoxycoumarin (CMDiFUEt)	5 mg
C6533	5-(and-6)-chloromethylfluorescein diethyl ether *mixed isomers*	5 mg
C22220	6-chloro-9-nitro-5-oxo-5*H*-benzo[a]phenoxazine (CNOB)	1 mg
C2944	coelenterazine	250 µg
C14260	coelenterazine cp	250 µg
C6779	coelenterazine f	250 µg
C6780	coelenterazine h	250 µg
C14261	coelenterazine hcp	250 µg
C6776	coelenterazine n	250 µg
C6777	Coelenterazine Sampler Kit *coelenterazine and five analogs, 25 µg each*	1 kit
C7933	coumarin-3-carboxylic acid, succinimidyl ester (SECCA)	25 mg
C684	3-cyano-7-ethoxycoumarin	10 mg
D12203	6,8-difluoro-7-ethoxy-4-methylcoumarin (DiFMUEt)	5 mg
D12200	6,8-difluoro-4-methylumbelliferyl octanoate (DiFMU octanoate)	10 mg
E6580	ELF® 97 esterase substrate (ELF® 97 acetate)	5 mg
E6583	ELF® 97 lipase substrate (ELF® 97 palmitate)	5 mg
E2882	7-ethoxy-4-trifluoromethylcoumarin	25 mg
F2900	*FAST* CAT® Chloramphenicol Acetyltransferase Assay Kit *100 assays*	1 kit
F6616	*FAST* CAT® Green (deoxy) Chloramphenicol Acetyltransferase Assay Kit *100 assays*	1 kit
F6617	*FAST* CAT® Yellow (deoxy) Chloramphenicol Acetyltransferase Assay Kit *100 assays*	1 kit
F6489	fluorescein mono-(4-guanidinobenzoate), hydrochloride	5 mg
F33951	Fluorocillin™ Green 345/530 β-lactamase substrate *precipitating product*	5 mg
G7702	glycerol tris-(1-pyrenebutyrate)	5 mg
L7085	D-luciferin, 1-(4,5-dimethoxy-2-nitrophenyl)ethyl ester (DMNPE-caged luciferin)	5 mg
L2911	D-luciferin, free acid	25 mg
L2916	D-luciferin, potassium salt	25 mg
L2912	D-luciferin, sodium salt	25 mg
L22172	D-luciferin, sodium salt *FluoroPure™ grade*	10 mg
P35901	*O*-pivaloyloxymethyl umbelliferone (C-POM) *lipase substrate* *special packaging*	5 x 100 µg
R12204	resazurin, sodium salt	10 mg
R441	resorufin benzyl ether (benzyloxyresorufin)	10 mg
R6564	Resorufin Ether Sampler Kit	1 kit
R352	resorufin ethyl ether (ethoxyresorufin)	5 mg
R351	resorufin methyl ether (methoxyresorufin)	5 mg
R1147	resorufin pentyl ether (pentoxyresorufin)	5 mg
V23111	Vybrant® Cytotoxicity Assay Kit *G6PD release assay* *1000 assays*	1 kit

For current prices or to order online, visit probes.invitrogen.com

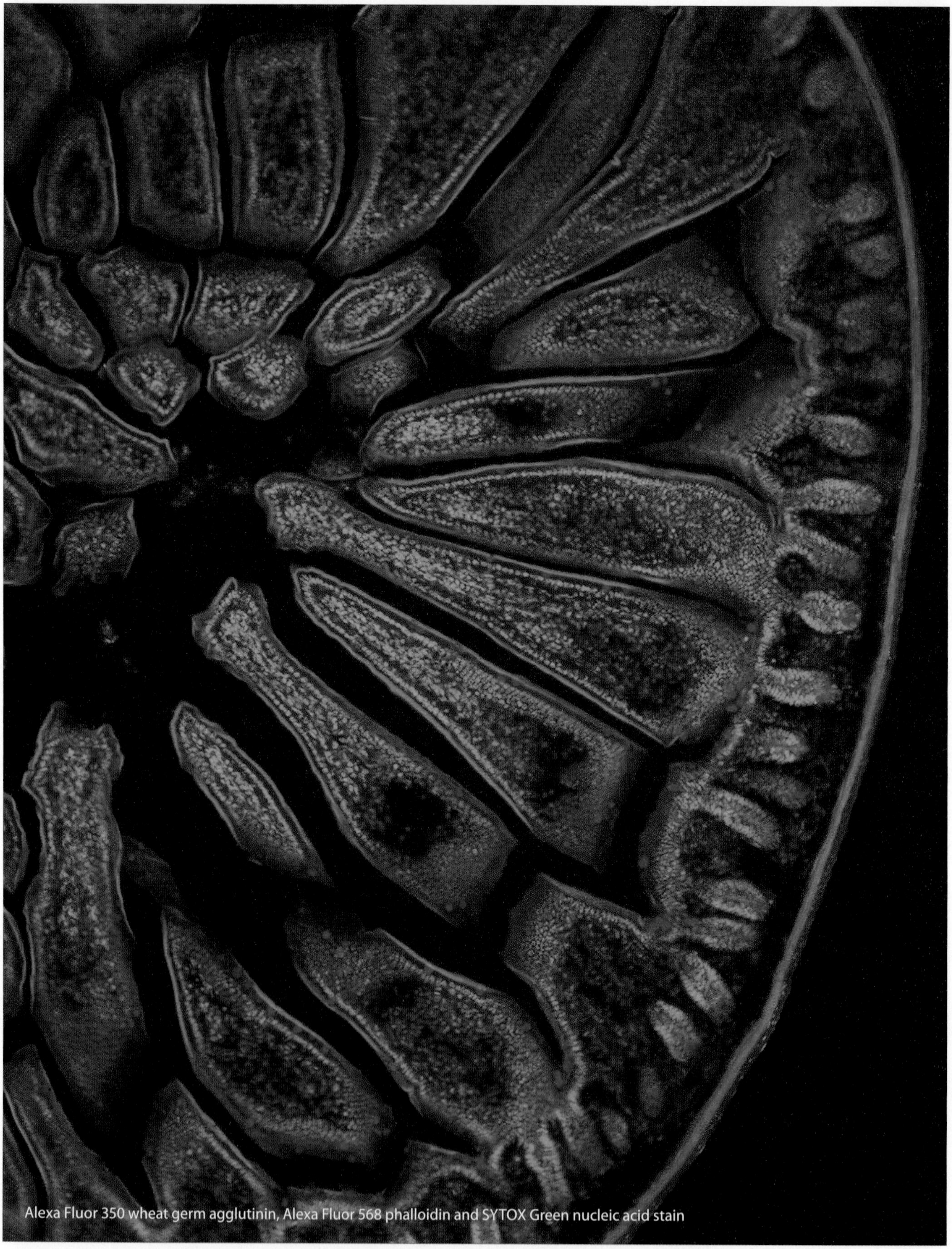

Alexa Fluor 350 wheat germ agglutinin, Alexa Fluor 568 phalloidin and SYTOX Green nucleic acid stain

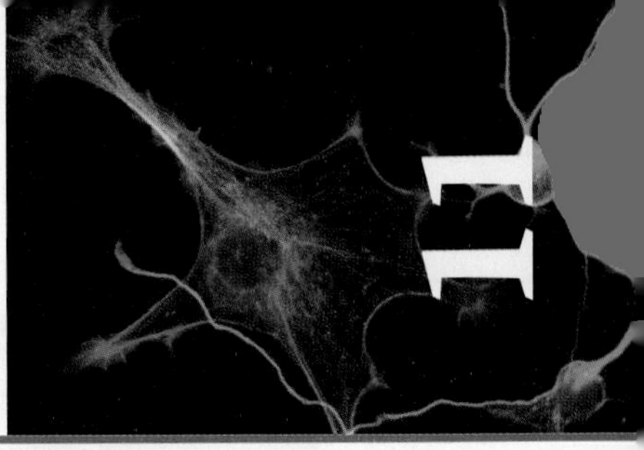

Chapter 11

Probes for Cytoskeletal Proteins

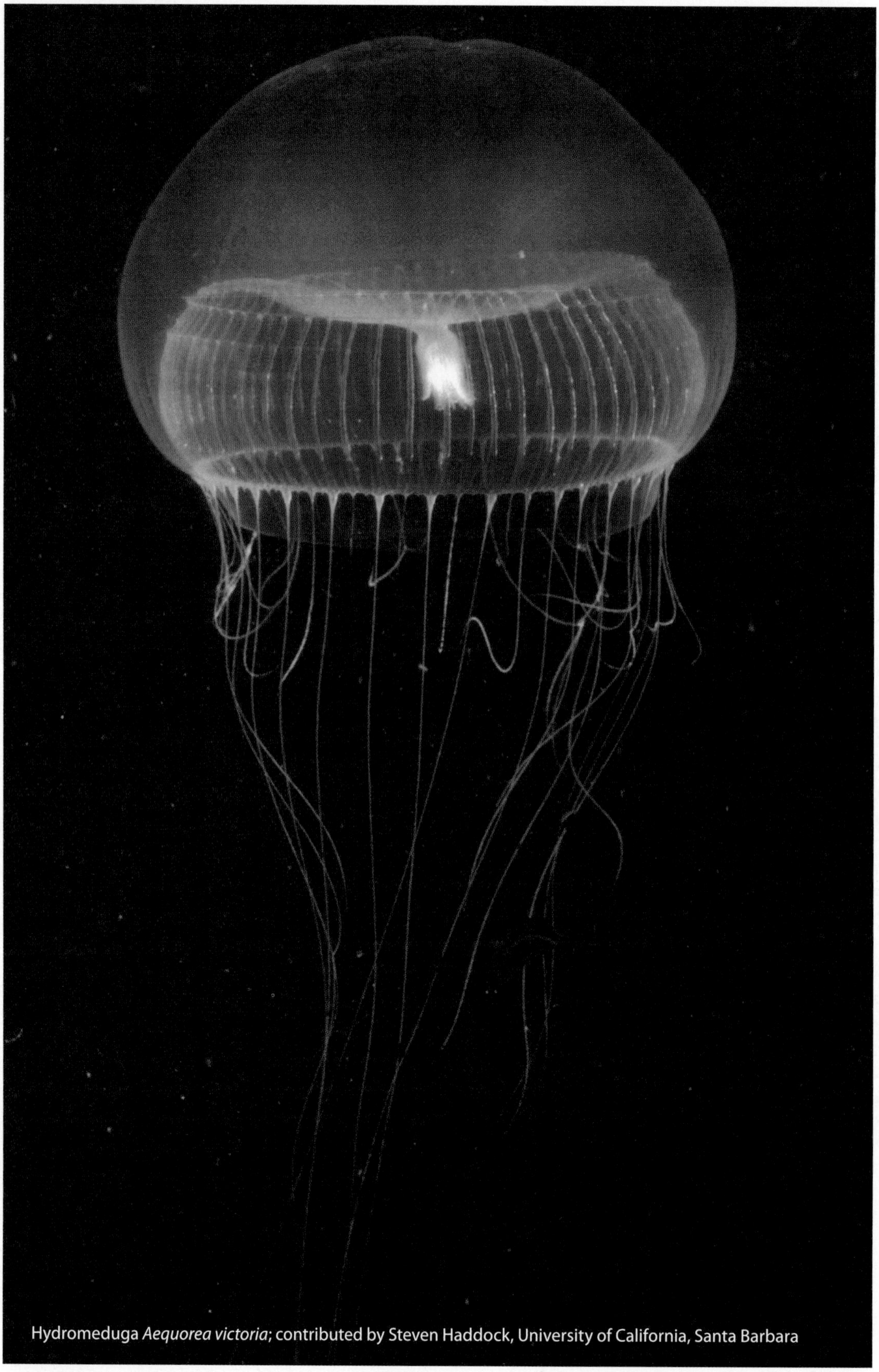

Hydromeduga *Aequorea victoria*; contributed by Steven Haddock, University of California, Santa Barbara

11.1 Probes for Actin

The cytoskeleton is an essential component of a cell's structure and one of the easiest to label with fluorescent reagents. Section 11.1 describes our probes for both monomeric actin (G-actin) and filamentous actin (F-actin); reagents for staining tubulin and other cytoskeletal proteins are described in Section 11.2.

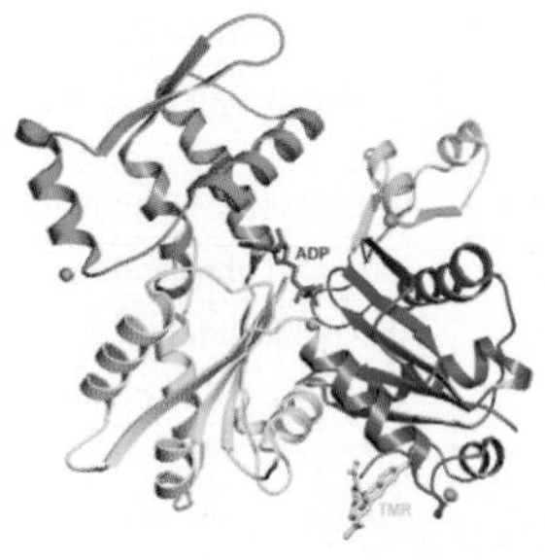

Figure 11.1 Ribbon diagram of the structure of uncomplexed actin in the ADP state. The four subdomains are represented in different colors, and ADP is bound at the center where the four subdomains meet. Four Ca^{2+} ions bound to the actin monomer are represented as gold spheres. In this structure, tetramethylrhodamine-5-maleimide (T6027) has been used to covalently attach the dye to a specific cysteine residue (Cys 374). Figure provided by Roberto Dominguez, Boston Biomedical Research Institute, Watertown, Massachusetts. Reprinted with permission from Science 293, 708 (2001). Copyright 2001 American Association for the Advancement of Science.

Unlabeled and Fluorescent Actin

Fluorescently labeled actin (Figure 11.1) is an important tool for investigating cytoskeleton dynamics *in vivo*.[1–5] Molecular Probes offers highly purified actin from rabbit muscle (A12375), as well as fluorescent actin conjugates labeled with four of our brightest and most photostable dyes. The green-fluorescent Alexa Fluor® 488 actin conjugate (A12373) has excitation and emission maxima similar to fluorescein actin (Figure 7.51), but it is brighter and more photostable, and its spectra are much less pH dependent. The red-orange–fluorescent Alexa Fluor® 568 (A12374, Actin), red-fluorescent Alexa Fluor® 594 (A34050) and far-red–fluorescent Alexa Fluor® 647 (A34051) actin conjugates are more fluorescent than the spectrally similar Lissamine rhodamine B, Texas Red® and Cy5 conjugates, respectively.

Our fluorescent actin conjugates are prepared by reacting amine residues of polymerized F-actin with the succinimidyl ester of the appropriate dye using a modification of the method described by Alberts and co-workers.[2] After labeling, the conjugates are subjected to depolymerization and subsequent polymerization to ensure that the actin conjugates are able to assemble properly. The labeled actin that polymerizes is then separated from remaining monomeric actin by centrifugation, depolymerized and packaged in monomeric form.

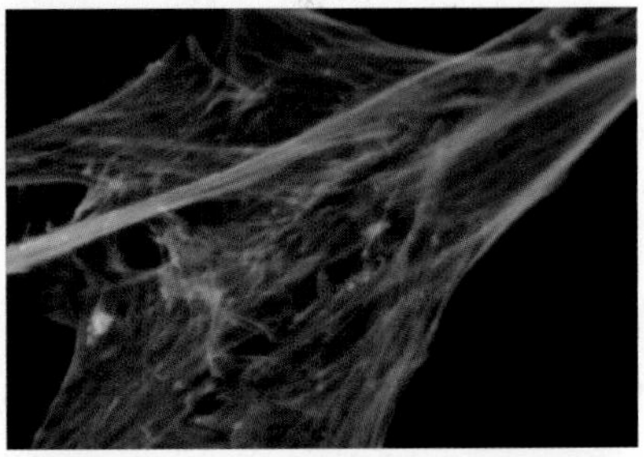

Figure 11.2 Chick embryo fibroblasts injected with the Alexa Fluor® 568 conjugate of actin from rabbit muscle (A12374). The cells were then fixed and permeabilized, and the filamentous actin was stained with coumarin phallacidin (C606). The double-exposure image was acquired using longpass filter sets appropriate for rhodamine and DAPI. Image contributed by Heiti Paves, Laboratory of Molecular Genetics, National Institute of Chemical Physics and Biophysics, Estonia.

Phallotoxins for F-Actin

Molecular Probes prepares numerous fluorescent and biotinylated derivatives of phalloidin and phallacidin for selectively labeling F-actin (Figure 11.3, Figure 11.4). Phallotoxins are bicyclic peptides isolated from the deadly *Amanita phalloides* mushroom[6] (www.grzyby.pl/gatunki/Amanita_phalloides.htm). They can be used interchangeably in most applications and bind competitively to the same sites on F-actin. Table 11.1 lists the available phallotoxin derivatives, along with their spectral properties. A detailed staining protocol is included with each phallotoxin derivative, and extensive bibliographies are available on our Web site (probes.invitrogen.com). One vial of the fluorescent phallotoxin contains sufficient reagent for staining ~300 microscope slide preparations; one vial of biotin-XX phalloidin, which must be used at a higher concentration, contains sufficient reagent for ~50 microscope slide preparations. We also offer unlabeled phalloidin (P3457) for blocking F-actin staining by labeled phallotoxins and for promoting actin polymerization.

Properties of Phallotoxin Derivatives

The fluorescent and biotinylated phallotoxin derivatives stain F-actin selectively at nanomolar concentrations and are readily water soluble, thus providing convenient labels for identifying and quantitating actin in tissue sections, cell cultures or cell-free preparations.[7–11] F-actin in live neurons can be efficiently labeled using cationic liposomes containing fluorescent phallotoxins, such as BODIPY® FL phallacidin[12] (B607). This procedure permits the labeling of entire cell cultures with minimum disruption. Because fluorescent phalloidin conjugates are not permeant to most live cells, they can be used to detect cells that have compromised membranes. However, it has been reported that unlabeled phalloidin, and potentially dye-labeled phalloidins, can penetrate the membranes of certain hypoxic cells.[13] An extensive study on visualizing the actin cytoskeleton with various fluorescent probes in cell preparations, as well as in live cells, has been published.[7]

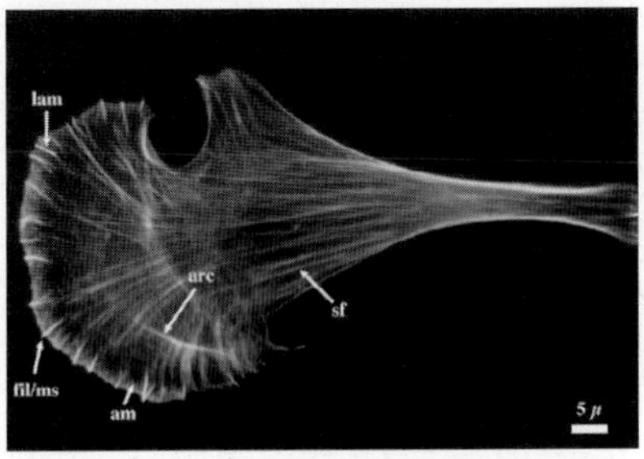

Figure 11.3 Actin filaments of chick heart fibroblasts stained with rhodamine phalloidin (R415). The subcompartments in the cytoskeleton are readily apparent and labeled as follows: **sf**, stress fiber; **lam**, lamellipodium; **fil/ms**, filipodium/microspike; **am**, actin meshwork; **arc**, dorsal arc. Figure reprinted from "Visualizing the Actin Cytoskeleton." J. Small *et al.* Microscopy Research and Technique 47, 3–17 (1999). Reprinted by permission of Wiley-Liss, Inc., a subsidiary of John Wiley & Sons, Inc., and J. Victor Small.

Labeled phallotoxins have similar affinity for both large and small filaments and bind in a stoichiometric ratio of about one phallotoxin per actin subunit in both muscle and nonmuscle cells; they reportedly do not bind to monomeric G-actin, unlike some antibodies against actin.[9,14] Phallotoxins have further advantages over antibodies for actin labeling, in that 1) their binding properties do not change appreciably with actin from different species, including plants and

Table 11.1 — Spectral characteristics of our F-actin–selective probes

Cat #	Actin-Selective Probe	Ex/Em *	Approximate MW
A22281	Alexa Fluor® 350 phalloidin	346/446 †	1100
C606	Coumarin phallacidin	355/443	1100
N354	NBD phallacidin	465/536	1040
A12379	Alexa Fluor® 488 phalloidin	495/517 †	1320
F432	Fluorescein phalloidin	496/516 †	1175
O7466	Oregon Green® 488 phalloidin	496/520 †	1180
B607	BODIPY® FL phallacidin	505/512	1125
O7465	Oregon Green® 514 phalloidin	511/528 †	1280
E7463	Eosin phalloidin	524/544	1500
A22282	Alexa Fluor® 532 phalloidin	528/555 †	1350
R415	Rhodamine phalloidin	554/573 †	1250
A22283	Alexa Fluor® 546 phalloidin	554/570 †	1800
B3475	BODIPY® 558/568 phalloidin	558/569	1115
A12380	Alexa Fluor® 568 phalloidin	578/600 †	1590
B7464	BODIPY® TR-X phallacidin	589/617	1400
A12381	Alexa Fluor® 594 phalloidin	593/617 †	1620
T7471	Texas Red®-X phalloidin	591/608 †	1490
A22284	Alexa Fluor® 633 phalloidin	625/645 †	1900
A34054	Alexa Fluor® 635 phalloidin	633/648 †	1900
B12382	BODIPY® 650/665 phalloidin	647/661	1200
A22287	Alexa Fluor® 647 phalloidin	649/666 †	1950
A22285	Alexa Fluor® 660 phalloidin	661/689 †	1750
A22286	Alexa Fluor® 680 phalloidin	677/699 †	1850
B7474	Biotin-XX phalloidin	NA	1300
P3457	Phalloidin	NA	790

* Excitation (Ex) and emission (Em) maxima, in nm. Spectra of phallotoxins are either in aqueous buffer, pH 7–9 (denoted †) or in methanol. NA = Not applicable.

animals; and 2) their nonspecific staining is negligible; thus, the contrast between stained and unstained areas is high.

Phallotoxins shift actin's monomer/polymer equilibrium toward the polymer, lowering the critical concentration for polymerization as much as 30-fold.[15,16] Furthermore, depolymerization of F-actin by cytochalasins, potassium iodide and elevated temperatures is inhibited by phallotoxin binding. Because the phallotoxin derivatives are relatively small, with approximate diameters of 12–15 Å and molecular weights below 2000 daltons, a wide variety of actin-binding proteins — including myosin, tropomyosin, troponin and DNase I — can still bind to actin after treatment with fluorescent phallotoxins. Even more significantly, phallotoxin-labeled actin filaments retain certain functional characteristics; labeled glycerinated muscle fibers still contract, and labeled actin filaments still move on solid-phase myosin substrates.[17–19]

Alexa Fluor® Phalloidins

We have taken advantage of the outstanding characteristics of our Alexa Fluor® dyes (Section 1.3) to create a series of Alexa Fluor® dye–labeled phalloidins (Figure 7.110, Figure 11.5, Figure 11.6, Figure 23.23), which are now the preferred F-actin stains for most applications across the full spectral range. The Alexa Fluor® phalloidin conjugates provide researchers with fluorescent probes that are superior in brightness and photostability to all other spectrally similar conjugates tested (Section 1.3; Figure 1.10, Figure 1.11). Spectra of the Alexa Fluor® dyes are given in Figure 1.17, Figure 1.24 and Figure 1.34. For improved fluorescence detection of F-actin in fixed and permeabilized cells, we encourage researchers to try these fluorescent phalloidins in their actin-labeling protocols. A series of videos showing Alexa Fluor® 488 phalloidin–stained actin[20] is available at the *Journal of Cell Biology* Web site (www.jcb.org/cgi/content/full/150/2/361/DC1).

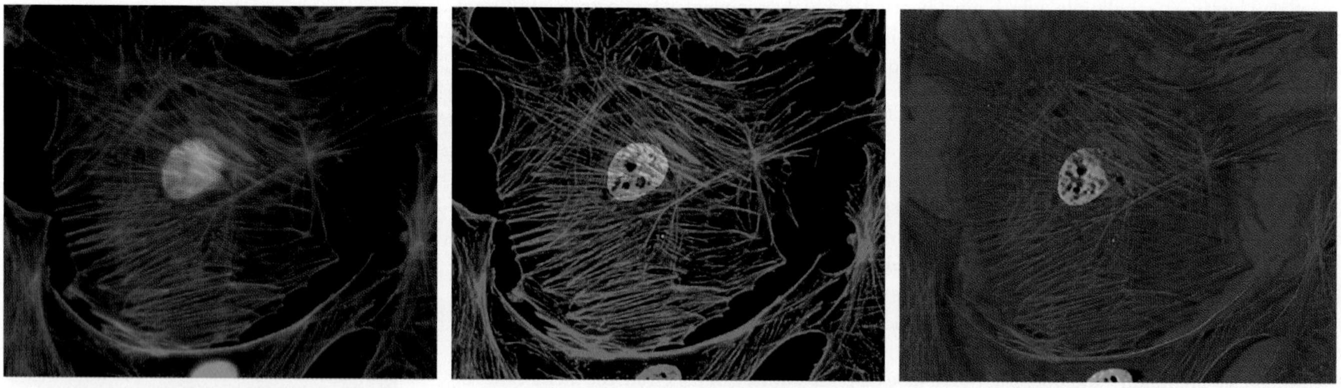

Figure 11.4 Fixed, permeabilized bovine pulmonary artery endothelial cells were labeled with Texas Red®-X phalloidin (T7471), which stains F-actin, and counterstained with DAPI (D1306, D3571, D21490). The panels show the unprocessed image (left panel), after deconvolution (middle panel) and after deconvolution and three-dimensional reconstruction (right panel). The image was deconvolved using Huygens software (Scientific Volume Imaging, www.svi.nl). 3-D reconstruction was performed using Imaris software (Bitplane AG, www.bitplane.com).

Oregon Green® Phalloidins

Green-fluorescent actin stains are popular reagents for labeling F-actin in fixed and permeabilized cells. Unfortunately, the green-fluorescent fluorescein phalloidin and NBD phallacidin photobleach rapidly, making their photography difficult. We have used two of our Oregon Green® dyes (Section 1.5) to prepare Oregon Green® 488 phalloidin (O7466) and the slightly longer-wavelength Oregon Green® 514 phalloidin (O7465, Figure 11.7). The excitation and emission spectra of the Oregon Green® 488 dye are virtually superimposable on those of fluorescein (Figure 7.21), and both the Oregon Green® 488 and Oregon Green® 514 dyes may be viewed with standard fluorescein optical filter sets (Table 23.9). As shown in Figure 11.8, Oregon Green® 514 phalloidin is more photostable than fluorescein phalloidin, making it easier to visualize and photograph (Figure 1.61).

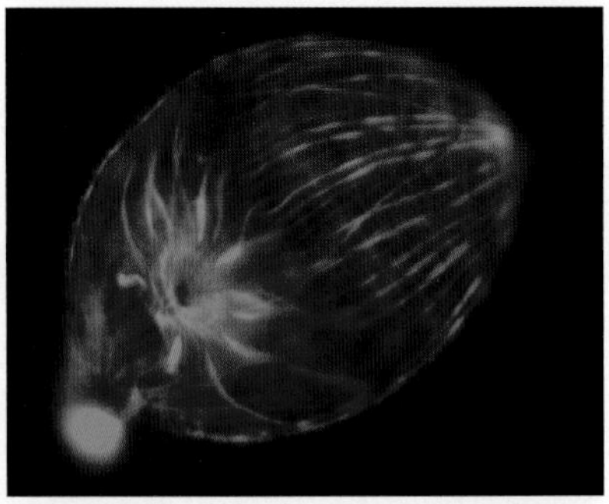

Figure 11.5 Actin filaments of the turbellarian flatworm *Archimonotresis* sp. stained with Alexa Fluor® 488 phalloidin (A12379) to reveal a meshwork of longitudinal, circular and diagonal muscles. The large, bright ring with muscle fibers radiating outward is the muscular pharynx, and the small, bright ring at the posterior is part of the reproductive system. This epifluorescence image was contributed by Matthew D. Hooge and Seth Tyler, University of Maine, Orono.

BODIPY® Phallotoxins

BODIPY® phallotoxin conjugates (B607, B3475, B7464, B12382; Figure 8.122, Figure 11.9, Figure 11.10) have some important advantages over the conventional NBD, fluorescein and rhodamine phallotoxins. BODIPY® dyes are more photostable than these traditional fluorophores [21] and have narrower emission bandwidths (Figure 1.43), making them especially useful for double- and triple-labeling experiments. BODIPY® FL phallacidin (B607), which reportedly gives a signal superior to that of fluorescein phalloidin,[22] has been used for quantitating F-actin and determining its distribution in cells.[23,24]

The BODIPY® FL, BODIPY® 558/568 and BODIPY® TR-X phallotoxins (B607, B3475, B7464) exhibit excitation and emission spectra similar to those of fluorescein, rhodamine B and Texas Red® dyes, respectively, and can be used with standard optical filter sets (Table 23.9). BODIPY® 650/665 phalloidin (B12382) is the longest-wavelength BODIPY® phallotoxin conjugate available, increasing the options for multicolor analysis. BODIPY® 650/665 phalloidin, Alexa Fluor® 647 phalloidin (A22287) and Alexa Fluor® 660 phalloidin (A22285) are among the few probes available that can be excited by the 647 nm spectral line of the Ar–Kr laser used in many confocal laser-scanning microscopes.

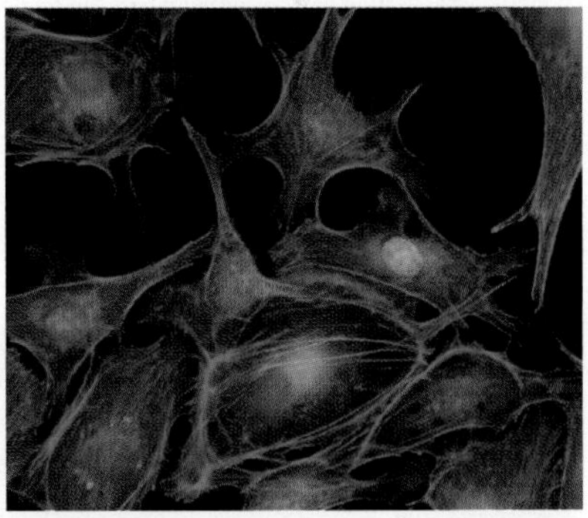

Figure 11.6 Subcellular structures in fixed and permeabilized bovine pulmonary artery endothelial cells visualized with several fluorescent dyes. Filamentous actin (F-actin) was identified with Alexa Fluor® 633 phalloidin (A22284), which is pseudocolored magenta. Lipophilic regions of the cell, including intracellular membranes, were stained with green-fluorescent $DiOC_6(3)$ (D273). Finally, nuclei were counterstained with blue-fluorescent DAPI (D1306, D3571, D21490). The image was acquired using filters appropriate for fluorescein and DAPI and a special filter (courtesy of Omega Optical) for the Alexa Fluor® 633 dye, consisting of a narrow band exciter (630DF10), dichroic (640DRLP) and emitter (660DF10).

Rhodamine Phalloidin and Other Red-Fluorescent Phalloidins

Rhodamine phalloidin (R415, Figure 11.3) has been the standard for red-fluorescent phallotoxins, with more than 1400 citations in our bibliography database. Rhodamine phalloidin is excited efficiently by the mercury-arc lamp in most fluorescence microscopes. However, our Alexa Fluor® 546, Alexa Fluor® 568, Alexa Fluor® 594 and Texas Red®-X phalloidins [25] (A22283,

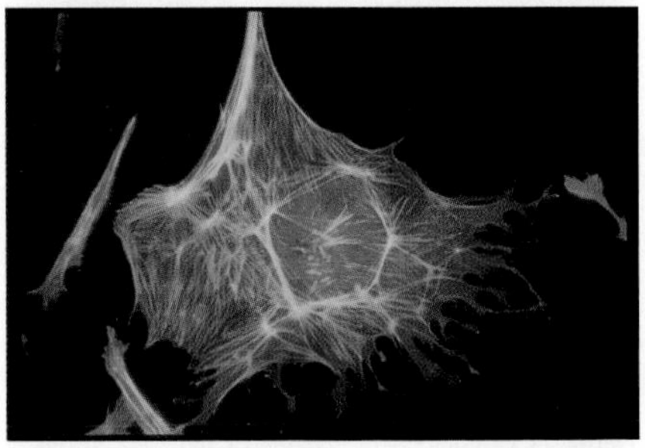

Figure 11.7 Simultaneous visualization of F- and G-actin in a bovine pulmonary artery endothelial cell using F-actin–specific Oregon Green® 488 phalloidin (O7466) and G-actin–specific Texas Red® deoxyribonuclease I (D972). The G-actin appears as diffuse red fluorescence that is more intense in the nuclear region where the cell thickness is greater and stress fibers are less dense. The image was obtained by taking multiple exposures through bandpass optical filter sets appropriate for fluorescein and the Texas Red® dye.

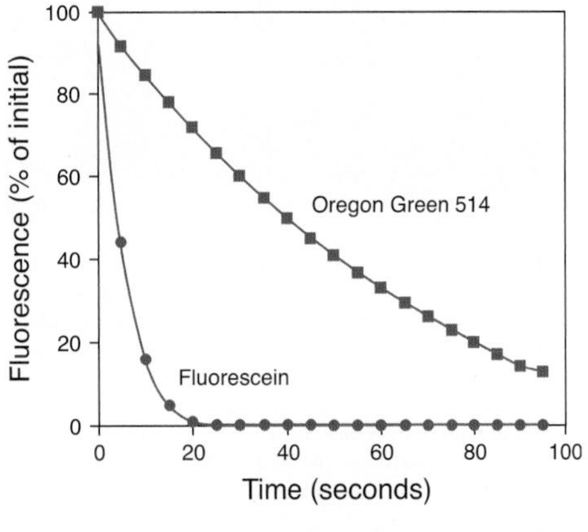

Figure 11.8 Photostability comparison for Oregon Green® 514 phalloidin (O7465) and fluorescein phalloidin (F432). CRE BAG 2 fibroblasts were fixed with formaldehyde, permeabilized with acetone and then stained with the fluorescent phallotoxins. Samples were continuously illuminated and images were acquired every 5 seconds using a Star 1 CCD camera (Photometrics); the average fluorescence intensity in the field of view was calculated with Image-1 software (Universal Imaging Corp.) and expressed as a fraction of the initial intensity. Three data sets, representing different fields of view, were averaged for each labeled phalloidin to obtain the plotted time courses.

A12380, A12381, T7471; Figure 7.92, Figure 11.11, Figure 11.12) will be welcome replacements for rhodamine phalloidin in many multicolor applications because their emission spectra are better separated from those of the green-fluorescent Alexa Fluor® 488, Oregon Green® and fluorescein dyes. Moreover, the Alexa Fluor® 568 and Texas Red®-X conjugates can be excited by the 568 nm spectral line of the Ar–Kr laser used in several confocal laser-scanning microscopes, whereas the tetramethylrhodamine dye used to prepare rhodamine phalloidin is poorly excited by this laser.

Other Labeled Phallotoxins, Including Eosin Phalloidin

The original yellow-green–fluorescent NBD phallacidin (N354) and green-fluorescent fluorescein phalloidin (F432) remain in use despite their relatively poor photostability (Figure 11.8). Photostability of fluorescein phalloidin and some other fluorescent phallotoxins can be considerably improved (Figure 23.29) by mounting the stained samples with our ProLong® Antifade Kit or ProLong® Gold antifade reagent (P7481, P36930, P36934; Section 23.1). We recommend the Alexa Fluor® 488 (Figure 11.7), Oregon Green® 488, Oregon Green® 514 and BODIPY® FL phallotoxins as the preferred green-fluorescent actin stains. Alexa Fluor® 350 phalloidin (A22281) and coumarin phallacidin (C606, Figure 11.2) are the only blue-fluorescent phallotoxin conjugates currently available for staining actin.[26]

We have also prepared eosin phalloidin (E7463), which has been shown to be useful for correlated fluorescence and electron microscopy studies (see Note 14.2 "Product Highlight: Fluorescent Probes for Photoconversion of Diaminobenzidine Reagents" in Section 14.3). Deerinck and colleagues have reported that eosin-mediated photooxidation of diaminobenzidine followed by treatment with osmium tetroxide yields an insoluble, electron-dense DAB oxidation product that can be visualized by either light or electron microscopy, allowing three-dimensional reconstructions at the electron microscopy level.[25,27] Specific subpopulations of F-actin in the rat central nervous system have been identified by electron microscopy using eosin phalloidin labeling followed by eosin-mediated photooxidation of diaminobenzidine.[25,28]

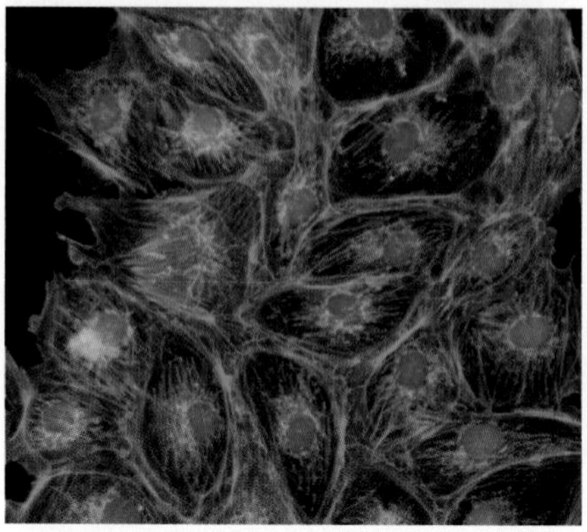

Figure 11.9 FluoCells® prepared slide #1 (F14780), consisting of bovine pulmonary artery endothelial cells incubated with MitoTracker® Red CMXRos (M7512) to label the mitochondria. After fixation and permeabilization, the cells were stained with BODIPY® FL phallacidin (B607) to label the filamentous actin (F-actin) and finally counterstained with DAPI (D1306, D3571, D21490) to label the nucleus. The multiple-exposure image was acquired using bandpass filters appropriate for Texas Red® dye, fluorescein and DAPI.

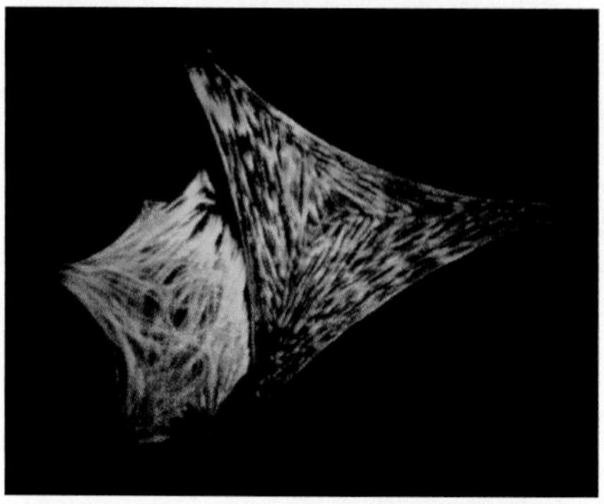

Figure 11.10 Actin labeled with BODIPY® FL phallacidin (B607) and vinculin, a cytoskeletal focal adhesion protein, tagged with a monoclonal anti-vinculin antibody that was subsequently probed with Texas Red® goat anti-mouse IgG antibody (T862). The large triangular cell is a fibroblast containing green actin stress fibers terminating in red focal adhesions. The neighboring polygonal cell, a rat neonatal cardiomyocyte, contains green striated actin in the myofibrils terminating in the focal adhesions. The close apposition of the two stains results in a yellowish-orange color. Image contributed by Mark B. Snuggs and W. Barry VanWinkle, University of Texas, Houston.

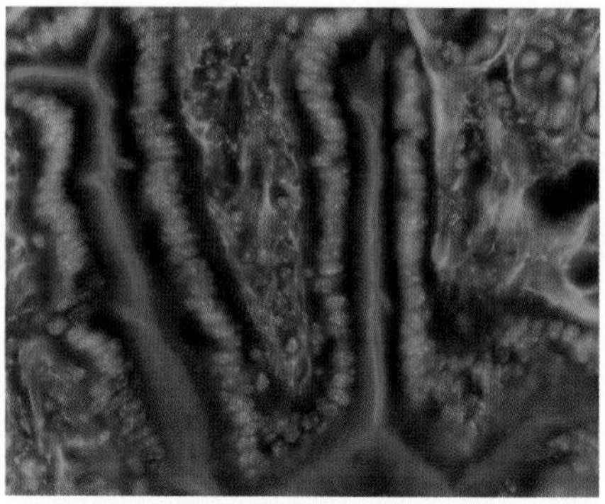

Figure 11.11 A section of mouse intestine stained with a combination of fluorescent stains. Fibronectin, an extracellular matrix adhesion molecule, was labeled using a chicken primary antibody against fibronectin and visualized using green-fluorescent Alexa Fluor® 488 goat anti–chicken IgG antibody (A11039). The filamentous actin (F-actin) prevalent in the brush border was stained with red-fluorescent Alexa Fluor® 568 phalloidin (A12380). Finally, the nuclei were stained with DAPI (D1306, D3571, D21490).

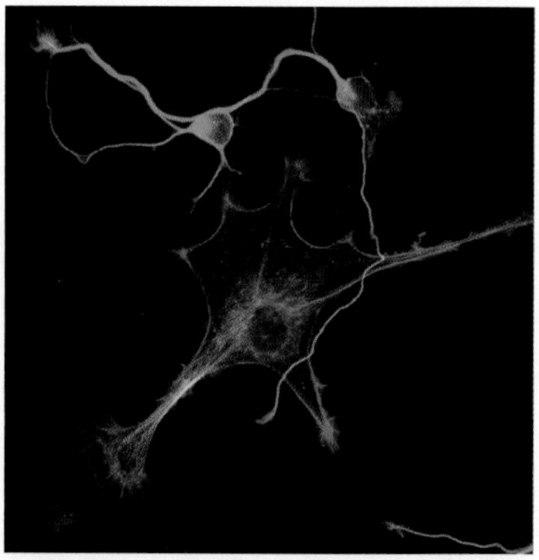

Figure 11.12 Confocal micrograph of the cytoskeleton of a mixed population of granule neurons and glial cells. The F-actin was stained with red-fluorescent Texas Red®-X phalloidin (T7471). The microtubules were detected with a mouse monoclonal anti-β-tubulin primary antibody and subsequently visualized with the green-fluorescent Alexa Fluor® 488 goat anti–mouse IgG antibody (A11001). The image was contributed by Jonathan Zmuda, Immunomatrix, Inc.

Biotin-XX phalloidin (B7474, Figure 6.25) also permits detection of F-actin by electron microscopy and light microscopy techniques.[29] This biotin conjugate can be visualized with fluorophore- or enzyme-labeled avidin and streptavidin (Section 7.6), with tyramide signal amplification (TSA) technology (Section 6.2), with our novel ELF® signal amplification technology (Figure 6.26) or potentially with NANOGOLD or Alexa Fluor® FluoroNanogold streptavidin (Section 7.6). Biotin-XX phalloidin, in conjunction with streptavidin or CaptAvidin™ agarose (S951, C21386; Section 7.6), can be used to precipitate F-actin from the cytosolic anti-phosphotyrosine–reactive fraction in macrophages stimulated with colony-stimulating factor-1.[30]

DNase I Conjugates for Staining G-Actin

Bovine pancreatic deoxyribonuclease (DNase I, ~31,000 daltons) binds to monomeric G-actin with an affinity of about 5×10^{-8} M.[31–35] Like unlabeled DNase I, our fluorescent DNase I conjugates (Table 11.2) selectively label G-actin and have proven very useful for detecting and quantitating the proportion of unpolymerized actin in a cell. Molecular Probes' scientists have triple-labeled endothelial cells with fluorescein DNase I, BODIPY® 581/591 phalloidin and a monoclonal anti-actin antibody detected with a Cascade Blue® dye–labeled secondary antibody[36] (C962, Section 7.2, Table 7.1). They found that the monoclonal antibody, which binds to both G-actin and F-actin, colocalized with the DNase I and phalloidin conjugates, suggesting that these three probes recognize unique binding sites on the actin molecule. Researchers can choose fluorescein (D970), Alexa Fluor® 488 (D12371), Oregon Green® 488 (D7497), Alexa Fluor® 594 (D12372) or Texas Red® (D972) DNase I conjugates (Table 11.2), depending on their multicolor application and their detection instrumentation.

Fluorescein DNase I and the Alexa Fluor® 488 and Alexa Fluor® 594 DNase I conjugates have been used in combination with fluorescently labeled phallotoxins to simultaneously visualize G-actin pools and filamentous F-actin[36–41] and to study the disruption of microfilament organization in live nonmuscle cells.[42] Rhodamine phalloidin (R415) has been used in conjunction with Oregon Green® 488 DNase I to determine the F-actin:G-actin ratio in *Dictyostelium* using confocal laser-scanning microscopy.[43] A mouse fibroblast labeled with both Texas Red® DNase I and Oregon Green® 488 phalloidin (O7466) permitted visualization of the G-actin and the complex network of F-actin throughout the cytoplasm, as well as at the cell periphery (Figure 11.7). The influence of cytochalasins on actin structure in monocytes has been quantitated by flow cytometry using Texas Red® DNase I and BODIPY® FL phallacidin (B607) to stain the G-actin and F-actin pools, respectively.[44] Fluorescent DNase I has also been used as a model system to study the interactions of nucleotides, cations and cytochalasin D with monomeric actin.[45]

Table 11.2 — Spectral characteristics of our G-actin–selective probes

Cat #	Actin-Selective Probe	Ex/Em *
D970	DNase I, fluorescein conjugate	494/517
D12371	DNase I, Alexa Fluor® 488 conjugate	495/519
D7497	DNase I, Oregon Green® 488 conjugate	496/516
D12372	DNase I, Alexa Fluor® 594 conjugate	590/617
D972	DNase I, Texas Red® conjugate	597/618

* Excitation (Ex) and emission (Em) maxima, in nm. Spectra of the DNase I conjugates are in aqueous buffer, pH 7–8.

Probes and Assays for Actin Quantitation and Polymerization

Assays for Quantitating F-Actin and G-Actin Polymerization

Quantitative assays for F-actin have employed fluorescein phalloidin,[46,47] rhodamine phalloidin,[48] BODIPY® FL phallacidin[24] and NBD phallacidin.[49] An F-actin assay based on fluorescein phalloidin was used to demonstrate the loss of F-actin from cells during apoptosis.[50] The addition of propidium iodide (P1304MP, P3566; FluoroPure™ Grade, P21493; Section 8.1) to the cell suspensions enabled these researchers to estimate the cell-cycle distributions of both the apoptotic and nonapoptotic cell populations. The change in F-actin content in proliferating adherent cells has been quantitated using the ratio of rhodamine phalloidin fluorescence to ethidium bromide fluorescence.[51] The spectral separation of the signals in this assay may be improved by using a green-fluorescent stain for F-actin and a high-affinity red-fluorescent nucleic acid stain, such as the combination of Alexa Fluor® 488 phalloidin (A12379) and ethidium homodimer-1 (E1169, Section 8.1).

The fluorescence of actin monomers labeled with pyrene iodoacetamide (P29) has been demonstrated to change upon polymerization, making this probe an excellent tool for following the kinetics of actin polymerization and the effects of actin-binding proteins on polymerization.[52–54]

Jasplakinolide: A Cell-Permeant F-Actin Probe

Molecular Probes offers jasplakinolide (J7473, Figure 11.13), a macrocyclic peptide isolated from the marine sponge *Jaspis johnstoni*.[55–57] Jasplakinolide is a potent inducer of actin polymerization *in vitro* by stimulating actin filament nucleation[58,59] and competes with phalloidin for actin binding[60] (K_d = 15 nM). Moreover, unlike other known actin stabilizers such as phalloidins and virotoxins, jasplakinolide appears to be somewhat cell permeant and therefore can potentially be used to manipulate actin polymerization in live cells. This peptide, which also exhibits fungicidal, insecticidal and antiproliferative activity,[56,61–63] is particularly useful for investigating cell processes mediated by actin polymerization and depolymerization, including cell adhesion, locomotion, endocytosis and vesicle sorting and release. Jasplakinolide has been reported to enhance apoptosis induced by cytokine deprivation.[64]

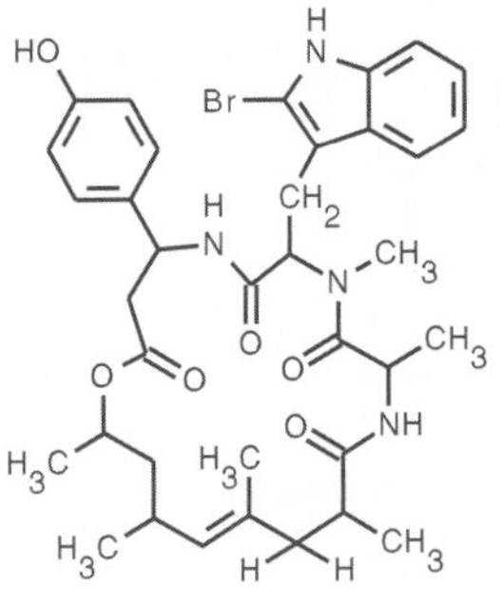

Figure 11.13 J7473 jasplakinolide.

Latrunculin A and Latrunculin B: Cell-Permeant Actin Antagonists

Latrunculins are powerful disruptors of microfilament organization. Isolated from a Red Sea sponge, these G-actin binding compounds inhibit fertilization and early embryological development,[65] alter the shape of cells[66,67] and inhibit receptor-mediated endocytosis.[68] Latrunculin A[64,66,67,69] (L12370, Figure 11.14) binds to monomeric G-actin in a 1:1 ratio at submicromolar concentrations[70] and is frequently used to establish the effects of F-actin disassembly on particular physiological functions such as ion transport[71] and protein localization.[72] The activity of latrunculin B (L22290) mimics that of latrunculin A in most applications.[66,68,73–75]

Fluorescent Cytochalasins

Our fluorescent cytochalasin derivatives promise to be useful probes for live-cell staining of actin filaments. Cytochalasins are a group of natural compounds that bind to actin and alter its polymerization. Activities reported for cytochalasin D, which binds to the barbed (faster-growing) end of actin with high affinity (K_d ~50 nM),[76] include capping the barbed end of actin, cleaving actin filaments and increasing the rate of actin assembly. Cytochalasin B, which binds elsewhere on actin, has been shown to increase the rate of actin assembly and is not believed to have a capping activity. We have prepared the green-fluorescent BODIPY® FL (C12377) and orange-fluorescent BODIPY® TMR (C12378) derivatives of cytochalasin D and the green-fluorescent BODIPY® FL derivative of cytochalasin B (C12376). BODIPY® TMR cytochalasin D has been shown to colocalize with Oregon Green® phalloidin in NIH 3T3 fibroblasts. Migrating human neutrophils appear to show fluorescent cytochalasin D staining approximately 1–2 µm inside the leading edge.[70]

Cofilin: An F-Actin Depolymerizing Factor

Molecular Probes offers high-purity, recombinant chicken muscle cofilin (C22280) isolated from *Escherichia coli*. Cofilin, along with the related actin–depolymerizing factor (ADF), promotes the depolymerization of actin filaments *in vivo*, a process that is required for a variety of cellular responses, including cytokinesis, chemotaxis and formation of lamellipodia.[77–81] This low molecular weight protein (~18,800 daltons) is ubiquitous in tissues of eukaryotes and particularly abundant in embryonic tissue and in developing and degenerating muscle. At pH <7.0, cofilin complexes with F-actin at a stoichiometry of 1:1 with the actin subunits; its name is derived from this cofilamentous structure. At pH >7.0, cofilin causes an increase in the G-actin pool and, in muscle, favors dissociation from the pointed (minus) ends of actin filaments. Cofilin binding to F-actin results in a loss of the phalloidin-binding site and is also competitive with tropomyosin binding. The activity of cofilin *in vivo* is regulated by the phosphorylation of cofilin by LIM kinase at a single serine residue in the N-terminal region. Phosphorylated cofilin does not bind to either G-actin or F-actin. LIM kinase is, in turn, regulated by Rho, a small GTPase of the Ras family.[82,83]

Molecular Probes' cofilin preparation has an estimated purity of >99% by SDS-polyacrylamide gel electrophoresis, and its actin-binding activity is confirmed by its co-migration with G-actin in native gel electrophoresis. The binding constant for our cofilin to the ATP-form of G-actin is ~0.2 µM.

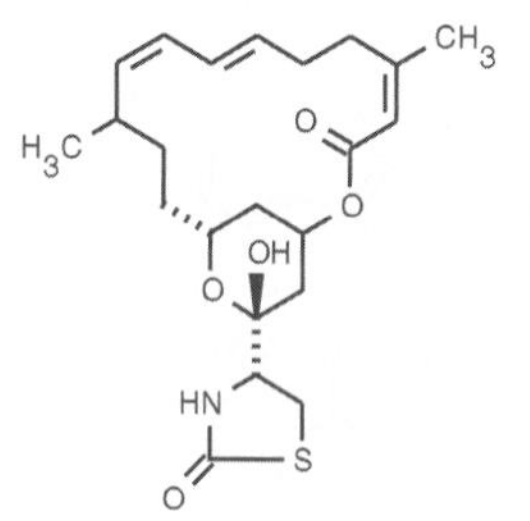

Figure 11.14 L12370 latrunculin A.

Assays for Actin-Binding Proteins

Enhancement of the fluorescence of certain phallotoxins upon binding to F-actin can be a useful tool for following the kinetics and extent of binding of specific actin-binding proteins. We have used the change in fluorescence of rhodamine phalloidin (R415) to determine the dissociation constant of various phallotoxins.[84] The enhancement of rhodamine phalloidin's fluorescence upon actin binding has also been used to measure the kinetics and extent of gelsolin severing of actin filaments.[85] In this study, the ion indicator mag-fura-5 (M3103, Section 19.2) was employed to determine the dependence of this severing on divalent ion concentrations. The affinity and rate constants for rhodamine phalloidin binding to actin are not affected by saturation of actin with either myosin subfragment-1 or tropomyosin, indicating that these two actin-binding proteins do not bind to the same sites as the phalloidin.[12]

In Section 11.2 are described our probes for tubulin and other cytoskeletal proteins, including the following probes for actin-binding proteins:

- Recombinant Endostatin protein (E23377), which binds to tropomyosin, an actin-binding protein
- Fluorescent phosphoinositides and related probes, which bind to actin-binding proteins, including cofilin I, through pleckstrin homology (PH) domains and other binding motifs
- Antibody to the synapsin I actin-binding protein (A6442)

References

1. Cell Struct Funct 22, 59 (1997); **2.** Development 103, 675 (1988); **3.** J Cell Biol 102, 1074 (1986); **4.** J Cell Biol 101, 597 (1985); **5.** Proc Natl Acad Sci U S A 75, 857 (1978); **6.** Proc Natl Acad Sci U S A 71, 2803 (1974); **7.** Microsc Res Tech 47, 3 (1999); **8.** Biophys J 74, 2451 (1998); **9.** Peptides of Poisonous Amanita Mushrooms, Rich A, Ed. (1986); **10.** Methods Enzymol 194, 729 (1991); **11.** J Muscle Res Cell Motil 9, 370 (1988); **12.** Neurosci Lett 207, 17 (1996); **13.** J Lab Clin Med 123, 357 (1994); **14.** Biochemistry 33, 14387 (1994); **15.** Eur J Biochem 165, 125 (1987); **16.** J Cell Biol 105, 1473 (1987); **17.** J Cell Biol 115, 67 (1991); **18.** Nature 326, 805 (1987); **19.** Proc Natl Acad Sci U S A 83, 6272 (1986); **20.** J Cell Biol 150, 361 (2000); **21.** J Cell Biol 114, 1179 (1991); **22.** J Cell Biol 127, 1637 (1994); **23.** J Cell Biol 116, 197 (1992); **24.** Histochem J 22, 624 (1990); **25.** J Histochem Cytochem 49, 1351 (2001); **26.** J Muscle Res Cell Motil 14, 594 (1993); **27.** J Cell Biol 126, 901 (1994); **28.** Brain Res 923, 1 (2001); **29.** J Cell Biol 130, 591 (1995); **30.** J Biol Chem 273, 17128 (1998); **31.** J Cell Sci 66, 39 (1984); **32.** Anal Biochem 135, 22 (1983); **33.** Exp Cell Res 147, 240 (1983); **34.** Eur J Biochem 104, 367 (1980); **35.** J Biol Chem 255, 5668 (1980); **36.** J Histochem Cytochem 42, 345 (1994); **37.** Protoplasma 209, 214 (1999); **38.** J Biol Chem 271, 20516 (1996); **39.** Lab Invest 73, 372 (1995); **40.** Biotech Histochem 68, 8 (1993); **41.** J Histochem Cytochem 40, 1605 (1992); **42.** Proc Natl Acad Sci U S A 87, 5474 (1990); **43.** J Cell Biol 142, 1325 (1998); **44.** J Biol Chem 269, 3159 (1994); **45.** Eur J Biochem 182, 267 (1989); **46.** Proc Natl Acad Sci U S A 77, 6624 (1980); **47.** J Cell Sci 100, 187 (1991); **48.** J Cell Biol 130, 613 (1995); **49.** J Cell Biol 98, 1265 (1984); **50.** Cytometry 20, 162 (1995); **51.** J Cell Biol 129, 1589 (1995); **52.** J Biol Chem 270, 7125 (1995); **53.** J Muscle Res Cell Motil 4, 253 (1983); **54.** Eur J Biochem 114, 33 (1981); **55.** J Cell Biol 137, 399 (1997); **56.** J Am Chem Soc 108, 3123 (1986); **57.** Tetrahedron Lett 27, 2797 (1986); **58.** Methods Mol Biol 161, 109 (2001); **59.** J Biol Chem 275, 5163 (2000); **60.** J Biol Chem 269, 14869 (1994); **61.** J Natl Cancer Inst 87, 46 (1995); **62.** Cancer Chemother Pharmacol 30, 401 (1992); **63.** Antimicrob Agents Chemother 32, 1154 (1988); **64.** J Biol Chem 274, 4259 (1999); **65.** Science 219, 493 (1983); **66.** J Biol Chem 275, 28120 (2000); **67.** FEBS Lett 213, 316 (1987); **68.** Exp Cell Res 166, 191 (1986); **69.** Cell Motil Cytoskeleton 13, 127 (1989); **70.** Howard Petty, Wayne State University, personal communication; **71.** J Biol Chem 272, 20332 (1997); **72.** Am J Physiol 272, C254 (1997); **73.** J Biol Chem 276, 23056 (2001); **74.** J Cell Sci 114, 1025 (2001); **75.** Cell Motil Cytoskeleton 48, 96 (2001); **76.** Arch Biochem Biophys 269, 181 (1989); **77.** J Histochem Cytochem 51, 411 (2003); **78.** Annu Rev Cell Dev Biol 15, 185 (1999); **79.** Curr Biol 9, R800 (1999); **80.** J Biol Chem 274, 33827 (1999); **81.** Trends Cell Biol 9, 364 (1999); **82.** J Biol Chem 275, 3577 (2000); **83.** Science 285, 895 (1999); **84.** Anal Biochem 200, 199 (1992); **85.** J Biol Chem 269, 32916 (1994).

Data Table — 11.1 Probes for Actin

Cat #	MW	Storage	Soluble	Abs	EC	Em	Solvent	Notes
A12379	~1320	F,L	MeOH, H_2O	494	78,000	517	pH 7	1, 2, 3
A12380	~1590	F,L	MeOH, H_2O	578	88,000	600	pH 7	1, 2, 3
A12381	~1620	F,L	MeOH, H_2O	593	92,000	617	pH 7	1, 2, 3
A22281	~1100	F,L	MeOH, H_2O	346	17,000	446	pH 7	1, 2, 3
A22282	~1350	F,L	MeOH, H_2O	528	81,000	555	pH 7	1, 2, 3
A22283	~1800	F,L	MeOH, H_2O	554	112,000	570	pH 7	1, 2, 3
A22284	~1900	F,L	MeOH, H_2O	621	159,000	639	MeOH	1, 2, 3, 4
A22285	~1650	F,L	MeOH, H_2O	668	132,000	697	MeOH	1, 2, 3, 4
A22286	~1850	F,L	MeOH, H_2O	684	183,000	707	MeOH	1, 2, 3, 4
A22287	~1950	F,L	MeOH, H_2O	650	275,000	672	MeOH	1, 2, 3, 4
A34054	~1850	F,L	MeOH, H_2O	622	145,000	640	MeOH	1, 2, 3, 4
B607	~1160	F,L	MeOH, H_2O	505	83,000	512	MeOH	1, 2, 3
B3416	~1150	F,L	MeOH, H_2O	584	145,000	592	MeOH	1, 2, 3
B3475	~1115	F,L	MeOH, H_2O	558	85,000	569	MeOH	1, 2, 3
B7464	~1400	F,L	MeOH	589	62,000	617	MeOH	1, 3, 5
B7474	~1300	F	MeOH, H_2O	<300		none		1, 2
B12382	~1200	F,L	MeOH	647	102,000	661	MeOH	1, 3, 5
C606	~1100	F,L	MeOH, H_2O	355	16,000	443	MeOH	1, 2, 3
C12376	753.69	F,D,L	DMSO	503	80,000	510	MeOH	
C12377	781.70	F,D,L	DMSO	504	80,000	511	MeOH	
C12378	887.83	F,D,L	DMSO	545	56,000	571	MeOH	
E7463	~1500	F,L	MeOH, H_2O	524	100,000	544	MeOH	1, 2, 3
F432	~1175	F,L	MeOH, H_2O	496	84,000	516	pH 8	1, 2, 3
J7473	709.68	F,D	MeOH	278	8,000	none	MeOH	
L12370	421.55	F,D	DMSO	<300		none		
L22290	395.51	F,D	DMSO	<300		none		
N354	~1040	F,L	MeOH, H_2O	465	24,000	536	MeOH	1, 2, 3
O7465	~1280	F,L	MeOH, H_2O	511	85,000	528	pH 9	1, 2, 3
O7466	~1180	F,L	MeOH, H_2O	496	86,000	520	pH 9	1, 2, 3
P29	385.20	F,D,L	DMF, DMSO	339	26,000	384-	MeOH	6, 7
P3457	~790	F	MeOH, H_2O	<300		see Notes		2, 8
R415	~1250	F,L	MeOH, H_2O	542	85,000	565	MeOH	1, 2, 3, 9
T7471	~1490	F,L	MeOH, H_2O	583	95,000	603	MeOH	1, 2, 3, 9

For definitions of the contents of this data table, see "Navigating *The Handbook*" in the introductory pages.

Notes

1. α-Bungarotoxin, EGF and phallotoxin conjugates have approximately 1 label per peptide.
2. Although this phallotoxin is water-soluble, storage in water is not recommended, particularly in dilute solution.
3. The value of EC listed for this phallotoxin conjugate is for the labeling dye in free solution. Use of this value for the conjugate assumes a 1:1 dye:peptide labeling ratio and no change of EC due to dye-peptide interactions.
4. In aqueous solutions (pH 7.0), Abs/Em = 625/645 nm for A22284, 633/648 nm for A34054, 649/666 nm for A22287, 661/689 nm for A22285 and 677/699 nm for A22286.
5. B7464 and B12382 are not directly soluble in H_2O. Aqueous dispersions can be prepared by dilution of a stock solution in MeOH.
6. Spectral data of the 2-mercaptoethanol adduct.
7. Iodoacetamides in solution undergo rapid photodecomposition to unreactive products. Minimize exposure to light prior to reaction.
8. This bicyclic peptide is very weakly fluorescent in aqueous solution (Em ~380 nm) (Biochim Biophys Acta 760, 411 (1983)).
9. In aqueous solutions (pH 7.0), Abs/Em = 554/573 nm for R415 and 591/608 nm for T7471.

Product List — 11.1 Probes for Actin

Cat #	Product Name	Unit Size
A12375	actin from rabbit muscle	1 mg
A12373	actin from rabbit muscle, Alexa Fluor® 488 conjugate *in solution*	200 µg
A12374	actin from rabbit muscle, Alexa Fluor® 568 conjugate *in solution*	200 µg
A34050	actin from rabbit muscle, Alexa Fluor® 594 conjugate *in solution*	200 µg
A34051	actin from rabbit muscle, Alexa Fluor® 647 conjugate *in solution*	200 µg
A22281	Alexa Fluor® 350 phalloidin	300 U
A12379	Alexa Fluor® 488 phalloidin	300 U
A22282	Alexa Fluor® 532 phalloidin	300 U
A22283	Alexa Fluor® 546 phalloidin	300 U
A12380	Alexa Fluor® 568 phalloidin	300 U
A12381	Alexa Fluor® 594 phalloidin	300 U
A22284	Alexa Fluor® 633 phalloidin	300 U
A34054	Alexa Fluor® 635 phalloidin	300 U
A22287	Alexa Fluor® 647 phalloidin	300 U
A22285	Alexa Fluor® 660 phalloidin	300 U
A22286	Alexa Fluor® 680 phalloidin	300 U
B7474	biotin-XX phalloidin	50 U
B607	BODIPY® FL phallacidin	300 U
B3475	BODIPY® 558/568 phalloidin	300 U
B3416	BODIPY® 581/591 phalloidin	300 U
B12382	BODIPY® 650/665 phalloidin	300 U
B7464	BODIPY® TR-X phallacidin	300 U
C22280	cofilin, chicken muscle, recombinant from *Escherichia coli*	50 µg
C606	coumarin phallacidin	300 U
C12376	cytochalasin B, BODIPY® FL conjugate	100 µg
C12377	cytochalasin D, BODIPY® FL conjugate	100 µg
C12378	cytochalasin D, BODIPY® TMR conjugate	100 µg
D12371	deoxyribonuclease I, Alexa Fluor® 488 conjugate	5 mg
D12372	deoxyribonuclease I, Alexa Fluor® 594 conjugate	5 mg
D970	deoxyribonuclease I, fluorescein conjugate	5 mg
D7497	deoxyribonuclease I, Oregon Green® 488 conjugate	5 mg
D972	deoxyribonuclease I, Texas Red® conjugate	5 mg
E7463	eosin phalloidin	300 U
F432	fluorescein phalloidin	300 U
J7473	jasplakinolide	100 µg
L12370	latrunculin A	100 µg
L22290	latrunculin B	100 µg
N354	*N*-(7-nitrobenz-2-oxa-1,3-diazol-4-yl)phallacidin (NBD phallacidin)	300 U
O7466	Oregon Green® 488 phalloidin	300 U
O7465	Oregon Green® 514 phalloidin	300 U
P3457	phalloidin	1 mg
P29	*N*-(1-pyrene)iodoacetamide	100 mg
R415	rhodamine phalloidin	300 U
T7471	Texas Red®-X phalloidin	300 U

For current prices or to order online, visit probes.invitrogen.com

11.2 Probes for Tubulin and Other Cytoskeletal Proteins

Fluorescent Tubulin

For researchers studying microtubule dynamics *in vitro* and *in vivo*, Molecular Probes offers the Oregon Green® 514 conjugate of highly purified, bovine brain tubulin (T12391, Figure 11.15), the standard source of tubulin for research. Our fluorescent tubulin preparation typically contains one or two Oregon Green® 514 fluorophores per tubulin dimer, and it is subjected to three cycles of temperature-dependent polymerization/depolymerization to select for functional subunits prior to packaging.[1,2]

Fluorescent tubulin has been employed to directly observe cell cycle–dependent microtubule dynamics[3] and mitotic spindle morphogenesis[4] in *Xenopus* oocyte extracts, to visualize tubulin transport in neurons[3] and to follow the loss of localized fluorescence that occurs after cells are treated with anti-microtubule agents.[5] Using tetramethylrhodamine-labeled tubulin and GTP-coated beads prepared from our yellow-green–fluorescent FluoSpheres® microspheres (Section 6.5, Table 6.7), Mitchison has identified an exchangeable GTP-binding site on the plus end of paclitaxel-stabilized fluorescent microtubules, suggesting that β-tubulin is exposed at the plus end and α-tubulin at the minus end of microtubules.[6]

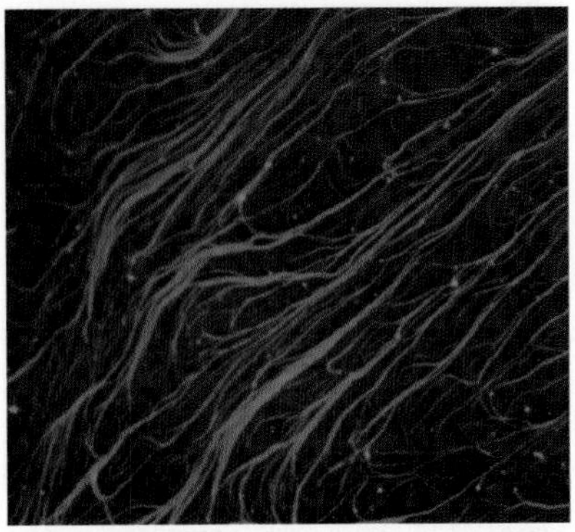

Figure 11.15 Microtubules formed from a solution of Oregon Green® 514 tubulin (T12391) in a polymerization buffer consisting of 0.5 mg GTP in 1 mL of 1% DMSO, 1 mM $MgCl_2$, 1 mM EDTA and 80 mM PIPES at pH 6.8. This solution was subsequently diluted 1:4, pipetted onto a glass slide and photographed using an epifluorescence microscope equipped with a longpass filter appropriate for fluorescein.

Tubulin-Selective Probes

Anti-α-Tubulin Monoclonal Antibody

When used in conjunction with an anti–mouse IgG secondary immunoreagent (Section 7.2, Table 7.1), Molecular Probes' anti–α-tubulin monoclonal antibody (A11126) enables researchers to visualize microtubules in fixed cells (Figure 7.42, Figure 7.91, Figure 7.92, Figure 11.16, Figure 11.17, Figure 11.18) and in fixed or frozen tissue sections from various species. This mouse monoclonal antibody, which recognizes amino acid residues 69–97 of the N-terminal structural domain, is also useful for detecting tubulin by ELISA or Western blotting, for screening expression libraries and as a probe for the N-terminal domain of α-tubulin.

The anti–α-tubulin monoclonal antibody is available either unlabeled (A11126) or as a biotin-XX conjugate (A21371). For detecting the biotinylated antibody, Molecular Probes carries a wide variety of fluorophore- and enzyme-labeled avidin, streptavidin and NeutrAvidin biotin-binding protein conjugates and NANOGOLD and Alexa Fluor® FluoroNanogold streptavidin (Section 7.6, Table 7.22).

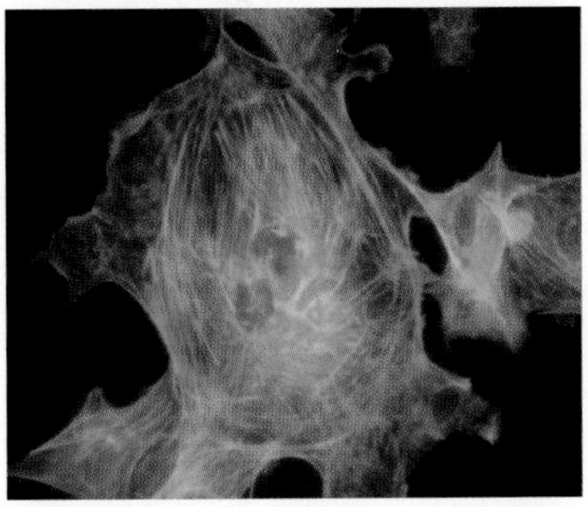

Figure 11.16 Bovine pulmonary artery endothelial cells were labeled with Alexa Fluor® 488 phalloidin (A12379) to stain F-actin and our mouse monoclonal anti–α-tubulin antibody (A11126) in combination with Alexa Fluor® 594 dye–conjugated $F(ab')_2$ fragment of goat anti–mouse IgG antibody (A11020) to stain microtubules. The multiple-exposure image was acquired using bandpass filter sets appropriate for Texas Red® dye and fluorescein.

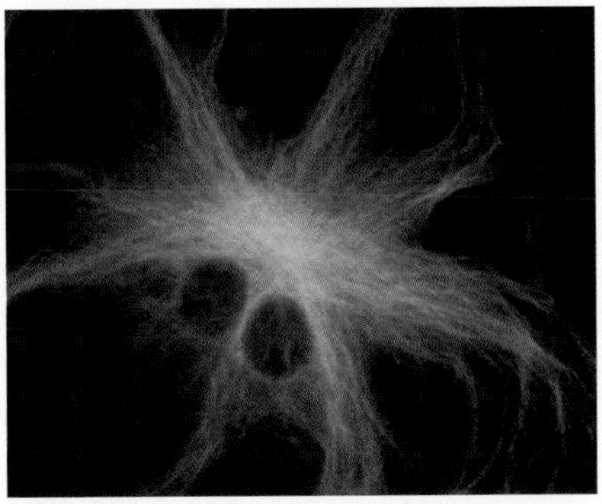

Figure 11.17 A bovine pulmonary artery endothelial cell labeled with mouse monoclonal anti–α-tubulin antibody (A11126) in combination with Alexa Fluor® 532 goat anti–mouse IgG antibody (A11002) to stain microtubules. The image was acquired using a bandpass filter set (excitation/emission 535 ± 17.5/590 ± 17.5 nm).

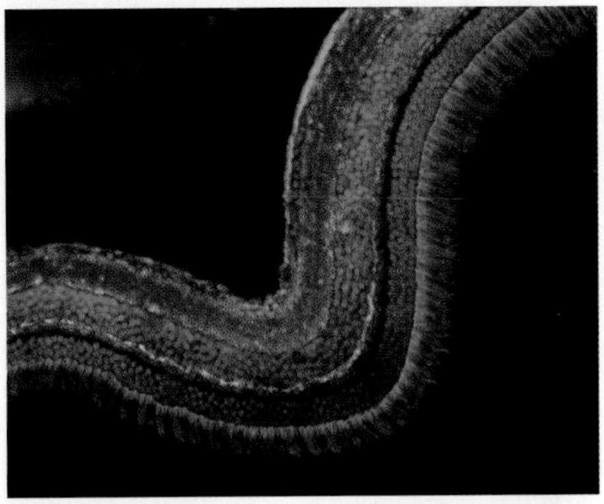

Figure 11.18 A zebrafish cryosection incubated with the biotin-XX conjugate of mouse monoclonal anti–α-tubulin antibody (A21371). The signal was amplified with TSA Kit #22, which includes HRP–streptavidin and Alexa Fluor® 488 tyramide (T20932). The sample was then incubated with the mouse monoclonal FRet 6 antibody and was visualized with Alexa Fluor® 647 goat anti-mouse IgG (A21235), which is pseudocolored magenta. Finally, the nuclei were counterstained with SYTOX® Orange nucleic acid stain (S11368).

We have extensively utilized the mouse IgG_1 monoclonal anti–α-tubulin antibody during development and evaluation of our Zenon® technology (Section 7.3, Table 7.13), with outstanding results (Figure 11.19, Figure 11.20). Labeling of our anti–α-tubulin antibody can be completed in minutes on even submicrogram quantities of the antibody, using the procedure described in Figure 7.59.

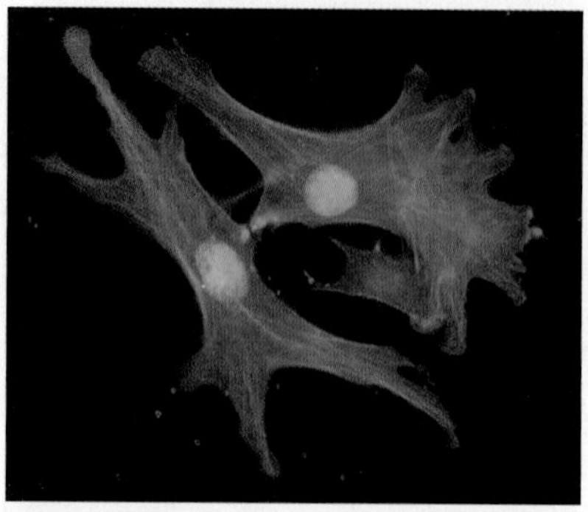

Figure 11.19 Fixed and permeabilized bovine pulmonary artery endothelial cells stained with Alexa Fluor® 350 phalloidin (A22281), an anti–α-tubulin antibody (A11126) and the anti-cdc6 peptide antibody (A21286). The anti–α-tubulin antibody was labeled with the Zenon® Alexa Fluor® 568 Mouse IgG_1 Labeling Kit (Z25006) and the anti-cdc6 peptide antibody was labeled with the Zenon® Alexa Fluor® 488 Mouse IgG_1 Labeling Kit (Z25002).

Paclitaxel

Molecular Probes offers paclitaxel (P3456) for *research purposes only* at a purity of >98% by HPLC. Paclitaxel, formerly referred to as taxol in some scientific literature, is the approved generic name for the anticancer pharmaceutical Taxol (a registered trademark of Bristol-Myers Squibb Co.). Paclitaxel promotes tubulin assembly, producing aggregates that cannot be depolymerized by dilution, calcium ions, cold or a number of microtubule-disrupting drugs.[7,8] Cultured cells treated with paclitaxel are blocked in the G_2 and M phases of the cell cycle.[9]

Fluorescent Paclitaxel Conjugates

Molecular Probes exclusively provides three fluorescent derivatives of paclitaxel: Oregon Green® 488 paclitaxel [10–12] (Flutax-2, P22310), BODIPY® FL paclitaxel (P7500) and BODIPY® 564/570 paclitaxel (P7501). These fluorescent paclitaxel derivatives are promising tools for imaging microtubule formation and motility. Their fluorescent attributes should also make these conjugates useful reagents for screening compounds that affect microtubule assembly.

Oregon Green® 488 paclitaxel [12] is an important probe for labeling tubulin filaments in live cells. The fluorescent label on this probe is attached by derivatizing the 7β-hydroxy group of native paclitaxel (Figure 11.21), a strategy that permits selective binding of the probe to microtubules with high affinity at 37°C [12] (K_d ~10^{-7} M). Oregon Green® 488 paclitaxel has been utilized in a high-throughput fluorescence polarization–based assay to screen for paclitaxel (Taxol) biomimetics.[10] Molecular Probes' scientists have successfully used Oregon Green® 488 paclitaxel to label microtubules of live HeLa (Figure 11.22), NIH 3T3, A-10 and BC3H1 cells. *Xenopus laevis* [13] and bovine brain [14] microtubules have also been stained with Oregon Green® 488 paclitaxel.

In the BODIPY® FL and BODIPY® 564/570 paclitaxel derivatives, the *N*-benzoyl substituent of the 3-phenylisoserine portion of native paclitaxel is replaced by a BODIPY® propionyl substituent (Figure 11.23). As an alternative to chemically modifying tubulin with a reactive fluorophore, a published method describes the use of these BODIPY® paclitaxel derivatives to generate fluorescent microtubules that are stable at room temperature for one week or longer.[15]

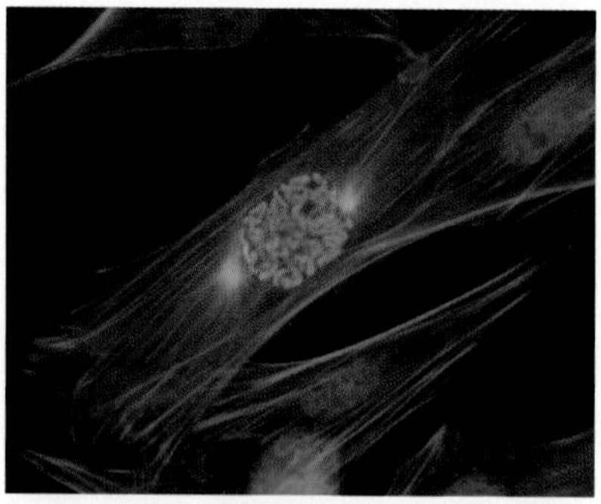

Figure 11.20 A prometaphase muntjac skin fibroblast stained with Alexa Fluor® 350 phalloidin (A22281), an anti–α-tubulin antibody (A11126) and an anti-cdc6 peptide antibody (A21286). The anti–α-tubulin antibody was prelabeled with the Zenon® Alexa Fluor® 488 Mouse IgG_1 Labeling Kit (Z25002) and the anti-cdc6 peptide antibody was prelabeled with the Zenon® Alexa Fluor® 647 Mouse IgG_1 Labeling Kit (Z25008).

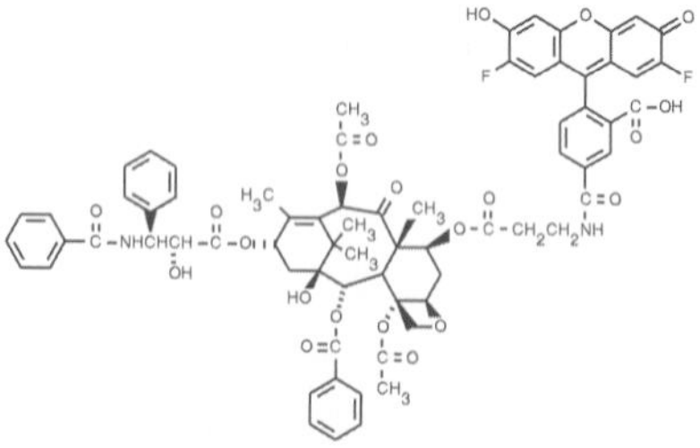

Figure 11.21 P22310 paclitaxel, Oregon Green® 488 conjugate (Oregon Green® 488 Taxol; Flutax-2).

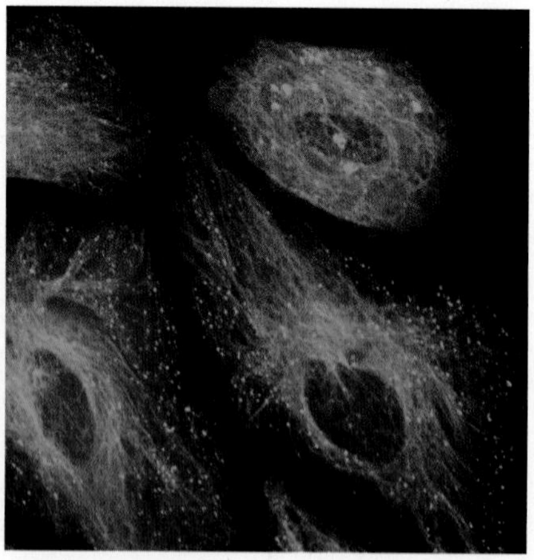

Figure 11.22 Microtubules were assembled, stabilized and visualized with the aid of green-fluorescent Oregon Green® 488 paclitaxel (P22310). Viable HeLa cells were incubated with the conjugate for one hour, followed by several washes with phosphate-buffered saline containing 2% bovine serum albumin. The image was acquired using a confocal laser-scanning microscope and a filter set appropriate for fluorescein.

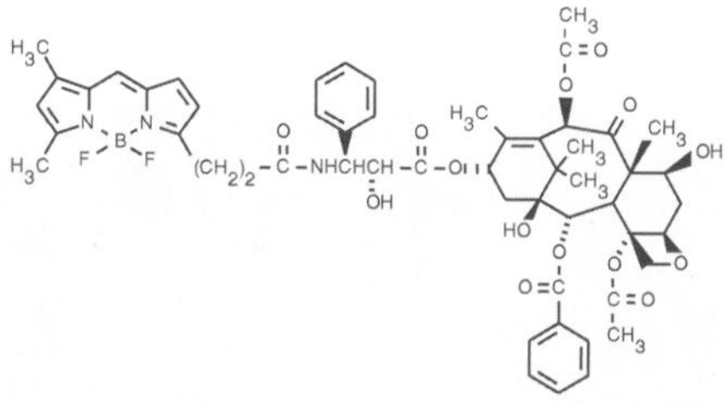

Figure 11.23 P7500 paclitaxel, BODIPY® FL conjugate (BODIPY® FL Taxol).

In contrast to the Oregon Green® 488 derivative, the BODIPY® FL and BODIPY® 564/570 paclitaxel derivatives do not appear to be suitable for labeling intracellular tubulin in most cases.

BODIPY® FL Vinblastine

BODIPY® FL vinblastine (V12390, Figure 11.24), a fluorescent analog of the anticancer drug vinblastine, is a useful probe for labeling β-tubulin and for investigating drug-transport mechanisms.[16,17] Vinblastine inhibits cell proliferation by capping microtubule ends, thereby suppressing mitotic spindle microtubule dynamics.[18] Another fluorescent vinblastine derivative, vinblastine 4′-anthranilate, reportedly binds to the central portion of the primary sequence of β-tubulin and inhibits polymerization.[16,19–21]

In addition, intracellular accumulation of vinblastine has been associated with a vinblastine-specific modulating site on P-glycoprotein, a drug-efflux pump that is overexpressed in multidrug-resistant (MDR) cells[22] (Section 15.6). This highly lipophilic P-glycoprotein substrate has also been used to study the role of P-glycoprotein in drug penetration through the blood-brain barrier.[23] Fluorescently labeled vinblastine analogs, including BODIPY® FL vinblastine, have been employed to measure drug-transport kinetics in MDR cells.[24]

Other Probes for Tubulin

The nuclear stain DAPI (D1306, D3571; FluoroPure™ Grade, D21490) binds tightly to purified tubulin *in vitro* without interfering with microtubule assembly or GTP hydrolysis. DAPI binds to tubulin at sites different from those of paclitaxel, colchicine and vinblastine, and its binding is accompanied by shifts in the absorption spectra and fluorescence enhancement. The affinity of DAPI for polymeric tubulin is sevenfold greater than for dimeric tubulin, making DAPI a sensitive tool for investigating microtubule assembly kinetics.[25–28] DAPI has been used to screen for potential antimicrotubule drugs in a high-throughput assay.[29]

Bis-ANS (B153) is a potent inhibitor of *in vitro* microtubule assembly.[30] This fluorescent probe binds to the hydrophobic clefts of proteins with an affinity about 10–100 times higher than that of 1,8-ANS (A47, Section 13.5) and exhibits a significant fluorescence enhancement upon binding. The bis-ANS binding site on tubulin lies near the critical contact region for microtubule assembly, but it is distinct from the binding sites for colchicine, vinblastine, podophyllotoxin and maytansine.[31–33] Bis-ANS was used to investigate structural changes in tubulin monomers and dimers during time- and temperature-dependent decay.[34,35]

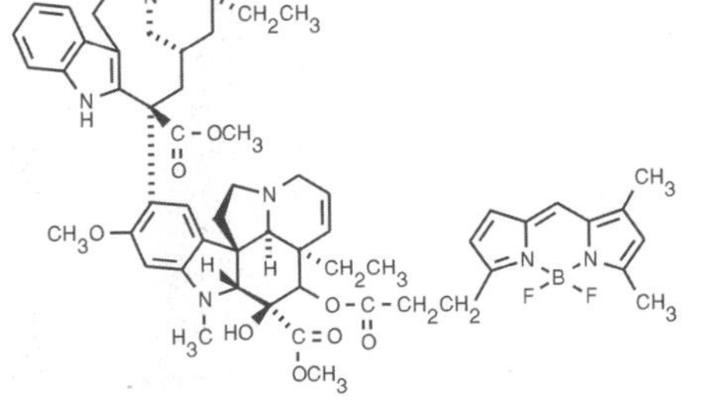

Figure 11.24 V12390 vinblastine, BODIPY® FL conjugate (BODIPY® FL vinblastine).

DCVJ (4-(dicyanovinyl)julolidine; D3923), which binds to a specific site on the tubulin dimer,[3] has been reported to be a useful probe for following polymerization of tubulin in live cells.[36] DCVJ staining in live cells is mostly blocked by cytochalasin D.[37] Additionally, DCVJ emits strong green fluorescence upon binding to bovine brain calmodulin.[38] The hydrophobic surfaces of tubulin have also been investigated with the environment-sensitive probes nile red[39] (N1142) and prodan[40] (P248).

Probes for Other Cytoskeletal Proteins

Phosphoinositides and Related Products

Many actin-binding proteins, including cofilin (C22280, Section 11.1), profilin, gelsolin, vinculin, dystrophin and talin, reportedly bind phosphoinositides — in particular, phosphatidylinositol 4,5-diphosphate (PtdIns(4,5)P_2) — through phosphoinositide-binding motifs that include C2 (PKC-conserved region 2), PH (pleckstrin homology), FYVE (Fab1p/YOTP/Vac1p/EEA1), ENTH (Epsin NH_2-terminal homology) and PX (phox or phagocyte oxidase) homology domains.[41] Consequently, our BODIPY® phosphatidylinositol phosphates (Section 17.4, Table 17.3), the Shuttle PIP carriers that transfer these probes into live cells (Figure 17.34) and other phosphatidylinositol-related products — PIP Strips and PIP MicroStrips membranes, PIP Array membranes and PIP Beads — in Section 17.4 may have considerable utility for detecting actin-binding proteins in solution and in cells.

Anti–Glial Fibrillary Acidic Protein (GFAP) Antibody

The 50,000-dalton type-III intermediate filament protein known as glial fibrillary acidic protein (GFAP) is a major structural component of astrocytes and some ependymal cells.[42] GFAP associates with the calcium-binding protein annexin II2-p11(2) and S-100.[43,44] Association with these proteins together with phosphorylation regulates GFAP polymerization. Astrocytes respond to brain injury by proliferation (astrogliosis); one of the first events to occur during astrocyte proliferation is increased GFAP expression. Molecular Probes' anti-GFAP antibody (A21282) and its Alexa Fluor® 488 and Alexa Fluor® 594 conjugates (A21294, A21295; Figure 11.25) can be used to aid in the identification of cells of glial lineage. Interestingly, antibodies to GFAP have been detected in individuals with dementia.[45] In the

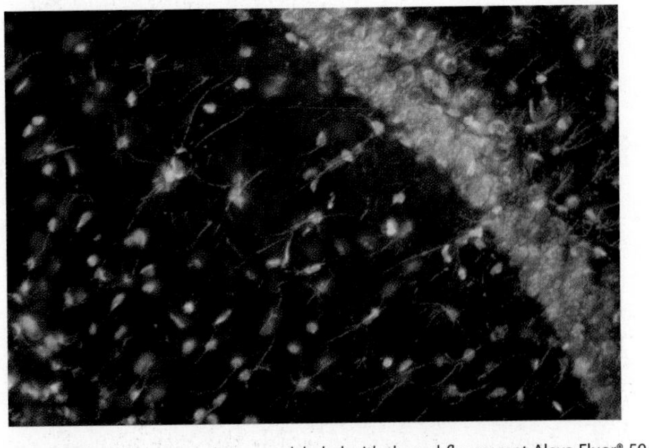

Figure 11.25 Rat brain cryosections were labeled with the red-fluorescent Alexa Fluor® 594 conjugate of anti–glial fibrillary acidic protein antibody (A21295). Nuclei were counterstained with TOTO®-3 iodide (T3604, pseudocolored blue).

central nervous system, anti-GFAP antibody stains both astrocytes and ependymal cells. In the peripheral nervous system, Schwann cells, satellite cells and enteric glial cells are stained. Tumors of glial origin contain high amounts of GFAP. No positive staining is observed in skin, connective tissue, adipose tissue, lymphatic tissue, muscle, gastrointestinal tract including liver and pancreas, kidney, ureter, and bladder. Molecular Probes' anti-GFAP antibody does not crossreact with vimentin, which is frequently co-expressed in glioma cells and some astrocytes, nor does it crossreact with Bergmann glia cells, gliomas or other glial cell–derived tumors.

Anti-Desmin Antibody

Desmin, encoded by a gene belonging to the intermediate filament protein gene family,[46–48] is the main intermediate filament in mature skeletal, cardiac and smooth muscle cells. Both striated and smooth muscle cells can be labeled by an anti-desmin antibody, although not all muscle tissue contains desmin (e.g., aorta smooth muscle). Identification of desmin is useful in distinguishing habdomyosarcomas and leiomyosarcomas from other vimentin-positive sarcomas. Molecular Probes offers a mouse IgG_1 monoclonal anti-desmin antibody (A21283), which can potentially be used with our fluorescent secondary antibodies (Table 7.5, Figure 12.27) as a marker for typing soft tissue sarcomas. Anti-desmin immunohistochemical staining in cell-block preparations may also be helpful in distinguishing mesothelial cells from carcinoma.[49] Our exclusive Zenon® Mouse IgG_1 Labeling Kits (Section 7.3, Table 7.13) should be useful for preparing fluorescent complexes of our mouse IgG_1 monoclonal anti-desmin antibody in almost any color, as well as for preparing enzyme complexes (Figure 7.59).

Anti-Synapsin I Antibody

Synapsin I, an actin-binding protein, is localized exclusively to synaptic vesicles and thus serves as an excellent marker for synapses in brain and other neuronal tissues.[50,51] Synapsin I inhibits neurotransmitter release, an effect that is abolished upon its phosphorylation by Ca^{2+}/calmodulin–dependent protein kinase II.[52] For assaying the localization and abundance of synapsin I by Western blot analysis, immunohistochemistry (Figure 17.12), enzyme-linked immunosorbent assay (ELISA) or immunoprecipitation, Molecular Probes offers a polyclonal rabbit anti–synapsin I antibody as an affinity-purified IgG fraction (A6442, Section 17.3). Although raised against bovine synapsin I, this antibody also recognizes human, rat and mouse synapsin I; it has little or no activity against synapsin II.

Endostatin Protein

The angiogenesis inhibitor endostatin is an endogenous 20,000-dalton carboxyl-terminal fragment of collagen XVIII (Figure 16.14) that induces regression of tumors in mice. Although its complete mechanism of action is being investigated, research has found that endostatin appears to trigger suppression of both apoptosis factors and cell proliferation genes, including *c-myc* gene expression, resulting in a potent antimigratory effect.[53] On the cell surface, endostatin has been shown to bind to glypicans or transmembrane heparan sulfate proteoglycans.[54,55] Once endocytosed, the protein has been demonstrated to bind to tropomyosin,[56] a protein that stabilizes the pointed end of actin filaments by slowing depolymerization.[57] Indirectly, endostatin appears to induce increases in cytosolic Ca^{2+} and cAMP.[53] Molecular Probes offers recombinant Endostatin protein (E23377) for research purposes; recombinant Angiostatin protein, another protein useful for angiogenesis research, is also available (A23375, Section 15.4).

References

1. Methods Enzymol 196, 478 (1991); **2.** Development 103, 675 (1988); **3.** Cell 62, 579 (1990); **4.** J Cell Biol 112, 925 (1991); **5.** J Cell Biol 130, 639 (1995); **6.** Science 261, 1044 (1993); **7.** J Biol Chem 269, 23399 (1994); **8.** Pharmacol Ther 25, 83 (1984); **9.** Cancer Treat Rep 62, 1219 (1978); **10.** Biochemistry 40, 11975 (2001); **11.** Cell Motil Cytoskeleton 49, 1 (2001); **12.** J Biol Chem 275, 26265 (2000); **13.** J Cell Biol 148, 883 (2000); **14.** Chem Biol 7, 275 (2000); **15.** Biotechniques 25, 188 (1998); **16.** Mol Pharmacol 62, 1238 (2002); **17.** Cancer Res 62, 6864 (2002); **18.** Mol Biol Cell 6, 1215 (1995); **19.** Mol Pharmacol 62, 1 (2002); **20.** FEBS Lett 416, 251 (1997); **21.** J Biol Chem 271, 14707 (1996); **22.** Eur J Biochem 244, 664 (1997); **23.** J Neurochem 67, 1688 (1996); **24.** Biochemistry 33, 12665 (1994); **25.** Acta Histochem 94, 54 (1993); **26.** Arch Biochem Biophys 303, 159 (1993); **27.** Eur J Biochem 165, 613 (1987); **28.** J Biol Chem 260, 2819 (1985); **29.** Anal Biochem 315, 49 (2003); **30.** J Biol Chem 259, 14647 (1984); **31.** Biochemistry 33, 11900 (1994); **32.** Biochemistry 33, 11891 (1994); **33.** Biochemistry 25, 3536 (1986); **34.** Biochemistry 37, 4687 (1998); **35.** Biochemistry 34, 13367 (1995); **36.** Biochemistry 28, 6678 (1989); **37.** Immunol Lett 33, 285 (1992); **38.** J Biochem (Tokyo) 109, 499 (1991); **39.** J Biol Chem 265, 14899 (1990); **40.** Eur J Biochem 204, 127 (1992); **41.** Chem Phys Lipids 101, 93 (1999); **42.** Neurochem Res 25, 1439 (2000); **43.** Biochem Biophys Res Commun 208, 910 (1995); **44.** Biochim Biophys Acta 1313, 268 (1996); **45.** J Neurol Sci 151, 41 (1997); **46.** Proc Natl Acad Sci U S A 73, 4344 (1976); **47.** J Cell Sci 23, 243 (1977); **48.** EMBO J 1, 1649 (1982); **49.** Acta Cytol 44, 976 (2000); **50.** Science 226, 1209 (1984); **51.** J Cell Biol 96, 1337 (1983); **52.** Molecular and Cellular Mechanisms of Neurotransmitter Release, Stjarne L, et al., Eds. pp. 31–45 (1994); **53.** FASEB J 15, 1044 (2001); **54.** Mol Cell 7, 811 (2001); **55.** Proc Natl Acad Sci U S A 98, 12509 (2001); **56.** J Biol Chem 276, 25190 (2001); **57.** Biochemistry 28, 1048 (1989).

Data Table — 11.2 Probes for Tubulin and Other Cytoskeletal Proteins

Cat #	MW	Storage	Soluble	Abs	EC	Em	Solvent	Notes
B153	672.85	L	pH >6	395	23,000	500	MeOH	1, 2
D1306	350.25	L	H_2O, DMF	344	23,000	450	pH 7	3
D3571	457.49	L	H_2O, MeOH	344	22,000	450	pH 7	3
D3923	249.31	L	DMF, DMSO	456	61,000	493	MeOH	4
D21490	350.25	L	H_2O, DMF	344	23,000	450	pH 7	3, 5
N1142	318.37	L	DMF, DMSO	552	45,000	636	MeOH	6
P248	227.31	L	DMF, MeCN	363	19,000	497	MeOH	7
P3456	853.92	F,D	MeOH, DMSO	228	30,000	none	MeOH	
P7500	1023.89	FF,D,L	DMSO	504	66,000	511	MeOH	
P7501	1098.98	FF,D,L	DMSO	565	121,000	571	MeOH	
P22310	1319.28	FF,D,L	DMSO, EtOH	494	80,000	522	pH 9	
V12390	1043.02	F,D,L	DMSO, DMF	503	83,000	510	MeOH	

For definitions of the contents of this data table, see "Navigating *The Handbook*" in the introductory pages.

Notes

1. B153 is soluble in water at 0.1–1.0 mM after heating.
2. Bis-ANS (B153) bound to tubulin has Abs = 392 nm, Em = 490 nm and a fluorescence quantum yield of 0.23 (Biochemistry 33, 11900 (1994)).
3. DAPI undergoes an approximately 9-fold fluorescence enhancement on binding to polymerized tubulin. Abs = 345 nm, Em = 446 nm (J Biol Chem 260, 2819 (1985)).
4. The absorption and fluorescence emission maxima of DCVJ (D3923) bound to tubulin are essentially the same as in methanol (Biochemistry 28, 6678 (1989)).
5. This product is specified to equal or exceed 98% analytical purity by HPLC.
6. The fluorescence emission maximum of nile red (N1142) bound to tubulin is 623 nm (J Biol Chem 265, 14899 (1990)).
7. The fluorescence emission maximum of prodan (P248) bound to tubulin is ~450 nm (Eur J Biochem 204, 127 (1992)).

Product List — 11.2 Probes for Tubulin and Other Cytoskeletal Proteins

Cat #	Product Name	Unit Size
A21283	anti-desmin, mouse IgG_1, monoclonal 131-15014 *1 mg/mL*	100 µL
A21282	anti-glial fibrillary acidic protein, mouse IgG_1, monoclonal 131-17719 (anti-GFAP) *1 mg/mL*	100 µL
A21294	anti-glial fibrillary acidic protein, mouse IgG_1, monoclonal 131-17719, Alexa Fluor® 488 conjugate (anti-GFAP, Alexa Fluor® 488 conjugate) *1 mg/mL*	50 µL
A21295	anti-glial fibrillary acidic protein, mouse IgG_1, monoclonal 131-17719, Alexa Fluor® 594 conjugate (anti-GFAP, Alexa Fluor® 594 conjugate) *1 mg/mL*	50 µL
A11126	anti-α-tubulin (bovine), mouse IgG_1, monoclonal 236-10501	50 µg
A21371	anti-α-tubulin (bovine), mouse IgG_1, monoclonal 236-10501, biotin-XX conjugate	50 µg
B153	bis-ANS (4,4′-dianilino-1,1′-binaphthyl-5,5′-disulfonic acid, dipotassium salt)	10 mg
D1306	4′,6-diamidino-2-phenylindole, dihydrochloride (DAPI)	10 mg
D21490	4′,6-diamidino-2-phenylindole, dihydrochloride (DAPI) *FluoroPure™ grade*	10 mg
D3571	4′,6-diamidino-2-phenylindole, dilactate (DAPI, dilactate)	10 mg
D3923	4-(dicyanovinyl)julolidine (DCVJ)	25 mg
E23377	Endostatin™ protein (human, recombinant) *1 mg/mL*	250 µL
N1142	nile red	25 mg
P3456	paclitaxel (Taxol equivalent) *for use in research only*	5 mg
P7501	paclitaxel, BODIPY® 564/570 conjugate (BODIPY® 564/570 Taxol)	10 µg
P7500	paclitaxel, BODIPY® FL conjugate (BODIPY® FL Taxol)	10 µg
P22310	paclitaxel, Oregon Green® 488 conjugate (Oregon Green® 488 Taxol; Flutax-2)	100 µg
P248	6-propionyl-2-dimethylaminonaphthalene (prodan)	100 mg
T12391	tubulin from bovine brain, Oregon Green® 514 conjugate *10 mg/mL*	10 µL
V12390	vinblastine, BODIPY® FL conjugate (BODIPY® FL vinblastine)	100 µg

For current prices or to order online, visit probes.invitrogen.com

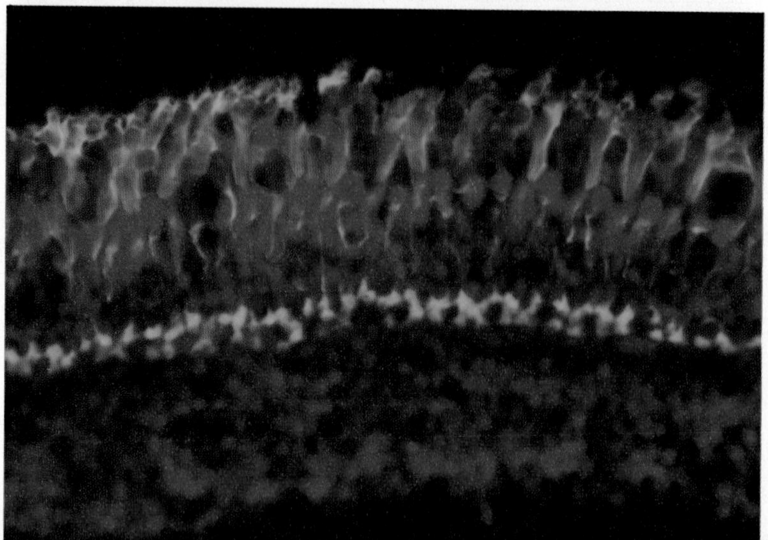

TSA Kit #9 and Hoechst 33258

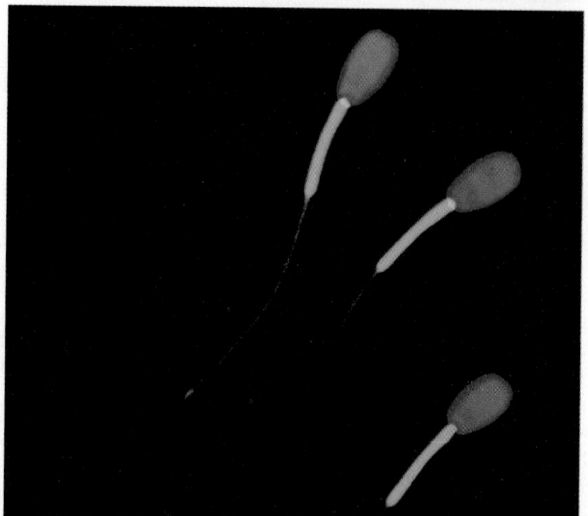

MitoTracker Green FM and Hoechst 33342; contributed by Peter Sutovsky, Oregon Health Sciences University

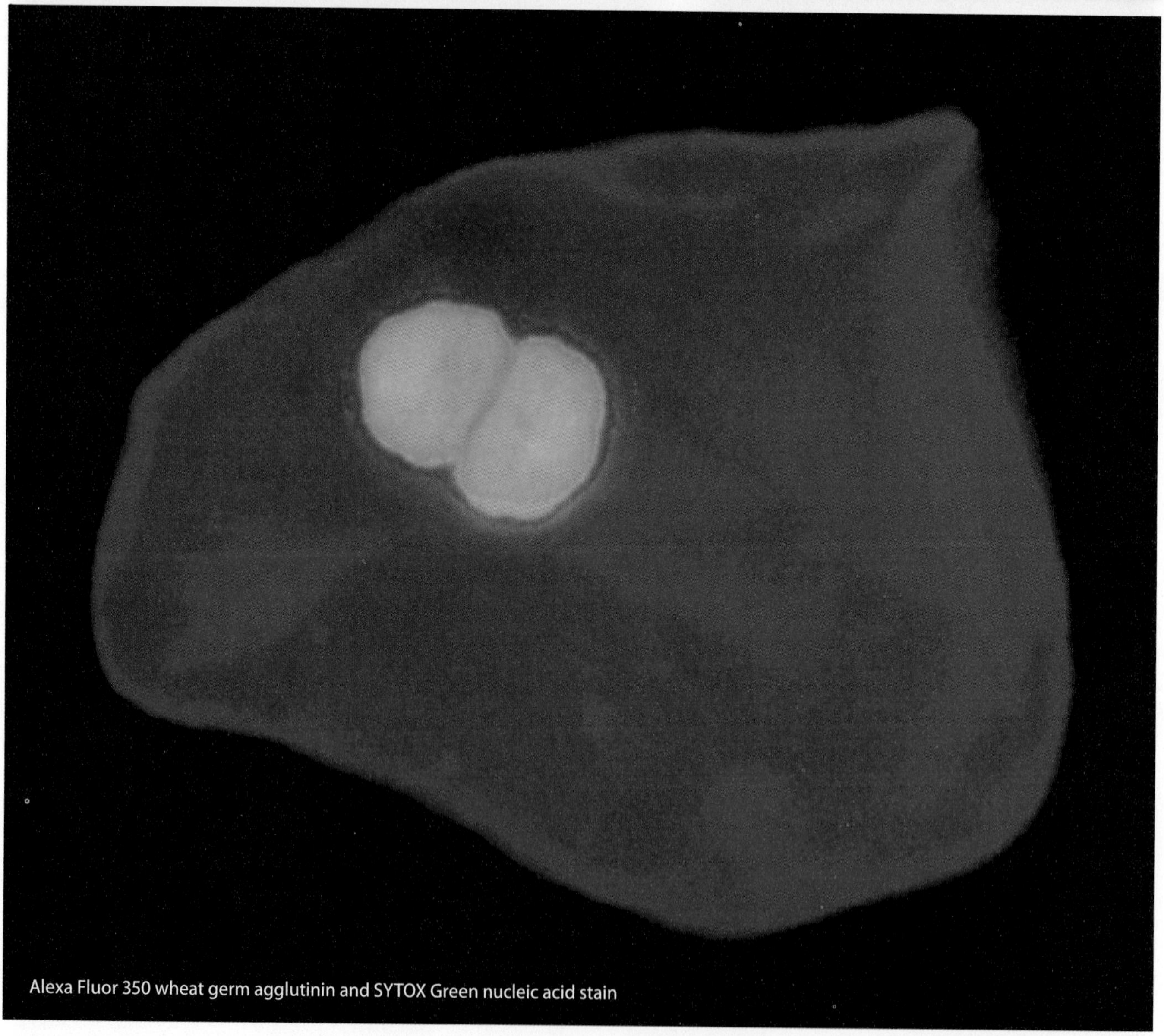

Alexa Fluor 350 wheat germ agglutinin and SYTOX Green nucleic acid stain

Chapter 12

Probes for Organelles

12.1 A Diverse Selection of Organelle Probes

Molecular Probes offers a diverse array of cell-permeant fluorescent stains that selectively associate with the mitochondria, lysosomes, endoplasmic reticulum and Golgi apparatus in live cells, including our exclusive MitoTracker®, MitoFluor™, LysoTracker®, LysoSensor™, RedoxSensor™ and ER-Tracker™ organelle stains (Table 12.1, Figure 12.1). These probes, which are compatible with most fluorescence instrumentation, provide researchers with powerful tools for investigating respiration, mitosis, apoptosis, multidrug resistance, substrate degradation and detoxification, intracellular transport and sorting and more. Moreover, unlike antibodies, these fluorescent probes can be used to investigate organelle structure and activity in live cells with minimal disruption of cellular function (Figure 12.2). Our live-cell organelle stains are particularly useful for demonstrating the colocalization of green-fluorescent protein (GFP) expression and selective organelle staining by our red-fluorescent organelle stains [1–4] (see Note 12.1 "Product Highlight: Fluorescent Probes for Use with GFP"). An excellent compendium of human diseases that affect intracellular transport processes through lysosomes, Golgi and endoplasmic reticulum (ER) has been published.[5] A particularly useful general review of cell organelles and other topics appears at the Cell Biology Topics web site (http://cellbio.utmb.edu/cellbio/).

We have also introduced a large collection of organelle-specific monoclonal antibodies for both mammalian and yeast cells that can be used for immunolocalization, immunoprecipitation and Western blot analysis. Our antibodies to mitochondrial proteins (Section 12.2, Table 12.4, Table 12.6, Figure 12.30) provide a unique set of tools for understanding the assembly and function of the mitochondria. Cell-permeant and -impermeant fluorescent stains for the nucleus are described in Chapter 8, probes for the cytoskeleton in Chapter 11, and plasma membrane stains in Chapter 13. A variety of probes for phagovacuoles, endosomes and lysosomes — including membrane markers as well as ligands for studying receptor-mediated endocytosis — are discussed in Section 16.1.

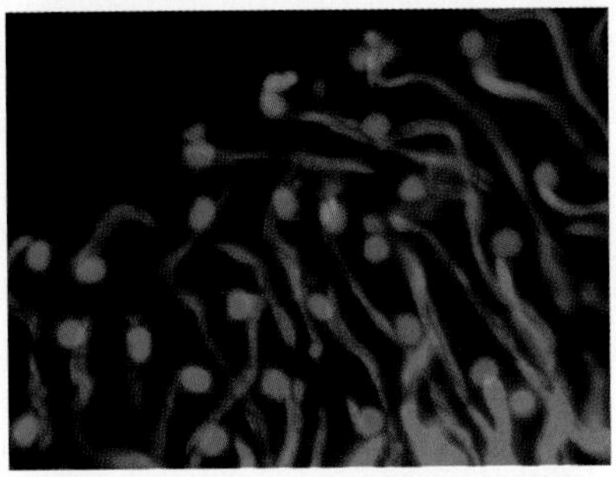

Figure 12.2 Euphyrene spermatozoa from the pupal testis of the gypsy moth (*Lymantria dispar*) that were incubated in a solution of MitoTracker® Red CMXRos (M7512). The sample was subsequently fixed and the nuclear material was counterstained with the blue-fluorescent dsDNA dye, DAPI (D1306, D3571, D21490). Image contributed by Laura K. Garvey, University of Connecticut.

References

1. Mol Biol Cell 11, 1789 (2000); 2. J Biol Chem 274, 37233 (1999); 3. Biochem Biophys Res Commun 242, 390 (1998); 4. J Biol Chem 272, 14817 (1997); 5. Traffic 1, 836 (2000).

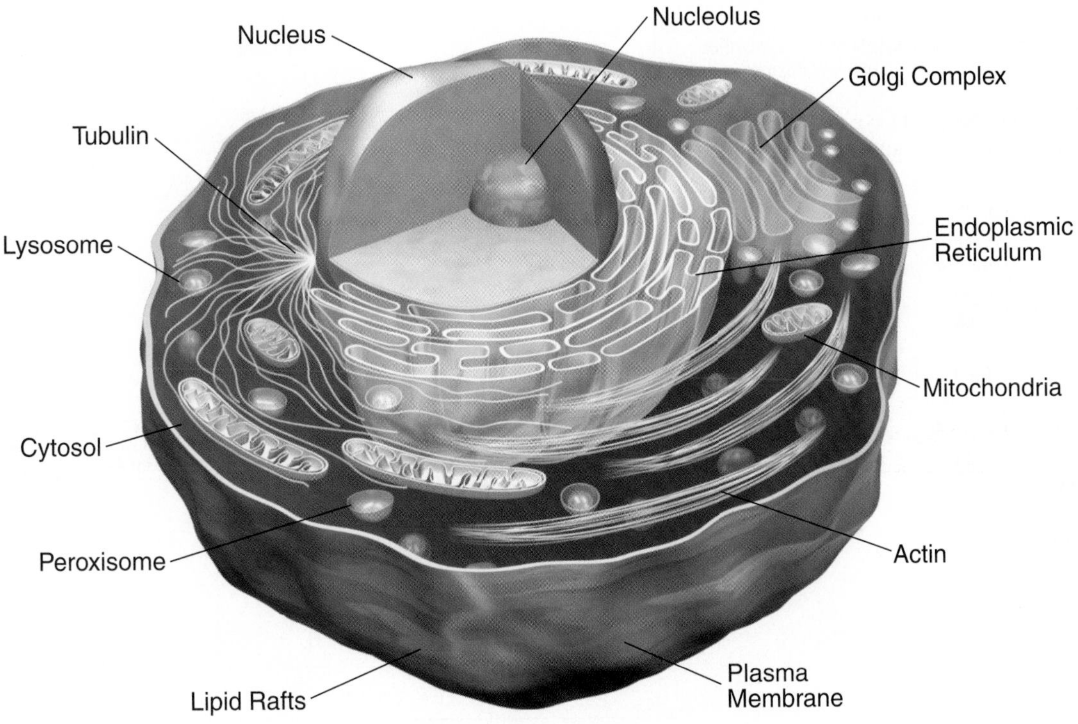

Figure 12.1 Diagram of an animal cell.

Table 12.1 — Molecular Probes' organelle-selective probes

Green-Fluorescent Probes		Yellow- and Orange-Fluorescent Probes		Red-Fluorescent Probes		Blue-Fluorescent and Nonfluorescent Probes	
Cat #	Probe	Cat #	Probe	Cat #	Probe	Cat #	Probe
Probes for Mitochondria — Section 12.2							
A1372	Nonyl acridine orange	D288	4-Di-1-ASP (DASPMI)	M7512	MitoTracker® Red CMXRos *	L6868	Lucigenin †
D273	DiOC$_6$(3)	D426	DASPEI	T3168	JC-1 ‡		
D378	DiOC$_7$(3) (for plant mitochondria)	M7510	MitoTracker® Orange CMTMRos *	D22421	JC-9 ‡		
M7502	MitoFluor™ Green	R634	Rhodamine 6G	M22425	MitoTracker® Red 580 *		
M7514	MitoTracker® Green FM *	R648MP	Rhodamine B, hexyl ester	M22424	MitoFluor™ Red 589		
R302, R22420	Rhodamine 123	T639	Tetramethylrosamine	M22422	MitoFluor™ Red 594		
S7529	SYTO® 18 yeast mitochondrial stain	T668	Tetramethylrhodamine, methyl ester	M22426	MitoTracker® Deep Red 633 *		
T3168	JC-1 ‡	T669	Tetramethylrhodamine, ethyl ester				
D22421	JC-9 ‡						
Probes for Mitochondria (Probes Requiring Intracellular Oxidation) — Section 12.2							
D632	Dihydrorhodamine 123	D633	Dihydrorhodamine 6G	M7513	MitoTracker® Red CM-H_2XRos *		
		M7511	MitoTracker® Orange CM-H_2TMRos *	R14060	RedoxSensor™ Red CC-1 §		
Probes for Acidic Organelles, Including Lysosomes — Section 12.3							
L7526	LysoTracker® Green DND-26	D113	Dansyl cadaverine	L7528	LysoTracker® Red DND-99	D1552	DAMP **
		L12491	LysoTracker® Yellow HCK-123	R14060	RedoxSensor™ Red CC-1 §	H22845	Hydroxystilbamidine
						L7525	LysoTracker® Blue DND-22
						L12490	LysoTracker® Blue-White DPX
Probes for Acidic Organelles, Including Lysosomes (pH-Sensitive Probes) — Section 12.3							
L7534	LysoSensor™ Green DND-153	A1301	Acridine orange	N3246	Neutral red	L7533	LysoSensor™ Blue DND-167
L7535	LysoSensor™ Green DND-189	L7545	LysoSensor™ Yellow/Blue DND-160 ‡			L7545	LysoSensor™ Yellow/Blue DND-160 ‡
		L22460	LysoSensor™ Yellow/Blue 10,000 MW dextran ‡			L22460	LysoSensor™ Yellow/Blue 10,000 MW dextran ‡
Probes for the Endoplasmic Reticulum — Section 12.4							
B7447	BODIPY® FL brefeldin A	B7449	BODIPY® 558/568 brefeldin A			E12353	ER-Tracker™ Blue-White DPX
D272	DiOC$_5$(3)	D282	DiIC$_{18}$(3)				
D273	DiOC$_6$(3)	D384	DiIC$_{16}$(3)				
		R648MP	Rhodamine B, hexyl ester				
		R634	Rhodamine 6G				
		T668	Tetramethylrhodamine, methyl ester				
		T669	Tetramethylrhodamine, ethyl ester				
Probes for the Golgi Apparatus — Section 12.4							
B7447	BODIPY® FL brefeldin A	B7449	BODIPY® 558/568 brefeldin A	D3521	BODIPY® FL C$_5$-ceramide ‡	B7450	Brefeldin A **
D3521	BODIPY® FL C$_5$-ceramide ‡			B22650	BODIPY® FL C$_5$-ceramide complexed to BSA ‡		
B22650	BODIPY® FL C$_5$-ceramide complexed to BSA ‡			D7540	BODIPY® TR ceramide ‡		
D3522	BODIPY® FL C$_5$-sphingo-myelin						
N1154	NBD C$_6$-ceramide						
N22651	NBD C$_6$-ceramide complexed to BSA						
N3524	NBD C$_6$-sphingomyelin						

* Aldehyde-fixable probe. † Chemiluminescent probe. ‡ Dual-emission spectrum. § The differential distribution of the oxidized product between mitochondria and lysosomes appears to depend on the oxidation–reduction (redox) potential of the cytosol. ** Nonfluorescent probe.

Note 12.1 — Product Highlight

Fluorescent Probes for Use with GFP

Probes for Multiplexed Detection of GFP-Expressing Cells

The green-fluorescent protein (GFP) reporter has added a new dimension to the analysis of protein localization, allowing real-time examination in living cells of processes that have conventionally been observed through immunocytochemical "snapshots" in fixed specimens.[1] Using other spectrally distinct probes and markers (Table 1) adds extra data dimensions and reference points to these experiments (Figure 1).

The majority of the applications summarized in Table 1 involve living cells, tissues and organisms. There are many other instances where research objectives call for complementary use of immunochemical and GFP-based protein localization techniques. These experiments demand the unmatched combination of brightness, photostability and spectral separation provided by our Alexa Fluor® dye–labeled secondary detection reagents. For two-color combinations with GFP, we recommend our Alexa Fluor® 555, Alexa Fluor® 568 or Alexa Fluor® 594 dye–labeled secondary antibodies (Section 7.2, Table 7.1). For three-color detection, add Alexa Fluor® 635 or Alexa Fluor® 647 dye-labeled antibodies. Some immunohistochemical procedures such as paraffin embedding of fixed tissue result in loss of the intrinsic fluorescence of GFP. In other cases, GFP expression levels may simply be too low for detection above background autofluorescence.[2] Antibodies to GFP provide remedies for these problems (Figure 2). We offer unlabeled mouse monoclonal and rabbit polyclonal antibodies to GFP (A6455, A11120, A11121, A11122; Section 7.5) as well as Alexa Fluor® dye–labeled rabbit polyclonal antibodies to GFP (A21311, A21312, A31851, A31852; Section 7.5).

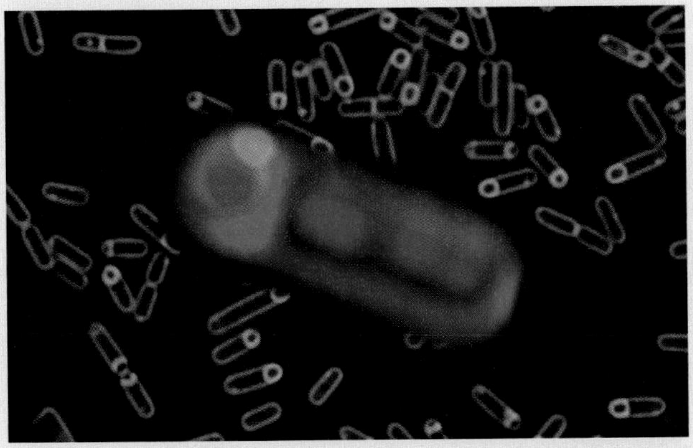

Figure 1. The morphology of sporulating *Bacillus subtilis* in the early stages of forespore engulfment. The membranes and chromosomes of both the forespore and the larger mother cell are stained with FM® 4-64 (red; T3166, T13320) and DAPI (blue; D1306, D3571, D21490), respectively. The small green-fluorescent patch indicates the localization of a GFP fusion to SPoIIIE, a protein essential for translocation of the forespore chromosome that may also regulate membrane fusion events (see Proc Natl Acad Sci U S A 96, 14553 (1999)). The background contains sporangia at various stages in the engulfment process stained with MitoTracker® Green FM (green, M7514) and FM® 4-64 (red).

Alexa Fluor® Dyes — Highly Fluorescent FRET Acceptors

Proximity-dependent fluorescence resonance energy transfer (FRET) allows detection of protein–protein interactions with much higher spatial resolution than conventional diffraction-limited microscopy.[3] Alexa Fluor dyes with strong absorption in the 500–600 nm wavelength range are excellent FRET acceptors from GFP (Table 2). An assay to detect activation of GFP–GTPase fusions developed by researchers at Scripps Research Institute[4] utilizes the GTPase-binding domain (PBD) of PAK1, a protein that binds to GTPases only in their activated GTP-bound form. GTPase activation is indicated by FRET from GFP to PDB labeled with Alexa Fluor 546 C_5-maleimide at a single N-terminal cysteine residue. This assay has been used to determine the location and dynamics of rac and Cdc42 GTPase activation in living cells.[4–6]

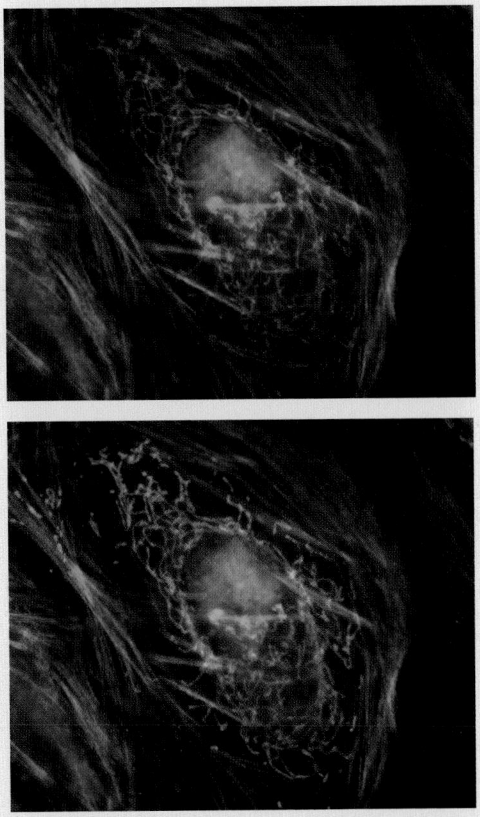

Figure 2. HeLa cell transfected with pShooter pCMV/myc/mito/GFP, then fixed and permeabilized. Green-fluorescent protein (GFP) localized in the mitochondria was labeled with mouse IgG2a anti-GFP antibody (A11120) and detected with orange-fluorescent Alexa Fluor® 555 goat anti-mouse IgG antibody (A21422), which colocalized with the dim GFP fluorescence. F-actin was labeled with green-fluorescent Alexa Fluor® 488 phalloidin (A12379), and the nucleus was stained with blue-fluorescent DAPI (D1306, D3571, D21490). The sample was mounted using ProLong® Gold antifade reagent (P36930). Some GFP fluorescence is retained in the mitochondria after fixation (top), but immunolabeling and detection greatly improve visualization (bottom).

continued on next page

continued from previous page

Normalizing Expression and Translation Signals

In 2002, researchers in Scott Fraser's laboratory at the California Institute of Technology reported a method of coinjecting Texas Red® dye–labeled 10,000 MW dextran and GFP vectors into sea urchin embryos. This method overcomes a multitude of problems inherent in making intra- and inter-embryo comparisons of gene expression levels using confocal microscopy. In particular, laser excitation and fluorescence collection efficiencies vary with the depth of the fluorescent protein in the embryo, and the orientation of different embryos on the coverslip varies relative to the microscope objective. Measuring the ratio of Texas Red® dextran and GFP fluorescence signals corrects for these spatial factors, providing a gene expression readout that is 2–50 times more accurate than conventional confocal microscopy procedures depending on the localization of GFP within an embryo.[7] A similar strategy was previously used to determine translation efficiencies of GFP-encoding mRNAs.[8]

References

1. Nat Rev Mol Cell Biol 3, 906 (2002); **2.** Anal Biochem 291, 175 (2001); **3.** J Cell Biol 160, 629 (2003); **4.** Science 290, 333 (2000); **5.** J Biol Chem 278, 31020 (2003); **6.** Nat Cell Biol 4, 32 (2002); **7.** Proc Natl Acad Sci U S A 99, 12895 (2002); **8.** J Cell Biol 147, 247 (1999).

Table 1 — Probes for multiplexed detection of GFP-expressing* cells

Target	Probe	Cat #	Ex/Em †	GFP Fusion Partner	Specimen	Reference
Physiological Indicators						
Intracellular Ca^{2+}	Fura-2 AM	F1201, F1221, F1225, F14185	335/505 ‡	Protein kinase C (PKC)	BHK cells	Biochem J 337, 211 (1999)
Intracellular Ca^{2+}	X-Rhod-1 AM	X14210	580/602	580/602 Trpm5 (melastatin-related cation channel)	CHO cells	Nat Neurosci 5, 1169 (2002)
Intracellular Ca^{2+}	Fura Red AM	F3020, F3021	488/650	GFP expressed specifically in pancreatic β-cells	Mouse pancreatic islets	Am J Physiol Endocrinol Metab 284, E177 (2003)
Intracellular pH	5-(and 6-)Carboxy SNARF®-1 AM ester acetate	C1271	568/635	Human growth hormone (hGH)	RIN1046-38 insulinoma cells	Am J Physiol Cell Physiol 283, C429 (2002)
Mitochondrial membrane potential	TMRM	T668	555/580	Cytochrome *c*	MCF-7 human breast carcinoma, HeLa	J Cell Sci 116, 525 (2003)
Superoxide (O_2^-)	Dihydroethidium	D1168	518/605	Cytochrome *c*	MCF-7 human breast carcinoma	J Biol Chem 278, 12645 (2003)
Synaptic activity	FM® 4-64	T3166, T13320	506/750 §	VAMP (vesicle-associated membrane protein)	Rat hippocampal neurons	Nat Neurosci 3, 445 (2000)
Receptors and Endocytosis						
Acetylcholine receptor	Tetramethylrhodamine α-bungarotoxin	T1175	553/577	Rapsyn (receptor-aggregating protein)	Zebrafish	J Neurosci 21, 5439 (2001)
Epidermal growth factor (EGF)	Rhodamine EGF	E3481	555/581	EGF receptor	MTLn3 rat mammary adenocarcinoma	Mol Biol Cell 11, 3873 (2000)
Endosomes	Transferrin from human serum, Alexa Fluor® 546 conjugate	T23364	556/573	β2-adrenergic receptor (β2AR)	HEK 293, rat hippocampal neurons	Brain Res 984, 21 (2003)
Endosomes	Transferrin from human serum, Alexa Fluor® 568 conjugate	T23365	578/603	PrP^c (cellular prion protein)	SN56 cells	J Biol Chem 277, 33311 (2002)
Endosomes	FM® 4-64	T3166, T13320	506/750 §	PrP^c (cellular prion protein)	SN56 cells	J Biol Chem 277, 33311 (2002)
Organelles						
Endoplasmic reticulum	ER-Tracker™ Blue-White DPX	E12353	375/520 ‡	HSD17B7 gene product (3-ketosteroid reductase)	HeLa, NIH 3T3	Mol Endocrinol 17, 1715 (2003)
Golgi complex	BODIPY® TR ceramide	D7540	589/617	PrP^c (cellular prion protein)	SN56 cells	J Biol Chem 277, 33311 (2002)
Lysosomes	LysoTracker® Red	L7528	577/590	Heparanase	Primary human fibroblasts, MDA-231 (human breast carcinoma)	Exp Cell Res 281, 50 (2002)

Table 1 — Probes for multiplexed detection of GFP-expressing* cells — continued

Target	Probe	Cat #	Ex/Em †	GFP Fusion Partner	Specimen	Reference
Mitochondria	MitoTracker® Red	M7512	578/599	Sam5p (mitochondrial carrier for S-adenosylme-thionine)	Yeast (*Saccharomyces cerevisiae*)	EMBO J 22, 5975 (2003)
Nuclear DNA	DAPI	D1306, D3571, D21490	358/461	Histone H2B	HeLa	Methods 29, 42 (2003)
Nuclear DNA	Hoechst 33342	H1399, H3570, H21492	350/461	Histone H1	BALB/c 3T3 fibroblasts	Nature 408, 877 (2000)
Nuclear DNA	SYTO® 17	S7579	621/634	HIV-1 integrase	HeLa	J Biol Chem 278, 33528 (2003)
Nuclear DNA	SYTO® 59	S11341	622/645	Microtubule plus-end binding protein	Porcine kidney epithelial cells (LLCPK)	Mol Biol Cell 14, 916 (2003)
Nuclear DNA	TO-PRO®-3	T3605	642/661	Citron kinase	HeLa	J Cell Sci 114, 3273 (2001)
Plasma membrane	DiI	D282, D3911, N22880	549/565	Synaptobrevin	*Xenopus* optic neurons	Nat Neurosci 4, 1093 (2001)
Other Subcellular Structures						
F-actin	Rhodamine phalloidin	R415	554/573	ERM (ezrin-radixin-moesin) proteins	Human peripheral blood T cells (PBT)	Nat Immunol 5, 272 (2004)
F-actin	Alexa Fluor® 568 phalloidin	A12380	578/603	Calponin	NIH 3T3	J Cell Sci 113 Pt 21, 3725 (2000)
Lipid rafts	Cholera toxin subunit B (recombinant), Alexa Fluor® 594 conjugate	C22842	590/617	Histocompatibility leukocyte antigen (HLA)-Cw4	NK cell–B-cell immunological synapse	Proc Natl Acad Sci U S A 98, 14547 (2001)
Cell Classification Markers						
Apoptotic cells	Annexin V, Alexa Fluor® 594 conjugate	A13203	590/617	GRASP65 (Golgi stacking protein)	HeLa	J Cell Biol 156, 495 (2002)
Transformed B lymphocytes (Raji cells)	CellTracker™ Orange CMTMR	C2927	550/575	ICAM-3 (intercellular adhesion molecule-3)	T-lymphocytes and antigen-presenting B cells	Nat Immunol 3, 159 (2002)
Cell-surface antigens	R-Phycoerythrin (streptavidin conjugate)	S866, S21388	565/575	GFP gene expression	NIH 3T3	Cytometry 25, 211 (1996)
Neurons	NeuroTrace® 530/615 red-fluorescent Nissl stain	N21482	530/620	Tau microtubule-binding protein (Purkinje cell marker)	Mouse brain slice	J Neurosci 23, 6392 (2003)
Neurons	Alexa Fluor® 594 hydrazide	A10438, A10442	588/613	Synaptophysin	*Aplysia californica* sensory neurons	Neuron 40, 151 (2003)

* This list covers only *Aequoria victoria* GFP, optimized mutants (e.g., EGFP) and green-fluorescent proteins from other species (e.g., *Renilla reniformis*). Fluorescent proteins with distinctly different excitation and emission characteristics (CFP, YFP, dsRed, etc.) are not included. † Fluorescence excitation (Ex) and emission (Em) maxima, in nm. ‡ Simultaneous imaging of GFP with fura-2 or ER-Tracker™ Blue-White DPX requires excitation wavelength–switching capability, because the fluorescence emission spectra overlap extensively. Even under these conditions, signal bleedthrough from one detection channel to the other may still be problematic, depending on the expression level and localization of the GFP chimera. See Biochem J 356, 345 (2001) for further discussion. § The fluorescence emission spectra of styryl dyes such as FM® 1-43 and FM® 4-64 are broad and extend into the green emission range of GFP. In some cases, FM® dye emission can overspill into the GFP detection channel, causing degraded resolution of image features. The excitation and emission spectra of FM® 1-43 overlap those of GFP more extensively than those of FM® 4-64. Therefore, using FM® 4-64 instead of FM® 1-43 is recommended to minimize this problem.

Table 2 — R_0 values for FRET from EGFP to Alexa Fluor® dyes*

Acceptor Dye	R_0 (Å)
Alexa Fluor® 546 dye	57
Alexa Fluor® 555 dye	63
Alexa Fluor® 568 dye	54
Alexa Fluor® 594 dye	53

* R_0 values in angstroms (Å) represent the distance at which fluorescence resonance energy transfer from the donor dye to the acceptor dye is 50% efficient. Values were calculated from spectroscopic data as outlined (see Note 1.2 "Technical Focus: Fluorescence Resonance Energy Transfer (FRET)" in Section 1.3).

12.2 Probes for Mitochondria

Mitochondria are found in eukaryotic cells, where they make up as much as 10% of the cell volume. They are pleomorphic organelles with structural variations depending on cell type, cell-cycle stage and intracellular metabolic state. The key function of mitochondria is energy production through oxidative phosphorylation (OxPhos) and lipid oxidation.[1,2] Several other metabolic functions are performed by mitochondria, including urea production and heme, non-heme iron and steroid biogenesis, as well as intracellular Ca^{2+} homeostasis. Mitochondria also play a pivotal role in apoptosis — a process by which unneeded cells are removed during development, and defective cells are selectively destroyed without surrounding organelle damage in somatic tissues[3–5] (Section 15.5). For many of these mitochondrial functions, there is only a partial understanding of the components involved, with even less information on mechanism and regulation.

Visualizing Mitochondria in Cells and Tissues

The morphology of mitochondria is highly variable. In dividing cells, the organelle can switch between a fragmented morphology with many ovoid-shaped mitochondria, as often shown in textbooks, and a reticulum in which the organelle is a single, many-branched structure. The cell cycle– and metabolic state–dependent changes in mitochondrial morphology are controlled by a set of proteins that cause fission and fusion of the organelle mass. Mutations in these proteins are the cause of several human diseases, indicating the importance of overall morphology for cell functioning (see Note 12.2 "Technical Focus: Mitochondria in Diseases"). Organelle morphology is also controlled by cytoskeletal elements, including actin filaments and microtubules. In nondividing tissue, overall mitochondrial morphology is very cell dependent, with mitochondria spiraling around the axoneme in spermatozoa, and ovoid bands of mitochondria intercalating between actomyosin filaments. There is emerging evidence of functionally significant heterogeneity of mitochondrial forms within individual cells.

The abundance of mitochondria varies with cellular energy level and is a function of cell type, cell-cycle stage and proliferative state. For example, brown adipose tissue cells,[6] hepatocytes[7] and certain renal epithelial cells[8] tend to be rich in active mitochondria, whereas quiescent immune-system progenitor or precursor cells show little staining with mitochondrion-selective dyes.[9] The number of mitochondria is reduced in Alzheimer's disease and their protein and nucleic acids are affected by reactive oxygen species, including nitric oxide[10] (Chapter 18).

Molecular Probes has a range of mitochondrion-selective dyes with which to monitor mitochondrial morphology and organelle functioning. The uptake of most mitochondrion-selective dyes is dependent on the mitochondrial membrane potential; nonyl acridine orange and possibly our MitoTracker® Green FM, MitoFluor™ Green and MitoFluor™ Red 589 probes are notable exceptions, although their membrane potential–independent uptake and fluorescence has been questioned in some cell types.[11,12] Mitochondrion-selective reagents enable researchers to probe mitochondrial activity, localization and abundance,[13,14] as well as to monitor the effects of some pharmacological agents, such as anesthetics that alter mitochondrial function.[15] Molecular Probes offers a variety of cell-permeant stains for mitochondria, as well as subunit-specific monoclonal antibodies directed against proteins in the oxidative phosphorylation (OxPhos) system, all of which are discussed below.

MitoTracker® Probes: Fixable Mitochondrion-Selective Probes

Although conventional fluorescent stains for mitochondria, such as rhodamine 123 and tetramethylrosamine, are readily sequestered by functioning mitochondria, they are subsequently washed out of the

Note 12.2 — Technical Focus

Mitochondria in Diseases

Given the multiple functions and numerous proteins present in the mitochondria, it is not surprising that genetically inherited defects of mitochondrial function are a major cause of morbidity and mortality in humans. In particular, there are several human diseases that have known defects in the proteins responsible for oxidative phosphorylation (OxPhos) in cells. Typically, such defects produce lactic acidemia, exercise intolerance or neurological disorders. Diseases of OxPhos are notoriously difficult to diagnose, and it is even more difficult to correlate their phenotype–genotype relationships. A subset of OxPhos defects is maternally inherited. These defects result from mutations in mitochondrial DNA (mtDNA), a small, 16-kb genome present in hundreds to thousands of copies per cell. mtDNA, which encodes 13 polypeptides of the OxPhos machinery, differs from the nuclear genome in its absence of histones, poor repair mechanisms and very limited recombination frequencies. As a result, mtDNA in somatic cells builds up mutations over time due to errors in replication that are not repaired and physical insult from a variety of toxins. Such accumulated mutations are implicated in a number of neurodegenerative diseases — notably Parkinson's and Alzheimer's diseases — where the mutation load triggers premature apoptotic or necrotic cell death. For example, a strong link has been established between exposure to the pesticide rotenone, a well-defined and specific inhibitor of OxPhos, and Parkinson's disease. mtDNA mutations function by reducing energy production within the cell and are thought to contribute to cancer and to aging. Likewise, mutations in the nuclear-encoded subunits of OxPhos have been found to regulate the life span in flies and worms. Many of the products listed in this section are useful tools for studying degenerative conditions, including our monoclonal antibodies specific for OxPhos proteins.[1]

Reference

1. "Immunological approaches to the characterization and diagnosis of mitochondrial disease." R.A. Capaldi, J. Murray, L. Byrne, M.S. Janes and M.F. Marusich, Mitochondrion (2004) in press.

cells once the mitochondrion's membrane potential is lost. This characteristic limits their use in experiments in which cells must be treated with aldehyde-based fixatives or other agents that affect the energetic state of the mitochondria. To overcome this limitation, Molecular Probes has developed MitoTracker® probes — a series of patented mitochondrion-selective stains that are concentrated by active mitochondria and well retained during cell fixation.[16] Because the MitoTracker® Orange, MitoTracker® Red and MitoTracker® Deep Red probes are also retained following permeabilization, the sample retains the fluorescent staining pattern characteristic of live cells during subsequent processing steps for immunocytochemistry, *in situ* hybridization or electron microscopy. In addition, MitoTracker® reagents eliminate some of the difficulties of working with pathogenic cells because, once the mitochondria are stained, the cells can be treated with fixatives before the sample is analyzed.

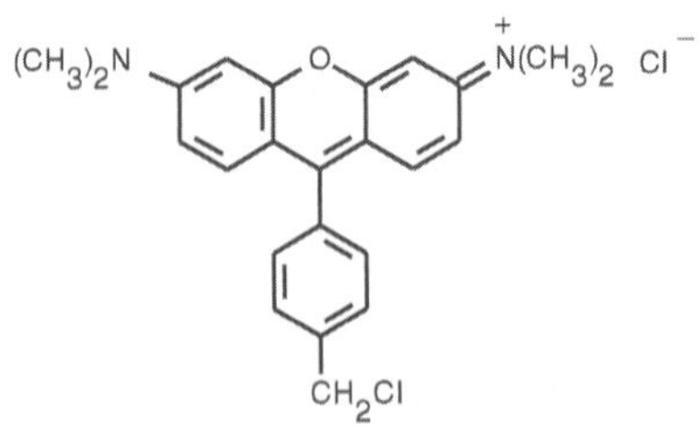

Figure 12.3 M7510 MitoTracker® Orange CMTMRos.

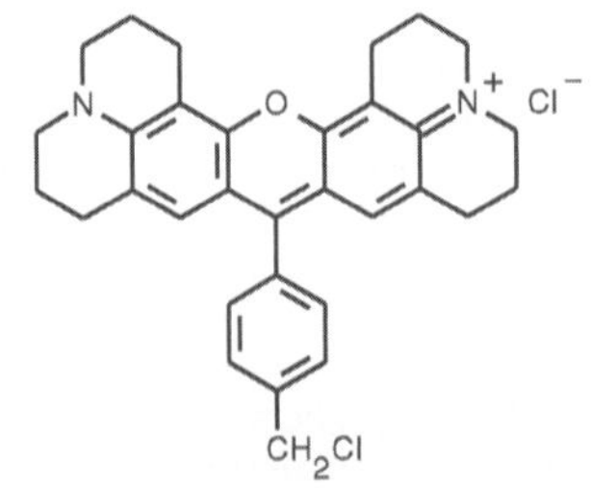

Figure 12.4 M7512 MitoTracker® Red CMXRos.

Properties of MitoTracker® Probes

MitoTracker® probes are cell-permeant mitochondrion-selective dyes that contain a mildly thiol-reactive chloromethyl moiety. The chloromethyl group appears to be responsible for keeping the dye associated with the mitochondria after fixation. To label mitochondria, cells are simply incubated in submicromolar concentrations of the MitoTracker® probe, which passively diffuses across the plasma membrane and accumulates in active mitochondria. Once their mitochondria are labeled, the cells can be treated with aldehyde-based fixatives to allow further processing of the sample; with the exception of MitoTracker® Green FM, subsequent permeabilization with cold acetone does not appear to disturb the staining pattern of the MitoTracker® dyes.

Molecular Probes offers seven MitoTracker® reagents that differ in spectral characteristics, oxidation state and fixability (Table 12.2). MitoTracker® probes are provided in specially packaged sets of 20 vials, each containing 50 µg for reconstitution as required.

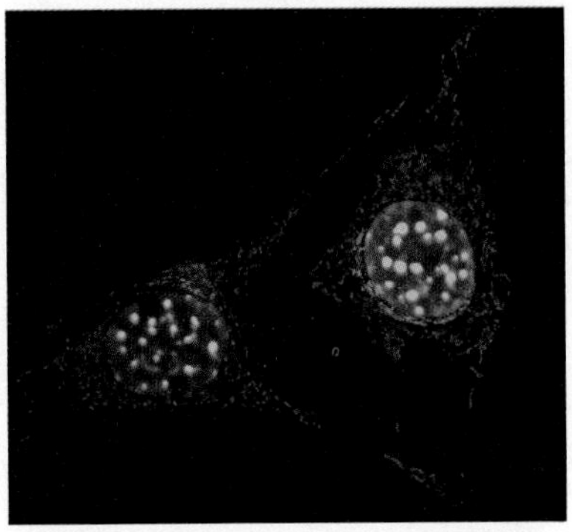

Figure 12.5 Live NIH 3T3 cells labeled with probes for mitochondria, Golgi and the nucleus. Mitochondria were labeled with MitoTracker® Red 580 (M22425), Golgi with BODIPY® FL ceramide (D3521, B22650), and the nucleus with Hoechst 33342 (H1399, H3570, H21492). The image was deconvolved using Huygens software (Scientific Volume Imaging).

Orange-, Red- and Infrared-Fluorescent MitoTracker® Dyes

We offer MitoTracker® derivatives of the orange-fluorescent tetramethylrosamine (MitoTracker® Orange CMTMRos, M7510; Figure 12.3) and the red-fluorescent X-rosamine (MitoTracker® Red CMXRos, M7512; Figure 12.4), as well as our newest derivatives, the MitoTracker® Red 580 and MitoTracker® Deep Red 633 probes (M22425, M22426; Figure 12.5, Figure 12.6). Because the MitoTracker® Red CMXRos, MitoTracker® Red 580 and MitoTracker® Deep Red 633 probes produce longer-wavelength fluorescence that is well resolved from the fluorescence of green-fluorescent dyes, they are suitable for multicolor labeling experiments (Figure 1.45, Figure 8.7, Figure 12.7, Figure 12.8, Figure 12.9), including those that employ image deconvolution techniques (see Note 12.3 "Technical Focus: Wide-Field Deconvolution Microscopy"). Also available are chemically reduced forms of the tetramethylrosamine (MitoTracker® Orange CM-H_2TMRos, M7511; Figure 12.10) and X-rosamine (MitoTracker® Red CM-H_2XRos, M7513; Figure 12.11) MitoTracker® probes. Unlike MitoTracker® Orange CMTMRos and MitoTracker® Red CMXRos, the reduced versions of these probes do not fluoresce until they enter an actively respiring cell, where they are oxidized to the fluorescent

Table 12.2 — Spectral characteristics of the MitoTracker® probes

Cat #	MitoTracker® Probe	Abs * (nm)	Em * (nm)	Oxidation State
M7514	MitoTracker® Green FM †	490	516	NA
M7510	MitoTracker® Orange CMTMRos	551	576	Oxidized
M7511	MitoTracker® Orange CM-H_2TMRos	551 ‡	576 ‡	Reduced
M7512	MitoTracker® Red CMXRos	578	599	Oxidized
M7513	MitoTracker® Red CM-H_2XRos	578 ‡	599 ‡	Reduced
M22425	MitoTracker® Red 580	581	644	NA
M22426	MitoTracker® Deep Red 633	644	665	NA

* Absorption (Abs) and fluorescence emission (Em) maxima, determined in methanol; values may vary somewhat in cellular environments. † MitoTracker® Green FM is nonfluorescent in aqueous environments. ‡ These reduced MitoTracker® probes are not fluorescent until oxidized. NA = Not applicable.

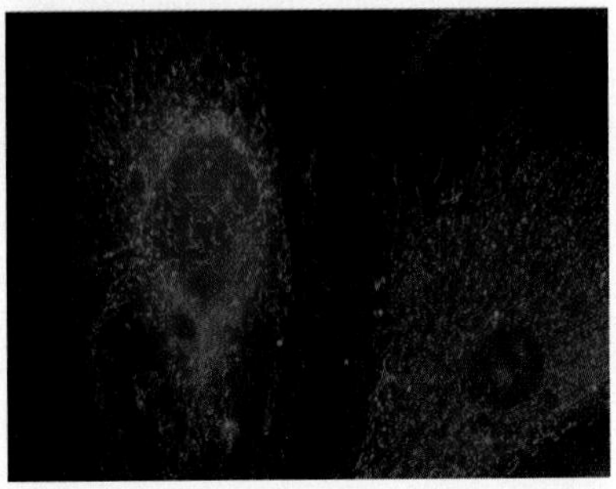

Figure 12.6 Mitochondria of live bovine pulmonary artery endothelial cells stained with the MitoTracker® Deep Red 633 dye (M22426).

Note 12.3 — Technical Focus

Wide-Field Deconvolution Microscopy

Wide-field deconvolution microscopy consists of a tripartite system: a conventional fluorescence microscope equipped with a movable z-axis stage that permits imaging of the specimen at different focus positions, a CCD camera for quantification of the light emitted by the specimen, and a software package that is capable of correcting for distortions and information loss inherent in the imaging process.

A dominant characteristic of images collected with a wide-field fluorescence microscope is that at some level the image becomes blurred. Blurring can come from two sources: 1) contributions of out-of-focus light to the imaging plane and 2) diffraction. Large scale blurring is the result of light that is reflected or emitted from objects above and below the focal plane. These contributions blur the in-focus object; generally the farther away the contribution is from the in-focus plane, the more blurred the image becomes. Diffraction is a result of the interaction of light with matter — the tendency of light waves to "bend" when they pass an obstacle. Even if an imaging system is perfectly focused, diffraction effects make it hard to discern details finer than roughly half the wavelength of the incident light. In the visible spectrum, the diffraction limit restricts resolution of objects smaller than ~200 nm (for blue light) to ~350 nm (for red light). Because many biologically interesting structures are smaller than 200 nm, the diffraction limit poses a serious limitation for optical microscopy.

Image restoration, or deconvolution, strives to correct these problems. When applied to wide-field data, deconvolution can significantly reduce blur contributions, resulting in increased resolution and greatly improved contrast[1] (Figure 1, Figure 2). Other types of microscopy may also benefit from deconvolution: confocal laser-scanning microscopy,[2] two-photon microscopy[2] (Figure 1.47) and 4Pi microscopy.[3] The combination of 4Pi microscopy and deconvolution is currently the pinnacle of optical resolution, allowing for resolution of objects at or below the diffraction limit.[4,5]

The mathematical algorithms for deconvolution take a variety of forms. The earliest algorithms, developed in the mid-1980s[6] employed techniques where the blur in each plane was suppressed by subtracting blurred versions of its "nearest neighbors." However, modern computing power has allowed far more sophisticated algorithms to become practical. For example, the fast maximum likelihood estimate (MLE) algorithm considers the light contributions made to that location by all other points within the measurement space. Doing so results in reassignment of the out-of-focus light back to the original source from which it has been estimated to have come. To improve accuracy, such algorithms function iteratively, refining the estimate of the true object in a step-by-step fashion.

Although requiring significant computing power, image deconvolution in conjunction with standard fluorescence imaging can provide significant improvements to the scientific value and quality of the images collected. Deconvolved images on our web site (probes.invitrogen.com) and in other publications make use of Huygens software (Scientific Volume Imaging), which utilizes an accelerated MLE algorithm. This software may be used for processing of time-resolved two- and three-dimensional multichannel images from wide-field, confocal, scanning disk confocal, two-photon and 4Pi microscopes. In all publications, we indicate in the picture captions when we have used deconvolution techniques to improve the resolution of the picture. Additional examples of pictures in which we have used image deconvolution include: Figure 1.114, Figure 11.4, Figure 12.5, Figure 12.34.

References

1. J Opt Soc Am A 8, 893 (1991); **2.** Bioimaging 4, 187 (1996); **3.** J Microsc 187, 1 (1997); **4.** Ultramicroscopy 87, 155 (2001); **5.** J Struct Biol 123, 236 (1998); **6.** Methods Cell Biol 30, 353 (1989).

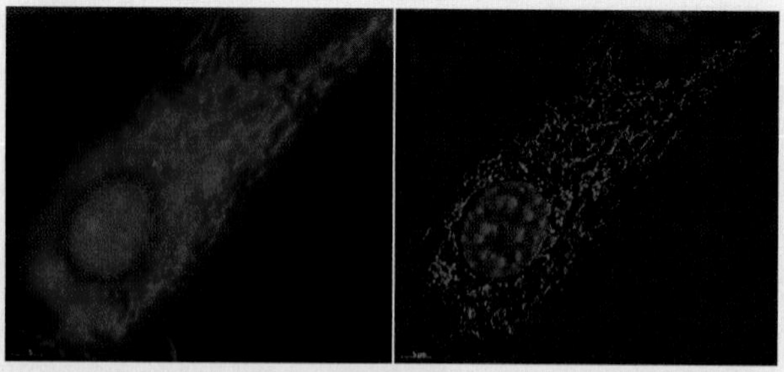

Figure 1. Bovine pulmonary artery endothelial cells were incubated with MitoTracker® Red 580 (M22425) to label the mitochondria. After fixation, the cells were counterstained with DAPI (D1306, D3571, D21490) to label the nucleus. The panels show the unprocessed image (left panel), and after deconvolution (right panel). The image was deconvolved using Huygens software (Scientific Volume Imaging). Deconvolution was performed using Imaris software (Bitplane AG).

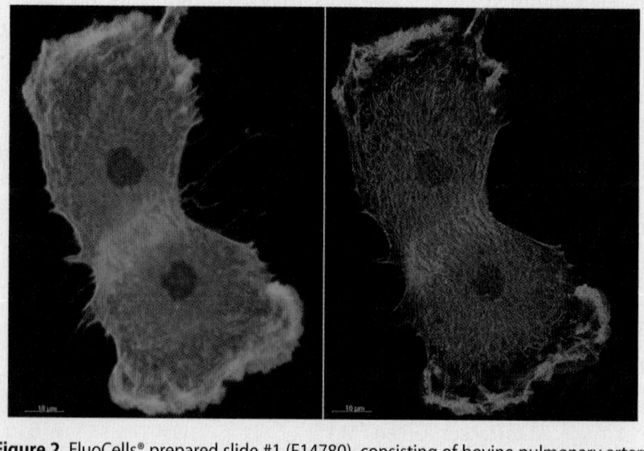

Figure 2. FluoCells® prepared slide #1 (F14780), consisting of bovine pulmonary artery endothelial cells incubated with MitoTracker® Red CMXRos (M7512) to label the mitochondria. After fixation and permeabilization, the cells were stained with BODIPY® FL phallacidin (B607) to label the filamentous actin (F-actin) and counterstained with DAPI (D1306, D3571, D21490) to label the nucleus. The panels show the unprocessed image (left panel), and after deconvolution (right panel). The image was deconvolved using Huygens software (Scientific Volume Imaging). Three-dimensional reconstruction was performed using Imaris software (Bitplane AG).

mitochondrion-selective probe and then sequestered in the mitochondria (Figure 12.12, Figure 12.49, Figure 15.13). The MitoTracker® probes have proven useful for:

- Assaying the role of a kinesin-like protein on germ plasm aggregation in *Xenopus* oocytes[17]
- Detecting early apoptosis (Section 15.5), which is marked by a disruption of mitochondrial transmembrane potential in all cell types studied[18–20]
- Determining the mechanism by which mitochondrial shape is established and maintained in yeast[21]
- Examining the time course of cell swelling in a human collecting-duct cell line using total internal reflection (TIR) microfluorimetry[22]
- Localizing a novel kinesin motor protein involved in transport of mitochondria along microtubules[23]
- Simultaneously observing fluorescent signals from a green-fluorescent protein (GFP) chimera and from the MitoTracker® dye[24–27] (see Note 12.1 "Product Highlight: Fluorescent Probes for Use with GFP" in Section 12.1)
- Studying the localization of mitochondria in fibroblasts transformed with cDNA of wild-type and mutant kinesin heavy chains[28]
- Visualizing mitochondria while characterizing the subcellular distribution of calcium channel subtypes in *Aplysia californica* bag cell neurons[29] and of the verotoxin B subunit in Vero cells[30]

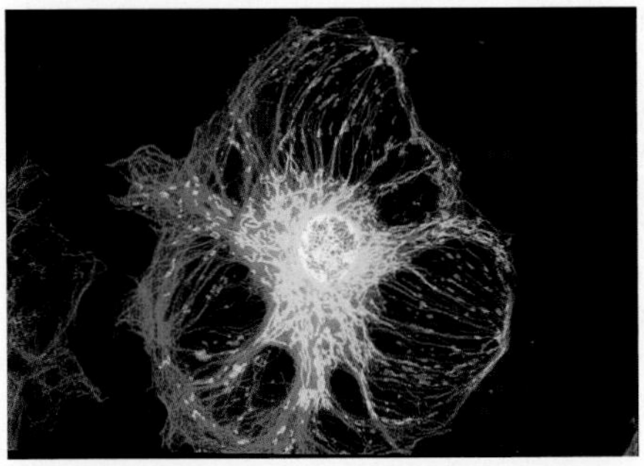

Figure 12.7 A bovine pulmonary artery endothelial cell (BPAEC) stained with mouse monoclonal anti–β-tubulin in conjunction with Oregon Green® 514 goat anti-mouse IgG antibody (O6383), MitoTracker® Red CMXRos (M7512) and DAPI (D1306, D3571, D21490).

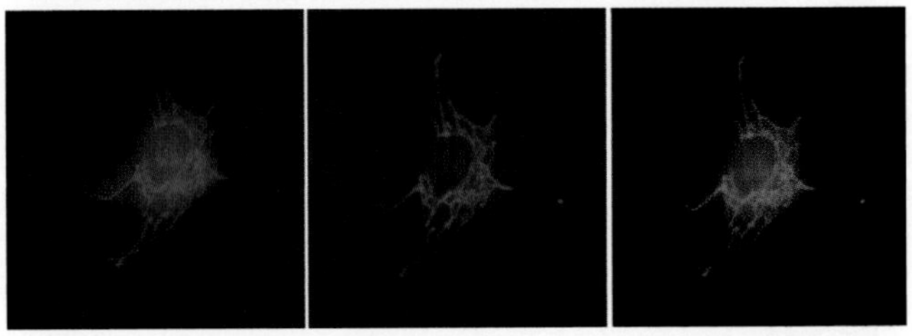

Figure 12.9 Live bovine pulmonary artery endothelial cells loaded with MitoTracker® Red CMXRos (M7512) then fixed and permeabilized. The cells were then treated with a cocktail containing two antibodies to cytochrome oxidase: the anti–OxPhos Complex IV subunit VIc (A6401) and anti–OxPhos Complex IV subunit I (A6403) antibodies. The mitochondria were then labeled with Alexa Fluor® 350 goat anti-mouse IgG antibody (A11045). The image on the right is an overlay of the first two images.

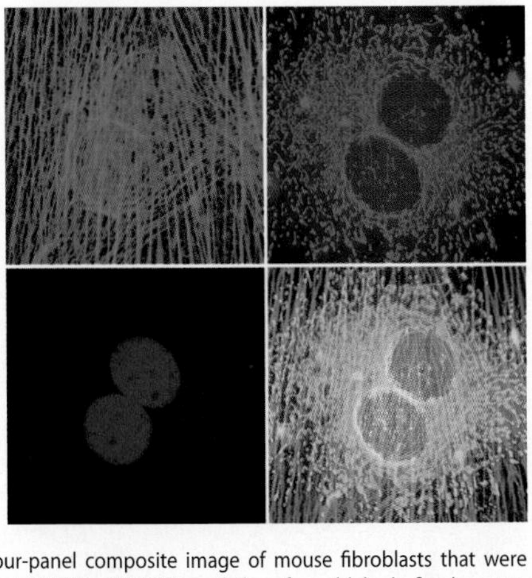

Figure 12.8 Four-panel composite image of mouse fibroblasts that were incubated with MitoTracker® Red CMXRos (M7512), and then formaldehyde-fixed, acetone-permeabilized and stained with the F-actin–specific probe, BODIPY® FL phallacidin (B607) and with DAPI (D1306, D3571, D21490). Images were obtained by taking single and multiple exposures through bandpass optical filter sets appropriate for fluorescein, the Texas Red® dye and DAPI.

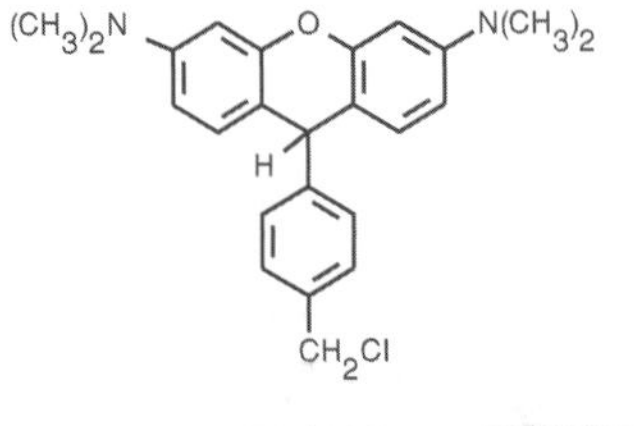

Figure 12.10 M7511 MitoTracker® Orange CM-H_2TMRos.

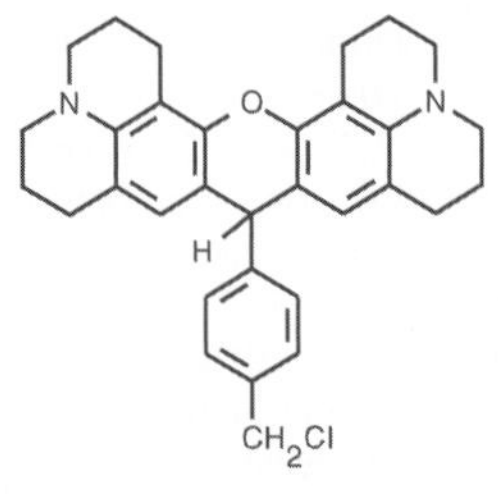

Figure 12.11 M7513 MitoTracker® Red CM-H_2XRos.

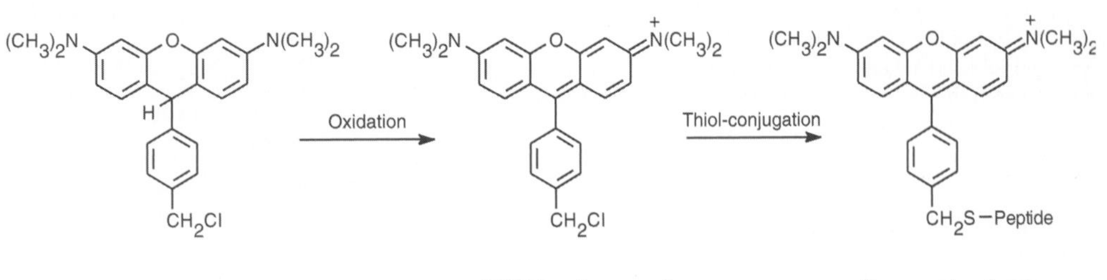

Figure 12.12 Intracellular reactions of our fixable, mitochondrion-selective MitoTracker® Orange CM-H_2TMRos (M7511). When this cell-permeant probe enters an actively respiring cell, it is oxidized to MitoTracker® Orange CMTMRos and sequestered in the mitochondria, where it can react with thiols on proteins and peptides to form aldehyde-fixable conjugates.

Our Vybrant® Apoptosis Assay Kit #11 (V35116, Section 15.5) utilizes MitoTracker® CMXRos in combination with Alexa Fluor® 488 annexin V in a two-color assay of apoptotic cells (Figure 15.92). MitoTracker® Orange CMTMRos and its reduced form CM-H_2TMRos have also been used to investigate the metabolic state of *Pneumocystis carinii* mitochondria.[31] Following fixation, the oxidized forms of the tetramethylrosamine and X-rosamine MitoTracker® dyes can be detected directly by fluorescence or indirectly with either anti-tetramethylrhodamine or anti–Texas Red® dye antibodies (A6397, A6399; Section 7.4).

MitoTracker® Green FM Probe

Mitochondria in cells stained with nanomolar concentrations of our patented MitoTracker® Green FM dye (M7514) exhibit bright green, fluorescein-like fluorescence (Figure 12.13, Figure 12.32, Figure 14.66, Figure 16.21). The MitoTracker® Green FM probe has the added advantage that it is essentially nonfluorescent in aqueous solutions and only becomes fluorescent once it accumulates in the lipid environment of mitochondria. Hence, background fluorescence is negligible, enabling researchers to clearly visualize mitochondria in live cells immediately following addition of the stain, without a wash step.

Unlike MitoTracker® Orange CMTMRos and MitoTracker® Red CMXRos, the MitoTracker® Green FM probe appears to preferentially accumulate in mitochondria regardless of mitochondrial membrane potential in certain cell types, making it a possible tool for determining mitochondrial mass[32,33] (see Note 12.4 "Product Highlight: Estimating Mitochondrial Mass"). Furthermore, the MitoTracker® Green FM dye is substantially more photostable than the widely used rhodamine 123 fluorescent dye and produces a brighter, more mitochondrion-selective signal at lower concentrations. Because its emission maximum is blue-shifted approximately 10 nm relative to the emission maximum of rhodamine 123, the MitoTracker® Green FM dye produces a fluorescent staining pattern that should be better resolved from that of red-fluorescent probes in double-labeling experiments. The MitoTracker® Green FM probe has been used to:

- Assay the differentiation state of *Trypanosoma brucei* bloodstream forms[34]
- Demonstrate mitochondrion-selective labeling by avidin, streptavidin and anti-biotin antibodies[35]
- Identify mitochondria in immunolocalization experiments in CHO cells[36]
- Label sperm in order to determine the fate of sperm mitochondria during fertilization and subsequent embryo development[37–39] (Figure 12.13, Figure 12.14)
- Monitor mitochondrial distribution and transport in Tau-expressing CHO cells[40]
- Study the regulation of calcium signaling by mitochondria in T lymphocytes[41]

The mitochondrial proteins that are selectively labeled by the MitoTracker® Green FM reagent have been separated by capillary electrophoresis.[42]

Note 12.4 — Product Highlight

Estimating Mitochondrial Mass

Accurate measurements of mitochondrial mass require a probe that will accumulate in mitochondria regardless of the mitochondrial membrane potential, a property displayed by several of our MitoTracker® and MitoFluor™ dyes — MitoFluor™ Green (M7502), MitoFluor™ Red 589 (M22424), MitoTracker® Red 580 (M22425) and MitoTracker® Deep Red 633 (M22426). Mitochondrial uptake of nonyl acridine orange (NAO, A1372) and MitoTracker® Green FM (M7514) has also been reported to be independent of mitochondrial membrane potential,[1,2] although studies have shown that this may not be true for all cell types.[3,4] Mitochondrial staining by nonyl acridine orange is attributed to binding of cardiolipin in the inner mitochondrial membrane,[5] suggesting that the observed fluorescence signal may not correlate with the "mass" of the entire mitochondria but instead may measure the amount of inner membrane present. Indeed, one study has shown that mitochondrial mass can increase while the mitochondrial volume remains unchanged.[6]

Mitochondrial mass varies with cell type and can be useful in separating populations of healthy cells (see Figure 1). The mitochondrial mass of a cell does change with time, as demonstrated by the loss of mitochondrial mass in studies of aging cells.[7] Changes in mitochondrial mass are also observed in apoptotic cells, but are not necessarily associated with the loss of mitochondrial membrane potential.[6,8]

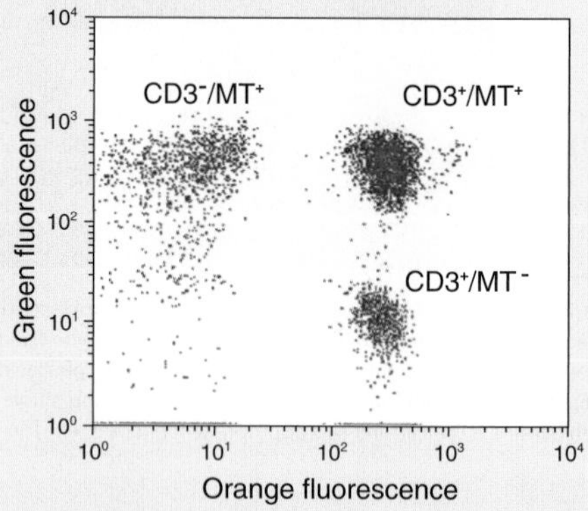

Figure 1. Peripheral blood mononuclear cells (PBMCs) stained with an orange-fluorescent R-phycoerythrin–labeled anti-CD3 antibody (A21333) and the green-fluorescent MitoTracker® Green dye (M7514). For comparison, CD3$^+$ PBMCs without MitoTracker® Green staining are shown on the same plot (lower right population). This figure demonstrates that the mitochondrial mass of PBMCs is approximately the same for CD3$^+$ and CD3$^-$ individuals.

References

1. Histochemistry 82, 51 (1985); **2.** Immunol Lett 61, 157 (1998); **3.** Basic Appl Histochem 33, 71 (1989); **4.** Cytometry 39, 203 (2000); **5.** Eur J Biochem 209, 267 (1992); **6.** Proc Natl Acad Sci U S A 98, 9505 (2001); **7.** Mech Ageing Dev 77, 83 (1994); **8.** Exp Cell Res 221, 281 (1995).

MitoFluor™ Probes: Nonfixable Mitochondrion-Selective Probes

MitoFluor™ Green Probe

As a companion to the MitoTracker® Green FM derivative, we have developed the MitoFluor™ Green probe [11] (M7502), which has a structure similar to MitoTracker® Green FM (Figure 12.15) but lacks its reactive chloromethyl moieties (Figure 12.16) and is not as well retained following fixation. As with MitoTracker® Green FM, the MitoFluor™ Green probe can selectively stain mitochondria in live cells.[11,43] The MitoFluor™ Green probe is also substantially more photostable than rhodamine 123, produces a brighter, more mitochondrion-selective signal at lower concentrations, and exhibits a blue-shifted emission maximum relative to that of rhodamine 123 that is better resolved from that of red-fluorescent probes in double-labeling experiments. Neither MitoTracker® Green FM, nor the MitoFluor™ Green probe, appears to be retained after cell permeabilization.

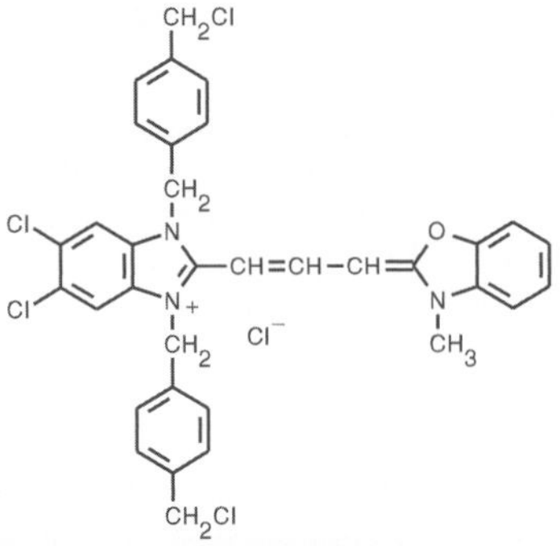

Figure 12.15 M7514 MitoTracker® Green FM.

Long-Wavelength MitoFluor™ Red Probes

We offer two mitochondria markers with long-wavelength fluorescence emission: MitoFluor™ Red 589 (M22424, Figure 12.17) and MitoFluor™ Red 594 [44] (M22422, Figure 12.17). The MitoFluor™ Red 589 probe appears to accumulate in mitochondria regardless of the mitochondria's membrane potential, making it a potentially useful stain for estimating mitochondrial mass. This probe has absorption and emission peaks at 588 nm and 622 nm, respectively, and can be viewed with filter sets appropriate for the Texas Red® dye. The MitoFluor™ Red 594 probe is a mitochondrial membrane potential–sensing dye that has been designed for optimal excitation by the 594 nm spectral line of the He–Ne laser. Both of these MitoFluor™ Red dyes

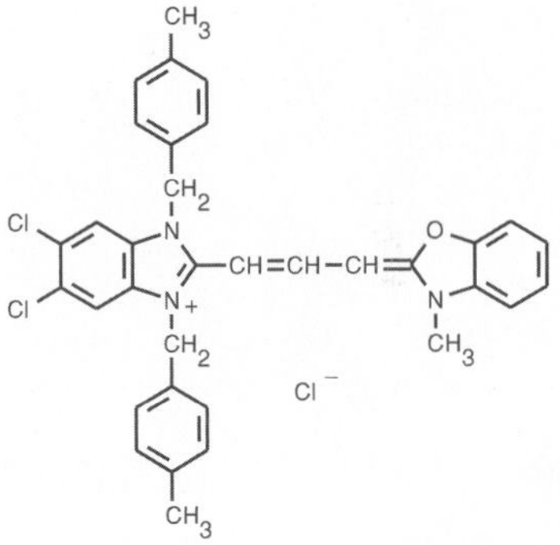

Figure 12.16 M7502 MitoFluor™ Green.

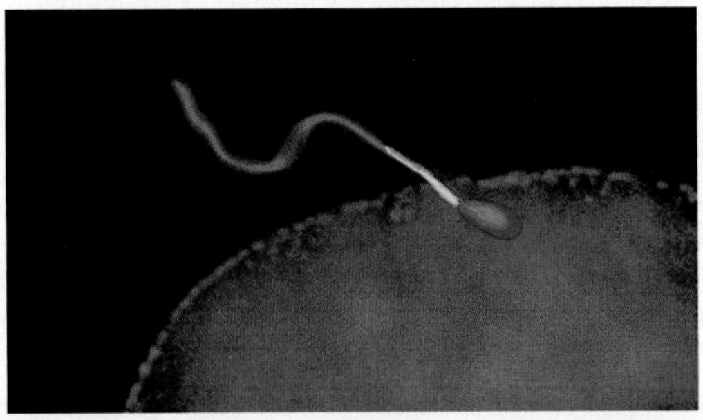

Figure 12.13 Bull sperm prelabeled with MitoTracker® Green FM (M7514) and used for *in vitro* fertilization of bovine oocytes (Biol Reprod 55, 1195 (1996)). After fertilization, eggs with bound or incorporated sperm were fixed in 2% formaldehyde, made permeable with Triton X-100 and labeled with an anti-tubulin antibody followed by a tetramethylrhodamine-labeled secondary antibody and counterstained with DAPI (D1306, D3571, D21490). Image contributed by Peter Sutovsky, University of Wisconsin.

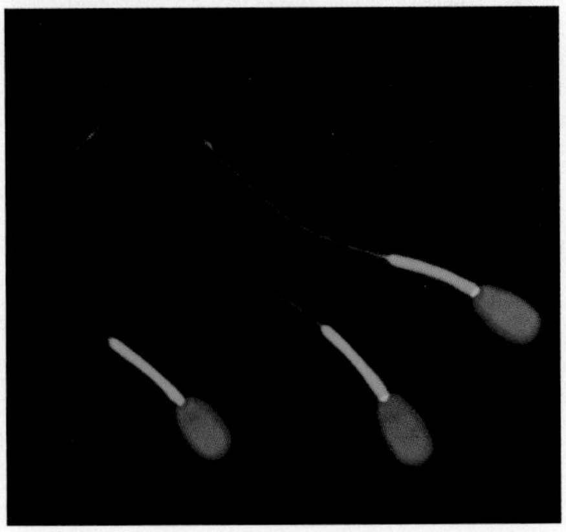

Figure 12.14 Live bull sperm stained simultaneously with MitoTracker® Green FM (M7514) and Hoechst 33342 (H1399, H3570, H21492), as reported in Mol Reprod Dev 47, 79 (1997). The image contributed by Peter Sutovsky, Oregon Regional Primate Resource Center, Oregon Health Sciences University, and used with the permission of Wiley-Liss, Inc., a subsidiary of John Wiley & Sons, Inc.

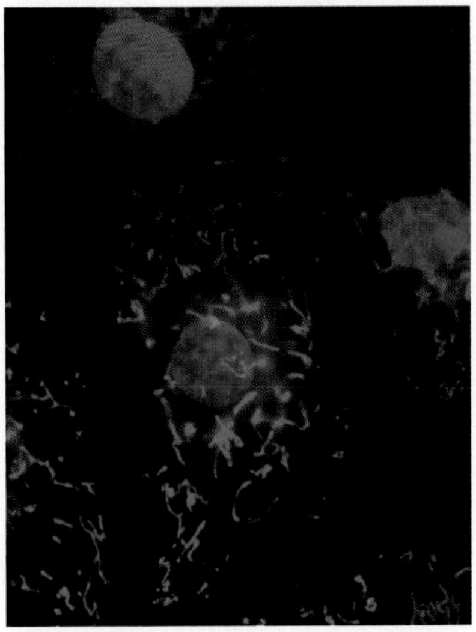

Figure 12.17 Viable bovine pulmonary artery endothelial cells incubated simultaneously with the red-fluorescent mitochondrial stain MitoFluor™ Red 594 (M22422) and the blue-fluorescent nuclear stain Hoechst 33342 (H1399, H3570, H21492). The image is a composite of two micrographs, using appropriate filter sets.

provide a clear spectral window below 600 nm for dual labeling with green-fluorescent probes, including other site-selective probes or GFP chimeras.

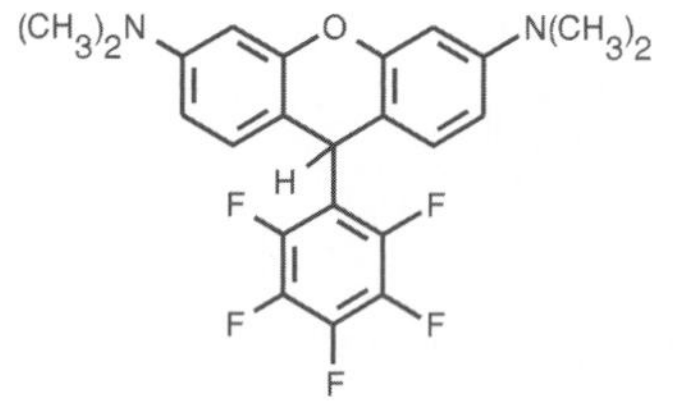

Figure 12.18 R14060 RedoxSensor™ Red CC-1.

RedoxSensor™ Red CC-1 Stain

RedoxSensor™ Red CC-1 (2,3,4,5,6-pentafluorotetramethyldihydrorosamine, R14060; Figure 12.18) stain is a unique probe whose fluorescence localization appears to be based on a cell's cytosolic redox potential. Once it passively enters live cells, the RedoxSensor™ Red CC-1 stain may be oxidized in the cytosol to a red-fluorescent product (excitation/emission maxima ~540/600 nm), which then accumulates in the mitochondria. Alternatively, this nonfluorescent probe may be transported to the lysosomes where it is oxidized. The differential distribution of the oxidized product between mitochondria and lysosomes appears to depend on the redox potential of the cytosol.[45] In proliferating cells, mitochondrial staining predominates; whereas in contact-inhibited cells, the staining is primarily lysosomal (Figure 18.15). The best method we have found to quantitate the distribution of the oxidized product is to use the mitochondrion-selective MitoTracker® Green FM stain (M7514) in conjunction with the RedoxSensor™ Red CC-1 stain.[45]

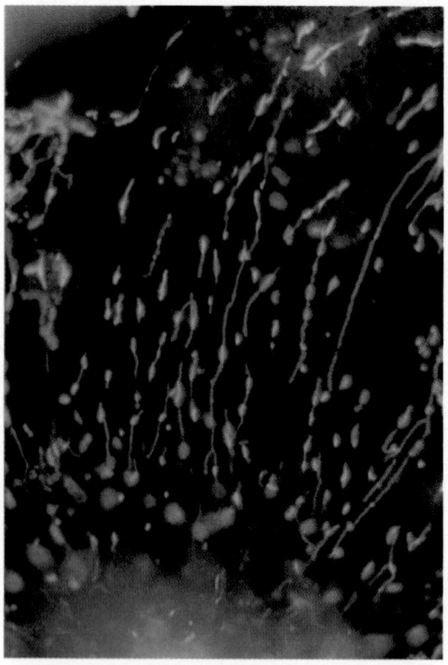

Figure 12.19 Potential-dependent staining of mitochondria in CCL64 fibroblasts by JC-1 (T3168). The mitochondria were visualized by epifluorescence microscopy using a 520 nm longpass optical filter. Regions of high mitochondrial polarization are indicated by red fluorescence due to J-aggregate formation by the concentrated dye. Depolarized regions are indicated by the green fluorescence of the JC-1 monomers. The image was contributed by Lan Bo Chen, Dana Farber Cancer Institute, Harvard Medical School.

JC-1 and JC-9: Dual-Emission Potential-Sensitive Probes

The green-fluorescent JC-1 probe (5,5′,6,6′-tetrachloro-1,1′,3,3′-tetraethylbenzimidazolylcarbocyanine iodide, T3168; Figure 22.13) exists as a monomer at low concentrations or at low membrane potential. However, at higher concentrations (aqueous solutions above 0.1 µM) or higher potentials, JC-1 forms red-fluorescent "J-aggregates" that exhibit a broad excitation spectrum and an emission maximum at ~590 nm (Figure 12.19, Figure 12.20, Figure 22.14). Thus, the emission of this cyanine dye can be used as a sensitive measure of mitochondrial membrane potential. Various types of ratio measurements are possible by combining signals from the green-fluorescent JC-1 monomer (absorption/emission maxima ~514/529 nm in water) and the J-aggregate (emission maximum 590 nm), which can be effectively excited anywhere between 485 nm and its absorption maximum at 585 nm (Figure 22.15). The ratio of red-to-green JC-1 fluorescence is dependent only on the membrane potential and not on other factors that may influence single-component fluorescence signals, such as mitochondrial size, shape and density. Optical filters designed for fluorescein and tetramethylrhodamine (Table 23.9) can be used to separately visualize the monomer and J-aggregate forms, respectively. Alternatively, both forms can be observed simultaneously using a standard fluorescein longpass optical filter set. Chen

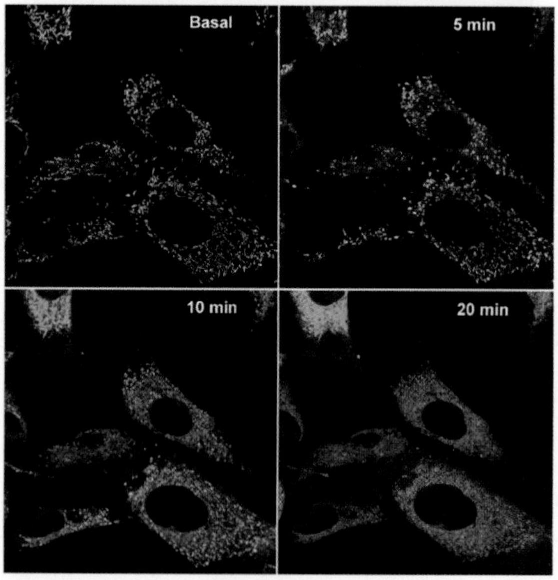

Figure 12.20 NIH 3T3 fibroblasts stained with JC-1 (T3168), showing the progressive loss of red J-aggregate fluorescence and cytoplasmic diffusion of green monomer fluorescence following exposure to hydrogen peroxide. Images show the same field of cells viewed before H_2O_2 treatment and 5, 10 and 20 minutes after treatment. The images were contributed by Ildo Nicoletti, Perugia University Medical School.

and colleagues have used JC-1 to investigate mitochondrial potentials in live cells by ratiometric techniques[46–48] (Figure 22.16). JC-1 has also been used to:

- Analyze the effects of drugs by flow cytometry[49]
- Detect human encephalomyopathy[50]
- Follow mitochondrial changes during apoptosis[51,52]
- Investigate mitochondrial poisoning, uncoupling and anoxia[53]
- Monitor effects of ellipticine on mitochondrial potential[54]

JC-1 has been combined with the reagents in our LIVE/DEAD® Sperm Viability Kit (L7011, Section 15.3) to permit simultaneous assessment of cellular integrity and mitochondrial function by flow cytometry.[55] We also offer JC-1 as part of the MitoProbe™ JC-1 Assay Kit for flow cytometry (M34152, Section 22.3). We have discovered another mitochondrial marker, JC-9 (3,3′-dimethyl-β-naphthoxazolium iodide, D22421; Figure 22.18), with a very different chemical structure (Figure 22.17) but similar potential-dependent spectroscopic properties. However, the green fluorescence of JC-9 is essentially invariant with membrane potential, whereas the red fluorescence is significantly increased at hyperpolarized membrane potentials.

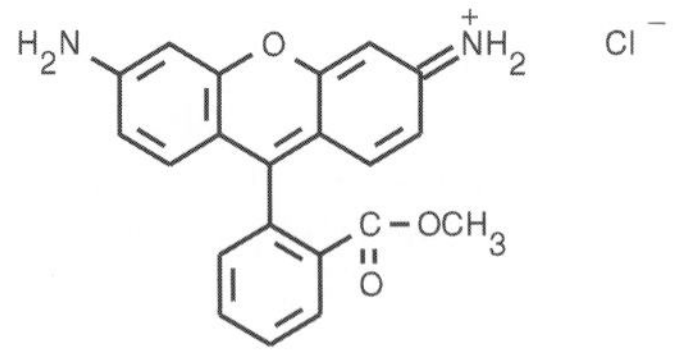

Figure 12.21 R302 rhodamine 123.

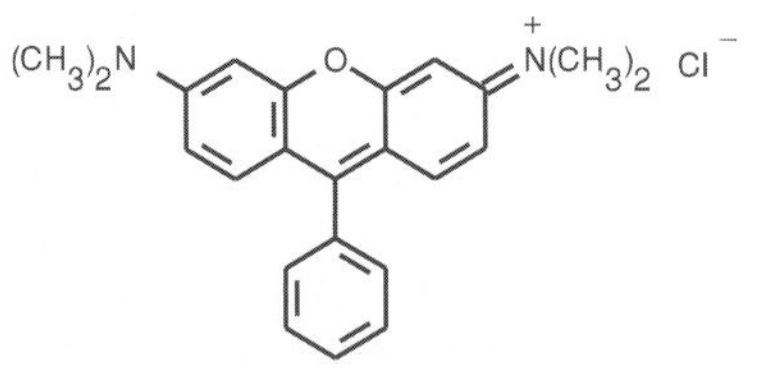

Figure 12.22 T639 tetramethylrosamine chloride.

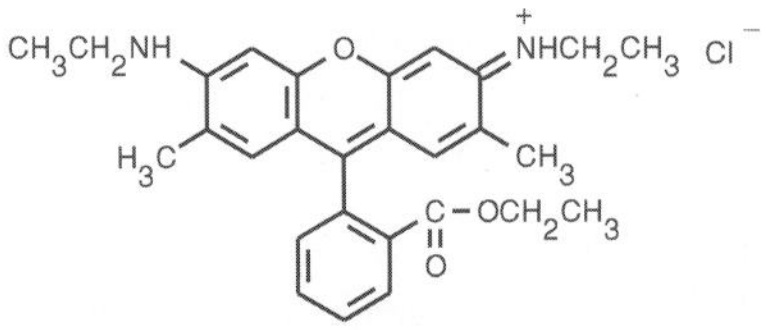

Figure 12.23 R634 rhodamine 6G chloride.

Mitochondrion-Selective Rhodamines and Rosamines

Rhodamine 123

Rhodamine 123 (R302; FluoroPure™ Grade, R22420; Figure 12.21) is a cell-permeant, cationic, fluorescent dye that is readily sequestered by active mitochondria without inducing cytotoxic effects.[56] Uptake and equilibration of rhodamine 123 is rapid (a few minutes) compared with dyes such as DASPMI (4-Di-1-ASP, D288), which may take 30 minutes or longer.[14] Viewed through a fluorescein longpass optical filter (Table 23.9), fluorescence of the mitochondria of cells stained by rhodamine 123 appears yellow-green. Viewed through a tetramethylrhodamine longpass optical filter, however, these same mitochondria appear red. Unlike the lipophilic rhodamine and carbocyanine dyes, rhodamine 123 apparently does not stain the endoplasmic reticulum.

Rhodamine 123 has been used with a variety of cell types such as presynaptic nerve terminals,[57] live bacteria,[58,59] plants[60,61] and human spermatozoa.[62] Using flow cytometry, researchers employed rhodamine 123 to sort respiratory-deficient yeast cells[63,64] and to isolate those lymphocytes that are responsive to mitogen stimulation.[65] Rhodamine 123 has also been used to study:

- Apoptosis[52,66]
- Axoplasmic transport of mitochondria[67]
- Bacterial viability and vitality[58]
- Mitochondrial enzymatic activities[68,69]
- Mitochondrial transmembrane potential and other membrane activities[15,60,70–73]
- Multidrug resistance[74–81] (Section 15.6)
- Mycobacterial drug susceptibility[82,83]
- Oocyte maturation[84]

Although rhodamine 123 is usually not retained by cells when they are washed, a variety of human carcinoma cell lines (but not sarcomas or leukemic cells) retain the dye for unusually long periods[85] (>24 hours), making rhodamine 123 a potential anticancer agent for photodynamic therapy.[86–91] Rhodamine 123 is known to be preferentially taken up and retained by mitochondria of carcinoma cells[92] and to inhibit their proliferation;[93,94] cardiac muscle cells also retain rhodamine 123 for days.[95]

Rosamines and Other Rhodamine Derivatives, Including TMRM and TMRE

Other mitochondrion-selective dyes include tetramethylrosamine (T639, Figure 12.22), whose fluorescence contrasts well with that of fluorescein for multicolor applications, and rhodamine 6G[89,96–98] (R634, Figure 12.23), which has an absorption maximum between that of rhodamine 123 and tetramethylrosamine. Tetramethylrosamine and rhodamine 6G have both been used to examine the efficiency of P-glycoprotein–mediated exclusion from multidrug-resistant cells[74] (Section 15.6). Rhodamine 6G has been employed to study microvascular reperfusion injury[99] and the stimulation and inhibition of F_1-ATPase from the thermophilic bacterium PS3.[100]

At low concentrations, certain lipophilic rhodamine dyes selectively stain mitochondria in live cells.[101] Molecular Probes' researchers have observed that low concentrations of the hexyl ester of rhodamine B (R 6, R648MP) accumulate selectively in mitochondria (Figure 12.24) and appear to be relatively nontoxic. We have included this probe in our Yeast Mitochondrial Stain Sampler Kit (Y7530, see below for description). At higher concentrations, rhodamine B hexyl ester and rhodamine 6G stain the endoplasmic reticulum of animal cells[101] (Section 12.4).

The accumulation of tetramethylrhodamine methyl and ethyl esters (TMRM, T668; TMRE, T669) in mitochondria and the endoplasmic reticulum has also been shown to be driven by their membrane potential[102,103] (Section 22.3). Moreover, because of their reduced hydrophobic character, these probes exhibit potential-independent binding to cells that is 10 to 20 times lower than that seen with rhodamine 6G.[104] Tetramethylrhodamine ethyl ester has been described as one of the best fluorescent dyes for dynamic and *in situ* quantitative measurements — better than rhodamine 123 — because it is rapidly and reversibly taken up by live cells.[105–107] TMRM and TMRE have been used to measure mitochondrial depolarization related to cytosolic Ca^{2+} transients[108] and to image time-dependent mitochondrial membrane potentials.[106] A high-throughput assay utilizes TMRE and our low-affinity Ca^{2+} indicator fluo-5N AM (F14204, Section 19.3) to screen inhibitors of the opening of the mitochondrial transition pore.[109] Researchers have also taken advantage of the red shift exhibited by TMRM, TMRE and rhodamine 123 upon membrane potential–driven mitochondrial uptake to develop a ratiometric method for quantitating membrane potential.[70]

Reduced Rhodamines and Rosamines

Inside live cells, the colorless dihydrorhodamines and dihydrotetramethylrosamine are oxidized to fluorescent products that stain mitochondria.[110] However, the oxidation may occur in organelles other than the mitochondria. Dihydrorhodamine 123 (D632, D23806; Figure 12.25) reacts with hydrogen peroxide in the presence of peroxidases,[111] iron or cytochrome *c*[112] to form rhodamine 123. This reduced rhodamine has been used to monitor reactive oxygen intermediates in rat mast cells[113] and to measure hydrogen peroxide in endothelial cells.[112] Dihydrorhodamine 6G (D633, Figure 12.26) is another reduced rhodamine that has been shown to be taken up and oxidized by live cells.[114–116] Chloromethyl derivatives of reduced rosamines (MitoTracker® Orange CM-H_2TMRos, M7511; MitoTracker® Red CM-H_2XRos, M7513), which can be fixed in cells by aldehyde-based fixatives, have been described above. The acetoxymethyl (AM) ester of dihydrorhod-2, which is prepared by chemical reduction of the calcium indicator rhod-2 AM (R1244, R1245MP; Section 19.3) has been extensively used to measure the relatively slow changes in intramitochondrial Ca^{2+} (Figure 19.33, Figure 19.39).

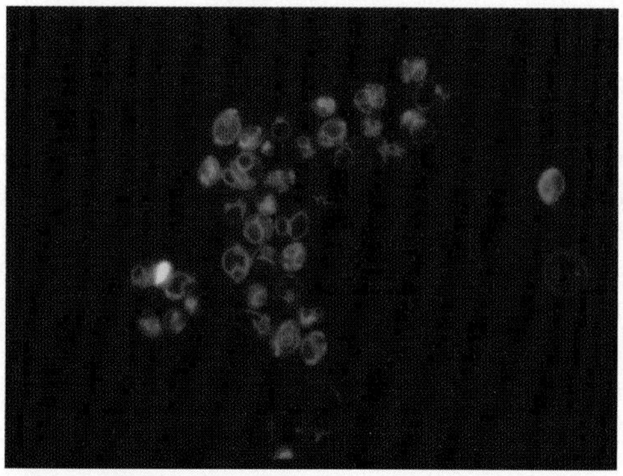

Figure 12.24 *Saccharomyces cerevisiae* stained sequentially with the red-fluorescent rhodamine B hexyl ester (R 6, R648MP), which selectively labels yeast mitochondria under these conditions, and the green-fluorescent yeast vacuole membrane marker MDY-64 (Y7536). These probes are also provided in our Yeast Mitochondrial Stain Sampler Kit (Y7530) and Yeast Vacuole Marker Sampler Kit (Y7531), respectively. Stained yeast were photographed in a single exposure through an Omega Optical triple-bandpass filter set.

Other Mitochondrion-Selective Probes

Carbocyanines

Most carbocyanine dyes with short (C_1–C_6) alkyl chains (Section 22.3) stain mitochondria of live cells when used at low concentrations (~0.5 µM or ~0.1 µg/mL); those with pentyl or hexyl substituents also stain the endoplasmic reticulum when used at higher concentrations (~5–50 µM or ~1–10 µg/mL). $DiOC_6(3)$ (D273) stains mitochondria in live yeast [21,117–119] and other eukaryotic cells,[98,120] as well as sarcoplasmic reticulum in beating heart cells.[121] It has also been used to demonstrate mitochondria moving along microtubules.[23] Photolysis of mitochondrion- or endoplasmic reticulum–bound $DiOC_6(3)$ specifically destroys the microtubules of cells without affecting actin stress fibers, producing a highly localized inhibition of intracellular organelle motility.[122] We have included $DiIC_1(5)$ and $DiOC_2(3)$ in two of our MitoProbe™ Assay Kits for flow cytometry (M34151, M34150; Section 22.3). Several other potential-sensitive carbocyanine probes described in Section 22.3 also stain mitochondria in live cultured cells.[98]

The carbocyanine $DiOC_7(3)$ (D378), which exhibits spectra similar to those of fluorescein, is a versatile dye that has been reported to be a sensitive probe for mitochondria in plant cells.[123] Its other uses include:

- Distinguishing cycling and noncycling fibroblasts [124] and viable and nonviable bacteria [125]
- Following the reorganization of the endoplasmic reticulum during fertilization in the ascidian egg [126]
- Identifying functional vasculature in murine tumors [127,128]
- Studying multidrug resistance [129] (Section 15.6)
- Visualizing the detailed morphology of neurites of Alzheimer's disease neurons [130]

Styryl Dyes

The styryl dyes DASPMI (4-Di-1-ASP, D288) and DASPEI (D426) can be used to stain mitochondria in live cells.[14] These dyes have large fluorescence Stokes shifts and are taken up relatively slowly as a function of membrane potential. The kinetics of mitochondrial staining with styrylpyridinium dyes has been investigated using the concentration jump method.[131] DASPMI and DASPEI have been shown to be useful for:

- Determining the distribution of mitochondria in yeast mutants [63]
- Long-term imaging of live mammalian nerve cells and their connections [132–134]
- Monitoring the metabolic state of *Pneumocystis carinii* mitochondria [31]
- Screening aberrant mitochondrial distribution and morphology in yeast [135]

Nonyl Acridine Orange

Nonyl acridine orange (A1372) is well retained in the mitochondria of live HeLa cells for up to 10 days, making it a useful probe for following mitochondria during isolation and after cell fusion.[136–138] The mitochondrial uptake of this metachromatic dye is reported not to depend on membrane potential. It is toxic at high concentrations [139] and apparently binds to cardiolipin in all mitochondria, regardless of their energetic state.[140–143] This derivative has been used to analyze mitochondria by flow cytometry,[144] to characterize multidrug resistance [145] (Section 15.6) and to measure changes in mitochondrial mass during apoptosis in rat thymocytes.[52]

Carboxy SNARF®-1 pH Indicator

A special cell-loading technique permits ratiometric measurement of intramitochondrial pH with our SNARF® dyes. Cell loading with 10 µM 5-(and 6-)carboxy SNARF®-1, acetoxymethyl ester, acetate (C1271, C1272; Section 20.2), followed by 4 hours of incubation at room temperature leads to highly selective localization of the carboxy SNARF®-1 dye in mitochondria (Figure 20.15), where it responds to changes in mitochondrial pH.[146]

CoroNa™ Red Chloride

As shown by colocalization with MitoTracker® Green FM, the CoroNa™ Red Na^+ indicator (C24430, C24431; Section 21.1) spontaneously localizes in the mitochondria (Figure 21.14) and may be useful for measuring intramitochondrial Na^+ transients.

Lucigenin

The well-known chemiluminescent probe lucigenin (L6868) accumulates in mitochondria of alveolar macrophages.[147] Relatively high concentrations of the dye (~100 µM) are required to obtain fluorescent staining; however, low concentrations reportedly yield a chemiluminescent response to stimulated superoxide generation within the mitochondria.[147] Lucigenin from Molecular Probes has been highly purified to remove a bright blue-fluorescent contaminant that is found in some commercial samples.

Yeast Mitochondrial Stain Sampler Kit

Because fluorescence microscopy has been extensively used to study yeast,[21,119] Molecular Probes offers a Yeast Mitochondrial Stain Sampler Kit (Y7530). This kit contains sample quantities of five different probes that have been found to selectively label yeast mitochondria. Both well-characterized and proprietary mitochondrion-selective probes are provided:

- Rhodamine 123 [64,148–150]
- Rhodamine B hexyl ester [101] (Figure 12.24)

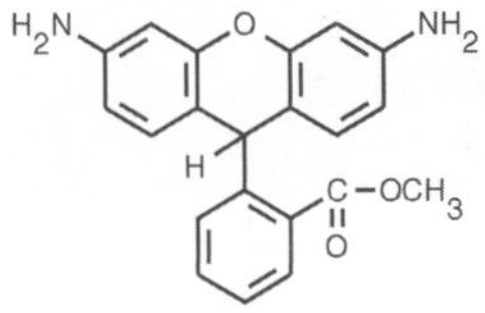

Figure 12.25 D632 dihydrorhodamine 123.

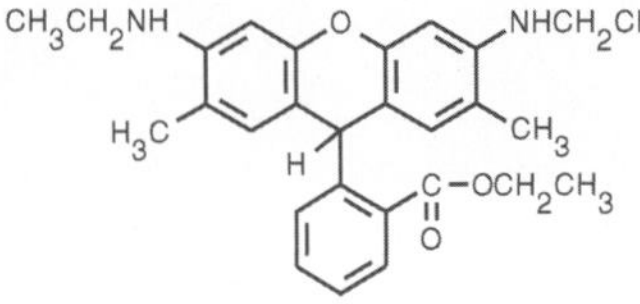

Figure 12.26 D633 dihydrorhodamine 6G.

- MitoTracker® Green FM
- SYTO® 18 yeast mitochondrial stain [151]
- $DiOC_6(3)$ [21,118,119,152–158]

The mitochondrion-selective nucleic acid stain included in this kit — SYTO® 18 yeast mitochondrial stain — exhibits a pronounced fluorescence enhancement upon binding to nucleic acids, resulting in very low background fluorescence even in the presence of dye. SYTO® 18 is an effective mitochondrial stain in live yeast but neither penetrates nor stains the mitochondria of higher eukaryotic cells. Each of the components of the Yeast Mitochondrial Stain Sampler Kit is also available separately, including the SYTO® 18 yeast mitochondrial stain (S7529).

Avidin Conjugates for Staining Mitochondria

Endogenously biotinylated proteins in mammalian cells, bacteria, yeast and plants — biotin carboxylase enzymes — are present almost exclusively in mitochondria, where biotin synthesis occurs;[159] consequently, mitochondria can be selectively stained by almost any fluorophore- or enzyme-labeled avidin or streptavidin derivative (Section 7.6; Table 7.22; Figure 12.27, Figure 12.28) without applying any biotinylated ligand. This staining, which can complicate the use of avidin–biotin techniques in sensitive cell-based assays, can be blocked by the reagents in our Endogenous Biotin-Blocking Kit (E21390, Section 7.6).

Antibodies to Mitochondrial Proteins

Monoclonal Antibodies Specific for Proteins in the Oxidative Phosphorylation System

Oxidative phosphorylation (OxPhos) activity occurs in the mitochondria and, in mammals, is catalyzed by five large membrane-bound protein complexes, namely NADH–ubiquinol oxidoreductase (Complex I), succinate–ubiquinol oxidoreductase (Complex II), ubiquinol–cytochrome *c* oxidoreductase (Complex III), cytochrome *c* oxidase (Complex IV) and ATP synthase (Complex V). The complexes are composed of multiple subunits, some of which are encoded in the mitochondrion and some in the nucleus. For example, mammalian cytochrome oxidase (COX) is composed of 13 subunits, three encoded by mitochondrial DNA (subunits I, II and III; Figure 12.29) and ten encoded by nuclear DNA. Assembly of each complex involves a coordinated association of prosthetic groups (hemes, non-heme irons, flavins and copper atoms) with some polypeptides made in the mitochondrion and others made in the cytosol and then translocated to the organelle. This complicated process is poorly defined but known to require various assembly factors, each of which is specific for a particular complex. Defects in assembly of one or more of these complexes contribute to several described mitochondrial diseases and possibly Alzheimer's and Parkinson's diseases.[160–165]

Antibodies against the various subunits of the OxPhos Complex are important tools for investigating mitochondrial biogenesis and studying OxPhos-related diseases (see Note 12.2 "Technical Focus: Mitochondria in Diseases"). Patient cell lines can now be screened for deficiencies in each of the OxPhos Complexes by simple Western blotting.[166,167] When compared with control cell lines, this screen

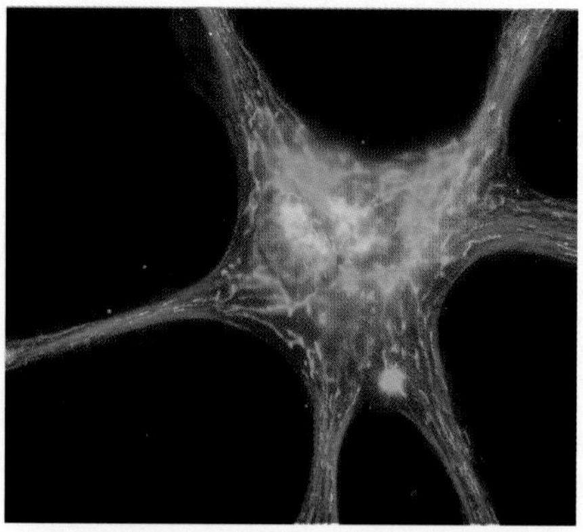

Figure 12.28 The cytoskeleton of a fixed and permeabilized bovine pulmonary artery endothelial cell detected using mouse monoclonal anti-α-tubulin antibody (A11126), visualized with Alexa Fluor® 647 goat anti–mouse IgG antibody (A21235) and pseudocolored magenta. Endogenous biotin in the mitochondria was labeled with green-fluorescent Alexa Fluor® 488 streptavidin (S11223) and DNA was stained with blue-fluorescent DAPI (D1306, D3571, D21490).

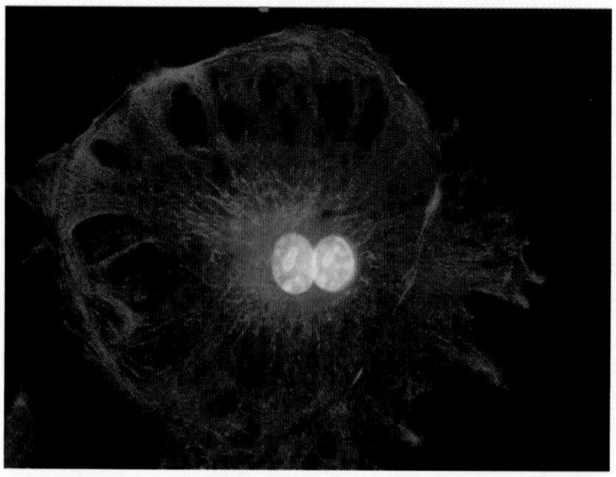

Figure 12.27 The intermediate filaments in bovine pulmonary artery endothelial cells, localized using our anti-desmin antibody (A21283), which was visualized with the Alexa Fluor® 647 goat anti–mouse IgG antibody (A21235). Endogenous biotin in the mitochondria was labeled with Alexa Fluor® 546 streptavidin (S11225) and DNA in the cell was stained with blue-fluorescent DAPI (D1306, D3571, D21490).

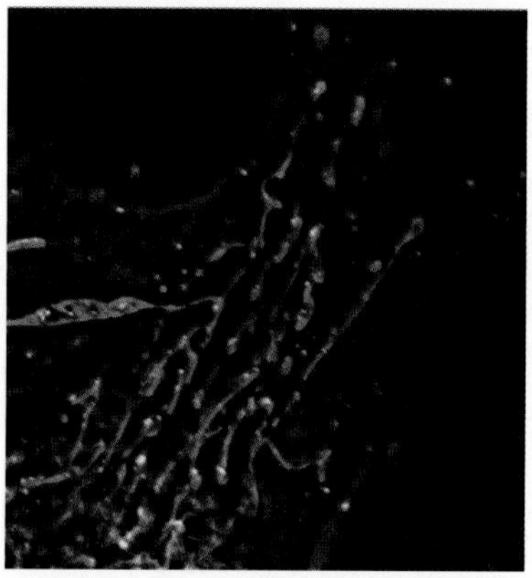

Figure 12.29 Mitochondrial DNA labeled with DAPI (D1306, D3571, D21490) and colocalized with MitoTracker® Red (M7512) in a bovine pulmonary artery endothelial cell. MitoTracker® Red was incubated with live cells, followed by fixation with 4% formaldehyde. Staining of the mitochondrial DNA by DAPI was performed after fixation.

provides information about relative subunit expression levels and can be combined with native gel electrophoresis or sucrose gradient centrifugation to gather additional information regarding the assembly state of the OxPhos Complex.[168] Many of our antibodies against subunits of the OxPhos Complex may also be used for immunohistochemical analysis. Image analysis of the antibody's staining pattern can reveal the relative expression and localization of a subunit. This approach has been particularly useful for studying OxPhos subunit expression in diseased muscle fibers [169] and for screening Complex IV–deficient patients.[170]

Molecular Probes offers a range of subunit-specific anti–OxPhos Complex mouse monoclonal antibodies that recognize proteins in the oxidative phosphorylation system (Table 12.3, Table 12.4, Table 12.5; Figure 12.30) and have proven useful in the characterization and diagnosis of mitochondrial disease.[171] One set of antibodies is against the Complex IV subunits of yeast, as this is the organism of choice for studying biogenesis of cytochrome oxidase. The remaining antibodies were generated against bovine or human material and were selected because they react with high specificity for the human form of the various proteins. All of our antibodies work well in Western blots and a majority can be used for immunohistochemistry, as listed in Table 12.4. These antibodies may also be employed to test other subcellular preparations for mitochondrial contamination. Stringent selection criteria were applied during the development of these monoclonal antibodies, including:

- Ability of the antibodies to detect native protein in solid-phase binding assays such as particle-concentration fluorescence immunoassays (PCFIAs) and enzyme-linked immunosorbent assays (ELISAs)
- Specificity for the appropriate denatured subunit in Western blots of whole-cell extracts and isolated mitochondria
- Where appropriate, specific mitochondrial subcellular localization of immunohistochemical reactivity in fixed cultured human cells

Detailed information regarding the IgG isotype and recommended working concentration is provided with each product. For detection of these monoclonal antibodies, Molecular Probes offers anti–mouse IgG secondary antibodies labeled with biotin, enzymes, NANOGOLD and Alexa Fluor® FluoroNanogold 1.4 nm gold clusters, Captivate™ ferrofluid or a wide range of fluorophores (Section 7.2, Table 7.1). The antibodies in this group (Table 7.15, Table 7.16, Table 7.17, Table 12.4) can also be complexed with the Zenon® labeling reagents in the corresponding Zenon® Antibody Labeling Kits (Section 7.3, Table 7.13) for detecting mitochondrial targets in cells (Figure 7.80, Figure 15.78).

Monoclonal Antibodies Specific for OxPhos Complex IV (Cytochrome Oxidase)

To facilitate the study of cytochrome oxidase (COX) structure and mitochondrial biogenesis, Molecular Probes offers subunit-specific mouse anti–OxPhos Complex IV monoclonal antibodies that have been derived from the human, bovine and yeast forms of COX. COX catalyzes the transfer of electrons from reduced cytochrome *c* to molecular oxygen, with a concomitant translocation of protons across the mitochondrial inner membrane.[172,173] This mitochondrial membrane–bound enzyme is composed of subunits that are encoded in both the mitochondria (COX subunits I, II and III) and the nucleus (all others), with a total of 13 subunits for mammalian COX and 11 subunits for yeast COX. The binding specificity exhibited by our anti–OxPhos Complex IV monoclonal antibody preparations allows researchers to investigate the regulation, assembly and orientation of COX subunits from a variety of organisms [174–178] (Table 12.3, Table 12.4, Table 12.5). Furthermore, because the antibodies to bovine COX also recognize the corresponding human COX subunits, the antibodies have proven valuable for analyzing human mitochondrial myopathies and related disorders.[166,169,179,180] Alexa Fluor® 488 and Alexa Fluor® 594 conjugates of anti–COX subunit I are also available for direct staining of mitochondria (A21296, A21297; Figure 7.79). Mouse monoclonal 1D6 anti–COX subunit 1 antibody (A6403), which recognizes the mitochondrial DNA–encoded COX subunit I, has been shown to be an effective tool for following mitochondrial DNA depletion in cultured fibroblasts treated with nucleoside reverse transcriptase inhibitors (NRTIs) and potentially for monitoring patients on a regimen of NRTIs for the treatment of HIV.[181]

Monoclonal Antibodies Specific for Complexes I, II, III and V

Molecular Probes supplies a large number of monoclonal antibodies to the OxPhos Complex (Table 12.4). These include antibodies specific for individual subunits of Complexes I, II, III and V, as well as

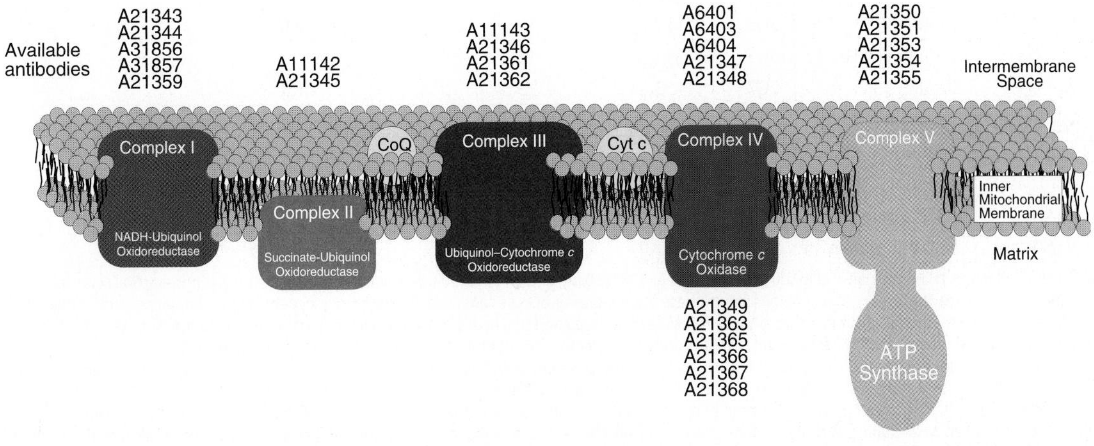

Figure 12.30. Major protein complexes of the oxidative phosphorylation (OxPhos) system and antibodies that recognize them.

Table 12.3 — Monoclonal antibodies to yeast oxidative phosphorylation complex IV (COX)

Cat Num *	Yeast COX Subunit Specificity	Mouse Monoclonal	Mouse Isotype	Suggested Concentration for Westerns (µg/mL)	Suggested Concentration for Immunocytochemistry (µg/mL)
A6405	Subunit I	11D8	$IgG_{2b,\kappa}$	0.5	NR
A6407	Subunit II	4B12	$IgG_{2a,\kappa}$	1	NR
A6408	Subunit III †	DA5	$IgG_{2a,\kappa}$	0.5	5–20
A6432	Subunit IV	1A12	$IgG_{1,\kappa}$	0.5	NR

* For all the antibodies listed in this table, the unit size is 250 µg, except for A6405, which is available in a unit size of 100 µg. † Monoclonal DA5 was raised against yeast COX, but it strongly crossreacts with *Neurospora crassa* COX subunit III. NR = Not recommended.

Table 12.4 — Monoclonal antibodies specific for proteins in the oxidative phosphorylation system

Cat Num *	Oxidative Complex	Subunit Specificity	Clone	Isotype	Suggested Concentration for Westerns (µg/mL)	Suggested Concentration for Immunocytochemistry (µg/mL)	Species Specificity †			
							Hum	Bov	Rat	Mou
A21344	I	39,000-dalton subunit	20C11	$IgG_{1,\kappa}$	0.5	NR	+	+	+	+
A21343	I	30,000-dalton subunit	3F9	$IgG_{1,\kappa}$	0.5	NR	+	+	ND	+
A31857	I	20,000-dalton subunit	20E9	$IgG_{1,\kappa}$	0.5–1	5	+	+	ND	+
A21359	I	17,000-dalton subunit	21C11	$IgG_{2b,\kappa}$	0.5	5–10	+	+	ND	+
A31856	I	15,000-dalton subunit	17G3	$IgG_{1,\kappa}$	0.1	1–10	±	+	±	–
A11142	II	70,000-dalton subunit	2E3	$IgG_{1,\kappa}$	0.1	0.1–0.5 ‡	+	+	+	+
A21345	II	30,000-dalton subunit	21A11	$IgG_{2a,\kappa}$	5	5–10 ‡	+	+	+	+
A21362	III	Core 1 subunit	16D10	$IgG_{1,\kappa}$	0.1	1–5	+	+	ND	+
A11143	III	Core 2 subunit	13G12	$IgG_{1,\kappa}$	0.4	NR	+	+	+	+
A21346	III	FeS subunit	5A5	$IgG_{2b,\kappa}$	0.5	NR	+	+	ND	+
A21361	III	10,000-dalton subunit	1H9	$IgG_{2a,\kappa}$	0.2	NR	–	+	ND	+
A6403	IV (COX)	Subunit I	1D6	$IgG_{2a,\kappa}$	2	2 ‡§	+	+	+	+
A6404	IV (COX)	Subunit II	12C4	$IgG_{2a,\kappa}$	2	5	+	–	±	±
A21347	IV (COX)	Subunit IV	10G8	$IgG_{2a,\kappa}$	0.5	5–10 ‡	+	+	–	–
A21348	IV (COX)	Subunit IV	20E8	$IgG_{2a,\kappa}$	0.5	NR	+	+	ND	ND
A21363	IV (COX)	Subunit Va	6E9	$IgG_{2a,\kappa}$	2	5	+	+	±	+
A21349	IV (COX)	Subunit Vb	16H12	$IgG_{2b,\kappa}$	2	5	+	+	+	+
A21365	IV (COX)	Subunit VIa-L **	14A3	$IgG_{1,\kappa}$	5	NR	+	–	±	+
A21366	IV (COX)	Subunit VIb	3F9	$IgG_{1,\kappa}$	1	NR	+	+	+	+
A6401	IV (COX)	Subunit VIc	3G5	$IgG_{2b,\kappa}$	2	NR	+	+	+	–
A21367	IV (COX)	Subunit VIIa-H/L ††	6D7	IgG_{2a}	10	NR	–	+	+	+
A21368	IV (COX)	Subunit VIIb	2G7	$IgG_{1,\kappa}$	25	NR	+	+	–	–
A21350	V (ATPase)	α subunit	7H10	$IgG_{2b,\kappa}$	0.5	1 §	+	+	+	+
A21351	V (ATPase)	β subunit	3D5	$IgG_{1,\kappa}$	0.2	1	+	+	ND	+
A21353	V (ATPase)	d subunit	7F9	$IgG_{2b,\kappa}$	5	5	+	+	ND	±
A21354	V (ATPase)	OSCP subunit ‡‡	4C11	$IgG_{1,\kappa}$	0.1	5–10	+	+	ND	–
A21355	V (ATPase)	Inhibitor protein §§	5E2	$IgG_{1,\kappa}$	0.5 ***	5–10 §	+	+	+	+

* For all the antibodies listed in this table, the unit size is 100 µg, except for A6408 (250 µg) and A11142 (50 µg). † Species specificity: Hum = human; Bov = bovine; Mou = mouse; (+) = strong reactivity; (±) = weak reactivity; (-) = no reactivity. ‡ When these monoclonal antibodies are used for immunocytochemistry experiments, paraformaldehyde-fixed target cells may require antigen retrieval methodology before the target cells are permeabilized and blocked. § These monoclonal antibodies yield the strongest and most consistent signals when used for indirect immunocytochemistry. ** The designations VIa-H and VIa-L refer to COX subunit VIa from bovine heart and liver, respectively. Monoclonal 14A3 recognizes COX subunit VIIa isotypes from liver. †† Monoclonal 6D7 recognizes COX subunit VIIa isotypes from both heart and liver. ‡‡ OSCP = oligomycin sensitivity–conferring protein. §§ Although not considered a member of Complex V, the ATPase inhibitor protein does associate with this OxPhos subsystem. *** A second protein band (~18,000 daltons) has been observed with this antibody in Western blots of Complex V preparations from human heart tissue. Although it is most likely the dimer of the ~10,000-dalton inhibitor protein, this has not been confirmed by the antibody supplier. We recommend caution when using this antibody for immunocyto- and immunohistochemistry applications because the antibody could interact with this unknown protein. ND = Not determined. NR = Not recommended.

the Complex V inhibitor protein. When these monoclonal antibodies are used in combination with the set of antibodies to cytochrome oxidase (Complex IV), the relative levels of all OxPhos enzyme complexes in normal and diseased tissues can be evaluated.

The mouse monoclonal 7H10 anti–OxPhos Complex V subunit (bovine) (anti–F_1F_0-ATPase subunit α, A21350) and mouse monoclonal 3D5 anti–OxPhos Complex V subunit (bovine) (anti–F_1F_0-ATPase subunit β, A21351) antibodies have also been shown to mimic angiostatin, a potent inhibitor of angiogenesis.[182] Angiostatin protein (A23375, Section 15.4), a recombinant form of natural angiostatin, targets the F_1F_0-ATP synthase and inhibits cell-surface ATP metabolism of endothelial cells, thereby blocking cell migration and proliferation that is essential for angiogenesis. This research demonstrated that these anti-ATPase antibodies had similar inhibitory effects, implying that they also compromised ATP metabolism and may function as angiostatin analogs.

SelectFX™ Alexa Fluor® 488 Cytochrome c Apoptosis Detection Kit

A distinctive feature of the early stages of programmed cell death is the disruption of active mitochondria.[4,5,183] This mitochondria disruption includes changes in the membrane potential, presumably due to the opening of the mitochondrial permeability transition pore, which allows passage of ions and small molecules. The resulting equilibration of ions leads in turn to the decoupling of the respiratory chain and then the release of cytochrome *c* into the cytosol.[184,185] The SelectFX™ Alexa Fluor® 488 Cytochrome *c* Apoptosis Detection Kit (S35115) provides all the reagents required to detect cytochrome *c* in fixed cells. The Alexa Fluor® 488 dye exhibits bright green fluorescence that is compatible with filters and instrument settings appropriate for fluorescein. Each kit contains:

- Mouse IgG_1 anti–cytochrome *c* antibody
- Highly cross-adsorbed Alexa Fluor® 488 goat anti–mouse IgG antibody

Table 12.5 — Molecular characteristics of components of the oxidative phosphorylation system

Complex	Name		Molecular Weight *	Alternative Name	Protein Number †	Gene Number ‡
I	NADH–ubiquinone oxidoreductase	39,000-dalton subunit	42.5	α subcomplex, 9	Q16795	NDUFA9
		30,000-dalton subunit	30.2	iron–sulfur protein 3	O75489	NDUFS3
		20,000-dalton subunit §	ND	ND	ND	ND
		17,000-dalton subunit	15.5	β subcomplex, 6	O95139	NDUFB6
		15,000-dalton subunit	15.1	α subcomplex, 6	P56556	NDUFA6
II	Succinate–ubiquinone oxidoreductase	70,000-dalton subunit	72.7	flavoprotein	P31040	SDHA
		30,000-dalton subunit	31.6	iron–sulfur protein	P21912	SDHB
III	Ubiquinone–cytochrome *c* oxidoreductase	Core 1 subunit	51.6	none	P31930	UQCRC1
		Core 2 subunit	48.5	none	P22695	UQCRC2
		Iron–sulfur subunit	29.6	Rieske iron–sulfur protein	P47985	UQCRFS1
		10,000-dalton subunit	9.6 **	subunit VII	P13271 **	UCRQ
IV	Cytochrome *c* oxidase (COX)	Subunit I	57.0	COX I	P00395	MTCO1
		Subunit II	25.6	COX II	P00403	MTCO2
		Subunit III	29.9	COX III	P00414	MTCO3
		Subunit IV	19.6	COX IV	P13073	COX4
		Subunit Va	16.8	COX Va	P20674	COX5A
		Subunit Vb	13.7	COX Vb	P10606	COX5B
		Subunit VIa-L ††	9.5 **	COX VIa	P13182 **	COX6A1
		Subunit VIb	10.0 **	COX VIb	P00429 **	COX6B
		Subunit VIc	8.8	COX VIc	P09669	COX6C
		Subunit VIIa-H/L ††	9.4	COX VIIa	P14406	COX7A2
		Subunit VIIb	9.2	COX VIIb	P24311	COX7B
V	ATP synthase	α subunit	59.8	F_1 complex, α subunit	P25705	ATP5A1
		β subunit	56.6	F_1 complex, β subunit	P06576	ATP5B
		d subunit	18.4	none	O75947	ATP5H
		OSCP subunit ‡‡	23.2	F_1 complex, O subunit	P48047	ATP5O
		Inhibitor protein (IP)	12.3 **	IF_1	P01096 **	ATPI

* Molecular weight in kilodaltons. † Protein reference numbers are from SWISS-PROT, an annotated protein sequence database (www.ebi.ac.uk/swissprot) and refer to the human sequence, unless otherwise noted. ‡ Gene reference numbers are from Genbank, which can be accessed through Entrez (www3.ncbi.nlm.nih.gov/Entrez). § While not confirmed, the antibody supplier has reported observations that strongly suggest that the target for monoclonal 20E9 (A31857) is mtDNA-encoded ND6 protein (NDU subunit 6, gene number MTND6) with a molecular weight of ~20 kilodaltons as determined by SDS-PAGE. The protein number has not yet been determined. These observations include its acidic isoelectric focusing point (pI<<5) and the loss of immunoreactivity in cells in which mtDNA is depleted. The only other 20-kilodalton Complex I protein with a similar isoelectric point (NDUFB8) is encoded by nuclear DNA. ** Protein number and molecular weight are for the bovine sequence. †† H = heart-specific isotope; L = liver-specific isotope. ‡‡ OSCP = oligomycin sensitivity–conferring protein.

- Concentrated fixative solution
- Concentrated phosphate-buffered saline (PBS)
- Concentrated permeabilization solution
- Concentrated blocking solution
- Detailed protocols for mammalian cell preparation and staining

The SelectFX™ Alexa Fluor® 488 Cytochrome *c* Apoptosis Detection Kit can be used in conjunction with probes for other cell targets to achieve multicolor cell staining.

Antibodies against Other Mitochondrial Proteins

Mitochondrial Porin

Mitochondrial porin is an outer-membrane protein that forms regulated channels (referred to as voltage-dependent anionic channels, or VDACs) between the cytosol and the mitochondrial inter-membrane space.[186] This abundant transmembrane protein forms a small pore (~3 nm) in the outer membrane, allowing molecules less than ~10,000 daltons to pass.[187] Due to its abundance, porin is often used as a standardization marker in Western blots when assaying for other mitochondrial proteins [168,188] and serves as an effective organelle marker for immunohistochemistry.[117] Monoclonal antibodies against both human and yeast porin are available from Molecular Probes (A21317, A31855, A6449; Table 12.6).

Pyruvate Dehydrogenase

Molecular Probes has available a series of antibodies against the human pyruvate dehydrogenase (PDH) complex (Table 12.6), a large, multienzyme assembly residing in the mitochondrial matrix and consisting of three catalytic activities: pyruvate dehydrogenase, dihydrolipoyl transacetylase and dihydrolipoyl dehydrogenase [189] (diaphorase). The PDH complex is responsible for the oxidative decarboxylation of pyruvate to form acetyl coenzyme A, which is in turn fed into the citric acid cycle. Deficiencies in the PDH complex lead to lactic acidosis;[190] severe cases can lead to developmental defects such as congenital brain malformation.[191] In addition to unlabeled subunit-specific anti-PDH antibodies, we offer the red-fluorescent Alexa Fluor® 594 conjugate of anti–PDH E1α subunit antibody (A31853), as well as the green-fluorescent Alexa Fluor® 488 conjugate of anti–PDH E2 subunit antibody (A31854).

Mitochondrial Protein Extracts

For researchers seeking a source of mitochondrial protein standards, Molecular Probes offers human heart mitochondrial proteins for SDS-polyacrylamide gel electrophoresis (M22430). This complete mitochondrial lysate has tested negative for hepatitis B and C, as well as HIV 1 and 2 in serology tests. Mitochondrial protein extracts are useful for comparing new mitochondrial protein preparations in SDS-polyacrylamide gels and for testing mitochondrial antibodies.

Table 12.6 — Monoclonal antibodies specific for mitochondrial proteins not associated with the oxidative phosphorylation system

Cat # *	Subunit Specificity	Clone	Isotype	Suggested Concentration for Westerns (µg/mL)	Suggested Concentration for Immunocytochemistry (µg/mL)	Species Specificity †				
						Hum	Bov	Rat	Mou	Ye
A21323, A31853 ‡	Pyruvate dehydrogenase E1α	9H9	$IgG_{1,\kappa}$	0.04	1	+	ND	ND	+	ND
A21324	Pyruvate dehydrogenase E1β	17A5	$IgG_{1,\kappa}$	5	NR	+	ND	+	+	ND
A21325, A31854 ‡	Pyruvate dehydrogenase E2	15D3	$IgG_{1,\kappa}$	0.01	0.1	+	ND	–	–	ND
A21326	Pyruvate dehydrogenase E2/E3bp	13G2	$IgG_{2a,\kappa}$	0.5	1	+	+	ND	+	ND
A21317	Mitochondrial porin (human)	20B12	$IgG_{2b,\kappa}$	1	0.5	+	ND	ND	+	ND
A31855	Mitochondrial porin (human)	31HL	$IgG_{2b,\kappa}$	ND	ND	+	ND	ND	ND	ND
A6449	Mitochondrial porin (yeast)	16G9	$IgG_{1,\kappa}$	0.5	5–20	ND	ND	ND	ND	+

* For all the antibodies listed in this table, the unit size is 100 µg, except for A6449, which is available in a unit size of 250 µg. † Species specificity: Hum = human; Bov = bovine; Mou = Mouse; Ye = yeast; (+) = strong reactivity; (–) = no reactivity. ‡ Fluorescent conjugate: A31853 is a red-fluorescent Alexa Fluor® 594 conjugate; A31854 is a green-fluorescent Alexa Fluor® 488 conjugate. ND = Not determined. NR = Not recommended.

References

1. Mitochondrion 1, 3 (2001); **2.** Trends Biochem Sci 25, 319 (2000); **3.** Methods Cell Biol 63, 467 (2001); **4.** Trends Cell Biol 10, 369 (2000); **5.** Science 289, 1150 (2000); **6.** FEBS Lett 170, 181 (1984); **7.** Arch Biochem Biophys 282, 358 (1990); **8.** J Microsc 132, 143 (1983); **9.** Cytometry 12, 179 (1991); **10.** J Neurosci 21, 3017 (2001); **11.** Cytometry 39, 203 (2000); **12.** Cell Biology: A Laboratory Handbook, 2nd Ed., Vol. 2, Celis JE, Ed. pp. 513–517 (1998); **13.** Microsc Res Tech 27, 198 (1994); **14.** Int Rev Cytol 122, 1 (1990); **15.** Biochem J 271, 269 (1990); **16.** J Histochem Cytochem 44, 1363 (1996); **17.** Cell 87, 823 (1996); **18.** J Biomol Screen 2, 249 (1997); **19.** Cytometry 25, 333 (1996); **20.** J Immunol 157, 512 (1996); **21.** J Cell Biol 126, 1375 (1994); **22.** J Biol Chem 271, 24365 (1996); **23.** Cell 79, 1209 (1994); **24.** J Biol Chem 273, 12415 (1998); **25.** J Biol Chem 272, 14817 (1997); **26.** Science 276, 1709 (1997); **27.** Cell 87, 629 (1996); **28.** J Cell Biol 131, 1039 (1995); **29.** J Neurosci 17, 1582 (1997); **30.** J Cell Biol 134, 1387 (1996); **31.** J Eukaryot Microbiol 41, 79S (1994); **32.** Immunol Lett 61, 157 (1998); **33.** Proc Natl Acad Sci U S A 98, 9505 (2001); **34.** Mol Biochem Parasitol 90, 381 (1997); **35.** J Histochem Cytochem 45, 1053 (1997); **36.** J Cell Biol 136, 1081 (1997); **37.** Mol Reprod Dev 47, 79 (1997); **38.** Zygote 5, 301 (1997); **39.** Biol Reprod 55, 1195 (1996); **40.** J Cell Biol 143, 777 (1998); **41.** J Cell Biol 137, 633 (1997); **42.** J Chromatogr B Analyt Technol Biomed Life Sci 793, 141 (2003); **43.** Mol Cell Biochem 172, 171 (1997); **44.** Biophys J 83, 502 (2002); **45.** Free Radic Biol Med 28, 1266 (2000); **46.** Fluorescent and Luminescent Probes for Biological Activity, Mason WT, Ed. pp. 124–132 (1993); **47.** Biochemistry 30, 4480 (1991); **48.** Proc Natl Acad Sci U S A 88, 3671 (1991); **49.** Biochem Biophys Res Commun 197, 40 (1993); **50.** Proc Natl Acad Sci U S A 92, 729 (1995); **51.** Neuron 15, 961 (1995); **52.** Exp Cell Res 214, 323 (1994); **53.** Cardiovasc Res 27, 1790 (1993); **54.** Biophys J 65, 1767 (1993); **55.** Reprod Toxicol 15, 5 (2001); **56.** Proc Natl Acad Sci U S A 77, 990 (1980); **57.** Nature 310, 53 (1984); **58.** J Appl Bacteriol 72, 410 (1992); **59.** FEMS Microbiol Lett 21, 153 (1984); **60.** Plant Physiol 98, 279 (1992); **61.** Planta 17, 346 (1987); **62.** J Histochem Cytochem 41, 1247 (1993); **63.** J Cell Biol 111, 967 (1990); **64.** Curr Genet 18, 265 (1990); **65.** Proc Natl Acad Sci U S A 78, 2383 (1981); **66.** J Cell Biol 123, 1207 (1993); **67.** Brain Res 528, 285 (1990); **68.** J Cell Biol 112, 385 (1991); **69.** Biochim Biophys Acta 975, 377 (1989); **70.** Biophys J 76, 469 (1999); **71.** Cytometry 15, 335 (1994); **72.** J Biol Chem 269, 14546 (1994); **73.** Biochem J 288, 207 (1992); **74.** Eur J Biochem 248, 104 (1997); **75.** Cytometry 17, 50 (1994); **76.** Eur J Cancer 30A, 1117 (1994); **77.** Mol Pharmacol 45, 1145 (1994); **78.** Proc Natl Acad Sci U S A 91, 4654 (1994); **79.** Mol Pharmacol 43, 51 (1993); **80.** Exp Cell Res 190, 69 (1990); **81.** Exp Cell Res 174, 168 (1988); **82.** Biochemistry 33, 7056 (1994); **83.** J Microbiol Methods 7, 139 (1987); **84.** Biol Reprod 30, 13 (1984); **85.** Ann NY Acad Sci 397, 299 (1982); **86.** Pharmacol Ther 63, 1 (1994); **87.** Exp Cell Res 192, 198 (1991); **88.** Photochem Photobiol 52, 703 (1990); **89.** Biophys J 56, 979 (1989); **90.** Cancer Res 49, 3961 (1989); **91.** Photochem Photobiol 48, 613 (1988); **92.** Cancer Res 45, 6093 (1985); **93.** Science 218, 1117 (1982); **94.** Biochem Biophys Res Commun 118, 717 (1984); **95.** Proc Natl Acad Sci U S A 79, 5292 (1982); **96.** Histochemistry 94, 303 (1990); **97.** Exp Pathol 31, 47 (1987); **98.** J Cell Biol 88, 526 (1981); **99.** Transplantation 58, 403 (1994); **100.** J Bioenerg Biomembr 25, 679 (1993); **101.** J Cell Sci 101, 315 (1992); **102.** Biophys J 56, 1053 (1989); **103.** Biophys J 53, 785 (1988); **104.** J Fluorescence 3, 265 (1993); **105.** Cell Biology: A Laboratory Handbook, Vol. 2, Celis JE, Ed. pp. 399–403 (1994); **106.** Biophys J 65, 2396 (1993); **107.** Optical Microscopy for Biology, Herman B, Jacobson K, Eds. pp. 131–142 (1990); **108.** Proc Natl Acad Sci U S A 91, 12579 (1994); **109.** Anal Biochem 295, 220 (2001); **110.** Methods Cell Biol 29, 103 (1989); **111.** Eur J Biochem 217, 973 (1993); **112.** Arch Biochem Biophys 302, 348 (1993); **113.** APMIS 102, 474 (1994); **114.** Free Radicals: A Practical Approach, Punchard NA, Ed. pp. 83–99 (1996); **115.** Proc Natl Acad Sci U S A 93, 1167 (1996); **116.** Methods Enzymol 172, 102 (1989); **117.** Mol Biol Cell 9, 917 (1998); **118.** Cell Motil Cytoskeleton 25, 111 (1993); **119.** Methods Cell Biol 31, 357 (1989); **120.** Methods Cell Biol 29, 125 (1989); **121.** Exp Cell Res 125, 514 (1980); **122.** Cancer Res 55, 2063 (1995); **123.** Plant Physiol 84, 1385 (1987); **124.** Nature 290, 593 (1981); **125.** J Appl Bacteriol 78, 309 (1995); **126.** J Cell Biol 120, 1337 (1993); **127.** Br J Cancer 62, 903 (1990); **128.** Br J Cancer 59, 706 (1989); **129.** Biochemistry 34, 3858 (1995); **130.** J Cell Biol 107, 2703 (1988); **131.** Histochemistry 99, 75 (1993); **132.** J Neurocytol 19, 67 (1990); **133.** J Neurosci 7, 1207 (1987); **134.** Trends Neurosci 10, 398 (1987); **135.** J Cell Biol 126, 1361 (1994); **136.** Histochemistry 82, 51 (1985); **137.** Histochemistry 80, 385 (1984); **138.** Histochemistry 79, 443 (1983); **139.** FEBS Lett 260, 236 (1990); **140.** J Dent Res 74, 1295 (1995); **141.** Eur J Biochem 228, 113 (1995); **142.** Eur J Biochem 194, 389 (1990); **143.** Biochem Biophys Res Commun 164, 185 (1989); **144.** Basic Appl Histochem 33, 71 (1989); **145.** Cancer Res 51, 4665 (1991); **146.** Biotechniques 30, 804 (2001); **147.** Free Radic Biol Med 17, 117 (1994); **148.** J Biol Chem 274, 543 (1999); **149.** Mol Biol Cell 9, 523 (1998); **150.** Yeast 14, 147 (1998); **151.** Biochim Biophys Acta 1366, 177 (1998); **152.** J Cell Biol 143, 359 (1998); **153.** J Cell Biol 143, 333 (1998); **154.** J Cell Biol 141, 1371 (1998); **155.** Cytometry 23, 28 (1996); **156.** J Cell Biol 130, 345 (1995); **157.** Mol Biol Cell 6, 1381 (1995); **158.** Biochem Int 2, 503 (1981); **159.** Histochemistry 100, 415 (1993); **160.** Biochim Biophys Acta 1366, 199 (1998); **161.** Biochim Biophys Acta 1366, 211 (1998); **162.** Curr Opin Cardiol 13, 190 (1998); **163.** Ann Neurol 44, S99 (1998); **164.** J Neural Transm 105, 855 (1998); **165.** Semin Liver Dis 18, 237 (1998); **166.** Biochim Biophys Acta 1362, 145 (1997); **167.** J Biol Chem 276, 8892 (2001); **168.** J Biol Chem 276, 16296 (2001); **169.** Biochim Biophys Acta 1315, 199 (1996); **170.** Brain 123, 591 (2000); **171.** "Immunological approaches to the characterization and diagnosis of mitochondrial disease." R.A. Capaldi, J. Murray, L. Byrne, M.S. Janes and M.F. Marusich, Mitochondrion (2004) in press; **172.** Science 283, 1488 (1999); **173.** Annu Rev Biochem 59, 569 (1990); **174.** Biochemistry 30, 3674 (1991); **175.** Biochim Biophys Acta 1225, 95 (1993); **176.** Methods Enzymol 260, 117 (1995); **177.** J Biol Chem 268, 18754 (1993); **178.** J Biol Chem 266, 7688 (1991); **179.** Pediatr Res 28, 529 (1990); **180.** Hum Mol Genet 6, 935 (1997); **181.** J Histochem Cytochem 52, 1011 (2004); **182.** Proc Natl Acad Sci U S A 98, 6656 (2001); **183.** Science 292, 624 (2001); **184.** Biochim Biophys Acta 1366, 151 (1998); **185.** Science 281, 1309 (1998); **186.** Biochim Biophys Acta 894, 109 (1987); **187.** J Biol Chem 273, 24406 (1998); **188.** Biochim Biophys Acta 1455, 35 (1999); **189.** J Biol Chem 272, 5757 (1997); **190.** Biochem J 239, 89 (1986); **191.** Neurology 53, 612 (1999).

Data Table — 12.2 Probes for Mitochondria

Cat #	MW	Storage	Soluble	Abs	EC	Em	Solvent	Notes
A1372	472.51	L	DMSO, EtOH	495	84,000	519	MeOH	
D273	572.53	D,L	DMSO	484	154,000	501	MeOH	
D288	366.24	L	DMF	475	45,000	605	MeOH	1
D308	366.24	L	DMF	461	38,000	585	MeOH	1
D378	600.58	D,L	DMSO	482	148,000	504	MeOH	
D426	380.27	L	DMF	461	39,000	589	MeOH	1
D632	346.38	F,D,L,AA	DMF, DMSO	289	7,100	none	MeOH	2, 3
D633	444.57	F,D,L,AA	DMF, DMSO	296	11,000	none	MeOH	2, 3
D22421	532.38	D,L	DMSO, DMF	522	143,000	535	$CHCl_3$	4
D23806	346.38	F,D,L,AA	DMSO	289	7,100	none	MeOH	3, 5
L6868	510.50	L	H_2O	455	7,400	505	H_2O	6, 7
M7502	602.99	L	DMSO	489	112,000	517	MeOH	
M7510	427.37	F,D,L	DMSO	551	102,000	576	MeOH	
M7511	392.93	F,D,L,AA	DMSO	235	57,000	none	MeOH	2, 3
M7512	531.52	F,D,L	DMSO	578	116,000	599	MeOH	
M7513	497.08	F,D,L,AA	DMSO	245	45,000	none	MeOH	2, 3
M7514	671.88	F,D,L	DMSO	490	119,000	516	MeOH	
M22422	647.10	F,D,L	DMSO	604	97,000	637	MeOH	
M22424	~550	F,D,L	DMSO	588	105,000	622	MeOH	8
M22425	724.00	F,D,L	DMSO	588	81,000	644	MeOH	
M22426	543.58	F,D,L	DMSO	640	194,000	662	MeOH	
R302	380.83	F,D,L	MeOH, DMF	507	101,000	529	MeOH	

Data Table — 12.2 Probes for Mitochondria — continued

Cat #	MW	Storage	Soluble	Abs	EC	Em	Solvent	Notes
R634	479.02	F,D,L	EtOH	528	105,000	551	MeOH	
R648MP	627.18	F,D,L	DMF, DMSO	556	123,000	578	MeOH	
R14060	434.41	F,D,L,AA	DMSO	239	52,000	none	MeOH	2, 9
R22420	380.83	F,D,L	MeOH, DMF	507	101,000	529	MeOH	10
S7529	~450	F,D,L	DMSO	483	64,000	none	pH 7	8, 11, 12
T639	378.90	L	DMF, DMSO	550	87,000	574	MeOH	
T668	500.93	F,D,L	DMSO, MeOH	549	115,000	573	MeOH	
T669	514.96	F,D,L	DMSO, EtOH	549	109,000	574	MeOH	
T3168	652.23	D,L	DMSO, DMF	514	195,000	529	MeOH	13

For definitions of the contents of this data table, see "Navigating *The Handbook*" in the introductory pages.

Notes

1. Abs and Em of styryl dyes are at shorter wavelengths in membrane environments than in reference solvents such as methanol. The difference is typically 20 nm for absorption and 80 nm for emission, but varies considerably from one dye to another. Styryl dyes are generally nonfluorescent in water.
2. This compound is susceptible to oxidation, especially in solution. Store solutions under argon or nitrogen. Oxidation may be induced by illumination.
3. These compounds are essentially colorless and nonfluorescent until oxidized. Oxidation products (in parentheses) are as follows: D632 and D23806 (R302); D633 (R634); M7511 (M7510); M7513 (M7512).
4. JC-9 exhibits long-wavelength J-aggregate emission at ~635 nm in aqueous solutions and polarized mitochondria.
5. This product is supplied as a ready-made solution in DMSO with sodium borohydride added to inhibit oxidation.
6. L6868 has much stronger absorption at shorter wavelengths (Abs = 368 nm (EC = 36,000 $cm^{-1}M^{-1}$)).
7. This compound emits chemiluminescence upon oxidation in basic aqueous solutions. Emission peaks are at 425 nm (L8455) and 470 nm (L6868).
8. MW: The preceding ~ symbol indicates an approximate value, not including counterions.
9. R14060 is colorless and nonfluorescent until oxidized. The spectral characteristics of the oxidation product (2,3,4,5,6-pentafluorotetramethylrosamine) are similar to those of T639.
10. This product is specified to equal or exceed 98% analytical purity by HPLC.
11. This product is supplied as a ready-made solution in the solvent indicated under "Soluble."
12. S7529 is fluorescent when bound to DNA (Abs = 490 nm, Em = 507 nm).
13. JC-1 forms J-aggregates with Abs/Em = 585/590 nm at concentrations above 0.1 µM in aqueous solutions (pH 8.0) (Biochemistry 30, 4480 (1991)).

Product List — 12.2 Probes for Mitochondria

Cat #	Product Name	Unit Size
A1372	acridine orange 10-nonyl bromide (nonyl acridine orange)	100 mg
A21359	anti-OxPhos Complex I 17 kDa subunit, mouse IgG_{2b}, monoclonal 21C11 *human mitochondrial reactivity*	100 µg
A21343	anti-OxPhos Complex I 30 kDa subunit, mouse IgG_1, monoclonal 3F9 *human mitochondrial reactivity*	100 µg
A21344	anti-OxPhos Complex I 39 kDa subunit, mouse IgG_1, monoclonal 20C11 *human mitochondrial reactivity*	100 µg
A11142	anti-OxPhos Complex II 70 kDa subunit, mouse IgG_1, monoclonal 2E3 *human mitochondrial reactivity*	50 µg
A21345	anti-OxPhos Complex II 30 kDa subunit, mouse IgG_{2a}, monoclonal 21A11 *human mitochondrial reactivity*	100 µg
A21361	anti-OxPhos Complex III 10 kDa subunit, mouse IgG_{2a}, monoclonal 1H9 *human mitochondrial reactivity*	100 µg
A21362	anti-OxPhos Complex III core 1 subunit, mouse IgG_1, monoclonal 16D10 *human mitochondrial reactivity*	100 µg
A11143	anti-OxPhos Complex III core 2 subunit, mouse IgG_1, monoclonal 13G12 *human mitochondrial reactivity*	100 µg
A21346	anti-OxPhos Complex III subunit FeS, mouse IgG_{2b}, monoclonal 5A5 *human mitochondrial reactivity*	100 µg
A6403	anti-OxPhos Complex IV subunit I, mouse IgG_{2a}, monoclonal 1D6 (anti-cytochrome oxidase subunit I) *human mitochondrial reactivity*	100 µg
A21296	anti-OxPhos Complex IV subunit I, mouse IgG_{2a}, monoclonal 1D6, Alexa Fluor® 488 conjugate (anti-cytochrome oxidase subunit I, Alexa Fluor® 488 conjugate) *1 mg/mL* *human mitochondrial reactivity*	100 µL
A21297	anti-OxPhos Complex IV subunit I, mouse IgG_{2a}, monoclonal 1D6, Alexa Fluor® 594 conjugate (anti-cytochrome oxidase subunit I, Alexa Fluor® 594 conjugate) *1 mg/mL* *human mitochondrial reactivity*	100 µL
A6404	anti-OxPhos Complex IV subunit II, mouse IgG_{2a}, monoclonal 12C4 (anti-cytochrome oxidase subunit II) *human mitochondrial reactivity*	100 µg
A21347	anti-OxPhos Complex IV subunit IV, mouse IgG_{2a}, monoclonal 10G8 (anti-cytochrome oxidase subunit IV) *human mitochondrial reactivity*	100 µg
A21348	anti-OxPhos Complex IV subunit IV, mouse IgG_{2a}, monoclonal 20E8 (anti-cytochrome oxidase subunit IV) *human mitochondrial reactivity*	100 µg
A21363	anti-OxPhos Complex IV subunit Va, mouse IgG_{2a}, monoclonal 6E9 (anti-cytochrome oxidase subunit Va) *human mitochondrial reactivity*	100 µg
A21349	anti-OxPhos Complex IV subunit Vb, mouse IgG_{2b}, monoclonal 16H12 (anti-cytochrome oxidase subunit Vb) *human mitochondrial reactivity*	100 µg
A21365	anti-OxPhos Complex IV subunit VIa-L, mouse IgG_1, monoclonal 14A3 (anti-cytochrome oxidase subunit VIa-L) *human mitochondrial reactivity*	100 µg
A21366	anti-OxPhos Complex IV subunit VIb, mouse IgG_1, monoclonal 3F9 (anti-cytochrome oxidase subunit VIb) *human mitochondrial reactivity*	100 µg
A6401	anti-OxPhos Complex IV subunit VIc, mouse IgG_{2b}, monoclonal 3G5 (anti-cytochrome oxidase subunit VIc) *human mitochondrial reactivity*	100 µg
A21367	anti-OxPhos Complex IV subunit VIIa-H/L, mouse IgG_{2a}, monoclonal 6D7 (anti-cytochrome oxidase subunit VIIa-H/L) *human mitochondrial reactivity*	100 µg
A21368	anti-OxPhos Complex IV subunit VIIb, mouse IgG_1, monoclonal 2G7 (anti-cytochrome oxidase subunit VIIb) *human mitochondrial reactivity*	100 µg

For current prices or to order online, visit probes.invitrogen.com

Cat #	Product Name	Unit Size
A6405	anti-OxPhos Complex IV subunit I (yeast), mouse IgG_{2b}, monoclonal 11D8 (anti-cytochrome oxidase subunit I (yeast))	100 µg
A6407	anti-OxPhos Complex IV subunit II (yeast), mouse IgG_{2a}, monoclonal 4B12 (anti-cytochrome oxidase subunit II (yeast))	250 µg
A6408	anti-OxPhos Complex IV subunit III (yeast), mouse IgG_{2a}, monoclonal DA5 (anti-cytochrome oxidase subunit III (yeast))	250 µg
A6432	anti-OxPhos Complex IV subunit IV (yeast), mouse IgG_1, monoclonal 1A12 (anti-cytochrome oxidase subunit IV (yeast))	250 µg
A21355	anti-OxPhos Complex V inhibitor protein, mouse IgG_1, monoclonal 5E2 (anti-ATP synthase IP; anti-F_1F_0-ATPase IP) *human mitochondrial reactivity*	100 µg
A21350	anti-OxPhos Complex V subunit α, mouse IgG_{2b}, monoclonal 7H10 (anti-ATP synthase subunit α; anti-F_1F_0-ATPase subunit α) *human mitochondrial reactivity*	100 µg
A21351	anti-OxPhos Complex V subunit β, mouse IgG_1, monoclonal 3D5 (anti-ATP synthase subunit β; anti-F_1F_0-ATPase subunit β) *human mitochondrial reactivity*	100 µg
A21353	anti-OxPhos Complex V subunit d, mouse IgG_{2b}, monoclonal 7F9 (anti-ATP synthase subunit d; anti-F_1F_0-ATPase subunit d) *human mitochondrial reactivity*	100 µg
A21354	anti-OxPhos Complex V subunit OSCP, mouse IgG_1, monoclonal 4C11 (anti-ATP synthase subunit OSCP; anti-F_1F_0-ATPase subunit OSCP) *human mitochondrial reactivity*	100 µg
A31856	anti-OxPhos Complex I 15 kDa subunit, mouse IgG_1, monoclonal 17G3 *human mitochondrial reactivity*	100 µg
A31857	anti-OxPhos Complex I 20 kDa subunit, mouse IgG_1, monoclonal 20E9 *human mitochondrial reactivity*	100 µg
A21317	anti-porin (human mitochondrial), mouse IgG_{2b}, monoclonal 20B12	100 µg
A31855	anti-porin (human mitochondrial), mouse IgG_{2b}, monoclonal 31HL *1 mg/mL*	100 µL
A6449	anti-porin (yeast mitochondrial), mouse IgG_1, monoclonal 16G9	250 µg
A21323	anti-pyruvate dehydrogenase E1α subunit (human mitochondrial), mouse IgG_1, monoclonal 9H9 (anti-PDH E1α subunit)	100 µg
A31853	anti-pyruvate dehydrogenase E1α subunit (human mitochondrial), mouse IgG_1, monoclonal 9H9, Alexa Fluor® 594 conjugate (anti-PDH E1α subunit, Alexa Fluor® 594 conjugate) *1 mg/mL*	100 µL
A21324	anti-pyruvate dehydrogenase E1β subunit (human mitochondrial), mouse IgG_1, monoclonal 17A5 (anti-PDH E1β subunit)	100 µg
A21325	anti-pyruvate dehydrogenase E2 subunit (human mitochondrial), mouse IgG_1, monoclonal 15D3 (anti-PDH E2 subunit)	100 µg
A21326	anti-pyruvate dehydrogenase E2/E3bp subunit (human mitochondrial), mouse IgG_{2a}, monoclonal 13G2 (anti-PDH E2/E3bp subunit)	100 µg
A31854	anti-pyruvate dehydrogenase E2 subunit (human mitochondrial), mouse IgG_1, monoclonal 15D3, Alexa Fluor® 488 conjugate (anti-PDH E2 subunit, Alexa Fluor® 488 conjugate) *1 mg/mL*	100 µL
D378	3,3′-diheptyloxacarbocyanine iodide ($DiOC_7(3)$)	100 mg
D273	3,3′-dihexyloxacarbocyanine iodide ($DiOC_6(3)$)	100 mg
D632	dihydrorhodamine 123	10 mg
D23806	dihydrorhodamine 123 *5 mM stabilized solution in DMSO*	1 mL
D633	dihydrorhodamine 6G	25 mg
D426	2-(4-(dimethylamino)styryl)-*N*-ethylpyridinium iodide (DASPEI)	1 g
D308	2-(4-(dimethylamino)styryl)-*N*-methylpyridinium iodide (2-Di-1-ASP)	1 g
D288	4-(4-(dimethylamino)styryl)-*N*-methylpyridinium iodide (4-Di-1-ASP)	1 g
D22421	3,3′-dimethyl-α-naphthoxacarbocyanine iodide (JC-9; $DiNOC_1(3)$)	5 mg
E21390	Endogenous Biotin-Blocking Kit *100 assays*	1 kit
L6868	lucigenin (bis-*N*-methylacridinium nitrate) *high purity*	10 mg
M22430	mitochondrial proteins (human heart) for SDS-polyacrylamide gel electrophoresis *2 mg/mL*	100 µL
M7502	MitoFluor™ Green	1 mg
M22424	MitoFluor™ Red 589	1 mg
M22422	MitoFluor™ Red 594	1 mg
M22426	MitoTracker® Deep Red 633 *special packaging*	20 x 50 µg
M7514	MitoTracker® Green FM *special packaging*	20 x 50 µg
M7511	MitoTracker® Orange CM-H_2TMRos *special packaging*	20 x 50 µg
M7510	MitoTracker® Orange CMTMRos *special packaging*	20 x 50 µg
M22425	MitoTracker® Red 580 *special packaging*	20 x 50 µg
M7513	MitoTracker® Red CM-H_2XRos *special packaging*	20 x 50 µg
M7512	MitoTracker® Red CMXRos *special packaging*	20 x 50 µg
R14060	RedoxSensor™ Red CC-1 *special packaging*	10 x 50 µg
R302	rhodamine 123	25 mg
R22420	rhodamine 123 *FluoroPure™ grade*	25 mg
R634	rhodamine 6G chloride	1 g
R648MP	rhodamine B, hexyl ester, perchlorate (R 6)	10 mg
S35115	SelectFX™ Alexa Fluor® 488 Cytochrome *c* Apoptosis Detection Kit *for fixed cells*	1 kit
S7529	SYTO® 18 yeast mitochondrial stain *5 mM solution in DMSO*	250 µL
T3168	5,5′,6,6′-tetrachloro-1,1′,3,3′-tetraethylbenzimidazolylcarbocyanine iodide (JC-1; $CBIC_2(3)$)	5 mg
T669	tetramethylrhodamine, ethyl ester, perchlorate (TMRE)	25 mg
T668	tetramethylrhodamine, methyl ester, perchlorate (TMRM)	25 mg
T639	tetramethylrosamine chloride	25 mg
Y7530	Yeast Mitochondrial Stain Sampler Kit	1 kit

For current prices or to order online, visit probes.invitrogen.com

12.3 Probes for Lysosomes, Peroxisomes and Yeast Vacuoles

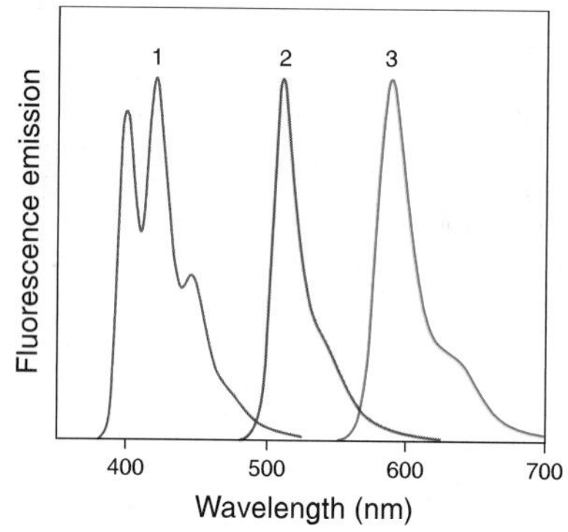

Figure 12.31 Normalized fluorescence emission spectra of 1) LysoTracker® Blue DND-22 (L7525), 2) LysoTracker® Green DND-26 (L7526) and 3) LysoTracker® Red DND-99 (L7528) in aqueous solutions, pH 6.0.

Molecular Probes' acidotropic reagents can be used to stain lysosomes and yeast vacuoles, as well as several other types of acidic compartments such as trans-Golgi vesicles, endosomes and subpopulations of coated vesicles in fibroblasts, secretory vesicles in insulin-secreting pancreatic β-cells, acrosomes of spermatozoa and plant vacuoles.[1] Lysosomes contain glycosidases, acid phosphatases, elastase, cathepsins, carboxypeptidases and a variety of other proteases. Chapter 10 describes a number of substrates for detecting the activity of these hydrolytic enzymes. An excellent compendium of human diseases that affect intracellular transport processes through lysosomes, Golgi and endoplasmic reticulum (ER) has been published.[2]

Like lysosomes, peroxisomes are single membrane–bound vesicles that contain digestive enzymes. The chief function of these basic organelles is to enzymatically oxidize fatty acids and to subsequently catalyze the breakdown of H_2O_2, a by-product of fatty acid degradation. Recently, interest in peroxisomes has increased, especially studies related to peroxisomal origin and maintenance.[3,4] Morphological abnormalities in peroxisomes related to disease states and diet have also been the subject of current research.[5,6] The SelectFX™ Alexa Fluor® 488 Peroxisome Labeling Kit (S34201), described below, provides an antibody-based method for labeling peroxisomes in fixed cells.

Figure 12.32 Bovine pulmonary artery endothelial cells (BPAEC) incubated simultaneously with 50 nM LysoTracker® Red DND-99 (L7528) and 75 nM MitoTracker® Green FM (M7514) at 37°C for 30 minutes. Both dyes showed excellent cellular retention, even after cells were fixed in 3% glutaraldehyde for 30 minutes. The image was deconvolved using Huygens software (Scientific Volume Imaging).

LysoTracker® Probes: Acidic Organelle–Selective Cell-Permeant Probes

Weakly basic amines selectively accumulate in cellular compartments with low internal pH and can be used to investigate the biosynthesis and pathogenesis of lysosomes.[7,8] One frequently used probe for acidic organelles, DAMP (D1552), is not fluorescent and therefore must be used in conjunction with anti-DNP antibodies (Section 7.4) directly or indirectly conjugated to a fluorophore or enzyme in order to visualize the staining pattern.[9] The fluorescent probes neutral red (N3246) and acridine orange (A1301, A3568) are also commonly used for staining acidic organelles, though they lack specificity.[1,10]

These limitations have motivated us to search for alternative acidic organelle–selective probes, both for short-term and long-term tracking studies. The LysoTracker® probes are fluorescent acidotropic probes for labeling and tracing acidic organelles in live cells. These probes have

Table 12.7 — Summary of our LysoTracker® and LysoSensor™ probes

Cat #	Probe	Abs * (nm)	Em * (nm)	pK_a
L7525	LysoTracker® Blue DND-22	373	422	ND
L12490	LysoTracker® Blue-White DPX	380	†	ND
L12491	LysoTracker® Yellow HCK-123	465	535	ND
L7526	LysoTracker® Green DND-26	504	511	ND
L7528	LysoTracker® Red DND-99	577	590	ND
L7533	LysoSensor™ Blue DND-167	373	425	5.1
L7535	LysoSensor™ Green DND-189	443	505	5.2
L7534	LysoSensor™ Green DND-153	442	505	7.5
L7545	LysoSensor™ Yellow/Blue DND-160	384 329	540 ‡ 440 §	3.9
L22460	LysoSensor™ Yellow/Blue 10,000 MW dextran	381 335	521 ‡ 452 §	4.2

* Absorption (Abs) and fluorescence emission (Em) maxima, determined in aqueous buffer or methanol; values may vary somewhat in cellular environments. † The emission is extremely sensitive to environment; stained lysosomes appear blue-white, although the emission maximum in methanol is 576 nm. ‡ At pH 3. § At pH 7; this dye has pH-dependent dual-excitation and dual-emission peaks (Figure 12.36). ND = Not determined.

several important features, including high selectivity for acidic organelles and effective labeling of live cells at nanomolar concentrations. Furthermore, the LysoTracker® probes are available in several fluorescent colors (Table 12.7, Figure 12.31), making them especially suitable for multicolor applications.

The LysoTracker® probes, which comprise a fluorophore linked to a weak base that is only partially protonated at neutral pH, are freely permeant to cell membranes and typically concentrate in spherical organelles (Figure 1.113, Figure 10.20, Figure 12.32, Figure 12.33). We have found that the fluorescent LysoTracker® probes must be used at very low concentrations — usually about 50 nM — to achieve optimal selectivity. Their mechanism of retention has not been firmly established but is likely to involve protonation and retention in the organelles' membranes, although staining is generally not reversed by subsequent treatment of the cells with weakly basic cell-permeant compounds. Furthermore, the larger acidic compartments of cells stained with LysoTracker® Red DND-99 (L7528; Figure 12.32, Figure 12.34) usually retain their staining pattern following fixation with aldehydes. Simultaneous staining of lysosomes by two LysoTracker® dyes — LysoTracker® Yellow HCK-123 (L12491) and LysoTracker® Red DND-99 (L7528) — yields identical staining patterns when viewed through either the bandpass filter set appropriate for fluorescein or a longpass filter set appropriate for rhodamine (Figure 12.33).

LysoTracker® Green DND-26 (L7526) was used to identify acidic compartments in a study of a membrane protein that facilitates vesicular sequestration of zinc,[11] to visualize acidic organelles labeled with rhodamine B in denervated skeletal muscle [12] and to assess acrosomal integrity in cryopreserved bovine spermatozoa.[13] This LysoTracker® probe also proved useful in a continuous assay for the secretion of pulmonary surfactant by exocytosis of lamellar bodies.[14] LysoTracker® Red DND-99 provided researchers with a probe for examining lysosome damage in *Trypanosoma brucei* after specific uptake of cytokine tumor necrosis factor-α,[15] for studying apoptosis in organogenesis-stage mouse embryos [16] and for determining the subcellular localization of receptor and channel proteins.[17–19]

Our kinetic studies on the internalization of LysoTracker® Green DND-26 (L7526) indicate that the dye is taken up by live cells within seconds.[20] Unfortunately, these lysosomal probes can exhibit an alkalinizing effect on the lysosomes, such that longer incubation with these probes can induce an increase in lysosomal pH. Therefore, we recommend incubating cells with these probes for only one to five minutes before imaging.

The LysoTracker® probes were principally developed for fluorescence microscopy applications. The lysosomal fluorescence in LysoTracker® dye–stained cells may constitute only a portion of total cellular fluorescence due to cellular autofluorescence or nonspecific staining. Consequently, successful application of these probes for quantitating the number of lysosomes by flow cytometry or fluorometry will likely depend on the particular cell lines and staining protocols used.

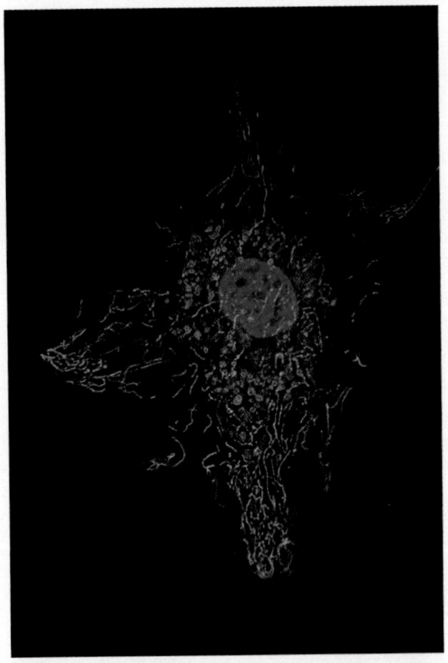

Figure 12.34 Live bovine pulmonary artery endothelial cells (BPAEC) were first stained with LysoTracker® Red DND-99 (L7528). Then, a solution of dihydrorhodamine 123 (D632, D23806) and Hoechst 33258 (H1398, H3569, H21491) was added and allowed to incubate with the cells for an additional 10 minutes before the cells were subsequently washed and visualized. The green-fluorescent oxidation product (rhodamine 123, R302) localized primarily to the mitochondria. The red-fluorescent LysoTracker® Red DND-99 stain accumulated in the lysosomes, and the blue-fluorescent Hoechst 33258 dye stained the nuclei. The image was acquired with filters appropriate for DAPI, fluorescein and the Texas Red® dye. The image was deconvolved using Huygens software (Scientific Volume Imaging). 3-D reconstruction was performed using Imaris software (Bitplane AG).

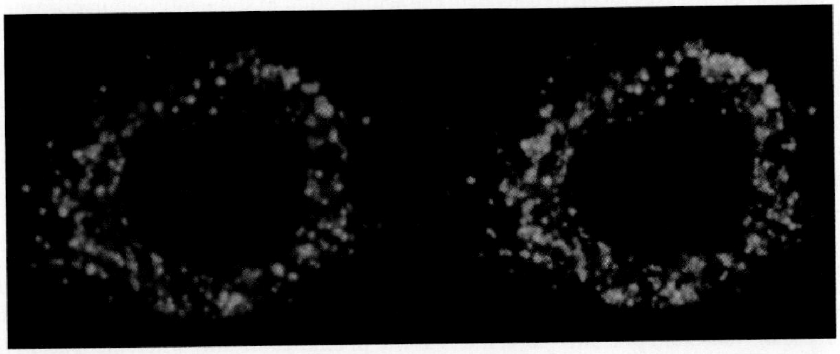

Figure 12.33 Rat fibroblasts stained with LysoTracker® Yellow HCK-123 (L12491) and LysoTracker® Red DND-99 (L7528). The lysosomes fluoresce green when visualized through a bandpass filter set appropriate for fluorescein (right image) and red when visualized through a longpass filter set appropriate for rhodamine (left image).

LysoSensor™ Probes: Acidic Organelle–Selective pH Indicators

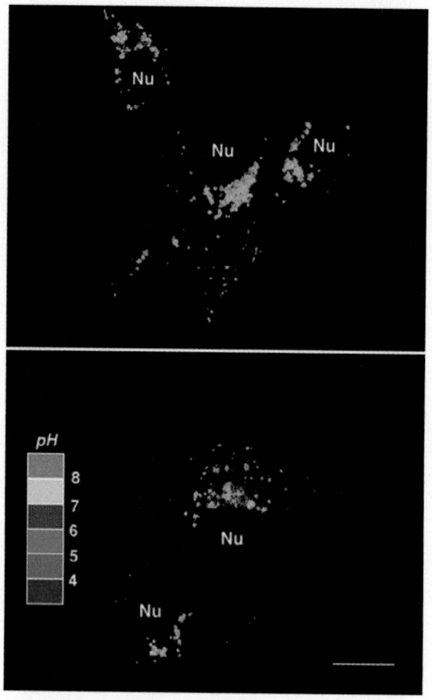

Figure 12.35 Dual-emission ratiometric measurement of lysosomal pH using LysoSensor™ Yellow/Blue DND-160 (L7545). Madin-Darby canine kidney cells were exposed to pH-calibration buffers (pH 4.5 or 7.0) in the presence of nigericin (N1495) and monensin. These pseudocolored images were constructed from two emission images at 450 +/- 33 nm and 510 +/- 20 nm, both excited at 365 +/- 8 nm.

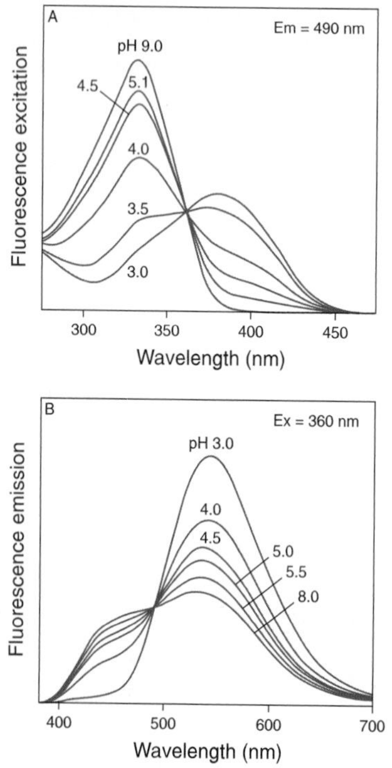

Figure 12.36 The pH-dependent spectral response of LysoSensor™ Yellow/Blue DND-160 (L7545): A) fluorescence excitation spectra and B) fluorescence emission spectra.

For researchers studying the dynamic aspects of lysosome biogenesis and function in live cells, we have developed the LysoSensor™ probes — fluorescent pH indicators that partition into acidic organelles. The LysoSensor™ dyes are acidotropic probes that appear to accumulate in acidic organelles as the result of protonation. This protonation also relieves the fluorescence quenching of the dye by its weakly basic side chain, resulting in an increase in fluorescence intensity. Thus, the LysoSensor™ reagents exhibit a pH-dependent increase in fluorescence intensity upon acidification, in contrast to the LysoTracker® probes, which exhibit fluorescence that is not substantially enhanced at acidic pH.

We offer five LysoSensor™ reagents that differ in color and pK_a (Table 12.7). Because these probes may localize in the membranes of organelles, it is probable that the pK_a values listed in Table 12.7 will not be equivalent to those measured in cellular environments and that only qualitative and semiquantitative comparisons of organelle pH will be possible. The blue- and green-fluorescent LysoSensor™ probes are available with optimal pH sensitivity in either the acidic or neutral range (pK_a ~5.2 or ~7.5 in aqueous buffers). With their low pK_a values, LysoSensor™ Blue DND-167 (L7533) and LysoSensor™ Green DND-189 (L7535) are almost nonfluorescent except when inside acidic compartments, whereas LysoSensor™ Green DND-153 (L7534) is brightly fluorescent at neutral pH. LysoSensor™ Yellow/Blue DND-160 (L7545, Figure 12.35) is unique in that it exhibits both dual-excitation and dual-emission spectral peaks that are pH dependent (Figure 12.36). LysoSensor™ Yellow/Blue DND-160 exhibits predominantly yellow fluorescence in acidic organelles, and in less acidic organelles it exhibits blue fluorescence. Dual-emission measurements facilitate ratio imaging of the pH in acidic organelles such as lysosomes,[21] myeloid leukemic cells[22] and acidic vacuoles of plant cells.[23] LysoSensor™ Yellow/Blue DND-160 has been used in conjunction with fluo-3 AM (F1241, F1242, F23915; Section 19.3) for simultaneous fluorescence measurements of H^+ and Ca^{2+} in rabbit gastric glands in order to determine the kinetics of acid secretion upon activation of the cholinergic and the cAMP-dependent pathways.[24]

We have prepared a 10,000 MW dextran conjugate of the LysoSensor™ Yellow/Blue dye (L22460). As this labeled dextran is taken up by the cells and moves through the endocytic pathway, the fluorescence of the LysoSensor™ dye changes from blue fluorescent in the near-neutral endosomes to longer-wavelength yellow fluorescent in the acidic lysosomes.[25] The greatest change in fluorescence emission occurs near the pK_a of the dye at pH ~3.9. Unlike the cell-permeant LysoSensor™ dyes, LysoSensor™ Yellow/Blue dextran allows measurement of pH in lysosomes using either fluorescence microscopy (Figure 12.37) or flow cytometry.

The cell-permeant probes in this section can be used singly (or potentially in combination) to investigate the acidification of lysosomes and alterations of lysosomal function or trafficking that occur in cells. For example, lysosomes in some tumor cells have a lower pH than normal lysosomes,[26] whereas other tumor cells contain lysosomes with higher pH.[27] In addition, cystic fibrosis and other diseases result in defects in the acidification of some intracellular organelles,[28] and the LysoSensor™ probes may prove useful in studying these aberrations. LysoSensor™ Green DND-189 has been used to selectively label acidic compartments within granule cell neurites[29] and, along with LysoSensor™ Green DND-153, to examine the acidification of endosomes and lysosomes in a mutant CHO cell line.[30] LysoSensor™ Yellow/Blue DND-160 was employed in a study that demonstrated the involvement of lysosomes in the acquired drug-resistance phenotype of a doxorubicin-selected variant of human U-937 myeloid leukemia cells.[22]

Kinetic studies on the internalization of LysoSensor™ Yellow/Blue DND-160 indicate that the probe is taken up by live cells within seconds. Unfortunately, this lysosomal probe can exhibit an alkalinizing effect on the lysosomes, such that longer incubation with this probe can induce an increase in lysosomal pH. Therefore, it is a useful pH indicator only when incubation times are kept short; we recommend incubating cells for only one to five minutes before imaging.

As with the LysoTracker® probes, the cell-permeant LysoSensor™ probes were originally developed for fluorescence microscopy applications. The lysosomal fluorescence in LysoSensor™ dye–stained cells may constitute only a portion of total cellular fluorescence due to cellular autofluorescence or nonspecific staining. Therefore, the successful application of these probes for quantitating the number of lysosomes or their pH by flow cytometry or fluorometry will likely depend on the particular cell lines and staining protocols used.

DAMP and Other Lysosomotropic Probes

DAMP

The reagent DAMP (*N*-(3-((2,4-dinitrophenyl)amino)propyl)-*N*-(3-aminopropyl)-methylamine, dihydrochloride; D1552; Figure 12.38) is a weakly basic amine that is taken up in acidic organelles of live cells. This cell-permeant acidotropic reagent can be detected with anti-DNP antibodies (Section 7.4), including those labeled with fluorochromes, ferritin, colloidal gold (as well as our NANOGOLD reagents for light and electron microscopy) or enzymes,[9] making DAMP broadly applicable for detecting acidic organelles by electron and light microscopy. For example, DAMP has been used to investigate:

- Acidification of yolk platelets in sea urchin embryos[31]
- Defective acidification of intracellular organelles in cells from cystic fibrosis patients[28]
- Dependence on pH of the conversion of proinsulin to insulin in beta cells[32]
- Development of autophagic vacuoles[33,34]
- Location of intracellular acidic compartments during viral infection[34]

As alternatives to DAMP, our cell-permeant fluorescent LysoTracker® and LysoSensor™ probes described above have significant potential in many of these applications. Because they can be visualized directly without any secondary detection reagents, the LysoTracker® and LysoSensor™ reagents enable researchers to study acidic organelles and follow their dynamic processes in live cells.

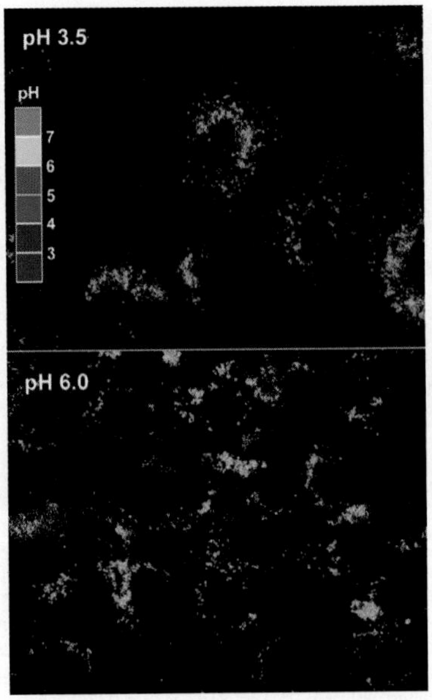

Figure 12.37 Dual-emission ratiometric measurement of lysosomal pH using a dextran conjugated with LysoSensor™ Yellow/Blue dextran (L22460). MDCK cells labeled with the fluorescent dextran were exposed to pH-calibration buffers (pH 3.5 or pH 6.0) in the presence of nigericin (N1495) and monensin. Pseudocolored images were constructed from two emission images at 450 ± 33 nm and 510 ± 20 nm, both excited at 365 ± 8 nm (Chem Biol 6, 411 (1999)).

RedoxSensor™ Red CC-1 Stain

The fluorescence localization of our RedoxSensor™ Red CC-1 stain (2,3,4,5,6-pentafluorotetramethyldihydrorosamine, R14060) appears to be based on a cell's cytosolic redox potential. Once it passively enters live cells, the RedoxSensor™ Red CC-1 stain may be oxidized in the cytosol to a red-fluorescent product (excitation/emission maxima ~540/600 nm), which then accumulates in the mitochondria. Alternatively, this nonfluorescent probe may be transported to the lysosomes where it is oxidized. The differential distribution of the oxidized product between mitochondria and lysosomes appears to depend on the redox potential of the cytosol.[35] In proliferating cells, mitochondrial staining predominates; whereas in contact-inhibited cells, the staining is primarily lysosomal (Figure 18.15). The best method we have found to quantitate the distribution of the oxidized product is to use the mitochondrion-selective MitoTracker® Green FM stain (M7514) in conjunction with the RedoxSensor™ Red CC-1 stain.[35]

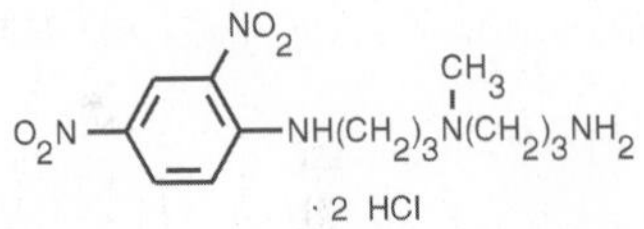

Figure 12.38 D1552 *N*-(3-((2,4-dinitrophenyl)amino)propyl)-*N*-(3-aminopropyl)methylamine, dihydrochloride (DAMP).

Other Lysosomotropic Probes

BODIPY® FL histamine (B22461) combines the pH-insensitive, bright green-fluorescent BODIPY® FL dye with the weakly basic imidazole moiety of histamine. When used at low concentrations, this probe selectively stains lysosomes (Figure 12.39).

As with the LysoTracker® and LysoSensor™ probes, the weak basicity of the amine group in Dapoxyl® (2-aminoethyl)sulfonamide (D10460) leads to its accumulation in acidic organelles. Dapoxyl® (2-aminoethyl)sulfonamide[36] (Figure 12.40) uptake by the acidic lumen of the intact acrosome of mouse sperm is accompanied by significant enhancement of this probe's fluorescence.[37] The fluorescence of Dapoxyl® (2-aminoethyl)sulfonamide is considerably reduced upon loss of the pH gradient at the onset of the acrosome reaction.[37]

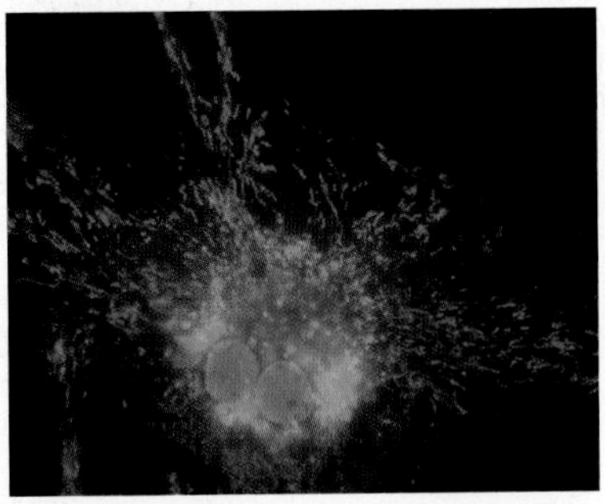

Figure 12.39 Viable bovine pulmonary artery endothelial cells simultaneously stained with BODIPY® FL histamine (B22461), MitoTracker® Red CMXRos (M7512) and Hoechst 33342 (H1399, H3570, H21492). Green-fluorescent BODIPY® FL histamine localized to lysosomes, red-fluorescent MitoTracker® Red CMXRos accumulated in the mitochondria, and the blue-fluorescent Hoechst 33342 dye stained the nuclei. This multiple-exposure image was acquired with bandpass filters appropriate for fluorescein, the Texas Red® dye and DAPI.

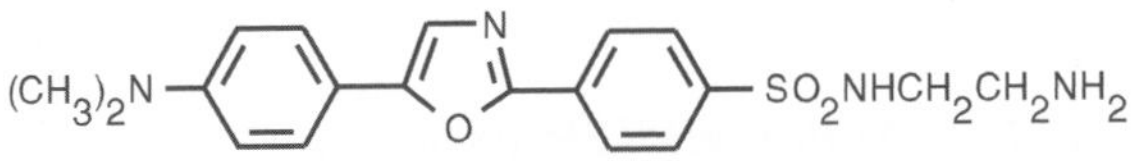

Figure 12.40 D10460 Dapoxyl® (2-aminoethyl)sulfonamide.

Our high-purity neutral red (N3246) is a common lysosomal probe that stains lysosomes a fluorescent red.[10,38] It has also been used to determine the number of adherent and nonadherent cells in a microplate assay[39] and to stain cells in brain tissue.[40,41]

In addition, dansyl cadaverine[42,43] (D113) and the DNA intercalator acridine orange[10,44] (A1301, A3568) have been reported to be useful lysosomotropic reagents. Dansyl cadaverine has been shown to selectively label autophagic vacuoles, at least some of which had already fused with lysosomes; it did not, however, accumulate in early or late endosomes.[45]

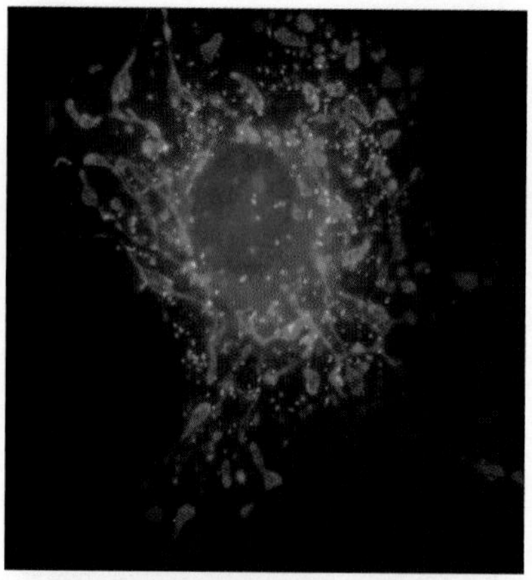

Figure 12.41 Peroxisome labeling in fixed and permeabilized bovine pulmonary artery endothelial cells. Peroxisomes were labeled using an antibody directed at peroxisomal membrane protein 70 (PMP-70) and detected with Alexa Fluor® 488 dye–labeled goat anti–mouse IgG (components of S34201). Mitochondria were stained with MitoTracker® Red CMXRos (M7512) prior to fixation; nuclei were stained with blue-fluorescent DAPI (D1306, D3571, D21490).

Ligands for Receptor-Mediated Endocytosis

In addition to these lysosomotropic probes, Molecular Probes prepares a wide variety of low-density lipoproteins (LDL) and fluorescent transferrin conjugates. Once internalized, LDL dissociates from its receptor and ultimately accumulates in lysosomes.[46] The contrasting fluorescence of DiI LDL (L3482, Section 16.1) and fluorescein transferrin (T2871, Section 16.1) permits their simultaneous use to follow the lysosomally directed pathway and the recycling pathways, respectively.[47] The pH sensitivity of fluorescein transferrin has been exploited to investigate events occurring during endosomal acidification.[48–51] Likewise, dextrans labeled with fluorescent pH indicators (Section 14.5, Section 20.4) can be used to monitor the uptake and internal processing of exogenous materials in acidic organelles through endocytosis.[52–57]

SelectFX™ Alexa Fluor® 488 Peroxisome Labeling Kit

Peroxisomes, single membrane–bound vesicles found in most eukaryotic cells, function to enzymatically oxidize fatty acids and to subsequently catalyze the breakdown of H_2O_2, a by-product of fatty acid degradation. The SelectFX™ Alexa Fluor® 488 Peroxisome Labeling Kit (S34201) provides all the reagents required for labeling peroxisomes in fixed cells, including cell fixation and permeabilization reagents. To specifically detect peroxisomes, this kit uses an antibody directed against peroxisomal membrane protein 70 (PMP 70), which is a high-abundance integral membrane protein in peroxisomes,[6] and an Alexa Fluor® 488 dye–labeled secondary antibody (Figure 12.41). The Alexa Fluor® 488 dye exhibits bright green fluorescence that is compatible with filters and instrument settings appropriate for fluorescein. PMP 70 is significantly induced by administration of hypolipidemic agents, in parallel with peroxisome proliferation and the induction of peroxisomal fatty acid β-oxidation enzymes.[6] Each kit contains:

- Rabbit IgG anti–peroxisomal membrane protein 70 (PMP 70) antibody
- Highly cross-adsorbed Alexa Fluor® 488 goat anti–rabbit IgG antibody
- Concentrated fixative solution
- Concentrated phosphate-buffered saline (PBS)
- Concentrated permeabilization solution
- Concentrated blocking solution
- Detailed protocols for mammalian cell preparation and staining

The SelectFX™ Alexa Fluor® 488 Peroxisome Labeling Kit can be used in conjunction with probes for other cell targets to achieve multicolor cell staining.

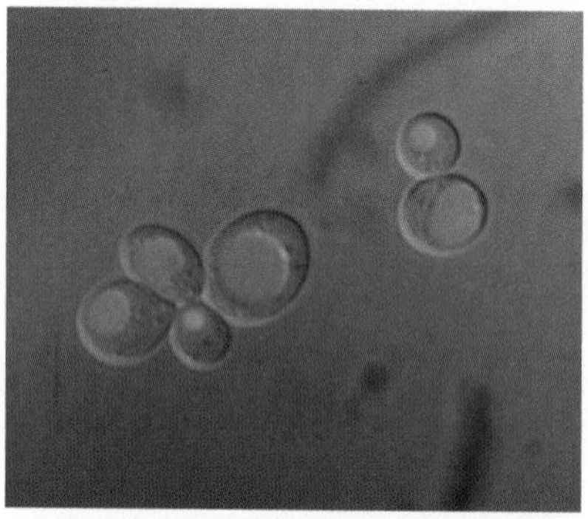

Figure 12.42 *Saccharomyces cerevisiae* vacuolar lumen stained with 7-amino-4-chloromethylcoumarin, L-arginine amide (Arg-CMAC), available in our Yeast Vacuole Marker Sampler Kit (Y7531). The kit contains three additional fluorescent vacuolar lumen stains plus a green-fluorescent vacuolar membrane stain. After staining, yeast were viewed by epifluorescence and DIC microscopy.

Cell-Permeant Probes for Yeast Vacuoles

Biogenesis of the yeast vacuole has been extensively studied as a model system for eukaryotic organelle assembly.[58–61] Using a combination of genetic and biochemical approaches, researchers have isolated a large collection of yeast vacuolar protein sorting (*vps*) mutants[62] and characterized the vacuolar H^+-ATPase (V-ATPase) responsible for compartment acidification.[63] To facilitate the investigation of yeast vacuole structure and function, Molecular Probes offers membrane-permeant reagents and a Yeast Vacuole Marker Sampler Kit (Y7531, Figure 12.42), as well as several monoclonal antibodies directed against vacuolar proteins, including V-ATPase.

FUN® 1 and FUN® 2 Cell Stains: Vital Stains for Yeast

The FUN® 1 (Figure 12.43) and FUN® 2 cell stains (F7030, F13150) exploit endogenous biochemical processing mechanisms that appear to be well conserved among different species of yeast and other fungi.[64,65] When used at micromolar concentrations, the FUN® 1 and FUN® 2 stains are freely taken up by several species of yeast and fungi and converted from a diffusely distributed pool of yellow-green–fluorescent intracellular stain into compact red-orange– or yellow-orange–fluorescent intravacuolar structures, respectively (Figure 12.44). This conversion requires both plasma membrane integrity and metabolic capability. Only metabolically active cells are marked clearly with fluorescent intravacuolar structures, while dead cells exhibit extremely bright, diffuse, yellow-green fluorescence[64,66] (Figure 15.38, Figure 15.42). FUN® 1 staining has been utilized to detect antifungal activity against *Candida* species[67] and to measure susceptibility of fungi to fungicides by flow cytometry.[68,69] The FUN® 1 cell stain is also available as a component in our LIVE/DEAD® Yeast Viability Kit (L7009, Section 15.3).

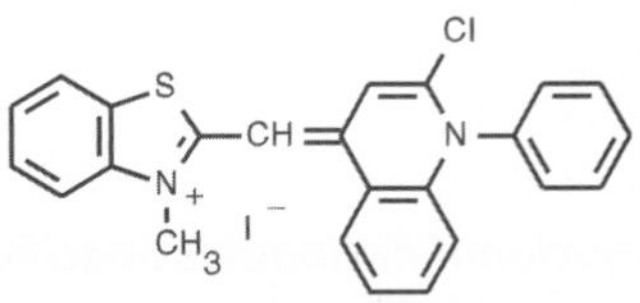

Figure 12.43 F7030 FUN® 1 cell stain.

FM® 4-64 and FM® 5-95

One of our FM® dyes, FM® 4-64 has been reported to selectively stain yeast vacuolar membranes with red fluorescence[70] (excitation/emission maxima ~515/640 nm). This lipophilic styryl dye is proving to be an important tool for visualizing vacuolar organelle morphology and dynamics, for studying the endocytic pathway and for screening and characterizing yeast endocytosis mutants.[71–76] We offer FM® 4-64 in 1 mg vials (T3166) or specially packaged in 10 vials of 100 µg each (T13320). The increasing number of successful applications for our FM® dyes has prompted us to synthesize FM® 5-95 (T23360), a slightly less lipophilic analog of FM® 4-64 with essentially identical spectroscopic properties.

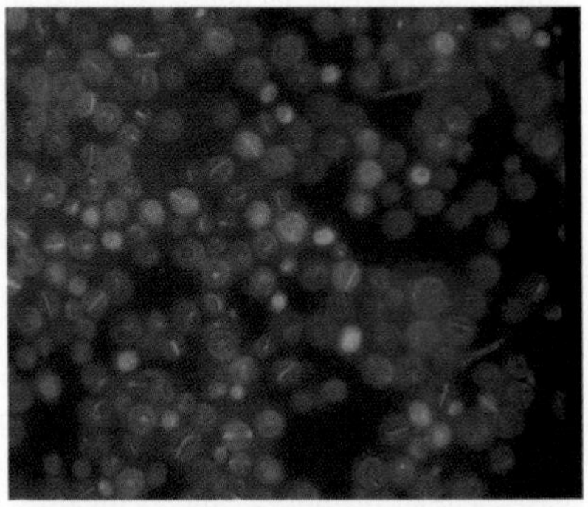

Figure 12.44 A culture of *Saccharomyces cerevisiae* incubated in medium containing the FUN® 1 viability indicator (F7030) and the counterstain Calcofluor White M2R, both of which are provided in our LIVE/DEAD® Yeast Viability Kit (L7009). Metabolically active yeast process the FUN® 1 dye, forming numerous red-fluorescent cylindrical structures within their vacuoles. Calcofluor stains the cell walls fluorescent blue, regardless of the yeast's metabolic state. The yeast were photographed in a single exposure through an Omega Optical triple bandpass filter set.

Yeast Vacuole Marker Sampler Kit

The Yeast Vacuole Marker Sampler Kit (Y7531) contains sample quantities of a series of both novel and well-established vacuole marker probes that show promise for the study of yeast cell biology:

- 5-(and 6-)Carboxy-2′,7′-dichlorofluorescein diacetate (carboxy-DCFDA)[58,70,77–81]
- CellTracker™ Blue CMAC[82]
- Aminopeptidase substrate Arg-CMAC (Figure 12.42)
- Dipeptidyl peptidase substrate Ala-Pro-CMAC
- Yeast vacuole membrane marker MDY-64[83] (Figure 12.24, Figure 12.45)

Our experiments have demonstrated that several cell-permeant derivatives of 7-amino-4-chloromethylcoumarin (CMAC) are largely sequestered within yeast vacuoles. The corresponding 7-amino-4-methylcoumarin derivatives are known to be substrates for yeast vacuolar enzymes.[84–86] This sampler kit's three coumarin-based vacuole markers selectively stain the lumen of the yeast vacuole. To complement the blue-fluorescent staining of the lumen, we provide a novel green-fluorescent membrane marker MDY-64 for staining the yeast vacuole membrane. Membrane staining can also be accomplished using the red-fluorescent probe FM® 4-64, as described below. The commonly used vacuole marker 5-(and 6-)carboxy-2′,7′-dichlorofluorescein diacetate (carboxy-DCFDA) is supplied for use as a standard.[58,78] Three of the components in the Yeast Vacuole Marker Sampler Kit — CellTracker™ Blue CMAC (C2110, Section 14.2), the proprietary yeast vacuole membrane marker MDY-64[83,87] (Y7536) and carboxy-DCFDA (C369, Section 15.2) — are also available separately for those researchers who find that one of these dyes is well suited for their application.

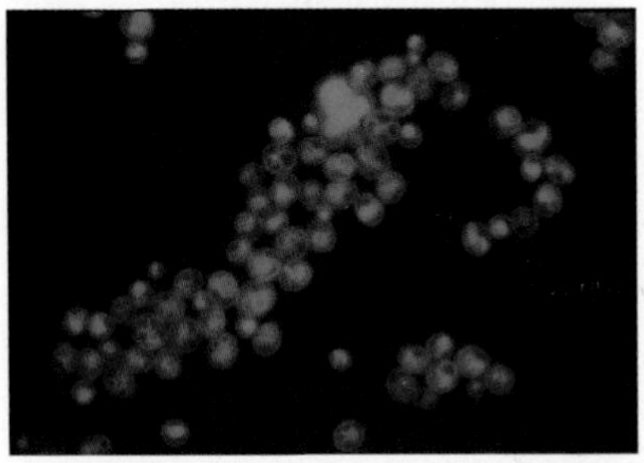

Figure 12.45 *Saccharomyces cerevisiae* vacuolar membranes stained with the yeast vacuole membrane marker MDY-64, which is available separately (Y7536) or in our Yeast Vacuole Marker Sampler Kit (Y7531). The kit contains four additional fluorescent vacuolar lumen stains.

Monoclonal Antibodies for Yeast Cell Biology

In addition to the anti–yeast COX (OxPhos Complex IV) monoclonal antibodies described in Section 12.2, Molecular Probes offers several other immunoreagents that have proven useful for studying many aspects of cell biology with the yeast *Saccharomyces cerevisiae* (Table 12.8). These products include antibodies directed against yeast vacuole, cytosolic and endosomal proteins (described below) and antibodies directed against yeast endoplasmic reticulum and Golgi proteins (Section 12.4). We have selected this set of monoclonal antibodies because they are compatible with both Western blotting of denatured proteins and protein immunolocalization in fixed yeast cells. Other potential uses of these antibodies include the development of ELISAs to determine either the level of enrichment of a particular yeast organelle or the level at which the organelle contaminates a subcellular fraction. Detailed information regarding the IgG isotype and recommended working concentrations is provided with each product. For detection of these monoclonal antibodies, Molecular Probes offers anti–mouse IgG secondary antibodies labeled with biotin, enzymes, NANOGOLD and Alexa Fluor® FluoroNanogold 1.4 nm gold clusters, Captivate™ ferrofluid and a wide range of fluorophores and enzymes (Section 7.2).

Monoclonal Antibodies Specific for Yeast Vacuolar Membranes

For the detection of yeast vacuolar membranes, we offer four monoclonal antibodies directed against integral or peripheral membrane proteins. Two of the antibodies are specific for integral membrane proteins of the yeast vacuoles: Monoclonal 1D3 (A6458) is specific for the 70,000-dalton vacuolar alkaline phosphatase (ALP), the product of the *PHO8* gene; this antibody is ideal for indirect immunofluorescence detection of vacuolar membranes in fixed yeast cells, as well as for detection of ALP by Western blotting.[88,89] Monoclonal 10D7 (A6426) recognizes the 100,000-dalton vacuolar H^+-ATPase (V-ATPase) subunit (the product of the *VPH1* gene[90]) and is especially useful for Western blotting.[76,88,91–93]

The other two antibodies are directed against peripheral membrane proteins of the yeast vacuoles, specifically two subunits of the V-ATPase complex that are associated with the cytosolic face of the yeast vacuolar membrane: monoclonal 13D11 (A6427) recognizes the 60,000-dalton subunit[62,76,89,91–93] (the B-subunit, the product of the *VMA2* or *VAT2* gene), whereas monoclonal 8B1 (A6422) binds the 69,000-dalton subunit[63,92,93] (the A-subunit, the product of the *VMA1* or *TFP1* gene). Both of these antibodies are useful for indirect immunofluorescence analysis, as well as for Western blotting.

Monoclonal Antibody Specific for the Yeast Vacuolar Lumen

For the detection of yeast vacuolar lumen, we offer monoclonal 10A5[94] (A6428). This antibody is specific for carboxypeptidase Y (CPY), a 61,000-dalton soluble glycoprotein located in the vacuolar lumen.[77] Monoclonal 10A5 is useful for indirect immunofluorescence, as well as for Western blotting.

Monoclonal Antibody Specific for the Yeast Endosomal Compartment

For the detection of the yeast endosomal compartment, we have available anti-Pep12p monoclonal 2C3[95,96] (A21273). Yeast Pep12p, also known as Vps6p, is a 37,000-dalton yeast endosomal protein of the t-SNARE or syntaxin family. Pep12 is localized via a C-terminal transmembrane domain, and the epitope recognized by monoclonal 2C3 is located in the N-terminal cytosolic domain.

Monoclonal Antibody Specific for the Yeast Cytosol

For the detection of yeast cytosol, we offer a monoclonal antibody directed against the 44,700-dalton yeast cytosolic protein phosphoglycerate kinase (PGK). Monoclonal 22C5 (A6457) can be used for the detection of yeast PGK by Western blotting (Section 9.4).

Table 12.8 — Monoclonal antibodies for yeast cell biology

Cat # *	Yeast Antigen Recognized by the Antibody	Yeast Subcellular Structure in which the Antigen Resides	Mouse Monoclonal	Mouse Isotype	Suggested Concentration for Westerns (µg/mL)	Suggested Concentration for Immunocytochemistry (µg/mL)
A6405	OxPhos Complex IV, subunit I	Mitochondrial inner membrane	11D8	$IgG_{2b,\kappa}$	0.5	NR
A6407	OxPhos Complex IV, subunit II	Mitochondrial inner membrane	4B12	$IgG_{2a,\kappa}$	1	NR
A6408	OxPhos Complex IV, subunit III †	Mitochondrial inner membrane	DA5	$IgG_{2a,\kappa}$	0.5	5–20 ‡
A6432	OxPhos Complex IV, subunit IV	Mitochondrial inner membrane	1A12	$IgG_{1,\kappa}$	0.5	NR
A6449	Mitochondrial porin	Mitochondrial outer membrane	16G9	$IgG_{1,\kappa}$	0.5	5–20 ‡
A6422	V-ATPase 69,000-dalton subunit	Vacuole membrane	8B1	$IgG_{2a,\kappa}$	0.25	20
A6426	V-ATPase 100,000-dalton subunit	Vacuole membrane	10D7	$IgG_{2a,\kappa}$	0.25	20
A6427	V-ATPase 60,000-dalton subunit	Vacuole membrane	13D11	$IgG_{1,\kappa}$	0.25	20 ‡
A6458	Alkaline phosphatase (ALP)	Vacuole membrane	1D3	$IgG_{1,\kappa}$	§	‡§
A6428	Carboxypeptidase Y (CPY)	Vacuole lumen	10A5	$IgG_{1,\kappa}$	0.5	20
A6429	Dol-P-Man synthase (Dpm1p)	Endoplasmic reticulum membrane	5C5	$IgG_{1,\kappa}$	4	NR
A21273	Pep12p	Endosomal membrane	2C3	$IgG_{1,\kappa}$	0.5	1
A21274	Vsp10p	Late-Golgi membrane	18C8	$IgG_{2a,\kappa}$	4	NR
A6457	3-Phosphoglycerate kinase (PGK)	Cytosol	22C5	$IgG_{1,\kappa}$	2	10

* For all the antibodies listed in this table, the unit size is 250 µg, except for A6408 (provided in a unit size of 100 µg), A6458 (provided as 2.5 mL of unpurified antibody in conditioned cell culture medium), A21273 (provided as 100 µL of a 0.5 mg/mL solution) and A21274 (provided as 500 µL of a 0.5 mg/mL solution). † Monoclonal DA5 was raised against yeast COX, but it strongly crossreacts with both *Neurospora crassa* and human COX subunit III. ‡ These monoclonal antibodies yield the strongest and most consistent signals when used for indirect immunofluorescence; the anti-ALP antibody is the most reliable monoclonal antibody for detecting yeast vacuolar membranes. § Monoclonal 1D3 is provided in solution; a 50–100-fold dilution is recommended for Westerns and a 2–3-fold dilution is recommended for immunocytochemistry. NR = Not recommended.

References

1. J Cell Biol 106, 539 (1988); **2.** Traffic 1, 836 (2000); **3.** Am J Hum Genet 73, 233 (2003); **4.** Mol Biol Cell 14, 2900 (2003); **5.** Mar Environ Res 54, 297 (2002); **6.** Cell Biochem Biophys 32 Spring, 131 (2000); **7.** Cell 52, 329 (1988); **8.** Lysosomes in Biology and Pathology, Dingle JT, Fell HB, Eds. (Complete Volume) (1969); **9.** Proc Natl Acad Sci U S A 81, 4838 (1984); **10.** Lysosomes in Biology and Pathology, Vol. 2, Dingle JT, Fell HB, Eds. pp. 600–628 (1969); **11.** EMBO J 15, 1784 (1996); **12.** J Histochem Cytochem 44, 267 (1996); **13.** Biol Reprod 56, 991 (1997); **14.** Proc Natl Acad Sci U S A 95, 1579 (1998); **15.** J Cell Biol 137, 715 (1997); **16.** Cytometry 33, 348 (1998); **17.** J Biol Chem 273, 22466 (1998); **18.** J Biol Chem 272, 14817 (1997); **19.** J Neurosci 17, 1582 (1997); **20.** Cytometry (Suppl 7) 52, abstract #426B (1994); **21.** Chem Biol 6, 411 (1999); **22.** Blood 89, 3745 (1997); **23.** Plant Cell 10, 685 (1998); **24.** J Physiol 537, 735 (2001); **25.** Nucleic Acids Res 30, 1338 (2002); **26.** Molecular Aspects of Anti-Cancer Drug Action, Neidle S, Waring MJ, Eds. pp. 233–282 (1983); **27.** J Biol Chem 265, 4775 (1990); **28.** Nature 352, 70 (1991); **29.** J Neurochem 69, 1927 (1997); **30.** J Cell Biol 139, 1183 (1997); **31.** J Cell Biol 117, 1211 (1992); **32.** J Cell Biol 126, 1149 (1994); **33.** J Cell Biol 111, 329 (1990); **34.** J Cell Biol 110, 1935 (1990); **35.** Free Radic Biol Med 28, 1266 (2000); **36.** Photochem Photobiol 66, 424 (1997); **37.** Mol Reprod Dev 55, 335 (2000); **38.** In Vitro Toxicol 3, 219 (1990); **39.** Anal Biochem 213, 426 (1993); **40.** Jpn J Physiol 43, 161 (1993); **41.** Brain Res 573, 1 (1992); **42.** Immunology 51, 319 (1984); **43.** J Immunol 131, 125 (1983); **44.** Anal Biochem 192, 316 (1991); **45.** Eur J Cell Biol 66, 3 (1995); **46.** J Cell Biol 121, 1257 (1993); **47.** J Cell Sci 107, 2177 (1994); **48.** Biochemistry 31, 5820 (1992); **49.** J Biol Chem 266, 3469 (1991); **50.** J Bioenerg Biomembr 23, 147 (1991); **51.** J Biol Chem 265, 6688 (1990); **52.** Cell Calcium 19, 157 (1996); **53.** J Biol Chem 269, 12918 (1994); **54.** Am J Physiol 258, C309 (1990); **55.** J Cell Physiol 131, 200 (1987); **56.** Proc Natl Acad Sci U S A 82, 8523 (1985); **57.** Exp Cell Res 150, 36 (1984); **58.** Methods Enzymol 194, 644 (1991); **59.** Trends Biochem Sci 14, 347 (1989); **60.** Molecular Biology of Intracellular Protein Sorting and Organelle Assembly, Bradshaw RA, et al., Eds pp. 173–186 (1988); **61.** Protein Transfer and Organelle Biogenesis, Das RC, Robbins PW, Eds. pp. 317–362 (1988); **62.** Mol Biol Cell 3, 1389 (1992); **63.** J Biol Chem 264, 19236 (1989); **64.** Biotechnol Intl 1, 291 (1997); **65.** Appl Environ Microbiol 63, 2897 (1997); **66.** J Cell Biol 126, 1375 (1994); **67.** Mycoses 39, 45 (1996); **68.** Cytometry 31, 307 (1998); **69.** J Clin Microbiol 35, 5 (1997); **70.** J Cell Biol 128, 779 (1995); **71.** J Cell Biol 146, 85 (1999); **72.** Science 285, 1084 (1999); **73.** J Cell Biol 135, 1535 (1996); **74.** J Cell Biol 135, 1485 (1996); **75.** Mol Biol Cell 7, 1375 (1996); **76.** Mol Biol Cell 7, 985 (1996); **77.** Eur J Cell Biol 65, 305 (1994); **78.** Methods Cell Biol 31, 357 (1989); **79.** Mol Biol Cell 6, 525 (1995); **80.** J Cell Biol 125, 283 (1994); **81.** J Cell Biol 111, 877 (1990); **82.** J Biol Chem 274, 1835 (1999); **83.** Fungal Genet Biol 24, 86 (1998); **84.** Methods Enzymol 194, 428 (1991); **85.** Arch Biochem Biophys 226, 292 (1983); **86.** FEBS Lett 131, 296 (1981); **87.** Fungal Genet Biol 24, 86 (1998); **88.** J Cell Biol 136, 287 (1997); **89.** Mol Cell Biol 16, 2700 (1996); **90.** J Biol Chem 267, 14294 (1992); **91.** J Biol Chem 272, 25928 (1997); **92.** J Biol Chem 268, 16845 (1993); **93.** J Biol Chem 267, 447 (1992); **94.** Genetics 144, 445 (1996); **95.** Traffic 1, 45 (2000); **96.** Mol Biol Cell 11, 305 (2000).

Data Table — 12.3 Probes for Lysosomes, Peroxisomes and Yeast Vacuoles

Cat #	MW	Storage	Soluble	Abs	EC	Em	Solvent	Notes
A1301	301.82	L	H_2O, EtOH	489	65,000	520	MeOH	
A3568	301.82	RR,L	H_2O	489	65,000	520	MeOH	1
B22461	385.22	F,D,L	DMSO	503	82,000	511	MeOH	
D113	335.46	L	EtOH, DMF	335	4,600	518	MeOH	
D1552	384.26	F,D,L	pH <7, DMF	349	16,000	none	MeOH	
D10460	386.47	L	DMF, DMSO	373	23,000	571	MeOH	
F7030	528.84	F,D,L	DMSO	508	71,000	none	pH 7	1, 2
F13150	387.33	F,D,L	DMSO	465	81,000	none	pH 7	1, 3
L7525	524.40	D,L	DMSO	373	9,600	422	pH 7	1, 4
L7526	398.69	F,D,L	DMSO	504	54,000	511	MeOH	1
L7528	399.25	F,D,L	DMSO	577	48,000	590	MeOH	1
L7532	292.42	F,D,L	DMSO	374	11,000	424	pH 5	1, 5
L7533	376.50	F,D,L	DMSO	373	11,000	425	pH 5	1, 5
L7534	356.43	F,D,L	DMSO	442	17,000	505	pH 5	1, 5
L7535	398.46	F,D,L	DMSO	443	16,000	505	pH 5	1, 5
L7545	366.42	F,D,L	DMSO	384	21,000	540	pH 3	1, 6
L12490	501.47	F,D,L	DMSO	380	26,000	576	MeOH	1
L12491	364.40	F,D,L	DMSO	466	22,000	536	MeOH	1
L22460	see Notes	F,D,L	H_2O	384	ND	540	pH 3	6, 7, 8
N3246	288.78	D,L	H_2O, EtOH	541	39,000	640	see Notes	9
R14060	434.41	F,D,L,AA	DMSO	239	52,000	none	MeOH	
T3166	607.51	D,L	H_2O, DMSO	558	48,000	734	CHCl3	10
T13320	607.51	D,L	H_2O, DMSO	558	46,000	734	CHCl3	10
T23360	565.43	D,L	H_2O, DMSO	560	43,000	734	CHCl3	10
Y7536	384.48	F,L	DMSO, DMF	456	27,000	505	MeOH	

For definitions of the contents of this data table, see "Navigating *The Handbook*" in the introductory pages.

Notes

1. This product is supplied as a ready-made solution in the solvent indicated under "Soluble."
2. F7030 is fluorescent when bound to DNA (Em = 538 nm). Uptake and processing of the dye by live yeast results in red-shifted fluorescence (Em ~590 nm).
3. F13150 is fluorescent when bound to DNA (Em = 510 nm). Uptake and processing of the dye by live yeast results in red-shifted fluorescence (Em ~550 nm).
4. L7525 has structured absorption and fluorescence spectra with additional peaks at Abs = 394 nm and Em = 401 nm.
5. This LysoSensor™ dye exhibits increasing fluorescence as pH decreases with no spectral shift. L7533 has additional absorption and fluorescence emission peaks at Abs = 394 nm and Em = 401 nm.
6. LysoSensor™ Yellow/Blue spectra are pH dependent. Abs and Em shift to shorter wavelengths at pH >5.
7. The molecular weight is nominally as specified in the product name but may have a broad distribution.
8. ND = not determined.
9. Spectra of N3246 are pH-dependent (pK_a ~6.7). Data reported are for 1:1 (v/v) EtOH/1% acetic acid.
10. FM® 4-64 and FM® 5-95 are nonfluorescent in water. For two-color imaging in GFP-expressing cells, these dyes can be excited at 568 nm with emission detection at 690–730 nm (Am J Physiol Cell Physiol 281, C624 (2001)).

Product List — 12.3 Probes for Lysosomes, Peroxisomes and Yeast Vacuoles

Cat #	Product Name	Unit Size
A1301	acridine orange	1 g
A3568	acridine orange *10 mg/mL solution in water*	10 mL
A6458	anti-alkaline phosphatase (yeast vacuolar), mouse IgG_1, monoclonal 1D3 *in conditioned culture medium*	2.5 mL
A6428	anti-carboxypeptidase Y (yeast vacuolar), mouse IgG_1, monoclonal 10A5 (anti-CPY)	250 µg
A6422	anti-H+-ATPase 69 kDa subunit (yeast vacuolar), mouse IgG_{2a}, monoclonal 8B1	250 µg
A6426	anti-H+-ATPase 100 kDa subunit (yeast vacuolar), mouse IgG_{2a}, monoclonal 10D7	250 µg
A6427	anti-H+-ATPase 60 kDa subunit (yeast vacuolar), mouse IgG_1, monoclonal 13D11	250 µg
A21273	anti-Pep12p (yeast), mouse IgG_1, monoclonal 2C3 *0.5 mg/mL*	100 µL
A6457	anti-3-phosphoglycerate kinase (yeast), mouse IgG_1, monoclonal 22C5 (anti-PGK)	250 µg
B22461	BODIPY® FL histamine	1 mg
D10460	Dapoxyl® (2-aminoethyl)sulfonamide	10 mg
D113	5-dimethylaminonaphthalene-1-(N-(5-aminopentyl))sulfonamide (dansyl cadaverine)	100 mg
D1552	N-(3-((2,4-dinitrophenyl)amino)propyl)-N-(3-aminopropyl)methylamine, dihydrochloride (DAMP)	100 mg
F7030	FUN® 1 cell stain *10 mM solution in DMSO*	100 µL
F13150	FUN® 2 cell stain *10 mM solution in DMSO*	100 µL
L7533	LysoSensor™ Blue DND-167 *1 mM solution in DMSO* *special packaging*	20 x 50 µL
L7532	LysoSensor™ Blue DND-192 *1 mM solution in DMSO* *special packaging*	20 x 50 µL
L7534	LysoSensor™ Green DND-153 *1 mM solution in DMSO* *special packaging*	20 x 50 µL
L7535	LysoSensor™ Green DND-189 *1 mM solution in DMSO* *special packaging*	20 x 50 µL
L22460	LysoSensor™ Yellow/Blue dextran, 10,000 MW, anionic, fixable	5 mg
L7545	LysoSensor™ Yellow/Blue DND-160 *1 mM solution in DMSO* *special packaging*	20 x 50 µL
L7525	LysoTracker® Blue DND-22 *1 mM solution in DMSO* *special packaging*	20 x 50 µL
L12490	LysoTracker® Blue-White DPX *1 mM solution in DMSO* *special packaging*	20 x 50 µL
L7526	LysoTracker® Green DND-26 *1 mM solution in DMSO* *special packaging*	20 x 50 µL
L7528	LysoTracker® Red DND-99 *1 mM solution in DMSO* *special packaging*	20 x 50 µL
L12491	LysoTracker® Yellow HCK-123 *1 mM solution in DMSO* *special packaging*	20 x 50 µL
N3246	neutral red *high purity*	25 mg
R14060	RedoxSensor™ Red CC-1 *special packaging*	10 x 50 µg
S34201	SelectFX™ Alexa Fluor® 488 Peroxisome Labeling Kit *for fixed cells*	1 kit
T3166	N-(3-triethylammoniumpropyl)-4-(6-(4-(diethylamino)phenyl)hexatrienyl)pyridinium dibromide (FM® 4-64)	1 mg
T13320	N-(3-triethylammoniumpropyl)-4-(6-(4-(diethylamino)phenyl)hexatrienyl)pyridinium dibromide (FM® 4-64) *special packaging*	10 x 100 µg
T23360	N-(3-trimethylammoniumpropyl)-4-(6-(4-(diethylamino)phenyl)hexatrienyl)pyridinium dibromide (FM® 5-95)	1 mg
Y7531	Yeast Vacuole Marker Sampler Kit	1 kit
Y7536	yeast vacuole membrane marker MDY-64	1 mg

For current prices or to order online, visit probes.invitrogen.com

12.4 Probes for the Endoplasmic Reticulum and Golgi Apparatus

The endoplasmic reticulum (ER) and Golgi apparatus (Figure 12.1) are primarily responsible for the proper sorting of lipids and proteins in cells.[1] Consequently, most of the cell-permeant probes for these organelles are either lipids or chemicals that affect protein movement. Several of the most effective probes for the Golgi apparatus are fluorescent ceramides and sphingolipids, which are discussed below and in Section 13.3. The lipophilicity of these probes enables their facile loading into live cells, usually from a dilute solution in dimethylsulfoxide. Certain aspects of lipid trafficking through the ER and Golgi apparatus related to signal transduction are described in Section 17.4.

An excellent compendium of human diseases that affect intracellular transport processes through lysosomes, Golgi and endoplasmic reticulum (ER) has been published.[2] Enzymes in the ER are also involved in synthesis of cholesterol and membranes and in the detoxification of hydrophobic drugs through the cytochrome P450 system (Section 10.6). Because several enzymes in the Golgi glycosylate lipids and proteins, some fluorescent lectins are useful markers for this organelle (Figure 12.46). Nissl bodies principally comprise ordered structures of alternate lamellae of rough endoplasmic reticulum and polyribosome arrays (Figure 8.37, Figure 14.42, Figure 14.39), and our NeuroTrace® fluorescent Nissl stains are described in Section 14.3.

In both live and fixed cells, the flattened membranous sacs of the ER and the Golgi apparatus can be stained with a variety of lipophilic probes and then distinguished by their morphology. For labeling fixed-cell preparations, we also offer antibodies specific for the yeast ER and for both mammalian and yeast Golgi proteins, as well as the SelectFX™ Alexa Fluor® 488 Endoplasmic Reticulum Labeling Kit (S34200), which contains an antibody directed against the ER-associated protein disulfide isomerase (PDI).

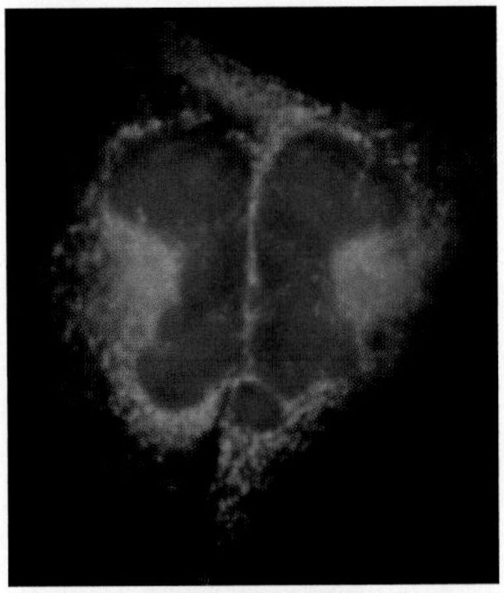

Figure 12.46 Fixed and permeabilized osteosarcoma cells simultaneously stained with the fluorescent lectins Alexa Fluor® 488 concanavalin A (Con A) (C11252) and Alexa Fluor® 594 wheat germ agglutinin (WGA) (W11262). Con A selectively binds α-glucopyranosyl residues, whereas WGA selectively binds sialic acid and *N*-acetylglucosaminyl residues. The nuclei were counterstained with blue-fluorescent Hoechst 33342 nucleic acid stain (H1399, H3570, H21492). The image was acquired using bandpass filter sets appropriate for the Texas Red® dye, fluorescein and AMCA.

ER-Tracker™ Blue-White DPX

ER-Tracker™ Blue-White DPX (E12353, Figure 12.47) is a highly selective and photostable stain for the ER in live cells[3–5] (Figure 12.48, Figure 12.49). Unlike the conventional ER stain $DiOC_6(3)$ (D273), ER-Tracker™ Blue-White DPX does not stain mitochondria, and staining at low concentrations does not appear to be toxic to cells. Moreover, our experiments indicate that the staining patterns are retained after fixation with aldehydes, although at reduced intensity.

ER-Tracker™ Blue-White DPX is a member of our Dapoxyl® dye family[6] and thus exhibits an unusually large Stokes shift and long-wavelength emission with a high extinction coefficient and high quantum yield when in a hydrophobic environment (Figure 1.112). Its fluorescence is highly environment sensitive — with increasing solvent polarity, the fluorescence maximum shifts to longer wavelengths and the quantum yield decreases — and peak fluorescence emission ranges from 430 nm to 640 nm. The ER-Tracker™ Blue-White DPX dye is readily visualized by two-photon microscopy.[7] We recommend visualizing its ER staining with a standard DAPI or UV longpass optical filter set (Table 23.9).

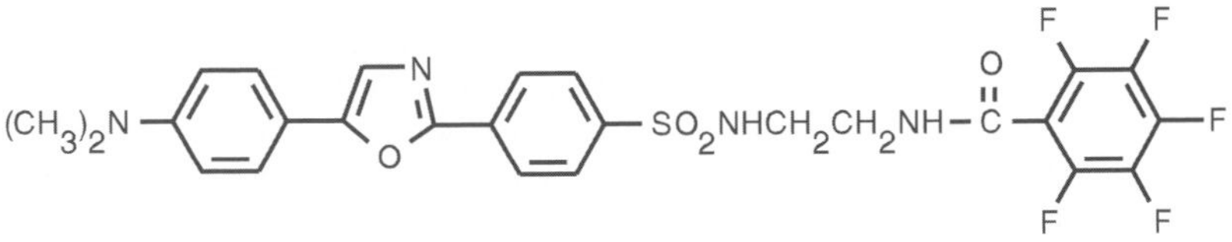

Figure 12.47 E12353 ER-Tracker™ Blue-White DPX.

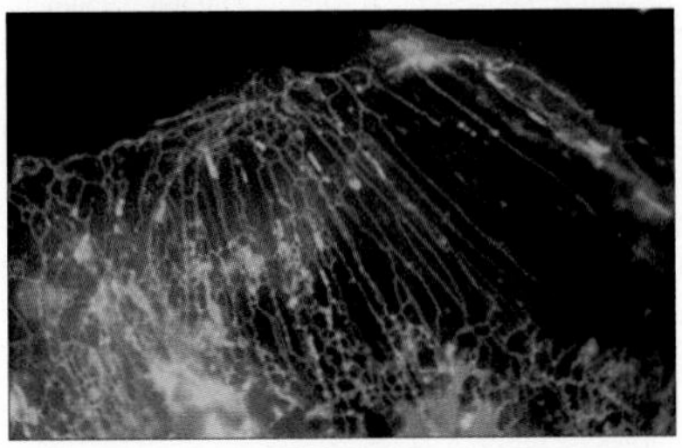

Figure 12.48 Live bovine pulmonary artery endothelial cells stained with ER-Tracker™ Blue-White DPX (E12353), a Dapoxyl® derivative. This image was acquired using a DAPI bandpass optical filter.

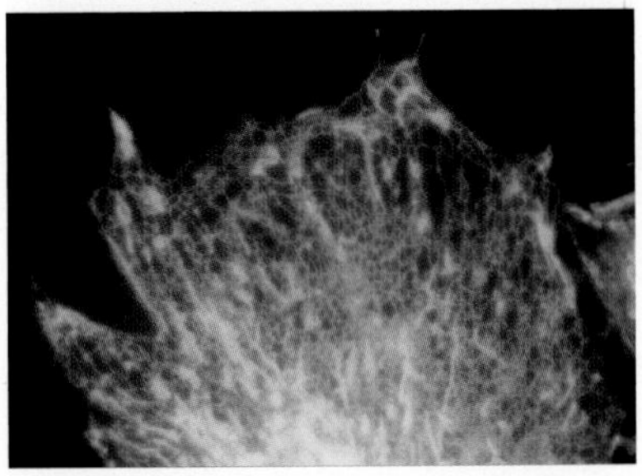

Figure 12.49 Live bovine pulmonary artery endothelial cells stained with ER-Tracker™ Blue-White DPX (E12353) and MitoTracker® Red CM-H_2XRos (M7513). The endoplasmic reticulum appears green and the mitochondria appear orange. The image was acquired using a fluorescence microscope equipped with a triple-bandpass filter set appropriate for DAPI, fluorescein and Texas Red® dyes.

Carbocyanine Dyes

Short-Chain Carbocyanine Dyes

Terasaki and co-workers used the short-chain carbocyanine $DiOC_6(3)$ (D273) to visualize the ER in both live and aldehyde-fixed cells.[8–10] This dye and the similar $DiOC_5(3)$ (D272) have since been used extensively to study structural interactions and dynamics of the ER in neurons,[11,12] yeast,[13] onion epidermis,[14] and to examine the morphological relationships between the ER, mitochondria, intermediate filaments and microtubules in various cell types.[15–17] $DiOC_6(3)$ and $DiOC_5(3)$ pass through the plasma membrane and stain intracellular membranes with a fluorescein-like fluorescence; ER membranes can easily be distinguished by their characteristic morphology.[18] Caution must be exercised, however, in using the carbocyanines as probes for the ER. It has been reported that ER staining with $DiOC_6(3)$ does not occur until the mitochondria round up and lose the fluorochrome.[19] Rhodamine 6G and the hexyl ester of rhodamine B (R634, R648MP; Section 12.2) appear to stain like $DiOC_6(3)$, except they are apparently less toxic and they fluoresce orange, providing possibilities for multicolor labeling.[18,20] When used at very low concentrations, these slightly lipophilic rhodamine dyes tend to stain only mitochondria of live cells[21] (Figure 12.24).

Long-Chain Carbocyanine Dyes

Terasaki and Jaffe have used the long-chain carbocyanines $DiIC_{16}(3)$ and $DiIC_{18}(3)$ (D384, D282) to label ER membranes. They achieved selective labeling of the ER by microinjecting a saturated solution of DiI in oil into sea urchin eggs.[22,23] This method has been successful in several other egg types but was not effective in molluscan or arthropod axons. As noted in Section 13.4 on dialkylcarbocyanine and dialkylaminostyryl probes, DiI diffuses only in continuous membranes.

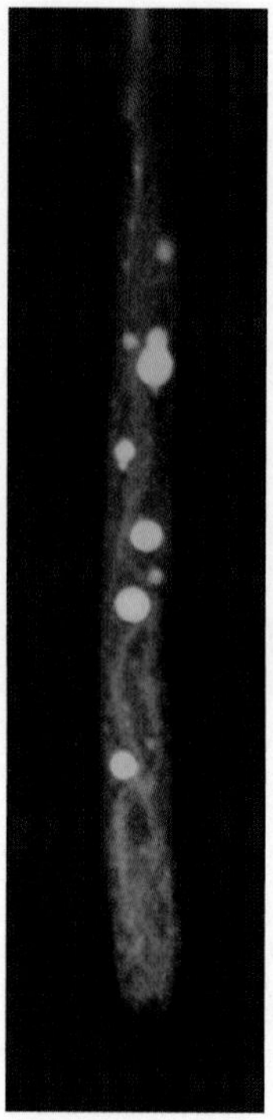

Figure 12.50 Endoplasmic reticulum (ER) of the hyphal tip cells of *Pisolithus tinctorius* were labeled with the red-orange–fluorescent BODIPY® 558/568 conjugate of brefeldin A (B7449), a reversible inhibitor of protein transport from the ER to the Golgi apparatus in many cell types and species. The motile tubular vacuole system was stained with green-fluorescent carboxy-DFFDA (Oregon Green® 488 carboxylic acid diacetate, O6151). Image contributed by Danielle Davies, University of New South Wales, Sydney, Australia.

Brefeldin A and Its Fluorescent Analogs

The fungal metabolite brefeldin A (BFA) has proven valuable for dissecting the cellular processes, including vesicle formation[24] and kinesin distribution,[25] involved in exporting newly synthesized proteins.[26] In addition to the natural product isolated from *Penicillium brefeldianum* (B7450), we offer green- and orange-fluorescent BODIPY® derivatives of brefeldin A[3,5,27,28] (B7447, B7449).

Brefeldin A

BFA (B7450) has multiple targets in cells.[29] Exposing cells to BFA causes a distortion in intracellular protein traffic from the ER to the Golgi apparatus and the eventual loss of Golgi apparatus morphology; removal of BFA completely reverses these effects.[26,30–34] BFA also alters the morphology of endosomes and lysosomes.[35] BFA has been used to prevent retinoic acid potentiation of immunotoxins,[36] to study translocation of proteins in polarized epithelial cells[37] and to investigate the regulation of ADP-ribosylation factor binding to the Golgi apparatus.[38] BFA action can be monitored using fluorescent endosomal markers such as lucifer yellow CH[35] (L453, L682, L1177, L12926; Section 14.3) and tetramethylrhodamine-labeled transferrin[39] (T2872, Section 16.1). Researchers have also used BFA to detect the intracellular expression of cytokines.[40,41] BFA disrupts Golgi-mediated intracellular transport and allows cytokines to accumulate, producing an enhanced cytokine signal that can be detected by flow cytometry.

Fluorescent Brefeldin A

The green-fluorescent BODIPY® FL and red-orange–fluorescent BODIPY® 558/568 BFA derivatives (B7447, B7449; Figure 12.50) are selectively localized in the ER and Golgi apparatus in four different cell lines.[28] BODIPY® 558/568 BFA may be used in conjunction with NBD C_6-ceramide (N1154) to investigate the ER and Golgi apparatus simultaneously. BODIPY® 558/568 BFA has also been used in combination with ER Tracker Blue-White DPX (E12353) to label the endoplasmic reticulum of hyphae.[5] However, the biological activity of the fluorescent BFA derivatives may be limited and may be dependent on cleavage of the BODIPY® fluorophore from BFA by intracellular esterases.[28] Two isomeric esters are isolated in the synthesis of the fluorescent brefeldins; we offer only "isomer 1" of each product.

Fluorescent Ceramide Analogs

NBD C_6-ceramide and BODIPY® FL C_5-ceramide (N1154, D3521;), both of which can be used with fluorescein optical filter sets (Table 23.9), are selective stains for the Golgi apparatus.[42–44] With spectral properties similar to those of Texas Red® dye, BODIPY® TR ceramide[45,46] (D7540) is especially useful for double-labeling experiments, including with chimeras of green-fluorescent proteins,[47,48] as well as for staining cells and tissues that have substantial amounts of green autofluorescence. In addition, the BODIPY® TR fluorophore is ideal for imaging microscopy with CCD cameras or other red-sensitive detectors. Uptake of fluorescent ceramides, at least in *Paramecium* cells, appears to be an ATP-dependent process.[49]

NBD C_6-Ceramide and NBD C_6-Sphingomyelin

NBD C_6-ceramide (N1154) has been used extensively as a selective stain of the trans-Golgi in both live and fixed cells.[50–57] Complexing fluorescent ceramides with bovine serum albumin (BSA) facilitates cell labeling without requiring the use of organic solvents to dissolve the probe.[42] For this application, we provide NBD C_6-ceramide complexed with defatted BSA (N22651). Researchers have employed NBD C_6-ceramide to investigate:

- Defective trans-Golgi acidification in cystic fibrosis[58]
- Effects of BFA (B7450) on the transport of proteins from the Golgi apparatus to the ER[30,32,59]
- Farber's disease, a genetically inherited disease of lipid metabolism[60]
- Inhibition of glycoprotein traffic through secretory pathways[61]
- Intracellular trafficking and targeting of thrombin receptors[62]
- Secretory activity during the isolation of secretion mutants by fluorescence-activated cell sorting[63]
- Subcellular distribution of the verotoxin B subunit in Vero cells[64]

Furthermore, the fluorescence of NBD C_6-ceramide is apparently sensitive to the cholesterol content of the Golgi apparatus, a phenomenon that is not observed with BODIPY® FL C_5-ceramide.[65] If NBD C_6-ceramide–containing cells are starved for cholesterol, the NBD C_6-ceramide that accumulates within the Golgi apparatus appears to be severely photolabile. However, this NBD photobleaching can be reduced by stimulation of cholesterol synthesis. Thus, NBD C_6-ceramide may be useful in monitoring the cholesterol content of the Golgi apparatus in live cells.[65]

NBD C_6-ceramide's conversion to the NBD C_6-glycosyl ceramide and NBD C_6-sphingomyelin (N3524) has been observed *in vivo*.[66–68] Metabolism of the probe in live Chinese hamster ovary (CHO) fibroblasts has been used to define lipid-transport pathways.[66,69] NBD C_6-ceramide is reported to be metabolized to NBD C_6-sphingomyelin in *Plasmodium falciparum*–infected erythrocytes, but not in normal erythrocytes.[70,71] Like NBD C_6-ceramide, NBD C_6-sphingomyelin has been used for the study of lipid trafficking between organelles.[69,72,73] Normal fibroblasts hydrolyze NBD C_6-sphingomyelin and process it through the Golgi apparatus.[74] However, in human skin fibroblasts from patients with Niemann–Pick disease, which is characterized by a lack of lysosomal sphingomyelinase activity, NBD C_6-sphingomyelin accumulates in the lysosomes.

BODIPY® Ceramides, BODIPY® Sphingomyelin and Related Derivatives

The green-fluorescent BODIPY® FL C_5-ceramide (D3521) is more fade-resistant and brighter than the NBD derivative and can likely be substituted for the NBD C_6-ceramide in many of its applications. The red-fluorescent BODIPY® TR ceramide (D7540) has proven useful for two-color immunofluorescence using a fluorescein-labeled antibody.[75] As with NBD C_6-ceramide, we also offer BODIPY® FL C_5-ceramide and BODIPY® TR C_5-ceramide complexed with defatted BSA (B22650, B34400) to facilitate cell labeling without the use of organic solvents to dissolve the probe.[42]

During normal resting intracellular transport, the kinetics of dye loading and transport may differ somewhat between the BODIPY® and NBD analogs.[76] BODIPY® FL C_5-ceramide has proven to be an excellent structural marker for the Golgi apparatus, visualized either by fluorescence microscopy[77,78] or, following diaminobenzidine (DAB) conversion, electron microscopy.[79–81] BODIPY® FL C_5-ceramide has also been used to:

- Delineate the Golgi apparatus in the cytoarchitecture of size-excluding compartments in live cells[82]
- Investigate both the inhibition of glycoprotein transport by ceramides[61] and the possible link between protein secretory pathways and sphingolipid biosynthesis[83]
- Isolate mammalian secretion mutants[63]
- Study sphingolipid distribution during human keratinocyte differentiation[84]
- Visualize tubovesicular membranes induced by *Plasmodium falciparum*[70,85]

BODIPY® FL C_5-ceramide exhibits concentration-dependent fluorescence properties that provide additional benefits for imaging the Golgi apparatus. At high concentrations, the nonpolar BODIPY® FL fluorophore forms excimers, resulting in a shift of the fluorophore's emission maximum from 515 nm (green) to ~620 nm (red). BODIPY® FL C_5-ceramide accumulation is sufficient for excimer formation in the trans-Golgi but not in the surrounding cytoplasm. Longpass optical filters that isolate the red emission can thus be used to selectively visualize the Golgi apparatus (Figure 12.51, Figure 12.52).

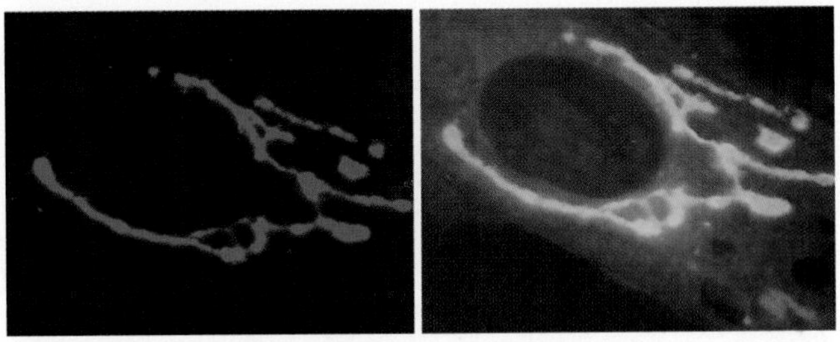

Figure 12.51 Selective staining of the Golgi apparatus using the green-fluorescent BODIPY® FL C_5-ceramide (D3521) (right panel). At high concentrations, the BODIPY® FL fluorophore forms excimers that can be visualized using a red longpass optical filter. The BODIPY® FL C_5-ceramide accumulation in the trans-Golgi is sufficient for excimer formation (left panel) (J Cell Biol 113, 1267 (1991)). Images contributed by Richard Pagano, Mayo Foundation.

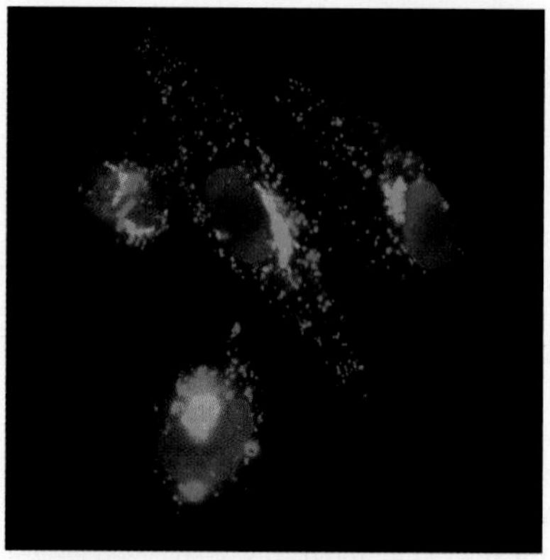

Figure 12.52 Viable Madin-Darby canine kidney (MDCK) cells sequentially stained with BODIPY® FL C_5-ceramide (D3521, B22650), LysoTracker® Red DND-99 (L7528) and Hoechst 33258 (H1398, H3569, H21491). Green-fluorescent BODIPY® FL C_5-ceramide localized to the Golgi apparatus, red-fluorescent LysoTracker® Red stain accumulated in the lysosomes, and the blue-fluorescent Hoechst 33258 dye stained the nuclei. The multiple-exposure image was acquired with bandpass filters appropriate for fluorescein, Texas Red® dye and DAPI.

Moreover, this two-color property can be used to quantitate BODIPY® FL C_5-ceramide accumulation by ratio imaging.[43,83,86] Like BODIPY® FL C_5-ceramide, the red-fluorescent BODIPY® TR ceramide appears to form long-wavelength excimers when concentrated in the Golgi apparatus; in this case, however, the excimers exhibit infrared fluorescence. In an unexpected application, it has been shown that cells infected with some intracellular bacteria, including *Chlamydia psittaci*, accumulate BODIPY® FL C_5-ceramide (D3521) in their inclusion membranes rather than in the Golgi of the host cells.[87,88] Certain CellTracker™ reagents (Section 14.2) that were used in combination with BODIPY® FL C_5-ceramide were also found to selectively label intracellular bacteria and parasites.[87]

We also offer BODIPY® FL C_5-sphingomyelin (D3522) — the likely metabolic product of BODIPY® FL C_5-ceramide[43] — as well as BODIPY® FL C_{12}-sphingomyelin[89] (D7711), BODIPY® FL C_5- and C_{12}-glucocerebrosides (D7548, D7547; Section 13.3) and BODIPY® FL C_5-lactosylceramide (D13951, B34402). The concentration-dependent fluorescence shift of BODIPY® FL C_5-sphingomyelin from green to red has been used to follow the initial steps of lipid uptake and transport by early endosomes through the cytoplasm.[90] BODIPY® FL C_5-glucocerebroside is reportedly internalized by endocytic and nonendocytic pathways that are quite different from those governing the internalization of BODIPY® FL C_5-sphingomyelin[91] (D3522). Addition of BODIPY® FL C_5-lactosylceramide to the culture medium of cells from patients with sphingolipid-storage diseases (sphingolipidosis) results in fluorescent product accumulation in lysosomes, whereas this probe accumulates in the Golgi apparatus of normal cells and cells from patients with other storage diseases.[92,93] Pagano and collaborators have published reviews of the use of BODIPY® ceramides and BODIPY® sphingolipids to study the endocytic pathway in mammalian cells.[42,94]

SelectFX™ Alexa Fluor® 488 Endoplasmic Reticulum Labeling Kit

The SelectFX™ Alexa Fluor® 488 Endoplasmic Reticulum Labeling Kit (S34200) provides all the reagents required to fix and permeabilize mammalian cells and then specifically label the ER. To achieve ER labeling, this kit employs a primary antibody directed against an ER-associated protein, protein disulfide isomerase (PDI), and an Alexa Fluor® 488 dye–labeled secondary antibody. The Alexa Fluor® 488 dye exhibits bright green fluorescence that is compatible with filters and instrument settings appropriate for fluorescein. Each kit contains:

- Mouse IgG_{2b} anti–protein disulfide isomerase (PDI) antibody
- Highly cross-adsorbed Alexa Fluor® 488 goat anti–mouse IgG antibody
- Concentrated fixative solution
- Concentrated phosphate-buffered saline (PBS)
- Concentrated permeabilization solution
- Concentrated blocking solution
- Detailed protocols for mammalian cell preparation and staining

The SelectFX™ Alexa Fluor® 488 Endoplasmic Reticulum Labeling Kit can be used in conjunction with probes for other cell targets to achieve multicolor cell staining.

Monoclonal Antibody Specific for the Yeast Endoplasmic Reticulum

For detection of yeast endoplasmic reticulum membranes, we offer the anti–dolichol phosphate mannose synthase (Dol-P-Man synthase, Dpm1p) monoclonal antibody (A6429). The yeast[95] Dol-P-Man synthase is an ~30,000-dalton integral membrane protein that resides in the endoplasmic reticulum; the monoclonal[96] antibody was prepared against the cytosolic domain of the protein.

Antibodies to Mammalian and Yeast Golgi Proteins

Anti–Human Golgin-97

Originally isolated from the serum of a patient with the autoimmune disease known as Sjögren's syndrome, anti–human golgin-97 antibodies recognize a 97,000-dalton protein called golgin-97, a member of the granin family of proteins and a peripheral membrane protein localized on the cytoplasmic face of the Golgi apparatus.[97] Because the antibody recognizes a protein unique to the Golgi apparatus of most vertebrate species, it is a useful for immunodetection and identification of the Golgi apparatus in cells, Western blotting and immunoprecipitation; however, we have a report that it may not work for rat cells (Figure 12.5, Figure 12.53, Figure 12.54). Molecular Probes offers mouse IgG_1 monoclonal anti–human golgin-97 antibody (A21270).

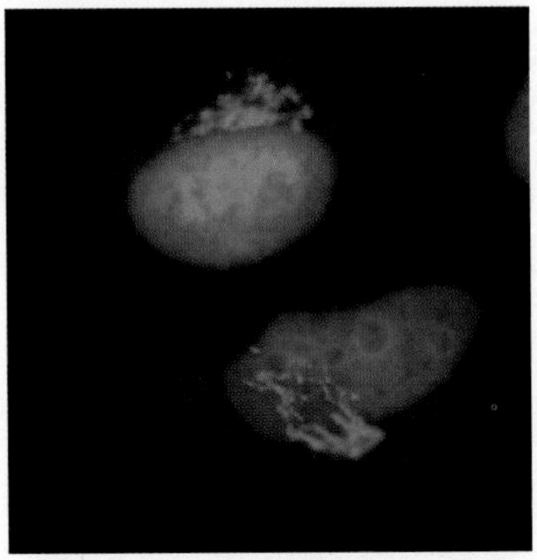

Figure 12.53 Fixed, permeabilized HeLa cells were labeled with anti-Golgin-97 antibody (A21270) and detected using Alexa Fluor® 647 goat anti-mouse IgG antibody (A21235). The cells were counterstained with SYTOX® Orange nucleic acid stain (S11368).

Monoclonal Antibody Specific for the Yeast Late-Golgi Compartment

For detection of the late-Golgi compartment of yeast, we offer a mouse monoclonal antibody to Vps10p (A21274). Yeast Vps10p is an ~180,000-dalton membrane protein that resides in the late-Golgi compartment. This monoclonal antibody is a valuable tool for detecting the late-Golgi compartment and late-Golgi membranes in yeast subcellular fractions by Western blot. However, due to the low abundance of the Vps10p antigen, this monoclonal antibody cannot be used to visualize Golgi by immunocytochemistry unless the signal is amplified, such as with our tyramide signal amplification (TSA) technology (Section 6.2).

Lectins for Staining the Golgi Apparatus

Wheat Germ Agglutinin and Concanavalin A

Various proteins and lipids found in the Golgi apparatus are glycosylated. Consequently, lectin conjugates (Section 7.7) have been found to be particularly useful for staining Golgi structures in fixed-cell preparations (Figure 7.110). Wheat germ agglutinin (WGA) staining of trans-Golgi has been considered a marker for this organelle.[98–100] Fluorescent conjugates of concanavalin A (Con A) also stain the Golgi but with reduced specificity.[101] Molecular Probes prepares WGA and Con A conjugates whose fluorescence spans the entire visible and near-infrared spectrum (Table 7.23). Our Alexa Fluor® conjugates of these important lectins are particularly recommended for their enhanced brightness and photostability. We also offer a Wheat Germ Agglutinin Stain Sampler Kit (W7024), which contains 1 mg quantities each of WGA conjugates of the Alexa Fluor® 350, Oregon Green® 488, tetramethylrhodamine and Texas Red®-X dyes.

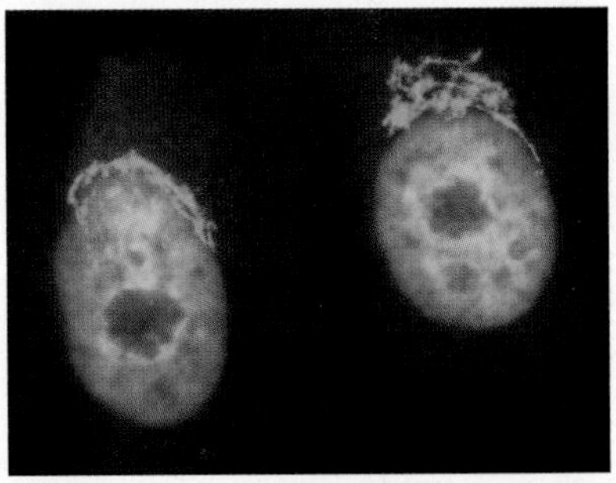

Figure 12.54 Fixed, permeabilized HeLa cells were labeled with anti–Golgin-97 antibody (A21270) and detected using Alexa Fluor® 488 goat anti–mouse IgG antibody (A11001). The cells were counterstained with DAPI (D1306, D3571, D21490). The image was deconvolved using Huygens software (Scientific Volume Imaging). 3-D reconstruction was performed using Imaris software (Bitplane AG).

Griffonia simplicifolia *Lectin GS-II*

Lectin GS-II from *Griffonia simplicifolia* is the only known lectin that binds with high selectivity to terminal, nonreducing α- and β-*N*-acetyl-D-glucosaminyl (GlcNAc) residues of glycoproteins. Because of the affinity of lectin GS-II for GlcNAc, conjugates of this lectin are useful for staining intermediate-to-trans Golgi — the site of *N*-acetylglucosaminyltransferase activity.[102] The Golgi apparatus of oligodendrocytes and ganglion neurons are readily stained by fluorescent GS-II conjugates. We have prepared the green-fluorescent Alexa Fluor® 488 (L21415, Figure 7.117), red-fluorescent Alexa Fluor® 594 (L21416) and far-red–fluorescent Alexa Fluor® 647 (L32451) conjugates of lectin GS-II for use in Golgi staining.

Helix pomatia *(Edible Snail) Agglutinin*

Helix pomatia agglutinin (HPA) selectively binds to terminal α-*N*-acetylgalactosaminyl residues — an intermediate sugar added in *O*-linkage to serine and threonine residues in *cis*-Golgi cisternae and then substituted with galactose and sialic acid in the *trans*-Golgi.[103] HPA conjugates are principally used as markers for the Golgi. Our fluorescent Alexa Fluor® 488, Alexa Fluor® 568, Alexa Fluor® 594 and Alexa Fluor® 647 conjugates of HPA [103] (L11271, L32452, L32453, L32454) should be particularly useful for Golgi staining.

References

1. Science 282, 2172 (1998); **2.** Traffic 1, 836 (2000); **3.** Fungal Genet Biol 29, 95 (2000); **4.** Mol Biol Cell 11, 1815 (2000); **5.** J Microsc 197, 239 (2000); **6.** Photochem Photobiol 66, 424 (1997); **7.** J Biol Chem 275, 22487 (2000); **8.** Cell Biology: A Laboratory Handbook, 2nd Ed., Vol. 2, Celis JE, Ed. pp.501–506 (1998); **9.** J Cell Biol 103, 1557 (1986); **10.** Cell 38, 101 (1984); **11.** J Cell Biol 127, 1021 (1994); **12.** Nature 310, 53 (1984); **13.** Cell Motil Cytoskeleton 25, 111 (1993); **14.** Eur J Cell Biol 52, 328 (1990); **15.** J Cell Biol 137, 1199 (1997); **16.** Biochem Cell Biol 70, 1174 (1992); **17.** Cell Motil Cytoskeleton 15, 71 (1990); **18.** J Cell Sci 101, 315 (1992); **19.** Microsc Res Tech 27, 198 (1994); **20.** J Cell Biol 143, 861 (1998); **21.** Histochemistry 94, 303 (1990); **22.** J Cell Biol 120, 1337 (1993); **23.** J Cell Biol 114, 929 (1991); **24.** J Cell Biol 122, 1197 (1993); **25.** J Cell Biol 128, 293 (1995); **26.** J Biol Chem 261, 11398 (1986); **27.** J Exp Med 190, 523 (1999); **28.** J Histochem Cytochem 43, 907 (1995); **29.** Cell 67, 449 (1991); **30.** J Biol Chem 268, 2341 (1993); **31.** J Cell Biol 116, 1071 (1992); **32.** Proc Natl Acad Sci U S A 88, 9818 (1991); **33.** Cell 60, 821 (1990); **34.** J Cell Biol 111, 2295 (1990); **35.** J Cell Biol 119, 273 (1992); **36.** J Cell Biol 125, 743 (1994); **37.** J Cell Biol 124, 83 (1994); **38.** Nature 364, 818 (1993); **39.** J Cell Biol 118, 267 (1992); **40.** Blood 86, 1357 (1995); **41.** J Immunol Methods 159, 197 (1993); **42.** Cell Biology: A Laboratory Handbook, 2nd Ed., Vol. 2, Celis JE, Ed. pp. 507–512 (1998); **43.** J Cell Biol 113, 1267 (1991); **44.** J Cell Biol 109, 2067 (1989); **45.** Infect Immun 68, 5960 (2000); **46.** Mol Biochem Parasitol 106, 21 (2000); **47.** Mol Biol Cell 11, 1789 (2000); **48.** J Biol Chem 274, 37233 (1999); **49.** J Histochem Cytochem 52, 557 (2004); **50.** J Biol Chem 268, 18390 (1993); **51.** Am J Physiol 260, G119 (1991); **52.** Neurochem Res 16, 551 (1991); **53.** Biochem Soc Trans 18, 361 (1990); **54.** Eur J Cell Biol 53, 173 (1990); **55.** Science 229, 1051 (1985); **56.** Science 228, 745 (1985); **57.** Proc Natl Acad Sci U S A 80, 2608 (1983); **58.** J Biol Chem 271, 15542 (1996); **59.** J Cell Biol 112, 567 (1991); **60.** Arch Biochem Biophys 208, 444 (1981); **61.** J Biol Chem 268, 4577 (1993); **62.** J Biol Chem 269, 27719 (1994); **63.** Mol Biol Cell 6, 135 (1995); **64.** J Cell Biol 134, 1387 (1996); **65.** Proc Natl Acad Sci U S A 90, 2661 (1993); **66.** J Cell Biol 111, 977 (1990); **67.** Biochemistry 27, 6197 (1988); **68.** J Cell Biol 105, 1623 (1987); **69.** J Cell Biol 108, 2169 (1989); **70.** J Cell Biol 124, 449 (1994); **71.** Mol Biochem Parasitol 49, 143 (1991); **72.** J Cell Biol 121, 1257 (1993); **73.** J Cell Biol 117, 259 (1992); **74.** J Cell Biol 111, 429 (1990); **75.** Proc Natl Acad Sci U S A 93, 10217 (1996); **76.** Methods Cell Biol 38, 221 (1993); **77.** Cytometry 14, 251 (1993); **78.** J Cell Biol 120, 399 (1993); **79.** J Cell Biol 127, 29 (1994); **80.** Cell 73, 1079 (1993); **81.** Eur J Cell Biol 58, 214 (1992); **82.** J Cell Sci 106, 565 (1993); **83.** Biochemistry 31, 3581 (1992); **84.** J Biol Chem 273, 9651 (1998); **85.** Science 276, 1122 (1997); **86.** FASEB J 8, 573 (1994); **87.** J Microbiol Methods 40, 265 (2000); **88.** EMBO J 15, 964 (1996); **89.** J Cell Biol 140, 39 (1998); **90.** Biophys J 72, 37 (1997); **91.** J Cell Biol 125, 769 (1994); **92.** Nat Cell Biol 1, 386 (1999); **93.** Lancet 354, 901 (1999); **94.** Ann N Y Acad Sci 845, 152 (1998); **95.** J Biol Chem 272, 25928 (1997); **96.** Guidebook to the Secretory Pathway , Rothblatt J, Novick P, Stevens TH, Eds. (Complete Volume) (1994); **97.** Arthritis Rheum 40, 1693 (1997); **98.** Cytometry 19, 112 (1995); **99.** J Cell Biol 85, 429 (1980); **100.** J Cell Biochem 66, 165 (1997); **101.** Exp Cell Res 207, 136 (1993); **102.** J Struct Biol 128, 131 (1999); **103.** Adv Immunol 34, 213 (1983).

Data Table — 12.4 Probes for the Endoplasmic Reticulum and Golgi Apparatus

Cat #	MW	Storage	Soluble	Abs	EC	Em	Solvent	Notes
B7447	554.44	F,D,L	DMSO, EtOH	503	83,000	510	MeOH	
B7449	608.51	F,D,L	DMSO, EtOH	559	80,000	568	MeOH	
B7450	280.36	F,D	DMSO, EtOH	<300		none		
B22650	~66,000	F,D,L	H_2O	505	91,000	511	MeOH	1, 2
B34400	~66,000	F,D,L	H_2O	589	65,000	616	MeOH	2
B34402	~66,000	F,D,L	H_2O	505	80,000	511	MeOH	1, 2
D272	544.47	D,L	DMSO	484	155,000	500	MeOH	
D273	572.53	D,L	DMSO	484	154,000	501	MeOH	
D282	933.88	L	DMSO, EtOH	549	148,000	565	MeOH	
D384	877.77	L	DMSO, EtOH	549	148,000	565	MeOH	
D3521	601.63	FF,D,L	$CHCl_3$, DMSO	505	91,000	511	MeOH	1
D3522	766.75	FF,D,L	see Notes	505	77,000	512	MeOH	1, 3
D7540	705.71	FF,D,L	$CHCl_3$, DMSO	589	65,000	616	MeOH	
D7546	759.42	FF,D,L	$CHCl_3$, DMSO	533	80,000	545	MeOH	
D7711	864.94	FF,D,L	DMSO	505	75,000	513	MeOH	1, 4
D13951	925.91	FF,D,L	DMSO, EtOH	505	80,000	511	MeOH	
E12353	580.53	F,D,L	DMSO	374	25,000	575	MeOH	4, 5
N1154	575.75	FF,D,L	$CHCl_3$, DMSO	466	22,000	536	MeOH	6
N3524	740.88	FF,D,L	see Notes	466	22,000	536	MeOH	3, 6
N22651	~66,000	F,D,L	H_2O	466	22,000	536	MeOH	2, 6

For definitions of the contents of this data table, see "Navigating *The Handbook*" in the introductory pages.

Notes

1. Em for BODIPY® FL sphingolipids shifts to ~620 nm when high concentrations of the probe (>5 mol %) are incorporated in lipid mixtures (J Cell Biol 113, 1267 (1991)).
2. This product is a lipid complexed with bovine serum albumin (BSA). Spectroscopic data are for the free lipid in MeOH.
3. Chloroform is the most generally useful solvent for preparing stock solutions of phospholipids (including sphingomyelins). Glycerophosphocholines are usually freely soluble in ethanol. Most other glycerophospholipids (phosphoethanolamines, phosphatidic acids and phosphoglycerols) are less soluble in ethanol, but solutions up to 1–2 mg/mL should be obtainable, using sonication to aid dispersion if necessary. Labeling of cells with fluorescent phospholipids can be enhanced by addition of cyclodextrins during incubation (J Biol Chem 274, 35359 (1999)).
4. This product is supplied as a ready-made solution in the solvent indicated under "Soluble."
5. ER-Tracker™ Blue-White DPX Abs = 372 nm, Em = 556 nm bound to phospholipid bilayer membranes. The emission spectrum is extremely broad (~200 nm at half-maximum). Fluorescence in water is very weak.
6. Fluorescence of NBD and its derivatives in water is relatively weak. QY and τ increase and Em decreases in aprotic solvents and other nonpolar environments relative to water (Biochemistry 16, 5150 (1977); Photochem Photobiol 54, 361 (1991)).

Product List — 12.4 Probes for the Endoplasmic Reticulum and Golgi Apparatus

Cat #	Product Name	Unit Size
A6429	anti-dolichol phosphate mannose synthase (yeast), mouse IgG_1, monoclonal 5C5	250 µg
A21270	anti-golgin-97 (human), mouse IgG_1, monoclonal CDF4 (anti-Golgi)	100 µg
A21273	anti-Pep12p (yeast), mouse IgG_1, monoclonal 2C3 *0.5 mg/mL*	100 µL
A21274	anti-Vps10p (yeast), mouse IgG_{2a}, monoclonal 18C8 *0.5 mg/mL*	500 µL
B22650	BODIPY® FL C_5-ceramide complexed to BSA	5 mg
B34402	BODIPY® FL C_5-lactosylceramide complexed to BSA	1 mg
B34400	BODIPY® TR C_5-ceramide complexed to BSA	5 mg
B7450	brefeldin A *from *Penicillium brefeldianum**	5 mg
B7449	brefeldin A, BODIPY® 558/568 conjugate *isomer 1*	25 µg
B7447	brefeldin A, BODIPY® FL conjugate *isomer 1*	25 µg
D7546	*N*-(2,6-dibromo-4,4-difluoro-5,7-dimethyl-4-bora-3a,4a-diaza-*s*-indacene-3-pentanoyl)sphingosine (BODIPY® FL Br_2C_5-ceramide)	250 µg
D7711	*N*-(4,4-difluoro-5,7-dimethyl-4-bora-3a,4a-diaza-*s*-indacene-3-dodecanoyl)sphingosyl phosphocholine (BODIPY® FL C_{12}-sphingomyelin) *1 mg/mL in DMSO*	250 µL
D3521	*N*-(4,4-difluoro-5,7-dimethyl-4-bora-3a,4a-diaza-*s*-indacene-3-pentanoyl)sphingosine (BODIPY® FL C_5-ceramide)	250 µg
D13951	*N*-(4,4-difluoro-5,7-dimethyl-4-bora-3a,4a-diaza-*s*-indacene-3-pentanoyl)sphingosyl 1-β-D-lactoside (BODIPY® FL C_5-lactosylceramide)	25 µg
D3522	*N*-(4,4-difluoro-5,7-dimethyl-4-bora-3a,4a-diaza-*s*-indacene-3-pentanoyl)sphingosyl phosphocholine (BODIPY® FL C_5-sphingomyelin)	250 µg
D7540	*N*-((4-(4,4-difluoro-5-(2-thienyl)-4-bora-3a,4a-diaza-*s*-indacene-3-yl)phenoxy)acetyl)sphingosine (BODIPY® TR ceramide)	250 µg
D384	1,1′-dihexadecyl-3,3,3′,3′-tetramethylindocarbocyanine perchlorate ($DiIC_{16}(3)$)	100 mg
D273	3,3′-dihexyloxacarbocyanine iodide ($DiOC_6(3)$)	100 mg
D282	1,1′-dioctadecyl-3,3,3′,3′-tetramethylindocarbocyanine perchlorate ('DiI'; $DiIC_{18}(3)$)	100 mg
D272	3,3′-dipentyloxacarbocyanine iodide ($DiOC_5(3)$)	100 mg
E12353	ER-Tracker™ Blue-White DPX *1 mM solution in DMSO* *special packaging*	20 x 50 µL
L21415	lectin GS-II from *Griffonia simplicifolia*, Alexa Fluor® 488 conjugate	500 µg
L21416	lectin GS-II from *Griffonia simplicifolia*, Alexa Fluor® 594 conjugate	500 µg
L32451	lectin GS-II from *Griffonia simplicifolia*, Alexa Fluor® 647 conjugate	500 µg
L11271	lectin HPA from *Helix pomatia* (edible snail), Alexa Fluor® 488 conjugate	1 mg
L32452	lectin HPA from *Helix pomatia* (edible snail), Alexa Fluor® 568 conjugate	1 mg
L32453	lectin HPA from *Helix pomatia* (edible snail), Alexa Fluor® 594 conjugate	1 mg
L32454	lectin HPA from *Helix pomatia* (edible snail), Alexa Fluor® 647 conjugate	1 mg
N22651	NBD C_6-ceramide complexed to BSA	5 mg
N1154	6-((*N*-(7-nitrobenz-2-oxa-1,3-diazol-4-yl)amino)hexanoyl)sphingosine (NBD C_6-ceramide)	1 mg
N3524	6-((*N*-(7-nitrobenz-2-oxa-1,3-diazol-4-yl)amino)hexanoyl)sphingosyl phosphocholine (NBD C_6-sphingomyelin)	1 mg
S34200	SelectFX™ Alexa Fluor® 488 Endoplasmic Reticulum Labeling Kit *for fixed cells*	1 kit
W11263	wheat germ agglutinin, Alexa Fluor® 350 conjugate	5 mg
W11261	wheat germ agglutinin, Alexa Fluor® 488 conjugate	5 mg
W11262	wheat germ agglutinin, Alexa Fluor® 594 conjugate	5 mg
W21404	wheat germ agglutinin, Alexa Fluor® 633 conjugate	5 mg
W21407	wheat germ agglutinin, Alexa Fluor® 660 conjugate	5 mg
W834	wheat germ agglutinin, fluorescein conjugate	5 mg
W11260	wheat germ agglutinin, Marina Blue® conjugate	5 mg
W6748	wheat germ agglutinin, Oregon Green® 488 conjugate	5 mg
W7024	Wheat Germ Agglutinin Sampler Kit *four fluorescent conjugates, 1 mg each*	1 kit
W849	wheat germ agglutinin, tetramethylrhodamine conjugate	5 mg
W21405	wheat germ agglutinin, Texas Red®-X conjugate	1 mg

For current prices or to order online, visit probes.invitrogen.com

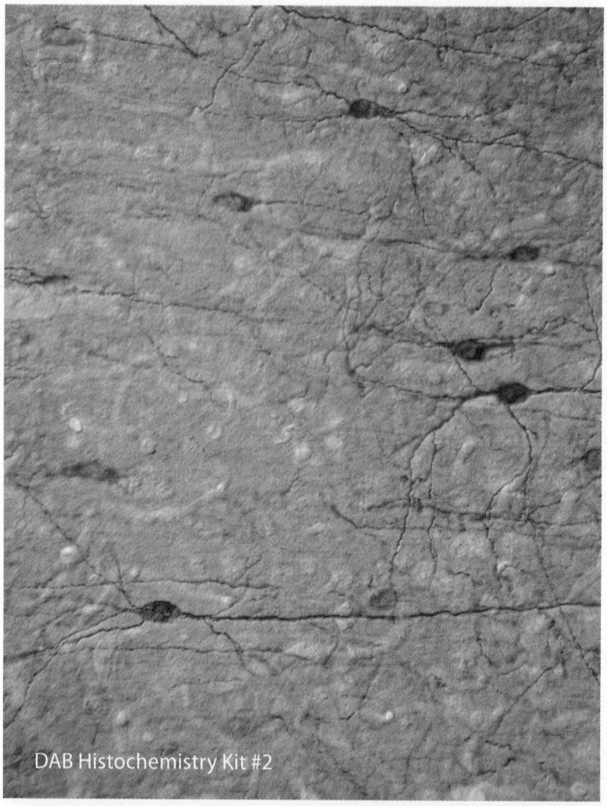

DAB Histochemistry Kit #2

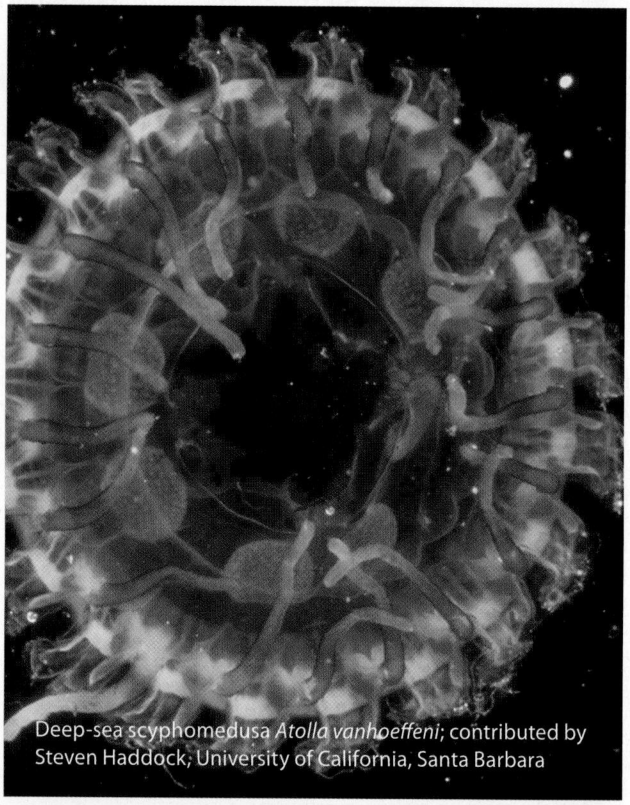

Deep-sea scyphomedusa *Atolla vanhoeffeni*; contributed by Steven Haddock, University of California, Santa Barbara

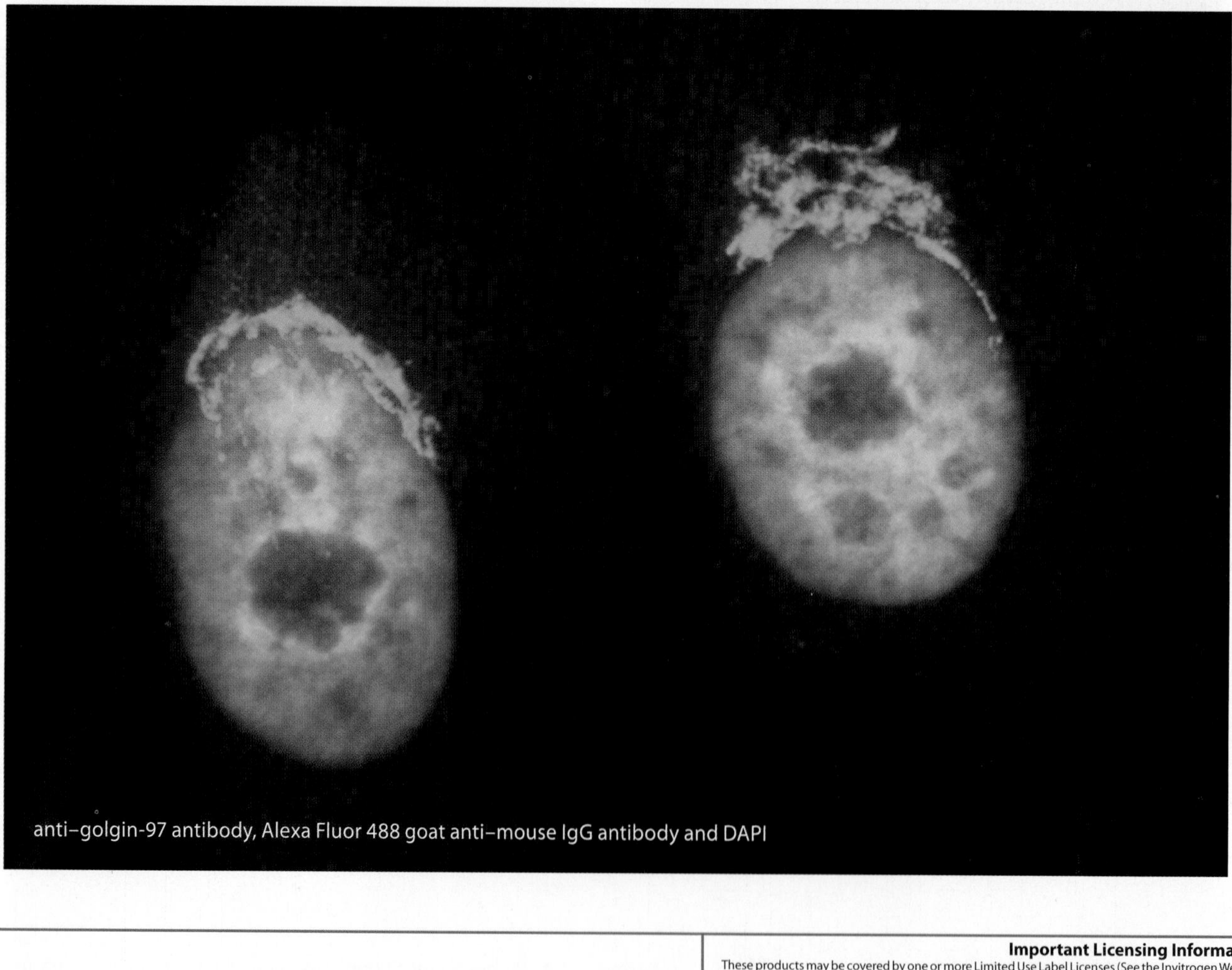

anti–golgin-97 antibody, Alexa Fluor 488 goat anti–mouse IgG antibody and DAPI

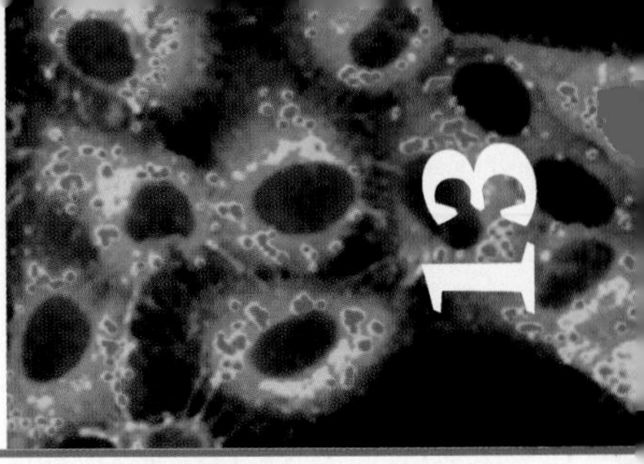

Chapter 13

Probes for Lipids and Membranes

13.1 Introduction to Membrane Probes

The plasma membranes and intracellular membranes of live cells and the artificial membranes of liposomes represent a significant area of application for fluorescent probes. Membrane probes include fluorescent analogs of natural lipids, as well as lipophilic organic dyes that have little structural resemblance to natural biomolecules (Figure 13.1). Molecular Probes offers a wide range of both types of membrane probes. Some probes are primarily used for structural and biophysical analysis of membranes, others for following lipid transport and metabolism in live cells (Figure 13.2) and some for investigating synaptosome recycling (Section 16.1) and lipid-mediated signal transduction processes (Chapter 17). Due to their low toxicity and stable retention, some lipid probes are particularly useful for long-term cell tracing (Section 14.4). Other, slightly less lipophilic probes are used as membrane markers of endocytosis and exocytosis (Section 16.1).

We offer fluorescent and, in a few cases, biotinylated analogs of five naturally occurring lipid classes — phospholipids, sphingolipids (including ceramides), fatty acids, triglycerides and steroids. A recent major addition to our selection of fluorescent phospholipid analogs is an extensive range of BODIPY® dye–labeled phosphatidylinositols developed in collaboration with Echelon Biosciences, Inc. Phospholipids are the principal building blocks of cell membranes. Most phospholipids are derivatives of glycerol comprising two fatty acyl residues (nonpolar tails) and a single phosphate ester substituent (polar head group). Despite their overall structural similarity (Figure 13.3), natural phospholipids exhibit subtle differences in their fatty acid compositions, degree of acyl chain unsaturation and type of polar head group.[1] These differences can produce significant variations in membrane physical properties, in the location of phospholipids in a lipid bilayer and in their biological activity. Fluorescent phospholipid analogs (Section 13.2) can be classified according to where the fluorophore is attached. The fluorophore can be attached to one (or both) of the fatty acyl chains or to the polar head group. The attachment position of the fluorophore determines whether it is located in the nonpolar interior or at the water/lipid interface when the phospholipid analog is incorporated into a lipid bilayer membrane (Figure 13.1).

Fatty acids are the building blocks for a diverse set of biomolecules. Some fatty acids (e.g., arachidonic acid) are important in cell signaling.[2] Fatty acids are liberated by the enzymatic action of phospho-

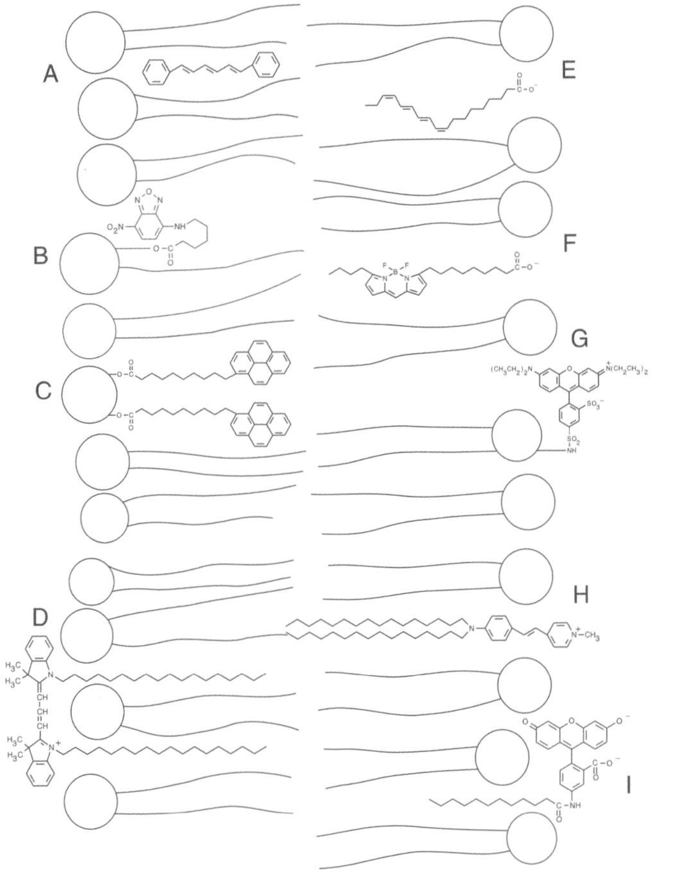

Figure 13.1 Location and orientation of representative fluorescent membrane probes in a phospholipid bilayer: **A)** DPH (D202), **B)** NBD-C_6-HPC (N3786), **C)** bis-pyrene-PC (B3782), **D)** DiI (D282), **E)** *cis*-parinaric acid (P36005), **F)** BODIPY® 500/510 C_4, C_9 (B3824), **G)** *N*-Rh-PE (L1392), **H)** DiA (D3883) and **I)** C_{12}-fluorescein (D109).

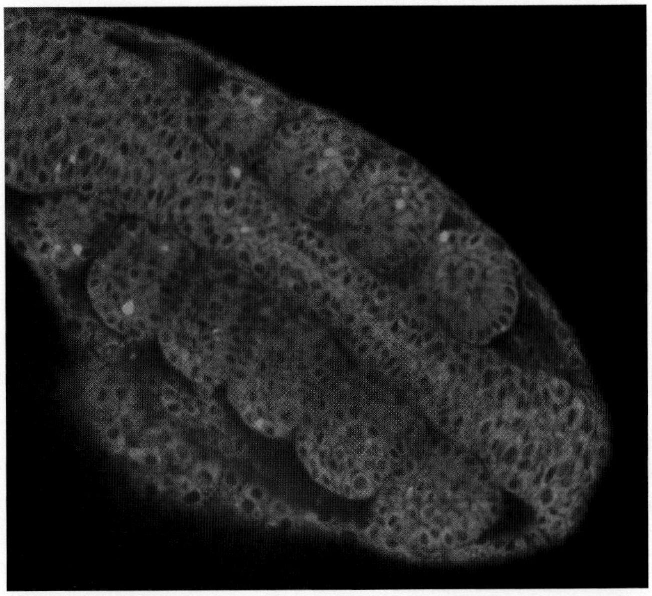

Figure 13.2 The cytoplasm of a live zebrafish embryo labeled with the green-fluorescent lipophilic tracer BODIPY® 505/515 (D3921). The image was contributed by Arantza Barrios, University College, London.

lipase A on phospholipids (Section 17.4) and also by various other lipases. Fluorescent fatty acids can often be used interchangeably with the corresponding phospholipids as membrane probes; however, fatty acids transfer more readily between aqueous and lipid phases.[3] Although fatty acids are ionized at neutral pH in water (pK_a ~5), their pK_a is typically ~7 in membranes, and thus a significant fraction of membrane-bound fatty acids are neutral species.[3] Certain fluorescent fatty acids (Section 13.2) are readily metabolized by live cells to phospholipids, mono-, di- and triacylglycerols, cholesteryl esters and other lipid derivatives.[4]

Sphingolipids play critical roles in processes such as proliferation, apoptosis, signal transduction and molecular recognition at cell surfaces.[1,5,6] Defects in the lysosomal breakdown of sphingolipids are the underlying cause of lipid storage disorders such as Niemann–Pick, Tay–Sachs, Krabbe's and Gaucher's diseases. The sphingolipids described in Section 13.3 include ceramides, sphingomyelins, glycosylceramides (cerebrosides) and gangliosides. The structural backbone of sphingolipids is the lipophilic amino–dialcohol sphingosine (2-amino-4-octadecen-1,3-diol, Figure 13.3) to which a single fatty acid residue is attached via an amide linkage. Our fluorescent analogs of sphingolipids are prepared by replacing the natural amide-linked fatty acid with a fluorescent analog. Sphingolipids with an unmodified hydroxyl group in the 1-position are classified as ceramides. As part of the lipid-sorting process in cells, ceramides are glycosylated to cerebrosides (Figure 13.3) or converted to sphingomyelins (Figure 13.3) in the Golgi complex. Glycosylated sphingolipids (cerebrosides and gangliosides) occur in the plasma membranes of all eukaryotic cells and are involved in cell recognition, signal transduction and modulation of receptor function.[7] Gangliosides have complex oligosaccharide head groups containing at least one sialic acid residue in place of the single galactose or glucose residues of cerebrosides.

Fluorescent cholesteryl esters and triglycerides (Section 13.3) can be used as structural probes and transport markers for these important lipid constituents of membranes and lipoproteins. They may also serve as fluorescent substrates for lipases and lipid-transfer proteins and can be incorporated into low-density lipoproteins (LDL, Section 16.1).

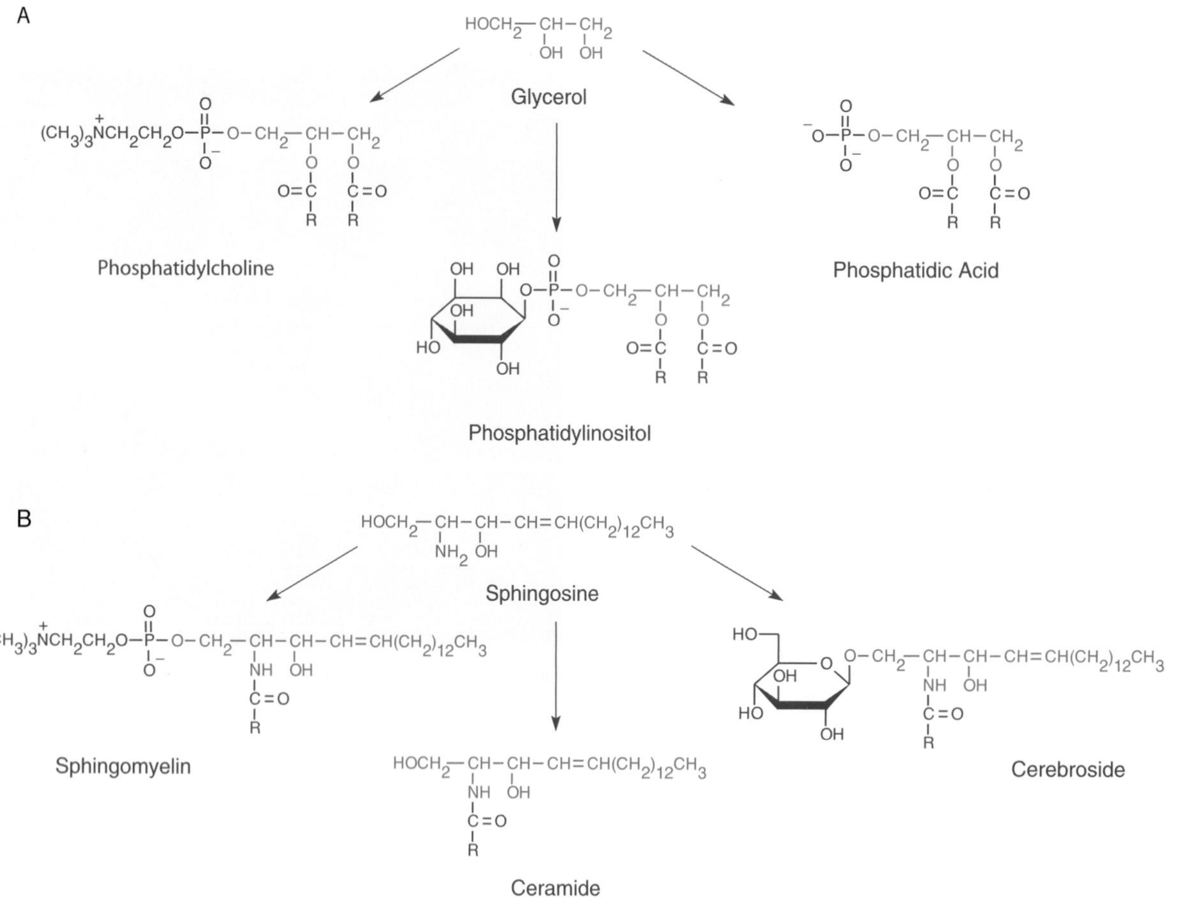

Figure 13.3 A) Phosphatidylcholines, phosphatidylinositols and phosphatidic acids are examples of glycerolipids derived from glycerol. **B)** Sphingomyelins, ceramides and cerebrosides are examples of sphingolipids derived from sphingosine. In all the structures shown, R represents the hydrocarbon tail portion of a fatty acid residue.

The probes described in Section 13.4 and Section 13.5 are not analogs of any particular biological lipid class, but they have a general structural resemblance that facilitates labeling of membranes, lipoproteins and other lipid-based molecular assemblies. Particularly notable members of this group are the lipophilic carbocyanines DiI (Figure 13.4), DiO, DiD and DiR, the lipid fluidity probes DPH and TMA-DPH and the membrane-surface probes ANS and laurdan. These probes generally have limited water solubility and exhibit substantially enhanced fluorescence upon partition into lipid environments. They can be classified as either amphiphilic (having both polar and nonpolar structural elements) or neutral (lacking charges and most soluble in very nonpolar environments). We use similar neutral lipophilic dyes for internal staining of our fluorescent polystyrene microspheres (Section 6.5).

In addition to the lipophilic probes described in this chapter, we have available the following related products:

- FM® dyes — amphiphilic probes for cell membrane labeling (Section 14.4, Section 16.1)
- Moderately lipophilic stains for the endoplasmic reticulum and Golgi apparatus (Section 12.4)
- Membrane potential–sensitive probes (Section 22.2, Section 22.3)
- Amplex® Red Phosphatidylcholine-Specific Phospholipase C Assay Kit (A12218, Section 17.4)
- Amplex® Red Phospholipase D Assay Kit (A12219, Section 17.4)
- Fluorescent and fluorogenic phospholipase A substrates (Section 17.4)
- Shuttle PIP carriers for loading phosphatidylinositol phosphates into live cells (Section 17.4, Figure 17.34)
- Antibodies to phosphatidylinositol phosphates (Section 7.5, Section 17.4)
- Pro-Q® Emerald 300 Lipopolysaccharide Gel Stain Kit (P20495, Section 3.2)
- Alexa Fluor® dye–labeled cholera toxin subunit B conjugates for labeling lipid rafts (Section 14.7)
- Annexin V conjugates for detection of phosphatidylserine exposure in apoptotic cell membranes (Section 15.5)
- Lipophilic Ca^{2+} indicators (Section 19.4) and pH indicators (Section 20.4)

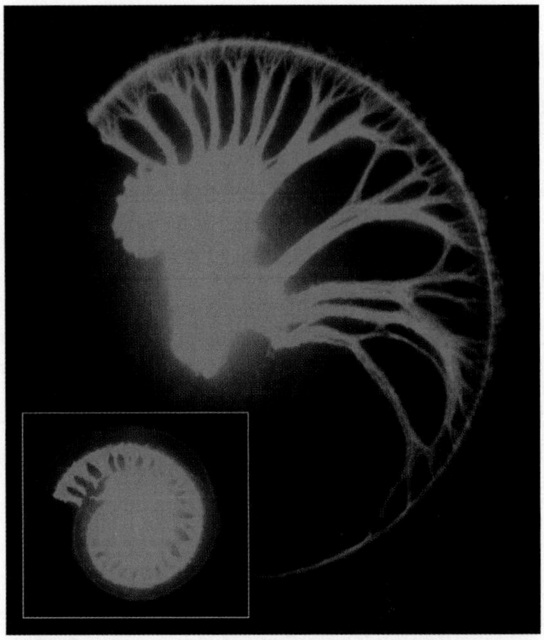

Figure 13.4 The neuronal tracer DiI (D282, D3911) used as a diagnostic tool to evaluate patterns of innervation in newborn mice cochlea. The larger image is of a mutant cochlea and the inset is of a wild-type cochlea. Image contributed by Bernd Fritzsch, Creighton University, and L. Reichardt and I. Farinas, Howard Hughes Medical Institute, San Francisco.

References

1. Annu Rev Biochem 66, 199 (1997); **2.** Biochim Biophys Acta 1212, 26 (1994); **3.** J Lipid Res 39, 467 (1998); **4.** Chem Phys Lipids 58, 111 (1991); **5.** Biochim Biophys Acta 1082, 113 (1991); **6.** Annu Rev Biochem 67, 27 (1998); **7.** Ann N Y Acad Sci 845, 57 (1998).

13.2 Fatty Acid Analogs and Phospholipids

The probes in this section and in Section 13.3 bear some structural resemblance to natural lipids. Included in this section are our fluorescent fatty acid analogs, as well as phospholipids wherein one or both fatty acid esters are replaced by fluorescent fatty acid esters. The fluorophores in these probes tend to remain buried in the hydrophobic interior of lipid bilayer membranes.[1,2] In this location, they are sensitive to membrane properties such as lipid fluidity, lateral domain formation and structural perturbation by proteins, drugs and other additives. Also included in this section are several head group–modified phospholipid analogs incorporating fluorophores, biotin or reactive groups (Table 13.1). Sphingolipids, steroids and lipopolysaccharides are discussed in Section 13.3. Important applications of the fluorescent phosphatidylinositol derivatives as probes for signal transduction and various fluorescent phospholipids as phospholipase substrates are further described in Section 17.4. A review of fluorescent lipid probes and their use in biological and biophysical research has been recently published.[3]

Table 13.1 — Phospholipids with labeled head groups

Label (Ex/Em or Application) *	Cat #
Dansyl (336/517)	D57
Marina Blue® (365/460)	M12652
Pacific Blue™ (410/455)	P22652
NBD (463/536)	N360
Fluorescein (496/519)	F362
Oregon Green® 488 (501/526)	O12650
BODIPY® FL (505/511)	D3800
BODIPY® 530/550	D3815
Tetramethylrhodamine (540/566)	T1391
Lissamine rhodamine (560/581)	L1392
BODIPY® 581/591	D3806
Texas Red® (582/601)	T1395MP
Biotin (<250/none)	B1550, B1616
Maleimide (thiol-reactive)	M1618

* Fluorescence excitation (Ex) and emission (Em) spectral maxima, in nm, are in methanol. The spectra may be different in membranes.

Fluorescent Fatty Acid Analogs

Our fluorescent fatty acid analogs have a fluorophore linked within the fatty acid chain or, more commonly, at the terminal (omega) carbon atom that is furthest from the carboxylate moiety. Although fluorescent fatty acid analogs are sometimes used as direct probes for membranes and liposomes, their most common applications have been for synthesis of fluorescent phospholipids and for metabolic incorporation by live cells. Our fluorescent fatty acids currently include derivatives based on the BODIPY®, nitrobenzoxadiazole (NBD), pyrene and dansyl fluorophores, as well as the naturally fluorescent polyunsaturated fatty acid, *cis*-parinaric acid.

BODIPY® Fatty Acids

Our patented BODIPY® fatty acids are, by far, the most fluorescent fatty acid analogs that we have available.[4] Their lack of ionic charge is unusual for long-wavelength fluorescent dyes and results in exclusive localization of the fluorophore within the membrane. BODIPY® derivatives typically have extinction coefficients greater than 90,000 $cm^{-1}M^{-1}$ with absorption maxima beyond 500 nm. The fluorophores in our current selection of BODIPY® fatty acids and their approximate absorption/emission maxima (in nm) are:

- BODIPY® 503/512 (BODIPY® FL; D3821, D3822, D3834, D3862)
- BODIPY® 500/510 (D3823, B3824, D3825)
- BODIPY® 530/550 (D3832)
- BODIPY® 558/568 (D3835)
- BODIPY® 581/591 (D3861)

The three BODIPY® 500/510 probes form a unique series in which the green-fluorescent fluorophore is located within the fatty acid chain at different distances from the terminal carboxylate group.[4] The overall length of the probe is constant and, including the fluorophore, is about equivalent to that of an 18-carbon fatty acid (Figure 13.5).

BODIPY® fatty acids are synthetic precursors to a wide variety of fluorescent phospholipids (described below) as well as several important sphingolipid probes described in Section 13.3. Some BODIPY® fatty acids are readily metabolized by live cells to phospholipids, di- and triacylglycerols, cholesteryl esters and other natural lipids.[5–8] Analysis of cellular lipid extracts by HPLC has shown that glycerophosphocholines constitute more than 90% of the products of biosynthetic incorporation of BODIPY® 500/510 dodecanoic acid (D3823) by BHK cells.[9] A useful spectroscopic property of BODIPY® dyes, in general, is the concentration-dependent formation of excited-state dimers

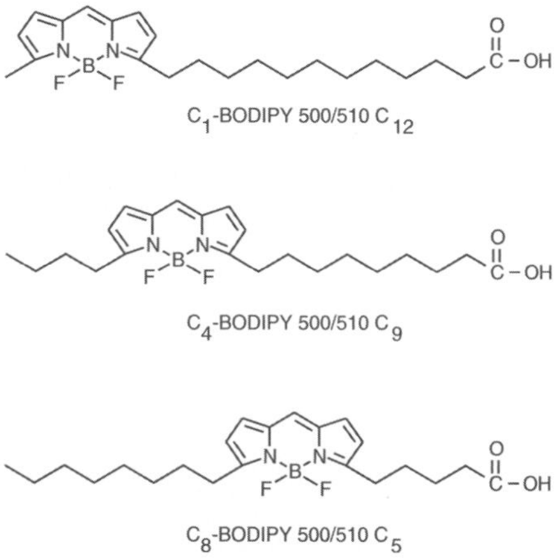

Figure 13.5 Structural representations showing the positional shift of the fluorophore with respect to the terminal carboxyl group in a homologous series of BODIPY® 500/510 fatty acids (D3823, B3824, D3825).

("excimers," Figure 13.6) with red-shifted emission. We have observed this phenomenon particularly with our green-fluorescent BODIPY® fatty acid derivatives, which undergo a considerable red shift in their emission when metabolically incorporated into lipophilic products[9] (Figure 13.7). Pyrene fatty acids (see below) also exhibit excimer formation (Figure 13.8) but their emission is at much shorter wavelengths than that of the BODIPY® dyes and they are therefore less useful for the study of live cells.

BODIPY® 581/591 undecanoic acid (D3861) is particularly useful for detecting reactive oxygen species in cells and membranes.[10–13] Oxidation of the polyunsaturated butadienyl portion of the BODIPY® 581/591 dye (Figure 18.6) truncates the conjugated π-electron system, resulting in a shift of the fluorescence emission peak from ~590 nm to ~510 nm.[10,13] This oxidation response mechanism is similar to that of the naturally occurring polyunsaturated fatty acid *cis*-parinaric acid (see below). In comparison to *cis*-parinaric acid, advantages of BODIPY® 581/591 undecanoic acid include:

- Long-wavelength excitation compatible with confocal laser-scanning microscopes and flow cytometers
- Avoidance of photooxidation effects induced by ultraviolet excitation
- Less interference by colored oxidant and antioxidant additives when detecting probe fluorescence[12]
- Greater resistance to spontaneous oxidation
- A red-to-green fluorescence shift, allowing the use of fluorescence ratio detection methods[10,13]

We also offer a phospholipid derivative of BODIPY® 581/591 undecanoic acid (D3806), which can be anticipated to have similar applications. An alternative technique for detecting lipid peroxidation utilizes the oxidation-induced decrease of concentration-dependent excimer formation by BODIPY® FL dye–labeled fatty acids.[14]

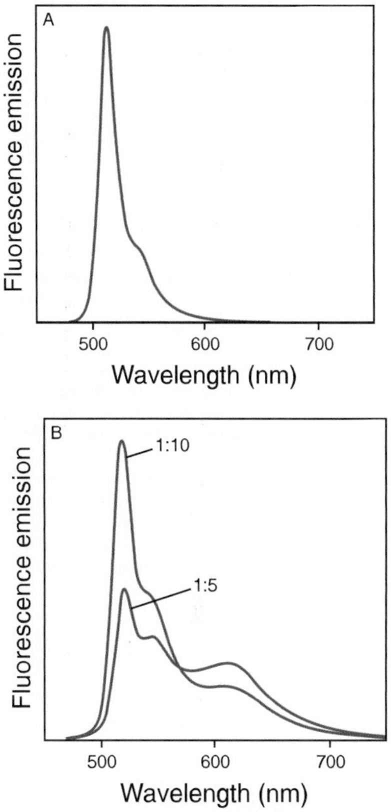

Figure 13.6 A) Fluorescence spectrum of β-C_8-BODIPY® 500/510 C_5-HPC (D3795) incorporated in DOPC (dioctadecenoylphosphocholine) liposomes at 1:100 mole:mole (labeled:unlabeled PC). **B)** Fluorescence spectra at high molar incorporation levels: 1:10 mole:mole and 1:5 mole:mole.

NBD Fatty Acids

Fluorescence of the nitrobenzoxadiazole (NBD) fluorophore is highly sensitive to its environment. Although it is moderately fluorescent in aprotic solvents, in aqueous solvents it is almost nonfluorescent.[15] The NBD fluorophore is moderately polar and both its homologous 6-carbon and 12-carbon fatty acid analogs (N316, N678) and the phospholipids derived from these probes (N3786, N3787) tend to sense the lipid–water interface region of membranes instead of the hydrophobic interior[16] (see part B of Figure 13.1). NBD fatty acids are not well metabolized by live cells.[8,17] The environmental sensitivity of NBD fatty acids can be usefully exploited to probe the ligand-binding sites of fatty acid and sterol carrier proteins.[18]

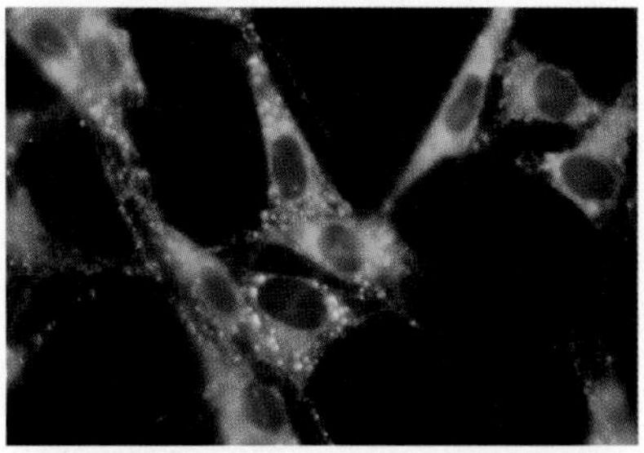

Figure 13.7 BHK cells incubated in medium containing the fluorescent fatty acid analog C_1-BODIPY® 500/510 C_{12} (D3823). This photomicrograph, obtained through a standard fluorescein longpass filter set, reveals reticular green-fluorescent staining as well as yellow-orange–fluorescent spherical structures. These fluorescent structures are indicative of the metabolic accumulation of BODIPY® dye–labeled neutral lipids in cytoplasmic droplets. Image contributed by Juha Kasurinen, University of Helsinki, Finland.

Pyrene Fatty Acids

The hydrophobic pyrene fluorophore is readily accommodated within the membrane.[19] Omega®-Pyrene derivatives of longer-chain fatty acids (Figure 13.9) were first described by Galla and Sackmann in 1975.[20] Molecular Probes has pyrene derivatives of the 4-, 6-, 10-, 12- and 16-carbon fatty acids (P1903MP, P3840, P31, P96, P243, respectively). Pyrenebutanoic acid — frequently called pyrenebutyric acid (P1903MP) — has rarely been used as a membrane probe; however, its conjugates have exceptionally long excited-state lifetimes (τ >100 nanoseconds) and are consequently useful for time-resolved fluorescence immunoassays and nucleic acid detection.[21,22] The long excited-state lifetime of pyrenebutyric acid also makes it useful as a probe for oxygen in cells[23–26] and lipid vesicles.[27]

Pyrene derivatives form excited-state dimers (excimers) with red-shifted fluorescence emission[28–30] (Figure 13.8). Pyrene excimers can even form when two pyrenes are tethered by a short trimethine spacer, as in 1,3-bis-(1-pyrenyl)propane (B311, Section 13.5). Pyrene excimer formation is commonly exploited for assaying membrane fusion[31,32] (see Note 13.1 "Technical Focus: Lipid-Mixing Assays of Membrane Fusion") and for detecting lipid domain formation.[33–35] Pyrene fatty acids are metabolically incorporated into phospholipids, di- and tri-acylglycerols and cholesteryl esters by live cells.[17,36,37] Other uses of pyrene fatty acids include:

- Investigating lipid transport mechanisms and transfer proteins[38–40]
- Detecting lipid–protein interactions[41,42]

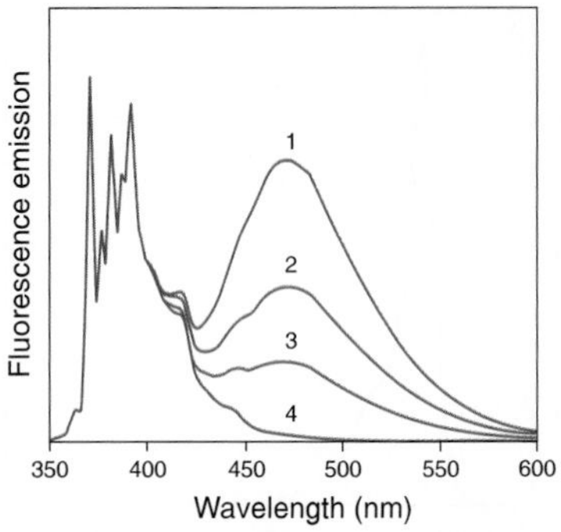

Figure 13.8 Excimer formation by pyrene in ethanol. Spectra are normalized to the 371.5 nm peak of the monomer. All spectra are essentially identical below 400 nm after normalization. Spectra are as follows: **1)** 2 mM pyrene, purged with argon to remove oxygen; **2)** 2 mM pyrene, air-equilibrated; **3)** 0.5 mM pyrene (argon-purged); and **4)** 2 µM pyrene (argon-purged). The monomer-to-excimer ratio (371.5 nm/470 nm) is dependent on both pyrene concentration and the excited-state lifetime, which is variable because of quenching by oxygen.

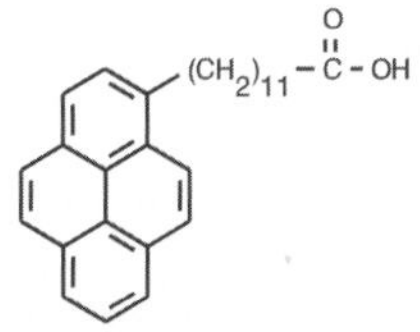

Figure 13.9 P96 1-pyrenedodecanoic acid.

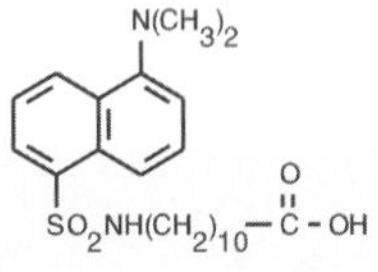

Figure 13.10 D94 11-((5-dimethylaminonaphthalene-1-sulfonyl)amino)undecanoic acid (DAUDA).

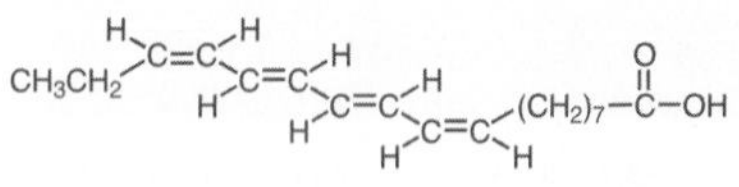

Figure 13.11 P36005 *cis*-parinaric acid.

- Investigating phospholipase A_2 action on lipid assemblies [43–45]
- Inducing photodynamic damage [46,47]
- Synthesizing fluorescent sphingolipid probes [48–51]

Dansyl Undecanoic Acid

Dansyl undecanoic acid (DAUDA, D94) incorporates a polar, environment-sensitive dansyl fluorophore that preferentially locates in the polar headgroup region of lipid bilayer membranes [52] (Figure 13.10). DAUDA exhibits a 60-fold fluorescence enhancement and a large emission spectral shift to shorter wavelengths on binding to certain proteins.[53] This property has been exploited to analyze fatty acid–binding proteins [53–56] and also to develop a fluorometric phospholipase A_2 assay (Section 17.4) based on competitive fatty acid displacement.[57–60]

cis-Parinaric Acid

The naturally occurring polyunsaturated fatty acid *cis*-parinaric acid (P36005, Figure 13.11) was initially developed as a membrane probe by Hudson and co-workers and published in 1975.[61] *cis*-Parinaric acid is the closest structural analog of intrinsic membrane lipids among currently available fluorescent probes. The chemical and physical properties of *cis*-parinaric acid have been well characterized. The lowest absorption band of *cis*-parinaric acid has two main peaks around 300 nm and 320 nm, with a high extinction coefficient. *cis*-Parinaric acid offers several experimentally advantageous optical properties, including a very large fluorescence Stokes shift (~100 nm) and an almost complete lack of fluorescence in water. In addition, the fluorescence decay lifetime of *cis*-parinaric acid varies from 1 to ~40 nanoseconds, depending on the molecular packing density in phospholipid bilayers. Consequently, minutely detailed information on lipid-bilayer dynamics can be obtained.[62] Selected applications of *cis*-parinaric acid include:

- Measurement of peroxidation in lipoproteins [63,64] and the relationship of peroxidation to cytotoxicity [65,66] and apoptosis [67–70]
- Evaluation of antioxidants [71–74]
- Structural characterization of lipoproteins [75]
- Investigation of the mechanism of fatty acid–binding proteins [76–78] and phospholipid-transfer proteins [79,80]
- Detection of lipid–protein interactions [81–83] and lipid clustering [84]
- High-affinity binding to a hydrophobic pocket between the heavy chain of myosin subfragment-1 and its essential light chain [85]
- Detection of lipoproteins following chromatographic separation [86]

The extensive unsaturation of *cis*-parinaric acid makes it quite susceptible to oxidation. Consequently, we offer *cis*-parinaric acid in a 10 mL unit size of a 3 mM solution in deoxygenated ethanol (P36005); if stored protected from light under an inert argon atmosphere at -20°C, this stock solution should be stable for at least six months. During experiments, we strongly advise handling *cis*-parinaric acid samples under inert gas and preparing solutions using degassed buffers and solvents. *cis*-Parinaric acid is also somewhat photolabile, undergoing photodimerization under intense illumination, resulting in loss of fluorescence.[87]

ADIFAB

Fatty acid–binding proteins are small cytosolic proteins found in a variety of mammalian tissues, and studies of their physiological function frequently involve fluorescent fatty acid probes.[88] To facilitate these studies, Molecular Probes offers ADIFAB (A3880), a dual-wavelength fluorescent indicator of free fatty acids [89–91] (Figure 17.42, Figure 17.43). ADIFAB is a conjugate of I-FABP, a rat intestinal fatty acid–binding protein with a low molecular weight (15,000 daltons) and a high binding affinity for free fatty acids, [92] and the polarity-sensitive acrylodan fluorophore (A433, Section 2.3). It is designed to provide quantitative monitoring of free fatty acids without resorting to separative biochemical methods.[44,93,94] With appropriate precautions, which are described in the product information sheet accompanying this product, ADIFAB can be used to determine free fatty acid concentrations between 1 nM and >20 µM.

Note 13.1 — Technical Focus

Lipid-Mixing Assays of Membrane Fusion

Fluorometric methods for assaying membrane fusion exploit processes, such as nonradiative energy transfer, fluorescence quenching and pyrene excimer formation, that are dependent on probe concentration.[1–8] Assays of membrane fusion report either the mixing of membrane lipids (described here) or the mixing of the aqueous contents of the fused entities (see Note 14.3 "Technical Focus: Assays of Volume Change, Membrane Fusion and Membrane Permeability" in Section 14.3). Chapter 13 describes additional methods for detecting membrane fusion based on image analysis.

NBD–Rhodamine Energy Transfer

Principle: Struck, Hoekstra and Pagano introduced lipid-mixing assays based on NBD–rhodamine energy transfer.[9] In this method (Figure 1), membranes labeled with a combination of fluorescence energy transfer donor and acceptor lipid probes — typically NBD-PE (N360, Section 13.2) and *N*-Rh-PE (L1392, Section 13.2), respectively — are mixed with unlabeled membranes. Fluorescence resonance energy transfer (FRET), detected as rhodamine emission at ~585 nm resulting from NBD excitation at ~470 nm, decreases when the average spatial separation of the probes is increased upon fusion of labeled membranes with unlabeled membranes. The reverse detection scheme, in which FRET increases upon fusion of membranes that have been separately labeled with donor and acceptor probes, has also proven to be a useful lipid-mixing assay.[10]

Applications: Applications of the NBD–rhodamine assay are described in footnoted references.[11–20]

Octadecyl Rhodamine B Self-Quenching

Principle: Lipid-mixing assays based on self-quenching of octadecyl rhodamine B (R18, O246; Section 13.5) were originally described by Hoekstra and co-workers.[21] Octadecyl rhodamine B self-quenching occurs when the probe is incorporated into membrane lipids at concentrations of 1–10 mole percent.[22] Unlike phospholipid analogs, octadecyl rhodamine B can readily be introduced into existing membranes in large amounts. Fusion with unlabeled membranes results in dilution of the probe, which is accompanied by increasing fluorescence[23,24] (excitation/emission maxima 560/590 nm) (Figure 2). The assay may be compromised by effects such as spontaneous transfer of the probe to unlabeled membranes, quenching of fluorescence by proteins and probe-related inactivation of viruses; the prevalence of these effects is currently debated.[25–27]

Applications: The octadecyl rhodamine B self-quenching assay is extensively used for detecting virus–cell fusion.[28–39]

Pyrene Excimer Formation

Principle: Pyrene-labeled fatty acids (e.g., P31, P96, P243; Section 13.2) can be biosynthetically incorporated into viruses and cells in sufficient quantities to produce the degree of labeling required for long-wavelength pyrene excimer fluorescence (Figure 13.8). This excimer fluorescence is diminished upon fusion of labeled membranes with unlabeled membranes (Figure 3). Fusion can be monitored by following the increase in the ratio of monomer (~400 nm) to excimer (~470 nm) emission, with excitation at about 340 nm. This method appears to circumvent some of the potential artifacts of the octadecyl rhodamine B self-quenching technique[26] and, therefore, provides a useful alternative for virus–cell fusion applications.

Applications: Applications of pyrene excimer assays for membrane fusion are described in the footnoted references.[26,28,40–43]

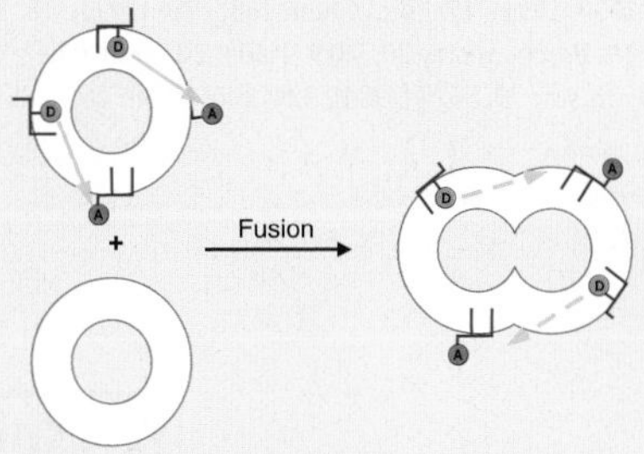

Figure 1. Pictorial representation of a lipid-mixing assay based on fluorescence resonance energy transfer (FRET). The average spatial separation of the donor (D) and acceptor (A) lipid probes increases upon fusion of labeled membranes with unlabeled membranes, resulting in decreased efficiency of proximity-dependent FRET (represented by yellow arrows). Decreased FRET efficiency is registered by increased donor fluorescence intensity and decreased acceptor fluorescence intensity.

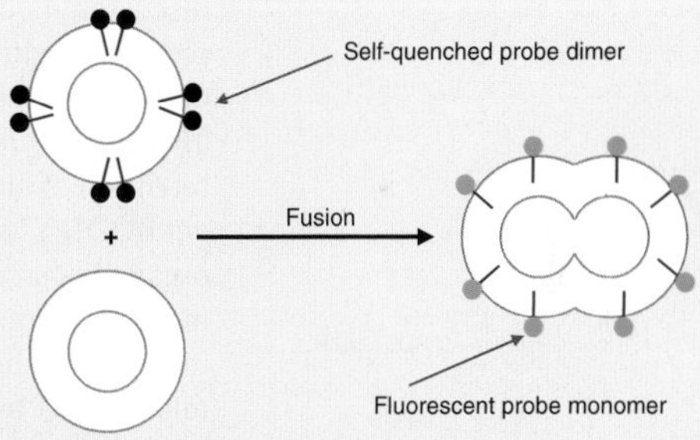

Figure 2. Pictorial representation of a lipid-mixing assay based on fluorescence self-quenching. Fluorescence of octadecyl rhodamine B (O246), incorporated at >1:100 with respect to host membrane lipids, is quenched due to dye–dye interactions. Fusion with unlabeled membranes causes dispersion of the probe, resulting in a fluorescence increase that is represented here by a color change from black to green.

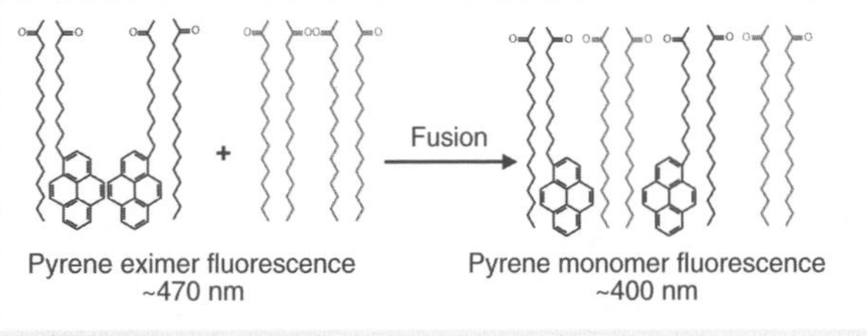

Figure 3. Pictorial representation of a lipid-mixing assay based on pyrene excimer formation (Figure 13.8). Locally concentrated pyrene-labeled lipid probes emit red-shifted fluorescence due to formation of excimers (excited state dimers). Probe dilution by unlabeled lipids as a result of membrane fusion is registered by the replacement of excimer emission by blue-shifted monomer fluorescence.

continued on next page

continued from previous page

References

1. Chem Phys Lipids 116, 39 (2002); **2.** Spectroscopic Membrane Probes, Vol. I, Lowe LM, Ed. pp. 161–191 (1988); **3.** Methods Enzymol 220, 3 (1993); **4.** Methods Enzymol 220, 15 (1993); **5.** Spectroscopic Membrane Probes, Vol. I, Loew LM, Ed. pp. 117–159 (1988); **6.** Annu Rev Biophys Biophys Chem 18, 187 (1989); **7.** Hepatology 12, 61S (1990); **8.** Biochemistry 26, 8435 (1987); **9.** Biochemistry 20, 4093 (1981); **10.** Methods Enzymol 221, 239 (1993); **11.** Biochemistry 33, 12615 (1994); **12.** Biochemistry 33, 5805 (1994); **13.** Biochemistry 33, 3201 (1994); **14.** Biophys J 67, 1117 (1994); **15.** J Biol Chem 269, 15124 (1994); **16.** J Biol Chem 269, 4050 (1994); **17.** J Biol Chem 268, 1716 (1993); **18.** Biochemistry 31, 2629 (1992); **19.** Biochemistry 30, 5319 (1991); **20.** J Biol Chem 266, 3252 (1991); **21.** Biochemistry 23, 5675 (1984); **22.** J Biol Chem 265, 13533 (1990); **23.** Biophys J 65, 325 (1993); **24.** Biophys J 58, 1157 (1990); **25.** Biochim Biophys Acta 1190, 360 (1994); **26.** Biochemistry 32, 11330 (1993); **27.** Biochemistry 32, 900 (1993); **28.** Biochemistry 33, 9110 (1994); **29.** Biochemistry 33, 1977 (1994); **30.** Biochim Biophys Acta 1191, 375 (1994); **31.** J Biol Chem 269, 5467 (1994); **32.** Biochem J 294, 325 (1993); **33.** J Biol Chem 268, 25764 (1993); **34.** J Biol Chem 268, 9267 (1993); **35.** Virology 195, 855 (1993); **36.** Biochemistry 31, 10108 (1992); **37.** Exp Cell Res 195, 137 (1991); **38.** J Virol 65, 4063 (1991); **39.** Biochemistry 29, 4054 (1990); **40.** EMBO J 12, 693 (1993); **41.** J Virol 66, 7309 (1992); **42.** Biochemistry 27, 30 (1988); **43.** Biochim Biophys Acta 860, 301 (1986).

Phospholipids with BODIPY® Dye–Labeled Acyl Chains

Phosphoinositides Labeled with BODIPY® Dyes

Phosphatidylinositol (PI or PtdIns) and its phosphorylated derivatives are relatively minor membrane constituents with a wide and diverse range of biological activity.[95] Phosphoinositides are functionally active in the transverse redistribution and lateral domain organization of membrane lipids[96–98] as well as a plethora of regulatory and signal transduction processes that are discussed in more detail elsewhere[95,99–103] (Section 17.4). We offer fluorescent analogs of phosphatidylinositol (PtdIns) and of its 3-, 4- and 5-phosphorylated derivatives[104] (Table 17.3). All of the fluorescent analogs are labeled with a BODIPY® dye on the *sn*-1 acyl chain (Figure 17.33). This labeling pattern maximizes the separation of the dye from the inositol ring and ensures retention of biological activity.[105] Each phosphoinositide analog is available with three different BODIPY® dye options (Table 17.3) for multicolor detection in combination with fluorescent organelle markers (Chapter 12), calcium indicators[105] (Chapter 19) or GFP chimeras. A sensitive method for analyzing these fluorescent phosphoinositides and other products of lipid-modifying enzymes has been developed using a microfluidic chip device that separates lipids based on micellar electrokinetic capillary chromatography.[106] Phosphoinositides can be delivered into live cells using polyamine reagents[105] or with the Shuttle PIP carriers (Figure 17.34), which are described in Section 17.4. Also described in Section 17.4 is our range of phosphoinositide affinity matrices and anti-phosphoinositide monoclonal antibodies.

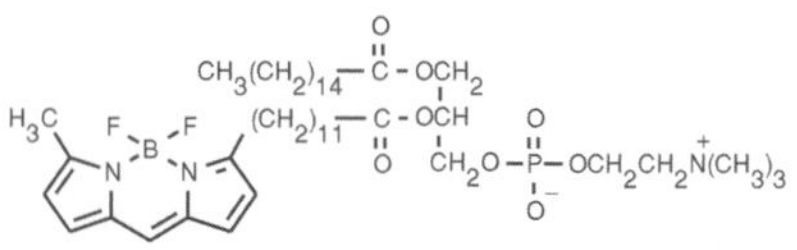

Figure 13.12 D3793 2-(4,4-difluoro-5-methyl-4-bora-3a,4a-diaza-*s*-indacene-3-dodecanoyl)-1-hexadecanoyl-*sn*-glycero-3-phosphocholine (β-BODIPY® 500/510 C_{12}-HPC).

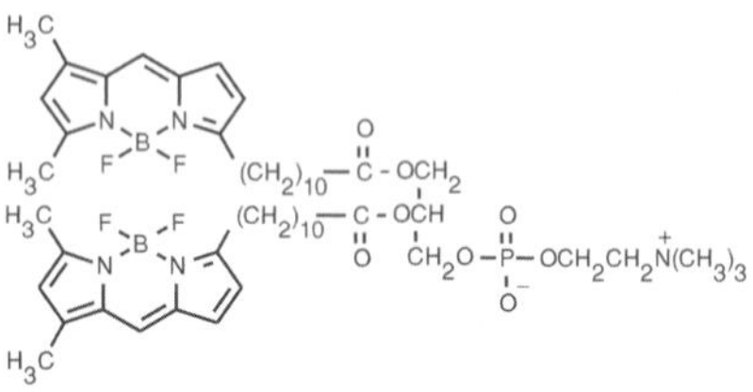

Figure 13.13 B7701 1,2-bis-(4,4-difluoro-5,7-dimethyl-4-bora-3a,4a-diaza-*s*-indacene-3-undecanoyl)-*sn*-glycero-3-phosphocholine (bis-BODIPY® FL C_{11}-PC).

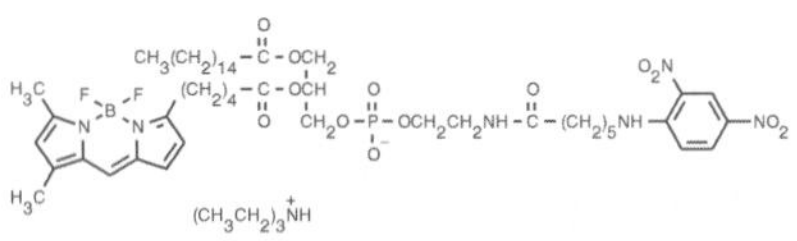

Figure 13.14 D23739 *N*-((6-(2,4-dinitrophenyl)amino)hexanoyl)-2-(4,4-difluoro-5,7-dimethyl-4-bora-3a,4a-diaza-*s*-indacene-3-pentanoyl)-1-hexadecanoyl-*sn*-glycero-3-phosphoethanolamine, triethylammonium salt (PED6).

Other BODIPY® Dye–Labeled Glycerophospholipids

We offer glycerophosphocholine analogs labeled with a single green-fluorescent BODIPY® 500/510 or BODIPY® FL fluorophore on the *sn*-2 acyl chain (D3792, D3793, D3795, D3803; Figure 13.12) or the *sn*-1 acyl chain (D3771). Our range of BODIPY® dye–labeled glycerophospholipids also includes:

- BODIPY® FL dye–labeled phosphatidic acid (D3805)
- BODIPY® 530/550 dye–labeled glycerophosphocholine (D3815)
- BODIPY® 581/591 dye–labeled glycerophosphocholine (D3806)

Phospholipids with two BODIPY® FL dye–labeled acyl chains (B7701, Figure 13.13) or one BODIPY® FL dye–labeled acyl chain and a dinitrophenyl quencher attached to the headgroup[107] (PED6, D23739, Figure 13.14) are designed primarily for detection of phospholipase A activity

(Section 17.4, Figure 17.24). PED6 is suitable both for performing high-throughput solution assays and for imaging phospholipase A_2 activity in live organisms (Figure 17.27).

The spectral properties of BODIPY® FL dye–labeled phospholipids are summarized in Table 13.2. Unlike the nitrobenzoxadiazole (NBD) fluorophore, the BODIPY® FL and BODIPY® 500/510 fluorophores are intrinsically lipophilic and readily localize in the membrane's interior.[1] The fluorophore is completely inaccessible to the membrane-impermeant anti–BODIPY® FL antibody (A5770, Section 7.4), which also recognizes the BODIPY® 500/510 derivative. As shown in Figure 13.15, the emission spectrum of the BODIPY® 500/510 fluorophore is much narrower than that of the NBD fluorophore. Because both the extinction coefficient of the BODIPY® 500/510 fluorophore and its quantum yield in a lipophilic environment (ε ~90,000 $cm^{-1}M^{-1}$ and QY ~0.9) are much higher than those of the NBD fluorophore (ε ~20,000 $cm^{-1}M^{-1}$ and QY ~0.3), much less BODIPY® 500/510 dye–labeled phospholipid is required for labeling membranes.[4]

Incorporation of high molar ratios (>10 mole %) of the BODIPY® 500/510 dye–labeled phospholipids into membranes results in a dramatic spectral shift of the fluorescence emission spectrum to longer wavelengths (Figure 13.6). We have also observed this spectral shift in the Golgi of live cells that have been labeled with our BODIPY® dye–labeled ceramides (Section 12.4, Figure 12.51) and with BODIPY® fatty acids that have been metabolically incorporated by cells (Figure 13.7). In fluorescence resonance energy transfer (FRET) measurements, the green-fluorescent BODIPY® 500/510 dye is an excellent donor to longer-wavelength BODIPY® probes[108,109] (Figure 13.16) and acceptor from dansyl-, DPH- or pyrene-labeled phospholipids.[110] These probe combinations offer several alternatives to the widely used NBD–rhodamine fluorophore pair for researchers using FRET techniques to study lipid transfer and membrane fusion.[108]

Applications

Once cells are labeled with a BODIPY® phospholipid, the probe shows little tendency to spontaneously transfer between cells.[111] Consequently, BODIPY® dye–labeled phospholipids have been used in a number of studies of cell membrane structure and properties:

- Despite their good photostability, BODIPY® lipids are useful for fluorescence recovery after photobleaching (FRAP) measurements of lipid diffusion.[112,113]
- Researchers have used BODIPY® fatty acids and phospholipids to visualize compartmentalization of specific lipid classes in *Schistosoma mansoni*[114] and fungi.[115,116]
- β-BODIPY® FL C_{12}-HPC (D3792) has been used to examine lipid–protein interactions involved in bacterial protein secretion via fluorescence resonance energy transfer (FRET) measurements[117] (see Note 1.2 "Technical Focus: Fluorescence Resonance Energy Transfer (FRET)" in Section 1.3).
- β-BODIPY® FL C_5-HPC[118] (D3803) has been used to characterize lipid domains by fluorescence correlation spectroscopy[119] (see Note 1.4 "Technical Focus: Fluorescence Correlation

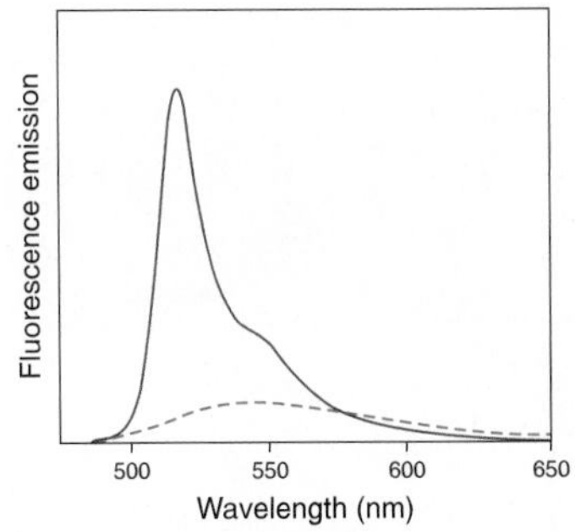

Figure 13.15 Fluorescence spectra (excitation at 475 nm) of β-BODIPY® 500/510 C_{12}-HPC (blue line peak at 516 nm, D3793) and NBD C_{12}-HPC (red line peak at 545 nm, N3787) incorporated in DOPC (dioctadecenoylglycerophosphocholine) liposomes at molar ratios of 1:400 mole:mole (labeled:unlabeled PC). The integrated intensities of the spectra are proportional to the relative fluorescence quantum yields of the two probes.

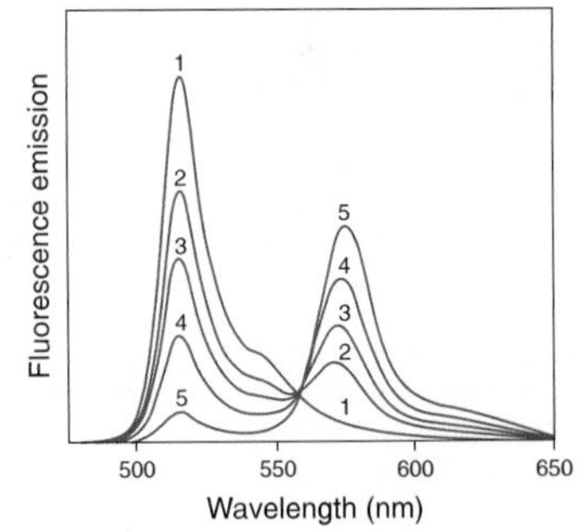

Figure 13.16 Fluorescence resonance energy transfer from β-BODIPY® 500/510 C_{12}-HPC (peak at 516 nm, D3793) to BODIPY® 558/568 C_{12} (peak at 572 nm, D3835) in DOPC (dioctadecenoylglycerophosphocholine) lipid bilayers using 475 nm excitation. Ratio of acceptors to donors is: **1)** 0; **2)** 0.2; **3)** 0.4; **4)** 0.8; and **5)** 2.0.

Table 13.2 — Spectral properties of some lipid probes

Spectral Property	Pyrene	DPH	NBD	BODIPY® FL
Ex/Em (nm) *	340/376	360/430	470/530	507/513
QY (τ) †	0.6 (>100 nanoseconds)	0.8 (4–8 nanoseconds)	0.32 (5–10 nanoseconds)	0.9 (6 nanoseconds)
Concentration Dependence	Excimer emission (~470 nm) at high concentrations.	Self-quenched at high concentrations.	Self-quenched at high concentrations.	Excimer emission (~620 nm) at high concentrations.
Environmental Sensitivity	Very sensitive to quenching by oxygen. Essentially nonfluorescent in water.	Essentially nonfluorescent in water.	Essentially nonfluorescent in water.	Relatively insensitive. Strongly fluorescent in both aqueous and lipid environments.

* Typical fluorescence excitation and emission maxima for membrane-intercalated probes. † QY = fluorescence quantum yield; τ = fluorescence decay lifetime. Typical values for membrane-intercalated probes are listed. These values may show significant environment-dependent variations.

Spectroscopy (FCS)" in Section 1.3), confocal laser-scanning microscopy[120] (Figure 13.17) and near-field scanning optical microscopy.[112,121]

- bis-BODIPY® FL C_{11}-PC (B7701) has BODIPY® FL dye–labeled *sn*-1 and *sn*-2 acyl groups (Figure 13.13), resulting in partially quenched fluorescence that increases when one of the acyl groups is hydrolyzed by phospholipase A_1 or A_2. The hydrolysis products are BODIPY® FL undecanoic acid (D3862) and BODIPY® FL dye–labeled lysophosphatidylcholine (Figure 17.24). The probe has been used successfully in human neutrophils, plants and zebrafish to detect phospholipase A activity[122–127] (Section 17.4).
- β-BODIPY® FL C_5-HPC (D3803) has been used to investigate the cellular uptake of antineoplastic ether lipids.[128]

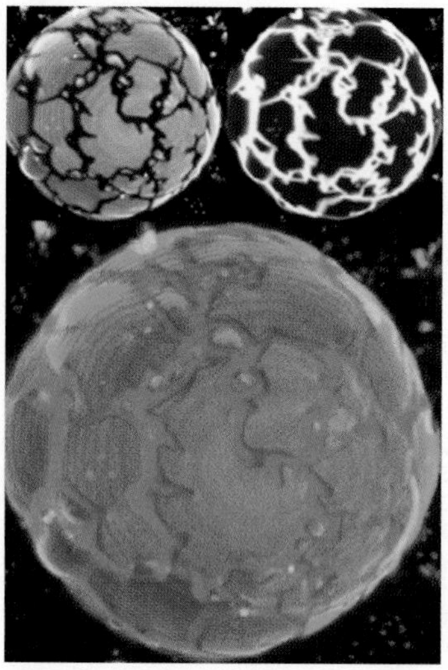

Figure 13.17 Confocal laser-scanning microscopy images of a giant unilamellar phospholipid vesicle (GUV). The lipid composition of this GUV was DPPC/DLPC = 1/1, with $DiIC_{20}(3)$ and β-BODIPY® FL C_5-HPC (D3803) dyes at mole fraction ~0.001. Excitation was at 488 nm. The upper right image is the fluorescence emission through a 585 nm longpass filter, thus almost exclusively from $DiIC_{20}(3)$. The upper left image is the emission through a 522 ± 35 nm bandpass filter, thus almost exclusively from β-BODIPY® FL C_5-HPC. The bottom image is color-merged, using the public domain NIH Image program. Image contributed by Gerald W. Feigenson, Cornell University, and reprinted with permission from Biophys J 80, 2775 (2001).

Phospholipid with DPH-Labeled Acyl Chain

Properties

The fluorescent phospholipid analog β-DPH HPC (D476) comprises diphenylhexatriene propionic acid (P459, Section 13.5, Figure 13.51) coupled to glycerophosphocholine at the *sn*-2 position (Figure 13.18). It is therefore related to the neutral membrane probe DPH (D202, Section 13.5, Figure 13.49) and the cationic TMA-DPH (T204, Section 13.5, Figure 13.50) and TMAP-DPH (P3900, Section 13.5, Figure 16.23) derivatives. DPH and its derivatives exhibit strong fluorescence enhancement when incorporated into membranes, as well as sensitive fluorescence polarization (anisotropy) responses to lipid ordering (see Note 1.5 "Technical Focus: Fluorescence Polarization (FP)" in Section 1.4). β-DPH HPC was originally devised to improve the localization of DPH in membranes.[129,130] Unlike underivatized DPH, it can be used to specifically label one leaflet of a lipid bilayer, facilitating analysis of membrane asymmetry.[131]

Applications

DPH derivatives are predominately used to investigate the structure and dynamics of the membrane interior either by fluorescence polarization or lifetime measurements. Researchers have used β-DPH HPC as a probe for lipid–protein interactions,[132–134] alcohol-induced perturbations of membrane structure,[135,136] molecular organization and dynamics of lipid bilayers[11,137–139] and lipid peroxidation.[140] Fluorescence lifetime measurements of β-DPH HPC provide a sensitive indicator of membrane fusion.[141–143] In addition to membrane fusion, β-DPH HPC has been used to monitor various other lipid-transfer processes.[144–146]

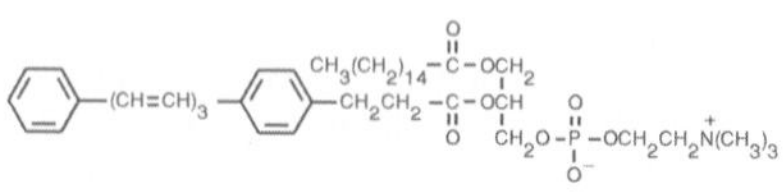

Figure 13.18 D476 2-(3-(diphenylhexatrienyl)propanoyl)-1-hexadecanoyl-*sn*-glycero-3-phosphocholine (β-DPH HPC).

Phospholipids with NBD-Labeled Acyl Chains

Properties

Our acyl-modified nitrobenzoxadiazole (NBD) phospholipid probes include both the NBD hexanoyl– and NBD dodecanoyl–glycerophosphocholines (NBD C_6-HPC, N3786; Figure 13.19 and NBD C_{12}-HPC, N3787). Table 13.2 compares the spectral properties of these probes with those of the BODIPY®, DPH and pyrene lipid probes. Unlike the BODIPY® phospholipids, the location of the relatively polar NBD fluorophore of NBD C_6-HPC and NBD C_{12}-HPC in phospholipid bilayers does *not* appear to conform to expectations based on the probe structure. A variety of physical evidence indicates that the NBD moiety "loops back" to the head-group region[147–150] (Figure 13.1). In fact, the fluorophore in this acyl-modified phospholipid appears to probe the same location as does the head group–labeled glycerophosphoethanolamine derivative NBD-PE[16] (N360, see below).

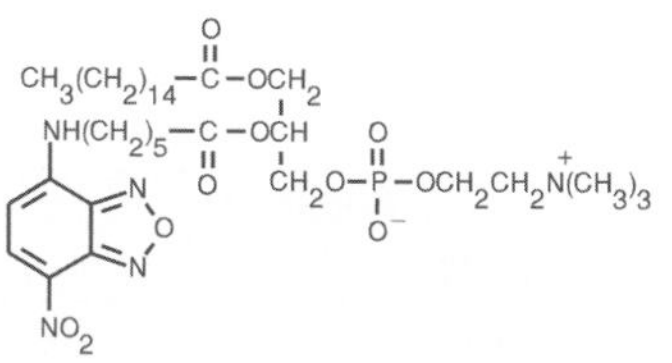

Figure 13.19 N3786 2-(6-(7-nitrobenz-2-oxa-1,3-diazol-4-yl)amino)hexanoyl-1-hexadecanoyl-*sn*-glycero-3-phosphocholine (NBD C_6-HPC).

These NBD probes transfer spontaneously between membranes, with NBD C_6-HPC transferring more rapidly than its more lipophilic C_{12} analog.[151,152] NBD C_6-HPC can be readily removed (back-exchanged) from the plasma membrane by incubating the labeled cells either with unlabeled lipid vesicles[153] or with bovine serum albumin.[154–156] This property is useful for quantitating lipid transfer and for studying phospholipid distribution asymmetry and transmembrane "flip-flop" rates in lipid bilayers.[16,157–162]

Applications

NBD acyl–modified probes are used for investigating lipid traffic, either by directly visualizing NBD fluorescence,[163–166] by exploiting NBD self-quenching [167–169] or by fluorescence resonance energy transfer methods.[151,163,170–172] Lateral domains in model monolayers, bilayers and cell membranes have been characterized using NBD phospholipids in conjunction with fluorescence recovery after photobleaching [173–175] (FRAP), fluorescence resonance energy transfer [176] (FRET) (see Note 1.2 "Technical Focus: Fluorescence Resonance Energy Transfer (FRET)" in Section 1.3) and direct microscopy techniques.[177–180] Transmembrane lipid distribution (see Note 13.1 "Technical Focus: Lipid-Mixing Assays of Membrane Fusion") has been assessed using fluorescence resonance energy transfer from NBD HPC to rhodamine DHPE [160,162,181] (L1392) or alternatively by selective dithionite ($S_2O_4^{2-}$) reduction of NBD phospholipids in the outer membrane monolayer [182] (Figure 13.20).

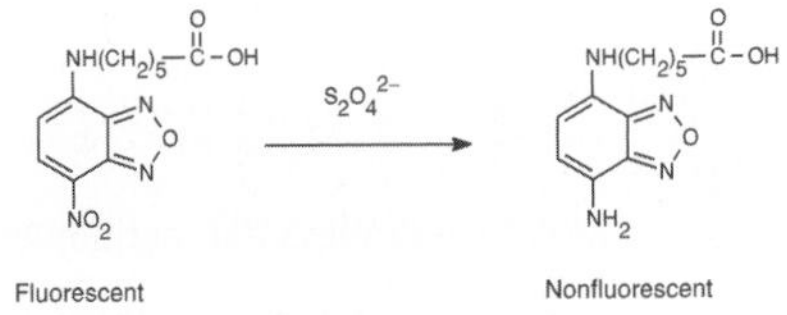

Figure 13.20 Dithionite reduction of 6-(*N*-(7-nitrobenz-2-oxa-1,3-diazol-4-yl)amino)hexanoic acid (NBD-X, N316). The elimination of fluorescence associated with this reaction, coupled with the fact that extraneously added dithionite is not membrane permeant, can be used to determine whether the NBD fluorophore is located in the external or internal monolayer of lipid bilayer membranes.

Phospholipids with Pyrene-Labeled Acyl Chains

Properties

Phospholipid analogs with pyrene-labeled *sn*-2 acyl chains (Figure 13.21) are among the most popular fluorescent membrane probes.[28,183,184] Molecular Probes offers pyrenedecanoyl-labeled glycerophospholipids with phosphocholine (H361), phosphoglycerol (H3809) and phosphomethanol (H3810) head groups.

The spectral properties of the pyrene lipid probes are summarized in Table 13.2. Of primary importance, in terms of practical applications, is the concentration-dependent formation of excited-state pyrene dimers (excimers), which exhibit a distinctive red-shifted emission (peak ~470 nm) (Figure 13.8).

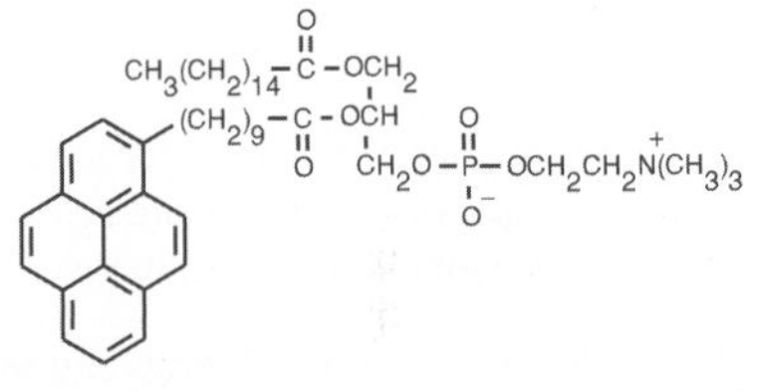

Figure 13.21 H361 1-hexadecanoyl-2-(1-pyrenedecanoyl)-*sn*-glycero-3-phosphocholine (β-py-C_{10}-HPC).

Applications

The excimer-forming properties of pyrene are well suited for monitoring membrane fusion (see Note 13.1 "Technical Focus: Lipid-Mixing Assays of Membrane Fusion") and phospholipid transfer processes.[36,185–189] The monomer/excimer emission ratio can also be used to characterize membrane structural domains and their dependence on temperature, lipid composition and other external factors.[190–193] Pyrenedecanoyl glycerophosphocholine (β-py-C_{10}-HPC, H361) has been used to elucidate the effect of extrinsic species such as Ca^{2+},[194] platelet-activating factor,[195] drugs,[196] membrane-associated proteins,[197–199] and ethanol and cholesterol [200,201] on lipid bilayer structure and dynamics. The anionic phosphoglycerol analog (H3809, Figure 13.22) is preferred as a substrate for secretory phosholipases A_2 relative to other phospholipid classes.[202,203] The long excited-state lifetime of pyrene (Table 13.2) renders the fluorescence of its conjugates very susceptible to oxygen quenching, and consequently these probes can be used to measure oxygen concentrations in solutions,[204] lipid bilayers [205] and cells.[206,207]

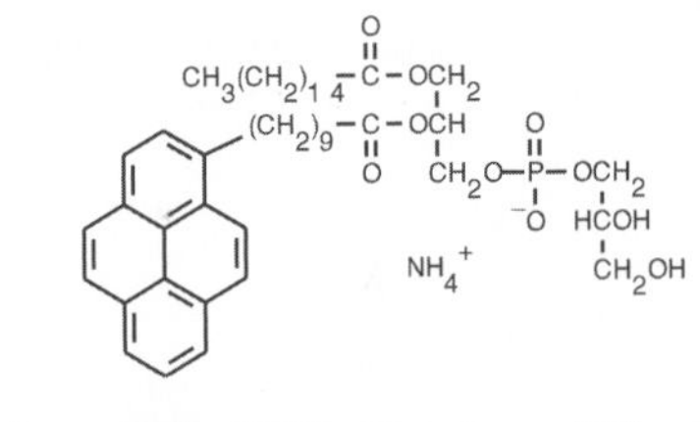

Figure 13.22 H3809 1-hexadecanoyl-2-(1-pyrenedecanoyl)-*sn*-glycero-3-phosphoglycerol, ammonium salt (β-py-C_{10}-PG).

Glycerophospholipids in which both alcohols are esterified to pyrene fatty acids, as in our bis-(1-pyrenebutanoyl)- and bis-(1-pyrenedecanoyl)glycerophosphocholines (B3781, B3782; Figure 13.23) show strong excimer fluorescence, with maximum emission near 470 nm.[28] Hydrolysis of either fatty acid ester by a phospholipase results in liberation of a pyrene fatty acid and an emission shift to shorter wavelengths, making these probes useful as phospholipase substrates [208–211] (Section 17.4).

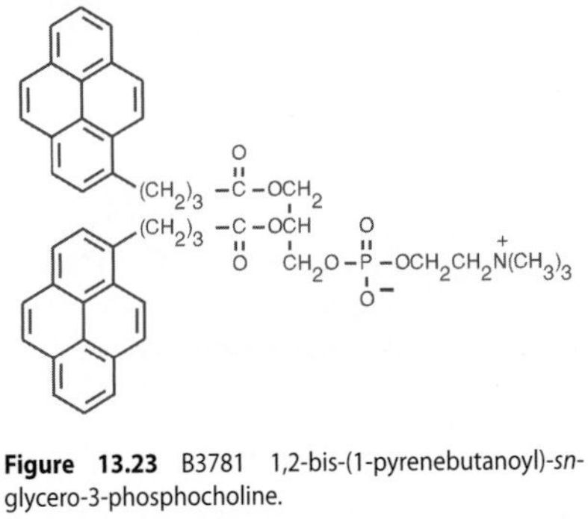

Figure 13.23 B3781 1,2-bis-(1-pyrenebutanoyl)-*sn*-glycero-3-phosphocholine.

Phospholipid with a Dansyl-Labeled Head Group

The phospholipid analog incorporating the environment-sensitive [212] dansyl fluorophore (dansyl DHPE, D57) is a useful probe of lipid–water interfaces.[52,213] It is sensitive to the interactions of a number of proteins, including protein kinase C,[214,215] annexins [216,217] and phospholipase A_2,[218–220] with membrane surfaces. Dansyl DHPE has also been used to examine the effects of cholesterol on the accessibility of the dansyl hapten to antibodies [221] (see Note 13.2 "Product Highlight: Antibodies for Detecting Membrane-Surface Labels").

Note 13.2 — Product Highlight

Antibodies for Detecting Membrane-Surface Labels

Molecular Probes offers antibodies that recognize the following labels:

- Alexa Fluor® 488 dye (A11094)
- Biotin (A11242, A31800, A31801)
- BODIPY® FL dye (A5770)
- Alexa Fluor® 405 and Cascade Blue® dyes (A5760)
- Dansyl (A6398)
- Dinitrophenyl chromophore (A6423, A6430, A6435, A11097)
- Fluorescein and Oregon Green® dyes (Section 7.4, Table 7.18)
- Green-fluorescent protein (GFP, A6455, A11120, A11121, A11122)
- Lucifer yellow (A5750, A5751)
- Tetramethylrhodamine (A6397)
- Texas Red® dye (A6399)

Fluorescent conjugates of several of these anti-dye and anti-hapten antibodies are also available; see Section 7.4 and Table 7.18 for complete product information. These antibodies can be used for direct detection of labeled phospholipids via fluorescence quenching [1,2] (or fluorescence enhancement, in the case of the anti-dansyl antibody). When used in conjunction with phospholipids with dye-labeled head groups (Table 13.1), they are important tools for:

- Studies of molecular recognition mechanisms at membrane surfaces [3]
- Lipid diffusion measurements [4,5]
- Quantitation of lipid internalization by endocytosis [6,7]

In addition to anti-fluorophore antibodies, we offer a selection of streptavidin conjugates (Section 7.6, Table 7.22) for detecting biotinylated phospholipids.

References

1. Biochemistry 38, 976 (1999); **2.** J Biol Chem 273, 22950 (1998); **3.** Angew Chem Int Ed Engl 29, 1269 (1990); **4.** J Cell Biol 120, 25 (1993); **5.** Proc Natl Acad Sci U S A 88, 6274 (1991); **6.** J Cell Biol 106, 1083 (1988); **7.** Cell 64, 393 (1991).

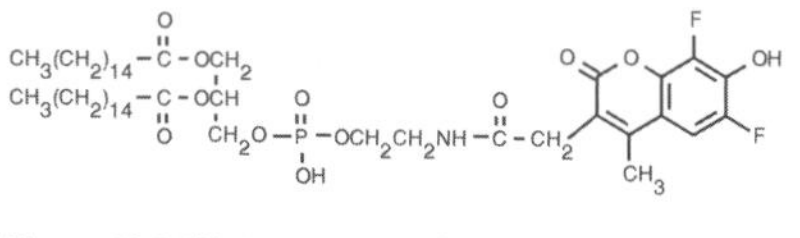

Figure 13.24 M12652 Marina Blue® 1,2-dihexadecanoyl-*sn*-glycero-3-phosphoethanolamine (Marina Blue® DHPE).

Phospholipid with a Marina Blue® Dye–Labeled Head Group

Marina Blue® DHPE (M12652) is optimally excited by the intense 365 nm spectral line of the mercury-arc lamp, and exhibits bright blue fluorescence emission near 460 nm. Significantly, the pK_a value of this 6,8-difluoro-7-hydroxycoumarin derivative (Figure 13.24) is 2–3 log units lower than that of nonfluorinated 7-hydroxycoumarin analogs, so Marina Blue® DHPE is expected to be strongly fluorescent in membranes, even at neutral pH.

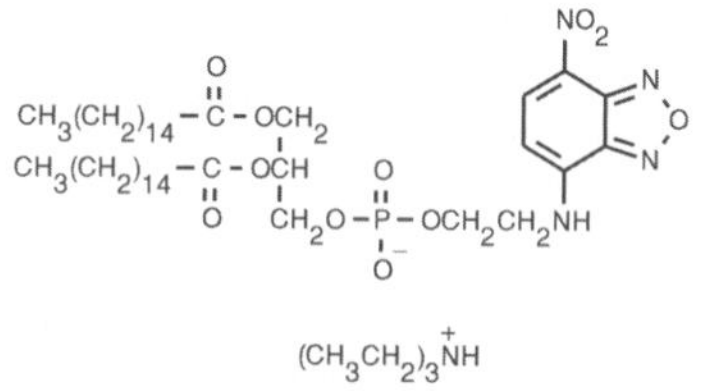

Figure 13.25 N360 *N*-(7-nitrobenz-2-oxa-1,3-diazol-4-yl)-1,2-dihexadecanoyl-*sn*-glycero-3-phosphoethanolamine, triethylammonium salt (NBD-PE).

Phospholipid with a Pacific Blue™ Dye–Labeled Head Group

The Pacific Blue™ dye–labeled phospholipid (Pacific Blue™ DMPE, P22652) is our only head group–labeled phospholipid with tetradecanoyl (myristoyl) esters rather than hexadecanoyl (palmitoyl) esters. This blue-fluorescent phospholipid is structurally similar to a phospholipid described by Gonzalez and Tsien for use in a FRET-based measurement of membrane potential.[222]

Phospholipid with an NBD-Labeled Head Group

The widely used membrane probe nitrobenzoxadiazolyldihexadecanoylglycerophosphoethanolamine [16] (NBD-PE, N360; Figure 13.25) has three important optical properties: photolability, which makes it suitable for photobleaching recovery measurements; concentration-dependent self-quenching; and fluorescence resonance energy transfer to rhodamine acceptors (usually rhodamine DHPE, L1392). Spectroscopic characteristics of NBD-PE are generally similar to those described for our phospholipids with NBD-labeled acyl chains (N3786, N3787). NBD-PE is frequently used in NBD–rhodamine fluorescence energy transfer experiments to monitor membrane fusion (see Note 13.1 "Technical Focus: Lipid-Mixing Assays of Membrane Fusion"). In addition, this method can be used to detect lipid domain formation [176] and intermembrane lipid transfer [223–226] and to determine the transbilayer distribution of phospholipids.[162] Attachment of the NBD fluorophore to the head group makes NBD-PE resistant to transfer between vesicles.[153] NBD-PE has been used in combination with either rhodamine DHPE (L1392) or Texas Red® DHPE (T1395MP) for visualizing the spatial relationships of lipid populations by fluorescence resonance energy transfer microscopy.[227] The nitro group of NBD can be reduced with sodium dithionite, irreversibly eliminating the dye's fluorescence (Figure 13.20). This technique can be employed to determine whether the probe is localized on the outer or inner leaflet of the cell membrane.[182,228–230] The argon-ion laser–excitable NBD-PE is also a frequent choice for fluorescence recovery after photobleaching (FRAP) measurements of lateral diffusion in membranes.[231–234] In addition, NBD-PE is of particular value for monitoring bilayer-to-hexagonal phase transitions, because these transitions cause an increase in NBD-PE's fluorescence intensity.[235–237]

Phospholipid with a Fluorescein-Labeled Head Group

Fluorescein-derivatized dihexadecanoylglycerophosphoethanolamine (fluorescein DHPE, F362; Figure 13.26) is a membrane-surface probe that is sensitive to both the local electrostatic potential and pH.[238–240] An anti-fluorescein/Oregon Green® antibody (A889, Section 7.4) has been employed in combination with fluorescein DHPE to investigate specific recognition interactions at membrane surfaces [241,242] (see Note 13.2 "Product Highlight: Antibodies for Detecting Membrane-Surface Labels").

Because of fluorescein's photolability, fluorescein DHPE is a useful reagent for measuring lateral diffusion in membranes using fluorescence photobleaching recovery methods.[243,244] Another technique, single-particle tracking (SPT), provides direct measurements of diffusion rates by calculating the trajectories of fluorescent polystyrene beads or colloidal gold particles from time-sequential images.[245,246] Molecular Probes' FluoSpheres® fluorescent microspheres (Section 6.5) were labeled with streptavidin and then coupled to fluorescein DHPE using a biotinylated conjugate of anti-fluorescein/Oregon Green® monoclonal 4-4-20 (A6421, Section 7.4). Diffusion rates measured with this bridged conjugate in glass-supported phospholipid bilayers were the same as those determined with streptavidin beads coupled directly to biotin-X DHPE (B1616). Fluorescein DHPE has also been used in conjunction with polyclonal anti-fluorescein/Oregon Green® antibody (A889, Section 7.4) to prepare colloidal gold probes for SPT diffusion measurements in supported phospholipid bilayers and in keratocyte plasma membranes.[247]

Phospholipid with an Oregon Green® 488 Dye–Labeled Head Group

With absorption and emission spectra that are virtually superimposable on those of fluorescein (Figure 7.21), our Oregon Green® 488 DHPE (O12650) provides an important alternative to fluorescein DHPE in its many applications. When compared with the fluorescein derivative, Oregon Green® 488 DHPE exhibits greater photostability and a lower pK_a ($pK_a = 4.7$ versus 6.4 for fluorescein); however, these pK_a values may differ when the probes are bound to membranes.

Phospholipid with a BODIPY® FL Dye–Labeled Head Group

Our phospholipid with the green-fluorescent BODIPY® FL dye attached to the head group (BODIPY® FL DHPE, D3800) has significant potential for studies of molecular recognition interactions at membrane surfaces (see Note 13.2 "Product Highlight: Antibodies for Detecting Membrane-Surface Labels"). Spectral properties of this BODIPY® probe is generally the same as those described above for phospholipids with BODIPY® FL dye–labeled acyl chains.

Phospholipids with Rhodamine- and Texas Red® Dye–Labeled Head Groups

The rhodamine-labeled phospholipids TRITC DHPE (T1391) and rhodamine DHPE (often referred to as *N*-Rh-PE, L1392; Figure 13.27) do not readily transfer between separated lipid bilayers.[151,248] This property has led to the extensive use of rhodamine DHPE for membrane fusion assays based on fluorescence resonance energy transfer from NBD-PE (see Note 13.1 "Technical Focus: Lipid-Mixing Assays

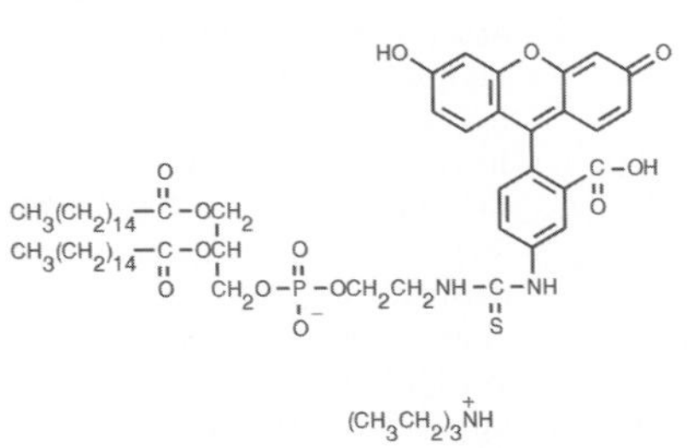

Figure 13.26 F362 *N*-(fluorescein-5-thiocarbamoyl)-1,2-dihexadecanoyl-*sn*-glycero-3-phosphoethanolamine, triethylammonium salt (fluorescein DHPE).

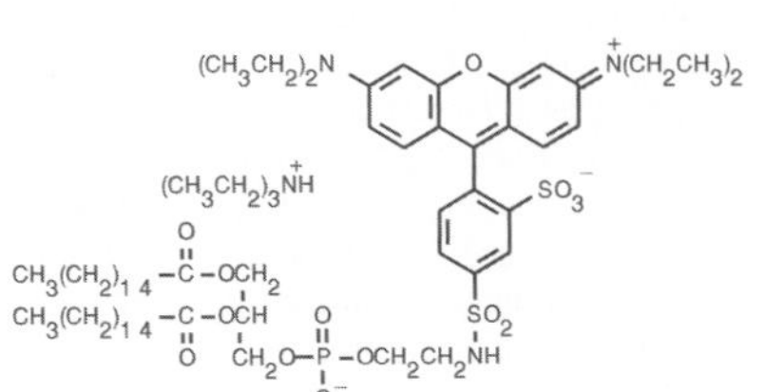

Figure 13.27 L1392 Lissamine rhodamine B 1,2-dihexadecanoyl-*sn*-glycero-3-phosphoethanolamine, triethylammonium salt (rhodamine DHPE).

of Membrane Fusion"). In addition, these probes are good resonance energy transfer acceptors from fluorescent lipid analogs such as the BODIPY® and NBD phospholipids[249] and from protein labels such as 5-iodoacetamidofluorescein 5-IAF, I30451; Section 2.2) and IAEDANS[250,251] (I14, Section 2.3). Rhodamine-labeled phospholipids have also been used as tracers for membrane traffic during endocytosis[252] and for lipid processing in hepatocytes.[253] Texas Red® DHPE (T1395MP) is principally employed as an energy transfer acceptor from NBD, BODIPY® and fluorescein lipid probes. The longer emission wavelength of the Texas Red® dye provides superior separation of the donor and acceptor emission signals in resonance energy transfer microscopy.[228,254] This technique has enabled visualization of ATP-dependent fusion of liposomes with the Golgi apparatus.[255] Membrane flux during hemagglutinin-mediated cell–cell fusion has been visualized using Texas Red® DHPE and the lipophilic carbocyanine DiI (D282, D3911; Section 13.4) as membrane labels.[256]

Phospholipids with Maleimide-Labeled and Biotinylated Head Groups

Molecular Probes offers phospholipids labeled with either biotin or thiol-reactive maleimide groups to facilitate binding of labeled membranes to other biomolecules. The maleimide-containing phospholipid (MMCC DHPE, M1618) forms stable crosslinks to thiolated biomolecules, allowing the coupling of antibodies to liposomes for targeted delivery to cells[257–260] and for immunoassays.[261–263] The biotinylated phospholipids (biotin DHPE, B1550 and biotin-X DHPE, B1616; Figure 13.28) can be used to couple avidin or streptavidin (Section 7.6) to cell membranes, liposomes and lipid monolayers.[264–267] Avidin can then be employed as a bridge for antibody coupling or for assembling liposomes into multiplex structures.[268,269] Liposomes incorporating biotinylated phospholipids can also be used to immobilize membrane-bound proteins for analysis by affinity chromatography.[270] Interactions of biotinylated lipids with streptavidin provide a model for molecular recognition processes at membrane surfaces.[271–273] The phase structure of lipid assemblies incorporating biotinylated phospholipids has been studied by X-ray diffraction,[230] ^{31}P NMR and differential scanning calorimetry.[274,275]

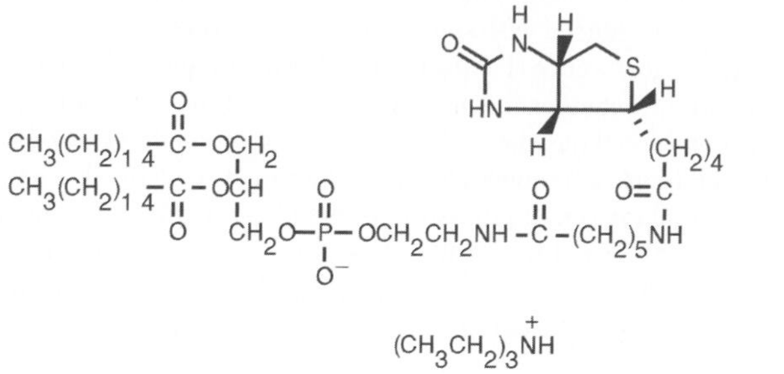

Figure 13.28 B1616 *N*-((6-(biotinoyl)amino)hexanoyl)-1,2-dihexadecanoyl-*sn*-glycero-3-phosphoethanolamine, triethylammonium salt (biotin-X DHPE).

References

1. Biochim Biophys Acta 1375, 13 (1998); **2.** Biochemistry 31, 5312 (1992); **3.** Chem Phys Lipids 116, 3 (2002); **4.** Anal Biochem 198, 228 (1991); **5.** J Biol Chem 276, 1391 (2001); **6.** J Biol Chem 272, 8531 (1997); **7.** Exp Parasitol 86, 133 (1997); **8.** Am J Physiol 269, G842 (1995); **9.** Biochem Biophys Res Commun 187, 1594 (1992); **10.** Methods Enzymol 319, 603 (2000); **11.** Biochim Biophys Acta 1487, 61 (2000); **12.** Anal Biochem 265, 290 (1998); **13.** FEBS Lett 453, 278 (1999); **14.** J Biochem Biophys Methods 35, 23 (1997); **15.** Photochem Photobiol 54, 361 (1991); **16.** Chem Phys Lipids 53, 1 (1990); **17.** Chem Phys Lipids 58, 111 (1991); **18.** Biochemistry 34, 11919 (1995); **19.** Biophys J 80, 832 (2001); **20.** J Am Chem Soc 97, 4114 (1975); **21.** Anal Biochem 174, 101 (1988); **22.** Anal Biochem 183, 231 (1989); **23.** Arch Biochem Biophys 341, 34 (1997); **24.** Exp Cell Res 89, 105 (1974); **25.** Adv Exp Med Biol 75, 47 (1975); **26.** Biochim Biophys Acta 591, 187 (1980); **27.** Photochem Photobiol 26, 221 (1977); **28.** Chem Phys Lipids 116, 57 (2002); **29.** Chem Phys Lipids 27, 199 (1980); **30.** Methods for Studying Membrane Fluidity, Aloia RC, et al., Eds. pp. 161–191 (1988); **31.** J Biol Chem 272, 3369 (1997); **32.** Biochemistry 32, 11330 (1993); **33.** J Biol Chem 271, 3085 (1996); **34.** Biophys J 60, 110 (1991); **35.** Biochim Biophys Acta 1106, 178 (1992); **36.** Chem Phys Lipids 50, 191 (1989); **37.** J Biol Chem 267, 6563 (1992); **38.** Biochemistry 33, 15382 (1994); **39.** J Biol Chem 273, 27800 (1998); **40.** Biophys J 72, 1732 (1997); **41.** Biochemistry 34, 7271 (1995); **42.** Biochemistry 34, 9913 (1995); **43.** J Neurosci Methods 100, 127 (2000); **44.** Biochemistry 37, 10709 (1998); **45.** Biochemistry 37, 14128 (1998); **46.** Biochim Biophys Acta 1402, 61 (1998); **47.** J Biol Chem 275, 21715 (2000); **48.** Chem Phys Lipids 65, 43 (1993); **49.** Biochemistry 29, 697 (1990); **50.** Biochemistry 26, 5943 (1987); **51.** Biochim Biophys Acta 918, 250 (1987); **52.** Biochemistry 37, 4603 (1998); **53.** Biochem J 238, 419 (1986); **54.** Biochem J 356, 387 (2001); **55.** Biochemistry 38, 16932 (1999); **56.** Analyst 117, 1859 (1992); **57.** Biochim Biophys Acta 1484, 195 (2000); **58.** Anal Biochem 212, 65 (1993); **59.** Biochem J 278, 843 (1991); **60.** Biochem J 266, 435 (1990); **61.** Proc Natl Acad Sci U S A 72, 1649 (1975); **62.** Spectroscopic Membrane Probes, Vol. I, Loew LM, Ed. pp. 43–62 (1988); **63.** Proc Natl Acad Sci U S A 91, 1183 (1994); **64.** Arch Biochem Biophys 297, 147 (1992); **65.** Biochim Biophys Acta 1330, 127 (1997); **66.** Neurochem Res 22, 1187 (1997); **67.** Biochemistry 39, 127 (2000); **68.** Biochemistry 37, 13781 (1998); **69.** Nature 378, 776 (1995); **70.** Cell 75, 241 (1993); **71.** Biochem Pharmacol 54, 937 (1997); **72.** Biochemistry 32, 10692 (1993); **73.** J Biol Chem 268, 10906 (1993); **74.** Anal Biochem 196, 443 (1991); **75.** Chem Phys Lipids 60, 1 (1991); **76.** Biochem J 349, 377 (2000); **77.** Biochemistry 33, 3327 (1994); **78.** J Biol Chem 268, 7885 (1993); **79.** Lipids 32, 1201 (1997); **80.** Biochemistry 29, 8548 (1990); **81.** Biochemistry 32, 12420 (1993); **82.** Biochemistry 30, 6195 (1991); **83.** Biochemistry 29, 6714 (1990); **84.** Biochemistry 31, 1816 (1992); **85.** Biophys J 72, 2268 (1997); **86.** Clin Chem 44, 2148 (1998); **87.** Proc Natl Acad Sci USA 77, 26 (1980); **88.** Mol Cell Biochem 123, 45 (1993); **89.** Mol Cell Biochem 192, 87 (1999); **90.** J Biol Chem 269, 23918 (1994); **91.** J Biol Chem 267, 23495 (1992); **92.** J Biol Chem 267, 23534 (1992); **93.** Biochemistry 37, 8011 (1998); **94.** J Lipid Res 36, 229 (1995); **95.** Cell 100, 603 (2000); **96.** Biochemistry 39, 5838 (2000); **97.** Biophys J 74, 731 (1998); **98.** Curr Biol 10, 311 (2000); **99.** Biochem J 360, 513 (2001); **100.** Biochem J 355, 249 (2001); **101.** J Biol Chem 274, 8347 (1999); **102.** J Biol Chem 274, 9907 (1999); **103.** Annu Rev Cell Dev Biol 14, 231 (1998); **104.** Biochem J 379, 527 (2004); **105.** Proc Natl Acad Sci U S A 97, 11286 (2000); **106.** Anal Biochem 314, 97 (2003); **107.** Anal Biochem 276, 27 (1999); **108.** Biochemistry 40, 8292 (2001); **109.** J Fluorescence 4, 295 (1994); **110.** Biochem Biophys Res Commun 207, 508 (1995); **111.** Biochemistry 36, 8840 (1997); **112.** Biophys J 74, 2184 (1998); **113.** Biophys J 71, 2656 (1996); **114.** J Cell Sci 106, 485 (1993); **115.** J Biochem (Tokyo) 129, 19 (2001); **116.** Biochim Biophys Acta 1438, 185 (1999); **117.** Biochemistry 35, 3063 (1996); **118.** Biophys J 83, 1511 (2002); **119.** Proc Natl Acad Sci U S A 96, 8461 (1999); **120.** Biophys J 80, 2775 (2001); **121.** J Cell Biol 130, 781 (1995); **122.** J Biol Chem 274, 19338 (1999); **123.** J Biol Chem 267, 21465 (1992); **124.** Plant Physiol 110, 979 (1996); **125.** Br J Pharmacol 124, 1675 (1998); **126.** J Biol Chem 272, 2542 (1997); **127.** Biochim Biophys Acta 1448, 390 (1999); **128.** Biochim Biophys Acta 1390, 73 (1998); **129.** Biochim Biophys Acta 692, 196 (1982); **130.** Biochemistry 37, 8180 (1998); **131.** J Biol Chem 271, 11627 (1996); **132.** Biochemistry 39, 10928 (2000); **133.** Biochemistry 38, 4604 (1999); **134.** Biochemistry 36, 4675 (1997); **135.** Biochemistry 36, 10630 (1997); **136.** Biochim Biophys Acta 946, 85 (1988); **137.** Biophys J 72, 2660 (1997); **138.** Biophys J 71, 892 (1996); **139.** Biophys J 71, 878 (1996); **140.** Methods Enzymol 233, 459 (1994); **141.** Biochemistry 36, 5827 (1997); **142.** Biochemistry 36, 6251 (1997); **143.** J Fluorescence 4, 153 (1994); **144.** J Biol Chem 271, 31878 (1996); **145.** Biochemistry 37, 16653 (1998); **146.** Biochemistry 30, 4193 (1991); **147.** Biophys J 80, 822 (2001); **148.** Biochemistry 32, 10826 (1993);

References — continued

149. Biochim Biophys Acta 938, 24 (1988); **150.** Biochemistry 26, 39 (1987); **151.** Biochemistry 21, 1720 (1982); **152.** Biochemistry 20, 2783 (1981); **153.** J Biol Chem 255, 5404 (1980); **154.** J Biol Chem 269, 22517 (1994); **155.** Biochemistry 32, 3714 (1993); **156.** Proc Natl Acad Sci U S A 86, 9896 (1989); **157.** J Biol Chem 275, 23065 (2000); **158.** Biophys J 78, 2628 (2000); **159.** Biochemistry 37, 14833 (1998); **160.** Biochemistry 33, 6721 (1994); **161.** Fluorescent and Luminescent Probes for Biological Activity, Mason WT, Ed. pp. 100–119 (1993); **162.** Biochemistry 31, 2865 (1992); **163.** J Cell Biol 123, 1403 (1993); **164.** J Cell Biol 113, 235 (1991); **165.** J Cell Biol 112, 267 (1991); **166.** J Biol Chem 265, 5337 (1990); **167.** Biochim Biophys Acta 1082, 255 (1991); **168.** Biochemistry 27, 1889 (1988); **169.** J Biol Chem 262, 14172 (1987); **170.** Biochemistry 40, 6475 (2001); **171.** Am J Physiol 267, G80 (1994); **172.** J Biol Chem 258, 5368 (1983); **173.** Biochemistry 33, 8225 (1994); **174.** J Cell Biol 112, 1143 (1991); **175.** J Cell Biol 105, 755 (1987); **176.** Biophys J 80, 1819 (2001); **177.** Biochemistry 33, 4483 (1994); **178.** Biochemistry 32, 12591 (1993); **179.** Chem Phys Lipids 57, 227 (1991); **180.** Proc Natl Acad Sci U S A 88, 1364 (1991); **181.** Chem Phys Lipids 57, 29 (1991); **182.** Biochemistry 37, 15114 (1998); **183.** Vesicles, Rosoff M, Ed. pp. 296–372 (1996); **184.** Pflugers Arch 414, 162 (1989); **185.** Biochim Biophys Acta 1487, 82 (2000); **186.** Biochim Biophys Acta 1467, 281 (2000); **187.** Biochemistry 32, 11074 (1993); **188.** Biochemistry 31, 5912 (1992); **189.** Biochemistry 29, 1593 (1990); **190.** Biochemistry 40, 4181 (2001); **191.** Biochemistry 37, 17562 (1998); **192.** Biophys J 66, 1981 (1994); **193.** Biophys J 63, 903 (1992); **194.** Biochemistry 27, 3433 (1988); **195.** Chem Phys Lipids 53, 129 (1990); **196.** J Biol Chem 268, 1074 (1993); **197.** Biochemistry 32, 11711 (1993); **198.** Biochemistry 32, 5411 (1993); **199.** Biochemistry 32, 5373 (1993); **200.** Biophys J 66, 729 (1994); **201.** J Biol Chem 272, 3573 (1997); **202.** Biochemistry 36, 14325 (1997); **203.** Biochemistry 38, 7803 (1999); **204.** Anal Chem 59, 279 (1987); **205.** Biophys J 47, 613 (1985); **206.** J Cell Physiol 107, 329 (1981); **207.** Biochim Biophys Acta 279, 393 (1972); **208.** Anal Biochem 116, 553 (1981); **209.** Biochim Biophys Acta 1192, 132 (1994); **210.** Anal Biochem 219, 1 (1994); **211.** Anal Biochem 232, 7 (1995); **212.** Biochim Biophys Acta 815, 351 (1985); **213.** Biochim Biophys Acta 1284, 191 (1996); **214.** J Biol Chem 272, 6167 (1997); **215.** Biochemistry 32, 66 (1993); **216.** Biochemistry 36, 8189 (1997); **217.** Biochemistry 33, 13231 (1994); **218.** Biochemistry 39, 9623 (2000); **219.** Biochemistry 37, 6697 (1998); **220.** Biochemistry 37, 8516 (1998); **221.** Biochim Biophys Acta 1104, 9 (1992); **222.** Chem Biol 4, 269 (1997); **223.** J Biol Chem 269, 10517 (1994); **224.** Biochemistry 29, 879 (1990); **225.** Biochim Biophys Acta 981, 178 (1989); **226.** Biochemistry 27, 3925 (1988); **227.** Methods Enzymol 171, 850 (1989); **228.** Biochemistry 33, 9968 (1994); **229.** Chem Phys Lipids 70, 205 (1994); **230.** Biochemistry 32, 14194 (1993); **231.** Biochemistry 16, 3836 (1977); **232.** J Cell Biol 122, 1253 (1993); **233.** J Cell Biol 115, 1585 (1991); **234.** J Cell Biol 115, 245 (1991); **235.** Biophys J 63, 309 (1992); **236.** Biochemistry 29, 2976 (1990); **237.** Biochemistry 27, 3947 (1988); **238.** Z Naturforsch [C] 55, 418 (2000); **239.** Biochim Biophys Acta 1374, 63 (1998); **240.** J Biol Chem 274, 29951 (1999); **241.** Biophys J 63, 823 (1992); **242.** J Am Chem Soc 103, 6797 (1981); **243.** Biophys J 66, 25 (1994); **244.** J Cell Biol 103, 807 (1986); **245.** J Membr Biol 135, 83 (1993); **246.** Proc Natl Acad Sci U S A 88, 6274 (1991); **247.** J Cell Biol 120, 25 (1993); **248.** Biochemistry 24, 6390 (1985); **249.** Biochemistry 20, 4093 (1981); **250.** J Biol Chem 266, 12082 (1991); **251.** Biochemistry 29, 1607 (1990); **252.** Eur J Cell Biol 53, 173 (1990); **253.** Biochem J 284, 259 (1992); **254.** J Cell Biol 103, 1221 (1986); **255.** Cell 55, 797 (1988); **256.** J Cell Biol 121, 543 (1993); **257.** J Immunol Methods 132, 25 (1990); **258.** Proc Natl Acad Sci U S A 87, 2448 (1990); **259.** Cancer Res 48, 5237 (1988); **260.** Proc Natl Acad Sci U S A 84, 246 (1987); **261.** Anal Biochem 280, 151 (2000); **262.** J Immunol Methods 134, 207 (1990); **263.** J Immunol Methods 100, 59 (1987); **264.** J Immunol Methods 158, 183 (1993); **265.** Anal Biochem 207, 341 (1992); **266.** Biophys J 59, 387 (1991); **267.** Biochim Biophys Acta 1028, 73 (1990); **268.** Anal Chem 73, 91 (2001); **269.** Science 264, 1753 (1994); **270.** Anal Biochem 280, 94 (2000); **271.** Angew Chem Int Ed Engl 29, 1269 (1990); **272.** Anal Biochem 217, 128 (1994); **273.** Biophys J 65, 2160 (1993); **274.** Biophys J 66, 31 (1994); **275.** Biochemistry 32, 9960 (1993).

Data Table — 13.2 Fatty Acid Analogs and Phospholipids

Cat #	MW	Storage	Soluble	Abs	EC	Em	Solvent	Notes
A37	504.71	F,L	DMSO	361	8,000	467	MeOH	1
A176	250.30	L	DMSO	366	8,900	414	MeOH	
A242	504.71	F,L	DMSO	362	8,400	470	MeOH	1
A3880	~15,350	FF,L,AA	H_2O	365	10,500	432	H_2O	2
B1550	1019.45	FF,D	see Notes	<300		none		3
B1616	1132.61	FF,D	see Notes	<300		none		3
B3781	797.88	FF,D,L	see Notes	342	75,000	471	EtOH	4
B3782	966.20	FF,D,L	see Notes	340	62,000	473	EtOH	5
B3794	881.93	FF,D,L	see Notes	510	92,000	515	EtOH	3, 6
B3824	404.31	F,L	DMSO	509	101,000	515	MeOH	6
B7701	1029.80	FF,D,L	see Notes	505	123,000	512	MeOH	3, 7
B22618	1371.47	F,D,L	DMSO	504	80,000	511	MeOH	6
B22619	1371.47	F,D,L	DMSO	504	80,000	511	MeOH	6
B22620	1371.47	F,D,L	DMSO	504	80,000	511	MeOH	6
B22621	948.84	F,D,L	DMSO	504	80,000	511	MeOH	6
B22622	1231.20	F,D,L	H_2O, DMSO	504	80,000	511	MeOH	6
B22623	1231.20	F,D,L	H_2O, DMSO	504	80,000	511	MeOH	6
B22624	1231.20	F,D,L	H_2O, DMSO	504	80,000	511	MeOH	6
B22625	1513.57	F,D,L	H_2O, DMSO	504	80,000	511	MeOH	6
B22626	1513.57	F,D,L	H_2O, DMSO	504	80,000	511	MeOH	6
B22627	1513.57	F,D,L	H_2O, DMSO	504	80,000	511	MeOH	6
B22628	1795.93	F,D,L	H_2O, DMSO	504	80,000	511	MeOH	6
B22631	1140.07	F,D,L	DMSO	544	60,000	570	MeOH	6
B22632	1422.43	F,D,L	H_2O, DMSO	544	60,000	570	MeOH	6
B22633	1422.43	F,D,L	H_2O, DMSO	544	60,000	570	MeOH	6
B22634	1422.43	F,D,L	H_2O, DMSO	544	60,000	570	MeOH	6
B22635	1704.79	F,D,L	H_2O, DMSO	544	60,000	570	MeOH	6
B22636	1704.79	F,D,L	H_2O, DMSO	544	60,000	570	MeOH	6
B22637	1704.79	F,D,L	H_2O, DMSO	544	60,000	570	MeOH	6
B22638	1987.16	F,D,L	H_2O, DMSO	544	60,000	570	MeOH	6
B22641	1166.08	F,D,L	DMSO	588	68,000	616	MeOH	6
B22642	1448.44	F,D,L	H_2O, DMSO	588	68,000	616	MeOH	6
B22643	1448.44	F,D,L	H_2O, DMSO	588	68,000	616	MeOH	6
B22644	1448.44	F,D,L	H_2O, DMSO	588	68,000	616	MeOH	6

Data Table — 13.2 Fatty Acid Analogs and Phospholipids — continued

Cat #	MW	Storage	Soluble	Abs	EC	Em	Solvent	Notes
B22645	1730.81	F,D,L	H_2O, DMSO	588	68,000	616	MeOH	6
B22646	1730.81	F,D,L	H_2O, DMSO	588	68,000	616	MeOH	6
B22647	1730.81	F,D,L	H_2O, DMSO	588	68,000	616	MeOH	6
B22648	2013.17	F,D,L	H_2O, DMSO	588	68,000	616	MeOH	6
D57	1026.44	FF,D,L	see Notes	336	4,500	517	MeOH	3
D94	434.59	F,L	DMSO, EtOH	335	4,800	519	MeOH	
D476	782.01	FF,D,L	see Notes	354	81,000	428	MeOH	3, 8
D3771	854.86	FF,D,L	see Notes	506	71,000	512	EtOH	3
D3792	895.95	FF,D,L	see Notes	506	86,000	513	EtOH	3, 6
D3793	881.93	FF,D,L	see Notes	509	86,000	513	EtOH	3, 6
D3795	881.93	FF,D,L	see Notes	508	89,000	516	EtOH	3, 6
D3799	1191.38	FF,D,L	see Notes	535	85,000	552	MeOH	3, 6
D3800	1067.23	FF,D,L	see Notes	505	87,000	511	MeOH	3, 6
D3803	797.77	FF,D,L	see Notes	503	80,000	512	MeOH	3, 6
D3805	746.68	FF,D,L	see Notes	504	79,000	511	MeOH	3, 6
D3806	897.88	FF,D,L	see Notes	582	124,000	593	MeOH	3, 6, 9
D3811	1541.81	FF,D,LL	see Notes	340	13,000	none	MeOH	3, 10, 11
D3815	921.91	FF,D,L	see Notes	534	64,000	552	MeOH	3, 6
D3821	474.44	F,L	DMSO	505	90,000	512	MeOH	6
D3822	418.33	F,L	DMSO	505	87,000	511	MeOH	6
D3823	404.31	F,L	DMSO	508	97,000	514	MeOH	6
D3825	404.31	F,L	DMSO	509	100,000	515	MeOH	6
D3832	542.47	F,L	DMSO	534	76,000	552	MeOH	6
D3834	320.15	F,L	DMSO, MeCN	505	96,000	511	MeOH	6
D3835	472.40	F,L	DMSO	559	91,000	568	MeOH	6
D3838	394.23	F,L	DMSO	564	148,000	570	MeOH	6
D3839	478.39	F,L	DMSO	564	145,000	570	MeOH	6
D3859	441.33	F,L	DMSO	578	100,000	590	MeOH	6
D3860	420.26	F,L	DMSO	582	140,000	591	MeOH	9
D3861	504.43	F,L	DMSO	582	140,000	591	MeOH	9
D3862	404.31	F,L	DMSO	505	92,000	510	MeOH	6
D12656	786.70	FF,D,L	see Notes	504	102,000	511	MeOH	3, 6
D23739	1136.13	FF,D,L	DMSO	505	92,000	511	MeOH	3, 12
F362	1182.54	FF,D,L	see Notes	496	88,000	519	MeOH	3, 13
H361	850.13	FF,D,L	see Notes	342	37,000	376	MeOH	3, 14, 15
H3790	928.24	FF,D,L	see Notes	442	29,000	448	EtOH	3, 16
H3809	856.09	FF,D,L	see Notes	341	38,000	376	MeOH	3, 14, 15
H3810	800.99	FF,D,L	see Notes	341	40,000	376	MeOH	3, 14, 15
H3818	794.02	FF,D,L	see Notes	341	37,000	377	MeOH	3, 14, 15
L1392	1333.81	FF,D,L	see Notes	560	75,000	581	MeOH	3
M1618	1012.40	FF,D	see Notes	<300		none		3
M12652	944.14	FF,D,L	see Notes	365	18,000	460	MeOH	3, 13
N316	294.27	L	DMSO	467	23,000	539	MeOH	17
N360	956.25	FF,D,L	see Notes	463	21,000	536	MeOH	3, 17
N678	378.43	L	DMSO	467	24,000	536	MeOH	17
N3786	771.89	FF,D,L	see Notes	465	21,000	533	EtOH	3, 17
N3787	856.05	FF,D,L	see Notes	465	22,000	534	EtOH	3, 17
O12650	1086.25	FF,D,L	see Notes	501	85,000	526	MeOH	3, 13
P31	372.51	L	DMF, DMSO	341	43,000	377	MeOH	14, 15
P58	1057.46	FF,D,L	see Notes	350	35,000	379	MeOH	
P96	400.56	L	DMF, DMSO	341	44,000	377	MeOH	14, 15
P243	456.67	L	DMF, DMSO	341	43,000	377	MeOH	14, 15
P646	450.62	L	DMF, DMSO	440	34,000	448	MeOH	16
P1619MP	990.43	FF,D	see Notes	281	4,900	none	MeOH	3
P1903MP	288.35	L	DMF, DMSO	341	43,000	376	MeOH	14, 15
P3840	316.40	L	DMF, DMSO	341	42,000	377	MeOH	14, 15
P22652	961.17	FF,D,L	see Notes	411	40,000	454	MeOH	3
P36005	276.42	FF,LL,AA	EtOH	304	77,000	416	MeOH	18, 19
R7712	1446.97	FF,D,L	see Notes	560	121,000	580	MeOH	3
T1391	1236.68	FF,D,L	see Notes	540	93,000	566	MeOH	3
T1395MP	1381.85	FF,D,L	see Notes	583	107,000	601	MeOH	3
T7710	1495.01	FF,D,L	see Notes	583	102,000	602	MeOH	3

For definitions of the contents of this data table, see "Navigating *The Handbook*" in the introductory pages.

Notes

1. Anthroyloxy derivatives have structured excitation spectra with peaks at about 380, 360, 345 and 328 nm, with the 360 nm peak the strongest. Emission is unstructured at 445 nm in phospholipid vesicles. The fluorescence lifetime for all anthroyloxy derivatives is about 11 nsec.
2. ADIFAB fatty acid indicator is a protein conjugate with a molecular weight of approximately 15,350. Em shifts from about 432 nm to 505 nm upon binding of fatty acids (Mol Cell Biochem 192, 87 (1999)).

3. Chloroform is the most generally useful solvent for preparing stock solutions of phospholipids (including sphingomyelins). Glycerophosphocholines are usually freely soluble in ethanol. Most other glycerophospholipids (phosphoethanolamines, phosphatidic acids and phosphoglycerols) are less soluble in ethanol, but solutions up to 1–2 mg/mL should be obtainable, using sonication to aid dispersion if necessary. Labeling of cells with fluorescent phospholipids can be enhanced by addition of cyclodextrins during incubation (J Biol Chem 274, 35359 (1999)).
4. Phospholipase A cleavage generates a fluorescent fatty acid (P1903MP) and a fluorescent lysophospholipid.
5. Phospholipase A cleavage generates a fluorescent fatty acid (P31) and a fluorescent lysophospholipid.
6. The absorption and fluorescence spectra of BODIPY® derivatives are relatively insensitive to the solvent.
7. Phospholipase A cleavage results in increased fluorescence with essentially no wavelength shift. The cleavage products are D3862 and a fluorescent lysophospholipid.
8. Diphenylhexatriene (DPH) and its derivatives are essentially nonfluorescent in water. Absorption and emission spectra have multiple peaks. The wavelength, resolution and relative intensity of these peaks are environment dependent. Abs and Em values are for the most intense peak in the solvent specified.
9. Oxidation of the polyunsaturated butadienyl portion of the BODIPY® 581/591 dye results in a shift of the fluorescence emission peak from ~590 nm to ~510 nm (Methods Enzymol 319, 603 (2000); FEBS Lett 453, 278 (1999)).
10. All photoactivatable probes are sensitive to light. They should be protected from illumination except when photolysis is intended.
11. This product is colorless and nonfluorescent until it is activated by ultraviolet photolysis. Photoactivation generates a fluorescein derivative with spectral characteristics similar to C1359.
12. Phospholipase A_2 cleavage results in increased fluorescence with essentially no wavelength shift. The cleavage products are D3834 and a dinitrophenylated lysophospholipid.
13. Spectra of this compound are in methanol containing a trace of KOH.
14. Alkylpyrene fluorescence lifetimes are up to 110 nanoseconds and are very sensitive to oxygen.
15. Pyrene derivatives exhibit structured spectra. The absorption maximum is usually about 340 nm with a subsidiary peak at about 325 nm. There are also strong absorption peaks below 300 nm. The emission maximum is usually about 376 nm with a subsidiary peak at 396 nm. Excimer emission at about 470 nm may be observed at high concentrations.
16. Perylene derivatives have fluorescence lifetimes of approximately 5 nanoseconds. Spectra are structured, with subsidiary peaks at 413 nm (absorption) and 477 nm (emission).
17. Fluorescence of NBD and its derivatives in water is relatively weak. QY and τ increase and Em decreases in aprotic solvents and other nonpolar environments relative to water (Biochemistry 16, 5150 (1977); Photochem Photobiol 54, 361 (1991)).
18. *Cis*-parinaric acid is highly oxygen-sensitive. Use under N_2 or Ar. *Cis*-parinaric acid is essentially nonfluorescent in water.
19. This product is supplied as a ready-made solution in the solvent indicated under "Soluble."

Product List — 13.2 Fatty Acid Analogs and Phospholipids

Cat #	Product Name	Unit Size
A3880	ADIFAB fatty acid indicator	200 µg
A176	9-anthracenepropionic acid	100 mg
A37	2-(9-anthroyloxy)stearic acid (2-AS)	100 mg
A242	6-(9-anthroyloxy)stearic acid (6-AS)	25 mg
B1616	*N*-((6-(biotinoyl)amino)hexanoyl)-1,2-dihexadecanoyl-*sn*-glycero-3-phosphoethanolamine, triethylammonium salt (biotin-X DHPE)	5 mg
B1550	*N*-(biotinoyl)-1,2-dihexadecanoyl-*sn*-glycero-3-phosphoethanolamine, triethylammonium salt (biotin DHPE)	10 mg
B7701	1,2-bis-(4,4-difluoro-5,7-dimethyl-4-bora-3a,4a-diaza-*s*-indacene-3-undecanoyl)-*sn*-glycero-3-phosphocholine (bis-BODIPY® FL C_{11}-PC)	100 µg
B3781	1,2-bis-(1-pyrenebutanoyl)-*sn*-glycero-3-phosphocholine	1 mg
B3782	1,2-bis-(1-pyrenedecanoyl)-*sn*-glycero-3-phosphocholine	1 mg
B22621	BODIPY® FL C_5, C_6-phosphatidylinositol (BODIPY® FL C_5, C_6-PtdIns)	50 µg
B22618	BODIPY® FL C_5, C_{16}-phosphatidylinositol 3-phosphate (BODIPY® FL C_5, C_{16}-PtdIns(3)P)	50 µg
B22622	BODIPY® FL C_5, C_6-phosphatidylinositol 3-phosphate (BODIPY® FL C_5, C_6-PtdIns(3)P)	50 µg
B22619	BODIPY® FL C_5, C_{16}-phosphatidylinositol 4-phosphate (BODIPY® FL C_5, C_{16}-PtdIns(4)P)	50 µg
B22623	BODIPY® FL C_5, C_6-phosphatidylinositol 4-phosphate (BODIPY® FL C_5, C_6-PtdIns(4)P)	50 µg
B22620	BODIPY® FL C_5, C_{16}-phosphatidylinositol 5-phosphate (BODIPY® FL C_5, C_{16}-PtdIns(5)P)	50 µg
B22624	BODIPY® FL C_5, C_6-phosphatidylinositol 5-phosphate (BODIPY® FL C_5, C_6-PtdIns(5)P)	50 µg
B22625	BODIPY® FL C_5, C_6-phosphatidylinositol 3,4-diphosphate (BODIPY® FL C_5, C_6-PtdIns(3,4)P_2)	50 µg
B22615	BODIPY® FL C_5, C_6-Phosphatidylinositol 3,4-Diphosphate Cell-Labeling Kit	1 kit
B22626	BODIPY® FL C_5, C_6-phosphatidylinositol 3,5-diphosphate (BODIPY® FL C_5, C_6-PtdIns(3,5)P_2)	50 µg
B22627	BODIPY® FL C_5, C_6-phosphatidylinositol 4,5-diphosphate (BODIPY® FL C_5, C_6-PtdIns(4,5)P_2)	50 µg
B22616	BODIPY® FL C_5, C_6-Phosphatidylinositol 4,5-Diphosphate Cell-Labeling Kit	1 kit
B22628	BODIPY® FL C_5, C_6-phosphatidylinositol 3,4,5-triphosphate (BODIPY® FL C_5, C_6-PtdIns(3,4,5)P_3)	50 µg
B22617	BODIPY® FL C_5, C_6-Phosphatidylinositol 3,4,5-Triphosphate Cell-Labeling Kit	1 kit
B22631	BODIPY® TMR-X C_6-phosphatidylinositol (BODIPY® TMR-X C_6-PtdIns)	50 µg
B22632	BODIPY® TMR-X C_6-phosphatidylinositol 3-phosphate (BODIPY® TMR-X C_6-PtdIns(3)P)	50 µg
B22633	BODIPY® TMR-X C_6-phosphatidylinositol 4-phosphate (BODIPY® TMR-X C_6-PtdIns(4)P)	50 µg
B22634	BODIPY® TMR-X C_6-phosphatidylinositol 5-phosphate (BODIPY® TMR-X C_6-PtdIns(5)P)	50 µg
B22635	BODIPY® TMR-X C_6-phosphatidylinositol 3,4-diphosphate (BODIPY® TMR-X C_6-PtdIns(3,4)P_2)	50 µg
B22636	BODIPY® TMR-X C_6-phosphatidylinositol 3,5-diphosphate (BODIPY® TMR-X C_6-PtdIns(3,5)P_2)	50 µg
B22637	BODIPY® TMR-X C_6-phosphatidylinositol 4,5-diphosphate (BODIPY® TMR-X C_6-PtdIns(4,5)P_2)	50 µg
B22638	BODIPY® TMR-X C_6-phosphatidylinositol 3,4,5-triphosphate (BODIPY® TMR-X C_6-PtdIns(3,4,5)P_3)	50 µg
B22641	BODIPY® TR-X C_6-phosphatidylinositol (BODIPY® TR-X C_6-PtdIns)	50 µg
B22642	BODIPY® TR-X C_6-phosphatidylinositol 3-phosphate (BODIPY® TR-X C_6-PtdIns(3)P)	50 µg
B22643	BODIPY® TR-X C_6-phosphatidylinositol 4-phosphate (BODIPY® TR-X C_6-PtdIns(4)P)	50 µg
B22644	BODIPY® TR-X C_6-phosphatidylinositol 5-phosphate (BODIPY® TR-X C_6-PtdIns(5)P)	50 µg
B22645	BODIPY® TR-X C_6-phosphatidylinositol 3,4-diphosphate (BODIPY® TR-X C_6-PtdIns(3,4)P_2)	50 µg
B22646	BODIPY® TR-X C_6-phosphatidylinositol 3,5-diphosphate (BODIPY® TR-X C_6-PtdIns(3,5)P_2)	50 µg
B22647	BODIPY® TR-X C_6-phosphatidylinositol 4,5-diphosphate (BODIPY® TR-X C_6-PtdIns(4,5)P_2)	50 µg
B22648	BODIPY® TR-X C_6-phosphatidylinositol 3,4,5-triphosphate (BODIPY® TR-X C_6-PtdIns(3,4,5)P_3)	50 µg
B3824	5-butyl-4,4-difluoro-4-bora-3a,4a-diaza-*s*-indacene-3-nonanoic acid (BODIPY® 500/510 C_4, C_9)	1 mg
B3794	2-(5-butyl-4,4-difluoro-4-bora-3a,4a-diaza-*s*-indacene-3-nonanoyl)-1-hexadecanoyl-*sn*-glycero-3-phosphocholine (β-C_4-BODIPY® 500/510 C_9-HPC)	100 µg

Product List — 13.2 Fatty Acid Analogs and Phospholipids — continued

Cat #	Product Name	Unit Size
D3771	2-decanoyl-1-(*O*-(11-(4,4-difluoro-5,7-dimethyl-4-bora-3a,4a-diaza-*s*-indacene-3-propionyl)amino)undecyl)-*sn*-glycero-3-phosphocholine	1 mg
D3822	4,4-difluoro-5,7-dimethyl-4-bora-3a,4a-diaza-*s*-indacene-3-dodecanoic acid (BODIPY® FL C_{12})	1 mg
D3792	2-(4,4-difluoro-5,7-dimethyl-4-bora-3a,4a-diaza-*s*-indacene-3-dodecanoyl)-1-hexadecanoyl-*sn*-glycero-3-phosphocholine (β-BODIPY® FL C_{12}-HPC)	100 µg
D3821	4,4-difluoro-5,7-dimethyl-4-bora-3a,4a-diaza-*s*-indacene-3-hexadecanoic acid (BODIPY® FL C_{16})	1 mg
D3834	4,4-difluoro-5,7-dimethyl-4-bora-3a,4a-diaza-*s*-indacene-3-pentanoic acid (BODIPY® FL C_5)	1 mg
D3805	2-(4,4-difluoro-5,7-dimethyl-4-bora-3a,4a-diaza-*s*-indacene-3-pentanoyl)-1-hexadecanoyl-*sn*-glycero-3-phosphate, diammonium salt (β-BODIPY® FL C_5-HPA)	100 µg
D3803	2-(4,4-difluoro-5,7-dimethyl-4-bora-3a,4a-diaza-*s*-indacene-3-pentanoyl)-1-hexadecanoyl-*sn*-glycero-3-phosphocholine (β-BODIPY® FL C_5-HPC)	100 µg
D3800	*N*-(4,4-difluoro-5,7-dimethyl-4-bora-3a,4a-diaza-*s*-indacene-3-propionyl)-1,2-dihexadecanoyl-*sn*-glycero-3-phosphoethanolamine, triethylammonium salt (BODIPY® FL DHPE)	100 µg
D12656	*N*-(4,4-difluoro-5,7-dimethyl-4-bora-3a,4a-diaza-*s*-indacene-3-propionyl)-1,2-dihexanoyl-*sn*-glycero-3-phosphoethanolamine, triethylammonium salt (BODIPY® FL dicaproyl PE)	100 µg
D3862	4,4-difluoro-5,7-dimethyl-4-bora-3a,4a-diaza-*s*-indacene-3-undecanoic acid (BODIPY® FL C_{11})	1 mg
D3832	4,4-difluoro-5,7-diphenyl-4-bora-3a,4a-diaza-*s*-indacene-3-dodecanoic acid (BODIPY® 530/550 C_{12})	1 mg
D3815	2-(4,4-difluoro-5,7-diphenyl-4-bora-3a,4a-diaza-*s*-indacene-3-pentanoyl)-1-hexadecanoyl-*sn*-glycero-3-phosphocholine (β-BODIPY® 530/550 C_5-HPC)	100 µg
D3799	*N*-(4,4-difluoro-5,7-diphenyl-4-bora-3a,4a-diaza-*s*-indacene-3-propionyl)-1,2-dihexadecanoyl-*sn*-glycero-3-phosphoethanolamine, triethylammonium salt (BODIPY® 530/550 DHPE)	100 µg
D3823	4,4-difluoro-5-methyl-4-bora-3a,4a-diaza-*s*-indacene-3-dodecanoic acid (BODIPY® 500/510 C_1, C_{12})	1 mg
D3793	2-(4,4-difluoro-5-methyl-4-bora-3a,4a-diaza-*s*-indacene-3-dodecanoyl)-1-hexadecanoyl-*sn*-glycero-3-phosphocholine (β-BODIPY® 500/510 C_{12}-HPC)	100 µg
D3825	4,4-difluoro-5-octyl-4-bora-3a,4a-diaza-*s*-indacene-3-pentanoic acid (BODIPY® 500/510 C_8, C_5)	1 mg
D3795	2-(4,4-difluoro-5-octyl-4-bora-3a,4a-diaza-*s*-indacene-3-pentanoyl)-1-hexadecanoyl-*sn*-glycero-3-phosphocholine (β-C_8-BODIPY® 500/510 C_5-HPC)	100 µg
D3860	4,4-difluoro-5-(4-phenyl-1,3-butadienyl)-4-bora-3a,4a-diaza-*s*-indacene-3-pentanoic acid (BODIPY® 581/591 C_5)	1 mg
D3806	2-(4,4-difluoro-5-(4-phenyl-1,3-butadienyl)-4-bora-3a,4a-diaza-*s*-indacene-3-pentanoyl)-1-hexadecanoyl-*sn*-glycero-3-phosphocholine (β-BODIPY® 581/591 C_5-HPC)	100 µg
D3861	4,4-difluoro-5-(4-phenyl-1,3-butadienyl)-4-bora-3a,4a-diaza-*s*-indacene-3-undecanoic acid (BODIPY® 581/591 C_{11})	1 mg
D3859	4,4-difluoro-5-(2-pyrrolyl)-4-bora-3a,4a-diaza-*s*-indacene-3-undecanoic acid (BODIPY® 576/589 C_{11})	1 mg
D3838	4,4-difluoro-5-styryl-4-bora-3a,4a-diaza-*s*-indacene-3-pentanoic acid (BODIPY® 564/570 C_5)	1 mg
D3839	4,4-difluoro-5-styryl-4-bora-3a,4a-diaza-*s*-indacene-3-undecanoic acid (BODIPY® 564/570 C_{11})	1 mg
D3835	4,4-difluoro-5-(2-thienyl)-4-bora-3a,4a-diaza-*s*-indacene-3-dodecanoic acid (BODIPY® 558/568 C_{12})	1 mg
D94	11-((5-dimethylaminonaphthalene-1-sulfonyl)amino)undecanoic acid (DAUDA)	100 mg
D57	*N*-(5-dimethylaminonaphthalene-1-sulfonyl)-1,2-dihexadecanoyl-*sn*-glycero-3-phosphoethanolamine, triethylammonium salt (dansyl DHPE)	25 mg
D23739	*N*-((6-(2,4-dinitrophenyl)amino)hexanoyl)-2-(4,4-difluoro-5,7-dimethyl-4-bora-3a,4a-diaza-*s*-indacene-3-pentanoyl)-1-hexadecanoyl-*sn*-glycero-3-phosphoethanolamine, triethylammonium salt (PED6)	1 mg
D476	2-(3-(diphenylhexatrienyl)propanoyl)-1-hexadecanoyl-*sn*-glycero-3-phosphocholine (β-DPH HPC)	1 mg
D3811	*N*-(DMNB-caged fluorescein)-1,2-dihexadecanoyl-*sn*-glycero-3-phosphoethanolamine, triethylammonium salt	1 mg
F362	*N*-(fluorescein-5-thiocarbamoyl)-1,2-dihexadecanoyl-*sn*-glycero-3-phosphoethanolamine, triethylammonium salt (fluorescein DHPE)	5 mg
H3790	1-hexadecanoyl-2-(3-perylenedodecanoyl)-*sn*-glycero-3-phosphocholine	1 mg
H361	1-hexadecanoyl-2-(1-pyrenedecanoyl)-*sn*-glycero-3-phosphocholine (β-py-C_{10}-HPC)	1 mg
H3809	1-hexadecanoyl-2-(1-pyrenedecanoyl)-*sn*-glycero-3-phosphoglycerol, ammonium salt (β-py-C_{10}-PG)	1 mg
H3810	1-hexadecanoyl-2-(1-pyrenedecanoyl)-*sn*-glycero-3-phosphomethanol, sodium salt (β-py-C_{10}-HPM)	1 mg
H3818	1-hexadecanoyl-2-(1-pyrenehexanoyl)-*sn*-glycero-3-phosphocholine (β-py-C_6-HPC)	1 mg
L1392	Lissamine™ rhodamine B 1,2-dihexadecanoyl-*sn*-glycero-3-phosphoethanolamine, triethylammonium salt (rhodamine DHPE)	5 mg
M1618	*N*-((4-maleimidylmethyl)cyclohexane-1-carbonyl)-1,2-dihexadecanoyl-*sn*-glycero-3-phosphoethanolamine, triethylammonium salt (MMCC DHPE)	5 mg
M12652	Marina Blue® 1,2-dihexadecanoyl-*sn*-glycero-3-phosphoethanolamine (Marina Blue® DHPE)	1 mg
N678	12-(*N*-(7-nitrobenz-2-oxa-1,3-diazol-4-yl)amino)dodecanoic acid	100 mg
N3787	2-(12-(7-nitrobenz-2-oxa-1,3-diazol-4-yl)amino)dodecanoyl-1-hexadecanoyl-*sn*-glycero-3-phosphocholine (NBD C_{12}-HPC)	5 mg
N316	6-(*N*-(7-nitrobenz-2-oxa-1,3-diazol-4-yl)amino)hexanoic acid (NBD-X)	100 mg
N3786	2-(6-(7-nitrobenz-2-oxa-1,3-diazol-4-yl)amino)hexanoyl-1-hexadecanoyl-*sn*-glycero-3-phosphocholine (NBD C_6-HPC)	5 mg
N360	*N*-(7-nitrobenz-2-oxa-1,3-diazol-4-yl)-1,2-dihexadecanoyl-*sn*-glycero-3-phosphoethanolamine, triethylammonium salt (NBD-PE)	10 mg
O12650	Oregon Green® 488 1,2-dihexadecanoyl-*sn*-glycero-3-phosphoethanolamine (Oregon Green® 488 DHPE)	1 mg
P22652	Pacific Blue™ 1,2-ditetradecanoyl-*sn*-glycero-3-phosphoethanolamine, triethylammonium salt (Pacific Blue™ DMPE)	1 mg
P36005	*cis*-parinaric acid *3 mM in ethanol*	10 mL
P646	3-perylenedodecanoic acid	10 mg
P1903MP	1-pyrenebutanoic acid *high purity*	100 mg
P31	1-pyrenedecanoic acid	25 mg
P96	1-pyrenedodecanoic acid	25 mg
P243	1-pyrenehexadecanoic acid	5 mg
P3840	1-pyrenehexanoic acid	100 mg
P58	*N*-(1-pyrenesulfonyl)-1,2-dihexadecanoyl-*sn*-glycero-3-phosphoethanolamine, triethylammonium salt (pyS DHPE)	25 mg
P1619MP	*N*-((2-pyridyldithio)propionyl)-1,2-dihexadecanoyl-*sn*-glycero-3-phosphoethanolamine, triethylammonium salt (PDP DHPE)	5 mg
R7712	Rhodamine Red™-X 1,2-dihexadecanoyl-*sn*-glycero-3-phosphoethanolamine, triethylammonium salt (Rhodamine Red™-X DHPE)	1 mg
T1391	*N*-(6-tetramethylrhodaminethiocarbamoyl)-1,2-dihexadecanoyl-*sn*-glycero-3-phosphoethanolamine, triethylammonium salt (TRITC DHPE)	1 mg
T1395MP	Texas Red® 1,2-dihexadecanoyl-*sn*-glycero-3-phosphoethanolamine, triethylammonium salt (Texas Red® DHPE)	1 mg
T7710	Texas Red®-X 1,2-dihexadecanoyl-*sn*-glycero-3-phosphoethanolamine, triethylammonium salt (Texas Red®-X DHPE)	1 mg

For current prices or to order online, visit probes.invitrogen.com

13.3 Sphingolipids, Steroids, Lipopolysaccharides and Related Probes

Sphingolipids

Structure and Activity

Sphingolipids are essential components of the plasma membrane of eukaryotic cells, where they are typically found in the outer leaflet. Although particularly abundant in mammalian cells, sphingolipids are also present in *Saccharomyces cerevisiae*,[1] other fungi and plants. Sphingolipids differ from phospholipids in being based on a lipophilic amino alcohol (sphingosine, Figure 13.3) rather than glycerol. Sphingolipids play important roles in signal transduction processes[2,3] (Chapter 17). Genetic defects in enzymes in the metabolic pathways of sphingolipid synthesis and degradation, including those involved in type I Gaucher's (Ashkenazi) disease, type A Niemann–Pick disease and Krabbe's disease,[4–8] and other lysosomal storage diseases, can be detected at the cellular level using our fluorescent analogs of sphingolipids. Ceramides are the biological building blocks of more complex sphingolipids. Metabolism of ceramides typically occurs in Golgi and endoplasmic reticulum membranes, and fluorescent ceramide analogs (Section 12.4) are important probes for measuring the intracellular distribution and transport of the labeled molecules in live cells.[9] If the hydroxyl group of the ceramide is esterified to phosphocholine, the sphingolipid is a sphingomyelin (Figure 13.3). The main pathway of sphingomyelin biosynthesis in mammalian cells is based on the transfer of phosphocholine from glycerophosphocholine to ceramide, catalyzed by sphingomyelin synthase in the Golgi membrane. Synthesis is followed by exocytosis of the sphingomyelin to the plasma membrane, apparently via a vesicular pathway and flip-flop to the outer membrane.[2] Sphingomyelinases, which are functionally analogous to phospholipase C in their chemistry, hydrolyze sphingomyelins back to ceramides. Generation of ceramides by hydrolysis of sphingomyelins appears to play a role in mediating the effects of exposure to tumor necrosis factor–α[10] (TNF-α), γ-interferon and several other agents, all of which induce an apoptosis-like cell death.[11–15] Molecular Probes' extensive assortment of reagents for following the diverse morphological and biochemical changes that occur during apoptosis are described in Section 15.5. Sensitive fluorescence-based measurements of sphingomyelinase activity using totally natural, unlabeled sphingomyelin as the substrate can be carried out using our Amplex® Red Sphingomyelinase Assay Kit (A12220), described below.

In glycosylsphingolipids, the free hydroxyl group of the ceramide is glycosylated to give a sphingosyl glycoside (cerebroside, Figure 13.29) or a ganglioside (Figure 13.30). These glycosphingolipids form cell-type–specific patterns at the cell surface that change with cell growth, differentiation, viral transformation and oncogenesis.[16] Glycosphingolipids interact at the cell surface with toxins, viruses and bacteria, as well as with receptors and enzymes[17] and are involved in cell-type–specific adhesion processes.[16] Gangliosides modulate the trophic factor–stimulated dimerization, tyrosine phosphorylation and subsequent signal transduction events of several tyrosine kinase receptors.[17] Ganglioside G_{M1} has antineurotoxic, neuroprotective and neurorestorative effects on various central neurotransmitter systems.[18] Gangliosides, including ganglioside G_{M1}, partition into lipid rafts — detergent-insoluble, sphingolipid- and cholesterol-rich membrane microdomains that form lateral assemblies in the plasma membrane.[19–25] Molecular Probes offers Vybrant® Lipid Raft Labeling Kits (V34403, V34404, V34405; see below), as well as Alexa Fluor® dye conjugates of subunit B of cholera toxin (Section 7.7), a protein that selectively binds to ganglioside G_{M1} in lipid rafts. We also offer sphingolipid arrays on nitrocellulose membranes (SphingoStrips, Section 17.4) for analyzing sphingolipid–protein interaction specificity.

BODIPY® Sphingolipids

Ceramides (*N*-acylsphingosines), like diacylglycerols, are lipid second messengers that function in signal transduction processes.[26–28] The concentration-dependent spectral properties of Molecular Probes' BODIPY® FL C_5-ceramide (D3521, B22650; Figure 13.31), BODIPY® FL C_5-sphingomyelin[29–31] (D3522, Figure 13.32) and BODIPY® FL C_{12}-sphingomyelin[32] (D7711) make them particularly suitable for investigating sphingolipid transport and metabolism,[31,33–36] in addition to their applications as structural markers for the Golgi complex[37] (Section 12.4, Figure 12.51). BODIPY® FL C_5-ceramide can be visualized by fluorescence microscopy[38,39] (Figure

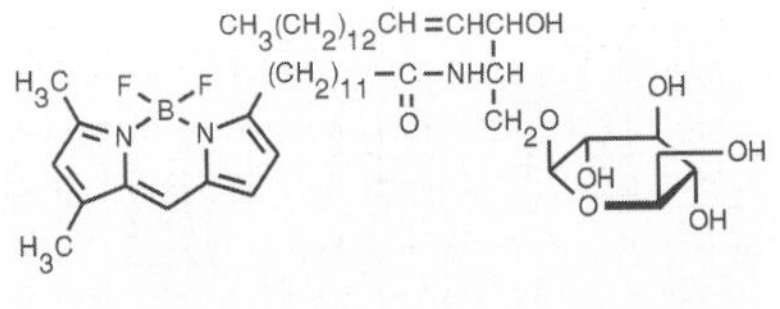

Figure 13.29 D7547 *N*-(4,4-difluoro-5,7-dimethyl-4-bora-3a,4a-diaza-*s*-indacene-3-dodecanoyl)sphingosyl 1-β-D-glucopyranoside (BODIPY® FL C_{12}-glucocerebroside).

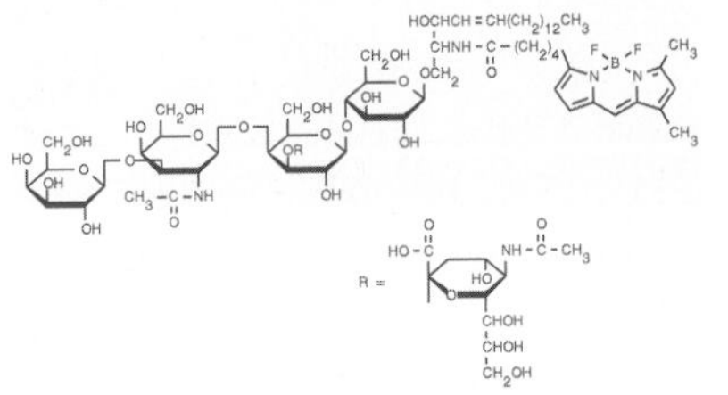

Figure 13.30 B13950 BODIPY® FL C_5-ganglioside G_{M1}.

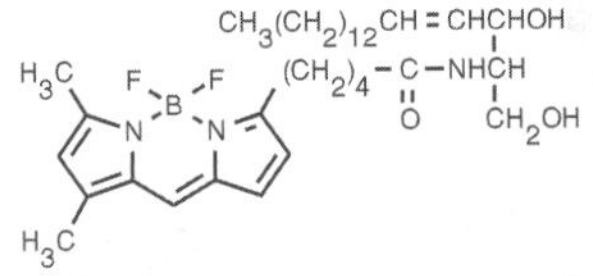

Figure 13.31 D3521 *N*-(4,4-difluoro-5,7-dimethyl-4-bora-3a,4a-diaza-*s*-indacene-3-pentanoyl)sphingosine (BODIPY® FL C_5-ceramide).

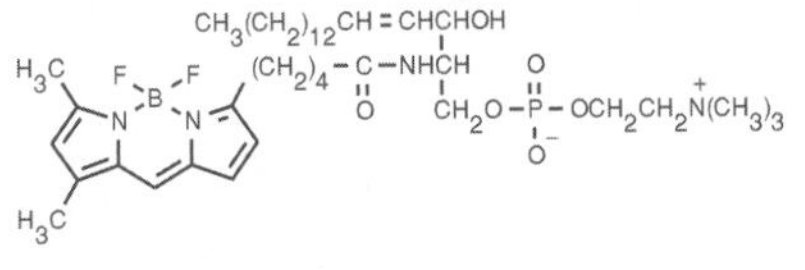

Figure 13.32 D3522 *N*-(4,4-difluoro-5,7-dimethyl-4-bora-3a,4a-diaza-*s*-indacene-3-pentanoyl)sphingosyl phosphocholine (BODIPY® FL C_5-sphingomyelin).

12.51, Figure 13.54, Figure 17.39) or by electron microscopy following diaminobenzidine (DAB) photoconversion to an electron-dense product.[40] (see Note 14.2 "Product Highlight: Fluorescent Probes for Photoconversion of Diaminobenzidine Reagents" in Section 14.3).

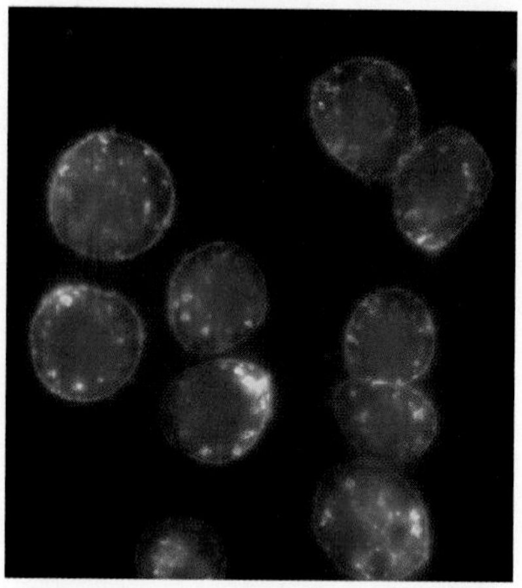

Figure 13.33 Live J774 macrophage cells labeled with BODIPY® FL C_5-ganglioside G_{M1} (B13950) and then with Alexa Fluor® 555 cholera toxin subunit B conjugate (C22843; also available as a component of V34404). Cells were then treated with anti–CT-B antibody (a component of V34404) to induce crosslinking. Yellow fluorescence indicates colocalization of the two dyes. Nuclei were stained with the blue fluorescent Hoechst 33342 dye (H1399, H3570, H21492).

Our range of BODIPY® sphingolipids also includes the long-wavelength light–excitable BODIPY® TR ceramide[41,42] (D7540, Figure 17.40), as well as BODIPY® FL C_5-lactosylceramide[43–48] (D13951), BODIPY® FL C_5-ganglioside G_{M1}[49] (B13950, Figure 13.30) and three BODIPY® FL cerebrosides[35,50] (glycosylated ceramides; D7519, D7547, D7548). All of Molecular Probes' sphingolipids are prepared from D-*erythro*-sphingosine and therefore have the same stereochemical conformation as natural biologically active sphingolipids.[51]

Complexing fluorescent lipids with bovine serum albumin (BSA) facilitates cell labeling by eliminating the need for organic solvents to dissolve the lipophilic probe — the BSA-complexed probe can be directly dissolved in water.[52] We offer four BODIPY® sphingolipid–BSA complexes for the study of lipid metabolism and trafficking, including BODIPY® FL C_5-ceramide, BODIPY® TR C_5-ceramide, BODIPY® FL C_5-ganglioside G_{M1} and BODIPY® FL C_5-lactosylceramide, each complexed with defatted BSA (B22650, B34400, B34401, B34402).

BODIPY® FL C_5-ceramide has been used to investigate the linkage of sphingolipid metabolism to protein secretory pathways[53–55] and neuronal growth.[46,56] Internalization of BODIPY® FL C_5-sphingomyelin (D3522) from the plasma membrane of human skin fibroblasts results in a mixed population of labeled endosomes that can be distinguished based on the concentration-dependent green (~515 nm) or red (~620 nm) emission of the probe[31] (Figure 12.51). BODIPY® C_5-sphingomyelin has also been used to assess sphingomyelinase gene transfer and expression in hematopoietic stem and progenitor cells.[4] Our BODIPY® FL C_5-lactosylceramide, BODIPY® FL C_5-ganglioside G_{M1} and BODIPY® FL cerebrosides should be useful tools for the study of glycosphingolipid transport and signaling pathways in cells[57,58] and for diagnosis of lipid-storage disorders such as Niemann–Pick disease,[59] Gaucher's disease, G_{M1} gangliosidosis, Morquio's syndrome and type IV mucolipidosis[6,7,48,60–65] (ML-IV). Addition of BODIPY® FL C_5-lactosylceramide to the culture medium of cells from patients with sphingolipid-storage diseases (sphingolipidosis) results in fluorescent product accumulation in lysosomes, whereas this probe accumulates in the Golgi apparatus of normal cells and cells from patients with other storage diseases.[45,47] BODIPY® FL C_5-ganglioside G_{M1} has been shown to form cholesterol-enhanced clusters in membrane complexes with amyloid β-protein in a model of Alzheimer's disease amyolid fibrils.[66] Colocalization of fluorescent cholera toxin B conjugates (Section 7.7) and BODIPY® FL C_5-ganglioside G_{M1} observed by fluorescence microscopy provides a direct indication of the association of these molecules in lipid rafts[49] (Figure 13.33, Figure 17.41). Studies by Martin and Pagano have shown that the internalization routes for BODIPY® FL C_5-glucocerebroside (D7548) follow both endocytic and nonendocytic pathways and are quite different from those for BODIPY® FL C_5-sphingomyelin.[50]

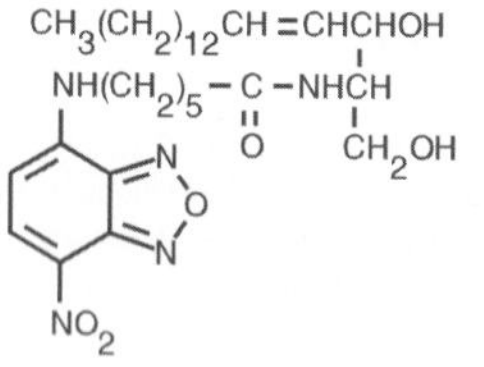

Figure 13.34 N1154 6-((*N*-(7-nitrobenz-2-oxa-1,3-diazol-4-yl)amino)hexanoyl)sphingosine (NBD C_6-ceramide).

NBD Sphingolipids

NBD C_6-ceramide (N1154, Figure 13.34) and NBD C_6-sphingomyelin (N3524) analogs predate their BODIPY® counterparts and have been extensively used for following sphingolipid metabolism in cells[9,57,67,68] and in multicellular organisms.[69] As with BODIPY® FL C_5-ceramide, we also offer NBD C_6-ceramide complexed with defatted BSA (N22651) to facilitate cell loading without the use of organic solvents to dissolve the probe.[52] Koval and Pagano have prepared NBD analogs of both the naturally occurring D-*erythro* and the nonnatural L-*threo* stereoisomers of sphingomyelin and have compared their intracellular transport behavior in Chinese hamster ovary (CHO) fibroblasts.[70]

NBD C_6-ceramide lacks the useful concentration-dependent optical properties of the BODIPY® FL analog and is less photostable; however, the fluorescence of NBD C_6-ceramide is apparently sensitive to the cholesterol content of the Golgi apparatus, a phenomenon that is not observed with BODIPY® FL C_5-ceramide. If NBD C_6-ceramide–containing cells are starved for cholesterol, the NBD C_6-ceramide that accumulates within the Golgi apparatus appears to be severely photolabile but this NBD photobleaching can be reduced by stimulation of cholesterol synthesis. Thus, NBD C_6-ceramide may be useful in monitoring the cholesterol content of the Golgi apparatus in live cells.[71]

Vybrant® Lipid Raft Labeling Kits

The Vybrant® Lipid Raft Labeling Kits (V34403, V34404, V34405) are designed to provide convenient, reliable and extremely bright fluorescent labeling of lipid rafts in live cells. Lipid rafts are detergent-insoluble, sphingolipid- and cholesterol-rich membrane microdomains that form lateral assemblies in the plasma membrane.[19–25] Lipid rafts also sequester glycophosphatidylinositol (GPI)-linked proteins and other signaling proteins and receptors, which may be regulated by their selective interactions with these membrane microdomains.[49,72–76] Recent research has demonstrated that lipid rafts play a role in a variety of cellular processes — including the compartmentalization of cell-signaling events,[77–84] the regulation of apoptosis[85–87] and the intracellular trafficking of certain membrane proteins and lipids[88–90] — as well as in the infectious cycles of several viruses and bacterial pathogens.[91–96] Examining the formation and regulation of lipid rafts is a critical step in understanding these aspects of eukaryotic cell function.

The Vybrant® Lipid Raft Labeling Kits (V34403, V34404, V34405) provide the key reagents for fluorescently labeling lipid rafts *in vivo* with our bright and extremely photostable Alexa Fluor® dyes (Figure 13.33, Figure 17.41). Live cells are first labeled with the green-fluorescent Alexa Fluor® 488, orange-fluorescent Alexa Fluor® 555 or red-fluorescent Alexa Fluor® 594 conjugate of cholera toxin subunit B (CT-B). This CT-B conjugate binds to the pentasaccharide chain of plasma membrane ganglioside G_{M1}, which selectively partitions into lipid rafts.[49,97,98] All of Molecular Probes' CT-B conjugates are prepared from recombinant CT-B and are completely free of the toxic subunit A, thus eliminating any concern for toxicity or ADP-ribosylating activity. An antibody that specifically recognizes CT-B is then used to crosslink the CT-B–labeled lipid rafts into distinct patches on the plasma membrane, which are easily visualized by fluorescence microscopy.[99,100] Each Vybrant® Lipid Raft Labeling Kit contains sufficient reagents to label 50 live-cell samples in a 2 mL assay, including:

- Recombinant cholera toxin subunit B (CT-B) labeled with the Alexa Fluor® 488 (in Kit V34403), Alexa Fluor® 555 (in Kit V34404) or Alexa Fluor® 594 (in Kit V34405) dye
- Anti–cholera toxin subunit B antibody (anti–CT-B)
- Concentrated phosphate-buffered saline (PBS)
- A detailed labeling protocol

Because they are compatible with various multilabeling schemes, the Vybrant® Lipid Raft Labeling Kits can also serve as important tools for identifying physiologically significant membrane proteins that associate with lipid rafts. Cells can be labeled with other live-cell probes during the lipid raft labeling protocol or immediately following the antibody crosslinking step, depending on the specific labeling requirements of the other probes. Alternatively, once the lipid rafts have been labeled and crosslinked, the cells can be fixed for long-term storage or fixed and permeabilized for subsequent labeling with antibodies or other probes that are impermeant to live cells.

Amplex® Red Sphingomyelinase Assay Kit

The Amplex® Red Sphingomyelinase Assay Kit (A12220) is designed for measuring sphingomyelinase activity in solution using a fluorescence microplate reader or fluorometer[101] (Figure 13.35). This assay should be useful for screening sphingomyelinase activators or inhibitors or for detecting sphingomyelinase activity in cell and tissue extracts. The assay, which uses natural sphingomyelin as the principal substrate, employs an enzyme-coupled detection scheme in which phosphocholine liberated by the action of sphingomyelinase is cleaved by alkaline phosphatase to generate choline. Choline is, in turn, oxidized by choline oxidase, generating H_2O_2, which drives the conversion of the Amplex® Red reagent (A12222, A22177; Section 10.5) to red-fluorescent resorufin (Figure 10.6). This sensitive assay technique has been employed to detect activation of acid sphingomyelinase associated with ultraviolet radiation–induced apoptosis[102] and to characterize an insecticidal sphingomyelinase C produced by *Bacillus cereus*.[103] The Amplex® Red Sphingomyelinase Assay Kit contains:

- Amplex® Red reagent
- Dimethylsulfoxide (DMSO)
- Horseradish peroxidase (HRP)
- H_2O_2 for use as a positive control
- Concentrated reaction buffer
- Choline oxidase from *Alcaligenes* sp.
- Alkaline phosphatase from calf intestine
- Sphingomyelin
- Triton X-100
- Sphingomyelinase from *Staphylococcus* sp.
- A detailed protocol

Each kit provides sufficient reagents for approximately 500 assays using a fluorescence microplate reader and a reaction volume of 200 µL per assay.

Steroids

Most steroids are neutral lipids and, as such, localize primarily within the cell's membranes, in lipid vacuoles and bound to certain lipoproteins. Our fluorescent analogs of these biomolecules, most of which are derived from our long-wavelength BODIPY® dyes, NBD dyes or pyrene dyes, are highly lipophilic probes. One application of these probes is to detect enzymatic activity — either *in vitro* or

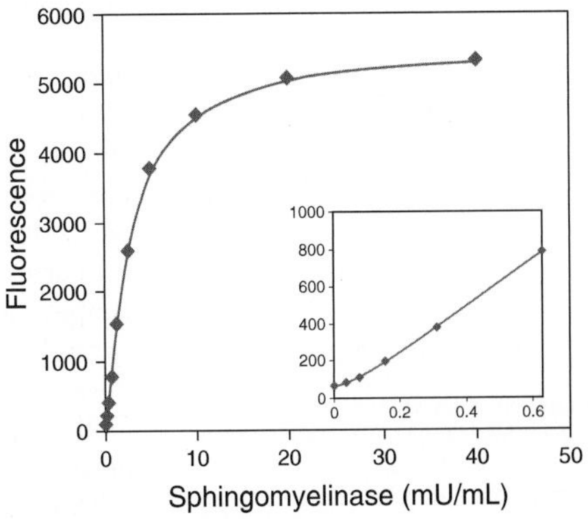

Figure 13.35 Measurement of sphingomyelinase activity using the Amplex® Red Sphingomyelinase Assay Kit (A12220). Each reaction contained 50 µM Amplex® Red reagent, 1 U/mL horseradish peroxidase (HRP), 0.1 U/mL choline oxidase, 4 U/mL of alkaline phosphatase, 0.25 mM sphingomyelin and the indicated amount of *Staphylococcus aureus* sphingomyelinase in 1X reaction buffer. Reactions were incubated at 37°C for one hour. Fluorescence was measured with a fluorescence microplate reader using excitation at 530 ± 12.5 nm and fluorescence detection at 590 ± 17.5 nm.

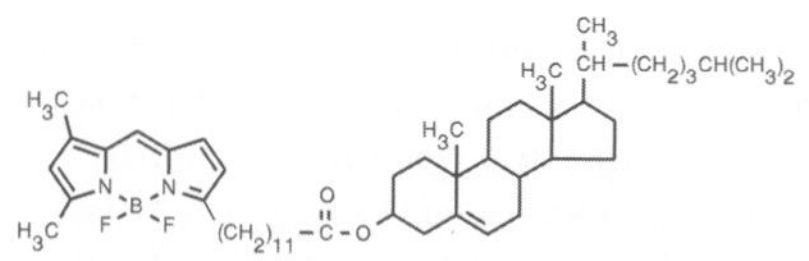

Figure 13.36 C3927MP cholesteryl 4,4-difluoro-5,7-dimethyl-4-bora-3a,4a-diaza-s-indacene-3-dodecanoate (cholesteryl BODIPY® FL C_{12}).

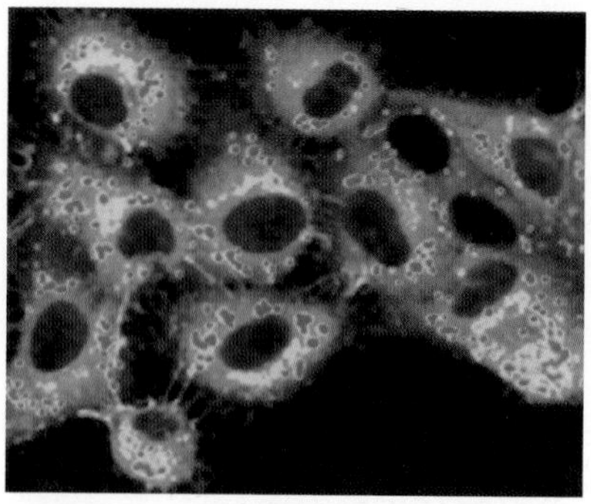

Figure 13.37 Selective uptake of cholesteryl esters (CE) in rat ovarian granulosa cells as monitored with cholesteryl BODIPY® FL C_{12} (C3927MP). The hormone-stimulated cells internalized and stored CEs derived from reconstituted high-density lipoprotein (HDL)–BODIPY® CE complexes (J Biol Chem 271, 16208 (1996)). A low-light (<100 µW beam power) computerized imaging system minimized any photobleaching of the fluorophore. This pseudocolored image uses yellow-green to illustrate the low-level fluorescence of the cytoplasmic membranes, yellow to illustrate the medium-level fluorescence of the Golgi, and red to illustrate the high-level fluorescence of the lipid droplets. Image contributed by Eve Reaven, VA Medical Center, Palo Alto, California.

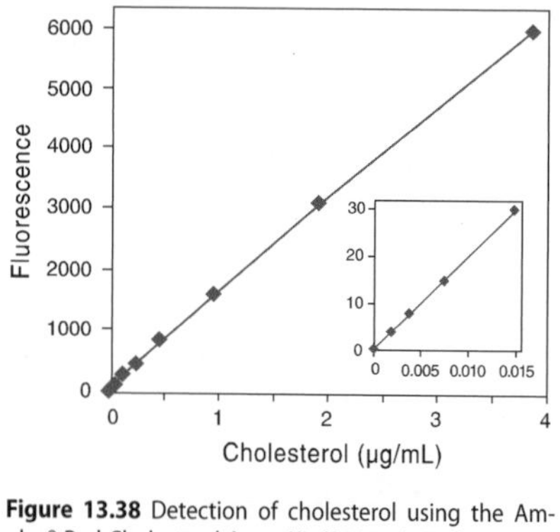

Figure 13.38 Detection of cholesterol using the Amplex® Red Cholesterol Assay Kit (A12216). Each reaction contained 150 µM Amplex® Red reagent, 1 U/mL HRP, 1 U/mL cholesterol oxidase, 1 U/mL cholesterol esterase and the indicated amount of cholesterol in 1X reaction buffer. Reactions were incubated at 37°C for 30 minutes. Fluorescence was measured with a fluorescence microplate reader using excitation at 560 ± 10 nm and fluorescence detection at 590 ± 10 nm. The inset shows the high sensitivity and excellent linearity of the assay at low levels of cholesterol (0–0.010 µg/mL).

in vivo — through hydrolysis of the fatty acid esters to fluorescent fatty acids.[104] Although the substrates and products typically have similar fluorescence properties, they are readily extracted by an organic solvent and separated by chromatography. Molecular Probes has also developed excellent fluorometric assays for cholesterol, cholesteryl esters and enzymes that metabolize natural cholesterol derivatives; the reagents for these are available in our Amplex® Red Cholesterol Assay Kits (A12216, see below).

Cholesteryl Esters

Cholesteryl esters consist of a fatty acid esterified to the 3β-hydroxyl group of cholesterol (Figure 13.36). These very nonpolar species are the predominant lipid components of atherosclerotic plaque and low- and high-density lipoprotein (LDL and HDL) cores. We offer cholesteryl esters of three of our BODIPY® fatty acids — BODIPY® FL C_{12} (C3927MP), BODIPY® 542/563 C_{11} (C12680) and BODIPY® 576/589 C_{11} (C12681) — all of which have long-wavelength visible emission and of diphenylhexatrienylpropionic acid (C7794), which has bright blue fluorescence only when it is in a lipid environment.[105] The BODIPY® FL cholesteryl ester (C3927MP) can be used as a tracer of cholesterol transport and receptor-mediated endocytosis of lipoproteins by fluorescence microscopy[106,107] (Figure 13.37) and as a general nonexchangeable membrane marker. Addition of methyl β-cyclodextrin to the BODIPY® FL cholesteryl ester is reported to facilitate its uptake by cells and tissues.[108] Researchers have extensively used our BODIPY® FL cholesteryl ester to measure cholesteryl ester–transfer protein (CETP) activity using fluorescence microplate readers.[109–112] The longer-wavelength BODIPY® 542/563 and BODIPY® 576/589 cholesteryl esters likely have similar applications.

Side Chain–Modified Cholesterol Analogs

Molecular Probes offers NBD- and pyrene-labeled cholesterol analogs in which the fluorophore replaces the terminal segment of cholesterol's flexible alkyl tail. Refer to Table 13.2 for a comparison of the spectral properties of these two fluorophores. The environment-sensitive NBD fluorophore of the NBD cholesterol analog (N1148) localizes in the membrane's interior, unlike the anomalous positioning of NBD-labeled phospholipid acyl chains[113] (Figure 13.1). As with other NBD lipid analogs, this probe is useful for investigating lipid transport processes[114,115] and lipid–protein interactions.[116,117] NBD cholesterol is selectively taken up by high-density lipoproteins via the scavenger receptor B1.[114] A lipid droplet–specific protein binds unesterified NBD cholesterol with extremely high affinity[114] (K_d = 2 nM). PMC oleate (P226) has been used to label LDL to detect receptor binding and internalization[118–121] and in acetylated LDL for following receptor-mediated endocytosis by the scavenger pathway[122] and also for selective photosensitization of cultured cells containing LDL receptors.[120]

Amplex® Red Cholesterol Assay Kit

The Amplex® Red Cholesterol Assay Kit (A12216) provides an exceptionally sensitive assay for both cholesterol and cholesteryl esters in complex mixtures that is suitable for use with either fluorescence microplate readers or fluorometers. The assay provided in this kit can detect as little as 5 ng/mL (5×10^{-4} mg/dL) cholesterol (Figure 13.38) and can accurately measure the cholesterol or cholesteryl ester content in the equivalent of 0.01 µL of human serum.[123] The assay uses an enzyme-coupled reaction scheme in which cholesteryl esters are hydrolyzed by cholesterol esterase into cholesterol, which is then oxidized by cholesterol oxidase to yield H_2O_2 and the corresponding ketone steroidal product (Figure 10.65). The H_2O_2 is then detected using the Amplex® Red reagent in combination with horseradish peroxidase (HRP). The Amplex® Red cholesterol assay is continuous and requires no separation or wash steps. These characteristics make the assay particularly well suited for the rapid and direct analysis of cholesterol in blood and food samples using automated instruments. By performing two separate measurements in the presence and absence of cholesterol esterase, this assay is also potentially useful for determining the fraction of cholesterol that is in the form of cholesteryl esters within a sample. In addition, by adding an excess of cholesterol to the reaction, this assay can be used to sensitively detect the activity of cholesterol oxidase. The Amplex® Red Cholesterol Assay Kit contains:

- Amplex® Red reagent
- Dimethylsulfoxide (DMSO)
- Horseradish peroxidase (HRP)
- H_2O_2 for use as a positive control

- Concentrated reaction buffer
- Cholesterol oxidase from *Streptomyces* sp.
- Cholesterol esterase from *Pseudomonas* sp.
- Cholesterol for preparation of a standard curve
- A detailed protocol

Each kit provides sufficient reagents for approximately 500 assays using a fluorescence microplate reader and a reaction volume of 100 µL per assay.

Fluorescent Triacylglycerol

The fluorescent triacylglycerol (1,2-dioleoyl-3-(1-pyrenedodecanoyl)-*rac*-glycerol (D6562) has a pyrene fatty acid ester replacing one of the three fatty acyl residues of a natural triacylglycerol (Figure 13.39). Pyrene has the important spectral property of forming excimers (Figure 13.8) when two fluorophores are in close proximity during the excited state. Pyrene triacylglycerols are useful for measuring cholesteryl ester transfer protein–mediated triacylglycerol transport between plasma lipoproteins.[124] It is also an excellent substrate for lipoprotein lipase and hepatic triacylglycerol lipase.[125]

Lipopolysaccharides

Molecular Probes offers fluorescent conjugates of lipopolysaccharides (LPS) from *Escherichia coli* and *Salmonella minnesota* (Section 16.1, Table 16.1) with three of our Alexa Fluor® dyes and with our BODIPY® FL fluorophore. LPS or endotoxins are complex macromolecules present on the outer cell walls of gram-negative bacteria. Recognition of LPS by binding to the CD14 cell-surface receptor of phagocytes (Figure 16.9) is the key initiation step in the mammalian immune response to infection by gram-negative bacteria. The structural core of LPS, and the primary determinant of its biological activity, is the *N*-acetylglucosamine derivative, lipid A (Figure 16.10). Two plasma proteins, LPS-binding protein (LBP) and soluble CD14 (sCD14), play primary roles in transporting LPS and mediating cellular responses.[126–131] If the fatty acid residues are removed from the lipid A component, the toxicity of the LPS can be reduced significantly. However, the mono- or diphosphoryl forms of lipid A are inherently toxic. In many gram-negative bacterial infections, LPS are responsible for clinically significant symptoms like fever, low blood pressure and tissue edema, which can lead to disseminated intravascular coagulation, organ failure and death. Studies also clearly indicate that LPS induce various signal transduction pathways, including those involving protein kinase C[132,133] and protein myristylation,[134] and stimulate a variety of immunochemical responses, including B lymphocyte[135] and G-protein activation.[136]

Our fluorescent BODIPY® FL and Alexa Fluor® LPS conjugates, which are labeled with succinimidyl esters of these dyes, allow researchers to follow LPS binding, transport and cell internalization processes. Lipopolysaccharide internalization activates endotoxin-dependent signal transduction in cardiomyocytes.[137] The Alexa Fluor® 488 LPS conjugates (L23351, L23356) selectively label microglia in a mixed culture containing oligodendrocyte precursors, astrocytes and microglia.[138] A biologically active conjugate of galactose oxidase–oxidized *S. minnesota* LPS and our Alexa Fluor® 488 hydrazide (A10436, Section 3.2; A10440, Section 14.3) has been used to elucidate molecular mechanisms of septic shock.[139] Aggregation of the BODIPY® FL derivative of *S. minnesota* strain R595 (L23355) in aqueous solution results in a spectral shift of the BODIPY® FL dye's emission maximum to ~620 nm. Addition of LBP results in a relatively small fluorescence increase, indicating that LPS remain aggregated upon binding. Subsequent addition of sCD14 results in a large increase in fluorescence intensity and a shift in emission maximum to ~510 nm, indicating LBP-mediated transfer of monomeric LPS to sCD14.[128] In one study, a BODIPY® FL derivative of LPS from *E. coli* strain LCD25 (L23350) was used to measure the transfer rate of LPS from monocytes to high-density lipoprotein[140] (HDL). Another study utilized a BODIPY® FL derivative of LPS from *S. minnesota* to demonstrate transport to the Golgi apparatus in neutrophils,[126,127] although this could have been due to probe metabolism. It has been reported that organelles other than the Golgi are labeled by some fluorescent or nonfluorescent LPS.[141,142] Cationic lipids are reported to assist the translocation of fluorescent lipopolysaccharides into live cells;[143] cell surface–bound LPS can be quenched by trypan blue[140] (Figure 16.24). Molecular Probes' fluorescent LPS can potentially be combined with other fluorescent indicators, such as Ca^{2+}-, pH- or organelle-specific stains, for monitoring intracellular localization and real-time changes in cellular response to LPS. We also offer the Pro-Q® Emerald 300 Lipopolysaccharide Gel Stain Kit (P20495, Section 3.2), which permits ultrasensitive analysis of unlabeled lipopolysaccharides in gel electrophoretograms (Figure 3.19, Figure 3.20, Figure 3.21).

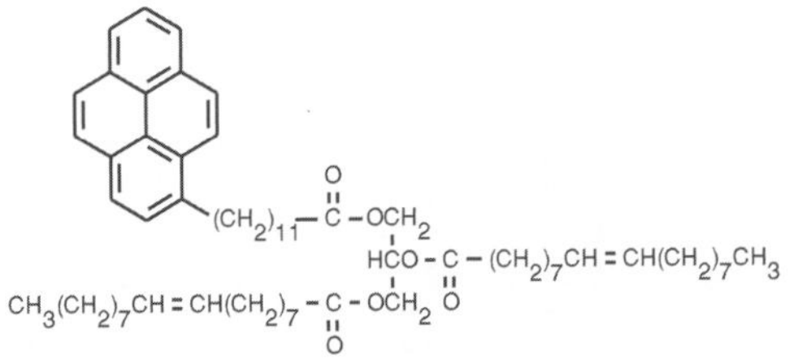

Figure 13.39 D6562 1,2-dioleoyl-3-(1-pyrenedodecanoyl)-*rac*-glycerol.

References

1. Annu Rev Biochem 67, 27 (1998); **2.** Prog Lipid Res 36, 153 (1997); **3.** Biochim Biophys Acta 1436, 233 (1998); **4.** Blood 93, 80 (1999); **5.** Biochim Biophys Acta 793, 169 (1984); **6.** Clin Chim Acta 124, 123 (1982); **7.** Clin Chim Acta 142, 313 (1984); **8.** J Cell Biol 111, 429 (1990); **9.** Methods Cell Biol 38, 221 (1993); **10.** J Biol Chem 268, 17762 (1993); **11.** Cell Signal 10, 685 (1998); **12.** Trends Biochem Sci 20, 73 (1995); **13.** Curr Opin Oncol 10, 552 (1998); **14.** J Inherit Metab Dis 21, 472 (1998); **15.** Science 259, 1769 (1993); **16.** Ann N Y Acad Sci 845, 139 (1998); **17.** Ann N Y Acad Sci 845, 57 (1998); **18.** J Neurochem 70, 1335 (1998); **19.** J Cell Biol 162, 365 (2003); **20.** J Lipid Res 44, 655 (2003); **21.** Eur J Biochem 269, 737 (2002); **22.** Science 290, 1721 (2000); **23.** Mol Membr Biol 16, 145 (1999); **24.** Trends Cell Biol 9, 87 (1999); **25.** Annu Rev Cell Dev Biol 14, 111 (1998); **26.** Biochemistry 40, 4893 (2001); **27.** Trends Cell Biol 10, 408 (2000); **28.** J Biol Chem 269, 3125 (1994); **29.** Chem Phys Lipids 102, 55 (1999); **30.** Ann N Y Acad Sci 845, 152 (1998); **31.** Biophys J 72, 37 (1997); **32.** J Cell Biol 140, 39 (1998); **33.** Methods Enzymol 312, 293 (2000); **34.** Methods Enzymol 312, 523 (2000); **35.** Frontiers in Bioactive Lipids, Vanderhoek JV, Ed. pp. 203–213 (1996); **36.** J Cell Biol 134, 1031 (1996); **37.** J Cell Biol 113, 1267

References — continued

(1991); **38.** Cytometry 14, 251 (1993); **39.** J Cell Biol 120, 399 (1993); **40.** Eur J Cell Biol 58, 214 (1992); **41.** Mol Biochem Parasitol 106, 21 (2000); **42.** Infect Immun 68, 5960 (2000); **43.** J Cell Biol 154, 535 (2001); **44.** Am J Physiol Lung Cell Mol Physiol 280, L938 (2001); **45.** Nat Cell Biol 1, 386 (1999); **46.** J Neurochem 73, 1375 (1999); **47.** Lancet 354, 901 (1999); **48.** Proc Natl Acad Sci U S A 95, 6373 (1998); **49.** J Cell Biol 147, 447 (1999); **50.** J Cell Biol 125, 769 (1994); **51.** Biophys J 77, 1498 (1999); **52.** Cell Biology: A Laboratory Handbook, 2nd Ed., Vol. 2, Celis JE, Ed. pp. 507–512 (1998); **53.** Mol Biol Cell 6, 135 (1995); **54.** J Biol Chem 268, 4577 (1993); **55.** Biochemistry 31, 3581 (1992); **56.** J Biol Chem 268, 14476 (1993); **57.** Biochim Biophys Acta 1113, 277 (1992); **58.** Brain Res 597, 108 (1992); **59.** Anal Biochem 293, 204 (2001); **60.** Biochim Biophys Acta 1455, 85 (1999); **61.** Traffic 1, 807 (2000); **62.** J Biol Chem 268, 14861 (1993); **63.** Biochim Biophys Acta 915, 87 (1987); **64.** Biochem Biophys Res Comm 18, 221 (1965); **65.** Anal Biochem 136, 223 (1984); **66.** J Biol Chem 276, 24985 (2001); **67.** Adv Cell Mol Biol Membranes 1, 199 (1993); **68.** Biochim Biophys Acta 1082, 113 (1991); **69.** Parasitology 105, 81 (1992); **70.** J Cell Biol 108, 2169 (1989); **71.** Proc Natl Acad Sci U S A 90, 2661 (1993); **72.** Proc Natl Acad Sci U S A 100, 5813 (2003); **73.** J Immunol 170, 1329 (2003); **74.** J Membr Biol 189, 35 (2002); **75.** Proc Natl Acad Sci U S A 98, 9098 (2001); **76.** Mol Biol Cell 10, 3187 (1999); **77.** Biochim Biophys Acta 1610, 247 (2003); **78.** Annu Rev Immunol 21, 457 (2003); **79.** Mol Immunol 38, 1247 (2002); **80.** Nat Rev Immunol 2, 96 (2002); **81.** Biol Res 35, 127 (2002); **82.** Nat Rev Mol Cell Biol 1, 31 (2000); **83.** J Exp Med 190, 1549 (1999); **84.** J Cell Biol 143, 637 (1998); **85.** Immunity 18, 655 (2003); **86.** J Biol Chem 277, 39541 (2002); **87.** Biochem Biophys Res Commun 297, 876 (2002); **88.** Biol Chem 383, 1475 (2002); **89.** J Cell Biol 153, 529 (2001); **90.** J Cell Sci 114, 3957 (2001); **91.** J Virol 77, 9542 (2003); **92.** Exp Cell Res 287, 67 (2003); **93.** Traffic 3, 705 (2002); **94.** J Clin Virol 22, 217 (2001); **95.** Curr Biol 10, R823 (2000); **96.** J Virol 74, 3264 (2000); **97.** Biochemistry 35, 16069 (1996); **98.** Mol Microbiol 13, 745 (1994); **99.** J Cell Biol 141, 929 (1998); **100.** J Biol Chem 269, 30745 (1994); **101.** Am J Pathol 161, 1061 (2002); **102.** J Biol Chem 276, 11775 (2001); **103.** Eur J Biochem 271, 601 (2004); **104.** J Lipid Res 36, 1602 (1995); **105.** Biochim Biophys Acta 735, 418 (1983); **106.** Proc Natl Acad Sci U S A 98, 1613 (2001); **107.** J Biol Chem 272, 25283 (1997); **108.** Am J Physiol 277, G1017 (1999); **109.** Biochemistry 34, 12560 (1995); **110.** Chem Phys Lipids 77, 51 (1995); **111.** Lipids 29, 811 (1994); **112.** J Lipid Res 34, 1625 (1993); **113.** J Phys Chem 103, 8180 (1999); **114.** J Biol Chem 275, 12769 (2000); **115.** J Lipid Res 40, 1747 (1999); **116.** Biochim Biophys Acta 1437, 37 (1999); **117.** J Biol Chem 274, 35425 (1999); **118.** J Biol Chem 273, 26138 (1998); **119.** Exp Cell Res 155, 389 (1984); **120.** Proc Natl Acad Sci U S A 78, 5717 (1981); **121.** J Supramol Struct 10, 467 (1979); **122.** J Biol Chem 269, 7631 (1994); **123.** J Biochem Biophys Methods 38, 43 (1999); **124.** J Biochem (Tokyo) 124, 237 (1998); **125.** Lipids 23, 605 (1988); **126.** J Exp Med 190, 523 (1999); **127.** J Exp Med 190, 509 (1999); **128.** J Biol Chem 271, 4100 (1996); **129.** J Exp Med 181, 1743 (1995); **130.** J Exp Med 180, 1025 (1994); **131.** J Exp Med 179, 269 (1994); **132.** J Biol Chem 259, 10048 (1984); **133.** J Exp Med 183, 1899 (1996); **134.** Proc Natl Acad Sci U S A 83, 5817 (1986); **135.** Adv Immunol 28, 293 (1979); **136.** Eur J Immunol 19, 125 (1989); **137.** Circ Res 88, 491 (2001); **138.** J Neurosci 22, 2478 (2002); **139.** Cytometry 41, 316 (2000); **140.** J Biol Chem 274, 34116 (1999); **141.** Electron Microsc Rev 5, 381 (1992); **142.** J Periodontol 56, 553 (1985); **143.** Biotechniques 28, 510 (2000).

Data Table — 13.3 Sphingolipids, Steroids, Lipopolysaccharides and Related Probes

Cat #	MW	Storage	Soluble	Abs	EC	Em	Solvent	Notes
A7509	341.53	F	DMSO, EtOH	<300		none		
B13950	1582.50	F,D,L	DMSO, EtOH	505	80,000	512	MeOH	1
B22650	~66,000	F,D,L	H_2O	505	91,000	511	MeOH	1, 2
B34400	~66,000	F,D,L	H_2O	589	65,000	616	MeOH	2
B34401	~66,000	F,D,L	H_2O	505	80,000	512	MeOH	1, 2
B34402	~66,000	F,D,L	H_2O	505	80,000	511	MeOH	1, 2
C212	656.99	D,L	$CHCl_3$	342	42,000	376	MeOH	3, 4
C3927MP	786.98	F,D,L	$CHCl_3$	505	86,000	511	MeOH	5
C7794	673.03	F,D,L	$CHCl_3$	361	81,000	430	$CHCl_3$	6
C12680	851.02	F,D,L	$CHCl_3$	543	57,000	563	MeOH	5
C12681	809.97	F,D,L	$CHCl_3$	579	98,000	590	MeOH	5
D3521	601.63	FF,D,L	$CHCl_3$, DMSO	505	91,000	511	MeOH	1
D3522	766.75	FF,D,L	see Notes	505	77,000	512	MeOH	1, 7
D6562	1003.54	FF,D,L,A	$CHCl_3$	341	40,000	376	MeOH	3, 4
D7519	861.96	FF,D,L	DMSO, EtOH	505	85,000	511	MeOH	1
D7540	705.71	FF,D,L	$CHCl_3$, DMSO	589	65,000	616	MeOH	
D7546	759.42	FF,D,L	$CHCl_3$, DMSO	533	80,000	545	MeOH	
D7547	861.96	FF,D,L	DMSO, EtOH	505	85,000	511	MeOH	1
D7548	763.77	FF,D,L	DMSO, EtOH	505	85,000	511	MeOH	1
D7711	864.94	FF,D,L	DMSO	505	75,000	513	MeOH	1, 8
D13951	925.91	FF,D,L	DMSO, EtOH	505	80,000	511	MeOH	1
N1148	494.63	L	$CHCl_3$, MeCN	469	21,000	537	MeOH	
N1154	575.75	FF,D,L	$CHCl_3$, DMSO	466	22,000	536	MeOH	9
N3524	740.88	FF,D,L	see Notes	466	22,000	536	MeOH	7, 9
N22651	~66,000	F,D,L	H_2O	466	22,000	536	MeOH	2, 9
P226	825.22	FF,D,L,A	$CHCl_3$, MeCN	344	44,000	377	$CHCl_3$	3, 4

For definitions of the contents of this data table, see "Navigating *The Handbook*" in the introductory pages.

Notes

1. Em for BODIPY® FL sphingolipids shifts to ~620 nm when high concentrations of the probe (>5 mol %) are incorporated in lipid mixtures (J Cell Biol 113, 1267 (1991)).
2. This product is a lipid complexed with bovine serum albumin (BSA). Spectroscopic data are for the free lipid in MeOH.
3. Alkylpyrene fluorescence lifetimes are up to 110 nanoseconds and are very sensitive to oxygen.
4. Pyrene derivatives exhibit structured spectra. The absorption maximum is usually about 340 nm with a subsidiary peak at about 325 nm. There are also strong absorption peaks below 300 nm. The emission maximum is usually about 376 nm with a subsidiary peak at 396 nm. Excimer emission at about 470 nm may be observed at high concentrations.
5. The absorption and fluorescence spectra of BODIPY® derivatives are relatively insensitive to the solvent.
6. Diphenylhexatriene (DPH) and its derivatives are essentially nonfluorescent in water. Absorption and emission spectra have multiple peaks. The wavelength, resolution and relative intensity of these peaks are environment dependent. Abs and Em values are for the most intense peak in the solvent specified.
7. Chloroform is the most generally useful solvent for preparing stock solutions of phospholipids (including sphingomyelins). Glycerophosphocholines are usually freely soluble in ethanol. Most other glycerophospholipids (phosphoethanolamines, phosphatidic acids and phosphoglycerols) are less soluble in ethanol, but solutions up to 1–2 mg/mL should be obtainable, using sonication to aid dispersion if necessary. Labeling of cells with fluorescent phospholipids can be enhanced by addition of cyclodextrins during incubation (J Biol Chem 274, 35359 (1999)).
8. This product is supplied as a ready-made solution in the solvent indicated under "Soluble."
9. Fluorescence of NBD and its derivatives in water is relatively weak. QY and τ increase and Em decreases in aprotic solvents and other nonpolar environments relative to water (Biochemistry 16, 5150 (1977); Photochem Photobiol 54, 361 (1991)).

Product List — 13.3 Sphingolipids, Steroids, Lipopolysaccharides and Related Probes

Cat #	Product Name	Unit Size
A7509	*N*-acetyl-D-erythro-sphingosine (acetyl ceramide; C_2-ceramide)	5 mg
A12216	Amplex® Red Cholesterol Assay Kit *500 assays*	1 kit
A12220	Amplex® Red Sphingomyelinase Assay Kit *500 assays*	1 kit
B22650	BODIPY® FL C_5-ceramide complexed to BSA	5 mg
B13950	BODIPY® FL C_5-ganglioside G_{M1}	25 µg
B34401	BODIPY® FL C_5-ganglioside G_{M1} complexed to BSA	1 mg
B34402	BODIPY® FL C_5-lactosylceramide complexed to BSA	1 mg
B34400	BODIPY® TR C_5-ceramide complexed to BSA	5 mg
C3927MP	cholesteryl 4,4-difluoro-5,7-dimethyl-4-bora-3a,4a-diaza-*s*-indacene-3-dodecanoate (cholesteryl BODIPY® FL C_{12})	1 mg
C12680	cholesteryl 4,4-difluoro-5-(4-methoxyphenyl)-4-bora-3a,4a-diaza-*s*-indacene-3-undecanoate (cholesteryl BODIPY® 542/563 C_{11})	1 mg
C12681	cholesteryl 4,4-difluoro-5-(2-pyrrolyl)-4-bora-3a,4a-diaza-*s*-indacene-3-undecanoate (cholesteryl BODIPY® 576/589 C_{11})	1 mg
C7794	cholesteryl 3-((6-phenyl)-1,3,5-hexatrienyl)phenylpropionate (cholesteryl DPH propionate)	5 mg
C212	cholesteryl 1-pyrenebutyrate	25 mg
D7546	*N*-(2,6-dibromo-4,4-difluoro-5,7-dimethyl-4-bora-3a,4a-diaza-*s*-indacene-3-pentanoyl)sphingosine (BODIPY® FL Br_2C_5-ceramide)	250 µg
D7519	*N*-(4,4-difluoro-5,7-dimethyl-4-bora-3a,4a-diaza-*s*-indacene-3-dodecanoyl)sphingosyl 1-β-D-galactopyranoside (BODIPY® FL C_{12}-galactocerebroside)	25 µg
D7547	*N*-(4,4-difluoro-5,7-dimethyl-4-bora-3a,4a-diaza-*s*-indacene-3-dodecanoyl)sphingosyl 1-β-D-glucopyranoside (BODIPY® FL C_{12}-glucocerebroside)	250 µg
D7711	*N*-(4,4-difluoro-5,7-dimethyl-4-bora-3a,4a-diaza-*s*-indacene-3-dodecanoyl)sphingosyl phosphocholine (BODIPY® FL C_{12}-sphingomyelin) *1 mg/mL in DMSO*	250 µL
D3521	*N*-(4,4-difluoro-5,7-dimethyl-4-bora-3a,4a-diaza-*s*-indacene-3-pentanoyl)sphingosine (BODIPY® FL C_5-ceramide)	250 µg
D7548	*N*-(4,4-difluoro-5,7-dimethyl-4-bora-3a,4a-diaza-*s*-indacene-3-pentanoyl)sphingosyl 1-β-D-glucopyranoside (BODIPY® FL C_5-glucocerebroside)	250 µg
D13951	*N*-(4,4-difluoro-5,7-dimethyl-4-bora-3a,4a-diaza-*s*-indacene-3-pentanoyl)sphingosyl 1-β-D-lactoside (BODIPY® FL C_5-lactosylceramide)	25 µg
D3522	*N*-(4,4-difluoro-5,7-dimethyl-4-bora-3a,4a-diaza-*s*-indacene-3-pentanoyl)sphingosyl phosphocholine (BODIPY® FL C_5-sphingomyelin)	250 µg
D7540	*N*-((4-(4,4-difluoro-5-(2-thienyl)-4-bora-3a,4a-diaza-*s*-indacene-3-yl)phenoxy)acetyl)sphingosine (BODIPY® TR ceramide)	250 µg
D6562	1,2-dioleoyl-3-(1-pyrenedodecanoyl)-*rac*-glycerol	1 mg
L23351	lipopolysaccharides from *Escherichia coli* serotype 055:B5, Alexa Fluor® 488 conjugate	100 µg
L23352	lipopolysaccharides from *Escherichia coli* serotype 055:B5, Alexa Fluor® 568 conjugate	100 µg
L23353	lipopolysaccharides from *Escherichia coli* serotype 055:B5, Alexa Fluor® 594 conjugate	100 µg
L23350	lipopolysaccharides from *Escherichia coli* serotype 055:B5, BODIPY® FL conjugate	100 µg
L23356	lipopolysaccharides from *Salmonella minnesota*, Alexa Fluor® 488 conjugate	100 µg
L23357	lipopolysaccharides from *Salmonella minnesota*, Alexa Fluor® 568 conjugate	100 µg
L23358	lipopolysaccharides from *Salmonella minnesota*, Alexa Fluor® 594 conjugate	100 µg
L23355	lipopolysaccharides from *Salmonella minnesota*, BODIPY® FL conjugate	100 µg
N22651	NBD C_6-ceramide complexed to BSA	5 mg
N1148	22-(*N*-(7-nitrobenz-2-oxa-1,3-diazol-4-yl)amino)-23,24-bisnor-5-cholen-3β-ol (NBD cholesterol)	10 mg
N1154	6-((*N*-(7-nitrobenz-2-oxa-1,3-diazol-4-yl)amino)hexanoyl)sphingosine (NBD C_6-ceramide)	1 mg
N3524	6-((*N*-(7-nitrobenz-2-oxa-1,3-diazol-4-yl)amino)hexanoyl)sphingosyl phosphocholine (NBD C_6-sphingomyelin)	1 mg
P226	1-pyrenemethyl 3β-(*cis*-9-octadecenoyloxy)-22,23-bisnor-5-cholenate (PMC oleate)	10 mg
V34403	Vybrant® Alexa Fluor® 488 Lipid Raft Labeling Kit *50 labelings*	1 kit
V34404	Vybrant® Alexa Fluor® 555 Lipid Raft Labeling Kit *50 labelings*	1 kit
V34405	Vybrant® Alexa Fluor® 594 Lipid Raft Labeling Kit *50 labelings*	1 kit

For current prices or to order online, visit probes.invitrogen.com

13.4 Dialkylcarbocyanine and Dialkylaminostyryl Probes

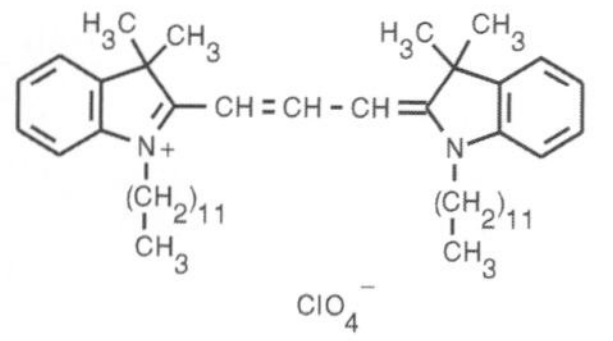

Figure 13.40 D383 1,1′-didodecyl-3,3,3′,3′-tetramethylindocarbocyanine perchlorate ($DiIC_{12}(3)$).

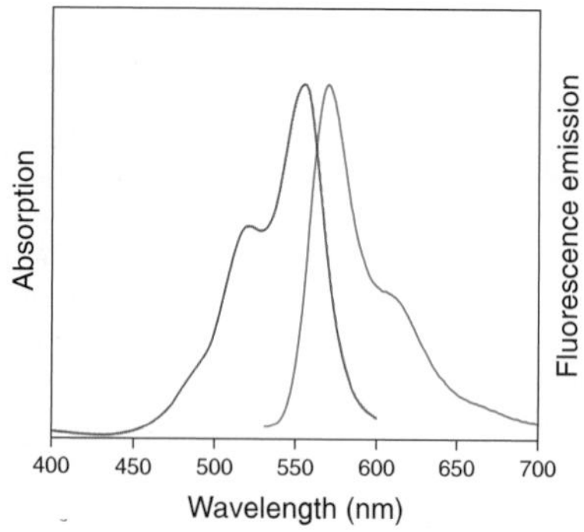

Figure 13.41 Absorption and fluorescence emission spectra of $DiIC_{18}(3)$ ("DiI") bound to phospholipid bilayer membranes.

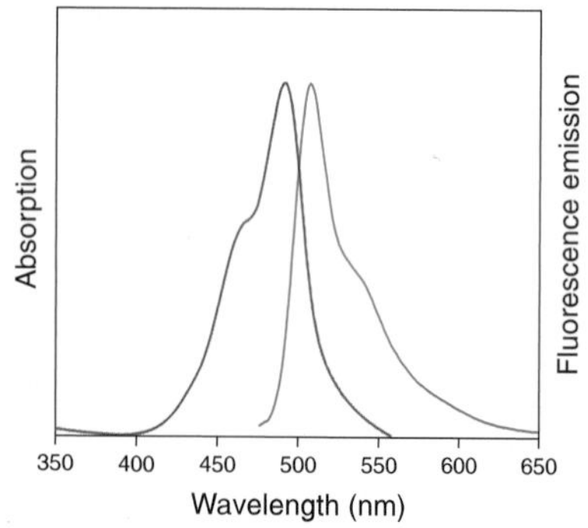

Figure 13.42 Absorption and fluorescence emission spectra of $DiOC_{18}(3)$ ("DiO") bound to phospholipid bilayer membranes.

The dyes in this section are all amphiphilic probes — molecules that comprise a charged fluorophore that localizes the probe at the membrane's surface and lipophilic aliphatic "tails" that insert into the membrane and thus anchor the probe to the membrane. In addition to being used to label model membranes, most of these probes are very useful for cell tracing applications (Section 14.4). Table 14.3 lists all of our lipophilic carbocyanine and aminostyryl tracers and compares their properties and uses. Our FM® dyes, which are also amphiphilic styryl dyes but with less lipophilic character than the dyes in this section, are particularly useful for labeling membranes of live cells and for following synaptosome recycling (Section 16.1).

Dialkylcarbocyanine Probes

Carbocyanines are among the most strongly light-absorbing dyes known and have proven to be useful tools in several different areas of research. Carbocyanines with short alkyl tails attached to the imine nitrogens are employed both as membrane-potential sensors (Section 22.3) and as organelle stains for mitochondria and the endoplasmic reticulum (Section 12.2, Section 12.4). Those with longer alkyl tails (≥12 carbons) have an overall lipophilic character that makes them useful for neuronal tracing [1] (Section 14.4), long-term labeling of cells in culture [2] (Section 14.4) and noncovalent labeling of lipoproteins (Section 16.1). This section describes the use and properties of dialkylcarbocyanines as general-purpose probes of membrane structure and dynamics.

DiI, DiO, DiD, DiR and Analogs

The most widely used carbocyanine membrane probes have been the octadecyl (C_{18}) indocarbocyanines (D282, D3911) and oxacarbocyanines (D275), often referred to by the generic acronyms DiI and DiO, or more specifically as $DiIC_{18}(3)$ and $DiOC_{18}(3)$, where the subscript is the number of carbon atoms in each alkyl tail and the bracketed numeral is the number of carbon atoms in the bridge between the indoline or benzoxazole ring systems (Figure 14.48, Figure 14.49). We also offer several variations on these basic structures (Table 14.3):

- DiI and DiO analogs with unsaturated alkyl tails (Δ^9-DiI, D3886; *FAST* DiO™, D3898; *FAST* DiI™, D3899, D7756)
- DiI and DiO analogs with shorter alkyl tails ($DiIC_{12}(3)$, D383; Figure 13.40; $DiIC_{16}(3)$, D384; $DiOC_{16}(3)$, D1125)
- Long-wavelength light–excitable carbocyanines (DiD, D307, D7757; Figure 14.50)
- Infrared light–excitable carbocyanine (DiR, D12731; Figure 14.51)
- Phenyl-substituted and sulfonated derivatives of DiI and DiO (see below)

Spectral Properties of Dialkylcarbocyanines

A review of relevant spectral and physical characteristics of lipophilic carbocyanines has been compiled by Wolf.[3] The spectral properties of dialkylcarbocyanines are largely independent of the lengths of the alkyl chains, and are instead determined by the heteroatoms in the terminal ring systems and the length of the connecting bridge. The $DiIC_n(3)$ probes have absorption and fluorescence spectra compatible with rhodamine (TRITC) optical filter sets (Table 23.9, Figure 13.41), whereas $DiOC_n(3)$ analogs can be used with fluorescein (FITC) optical filter sets (Table 23.9, Figure 13.42). The emission maxima of $DiIC_{18}(3)$ and $DiOC_{18}(3)$ incorporated in dioctadecenoylphosphocholine (dioleoyl PC or DOPC) liposomes (Figure 13.43) are similar to those of the dyes in methanol.

The very large molar extinction coefficients of carbocyanine fluorophores are their most outstanding spectral property. Their fluorescence quantum yields are only modest — about 0.07 for DiI in methanol [4] and about three-times greater in amphiphilic solvents such as octanol.[5] Their fluorescence in water is quite weak.[6] The excited-state lifetimes of carbocyanine fluorophores in lipid environments are short (~1 nanosecond), which is an advantage for flow cytometry applications because it allows more excitation/de-excitation cycles during flow transit;[7] the overall decay is multi-exponential.[8] Dialkylcarbocyanines are also exceptionally photostable.[9]

The red He–Ne laser–excitable indodicarbocyanines such as $DiIC_{18}(5)$ (DiD, D307, D7757) have long-wavelength absorption and red emission (Figure 13.43, Figure 13.44). Their extinction coefficients are somewhat larger and fluorescence quantum yields much larger than those of carbocyanines such as $DiIC_{18}(3)$.[5] Moreover, photoexcitation of $DiIC_{18}(5)$ seems to cause less collateral damage than photoexcitation of $DiIC_{18}(3)$ in live cells.[10] Our $DiIC_{18}(7)$ tricarbocyanine probe (DiR, D12731) has excitation and emission in the infrared (Figure 13.45), which may make the dye useful as an *in vivo* tracer for labeled cells and liposomes in live organisms.

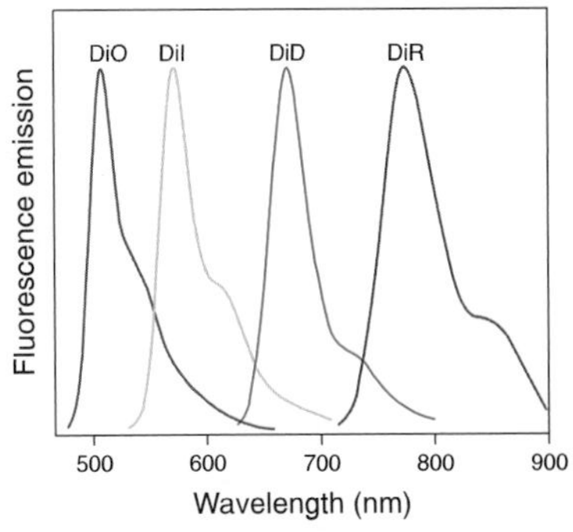

Figure 13.43 Normalized fluorescence emission spectra of DiO (D275), DiI (D282), DiD (D307) and DiR (D12731) bound to phospholipid bilayer membranes.

Substituted DiI and DiO Derivatives

Molecular Probes' scientists have synthesized various derivatives of DiI, DiO and DiD. All of these derivatives have octadecyl (C_{18}) tails identical to those of DiI (D282, D3911) and DiO (D275), thereby preserving the excellent membrane retention characteristics of the parent molecules. A variety of substitutions have been made on the indoline or benzoxazole ring systems:

- Chloromethylbenzamido DiI derivatives (CellTracker™ CM-DiI, C7000, C7001; Figure 14.58)
- Diphenyl DiI (5,5′-Ph_2-$DiIC_{18}(3)$, D7779)
- Anionic sulfophenyl[11] (SP-$DiIC_{18}(3)$, D7777; SP-$DiOC_{18}(3)$, D7778) or sulfonate ($DiIC_{18}(3)$-DS, D7776; $DiIC_{18}(5)$-DS, D12730) derivatives

Although these derivatives have primarily been developed to provide improved fixation and labeling in long-term cell tracing applications (Section 14.4), they also offer several features that can potentially be exploited for investigations of membrane structure and dynamics. For researchers wishing to carry out comparative evaluations, our Lipophilic Tracer Sampler Kit (L7781) provides 1 mg samples of four of the newer derivatives (D7776, D7777, D7778, D7779) and 1 mg samples of DiI, DiO, DiD, DiR and DiA. The fluorescence quantum yields of the sulfophenyl and phenyl derivatives (measured in methanol) are generally two- to threefold greater than those of DiI and DiO. In particular, we have found that the sulfophenyl derivatives (D7777, D7778) bound to phospholipid model membranes have approximately fivefold higher quantum yields than DiI and DiO. $DiIC_{18}(5)$-DS (D12730) has been used in combination with an NBD-labeled glycerophosphoserine probe in a novel resonance energy transfer assay that detects inner monolayer membrane hemifusion, avoiding erroneous indications of membrane fusion due to lipid mixing and other environmental effects in the outer monolayer.[12] The negative charge and greater water solubility of the sulfonated carbocyanines results in modified lateral and transverse distributions of these probes in lipid bilayers relative to those of DiI and DiO. This characteristic has been exploited to identify plasma membrane lipid domains that are responsive to electrical stimulation of outer hair cells in the inner ear.[13]

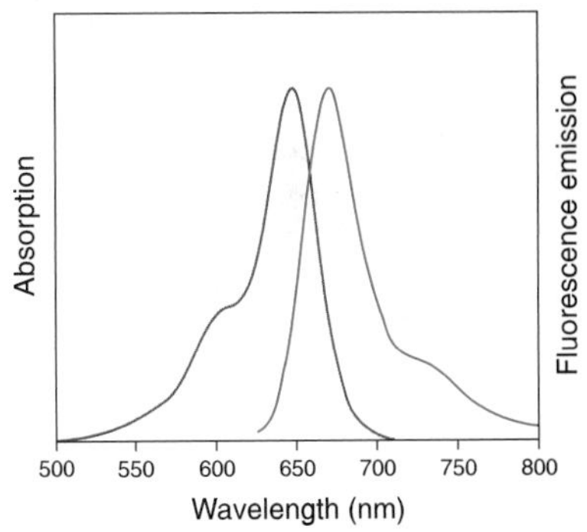

Figure 13.44 Absorption and fluorescence emission spectra of $DiIC_{18}(5)$ ("DiD") bound to phospholipid bilayer membranes.

DiI and DiO as Probes of Membrane Structure

The orientation of $DiIC_{18}(3)$ in membranes has been determined by fluorescence polarization microscopy.[14] The long axis of the fluorophore is parallel to the membrane surface, and the two alkyl chains protrude perpendicularly into the lipid interior (Figure 13.1). There are conflicting reports in the literature regarding the ease of transbilayer migration ("flip-flop") of lipophilic indocarbocyanines.[15–17] The lateral partitioning behavior of dialkylindocarbocyanines in membranes has been investigated by fluorescence recovery after photobleaching (FRAP),[18] calorimetry,[19] lifetime measurements[8] and fluorescence resonance energy transfer techniques[20] (see Note 1.2 "Technical Focus: Fluorescence Resonance Energy Transfer (FRET)" in Section 1.3). These studies demonstrate that the probe distribution between coexisting fluid and gel phases depends on the similarity of the alkyl chain lengths of the probe and the lipid. In general, the more dissimilar the lengths, the greater the preference for fluid-phase over gel-phase lipids. For example, the shorter-chain $DiIC_{12}(3)$ has a substantial preference for the fluid phase (~6:1) in DOPC, whereas $DiIC_{18}(3)$ is predominantly distributed in the gel phase[21] (~1:10). Consequently, long-chain dialkylcarbocyanines are among the best probes for detecting particularly rigid gel phases.

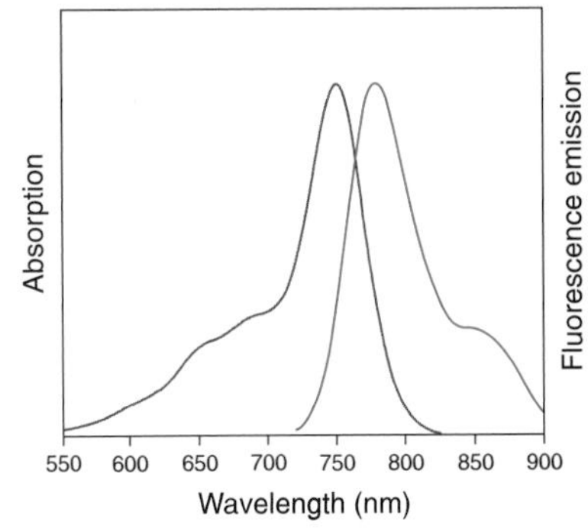

Figure 13.45 Absorption and fluorescence emission spectra of $DiIC_{18}(7)$ ("DiR") bound to phospholipid bilayer membranes.

Lipophilic carbocyanines have been used to visualize membrane fusion and cell permeabilization that occurs in response to electric fields,[22–24] as well as fusion of liposomes with planar bilayers.[25] Membrane fusion can also be measured by fluorescence resonance energy transfer to $DiIC_{18}(3)$ from dansyl- or NBD-labeled phospholipid donors[26] or by direct imaging.[27] In Langmuir–Blodgett films, excited-state energy transfer from $DiIC_{18}(3)$ to $DiIC_{18}(5)$ is exceptionally efficient because of the favorable orientations of the fluorophores.[28] Energy transfer from

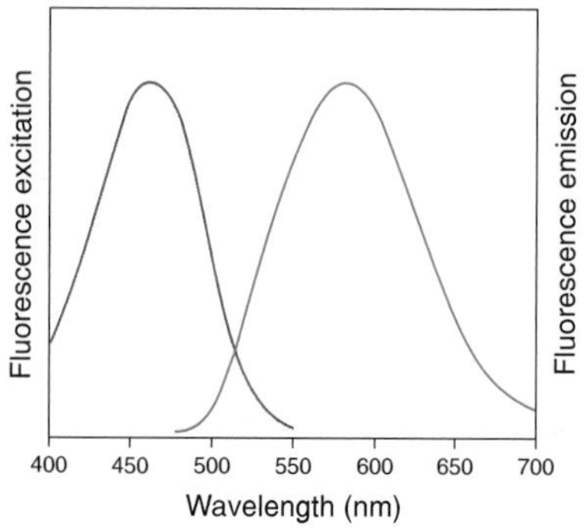

Figure 13.46 Fluorescence excitation and emission spectra of DiA bound to phospholipid bilayer membranes.

$DiIC_{18}(5)$ to $DiIC_{18}(7)$ should be similarly effective. Lipophilic carbocyanines have also been used to elicit photosensitized destabilization of liposomes,[29] to sensitize photoaffinity labeling of the viral glycoprotein hemagglutinin,[30] to image membrane domains in lipid monolayers[31] and to develop a fiber-optic potassium sensor.[32]

DiI and DiO as Probes of Membrane Dynamics

Despite their reasonably good photostability, dialkylcarbocyanines are widely employed to measure lateral diffusion processes using fluorescence recovery after photobleaching (FRAP) techniques.[33–36] Their lateral diffusion coefficients in isolated fluid- and gel-phase bilayers are independent of the carbocyanine alkyl chain length.[18] Phase-separated populations of lipophilic carbocyanine dyes can be distinguished by their diffusion rates and can therefore be used to define lateral domains in cell membranes.[37,38] Combined lateral diffusion measurements of labeled proteins and lipids have demonstrated that transformed[39] and permeabilized[40] cells show marked changes in protein diffusion whereas lipid diffusion rates remain unchanged. In other cases, coupling of lipid and protein mobility has been identified in the form of relatively immobilized lipid domains in yeast plasma membranes[41] and around IgE receptor complexes.[42] A different photobleaching technique, which depends on the *absence* of diffusional fluorescence recovery, was employed to determine lipid flow direction in locomoting cells by following the movement of a photobleached stripe of $DiIC_{16}(3)$[43] (D383).

Dialkylaminostyryl Probes

The lipophilic aminostyryl probes 4-Di-10-ASP (D291); DiA, (D3883, Figure 14.62) and *FAST* DiA™ (D3897, D7758) insert in membranes with their two alkyl tails and their fluorophore oriented parallel to the phospholipid acyl chains[44] (Figure 13.1). When these dialkylaminostyryl probes bind to membranes, they exhibit a strong fluorescence enhancement; their fluorescence in water is minimal. The interfacial solvation of the aminostyryl fluorophore causes a large blue shift of the absorption spectrum of the membrane-bound probe.[44] The absorption maximum of DiA is 456 nm when incorporated into DOPC liposomes and 490 nm when in methanol. The fluorescence emission maximum of DiA in the membrane environment is 590 nm, which is quite close to that observed for probes with shorter alkyl tails such as 4-Di-10-ASP.[44] However, its fluorescence spectrum is very broad, with appreciable intensity from about 510 nm to 690 nm (Figure 13.46). Consequently, DiA can be detected as green, orange or even red fluorescence, depending on the optical filter employed. Like the lipophilic carbocyanines, DiA is commonly used for neuronal membrane tracing (Section 14.4). *FAST* DiA™ (D3897, D7758), the diunsaturated analog of DiA, is intended to facilitate these studies by possibly accelerating dye diffusion within the membrane.

Our FM® 1-43 (Figure 16.19), FM® 1-43FX, FM® 4-64 and FM® 5-95 dyes, which are discussed in detail in Section 16.1, are styryl dyes with structurally similar high Stokes shifts of their fluorescence emission but less lipophilic character. These dyes are used to define the outer membranes of liposomes and live cells (Figure 16.21) and to detect synaptosome recycling (Figure 16.17).

References

1. Trends Neurosci 12, 333 (1989); **2.** Histochemistry 97, 329 (1992); **3.** Spectroscopic Membrane Probes, Vol. I, Loew LM, Ed. pp. 193–220 (1988); **4.** Handbook of Biological Confocal Microscopy, 2nd Ed., Pawley JB, Ed. pp. 267–279 (1995); **5.** Biochemistry 13, 3315 (1974); **6.** Chem Phys Lipids 109, 175 (2001); **7.** Flow Cytometry Sorting, 2nd Ed., Melamed MR, Lindmo T, Mendelsohn ML, Eds. pp. 209–225 (1990); **8.** Biochemistry 24, 5176 (1985); **9.** J Cell Biol 100, 1309 (1985); **10.** J Histochem Cytochem 32, 608 (1984); **11.** Bioorg Med Chem Lett 6, 1479 (1996); **12.** Biochim Biophys Acta 1467, 227 (2000); **13.** Mol Biol Cell 9, 80a, abstract #461 (1998); **14.** Biophys J 26, 557 (1979); **15.** J Cell Biol 103, 807 (1986); **16.** Biochemistry 24, 582 (1985); **17.** Nature 294, 718 (1981); **18.** Biochemistry 19, 6199 (1980); **19.** Biochim Biophys Acta 1191, 164 (1994); **20.** Biochim Biophys Acta 1467, 101 (2000); **21.** Biochim Biophys Acta 1023, 25 (1990); **22.** Biophys J 67, 427 (1994); **23.** Biophys J 65, 568 (1993); **24.** Biochemistry 29, 8337 (1990); **25.** J Membr Biol 109, 221 (1989); **26.** Biochim Biophys Acta 735, 243 (1983); **27.** J Cell Biol 121, 543 (1993); **28.** Chem Phys Lett 159, 231 (1989); **29.** FEBS Lett 467, 52 (2000); **30.** J Biol Chem 269, 14614 (1994); **31.** Biophys J 65, 1019 (1993); **32.** Analyst 115, 353 (1990); **33.** Biochemistry 16, 3836 (1977); **34.** Biophys J 75, 1131 (1998); **35.** Biophys J 68, 766 (1995); **36.** Bioessays 6, 117 (1987); **37.** Chem Phys Lipids 73, 139 (1994); **38.** J Cell Biol 112, 1143 (1991); **39.** Biochim Biophys Acta 1107, 193 (1992); **40.** J Cell Physiol 158, 7 (1994); **41.** J Membr Biol 131, 115 (1993); **42.** J Cell Biol 125, 795 (1994); **43.** Science 247, 1229 (1990); **44.** Biophys J 34, 353 (1981).

Data Table — 13.4 Dialkylcarbocyanine and Dialkylaminostyryl Probes

Cat #	MW	Storage	Soluble	Abs	EC	Em	Solvent	Notes
C7000	1051.50	F,D,L	DMSO, EtOH	553	134,000	570	MeOH	
C7001	1051.50	F,D,L	DMSO, EtOH	553	134,000	570	MeOH	
D275	881.72	L	DMSO, DMF	484	154,000	501	MeOH	
D282	933.88	L	DMSO, EtOH	549	148,000	565	MeOH	
D291	618.73	L	DMSO, EtOH	492	53,000	612	MeOH	1
D307	959.92	L	DMSO, EtOH	644	260,000	665	MeOH	2
D383	765.56	L	DMSO, EtOH	549	144,000	565	MeOH	3
D384	877.77	L	DMSO, EtOH	549	148,000	565	MeOH	
D1125	825.61	L	DMSO, DMF	484	156,000	501	MeOH	
D3883	787.05	L	DMSO, EtOH	491	52,000	613	MeOH	1
D3886	925.49	F,L,AA	DMSO, EtOH	549	144,000	564	MeOH	2
D3897	835.09	F,L,AA	DMSO, EtOH	492	49,000	612	MeOH	1, 2
D3898	873.65	F,L,AA	DMSO, DMF	484	138,000	499	MeOH	
D3899	925.82	F,L,AA	DMSO, EtOH	549	143,000	564	MeOH	2
D3911	933.88	L	DMSO, EtOH	549	148,000	565	MeOH	
D7756	1017.97	F,L,AA	DMSO, EtOH	549	148,000	564	MeOH	
D7757	1052.08	L	DMSO, EtOH	644	193,000	663	MeOH	
D7758	899.80	F,L,AA	DMSO, EtOH	492	41,000	612	MeOH	1
D7766	1091.67	L	DMSO, EtOH	558	128,000	575	MeOH	
D7776	993.54	L	DMSO, EtOH	555	144,000	570	MeOH	
D7777	1145.73	L	DMSO, EtOH	556	164,000	573	MeOH	
D7778	1115.55	L	DMSO, EtOH	497	175,000	513	MeOH	
D7779	1022.08	L	DMSO, EtOH	576	140,000	599	MeOH	
D12730	1019.58	L	DMSO, EtOH	650	247,000	670	MeOH	
D12731	1013.41	L	DMSO, EtOH	748	270,000	780	MeOH	
F6999	1017.06	L	DMSO, EtOH	553	133,000	570	MeOH	

For definitions of the contents of this data table, see "Navigating *The Handbook*" in the introductory pages.

Notes

1. Abs and Em of styryl dyes are at shorter wavelengths in membrane environments than in reference solvents such as methanol. The difference is typically 20 nm for absorption and 80 nm for emission, but varies considerably from one dye to another. Styryl dyes are generally nonfluorescent in water.
2. This product is intrinsically a liquid or an oil at room temperature.
3. This product is intrinsically a sticky gum at room temperature.

Product List — 13.4 Dialkylcarbocyanine and Dialkylaminostyryl Probes

Cat #	Product Name	Unit Size
C7001	CellTracker™ CM-DiI	1 mg
C7000	CellTracker™ CM-DiI *special packaging*	20 x 50 µg
D7766	5,5′-dibromo-1,1′-dioctadecyl-3,3,3′,3′-tetramethylindocarbocyanine perchlorate (Br_2-$DiIC_{18}(3)$)	5 mg
D291	4-(4-(didecylamino)styryl)-*N*-methylpyridinium iodide (4-Di-10-ASP)	25 mg
D383	1,1′-didodecyl-3,3,3′,3′-tetramethylindocarbocyanine perchlorate ($DiIC_{12}(3)$)	100 mg
D3883	4-(4-(dihexadecylamino)styryl)-*N*-methylpyridinium iodide (DiA; 4-Di-16-ASP)	25 mg
D1125	3,3′-dihexadecyloxacarbocyanine perchlorate ($DiOC_{16}(3)$)	25 mg
D384	1,1′-dihexadecyl-3,3,3′,3′-tetramethylindocarbocyanine perchlorate ($DiIC_{16}(3)$)	100 mg
D7758	4-(4-(dilinoleylamino)styryl)-*N*-methylpyridinium 4-chlorobenzenesulfonate (*FAST* DiA™ solid; $DiA^{9,12}$-C_{18}ASP, CBS)	5 mg
D3897	4-(4-(dilinoleylamino)styryl)-*N*-methylpyridinium iodide (*FAST* DiA™ oil; $DiA^{9,12}$-C_{18}ASP, I)	5 mg
D3898	3,3′-dilinoleyloxacarbocyanine perchlorate (*FAST* DiO™ solid; $DiO\Delta^{9,12}$-$C_{18}(3)$, ClO_4)	5 mg
D7756	1,1′-dilinoleyl-3,3,3′,3′-tetramethylindocarbocyanine, 4-chlorobenzenesulfonate (*FAST* DiI™ solid; $DiI\Delta^{9,12}$-$C_{18}(3)$, CBS)	5 mg
D3899	1,1′-dilinoleyl-3,3,3′,3′-tetramethylindocarbocyanine perchlorate (*FAST* DiI™ oil; $DiI\Delta^{9,12}$-$C_{18}(3)$, ClO_4)	5 mg
D7779	1,1′-dioctadecyl-5,5′-diphenyl-3,3,3′,3′-tetramethylindocarbocyanine chloride (5,5′-Ph_2-$DiIC_{18}(3)$)	5 mg
D7778	3,3′-dioctadecyl-5,5′-di(4-sulfophenyl)oxacarbocyanine, sodium salt (SP-$DiOC_{18}(3)$)	5 mg
D7777	1,1′-dioctadecyl-6,6′-di(4-sulfophenyl)-3,3,3′,3′-tetramethylindocarbocyanine (SP-$DiIC_{18}(3)$)	5 mg
D275	3,3′-dioctadecyloxacarbocyanine perchlorate ('DiO'; $DiOC_{18}(3)$)	100 mg
D7776	1,1′-dioctadecyl-3,3,3′,3′-tetramethylindocarbocyanine-5,5′-disulfonic acid ($DiIC_{18}(3)$-DS)	5 mg
D282	1,1′-dioctadecyl-3,3,3′,3′-tetramethylindocarbocyanine perchlorate ('DiI'; $DiIC_{18}(3)$)	100 mg
D3911	1,1′-dioctadecyl-3,3,3′,3′-tetramethylindocarbocyanine perchlorate ('DiI'; $DiIC_{18}(3)$) *crystalline*	25 mg
D7757	1,1′-dioctadecyl-3,3,3′,3′-tetramethylindodicarbocyanine, 4-chlorobenzenesulfonate salt ('DiD' solid; $DiIC_{18}(5)$ solid)	10 mg
D12730	1,1′-dioctadecyl-3,3,3′,3′-tetramethylindodicarbocyanine-5,5′-disulfonic acid ($DiIC_{18}(5)$-DS)	5 mg
D307	1,1′-dioctadecyl-3,3,3′,3′-tetramethylindodicarbocyanine perchlorate ('DiD' oil; $DiIC_{18}(5)$ oil)	25 mg
D12731	1,1′-dioctadecyl-3,3,3′,3′-tetramethylindotricarbocyanine iodide ('DiR'; $DiIC_{18}(7)$)	10 mg
D3886	1,1′-dioleyl-3,3,3′,3′-tetramethylindocarbocyanine methanesulfonate (Δ^9-DiI)	25 mg
F6999	FM® DiI *special packaging*	20 x 50 µg
L7781	Lipophilic Tracer Sampler Kit	1 kit

For current prices or to order online, visit probes.invitrogen.com

13.5 Other Nonpolar and Amphiphilic Probes

Amphiphilic Derivatives of Rhodamines, Fluoresceins and Coumarins

Each of our amphiphilic probes comprises a moderately polar fluorescent dye with a lipophilic "tail." When used to stain membranes, including liposomes, the lipophilic portion of the probe tends to insert in the membrane and the polar fluorophore resides on the surface (Figure 13.1), where it senses the membrane's surface environment and the surrounding medium.[1] Our lipophilic carbocyanines and styryl dyes (Section 13.4) are also amphiphilic molecules with a similar binding mode.

This section includes the classic membrane probes DPH, TMA-DPH, ANS, bis-ANS, TNS, prodan, laurdan and nile red, and also some lipophilic BODIPY® and Dapoxyl® dyes developed at Molecular Probes. Although they bear little resemblance to natural products, these probes tend to localize within cell membranes or liposomes or at their aqueous interfaces, where they are often used to report on characteristics of their local environment, such as viscosity, polarity and lipid order.

Octadecyl Rhodamine B

The relief of octadecyl rhodamine B (R18, O246; Figure 13.47) fluorescence self-quenching can be used to monitor membrane fusion[2–7] — one of several experimental approaches developed for this application (see Note 13.1 "Technical Focus: Lipid-Mixing Assays of Membrane Fusion" in Section 13.2). Octadecyl rhodamine B has been reported to undergo a potential-dependent "flip-flop" from one monolayer of a fluid-state phospholipid bilayer membrane to the other, with partial relief of its fluorescence quenching.[8,9] Investigators have used octadecyl rhodamine B in conjunction with video microscopy[10–12] or digital imaging techniques[13] to monitor viral fusion processes. Membrane fusion can also be followed by monitoring fluorescence resonance energy transfer to octadecyl rhodamine B from an acylaminofluorescein donor such as 5-octadecanoylamino-fluorescein[5,7,14,15] (O322). Fluorescence resonance energy transfer from fluorescein or dansyl labels to octadecyl rhodamine B has been used for structural studies of the blood coagulation factor IXa, EGF receptor and receptor-bound IgE.[16–18] Octadecyl rhodamine B has also been used to stain kinesin-generated membrane tubules,[19] to characterize detergent micelles,[20] to assay for lysosomal degradation of lipoproteins[21] and to investigate the influence of proteins on lipid dynamics using time-resolved fluorescence anisotropy.[22]

Lipophilic Fluoresceins

The lipophilic fluorescein probes bind to membranes with the fluorophore at the aqueous interface and the alkyl tail protruding into the lipid interior (Figure 13.1). 5-Dodecanoylaminofluorescein (D109) is the hydrolysis product of our ImaGene Green™ C_{12}-FDG β-galactosidase substrate (D2893, Section 10.2). We also offer the homologous membrane probes, 5-hexadecanoyl- and 5-octadecanoylaminofluorescein[1,15,23] (H110, O322) and the octadecyl ester of fluorescein[24,25] (F3857).

Lipophilic fluorescein probes are commonly utilized for fluorescence recovery after photobleaching (FRAP) measurements of lipid lateral diffusion.[26] Some researchers have reported that 5-hexadecanoylaminofluorescein stays predominantly in the outer membrane leaflet of epithelia and does not pass through tight junctions, whereas the dodecanoyl derivative can "flip-flop" to the inner leaflet at 20°C (but not at <10°C) and may also pass through tight junctions.[27,28] More recent studies have indicated that the lack of tight junction penetration of 5-hexadecanoylaminofluorescein is due to probe aggregation rather than a significant difference in its transport properties.[29]

A Lipophilic Coumarin

4-Heptadecyl-7-hydroxycoumarin (H22730, Figure 13.48) is an alkyl derivative of the pH-sensitive blue-fluorescent 7-hydroxycoumarin (umbelliferone) fluorophore. As with other lipophilic coumarins,[30] 4-heptadecyl-7-hydroxycoumarin is primarily useful as a probe of membrane surfaces. Deprotonation of the 7-hydroxyl group is expected to be strongly dependent on membrane-surface electrostatic potential. The pK_a of 4-heptadecyl-7-hydroxycoumarin varies from 6.35 in the cationic detergent CTAB to 11.15 in the anionic detergent sodium dodecyl sulfate (SDS), as measured by its fluorescence response.[31] However, its pK_a in lipid assemblies is strongly dependent on the ionic composition of the membrane surface,[31,32] making it a sensitive probe of membrane-surface electrostatic potential.[33] 4-Heptadecyl-7-hydroxycoumarin has been used to measure pH differences at membrane interfaces in isolated plasma membranes of normal and multidrug-resistant murine leukemia cells.[34,35] 4-Heptadecyl-7-hydroxycoumarin has also been employed as a structural probe for the head-group region of phospholipid bilayers.[36]

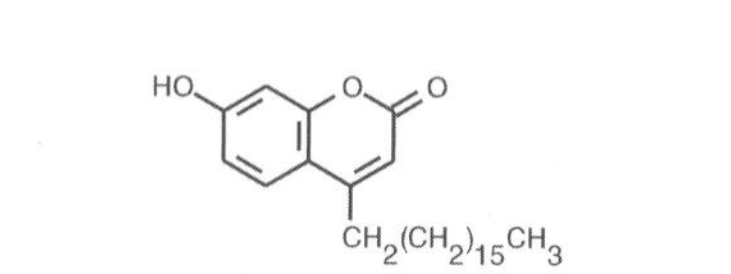

Figure 13.47 O246 octadecyl rhodamine B chloride (R18).

Figure 13.48 H22730 4-heptadecyl-7-hydroxycoumarin.

DPH and DPH Derivatives

Diphenylhexatriene (DPH)

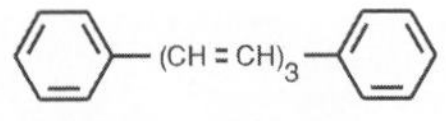

Figure 13.49 D202 1,6-diphenyl-1,3,5-hexatriene (DPH).

1,6-Diphenyl-1,3,5-hexatriene (DPH, D202; Figure 13.49) continues to be a popular fluorescent probe of membrane interiors. We also offer the cationic DPH derivatives TMA-DPH (T204, Figure 13.50) and TMAP-DPH (P3900), the anionic derivative DPH propionic acid (P459, Figure 13.51), as well as the phospholipid analog (D476, Section 13.2, Figure 13.18) and cholesteryl ester (C7794, Section 13.3). The orientation of DPH within lipid bilayers is loosely constrained. It is generally assumed to be oriented parallel to the lipid acyl chain axis (Figure 13.1), but it can also reside in the center of the lipid bilayer parallel to the surface, as demonstrated by time-resolved fluorescence anisotropy and polarized fluorescence measurements of oriented samples.[37–40] DPH shows no partition preference between coexisting gel- and fluid-phase phospholipids.[41] Intercalation of DPH and its derivatives into membranes is accompanied by strong enhancement of their fluorescence; their fluorescence is practically negligible in water. The fluorescence decay of DPH in lipid bilayers is complex.[42–44] Fluorescence decay data are often analyzed in terms of continuous lifetime distributions,[45–48] which are in turn interpreted as being indicative of lipid environment heterogeneity.

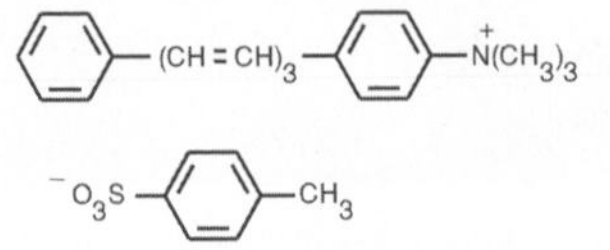

Figure 13.50 T204 1-(4-trimethylammoniumphenyl)-6-phenyl-1,3,5-hexatriene *p*-toluenesulfonate (TMA-DPH).

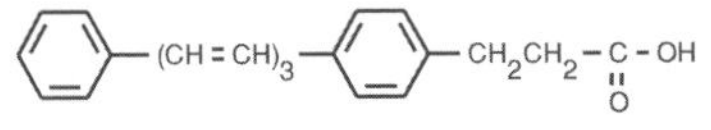

Figure 13.51 P459 3-(4-(6-phenyl)-1,3,5-hexatrienyl)-phenylpropionic acid (DPH propionic acid).

DPH and its derivatives are cylindrically shaped molecules with absorption and fluorescence emission transition dipoles aligned approximately parallel to their long molecular axis. Consequently, their fluorescence polarization is high in the absence of rotational motion and is very sensitive to reorientation of the long axis resulting from interactions with surrounding lipids. These properties have led to their extensive use for membrane fluidity measurements.[49] The exact physical interpretation of these measurements has some contentious aspects. For instance, the probes are largely sensitive to only the angular reorientation of lipid acyl chains — a motion that does not necessarily correlate with other dynamic processes such as lateral diffusion.[50] Reviews on this subject[39,49,51,52] should be consulted for further discussion. Time-resolved fluorescence polarization measurements of lipid order are more physically rigorous because they allow the angular range of acyl chain reorientation ("lipid order") to be resolved from its rate, and considerable research has been devoted to the interpretation of these measurements.[37,45,53,54]

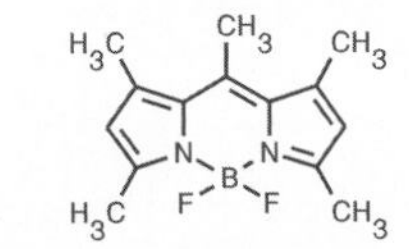

Figure 13.52 D3922 4,4-difluoro-1,3,5,7,8-pentamethyl-4-bora-3a,4a-diaza-*s*-indacene (BODIPY® 493/503).

TMA-DPH and TMAP-DPH

To improve the localization of DPH in the membrane, the derivative TMA-DPH (T204, Figure 13.50) was introduced, which contains a cationic trimethylammonium substituent that acts as a surface anchor.[55–57] A newer version of this probe, TMAP-DPH (P3900, Figure 16.23), incorporates an additional three-carbon spacer between the fluorophore and the trimethylammonium substituent.[55] Like DPH, these derivatives readily partition from aqueous dispersions into membranes and other lipid assemblies, accompanied by strong fluorescence enhancement. The lipid–water partition coefficients (K_p) for TMA-DPH and TMAP-DPH ($K_p = 2.4 \times 10^5$ and 2.9×10^5, respectively) are lower than for DPH ($K_p = 1.3 \times 10^6$), reflecting the increased water solubility caused by their polar substituents.[58] The partitioning properties of TMAP-DPH in multilamellar liposomes have been described.[55,59,60] The fluorescence decay lifetime of TMA-DPH is more sensitive to changes in lipid composition and temperature than is the fluorescence decay lifetime of DPH.[61–63]

Staining of cell membranes by TMA-DPH is much more rapid than staining by DPH. However, the duration of plasma membrane surface staining by TMA-DPH before internalization into the cytoplasm is quite prolonged.[64,65] As a consequence, TMA-DPH introduced into Madin–Darby canine kidney (MDCK) cell plasma membranes does not diffuse through tight junctions and remains in the apical domain, whereas the anionic DPH propionic acid (P459, Figure 13.51) accumulates rapidly in intracellular membranes.[66] TMA-DPH residing in the plasma membrane can be extracted by washing with medium, thus providing a method for isolating internalized probe and monitoring endocytosis[67] (Section 16.1). Furthermore, because TMA-DPH is virtually nonfluorescent in water and binds in proportion to the available membrane surface,[68] its fluorescence intensity is sensitive to increases in plasma membrane surface area resulting from exocytosis.[67,69,70]

TMA-DPH fluorescence polarization measurements can be combined with video microscopy to provide spatially resolved images of phospholipid order in large liposomes and single cells.[71–74]

Information regarding lipid order heterogeneity among cell populations can be obtained in a similar way using flow cytometry.[75–77]

DPH Propionic Acid

DPH propionic acid (P459, Figure 13.51) has principally been used as a synthetic intermediate for preparation of phospholipids (for example, D476; Section 13.2) and other molecules. When used as a membrane probe, its location within the lipid bilayer interior is dependent on the ionization state of its carboxylate group.[55] DPH propionic acid has been used together with DPH as a probe for lipid–protein interactions[78] and ethanol-induced perturbations of membrane structure.[79]

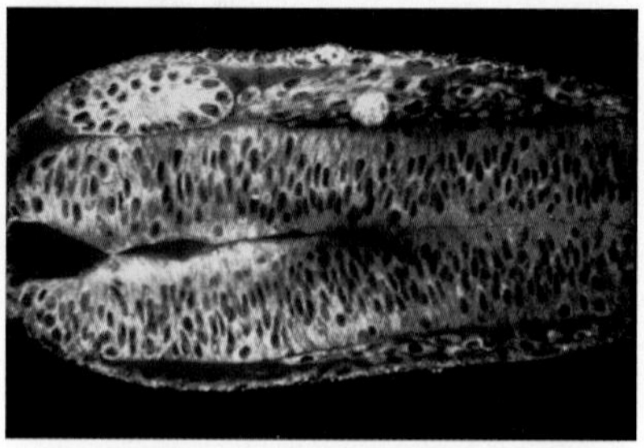

Figure 13.53 Dorsal view of the midbrain/hindbrain region of a 15-somite stage zebrafish embryo labeled with BODIPY® 505/515 (D3921). BODIPY® 505/515 localizes in lipidic yolk platelets, producing selective cytoplasmic staining. This pseudocolored confocal image was obtained using a Bio-Rad MRC-600 microscope. Image contributed by Mark Cooper, University of Washington.

Nonpolar BODIPY® Probes

Molecular Probes' nonpolar derivatives of the BODIPY® fluorophore offer an unusual combination of nonpolar structure (Figure 13.52) and long-wavelength absorption and fluorescence.[80] These dyes have potential applications as stains for neutral lipids and as tracers for oils and other nonpolar liquids. Staining with the BODIPY® 493/503 dye (D3922) has been shown by flow cytometry to be more specific for cellular lipid droplets than staining with nile red[81] (N1142). The low molecular weight of the BODIPY® 493/503 dye (262 daltons) results in the probe having a relatively fast diffusion rate in membranes.[82] The BODIPY® 493/503 dye has also been used to detect neutral compounds in a microchip channel separation device.[83] BODIPY® 505/515 (D3921) rapidly permeates cell membranes of live zebrafish embryos,[84,85] selectively staining cytoplasmic yolk platelets. This staining provides dramatic contrast enhancement of cytoplasm relative to nucleoplasm and interstitial spaces, allowing individual cell boundaries and cell nuclei to be imaged clearly with a confocal laser-scanning microscope (Figure 13.2, Figure 13.53). The very long–wavelength BODIPY® 665/676 dye (B3932) has fluorescence that is not visible to the human eye; however, it has found use as a probe for reactive oxygen species[86] (Section 18.2). BODIPY® FL C_5-ceramide (D3521, B22650; Section 13.3) stains the plasma membrane, Golgi apparatus and cytoplasmic particles within the superficial enveloping layer (EVL) of the embryos. However, once the fluorescent lipid percolates through the EVL epithelium, it remains localized within the interstitial fluid of the embryo and freely diffuses between cells (Figure 13.54). Vital staining with BODIPY® FL C_5-ceramide thus allows hundreds of cells to be imaged *en masse* during morphogenetic movements.[84,87] BODIPY® dyes have small fluorescence Stokes shifts, extinction coefficients that are typically greater than 80,000 $cm^{-1}M^{-1}$ and high fluorescence quantum yields that are not diminished in water.[88] Their photostability is generally high; this, together with other favorable characteristics (very low triplet–triplet absorption), results in excellent performance of the BODIPY® 493/503 and BODIPY® 505/515 dyes as flashlamp-pumped laser dyes.[89,90]

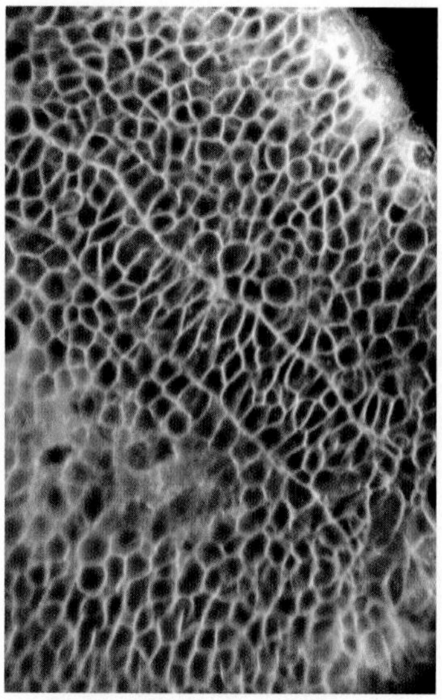

Figure 13.54 Cells in the notochord rudiment of a zebrafish embryo undergoing mediolateral intercalation to lengthen the forming notochord. BODIPY® FL C_5-ceramide (D3521) localizes in the interstitial fluid of the zebrafish embryo and freely diffuses between cells, illuminating cell boundaries. This confocal image was obtained using a Bio-Rad MRC-600 microscope. Image contributed by Mark Cooper, University of Washington.

Pyrene, Nile Red and Bimane Probes

Nonpolar Pyrene Probe

1,3-Bis-(1-pyrene)propane (B311) has two pyrene moieties linked by a three-carbon alkylene spacer. This probe is somewhat analogous to the bis-pyrenyl phospholipids (Section 13.2) in that excimer formation (and, consequently, the fluorescence emission wavelength) is controlled by intramolecular rather than bimolecular interactions. Thus, the probe is highly sensitive to constraints imposed by its environment, and can therefore be used as a viscosity sensor for interior regions of lipoproteins, membranes, micelles, liquid crystals and synthetic polymers.[91,92] Because excimer formation results in a spectral shift (Figure 13.8), the probe may be useful for ratio imaging of molecular mobility.[93] However, pyrene fatty acids (Section 13.2) appear to be preferable for this purpose because the uptake of 1,3-bis-(1-pyrene)propane by cells is limited.

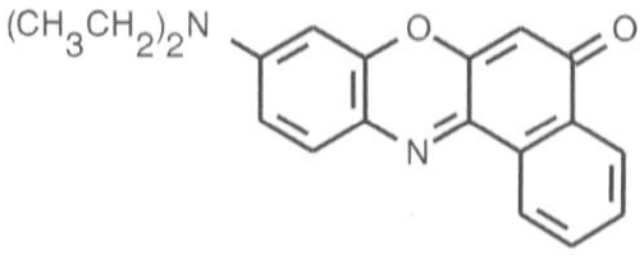

Figure 13.55 N1142 nile red.

Nile Red

The phenoxazine dye nile red (N1142, Figure 13.55) is used to localize and quantitate lipids, particularly neutral lipid droplets within cells.[81,94–96] It is selective for neutral lipids such as cholesteryl esters[97,98] (and also, therefore, for lipoproteins) and is suitable for staining lysosomal phospholipid inclusions.[99] Nile red is almost nonfluorescent in water and other polar solvents but undergoes fluorescence enhancement and large absorption and emission blue shifts in nonpolar environments.[100,101] Its fluorescence enhancement upon binding to proteins is weaker than that produced by its association with lipids[101] (Figure 13.56). Ligand-binding studies on tubulin and tryptophan synthase[102] have exploited the environmental sensitivity of nile red's fluorescence. Nile red has also been used to detect sphingolipids on thin-layer chromatograms[103] and to stain proteins after SDS-polyacrylamide gel electrophoresis.[104]

Bimane Azide

Bimane azide (B30600) is a small blue-fluorescent photoreactive alkyl azide (excitation/emission maxima ~375/458 nm) for photoaffinity labeling of proteins, potentially including membrane proteins from within the cell membrane. This reactive fluorophore's small size may reduce the likelihood that the label will interfere with the function of the biomolecule, an important advantage for site-selective probes.

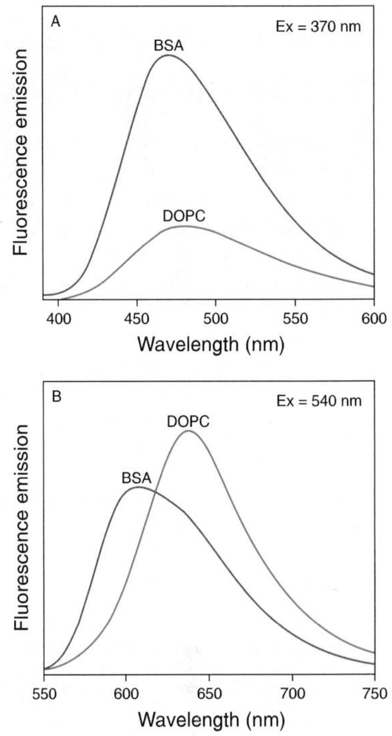

Figure 13.56 Fluorescence emission spectra of **A)** 1,8-ANS (A47) and **B)** nile red (N1142) bound to protein and phospholipid vesicles. Samples comprised 1 µM dye added to 20 µM bovine serum albumin (BSA) or 100 µM dioctadecenoylglycerophosphocholine (DOPC).

Membrane Probes with Environment-Sensitive Spectral Shifts

Prodan and Laurdan

Prodan (P248, Figure 13.57), introduced by Weber and Farris in 1979, has both electron-donor and electron-acceptor substituent, resulting in a large excited-state dipole moment and extensive solvent polarity–dependent fluorescence shifts[105] (Figure 13.58). Several variants of the original probe have since been prepared, including the lipophilic derivative laurdan (D250, Figure 13.59) and thiol-reactive derivatives acrylodan and badan (A433, B6057; Section 2.3), which can be used to confer the environment-sensitive properties of this fluorophore on bioconjugates. When prodan or its derivatives are incorporated into membranes, their fluorescence spectra are sensitive to the physical state of the surrounding phospholipids.[106] In membranes, prodan appears to localize at the surface,[107] although Fourier transform infrared (FTIR) measurements indicate some degree of penetration into the lipid interior.[108] Excited-state relaxation of prodan is sensitive to the nature of the linkage (ester or ether) between phospholipid hydrocarbon tails and the glycerol backbone.[109] In contrast, laurdan's excited-state relaxation is independent of head-group type, and is instead determined by water penetration into the lipid bilayer.[110,111] Two-photon infrared excitation techniques have been successfully applied to both prodan and laurdan, although both probes nominally require ultraviolet excitation[112–115] (~360 nm).

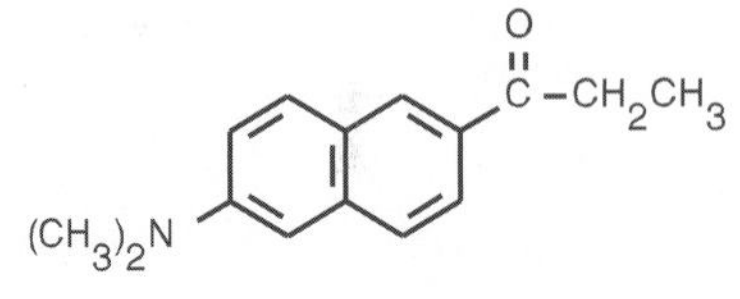

Figure 13.57 P248 6-propionyl-2-dimethylaminonaphthalene (prodan).

Much experimental work using these probes has sought to characterize coexisting lipid domains based on their distinctive fluorescence spectra,[113,116–120] an approach that is intrinsically amenable to dual-wavelength ratio measurements.[111,121] Other applications include detecting nonbilayer lipid phases,[122,123] mapping changes in membrane structure induced by cholesterol and alcohols[124–127] and assessing the polarity of lipid/water interfaces.[128,129] Like ANS (see below), prodan is also useful as a noncovalently interacting probe for proteins.[130–133]

Dapoxyl® Derivatives

Molecular Probes has developed a variety of probes based on our Dapoxyl® fluorophore.[134] Dapoxyl® sulfonamide derivatives exhibit UV absorption with maxima near 370 nm, extinction coefficients >24,000 $cm^{-1}M^{-1}$ and Stokes shifts in excess of 200 nm (Figure 1.111). Dapoxyl® sulfonic acid (D12800) is an amphiphilic Dapoxyl® derivative with generally similar properties and applications to anilinonaphthalene sulfonate (ANS) (see Note 13.3 "Product Highlight: Monitoring Protein-Folding Processes with Anilinonaphthalenesulfonate Dyes"). Both ANS and Dapoxyl® sulfonic acid have been used in a drug-discovery assay based on the detection of protein thermal denaturation shifts.[135] Reactive versions of the Dapoxyl® probes are described in Section 1.7, Section 2.3 and Section 3.3.

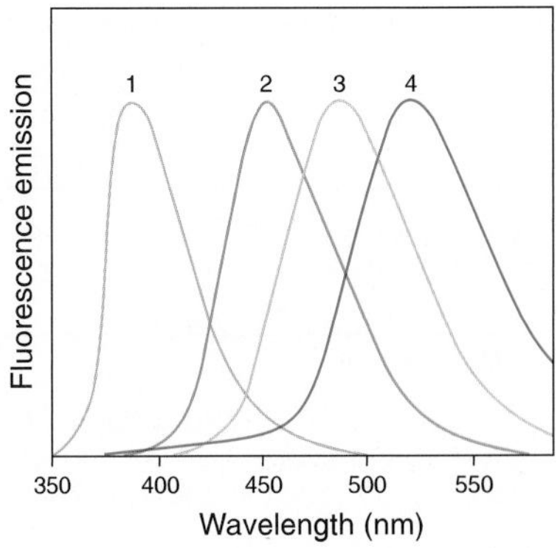

Figure 13.58 Normalized emission spectra of prodan (P248) excited at 345 nm in **1)** cyclohexane, **2)** dimethylformamide, **3)** ethanol and **4)** water.

Note 13.3 — Product Highlight

Monitoring Protein-Folding Processes with Anilinonaphthalenesulfonate Dyes

1,8-ANS (A47) and bis-ANS (B153) have proved to be sensitive probes for partially folded intermediates in protein-folding pathways (Table 1). The basis of these applications is the strong fluorescence enhancement exhibited by these amphiphilic dyes when their exposure to water is lowered (Figures 1 and 2). Consequently, fluorescence of ANS increases substantially when proteins to which it is bound undergo transitions from unfolded to fully or partially folded states that provide shielding from water. Molten globule intermediates are characterized by particularly high ANS fluorescence intensities due to the exposure of hydrophobic core regions that are inaccessible to the dye in the native structure.[1] Binding of 1,8-ANS and bis-ANS to proteins is noncovalent and involves a combination of electrostatic and hydrophobic modes.[2–6] Some investigators have noted that the dye-binding event itself may induce protein conformational changes, indicating the advisability of correlating ANS fluorescence measurements with data obtained using other physical techniques.[5,7–9] In particular, high-resolution structural analysis of an ANS–protein complex by X-ray crystallography has demonstrated the occurrence of local rearrangements of the protein structure to accommodate the dye.[10]

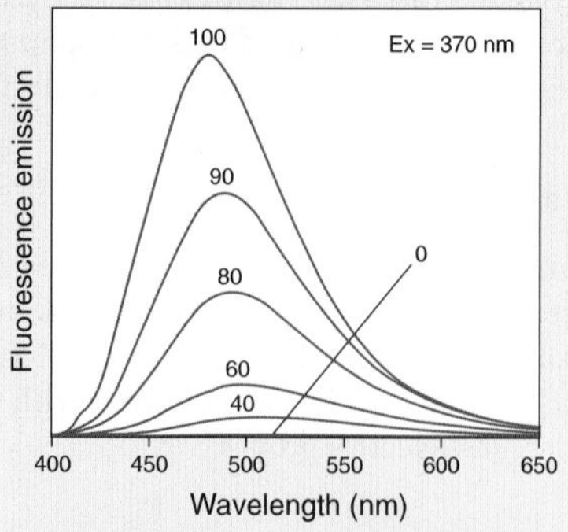

Figure 1. Fluorescence emission spectra of equal concentrations of 1,8-ANS (A47) in ethanol:water mixtures. The labels adjacent to each curve indicate the percentage of ethanol in the solvent mixture.

Table 1. Applications of ANS and bis-ANS as indicators of protein folding

Protein	Reference
Actin	Biochemistry 38, 6261 (1999)
Carbonic anhydrase	Biochemistry 40, 2653 (2001)
Cathepsin	Biochemistry 39, 12382 (2000)
α- and β-Crystallins	Biochemistry 39, 1420 (2000); J Biol Chem 275, 4565 (2000); J Biol Chem 275, 22009 (2000)
Cytochrome *c*	Biochemistry 38, 13635 (1999)
Glucose/xylose isomerase	Eur J Biochem 267, 6331 (2000)
Glutathione transferase	Biochemistry 39, 12336 (2000); Biochemistry 38, 16686 (1999)
GroEL	Biochemistry 40, 4484 (2001); J Biol Chem 275, 33504 (2000); J Mol Biol 276, 505 (1998)
Human serum albumin (HSA)	Biochim Biophys Acta 1476, 139 (2000); Eur J Biochem 266, 26 (1999)
α-Lactalbumin	Biochemistry 40, 2138 (2001); Proteins 42, 237 (2001)
β-Lactoglobulin	Biochemistry 39, 3565 (2000); Eur J Biochem 267, 3957 (2000)
Lysozyme	Biochemistry 39, 3248 (2000); Biochemistry 37, 6772 (1998)
β_2-Microglobulin	J Mol Biol 307, 379 (2001); Biochemistry 39, 8735 (2000)
Phospholipase A_2	Biochemistry 38, 2919 (1999)
Ricin	J Biol Chem 275, 9263 (2000)
α-Synuclein	J Biol Chem 276, 10737 (2001)
Rhodanese	J Biol Chem 275, 33504 (2000); J Biol Chem 274, 33795 (1999)

Figure 2. Fluorescence enhancement of 1,8-ANS (1-anilinonaphthalene-8-sulfonic acid, A47) upon binding to protein. The image shows aqueous solutions of 1,8-ANS excited by ultraviolet light. Addition of protein (bovine serum albumin) to the solution in the cuvette on the left results in intense blue fluorescence. In comparison, the fluorescence of uncomplexed free dye in the cuvette on the right is negligible.

References

1. Biopolymers 31, 119 (1991); **2.** Biophys J 74, 422 (1998); **3.** Biophys J 70, 69 (1996); **4.** Biochemistry 33, 7536 (1994); **5.** Biopolymers 49, 451 (1999); **6.** Biochem J 282, 589 (1992); **7.** Biochemistry 38, 13635 (1999); **8.** Biophys J 75, 2195 (1998); **9.** Biochemistry 40, 4484 (2001); **10.** Proc Natl Acad Sci U S A 97, 6345 (2000).

Anilinonaphthalenesulfonate (ANS) and Related Derivatives

The use of anilinonaphthalene sulfonates (ANS) as fluorescent probes dates back to the pioneering work of Weber in the 1950s, and this class of probes remains valuable for studying both membrane surfaces and proteins. Slavik's 1982 review of its properties is recommended reading, especially for the extensive compilation of spectral data.[136] The primary member of this class, 1,8-ANS (A47, Figure 13.60), and its analogs 2,6-ANS (A50) and 2,6-TNS (T53) are all essentially nonfluorescent in water, only becoming appreciably fluorescent when bound to membranes (quantum yields ~0.25) or proteins (quantum yields ~0.7) [136–138] (Figure 13.56). This property makes them sensitive indicators of protein folding, conformational changes [139–142] and other processes that modify the exposure of the probe to water (see Note 13.3 "Product Highlight: Monitoring Protein-Folding Processes with Anilinonaphthalenesulfonate Dyes"). Fluorescence of 2,6-ANS is also enhanced by cyclodextrins, permitting a sensitive method for separating and analyzing cyclodextrins with capillary electrophoresis.[143]

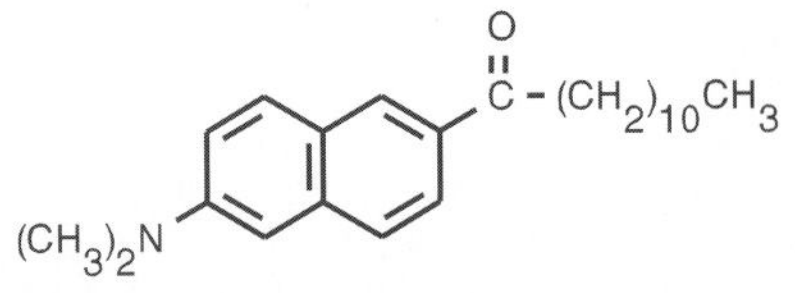

Figure 13.59 D250 6-dodecanoyl-2-dimethylaminonaphthalene (laurdan).

Bis-ANS

Bis-ANS (B153, Figure 13.61) is superior to 1,8-ANS as a probe for nonpolar cavities in proteins, often binding with an affinity that is orders-of-magnitude higher.[144–147] Bis-ANS has particularly high affinity for nucleotide-binding sites of some proteins.[148–150] It is also useful as a structural probe for tubulin [151,152] and as an inhibitor of microtubule assembly.[153–155] Covalent photoincorporation of bis-ANS into proteins has been reported.[156]

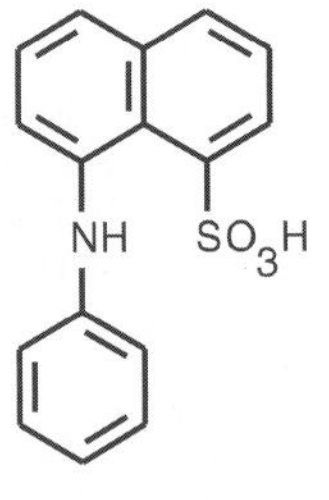

Figure 13.60 A47 1-anilinonaphthalene-8-sulfonic acid (1,8-ANS).

DCVJ

The styrene derivative DCVJ (D3923) is a sensitive indicator of tubulin assembly and actin polymerization.[157,158] The fluorescence quantum yield of DCVJ is strongly dependent on environmental rigidity, resulting in large fluorescence increases when the dye binds to antibodies [159] and when it is compressed in synthetic polymers or phospholipid membrane interiors.[160,161] DCVJ has been used for microviscosity measurements of phospholipid bilayers.[161]

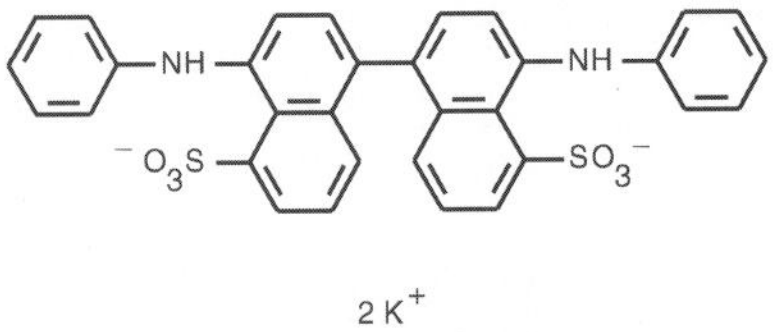

Figure 13.61 B153 bis-ANS (4,4′-dianilino-1,1′-binaphthyl-5,5′-disulfonic acid, dipotassium salt).

4-Amino-4′-Benzamidostilbene-2,2′-Disulfonic Acid

The disodium salt of 4-amino-4′-benzamidostilbene-2,2′-disulfonic acid (MBDS or BADS, A11760) has much lower residual fluorescence in water than does ANS. Upon binding to the hydrophobic pockets of certain proteins, its fluorescence is strongly enhanced.[162,163] The nearly 100-fold increase in MBDS's fluorescence upon forming a 1:1 complex with human serum albumin is useful for quantitation of that protein.[162] The compound is also an inhibitor of erythrocyte band 3 and other anion transporters [163,164] (Section 16.3).

References

1. Biochim Biophys Acta 1374, 63 (1998); **2.** Biophys J 77, 943 (1999); **3.** Photochem Photobiol 60, 563 (1994); **4.** Biophys Chem 34, 283 (1989); **5.** Techniques in Somatic Cell Genetics, Shay JW, Ed. pp. 101–109 (1982); **6.** Biochemistry 23, 5675 (1984); **7.** J Cell Sci 28, 167 (1977); **8.** Biophys J 71, 2680 (1996); **9.** Biochim Biophys Acta 1237, 121 (1995); **10.** Biophys J 63, 710 (1992); **11.** J Gen Physiol 97, 1101 (1991); **12.** Proc Natl Acad Sci U S A 87, 1850 (1990); **13.** FEBS Lett 250, 487 (1989); **14.** Biophys J 76, 1812 (1999); **15.** Biochim Biophys Acta 1189, 175 (1994); **16.** J Biol Chem 267, 17012 (1992); **17.** Biochemistry 30, 9125 (1991); **18.** Biochemistry 29, 8741 (1990); **19.** J Cell Biol 107, 2233 (1988); **20.** Langmuir 10, 658 (1994); **21.** Eur J Cell Biol 59, 116 (1992); **22.** Eur Biophys J 18, 277 (1990); **23.** FEBS Lett 257, 10 (1989); **24.** Cytometry 24, 368 (1996); **25.** Biophys J 70, 988 (1996); **26.** J Cell Sci 100, 473 (1991); **27.** Exp Cell Res 181, 375 (1989); **28.** Nature 294, 718 (1981); **29.** Biochem Biophys Res Commun 184, 160 (1992); **30.** Biochim Biophys Acta 1284, 191 (1996); **31.** J Phys Chem 81, 1755 (1977); **32.** Biochim Biophys Acta 323, 326 (1973); **33.** Methods Enzymol 171, 376 (1989); **34.** Biochemistry 29, 7275 (1990); **35.** Biochim Biophys Acta 729, 185 (1983); **36.** Biochemistry 24, 573 (1985); **37.** Biochemistry 30, 5565 (1991); **38.** Chem Phys Lipids 57, 39 (1991); **39.** Biochimie 71, 23 (1989); **40.** Biochim Biophys Acta 859, 209 (1986); **41.** Biochim Biophys Acta 941, 102 (1988); **42.** Biophys Chem 48, 205 (1993); **43.** Biophys J 59, 466 (1991); **44.** Biophys J 56, 723 (1989); **45.** Biophys Chem 48, 337 (1994); **46.** Biochim Biophys Acta 1104, 273 (1992); **47.** Biochemistry 29, 3248 (1990); **48.** Chem Phys Lipids 50, 1 (1989); **49.** Chem Phys Lipids 64, 99 (1993); **50.** Biochim Biophys Acta 649, 471 (1981); **51.** Chem Phys Lipids 64, 117 (1993); **52.** Biochim Biophys Acta 854, 38 (1986); **53.** Chem Phys 185, 393 (1994); **54.** Chem Phys Lett 216, 559 (1993); **55.** Biochemistry 37, 8180 (1998); **56.** Biochemistry 27, 7723 (1988); **57.** Biochemistry 20, 7333 (1981); **58.** Biochem Biophys Res Commun 181, 166 (1991); **59.** Chem Phys Lipids 66, 135 (1993); **60.** J Fluorescence 3, 145 (1993); **61.** Chem Phys Lipids 55, 29 (1990); **62.** Biochemistry 26, 5121 (1987); **63.** Biochemistry 26, 5113 (1987); **64.** Biochim Biophys Acta 845, 60 (1985); **65.** Cell Biophys 5, 129 (1983); **66.** Am J Physiol 255, F22 (1988); **67.** Cell Biology: A Laboratory Handbook, 2nd Ed., Vol. 2, Celis JE, Ed. pp. 63–69 (1998); **68.** Biochemistry 25, 2149 (1986); **69.** J Cell Biol 135, 1741 (1996); **70.** Biochim Biophys Acta 1147, 194 (1993); **71.** Fluorescent and Luminescent Probes for Biological Activity, Mason WT, Ed. pp. 420–425 (1993); **72.** Am J Physiol 260, C1 (1991); **73.** FASEB J 5, 2078 (1991); **74.** Biophys J 57, 1199 (1990); **75.** Cytometry 39, 151 (2000); **76.** Biochim Biophys Acta 1067, 71 (1991); **77.** Plant Physiol 94, 729 (1990); **78.** Biochemistry 37, 16653 (1998); **79.** Biochemistry 34, 5945 (1995); **80.** J Photochem Photobiol A 121, 177 (1999); **81.** Cytometry 17, 151 (1994); **82.** Biophys J 71, 2656 (1996); **83.** Electrophoresis 24, 3253 (2003); **84.** Methods Mol Biol 122, 185 (1999); **85.** Neuron 20, 1081 (1998); **86.** J Agric Food Chem 48,

References — continued

1150 (2000); **87.** Methods Cell Biol 59, 179 (1999); **88.** Anal Biochem 198, 228 (1991); **89.** Heteroatomic Chem 1, 389 (1990); **90.** Optics Comm 70, 425 (1989); **91.** Arch Pharm Res 20, 1 (1997); **92.** Biochim Biophys Acta 1149, 86 (1993); **93.** Eur J Cell Biol 65, 172 (1994); **94.** J Histochem Cytochem 45, 743 (1997); **95.** J Cell Biol 123, 1567 (1993); **96.** Exp Cell Res 199, 29 (1992); **97.** J Cell Biol 108, 2201 (1989); **98.** J Chromatogr 421, 136 (1987); **99.** Histochemistry 97, 349 (1992); **100.** Anal Chem 62, 615 (1990); **101.** Anal Biochem 167, 228 (1987); **102.** J Biol Chem 270, 6357 (1995); **103.** Anal Biochem 208, 121 (1993); **104.** Biotechniques 21, 625 (1996); **105.** Photochem Photobiol 58, 499 (1993); **106.** Photochem Photobiol 70, 557 (1999); **107.** Biochemistry 27, 399 (1988); **108.** Biochemistry 28, 8358 (1989); **109.** Biochemistry 29, 11134 (1990); **110.** Biophys J 66, 763 (1994); **111.** Biophys J 60, 179 (1991); **112.** Anal Chem 73, 2302 (2001); **113.** Biophys J 78, 290 (2000); **114.** Biophys J 77, 2090 (1999); **115.** Biophys J 72, 2413 (1997); **116.** Biophys J 80, 1417 (2001); **117.** Biophys J 66, 120 (1994); **118.** Photochem Photobiol 57, 420 (1993); **119.** Biophys J 57, 1179 (1990); **120.** J Biol Chem 265, 20044 (1990); **121.** Photochem Photobiol 57, 403 (1993); **122.** Biochemistry 31, 1550 (1992); **123.** Biophys J 57, 925 (1990); **124.** Biochim Biophys Acta 1511, 330 (2001); **125.** Biophys J 68, 1895 (1995); **126.** Biophys J 65, 1404 (1993); **127.** Biochemistry 31, 9473 (1992); **128.** J Biol Chem 269, 10298 (1994); **129.** J Biol Chem 269, 7429 (1994); **130.** Biochemistry 37, 7167 (1998); **131.** Biochem J 290, 411 (1993); **132.** Eur J Biochem 204, 127 (1992); **133.** Nature 319, 70 (1986); **134.** J Photochem Photobiol A 131, 95 (2000); **135.** J Biomol Screen 6, 429 (2001); **136.** Biochim Biophys Acta 694, 1 (1982); **137.** Biophys J 74, 422 (1998); **138.** Biochemistry 7, 3381 (1968); **139.** Biochemistry 38, 2110 (1999); **140.** Biochemistry 37, 4621 (1998); **141.** Biochemistry 37, 13862 (1998); **142.** Biochemistry 37, 16802 (1998); **143.** J Chromatogr A 680, 233 (1994); **144.** Arch Biochem Biophys 268, 239 (1989); **145.** Biochemistry 24, 3852 (1985); **146.** Biochemistry 24, 2034 (1985); **147.** Biochemistry 8, 3915 (1969); **148.** Biochemistry 31, 2982 (1992); **149.** Biochim Biophys Acta 1040, 66 (1990); **150.** Proc Natl Acad Sci U S A 74, 2334 (1977); **151.** Biochemistry 37, 4687 (1998); **152.** Biochemistry 33, 11891 (1994); **153.** Biochemistry 37, 17571 (1998); **154.** Biochemistry 31, 6470 (1992); **155.** J Biol Chem 259, 14647 (1984); **156.** Biochemistry 34, 7443 (1995); **157.** Anal Biochem 204, 110 (1992); **158.** Biochemistry 28, 6678 (1989); **159.** Biochemistry 32, 7589 (1993); **160.** Chem Phys 169, 351 (1993); **161.** Biochemistry 25, 6114 (1986); **162.** Biochim Biophys Acta 229, 547 (1971); **163.** Am J Physiol 259, C439 (1990); **164.** Biochemistry 31, 12610 (1992).

Data Table — 13.5 Other Nonpolar and Amphiphilic Probes

Cat #	MW	Storage	Soluble	Abs	EC	Em	Solvent	Notes
A47	299.34	L	pH >6, DMF	372	7,800	480	MeOH	1
A50	299.34	L	DMF	319	27,000	422	MeOH	1
A11760	518.47	L	H_2O	342	37,000	450	pH 7	
B153	672.85	L	pH >6	395	23,000	500	MeOH	1, 2
B162	542.76	L	MeCN, $CHCl_3$	345	69,000	378	$CHCl_3$	3
B311	444.57	L	MeCN, $CHCl_3$	344	80,000	378	MeOH	3
B3932	448.32	F,L	DMSO, $CHCl_3$	665	161,000	676	MeOH	4
B30600	233.23	F,D,L	DMSO	375	6,000	458	MeOH	
D69	628.98	L	MeCN, DMF	486	27,000	543	MeOH	6
D109	529.63	L	DMSO, EtOH	495	85,000	518	MeOH	7
D202	232.32	L	DMF, MeCN	350	88,000	452	MeOH	8, 9
D250	353.55	L	DMF, MeCN	364	20,000	497	MeOH	10
D3921	248.08	F,L	EtOH, DMSO	502	98,000	510	MeOH	4
D3922	262.11	F,L	EtOH, DMSO	493	89,000	504	MeOH	4
D3923	249.31	L	DMF, DMSO	456	61,000	493	MeOH	
D7760	452.08	L	DMSO, EtOH	394	18,000	494	MeOH	7
D12760	436.58	L	DMSO, EtOH	366	15,000	454	MeOH	7
D12800	366.37	L	DMSO, H_2O	358	25,000	517	MeOH	11
F3857	584.79	L	DMSO, EtOH	504	95,000	525	MeOH	7
H110	585.74	L	DMSO, EtOH	497	92,000	519	MeOH	7
H1387	517.24	L	DMSO, EtOH	357	17,000	488	MeOH	12
H22730	400.60	L	DMSO, EtOH	366	20,000	453	MeOH	7
N1142	318.37	L	DMF, DMSO	552	45,000	636	MeOH	13
O246	731.50	F,DD,L	DMSO, EtOH	556	125,000	578	MeOH	14
O322	613.79	L	DMSO, EtOH	497	84,000	519	MeOH	7
O3852	658.89	L	DMSO, EtOH	497	80,000	519	MeOH	7
P65	219.29	L	MeOH, DMF	337	8,100	426	MeOH	
P80	304.30	L	DMF	344	42,000	376	MeOH	15, 16
P244	274.36	L	DMF, $CHCl_3$	341	41,000	376	MeOH	16
P248	227.31	L	DMF, MeCN	363	19,000	497	MeOH	10
P394	344.50	L	DMF, $CHCl_3$	341	42,000	377	MeOH	16
P459	304.39	L	DMF, DMSO	354	82,000	430	MeOH	8
P3900	503.70	D,L	DMF, DMSO	354	85,000	429	MeOH	8
T53	335.35	L	DMF	318	26,000	443	MeOH	1
T204	461.62	D,L	DMF, DMSO	355	75,000	430	MeOH	8

For definitions of the contents of this data table, see "Navigating *The Handbook*" in the introductory pages.

Notes

1. Fluorescence quantum yields of ANS and its derivatives are environment-dependent and are particularly sensitive to the presence of water. QY of A47 is about 0.4 in EtOH, 0.2 in MeOH and 0.004 in water. Em is also somewhat solvent-dependent (Biochim Biophys Acta 694, 1 (1982)).
2. B153 is soluble in water at 0.1–1.0 mM after heating.
3. Absorption spectra of bis-pyrenyl alkanes have additional peaks at ~325 nm and <300 nm. Emission spectra include both monomer (~380 nm and ~400 nm) and excimer (~470 nm) peaks.
4. The absorption and fluorescence spectra of BODIPY® derivatives are relatively insensitive to the solvent.
5. This product is supplied as a ready-made solution in the solvent indicated under "Soluble."

6. Fluorescence of NBD and its derivatives in water is relatively weak. QY and τ increase and Em decreases in aprotic solvents and other nonpolar environments relative to water (Biochemistry 16, 5150 (1977); Photochem Photobiol 54, 361 (1991)).
7. Spectra of this product are pH-dependent. Data listed are for basic solutions prepared in methanol containing a trace of KOH.
8. Diphenylhexatriene (DPH) and its derivatives are essentially nonfluorescent in water. Absorption and emission spectra have multiple peaks. The wavelength, resolution and relative intensity of these peaks are environment dependent. Abs and Em values are for the most intense peak in the solvent specified.
9. Stock solutions of DPH (D202) are often prepared in in tetrahydrofuran (THF). Long-term storage of THF solutions is not recommended because of possible peroxide formation in that solvent.
10. The emission spectrum of P248 is solvent-dependent. Em = 401 nm in cyclohexane, 440 nm in $CHCl_3$, 462 nm in MeCN, 496 nm in EtOH and 531 nm in H_2O (Biochemistry 18, 3075 (1979)). Abs is only slightly solvent dependent. The emission spectra of D250 in these solvents are similar to those of P248.
11. Em = 520 nm when bound to phospholipid bilayer membranes. Fluorescence in H_2O is weak (Em ~600 nm).
12. Em of H1387 is significantly shifted in other solvents (Biochemistry 22, 5714 (1983)).
13. The absorption and fluorescence spectra and fluorescence quantum yield of N1142 are highly solvent-dependent (J Lipid Res 26, 781 (1985); Anal Biochem 167, 228 (1987)).
14. This product is intrinsically a sticky gum at room temperature.
15. P80 fluorescence lifetime is 62 nanoseconds in water, 57 nanoseconds in phospholipid vesicles and 140 nanoseconds in cetyltrimethylammonium micelles.
16. Pyrene derivatives exhibit structured spectra. The absorption maximum is usually about 340 nm with a subsidiary peak at about 325 nm. There are also strong absorption peaks below 300 nm. The emission maximum is usually about 376 nm with a subsidiary peak at 396 nm. Excimer emission at about 470 nm may be observed at high concentrations.

Product List — 13.5 Other Nonpolar and Amphiphilic Probes

Cat #	Product Name	Unit Size
A11760	4-amino-4′-benzamidostilbene-2,2′-disulfonic acid, disodium salt (MBDS)	100 mg
A47	1-anilinonaphthalene-8-sulfonic acid (1,8-ANS) *high purity*	100 mg
A50	2-anilinonaphthalene-6-sulfonic acid (2,6-ANS)	100 mg
B30600	bimane azide	5 mg
B153	bis-ANS (4,4′-dianilino-1,1′-binaphthyl-5,5′-disulfonic acid, dipotassium salt)	10 mg
B3932	(*E,E*)-3,5-bis-(4-phenyl-1,3-butadienyl)-4,4-difluoro-4-bora-3a,4a-diaza-*s*-indacene (BODIPY® 665/676)	5 mg
B162	1,10-bis-(1-pyrene)decane	25 mg
B311	1,3-bis-(1-pyrenyl)propane	25 mg
D12800	Dapoxyl® sulfonic acid, sodium salt	10 mg
D3923	4-(dicyanovinyl)julolidine (DCVJ)	25 mg
D12760	6,8-difluoro-4-heptadecyl-7-hydroxycoumarin (C_{17}DiFU)	10 mg
D3922	4,4-difluoro-1,3,5,7,8-pentamethyl-4-bora-3a,4a-diaza-*s*-indacene (BODIPY® 493/503)	10 mg
D3921	4,4-difluoro-1,3,5,7-tetramethyl-4-bora-3a,4a-diaza-*s*-indacene (BODIPY® 505/515)	10 mg
D69	4-dihexadecylamino-7-nitrobenz-2-oxa-1,3-diazole (NBD dihexadecylamine)	100 mg
D7760	4-(*N,N*-dimethyl-*N*-tetradecylammonium)methyl-(7-hydroxycoumarin) chloride (U-6)	10 mg
D202	1,6-diphenyl-1,3,5-hexatriene (DPH)	100 mg
D109	5-dodecanoylaminofluorescein	100 mg
D250	6-dodecanoyl-2-dimethylaminonaphthalene (laurdan)	100 mg
F3857	fluorescein octadecyl ester	10 mg
H22730	4-heptadecyl-7-hydroxycoumarin	10 mg
H110	5-hexadecanoylaminofluorescein	100 mg
H1387	6-hexadecanoyl-2-(((2-(trimethylammonium)ethyl)methyl)amino)naphthalene chloride (patman)	5 mg
N1142	nile red	25 mg
O322	5-octadecanoylaminofluorescein	100 mg
O3852	*N*-octadecyl-*N*′-(5-(fluoresceinyl))thiourea (F18)	25 mg
O246	octadecyl rhodamine B chloride (R18)	10 mg
P459	3-(4-(6-phenyl)-1,3,5-hexatrienyl)phenylpropionic acid (DPH propionic acid)	25 mg
P3900	*N*-((4-(6-phenyl-1,3,5-hexatrienyl)phenyl)propyl)trimethylammonium *p*-toluenesulfonate (TMAP-DPH)	5 mg
P65	*N*-phenyl-1-naphthylamine	1 g
P248	6-propionyl-2-dimethylaminonaphthalene (prodan)	100 mg
P244	1-pyrenebutanol	100 mg
P394	1-pyrenenonanol	25 mg
P80	1-pyrenesulfonic acid, sodium salt	1 g
T53	2-(*p*-toluidinyl)naphthalene-6-sulfonic acid, sodium salt (2,6-TNS)	100 mg
T204	1-(4-trimethylammoniumphenyl)-6-phenyl-1,3,5-hexatriene *p*-toluenesulfonate (TMA-DPH)	25 mg

For current prices or to order online, visit probes.invitrogen.com

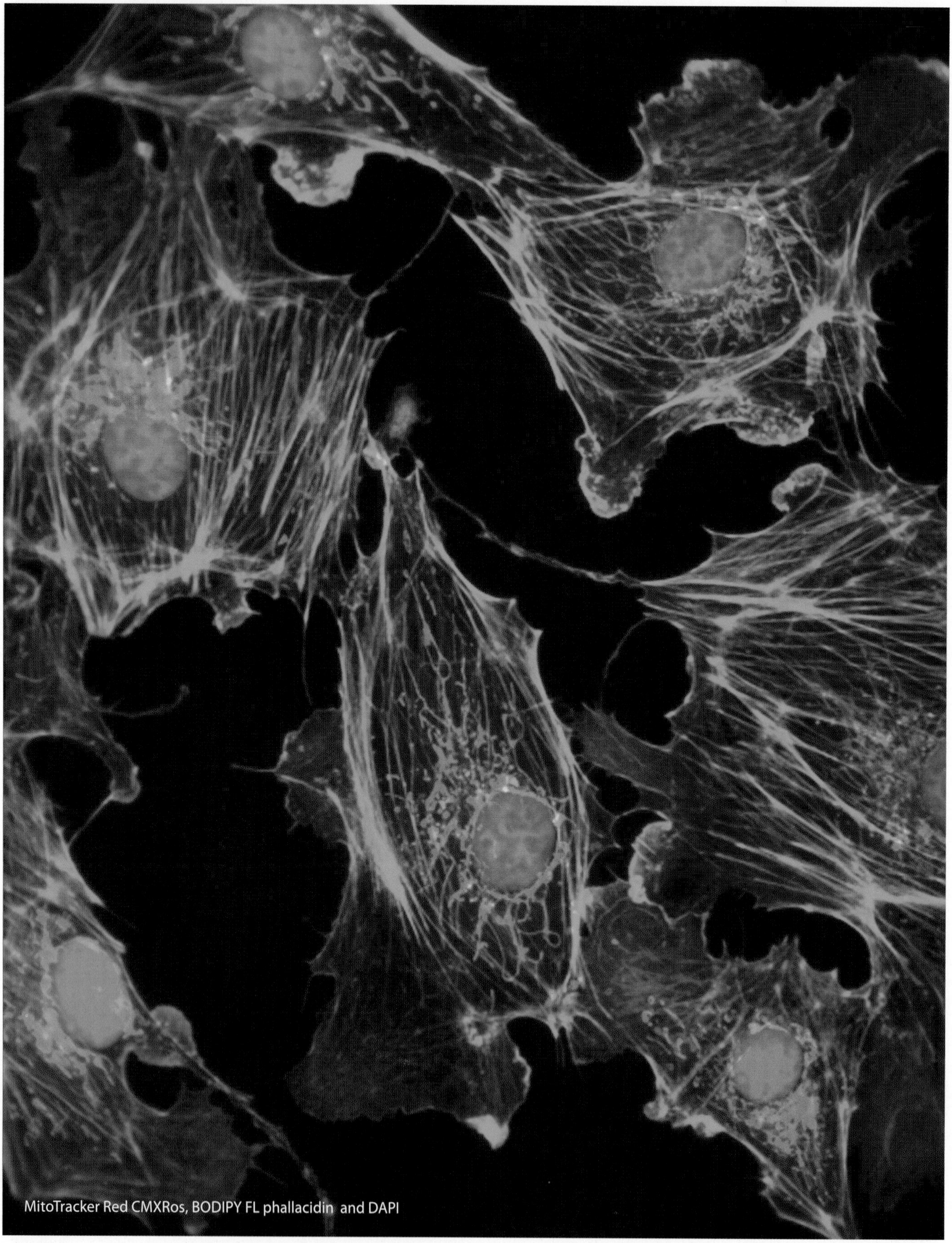

MitoTracker Red CMXRos, BODIPY FL phallacidin and DAPI

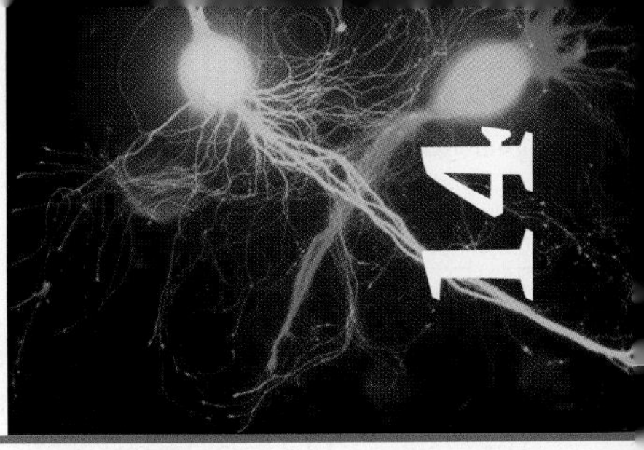

Chapter 14

Fluorescent Tracers of Cell Morphology and Fluid Flow

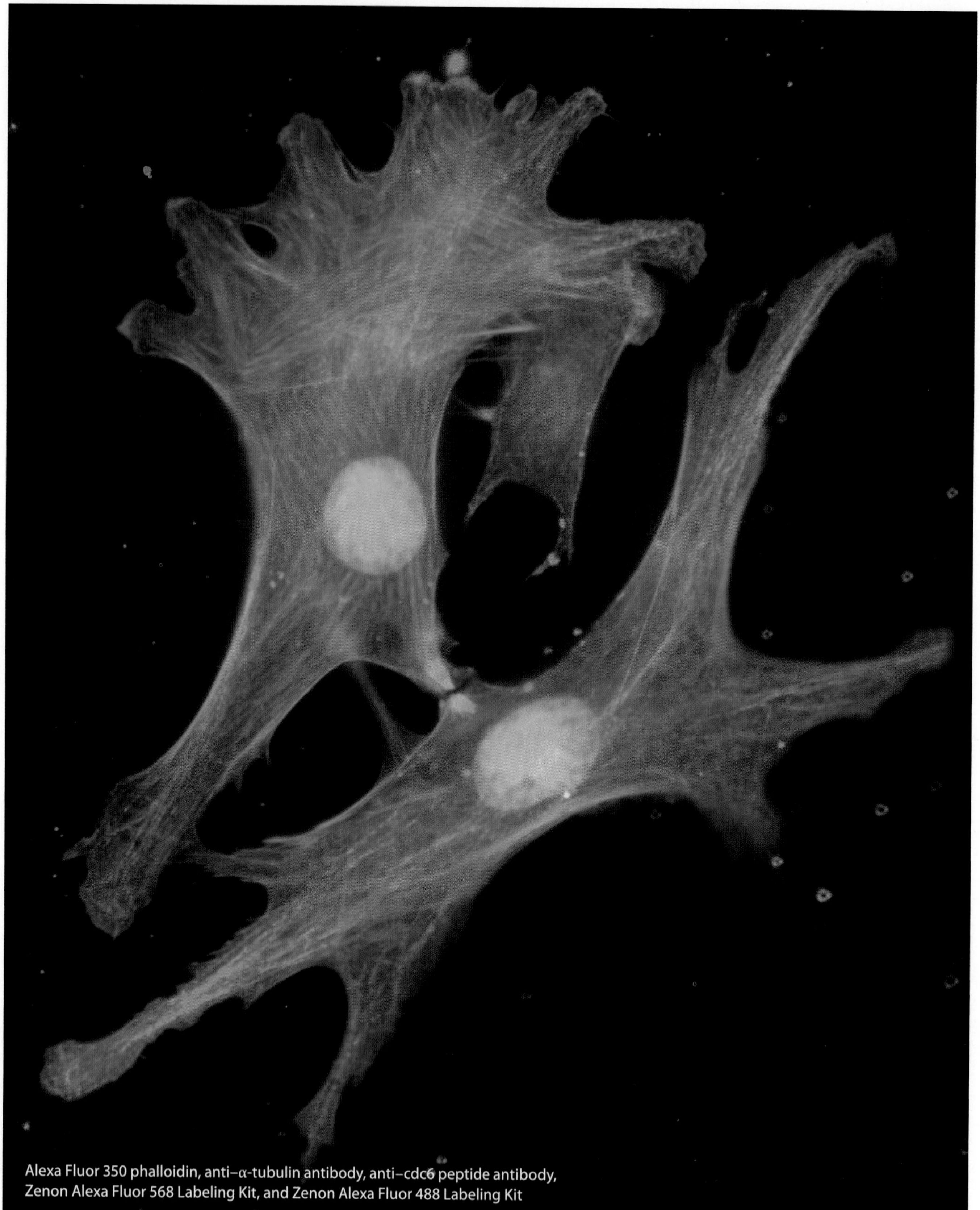

Alexa Fluor 350 phalloidin, anti–α-tubulin antibody, anti–cdc6 peptide antibody, Zenon Alexa Fluor 568 Labeling Kit, and Zenon Alexa Fluor 488 Labeling Kit

14.1 Choosing a Tracer

To serve as an effective tracer of cell morphology, a fluorescent probe or other detectable molecule must have the capacity for localized introduction into a cell or organelle, as well as long-term retention within that structure. If used with live cells and tissues, then the tracer should also be biologically inert and nontoxic. When these conditions are satisfied, the fluorescence or other detectable properties of the tracer can be used to track the position of the tracer over time. Fluorescent tracers can be employed to investigate flow in capillaries, to define neuronal cell connectivity and to study dye translocation through gap junctions, as well as to follow cell division, cell lysis or liposome fusion. Furthermore, they can be used to track the movements of labeled cells in culture, tissues or intact organisms. The review of techniques for tracing neuronal pathways by Vercelli et al.[1] is particularly recommended.

Although the predominant tracers have been fluorescent, not all of the useful tracers are intrinsically detectable. For example, biotin derivatives are widely used as polar tracers, especially in neurons. However, when a biotinylated or haptenylated tracer is used in live cells, detection requires cell fixation and permeabilization to allow access to fluorescent dye– or enzyme-labeled conjugates of avidin and streptavidin (Section 7.6, Table 7.22) or of antibodies (Section 7.2, Section 7.3, Section 7.4; Table 7.1).

In many of these tracing applications, the physical dimensions of the tracer molecule are an important consideration. Molecular Probes offers fluorescent tracers ranging in size from small molecules about 1 nm in diameter to polystyrene microspheres up to 15 µm in diameter. This chapter discusses our diverse selection of fluorescent tracers, as well as biotin derivatives and other tracers:

- **Cell-permeant cytoplasmic labels** (Section 14.2). Molecular Probes has developed several thiol-reactive CellTracker™ probes (Figure 14.17, Figure 15.1), which yield fluorescent products that are retained in many live cells through several generations and are not transferred to adjacent cells in a population, except possibly by transport through gap junctions. These probes represent a significant breakthrough in the cellular retention of fluorescent dyes and are ideal long-term tracers for transplanted cells or tissues.
- **Microinjectable cytoplasmic labels** (Section 14.3). Polar tracers such as lucifer yellow CH, Cascade Blue® hydrazide, the Alexa Fluor® hydrazides, sulforhodamine 101 and biocytin are membrane-impermeant probes that are usually introduced into cells by whole-cell patch clamping, iontophoresis, osmotic lysis of pinocytic vesicles or comparable methods[2,3] (Table 14.1). These tracers are commonly used to investigate cell–cell and cell–liposome fusion, as well as membrane permeability[4] and transport through gap junctions[5,6] or cell uptake during pinocytosis (Section 16.1).
- **Nissl stains for retrograde tracing in neurons.** We have developed five fluorescent Nissl stains that not only provide a wide spectrum of fluorescent colors (Figure 14.39, Figure 14.40, Figure 14.41, Figure 14.42) for staining neurons, but also are more sensitive than the conventional dyes (Section 14.3).
- **Membrane tracers — DiI, DiO, DiD, DiR, DiA, R18, FM® 1-43, FM® 4-64 and their analogs** (Section 14.4). Lipophilic carbocyanine, aminostyryl and rhodamine dyes can be introduced into membranes by direct application of a dye crystal onto a cell, by bulk loading from aqueous dispersions prepared from our Vybrant® DiI, DiO and DiD cell-labeling solutions or by application of the NeuroTrace® DiI, DiO and DiD tissue-labeling pastes. Lateral diffusion of the dye within the membrane eventually stains the entire cell. These probes are widely used for neuroanatomical tracing and long-term assays of cell–cell association. Some of our DiI and DiO analogs exhibit superior solubility and brightness and, in some cases, produce a cell-staining pattern that persists through fixation by aldehyde-based reagents and through acetone permeabilization (Figure 14.1).
- **Fluorescent and biotinylated dextran conjugates** (Section 14.5). Dextran conjugates are ideal cell-lineage tracers because they are relatively inert, exhibit low toxicity and are retained in cells for long periods. These membrane-impermeant probes are usually loaded into cells by invasive techniques such as microinjection, whole-cell patch clamping, scrape loading, microprojectile bombardment, electroporation or osmotic shock (Table 14.1). Availability of dextrans in a range of molecular weights makes them useful as size-exclusion probes for determining pore sizes in membranes.

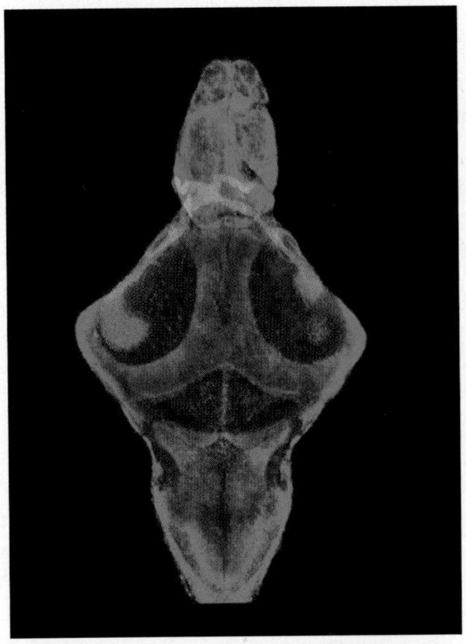

Figure 14.1 The tracer DiI (D282, D3911) used as a diagnostic tool to evaluate retinal and tectal patterns in a chimeric five-day-old zebrafish brain. *Acerebellar* (*Fgf8*) is required for development of midbrain polarity and correct retinotopic mapping of retinal ganglion cell axons. One eye of this brain was wild type, whereas the other was mutant for *fgf8* (derived from homozygous acerebellar donors). The chimera was obtained by transplanting eye primordia, and the eyes were subsequently removed for photography. Retinal ganglion cell axons in the dorsonasal retina were labeled with DiI and nuclei were counterstained with SYTOX® Green nucleic acid stain (S7020). Axons from the right, wild-type eye terminate correctly in the posterior tectum only, whereas axons from the left, mutant eye terminate inappropriately in the anterior and posterior tectum. This digital image, previously published on the cover of Development 125 (13) (1999), was created by Alexander Picker and Michael Brand, Neurobiology, University of Heidelberg. The image is used with the permission of The Company of Biologists, Ltd.

- **Fluorescent microspheres** (Section 14.6). Molecular Probes' FluoSpheres® and TransFluoSpheres® fluorescent microspheres — which contain ~10^2 to ~10^{10} fluorescent dyes per bead — are the most intensely fluorescent tracers available (Table 6.5, Table 6.6; Figure 14.2). Although other multiply labeled particles such as our BioParticles® fluorescent bacteria (Section 16.1) may be used as tracers, they are often not biologically inert nor are they as physically durable as fluorescent microspheres. These properties make fluorescent beads particularly useful as long-term markers for transplantation studies. Submicron microspheres can be injected into cells or taken up by phagocytosis (Section 16.1). Much larger (10–15 µm) beads provide an alternative to radioactive microspheres for determination of organ blood flow, and intermediate-sized (1–5 µm) microspheres are useful for studies that trace inhaled particles.
- **Proteins and protein conjugates** (Section 14.7). Our fluorescent protein tracers have molecular weights ranging from ~12,000 (cholera toxin subunit B conjugates) to ~240,000 daltons (B- and R-phycoerythrin). Their applications are sometimes similar to those of the fluorescent dextrans; however, unlike the polydisperse dextrans, fluorescent protein tracers have molecular weights that are reasonably well defined.

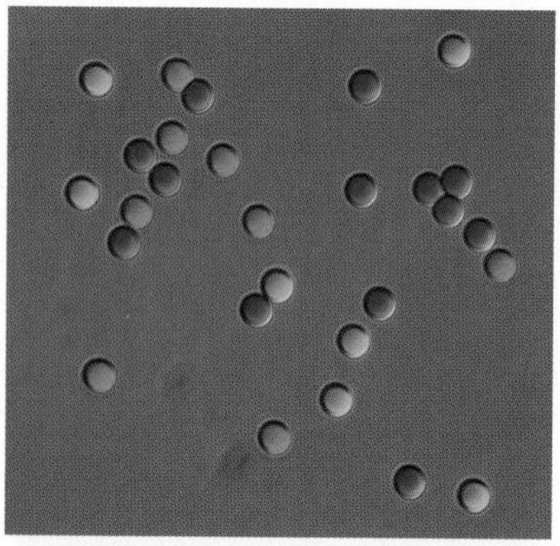

Figure 14.2 A photomicrograph of a multicolor mixture of Molecular Probes' FluoSpheres® fluorescent microspheres overlaid with a differential interference contrast (DIC) image of the same field. Molecular Probes applies its proprietary fluorescent dye technology to produce a range of intensely fluorescent FluoSpheres® microspheres labeled with biotin, streptavidin and NeutrAvidin biotin-binding protein, providing important tools for improving the sensitivity of flow cytometry applications and immunodiagnostic assays.

References

1. Brain Res Bull 51, 11 (2000); **2.** J Neurosci Methods 117, 159 (2002); **3.** Methods Cell Biol 29, 153 (1989); **4.** Cytometry 21, 230 (1995); **5.** Cell 84, 381 (1996); **6.** Biochim Biophys Acta 988, 319 (1989).

14.2 Membrane-Permeant Reactive Tracers for Long-Term Cell Labeling

Thiol-Reactive CellTracker™ Probes

Molecular Probes' CellTracker™ reagents are fluorescent chloromethyl derivatives that freely diffuse through the membranes of live cells (Figure 14.3, Figure 14.4, Figure 14.5). Once inside the cell, these mildly thiol-reactive probes undergo what is believed to be a glutathione *S*-transferase–mediated reaction to produce membrane-impermeant glutathione–fluorescent dye adducts, although our experiments suggest that they may also react with other intracellular components

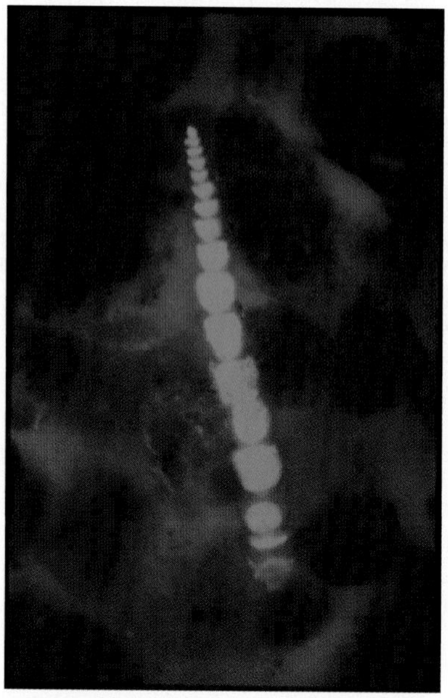

Figure 14.3 Detection of organisms in marine sediments by incubating an intact sediment core sample with the fixable, cell-permeant CellTracker™ Green CMFDA (C2925, C7025). The core sample was subsequently embedded, sectioned and examined for fluorescently labeled organisms. The micrograph reveals the microorganism *Leptohalysis scotti*, a marine benthic foraminiferan. Image contributed by Joan M. Bernhard, Wadsworth Center, New York State Department of Health.

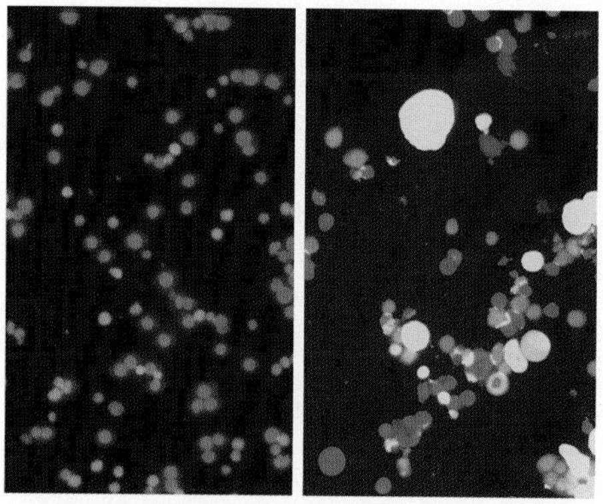

Figure 14.4 HL60 cells that have been stained with CellTracker™ Orange CMTMR (C2927) and then mixed with WEHI 7.1 cells stained with CellTracker™ Green CMFDA (C2925, C7025) (left panel). Several minutes after initiating cell–cell electrofusion, a CMTMR-stained HL60 cell is observed fusing with a CMFDA-stained WEHI 7.1 cell; cytoplasmic mixing is evident by the appearance of yellow fluorescence. After electrofusion is complete, dual-fluorescing (yellow) hybrids can be easily distinguished (right panel). Images contributed by Mark J. Jaroszeski, University of South Florida.

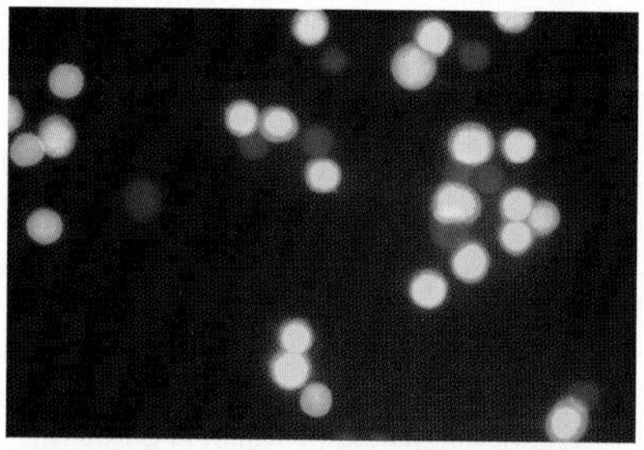

Figure 14.5 Individual populations of mouse myeloma (P3X) cells stained with our reactive tracers — CellTracker™ Orange CMTMR (C2927), CellTracker™ Green CMFDA (C2925) and CellTracker™ Blue CMAC (C2110). Each of three cell populations was stained with a different tracer and then the populations were mixed, demonstrating that these tracers allow simultaneous long-term monitoring of different groups of cells in transplantation and other assays.

(Figure 14.6). Regardless of the mechanism, many cell types loaded with the CellTracker™ probes are both fluorescent and viable for at least 24 hours after loading and often through several cell divisions. Most other cell-permeant fluorescent dyes, including the acetoxymethyl (AM) esters of calcein and BCECF (Section 15.2), are retained in viable cells for no more than a few hours at physiological temperatures (Figure 15.3). Furthermore, unlike the free dye, the peptide–fluorescent dye adducts contain amino groups and can therefore be covalently linked to surrounding biomolecules by fixation with formaldehyde or glutaraldehyde. This property permits long-term storage of the labeled cells or tissue and, in cases where the anti-dye antibody is available (see below), amplification of the conjugate by standard immunohistochemical techniques. Fixation without loss of the tracer also facilitates the safe handling and analysis of cells containing pathogens.

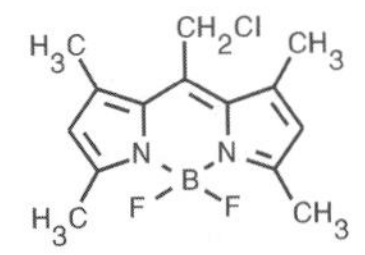

Figure 14.11 C2102 CellTracker™ Green BODIPY (8-chloromethyl-4,4-difluoro-1,3,5,7-tetramethyl-4-bora-3a,4a-diaza-s-indacene).

CellTracker™ Probes in a Variety of Fluorescent Colors

Molecular Probes' patented CellTracker™ product line includes reactive chloromethyl derivatives of:

- Blue-fluorescent 7-aminocoumarin (CellTracker™ Blue CMAC, C2110, Figure 14.7)
- Blue-fluorescent 7-hydroxycoumarin (CellTracker™ Blue CMHC, C2111, Figure 14.8)
- Blue-fluorescent 6,8-difluoro-7-hydroxycoumarin (CellTracker™ Blue CMF$_2$HC, C12881, Figure 14.9)
- Green-fluorescent fluorescein diacetate (CellTracker™ Green CMFDA, C2925 and C7025, Figure 14.6, Figure 14.10)
- Green-fluorescent BODIPY® derivative (CellTracker™ Green BODIPY®, C2102, Figure 14.11)
- Orange-fluorescent tetramethylrhodamine (CellTracker™ Orange CMTMR, C2927, Figure 14.12)
- Orange-fluorescent CellTracker™ Orange CMRA (C34551, Figure 14.13)
- Red-fluorescent CellTracker™ Red CMTPX (C34552, Figure 14.14)

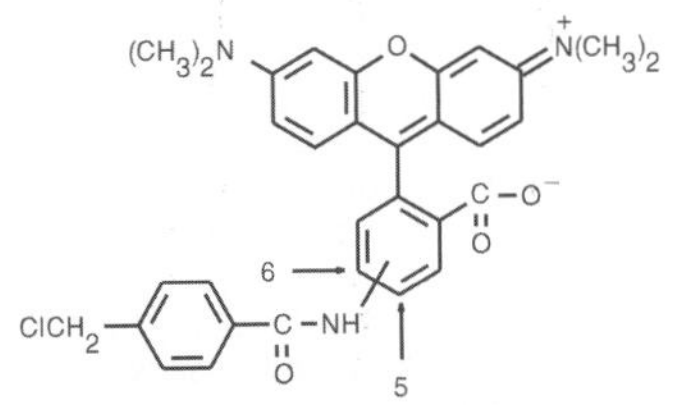

Figure 14.12 C2927 CellTracker™ Orange CMTMR (5-(and-6)-(((4-chloromethyl)benzoyl)amino)tetramethylrhodamine).

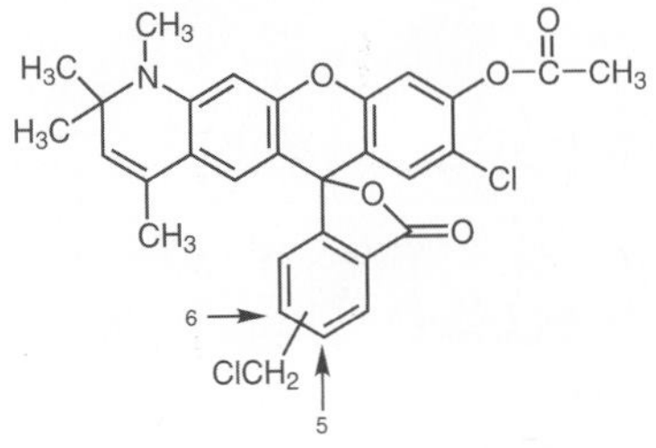

Figure 14.13 C34551 CellTracker™ Orange CMRA.

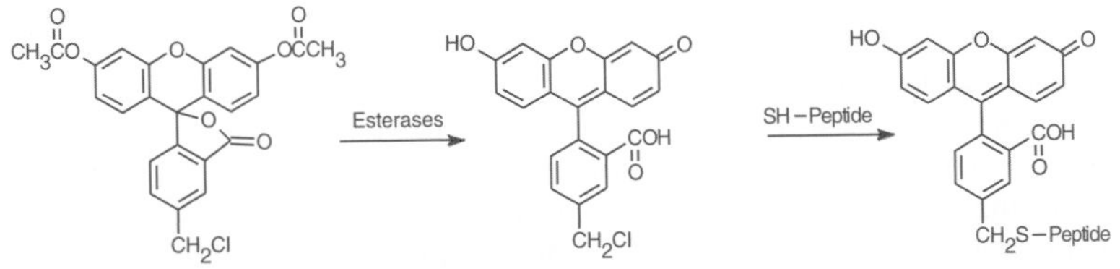

Figure 14.6 Intracellular reactions of our fixable CellTracker™ Green CMFDA (5-chloromethylfluorescein diacetate; C2925, C7025). Once this membrane-permeant probe enters a cell, esterase hydrolysis converts nonfluorescent CMFDA to fluorescent 5-chloromethylfluorescein, which can then react with thiols on proteins and peptides to form aldehyde-fixable conjugates. This probe may also react with intracellular thiol-containing biomolecules first, but the conjugate is nonfluorescent until its acetates are removed.

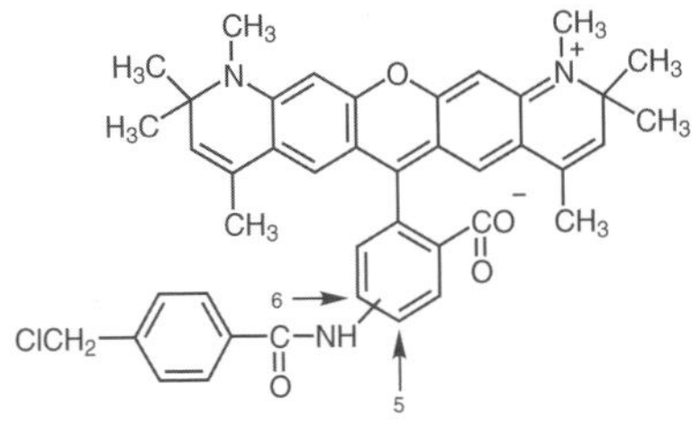

Figure 14.14 C34552 CellTracker™ Red CMTPX.

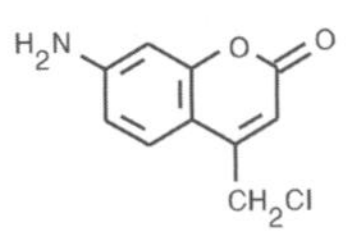

Figure 14.7 C2110 CellTracker™ Blue CMAC (7-amino-4-chloromethylcoumarin).

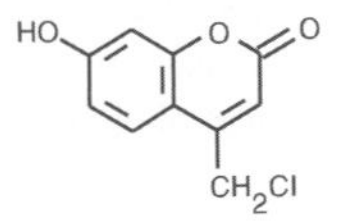

Figure 14.8 C2111 CellTracker™ Blue CMHC (4-chloromethyl-7-hydroxycoumarin).

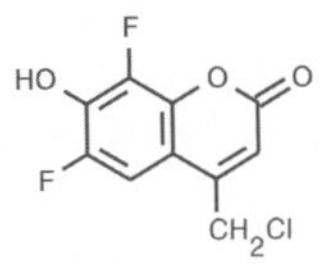

Figure 14.9 C12881 CellTracker™ Blue CMF$_2$HC (4-chloromethyl-6,8-difluoro-7-hydroxycoumarin).

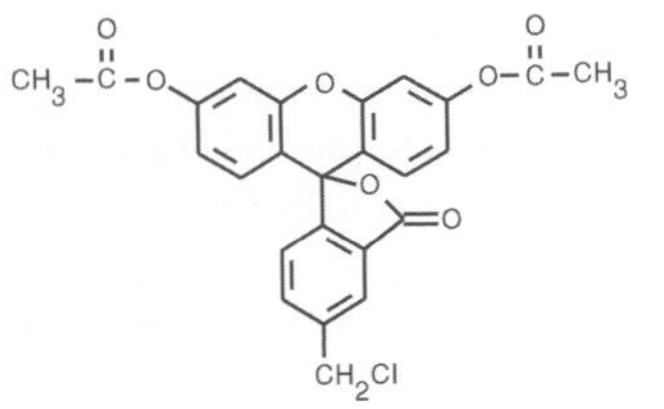

Figure 14.10 C2925 CellTracker™ Green CMFDA (5-chloromethylfluorescein diacetate).

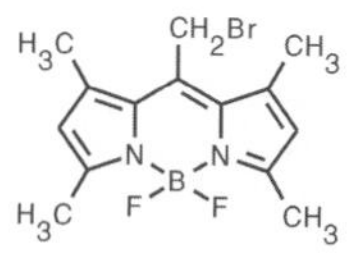

Figure 14.15 B2103 8-bromomethyl-4,4-difluoro-1,3,5,7-tetramethyl-4-bora-3a,4a-diaza-*s*-indacene (BODIPY® 493/503 methyl bromide).

Figure 14.16 B22802 8-bromomethyl-4,4-difluoro-3,5-bis-(2-thienyl)-4-bora-3a,4a-diaza-*s*-indacene (BODIPY® 630/650 methyl bromide).

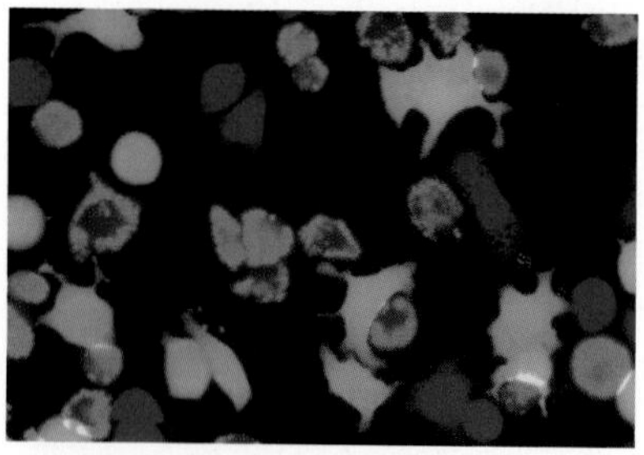

Figure 14.17 Rat basophilic leukemia (RBL) cells labeled in suspension with CellTracker™ Blue CMAC (C2110), CellTracker™ Green CMFDA (C2925, C7025) or CellTracker™ Orange CMTMR (C2927) prior to plating. The image was acquired using optical filter sets appropriate for DAPI, fluorescein and the Texas Red® dye.

CellTracker™ Green CMFDA freely diffuses into the cell, where cytosolic esterases cleave the acetate groups, releasing the fluorescent product; CellTracker™ Orange CMRA also requires esterase cleavage to activate its fluorescence. The CellTracker™ Blue CMAC, CMHC and CMF_2HC, CellTracker™ Green BODIPY®, CellTracker™ Orange CMTMR and CellTracker™ Red CMTPX probes do not require enzymatic cleavage to activate their fluorescence. CellTracker™ Orange CMRA is a rhodol-based fluorophore with an overall net charge at neutral pH that is expected to be negative, in contrast with the overall net positive charge of the tetramethylrhodamine-based CellTracker™ Orange CMTMR. Thus, unlike CellTracker™ Orange CMTMR, CellTracker™ Orange CMRA should remain primarily in the cytoplasm instead of being sequestered inside actively respiring mitochondria. The long-wavelength CellTracker™ Red CMTPX exhibits bright red fluorescence that is easily distinguished from that of blue-, green- and far-red–fluorescent probes, including CellTracker™ Green CMFDA. Because the spectral overlap between CellTracker™ Red CMTPX and this green fluorophore is minimized, the potential for fluorescence resonance energy transfer (FRET) in a multicolor labeling experiment is reduced and the ability to discriminate signals is enhanced.

Our related MitoTracker® probes (Section 12.2) and other mitochondrial stains may be similarly useful for tracing actively metabolizing cells. We also offer BODIPY® 493/503 methyl bromide (B2103, Figure 14.15), a green-fluorescent dye and BODIPY® 630/650 methyl bromide (B22802, Figure 14.16), a far-red–fluorescent dye, which have slightly greater thiol-reactivity than do chloromethyl derivatives. BODIPY® 630/650 methyl bromide is our longest-wavelength cell-permeant tracer and its fluorescence can be excited by either the 633 nm spectral line of the He–Ne laser or the 647 nm spectral line of the krypton-ion laser used in many confocal laser-scanning microscopes and flow cytometers.

Applications for CellTracker™ Probes

The thiol-reactive CellTracker™ Green CMFDA — which is particularly easy to use as a tracer — is suitable for long-term cell labeling and has been used in a wide variety of applications, including studies of:

- Cell adhesion,[1,2] including adhesion on prosthetic surfaces[3]
- Cell communication through gap junctions[4]
- Cell migration (chemotaxis)[5] (Section 15.6)
- Cell tracing in mixed cultures[1,6] (Figure 14.4)
- Platelet labeling without activation and their *in vivo* tracing for days[7]
- Long-term viability and cytotoxicity assays[8,9] (Section 15.2)
- Transplantation[10]
- Multidrug resistance and transport of the glutathione adduct by the multispecific organic anion transporter[11,12] (Section 15.6)
- Tumor cell death in culture[13]
- Keratocytes in intact cornea[14]
- Glutathione content in cells[4,15–17] (Section 15.6)
- Fungal growth and differentiation[18]
- Ingestion of live, fluorescently labeled protists by mixotrophic dinoflagellates[19]
- Cell–cell and cell–liposome fusion[20–24]
- Vacuolar morphology in yeast[25]

Virtually any of the other CellTracker™ probes could be used for the same applications as above and combinations of two (or more) CellTracker™ probes or use of CellTracker™ probes in conjunction with the lipophilic tracers described in Section 14.4 often permit simultaneous, multicolor applications (Figure 14.17). We particularly recommend the combination of CellTracker™ Green CMFDA and our chloromethyl SNARF® pH indicator (C6826, see below) for two-color tracing. Both dyes can be excited near 490 nm and the green-fluorescent CellTracker™ Green CMFDA–stained cells can be distinguished from the red-fluorescent chloromethyl SNARF® dye–stained cells, provided that the fluorescence intensities of the stained cells are similar. Our deep red-fluorescent BODIPY® 630/650 methyl bromide dye (B22802, see below) can be utilized as a third dye for triple staining and the blue-fluorescent CellTracker™ dyes (C2110, C2111, C12881) or monobromobimane (M1378, see below) can be added as a fourth label.

CellTracker™ Green CMFDA was used to track wild-type and myosin II mutant *Dictyostelium discoideum* cells within aggregation streams during early multicellular morphogenesis; differentiation and morphogenesis pathways were reportedly unaffected in labeled cells imaged over several days by confocal laser-scanning microscopy.[26,27] CellTracker™ Green BODIPY® was used to label CD4 T cells and follow their activation and proliferation in mice with the immunodeficiency syndrome MAIDS.[28] CellTracker™ Green CMFDA and some other CellTracker™ dyes have been utilized to selectively label intracellular *Chlamydia psittaci* in infected cells.[29] This unexpected application of the CellTracker™ dyes could be important for *in vivo* labeling of obligate intracellular bacteria and parasites for which no genetic tools exist. Additionally, intracellular bacteria accumulated BODIPY® FL C_5-ceramide (D3521, B22650; Section 12.4) in their inclusion membranes rather than labeling the Golgi of the host cells.[29,30]

CellTracker™ Orange CMTMR has been used to stain the cytoplasm of *engrailed*-expressing *Drosophila* cells in an *in vitro* reconstruction experiment,[31] to follow T-cell differentiation and maturation[32] and to trace implanted tumor cells for at least two weeks.[33,34] Chlamydia labeled with CellTracker™ Orange CMTMR continued to grow and differentiate, and labeled chlamydia isolated from infected cells remained infectious.[29] Both the CellTracker™ Green CMFDA and CellTracker™ Orange CMTMR probes have been employed in a flow cytometry method for quantitating cell–cell electrofusion products[22,23] (Figure 14.4) and in two-color imaging to detect cell–cell association.[2,35]

Metabolic activity and drug-induced cytotoxicity were measured with CellTracker™ Blue CMAC in a fluorescence-based microplate assay.[36] Peptidase substrates derived from CellTracker™ Blue CMAC yield blue-fluorescent products that are well retained in live cells[37] (Section 10.4). Our CellTracker™ Blue CMF_2HC (C12881) has a low pK_a that ensures that the dye's conjugates will be ionized and have bright blue fluorescence in the cytoplasm. CellTracker™ Blue CMAC was used in combination with calcein AM (C1430, C3099, C3100MP; Section 15.6) and the lipophilic tracer DiI (D282, D3911, V22885; Section 14.4) to identify lipid mixing and cytoplasm mixing between labeled effector cells and labeled target cells.[21]

The ability to fix the intracellular products of CellTracker™ Green CMFDA, CellTracker™ Green BODIPY® and CellTracker™ Orange CMTMR in permeabilized cells permits the stained cells to be probed with our anti-fluorescein/Oregon Green®, anti–BODIPY® FL and anti-tetramethylrhodamine antibodies, respectively (Section 7.4, Table 7.18). After antibody staining, these cells can be developed for electron microscopy using standard immunohistochemical techniques or for fluorescence amplification by our ultrasensitive tyramide signal amplification (TSA) and Enzyme-Labeled Fluorescence (ELF®) technologies (Section 6.2, Section 6.3).

Other Thiol-Reactive Tracers

PFB Aminofluorescein Diacetate

The green-fluorescent intracellular hydrolysis product of our patented pentafluorobenzoyl aminofluorescein diacetate (PFB-FDA, P12880, Figure 14.18) — PFB aminofluorescein[38] (PFB-F, P12925; Section 14.3) — localizes in the cytoplasm, is well retained in cells with intact cell membranes (even through cell division) and can be fixed in cells by formaldehyde or glutaraldehyde. PFB-F appears to be retained in viable cells by two mechanisms: 1) retention of the relatively lipophilic PFB group in the cell membrane, and 2) glutathione *S*-transferase–catalyzed reaction of PFB-F with intracellular glutathione. In addition, the relatively high lipophilicity of PFB-FDA facilitates passive cell loading: cells are simply incubated at 37°C in 1–10 µM substrate in standard culture medium. Thus, like our CellTracker™ Green CMFDA (C2925, C7025), PFB-FDA may prove useful for long-term cell labeling.

Chloromethyl Derivatives of SNARF®-1, a Dihydrofluorescein and a Microsomal Dealkylase Substrate

Although they were designed for other purposes, the chloromethyl derivatives of our SNARF®-1 pH indicator (C6826, Figure 14.19) and of 2′,7′-dichlorodihydrofluorescein diacetate, acetate ester ($CM-H_2DCFDA$, C6827, Figure 14.20) possess some unique properties for tracking cells. As with the CellTracker™ probes, cytoplasmic enzymes hydrolytically remove the acetate groups from the membrane-permeant probes, and the chloromethyl moieties become conjugated to

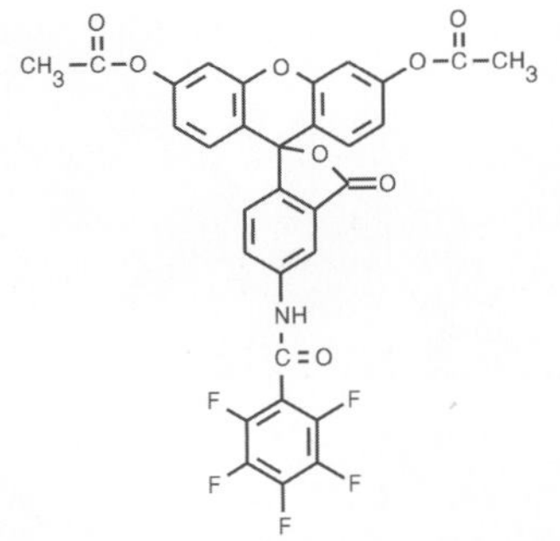

Figure 14.18 P12880 5-(pentafluorobenzoylamino)fluorescein diacetate (PFB-FDA).

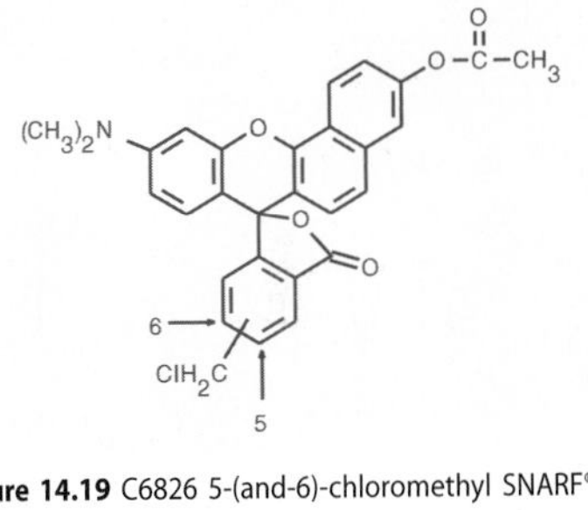

Figure 14.19 C6826 5-(and-6)-chloromethyl SNARF®-1, acetate.

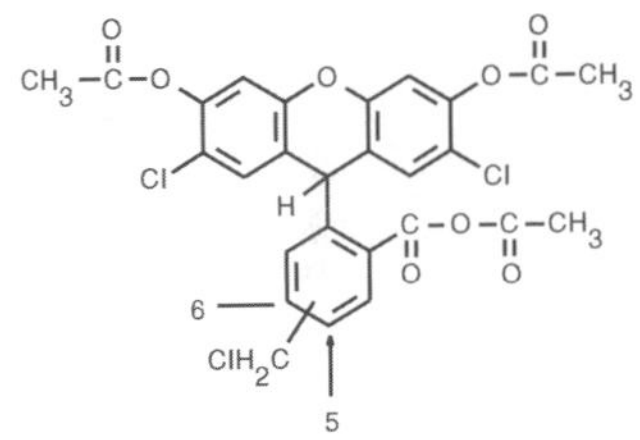

Figure 14.20 C6827 5-(and-6)-chloromethyl-2′,7′-dichlorodihydrofluorescein diacetate, acetyl ester ($CM-H_2DCFDA$).

intracellular thiols. With its long Stokes shift (Figure 20.13), the SNARF®-1 derivative is the only cell tracking dye that has bright, easily distinguished, red-orange fluorescence in the cytoplasm when excited at the same wavelengths used for the green-fluorescent CellTracker™ Green CMFDA (Figure 14.21). This property may permit simultaneous or sequential tracking of two cell populations by either microscopy or flow cytometry, provided the cells are stained to similar intensities. The broad visible absorption of the SNARF®-1 dye (Figure 20.12) also permits cells stained by this dye to be excited using filters optimized for tetramethylrhodamine (Table 23.9) and detected independently from any CellTracker™ Green CMFDA–stained cells.

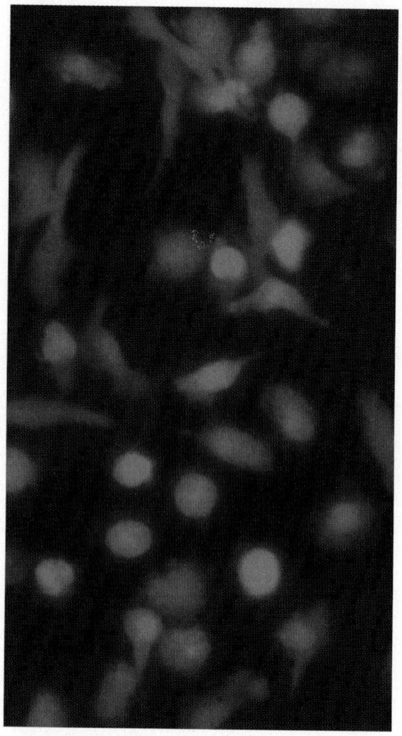
Figure 14.21 Human neutrophils loaded with 5-(and-6)-chloromethyl SNARF®-1 acetate (C6826).

As with other dihydrofluorescein derivatives (Section 18.2), CM-H_2DCFDA requires an additional oxidation step before becoming fluorescent. This probe is potentially useful for following stimulation of oxidative activity by external agents or natural killer (NK) cells over extended periods, as well as for passively labeling cells that lack appropriate oxidative activity and then following their ingestion by scavengers such as neutrophils. CM-H_2DCFDA has been used to measure intracellular reactive oxygen species (ROS) in cardiac myocytes [39] and in human embryonic kidney 293 (HEK293) cells stably transfected with the human vanilloid receptor 1 (VR1) cation channel.[40]

The chloromethyl fluorescein ether (C6533, Section 10.6) becomes fluorescent only in cells that have the required microsomal dealkylase activity to remove its ethyl ether moieties. Its thiol-reactive chloromethyl group ensures retention of its fluorescent products in live cells.

Bimanes: Blue-Fluorescent Reactive Tracers

The bimane derivatives, monobromobimane (mBBr, M1378; FluoroPure™ Grade, M20381), monochlorobimane (mBCl, M1381MP) and monobromotrimethylammoniobimane (qBBr, M1380), are important thiol-derivatization reagents (Section 2.3). The essentially nonfluorescent mBBr and mBCl dyes are known to passively diffuse across the plasma membrane into the cytoplasm, where they form blue-fluorescent adducts with intracellular glutathione and thiol-containing proteins (Section 15.6). Although the blue fluorescence of their thiol adducts is much weaker than that of our CellTracker™ Blue dyes (CMAC, C2110; CMHC, C2111; CMF_2HC, C12881), mBBr and mBCl have been shown to serve as effective tracers of gap-junctional communication.[4] Likewise, the bimane qBBr is a water-soluble quaternary ammonium salt that may be suitable as a microinjectable tracer.

Amine-Reactive Tracers

Amine-Reactive Fluorescein Probes

The carboxyfluorescein diacetate succinimidyl esters (C1157, C1165) and the carboxyeosin diacetate succinimidyl ester (C22803) may have applications similar to the CellTracker™ probes.[41] These amine-reactive reagents can passively diffuse into cells and are colorless and nonfluorescent until their acetate groups are cleaved by intracellular esterases to yield the highly fluorescent, amine-reactive fluorophores. Upon reaction with amine-containing residues of intracellular proteins, these probes form dye–protein adducts that are well retained in cells as they move and divide during embryonic development.[41,42] In addition, the probes survive subsequent fixation with formaldehyde or glutaraldehyde. Because it is intrinsically more reactive, the succinimidyl ester of CFDA is more likely to react at sites on the extracellular surface than is CMFDA. If that is undesirable, it may be possible to quench much of the fluorescence of outer-membrane fluorescein conjugates by acidifying the extracellular medium, by addition of trypan blue (Figure 16.24) or by incubating with anti-fluorescein/Oregon Green® antibody [43] (A889, Section 7.4).

The succinimidyl ester of carboxyfluorescein diacetate (5(6)-CFDA, SE; C1157), which is frequently termed CFSE, is a particularly useful probe for tracing transplanted cells.[42,44] Once incorporated into cells, CFDA SE remains there — even through cell division — thus preventing transfer to unlabeled cells.[45] Homing and proliferation of CFDA SE–labeled thymocytes has been extensively studied.[46–48] The feasibility of using cell-permeant fluorescent tracers to follow asynchronous cell division of natural killer (NK) cells, B cells, T cells, thymocytes, lymphocytes, fibroblasts and hematopoietic cells has been demonstrated with CFDA SE [46,49–58] (Figure 15.65). Lymphocytes labeled with CFDA SE were detected up to eight weeks after injection into mice during lymphocyte migration studies,[59–61] and similarly labeled hepatocytes were easily located by fluorescence microscopy even 20 days after intrahepatic transplantation.[62] CFDA SE has also been successfully employed to quantitate adhesion of neutrophils [63] and leukocytes,[64] to assay T-cadherin–mediated cell aggregation,[65] to follow neurite growth in an *in vitro* bioassay [66] and to trace fetal cells in culture.[67] Different loading concentrations of CFDA SE can be used to produce cells that can be distinguished by their relative brightness.[68] CFDA SE has been utilized for tracing the transport of viable bacterial cells in groundwater under no-growth conditions for periods of at least 28 days.[69] Carboxyeosin diacetate succinimidyl ester (C22803) has applications that are expected to be similar to CFDA SE; however, its fluorescence can be excited and detected at longer wavelengths, possibly permitting two-color tracing experiments of mixed-cell populations. Eosin derivatives are also effective reagents for photoablation of cells (Section 1.5).

CFDA SE is also available conveniently packaged for cell-tracing applications in our Vybrant® CFDA SE Cell Tracer Kit (V12883, Figure 15.65) and for cell proliferation studies in our CellTrace™ Cell Proliferation Kit (C34554, Figure 15.66). The fluorescent CFDA SE product has excitation/emission maxima of ~492/517 nm and can be detected using a fluorescence microscope, flow cytometer or fluorescence microplate reader. Each kit includes 10 single-use vials of CFDA SE, as well as high-quality anhydrous DMSO and a complete protocol.

Unlike CFDA SE, fluorescence of the intracellular hydrolysis products of the succinimidyl ester of 5-(and 6-)carboxy-2′,7′-dichlorofluorescein diacetate (C1165) is relatively insensitive to fluctuations in pH. This amine-reactive tracer was reported to be more useful than the lipophilic marker DiI (D282, Section 14.4) in an investigation of palatal fusion in rodent embryos.[70]

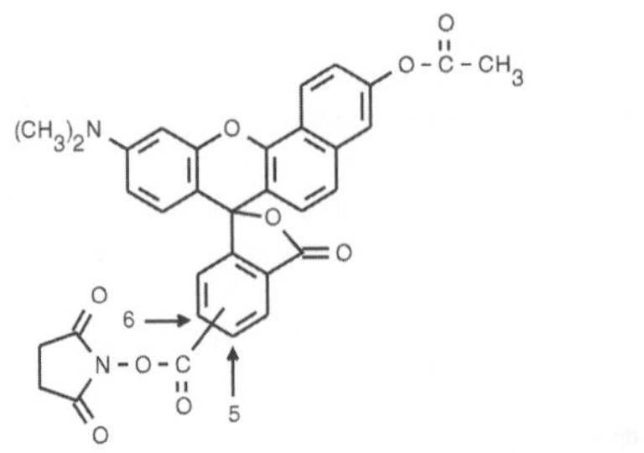

Figure 14.22 S22801 SNARF®-1 carboxylic acid, acetate, succinimidyl ester.

Amine-Reactive SNARF®-1 Carboxylic Acid Acetate

To permit simultaneous long-term tracing of mixed-cell populations using different fluorescent colors, we have developed an amine-reactive probe whose applications should be similar to those of CFDA SE. Cells labeled with our succinimidyl ester of SNARF®-1 carboxylic acid acetate (S22801, Figure 14.22) have a red-orange fluorescence that can easily be distinguished from that of cells loaded with green-fluorescent tracers such as CFDA SE. However, the fluorescence intensity of cells loaded with this SNARF®-1 derivative will not be as high as that of cells loaded with the same concentration of CFDA SE. Thus, it is necessary to adjust the reagent concentration and/or select optical filters to appropriately balance the fluorescence intensities when doing two-color experiments.

CellTrace™ Oregon Green® 488 Carboxylic Acid Diacetate Succinimidyl Ester

The succinimidyl ester of Oregon Green® 488 carboxylic acid diacetate (carboxy-DFFDA SE) offers several important advantages over CFDA SE as a fluorescent cell tracer. Unlike fluorescein derivatives, Oregon Green® 488 derivatives exhibit bright green fluorescence that is not pH dependent at typical cellular pH values. Moreover, Oregon Green® 488 probes are usually brighter and more photostable than fluorescein probes. This amine-reactive, cell-permeant Oregon Green® 488 derivative should provide a bright fluorescent signal for long-term cell tracing experiments. We offer carboxy-DFFDA SE in a 1 mg unit size (O34550) and specially packaged in a set of 20 vials, each containing 50 µg (CellTrace™ Oregon Green® 488 carboxylic acid diacetate succinimidyl ester, C34555).

CellTrace™ Far Red DDAO-SE

CellTrace™ Far Red DDAO-SE (C34553) is a fixable, far-red–fluorescent tracer for long-term cell labeling. The succinimidyl ester (SE) reactive group forms a strong covalent attachment to primary amines that occur in proteins and other biomolecules inside and outside of cells. With its far-red fluorescence, CellTrace™ Far Red DDAO-SE has minimal spectral overlap with most other fluorophores (Figure 10.7) and thus can be used simultaneously with almost any blue, green or orange fluorophores. The far-red emission of DDAO-SE can be easily imaged using microscopes, fluorometers and flow cytometers, though it is near the limit of unaided human vision.

References

1. J Cell Biol 133, 445 (1996); **2.** J Biol Chem 272, 23285 (1997); **3.** J Thorac Cardiovasc Surg 108, 1043 (1994); **4.** Cytometry 14, 747 (1993); **5.** J Biol Chem 272, 29380 (1997); **6.** J Cell Biol 128, 405 (1995); **7.** Am J Hematol 56, 17 (1997); **8.** Toxicol Appl Pharmacol 112, 235 (1992); **9.** Connect Tissue Res 33, 233 (1996); **10.** J Orthop Res 15, 791 (1997); **11.** J Cell Sci 111, 1137 (1998); **12.** Int J Cancer 76, 55 (1998); **13.** Cancer Res 58, 4525 (1998); **14.** Curr Eye Res 15, 165 (1996); **15.** Melanoma Res 5, 107 (1995); **16.** Cytometry 15, 349 (1994); **17.** Cytometry 12, 184 (1991); **18.** Biotech Histochem 70, 57 (1995); **19.** Aquat Microbial Ecol 10, 139 (1996); **20.** J Virol 74, 5629 (2000); **21.** J Cell Biol 140, 315 (1998); **22.** Anal Biochem 216, 271 (1994); **23.** Biophys J 67, 1574 (1994); **24.** Methods Mol Biol 48, 355 (1995); **25.** J Biol Chem 274, 1835 (1999); **26.** Dev Biol 170, 434 (1995); **27.** J Cell Sci 108, 1105 (1995); **28.** J Immunol 169, 722 (2002); **29.** J Microbiol Methods 40, 265 (2000); **30.** EMBO J 15, 964 (1996); **31.** Nature 363, 549 (1993); **32.** Stem Cells 14, 132 (1996); **33.** Anticancer Res 15, 719 (1995); **34.** Prostate 35, 1 (1998); **35.** J Biol Chem 272, 21373 (1997); **36.** Clin Chem 41, 1906 (1995); **37.** J Biol Chem 268, 23593 (1993); **38.** Anal Biochem 269, 410 (1999); **39.** J Biol Chem 274, 19323 (1999); **40.** J Pharmacol Exp Ther 300, 9 (2002); **41.** J Cell Biol 101, 610 (1985); **42.** J Cell Biol 103, 2649 (1986); **43.** Proc Natl Acad Sci U S A 78, 7540 (1981); **44.** Cell Transplant 3, 397 (1994); **45.** J Cell Sci 102, 789 (1992); **46.** J Immunol 160, 3666 (1998); **47.** J Immunol 157, 3412 (1996); **48.** Exp Cell Res 240, 75 (1998); **49.** J Exp Med 189, 265 (1999); **50.** J Immunol 162, 735 (1999); **51.** Cell Immunol 188, 1 (1998); **52.** Cytometry 34, 143 (1998); **53.** Eur J Immunol 28, 1040 (1998); **54.** J Immunol 161, 5260 (1998); **55.** Br J Haematol 98, 528 (1997); **56.** J Biol Chem 274, 3541 (1999); **57.** J Exp Med 184, 277 (1996); **58.** J Immunol Methods 171, 131 (1994); **59.** J Immunol Methods 286, 69 (2004); **60.** J Immunol Methods 133, 87 (1990); **61.** Cytometry 13, 739 (1992); **62.** Transplant Proc 24, 2820 (1992); **63.** J Immunol Methods 172, 25 (1994); **64.** J Immunol Methods 172, 115 (1994); **65.** J Cell Biol 119, 451 (1992); **66.** J Neurosci Methods 39, 193 (1991); **67.** J Neurosci Methods 44, 7 (1992); **68.** J Exp Med 183, 2313 (1996); **69.** Appl Environ Microbiol 66, 4486 (2000); **70.** Development 116, 1087 (1992).

Data Table — 14.2 Membrane-Permeant Reactive Tracers for Long-Term Cell Labeling

Cat #	MW	Storage	Soluble	Abs	EC	Em	Solvent	Notes
B2103	341.00	F,D,L	DMSO, MeCN	533	62,000	561	$CHCl_3$	1
B22802	449.14	F,D,L	DMSO, MeCN	658	73,000	678	$CHCl_3$	2
C1157	557.47	F,D	DMF, DMSO	<300		none		3
C1165	626.36	F,D	DMF, MeCN	<300		none		4
C2102	296.55	F,D,L	DMSO	522	72,000	529	MeOH	
C2110	209.63	F,D,L	DMSO	353	14,000	466	pH 9	5
C2111	210.62	F,D,L	DMSO	372	16,000	470	pH 9	6
C2925	464.86	F,D	DMSO	<300		none		3
C2927	554.04	F,D,L	DMSO	541	91,000	565	MeOH	
C6826	499.95	F,D	DMSO	<350		none		7
C6827	577.80	F,D,AA	DMSO	287	9,100	none	MeOH	8
C7025	464.86	F,D	DMSO	<300		none		3
C12881	246.60	F,D,L	DMSO	371	16,000	464	pH 9	6
C22803	873.05	F,D	DMSO	<300		none		9
C34551	550.44	F,D,L	DMSO	348	6,300	none	MeCN	10
C34552	686.25	F,D,L	DMSO	577	118,000	602	MeOH	
C34553	505.35	F,D,L	DMSO	647	35,000	657	pH 10	
M1378	271.11	F,L	DMF, MeCN	398	5,000	see Notes	pH 7	12
M1380	409.12	L	H_2O	378	5,500	see Notes	pH 7	12, 13
M1381MP	226.66	F,L	DMSO	380	6,000	see Notes	MeOH	12
M20381	271.11	F,L	DMF, MeCN	398	5,000	see Notes	pH 7	12, 14
O34550	593.45	F,D,L	DMSO	<300		none		15
P12880	625.46	F,D	DMSO	<300		none		16
P13290	627.48	F,D,AA	DMSO	259	22,000	none	MeOH	17
S22801	592.56	F,D	DMSO	<350		none		7
T7017	803.93	F,D	DMSO	<300		none		18

For definitions of the contents of this data table, see "Navigating *The Handbook*" in the introductory pages.

Notes

1. B2103 spectra are for the unreacted reagent. The thiol adduct has Abs = 493 nm, Em = 503 nm in MeOH.
2. B22802 spectral data are for the unreacted reagent. The thiol adduct has Abs = 629 nm, Em = 647 nm in dichloromethane (CH_2Cl_2).
3. Acetate hydrolysis of this compound yields a fluorescent product with similar pH-dependent spectral characteristics to C1904.
4. C1165 is converted to a fluorescent product with spectra similar to C368 after acetate hydrolysis.
5. C2110 in MeOH: Abs = 364 nm (EC = 16,000 $cm^{-1}M^{-1}$), Em = 454 nm.
6. Spectra of hydroxycoumarins are pH-dependent. Below the pK_a, Abs shifts to shorter wavelengths (325–340 nm) and fluorescence intensity decreases. Approximate pK_a values are 7.8 (H189, C2111), 7.5 (H185), 7.3 (T659) and 4.9 (D6566, C12881).
7. C6826 and S22801 are converted to fluorescent products with spectra similar to C1270 after acetate hydrolysis.
8. Acetate hydrolysis and subsequent oxidation of C6827 generate a fluorescent 2′,7′-dichlorofluorescein derivative with spectra similar to C368.
9. Acetate hydrolysis of C22803 yields a fluorescent product with spectra similar to 5-carboxyeosin, Abs = 519 nm (EC = 100,000 $cm^{-1}M^{-1}$), Em = 542 nm in pH 9 buffer.
10. The fluorescent phenolic dye generated by acetate hydrolysis of C34551 has Abs = 550 nm (EC = 72,000 $cm^{-1}M^{-1}$), Em = 572 nm in pH 7 buffer.
11. This product is supplied as a ready-made solution in the solvent indicated under "Soluble."
12. Bimanes are almost nonfluorescent until reacted with thiols. For monobromobimane conjugated to glutathione, Abs = 394 nm, Em = 490 nm (QY ~0.1–0.3) in pH 8 buffer (Methods Enzymol 143, 76 (1987); Methods Enzymol 251, 133 (1995)).
13. Unstable in water. Use immediately.
14. This product is specified to equal or exceed 98% analytical purity by HPLC.
15. Acetate hydrolysis of this compound yields a fluorescent product with similar spectral characteristics to O6146.
16. P12880 is converted to a fluorescent product (P12925) after acetate hydrolysis.
17. Acetate hydrolysis and subsequent oxidation of P13290 generate P12925.
18. T7017 is converted to a fluorescent product (Abs = 545 nm (EC = 111,000 $cm^{-1}M^{-1}$), Em = 561 nm in MeOH) after acetate hydrolysis.

Product List — 14.2 Membrane-Permeant Reactive Tracers for Long-Term Cell Labeling

Cat #	Product Name	Unit Size
B22802	8-bromomethyl-4,4-difluoro-3,5-bis-(2-thienyl)-4-bora-3a,4a-diaza-*s*-indacene (BODIPY® 630/650 methyl bromide)	1 mg
B2103	8-bromomethyl-4,4-difluoro-1,3,5,7-tetramethyl-4-bora-3a,4a-diaza-*s*-indacene (BODIPY® 493/503 methyl bromide)	5 mg
C1165	5-(and-6)-carboxy-2',7'-dichlorofluorescein diacetate, succinimidyl ester *mixed isomers*	25 mg
C22803	5-(and-6)-carboxyeosin diacetate, succinimidyl ester *mixed isomers*	5 mg
C1157	5-(and-6)-carboxyfluorescein diacetate, succinimidyl ester (5(6)-CFDA, SE; CFSE) *mixed isomers*	25 mg
C34554	CellTrace™ CFSE Cell Proliferation Kit *for flow cytometry*	1 kit
C34553	CellTrace™ Far Red DDAO-SE *special packaging*	20 x 50 µg
C2110	CellTracker™ Blue CMAC (7-amino-4-chloromethylcoumarin)	5 mg
C12881	CellTracker™ Blue CMF$_2$HC (4-chloromethyl-6,8-difluoro-7-hydroxycoumarin)	5 mg
C2111	CellTracker™ Blue CMHC (4-chloromethyl-7-hydroxycoumarin)	5 mg
C2102	CellTracker™ Green BODIPY® (8-chloromethyl-4,4-difluoro-1,3,5,7-tetramethyl-4-bora-3a,4a-diaza-*s*-indacene)	5 mg
C2925	CellTracker™ Green CMFDA (5-chloromethylfluorescein diacetate)	1 mg
C7025	CellTracker™ Green CMFDA (5-chloromethylfluorescein diacetate) *special packaging*	20 x 50 µg
C34551	CellTracker™ Orange CMRA *special packaging*	20 x 50 µg
C2927	CellTracker™ Orange CMTMR (5-(and-6)-(((4-chloromethyl)benzoyl)amino)tetramethylrhodamine) *mixed isomers*	1 mg
C34552	CellTracker™ Red CMTPX *special packaging*	20 x 50 µg
C6827	5-(and-6)-chloromethyl-2',7'-dichlorodihydrofluorescein diacetate, acetyl ester (CM-H$_2$DCFDA) *mixed isomers* *special packaging*	20 x 50 µg
C6826	5-(and-6)-chloromethyl SNARF®-1, acetate *mixed isomers* *special packaging*	20 x 50 µg
M1378	monobromobimane (mBBr)	25 mg
M20381	monobromobimane (mBBr) *FluoroPure™ grade*	25 mg
M1380	monobromotrimethylammoniobimane bromide (qBBr)	25 mg
M1381MP	monochlorobimane (mBCl)	25 mg
O34550	Oregon Green® 488 carboxylic acid diacetate, succinimidyl ester (carboxy-DFFDA, SE) *mixed isomers*	1 mg
P13290	5-(pentafluorobenzoylamino)dihydrofluorescein diacetate (PFB-H$_2$FDA)	5 mg
P12880	5-(pentafluorobenzoylamino)fluorescein diacetate (PFB-FDA)	5 mg
S22801	SNARF®-1 carboxylic acid, acetate, succinimidyl ester *special packaging*	10 x 50 µg
T7017	2',4',5',7'-tetrabromo-4,5,6,7-tetrafluorofluorescein diacetate (Br$_4$TFFDA)	5 mg
V12883	Vybrant® CFDA SE Cell Tracer Kit	1 kit

For current prices or to order online, visit probes.invitrogen.com

14.3 Polar Tracers

Fixable Polar Tracers

Molecular Probes prepares a wide variety of highly water-soluble dyes and other detectable probes that can be used as cell tracers. Polar tracers can also be incorporated into liposomes to generate polymeric fluorescent tracers or antibody-labeling reagents.[1–5]

In most cases, the polarity of these water-soluble probes is too high to permit them to passively diffuse through cell membranes. Consequently, special methods for loading the dyes into cells must be employed, including microinjection, pinocytosis or techniques that temporarily permeabilize the cell's membrane[6,7] (Table 14.1). Our Influx™ pinocytic cell-loading reagent (I14402, Figure 14.47; see below and Section 19.8) is particularly useful for loading many of the polar tracers in this section — as well as the dextrans and fluorescent proteins described in Section 14.5 and Section 14.7 — into many types of cells (Figure 14.43, Figure 14.44, Figure 14.45, Figure 14.46). Permeabilization of cells with staphylococcal α-toxin[8] or the saponin ester β-escin is reported to make the membrane of smooth muscle cells permeable to low molecular weight (<1000 daltons) molecules, while retaining high molecular weight compounds.[9–11] Electroporation has been used to transport several of the polar tracers through the skin[12] and into cells.[13,14] Many of these tracers can also be loaded into cells noninvasively as their cell-permeant acetoxymethyl (AM) esters, which are discussed in more detail in Section 15.2.

For ultrasensitive detection of polar tracers that are based on fluorescein, Oregon Green®, Cascade Blue®, lucifer yellow, tetramethylrhodamine or BODIPY® FL dyes in fixed-cell preparations, we recommend use of our TSA Kits (Section 6.2, Table 6.1) that contain an Alexa Fluor®, Oregon Green® 488 or Pacific Blue™ tyramide. The TSA Kits that utilize anti–mouse IgG or anti–rabbit IgG antibody conjugates of horseradish peroxidase (HRP) can be combined with an antibody to any of these fluorophores (Section 7.4, Table 7.18) to yield excellent spatial resolution and extremely bright signals that should be detectable in the finest biological structures. Following fixation, biotinylated tracers such as biocytin and biotin ethylenediamine, can be detected using the reagents in our TSA Kits that contain horseradish peroxidase streptavidin and a fluorescent tyramide.

Biotinylated polar tracers can be directly detected in light microscopy with the Diaminobenzidine (DAB) Histochemistry Kit #3

Table 14.1 — Techniques for loading molecules into the cytoplasm

Method of Plasma Membrane Breach *	Size of Molecules Loaded (MW) †
Chemical	
ATP[1]	1000
Influx™ pinocytic cell-loading reagent[2] (I14402)	Variable
EDTA[3]	10,000
$Ca_3(PO_4)_2$[4]	(DNA)
DEAE-dextran[5]	(DNA)
α-Toxin of *Staphylococcus aureus*[6,7]	1000
Transferrin polylysine[8]	(DNA)
Vehicle	
Red blood cell fusion[9,10]	300,000
Vesicle and liposome fusion[11,12]	Very high
Mechanical	
Microinjection[13]	Very high
Whole-cell patch clamping[14]	Very high
Hypoosmotic shock[15]	10,000
Osmotic lysis of pinosomes[16]	Very high
Scrape loading[17]	500,000; (DNA)
Agitation in cold[17]	500,000
Sonication (mild)[18]	70,000; (DNA)
Microprojectile bombardment[19–21]	10,000; (DNA)
Glass beads[22]	150,000
Scratching to wound culture[23]	150,000
Electrical	
Electroporation[24]	(DNA)

* Original reports or important variations. Table adapted with permission from McNeil, P.L., in *Fluorescence Microscopy of Living Cells in Culture, Part A.*[25] † Molecular weight (MW) of largest molecules reported loaded (DNA is listed separately if it has been successfully introduced by a technique).

1. Biochem Biophys Res Commun 67, 1581 (1975); **2.** J Virol 76, 11505 (2002); **3.** J Biol Chem 260, 2069 (1985); **4.** Virology 52, 456 (1973); **5.** Virology 27, 434 (1965); **6.** Methods Cell Biol 31, 63 (1989); **7.** Neuroscience 23, 1143 (1987); **8.** Biotechniques 20, 905 (1996); **9.** Cell 5, 371 (1975); **10.** J Cell Biol 101, 19 (1985); **11.** Neurosci Lett 207, 17 (1996); **12.** Methods Cell Biol 14, 33 (1976); **13.** Hoppe Seylers Z Physiol Chem 352, 527 (1971); **14.** J Neurosci Methods 117, 159 (2002); **15.** Science 217, 252 (1982); **16.** Cell 29, 33 (1982); **17.** J Cell Biol 98, 1556 (1984); **18.** Eur J Cell Biol 40, 242 (1986); **19.** J Neurosci Methods 119, 37 (2002); **20.** Nature 418, 177 (2002); **21.** Nature 327, 70 (1987); **22.** J Cell Sci 88, 669 (1987); **23.** Science 238, 548 (1987); **24.** Biochem Biophys Res Commun 107, 584 (1982); **25.** Methods Cell Biol 29, 153 (1989).

(D22187, Section 7.6) or with the NANOGOLD or Alexa Fluor® FluoroNanogold 1.4 nm gold cluster streptavidin (N24918, A24926, A24927; Section 7.6). The signal of the gold clusters can be further enhanced for electron microscopy with the LI Silver (LIS) Enhancement Kit (L24919, Section 7.2, Figure 7.57).

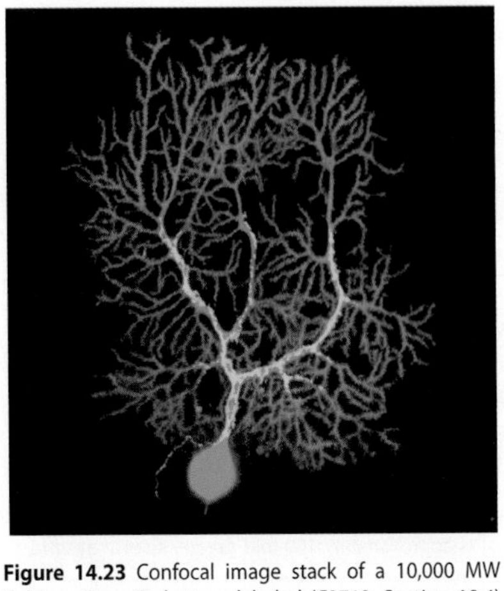

Figure 14.23 Confocal image stack of a 10,000 MW Calcium Green™ dextran–labeled (C3713, Section 19.4) climbing fiber in a sagittal cerebellar slice, showing incoming axon and terminal arborization (in yellow). The Purkinje cell innervated by this climbing fiber was labeled with Alexa Fluor® 568 hydrazide (A10437, A10441) via a patch pipette and visually identified using bright-field microscopy. Image contributed by Anatol Kreitzer, Department of Neurobiology, Harvard Medical School.

Alexa Fluor® Hydrazides and Hydroxylamines

Molecular Probes' selection of fluorescent hydrazide and hydroxylamine derivatives continues to expand (Table 3.1). The blue-fluorescent Alexa Fluor® 350 hydrazide and Alexa Fluor® 350 hydroxylamine (A10439, A30627), green-fluorescent Alexa Fluor® 488 hydrazide and Alexa Fluor® 488 hydroxylamine (A10436, A10440, A30629; Figure 3.16), orange-fluorescent Alexa Fluor® 555 and Alexa Fluor® 568 hydrazides (A20501MP, A10437, A10441; Figure 14.23), red-fluorescent Alexa Fluor® 594 hydrazide [15] (A10438, A10442) and far-red–fluorescent Alexa Fluor® 633 hydrazide, Alexa Fluor® 647 hydrazide and Alexa Fluor® 647 hydroxylamine (A30634, A20502, A30632) are likely the best overall polar tracers in each of their various spectral ranges.[16] These low molecular weight, cell membrane–impermeant molecules (Alexa Fluor® 350 hydrazide, 349 daltons; Alexa Fluor® 350 hydroxylamine, 585 daltons; ~570–760 daltons for the Alexa Fluor® 488, 568 and 594 hydrazides and hydroxylamine; and about 1200 daltons for the Alexa Fluor® 555 and 647 hydrazides and hydroxylamine) possess several properties that are superior to those of the widely used neuronal tracer lucifer yellow CH (L453, L682, L1177, L12926). Like lucifer yellow CH, the hydrazide moiety of the Alexa Fluor® derivatives makes these tracers fixable by common aldehyde-based fixatives. We have determined that Alexa Fluor® 594 hydrazide has a water solubility of ~84 mg/mL and the other Alexa Fluor® hydrazides are likely to have comparable or higher water solubility. Our rabbit polyclonal antibody to the Alexa Fluor® 488 fluorophore (A11094, Section 7.4) quenches the fluorescence of the Alexa Fluor® 488 dye (see Note 14.1 "Product Highlight: Anti–Lucifer Yellow Dye, Anti–Alexa Fluor® 405/Cascade Blue® Dye and Anti–Alexa Fluor® 488 Dye Antibodies") and, following cell fixation and permeabilization, can be used in conjunction with the reagents in our Tyramide Signal Amplification (TSA) or Enzyme-Labeled Fluorescence (ELF®) Kits (Section 6.2, Section 6.3) to amplify the signal or with the anti–rabbit IgG conjugate of NANOGOLD or Alexa Fluor® FluoroNanogold 1.4 nm gold clusters (N24916, A24926, A24927; Section 7.2) and the associated LI Silver Enhancement Kit (L24919, Section 7.2) for correlated fluorescence and light microscopy studies.

Note 14.1 — Product Highlight

Anti–Lucifer Yellow Dye, Anti–Alexa Fluor® 405/Cascade Blue® Dye and Anti–Alexa Fluor® 488 Dye Antibodies

Molecular Probes' anti–lucifer yellow dye antibodies were specifically developed to overcome certain limitations of lucifer yellow CH (L453, L682, L12926, L1177). Lucifer yellow CH is an aldehyde-fixable fluorescent cell tracer that has long been used by neuroscientists to identify patterns of gap junctional communication,[1] to assay the outgrowth of developing neurons[2] and to characterize the morphology of neurons from which electrical recordings have been made.[3] Even though the cell soma of a lucifer yellow CH–filled neuron may be brightly stained, its finer processes can sometimes be faint and may fade rapidly or be obscured by the more intensely stained portions of the neuron. Investigators have been able to overcome these limitations by using anti–lucifer yellow dye antibodies in conjunction with standard enzyme-mediated immunohistochemical methods to develop a more permanent, fade-free signal for light microscopy.[4–7] Anti–lucifer yellow dye antibodies have also been used to develop tissue for electron microscopy[8] and to distinguish neurons filled with lucifer yellow CH from those injected with the lectin *Phaseolus vulgaris* leucoagglutinin[9] (PHA-L). Molecular Probes' lithium salt of Cascade Blue® hydrazide (C3239), which can also be fixed in place with aldehyde-based fixatives, can potentially be used as a second label with lucifer yellow CH to characterize the morphology of interacting neurons. For these applications, Molecular Probes offers unconjugated and biotinylated rabbit polyclonal anti–lucifer yellow dye (A5750, A5751) and anti–Alexa Fluor® 405/Cascade Blue® dye (A5760) antibodies. Similarly, our rabbit polyclonal anti–Alexa Fluor® 488 dye antibody (A11094) can be used to detect Alexa Fluor® 488 hydrazide (A10436, A10440), Alexa Fluor® 488 hydroxylamine (A30629), Alexa Fluor® cadaverine (A30676) and Alexa Fluor® 488 biocytin (A12924) in fixed-cell preparations. See Section 7.4 (Table 7.18) for a complete description of these and other anti-fluorophore and anti-biotin antibodies.

References

1. Nature 292, 17 (1981); **2.** Science 242, 700 (1988); **3.** J Neurosci Methods 36, 309 (1991); **4.** J Neurosci 14, 5267 (1994); **5.** J Neurosci Methods 41, 45 (1992); **6.** J Comp Neurol 296, 598 (1990); **7.** Dev Biol 94, 391 (1982); **8.** Circ Res 70, 49 (1992); **9.** J Neurosci Methods 33, 207 (1990).

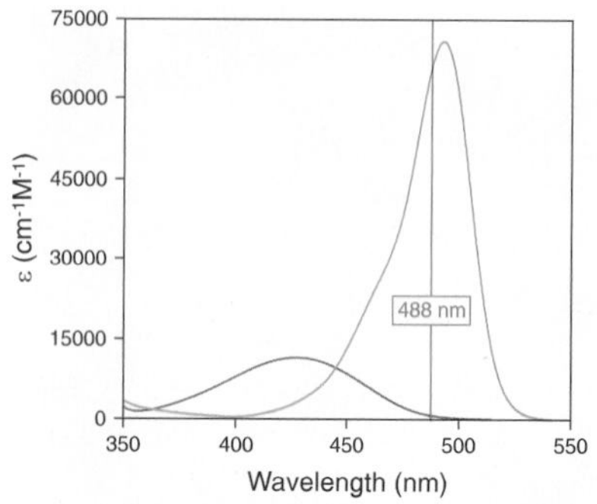

Figure 14.24 Absorption spectra showing that the molar extinction coefficient (ε) at 488 nm of Alexa Fluor® 488 hydrazide (A10436, A10440) in water (green line) is approximately 100-fold greater than that of lucifer yellow CH (L453, L682, L1177, L12926) in water (blue line).

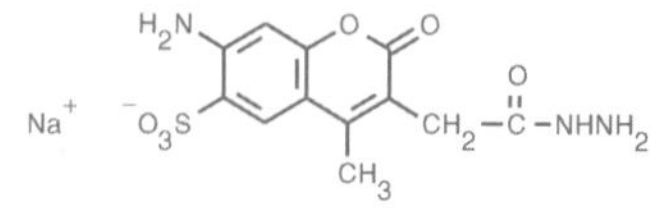

Figure 14.25 A10439 Alexa Fluor® 350 hydrazide, sodium salt.

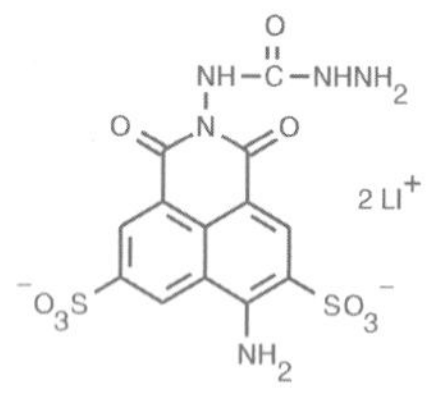

Figure 14.26 L453 lucifer yellow CH, lithium salt.

Although lucifer yellow CH can be used for confocal laser-scanning microscopy, its extinction coefficient at the 488 nm spectral line of the argon-ion laser (~700 $cm^{-1}M^{-1}$) is only about 1% of that of Alexa Fluor® 488 hydrazide and Alexa Fluor® 488 hydroxylamine (≥71,000 $cm^{-1}M^{-1}$) (Figure 14.24). Furthermore, the high photostability of the Alexa Fluor® dyes permits their detection in very fine structures that cannot be seen with lucifer yellow CH staining. Alexa Fluor® 555 hydrazide, Alexa Fluor® 568 hydrazide and the Alexa Fluor® 594 hydrazide can be efficiently excited by the 568 nm spectral line of the Ar–Kr mixed-gas laser, and Alexa Fluor® 633 hydrazide, Alexa Fluor® 647 hydrazide and Alexa Fluor® 647 hydroxylamine can be excited by the red light–emitting He–Ne laser. All of these Alexa Fluor® dyes are remarkably bright and photostable. In addition, the Alexa Fluor® hydrazide salts have high water solubility (typically greater than 8%). We offer the Alexa Fluor® 488, Alexa Fluor® 568 and Alexa Fluor® 594 hydrazides either as solids (A10436, A10437, A10438) or as 10 mM solutions in 200 mM KCl (A10440, A10441, A10442). The 10 mM solutions have been filtered through a 0.2 µm filter to remove any insoluble material prior to packaging. Alexa Fluor® 555 hydrazide, Alexa Fluor® 633 hydrazide and Alexa Fluor® 647 hydrazide (A20501MP, A30634, A20502) and Alexa Fluor® 350, Alexa Fluor® 488 and Alexa Fluor® 647 hydroxylamines (A30627, A30629, A30632) are only available as solids. Our Alexa Fluor® 350 hydrazide and Alexa Fluor® 350 hydroxylamine, which are sulfonated coumarin derivatives (Figure 14.25), are some of the few polar tracers that exhibit bright blue fluorescence. The water-soluble, thiol-reactive Alexa Fluor® maleimides (Section 2.2) may also be useful as polar tracers.

Other Alexa Fluor® Derivatives

To allow amplification of signals, especially in the finer processes of dye-filled neurons, we also offer Alexa Fluor® 488 biocytin (A12924), Alexa Fluor® 546 biocytin (A12923) and Alexa Fluor® 594 biocytin (A12922). These unique probes combine our Alexa Fluor® 488, Alexa Fluor® 546 and Alexa Fluor® 594 fluorophores with biotin and an aldehyde-fixable primary amine (see "Fluorescent Biotin Derivatives," below). In addition, we offer the bright blue-fluorescent Alexa Fluor® 405 cadaverine (A30675, see below) as well as several other Alexa Fluor® cadaverines (Table 3.1), all of which should be useful as tracing molecules because they are exceptionally bright, small and water soluble, and they each contain an aldehyde-fixable functional group. Alexa Fluor® 546 biocytin has been used to label streptavidin-coated particles in order to quantitate fluorescence signals in an automated imaging system designed for analyzing immobilized particle arrays.[17]

Lucifer Yellow CH

Lucifer yellow CH (LY-CH or LY, Figure 14.26) has long been a favorite tool for studying neuronal morphology because it contains a carbohydrazide (CH) group that allows it to be covalently linked to surrounding biomolecules during aldehyde-based fixation.[18,19] Loading of this polar tracer and other similar impermeant dyes is usually accomplished by microinjection,[20] pinocytosis,[21] scrape loading,[22] ATP-induced permeabilization[23] or osmotic shock[24] (Table 14.1), but can also be accomplished in cell suspensions or with adherent cells by using our Influx™ pinocytic cell-loading reagent (I14402). Lucifer yellow CH localizes in the plant vacuole when taken up either through what is thought to be anion-transport channels[25–27] or by fluid-phase endocytosis.[28] Upon injection into the epidermal cells of *Egeria densa* leaves, lucifer yellow CH reportedly moved into the cytoplasm of adjacent cells, localized in the plant vacuole or moved in and out of the nucleus.[29] The lithium salt of lucifer yellow CH is widely used for microinjection because of its relatively high water solubility (~8%). In addition to the solid (L453), we offer the lithium salt of lucifer yellow CH as a filtered 100 mM solution (L12926), ready for microinjection. The potassium salt (L1177, solubility ~1%) or the ammonium salt of lucifer yellow CH (L682, solubility ~6%) may be preferred in applications where lithium ions interfere with biological function.

Although its low absorbance at 488 nm (ε ~700 $cm^{-1}M^{-1}$) (Figure 14.24) makes it inefficiently excited with the argon-ion laser, lucifer yellow CH has been used as a neuronal tracer in some confocal laser-scanning microscopy studies.[30–32] For electron microscopy studies, lucifer yellow CH can be used to photoconvert diaminobenzidine (DAB) into an insoluble, electron-dense reaction product[33–35] (see Note 14.2 "Product Highlight: Fluorescent Probes for Photoconversion of Diaminobenzidine Reagents"). Alternatively, rabbit anti–lucifer yellow dye antibodies (Section 7.4) can be used in conjunction with our goat anti–rabbit IgG antibody conjugated to either NANOGOLD or Alexa Fluor® FluoroNanogold 1.4 nm gold clusters (Section 7.2) and the

Note 14.2 — Product Highlight

Fluorescent Probes for Photoconversion of Diaminobenzidine Reagents

Photoconversion of Diaminobenzidine

Molecular Probes offers a variety of fluorescent probes for photoconverting diaminobenzidine (DAB), enabling researchers to take advantage of an important development in correlated fluorescence, transmitted and electron microscopy. In 1982, Maranto first described the use of the fluorophore lucifer yellow for DAB photoconversion.[1] When a fluorophore is exposed to light of an appropriate wavelength, excitation from the electronic ground state to a higher singlet state occurs. Instead of emitting a photon, the excited state of the fluorophore may undergo intersystem crossing to the triplet state. Transfer of energy to ground state triplet oxygen ($^3O_2$) generates toxic and highly reactive singlet oxygen ($^1O_2$), which is capable of causing damage to lipids, proteins and nucleic acids.[2] However, the reactive potential of $^1O_2$ can also be harnessed to oxidize diaminobenzidine (DAB) into an electron-opaque osmiophilic precipitate within cells. The resulting DAB reaction product exhibits exceptionally uniform, nondiffusible staining properties, making it extremely useful for subsequent electron microscopy investigation of cellular ultrastructure.[1] Punctate background staining can reportedly be eliminated without affecting the DAB photoconversion signal by treating the sample with the peroxisomal catalase inhibitor aminotriazole.[3]

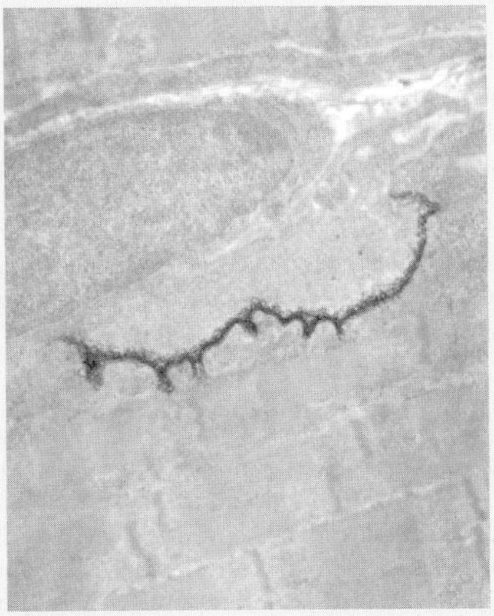

Electron micrograph of a 80 nm–thick section of formaldehyde-fixed rat soleus muscle, which was first stained with eosin α-bungarotoxin and then used to photoconvert DAB into an insoluble osmiophilic polymer. Photo contributed by Thomas J. Deerinck, University of California, San Diego.

Eosin Probes

In 1994, Deerinck and colleagues reported a simple method for eosin-mediated photoconversion of DAB.[4,5] Halogenated derivatives of fluorescein dyes are known to be effective photosensitizers and singlet oxygen generators.[6] Eosin is a brominated analog of fluorescein that has a $^1O_2$ yield 19 times greater than fluorescein and is an excellent dye for photoconverting DAB.[4,7] Furthermore, the small size of eosin promotes exceptional penetration into tissues resulting in increased resolution for electron microscopy.[8] We offer amine- and thiol-reactive eosin and erythrosin derivatives for preparing eosin- or erythrosin-based secondary detection reagents (Section 1.5, Section 2.2). Some other fluorescent tracers that have been used to photoconvert DAB include:[9]

- BODIPY® FL C_5-ceramide [10] (D3521, B22650; Section 12.4)
- DiI [11,12] (D282, Section 14.4)
- Fluorescent polystyrene microspheres [13] (Section 6.5, Table 6.7)
- Fluoro-ruby dextran [14] (D1817, Section 14.5)
- Lucifer yellow [15] (L453, L12926; Section 14.3)
- Propidium iodide [16] (P1304MP, P3566, P21493; Section 8.1)

References

1. Science 217, 953 (1982); **2.** J Photochem Photobiol B 11, 241 (1991); **3.** J Histochem Cytochem 46, 1085 (1998); **4.** J Cell Biol 126, 901 (1994); **5.** J Cell Biol 126, 877 (1994); **6.** Adv Photochem 18, 315 (1993); **7.** Photochem Photobiol 37, 271 (1983); **8.** J Histochem Cytochem 49, 1351 (2001); **9.** Neuroscience Protocols, Wouterlood FG, Ed. 93-050-06, pp. 01–13 (1993); **10.** Cell 73, 1079 (1993); **11.** J Histochem Cytochem 38, 725 (1990); **12.** Neuroscience 28, 3 (1989); **13.** Brain Res 630, 115 (1993); **14.** J Histochem Cytochem 41, 777 (1993); **15.** J Neurosci Methods 36, 309 (1991); **16.** J Neurosci Methods 45, 87 (1992).

LI Silver (LIS) Enhancement Kit (L24919, Section 7.2) to develop a more permanent, fade-free colorimetric or electron-dense signal from dye-filled neurons that is suitable for light or electron microscopy[36–41] (see Note 14.1 "Product Highlight: Anti–Lucifer Yellow Dye, Anti–Alexa Fluor® 405/Cascade Blue® Dye and Anti–Alexa Fluor® 488 Dye Antibodies").

Intracellular injection of lucifer yellow CH has been extensively employed to delineate neuronal morphology in live neurons[42–44] (Figure 14.27) and in fixed brain slices,[36] as well as to investigate intercellular communication through gap junctions.[45–47] Lucifer yellow CH can also be used to label neurons by using dye-filled electrodes during electrophysiological recording in order to correlate neuronal function with structure and connectivity.[20]

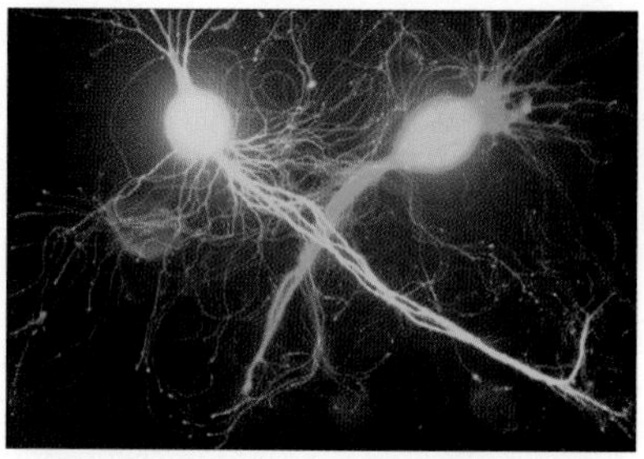

Figure 14.27 Cultured left-upper quadrant neurons from *Aplysia californica* that have been microinjected with either lucifer yellow CH (L453, L682, L1177, L12926) or sulforhodamine 101 (S359). These neurons display an extensive array of overlapping processes (J Neurophysiol 66, 316 (1991)). Image contributed by David Kleinfeld, AT&T Bell Laboratories, and Brian Salzberg, University of Pennsylvania School of Medicine.

Other Lucifer Yellow Derivatives

Like lucifer yellow CH, lucifer yellow ethylenediamine (A1339) is fixable with standard aldehyde-based fixatives and can be used as a building block for new lucifer yellow derivatives.[48] The thiol-reactive lucifer yellow iodoacetamide (L1338) can also be used as a microinjectable polar tracer, as well as for preparing fluorescent liposomes[1] and for detecting the accessibility of thiols in membrane-bound proteins.[49–51] In addition to these lucifer yellow derivatives, we offer a lucifer yellow–conjugated 10,000 MW dextran (D1825, Section 14.5).

Cascade Blue® Hydrazide

Molecular Probes' Cascade Blue® hydrazide is a fixable analog of the nonfixable, bright blue-fluorescent tracer methoxypyrenetrisulfonic acid[52] (MPTS, M395). All of the Cascade Blue® hydrazide derivatives have reasonable water solubility, ~1% for the sodium and potassium salts (C687, C3221) and ~8% for the lithium salt (C3239). They also exhibit a higher absorbance ($\varepsilon_{400\ nm}$ >28,000 $cm^{-1}M^{-1}$) and quantum yield (~0.54 in water) than lucifer yellow CH. In addition, Cascade Blue® derivatives have good photostability and emissions that are well resolved from those of fluorescein and lucifer yellow CH.[53] Cascade Blue® hydrazide, which readily passes through gap junctions, and lucifer yellow derivatives can be simultaneously excited at <410 nm (Figure 14.28) for two-color detection at about 430 and 530 nm.[54] Cascade Blue® dyes, lucifer yellow CH and sulforhodamine 101 can be used in combination for three-color mapping of neuronal processes (Figure 14.29). Molecular Probes also offers anti–Alexa Fluor® 405/Cascade Blue® dye antibodies (Section 7.4) for localizing Cascade Blue® dye–filled cells following fixation (see Note 14.1 "Product Highlight: Anti–Lucifer Yellow Dye, Anti–Alexa Fluor® 405/Cascade Blue® Dye and Anti–Alexa Fluor® 488 Dye Antibodies"). Like lucifer yellow CH, Cascade Blue® hydrazide and some other polar tracers are taken up by plants and sequestered into their central vacuoles. In onion epidermal cells, this uptake of Cascade Blue® hydrazide is blocked by probenecid, indicating that transfer may be through anion-transport channels.[26,27]

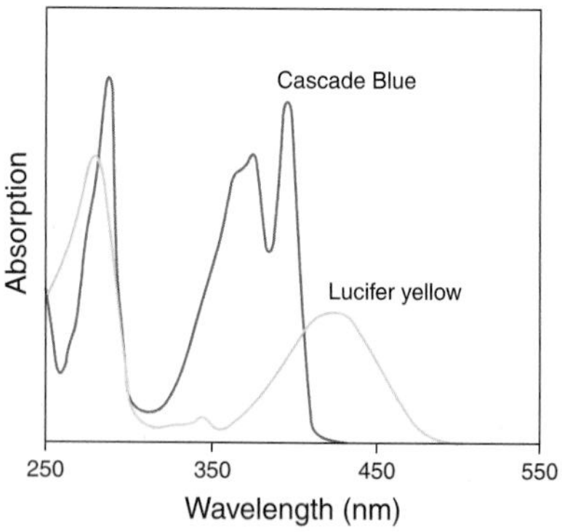

Figure 14.28 Absorption spectra for equal concentrations of Cascade Blue® hydrazide (C687, C3221, C3239) and lucifer yellow CH (L453, L682, L1177, L12926) in water.

Other Cascade Blue® and Alexa Fluor® 405 Derivatives

Cascade Blue® acetyl azide (C2284) and Alexa Fluor® 405 succinimidyl ester (A30000, A30100) are water-soluble, amine-reactive tracers that can be introduced either by microinjection or by fusion of dye-filled liposomes with cells. Once inside the cell, these derivatives will react with the amine groups of intracellular proteins. Cascade Blue® ethylenediamine (C621) and Alexa Fluor® 405 cadaverine (previously called Cascade Blue® cadaverine, A30675) are aldehyde-fixable fluorophores with reactive properties similar to those of the ethylenediamine derivative of lucifer yellow (A1339). A Cascade Blue® dye–labeled 10,000 MW dextran (D1976, Section 14.5) is also available. This dextran conjugate is a component of our Vybrant® Cell Lineage Tracing Kit (V22915, Section 14.5, Figure 7.75).

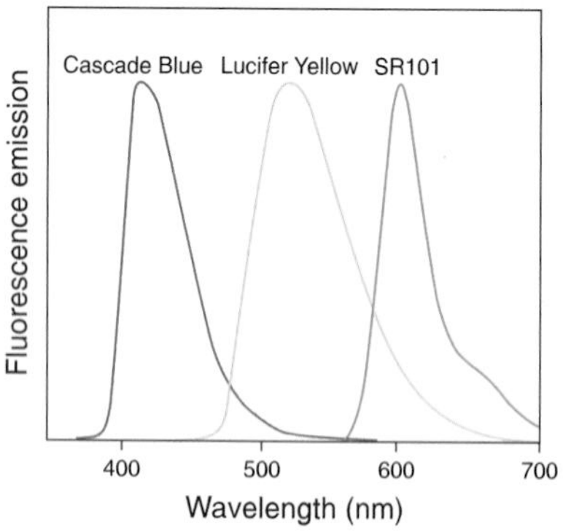

Figure 14.29 Normalized fluorescence emission spectra for Cascade Blue® hydrazide (C687, C3221, C3239), lucifer yellow CH (L453, L682, L1177, L12926) and sulforhodamine 101 (S359) in water.

Biocytin and Other Biotin Derivatives

Biocytin (ε-biotinoyl-L-lysine, B1592, Figure 14.30), DSB-X™ desthiobiocytin (ε-desthiobiotinoyl–L-lysine, D20652), DSB-X™ biotin ethylenediamine (D30752) and biotin ethylenediamine (A1593), which is structurally identical (Figure 14.31) to Neurobiotin (a trademark of Vector Laboratories), are microinjectable anterograde and transneuronal tracers.[55–58] Retrograde transport of biocytin and biotin ethylenediamine in neurons has also been reported.[59,60] These water-soluble tracers are often used to label neurons during electrophysiological measurements in order to correlate neuronal function with structure and connectivity.[61–64] Biotin cadaverine

(A1594) and biotin-X cadaverine (B1596) have slightly longer spacers than their ethylenediamine counterparts, making the hapten more accessible to the deep biotin-binding site in avidins.[65–67]

Biocytin, DSB-X™ desthiobiocytin, biotin ethylenediamine, DSB-X™ biotin ethylenediamine, biotin cadaverine and biotin-X cadaverine all contain primary amines and can therefore be fixed in cells with formaldehyde or glutaraldehyde and subsequently detected using fluorescent- or enzyme-labeled avidin or streptavidin second-step reagents or with NANOGOLD and Alexa Fluor® FluoroNanogold streptavidin[68] (Section 7.6). Biocytin hydrazide (B1603) and DSB-X™ biotin hydrazide (D20653) can serve as aldehyde-fixable tracers and as reactive probes for labeling glycoproteins and nucleic acids (Section 4.2).

DSB-X™ desthiobiocytin, DSB-X™ biotin ethylenediamine and DSB-X™ biotin hydrazide bind to avidin and streptavidin derivatives reversibly (Section 7.6, Figure 7.103). Thus, an aldehyde-fixed preparation of a neuron that has been traced using one of these DSB-X™ biotin derivatives can first be detected with a fluorescent derivative of avidin then stripped with unlabeled biotin (B20656, Section 4.2) and reprobed with a reagent that yields a permanent signal, such as diaminobenzidine, which is used in our Diaminobenzidine (DAB) Histochemistry Kit #3 (D22187), or with our NANOGOLD and Alexa Fluor® FluoroNanogold conjugates of streptavidin (Section 7.6).

As with the reactive lucifer yellow, and Cascade Blue® and Alexa Fluor® 405 derivatives discussed above, amine- or thiol-reactive biotin derivatives are useful for intracellular labeling applications. The succinimidyl esters of biotin and biotin-X (B1513, B1582) have been used to trace retinal axons in avian embryos.[69] Because they are more water soluble, the *sulfo*succinimidyl esters of biotin-X and biotin-XX (B6353, B6352) or the thiol-reactive biocytin maleimide (M1602) may be preferred for these applications.

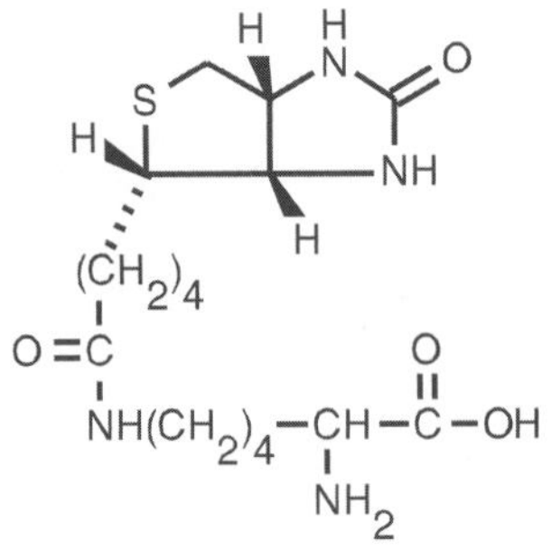

Figure 14.30 B1592 biocytin (ε-biotinoyl-L-lysine).

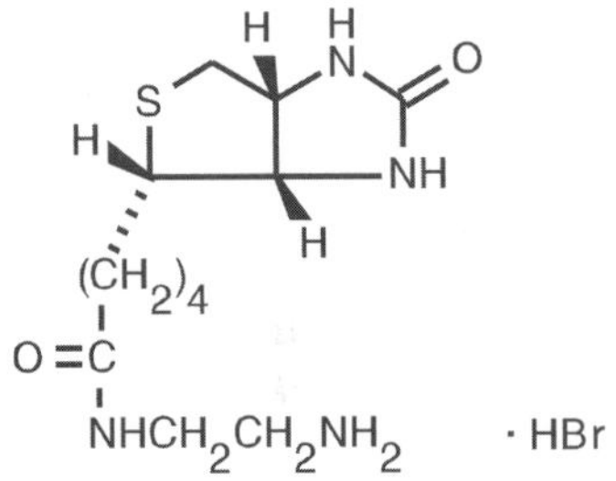

Figure 14.31 A1593 *N*-(2-aminoethyl)biotinamide, hydrobromide (biotin ethylenediamine).

Fluorescent Biotin Derivatives

Fluorescence of the finer processes of dye-filled neurons may fade rapidly or be obscured by the more intensely stained portions of the neuron, necessitating further amplification of the signal or other ultrastructural detection methods. Lucifer yellow biocytin (L6950), Alexa Fluor® 488 biocytin (A12924), Alexa Fluor® 546 biocytin (A12923), Alexa Fluor® 594 biocytin (A12922), Oregon Green® 488 biocytin (O12920) and tetramethylrhodamine biocytin (T12921) each incorporate a fluorophore, biotin and an aldehyde-fixable primary amine into a single molecule, thus enabling researchers to amplify the signals of these tracers with fluorescent or enzyme-labeled avidin or streptavidin conjugates (Section 7.6). Although our lucifer yellow cadaverine biotin-X (L2601) lacks a primary amine, it was reported that this tracer was well retained in aldehyde-fixed tissues, even after sectioning, extraction with detergents and several washes.[70,71] Because fluorescent biocytin derivatives contain free primary amines, they should be even more efficiently fixed by formaldehyde or glutaraldehyde.

PFB Aminofluorescein

5-(Pentafluorobenzoylamino)fluorescein[72] (PFB-F, P12925), which localizes in the cytoplasm, is well retained in cells with intact cell membranes (even through cell division) and is fixable by formaldehyde and glutaraldehyde. PFB-F appears to be retained in viable cells by two mechanisms: 1) retention of the relatively lipophilic PFB group of the hydrolysis products in the cell membrane, and 2) glutathione *S*-transferase–catalyzed reaction of the hydrolysis products with intracellular glutathione. Following fixation, adducts of the probe can be amplified using anti-fluorescein/Oregon Green® antibodies (Section 7.4). PFB-F is easily loaded into live cells as its colorless and nonfluorescent diacetate (PFB-FDA, P12880; Section 14.2, Figure 14.18) or by microinjection of PFB-F solutions that have been adjusted to a physiological pH.

Nonfixable Polar Tracers

Polar fluorescent dyes are commonly used to investigate fusion, lysis and gap-junctional communication and to detect changes in cell or liposome volume. These events are primarily monitored by following changes in the dye's fluorescence caused by interaction with nearby molecules. For example, because the fluorescence of many dyes at high concentrations is quenched, various processes that result in a dilution of the dyes, such as lysis or fusion of fluorescent dye–filled cells or liposomes, can produce an increase in fluorescence, thereby providing an easy method for monitoring these events. Cell–cell and cell–liposome fusion, as well as membrane permeability and transport through gap junctions, can all be monitored using these methods. Furthermore, a fluorogenic substrate can be incorporated within a liposome or cell that lacks the enzymatic activity to generate a fluorescent product; subsequent fusion with a cell that contains the appropriate enzyme, including reporter enzymes introduced by gene transfection, will release a fluorescent product.[73] Several water-soluble substrates (e.g., fluorescein digalactoside and fluorescein diphosphate; Chapter 10) may be useful for this application. Also, highly polar esterase substrates such as the colorless and nonfluorescent 5-sulfofluorescein diacetate (SFDA, S1129) can be incorporated into liposomes and their uptake monitored by the increase in fluorescence following liposome fusion with cells and intracellular hydrolysis of the acetate esters. These polar tracers are impermeant to most cell membranes and must be incorporated into cells by one of a variety of invasive techniques (Table 14.1); many of these dyes are lost from the cell upon disruption of the cell membrane.

An ultrasensitive fusion assay that is applicable to following fusion of even single vesicles utilizes an almost nonfluorescent potassium salt of an ion-sensitive indicator such as fluo-3 (F1240, F3715; Section 19.3) in one vesicle and a polyvalent ion such as Ca^{2+} — or perhaps better La^{3+}, which causes greater enhancement of the fluorescence of fluo-3 — in a second vesicle.[74]

Fluorescein Derivatives

The self-quenching of fluorescein derivatives provides a means of determining their concentration in dynamic processes such as lysis or fusion of dye-filled cells or liposomes (see Note 14.3 "Technical

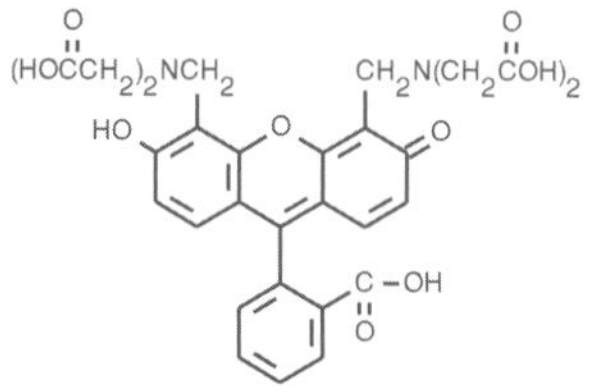

Figure 14.32 C481 calcein.

Note 14.3 — Technical Focus

Assays of Volume Change, Membrane Fusion and Membrane Permeability

Assays of membrane fusion report either the mixing or leakage of the aqueous contents of the fused entities (described here) or the mixing of membrane lipids (see Note 13.1 "Technical Focus: Lipid-Mixing Assays of Membrane Fusion" in Section 13.2). Leakage of aqueous contents from cells or vesicles as a result of lysis, fusion or physiological permeability can be detected fluorometrically using low molecular weight soluble tracers. Assays designed to detect solution mixing often rely on a fluorophore and quencher pair, whereas assays that detect solution leakage into the external medium typically exploit the self-quenching properties of a fluorophore.

Fluorescence Quenching Assays with ANTS/DPX

Originally developed by Smolarsky and co-workers to follow complement-mediated immune lysis,[1] the ANTS/DPX fluorescence quenching assay has since been widely used to detect membrane fusion.[2] This assay is based on the collisional quenching of the polyanionic fluorophore ANTS by the cationic quencher DPX (Figure 1). Separate vesicle populations are loaded with 25 mM ANTS (A350) in 40 mM NaCl and 90 mM DPX (X1525).

Vesicle fusion results in quenching of ANTS fluorescence monitored at 530 nm, with excitation at 360 nm. External leakage of vesicle contents does not cause quenching due to the accompanying high dilution of ANTS and DPX. For assays of vesicle leakage, ANTS (12.5 mM) and DPX (45 mM) can be co-encapsulated into liposomes; upon dilution into surrounding medium, ANTS fluorescence will increase because quenching by DPX will be diminished.

Examples employing ANTS/DPX quenching include studies of the role of amino lipids[3] and phospholipid asymmetry[4] in membrane fusion; glycoprotein-mediated viral fusion with membranes;[5] and the interactions of vesicle membranes with annexins,[6] HIV fusion peptide[7] and apolipoprotein.[8]

Additional Dye/Quencher Pairs

The fluorescence of HPTS and pyrenetetrasulfonic acid is also effectively quenched by DPX.[9–11] Thallium (Tl^+) and cesium (Cs^+) ions quench the fluorescence of ANTS, pyranine (HPTS, H348), pyrenetetrasulfonic acid (P349) and some other polyanionic fluorophores. A review by Garcia[12] describes how fluorescence quenching with a variety of dye/quencher pairs can be used to determine transmembrane ion permeability.

Fluorescence Enhancement Assays with Tb^{3+}/DPA

In the Tb^{3+}/dipicolinic acid (DPA) assay, which was originally described by Wilschut and Papahadjopoulos,[13,14] separate vesicle populations are loaded with 2.5 mM $TbCl_3$ (T1247) in 50 mM sodium citrate, or 50 mM DPA in 20 mM NaCl.

Vesicle fusion results in formation of Tb^{3+}/DPA chelates that are ~10,000 times more fluorescent than free Tb^{3+} (Figure 2). Fluorescence of the chelates is detected at 490 nm or 545 nm, with excitation at 276 nm. Including Ca^{2+} and EDTA in the external medium inhibits formation of the complex outside the fused vesicles. The Tb^{3+}/DPA fluorescence enhancement assay has been used to investigate the role of phospholipid conformation in vesicle fusion[15] and the interaction of cardiotoxin with phospholipid vesicles.[16]

Self-Quenching Assays with Fluorescein Derivatives

Fluorescence of carboxyfluorescein (C194, C1904) or calcein (C481) is >95% self-quenched at concentrations >100 mM. Concentrated

continued on next page

continued from previous page

solutions of these water-soluble dyes are encapsulated in liposomes, which are then separated from any remaining free dye by gel filtration. Upon addition of a fusogen or other permeabilizing agent, dye release is accompanied by an increase in fluorescence (excitation/emission maxima 490 nm/520 nm). Complete lysis of the liposomes with 0.1% Triton X-100 can be used to determine the assay endpoint. Calcein may be preferred over carboxyfluorescein because of higher net charge and lower pH sensitivity. Note that this assay will detect any process that causes leakage of aqueous contents, including fusion, lysis or permeabilization. In a modification of this assay designed to specifically detect vesicle fusion, a nonfluorescent Co^{2+} complex of calcein contained in a vesicle is disrupted upon fusion with a second vesicle that delivers EDTA, a chelator of Co^{2+}.[17,18] Studies employing carboxyfluorescein self-quenching include investigations of interactions of membranes with mycobacterial glycopeptidolipids[19] and with HIV glycoprotein peptide fragments.[20]

References

1. J Immunol Methods 15, 255 (1977); **2.** Biochemistry 24, 3099 (1985); **3.** Biochemistry 33, 12573 (1994); **4.** Biochemistry 31, 4262 (1992); **5.** Biochemistry 34, 1084 (1995); **6.** Biochemistry 32, 14194 (1993); **7.** Biochemistry 33, 3201 (1994); **8.** J Biol Chem 268, 22112 (1993); **9.** Biochim Biophys Acta 1142, 277 (1993); **10.** Am J Physiol 262, G30 (1992); **11.** Biochim Biophys Acta 1024, 352 (1990); **12.** Methods Enzymol 207, 501 (1992); **13.** Biochemistry 19, 6011 (1980); **14.** Nature 281, 690 (1979); **15.** Biochemistry 33, 5805 (1994); **16.** J Biol Chem 269, 14473 (1994); **17.** Biophys J 55, 973 (1989); **18.** J Biol Chem 257, 13892 (1982); **19.** Biochemistry 33, 7056 (1994); **20.** J Biol Chem 267, 7121 (1992).

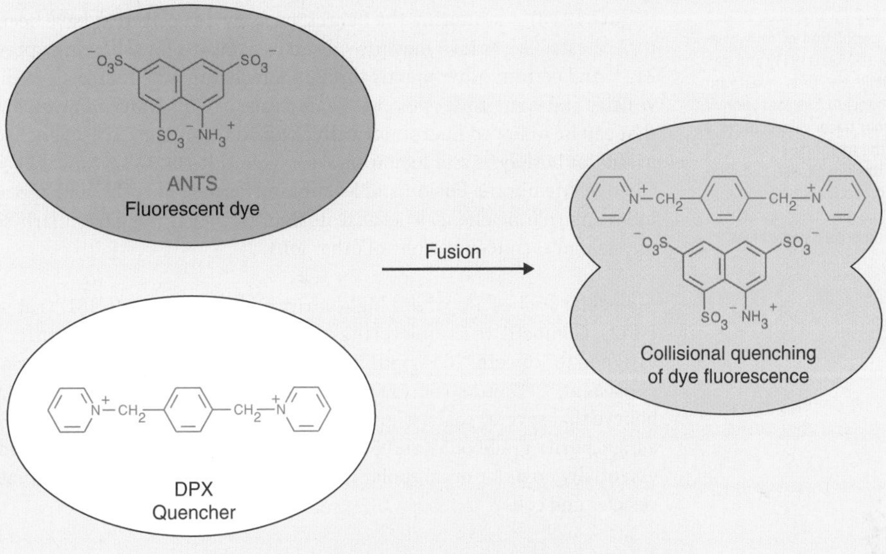

Figure 1 Pictorial representation of the ANTS/DPX vesicle-fusion assay.

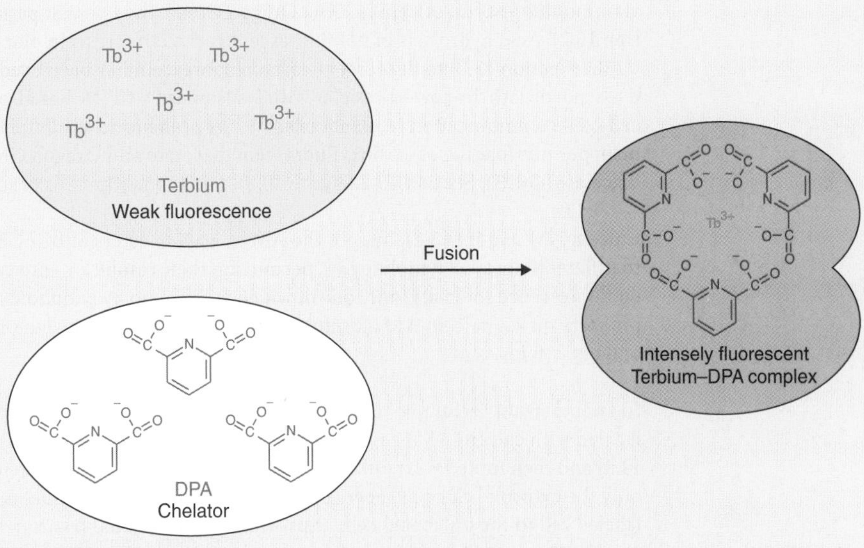

Figure 2 Pictorial representation of the terbium/dipicolinic acid (DPA) fluorescence enhancement assay for vesicle fusion.

Focus: Assays of Volume Change, Membrane Fusion and Membrane Permeability"). Calcein (C481) — a polyanionic fluorescein derivative that has about six negative and two positive charges at pH 7 (Figure 14.32) — as well as BCECF (B1151, Figure 20.6), carboxyfluorescein (C194; FluoroPure™ Grade, C1904), the 5-isomer of Oregon Green® 488 carboxylic acid (O6146) and fluorescein-5-(and 6-)sulfonic acid (F1130) are all soluble in water at >100 mM at pH 7. Unlike the other fluorescein derivatives, both calcein and Oregon Green® 488 carboxylic acid exhibit fluorescence that is essentially independent of pH between 6.5 and 12.

A
B

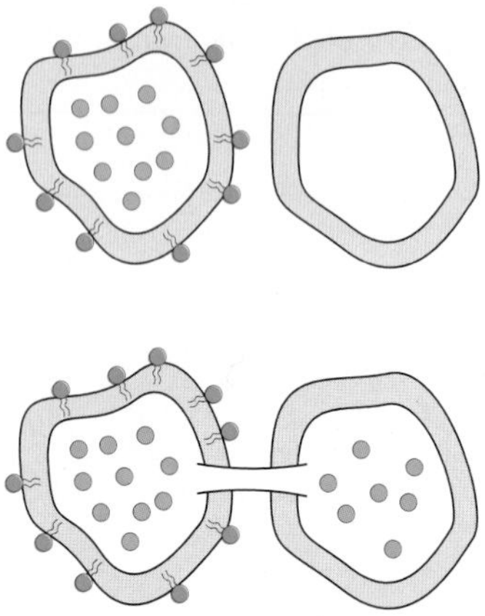

Figure 14.33 A simple technique for the study of gap junctional communication. A population of cells is labeled simultaneously with DiI (D282, D3911) and calcein AM (C1430, C3099, C3100MP), and then mixed with an unlabeled cell population (panel A). The formation of gap junctions allows the cytosolic tracer calcein to cross into the unlabeled cell, while the membrane-bound DiI does not (panel B). Cells from the initial unlabeled population that have taken part in gap junctional communication will therefore display the green fluorescence of calcein while lacking the red-fluorescent signal of DiI.

These five green-fluorescent polar tracers are widely used for investigating:

- Cell volume changes in neurons and other cells [75–78]
- Gap junctional communication [79–81]
- Liposome formation, fusion and targeting [82–85]
- Membrane integrity and permeability [86–97]
- Angiography [98]

Fluorescence of calcein (but not of carboxyfluorescein or fluorescein sulfonic acid) is strongly quenched by Fe^{3+}, Co^{2+}, Cu^{2+} and Mn^{2+} at physiological pH but not by Ca^{2+} or Mg^{2+} ions [99,100] (Figure 19.78). Monitoring the fluorescence level of cells that have been loaded with calcein (or its AM ester, see below) may provide an easy means for following uptake of Fe^{3+}, Co^{2+}, Cu^{2+}, Mn^{2+} and certain other metals through ion channels.[101] Increases in the internal volume of lipid vesicles and virus envelopes cause a decrease in Co^{2+}-induced quenching of calcein, a change that can be followed fluorometrically.[102] In addition, the Co^{2+}-quenched calcein complex is useful for both lysis and fusion assays [103] (see Note 14.3 "Technical Focus: Assays of Volume Change, Membrane Fusion and Membrane Permeability"). Calcein is a preferred reagent for following volume changes because its fluorescence is not particularly sensitive to either pH or physiological concentrations of other ions.[76]

Molecular Probes prepares a high-purity grade of calcein (C481) that is generally >97% pure by HPLC. Competitive commercial-grade calcein is typically <50% pure. The chemical structure assigned to "calcein" in various literature references and by commercial sources has been inconsistent;[104,105] our structure (Figure 14.32) has been confirmed by NMR spectroscopy, and we believe that several past assignments of other structures to calcein were incorrect. We also offer a high-purity grade of 5-(and 6-)carboxyfluorescein (FluoroPure™ Grade, C1904) that contains essentially no polar or nonpolar impurities that might alter transfer rates of the dye between vesicles and cells.[106]

Cell-Permeant Fluorescein Derivatives

Cell-permeant versions of carboxyfluorescein, fluorescein sulfonic acid, 5-(pentafluorobenzoylamino)fluorescein, calcein and the Oregon Green® dyes permit passive loading of cells (Section 15.2). Acid hydrolysis of nonfluorescent carboxyfluorescein diacetate (CFDA; C195, C1361, C1362; Section 15.2) to fluorescent carboxyfluorescein has been used to detect the fusion of dye-loaded clathrin-coated vesicles with lysosomes.[107] CFDA has also been used to investigate cell–cell communication in plant cells.[108–110] A probenecid-inhibitable anion-transport mechanism permits loading of carboxyfluorescein diacetate and Oregon Green® 488 carboxylic acid diacetate (O6151, Section 15.2, Figure 15.8) into hyphal tip-cells of some fungi.[111]

Calcein AM (Figure 15.2), but not the AM or acetate esters of BCECF or CFDA, is reported to differentially label lymphocytes, permitting their resolution into two populations based on fluorescence intensity, only one of which is taken up by lymphoid organs. This unique property makes calcein AM a useful probe for determining the lymph node homing potential of lymphocytes.[112]

In an important technique for studying gap junctional communication, cells are simultaneously labeled with calcein AM (C1430, C3099, C3100MP) and DiI (D282, D3911, V22885; Section 14.4) and then mixed with unlabeled cells (Figure 14.33). When gap junctions are established, only the cytosolic calcein tracer (but not the DiI membrane probe) is transferred from the labeled cell to the unlabeled cell. Thus, after gap-junctional transfer, the initially unlabeled cells exhibit the green fluorescence of calcein but not the red fluorescence of DiI.[79,113–116] This assay can be followed by either imaging or flow cytometry. A similar quantitative assay that combines calcein AM and the lipid tracer PKH26 [117] (structurally equivalent to the reagent in our Vybrant®

DiI cell-labeling solution, V22885, Section 14.4) to detect gap junction–mediated communication between cells in culture has also been described.[118] In addition, calcein AM and DiI have been combined for use in following cell fusion.[119]

Fluorescein Substitutes

Chapter 1 describes several of our proprietary green-fluorescent dyes that have exceptional optical properties, including our Alexa Fluor® 488 dye (Section 1.3), BODIPY® FL dye (Section 1.4) and Oregon Green® dyes (Section 1.5). Not only do these innovative fluorescein substitutes exhibit high absorbance and quantum yields in aqueous solution, but the dyes are significantly more photostable than fluorescein (Figure 1.46, Figure 7.23, Figure 11.8; Figure 1.61) and their fluorescence is less sensitive to pH (Figure 1.12). Their greater photostability makes them the preferred green-fluorescent dyes for fluorescence microscopy. In addition to their membrane-permeant versions, which are described in Section 15.2, highly water-soluble derivatives of these fluorescein substitutes are available for use as polar tracers:

- Oregon Green® 514 carboxylic acid (O6138, Figure 1.63), which is highly photostable and has little pH sensitivity at near-neutral pH
- BODIPY® 492/515 disulfonic acid[120] (D3238), which has high absorbance, narrow spectral bandwidths and bright green, pH-independent fluorescence
- Carboxy-2′,7′-dichlorofluorescein (C368), which has a lower pK_a than fluorescein

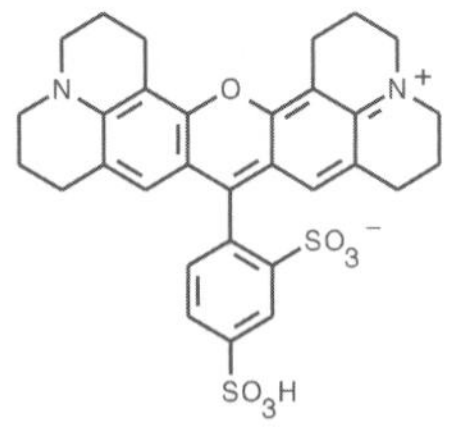

Figure 14.34 S359 sulforhodamine 101.

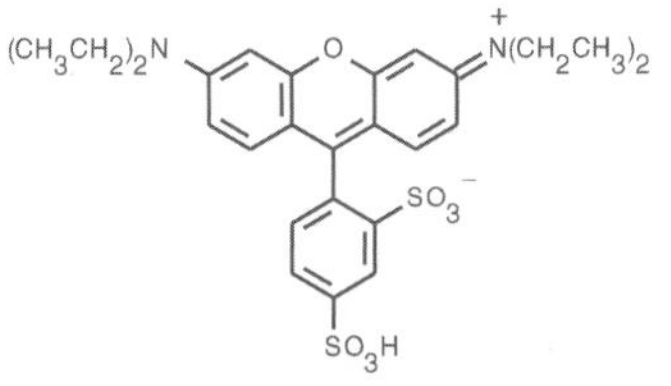

Figure 14.35 S1307 sulforhodamine B.

Sulforhodamines

Sulforhodamine 101 (S359, Figure 14.34) and sulforhodamine B (S1307, Figure 14.35) are orange- to red-fluorescent, very water-soluble sulfonic acid tracers with strong absorbance and good photostability.

Sulforhodamine 101 — the precursor to reactive Texas Red® derivatives — has been the preferred red-fluorescent polar tracer for use in combination with lucifer yellow CH, carboxyfluorescein or calcein[121–123] (Figure 14.27). Activity-dependent uptake of sulforhodamine 101 during nerve stimulation has been reported[124–128] (Figure 14.36). Because it is chemically stable, can be prepared in high purity and has a fluorescence quantum yield of nearly 1.0, we have included sulforhodamine 101 in our Reference Dye Sampler Kit (R14782, Section 23.1), along with four other dyes whose spectra cover the visible wavelengths.

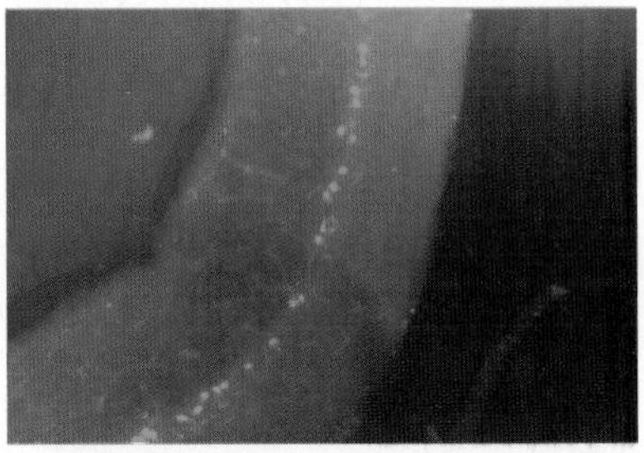

Figure 14.36 An *in vitro* brainstem–cerebellum preparation, from the turtle *Chrysemys picta*, soaked in 0.01% sulforhodamine 101 (S359). Following stimulation of the cerebellorubral circuits, the Purkinje cells in the preparation took up the dye. The distinctive pattern of neuronal labeling suggests that motor programs are highly distributed in the red nucleus, cerebellum and brainstem (J Neurosci 12, 3187 (1992)). The image was contributed by Joyce Keifer, The McGaw Medical Center, Northwestern University.

Sulforhodamine B is a low-cost alternative to sulforhodamine 101 for investigating neuronal morphology,[129,130] preparing fluorescent liposomes,[131] studying cell–cell communications[132,133] and following phagosome–lysosome uptake and fusion.[121,134–136]

Hydroxycoumarins

7-Hydroxycoumarin-3-carboxylic acid (H185) is a blue-fluorescent polar tracer (excitation/emission maxima of ~388/445 nm) with uses that complement those of calcein and the other green-fluorescent polar tracers.[115] The membrane-permeant AM ester of calcein blue (C1429, Section 15.2), another coumarin-based tracer, can be used for passive loading of cells.[137]

Polysulfonated Pyrenes

HPTS (8-hydroxypyrene-1,3,6-trisulfonic acid, also known as pyranine, H348; Figure 20.22) is a unique pH-sensitive tracer. It fluoresces blue in acidic solutions and in acidic organelles,[138–140] but fluoresces green in more basic organelles.[141] In addition to its use as a probe for proton translocation,[142–145] HPTS has been employed for intracellular labeling of neurons[146] and for delineating the cellular pathway of photosynthate transfer in the developing wheat grain.[147] HPTS forms a nonfluorescent complex with the cationic quencher DPX (X1525), and several assays have been described that monitor the increase in HPTS fluorescence that occurs upon lysis or fusion of liposomes or cells containing this quenched complex[140,148–150] (see Note 14.3 "Technical Focus: Assays of Volume Change, Membrane Fusion and Membrane Permeability"). HPTS has also been used as a viscosity probe in unilamellar phospholipid vesicles.[151]

The pH-insensitive methyl ether of HPTS[152] (MPTS, M395), 8-aminopyrene-1,3,6-trisulfonic acid (APTS, A6257) and 1,3,6,8-pyrenetetrasulfonic acid (P349) are all extremely soluble in water (>25%); they have been utilized as blue-fluorescent tracers.[153–156] As with HPTS, fluorescence of MPTS, APTS and 1,3,6,8-pyrenetetrasulfonic acid is quenched by DPX [140,149,157] (see Note 14.3 "Technical Focus: Assays of Volume Change, Membrane Fusion and Membrane Permeability") and by the cationic spin label CAT 1 [158] (T506, see below). These quenched-fluorophore complexes are useful for following lysis of cells and liposomes.

ANTS–DPX

The polyanionic dye ANTS (A350) is often used in combination with the cationic quencher DPX (X1525) for membrane fusion or permeability assays, including complement-mediated immune lysis [159] (see Note 14.3 "Technical Focus: Assays of Volume Change, Membrane Fusion and Membrane Permeability"). Thallium (Tl^+) and cesium (Cs^+) ions quench the fluorescence of ANTS, pyrenetetrasulfonic acid and some other polyanionic fluorophores.[160,161] A review by Garcia [154] describes how this quenching effect can be utilized to determine transmembrane ion permeability. The unusually high Stokes shift of ANTS in water (>150 nm) separates its emission from much of the autofluorescence of biological samples. An approximately fourfold enhancement of the quantum yield of ANTS is induced by D_2O — a spectral characteristic that has been used to determine water permeability in red blood cell ghosts and kidney collecting tubules.[162,163] ANTS has also been employed as a neuronal tracer.[146] 7-Aminonaphthalene-1,3-disulfonic acid (ANDS, A22840) has properties similar to ANTS, including a similarly high Stokes shift.

Lanthanide Chelates

Terbium ion (Tb^{3+} from $TbCl_3$, T1247) forms a chelate with dipicolinic acid (DPA) that is ~10,000 times more fluorescent than free Tb^{3+}. Fusion of vesicles that have been separately loaded with DPA and Tb^{3+} results in enhanced fluorescence, providing the basis for liposome fusion assays (see Note 14.3 "Technical Focus: Assays of Volume Change, Membrane Fusion and Membrane Permeability"). The fluorescence emission spectrum of the Tb^{3+}/DPA complex exhibits two sharp peaks at 491 nm and 545 nm. With a millisecond radiative lifetime, Tb^{3+} chelates are also useful for time-resolved detection in immunoassays.[164] Naphthoyltrifluoroacetone (T411) and its derivatives, which require solubilization with 0.1% Triton X-100 for use in aqueous systems, are widely used as Tb^{3+} chelators.

TOTO®, YOYO® and SYTO® Nucleic Acid Stains

Our high-affinity nucleic acid stains, including TOTO®-1 and YOYO®-1 (T3600, Y3601; Chapter 8), form tight complexes with nucleic acids with slow off-rates for release of the dye. Consequently, nucleic acids that have been prelabeled with these dyes can be traced in cells following microinjection or during gene transfer (Figure 10.11). The cell-to-cell transport via plasmodesmata of TOTO®-1 dye–labeled RNA, single-stranded DNA and double-stranded DNA has been determined following microinjection of the labeled nucleic acids into plant cells.[165–168]

Khoobehi and Peyman have demonstrated the use of our cell-permeant SYTO® nucleic acid stains as ophthalmological tracers of blood flow. White blood cells were passively loaded with the green-fluorescent SYTO® 16 dye (S7578, Section 8.1) or the red-fluorescent SYTO® 59 dye (S11341, Section 8.1). Red blood cell membranes were labeled with DiD (D307, Section 14.4). By using an argon-ion laser to excite SYTO® 16 and a red light–emitting He–Ne laser to excite both SYTO® 59 and DiD, they were able to follow the relative mobility of the two types of blood cells.[169,170]

Caged Fluorescent Dye Tracers

UV photolysis of photoactivatable fluorescent dyes provides a means of controlling — both spatially and temporally — the release of fluorescent tracers (Section 5.3). Thus, caged dyes enable researchers to follow the movement of individual molecules and cellular structures,[171–173] as well as to study cell lineage in live organisms (Figure 5.24). CMNB-caged fluorescein [174,175] (F7103, Figure 14.37) is colorless and nonfluorescent until it is photolyzed at <365 nm to the intensely green-fluorescent free dye. Movement of the liberated fluorophore from the site of photolysis can then be followed. Our caged fluorophore–labeled dextrans are described in Section 14.5. The succinimidyl ester of CMNB-caged carboxyfluorescein (C20050, Section 1.4, Figure 1.59), which is water soluble at pH 7, is useful for preparation of other caged dye tracers, including those of proteins.

Fluorescent Retrograde Tracers

Anterograde and retrograde tracing of neurons has utilized a wide variety of fluorescent and nonfluorescent probes. See particularly the review by Vercelli and collaborators for information on suitable probes and labeling methods.[59] Among the retrograde and anterograde tracers are biotin derivatives and polar fluorescent dyes (this Section), lipophilic tracers such as DiI (D282, Section 14.4), dextran conjugates (Section 14.5), fluorescent microspheres (Section 14.6) and protein conjugates, including lectins (Section 14.7).

True Blue and Nuclear Yellow

The popular retrograde tracer true blue (T1323) is a UV light–excitable, divalent cationic dye that stains the cytoplasm with blue fluorescence.[176–180] For two-color neuronal mapping, true blue has been combined with longer-wavelength tracers such as nuclear yellow [176,181–183] (Hoechst S769121, N21485) or diamidino yellow,[184–187] which primarily stain the neuronal nucleus with yellow fluorescence (Figure 7.118, Figure 8.126, Figure 8.143). Fluorescent microspheres have also been used as a counterstain with true blue.[188] True blue is reported to be a less cytotoxic retrograde tracer than Fluoro-Gold [177]

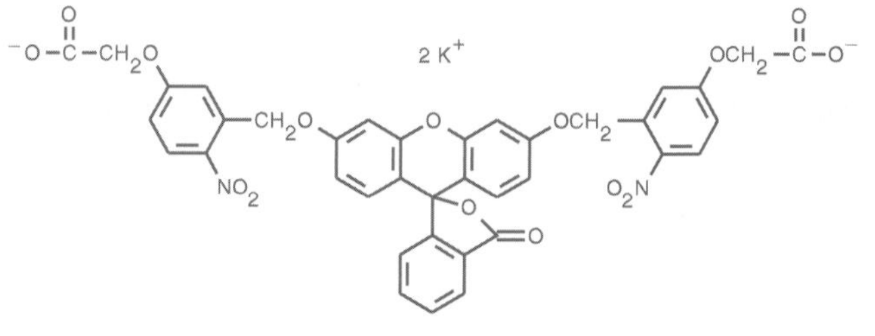

Figure 14.37 F7103 fluorescein bis-(5-carboxymethoxy-2-nitrobenzyl) ether, dipotassium salt (CMNB-caged fluorescein).

and to be a more efficient retrograde tracer than diamidino yellow.[178] Both true blue and nuclear yellow are stable when subjected to immunohistochemical processing and can be used to photoconvert DAB into an insoluble, electron-dense reaction product.[33,34,189,190]

Hydroxystilbamidine and Aminostilbamidine

Hydroxystilbamidine methanesulfonate (H22845, Figure 8.34) is an interesting probe originally developed as a trypanocide at May and Baker by the same group that developed ethidium bromide.[191,192] Hydroxystilbamidine has been identified by Wessendorf[193] as the active component of a dye that was named Fluoro-Gold by Schmued and Fallon[194] and later sold for retrograde tracing under that trademark by Fluorochrome, Inc.[195] The use of hydroxystilbamidine as a histochemical stain and as a retrograde tracer for neurons apparently goes back to the work of Snapper and collaborators in the early 1950s who, while studying the effects of hydroxystilbamidine on multiple myeloma, showed that therapeutically administered hydroxystilbamidine gives selective staining of ganglion cells.[196,197] The comprehensive article by Wessendorf[193] also describes several other early applications of hydroxystilbamidine that do not include its therapeutic uses:

- As an AT-selective, nonintercalating nucleic acid stain for discriminating between DNA and RNA[198–200] (Section 8.1)
- For histochemical staining of DNA, mucosubstances and elastic fibers, as well as mast cells[201]
- As a ribonuclease inhibitor[202]
- For lysosomal staining of live cells[203–208] (Section 12.3)

The weakly basic properties of hydroxystilbamidine that result in its uptake by lysosomes are reportedly important for its mechanism of retrograde transport.[193,203] Hydroxystilbamidine (as its isethionate salt, which is not available from Molecular Probes) is reported to be nonmutagenic in *Salmonella typhimurium* by the Ames test[201] and has been used therapeutically in large doses[209,210] (up to 225 mg i.v. daily). However, the product sold as Fluoro-Gold is reported to be toxic to some cells[177] and may cause necrosis at sites of injection.[194,211]

Molecular Probes introduced a product that we called hydroxystilbamidine (formerly catalog number H7599) in April 1995; however, we subsequently discovered that the chemical structure of our original "hydroxystilbamidine" corresponded to a novel dye that we now call aminostilbamidine (A22850, Figure 14.38). Apparently, aminostilbamidine functions at least as well as authentic hydroxystilbamidine as a tracer because several publications, including some recent papers, have utilized our original material for this purpose. However, aminostilbamidine does not show the spectral shifts with DNA and RNA that are observed with authentic hydroxystilbamidine. References to applications of aminostilbamidine (A22850) refer to material provided by Molecular Probes under the name "hydroxystilbamidine" that was actually aminostilbamidine. We recommend that those who have successfully used our former product now use aminostilbamidine (A22850).

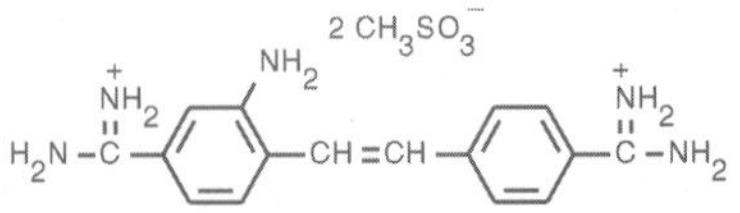

Figure 14.38 A22850 aminostilbamidine, methanesulfonate.

Propidium Iodide and DAPI for Retrograde Tracing

A variety of other low molecular weight dyes have been used as fluorescent retrograde neuronal tracers.[212,213] These include propidium iodide[214,215] (P1304MP; FluoroPure™ Grade, P21493) and DAPI.[216,217] Both propidium iodide and DAPI can be used to photoconvert DAB into an insoluble, electron-dense product.[33,34,218] The lactate salt of DAPI (D3571) has much higher water solubility than the chloride salt (D1306; FluoroPure™ Grade, D21490), making it the preferred form for microinjection.

NeuroTrace® Fluorescent Nissl Stains

The Nissl substance, described by Franz Nissl more than 100 years ago, is unique to neuronal cells.[219] Composed of an extraordinary amount of rough endoplasmic reticulum, the Nissl substance reflects the unusually high protein synthesis capacity of neuronal cells. Various fluorescent or chromophoric "Nissl stains" have been used for this counterstaining, including acridine orange,[220] ethidium bromide,[220] neutral red (N3246, Section 15.2), cresyl violet,[221] methylene blue, safranin-O and toluidine blue-O.[222] We have developed five fluorescent Nissl stains (Table 14.2) that not only provide a wide spectrum of fluorescent colors for staining neurons, but also are far more sensitive than the conventional dyes:

- NeuroTrace® 435/455 blue-fluorescent Nissl stain (N21479, Figure 14.39)
- NeuroTrace® 500/525 green-fluorescent Nissl stain (N21480; Figure 7.84, Figure 8.37, Figure 14.40, Figure 14.60)
- NeuroTrace® 515/535 yellow-fluorescent Nissl stain (N21481, Figure 14.41)
- NeuroTrace® 530/615 red-fluorescent Nissl stain (N21482; Figure 8.143, Figure 14.42)
- NeuroTrace® 640/660 deep red–fluorescent Nissl stain (N21483)

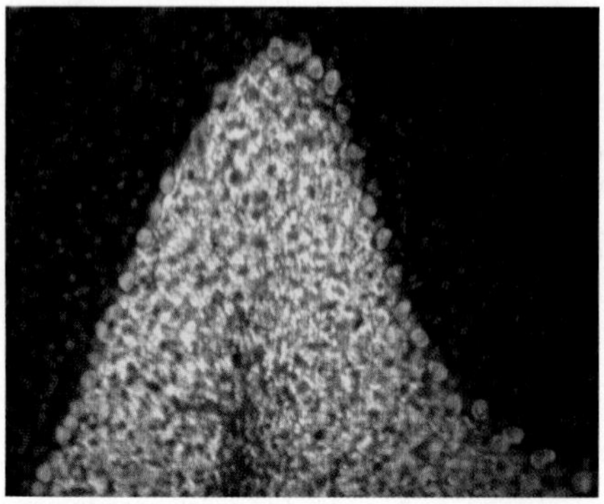

Figure 14.39 Mouse brain section stained with NeuroTrace® 435/455 blue-fluorescent Nissl stain (N21479) and counterstained with nuclear yellow (N21485).

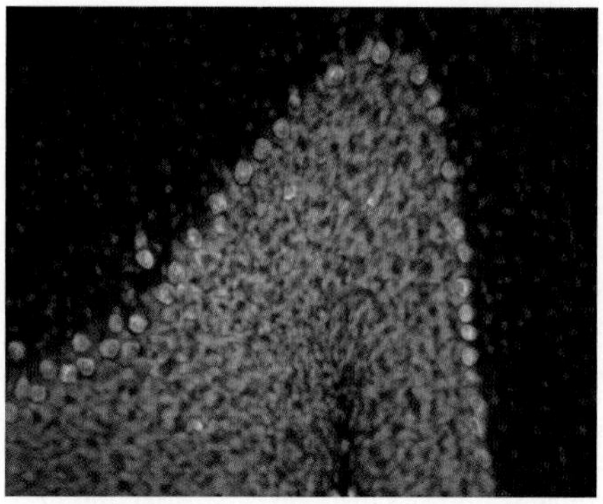

Figure 14.41 Mouse brain section stained with NeuroTrace® 515/535 yellow-fluorescent Nissl stain (N21481) and counterstained with nuclear yellow (N21485).

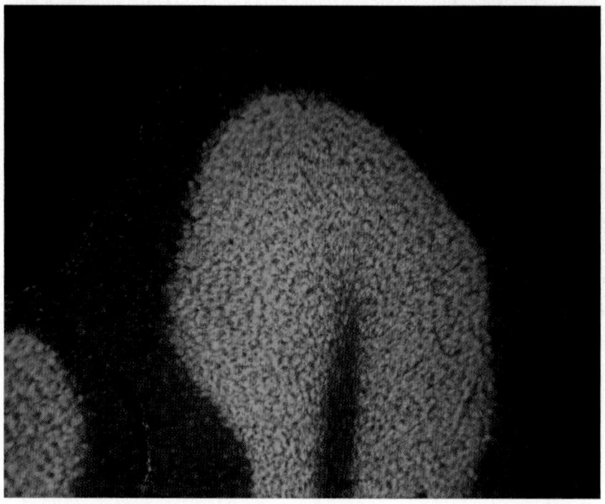

Figure 14.40 A mouse brain cryosection stained with the neuron-selective NeuroTrace® 500/525 green-fluorescent Nissl stain (N21480). The nuclei of the non-neuronal cells appear blue after incubation with the cell-permeant DNA counterstain, DAPI (D1306, D3571, D21490). The image is a composite of two micrographs acquired using filter sets appropriate for fluorescein and DAPI.

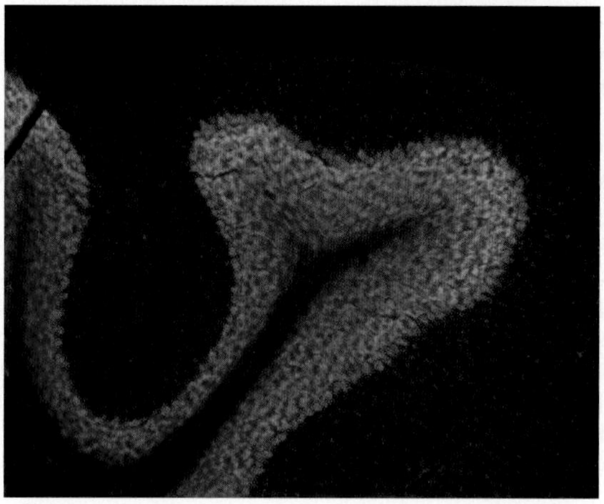

Figure 14.42 Neural somata labeled with NeuroTrace® 530/615 red-fluorescent Nissl stain (N21482). Nuclei in this mouse cerebellum section were counterstained with DAPI (D1306, D3571, D21490). The image is a composite of two micrographs acquired using filters appropriate for tetramethylrhodamine and DAPI.

Table 14.2 — Fluorescence characteristics of NeuroTrace® fluorescent Nissl stains

Cat #	Fluorescent Color	Ex *	Em *	Signal Using Various Filter Sets †				
				405 ± 20 445 ≥450	485 ± 11 505 535 ± 17.5	510 ± 11.5 540 ≥550	560 ± 20 590 610 ± 10	640 ± 10 660 682 ± 11
N21479	blue	435	455	+++	+	–	–	–
N21480	green	500	525	–	+++	+++	–	–
N21481	yellow	515	535	–	+++	+++	+++	–
N21482	red	530	615	–	–	++	+++	–
N21483	deep red	640	660	–	–	– ‡	–	++

* Approximate fluorescence excitation (Ex) and emission (Em) maxima, in nm. † Spectral characteristics in nm of the excitation filter, dichroic mirror and emission filter are shown top to bottom for each filter set. Relative signal strength for each filter combination is indicated with pluses and minuses. ‡ High background fluorescence.

In addition, the Nissl substance redistributes within the cell body in injured or regenerating neurons. Therefore, these Nissl stains can also act as markers for the physiological state of the neuron. Staining by the Nissl stains is completely eliminated by pretreatment of tissue specimens with RNase; however, these dyes are not specific stains for RNA in solutions. The best stains for the Nissl substance — including our NeuroTrace® dyes and the fluorescent retrograde tracers mentioned above — are usually nucleic acid stains, indicating that NeuroTrace® Nissl stains may also be useful for retrograde tracing, although we have not yet tested them for that purpose. The strong fluorescence (emission maximum ~515–520 nm) of NeuroTrace® 500/525 green-fluorescent Nissl stain (N21480) makes it the preferred dye for use as a counterstain in combination with orange- or red-fluorescent neuroanatomical tracers such as DiI [223] (D282, D3911, V22885; Section 14.4).

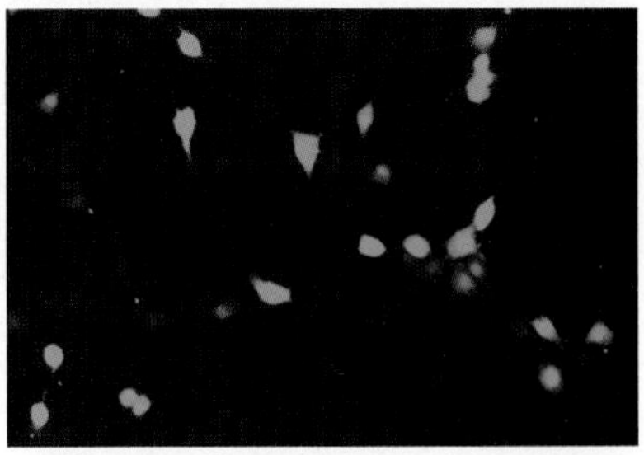

Figure 14.43 3T3 cells loaded with calcein (C481) using the Influx™ pinocytic cell-loading reagent (I14402). The image was acquired using a fluorescence microscope equipped with a cooled CCD camera and a bandpass filter set appropriate for fluorescein.

Polar Spin Label

The highly water-soluble cationic spin label 4-trimethylammonium-2,2,6,6-tetramethylpiperidine-1-oxyl iodide (CAT 1, T506) has been used to:

- Quench fluorescent dyes in solutions, cells and cell membranes [224]
- Detect oxygen gradients and oxidation–reduction properties of cells [225–229]
- Study liposome permeability [224,229]

Signal Amplification of Polar Tracers

Polar tracers such as Cascade Blue® hydrazide, lucifer yellow CH, Alexa Fluor® 488 hydrazide and biocytin penetrate even the finest structures of neurons and other cells; however, as the thickness of the sample is decreased, the fluorescence signal is reduced. Consequently, it may be necessary to further amplify the signal by secondary detection methods. We provide rabbit polyclonal antibodies to the Alexa Fluor® 488, Alexa Fluor® 405/Cascade Blue®, lucifer yellow, fluorescein, BODIPY® FL, tetramethylrhodamine and Texas Red® fluorophores (Section 7.4, Table 7.18) and a vast number of dye- or enzyme-labeled anti-rabbit antibodies (Section 7.2, Table 7.1). Our polyclonal and monoclonal antibodies to fluorescein crossreact strongly with the Oregon Green® dyes and somewhat with Rhodamine Green™ fluorophores, and our anti-tetramethylrhodamine and anti–Texas Red® antibodies crossreact with tetramethylrhodamine, Lissamine rhodamine B, Rhodamine Red™ and Texas Red® dyes. For the greatest signal amplification, however, Molecular Probes' ELF® 97 Immunohistochemistry Kit and ELF® 97 Cytological Labeling Kits (E6600, E6603; Section 6.3), several of our TSA (Tyramide Signal Amplification) Kits (Section 6.2, Table 6.1) and our Diaminobenzidine (DAB) Histochemistry Kits (D22185, Section 7.2; D22187, Section 7.6) can be utilized directly to detect aldehyde-fixed biotin derivatives or combined with antibodies to aldehyde-immobilized, fluorophore-labeled polar tracers to further amplify the signal — making it possible to detect ultrafine structures accessible to these probes. The relatively small size and easy penetration into tissues makes the streptavidin conjugates of the NANOGOLD, Alexa Fluor® 488 FluoroNanogold and Alexa Fluor® 594 FluoroNanogold 1.4 nm gold clusters (N24918, A24926, A24927; Section 7.6) useful for ultrastructural studies of biotinylated tracers, particularly in combination with the LI Silver Enhancement Kit (L24919, Section 7.6, Figure 7.57).

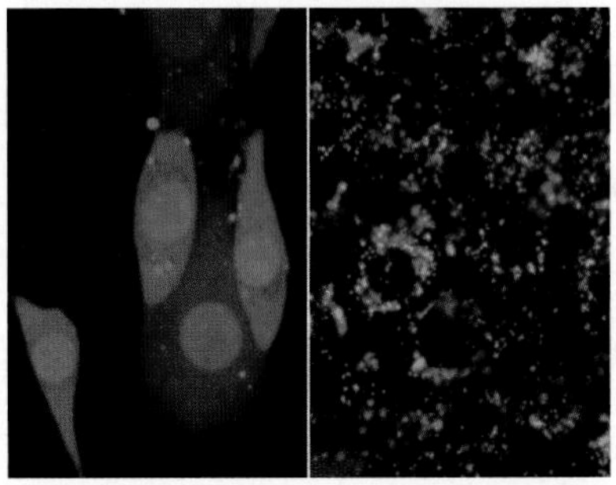

Figure 14.44 Adherent CRE BAG 2 cells passively loaded with the membrane-impermeant polar tracer Alexa Fluor® 594 hydrazide (A10438, A10442). The image on the left illustrates the relatively uniform, cytoplasmic labeling one can obtain with the Influx™ pinocytic cell-loading reagent (I14402), compared to the punctate labeling that results from pinocytic uptake in normal growth medium (right panel). Both images were acquired using a bandpass filter set appropriate for rhodamine dyes.

Influx™ Pinocytic Cell-Loading Reagent

The Influx™ pinocytic cell-loading reagent (I14402) opens up new research possibilities by facilitating the loading of just about any water-soluble material into live cells (Figure 14.43. Figure 14.44, Figure 14.45, Figure 14.46). Over the years, we have had many requests for a simple method to introduce polar compounds into many cells simultaneously without significantly altering normal cell function. We now offer an alternative to microinjection, electroporation and other invasive procedures.

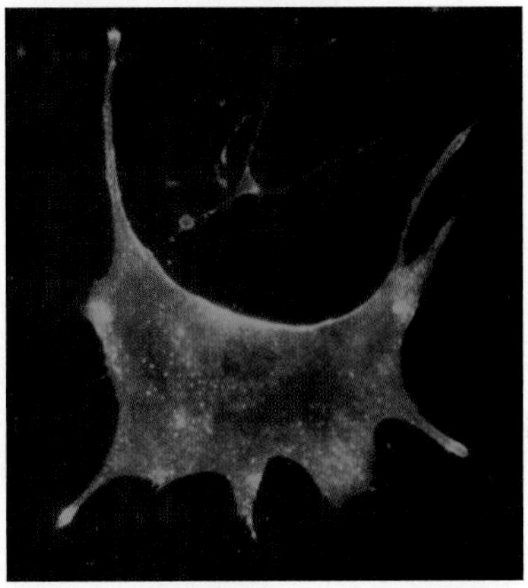

Figure 14.45 BPAE cells loaded with Alexa Fluor® 488 wheat germ agglutinin (W11261) using the Influx™ cell-loading reagent (I14402). The image was acquired using a fluorescence microscope equipped with a cooled CCD camera and a bandpass filter set appropriate for fluorescein.

Our Influx™ pinocytic cell-loading reagent works via a rapid and simple technique based on the osmotic lysis of pinocytic vesicles, an approach introduced by Okada and Rechsteiner.[24] The probe is simply mixed at high concentration with the Influx™ reagent blended into growth medium, then incubated with the cells in the medium to allow pinocytic uptake of the surrounding solution. Subsequent transfer of the cells to a slightly hypotonic medium results in bursting of the pinocytic vesicles within the cells and the release of the probe into the cytosol (Figure 14.47).

The Influx™ pinocytic cell-loading reagent is highly effective for loading a diverse array of probes — including calcein (Figure 14.46, Figure 14.43), Alexa Fluor® hydrazides (Figure 14.44), dextran conjugates of fluorophores[230] and ion indicators (Figure 19.100), fura-2 salts, Oregon Green® 514 dye–labeled tubulin, Alexa Fluor® 488 dye–labeled actin, heparin, hydroxyurea,[231] DNA, oligonucleotides,[232] SYTOX® Green nucleic acid stain and propidium iodide — into a variety of cell lines. We (or other researchers) have successfully tested the reagent and loading method with:

- Bovine pulmonary artery endothelial cells (BPAEC)
- Human epidermoid carcinoma cells (A431)
- Human T cell leukemia cells (Jurkat)
- Murine fibroblasts (NIH 3T3 and CRE BAG 2)
- Murine monocyte-macrophages (RAW264.7 and J774A.1)
- Murine myeloma cells (P3x63AG8)
- Rat basophilic leukemia cells (RBL)

More than 80% of the cells remained viable, as determined by subsequent exclusion of propidium iodide.

In addition to the Influx™ pinocytic cell-loading reagent and cell growth medium, all that is required to perform the loading procedure is sterile deionized water and the fluorescent probe or other polar molecule of interest. Cell labeling can be accomplished in a single 30-minute loading cycle and may be enhanced by repetitive loading. Although most types of cells load quickly and easily, optimal conditions for loading must be determined for each cell type. It is also important to note that cell-to-cell variability in the degree of loading is typical (Figure 14.44) and that higher variability is generally observed when using large compounds, such as >10,000 MW dextrans and proteins.

The Influx™ pinocytic cell-loading reagent is packaged as a set of 10 tubes (I14402), each containing sufficient material to load 50 samples of cells grown on coverslips following the standard protocol supplied. Cells in suspension or in culture flasks may also be easily loaded; however, the number of possible cell loadings will depend on the cell suspension volume or size of culture flask used. The information provided with the Influx™ reagent includes general guidelines and detailed suggestions for optimizing cell loading. Use of the custom coverslip mini-rack (C14784, Section 23.3, Figure 23.54) or coverslip maxi-rack (C24784, Section 23.3, Figure 23.55) facilitates cell loading and slide handling when using the Influx™ reagent.

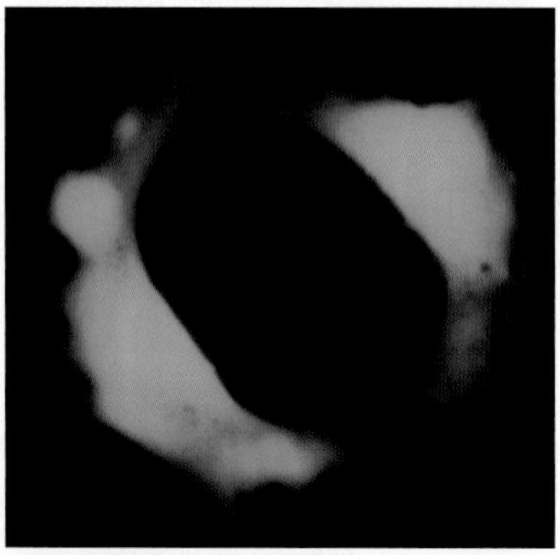

Figure 14.46 BPAEC cells loaded with calcein (C481) using the Influx™ cell-loading reagent (I14402). The image was acquired using a fluorescence microscope equipped with a cooled CCD camera and a bandpass filter set appropriate for fluorescein.

Loading $P2X_7$ Receptor–Expressing Cells

$P2X_7$ receptor–expressing cells such as macrophages and thymocytes exhibit reversible pore opening that can be exploited to provide an entry pathway for intracellular loading of both cationic and anionic fluorescent dyes with molecular weights of up to 900 daltons.[23,233,234] Pore opening is induced by treatment with 5 mM ATP for five minutes and subsequently reversed by addition of divalent cations (Ca^{2+} or Mg^{2+}). Dyes that have been successfully loaded into macrophage cells by this method include:

- Ca^{2+} indicator: fura-2 (F1200, F6799; Section 19.2)
- pH indicator: HPTS (H348)
- Aqueous tracers: lucifer yellow CH (L453, L682, L1177, L12926) and 6-carboxyfluorescein (C1360, Section 1.5)
- Nucleic acid stain: YO-PRO®-1 (Y3603, Section 8.1)

One of the most potent and widely used P2X receptor agonists, BzBzATP (2′-(or 3′-)*O*-(4-benzoylbenzoyl)adenosine 5′-triphosphate, B22358; Section 17.3), is available from Molecular Probes,[235,236] along with the corresponding GTP derivative (B22357, Section 17.3). Both BzBzATP and BzBzGTP have more general applications for site-directed irreversible modification of nucleotide-binding proteins via photoaffinity labeling;[237,238] see Section 17.3 for more information on our nucleotide analogs.

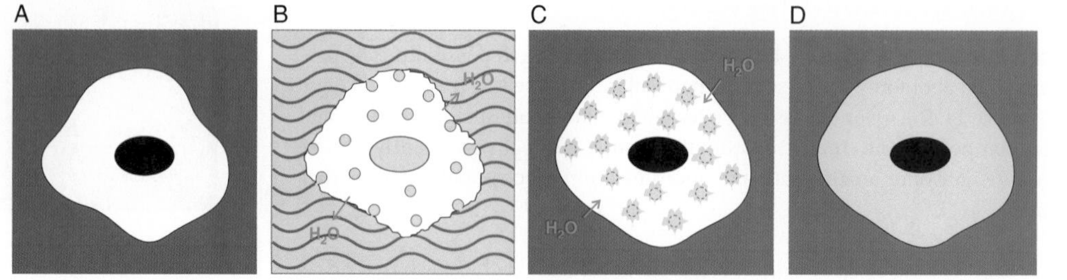

Figure 14.47 Principle of the Influx™ reagent pinocytic cell-loading method (I14402). Cultured cells are A) placed in hypertonic Influx™ loading reagent, along with the material to be loaded into the cells (yellow fluid, B), allowing the material to be carried into the cells via pinocytic vesicles. When the cells are placed in hypotonic medium, C) the pinocytic vesicles burst, D) releasing their contents into the cytosol.

References

1. J Fluorescence 3, 33 (1993); **2.** Photochem Photobiol 56, 325 (1992); **3.** J Immunol Methods 121, 1 (1989); **4.** Cytometry 8, 562 (1987); **5.** J Immunol Methods 100, 59 (1987); **6.** Proc Natl Acad Sci U S A 98, 4295 (2001); **7.** Methods Cell Biol 29, 153 (1989); **8.** Cell Biology: A Laboratory Handbook, 2nd Ed., Vol. 4, Celis JE, Ed. pp. 103–110 (1998); **9.** Annu Rev Physiol 52, 857 (1990); **10.** J Biol Chem 264, 5339 (1989); **11.** Methods Cell Biol 31, 63 (1989); **12.** J Pharm Sci 87, 1368 (1998); **13.** Methods Mol Biol 48, 93 (1995); **14.** Mol Biotechnol 4, 129 (1995); **15.** Proc Natl Acad Sci U S A 96, 121 (1999); **16.** J Neurosci 24, 722 (2004); **17.** Anal Chem 75, 1147 (2003); **18.** Nature 292, 17 (1981); **19.** Cell 14, 741 (1978); **20.** J Neurosci Methods 36, 309 (1991); **21.** J Cell Biol 104, 1217 (1987); **22.** Exp Cell Res 168, 422 (1987); **23.** J Biol Chem 262, 8884 (1987); **24.** Cell 29, 33 (1982); **25.** FEBS Lett 420, 86 (1997); **26.** Protoplasma 199, 198 (1997); **27.** J Cell Sci 99, 557 (1991); **28.** Planta 179, 257 (1989); **29.** Planta 181, 129 (1990); **30.** J Neurosci Methods 52, 111 (1994); **31.** J Neurosci Methods 47, 23 (1993); **32.** Scanning Microsc 5, 619 (1991); **33.** Neuroscience Protocols, Wouterlood FG, Ed. 93-050-06, pp. 01–13 (1993); **34.** Microsc Res Tech 24, 2 (1993); **35.** J Histochem Cytochem 36, 555 (1988); **36.** J Neurosci Methods 53, 87 (1994); **37.** J Neurosci 14, 5267 (1994); **38.** J Neurosci Methods 41, 45 (1992); **39.** J Comp Neurol 296, 598 (1990); **40.** J Neurosci Methods 33, 207 (1990); **41.** Dev Biol 94, 391 (1982); **42.** J Neurosci 15, 1755 (1995); **43.** J Neurosci 15, 1506 (1995); **44.** J Neurosci 14, 5077 (1994); **45.** Experientia 50, 124 (1994); **46.** J Neurosci 14, 999 (1994); **47.** Methods Enzymol 234, 235 (1994); **48.** Anal Biochem 211, 210 (1993); **49.** J Biol Chem 273, 22545 (1998); **50.** Biochem Soc Trans 23, 38S (1995); **51.** Biochemistry 30, 11245 (1991); **52.** Anal Biochem 198, 119 (1991); **53.** Nature 367, 69 (1994); **54.** J Anat 191, 355 (1997); **55.** Brain Res 564, 1 (1991); **56.** J Neurosci 14, 3805 (1994); **57.** J Neurosci Methods 41, 31 (1992); **58.** J Neurosci Methods 37, 141 (1991); **59.** Brain Res Bull 51, 11 (2000); **60.** J Neurosci Methods 39, 163 (1991); **61.** Nature 377, 734 (1995); **62.** J Neurosci 14, 5778 (1994); **63.** J Neurosci 14, 4338 (1994); **64.** J Neurosci 14, 1812 (1994); **65.** J Biol Chem 269, 24596 (1994); **66.** Anal Biochem 205, 166 (1992); **67.** Biochem J 251, 935 (1988); **68.** Neuroscience Protocols, Wouterlood FG, Ed. 93-050-20, pp. 01–16 (1993); **69.** Dev Biol 119, 322 (1987); **70.** J Neurosci Methods 53, 23 (1994); **71.** J Neurosci Methods 46, 59 (1993); **72.** Anal Biochem 269, 410 (1999); **73.** Anal Lett 18, 1847 (1985); **74.** Science 283, 1892 (1999); **75.** Meth Neurosci 27, 361 (1995); **76.** Neuroscience 69, 283 (1995); **77.** J Biol Chem 267, 17658 (1992); **78.** Biochim Biophys Acta 1052, 278 (1990); **79.** Biotechniques 18, 490 (1995); **80.** Biophys J 66, 1915 (1994); **81.** J Biol Chem 268, 706 (1993); **82.** J Pharm Sci 83, 276 (1994); **83.** J Cell Biol 123, 1845 (1993); **84.** Anal Biochem 207, 109 (1992); **85.** Biochim Biophys Acta 1106, 23 (1992); **86.** Am J Physiol Gastrointest Liver Physiol 268, 361 (1995); **87.** Am J Physiol Gastrointest Liver Physiol 281, G833 (2001); **88.** J Biol Chem 273, 27438 (1998); **89.** Am J Physiol 272, G923 (1997); **90.** Biochemistry 34, 1606 (1995); **91.** Biophys J 68, 1864 (1995); **92.** J Biol Chem 269, 14473 (1994); **93.** J Cell Biol 127, 1885 (1994); **94.** Biochemistry 31, 12424 (1992); **95.** Biochemistry 31, 9912 (1992); **96.** Anal Biochem 172, 403 (1988); **97.** Biochemistry 27, 5713 (1988); **98.** Int Ophthalmol 17, 349 (1993); **99.** Chem Pharm Bull (Tokyo) 39, 227 (1991); **100.** Biochim Biophys Acta 691, 332 (1982); **101.** J Biol Chem 274, 13375 (1999); **102.** Anal Biochem 134, 26 (1983); **103.** J Biol Chem 257, 13892 (1982); **104.** Anal Chem 35, 1035 (1963); **105.** Anal Chem 31, 456 (1959); **106.** Biochim Biophys Acta 649, 183 (1981); **107.** Cell 32, 921 (1983); **108.** J Neurochem 57, 1270 (1991); **109.** J Cell Biol 106, 715 (1988); **110.** Science 232, 525 (1986); **111.** Protoplasma 199, 18 (1997); **112.** Cytometry 13, 739 (1992); **113.** Exp Neurol 156, 16 (1999); **114.** J Neurosci Res 49, 19 (1997); **115.** J Cell Biol 130, 987 (1995); **116.** In Vitro Cell Dev Biol 30, 796 (1994); **117.** Not available from Molecular Probes; **118.** J Cell Biol 122, 157 (1993); **119.** J Cell Biol 131, 655 (1995); **120.** J Fluorescence 7, 45 (1997); **121.** Methods Enzymol 221, 234 (1993); **122.** J Biol Chem 267, 18424 (1992); **123.** J Cell Biol 108, 2241 (1989); **124.** J Neurosci 15, 5036 (1995); **125.** J Physiol 478, 265 (1994); **126.** Exp Brain Res 97, 239 (1993); **127.** J Neurosci 12, 3187 (1992); **128.** Nature 314, 357 (1985); **129.** J Neurosci 14, 6886 (1994); **130.** J Neurosci 12, 2960 (1992); **131.** FEBS Lett 305, 185 (1992); **132.** Am J Physiol 252, H223 (1987); **133.** Proc Natl Acad Sci U S A 84, 2272 (1987); **134.** J Cell Biol 104, 1749 (1987); **135.** J Leukoc Biol 41, 111 (1987); **136.** J Leukoc Biol 36, 273 (1984); **137.** Science 251, 81 (1991); **138.** Proc Natl Acad Sci U S A 92, 3156 (1995); **139.** J Biol Chem 268, 6742 (1993); **140.** Biochim Biophys Acta 1024, 352 (1990); **141.** Pharm Res 7, 824 (1990); **142.** J Neurochem 62, 2022 (1994); **143.** Nature 370, 379 (1994); **144.** Biochemistry 32, 7669 (1993); **145.** Biochim Biophys Acta 1111, 17 (1992); **146.** Neuron 11, 801 (1993); **147.** Plant Cell Environ 17, 257 (1994); **148.** J Gen Virol 75, 3477 (1994); **149.** Am J Physiol 262, G30 (1992); **150.** Plant Physiol 86, 999 (1988); **151.** Arch Biochem Biophys 202, 650 (1980); **152.** J Cell Biol 133, 617 (1996); **153.** Biochemistry 38, 134 (1999); **154.** Methods Enzymol 207, 501 (1992); **155.** Biophys J 54, 595 (1988); **156.** J Gen Physiol 83, 819 (1984); **157.** Biochim Biophys Acta 1142, 277 (1993); **158.** J Am Chem Soc 100, 3234 (1978); **159.** J Immunol Methods 15, 255 (1977); **160.** Proc Natl Acad Sci U S A 78, 775 (1981); **161.** Proc Natl Acad Sci U S A 77, 4509 (1980); **162.** Biochemistry 28, 824 (1989); **163.** Biophys J 54, 587 (1988); **164.** J Immunol Methods 147, 13 (1992); **165.** Plant J 12, 931 (1997); **166.** Science 270, 1980 (1995); **167.** Virology 207, 345 (1995); **168.** Cell 76, 925 (1994); **169.** Biophotonics Int 6, 56 (1999); **170.** Anal Chem 71, 5131 (1999); **171.** Anal Chem 75, 1387 (2003); **172.** Annu Rev Physiol 55, 755 (1993); **173.** Biotechniques 23, 268 (1997); **174.** Phys Fluids 9, 717 (1997); **175.** Exp Fluids 21, 237 (1996); **176.** Neuroscience 60, 125 (1994); **177.** Neurosci Lett 128, 137 (1991); **178.** J Neurosci Methods 35, 175 (1990); **179.** J Neurosci Methods 32, 15 (1990); **180.** Meth Neurosci 3, 275 (1990); **181.** Neuroscience 28, 725 (1989); **182.** Acta Anat (Basel) 122, 158 (1985); **183.** Neurosci Lett 18, 25 (1980); **184.** Brain Res 508, 289 (1990); **185.** Brain Res Bull 24, 341 (1990); **186.** J Neurosci Methods 16, 175 (1986); **187.** Exp Brain Res 51, 179 (1983); **188.** Brain Res 486, 334 (1989); **189.** J Comp Neurol 258, 230 (1987); **190.** J Neurosci Methods 14, 273 (1985); **191.** J Ultrastruct Res 37, 200 (1971); **192.** 567 (1946); **193.** Brain Res 553, 135 (1991); **194.** Brain Res 377, 147 (1986); **195.** US 4,716,905; **196.** Cancer 4, 1246 (1951); **197.** J Lab Clin Med 37, 562 (1951); **198.** Biochim Biophys Acta 407, 43 (1975); **199.** Biochim Biophys Acta 407, 24 (1975); **200.** Biochemistry 12, 4827 (1973); **201.** Histochemistry 74, 107 (1982); **202.** J Cell Biol 87, 292 (1980); **203.** J Neurocytol 18, 333 (1989); **204.** J Cell Biol 90, 665 (1981); **205.** J Cell Biol 90, 656 (1981); **206.** Infect Immun 11, 441 (1975); **207.** Biochem Pharmacol 19, 1251 (1970); **208.** Life Sci 3, 1407 (1964); **209.** Mayo Clin Proc 58, 223 (1983); **210.** Rev Infect Dis 2, 625 (1980); **211.** Brain Res 533, 329 (1990); **212.** Proc Natl Acad Sci USA 79, 2898 (1982); **213.** J Cell Biol 89, 368 (1981); **214.** J Comp Neurol 303, 255 (1991); **215.** Neurosci Lett 117, 285 (1990); **216.** Photochem Photobiol 46, 45 (1987); **217.** Brain Res Rev 8, 99 (1984); **218.** J Neurosci Methods 45, 87 (1992); **219.** Neuroscience Protocols, Wouterlood FG, Ed. 93-050-12, pp. 01–07 (1993); **220.** Proc Natl Acad Sci U S A 77, 2260 (1980); **221.** J Neurosci Methods 33, 129 (1990); **222.** J Neurosci Methods 72, 49 (1997); **223.** Neurosci Lett 184, 169 (1995); **224.** J Membr Biol 109, 41 (1989); **225.** Biochemistry 28, 2496 (1989); **226.** J Cell Physiol 140, 505 (1989); **227.** Biochim Biophys Acta 970, 270 (1988); **228.** Biochim Biophys Acta 888, 82 (1986); **229.** J Pharm Sci 75, 334 (1986); **230.** J Virol 76, 11505 (2002); **231.** J Virol 76, 5167 (2002); **232.** EMBO J 21, 1743 (2002); **233.** J Physiol 519 Pt 2, 335 (1999); **234.** Am J Physiol 275, C1158 (1998); **235.** J Physiol 519 Pt 3, 723 (1999); **236.** Mol Pharmacol 56, 1171 (1999); **237.** J Neurochem 61, 1657 (1993); **238.** Biochemistry 28, 3989 (1989).

Data Table — 14.3 Polar Tracers

Cat #	MW	Storage	Soluble	Abs	EC	Em	Solvent	Notes
A350	427.33	L	H_2O	353	7,200	520	H_2O	
A1339	491.57	L	H_2O	425	12,000	532	H_2O	
A1340	533.65	L	H_2O	426	11,000	531	H_2O	
A1593	367.30	NC	DMF, DMSO	<300		none		
A1594	442.50	NC	DMF, DMSO	<300		none		
A6257	523.39	D,L	H_2O	424	19,000	505	pH 7	
A10436	570.48	D,L	H_2O	493	71,000	517	pH 7	
A10437	730.74	D,L	H_2O	576	86,000	599	pH 7	1
A10438	758.79	D,L	H_2O	588	97,000	613	pH 7	1
A10439	349.29	L	H_2O, DMSO	345	13,000	445	pH 7	
A10440	570.48	FF,L	H_2O	493	71,000	517	pH 7	2
A10441	730.74	FF,L	H_2O	576	86,000	599	pH 7	2
A10442	758.79	FF,L	H_2O	588	97,000	613	pH 7	2
A12922	1141.31	D,L	DMSO, H_2O	591	80,000	618	pH 7	
A12923	1209.66	D,L	DMSO, H_2O	556	99,000	572	pH 7	
A12924	974.98	D,L	DMSO, H_2O	494	62,000	520	pH 7	
A20501MP	~1150	D,L	H_2O	554	150,000	567	pH 7	
A20502	~1200	D,L	H_2O	649	250,000	666	pH 7	
A22840	341.39	L	H_2O	350	4,200	450	pH 7	3
A22850	471.55	F,D,L	H_2O, DMSO	361	17,000	536	pH 7	
A30000	1028.26	F,DD,L	H_2O, DMSO	400	35,000	424	pH 7	4, 5, 6
A30627	584.52	F,D,L	H_2O, DMSO	353	20,000	437	MeOH	7
A30629	895.07	F,D,L	H_2O, DMSO	494	77,000	518	pH 7	7
A30632	~1220	F,D,L	H_2O, DMSO	651	250,000	672	MeOH	7
A30634	~950	D,L	H_2O, DMSO	624	110,000	643	pH 7	
A30675	666.58	F,D,L	H_2O	399	29,000	422	H_2O	
B1151	520.45	L	pH >6	503	90,000	528	pH 9	8
B1370	831.01	L	DMF, pH >6	494	75,000	518	pH 9	8
B1513	341.38	F,D	DMF, DMSO	<300		none		
B1582	454.54	F,D	DMF, DMSO	<300		none		
B1592	372.48	NC	H_2O	<300		none		
B1596	555.65	NC	DMF, DMSO	<300		none		
B1597	399.55	NC	DMF, DMSO	<300		none		
B1603	386.51	D	pH >6, DMF	<300		none		
B6350	499.67	D	pH >6, DMF	<300		none		
B6352	669.74	F,D	DMF, pH >6	<300		none		5
B6353	556.58	F,D	DMF, pH >6	<300		none		5
B6357	347.49	D	DMSO, H_2O	<300		none		
B10570	644.70	L	DMSO	494	68,000	523	pH 9	8
C194	376.32	L	pH >6, DMF	492	75,000	517	pH 9	8
C368	445.21	L	pH >6, DMF	504	107,000	529	pH 8	9
C481	622.54	L	pH >5	494	77,000	517	pH 9	10, 11
C621	624.49	L	H_2O	399	30,000	423	H_2O	4
C687	596.44	L	H_2O	399	30,000	421	H_2O	4, 12
C1430	994.87	F,D	DMSO	<300		none		13
C1904	376.32	L	pH >6, DMF	492	78,000	517	pH 9	3, 8
C2284	607.42	F,D,LL	H_2O, MeOH	396	29,000	410	MeOH	4, 14
C3099	994.87	F,D	DMSO	<300		none		2, 13
C3100MP	994.87	F,D	DMSO	<300		none		13
C3221	644.77	L	H_2O	399	31,000	419	H_2O	4, 12
C3239	548.29	L	H_2O	399	29,000	419	H_2O	4, 12
D530	279.83	D,L	H_2O, MeOH	<300		none		
D1306	350.25	L	H_2O, DMF	344	23,000	450	pH 7	
D1389	775.54	L	H_2O	653	166,000	674	MeOH	
D3238	484.20	F,D,L	H_2O	490	97,000	515	H_2O	15
D3571	457.49	L	H_2O, MeOH	344	22,000	450	pH 7	
D7060	719.55	FF,LL	H_2O, DMSO	402	24,000	none	H_2O	16, 17
D20652	342.44	NC	H_2O	<300		none		
D20653	341.45	D	DMSO	<300		none		
D21490	350.25	L	H_2O, DMF	344	23,000	450	pH 7	3
D30752	405.97	F,DD	DMF, DMSO	<300		none		
E6960	366.41	D	H_2O	337	17,000	613	H_2O	18, 19
F1130	478.32	D,L	H_2O, DMF	495	76,000	519	pH 9	8
F7103	826.81	FF,D,LL	H_2O, DMSO	333	15,000	none	DMSO	14, 17, 20
H185	206.15	L	pH >6, DMF	386	29,000	448	pH 10	21
H348	524.37	D,L	H_2O	454	24,000	511	pH 9	22
H22845	472.53	F,D,L	H_2O, DMSO	345	31,000	450	pH 5	23
L453	457.24	L	H_2O	428	12,000	536	H_2O	24
L682	479.44	L	H_2O	428	12,000	533	H_2O	24
L1177	521.56	L	H_2O	427	12,000	535	H_2O	24

Cat #	MW	Storage	Soluble	Abs	EC	Em	Solvent	Notes
L1338	659.51	F,D,L	H_2O	426	11,000	531	pH 7	25
L2601	873.10	D,L	H_2O	428	11,000	531	H_2O	
L6950	850.03	D,L	H_2O	428	11,000	532	pH 7	
L12926	457.24	FF,L	H_2O	428	12,000	536	H_2O	2
M395	538.40	L	H_2O	404	29,000	435	pH 8	26
M1602	523.60	F,D	pH >6, DMF	<300		none		
N21479	see Notes	F,D,L	DMSO	435	see Notes	457	H_2O/RNA	2, 27, 28
N21480	see Notes	F,D,L	DMSO	497	see Notes	524	H_2O/RNA	2, 27, 28
N21481	see Notes	F,D,L	DMSO	515	see Notes	535	H_2O/RNA	2, 27, 28
N21482	see Notes	F,D,L	DMSO	530	see Notes	619	H_2O/RNA	2, 27, 28
N21483	see Notes	F,D,L	DMSO	644	see Notes	663	H_2O/RNA	2, 27, 28
O6135	448.35	L	pH >6, DMF	497	84,000	517	pH 9	
O6138	512.36	L	pH >6, DMF	506	86,000	526	pH 9	29
O6146	412.30	L	pH >6, DMF	492	85,000	518	pH 9	30
O12920	887.39	L	DMSO, H_2O	495	66,000	522	pH 9	30
P349	610.42	L	H_2O	374	51,000	403	H_2O	
P1304MP	668.40	L	H_2O, DMSO	493	5,900	636	H_2O	
P12925	541.39	F,D,L	DMSO, EtOH	492	80,000	516	pH 10	8
P21493	668.40	L	H_2O, DMSO	493	5,900	636	H_2O	3
S359	606.71	L	H_2O	586	108,000	605	H_2O	
S1129	518.43	F,D	DMSO	<300		none		31
S1307	558.66	L	H_2O	565	84,000	586	H_2O	
S6957	552.59	D,L	DMSO, H_2O	529	75,000	548	MeOH	
T411	266.22	D,L	DMF, EtOH	337	17,000	483	MeOH	
T506	341.25	F,D	H_2O, MeOH	<300		none		
T1247	373.38	D	H_2O	270	4,700	545	H_2O	19, 32
T1323	417.29	L	DMSO	375	68,000	403	H_2O	
T6931	790.79	D,L	pH >6, DMSO	414	416,000	645	pH 9	
T6932	934.98	D,L	H_2O, DMSO	413	472,000	645	pH 9	33
T12921	869.09	D,L	DMSO	554	103,000	581	pH 7	
X1525	422.16	D	H_2O	259	8,800	none	H_2O	

For definitions of the contents of this data table, see "Navigating *The Handbook*" in the introductory pages.

Notes

1. Maximum solubility in water is ~8% for A10437 and A10438.
2. This product is supplied as a ready-made solution in the solvent indicated under "Soluble."
3. This product is specified to equal or exceed 98% analytical purity by HPLC.
4. The Alexa Fluor® 405 and Cascade Blue® dyes have a second absorption peak at about 376 nm with EC ~80% of the 395–400 nm peak.
5. This sulfonated succinimidyl ester derivative is water-soluble and may be dissolved in buffer at ~pH 8 for reaction with amines. Long-term storage in water is NOT recommended due to hydrolysis.
6. A30100 is an alternative packaging of A30000 but is otherwise identical.
7. Aqueous stock solutions should be used within 24 hours; long-term storage is NOT recommended.
8. Absorption and fluorescence of fluorescein derivatives are pH-dependent. Extinction coefficients and fluorescence quantum yields decrease markedly at pH <7.
9. Absorption and fluorescence of dichlorofluorescein derivatives are pH-dependent. Extinction coefficients and fluorescence quantum yields decrease markedly at pH <5.
10. C481 fluorescence is strongly quenched by micromolar concentrations of Fe^{3+}, Co^{2+}, Ni^{2+} and Cu^{2+} at pH 7 (Am J Physiol 268, C1354 (1995); J Biol Chem 274, 13375 (1999)).
11. $K_d(Co^{2+})$ for calcein is 120 nM, determined in 10 mM HEPES, 1 µM Ca^{2+}, 1 mM Mg^{2+}, 100 mM KCl (Anal Biochem 248, 31 (1997)).
12. Maximum solubility in water is ~1% for C687, ~1% for C3221 and ~8% for C3239.
13. Calcein AM is converted to fluorescent calcein (C481) after acetoxymethyl ester hydrolysis.
14. Unstable in water. Use immediately.
15. The absorption and fluorescence spectra of BODIPY® derivatives are relatively insensitive to the solvent.
16. D7060 is converted to fluorescent HPTS (H348) upon ultraviolet photolysis.
17. All photoactivatable probes are sensitive to light. They should be protected from illumination except when photolysis is intended.
18. Absorption and luminescence of E6960 are extremely weak unless it is chelated. Data are for the detergent-solubilized NTA (T411) chelate.
19. MW is for the hydrated form of this product.
20. This product is colorless and nonfluorescent until it is activated by ultraviolet photolysis. Photoactivation generates a fluorescein derivative with spectral characteristics similar to C1359.
21. Spectra of hydroxycoumarins are pH-dependent. Below the pK_a, Abs shifts to shorter wavelengths (325–340 nm) and fluorescence intensity decreases. Approximate pK_a values are 7.8 (H189, C2111), 7.5 (H185), 7.3 (T659) and 4.9 (D6566, C12881).
22. H348 spectra are pH-dependent.
23. Hydroxystilbamidine in H_2O has a wide emission bandwidth, with a second peak at ~600 nm.
24. Maximum solubility in water is ~8% for L453, ~6% for L682 and ~1% for L1177.
25. Iodoacetamides in solution undergo rapid photodecomposition to unreactive products. Minimize exposure to light prior to reaction.
26. Maximum solubility for M395 in water is ~25%.
27. This product is essentially nonfluorescent except when bound to DNA or RNA.
28. The active ingredient of this product is an organic dye with MW <1000. The exact MW and extinction coefficient values for this dye are proprietary.
29. Absorption and fluorescence of Oregon Green® 514 derivatives are pH-dependent only in moderately acidic solutions (pH <5).
30. Absorption and fluorescence of Oregon Green® 488 derivatives are pH-dependent only in moderately acidic solutions (pH <5).
31. S1129 is converted to a fluorescent product (F1130) after acetate hydrolysis.
32. Absorption and luminescence of T1247 are extremely weak unless it is chelated. Data are for dipicolinic acid (DPA) chelate. The luminescence spectrum has secondary peak at 490 nm.
33. The absorption spectrum of T6932 also contains much weaker bands in the 500–650 nm wavelength range. Absorption and fluorescence are pH-dependent. Abs = 434 nm at pH <5.

Product List — 14.3 Polar Tracers

Cat #	Product Name	Unit Size
A12924	Alexa Fluor® 488 biocytin, disodium salt (biocytin Alexa Fluor® 488)	250 µg
A12923	Alexa Fluor® 546 biocytin, sodium salt (biocytin Alexa Fluor® 546)	250 µg
A12922	Alexa Fluor® 594 biocytin, sodium salt (biocytin Alexa Fluor® 594)	250 µg
A30675	Alexa Fluor® 405 cadaverine, trisodium salt	1 mg
A30627	Alexa Fluor® 350 C_5-aminooxyacetamide, trifluoroacetate salt (Alexa Fluor® 350 hydroxylamine)	1 mg
A30629	Alexa Fluor® 488 C_5-aminooxyacetamide, bis(triethylammonium) salt (Alexa Fluor® 488 hydroxylamine)	1 mg
A30632	Alexa Fluor® 647 C_5-aminooxyacetamide, bis(triethylammonium) salt (Alexa Fluor® 647 hydroxylamine)	1 mg
A30000	Alexa Fluor® 405 carboxylic acid, succinimidyl ester	1 mg
A30100	Alexa Fluor® 405 carboxylic acid, succinimidyl ester	5 mg
A10439	Alexa Fluor® 350 hydrazide, sodium salt	5 mg
A10436	Alexa Fluor® 488 hydrazide, sodium salt	1 mg
A20501MP	Alexa Fluor® 555 hydrazide, tris(triethylammonium) salt	1 mg
A10437	Alexa Fluor® 568 hydrazide, sodium salt	1 mg
A10438	Alexa Fluor® 594 hydrazide, sodium salt	1 mg
A30634	Alexa Fluor® 633 hydrazide, bis(triethylammonium) salt	1 mg
A20502	Alexa Fluor® 647 hydrazide, tris(triethylammonium) salt	1 mg
A10440	Alexa Fluor® 488 hydrazide, sodium salt *for microinjection* *10 mM in 200 mM KCl*	125 µL
A10441	Alexa Fluor® 568 hydrazide, sodium salt *for microinjection* *10 mM in 200 mM KCl*	125 µL
A10442	Alexa Fluor® 594 hydrazide, sodium salt *for microinjection* *10 mM in 200 mM KCl*	125 µL
A1339	*N*-(2-aminoethyl)-4-amino-3,6-disulfo-1,8-naphthalimide, dipotassium salt (lucifer yellow ethylenediamine)	25 mg
A1593	*N*-(2-aminoethyl)biotinamide, hydrobromide (biotin ethylenediamine)	25 mg
A22840	7-aminonaphthalene-1,3-disulfonic acid, potassium salt (ANDS) *FluoroPure™ grade*	1 g
A350	8-aminonaphthalene-1,3,6-trisulfonic acid, disodium salt (ANTS)	1 g
A1340	*N*-(5-aminopentyl)-4-amino-3,6-disulfo-1,8-naphthalimide, dipotassium salt (lucifer yellow cadaverine)	25 mg
A1594	*N*-(5-aminopentyl)biotinamide, trifluoroacetic acid salt (biotin cadaverine)	25 mg
A6257	8-aminopyrene-1,3,6-trisulfonic acid, trisodium salt (APTS)	10 mg
A22850	aminostilbamidine, methanesulfonate	10 mg
B1592	biocytin (ε-biotinoyl-L-lysine)	100 mg
B1603	biocytin hydrazide	25 mg
B10570	biotin-4-fluorescein	5 mg
B1582	6-((biotinoyl)amino)hexanoic acid, succinimidyl ester (biotin-X, SE; biotinamidocaproate, *N*-hydroxysuccinimidyl ester)	100 mg
B6353	6-((biotinoyl)amino)hexanoic acid, sulfosuccinimidyl ester, sodium salt (Sulfo-NHS-LC-Biotin; biotin-X, SSE)	25 mg
B1597	2-(((*N*-(biotinoyl)amino)hexanoyl)amino)ethylamine (biotin-X ethylenediamine)	10 mg
B6352	6-((6-((biotinoyl)amino)hexanoyl)amino)hexanoic acid, sulfosuccinimidyl ester, sodium salt (biotin-XX, SSE)	25 mg
B1596	5-(((*N*-(biotinoyl)amino)hexanoyl)amino)pentylamine, trifluoroacetic acid salt (biotin-X cadaverine)	10 mg
B1370	5-((*N*-(5-(*N*-(6-(biotinoyl)amino)hexanoyl)amino)pentyl)thioureidyl)fluorescein (fluorescein biotin)	5 mg
B6350	ε-(6-(biotinoyl)amino)hexanoyl-L-lysine, hydrazide (biocytin-X hydrazide)	25 mg
B1513	D-biotin, succinimidyl ester (succinimidyl D-biotin)	100 mg
B6357	*S*-biotinylhomocysteine	5 mg
B1151	2',7'-bis-(2-carboxyethyl)-5-(and-6)-carboxyfluorescein (BCECF acid) *mixed isomers*	1 mg
C481	calcein *high purity*	100 mg
C1430	calcein, AM	1 mg
C3099	calcein, AM *1 mg/mL solution in dry DMSO*	1 mL
C3100MP	calcein, AM *special packaging*	20 x 50 µg
C368	5-(and-6)-carboxy-2',7'-dichlorofluorescein *mixed isomers*	100 mg
C1904	5-(and-6)-carboxyfluorescein (5(6)-FAM) *FluoroPure™ grade* *mixed isomers*	100 mg
C194	5-(and-6)-carboxyfluorescein *mixed isomers*	5 g
C2284	Cascade Blue® acetyl azide, trisodium salt	5 mg
C621	Cascade Blue® ethylenediamine, trisodium salt	10 mg
C3239	Cascade Blue® hydrazide, trilithium salt	10 mg
C3221	Cascade Blue® hydrazide, tripotassium salt	10 mg
C687	Cascade Blue® hydrazide, trisodium salt	10 mg
D1306	4',6-diamidino-2-phenylindole, dihydrochloride (DAPI)	10 mg
D21490	4',6-diamidino-2-phenylindole, dihydrochloride (DAPI) *FluoroPure™ grade*	10 mg
D3571	4',6-diamidino-2-phenylindole, dilactate (DAPI, dilactate)	10 mg
D3238	4,4-difluoro-1,3,5,7,8-pentamethyl-4-bora-3a,4a-diaza-*s*-indacene-2,6-disulfonic acid, disodium salt (BODIPY® 492/515 disulfonate)	10 mg
D7060	8-((4,5-dimethoxy-2-nitrobenzyl)oxy)pyrene-1,3,6-trisulfonic acid, trisodium salt (DMNB-caged HPTS)	5 mg
D530	4-(*N*,*N*-dimethyl-*N*-(2-hydroxyethyl))ammonium-2,2,6,6-tetramethylpiperidine-1-oxyl chloride (TEMPO choline)	25 mg
D1389	*N*,*N*'-di(3-trimethylammoniumpropyl)thiadicarbocyanine tribromide	10 mg
D30752	DSB-X™ biotin ethylenediamine (desthiobiotin-X ethylenediamine, hydrochloride)	1 mg

For current prices or to order online, visit probes.invitrogen.com

Cat #	Product Name	Unit Size
D20653	DSB-X™ biotin hydrazide	5 mg
D20652	DSB-X™ desthiobiocytin (ε-desthiobiotinoyl-L-lysine)	5 mg
E6960	europium(III) chloride, hexahydrate *99.99%*	1 g
F7103	fluorescein bis-(5-carboxymethoxy-2-nitrobenzyl) ether, dipotassium salt (CMNB-caged fluorescein)	5 mg
F1130	fluorescein-5-(and-6)-sulfonic acid, trisodium salt	100 mg
H185	7-hydroxycoumarin-3-carboxylic acid *reference standard*	100 mg
H348	8-hydroxypyrene-1,3,6-trisulfonic acid, trisodium salt (HPTS; pyranine)	1 g
H22845	hydroxystilbamidine, methanesulfonate	10 mg
I14402	Influx™ pinocytic cell-loading reagent *makes 10 x 5 mL*	1 set
L6950	lucifer yellow biocytin, potassium salt (biocytin lucifer yellow)	5 mg
L2601	lucifer yellow cadaverine biotin-X, dipotassium salt	10 mg
L682	lucifer yellow CH, ammonium salt	25 mg
L453	lucifer yellow CH, lithium salt	25 mg
L12926	lucifer yellow CH, lithium salt *for microinjection* *100 mM in water*	100 µL
L1177	lucifer yellow CH, potassium salt	25 mg
L1338	lucifer yellow iodoacetamide, dipotassium salt	25 mg
M1602	N^{α}-(3-maleimidylpropionyl)biocytin	25 mg
M395	8-methoxypyrene-1,3,6-trisulfonic acid, trisodium salt (MPTS)	100 mg
N21479	NeuroTrace® 435/455 blue fluorescent Nissl stain *solution in DMSO*	1 mL
N21480	NeuroTrace® 500/525 green fluorescent Nissl stain *solution in DMSO*	1 mL
N21481	NeuroTrace® 515/535 yellow fluorescent Nissl stain *solution in DMSO*	1 mL
N21482	NeuroTrace® 530/615 red fluorescent Nissl stain *solution in DMSO*	1 mL
N21483	NeuroTrace® 640/660 deep-red fluorescent Nissl stain *solution in DMSO*	1 mL
O12920	Oregon Green® 488 biocytin (biocytin Oregon Green® 488)	5 mg
O6146	Oregon Green® 488 carboxylic acid *5-isomer*	5 mg
O6135	Oregon Green® 500 carboxylic acid *5-isomer*	5 mg
O6138	Oregon Green® 514 carboxylic acid	5 mg
P12925	5-(pentafluorobenzoylamino)fluorescein (PFB-F)	5 mg
P1304MP	propidium iodide	100 mg
P21493	propidium iodide *FluoroPure™ grade*	100 mg
P349	1,3,6,8-pyrenetetrasulfonic acid, tetrasodium salt	100 mg
S1129	5-sulfofluorescein diacetate, sodium salt (SFDA)	25 mg
S359	sulforhodamine 101	25 mg
S1307	sulforhodamine B	5 g
S6957	sulforhodamine G	5 g
T1247	terbium(III) chloride, hexahydrate	1 g
T6931	tetrakis-(4-carboxyphenyl)porphine (TCPP)	5 mg
T6932	tetrakis-(4-sulfophenyl)porphine (TSPP)	5 mg
T12921	5-(and-6)-tetramethylrhodamine biocytin (biocytin TMR)	5 mg
T411	2-((trifluoroacetyl)acetyl)naphthalene (naphthoyltrifluoroacetone)	100 mg
T506	4-trimethylammonium-2,2,6,6-tetramethylpiperidine-1-oxyl iodide (CAT 1)	100 mg
T1323	true blue chloride	5 mg
X1525	*p*-xylene-bis-pyridinium bromide (DPX)	1 g

For current prices or to order online, visit probes.invitrogen.com

14.4 Fluorescent Lipophilic Tracers

Cell membranes provide a convenient conduit for loading live and fixed cells with lipophilic dyes. Not only can cells tolerate a high concentration of the lipophilic dye, but also lateral diffusion of the dye within the membrane can serve to stain the entire cell, even if the dye is applied locally. These properties have made lipophilic carbocyanine and aminostyryl dyes particularly important for anterograde and retrograde tracing in neuronal cells.[1,2] Lipophilic tracers are used to label cells,[3–5] organelles,[6,7] liposomes,[8] viruses[9] and lipoproteins[10] in a wide variety of long-term tracing applications, including cell transplantation, migration, adhesion and fusion studies. The distinguishing features of these carbocyanine and aminostyryl tracers are summarized in Table 14.3. Other lipophilic probes described in Chapter 13 have also been used as tracers for liposomes. For example, incorporation of a BODIPY® FL cholesterol derivative (C3927MP, Section 13.3) in liposomes is virtually irreversible and the dye-labeled liposomes have been conjugated to antibodies for immunotargeting applications.[11]

Table 14.3 — Summary of our lipophilic carbocyanine and aminostyryl tracers

Cat #	Probe *	Features of Carbocyanine or Aminostyryl Tracers
DiI and Analogs		
D282	DiIC$_{18}$(3) "DiI"	Red-orange–fluorescent lipophilic probe; widely used as a neuronal tracer
D3911	DiIC$_{18}$(3) "DiI"	Large-crystal form of D282 to facilitate direct application of crystals to membranes
D384	DiIC$_{16}$(3)	Shorter-chain DiI analog that may incorporate into membranes more easily than DiI
D383	DiIC$_{12}$(3)	Shorter-chain DiI analog that may incorporate into membranes more easily than DiI
D3899	*FAST* DiI™ oil	Unsaturated DiI analog that reportedly migrates ~50% faster than DiI within membranes
D7756	*FAST* DiI™	Solid form of D3899 to facilitate direct application of crystals to membranes
D3886	Δ^9-DiI oil	Unsaturated DiI analog that may migrate faster than DiI within membranes
C7000 C7001	CellTracker™ CM-DiI	Chloromethylated DiI analog with enhanced solubility in culture medium; potentially retained after fixation and permeabilization
D7779	5,5′-Ph$_2$-DiIC$_{18}$(3)	More lipophilic DiI analog with a higher quantum yield and longer-wavelength spectra (red-shifted ~20 nm)
D7777	SP-DiIC$_{18}$(3)	Anionic DiI analog with enhanced solubility in culture medium; potentially retained after fixation and permeabilization
D7776	DiIC$_{18}$(3)-DS	Anionic DiI analog with enhanced solubility in culture medium; potentially retained after fixation
DiD		
D307	DiIC$_{18}$(5) oil "DiD"	Much longer-wavelength DiI analog; useful in autofluorescent samples and as a second tracer in combination with DiI
D7757	DiIC$_{18}$(5) "DiD"	Solid form of D307 to facilitate direct application of crystals to membranes
D12730	DiIC$_{18}$(5)-DS	Anionic DiD analog with enhanced solubility in culture medium
DiR		
D12731	DiIC$_{18}$(7) "DiR"	DiI analog with absorption and emission in the near-infrared region, where many tissues are optically transparent
DiO and Analogs		
D275	DiOC$_{18}$(3) "DiO"	Yellow-green–fluorescent lipophilic probe; widely used as a second tracer in combination with DiI
D1125	DiOC$_{16}$(3)	Shorter-chain DiO analog that may incorporate into membranes more easily than DiO
D3898	*FAST* DiO™	Unsaturated DiO analog that reportedly migrates ~50% faster than DiO within membranes
D7778	SP-DiOC$_{18}$(3)	Anionic DiO analog with enhanced water solubility; potentially retained after fixation
DiA and Analogs		
D3883	4-Di-16-ASP "DiA"	Yellow-green–fluorescent lipophilic probe; useful as a second tracer with DiI
D3897	*FAST* DiA™ oil	Unsaturated DiA analog that may migrate faster than DiA within membranes
D7758	*FAST* DiA™	Solid form of D3897 to facilitate direct application of crystals to membranes
D291	4-Di-10-ASP	Shorter-chain DiA analog that may incorporate into membranes more easily than DiA

* Probe is in solid form unless otherwise specified.

Long-Chain Carbocyanines: DiI, DiO and Analogs

DiI, DiO, DiD and DiR

The lipophilic carbocyanines DiI ($DiIC_{18}(3)$, Figure 14.48), DiO ($DiOC_{18}(3)$, Figure 14.49), DiD ($DiIC_{18}(5)$, Figure 14.50) and DiR ($DiIC_{18}(7)$, Figure 14.51) are weakly fluorescent in water but highly fluorescent and quite photostable when incorporated into membranes (Figure 14.52). They have extremely high extinction coefficients (ε >125,000 $cm^{-1}M^{-1}$ at their longest-wavelength absorption maximum) though modest quantum yields, and short excited-state lifetimes (~1 nanosecond) in lipid environments. Once applied to cells, the dyes diffuse laterally within the plasma membrane, resulting in staining of the entire cell. Transfer of these probes between intact membranes is usually negligible. DiI and its analogs usually exhibit very low cell toxicity; however, moderate inhibition of electron transport chain activity has been reported for some analogs.[12]

DiI, DiO, DiD and DiR exhibit distinct orange, green, red and infrared fluorescence, respectively (Figure 13.43), thus facilitating multicolor imaging.[13] DiO (D275) and DiI (D282, D3911) can be used with standard fluorescein and rhodamine optical filters (Table 23.9), respectively. Iontophoretic application of these lipophilic dyes to nerve terminals at a single neuromuscular junction in living animals permits tracing of other synaptic terminals of the same motor unit.[14] The He–Ne laser–excitable DiD (D307, D7757) has much longer-wavelength excitation and emission spectra than those of DiI, providing a valuable alternative for labeling cells and tissues that have significant intrinsic fluorescence at wavelengths in the same range as DiI fluorescence (Figure 14.53). DiD was used as a population marker in a flow cytometric study that also employed indo-1 to monitor intracellular Ca^{2+} mobilization.[15] In an improved technique for tracking ocular blood flow, DiD was employed in conjunction with SYTO® 16 and SYTO® 59 nucleic acid stains (S7578, S11341; Section 8.1) to label red and white blood cells that could then be observed with a scanning laser ophthalmoscope.[16] Our heptamethine carbocyanine probe $DiIC_{18}(7)$ (DiR, D12731) has even further red-shifted spectra, with absorption and emission maxima in the near-infrared region (absorption/emission maxima = 748/780 nm in methanol, Figure 13.43). Because the fluorescence of this dye is invisible to the human eye, it must be detected using a CCD camera or other near-infrared photosensitive device. The high transmission of infrared light through cells and tissues and low level of autofluorescence in the infrared may make DiR particularly useful as an *in vivo* tracer for labeled cells and liposomes in living organisms. Photoconversion of diaminobenzidine (DAB) by lipid tracers, including DiI and DiO derivatives, produces an insoluble, electron-dense reaction product[14,17–20] (see Note 14.2 "Product Highlight: Fluorescent Probes for Photoconversion of Diaminobenzidine Reagents" in Section 14.3).

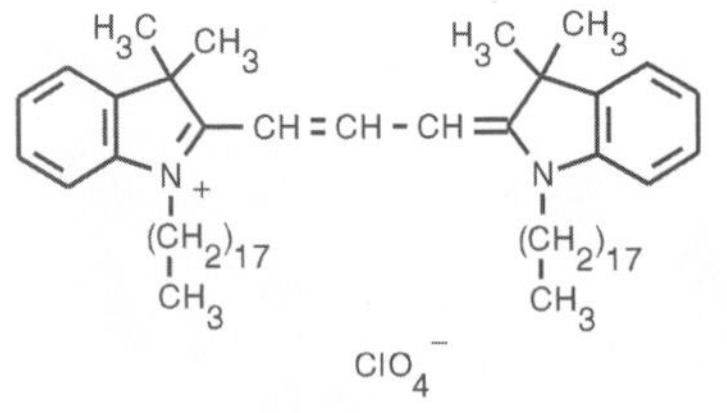

Figure 14.48 D282 1,1'-dioctadecyl-3,3,3',3'-tetramethylindocarbocyanine perchlorate ('DiI'; $DiIC_{18}(3)$).

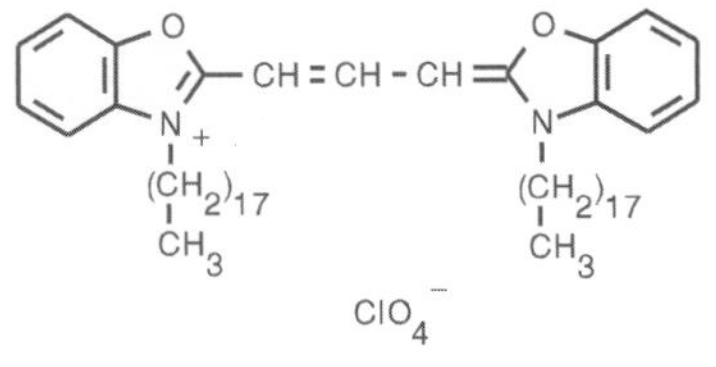

Figure 14.49 D275 3,3'-dioctadecyloxacarbocyanine perchlorate ('DiO'; $DiOC_{18}(3)$).

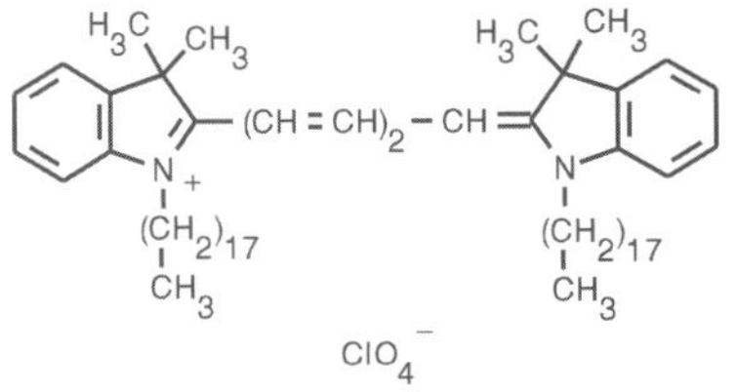

Figure 14.50 D307 1,1'-dioctadecyl-3,3,3',3'-tetramethylindodicarbocyanine perchlorate ('DiD' oil; $DiIC_{18}(5)$ oil).

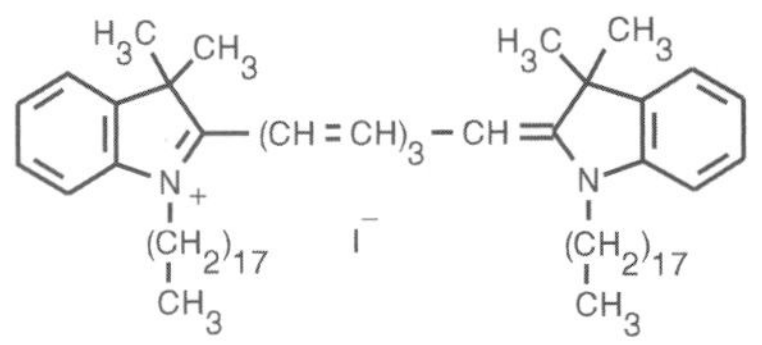

Figure 14.51 D12731 1,1'-dioctadecyl-3,3,3',3'-tetramethylindotricarbocyanine iodide ('DiR'; $DiIC_{18}(7)$).

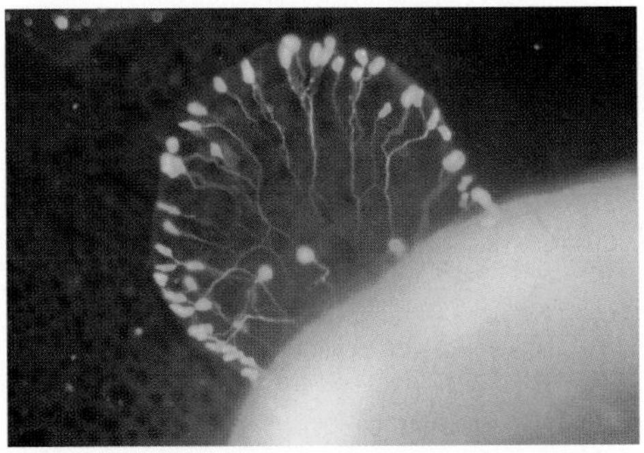

Figure 14.52 The rear fin of a squid embryo that has been labeled with $DiIC_{18}(3)$ (DiI; D282, D3911), showing selective staining of a population of ciliated sensory neurons whose cell bodies line the periphery of the fin. The dye was applied by soaking the embryos in a solution; no injection was used. Image contributed by Rachel Fink, Mount Holyoke College.

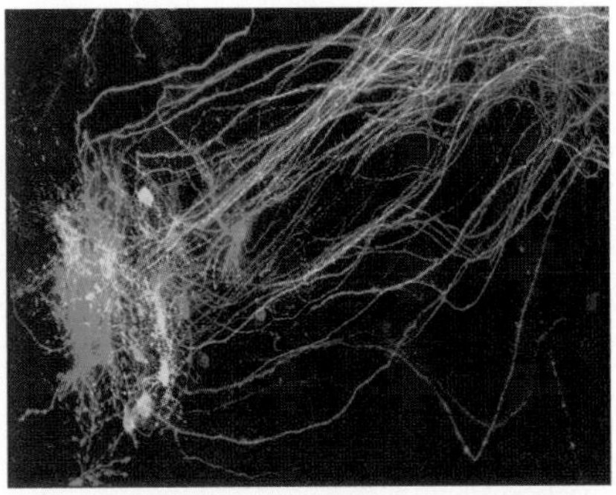

Figure 14.53 Pseudocolored confocal microscope image of retrogradely labeled neurons in the ventrobasal nucleus of the thalamus in newborn mouse. Paired dye deposits of DiI ($DiIC_{18}(3)$, D282, D3911; pseudocolored green) and DiD ($DiIC_{18}(5)$, D307, D7757; pseudocolored red) were injected into this 500 µm–thick section, which was then fixed with paraformaldehyde and incubated for two weeks at 37°C to allow retrograde dye transport to proceed. Image contributed by Ariel Agmon, West Virginia University.

Vybrant® DiI, DiO and DiD Cell-Labeling Solutions

The highly lipophilic nature of DiI, DiO and DiD has often posed an obstacle to uniform cellular labeling in aqueous culture media.[21] This technical difficulty has somewhat limited the use of these tracers in cell–cell fusion,[22,23] cellular adhesion [24,25] and migration [26] applications. The Vybrant® DiI cell-labeling solution (V22885) is a dye-delivery solution that can be added directly to normal culture media to uniformly label suspended or attached culture cells. The complementary Vybrant® DiO and DiD cell-labeling solutions (V22886, V22887) allow cell populations to be marked in distinctive fluorescent colors for identification after mixing (Figure 13.43, Figure 14.54). Cells that have fused or that have formed stable clusters can be identified by double labeling (Figure 14.55). Each 1 mM solution of DiI, DiO or DiD has been filtered through a 0.2 µm polycarbonate filter. All three cell-labeling solutions are also available in the Vybrant® Multicolor Cell-Labeling Kit (V22889). A Vybrant® CM-DiI labeling solution is also available (V22888, see below under CM-DiI).

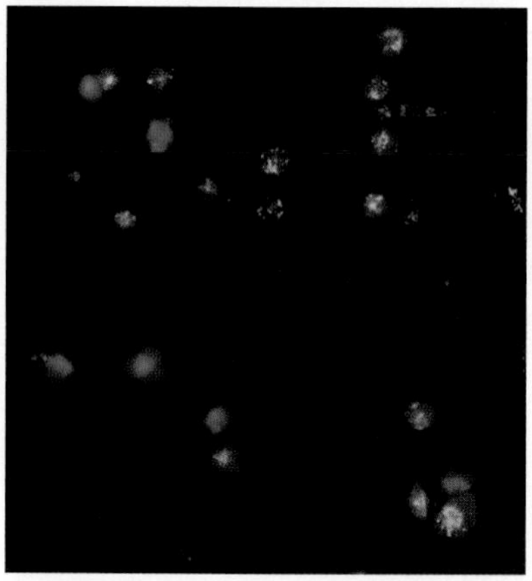

Figure 14.54 Three populations of P3X cells that were mixed after being separately labeled with the Vybrant® DiI, DiO and DiD cell-labeling solutions (V22885, V22886, V22887).

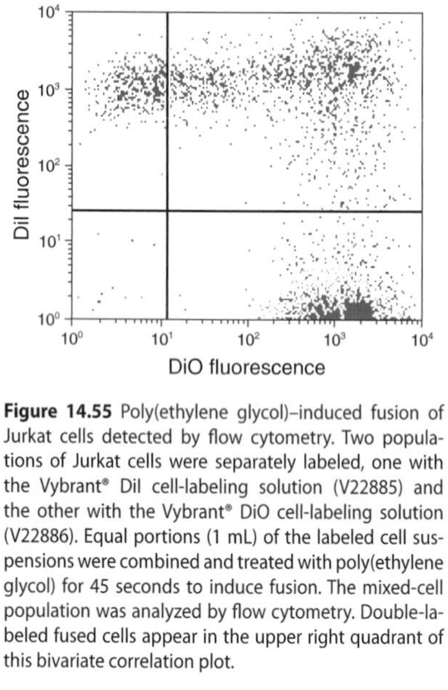

Figure 14.55 Poly(ethylene glycol)–induced fusion of Jurkat cells detected by flow cytometry. Two populations of Jurkat cells were separately labeled, one with the Vybrant® DiI cell-labeling solution (V22885) and the other with the Vybrant® DiO cell-labeling solution (V22886). Equal portions (1 mL) of the labeled cell suspensions were combined and treated with poly(ethylene glycol) for 45 seconds to induce fusion. The mixed-cell population was analyzed by flow cytometry. Double-labeled fused cells appear in the upper right quadrant of this bivariate correlation plot.

NeuroTrace® DiI, DiO and DiD Tissue-Labeling Pastes

NeuroTrace® DiI, DiO and DiD tissue-labeling pastes (N22880, N22881, N22882) consist of DiI, DiO and DiD, respectively, mixed into an inert, water-resistant gel. All three formulations are available in the convenient NeuroTrace® Multicolor Tissue-Labeling Kit (N22884). A NeuroTrace® CM-DiI tissue-labeling paste is also available (N22883, see below under CM-DiI). These pastes are ready to use as supplied and can be applied directly to live or fixed tissue specimens using the tip of a needle. This method of application improves the penetration of the dye into bundled neurons, labeling axons both on and below the surface. In similar situations, direct application of dye crystals or microinjection of concentrated solutions will only label neurons on the surface. This labeling method has also been found to increase the rate of dye transport by 50–80%.[27]

FAST *DiI™* and FAST *DiO™*

Diffusion of lipophilic carbocyanine tracers from the point of their application to the terminus of a neuron can take several days to weeks.[2] The diffusion process appears to be accelerated by introducing unsaturation in the alkyl tails of the probes. Molecular Probes' *FAST* DiI™[28–30] (D3899, D7756; Figure 14.56) and *FAST* DiO™[31] (D3898, Figure 14.57) have diunsaturated linoleyl ($C_{18:2}$) tails in place of the saturated octadecyl tails ($C_{18:0}$) of DiI and DiO. Migration of the unsaturated analogs is reported to be at least 50% faster than that of DiI and DiO.[32] *FAST* DiI™ and the shorter chain $DiIC_{12}(3)$ (D383) internalize during endocytic sorting of lipids and are mainly found in the endocytic recycling compartment, whereas the 16-carbon $DiIC_{16}(3)$ (D384) is delivered to late endosomes.[33] The perchlorate salt of *FAST* DiI™ does not crystallize and is a viscous oil (D3899); however, the 4-chlorobenzenesulfonate salt of *FAST* DiI™ (D7756) is a solid, making its crystals suitable for direct application to cells. We also offer a monounsaturated *cis*-9-octadecenyl ($C_{18:1}$) analog of DiI (Δ^9-DiI, D3886).

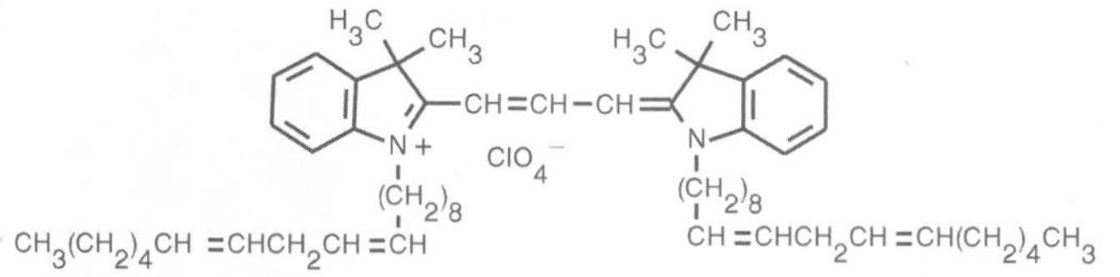

Figure 14.56 D3899 1,1′-dilinoleyl-3,3,3′,3′-tetramethylindocarbocyanine perchlorate (*FAST* DiI oil; $DiI\Delta^{9,12}$-$C_{18}(3)$, ClO_4).

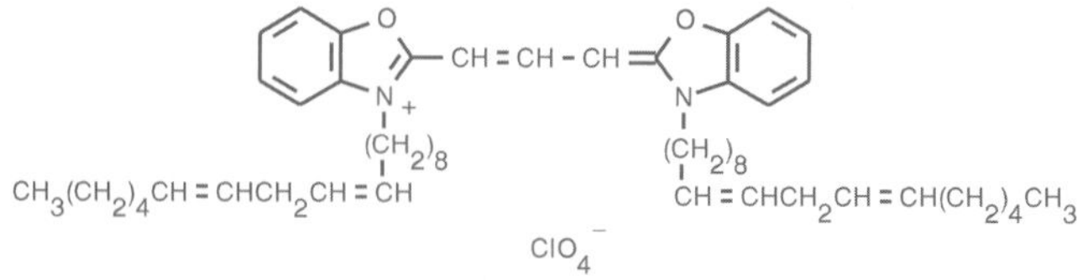

Figure 14.57 D3898 3,3′-dilinoleyloxacarbocyanine perchlorate (*FAST* DiO solid; $DiO\Delta^{9,12}$-$C_{18}(3)$, ClO_4).

Other DiO and DiI Analogs

Several other lipophilic carbocyanines are also useful tracers for labeling cell membranes. Some scientists find the slightly less lipophilic $DiIC_{12}(3)$ (D383), $DiIC_{16}(3)$ (D384) and $DiOC_{16}(3)$ (D1125) easier to load into cell suspensions than their C_{18} homologs. $DiIC_{16}(3)$ has been used in numerous tracing applications, including to measure:

- Cortical rotation during fertilization of frog eggs [34]
- Lipid diffusion in membranes by fluorescence recovery after photobleaching (FRAP) [35]
- Lipid flow during cell motility [36]
- Membrane fusion induced by electric fields [37]

The phenyl-substituted carbocyanine tracer 5,5′-Ph_2-$DiIC_{18}(3)$ (D7779) is more lipophilic than DiI and DiO but also significantly more fluorescent, at least in methanol. 5,5′-Ph_2-$DiIC_{18}(3)$ has spectra that fall between those of $DiIC_{18}(3)$ and $DiIC_{18}(5)$. This probe has potential for retrograde or anterograde neuronal tracing or other long-term tracing studies; however, we are not aware of it having been tested in these applications.

Neuronal Tracing Studies with DiI and DiO Analogs

DiI, DiO and DiD are widely used to label neuronal projections in live and fixed tissue. Our bibliography on DiI contains over 1000 papers on its applications. The dyes insert into the outer leaflet of the plasma membrane and diffuse laterally, producing detailed labeling of fine neuronal projections. DiI has been reported to diffuse about 6 mm/day in live tissue but more slowly in fixed specimens.[2] The dyes usually do not transfer from labeled to unlabeled cells, unless the membrane of the labeled cell is disrupted, and apparently do not transfer through gap junctions.

Motoneurons labeled with DiI have been reported to remain viable up to four weeks in culture and one year *in vivo*.[38] Staining of neurons in fixed tissue with DiI has been reported to persist for at least two years.[19,39] DiI and DiD can be used simultaneously for two-color tracing [13,40] (Figure 14.53) and as a fluorescence donor–acceptor pair in excited-state energy transfer studies.[41,42] Combinations of DiO, DiI, DiD and DiR may permit three- or even four-color measurements (Figure 13.43).

Cell labeling with the lipophilic carbocyanines is generally performed by direct application of a dye crystal or dye-coated paper, metal or glass probe or by microinjection onto single cells from a solution in dimethylformamide or dimethylformamide/ethanol.[43,44] A method has been described for iontophoretic loading of cells with DiI and other lipid tracers.[45] We also offer DiI in the form of extra-large crystals (D3911), which many researchers prefer for direct application to tissue. Detailed protocols for DiI labeling and confocal laser-scanning microscopy have been published.[46,47] DiI has also been used to mark sites of microinjection by coating the outside of the glass micropipette with the dye.[48]

An interesting paper [49] describes "DiOlistic labeling" of living or fixed cells and tissues using a "gene gun" to deliver pellets coated with lipophilic carbocyanine dyes DiO, DiI and DiD. This procedure permits rapid labeling at high densities with relatively high spatial resolution. By using combinations of dyes, these researchers visualized at least seven easily distinguishable colors.

Long-Term Cell Tracing with Membrane Tracers

Lipophilic carbocyanine tracers like DiI are also ideal labels for long-term cell tracing *in vivo* and *in vitro*,[50] including studies of cell migration, transplantation,[51] adhesion and fusion.[52] The presence of DiI and DiO in the cell membrane does not appreciably affect cell viability, development or other basic physiological properties.[2,21] Labeling of cell suspensions for long-term tracing is typically performed from aqueous dispersions of the dyes.[53] Stock solutions of most of the tracers may be prepared in alcohol or dimethylsulfoxide (DMSO) and then added to cell suspensions. Several analogs of DiI that are more soluble in culture medium should facilitate this method of labeling (see below). Alternatively, the endoplasmic reticulum (ER) has been selectively labeled by microinjecting sea urchin eggs with DiI from a solution in soybean oil, enabling researchers to follow ER reorganization during fertilization.[6]

Tissue Processing and Electron Microscopy with Long-Chain Carbocyanines

Methods have been developed to allow immunofluorescent labeling of tissue containing neurons stained with DiI.[54] Polyacrylamide has been employed to embed DiI-stained brain tissue for vibratome sectioning [55] — a method that has been reported to preserve DiI labeling better than cryostat sectioning.[56] Also, see below for a discussion of some DiI and DiO analogs that may be better retained through fixation and permeabilization procedures.

DiI and DiO Analogs, Including Membrane Tracers Retained through Fixation

CM-DiI

CellTracker™ CM-DiI (C7000, C7001) is a DiI derivative that is somewhat more water-soluble than $DiIC_{18}(3)$, thus facilitating the preparation of staining solutions for cell suspensions and fixed cells. In addition to its improved solubility in culture medium, CellTracker™ CM-DiI contains a thiol-reactive chloromethyl moiety (Figure 14.58) that allows the dye to covalently bind to cellular thiols. Thus, unlike other membrane stains, the label is well retained in some cells

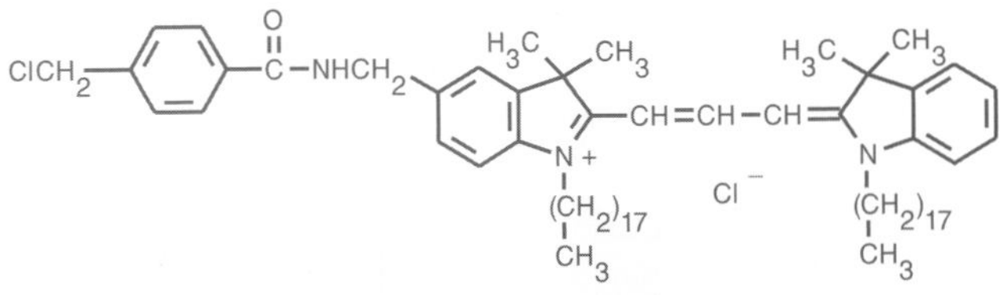

Figure 14.58 C7000 CellTracker™ CM-DiI.

throughout fixation and permeabilization steps[57,58] (Figure 14.59, Figure 14.60). Membrane staining with CellTracker™ CM-DiI persists following routine paraffin processing.[57] CellTracker™ CM-DiI is particularly useful in experiments that combine membrane labeling with subsequent immunohistochemical analysis, fluorescence *in situ* hybridization or electron microscopy.[59] As examples, CM-DiI was used for combined neuronal tract tracing and immunohistochemistry in zebrafish (Figure 14.61), for lineage tracing in dorsal epithelial somites[60] and for studying the interaction of neuronal microtubule-associated protein tau with the neural plasma membrane.[58] CM-DiI labeling of lymphocytes has been used to trace their circulation following reinfusion.[57,61] Similarly, cationic liposome complexes of DNA have been labeled with CM-DiI to identify their organ and cellular distribution following injection into mice.[62,63]

In addition to providing CM-DiI as a 1 mg solid (C7001) or specially packaged as a set of 20 vials, each containing 50 µg of CM-DiI, we have available the Vybrant® CM-DiI cell-labeling solution (V22888) and NeuroTrace® CM-DiI tissue-labeling paste (N22883) for the most efficient labeling of cell suspension and tissues, respectively, with this useful aldehyde-fixable tracer.

Sulfonated Carbocyanines

Because of poor solubility in water, it is often difficult to load the long-chain carbocyanine dyes such as DiI, DiO and PKH dyes into cells in suspension. For example, to prevent dye precipitation, labeling with the PKH dyes requires the use of special osmolarity regulating agents and the absence of any salt in the staining buffer.[50] To facilitate the staining of cells with long-chain carbocyanine dyes, we have developed sulfonated cyanine dyes[64] — SP-DiIC$_{18}$(3)[65] (D7777), SP-DiOC$_{18}$(3) (D7778), DiIC$_{18}$(3)-DS[66] (D7776) and DiIC$_{18}$(5)-DS (D12730) — that retain the 18-carbon lipophilic chains of DiI, DiD and DiO but exhibit improved solubility in culture medium. Cells can be labeled with these dyes by simply diluting a DMSO stock solution of the dye to a labeling concentration of 1–10 µM in unmodified culture medium. We have determined that these sulfonated dyes are completely soluble at 20 µM for at least one hour in Dulbecco's phosphate-buffered saline and Hanks' balanced salt solution; aggregation begins after a few hours in solution. Uptake of the anionic carbocyanine dyes in live cells is usually slower than that of cationic carbocyanine dyes, and the resulting staining patterns may be quite different.

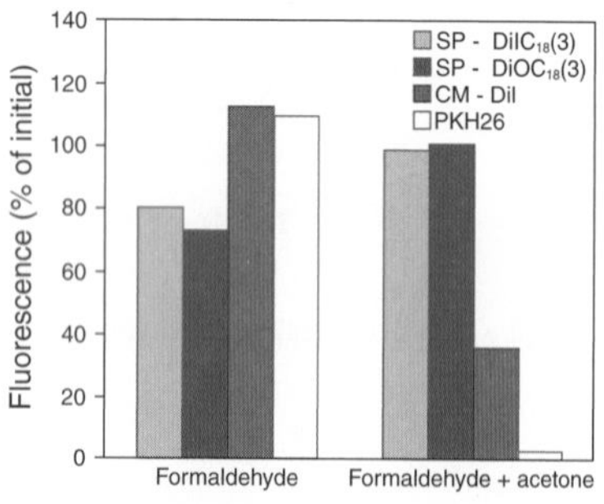

Figure 14.59 Persistence of lipophilic tracer fluorescence following fixation. Cultured human B cells were stained with 20 µM SP-DiOC$_{18}$(3) (D7778), SP-DiIC$_{18}$(3) (D7777), CM-DiI (C7000, C7001) or PKH26 and then fixed with 3.7% formaldehyde or 3.7% formaldehyde + acetone. The fixed cells were analyzed by flow cytometry to generate a comparison of their fluorescence with that of the original live-cell population.

The negatively charged sulfonate groups in the dyes also reduce the tendency of the dyes to aggregate in the membranes, which is a major cause of fluorescence quenching; thus, the fluorescence quantum yield of the bound dyes may be greater than that of DiI and DiO. In addition, the higher molar absorptivities of SP-DiIC$_{18}$(3) and especially SP-DiOC$_{18}$(3) relative to those of DiI and DiO make these dyes brighter. Therefore, compared with other carbocyanine membrane probes, these sulfonated dyes may be preferred when cells cannot tolerate excess dye or osmolarity-regulating reagents or when a subsequent fixation and lipid extraction step is required (see below). However, like DiI, DiO and the PKH dyes, these sulfonated carbocyanines also stain intracellular membranes. Also, although we have seen good retention of these anionic carbocyanine dyes in cells, their greater water solubility could result in some increase in dye transfer between cells.

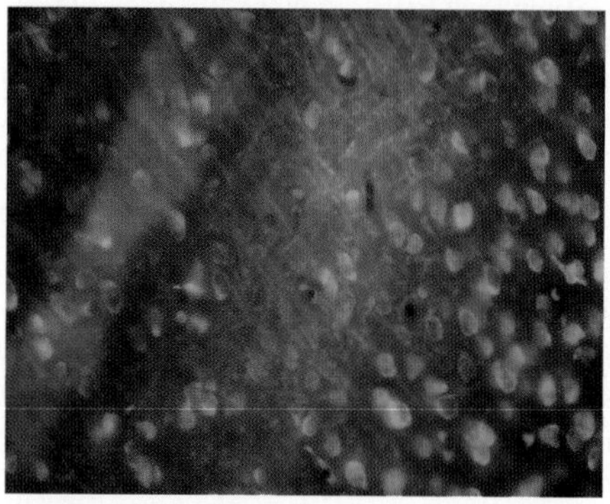

Figure 14.60 Neural somata from a mouse brain section labeled with NeuroTrace® 500/525 green-fluorescent Nissl stain (N21480). Nuclei are labeled with DAPI (D1306, D3571, D21490). Myelin and other lipophilic areas are illustrated with the aid of the red-orange fluorescence from CellTracker™ CM-DiI (C7000, C7001). The image is a composite of three micrographs acquired using filters appropriate for fluorescein, tetramethylrhodamine and DAPI.

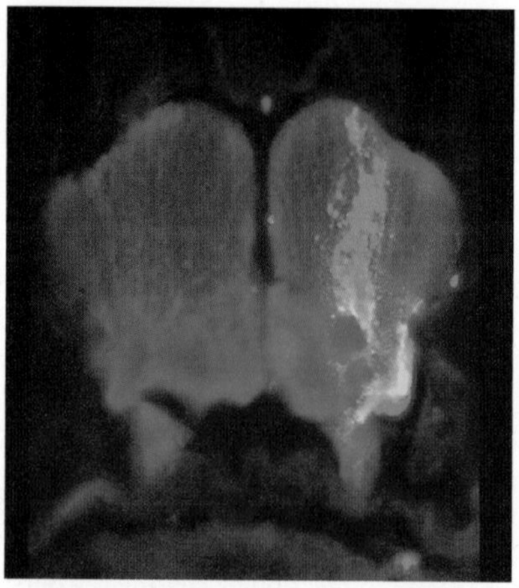

Figure 14.61 A 30 µm–thick section of a zebrafish embryo stained with CellTracker™ CM-DiI (C7000, C7001) prior to immunohistochemical analysis. A one-day-old zebrafish embryo was immobilized and impaled in the hindbrain with a microelectrode filled with 1 mg/mL CellTracker™ CM-DiI in 95% ethanol. One day later, the brain was fixed, embedded, frozen in liquid nitrogen and sectioned on a cryostat. After blocking with 0.1% Triton X-100 in PBS containing 2% BSA and 2% normal goat serum, the 30 µm–thick section was incubated with primary anti-glial antibody in conjunction with fluorescein goat anti–mouse IgG antibody. This section was then viewed sequentially through optical filter sets appropriate for rhodamine and fluorescein, and the resulting images were superimposed. The image was contributed by William Trevarrow, Beckman Institute, California Institute of Technology.

Some applications require retention of the membrane stain in place following aldehyde-mediated fixation and lipid extraction. In contrast to labeling with DiI, DiO or the PKH dyes,[52] cell labeling with some of these sulfonated carbocyanines appears to be compatible with standard aldehyde-based fixation methods and acetone treatment, at least in some cell lines. Although the mechanism for cell retention of the sulfonated carbocyanines has not been determined, we have observed excellent retention of staining of human B cells with SP-DiIC_{18}(3) and SP-DiOC_{18}(3), whereas virtually all of the PKH26 dye (which is structurally identical to DiIC_{18}(3)) is lost during the lipid extraction step (Figure 14.59). CM-DiI (C7000, C7001, N22883, V22888; see above) is also well retained during this processing. Furthermore, we have observed that acetone treatment actually enhances the fluorescence of some cells stained with SP-DiIC_{18}(3) and especially with SP-DiOC_{18}(3), a phenomenon that has not been seen with other carbocyanine-derived membrane stains. Although these properties have not yet been extensively tested, they could make SP-DiIC_{18}(3) and SP-DiOC_{18}(3) particularly useful for immunochemistry and other histochemical studies that may require tissue dehydration, clearing and membrane extraction.

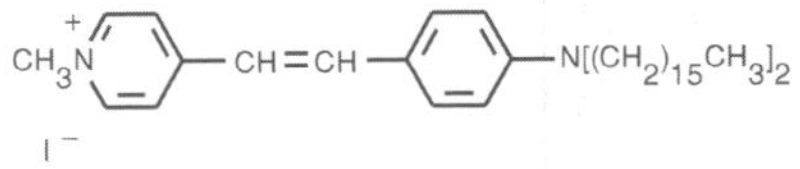

Figure 14.62 D3883 4-(4-(dihexadecylamino)styryl)-*N*-methylpyridinium iodide (DiA; 4-Di-16-ASP).

DiA and *FAST* DiA™

Reports from several researchers indicate that DiA (4-Di-16-ASP, D3883, Figure 14.62) is a better neuronal tracer than DiO for multicolor labeling with DiI.[67–69] DiA diffuses more rapidly in membranes and is more soluble than DiO, thus facilitating cell labeling. For example, DiA and DiI have been used together to investigate the interactions between dorsal root axons and their targets[70] and axon outgrowth in the retina.[71] DiA can be excited between 440 nm and 500 nm, and its maximum emission in DOPC vesicles is at ~590 nm (Figure 13.46) (red-orange fluorescence). Its fluorescence in cells, however, is usually bright green to yellow-green (depending on the optical filter set used). The polyunsaturated *FAST* DiA™, offered in both oil (D3897) and crystalline solid (D7758) form, may diffuse faster in membranes than DiA. The C_{10} analog of DiA, 4-Di-10-ASP (D291), has been used as a retrograde tracer to monitor injury-induced degradation of rat neurons *in vivo* and the role of microglial cells in removing debris resulting from natural and axotomy-induced neuronal cell death[72–74] (Figure 14.63). 4-Di-10-ASP staining of microglia can persist for at least 12 months and can be used for DAB photoconversion[72] (see Note 14.2 "Product Highlight: Fluorescent Probes for Photoconversion of Diaminobenzidine Reagents" in Section 14.3). Axonal outgrowth of retinal ganglion cells stained with 4-Di-10-ASP has been observed.[75]

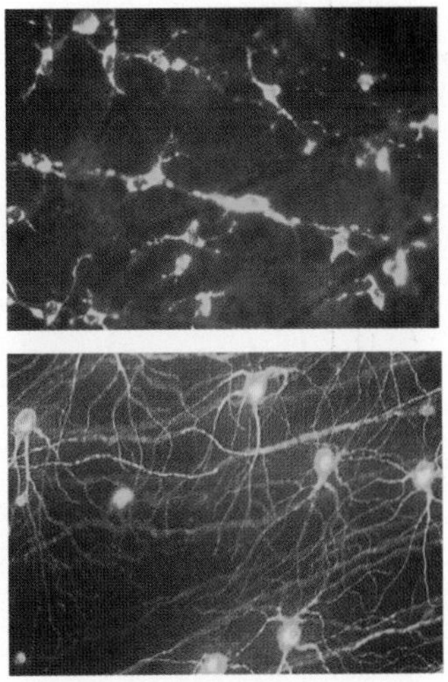

Figure 14.63 Rat retinal ganglion cells that have been allowed to regenerate for two months after transection into a grafted peripheral nerve piece and then labeled with 4-Di-10-ASP (D291), which is retrogradely transported within the regenerated axons and finest dendrites (bottom panel). Microglial cells in the retina were transcellularly labeled with 4-Di-10-ASP after phagocytosing degenerated ganglion cells (top panel). The images were contributed by Solon Thanos, University of Tübingen School of Medicine.

Lipophilic Tracer Sampler Kit

For researchers wishing to investigate the suitability of this group of membrane probes for a particular application, we have prepared a Lipophilic Tracer Sampler Kit (L7781). This kit contains 1 mg samples of nine different membrane stains, including both relatively new and well-established tracers:

- DiIC_{18}(3) (DiI), DiIC_{18}(3)-DS, SP-DiIC_{18}(3), 5,5′-Ph_2-DiIC_{18}(3)
- DiOC_{18}(3) (DiO), SP-DiOC_{18}(3)
- DiIC_{18}(5) (DiD), DiIC_{18}(7) (DiR)
- 4-Di-16-ASP (DiA)

Octadecyl Rhodamine B

Octadecyl rhodamine B (R18, O246) is a lipophilic cation that has been extensively used as a membrane probe[76–79] (see Note 13.1 "Technical Focus: Lipid-Mixing Assays of Membrane Fusion" in Section 13.2). Viral particles that have been labeled with high concentrations of R18 have fluorescence that is highly self-quenched; fusion of the particle with cell membranes relieves the quenching, making the receptor cell highly fluorescent.[77,80,81] Dequenching of the fluorescence of R18 is a useful method for following a variety of other processes that involve large changes in the membrane volume accessible to the probe, including:

- Disintegration of R18-labeled low-density lipoproteins (LDL) in lysosomes[82]
- Fusion of lysosomes with late endosomes[83]
- Fusion of endocytic vesicles of reticulocytes with liposomes[84]
- Receptor clustering on cell surfaces[85]

Plasma Membrane Stains

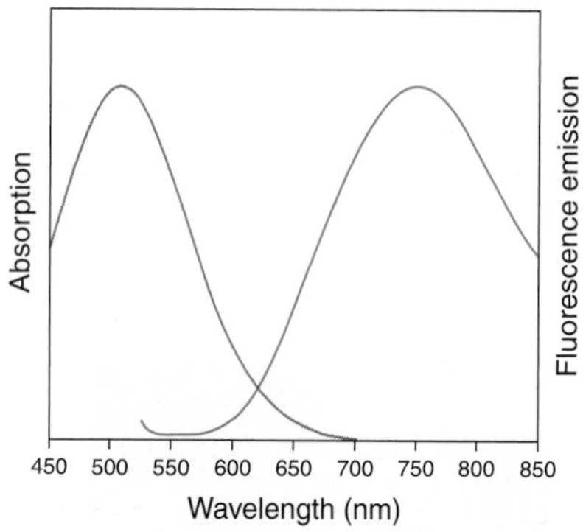

Figure 14.64 Absorption and fluorescence emission spectra of FM® 4-64 bound to zwitterionic detergent (CHAPS) micelles.

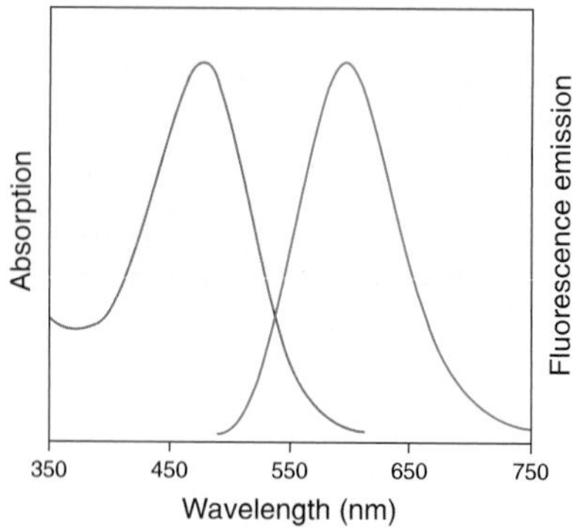

Figure 14.65 Absorption and fluorescence emission spectra of FM® 1-43 bound to phospholipid bilayer membranes.

Although the lipophilic cyanine and styryl dyes described above are useful for staining cell membranes, they are relatively difficult to apply to cells and they do eventually internalize, staining all cell membranes. In contrast, FM® 1-43 (T3163, T35356), FM® 4-64 (T3166, T13320) and RH 414 (T1111) are easily applied to cells, where they bind rapidly and reversibly to the plasma membrane with strong fluorescence enhancement.[86–88] These three probes have large Stokes shifts and can be excited by the argon-ion laser. Because we have found that small differences in the polarity of these probes can play a large role in their rates of uptake and their retention properties, we have introduced FM® 5-95 (T23360), a slightly less lipophilic analog of FM® 4-64 with essentially identical spectroscopic properties.

FM® 1-43 and FM® 4-64

FM® 1-43 is efficiently excited with standard fluorescein optical filters (Table 23.9) but poorly excited with standard tetramethylrhodamine optical filters. FM® 1-43 has been used to outline membranes in sea urchin eggs.[89] This styryl dye has also proven extremely valuable for identifying actively firing neurons and for investigating the mechanisms of activity-dependent vesicle cycling in widely different species[90–94] (Section 16.1). We offer FM® 1-43 in a 1 mg vial (T3163) or specially packaged in 10 vials of 100 µg each (T35356).

FM® 1-43FX is an FM® 1-43 analog that has been modified to contain an aliphatic amine. This modification makes the probe fixable with aldehyde-based fixatives including formaldehyde and glutaraldehyde. FM® 1-43FX has been used to study synaptic vesicle cycling in cone photoreceptor terminals[90] and to investigate the functional maturation of glutamatergic synapses.[95] FM® 1-43FX is available specially packaged in 10 vials of 100 µg each (F35355).

Membranes labeled with FM 4-64 exhibit long-wavelength red fluorescence (Figure 14.64) that can be distinguished from the green fluorescence of FM® 1-43 (Figure 14.65) staining with the proper optical filter sets, thus permitting two-color observation of membrane recycling in real time.[96,97] FM® 4-64 selectively stains yeast vacuolar membranes and is an important tool for visualizing vacuolar organelle morphology and dynamics and for studying the endocytic pathway in yeast[98] (Section 12.3). In addition, FM® 4-64 staining has been used to visualize membrane migration and fusion during *Bacillus subtilis* sporulation — movements that can be correlated with the translocation of green-fluorescent protein–labeled proteins[99] (Figure 14.66, Figure 16.21). We offer FM® 4-64 in a 1 mg vial (T3166) or specially packaged in 10 vials of 100 µg each (T13320).

RH 414

Membranes stained with RH 414 (T1111) exhibit orange fluorescence when observed through a longpass optical filter that permits passage of light beyond 510 nm.[88,100,101] In a confocal laser-scanning microscopy study, the subcellular distribution of L-type Ca^{2+} channels in olfactory bulb neurons was determined using intensity ratio measurements of the green fluorescence of DM-BODIPY® dihydropyridine (D7443, Section 16.3) to the red fluorescence of RH 414–stained plasma membranes[102] (Figure 16.37). In this method, staining of the plasma membrane by RH 414 was used to control for optical artifacts and differences in membrane surface area in the optical section. RH 414 has also been used as to follow vacuolization of the transverse tubules of frog skeletal muscle[103] and to measure membrane potential (Chapter 22).

NanoOrange® Reagent

The NanoOrange® protein quantitation reagent (N6666, Section 9.2), which is essentially nonfluorescent in aqueous solution, binds to the lipophilic coating around proteins in SDS gels, resulting in bright orange fluorescence.[104] The NanoOrange® reagent has also been used to rapidly stain flagella of live marine bacteria in seawater.[105] From our experience with the NanoOrange® reagent, the dye may also be useful as a general nontoxic stain for plasma membranes.

References

1. Brain Res Bull 51, 11 (2000); **2.** Trends Neurosci 12, 333 (1989); **3.** Neuron 13, 813 (1994); **4.** Biotechniques 13, 580 (1992); **5.** Development 106, 809 (1989); **6.** J Cell Biol 114, 929 (1991); **7.** J Struct Biol 105, 154 (1990); **8.** J Membr Biol 109, 221 (1989); **9.** Cytometry 14, 16 (1993); **10.** J Cell Biol 90, 595 (1981); **11.** Proc Natl Acad Sci U S A 94, 8795 (1997); **12.** Biochem Pharmacol 49, 1303 (1995); **13.** J Neurosci 15, 549 (1995); **14.** J Neurosci Methods 93, 13 (1999); **15.** Science 257, 96 (1992); **16.** Biophotonics Int 6, 56 (1999); **17.** J Neurosci 14, 6815 (1994); **18.** Microsc Res Tech 24, 2 (1993); **19.** J Histochem Cytochem 38, 725 (1990); **20.** Neuroscience 28, 3 (1989); **21.** J Cell Biol 103, 171 (1986); **22.** J Cell Biol 135, 63 (1996); **23.** Cytometry 21, 160 (1995); **24.** J Biol Chem 273, 33354 (1998); **25.** J Cell Biol 136, 1109 (1997); **26.** Anticancer Res 18, 4181 (1998); **27.** H. Richard Koerber, University of Pittsburgh School of Medicine, personal communication; **28.** Neuroreport 8, 3965 (1997); **29.** Biophys J 70, 988 (1996); **30.** J Cell Biol 134, 1427 (1996); **31.** Neuron 17, 91 (1996); **32.** Andrea Elberger, University of Tennessee, personal communication; **33.** J Cell Biol 144, 1271 (1999); **34.** J Cell Biol 114, 1017 (1991); **35.** J Cell Biol 103, 1745 (1986); **36.** Science 247, 1229 (1990); **37.** Biochemistry 29, 8337 (1990); **38.** J Comp Neurol 302, 729 (1990); **39.** Exp Neurol 102, 92 (1988); **40.** J Cell Biol 126, 519 (1994); **41.** Chem Phys Lett 159, 231 (1989); **42.** Thin Solid Films 132, 55 (1985); **43.** Neuron 7, 819 (1991); **44.** J Neurosci 10, 3947 (1990); **45.** Methods Cell Biol 51, 147 (1996); **46.** Three-Dimensional Confocal Microscopy, Stevens JK, Mills LR, Trogadis JE, Eds. pp. 325–351 (1994); **47.** Neuroscience Protocols, Wouterlood FG, Ed. 93-050-16, pp. 01–20 (1993); **48.** J 75, 2558 (1998); **49.** Neuron 27, 219 (2000); **50.** US 4,762,701; **51.** Cell Transplant 6, 455 (1997); **52.** Methods Cell Biol 33, 469 (1990); **53.** Histochemistry 97, 329 (1992); **54.** J Histochem Cytochem 38, 735 (1990); **55.** J Neurosci Methods 42, 65 (1992); **56.** J Neurosci Methods 42, 45 (1992); **57.** J Immunol Methods 194, 181 (1996); **58.** J Cell Biol 131, 1327 (1995); **59.** Science 278, 474 (1997); **60.** Development 130, 4325 (2003); **61.** Blood 91, 1653 (1998); **62.** Am J Physiol 273, H387 (1997); **63.** J Biol Chem 272, 1117 (1997); **64.** Bioorg Med Chem Lett 6, 1479 (1996); **65.** J Cell Biol 147, 105 (1999); **66.** Blood 96, 1180 (2000); **67.** J Neurosci 15, 3475 (1995); **68.** J Neurosci 15, 990 (1995); **69.** Trends Neurosci 13, 14 (1990); **70.** J Neurosci 12, 3494 (1992); **71.** Vis Neurosci 10, 117 (1993); **72.** Trends Neurosci 17, 177 (1994); **73.** J Neurosci 13, 455 (1993); **74.** Eur J Neurosci 3, 1189 (1991); **75.** J Neurosci 15, 5514 (1995); **76.** Biochemistry 33, 1820 (1994); **77.** Biochim Biophys Acta 1191, 375 (1994); **78.** Techniques in Somatic Cell Genetics, Shay JW, Ed. pp. 101–109 (1982); **79.** J Cell Sci 28, 167 (1977); **80.** Biochem J 300, 347 (1994); **81.** J Biol Chem 269, 5467 (1994); **82.** Eur J Cell Biol 59, 116 (1992); **83.** J Cell Biol 126, 1173 (1994); **84.** J Biol Chem 270, 17823 (1995); **85.** Biophys J 67, 1280 (1994); **86.** EMBO J 12, 5209 (1993); **87.** J Neurosci 13, 834 (1993); **88.** Science 255, 200 (1992); **89.** J Cell Biol 131, 1183 (1995); **90.** Neuron 41, 755 (2004); **91.** J Biol Chem 275, 15279 (2000); **92.** J Neurochem 73, 2227 (1999); **93.** Annu Rev Neurosci 22, 1 (1999); **94.** Proc R Soc Lond B Biol Sci 255, 61 (1994); **95.** Neuron 29, 469 (2001); **96.** J Cell Biol 131, 679 (1995); **97.** J Neurosci 15, 8246 (1995); **98.** J Cell Biol 128, 779 (1995); **99.** Proc Natl Acad Sci U S A 96, 14553 (1999); **100.** J Neurosci 15, 6327 (1995); **101.** J Neurosci 12, 363 (1992); **102.** J Neurosci Methods 59, 183 (1995); **103.** J Muscle Res Cell Motil 16, 401 (1995); **104.** Biotechniques 34, 850 (2003); **105.** Appl Environ Microbiol 66, 3632 (2000).

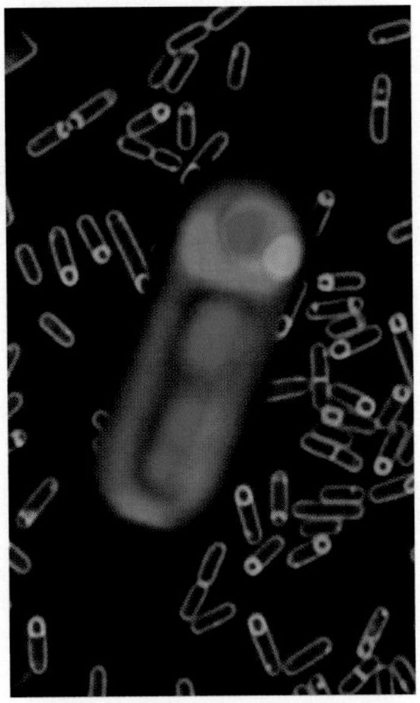

Figure 14.66 The morphology of sporulating *Bacillus subtilis* in the early stages of forespore engulfment. The membranes and chromosomes of both the forespore and the larger mother cell are stained with FM® 4-64 (red; T3166, T13320) and DAPI (blue, D1306, D3571, D21490), respectively. The small green-fluorescent patch indicates the localization of a GFP fusion to SPoIIIE, a protein essential for translocation of the forespore chromosome that may also regulate membrane fusion events (see Proc Natl Acad Sci U S A 96, 14553 (1999)). The background contains sporangia at various stages in the engulfment process stained with MitoTracker® Green FM (green, M7514) and FM® 4-64 (red).

Data Table — 14.4 Fluorescent Lipophilic Tracers

Cat #	MW	Storage	Soluble	Abs	EC	Em	Solvent	Notes
C7000	1051.50	F,D,L	DMSO, EtOH	553	134,000	570	MeOH	
C7001	1051.50	F,D,L	DMSO, EtOH	553	134,000	570	MeOH	
D275	881.72	L	DMSO, DMF	484	154,000	501	MeOH	
D282	933.88	L	DMSO, EtOH	549	148,000	565	MeOH	
D291	618.73	L	DMSO, EtOH	492	53,000	612	MeOH	1
D307	959.92	L	DMSO, EtOH	644	260,000	665	MeOH	2
D383	765.56	L	DMSO, EtOH	549	144,000	565	MeOH	3
D384	877.77	L	DMSO, EtOH	549	148,000	565	MeOH	
D1125	825.61	L	DMSO, DMF	484	156,000	501	MeOH	
D3883	787.05	L	DMSO, EtOH	491	52,000	613	MeOH	1
D3886	925.49	F,L,AA	DMSO, EtOH	549	144,000	564	MeOH	2
D3897	835.09	F,L,AA	DMSO, EtOH	492	49,000	612	MeOH	1, 2
D3898	873.65	F,L,AA	DMSO, DMF	484	138,000	499	MeOH	
D3899	925.82	F,L,AA	DMSO, EtOH	549	143,000	564	MeOH	2
D3911	933.88	L	DMSO, EtOH	549	148,000	565	MeOH	
D7756	1017.97	F,L,AA	DMSO, EtOH	549	148,000	564	MeOH	
D7757	1052.08	L	DMSO, EtOH	644	193,000	663	MeOH	
D7758	899.80	F,L,AA	DMSO, EtOH	492	41,000	612	MeOH	1
D7766	1091.67	L	DMSO, EtOH	558	128,000	575	MeOH	
D7776	993.54	L	DMSO, EtOH	555	144,000	570	MeOH	
D7777	1145.73	L	DMSO, EtOH	556	164,000	573	MeOH	
D7778	1115.55	L	DMSO, EtOH	497	175,000	513	MeOH	
D7779	1022.08	L	DMSO, EtOH	576	140,000	599	MeOH	
D12730	1019.58	L	DMSO, EtOH	650	247,000	670	MeOH	
D12731	1013.41	L	DMSO, EtOH	748	270,000	780	MeOH	
F6999	1017.06	L	DMSO, EtOH	553	133,000	570	MeOH	
F35355	560.09	D,L	H_2O, DMSO	510	50,000	626	MeOH	1

Data Table — 14.4 Fluorescent Lipophilic Tracers — continued

Cat #	MW	Storage	Soluble	Abs	EC	Em	Solvent	Notes
N22880	933.88	L	see Notes	549	148,000	565	MeOH	4
N22881	881.72	L	see Notes	484	154,000	501	MeOH	4
N22882	1052.08	L	see Notes	644	260,000	665	MeOH	4
N22883	1051.50	F,L	see Notes	553	134,000	570	MeOH	4
O246	731.50	F,DD,L	DMSO, EtOH	556	125,000	578	MeOH	3
T1111	581.48	D,L	DMSO, EtOH	532	55,000	716	MeOH	5
T3163	611.55	D,L	H_2O, DMSO	510	56,000	626	MeOH	1, 6
T3166	607.51	D,L	H_2O, DMSO	558	48,000	734	$CHCl_3$	7
T13320	607.51	D,L	H_2O, DMSO	558	46,000	734	$CHCl_3$	7
T23360	565.43	D,L	H_2O, DMSO	560	43,000	734	$CHCl_3$	7
T35356	611.55	D,L	H_2O, DMSO	510	56,000	626	MeOH	1, 6
V22885	933.88	L	see Notes	549	148,000	565	MeOH	8
V22886	881.72	L	see Notes	484	154,000	501	MeOH	8
V22887	1052.08	L	see Notes	644	193,000	663	MeOH	8
V22888	1051.50	F,L	see Notes	553	134,000	570	MeOH	8

For definitions of the contents of this data table, see "Navigating *The Handbook*" in the introductory pages.

Notes

1. Abs and Em of styryl dyes are at shorter wavelengths in membrane environments than in reference solvents such as methanol. The difference is typically 20 nm for absorption and 80 nm for emission, but varies considerably from one dye to another. Styryl dyes are generally nonfluorescent in water.
2. This product is intrinsically a liquid or an oil at room temperature.
3. This product is intrinsically a sticky gum at room temperature.
4. This product consists of a tracer dye mixed into an inert gel for direct application to tissues. Molecular weight and spectroscopic data are for the free dye.
5. RH 414 Abs ~500 nm, Em ~635 nm when bound to phospholipid bilayer membranes.
6. FM® 1-43 Abs = 479 nm, Em = 598 nm bound to phospholipid bilayer membranes. Em = 565 nm bound to synaptosomal membranes (Neuron 12, 1235 (1994)).
7. FM® 4-64 and FM® 5-95 are nonfluorescent in water. For two-color imaging in GFP-expressing cells, these dyes can be excited at 568 nm with emission detection at 690–730 nm (Am J Physiol Cell Physiol 281, C624 (2001)).
8. This product is supplied as a ready-made staining solution.

Product List — 14.4 Fluorescent Lipophilic Tracers

Cat #	Product Name	Unit Size
C7001	CellTracker™ CM-DiI	1 mg
C7000	CellTracker™ CM-DiI *special packaging*	20 x 50 µg
D7766	5,5′-dibromo-1,1′-dioctadecyl-3,3,3′,3′-tetramethylindocarbocyanine perchlorate (Br_2-DiIC_{18}(3))	5 mg
D291	4-(4-(didecylamino)styryl)-*N*-methylpyridinium iodide (4-Di-10-ASP)	25 mg
D383	1,1′-didodecyl-3,3,3′,3′-tetramethylindocarbocyanine perchlorate (DiIC_{12}(3))	100 mg
D3883	4-(4-(dihexadecylamino)styryl)-*N*-methylpyridinium iodide (DiA; 4-Di-16-ASP)	25 mg
D1125	3,3′-dihexadecyloxacarbocyanine perchlorate (DiOC_{16}(3))	25 mg
D384	1,1′-dihexadecyl-3,3,3′,3′-tetramethylindocarbocyanine perchlorate (DiIC_{16}(3))	100 mg
D7758	4-(4-(dilinoleylamino)styryl)-*N*-methylpyridinium 4-chlorobenzenesulfonate (*FAST* DiA™ solid; DiΔ^{9,12}-C_{18}ASP, CBS)	5 mg
D3897	4-(4-(dilinoleylamino)styryl)-*N*-methylpyridinium iodide (*FAST* DiA™ oil; DiΔ^{9,12}-C_{18}ASP, I)	5 mg
D3898	3,3′-dilinoleyloxacarbocyanine perchlorate (*FAST* DiO™ solid; DiOΔ^{9,12}-C_{18}(3), ClO_4)	5 mg
D7756	1,1′-dilinoleyl-3,3,3′,3′-tetramethylindocarbocyanine, 4-chlorobenzenesulfonate (*FAST* DiI™ solid; DiIΔ^{9,12}-C_{18}(3), CBS)	5 mg
D3899	1,1′-dilinoleyl-3,3,3′,3′-tetramethylindocarbocyanine perchlorate (*FAST* DiI™ oil; DiIΔ^{9,12}-C_{18}(3), ClO_4)	5 mg
D7779	1,1′-dioctadecyl-5,5′-diphenyl-3,3,3′,3′-tetramethylindocarbocyanine chloride (5,5′-Ph_2-DiIC_{18}(3))	5 mg
D7778	3,3′-dioctadecyl-5,5′-di(4-sulfophenyl)oxacarbocyanine, sodium salt (SP-DiOC_{18}(3))	5 mg
D7777	1,1′-dioctadecyl-6,6′-di(4-sulfophenyl)-3,3,3′,3′-tetramethylindocarbocyanine (SP-DiIC_{18}(3))	5 mg
D275	3,3′-dioctadecyloxacarbocyanine perchlorate ('DiO'; DiOC_{18}(3))	100 mg
D7776	1,1′-dioctadecyl-3,3,3′,3′-tetramethylindocarbocyanine-5,5′-disulfonic acid (DiIC_{18}(3)-DS)	5 mg
D282	1,1′-dioctadecyl-3,3,3′,3′-tetramethylindocarbocyanine perchlorate ('DiI'; DiIC_{18}(3))	100 mg
D3911	1,1′-dioctadecyl-3,3,3′,3′-tetramethylindocarbocyanine perchlorate ('DiI'; DiIC_{18}(3)) *crystalline*	25 mg
D7757	1,1′-dioctadecyl-3,3,3′,3′-tetramethylindodicarbocyanine, 4-chlorobenzenesulfonate salt ('DiD' solid; DiIC_{18}(5) solid)	10 mg
D12730	1,1′-dioctadecyl-3,3,3′,3′-tetramethylindodicarbocyanine-5,5′-disulfonic acid (DiIC_{18}(5)-DS)	5 mg
D307	1,1′-dioctadecyl-3,3,3′,3′-tetramethylindodicarbocyanine perchlorate ('DiD' oil; DiIC_{18}(5) oil)	25 mg
D12731	1,1′-dioctadecyl-3,3,3′,3′-tetramethylindotricarbocyanine iodide ('DiR'; DiIC_{18}(7))	10 mg
D3886	1,1′-dioleyl-3,3,3′,3′-tetramethylindocarbocyanine methanesulfonate (Δ^9-DiI)	25 mg
F35355	FM® 1-43FX *fixable analog of FM® 1-43 membrane stain*	10 x 100 µg
F6999	FM® DiI *special packaging*	20 x 50 µg
L7781	Lipophilic Tracer Sampler Kit	1 kit
N22883	NeuroTrace® CM-DiI tissue-labeling paste	100 mg
N22882	NeuroTrace® DiD tissue-labeling paste	500 mg

For current prices or to order online, visit probes.invitrogen.com

Cat #	Product Name	Unit Size
N22880	NeuroTrace® DiI tissue-labeling paste	500 mg
N22881	NeuroTrace® DiO tissue-labeling paste	500 mg
N22884	NeuroTrace® Multicolor Tissue-Labeling Kit *DiO, DiI, DiD pastes, 500 mg each*	1 kit
O246	octadecyl rhodamine B chloride (R18)	10 mg
T3163	*N*-(3-triethylammoniumpropyl)-4-(4-(dibutylamino)styryl)pyridinium dibromide (FM® 1-43)	1 mg
T35356	*N*-(3-triethylammoniumpropyl)-4-(4-(dibutylamino)styryl)pyridinium dibromide (FM® 1-43) *special packaging*	10 x 100 µg
T1111	*N*-(3-triethylammoniumpropyl)-4-(4-(4-(diethylamino)phenyl)butadienyl)pyridinium dibromide (RH 414)	5 mg
T3166	*N*-(3-triethylammoniumpropyl)-4-(6-(4-(diethylamino)phenyl)hexatrienyl)pyridinium dibromide (FM® 4-64)	1 mg
T13320	*N*-(3-triethylammoniumpropyl)-4-(6-(4-(diethylamino)phenyl)hexatrienyl)pyridinium dibromide (FM® 4-64) *special packaging*	10 x 100 µg
T23360	*N*-(3-trimethylammoniumpropyl)-4-(6-(4-(diethylamino)phenyl)hexatrienyl)pyridinium dibromide (FM® 5-95)	1 mg
V22888	Vybrant® CM-DiI cell-labeling solution	1 mL
V22887	Vybrant® DiD cell-labeling solution	1 mL
V22885	Vybrant® DiI cell-labeling solution	1 mL
V22886	Vybrant® DiO cell-labeling solution	1 mL
V22889	Vybrant® Multicolor Cell-Labeling Kit *DiO, DiI, DiD solutions, 1 mL each*	1 kit

For current prices or to order online, visit probes.invitrogen.com

14.5 Fluorescent and Biotinylated Dextrans

Dextrans are hydrophilic polysaccharides characterized by their moderate to high molecular weight, good water solubility and low toxicity. They are widely used as both anterograde and retrograde tracers in neurons [1,2] and for numerous other applications; see our bibliography of dextran applications (D8998) for specific literature citations. Dextrans are biologically inert due to their uncommon poly-(α-D-1,6-glucose) linkages, which render them resistant to cleavage by most endogenous cellular glycosidases. They also usually have low immunogenicity. Molecular Probes offers almost 100 fluorescent and biotinylated dextran conjugates in several molecular weight ranges.

Properties of Our Dextran Conjugates

A Wide Selection of Substituents

Molecular Probes' dextrans are conjugated to biotin or a wide variety of fluorophores, including five of our Alexa Fluor® dyes (Table 14.4). In particular, we would like to highlight the dextran conjugates of our Alexa Fluor® 488, Oregon Green® and Rhodamine Green™ dyes, which are significantly brighter and more photostable than most fluorescein dextrans. Dextran-conjugated fluorescent indicators for calcium and magnesium ions (Section 19.4) and for pH (Section 20.4) are described with their corresponding ion indicators in other chapters.

Dextran Size

Molecular Probes' dextrans include those with nominal molecular weights (MW) of 3000; 10,000; 40,000; 70,000; 500,000; and 2,000,000 daltons (Table 14.4). Because unlabeled dextrans are polydisperse — and may become more so during the chemical processes required for their modification and purification — the actual molecular weights present in a particular sample may have a broad distribution. For example, our "3000 MW" dextran preparations contain polymers with molecular weights predominantly in the range of ~1500–3000 daltons, including the dye or other label.

Degree of Substitution of Our Dextrans

Dextrans from other commercial sources usually have a degree of substitution of 0.2 or fewer dye molecules per dextran molecule for dextrans in the 10,000 MW range. Our dextrans, however, typically contain 0.3–0.7 dyes per dextran in the 3000 MW range, 0.5–2 dyes per dextran in the 10,000 MW range, 2–4 dyes in the 40,000 MW range and 3–6 dyes in the 70,000 MW range. The actual degree of substitution is indicated on the product's label. If too many fluorophores are conjugated to the dextran molecule, quenching and undesired interactions with cellular components may occur. We have found our degree of substitution to be optimal for most applications, yielding dextrans that are typically much more fluorescent than the labeled dextrans available from other sources, thus permitting lower quantities to be used for intracellular tracing. It has been reported that some commercially available fluorescein isothiocyanate (FITC) dextrans yield spurious results in endocytosis studies because of the presence of free dye or metal contamination.[3,4] To overcome this problem, Molecular Probes removes as much of the free dye as possible by a combination of precipitation, dialysis, gel filtration and other techniques. The fluorescent dextran is then assayed by thin-layer chromatography (TLC) to ensure that it is free of low molecular weight dyes. Molecular Probes prepares several unique products that have two or even three different labels, including our fluoro-ruby, mini-ruby and micro-ruby products, described below. Not all of the individual dextran molecules of these products are expected to have all the substituents, or to be equally fixable, particularly in conjugates of the lowest molecular weight dextrans.

Dextran Net Charge and Method of Substitution

The net charge on the dextran depends on the fluorophore and the method of preparing the conjugate. Molecular Probes prepares most of its dextrans by reacting a water-soluble amino dextran (D1860, D1861, D1862, D3330, D7144) with the succinimidyl ester of the appropriate dye, rather than reacting a native dextran with isothiocyanate derivatives such as FITC. This method provides superior amine selectivity and yields an amide linkage, which is somewhat more stable than the corresponding thioureas formed from isothiocyanates. Except for the Rhodamine Green™ and Alexa Fluor® 488 conjugates, once the dye has been added, the unreacted amines on the dextran are capped to yield a neutral or anionic dextran. In the case of the Rhodamine Green™ and Alexa Fluor® 488 dextrans, the unreacted amines on the dextran are not capped after dye conjugation. Thus, these dextran conjugates may be neutral, anionic or cationic. The Alexa Fluor®, Cascade Blue®, lucifer yellow, fluorescein and Oregon Green® dextrans are intrinsically anionic, whereas most of the dextrans labeled with the zwitterionic rhodamine B, tetramethylrhodamine and Texas Red® dyes are essentially neutral. To produce more highly anionic dextrans, Molecular Probes has developed a proprietary procedure for adding negatively charged groups to the dextran carriers; these products are designated "polyanionic" dextrans.

Dextran Fixability

Some applications require that the dextran tracer be treated with formaldehyde or glutaraldehyde for subsequent analysis.[5,6] For these applications, Molecular Probes offers "lysine-fixable" versions of most of our dextran conjugates of fluorophores or biotin. These dextrans have covalently bound lysine residues that permit dextran tracers to be conjugated to surrounding biomolecules by aldehyde-mediated fixation for subsequent detection by immunohistochemical and ultrastructural techniques. We have also shown that all of our Alexa Fluor® dextran conjugates can be fixed with aldehyde-based fixatives.

Loading Cells with Dextrans and Subsequent Tissue Processing

Unless taken up by an endocytic process, dextran conjugates are membrane impermeant and usually must be loaded by relatively invasive techniques (Table 14.1). As with the lipophilic tracers in Section 14.4, crystals of the dextran conjugates have been successfully loaded by simply placing them directly on some kinds of samples.[7] We have found our Influx™ pinocytic cell-loading reagent (I14402, Section 14.3, Section 19.8) to be particularly useful for loading dextrans into a variety of adherent and nonadherent cells[8] (Figure 19.100). Sterile filtration of dextran solutions before use with live cells is highly recommended.[9] Biotin and biotinylated biomolecules with molecular weights up to >100,000 daltons are taken up by some plant cells through an endocytic pathway.[10,11]

Table 14.4 — Molecular Probes' selection of dextran conjugates

Label(s) (Absorption/Emission Maxima) *	3000 MW	10,000 MW	40,000 MW	70,000 MW	500,000 MW	2,000,000 MW
Cascade Blue® (400/420)	D7132 †	D1976 †				
Lucifer yellow (428/532)		D1825 †				
Alexa Fluor® 488 (494/521)		D22910 ‡				
Oregon Green® 488 (496/524)		D7170, D7171 †		D7172, D7173 †		
Fluorescein (494/518)	D3305, D3306 †	D1821, D1820 †	D1844 D1845 †	D1823, D1822 †	D7136 †	D7137 †
Fluorescein + biotin (494/518)	D7156 †	D7178 †				
DMNB-caged fluorescein (494/518) §		D3310				
DMNB-caged fluorescein + biotin (494/518) §		D7146 †				
Rhodamine Green™ (502/527)	D7163	D7153 †				
BODIPY® FL (505/513)		D7168 ‡				
Oregon Green® 514 (511/530)		D7175 †		D7176		
CMNCBZ-caged carboxy-Q-rhodamine (545/575) §		D34678				
Tetramethylrhodamine (555/580)	D3307, D3308 †	D1816, D1817 † D1868 ‡	D1842	D1819, D1818 †		D7139 †
Tetramethylrhodamine + biotin (555/580)	D7162 †	D3312 †				
Alexa Fluor® 546 (556/573)		D22911 ‡				
Rhodamine B (570/590)		D1824		D1841		
Alexa Fluor® 568 (578/603)		D22912 ‡				
Alexa Fluor® 594 (590/617)		D22913 ‡				
Texas Red® (595/615)	D3329, D3328 †	D1828, D1863 †	D1829	D1830, D1864 †		
Alexa Fluor® 647 (650/668)		D22914 ‡				
Biotin (<300/none)	D7135 †	D1956 †		D1957 †	D7142 †	
Amino (<300/none)	D3330	D1860	D1861	D1862	D7144	

* Approximate absorption and emission maxima, in nm, for conjugates. † "Lysine-fixable" dextrans contain lysines and can therefore be fixed in place with formaldehyde or glutaraldehyde. ‡ "Fixable" dextrans contain free amines (but not lysines) and can be fixed in place with formaldehyde or glutaraldehyde. § Absorption and emission maxima are for the conjugate following photolysis.

Our lysine-fixable dextrans and Alexa Fluor® dextrans can be fixed in place with formaldehyde or glutaraldehyde, permitting subsequent tissue processing, such as sectioning. A protocol has been published for embedding tissues in plastic for high-resolution characterization of neurons filled with lysine-fixable fluorescent dextrans.[12] Fixation of biotinylated or fluorescent dextrans also permits the use of fluorescent- or enzyme-labeled conjugates of avidin and streptavidin (Section 7.6, Table 7.22) or of anti-dye antibodies (Section 7.4, Table 7.18), respectively. These techniques can amplify the signal, which is important for detecting fine structure in sections or for changing the detection mode.[13] We provide antibodies to the Alexa Fluor® 488, Alexa Fluor® 405/Cascade Blue®, lucifer yellow, fluorescein, BODIPY® FL, tetramethylrhodamine and Texas Red® fluorophores and to the 2,4-dinitrophenyl (DNP) and nitrotyrosine haptens (Section 7.4). Our antibodies to fluorescein crossreact strongly with the Oregon Green® dyes and somewhat with the Rhodamine Green™ fluorophore, and our anti-tetramethylrhodamine and anti–Texas Red® dye antibodies crossreact with tetramethylrhodamine, Lissamine rhodamine B, Rhodamine Red™ and Texas Red® dyes. Molecular Probes' ELF® 97 Immunohistochemistry Kit and ELF® 97 Cytological Labeling Kit (E6600, E6603; Section 6.3) and several of our TSA (Tyramide Signal Amplification) Kits (Section 6.2) can be utilized directly with biotinylated dextrans or combined with antibodies to the fluorophore-labeled dextrans to further amplify the signal, making it possible to detect ultrafine structures accessible to these dextran conjugates. The NANOGOLD and Alexa Fluor® FluoroNanogold conjugates of secondary antibodies (Section 7.2) and streptavidin (Section 7.6) can be utilized to allow detection of labeled dextrans in fixed-cell preparations by light microscopy or, following silver enhancement with the LI Silver Enhancement Kit (L24919, Section 7.2), by electron microscopy.

Photoconversion of neurons labeled with lysine-fixable fluorescent dextrans in the presence of diaminobenzidine (DAB) using our Diaminobenzidine (DAB) Histochemistry Kits (Section 7.2, Section 7.6) can be used to produce electron-dense products for electron microscopy[14] (see Note 14.2 "Product Highlight: Fluorescent Probes for Photoconversion of Diaminobenzidine Reagents" in Section 14.3). Electron-dense products can also be generated from peroxidase or colloidal gold conjugates of avidin, streptavidin or anti-dye antibodies.[15]

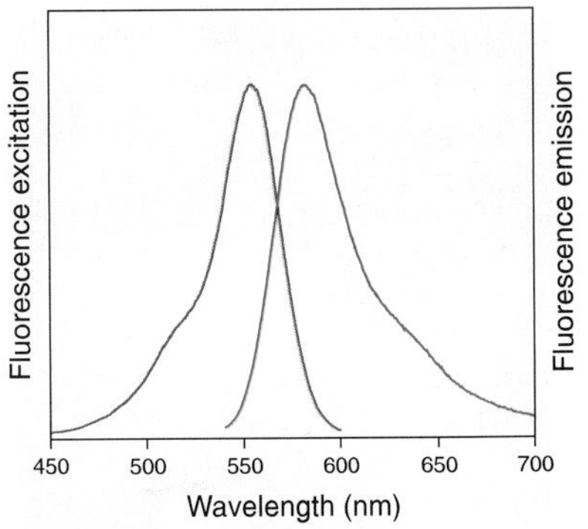

Figure 14.67 Fluorescence excitation and emission spectra of tetramethylrhodamine-labeled 10,000 MW dextran (fluoro-ruby) in pH 7.0 buffer.

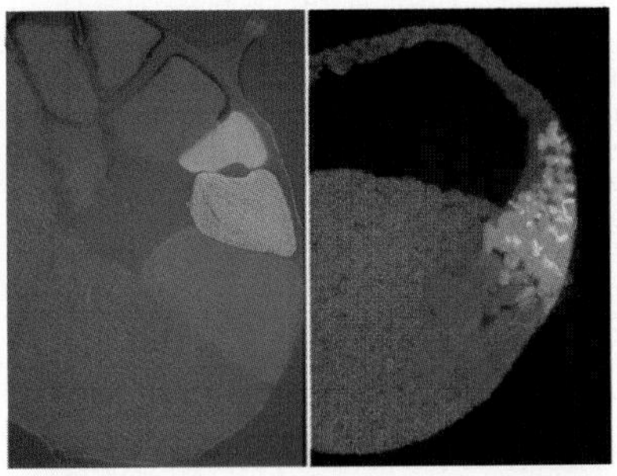

Figure 14.68 Lineage tracing of three dorsal blastomeres of 32-cell *Xenopus laevis* embryos injected with Molecular Probes' fluorescent dextran conjugates. The tier 1 dorsal (A1) blastomere was injected with lysine-fixable 10,000 MW fluorescein dextran (D1820), the tier 2 dorsal (B1) blastomere with lysine-fixable 10,000 MW Texas Red® dextran (D1863), and the tier 3 dorsal (C3) blastomere with lysine-fixable 10,000 MW Cascade Blue® dextran (D1976). Embryos were fixed in formaldehyde, embedded and sectioned. The image on the left shows a 13 µm–thick section of a stage 6 (32-cell) embryo fixed right after injection; this section exhibits significant autofluorescence due to the presence of residual yolk. The image on the right is a stage 10 (early gastrula) embryo. Triple-exposure photographs of the sectioned embryos were taken on a Zeiss Axiophot with a 10× objective. Images contributed by Marie Vodicka, University of California, Berkeley.

Neuronal Tracing with Dextrans

Fluorescent and biotinylated dextrans are routinely employed to trace neuronal projections. Dextrans can function efficiently as anterograde or retrograde tracers,[2] depending on the study method and tissue type used. Active transport of dextrans occurs only in live, not fixed tissue.[16] Comparative studies of rhodamine isothiocyanate, rhodamine B dextran (D1824) and lysinated tetramethylrhodamine dextran (fluoro-ruby, D1817) have shown that the dextran conjugates produce less diffusion at injection sites and more permanent labeling than do the corresponding free dyes.[5] Dextran conjugates with molecular weights up to 70,000 daltons have been employed as neuronal tracers in a wide variety of species. The availability of fluorescent dextran conjugates with different sizes and charges permitted the analysis of direction and rate of axonal transport in the squid giant axon.[17]

Multilabeled Dextrans

Our fixable dextrans, most of which are lysinated dextrans (see the products marked by a single dagger (†) in Table 14.4), are generally preferred for neuronal tracing because they may transport more effectively and can be fixed in place with aldehydes after labeling. Molecular Probes prepares a number of multilabeled dextrans that are fixable, including some that have acquired the distinction of unique names in various publications:

- Fluoro-ruby[5,14,18–23] — a red-orange–fluorescent, aldehyde-fixable 10,000 MW dextran labeled with both tetramethylrhodamine and lysine (D1817, Figure 14.67). 3000 MW, 70,000 MW and 2,000,000 MW versions of fluoro-ruby are also available (D3308, D1818, D7139).
- Fluoro-emerald[19,23,24] — a green-fluorescent, aldehyde-fixable 10,000 MW dextran labeled with both fluorescein and lysine (D1820; Figure 14.68, Figure 14.69, Figure 14.70). 3000 MW, 40,000 MW, 70,000 MW, 500,000 MW and 2,000,000 MW versions of fluoro-emerald are also available[25,26] (D3306, D1845, D1822, D7136, D7137).

- Micro-ruby (D7162) and mini-ruby[27–31] (D3312) — red-orange–fluorescent, aldehyde-fixable 3000 MW and 10,000 MW dextrans simultaneously labeled with tetramethylrhodamine, biotin and lysine.
- Micro-emerald (D7156) and mini-emerald (D7178) — green-fluorescent, aldehyde-fixable dextrans simultaneously labeled with fluorescein, biotin and lysine.
- Biotinylated dextran amine (BDA)[1,9,32–39] — nonfluorescent, aldehyde-fixable dextrans simultaneously labeled with both biotin and lysine. These are available in several molecular weights (D1956, D1957, D7135, D7142; Table 14.4). A useful review has been published on the BDA products.[40]

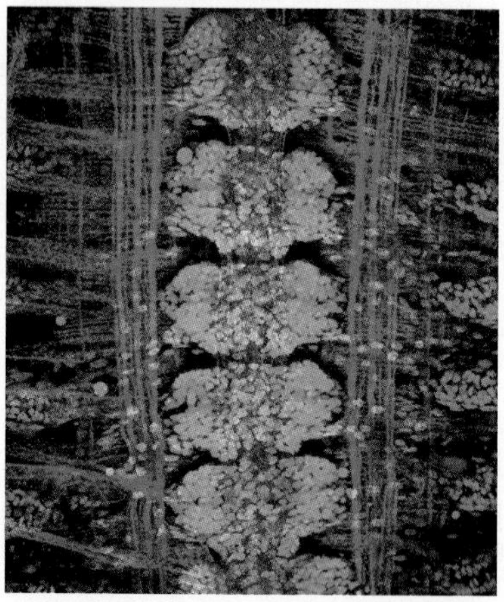

Figure 14.69 Development of the leech central nervous system into segments was characterized with the cell lineage tracer lysine-fixable 10,000 MW fluorescein dextran (fluoro-emerald, D1820). Fluoro-emerald was injected into a neuroectodermal cell of a leech embryo. The teloblast eventually differentiated into five segmentally iterated ganglia labeled with fluoro-emerald (pseudocolored blue in this image). Associated muscle fibers were identified with a Lan 3-14 monoclonal antibody and visualized with a Cy3 antibody (pseudocolored red). Nuclei were counterstained with TOTO®-3 dye (T3604, pseudocolored green). Image reprinted from the cover of Development 127 (4) (2000), used with the permission of The Company of Biologists Ltd.

Fluoro-ruby and fluoro-emerald (Figure 14.70) have been extensively employed for retrograde and anterograde neuronal tracing,[5] transplantation[21] and cell-lineage tracing.[2,20,22,23,41] Both products can be used to photoconvert DAB into an insoluble, electron-dense reaction product.[14] Like fluoro-ruby and fluoro-emerald, micro-ruby and mini-ruby are brightly fluorescent, making it easy to visualize the electrode during the injection process. DiI (D282, Section 14.4) or other lipophilic probes in Section 14.4 can be used to mark the sites of microinjection.[42] In addition, because these dextrans include a covalently linked biotin, filled cells can be probed with standard enzyme-labeled avidin or streptavidin conjugates or with NANOGOLD and FluoroNanogold streptavidin (Section 7.6) to produce a permanent record of the experiment.[43] Mini-ruby has proven useful for intracellular filling in fixed brain slices[28] and has been reported to produce staining comparable to that achieved with lucifer yellow CH[27] (L453, L682, L1177, L12926; Section 14.3). Moreover, the use of mini-ruby in conjunction with standard peroxidase-mediated avidin–biotin methods does not cause co-conversion of lipofuscin granules found in adult human brain, a common problem during photoconversion of lucifer yellow CH.[27] The lysine-fixable micro-emerald and mini-emerald — dextrans that are triply labeled with fluorescein, biotin and lysine — provide a contrasting color that is better excited by the argon-ion laser of confocal laser-scanning microscopes; they have uses similar to micro-ruby and mini-ruby, respectively.

3000 MW Dextrans

The nominally 3000 MW dextrans offer several advantages over higher molecular weight dextrans, including faster axonal diffusion and greater access to peripheral cell processes[25] (Figure 14.71). Our "3000 MW" dextran preparations contain polymers with molecular weight predominantly in the range of ~1500–3000 daltons, including the dye or other label. Our list of 3000 MW dextrans includes fluorescein, Rhodamine Green™, tetramethylrhodamine, Texas Red® and biotin conjugates. We also offer lysine-fixable 3000 MW dextrans that are simultaneously labeled with both fluorescein and biotin (micro-emerald, D7156) or tetramethylrhodamine and biotin (micro-ruby, D7162).

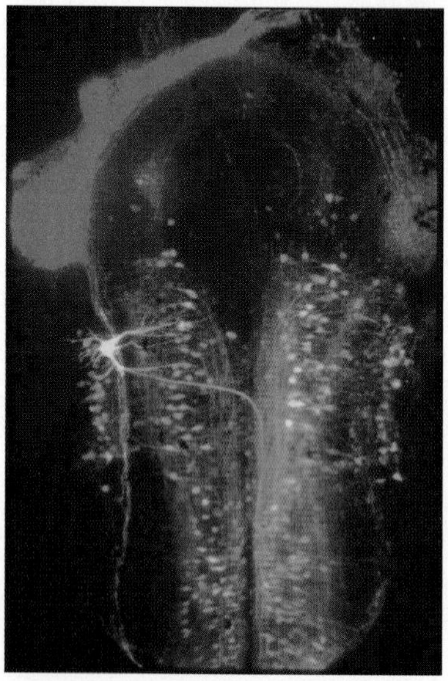

Figure 14.70 A whole-mount of the embryonic brain of *Xenopus laevis* that has been double-labeled with our lysine-fixable 10,000 MW fluorescein dextran (fluoro-emerald, D1820) and lysine-fixable 10,000 MW tetramethylrhodamine dextran (fluoro-ruby, D1817). The tetramethylrhodamine dextran was used to label the neurons projecting from the retina, whereas the fluorescein dextran was applied to the transected spinal cord, thus allowing the detailed evaluation of the topological relationship of these two populations of neurons (Neurosci Lett 127, 150 (1991)). Image contributed by Martina Manns and Bernd Fritzsch, Creighton University.

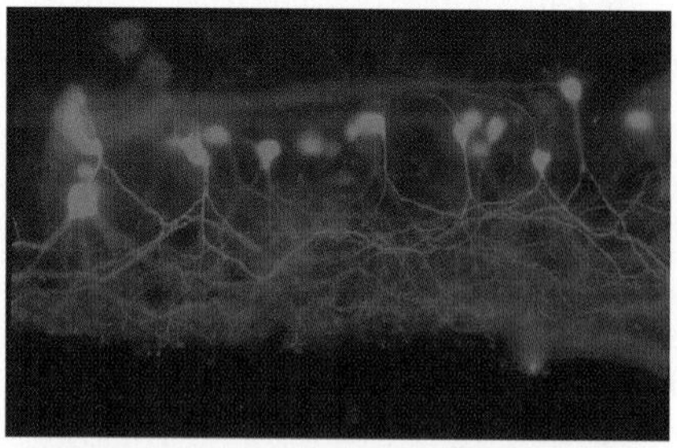

Figure 14.71 Secondary motor neurons in a spinal cord whole mount of a male western mosquitofish (*Gambusia affinis affinis*) that have been labeled with lysine-fixable 3000 MW Texas Red® dextran (D3328). The dextran crystals were applied to the bipinnate inclinator muscles of the anal appendicular support fin, and the dye was transported from the axons to cell body and dendrites. Motor neurons were visualized and photographed through a bandpass optical filter appropriate for Texas Red® dye, by epifluorescence microscopy. Image contributed by E. Rosa-Molinar, University of Nebraska Medical Center, and Bernd Fritzsch, Creighton University.

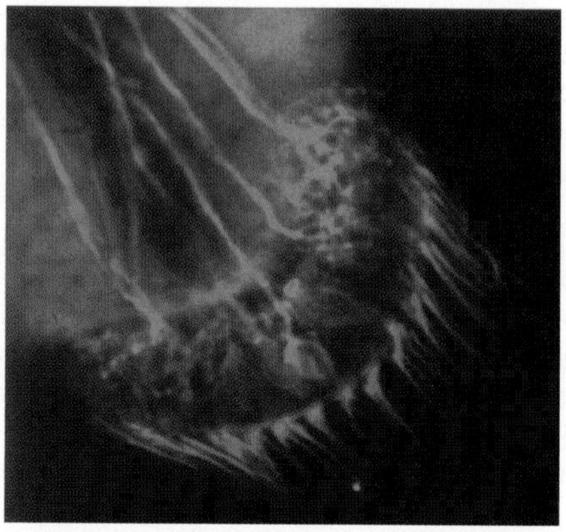

Figure 14.72 The attached eighth nerve from the vestibular labyrinth of a turtle, *Pseudemys scripta*, exposed to lysine-fixable 3000 MW tetramethylrhodamine dextran (D3308) and incubated with F-actin–specific BODIPY® FL phallacidin (B607). F-actin–labeled ciliary bundles were stained green by the phallacidin, and the calyceal and bouton endings of their primary afferents were stained red by the dextran. This image is a projection of 40 confocal images. Image contributed by Laura DiCaprio and Ellengene Peterson, Ohio University.

The 3000 MW fluorescein dextran and tetramethylrhodamine dextran (D3306, D3308; Figure 14.72, Figure 14.73) have been observed to readily undergo both anterograde and retrograde movement in live cells.[19,25] These 3000 MW dextrans appear to passively diffuse within the neuronal process, as their intracellular transport is not effectively inhibited by colchicine or nocodazole, both of which disrupt active transport by depolymerizing microtubules.[25] Moreover, these small dextrans diffuse at rates equivalent to those of smaller tracers such as sulforhodamine 101 and biocytin (~2 millimeters/hour at 22°C) and about twice as fast as 10,000 MW dextrans. The relatively low molecular weight of the dextrans may result in transport of some labeled probes through gap junctions (see below). By use of anti-tetramethylrhodamine antibodies (A6397, Section 7.4) and peroxidase–anti-peroxidase complex staining, the signal from tetramethylrhodamine-conjugated dextrans can be detected in the fine dendrite configuration of cortical projection neurons.[13]

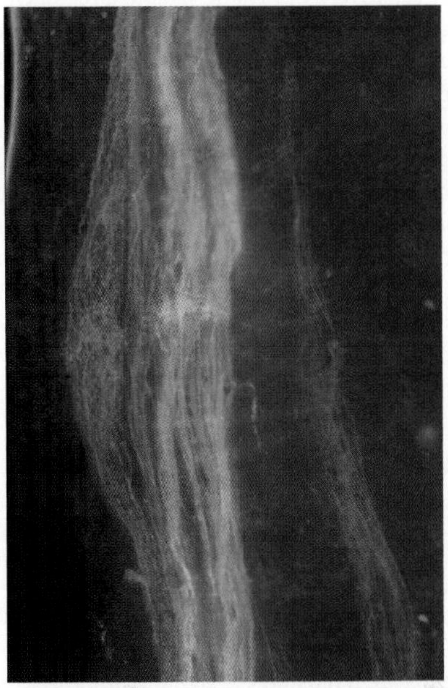

Figure 14.73 The antero-ventral and antero-dorsal lateral line nerves in an *Ambystoma mexicanum* whole-mounted brain after labeling with 3000 MW Rhodamine Green™ dextran (D7163) and lysine-fixable 3000 MW tetramethylrhodamine dextran (D3308), respectively. In both cases, the dextran was applied to the respective cut cranial nerves. This photomicrograph shows the four segregated ventral fascicles of the mechanosensory lateral line fibers and the intermingling of the dorsal electrosensory fibers. Image contributed by Bernd Fritzsch, Creighton University.

NeuroTrace® BDA-10,000 Neuronal Tracer Kit

The NeuroTrace® BDA-10,000 Neuronal Tracer Kit (N7167) contains convenient amounts of each of the components required for neuroanatomical tracing using BDA methods,[40] including:

- Lysine-fixable, biotinylated 10,000 MW dextran amine (BDA-10,000)
- Horseradish peroxidase avidin (HRP avidin)
- 3,3′-Diaminobenzidine (DAB)
- A rigorously tested protocol that ensures fast and simple tracing experiments

The neuronal tracer BDA-10,000 is transported over long distances and fills fine processes bidirectionally, including boutons in the anterograde direction and dendritic structures in the retrograde direction.[9,36–39] Two days to two weeks after BDA-10,000 is injected into the desired region of the brain, the brain tissue can be fixed and sectioned. BDA-10,000 can also be applied to cut nerves and allowed to transport. Following incubation with HRP avidin and then DAB, the electron-dense DAB reaction product can be viewed by either light or electron microscopy[40,43] (Figure 14.74). The NeuroTrace® BDA-10,000 labeling method can be readily combined with other anterograde or retrograde labeling methods or with immunohistochemical techniques. BDA-10,000 is available as a separate product (D1956), as are BDA derivatives with other molecular weights — BDA-3000[44] (D7135), BDA-70,000 (D1957) and BDA-500,000 (D7142). A detailed protocol that utilizes our BDA-10,000 probe, HRP streptavidin (S911, Section 7.6) and tetramethylbenzidine to anterogradely label fine processes in neurons has been published.[1]

Cell Lineage Tracing with Dextrans

Fluorescent dextrans — particularly the fluorescein and rhodamine conjugates — have been used extensively for tracing cell lineage.[22,45,46] In this technique, the dextran is microinjected into a single cell of the developing embryo, and the fate of that cell and its daughters can be followed *in vivo* (Figure 14.68). Examples using this method include studies of:

- Dorsoventral axis determination in zebrafish mutants[47]
- Early cell-fate commitment and lineage restrictions in developing zebrafish[48–50]
- Lineage and dopamine phenotype in tadpole hypothalamus[51]
- Migration of neural crest cells in *Xenopus*[52]
- Neural crest cell fate in zebrafish[53]
- Progeny tracing in the grasshopper neuroblast[9]

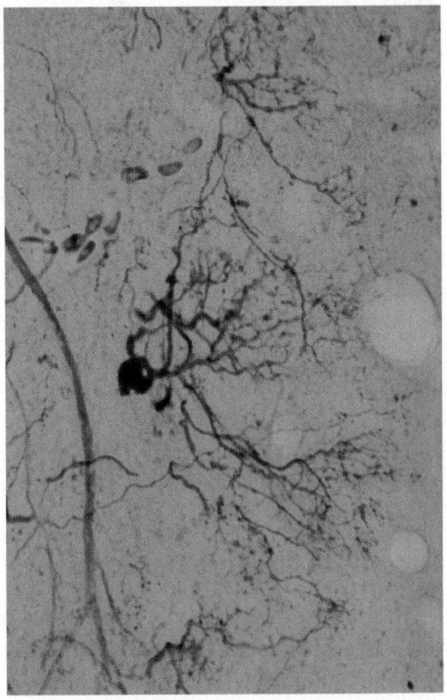

Figure 14.74 A mitral cell in the olfactory bulb of a chinook salmon that has been retrogradely labeled using the NeuroTrace® BDA-10,000 Neuronal Tracer Kit (N7167).

Developmental studies show that the lysinated fluorescent dextrans are also suitable for cell ablation studies, presumably through the generation of oxygen radicals.[54]

The lysine-fixable tetramethylrhodamine and Texas Red® dextran conjugates (Table 14.4) are most frequently cited for lineage tracing studies; they are often preferred over other conjugates because they have bright fluorescence and are relatively photostable. Our Alexa Fluor® 546, Alexa Fluor® 568, Alexa Fluor® 594 and Alexa Fluor® 647 dextrans (D22911, D22912, D22913, D22914) are likely to provide equal or superior performance as orange- to red-fluorescent polar tracers. As a second color, particularly in combination with the Texas Red® dextrans, people have most often used our lysine-fixable fluorescein dextrans (e.g., D3306, D1820, D1822). However, the photostability of fluorescein conjugates is not as high as that of the tetramethylrhodamine and Texas Red® conjugates. Consequently, we recommend our green-fluorescent Alexa Fluor® 488 dextran conjugate (D22910) or, alternatively, our lysine-fixable Oregon Green® 488 (D7171, D7173), Oregon Green® 514 (D7175) and Rhodamine Green™ (D7153) dextran conjugates; see Figure 1.46, Figure 7.23 and Figure 11.8 for a comparison of the photostability of the Alexa Fluor® 488, Oregon Green® and Rhodamine Green™ dyes and fluorescein. The more photostable dextrans may also be less phototoxic in cells. Although these fixable conjugates can be employed with long-term preservation of the tissue, some researchers prefer to co-inject a fluorescent, nonlysinated dextran along with a nonfluorescent, lysine-fixable biotin dextran (BDA, Table 14.4). The nonfluorescent BDA can then be fixed in place with aldehyde-based fixatives and probed with any of our fluorescent or enzyme-labeled streptavidin and avidin conjugates described in Section 7.6 (Table 7.22).

Vybrant® Cell Lineage Tracing Kit

The Vybrant® Cell Lineage Tracing Kit (V22915) combines an aldehyde-fixable Cascade Blue® dextran with the superior brightness of our red-orange–fluorescent Alexa Fluor® 546 dye to permit the detection of widely differentiated cell lineages. The Cascade Blue® dextran is first injected into the desired parent cells. After differentiation, the cells are fixed and the signal is amplified using a rabbit IgG against the Cascade Blue® dye and an Alexa Fluor® 546 conjugate of goat anti–rabbit IgG antibody as the detection reagent (Figure 7.75). The red-orange–fluorescent Alexa Fluor® 546 dye can be viewed using filters appropriate for tetramethylrhodamine (Table 23.9). The Vybrant® Cell Lineage Tracing Kit contains:

- Lysine-fixable, 10,000 MW Cascade Blue® dextran
- Rabbit IgG anti–Alexa Fluor® 405/Cascade Blue® dye antibody
- Alexa Fluor® 546 goat anti–rabbit IgG antibody conjugate
- A detailed experimental protocol

High MW Dextran Conjugates

Our 500,000 and 2,000,000 MW fluorescent dextrans (Table 14.4) may be particularly useful for lineage tracing at early stages of development, although these biopolymers have lower water solubility and a greater tendency to precipitate or clog microinjection needles than our lower molecular weight dextrans. Some studies suggest that lower molecular weight dextrans may leak from blastomeres, complicating analysis. Injection of 2,000,000 MW fluorescein- and Texas Red® dye–conjugated dextrans into separate cells of the two-cell stage zebrafish embryo allowed the construction of a fate map.[55] The 500,000 MW and 2,000,000 MW dextrans are labeled with fluorescein, tetramethylrhodamine or Texas Red® dyes or with biotin, and all contain aldehyde-fixable lysine groups. The nonfluorescent 500,000 MW aminodextran (D7144) can be conjugated with the researcher's choice of amine-reactive reagents.

Caged Fluorophore Dextrans

Dextrans with caged fluorophores are of particular interest to developmental biologists, because they can be injected early in development when the cells are large, and then later activated with UV illumination when the cells of interest may be small or buried in tissue[56–58] (Figure 5.24). A caged fluorescein dextran conjugate has been used in this way to demonstrate lineage restriction boundaries in the early *Drosophila* embryo.[59] Two-photon excitation has been used to photoactivate a caged fluorescein dextran at the two-cell stage of sea urchin embryo development.[60] We offer a 10,000 MW dextran conjugate of DMNB-caged fluorescein[58,61,62] (D3310, Figure 5.24) and its lysine-fixable, biotinylated analog (D7146), as well as a 10,000 MW dextran conjugate of CMNCBZ-caged carboxy-Q-rhodamine (D34678) that exhibits orange fluorescence (excitation/emission maxima ~545/575 nm) after photolysis. See Section 5.3 for a discussion of caged probes and Section 14.3 for a description of our lower molecular weight caged tracers for microinjection.

Studying Intercellular Communication with Dextrans

The size of dextrans can be exploited to study connectivity between cells. Examples include studies of the passage of 3000 MW dextrans through plasmodesmata[26] and modulation of gap junctional communication by transforming growth factor–β_1 and forskolin.[63] However, the dispersion of molecular weights in our "3000 MW" dextran preparations, which contain polymers with total molecular weights predominantly in the range of ~1500–3000 daltons but may also contain molecules <1500 daltons, may complicate such analyses.

An important experimental approach to identifying cells that form gap junctions makes use of simultaneous introduction of the polar tracer lucifer yellow CH (~450 daltons) and a tetramethylrhodamine 10,000 MW dextran. Because low molecular weight tracers like lucifer yellow CH (L453, L12926; Section 14.3) pass through gap junctions and dextrans do not, the initially labeled cell exhibits red fluorescence, whereas cells connected through gap junctions have yellow fluorescence[63] (Figure 14.75). This technique has been used to follow the loss of intercellular communication in adenocarcinoma cells,[64] to show the re-establishment of communication during wound healing in *Drosophila*[65] and to investigate intercellular communication at different stages in *Xenopus* embryos.[66,67] Similar experiments could employ our lucifer yellow 10,000 MW dextran (D1825) and a low molecular weight red-fluorescent tracer such as sulforhodamine 101 (S359, Section 14.3) or a blue-fluorescent dye

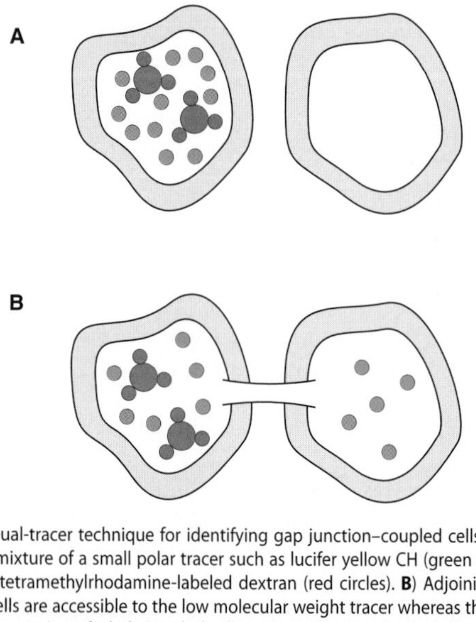

Figure 14.75 Dual-tracer technique for identifying gap junction–coupled cells. **A**) Cells are labeled with a mixture of a small polar tracer such as lucifer yellow CH (green circles) and a relatively large tetramethylrhodamine-labeled dextran (red circles). **B**) Adjoining gap junction–coupled cells are accessible to the low molecular weight tracer whereas the much larger dextran conjugate is excluded. Coupled cells with single-color lucifer yellow CH labeling are readily distinguished from initially labeled cells with dual fluorescence.

such as Cascade Blue® hydrazide or Alexa Fluor 405 cadaverine (C687, A30675; Section 14.3).

Simultaneous loading of cells with two (or more) dextrans that differ in both their molecular weight and in the dye's fluorescence properties has been used to assess subcellular heterogeneities in the submicroscopic structure of cytoplasm.[68]

Probing Membrane Permeability with Dextrans

Labeled dextrans are often used to investigate the exclusion or transfer of macromolecules across cell membranes. For example, fluorescent dextrans have been used to monitor the effectiveness of electroporation, a technique that produces pores in the cell membrane, thus providing a convenient method for introducing materials such as exogenous DNA. Fluorescein dextrans with molecular weights ranging from 4000 to 150,000 daltons were used to determine the effect of electroporation variables — pulse size, shape and duration — on plasma-membrane pore size in chloroplasts,[69] red blood cells[70] and fibroblasts.[71] Fluorescence recovery after photobleaching (FRAP) techniques have been used to monitor nucleocytoplasmic transport of fluorescent dextrans of various molecular weights, allowing the determination of the size-exclusion limit of the nuclear pore membrane,[72–74] as well as to study the effect of epidermal growth factor and insulin on the nuclear membrane and on nucleocytoplasmic transport.[75,76]

Microinjected 3000 MW fluorescent dextrans concentrate in interphase nuclei of *Drosophila* embryos, whereas 40,000 MW dextrans remain in the cytoplasm and enter the nucleus only after breakdown of the nuclear envelope during prophase. This size-exclusion phenomenon was used to follow the cyclical breakdown and reformation of the nuclear envelope during successive cell divisions.[77] Similarly, our 10,000 MW Calcium Green™ dextran conjugate (C3713, Section 19.4) was shown to diffuse across the nuclear membrane of isolated nuclei from *Xenopus laevis* oocytes, but the 70,000 MW and 500,000 MW conjugates could not.[78] Significantly, depletion of nuclear Ca^{2+} stores by inositol 1,4,5-triphosphate (Ins 1,4,5-P_3, I3716; Section 17.2) or by calcium chelators (Section 19.8) blocked nuclear uptake of the 10,000 MW Calcium Green™ dextran conjugate but not entry of lucifer yellow CH. Our 3000 MW Calcium Green™ dextran conjugate (C6765) is actively transported in adult nerve fibers over a significant distance and is retained in presynaptic terminals in a form that allows monitoring of presynaptic Ca^{2+} levels.[79] Fluorescent dextrans with molecular weights up to 20,000 daltons are reported to be taken up by the feeding tubes of nematodes, but 40,000 MW and 70,000 MW dextrans are not.[80]

Following Endocytosis and Fusion with Dextrans

Some of the dyes that Molecular Probes uses to prepare its dextran conjugates exhibit fluorescence that is sensitive to the pH of the medium (Chapter 20). Consequently, internalization of labeled dextrans into acidic organelles of cells can often be tracked by measuring changes in the fluorescence of the dye.[81,82] Fluorescence of fluorescein-labeled dextrans is strongly quenched upon acidification (Figure 20.2); however, fluorescein's lack of a spectral shift in acidic solution makes it difficult to discriminate between internalized probe that is quenched and the residual fluorescence of the external medium. Dextran conjugates that either shift their emission spectra, such as the SNARF® dextrans, or undergo significant shifts of their excitation spectra, such as BCECF, Oregon Green® and HPTS dextrans, are much more useful for following the internalization by ratio imaging (see Note 19.1 "Technical Focus: Loading and Calibration of Intracellular Ion Indicators" in Section 19.1). Our pH indicator conjugates and their optical responses are described in Section 20.4.

Discrimination of internalized fluorescent dextrans from external dextrans can be improved by adding a reagent that quenches the fluorescence of the external probe. For example, our anti-dye antibodies (Section 7.4) usually quench the fluorescence of their cognate dyes and may be useful for discriminating between externally bound dextrans and internalized dextrans. In addition, trypan blue can also be used as a quencher for some of the external dextran conjugates.

Fluorescent dextrans can also be encapsulated in liposomes.[83–85] Using Texas Red®– and fluorescein-labeled dextrans encapsulated in liposomes, researchers have obtained evidence that antigen processing occurs within dense lysosomes, rather than in earlier endocytic compartments.[86] Researchers have also used liposome-encapsulated fluorescent dextrans to investigate liposome fusion with isolated nuclei[87] and the effect of additives on vesicle size.[88] Intracellular fusion of endosomes has been monitored with a BODIPY® FL avidin conjugate by following the fluorescence enhancement that occurs when it complexes with a biotinylated dextran.[89] We have found our Oregon Green® 514 streptavidin (S6369, Section 7.6) to have an over 15-fold increase in fluorescence intensity upon binding free biotin, which may make it the preferred probe for this application (Figure 16.25).

Tracing Fluid Transport with Dextrans

Fluorescent dextrans are important tools for studying the hydrodynamic properties of the cytoplasmic matrix. The intracellular mobility of these fluorescent tracers can be investigated using fluorescence recovery after photobleaching (FRAP) techniques. We offer a range of dextran sizes, thus providing a variety of hydrodynamic radii for investigating both the nature of the cytoplasmic matrix and the permeability of the surrounding membrane. Because of their solubility and biocompatibility, fluorescent dextrans have been used to monitor *in vivo* tissue permeability and flow in the uveoscleral tract,[90,91] capillaries[92,93] and proximal tubules,[94] as well as diffusion of high molecular weight substances in the brain's extracellular environment.[95] Fluorescent dextrans have also been used to assess permeability of the blood–brain barrier[96] and to monitor blood flow.[97]

The 10,000 MW DMNB-caged fluorescein dextran (D3310, Figure 5.24), the corresponding triple-labeled DMNB-caged fluorescein, biotin and lysine dextran (D7146) and the 10,000 MW CMNCBZ-caged carboxy-Q-rhodamine dextran (D34678) are fluorescent only after UV photolysis,[61,98–100] enabling researchers to conduct photoactivation of fluorescence (PAF) experiments analogous to FRAP experiments in which the fluorophore is photoactivated upon illumination rather than bleached (Figure 7.74). DMNB-caged fluorescein dextran yields a green-fluorescent fluorescein dextran (excitation/emission maxima ~494/518 nm) and the CMNCBZ-caged carboxy-Q-rhodamine dextran exhibits orange fluorescence (excitation/emission maxima ~545/575 nm) after photolysis. Measuring the bright signal of the photoactivated fluorophore against a dark background should be intrinsically more sensitive than measuring a dark (photobleached) region against a bright field. In a collaboration with Walter Lempert of Princeton University, we have shown caged fluorescein dextran (D3310) to be an effective probe for tracing vortices in water using a technique called photoactivated nonintrusive tracking of molecular motion [101] (PHANTOMM). Furthermore, diffusional coupling between dendritic spines and shafts was measured both by FRAP experiments with fluorescein dextran and by PAF experiments with DMNB-caged fluorescein dextran.[62] DMNB-caged fluorescein was also employed to evaluate a system that combined confocal laser-scanning microscopy with local photolysis of caged compounds.[98]

Our Bibliography of Dextran Applications

Our bibliography of dextran applications (D8998) contains over 1300 references, and continuously updated copies are available upon request from our Technical Assistance Department or through our web site (probes.invitrogen.com). It includes references in which dextrans from several different sources were used. Because the source, molecular weight of the dextran, net charge, degree of substitution and nature of the dye may significantly affect the application, the methods described in this section and in the references in our bibliography should be considered guides rather than definitive protocols. In most cases, however, our fluorescent dextrans are much brighter and have higher negative charge than dextrans available from other sources. Furthermore, we use rigorous methods for removing as much unconjugated dye as practical, and then assay our dextran conjugates by thin-layer chromatography to ensure the absence of low molecular weight contaminants. A product information sheet for dextrans is also available.

References

1. J Neurosci Methods 109, 81 (2001); **2.** Brain Res Bull 51, 11 (2000); **3.** J Cell Sci 96, 721 (1990); **4.** J Cell Biol 105, 1981 (1987); **5.** Brain Res 526, 127 (1990); **6.** Brain Res Bull 25, 139 (1990); **7.** J Neurosci Methods 81, 169 (1998); **8.** J Virol 76, 11505 (2002); **9.** J Neurosci 14, 5766 (1994); **10.** Plant Physiol 98, 673 (1992); **11.** Plant Physiol 93, 1492 (1990); **12.** Biotech Histochem 67, 153 (1992); **13.** J Neurosci Methods 65, 157 (1996); **14.** J Histochem Cytochem 41, 777 (1993); **15.** Brain Res Bull 30, 115 (1993); **16.** Trends Neurosci 13, 14 (1990); **17.** Proc Natl Acad Sci U S A 92, 11500 (1995); **18.** Mol Biol Cell 6, 1491 (1995); **19.** J Neurosci Methods 53, 35 (1994); **20.** Nature 363, 630 (1993); **21.** Proc Natl Acad Sci U S A 90, 1310 (1993); **22.** Nature 344, 431 (1990); **23.** Dev Biol 109, 509 (1985); **24.** J Cell Biol 128, 293 (1995); **25.** J Neurosci Methods 50, 95 (1993); **26.** Plant J 4, 567 (1993); **27.** J Neurosci Methods 55, 105 (1994); **28.** Brain Res 608, 78 (1993); **29.** J Neurosci Methods 74, 9 (1997); **30.** Glia 20, 145 (1997); **31.** Hippocampus 8, 57 (1998); **32.** J Neurosci 15, 5222 (1995); **33.** J Neurosci 15, 5139 (1995); **34.** J Neurosci Methods 53, 23 (1994); **35.** J Neurosci Methods 52, 153 (1994); **36.** Brain Res 607, 47 (1993); **37.** J Neurosci Methods 48, 75 (1993); **38.** J Neurosci Methods 45, 35 (1992); **39.** J Neurosci Methods 41, 239 (1992); **40.** J Neurosci Methods 103, 23 (2000); **41.** Development 104 Suppl, 231 (1988); **42.** Biophys J 75, 2558 (1998); **43.** Neuroscience Protocols, Wouterlood FG, Ed. 93-050-14, pp. 01–14 (1993); **44.** J Neurosci Methods 76, 167 (1997); **45.** Science 252, 569 (1991); **46.** Development 108, 581 (1990); **47.** Nature 370, 468 (1994); **48.** Development 120, 483 (1994); **49.** Science 265, 517 (1994); **50.** Science 261, 109 (1993); **51.** J Neurosci 12, 1351 (1992); **52.** Development 118, 363 (1993); **53.** Development 120, 495 (1994); **54.** Dev Biol 120, 520 (1987); **55.** Nature 361, 451 (1993); **56.** Dev Biol 201, 247 (1998); **57.** Methods Mol Biol 135, 349 (2000); **58.** Biochem Cell Biol 75, 551 (1997); **59.** Cell 68, 923 (1992); **60.** Dev Biol 175, 177 (1996); **61.** Anal Chem 70, 2459 (1998); **62.** Science 272, 716 (1996); **63.** J Neurosci 15, 262 (1995); **64.** Proc Natl Acad Sci U S A 85, 473 (1988); **65.** Dev Biol 127, 197 (1988); **66.** J Cell Biol 110, 115 (1990); **67.** Dev Biol 129, 265 (1988); **68.** J Immunol 157, 3396 (1996); **69.** Biophys J 58, 823 (1990); **70.** Bioelectrochem Bioenerg 20, 57 (1988); **71.** Biotechniques 6, 550 (1988); **72.** J Cell Biol 102, 1183 (1986); **73.** EMBO J 3, 1831 (1984); **74.** J Biol Chem 258, 11427 (1983); **75.** J Cell Biol 110, 559 (1990); **76.** Biochemistry 26, 1546 (1987); **77.** Biotechniques 17, 730 (1994); **78.** Science 270, 1835 (1995); **79.** Neurosci Lett 258, 124 (1998); **80.** Parasitology 109, 249 (1994); **81.** FASEB J 8, 573 (1994); **82.** J Cell Sci 105, 861 (1993); **83.** Agr Biol Chem 50, 399 (1986); **84.** FEBS Lett 179, 148 (1985); **85.** J Cell Biol 99, 1989 (1984); **86.** Cell 64, 393 (1991); **87.** Biochemistry 26, 765 (1987); **88.** Biochemistry 29, 4582 (1990); **89.** Biophys J 71, 487 (1996); **90.** Proc Natl Acad Sci U S A 85, 2315 (1988); **91.** Arch Ophthalmol 105, 844 (1987); **92.** Microvasc Res 36, 172 (1988); **93.** Am J Physiol 245, H495 (1983); **94.** Am J Physiol 253, F366 (1987); **95.** Biophys J 65, 2277 (1993); **96.** Pflugers Arch 427, 86 (1994); **97.** J Cereb Blood Flow Metab 13, 359 (1993); **98.** Neuron 15, 755 (1995); **99.** Biophys J 74, 3302 (1998); **100.** AIAA Journal 34, 449 (1996); **101.** Exp Fluids 18, 249 (1995).

Product List — 14.5 Fluorescent and Biotinylated Dextrans

Cat #	Product Name	Unit Size
D22910	dextran, Alexa Fluor® 488; 10,000 MW, anionic, fixable	5 mg
D22911	dextran, Alexa Fluor® 546; 10,000 MW, anionic, fixable	5 mg
D22912	dextran, Alexa Fluor® 568; 10,000 MW, anionic, fixable	5 mg
D22913	dextran, Alexa Fluor® 594; 10,000 MW, anionic, fixable	5 mg
D22914	dextran, Alexa Fluor® 647; 10,000 MW, anionic, fixable	5 mg
D3330	dextran, amino, 3000 MW	2 mg
D1860	dextran, amino, 10,000 MW	100 mg
D1861	dextran, amino, 40,000 MW	1 g
D1862	dextran, amino, 70,000 MW	1 g
D7144	dextran, amino, 500,000 MW	1 g
D34678	dextran, 5-(and-6)-carboxy-Q-rhodamine, CMNCBZ-caged, 10,000 MW, anionic	100 mg
D7135	dextran, biotin, 3000 MW, lysine fixable (BDA-3000)	5 mg
D7134	dextran, biotin, 3000 MW, neutral	10 mg
D1956	dextran, biotin, 10,000 MW, lysine fixable (BDA-10,000)	10 mg
D1957	dextran, biotin, 70,000 MW, lysine fixable (BDA-70,000)	25 mg
D7142	dextran, biotin, 500,000 MW, lysine fixable (BDA-500,000)	25 mg
D7168	dextran, BODIPY® FL, 10,000 MW, fixable	10 mg
D7132	dextran, Cascade Blue®, 3000 MW, anionic, lysine fixable	5 mg
		10 mg

For current prices or to order online, visit probes.invitrogen.com

Cat #	Product Name	Unit Size
D1976	dextran, Cascade Blue®, 10,000 MW, anionic, lysine fixable	25 mg
D12980	dextran, 4',5'-dichloro-2',7'-dimethoxyfluorescein, 10,000 MW, anionic	5 mg
D12981	dextran, 4',5'-dichloro-2',7'-dimethoxyfluorescein, 70,000 MW, anionic	5 mg
D12983	dextran, 2,4-dinitrophenyl-X, 10,000 MW, lysine fixable	25 mg
D3309	dextran, DMNB-caged fluorescein, 3000 MW, anionic	5 mg
D3310	dextran, DMNB-caged fluorescein, 10,000 MW, anionic	5 mg
D7146	dextran, DMNB-caged fluorescein and biotin, 10,000 MW, lysine fixable	5 mg
D7147	dextran, DMNB-caged fluorescein and biotin, 70,000 MW, lysine fixable	5 mg
D7166	dextran, eosin, 10,000 MW, anionic, lysine fixable	25 mg
D3305	dextran, fluorescein, 3000 MW, anionic	10 mg
D3306	dextran, fluorescein, 3000 MW, anionic, lysine fixable	10 mg
D1821	dextran, fluorescein, 10,000 MW, anionic	25 mg
D1820	dextran, fluorescein, 10,000 MW, anionic, lysine fixable (fluoro-emerald)	25 mg
D1844	dextran, fluorescein, 40,000 MW, anionic	25 mg
D1845	dextran, fluorescein, 40,000 MW, anionic, lysine fixable	25 mg
D1823	dextran, fluorescein, 70,000 MW, anionic	25 mg
D1822	dextran, fluorescein, 70,000 MW, anionic, lysine fixable	25 mg
D1815	dextran, fluorescein, 70,000 MW, polyanionic	25 mg
D7136	dextran, fluorescein, 500,000 MW, anionic, lysine fixable	10 mg
D7137	dextran, fluorescein, 2,000,000 MW, anionic, lysine fixable	10 mg
D7156	dextran, fluorescein and biotin, 3000 MW, anionic, lysine fixable (micro-emerald)	5 mg
D7178	dextran, fluorescein and biotin, 10,000 MW, anionic, lysine fixable (mini-emerald)	10 mg
D1825	dextran, lucifer yellow, 10,000 MW, anionic, lysine fixable	25 mg
D7170	dextran, Oregon Green® 488; 10,000 MW, anionic	5 mg
D7171	dextran, Oregon Green® 488; 10,000 MW, anionic, lysine fixable	5 mg
D7172	dextran, Oregon Green® 488; 70,000 MW, anionic	5 mg
D7173	dextran, Oregon Green® 488; 70,000 MW, anionic, lysine fixable	5 mg
D7174	dextran, Oregon Green® 514; 10,000 MW, anionic	5 mg
D7175	dextran, Oregon Green® 514; 10,000 MW, anionic, lysine fixable	5 mg
D7176	dextran, Oregon Green® 514; 70,000 MW, anionic	5 mg
D1824	dextran, rhodamine B, 10,000 MW, neutral	25 mg
D1841	dextran, rhodamine B, 70,000 MW, neutral	25 mg
D7163	dextran, Rhodamine Green™, 3000 MW	5 mg
D7153	dextran, Rhodamine Green™, 10,000 MW, lysine fixable	10 mg
D3307	dextran, tetramethylrhodamine, 3000 MW, anionic	10 mg
D3308	dextran, tetramethylrhodamine, 3000 MW, anionic, lysine fixable	10 mg
D1868	dextran, tetramethylrhodamine, 10,000 MW, anionic, fixable	25 mg
D1817	dextran, tetramethylrhodamine, 10,000 MW, lysine fixable (fluoro-ruby)	25 mg
D1816	dextran, tetramethylrhodamine, 10,000 MW, neutral	25 mg
D1842	dextran, tetramethylrhodamine, 40,000 MW, neutral	25 mg
D1818	dextran, tetramethylrhodamine, 70,000 MW, lysine fixable	25 mg
D1819	dextran, tetramethylrhodamine, 70,000 MW, neutral	25 mg
D7139	dextran, tetramethylrhodamine, 2,000,000 MW, lysine fixable	10 mg
D7162	dextran, tetramethylrhodamine and biotin, 3000 MW, lysine fixable (micro-ruby)	5 mg
D3312	dextran, tetramethylrhodamine and biotin, 10,000 MW, lysine fixable (mini-ruby)	10 mg
D3328	dextran, Texas Red®, 3000 MW, lysine fixable	10 mg
D3329	dextran, Texas Red®, 3000 MW, neutral	10 mg
D1863	dextran, Texas Red®, 10,000 MW, lysine fixable	25 mg
D1828	dextran, Texas Red®, 10,000 MW, neutral	25 mg
D1829	dextran, Texas Red®, 40,000 MW, neutral	25 mg
D1864	dextran, Texas Red®, 70,000 MW, lysine fixable	25 mg
D1830	dextran, Texas Red®, 70,000 MW, neutral	25 mg
N7167	NeuroTrace® BDA-10,000 Neuronal Tracer Kit	1 kit
V22915	Vybrant® Cell Lineage Tracing Kit	1 kit

For current prices or to order online, visit probes.invitrogen.com

14.6 FluoSpheres® and TransFluoSpheres® Microspheres for Tracing

FluoSpheres® and TransFluoSpheres® polystyrene microspheres satisfy several prerequisites of ideal long-term biological tracers. Because the dyes in our microspheres are incorporated throughout the microsphere rather than just on its surface, the fluorescence output per microsphere is significantly greater than that obtained from protein or dextran conjugates (Table 6.6) and is relatively immune to photobleaching and other environment-dependent effects. FluoSpheres® and TransFluoSpheres® microspheres are also biologically inert and physically durable, and they are available from Molecular Probes with a large number of uniform sizes and surface properties. Furthermore, their spectral properties can be freely manipulated during manufacture without altering their surface properties. Our current carboxylate-modified fluorescent microspheres have much higher surface charges than were previously available, making them more hydrophilic and thus more useful as tracers. The additional carboxylate groups also make it easier to couple the microspheres to proteins and other biomolecules. See Section 6.5 for an extensive discussion of the properties of our FluoSpheres® and TransFluoSpheres® polystyrene beads. Molecular Probes also makes numerous fluorescent microsphere products that are useful as standards for imaging (Section 23.1) and flow cytometry (Section 23.2).

Availability of intensely fluorescent, highly uniform microspheres in different colors and sizes permits diverse applications in tracking particles and cells, tracing fluid dynamics and amplifying signals. In addition, measuring the effect of various interventions on regional blood flow is an important quantitative application of fluorescent microspheres. Using a mixture of beads of different sizes, each labeled with a different fluorescent color, researchers can discriminate the size dependence of uptake or transport of microspheres *in vivo* in cells, capillaries, lung or other tissues.[1] Our smallest microspheres can be microinjected into cells (see below) or are actively taken up by phagocytosis (Section 16.1).

Fluorescent Microspheres for Regional Blood Flow Studies

Relatively large radiolabeled microspheres (10–15 µm in diameter) have long been used for regional blood flow studies in tissues and organs. However, fluorescent microspheres have been shown to be superior to radioactive microspheres in chronic blood flow measurements.[2] In most cases, the microspheres are injected at desired locations in the circulatory system and eventually lodge in the capillaries, where they can later be counted in dissected tissue sections. To eliminate the hazards, expense and disposal problems of the radiolabeled microspheres,[3] researchers have turned to fluorescent and colored microspheres for measuring myocardial and cortical blood flow.[4–11] In addition, blood flow in brain cortex has been measured using much smaller microspheres (1.3 µm) by determining velocities of individual fluorescent beads with strobe epi-illumination.[12] Blood flow measurements using fluorescent microspheres in other organs, including the kidney,[13,14] lung,[15–21] pancreas,[22] adrenal glands,[23] and teeth,[24] are equally feasible. Our 0.1 µm and 0.2 µm FluoSpheres® microspheres have been used to trace new blood vessel development, which is important for the study of tumor angiogenesis and microvascular continuity. These small microspheres completely fill the vessels and remain in place following histological sectioning.[25] Fluorescent dextrans (Section 14.5) also have been used to make direct measurement of capillary transit times using intravital microscopy.[26,27]

FluoSpheres® Microspheres for Blood Flow Determination

Molecular Probes has used its proprietary fluorescent dye technology to produce a range of intensely fluorescent FluoSpheres® microspheres specifically designed for regional blood flow determination (Table 14.5). Regional blood flow studies using our FluoSpheres® polystyrene microspheres for blood flow determination (Figure 14.76) have been validated in several side-by-side comparisons with radioactively labeled microspheres[8,28–31] (see Note 14.4 "Product Highlight: Fluorescent Microspheres for Blood Flow Determination"). The two methods exhibit equivalent detection sensitivity, and excellent correlation

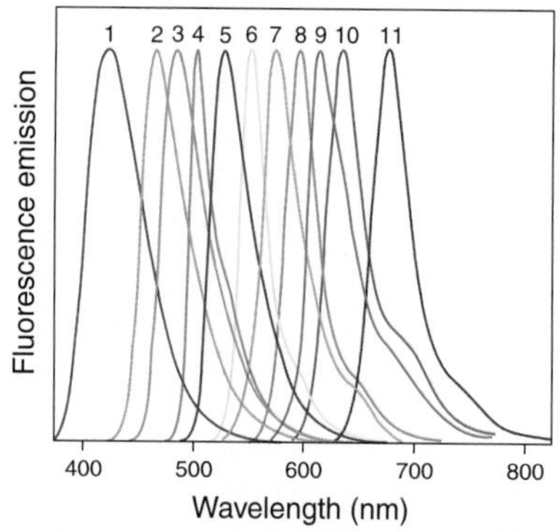

Figure 14.76 Normalized fluorescence emission spectra of the dyes contained in FluoSpheres® polystyrene microspheres for blood flow determination, after extraction into 2-ethoxyethyl acetate (Cellosolve acetate). The eleven colors of fluorescent microspheres represented are: **1)** blue, **2)** blue-green, **3)** green, **4)** yellow-green, **5)** yellow, **6)** orange, **7)** red-orange, **8)** red, **9)** carmine, **10)** crimson and **11)** scarlet.

Table 14.5 — FluoSpheres® microspheres for blood flow determination

Color (Ex/Em *)	Bead diameter	
	15 µm	10 µm
Blue (365/415)	F8837	F8829
Blue-green (430/465)	F8838	F8830
Green (450/480)	F21010	
Yellow-green (505/515)	F8844	F8836
Yellow (515/534)	F21011	
Orange (540/560)	F8841	F8833
Red-orange (565/580)	F21012	
Red (580/605)	F8842	F8834
Carmine (580/620)	F21013	
Crimson (625/645)	F8839	F8831
Scarlet (645/680)	F8843	

* Fluorescence excitation and emission maxima of the encapsulated dye measured in 2-ethoxyethyl acetate. All FluoSpheres® microspheres for blood flow determination are supplied as suspensions containing 1.0×10^6 beads/mL (15 µm microspheres) or 3.6×10^6 beads mL (10 µm microspheres) in a unit size of 10 mL.

Note 14.4 — Product Highlight

Fluorescent Microspheres for Blood Flow Determination

For about 30 years, radioactively labeled microspheres have been used as tracers to estimate regional organ perfusion. In order to minimize radiation exposure and to reduce expensive storage and disposal of radioactive materials, researchers are replacing the radiolabeled beads in these studies with fluorescent microspheres.[1-5] Molecular Probes' intensely fluorescent FluoSpheres® and TransFluoSpheres® beads for blood flow determination and tracer studies are especially designed for these applications. Because they are chemically inert, our fluorescent microspheres often can be left in the animal for months before analysis without significant loss of resolution or subsequent detectability. Radioactive (^{125}I) beads and fluorescent FluoSpheres® beads yielded comparable results when used to assess coronary blood flow in dogs,[6] as well as to measure perfusion of dog lung, pig heart and pig kidney.[7] Our 10 µm and 15 µm fluorescent microspheres are used for larger blood vessels, while our 1 µm FluoSpheres® and 2 µm TransFluoSpheres® products for tracing are used for the study of microcirculation and in regional pulmonary ventilation experiments.[8-10]

Additional technical support, including a detailed applications manual on the use of fluorescent microspheres for blood flow determination, is available from the Fluorescent Microsphere Resource Center (FMRC) at the University of Washington, Seattle. Contact information is listed at their web site (http://fmrc.pulmcc.washington.edu/).

References

1. J Neurosci Methods 122, 149 (2003); **2.** Biotech Histochem 73, 291 (1998); **3.** Am J Physiol 275, H110 (1998); **4.** J Cereb Blood Flow Metab 13, 359 (1993); **5.** J Auton Nerv Syst 30, 159 (1990); **6.** Circ Shock 41, 156 (1993); **7.** J Appl Physiol 74, 2585 (1993); **8.** Toxicol Appl Pharmacol 153, 28 (1998); **9.** J Appl Physiol 85, 2344 (1998); **10.** J Appl Physiol 82, 943 (1997).

FluoSpheres® and TransFluoSpheres® Beads for Blood Flow Determination

Cat #	Product Name
F8890	FluoSpheres® Blood Flow Determination Fluorescent Color Kit #1, polystyrene microspheres, 10 µm *seven colors, 10 mL each* *3.6 × 10⁶ beads/mL*
F8891	FluoSpheres® Blood Flow Determination Fluorescent Color Kit #2, polystyrene microspheres, 15 µm *seven colors, 10 mL each* *1.0 × 10⁶ beads/mL*
F8892	FluoSpheres® Blood Flow Determination Fluorescent Color Kit #3, polystyrene microspheres, 15 µm *five colors, 10 mL each* *1.0 × 10⁶ beads/mL*
F21015	FluoSpheres® Blood Flow Determination Fluorescent Color Kit #4, polystyrene microspheres, 15 µm *four colors, 10 mL each* *1.0 × 10⁶ beads/mL*

Fluorescent Color Kits for Regional Blood Flow Determination

Cat #	Product Name
F13080	FluoSpheres® polystyrene microspheres, 1.0 µm, blue-green–fluorescent (430/465) *for tracer studies* *1.0 × 10^{10} beads/mL*
F13081	FluoSpheres® polystyrene microspheres, 1.0 µm, yellow-green–fluorescent (505/515) *for tracer studies* *1.0 × 10^{10} beads/mL*
F13082	FluoSpheres® polystyrene microspheres, 1.0 µm, orange-fluorescent (540/560) *for tracer studies* *1.0 × 10^{10} beads/mL*
F13083	FluoSpheres® polystyrene microspheres, 1.0 µm, red-fluorescent (580/605) *for tracer studies* *1.0 × 10^{10} beads/mL*
T13090	TransFluoSpheres® polystyrene microspheres, 2.0 µm (633/760) *for tracer studies* *1.0 × 10^9 beads/mL*
F8829	FluoSpheres® polystyrene microspheres, 10 µm, blue-fluorescent (365/415) *for blood flow determination* *3.6 × 10^6 beads/mL*
F8830	FluoSpheres® polystyrene microspheres, 10 µm, blue-green–fluorescent (430/465) *for blood flow determination* *3.6 × 10^6 beads/mL*
F8836	FluoSpheres® polystyrene microspheres, 10 µm, yellow-green–fluorescent (505/515) *for blood flow determination* *3.6 × 10^6 beads/mL*
F8833	FluoSpheres® polystyrene microspheres, 10 µm, orange-fluorescent (540/560) *for blood flow determination* *3.6 × 10^6 beads/mL*
F8834	FluoSpheres® polystyrene microspheres, 10 µm, red-fluorescent (580/605) *for blood flow determination* *3.6 × 10^6 beads/mL*
F8831	FluoSpheres® polystyrene microspheres, 10 µm, crimson-fluorescent (625/645) *for blood flow determination* *3.6 × 10^6 beads/mL*
F8837	FluoSpheres® polystyrene microspheres, 15 µm, blue-fluorescent (365/415) *for blood flow determination* *1.0 × 10^6 beads/mL*
F8838	FluoSpheres® polystyrene microspheres, 15 µm, blue-green–fluorescent (430/465) *for blood flow determination* *1.0 × 10^6 beads/mL*
F21010	FluoSpheres® polystyrene microspheres, 15 µm, green-fluorescent (450/480) *for blood flow determination* *1.0 × 10^6 beads/mL*
F8844	FluoSpheres® polystyrene microspheres, 15 µm, yellow-green–fluorescent (505/515) *for blood flow determination* *1.0 × 10^6 beads/mL*
F21011	FluoSpheres® polystyrene microspheres, 15 µm, yellow-fluorescent (515/534) *for blood flow determination* *1.0 × 10^6 beads/mL*
F8841	FluoSpheres® polystyrene microspheres, 15 µm, orange-fluorescent (540/560) *for blood flow determination* *1.0 × 10^6 beads/mL*
F21012	FluoSpheres® polystyrene microspheres, 15 µm, red-orange–fluorescent (565/580) *for blood flow determination* *1.0 × 10^6 beads/mL*
F8842	FluoSpheres® polystyrene microspheres, 15 µm, red-fluorescent (580/605) *for blood flow determination* *1.0 × 10^6 beads/mL*
F21013	FluoSpheres® polystyrene microspheres, 15 µm, carmine-fluorescent (580/620) *for blood flow determination* *1.0 × 10^6 beads/mL*
F8839	FluoSpheres® polystyrene microspheres, 15 µm, crimson-fluorescent (625/645) *for blood flow determination* *1.0 × 10^6 beads/mL*
F8843	FluoSpheres® polystyrene microspheres, 15 µm, scarlet-fluorescent (645/680) *for blood flow determination* *1.0 × 10^6 beads/mL*

between the flow measurements has been reported. In addition, techniques have been developed to extract the microspheres and the fluorescent dyes they contain from tissue samples, allowing blood flow quantitation to be performed using readily available instrumentation such as spectrofluorometers and fluorescence microplate readers.[6] Up to seven simultaneously circulating tracers can be discriminated based on uncompensated fluorescent color differences. With spectral spillover corrections, the number of simultaneously detectable tracers can be increased to thirteen.[32] Microspheres that have been perfused or injected into tissues and organs retain their fluorescence following histological serial sectioning.[4,33] Our FluoSpheres® microspheres for blood flow determination, which are available in eleven distinguishable fluorescent colors (Figure 14.76), are also compatible with blood flow analyzer systems that perform automated extraction and analysis.[34]

FluoSpheres® Color Kits for Regional Blood Flow Studies

Molecular Probes offers four different FluoSpheres® Blood Flow Determination Fluorescent Color Kits (Table 14.6):

- Kit #1 (F8890) contains 10 mL vials of 10 µm microspheres in seven fluorescent colors (blue, blue-green, yellow-green, orange, red, crimson and scarlet).
- Kit #2 (F8891) contains 10 mL vials of 15 µm microspheres in seven fluorescent colors (blue, blue-green, yellow-green, orange, red, crimson and scarlet).
- Kit #3 (F8892) contains 10 mL vials of 15 µm microspheres in five fluorescent colors (blue-green, yellow-green, orange, red and crimson).
- Kit #4 (F21015) contains 10 mL vials of 15 µm microspheres in four additional fluorescent colors (green, yellow, carmine and red-orange), which are spectrally distinguishable from the dyes in Kits #2 and #3 (Figure 14.76).

The aqueous suspensions of 10 µm and 15 µm beads contain 3.6 million and 1 million microspheres per mL, respectively. All kits include a detailed protocol. Each of the colors of FluoSpheres® microspheres for blood flow studies can also be purchased separately (Table 14.5).

Regional Blood Flow in Live Animals

Molecular Probes' 2.0 µm TransFluoSpheres® polystyrene microspheres (633/760) (T13090) have been successfully used to measure retinal and choroidal blood circulation in live rhesus monkeys.[35] In the past, researchers using fluorescent microspheres performed their measurements on sectioned tissues. Now, because these 2.0 µm TransFluoSpheres® beads emit in the infrared region of the spectrum, blood circulation can be detected in some tissues in real time and regional blood circulation measurements can be made in live animals.[36]

Table 14.6 — FluoSpheres® blood flow and color kits

Catalog #	Application	Bead Size	Concentration	Number of Colors
F8890	Blood flow determination	10 µm	3.6×10^6 beads/mL	7 colors, 10 mL each
F8891	Blood flow determination	15 µm	1.0×10^6 beads/mL	7 colors, 10 mL each
F8892	Blood flow determination	15 µm	1.0×10^6 beads/mL	5 colors, 10 mL each
F21015	Blood flow determination	15 µm	1.0×10^6 beads/mL	4 colors, 10 mL each
F10720	Microinjection/tracing	0.04 µm	5% solids	4 colors, 1 mL each

Fluorescent Microsphere Resource Center

Additional technical support, including a detailed applications manual on the use of fluorescent microspheres for blood flow determination, is available from the Fluorescent Microsphere Resource Center (FMRC) at the University of Washington, Seattle. The FMRC can be contacted by phone (206) 685–9479 or fax (206) 685–8673. Information can also be obtained from their web site at http://fmrc.pulmcc.washington.edu/.

Alternative Method for Measuring Blood Flow

In a novel technique that does not use microspheres but may be useful for diagnosing diabetic retinopathy and other diseases that cause a breakdown in vascular tissue, the lipophilic carbocyanine dye DiD (D307, Section 14.4) was employed in conjunction with SYTO® 16 and SYTO® 59 nucleic acid stains (S7578, S11341; Section 8.1) to label red and white blood cells.[37] These labeled cells were then observed with a scanning laser ophthalmoscope equipped with both an argon-ion laser and a He–Ne laser.

Particle and Cell Tracking with Fluorescent Microspheres

In addition to our microspheres specially designed for blood flow studies, Molecular Probes offers a wide range of fluorescent FluoSpheres® carboxylate-modified microspheres in different fluorescent colors, bead diameters and surface functional groups (see Table 6.7 for a complete list). Of particular interest are our FluoSpheres® beads with 0.04 µm diameters and FluoSpheres® beads for tracer studies with 1 µm diameters, which have been specially formulated to perform well in cell tracking and particle tracking studies, respectively.

FluoSpheres® Beads with 0.04 µm Diameters for Microinjection

Unlike our other fluorescent microspheres, most of which come in aqueous suspensions containing 2% solids and 2 mM sodium azide as a preservative, FluoSpheres® beads with 0.04 µm diameters are prepared as aqueous suspensions containing 5% solids without preservatives. At more than double the concentration of our standard FluoSpheres® microspheres, these carboxylate-modified 0.04 µm beads are well suited to applications requiring microinjectable tracers. Yellow-green–, orange-, red- and dark red–fluorescent colors are available either individually (F8795, F8792, F8793, F8789) or in the FluoSpheres® Fluorescent Color Kit (F10720). In addition, the red-orange– and infrared-fluorescent colors are available individually (F8794, F8791). Use of the dark red– and infrared-fluorescent FluoSpheres® microspheres should permit greater light penetration through tissues. In many biological systems, the concentrated fluorescence and spherical shape of the FluoSpheres® beads permit them to be detected against a relatively high but diffuse background fluorescence. However, our TransFluoSpheres® microspheres (Table 14.7) — microspheres with an extremely large Stokes shifts — are preferred for some studies because their fluorescence may be better resolved from the tissue's autofluorescence (Figure 6.49).

FluoSpheres® Beads with 1.0 µm Diameters for Tracer Studies

Our FluoSpheres® fluorescent microspheres for tracer studies are 1.0 µm polystyrene beads for analysis by tissue extraction (Table 14.7). Because the dye content of these microspheres is much higher than that of other fluorescent microspheres, stronger signals can be generated using fewer microspheres per tracing experiment. These heavily dye-loaded beads are available in four well-resolved fluorescent colors: blue-green (F13080), yellow-green (F13081), orange (F13082) and red (F13083), with excitation/emission maxima at approximately 430/465, 505/515, 540/560 and 580/605 nm, respectively (the emission spectra are shown as peaks 2, 4, 6 and 8 of Figure 14.76). Aerosols containing these fluorescent microspheres have been used to acquire high-resolution maps of regional pulmonary ventilation.[20] Transport of these fluorescent microspheres through tissues can be determined using methods that have been developed for regional blood flow determination or by confocal laser-scanning microscopy.[38] As with the FluoSpheres® beads for blood flow determination, the microspheres and the fluorescent dyes they contain are first extracted from the tissue sample, and then the fluorescence is quantitated on a spectrofluorometer or fluorescence microplate reader. This technique is described in the accompanying product literature.

Europium and Platinum Luminescent Microspheres for Time-Resolved Fluorometry

Detecting a low level of protein or DNA targets in a tissue sample or on a membrane using classic fluorochromes is sometimes difficult and prone to errors because specific fluorescence signals tend to be low and are usually mixed with nonspecific signals and autofluorescence. One approach to improve detectability is the use of time-resolved luminescence reagents, such as our FluoSpheres® europium luminescent microspheres (Table 14.8) and FluoSpheres® platinum luminescent microspheres (Table 14.8). The FluoSpheres® europium beads contain Eu^{3+} coordination complexes with luminescence decay times of >600 microseconds — much longer than the <50 nanosecond decay time of conventional fluorophores and autofluorescence. The luminescence of the Pt^{2+} chelate in the FluoSpheres® platinum luminescent microspheres has a decay time of >40 microseconds. Thus, time-gated fluorescence detection using these microspheres results in complete rejection of autofluorescence signals.[39–47] In addition, the europium luminescent microspheres feature long-wavelength emission (610–650 nm) that is well separated from their excitation peak (340–390 nm) (Figure 6.47). The platinum luminescent microspheres are maximally excited near 390 nm with narrow emission that is maximal near 650 nm (Figure 6.48). Because of these unusually large Stokes shifts, filter combinations can be chosen that effectively isolate the desired luminescence signal. The narrow emissions and different lifetimes permit simultaneous use of the europium and platinum luminescent microspheres as tracers. These microspheres are available with nominal diameters of 0.04 µm, 0.2 µm or 1.0 µm (Table 14.7).

Microspheres for Monitoring Airflow

A cubic foot of air may contain hundreds of thousands of airborne particles such as viruses, bacteria, pollen, mold spores and gaseous chemicals (Figure 14.77). To combat harmful airborne particles, many types of air filters and instruments for detecting airborne particles have been developed for medical and defense purposes. Because most airborne particles are small (typically 10–150 nm, below microscopic resolution) and are difficult to detect, verification

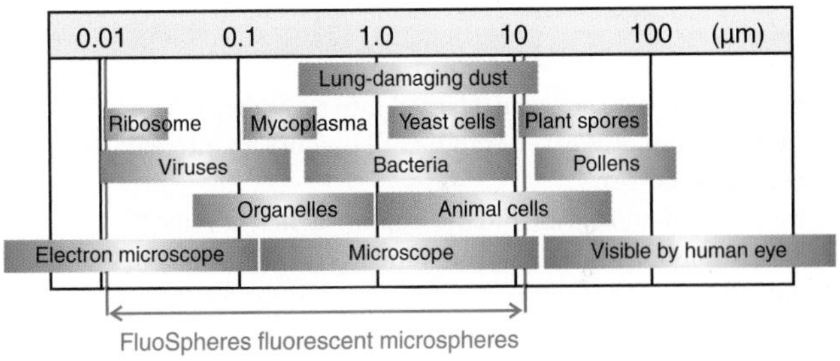

Figure 14.77 FluoSpheres® microsphere sizes relative to common airborne particles.

Table 14.7 — FluoSpheres® and TransFluoSpheres® microspheres for tracing

Color (Ex/Em *)	Size			
	0.04 µm	0.2 µm	1.0 µm	2.0 µm
Blue-green (430/465)			F13080 †	
Yellow-green (505/515)	F8795 ‡		F13081 †	
Orange (540/560)	F8792 ‡		F13082 †	
Red-orange (565/580)	F8794 ‡			
Red (580/605)	F8793 ‡		F13083 †	
Dark red (660/680)	F8789 ‡			
Infrared (715/755)	F8791 §			
Europium (365/610)	F20880 **	F20881 **	F20882 **	
Platinum (390/650)	F20886 **	F20887 **	F20888 **	
TransFluoSpheres® (633/760)				T13090 ††

* Fluorescence or luminescence excitation and emission maxima, in nm. † 1×10^{10} beads/mL, 5 mL unit size. ‡ 5% solids, 1.0 mL unit size. § 5% solids, 0.4 mL unit size. ** 0.5% solids, 2.0 mL unit size. †† 1×10^{9} beads/mL, 0.5 mL unit size.

Table 14.8 — Molecular Probes' europium and platinum luminescent FluoSpheres® microspheres*

Type of Microsphere	Size		
	0.04 µm	0.2 µm	1.0 µm
Carboxylate-Modified Microspheres			
Europium (365/610)	F20880	F20881	F20882
Platinum (390/650)	F20886	F20887	F20888
NeutrAvidin-Coated Microspheres			
Europium	F20883	F20884	F20885
Platinum	F20889	F20890	F20891

* Luminescent FluoSpheres® microspheres are supplied as aqueous suspensions containing 0.5% solids. The approximate absorption and emission maxima are 365/610 nm and 390/650 nm for the europium and platinum labeled microspheres, respectively.

of the function of these filters and instruments can be a challenge. Our FluoSpheres® microspheres are specially stained fluorescent polystyrene beads that can mimic airborne particles [20] and be used as unique markers to verify equipment reliability. A single "virus-sized" 20 nm diameter FluoSpheres® microsphere carries 100–200 fluorophore molecules and so emits sufficiently bright fluorescence for easy detection.

Transplantation and Migration Studies with Fluorescent Microspheres

Labeling cells with fluorescent microspheres prior to transplantation enables researchers to distinguish cell types and analyze graft migration in the host over extended time periods. Unlike other tracers, most of which rapidly diffuse or leach from their site of application in tissues, fluorescent microspheres tend to remain in place for periods of at least months. Their stability and biological inertness give them considerable potential for transplantation studies. Moreover, the intense fluorescence, high uniformity and low debris content of our FluoSpheres® polystyrene microspheres will circumvent many of the problems encountered in use of fluorescent microspheres from other sources. Cells are generally labeled with microspheres by microinjection or other invasive methods (Table 14.1). Potential problems of sterility, unequal uptake and translocation of the beads by the cells need to be considered before using fluorescent microspheres in transplantation and other cell tracing studies.[48] It has been reported that polystyrene microspheres for transplantation studies can be sterilized by heating below their softening temperature.[49]

Some published transplantation applications for fluorescent microspheres obtained from various sources include studies designed to trace:

- Cholinergic neurons transplanted into an embryo [50]
- Implantation of Weaver granule cell precursors into wild-type cerebellar cortex [51]
- Injection of myoblasts into dystrophin-deficient mice [52]
- Migration of neutrophils from lung to tracheobronchial lymph node [53]
- Migration of transplanted neurons into regions of continuing neuronal degeneration in adult mice [54]
- Projection of efferent fibers in neural grafts [55]
- Transplantation of fetal rat brain cells into host brains [56]
- Transplantation of autologous peritoneal macrophages into spinal cord compression lesions [57]
- Tumor-cell invasion in the adult rat brain by human glioma cells [58]

Fluorescent microspheres have also been used to visualize the injection sites of *in vivo* gene transfer in tissues.[59]

Several other probes from Molecular Probes may also be useful for transplantation studies, including CellTracker™ dyes (Section 14.2), the succinimidyl ester of carboxyfluorescein diacetate [60,61] (5(6)-CFDA, SE; CFSE; C1157; Section 14.2), fluorescent dextrans [62] (Section 14.5) and lipophilic tracers (Section 14.4).

Neuronal Tracing with Fluorescent Microspheres

Katz, the first scientist to use fluorescent microspheres as neuronal tracers, demonstrated that rhodamine-labeled microspheres could undergo retrograde transport.[63] Although the mechanism of microsphere transport is not completely understood, the process can apparently be facilitated by using a high concentration of particles with small diameters (<0.05 µm) and high negative surface-charge densities.[64–66] Fluorescent microspheres are also suitable for retrograde tracing because they are not cytotoxic and persist for extraordinarily long periods in nerve cells. The fluorescence intensity of microsphere-labeled neuronal perikarya in rats was found to be undiminished one year after injection.[67] Adsorption of neuroactive proteins, including neurotrophins, on small-diameter fluorescent microspheres provides a means of locating their *in vivo* and *in vitro* microinjection sites and of following retrograde transport in the central nervous system.[68] Our fluorescent microspheres are also becoming important tracers in ophthalmological studies [35,69,70] where they undergo retrograde transport.[71,72]

Our red-fluorescent, carboxylate-modified FluoSpheres® beads [73,74] (F8793) are retrogradely transported in rat lumbosacral ventral root axons that have been subjected to peripheral crush injury.[75] In this study, the fluorescent beads were used to photoconvert diaminobenzidine (DAB) into an insoluble, electron-dense reaction product in order to facilitate ultrastructural analysis by electron microscopy (see Note 14.2 "Product Highlight: Fluorescent Probes for Photoconversion of Diaminobenzidine Reagents" in Section 14.3). Because retrograde transport of fluorescent microspheres appears to be extremely sensitive to the microsphere's size, surface-charge density and concentration, references for neuronal tracing in our bibliography of microsphere applications (see below) may not always be applicable to our current products.

Following Phagocytosis with Fluorescent Microspheres

Many cell types actively ingest opsonized or nonopsonized fluorescent microspheres (Section 16.1). The preferred microspheres are about 0.5–2 µm in diameter. Confocal laser-scanning microscopy can distinguish between ingested beads and those simply bound to the surface.[76] Flow cytometry, fluorescence microscopy and fluorescence spectrometry have been used to quantitate phagocytosis by macrophage cells [77–81] and protozoan cells.[82] Macrophage cells in primary cultures of rat cerebral cortex have been identified by their ability to selectively phagocytose fluorescent microspheres;[83] macrophage cells have also been sorted based on the absolute number of microspheres phagocytosed.[81] Fluorescent microsphere uptake has been used as a model for alveolar macrophage cell translocation and clearance of inhaled aerosols containing environmental particulates.[38,84,85] As with our fluorescent microspheres for blood flow determination (see above), solvent extraction of the fluorescent dye from the beads can be used to quantitate microsphere uptake by macrophage cells.[86]

For the study of collagen phagocytosis, Molecular Probes manufactures yellow-green–fluorescent FluoSpheres® collagen I–labeled microspheres in either 1.0 µm or 2.0 µm diameters (F20892, F20893; Section 16.1). Fibroblasts phagocytose and then intracellularly digest collagen. These activities play an important role in the remodeling of the extracellular matrix during normal physiological turnover of connective tissues, in development, in wound repair and possibly in aging and various disorders. A well-established procedure for observing collagen phagocytosis by either flow cytometry or fluorescence microscopy involves the use of collagen-coated fluorescent microspheres, which attach to the cell surface and become engulfed by fibroblasts.[87–89]

Tracking the Movement of Proteins and Other Biomolecules with Fluorescent Microspheres

FluoSpheres® microspheres can serve as bright, inert and extremely photostable labels for tracking particle movement and other dynamic processes over extended time periods. The intense fluorescence of our FluoSpheres® beads permits the detection and tracking of very small single particles in three dimensions.[90–92] Examples of the diverse applications of fluorescent microspheres include studies designed to track or quantitate:

- Binding of kinetochores to microtubules *in vitro*[92,93]
- Brownian motion in protein[94] and dextran solutions[95]
- Exchangeable GTP-binding sites on paclitaxel-stabilized fluorescent microtubules[96]
- Direction and rate of axonal transport in the squid giant axon[97]
- Fluid dynamics and flow in brain arterioles[98] and peripheral lymph[99]
- Injection sites in tissues[100,101]
- Lateral diffusion of lipids and receptors in membranes[91,102–104]
- Movement of microinjected microspheres poleward during mitosis of sea urchin eggs[105] and sand dollar eggs[106]
- Particle flow through a model biofilm containing *Pseudomonas aeruginosa*, *P. fluorescens* and *Klebsiella pneumoniae* using confocal laser-scanning microscopy[107] (Figure 14.78)
- Size dependence of particle-uptake and particle-distribution measurements in rat gastrointestinal mucosa[108]
- Three-dimensional motion of microspheres in order to assess water permeability in individual Chinese hamster ovary (CHO) cells expressing CHIP28 water channels[90]
- Uptake of seawater by starfish[109]

Fluorescent microspheres have been used with optical tweezers[110] to control the movement of single myosin filaments[111] or kinesin molecules[112] and for imaging at suboptical resolution by scanning luminescence X-ray microscopy.[113] In addition, our 0.1 µm red-fluorescent carboxylate-modified microspheres (F8801, Section 6.3) have been used to model particle distribution and penetration of adenovirus-mediated gene transfer in human bronchial submucosal glands using xenografts.[114]

Our Bibliography of Microspheres Applications

Our bibliography of microsphere applications (M8997) contains over 1200 references, and continuously updated copies are available upon request from our Technical Assistance Department or through our web site (probes.invitrogen.com). This bibliography includes references in which microspheres from several different sources were used. Because the source, surface properties and size of the microspheres may affect the application, the methods described in these references should be considered guides rather than definitive protocols. In particular, the bibliography lists several references that cite the use of fluorescent microspheres for retrograde tracing, and our FluoSpheres® beads have been inconsistent in this application.

References

1. Am J Physiol 271, H996 (1996); **2.** Am J Physiol 275, H110 (1998); **3.** Circ Res 21, 163 (1967); **4.** J Neurosci Methods 122, 149 (2003); **5.** Cardiovasc Res 28, 1467 (1994); **6.** Am J Physiol 269, H725 (1995); **7.** Am J Cardiovasc Pathol 4, 352 (1993); **8.** Circ Shock 41, 156 (1993); **9.** Circulation 83, 974 (1991); **10.** J Auton Nerv Syst 30, 159 (1990); **11.** Am J Physiol 251, H863 (1986); **12.** J Cereb Blood Flow Metab 13, 359 (1993); **13.** Kidney Int 20, 230 (1981); **14.** Nephrol Dial Transplant 13, 594 (1998); **15.** Clin Sci (Colch) 94, 453 (1998); **16.** Arch Int Physiol Biochim Biophys 100, 263 (1992); **17.** J Appl Physiol 84, 2010 (1998); **18.** Anesthesiology 88, 1291 (1998); **19.** J Appl Physiol 84, 1278 (1998); **20.** J Appl Physiol 82, 943 (1997); **21.** J Appl Physiol 81, 1062 (1996); **22.** Am J Physiol 265, G587 (1993); **23.** J Appl Physiol 84, 82 (1998); **24.** Acta Odontol Scand 56, 57 (1998); **25.** Mol Ther 1, 82 (2000); **26.** Acta Radiol 35, 176 (1994); **27.** Science 218, 379 (1982); **28.** J Appl Physiol 95, 1153 (2003); **29.** Am J Physiol 276, H1150 (1999); **30.** Cardiovasc Res 30, 405 (1995); **31.** J Appl Physiol 74, 2585 (1993); **32.** Am J Physiol Heart Circ Physiol 280, H2496 (2001); **33.** Biotech Histochem 73, 291 (1998); **34.** Can J Physiol Pharmacol 75, 959 (1997); **35.** Ophthalmic Surg Lasers 28, 937 (1997); **36.** Visualizing submicron particles in blood flow in the eye of an animal is covered by US 5,437,274 owned by Louisiana State University. Purchase of these products does not convey a license under this patent; **37.** Biophotonics Int 6, 56 (1999); **38.** Microsc Res Tech 26, 437 (1993); **39.** J Photochem Photobiol B 27, 3 (1995); **40.** Clin Chem 43, 1937 (1997); **41.** Biophys J 74, 2210 (1998); **42.** J Histochem Cytochem 44, 1091 (1996); **43.** Histochem J 31, 45 (1999); **44.** Biochemistry 37, 2372 (1998); **45.** Cytometry 24, 312 (1996); **46.** J Histochem Cytochem 45, 1279 (1997); **47.** J Histochem Cytochem 47, 183 (1999); **48.** J Neurosci Methods 44, 7 (1992); **49.** Brain Res 447, 223 (1988); **50.** Nature 324, 569 (1986); **51.** Science 260, 367 (1993); **52.** J Histochem Cytochem 41, 1579 (1993); **53.** J Leukoc Biol 41, 95 (1987); **54.** J Neurosci 15, 8378 (1995); **55.** Brain Res 487, 225 (1989); **56.** J Neurosci Methods 27, 121 (1989); **57.** J Neurosci Res 51, 316 (1998); **58.** Int J Cancer 62, 767 (1995); **59.** Biotechniques 28, 470 (2000); **60.** Cell Transplant 3, 397 (1994); **61.** J Cell Biol 103, 2649 (1986); **62.** Proc Natl Acad Sci U S A 90, 1310 (1993); **63.** Nature 310, 498 (1984); **64.** Brain Res 522, 90 (1990); **65.** J Neurosci Methods 29, 1 (1989); **66.** J Neurosci Methods 24, 1 (1988); **67.** Brain Res 524, 339 (1990); **68.** Biotechniques 23, 928 (1997); **69.** Ophthalmic Surg Lasers 29, 506 (1998); **70.** Ophthalmology 104, 753 (1997); **71.** Brain Behav Evol 48, 221 (1996); **72.** Nat Med 3, 244 (1997); **73.** J Biol Chem 273, 24983 (1998); **74.** Neurosci Lett 207, 53 (1996); **75.** Brain Res 630, 115 (1993); **76.** J Leukoc Biol 45, 277 (1989); **77.** Cell Immunol 156, 508 (1994); **78.** Cytometry 12, 677 (1991); **79.** J Cell Biol 115, 59 (1991); **80.** J Immunol Methods 88, 175 (1986); **81.** Science 215, 64 (1982); **82.** Cytometry 11, 875 (1990); **83.** J Neurosci Res 26, 74 (1990); **84.** Cytometry 20, 23 (1995); **85.** Science 230, 1277 (1985); **86.** Anal Biochem 152, 167 (1986); **87.** Exp Cell Res 237, 383 (1997); **88.** J Cell Physiol 155, 461 (1993); **89.** J Cell Biol 98, 1947 (1984); **90.** Biophys J 67, 1291 (1994); **91.** J Cell Biol 127, 963 (1994); **92.** Nature 359, 533 (1992); **93.** J Cell Biol 127, 995 (1994); **94.** J Cell Biol 110, 1645 (1990); **95.** Macromolecules 24, 599 (1991); **96.** Science 261, 1044 (1993); **97.** Proc Natl Acad Sci U S A 92, 11500 (1995); **98.** Microvasc Res 43, 235 (1992); **99.** Lymphology 27, 108 (1994); **100.** J Neurosci 15, 4209 (1995); **101.** J Appl Physiol 68, 1157 (1990); **102.** J Membr Biol 144, 231 (1995); **103.** Meth Neurosci 19, 320 (1994); **104.** J Membr Biol 135, 83 (1993); **105.** Cell Motil Cytoskeleton 8, 293 (1987); **106.** Dev Growth Differ 28, 461 (1986); **107.** Appl Environ Microbiol 60, 2711 (1994); **108.** J Pharm Pharmacol 42, 821 (1990); **109.** J Exp Zool 255, 262 (1990); **110.** Biophotonics Int 6, 44 (1999); **111.** Biophys J 66, 769 (1994); **112.** Science 260, 232 (1993); **113.** J Microsc 172, 121 (1993); **114.** Am J Physiol 268, L657 (1995).

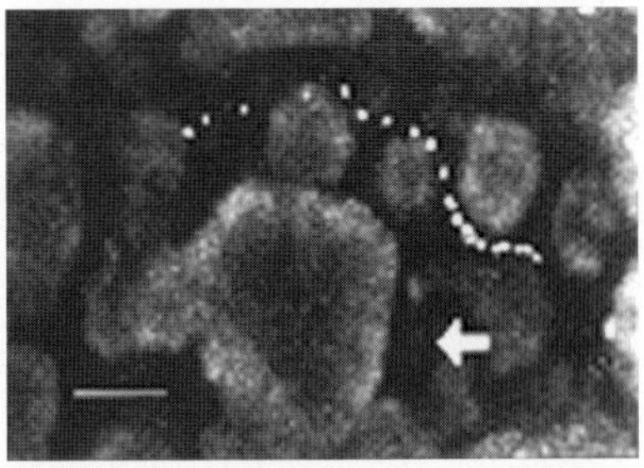

Figure 14.78 Superimposed time sequence image (2.3-second intervals), showing a single bead moving through a biofilm channel. Autofluorescence of the cell clusters can be seen as lighter areas relative to the channels. The direction of bulk fluid flow is indicated by the arrow. Photo contributed by Paul Stoodley, Exeter University, and Dirk DeBeer, Max Planck Institute of Marine Biology.

Product List — 14.6 FluoSpheres® and TransFluoSpheres® Microspheres for Tracing

Cat #	Product Name	Unit Size
F8890	FluoSpheres® Blood Flow Determination Fluorescent Color Kit #1, polystyrene microspheres, 10 µm *seven colors, 10 mL each* *3.6x10^6 beads/mL*	1 kit
F8891	FluoSpheres® Blood Flow Determination Fluorescent Color Kit #2, polystyrene microspheres, 15 µm *seven colors, 10 mL each* *1.0x10^6 beads/mL*	1 kit
F8892	FluoSpheres® Blood Flow Determination Fluorescent Color Kit #3, polystyrene microspheres, 15 µm *five colors, 10 mL each* *1.0x10^6 beads/mL*	1 kit
F21015	FluoSpheres® Blood Flow Determination Fluorescent Color Kit #4, polystyrene microspheres, 15 µm *four colors, 10 mL each* *1.0x10^6 beads/mL*	1 kit
F8789	FluoSpheres® carboxylate-modified microspheres, 0.04 µm, dark red fluorescent (660/680) *5% solids, azide free*	1 mL
F8791	FluoSpheres® carboxylate-modified microspheres, 0.04 µm, infrared fluorescent (715/755) *5% solids, azide free*	0.4 mL
F8792	FluoSpheres® carboxylate-modified microspheres, 0.04 µm, orange fluorescent (540/560) *5% solids, azide free*	1 mL
F8793	FluoSpheres® carboxylate-modified microspheres, 0.04 µm, red fluorescent (580/605) *5% solids, azide free*	1 mL
F8794	FluoSpheres® carboxylate-modified microspheres, 0.04 µm, red-orange fluorescent (565/580) *5% solids, azide free*	1 mL
F8795	FluoSpheres® carboxylate-modified microspheres, 0.04 µm, yellow-green fluorescent (505/515) *5% solids, azide free*	1 mL
F20880	FluoSpheres® carboxylate-modified microspheres, 0.04 µm, europium luminescent (365/610) *0.5% solids*	2 mL
F20881	FluoSpheres® carboxylate-modified microspheres, 0.2 µm, europium luminescent (365/610) *0.5% solids*	2 mL
F20882	FluoSpheres® carboxylate-modified microspheres, 1.0 µm, europium luminescent (365/610) *0.5% solids*	2 mL
F20886	FluoSpheres® carboxylate-modified microspheres, 0.04 µm, platinum luminescent (390/650) *0.5% solids*	2 mL
F20887	FluoSpheres® carboxylate-modified microspheres, 0.2 µm, platinum luminescent (390/650) *0.5% solids*	2 mL
F20888	FluoSpheres® carboxylate-modified microspheres, 1.0 µm, platinum luminescent (390/650) *0.5% solids*	2 mL
F10720	FluoSpheres® Fluorescent Color Kit, carboxylate-modified microspheres, 0.04 µm *four colors, 1 mL each* *5% solids, azide free*	1 kit
F13080	FluoSpheres® polystyrene microspheres, 1.0 µm, blue-green fluorescent (430/465) *for tracer studies* *1.0x10^{10} beads/mL*	5 mL
F13082	FluoSpheres® polystyrene microspheres, 1.0 µm, orange fluorescent (540/560) *for tracer studies* *1.0x10^{10} beads/mL*	5 mL
F13083	FluoSpheres® polystyrene microspheres, 1.0 µm, red fluorescent (580/605) *for tracer studies* *1.0x10^{10} beads/mL*	5 mL
F13081	FluoSpheres® polystyrene microspheres, 1.0 µm, yellow-green fluorescent (505/515) *for tracer studies* *1.0x10^{10} beads/mL*	5 mL
F8829	FluoSpheres® polystyrene microspheres, 10 µm, blue fluorescent (365/415) *for blood flow determination* *3.6x10^6 beads/mL*	10 mL
F8830	FluoSpheres® polystyrene microspheres, 10 µm, blue-green fluorescent (430/465) *for blood flow determination* *3.6x10^6 beads/mL*	10 mL
F8831	FluoSpheres® polystyrene microspheres, 10 µm, crimson fluorescent (625/645) *for blood flow determination* *3.6x10^6 beads/mL*	10 mL
F8833	FluoSpheres® polystyrene microspheres, 10 µm, orange fluorescent (540/560) *for blood flow determination* *3.6x10^6 beads/mL*	10 mL
F8834	FluoSpheres® polystyrene microspheres, 10 µm, red fluorescent (580/605) *for blood flow determination* *3.6x10^6 beads/mL*	10 mL
F8836	FluoSpheres® polystyrene microspheres, 10 µm, yellow-green fluorescent (505/515) *for blood flow determination* *3.6x10^6 beads/mL*	10 mL
F8837	FluoSpheres® polystyrene microspheres, 15 µm, blue fluorescent (365/415) *for blood flow determination* *1.0x10^6 beads/mL*	10 mL
F8838	FluoSpheres® polystyrene microspheres, 15 µm, blue-green fluorescent (430/465) *for blood flow determination* *1.0x10^6 beads/mL*	10 mL
F8839	FluoSpheres® polystyrene microspheres, 15 µm, crimson fluorescent (625/645) *for blood flow determination* *1.0x10^6 beads/mL*	10 mL
F8841	FluoSpheres® polystyrene microspheres, 15 µm, orange fluorescent (540/560) *for blood flow determination* *1.0x10^6 beads/mL*	10 mL
F8842	FluoSpheres® polystyrene microspheres, 15 µm, red fluorescent (580/605) *for blood flow determination* *1.0x10^6 beads/mL*	10 mL
F8843	FluoSpheres® polystyrene microspheres, 15 µm, scarlet fluorescent (645/680) *for blood flow determination* *1.0x10^6 beads/mL*	10 mL
F8844	FluoSpheres® polystyrene microspheres, 15 µm, yellow-green fluorescent (505/515) *for blood flow determination* *1.0x10^6 beads/mL*	10 mL
F21013	FluoSpheres® polystyrene microspheres, 15 µm, carmine fluorescent (580/620) *for blood flow determination* *1.0x10^6 beads/mL*	10 mL
F21010	FluoSpheres® polystyrene microspheres, 15 µm, green fluorescent (450/480) *for blood flow determination* *1.0x10^6 beads/mL*	10 mL
F21012	FluoSpheres® polystyrene microspheres, 15 µm, red-orange fluorescent (565/580) *for blood flow determination* *1.0x10^6 beads/mL*	10 mL
F21011	FluoSpheres® polystyrene microspheres, 15 µm, yellow fluorescent (515/534) *for blood flow determination* *1.0x10^6 beads/mL*	10 mL
T13090	TransFluoSpheres® polystyrene microspheres, 2.0 µm (633/760) *for tracer studies* *1.0x10^9 beads/mL*	0.5 mL

For current prices or to order online, visit probes.invitrogen.com

14.7 Protein Conjugates

Unlike the polydisperse dextrans (Section 14.5), fluorescent protein tracers have molecular weights that are reasonably well defined (bovine serum albumin (BSA) ~66,000 daltons; ovalbumin ~45,000; codfish parvalbumin 12,328 daltons,[1] casein ~23,600 daltons; monomeric subunit B of cholera toxin ~12,000 daltons; horseradish peroxidase (HRP) ~40,000 daltons; soybean trypsin inhibitor ~21,500 daltons; *Phaseolus vulgaris* leucoagglutinin (PHA-L) ~126,000 daltons). Some of their applications are similar to those of dextran tracers, although protein conjugates may be more susceptible to proteolysis. However, through creative modifications of the proteins, researchers have been able to use these conjugates to target receptors, detect protease activity and measure intracellular pH. Some applications of fluorescent protein conjugates as tracers include:

- Quantitative studies of electroporation [2,3]
- Reconstitution of functional nuclear pores [4]
- Macromolecule trafficking to endocytic compartments [5]
- Measurement of plasma volume in rats [6]

Tyramide signal amplification (TSA) technology (see Section 6.2 and below) combined with HRP and its conjugates promises to become a major tool for retrograde and anterograde labeling of neurons and other cells (Figure 14.79).

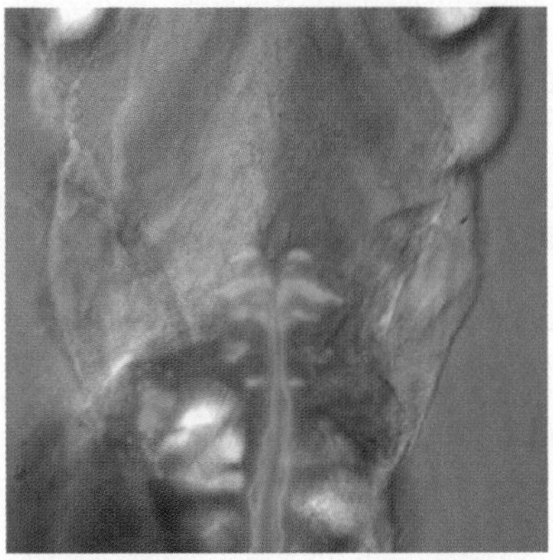

Figure 14.79 Horseradish peroxidase (HRP)–filled reticulospinal neurons of the hindbrain of a whole-mount zebrafish larva were detected using green-fluorescent Alexa Fluor® 488 tyramide (TSA Kit #2, T20912). The spinal cord was labeled by transection in the presence of HRP (1 mg/mL). After a two-hour incubation, the specimen was fixed and the HRP was visualized using Alexa Fluor® 488 tyramide. This figure represents a projection (performed with AutoQuant Imaging, Inc., software) of a stack of 30 images.

Albumin Conjugates

Fluorescent BSA, Ovalbumin and Parvalbumin

Molecular Probes supplies bovine serum albumin (BSA) fluorescently labeled with our fluorescein, tetramethylrhodamine, Texas Red® and BODIPY® FL dyes (A23015, A23016, A23017, A2750). We have also prepared conjugates of BSA with our outstanding Alexa Fluor® 488, Alexa Fluor® 594 and Alexa Fluor® 647 dyes (A13100, A13101, A34785), which provide particularly bright, photostable and pH-insensitive fluorescence.

In addition to the BSA conjugates, Molecular Probes prepares the fluorescein and Texas Red® conjugates of ovalbumin (O23020, O23021), as well as the brightly fluorescent Alexa Fluor® 488, Alexa Fluor® 594 and Alexa Fluor® 647 conjugates (O34781, O34783, O34784). Ovalbumin is a protein with a relatively low molecular weight (~45,000 daltons) that has been used to follow endocytic internalization [7,8] and to estimate microvasculature transport-pathway sizes.[9] We also offer the Alexa Fluor® 488 conjugate of codfish parvalbumin (P23012), which is the smallest (molecular weight 12,328 daltons [1]) fluorescent protein tracer in this section.

Dinitrophenylated Bovine Serum Albumin

We offer BSA that has been conjugated to multiple dinitrophenyl hapten molecules (DNP-BSA, A23018), a reagent that is commonly used to study Fc receptor–mediated immune function [10–12] and the IgE- and IgG-mediated responses to crosslinking of DNP-specific antibodies.[13,14] Our dinitrophenylated BSA typically has ~25 dinitrophenyl substituents per molecule of BSA. For these studies, Molecular Probes offers rabbit anti-DNP antibody prepared against DNP-conjugated keyhole limpet hemocyanin (anti–DNP-KLH antibody, A6430; Section 7.4), as well as the Alexa Fluor® 488 dye, fluorescein and biotin-XX conjugates of this important antibody (A11097, A6423, A6435; Section 7.4).

DQ™ BSA, DQ™ Ovalbumin, DQ™ Collagen and Anti–BSA Antibodies

Our patented DQ™ substrates, including the DQ™ Green BSA and DQ™ Red BSA (D12050, D12051) and DQ™ ovalbumin (D12053), are based on the strong fluorescence quenching effect observed when proteins are heavily conjugated with BODIPY® dyes or, in the case of DQ™ collagen conjugates (D12052, D12060), with multiple fluorescein dyes. Upon hydrolysis of the proteins to single dye–labeled peptides by proteases, this quenching is relieved (Figure 10.56). This technology provides an easy continuous assay for numerous proteases (Section 10.4). When complexed to rabbit anti–BSA IgG (A11133), the DQ™ BSA products are phagocytosed into live cells via the Fc receptor (Section 16.1, Figure 16.5), where they are broken down into fluorescent peptides [15,16] (Figure 10.56). DQ™ Green BSA, which gives bright green fluorescence upon proteolysis, and DQ™ Red BSA, which yields red-fluorescent hydrolysis products, are packaged in sets of five vials, each containing 1 mg of the substrate. Our Fc OxyBURST® Green assay reagent (F2902, Section 16.1), which is based on a similar concept, comprises BSA that has been conjugated to a dihydrofluorescein derivative and then complexed with anti-BSA IgG (Figure 16.2). Upon binding to the Fc receptor, the immune complex is internalized and oxidized to a fluorescent product within the phagovacuole [17,18] (Section 16.1).

We have found our highly quenched DQ™ ovalbumin (D12053) to be particularly useful for antigen processing and presentation studies. Ovalbumin conjugates are internalized via the mannose receptor–mediated endocytosis pathway and are recognized by antigen-presenting cells. BSA that was heavily labeled with fluorescein (FITC) has been used for these studies.[19] However, fluorescence of the intracellular hydrolysis products of FITC BSA is significantly decreased by the acidity of the phagovacuole. In contrast, the bright fluorescence of the BODIPY® FL fluorophore in DQ™ ovalbumin is completely independent of the pH. The fluorescence generated after DQ™ collagen (D12052) is hydrolyzed by cellular collagenase has been used to visualize the migratory pathway followed by tumor cells during invasion of a gelatin matrix and to image proteolysis by living breast cancer cells.[20,21]

Alexa Fluor® 488 Parvalbumin

Parvalbumin, a stable and protease-resistant protein with a molecular weight of 12,328 daltons, is found in the skeletal muscle of vertebrates and the endocrine glands of mammals.[22] Our Alexa Fluor® 488 conjugate of codfish parvalbumin (P23012) has bright green, photostable fluorescence, making this conjugate a potentially useful aldehyde-fixable tracer for microinjection into cells, including neurons.

Casein Conjugates

BODIPY® FL casein and BODIPY® TR-X casein, which are components of two of our EnzChek® Protease Assay Kits (E6638, E6639), are substrates for metallo-, serine, acid and sulfhydryl proteases, including cathepsin, chymotrypsin, elastase, papain, pepsin, thermolysin and trypsin [23] (Section 10.4). The casein-based substrates are heavily labeled and therefore highly quenched conjugates; they typically exhibit <3% of the fluorescence of the corresponding free dyes. Protease-catalyzed hydrolysis relieves this quenching, yielding brightly fluorescent peptides (Figure 10.56). The EnzChek® Protease Assay Kits, as well as the DQ™ BSA and DQ™ ovalbumin substrates mentioned above, have significant potential as:

- Detectors of protease contamination in culture media
- Fluorogenic substrates for circulating or secreted proteases in extracellular fluids
- Nontoxic, pH-insensitive markers for phagocytic cells, which will ingest and eventually cleave the quenched casein substrates to yield fluorescent BODIPY® FL– or BODIPY® TR-X–labeled peptides
- Microinjectable tracers to detect enhanced protease activity associated with cell activation and fusion
- Nontoxic markers for assessing various cell-loading and cell-transfection techniques, including electroporation, high-velocity microprojectiles, scrape loading and related methods (Table 14.1)

The peptide hydrolysis products of BODIPY® FL casein exhibit green fluorescence that is optimally excited by the argon-ion laser at 488 nm, permitting flow sorting of the cells. The red-fluorescent BODIPY® TR-X–labeled peptides, with excitation and emission spectra similar to those of the Texas Red® fluorophore, should be useful for multilabeling experiments or measurements in the presence of green autofluorescence. Following intracellular hydrolysis, some of the lower molecular weight fluorescent peptides may diffuse into other organelles or pass thorough gap junctions.

Phaseolus vulgaris Leucoagglutinin: An Important Anterograde Tracer

Phaseolus vulgaris leucoagglutinin (PHA-L) is a widely used lectin for anterograde axonal tracing.[24–26] Iontophoretically injected PHA-L clearly demonstrates the morphological features of the filled neurons at the injection site and the labeled axons and axon terminals. Furthermore, PHA-L that has been transported is not degraded over long periods. PHA-L has been used in combination with our biotin dextran amines [27–30] (BDA dextrans, Section 14.5) or the fluorescent dextrans fluoro-ruby and mini-ruby [29,31,32] (D1817, D3312; Section 14.5) to demonstrate their similar transport properties and to show the distribution of anterograde-labeled fibers.[33–35] PHA-L has been simultaneously injected with the retrograde tracer hydroxystilbamidine (H22845, Section 14.3) for double-labeling experiments.[36,37] Our Alexa Fluor® 488, Alexa Fluor® 568, Alexa Fluor® 594 and Alexa Fluor® 647 conjugates of PHA-L (L11270, L32455, L32456, L32457) should provide exceptionally bright and photostable labeling.

Cholera Toxin Subunit B

Cholera toxin comprises two subunits, A and B, arranged in an AB_5 conformation. Subunit A is an ADP-ribosyltransferase, which disrupts the proper signaling of G proteins and eventually leads to dehydration of the cell.[38] The 12,000-dalton nontoxic subunit B ("choleragenoid"), which is assembled into a 60,000-dalton pentamer above pH 2,[39] allows the protein complex to bind to cellular surfaces via the pentasaccharide chain of ganglioside G_{M1}.[40]

Cholera toxin subunit B and its conjugates are emerging as superior tracers for retrograde labeling of neurons.[41,42] Researchers have used cholera toxin subunit B in a variety of applications, including tracing of rat forebrain afferents,[43] projections of the parabrachial region[44] and neurons of the urinary bladder wall.[45] Cholera toxin subunit B conjugates bind to the pentasaccharide chain of ganglioside G_{M1} on neuronal cell surfaces and are actively taken up and transported; alternatively, they can be injected by iontophoresis. Unlike the carbocyanine-based neuronal tracers such as DiI (D282, D3911, V22885; Section 14.4), cholera toxin subunit B conjugates can be used on tissue sections that will be fixed and frozen.[46]

Fluorescent cholera toxins are also markers of lipid rafts — regions of cell membranes high in ganglioside G_{M1} that are thought to be important in cell signaling[39,40,47] (Figure 17.41, Figure 13.33). The Vybrant® Lipid Raft Labeling Kits (V34403, V34404, V34405; Section 17.4) provide the key reagents, including fluorescent cholera toxin subunit B conjugates, for fluorescently labeling lipid rafts *in vivo* with our bright and extremely photostable Alexa Fluor® dyes (Figure 13.33, Figure 17.41). All of Molecular Probes' cholera toxin subunit B conjugates are prepared from recombinant cholera toxin subunit B, which is completely free of the toxic subunit A, thus eliminating any concern for toxicity or ADP-ribosylating activity. Our Alexa Fluor® 488 (C22841, C34775), Alexa Fluor® 555 (C22843, C34776), Alexa Fluor® 594 (C22842, C34777) and Alexa Fluor® 647 (C34778) conjugates of cholera toxin subunit B combine this versatile tracer with the superior brightness of our Alexa Fluor® dyes to provide sensitive and selective receptor labeling and neuronal tracing. We also offer biotin-XX (C34779) and horseradish peroxidase (C34780) conjugates of cholera toxin subunit B, which, in conjunction with sensitive secondary detection methods such as diaminobenzidine (DAB) and tyramide signal amplification (TSA), can be used as retrograde tracers in neurons.

Peroxidase, Peroxidase Conjugates and Tyramide Signal Amplification

Horseradish peroxidase (HRP) conjugates of lectins — particularly of wheat germ agglutinin (WGA) and cholera toxin — are important anterograde (and sometimes retrograde) neuronal tracers. Although we currently do not provide the HRP-labeled lectins, the tyramide signal amplification (TSA) technology (Section 6.2) represents an exciting opportunity to directly label HRP-injected neurons with fluorescent tyramides of several of our Alexa Fluor® dyes or the Oregon Green® 488 or Pacific Blue™ dyes (Table 6.1, Figure 14.79) or indirectly label neurons or other HRP-containing cells with biotin-XX tyramide, DSB-X™ biotin tyramide or dinitrophenyl-X tyramide (Table 6.1). TSA using a biotin tyramide has been reported to be successful in vagal afferents.[48,49] Because biotin-XX tyramide and DSB-X™ biotin tyramide can be detected with any fluorescent, luminescent or heavy atom avidin or streptavidin derivative (Section 7.6, Table 7.22) or converted to a precipitate for electron microscopy observation, we anticipate that TSA will become a major tool for labeling neurons with high sensitivity and spatial resolution and low background staining.

Phycobiliproteins

Phycobiliproteins make effective polar tracers because they are intensely fluorescent, are very soluble in water and have a low tendency to bind nonspecifically to cells. These intrinsically fluorescent biomolecules are stable proteins that are monodisperse and substantially larger than albumins, with molecular weights of 240,000 daltons (B- and R-phycoerythrin, P800, P801) and 104,000 daltons (allophycocyanin, A803, or crosslinked allophycocyanin, A819). Phycobiliproteins have been employed as tracers to:

- Follow nucleocytoplasmic transport of proteins[50–52]
- Measure permeability of reconstituted nuclear pores[4]
- Assess nuclear exclusion of nonnuclear proteins[53] and soluble cytoplasmic factors involved in protein import[54]
- Observe transport through single transporters in cells[55]

Phycoerythrin has also been conjugated to nuclear-localization peptide sequences to follow nuclear import processes.[50–52,56] B-phycoerythrin can pass through pores in erythrocyte membranes created by streptolysin O.[55] Single molecules of R-phycoerythrin have been imaged and tracked within mammalian cells.[57] Unlike our DQ™ and EnzChek® protease substrates (Section 10.4), proteolysis of phycobiliproteins results in the loss of most of their intrinsic fluorescence.

Fluorescent Histones

Our green-fluorescent Alexa Fluor® 488 conjugate of lysine-rich calf thymus histone H1 (H13188) has been successfully used in a yeast nuclear-import assay.[58,59] The Alexa Fluor® 488 histone H1 conjugate is both more fluorescent and much more photostable than the fluorescein conjugate of histones. Fluorescent dye–labeled histones have been reported to be useful for following endocytosis.[60,61] The combination of fluorescent dextrans (Section 14.5) and fluorescent histones has been used to demonstrate nuclear envelope breakdown during anaphase.[62] Although histones have relatively low molecular weights (~12,000–15,000 daltons), transport of fluorescent histones is apparently a receptor-mediated process.[63,64]

Fluorescent α-Crystallin

α-Crystallin is a large, polydisperse heat shock protein that accounts for up to 50% of the total protein content in vertebrate lenses. This protein complex is composed of many copies of two types of homologous subunits, αA and αB crystallin, and has an average molecular mass of ~800,000 daltons.[65] In the eye, α-crystallin helps to maintain the proper refractive index of the lens, which it may do in part by acting as a molecular chaperone to prevent denaturation of other lens proteins.[65–67] Fluorescent α-crystallin conjugates have been used to characterize the interaction of this protein with fiber cell plasma membranes, which increases with age or the onset of cataracts. To facilitate these investigations, Molecular Probes offers a green-fluorescent conjugate of α-crystallin using our outstanding Alexa Fluor® 488 dye (C23010), which yields bright, photostable and pH-insensitive fluorescence between pH 4 and pH 10.

Alexa Fluor® 488 Soybean Trypsin Inhibitor

Soybean trypsin inhibitor (SBTI) conjugates do not appear to have been used previously as polar tracers. However, the high water solubility and chemical stability of SBTI may make its green-fluorescent Alexa Fluor® 488 conjugate (T23011) a useful tracer for various studies. This conjugate has been reported to be a useful probe for the acrosome reaction of spermatozoa.[68]

References

1. Allergy 38, 449 (1983); **2.** Biophys J 66, 1522 (1994); **3.** Biophys J 65, 414 (1993); **4.** J Biol Chem 269, 9289 (1994); **5.** J Biol Chem 270, 1443 (1995); **6.** J Appl Physiol 76, 485 (1994); **7.** Infect Immun 64, 2585 (1996); **8.** J Neurosci Res 40, 694 (1995); **9.** Microcirculation 5, 275 (1998); **10.** Cell Regul 2, 181 (1991); **11.** FEBS Lett 270, 115 (1990); **12.** Cell 58, 317 (1989); **13.** J Biol Chem 270, 4013 (1995); **14.** Mol Biol Cell 6, 825 (1995); **15.** Eur J Cell Biol 75, 192 (1998); **16.** J Leukoc Biol 62, 329 (1997); **17.** J Leukoc Biol 43, 304 (1988); **18.** J Immunol Methods 130, 223 (1990); **19.** J Immunol 159, 2177 (1997); **20.** FASEB J 15, 932 (2001); **21.** Neoplasia 2, 496 (2000); **22.** Eur J Biochem 222, 21 (1994); **23.** Anal Biochem 251, 144 (1997); **24.** Brain Res Bull 51, 11 (2000); **25.** Neurosci Lett 45, 285 (1984); **26.** Brain Res 290, 219 (1984); **27.** J Neurosci Methods 48, 75 (1993); **28.** Histochem Cell Biol 110, 509 (1998); **29.** J Comp Neurol 403, 158 (1999); **30.** J Neurosci 18, 10525 (1998); **31.** J Comp Neurol 302, 159 (1990); **32.** Anat Embryol (Berl) 194, 559 (1996); **33.** Histochem Cell Biol 107, 391 (1997); **34.** Brain Res Bull 40, 219 (1996); **35.** Neuroscience 82, 1151 (1998); **36.** Neurosci Lett 168, 119 (1994); **37.** Brain Res Bull 33, 445 (1994); **38.** J Biol Chem 255, 1252 (1980); **39.** Biochemistry 35, 16069 (1996); **40.** Mol Microbiol 13, 745 (1994); **41.** Brain Res 243, 215 (1982); **42.** Brain Res 231, 33 (1982); **43.** Neuroscience 82, 443 (1998); **44.** Brain Res 816, 364 (1999); **45.** Neuroscience 87, 275 (1998); **46.** J Neurosci 22, 9419 (2002); **47.** J Cell Biol 147, 447 (1999); **48.** J Comp Neurol 412, 161 (1999); **49.** J Histochem Cytochem 46, 527 (1998); **50.** Biochim Biophys Acta 930, 419 (1987); **51.** Exp Cell Res 178, 318 (1988); **52.** J Cell Sci 108, 1849 (1995); **53.** J Cell Biol 103, 2091 (1986); **54.** J Cell Biol 111, 807 (1990); **55.** J Microsc 192, 114 (1998); **56.** J Membr Biol 146, 239 (1995); **57.** Biophys J 79, 2188 (2000); **58.** J Cell Biol 123, 785 (1993); **59.** Jim Campanella, Lehigh University, personal communication; **60.** Biochem Cell Biol 68, 729 (1990); **61.** J Biol Chem 257, 1695 (1982); **62.** Biotechniques 17, 730 (1994); **63.** J Cell Biochem 64, 573 (1997); **64.** Cell 60, 999 (1990); **65.** J Biol Chem 271, 29060 (1996); **66.** Eye 13, 403 (1999); **67.** Proc Natl Acad Sci U S A 97, 3260 (2000); **68.** Zygote 8, 127 (2000).

Product List — 14.7 Protein Conjugates

Cat #	Product Name	Unit Size
A13100	albumin from bovine serum (BSA), Alexa Fluor® 488 conjugate	5 mg
A13101	albumin from bovine serum (BSA), Alexa Fluor® 594 conjugate	5 mg
A34785	albumin from bovine serum (BSA), Alexa Fluor® 647 conjugate	5 mg
A2750	albumin from bovine serum (BSA), BODIPY® FL conjugate	5 mg
A23018	albumin from bovine serum (BSA), 2,4-dinitrophenylated (DNP-BSA)	5 mg
A23015	albumin from bovine serum (BSA), fluorescein conjugate	5 mg
A23016	albumin from bovine serum (BSA), tetramethylrhodamine conjugate	5 mg
A23017	albumin from bovine serum (BSA), Texas Red® conjugate	5 mg
A803	allophycocyanin *4 mg/mL*	0.5 mL
A819	allophycocyanin, crosslinked (APC-XL) *4 mg/mL*	250 µL
A11133	anti-albumin (bovine serum), rabbit IgG fraction (anti-BSA) *2 mg/mL*	0.5 mL
C22841	cholera toxin subunit B (recombinant), Alexa Fluor® 488 conjugate	500 µg
C34775	cholera toxin subunit B (recombinant), Alexa Fluor® 488 conjugate	100 µg
C22843	cholera toxin subunit B (recombinant), Alexa Fluor® 555 conjugate	500 µg
C34776	cholera toxin subunit B (recombinant), Alexa Fluor® 555 conjugate	100 µg
C22842	cholera toxin subunit B (recombinant), Alexa Fluor® 594 conjugate	500 µg
C34777	cholera toxin subunit B (recombinant), Alexa Fluor® 594 conjugate	100 µg
C34778	cholera toxin subunit B (recombinant), Alexa Fluor® 647 conjugate	100 µg
C34779	cholera toxin subunit B (recombinant), biotin-XX conjugate	100 µg
C34780	cholera toxin subunit B (recombinant), horseradish peroxidase conjugate	100 µg
D12060	DQ™ collagen, type I from bovine skin, fluorescein conjugate	1 mg
D12052	DQ™ collagen, type IV from human placenta, fluorescein conjugate	1 mg
D12050	DQ™ Green BSA *special packaging*	5 x 1 mg
D12053	DQ™ ovalbumin *special packaging*	5 x 1 mg
D12051	DQ™ Red BSA *special packaging*	5 x 1 mg
E6638	EnzChek® Protease Assay Kit *green fluorescence* *100-1000 assays*	1 kit
E6639	EnzChek® Protease Assay Kit *red fluorescence* *100-1000 assays*	1 kit
H13188	histone H1 from calf thymus, Alexa Fluor® 488 conjugate	1 mg
L11270	lectin PHA-L from *Phaseolus vulgaris* (red kidney bean), Alexa Fluor® 488 conjugate	1 mg
L32455	lectin PHA-L from *Phaseolus vulgaris* (red kidney bean), Alexa Fluor® 568 conjugate	1 mg
L32456	lectin PHA-L from *Phaseolus vulgaris* (red kidney bean), Alexa Fluor® 594 conjugate	1 mg
L32457	lectin PHA-L from *Phaseolus vulgaris* (red kidney bean), Alexa Fluor® 647 conjugate	1 mg
O34781	ovalbumin, Alexa Fluor® 488 conjugate	2 mg
O34782	ovalbumin, Alexa Fluor® 555 conjugate	2 mg
O34783	ovalbumin, Alexa Fluor® 594 conjugate	2 mg
O34784	ovalbumin, Alexa Fluor® 647 conjugate	2 mg
O23020	ovalbumin, fluorescein conjugate	5 mg
O23021	ovalbumin, Texas Red® conjugate	5 mg
P23012	parvalbumin from codfish, Alexa Fluor® 488 conjugate	1 mg
P800	B-phycoerythrin *4 mg/mL*	0.5 mL
P801	R-phycoerythrin *4 mg/mL*	0.5 mL
T23011	trypsin inhibitor from soybean, Alexa Fluor® 488 conjugate	1 mg

For current prices or to order online, visit probes.invitrogen.com

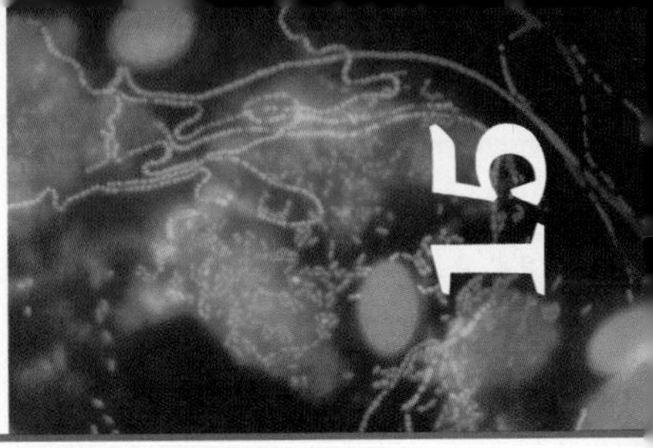

Chapter 15

Assays for Cell Viability, Proliferation and Function

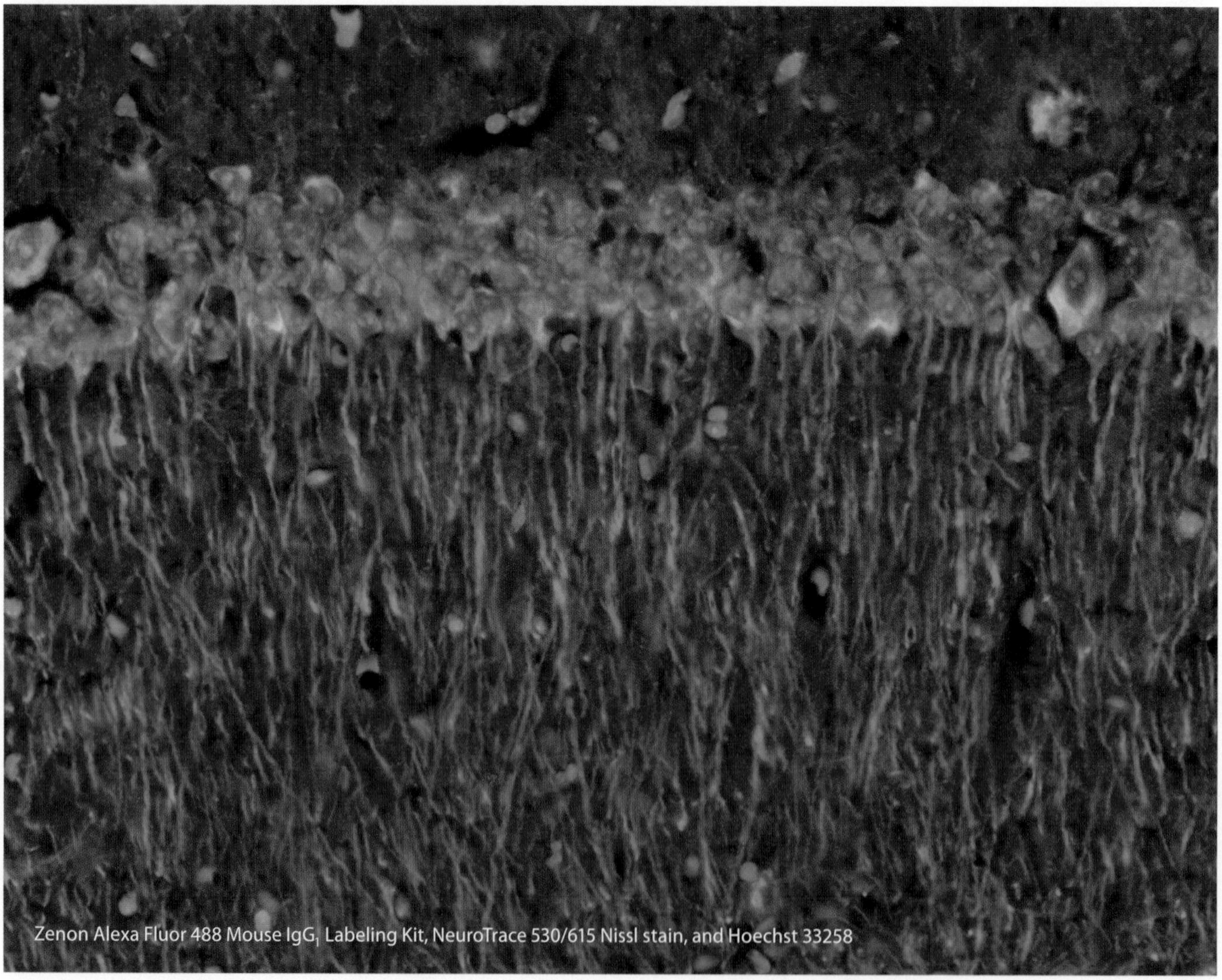
Zenon Alexa Fluor 488 Mouse IgG$_1$ Labeling Kit, NeuroTrace 530/615 Nissl stain, and Hoechst 33258

15.1 Overview of Probes for Cell Viability, Cell Proliferation and Live-Cell Function

Cell viability, cell proliferation and many important live-cell functions — including apoptosis, cell adhesion, chemotaxis, multidrug resistance, endocytosis, secretion and signal transduction — can be stimulated or monitored with various chemical and biological reagents. Many of these processes lead to changes in intracellular radicals (Chapter 18), free-ion concentrations (Chapter 19, Chapter 20, Chapter 21) or membrane potential (Chapter 22) that can be followed with appropriately responsive fluorescent indicators. This chapter discusses important reagents and assays for detecting these diverse cell processes in live cells. It also includes our important antibodies to cell cycle–related markers (for example, cyclins and bromodeoxyuridine (BrdU)), which are useful in fixed-cell preparations (Section 15.4). Many of the assays in this chapter can be analyzed on a cell-by-cell basis, and some are equally suitable for detection by microscopy, by flow cytometry or with a microplate reader. Almost all of the assays have the capacity for high-throughput analysis.

Our viability and cytotoxicity assay reagents (Section 15.2) and kits (Section 15.3) are principally used to enumerate the proportion of live and dead cells in a population. In contrast, proliferation assays (Section 15.4) are primarily designed to monitor the growth rate of a cell population or to detect daughter cells in a growing population. Fluorescence-based cell viability and proliferation assays are generally less hazardous and less expensive than radioisotopic techniques, more sensitive than colorimetric methods and more convenient than animal testing methods.[1] Unlike ^{51}Cr-release assays, fluorescence-based assays of cell-mediated cytotoxicity do not require large samples, which can be difficult to obtain from patients.[2] Furthermore, fluorescence-based protocols are more convenient than the trypan blue–based exclusion assay. This common colorimetric method for determining cell viability must be completed within 3–5 minutes because the number of blue-staining cells increases with time after addition of the dye.[3]

Fluorescent dye–based assays for cell viability and cytotoxicity are reliable and easy to perform. Our stand-alone reagents for these assays are described in Section 15.2, whereas our kits for viability and cytotoxicity analysis are discussed in Section 15.3. Molecular Probes' LIVE/DEAD® Viability Assay Kits (Section 15.3) give researchers a choice of viability/cytotoxicity assays suitable for bacteria, fungi or higher eukaryotic cells (Table 15.2). Our LIVE/DEAD® Reduced Biohazard Kits (Section 15.3) permit the original viability status of a mixed-cell population to be determined following treatment by aldehyde-based fixatives to kill pathogens. In each case, these viability assay kits provide the reagents and a simple protocol for simultaneous two-color assessment of numbers of live and dead cells. We also offer several proliferation assay kits that enable researchers to rapidly monitor numbers of adherent or nonadherent cells based on the presence of newly replicated DNA, the total nucleic acid content or the total protein content (Section 15.4).

The diversity of live cells and their environments (Figure 15.1) makes it impossible to devise a single viability or enumeration assay applicable to all cell types. Because viability is not easily defined in terms of a single physiological or morphological parameter, it is often desirable to combine several different measures, such as enzymatic activity, membrane permeability and oxidation–reduction (redox) potential. Each assay method has inherent advantages and limitations and may introduce specific biases into the experiment; thus, different applications often call for different approaches.

Apoptosis research is a burgeoning field in which fluorescent probes are having a major impact. Consequently, Section 15.5 focuses on our probes for monitoring apoptosis, including our proprietary reagents for selectively detecting apoptotic cells based on their cell-permeability properties, as well as some exclusive conjugates of annexin V phosphatidylserine-binding protein.

In addition to our probes for cell viability, cell proliferation and apoptosis, several of the reagents for live-cell function described in Section 15.6 can be used to develop assays that measure a particular biochemical parameter of interest. There is a significant overlap between probes for cell viability and probes for live-cell functions. For example, fluorogenic esterase substrates are commonly used to detect viability and proliferation, as well as to monitor cell adhesion, apoptosis and multidrug resistance. Likewise, cell-permeant and cell-impermeant nucleic acid stains are widely applicable to many live-cell function assays. We have organized discussions in this chapter according to several commonly studied cell processes in order to highlight the many published applications for these probes and foster the development of new applications.

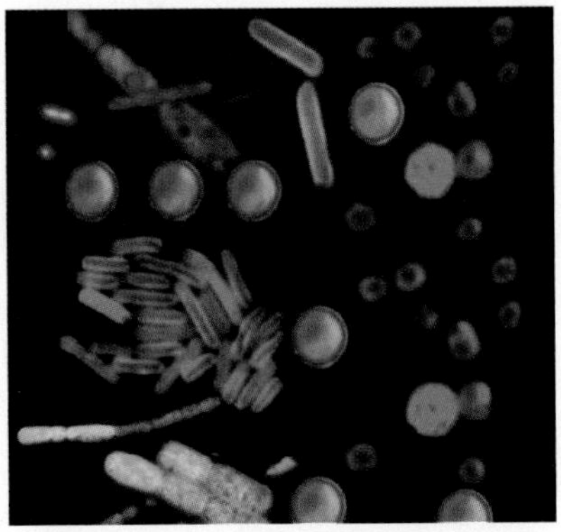

Figure 15.1 Collage of images of cyanobacteria stained with various blue- or green-fluorescent probes to complement the natural red autofluorescence from chlorophyll and phycobilisomes. The round cells are *Synechocystis* sp. (strain PCC 6803), and their membranes were labeled with green-fluorescent BODIPY® FL propionic acid (D2183). The cylindrical cells are *Synechococcus* sp. (strain PCC 7942), stained with blue-fluorescent DAPI (D1306, D3571, D21490). The filamentous cyanobacteria, *Anabaena cylindrica*, were labeled with either the green-fluorescent cystosolic stain, CellTracker™ Green BODIPY® (C2102), or with the lipophilic membrane stain BODIPY® FL (D2183). The image was contributed by Mary Sarcina, University College, London.

References

1. Principles and Methods of Toxicology, 3rd Ed., Hayes AW, Ed. pp. 1231–1258 (1994); **2.** Hum Immunol 37, 264 (1993); **3.** J Histochem Cytochem 33, 77 (1985).

15.2 Viability and Cytotoxicity Assay Reagents

Fluorometric assays of cell viability and cytotoxicity are easy to perform with the use of a fluorescence microscope, fluorometer, fluorescence microplate reader or flow cytometer,[1] and they offer many advantages over traditional colorimetric and radioactivity-based assays. This section describes our numerous reagents for conducting viability and cytotoxicity assays in a wide variety of cells, including those of animal origin as well as bacteria and yeast. Following this discussion of individual reagents is Section 15.3, which contains a thorough description of each of our viability and cytotoxicity kits, including the:

- LIVE/DEAD® Viability/Cytotoxicity Kit (L3224)
- LIVE/DEAD® Reduced Biohazard Cell Viability Kits (L7013, L23101, L23102, L23105)
- LIVE/DEAD® Cell-Mediated Cytotoxicity Kit (L7010)
- LIVE/DEAD® Sperm Viability Kit (L7011)
- LIVE/DEAD® Cell Vitality Assay Kit (L34951)
- LIVE/DEAD® Yeast Viability Kit (L7009)
- LIVE/DEAD® *Bac*Light™ Bacterial Viability Kits (L7007, L7012, L13152, L34856)
- ViaGram™ Red+ Bacterial Gram Stain and Viability Kit (V7023)
- Vybrant® Cytotoxicity Assay Kit *G6PD release assay* (V23111)
- Vybrant® Cell Metabolic Assay Kit *with C_{12}-resazurin* (V23110)

Many of these reagents and assay kits have been developed and patented by Molecular Probes' scientists and are exclusively available from Molecular Probes and its distributors. Also discussed in this section and Section 15.3 are our unique single-step reagents and kits for assessing gram sign and for simultaneously determining gram sign and viability of bacteria, as well as our novel fluorescent antibiotics. Section 15.4 describes our important probes for quantitating cell proliferation, analyzing the cell cycle and detecting the presence of bacteria and mycoplasma.

Viability/Cytotoxicity Assays Using Esterase Substrates

Molecular Probes prepares a wide variety of fluorogenic esterase substrates — including calcein AM, BCECF AM and various fluorescein diacetate derivatives — that can be passively loaded into adherent and nonadherent cells. These cell-permeant esterase substrates serve as viability probes that measure both enzymatic activity, which is required to activate their fluorescence, and cell-membrane integrity, which is required for intracellular retention of their fluorescent products.

As electrically neutral or near-neutral molecules, the esterase substrates freely diffuse into most cells. In general, cell loading of acetate or acetoxymethyl ester derivatives is accomplished by initially preparing a 1–10 mM stock solution of the dye in dimethylsulfoxide (DMSO) and then diluting the stock solution into the cell medium to a final concentration of 1–25 µM (see Note 19.1 "Technical Focus: Loading and Calibration of Intracellular Ion Indicators" in Section 19.1). Once inside the cell, these nonfluorescent substrates are converted by nonspecific intracellular esterases into fluorescent products that are retained by cells with intact plasma membranes. In contrast, both the unhydrolyzed substrates and their products rapidly leak from dead or damaged cells with compromised membranes, even when the cells retain some residual esterase activity. Low incubation temperatures and highly charged esterase products usually favor retention, although the rate of dye loss from viable cells also depends to a large extent on cell type (see "Multidrug Resistance" in Section 15.6). For example, mast cells and epithelial cells actively secrete many polar products.[2,3] Table 15.1 lists Molecular Probes' esterase substrates that have been used for cell viability studies and compares their cell loading, retention and pH sensitivity. Many of the applications of these esterase substrates — for example, viability, cytotoxicity and adhesion assays — closely parallel those of ^{51}Cr-release assays, except that the fluorescent probes do not carry the risks or the disposal costs associated with the use of radioactive materials.

CellTrace™ Calceins: Calcein AM, Calcein Blue AM and Calcein Red-Orange AM

Of the dyes listed in Table 15.1, calcein AM (C1430, C3099, C3100MP; Figure 15.2) stands out as the premier indicator of cell viability due to its superior cell retention and the relative insensitivity of its fluorescence to pH in the physiological range.[4–7] Calcein AM, also called CellTrace™ calcein green AM (C34852), is also the best single probe available for use in assays for cell adhesion, chemotaxis and multidrug resistance (Section 15.6). Calcein (C481, Section 14.3), which is the hydrolysis product of calcein AM, is a polyanionic fluorescein derivative (Figure 14.32) that has about six negative charges and two positive charges at pH 7.[8] Calcein is better retained in viable cells than are fluorescein, carboxyfluorescein and BCECF (Figure 15.3) and tends to have brighter fluorescence in a number of mammalian cell types. Calcein AM has the ability to penetrate intact cornea, revealing cell viability, morphology and organization of living cornea.[9,10] Furthermore, unlike some other dyes — including BCECF AM — calcein AM does not interfere with leukocyte chemotaxis or superoxide production, nor does it affect lymphocyte–target cell conjugation.[6,11–14] Leakage of calcein from calcein AM–loaded cells has been used to measure the increase in membrane permeability that occurs above physiological temperatures,[15] as well as to assay for cytotoxic T lymphocyte activity.[5] Fluorescence of extracellular calcein that has leaked from cells or that has been lost during secretion, lysis or ATP-dependent anion transport can be quenched by 5 µM Co^{2+} ion (panel R, Figure 19.76) or by Mn^{2+} ion. Heavy-atom quenching of calcein provides a means of detecting dye leakage and quantitating only the intracellular fluorescence.[16]

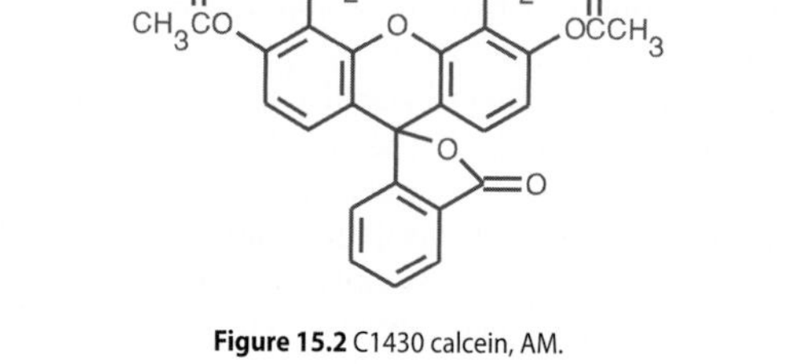

Figure 15.2 C1430 calcein, AM.

Table 15.1 — Esterase substrates for cell viability studies

Esterase Substrate (Cat #)	Properties in Cells	pK_a of Product *
BCECF AM (B1150, B1170, B3051)	• Quite well retained • Released during cytolysis • pH-sensitive fluorescence	7.0
Calcein AM (C1430, C3099, C3100MP)	• Quite well retained • Released during cytolysis • Not as pH-sensitive as BCECF	5
Carboxyeosin diacetate, succinimidyl ester (C22803, Section 15.4)	• Well retained by reaction with amines • Useful for DAB photoconversion • Phosphorescent	<5 †
Carboxy-2′,7′-dichlorofluorescein diacetate (carboxy-DCFDA, C369)	• Moderately well retained • Not as pH-sensitive as CFDA	4.8
Carboxyfluorescein diacetate (5(6)-CFDA, C195)	• Moderately well retained • pH-sensitive fluorescence	6.4
Carboxyfluorescein diacetate, acetoxymethyl ester (5-CFDA, AM; C1354)	• Easier to load than CFDA yet yields the same product upon hydrolysis • pH-sensitive fluorescence	6.4
Carboxyfluorescein diacetate, succinimidyl ester (5(6)-CFDA, SE; C1157, Section 15.4)	• Well retained by reaction with amines • Not completely released during cytolysis • pH-sensitive fluorescence	6.4 †
CellTracker™ Green CMFDA (CMFDA; C2925, C7025)	• Well retained by reaction with thiols • Not completely released during cytolysis • pH-sensitive fluorescence	6.4 †
Chloromethyl SNARF®-1, acetate (C6826)	• Well retained by reaction with thiols • Not completely released during cytolysis • Long-wavelength, pH-sensitive fluorescence	7.5 †
Fluorescein diacetate (F1303)	• Poorly retained • pH-sensitive fluorescence • Inexpensive	6.4
Oregon Green® 488 carboxylic acid diacetate (carboxy-F_2FDA, O6151)	• Moderately well retained • Not as pH-sensitive as CFDA	4.7

* Approximate pK_a values in aqueous solvents. The actual pK_a of the indicator will vary somewhat depending upon experimental conditions. † pK_a of the unconjugated hydrolysis product; after conjugation to an intracellular amine or thiol, the actual pK_a value may be different.

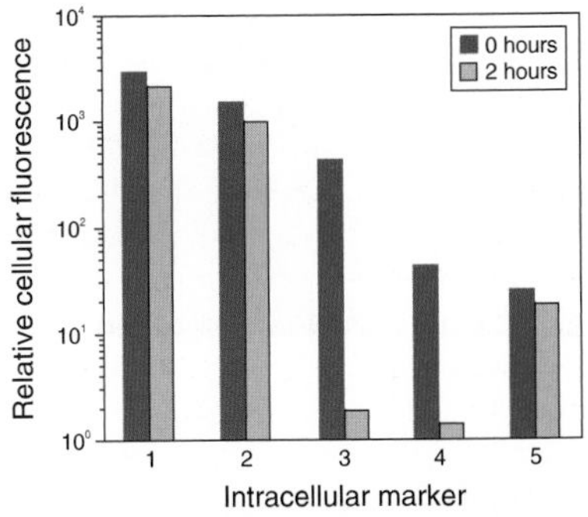

Figure 15.3 Loading and retention characteristics of intracellular marker dyes. Cells of a human lymphoid line (GePa) were loaded with the following cell-permeant acetoxymethyl ester (AM) or acetate derivatives of fluorescein: 1) calcein AM (C1430, C3099, C3100MP), 2) BCECF AM (B1150), 3) fluorescein diacetate (FDA, F1303), 4) carboxyfluorescein diacetate (CFDA, C1354) and 5) CellTracker™ Green CMFDA (5-chloromethylfluorescein diacetate, C2925, C7025). Cells were incubated in 4 µM staining solutions in Dulbecco's modified eagle medium containing 10% fetal bovine serum (DMEM+) at 37°C. After incubation for 30 minutes, cell samples were immediately analyzed by flow cytometry to determine the average fluorescence per cell at time zero (0 hours). Retained cell samples were subsequently washed twice by centrifugation, resuspended in DMEM+, maintained at 37°C for 2 hours and then analyzed by flow cytometry. The decrease in the average fluorescence intensity per cell in these samples relative to the time zero samples indicates the extent of intracellular dye leakage during the 2-hour incubation period.

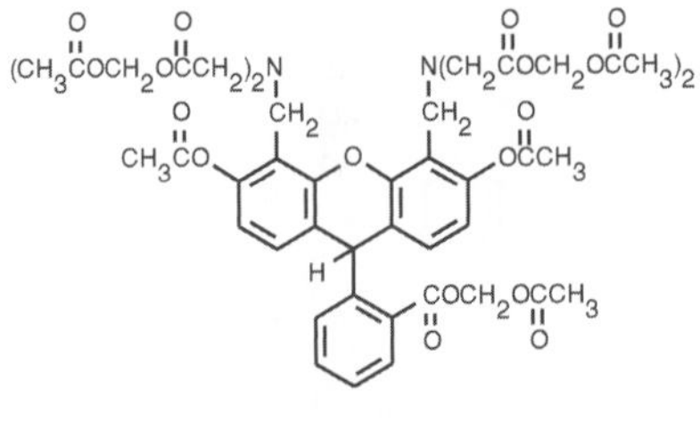

Figure 15.4 D23805 dihydrocalcein, AM.

Dihydrocalcein AM (Figure 15.4) is a reasonably stable, chemically reduced form of calcein AM that requires *both* hydrolysis by intracellular esterases and oxidation within the cell to produce the green-fluorescent calcein dye. Dihydrocalcein AM resembles 2′,7′-dichlorodihydrofluorescein diacetate (D399, Figure 16.1), the important indicator for oxidative activity in cells (see below), except that its oxidation product (calcein, Figure 14.32) should be better retained in cells than is the oxidation product of 2′,7′-dichlorodihydrofluorescein diacetate. Dihydrocalcein AM (D23805) is available as a set of 20 vials, each containing 50 µg of the product.

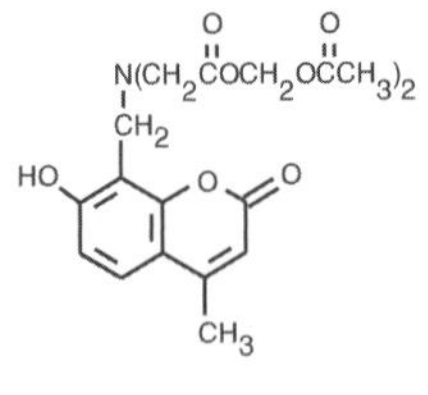

Figure 15.5 C1429 calcein blue, AM.

Calcein blue AM, also called CellTrace™ calcein blue AM (C1429, C34853; Figure 15.5), is a viability indicator for use with instruments optimized for the detection of blue fluorescence.[17,18] This tracer possesses AM esters that allow its passive diffusion across cell membranes. Before de-esterification, CellTrace™ calcein blue AM is only weakly fluorescent (excitation/emission maxima ~322/435 nm). Upon cleavage of the AM esters by intracellular esterases, however, this tracer becomes relatively polar and is retained by cells for several hours. In addition, its fluorescence intensity increases and its fluorescence spectra shift to longer wavelengths, with excitation/emission maxima of ~360/449 nm. Calcein blue AM is useful for viability measurements in combination with our SYTOX® Green nucleic acid stain (see below) and other green- or red-fluorescent probes.

In addition to the blue-fluorescent CellTrace™ calcein blue AM and the green-fluorescent CellTrace™ calcein green AM, we offer CellTrace™ calcein red-orange AM (C34851). Upon cleavage by intracellular esterases, CellTrace™ calcein red-orange (excitation/emission maxima ~576/589 nm) is well retained by live cells that possess intact plasma membranes. Unlike calcein AM, CellTrace™ calcein red-orange AM is intrinsically fluorescent; thus, an additional wash step may be necessary to minimize background fluorescence from dye that is not taken up by cells.

CellTrace™ calcein red-orange AM is a useful cell tracer and indicator of cell viability and can be used in combination with blue- and green-fluorescent probes.

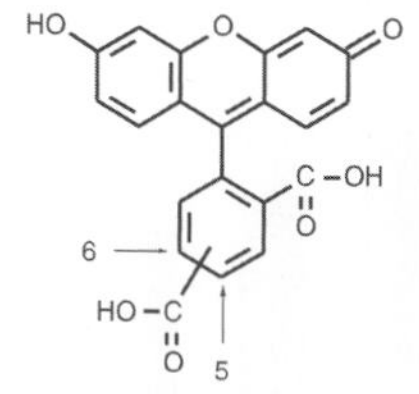

Figure 15.6 C194 5-(and-6)-carboxyfluorescein.

BCECF AM

BCECF AM (B1150, B1170, B3051) is extensively used for detecting cytotoxicity [19] and for determining the ability of surviving cells to proliferate.[20,21] The intracellular hydrolysis product of BCECF AM, BCECF (B1151, Section 20.2), has 4–5 negative charges (Figure 20.6), a property that considerably improves its cell retention in viable cells over that of fluorescein or carboxyfluorescein (Figure 15.3). However, because the emission intensity of BCECF is only half-maximal at pH 7.0 ($pK_a = 6.98$, Figure 20.3) — and is even further reduced in a cell's acidic compartments — the signal intensity of BCECF may be less than optimal in some cell viability and cell adhesion assays.

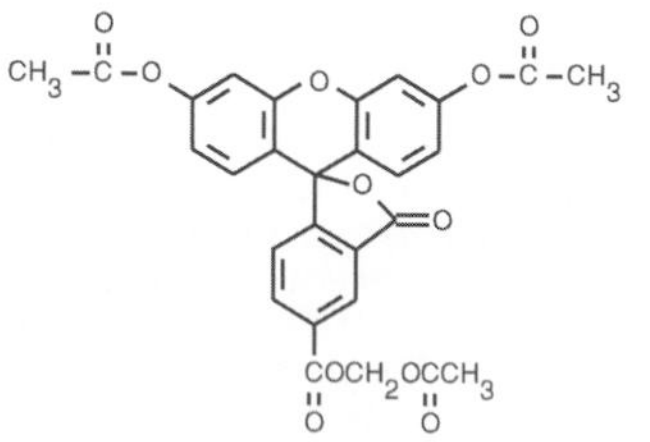

Figure 15.7 C1354 5-carboxyfluorescein diacetate, acetoxymethyl ester (5-CFDA, AM).

Using monoclonal antibodies known to either enhance or inhibit natural killer (NK) cell function, researchers found that BCECF AM was at least as effective as ^{51}Cr for measuring NK activity. Furthermore, the fluorescence-based assay could be performed with smaller samples.[22] BCECF AM has also been used to screen for trypanocidal activity [23] and viability of islets.[24]

Fluorescein Diacetate

Fluorescein diacetate (FDA, F1303) was one of the first probes to be used as a fluorescent indicator of cell viability.[25–27] FDA is still occasionally used to detect cell adhesion [28] or, in combination with propidium iodide (P1304MP; P3566; FluoroPure™ Grade, P21493), to determine cell viability.[29,30] However, fluorescein, (F1300, Section 20.2) which is formed by intracellular hydrolysis of FDA, rapidly leaks from cells (Figure 15.3). Thus, other cell-permeant dyes such calcein AM and BCECF AM are now preferred for cell viability assays.

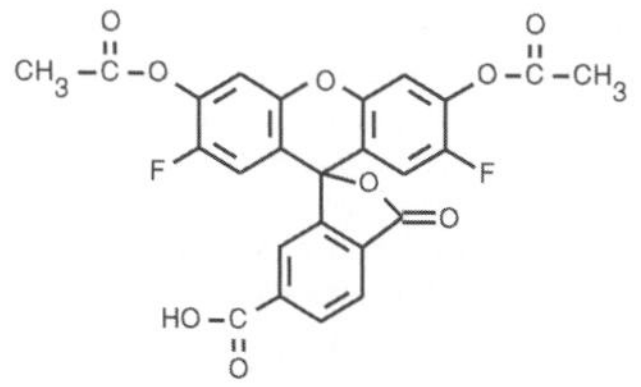

Figure 15.8 O6151 Oregon Green® 488 carboxylic acid diacetate (carboxy-DFFDA).

Carboxyfluorescein Diacetate and Its Derivatives

The high leakage rate of fluorescein from cells [27,31] prompted the development of carboxyfluorescein diacetate (CFDA), which was originally used to measure intracellular pH [32] but was soon adapted for use as a cell viability indicator.[33,34] Upon hydrolysis by intracellular nonspecific esterases, CFDA forms carboxyfluorescein (5(6)-FAM, C194, C1904; Section 14.3). As compared with fluorescein, carboxyfluorescein contains extra negative charges (Figure 15.6) and is therefore better retained in cells [6] (Figure 15.3). CFDA is moderately permeant to most cell membranes, with uptake greater at pH 6.2 than at pH 7.4.[32] The mixed-isomer preparation of CFDA (5(6)-CFDA, C195) is usually adequate for cell viability measurements; however, we also prepare high-purity single isomers of CFDA (C1361, C1362). In addition, we offer the electrically neutral AM ester of CFDA (5-CFDA, AM; C1354; Figure 15.7), which can be loaded into cells at lower concentrations than CFDA. Upon hydrolysis by intracellular esterases, this AM ester also yields carboxyfluorescein.[35–37] CFDA, CFDA AM and sulfofluorescein diacetate (see below) have been proposed for detection of living organisms on Mars.[38] Hemoglobin can be used to quench extracellular fluorescence due to leakage of probes or leakage of products, such as fluorescein or carboxyfluorescein.[39] Alternatively, antibodies directed against the fluorescein hapten (Section 7.4, Table 7.18) or the membrane-impermeant reagent trypan blue can be used to quench low levels of extracellular fluorescence of some fluorescein-based dyes (Figure 16.24).

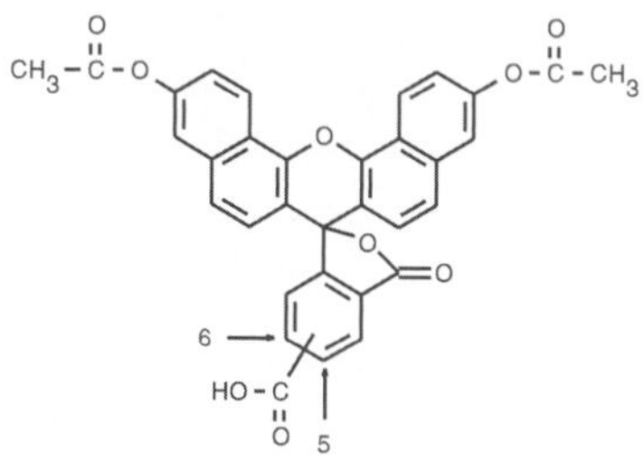

Figure 15.9 C13196 5-(and-6)-carboxynaphthofluorescein diacetate.

CFDA has been used as a viability probe with a variety of cells, including bacteria,[40] fungi (e.g., *Saccharomyces cerevisiae*),[41] spermatozoa,[42] natural killer (NK) cells [19,43] and tumor cells.[44] Cytotoxicity assays using either CFDA or 5-(and 6-)carboxy-2′,7′-dichlorofluorescein diacetate (carboxy-DCFDA, C369) show good correlation with results obtained using the radioisotopic ^{51}Cr-release method.[19,45] With its low pK_a, carboxy-DCFDA is frequently used as a selective probe for the relatively acidic yeast vacuole.[46–48] Oregon Green® 488 carboxylic acid diacetate (carboxy-DFFDA; O6151, C34555; Figure 15.8) also exhibits a low pK_a (~4.7, Figure 20.30) and may be similarly useful as a vital stain. Its intracellular hydrolysis product — Oregon Green® 488 carboxylic acid (O6146, Section 1.5, Figure 1.62) — is more photostable than carboxyfluorescein (Figure 1.46).

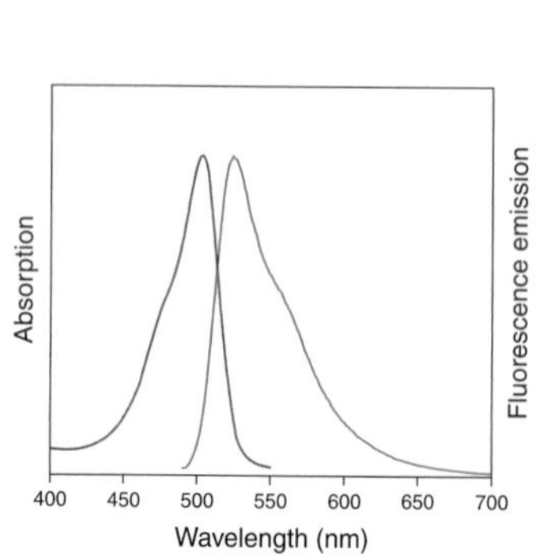

Figure 15.10 Absorption and fluorescence emission spectra of the SYTOX® Green nucleic acid stain bound to DNA.

Sulfofluorescein Diacetate

Sulfofluorescein diacetate (SFDA, S1129), which is converted by intracellular esterases to fluorescein sulfonic acid (F1130, Section 14.3), is more polar than CFDA and consequently may be more difficult to load into some viable cells. However, SFDA's polar hydrolysis product, fluorescein sulfonic acid, is better retained in viable cells than is carboxyfluorescein.[49–52] SFDA was used to stain live bacteria and fungi in soil; little interference from autofluorescence of soil minerals or detritus was observed.[17,53]

CellTracker™ Green CMFDA

Molecular Probes' patented CellTracker™ dyes are thiol-reactive fluorescent dyes that are retained in many live cells through several generations (Figure 15.3) and are not transferred to adjacent cells in a population (Figure 14.4, Figure 14.5, Figure 14.17), except possibly through gap junctions. These dyes represent a significant breakthrough in the cellular retention of fluorescent probes and are ideal long-term tracers for transplanted cells or tissues (Section 14.2).

CellTracker™ Green CMFDA (C2925, C7025; Figure 14.10) freely diffuses into the cell, where its weakly thiol-reactive chloromethyl moieties react with intracellular thiols and their acetate groups are cleaved by cytoplasmic esterases (Figure 14.6), generating the fluorescent product (Figure 14.3). The other CellTracker™ probes (coumarin, BODIPY® and tetramethylrhodamine derivatives; Section 14.2) do not require enzymatic cleavage to activate their fluorescence. Because the CellTracker™ dyes may react with both glutathione and proteins, cells with membranes that become compromised after staining may retain some residual fluorescent conjugates. However, use of a membrane-impermeant probe such as propidium iodide (P1304MP; P3566; FluoroPure™ Grade, P21493), SYTOX® Blue (S11348), SYTOX® Orange (S11368) or one of our "dimeric" or "monomeric" nucleic acid stains (see below) in combination with CellTracker™ Green CMFDA should permit relatively long-term cytotoxicity assays. CellTracker™ Green CMFDA and ethidium homodimer-1 (EthD-1, E1169) have been used to detect viable and nonviable cells in rat and human coronary and internal thoracic arteries sampled at autopsy[54] and in connective tissue explants.[55]

Pentafluorobenzoyl Aminofluorescein Diacetate

The green-fluorescent 5-(pentafluorobenzoyl)aminofluorescein (PFB-F, P12925; Section 14.3) — the intracellular hydrolysis product of PFB aminofluorescein diacetate (PFB-FDA, P12880) — localizes in the cytoplasm, is well retained in cells with intact cell membranes (even through cell division) and is fixable by formaldehyde and glutaraldehyde. PFB-F appears to be retained in viable cells by two mechanisms: 1) retention of the relatively lipophilic PFB group of the hydrolysis products in the cell membrane, and 2) glutathione *S*-transferase–catalyzed reaction of the hydrolysis products with intracellular glutathione.[56] In addition, the relatively high lipophilicity of PFB-FDA facilitates passive cell loading: cells are simply incubated at 37°C in 1–10 µM PFB-FDA in standard culture medium. Thus, like our CellTracker™ Green CMFDA, PFB-FDA should prove useful for long-term cell labeling.

Chloromethyl SNARF®-1 Acetate

Chloromethyl SNARF®-1 acetate (C6826, Figure 14.19) is the only cell-tracking dye (and pH indicator) that exhibits bright red cytoplasmic fluorescence (Figure 14.21) when excited at the same wavelengths used to excite the green-fluorescent hydrolysis product of CMFDA (Figure 20.11). The spectral characteristics of these two dyes permit simultaneous tracking of two cell populations by either fluorescence microscopy or flow cytometry. The large Stokes shift of the SNARF® fluorophore also makes chloromethyl SNARF®-1 acetate useful as a viability indicator in cells that exhibit green autofluorescence when excited by the 488 nm spectral line of the argon-ion laser.

Carboxynaphthofluorescein Diacetate

Carboxynaphthofluorescein diacetate (C13196, Figure 15.9), which is cleaved by intracellular esterases to yield red-fluorescent carboxynaphthofluorescein (excitation/emission maxima ~598/668 nm), is the only long-wavelength tracer of this type that can be passively loaded into live cells.[57] Like chloromethyl SNARF®-1 acetate, carboxynaphthofluorescein diacetate is usually used in combination with a green-fluorescent tracer for detecting cell–cell interactions.

Viability/Cytotoxicity and Gram Stain Assays Using Nucleic Acid Stains

To simultaneously detect both the live-cell and dead-cell populations, viability assessments of animal cells, bacteria and yeast frequently employ polar and therefore cell-impermeant nucleic acid stains to detect the dead-cell population. Nucleic acid stains are most often used in combination with intracellular esterase substrates (see above), membrane-permeant nucleic acid stains (see below), membrane potential–sensitive probes (Chapter 22), organelle probes (Chapter 12) or cell-permeant indicators (Chapter 19, Chapter 20 and Chapter 21) to detect the live-cell population. Although many other cell-impermeant dyes could be used to detect dead cells, the high concentrations of nucleic acids in cells, coupled with the large fluorescence enhancement exhibited by most of our nucleic acid stains upon binding, make cell-impermeant nucleic acid stains the logical candidates for viability probes. See Table 8.2 for a list of several cell-impermeant nucleic acid stains and Section 8.1 for a general discussion of dye binding to nucleic acids.

SYTOX® Green, SYTOX® Orange and SYTOX® Blue Nucleic Acid Stains

Many polar nucleic acid stains will enter eukaryotic cells with damaged plasma membranes yet will not stain dead bacteria with damaged plasma membranes. Our patented SYTOX® Green nucleic acid stain (S7020) is a high-affinity probe that easily penetrates eukaryotic cells and both gram-positive and gram-negative bacteria with compromised plasma membranes, yet is completely excluded from live cells.[58] After brief incubation with the SYTOX® Green nucleic acid stain, dead bacteria fluoresce bright green when excited with the 488 nm spectral line of the argon-ion laser or any other 470–490 nm source (Figure 15.10). These properties, combined with its ~1000-fold fluorescence enhancement upon nucleic acid binding, make our SYTOX® Green stain a simple and quantitative dead-cell indicator for use with fluorescence microscopes, fluorometers, fluorescence microplate readers or flow cytometers (Figure 15.11). We have taken advantage of the sensitivity of the SYTOX® Green nucleic acid stain in our ViaGram™ Red$^+$ Bacterial Gram Stain and Viability Kit (V7023) and in our Vybrant® Apoptosis Assay Kit #1 (V13240, Section 15.5). A significant application of the SYTOX® Green nucleic acid stain is the high-throughput screening of bacteria for antibiotic susceptibility by fluorescence microscopy, by flow cytometry or in a fluorescence microplate reader.[59]

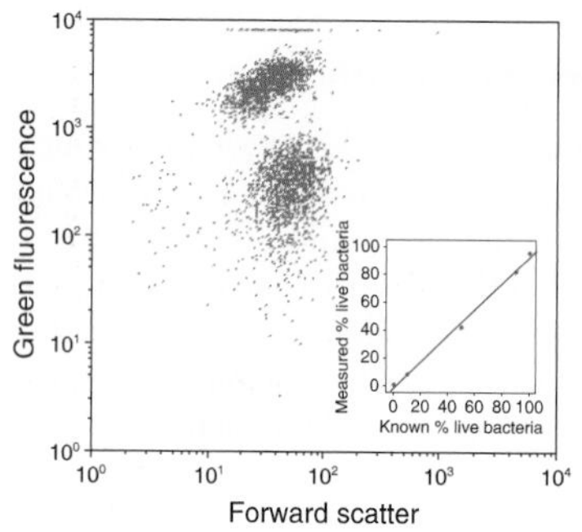

Figure 15.11 Quantitative flow cytometric analysis of *Escherichia coli* viability using the SYTOX® Green nucleic acid stain (S7020). A bacterial suspension containing an equal number of live and isopropyl alcohol–killed *E. coli* was stained with SYTOX® Green and analyzed using excitation at 488 nm. A bivariate frequency distribution for forward light scatter versus log fluorescence intensity (collected with a 510 nm longpass optical filter) shows two clearly distinct populations. When live and dead bacteria were mixed in varying proportions, a linear relationship between the population numbers and the actual percentage of live cells in the sample was obtained (see inset).

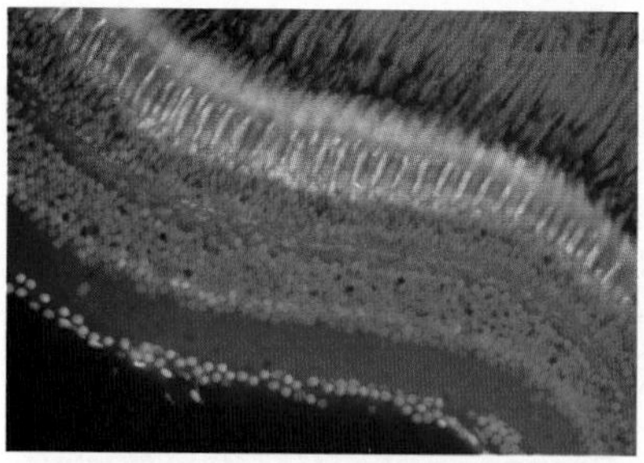

Figure 15.12 A frozen section of zebrafish retina stained with mouse monoclonal antibody FRet 43 in conjunction with Texas Red®-X goat anti–mouse IgG (T6390), Alexa Fluor® 350 wheat germ agglutinin (W11263) and SYTOX® Green nucleic acid stain (S7020).

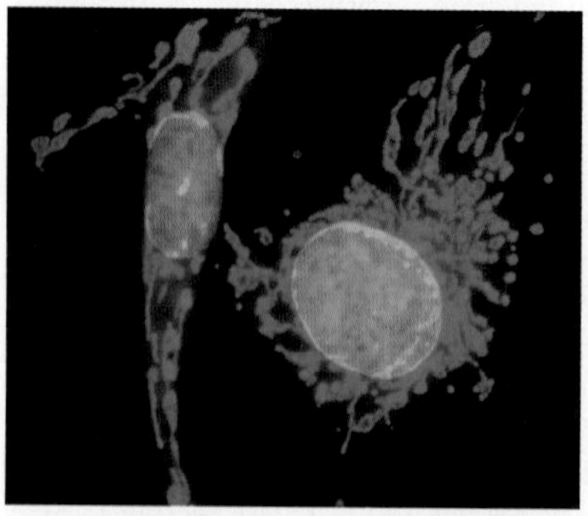

Figure 15.13 The mitochondria of bovine pulmonary artery endothelial cells stained with MitoTracker® Red CM-H_2XRos (M7513). The cells were subsequently fixed, permeabilized and treated with RNase. Then the nuclei were stained with SYTOX® Green nucleic acid stain (S7020). The multiple-exposure photomicrograph was acquired using a fluorescence microscope equipped with bandpass filter sets appropriate for fluorescein and Texas Red® dyes.

The SYTOX® Green nucleic acid stain as a tool for viability assessment is not restricted to bacteria; it is also a very effective cell-impermeant counterstain in eukaryotic systems (Section 8.6). It can be used in conjunction with blue- and red-fluorescent labels for multiparameter analyses in fixed cells and tissue sections (Figure 8.7, Figure 15.12, Figure 15.13). Furthermore, it should be possible to combine the SYTOX® Green nucleic acid stain with one of the membrane-permeant nucleic acid stains in our SYTO® Red-, SYTO® Blue- or SYTO® Orange-Fluorescent Nucleic Acid Stain Sampler Kits (S11340, S11350, S11360) for two-color visualization of dead and live cells.

Like the SYTOX® Green reagent, our SYTOX® Orange and SYTOX® Blue nucleic acid stains (S11368, S11348) are high-affinity nucleic acid stains that only penetrate cells with compromised plasma membranes. The SYTOX® Orange nucleic acid stain (S11368, Figure 11.18) has absorption/emission maxima of 547/570 nm when bound to DNA and is optimally detected using filters appropriate for rhodamine dyes (Table 23.9). As with the other SYTOX® dyes, the SYTOX® Orange stain is virtually nonfluorescent except when bound to nucleic acids and can be used to detect cells that have compromised membranes without a wash step.

Our SYTOX® Blue nucleic acid stain labels both DNA and RNA with extremely bright fluorescence centered near 480 nm (Figure 8.119), making it an excellent fluorescent indicator of cell viability (Figure 15.14). Unlike many blue-fluorescent dyes, the SYTOX® Blue stain is efficiently excited by tungsten–halogen lamps and other sources with relatively poor emission in the UV portion of the spectrum. The brightness of the SYTOX® Blue complex with nucleic acids allows sensitive detection of stained cells with fluorometers, fluorescence microplate readers, arc-lamp–equipped flow cytometers and epifluorescence microscopes, including those not equipped with UV light–pass optics.

Quantitation of membrane-compromised bacterial cells carried out with the SYTOX® Blue stain yields results identical to those obtained in parallel assays using the SYTOX® Green stain. Like the SYTOX® Green stain, the SYTOX® Blue stain does not interfere with bacterial cell growth. Because their emission spectra overlap somewhat, we have found that it is not ideal to use SYTOX® Blue stain and green-fluorescent dyes together in the same application, except when the green-fluorescent dye is excited beyond the absorption of the SYTOX® Blue dye (e.g., at >480 nm). However, emission of the SYTOX® Blue complex with nucleic acids permits clear discrimination from red- and orange-fluorescent probes, facilitating development of multicolor assays with minimal spectral overlap between signals.

Dimeric and Monomeric Cyanine Dyes

The patented dimeric and monomeric cyanine dyes in the TOTO® and TO-PRO® series (Table 8.2) are essentially nonfluorescent unless bound to nucleic acids and have extinction coefficients 10–20 times greater than that of DNA-bound propidium iodide. Spectra of the nucleic acid–bound dyes cover the entire visible spectrum and into the infrared region (Figure 8.1). These dyes are typically impermeant to the membranes of live cells [60] but brightly stain dead cells that have compromised membranes. However, YO-PRO®-1 and other polar stains are taken up by some live cells via the $P2X_{1-7}$ receptors [61] and by apoptotic cells (Section 15.5), so care needs to be taken when assaying cell viability with nucleic acid stains. The POPO™-1 and BOBO™-1 dyes may be useful blue-fluorescent dead-cell stains, and the YOYO®-3 and TOTO®-3 dyes and the corresponding YO-PRO®-3 and TO-PRO®-3 dyes have excitation maxima beyond 600 nm when bound to DNA. Our JOJO™-1 and JO-PRO™-1 dyes exhibit orange fluorescence (~545 nm) upon binding to nucleic acids and can be excited with a 532 nm Nd:YAG laser. The LOLO™-1 and LO-PRO™-1 nucleic acid stains have longer-wavelength fluorescence (~580 nm) and are maximally excited by the 568 nm spectral line of the krypton-ion laser.

One cell viability assay utilizes YOYO®-1 fluorescence before and after treatment with digitonin as a measure of the dead cells and total cells, respectively, in the sample.[62] The YOYO®-3 dye was used as a stain for dead cells in an assay designed to correlate cell cycle with metabolism in single cells.[63] In addition to their use as dead-cell stains, both the dimeric and monomeric cyanine dyes are also proving useful for staining viruses. TOTO®-1 dye–staining and flow cytometric analysis gave better discrimination of live and dead lactic acid bacteria in several species than did propidium iodide.[64] Viruses stained with the YOYO®-1 and POPO™-1 dyes have been employed to identify and quantitate bacteria and cyanobacteria in marine microbial communities.[65] The YO-PRO®-1 dye has been used to count viruses in marine and freshwater environments by epifluorescence microscopy [66] and is also selectively permeant to apoptotic cells [67]

(Section 15.5). TO-PRO®-3 (T3605, Section 15.4) has been utilized to demonstrate transient permeabilization of bacterial by sublethal doses of antibiotics.[68]

Our Nucleic Acid Stains Dimer Sampler Kit (N7565) provides a total of eight cyanine dyes that span the visible spectrum. This kit should be useful when screening dyes for their utility in viability and cytotoxicity assays.

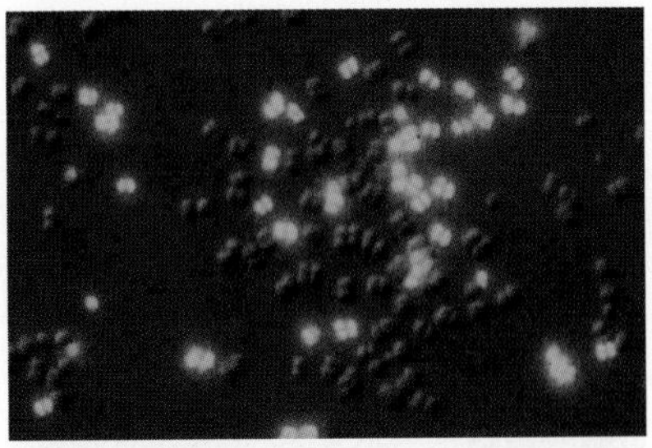

Figure 15.14 A mixed population of live and isopropyl alcohol–killed *Micrococcus luteus* stained with SYTOX® Blue nucleic acid stain (S11348), which does not penetrate intact plasma membranes. Dead cells exhibit bright blue-fluorescent staining. The image was acquired using a longpass optical filter set appropriate for the Cascade Blue® dye.

Ethidium and Propidium Dyes

The red-fluorescent, cell-impermeant ethidium and propidium dyes — ethidium bromide (E1305, E3565), ethidium homodimer-1 (EthD-1, E1169; Figure 8.18) and propidium iodide (P1304MP, P3566; FluoroPure™ Grade, P21493) — can all be excited by the argon-ion laser and are therefore useful for detecting and sorting dead cells by flow cytometry.[69,70] Moreover, these dyes have large Stokes shifts and may be used in combination with fluorescein-based probes (such as calcein, CellTracker™ Green CMFDA or BCECF) or green-fluorescent SYTO® dyes (Table 8.3) for two-color applications (Figure 15.50, Figure 15.15, Figure 15.16). Both propidium iodide and ethidium bromide have been extensively used to detect dead or dying cells,[71–75] although ethidium bromide may be somewhat less reliable because it is not as highly charged. EthD-1 and propidium iodide are superior to ethidium bromide for two-color flow cytometric viability assays in which either BCECF AM or calcein AM is used as the live-cell stain because their spectra do not overlap as much with those of the green-fluorescent esterase probes.[21]

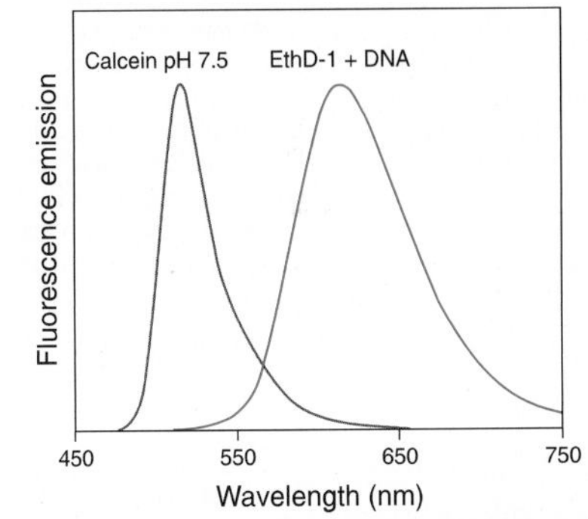

Figure 15.15 Normalized fluorescence emission spectra of calcein (C481) and DNA-bound ethidium homodimer-1 (EthD-1, E1169), illustrating the clear spectral separation that allows simultaneous visualization of live and dead eukaryotic cells with Molecular Probes' LIVE/DEAD® Viability/Cytotoxicity Kit (L3224).

With its high affinity for DNA and low membrane permeability,[76–79] EthD-1 is often the preferred red-fluorescent dead-cell indicator. EthD-1 binds to nucleic acids 1000 times more tightly than does ethidium bromide and undergoes about a 40-fold enhancement of fluorescence upon binding.[78,80] When used as a viability indicator, EthD-1 typically does not require a wash step. Also, the high affinity of EthD-1 permits the use of very low concentrations to stain dead cells, thus avoiding the use of large quantities of the potentially hazardous ethidium bromide or propidium iodide. EthD-1, the dead-cell indicator in our LIVE/DEAD® Viability/Cytotoxicity Kit (L3224, see below), has been used alone[81] or in combination with calcein AM[82] to detect tumor necrosis factor activity and to assay neuronal cell death.[72,83,84] Ethidium homodimer-2 (E3599, Figure 8.19), which under our trademark DEAD Red™ is used as the necrotic-cell indicator in our LIVE/DEAD® Reduced Biohazard Cell Viability Kit #1 (L7013, Section 15.3), has a particularly low dissociation rate from cellular nucleic acids, permitting its use for selective marking of dead-cell populations that need to be observed over several hours. Our DEAD Red™ nucleic acid stain has proven useful for determining brain stem lesion size *in vivo* in rats following a neurotoxin injection.[85] Live and dead cells of the yeast-like fungus *Aureobasidium pullulans* have been identified on microscope slides as well as leaf surfaces using CellTracker™ Blue CMAC (C2110, Section 14.2) in conjunction with the DEAD Red™ nucleic acid stain.[86]

Ethidium Monoazide

Ethidium monoazide (E1374) is a fluorescent photoaffinity label that, after photolysis, binds covalently to nucleic acids in solution and in cells with compromised membranes.[87,88] A mixed population of live and dead cells incubated with this membrane-impermeant dye can be illuminated with a visible-light source, washed, fixed and then analyzed in order to determine the viability of the cells at the time of photolysis.[88] Thus, ethidium monoazide reduces some of the hazards inherent in working with pathogenic samples because, once stained, samples can be treated with fixatives before analysis by fluorescence microscopy or flow cytometry. Immunocytochemical analyses requiring fixation are also compatible with this ethidium monoazide–based viability assay. We have developed an alternative two-color fluorescence-based assay for determining the original viability of fixed samples that employs our cell-permeant, green-fluorescent SYTO® 10 and cell-impermeant, red-fluorescent DEAD Red™ nucleic acid stains; the LIVE/DEAD® Reduced Biohazard Cell Viability Kit #1 (L7013) is described in Section 15.3.

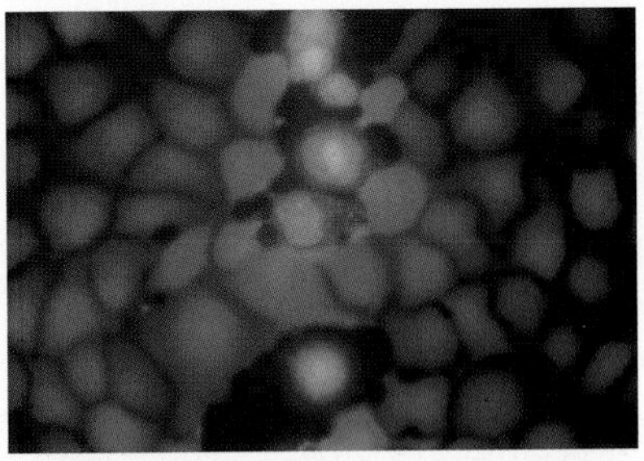

Figure 15.16 Live and dead kangaroo rat (PtK2) cells stained with ethidium homodimer-1 and the esterase substrate calcein AM, both of which are provided in our LIVE/DEAD® Viability/Cytotoxicity Kit (L3224). Live cells fluoresce a bright green, whereas dead cells with compromised membranes fluoresce red-orange.

Hexidium Iodide: A Fluorescent Gram Stain

Ethidium bromide is only marginally permeant to cell membranes or bacteria; however, we found that our patented hexidium iodide stain (H7593) has the right combination of polarity and permeability (Figure 8.17) to allow it to rapidly stain most gram-positive bacteria while being excluded by the less-permeant membranes of most gram-negative bacteria[89] (Figure 15.53). Combining the red-orange–fluorescent hexidium iodide reagent with a green-fluorescent, membrane-permeant nucleic acid stain — as in our LIVE *Bac*Light™ Bacterial Gram Stain Kit (L7005, Section 15.3) — enables taxonomic classification of most bacteria in minutes, using a single staining solution, no fixatives and no wash steps. This rapid gram stain assay should be useful in both clinical and research settings. The validity of using hexidium iodide in combination with the SYTO® 13 green-fluorescent nucleic acid stain to correctly predict the gram sign of 45 clinically relevant organisms, including several known to be gram variable, has been demonstrated.[89] The method of use of hexidium iodide as a gram stain is described further in Section 15.3.

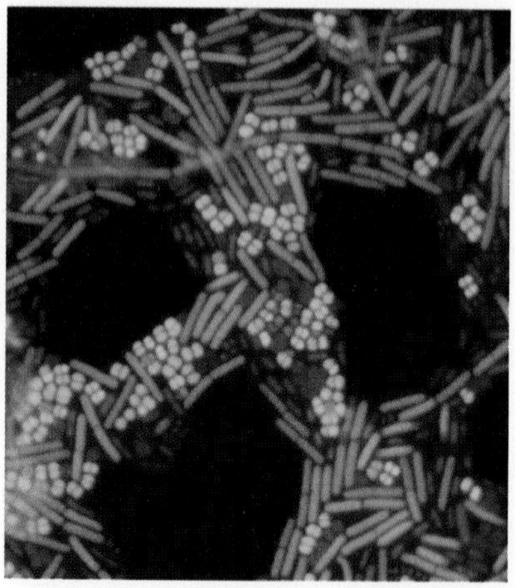

Figure 15.17 A mixed population of live and isopropyl alcohol–killed *Micrococcus luteus* and *Bacillus cereus* stained with the LIVE/DEAD® *Bac*Light™ Bacterial Viability Kit (L7007, L7012). Bacteria with intact cell membranes exhibit green fluorescence, whereas bacteria with damaged membranes exhibit red fluorescence. Prior to imaging, the bacteria were placed onto a polycarbonate filter and immersed in *Bac*Light™ mounting oil. This multiple exposure image was acquired with a triple-bandpass optical filter set appropriate for simultaneous imaging of DAPI, fluorescein and Texas Red® dyes.

SYTO® Nucleic Acid Stains for DNA and RNA

Our patented SYTO® family of dyes, all of which are listed in Table 8.3, are essentially nonfluorescent until they bind to nucleic acids, whereupon their fluorescence quantum yield may increase by 1000-fold or more. These dyes are freely permeant to most cells, although their rate of uptake and ultimate staining pattern may be cell dependent. Their affinity for nucleic acids is moderate and they can be displaced by higher-affinity nucleic acid stains such as SYTOX® Green, propidium iodide, the ethidium dimers and all of the monomeric and dimeric nucleic acid stains described above. Because the membrane of intact cells offers a barrier to entry of these higher-affinity nucleic acid stains, it is common to combine, for instance, a green-fluorescent SYTO® dye with a red-fluorescent, high-affinity nucleic acid stain such as propidium iodide, one of the ethidium homodimers, or TOTO®-3 for simultaneous staining of the live- and dead-cell populations. Although the green-fluorescent SYTO® dye will still bind to nucleic acids in dead cells, it will be displaced or its fluorescence quenched by the red-fluorescent dye, resulting in a yellow-, orange- or red-fluorescent dead-cell population. This principle is the basis of our LIVE/DEAD® *Bac*Light™ Bacterial Viability Kits (L7007, L7012, L13152; Figure 15.17), our LIVE/DEAD® Sperm Viability Kit (L7011) and our LIVE *Bac*Light™ Bacterial Gram Stain Kit (L7005), which are all discussed in Section 15.3. Five sampler kits of the SYTO® dyes (S7554, S7572, S11340, S11350, S11360) provide a total of 32 SYTO® dyes with emission maxima that range from 441 nm to 678 nm. All of the SYTO® dyes in the sampler kits are also available individually (Section 8.1), as well as several other recently introduced SYTO® green-fluorescent (S32704, S32705, S32706, S34854, S34855) and SYTO® orange-fluorescent (S32707) nucleic acid stains. The SYTO® 13 green-fluorescent nucleic acid stain (S7575) has been used in combination with:

- Ethidium bromide for studies of tissue cryopreservation [90]
- Hexidium iodide for simultaneous viability and gram sign determination of clinically relevant bacteria [89]
- Ethidium homodimer-1 for quantitation of neurotoxicity [72,91]
- Propidium iodide to detect the effects of surfactants on *Escherichia coli* viability [92]

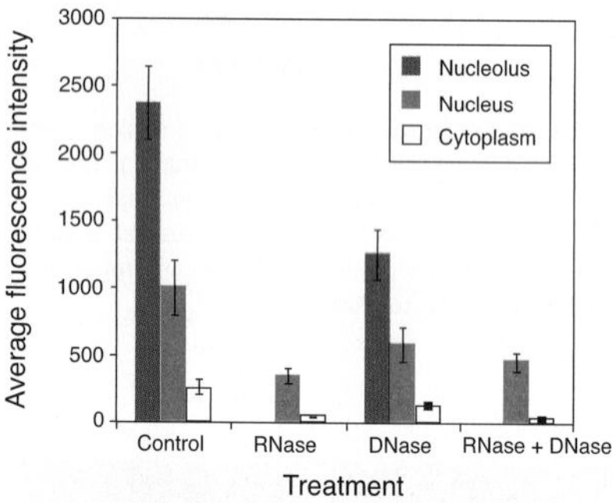

Figure 15.18 Methanol-fixed bovine pulmonary artery endothelial cells treated with RNase, DNase or both, and then labeled with SYTO® RNASelect™ Green cell stain (S32703). Removal of RNA with RNase prevented nucleolar labeling and greatly decreased nuclear and cytoplasmic labeling. Use of DNase resulted in less of a loss of label intensity in these cell compartments, reflecting the RNA-selective nature of this dye.

SYTO® RNASelect™ Green-Fluorescent Cell Stain

SYTO® RNASelect™ green-fluorescent cell stain (S32703) is a cell-permeant nucleic acid stain that selectively stains RNA (Figure 15.18). Although virtually nonfluorescent in the absence of nucleic acids, SYTO® RNASelect™ stain exhibits bright green fluorescence when bound to RNA (absorption/emission maxima ~490/530 nm), but only weak fluorescence when bound to DNA (Figure 8.12). Filter sets that are suitable for imaging cells labeled with fluorescein (FITC) will work well for imaging cells stained with SYTO® RNASelect™ stain (Figure 15.19, Figure 15.20).

Eukaryotic cells stained with the SYTO® RNASelect™ dye show a staining pattern consistent with that of an RNA-selective probe. Maximal fluorescence is observed in the nucleoli, with faint fluorescence throughout the nucleus. Weak fluorescence is also seen throughout the cytoplasm, predominantly associated with mitochondria. The RNA localization of the SYTO® RNASelect™ stain is further supported by RNase and DNase treatments: 1) upon treatment with RNase, the nucleolar and cytoplasmic intensities are significantly reduced, as compared with control cells; 2) upon treatment with DNase, there is no significant loss of fluorescence; and 3) upon treatment with both RNase and DNase, the staining pattern is the same as that observed with RNase treatment alone.

Because the SYTO® RNASelect™ green-fluorescent cell stain is cell permeant, it is suitable for use in live cells. After the cells have been stained, they may be fixed in methanol with minimal loss of the staining pattern. If desired, cells can also be fixed in methanol before staining RNA with the SYTO® RNASelect™ stain. Fixation with formaldehyde alters the staining pattern and is not recommended.

FUN® 1 and FUN® 2: Unique Stains for Assessing Viability of Yeast and Fungi

Our patented FUN® 1 and FUN® 2 dyes (F7030, F13150) are structurally related to the SYTO® dyes; however, both dyes contain substituents (Figure 12.43) that apparently make them chemically reactive with intracellular components of yeast, provided that the yeast are metabolically active. The FUN® 1 and FUN® 2 stains are freely taken up by several species of yeast and fungi and converted from a diffusely distributed pool of yellow-green–fluorescent intracellular stain into compact red-orange– or yellow-orange–fluorescent intravacuolar structures, respectively (Figure 15.41). Conversion of the FUN® 1 and FUN® 2 dyes to products with longer-wavelength emission (Figure 15.38) requires both plasma membrane integrity and metabolic capability. Only metabolically active cells are marked clearly with fluorescent intravacuolar structures, while dead cells exhibit extremely bright, diffuse, yellow-green fluorescence.[58,93] The FUN® 1 cell stain is also available as a component in our LIVE/DEAD® Yeast Viability Kit (L7009, Section 15.3).

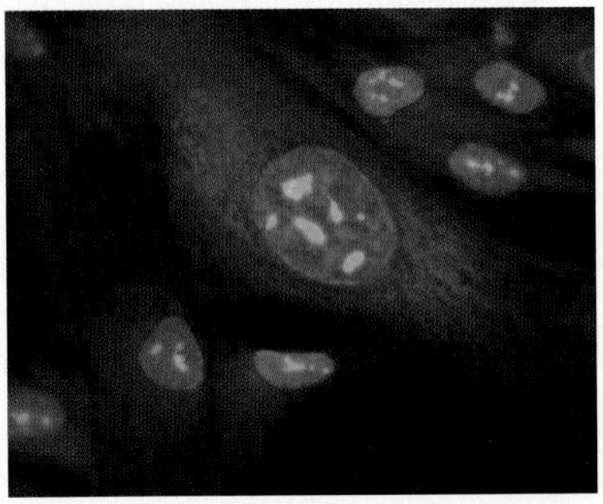

Figure 15.19 Methanol-fixed MRC-5 cells stained with SYTO® RNASelect™ green-fluorescent cell stain (S32703). Nuclei were stained with DAPI (D1306, D3571, D21490); the densely stained areas are nucleoli.

7-Aminoactinomycin D

7-AAD (7-aminoactinomycin D, A1310; Section 15.4) is a fluorescent intercalator that undergoes a spectral shift upon association with DNA. 7-AAD/DNA complexes can be excited by the argon-ion laser and emit beyond 610 nm (Figure 8.32), making this nucleic acid stain useful for multicolor fluorescence microscopy, confocal laser-scanning microscopy and flow cytometry. 7-AAD appears to be generally excluded from live cells, although it has been reported to label the nuclear region of live cultured mouse L cells and salivary gland polytene chromosomes of *Chironomus thummi thummi* larvae.[94] 7-AAD is also a useful marker for apoptotic cell populations (Section 15.5) and has been utilized to discriminate dead cells from apoptotic and live cells.[95] In addition, 7-AAD can be used in combination with conjugates of R-phycoerythrin (Section 6.4) in three-color flow cytometry protocols.

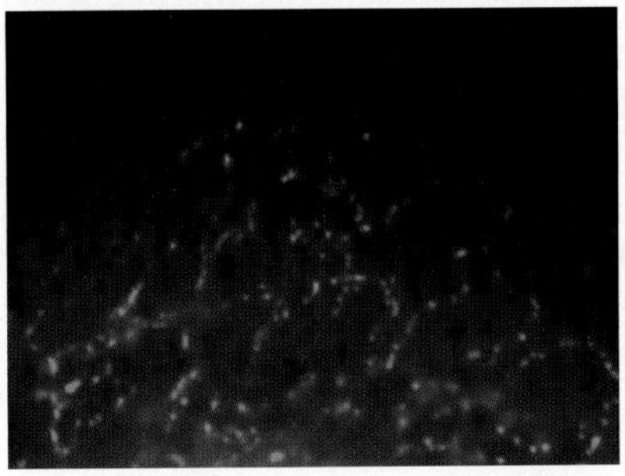

Figure 15.20 Methanol-fixed MRC-5 cells stained with SYTO® RNASelect™ green-fluorescent cell stain (S32703).

Viability/Cytotoxicity Assays That Measure Oxidation or Reduction

Metabolically active cells can oxidize or reduce a variety of probes, providing a measure of cell viability and overall cell health. This measure of viability is distinct from that provided by probes designed to detect esterase activity or cell permeability. Detecting oxidative activity and reactive oxygen species (ROS) in cells is also discussed in Section 18.2.

High-Purity Resazurin

Resazurin (R12204, Figure 15.21) has been extensively used as an oxidation–reduction indicator to detect bacteria and yeast in broth cultures and milk,[96,97] to assess the activity of sperm[98,99] and to assay bile acids[100,101] and triglycerides.[102] Resazurin reduction also occurs with other mammalian cells, including neurons,[103] corneal endothelial cells,[104] lymphocytes, lymphoid tumor cells and hybridoma cells.[105] Furthermore, resazurin has been used in high-throughput screening assays for compounds that act against *Mycobacterium tuberculosis*.[106] However, correlation of the results obtained with resazurin and bioluminescent assays for ATP has been reported to be poor.[107] Recently, resazurin has been sold under the name alamarBlue (a trademark of AccuMed International, Inc.) and has been reported to be useful for quantitatively measuring cell-mediated cytotoxicity,[108] cell proliferation[109,110] and mitochondrial metabolic activity in isolated neural tissue.[111] Several of our bibliography references on resazurin describe studies in which the alamarBlue reagent was the form of resazurin utilized. Our resazurin has been purified to remove fluorescent and colored products typically found in other commercial resazurin preparations, including the alamarBlue reagent.

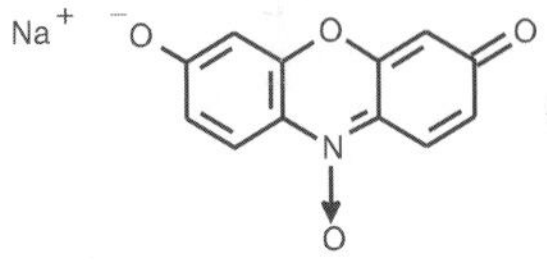

Figure 15.21 R12204 resazurin, sodium salt.

Dodecylresazurin: A Superior Probe for Cell Metabolic Studies

Dodecylresazurin (C_{12}-resazurin), which is available only as a component of our Vybrant® Cell Metabolic Assay Kit (V23110, Section 15.3), LIVE/DEAD® Cell Vitality Assay Kit (L34951, Section 15.3) and Vybrant® Apoptosis Assay Kit #10 (V35114, Section 15.5), has several properties that make it superior to resazurin (and alamarBlue) for detecting metabolic activity in cells:

- C_{12}-resazurin is freely permeant to the membranes of most cells.
- Less C_{12}-resazurin is required for equivalent sensitivity.

- Unlike resazurin, which yields a product (resorufin) that rapidly leaks from viable cells, the product of reduction of C_{12}-resazurin — C_{12}-resorufin — is relatively well retained by single cells, permitting flow cytometric assay of cell metabolism and viability on a single-cell basis (Figure 15.33).
- The fluorescence developed by reduction of C_{12}-resazurin is directly proportional to cell number, and the assay is capable of detecting very low numbers of cells, even in a high-throughput microplate assay (Figure 15.34).

Dihydrorhodamines and Dihydrofluoresceins

Fluorescein, rhodamine and various other dyes can be chemically reduced to colorless, nonfluorescent leuco dyes. These "dihydro" derivatives are readily oxidized back to the parent dye by some reactive oxygen species (Section 18.2) and thus can serve as fluorogenic probes for detecting oxidative activity in cells and tissues.[112–114] Because reactive oxygen species are produced by live but not dead cells, fluorescent oxidation products that are retained in cells can be used as viability indicators for single cells or cell suspensions. Some probes that are useful for detecting oxidative activity in metabolically active cells include:

- H_2DCFDA [115] (2′,7′-dichlorodihydrofluorescein diacetate, D399, Figure 18.7), carboxy-H_2DCFDA (5-(and 6-)carboxy-2′,7′-dichlorodihydrofluorescein diacetate, C400) and the acetoxymethyl ester of H_2DCFDA (C2938, Figure 15.100), all of which require both intracellular deacetylation and oxidation to yield green-fluorescent products [116–118]
- CM-H_2DCFDA (chloromethyl-2′,7′-dichlorodihydrofluorescein diacetate, acetyl ester, C6827), which is analogous to H_2DCFDA, except that it forms a mildly thiol-reactive fluorescent product after oxidation by metabolically active cells (Figure 18.10), permitting significantly longer-term measurements [119,120]
- Dihydrocalcein AM (D23805), our newest dihydrofluorescein derivative, which is converted intracellularly to calcein, a green-fluorescent dye with superior cell retention (Figure 15.3)
- Dihydrorhodamine 123 (D632, D23806; Figure 15.22) and dihydrorhodamine 6G (D633), which are oxidized in viable cells to the mitochondrial stains rhodamine 123 [121–124] and rhodamine 6G,[125,126] respectively
- Dihydroethidium (also known as hydroethidine; D1168, D11347, D23107; Figure 15.23), which forms the nucleic acid stain ethidium following oxidation [127,128] and has proven useful for detecting the viability of intracellular parasites [129]
- Luminol (L8455), which is useful for chemiluminescence-based detection of oxidative events in cells rich in peroxidases, including granulocytes [130–133] and spermatozoa [134]

These probes are all described in more detail in Section 18.2, which includes products for assaying oxidative activity in live cells and tissues.

RedoxSensor™ Red CC-1 Stain

The fluorescence localization of our RedoxSensor™ Red CC-1 stain (2,3,4,5,6-pentafluorotetramethyldihydrorosamine, R14060; Figure 12.18) appears to be based on a cell's cytosolic redox potential. Once it passively enters live cells, the RedoxSensor™ Red CC-1 stain may be oxidized in the cytosol to a red-fluorescent product (excitation/emission maxima ~540/600 nm), which then accumulates in the mitochondria. Alternatively, this nonfluorescent probe may be transported to the lysosomes where it is oxidized. The differential distribution of the oxidized product between mitochondria and lysosomes appears to depend on the redox potential of the cytosol.[135] In proliferating cells, mitochondrial staining predominates; whereas in contact-inhibited cells, the staining is primarily lysosomal (Figure 18.15). The best method we have found to quantitate the distribution of the oxidized product is to use the mitochondrion-selective MitoTracker® Green FM stain (M7514) in conjunction with the RedoxSensor™ Red CC-1 stain.[135]

Tetrazolium Salts

Tetrazolium salts are widely used for detecting redox potential of cells for viability, cytotoxicity and proliferation assays.[136–141] Following reduction, these water-soluble, colorless compounds form uncharged, brightly colored but nonfluorescent formazans. Several of the formazans precipitate out of solution and are useful for histochemical localization of the site of reduction or, after solubilization in organic solvent, for quantitation by standard spectrophotometric techniques.

Reduction of MTT (M6494) remains the most common assay for tetrazolium salt–based viability testing.[142–144] Molecular Probes' convenient Vybrant® MTT Cell Proliferation Assay Kit (V13154, Section 15.4) provides a simple method for determining cell number using standard microplate absorbance readers. MTT has also been used to measure adhesion of HL60 leukemia cells onto endothelial cells.[145] In addition to dehydrogenases, MTT is reduced by glutathione *S*-transferase [146] (GST). Therefore, MTT may not always be a reliable cell viability probe in cells treated with compounds that affect GST activity.

Unlike MTT's purple-colored formazan product, the extremely water-soluble, orange-colored formazan product of XTT (X6493) does not require solubilization prior to quantitation, thereby reducing the assay time in many viability assay protocols. Moreover, the sensitivity of the XTT reduction assay is reported to be similar to or better than that of the MTT reduction assay.[137] The XTT reduction assay is particularly useful for high-throughput screening of antiviral and antitumor agents and for assessing the effect of cytokines on cell proliferation.[141,147–150] NBT (N6495) forms a deep blue–colored precipitate that is commonly used to indicate oxidative metabolism.[151,152]

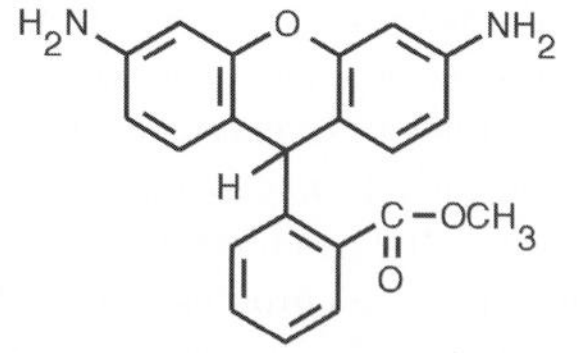

Figure 15.22 D632 dihydrorhodamine 123.

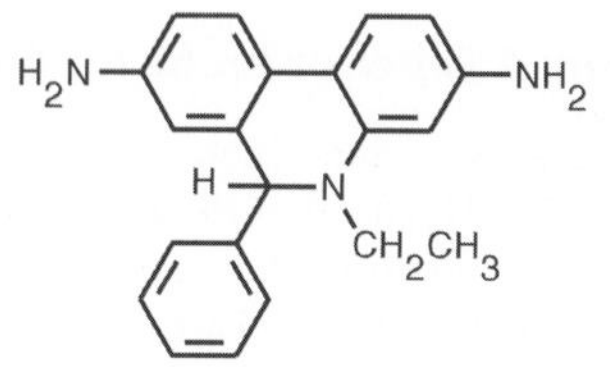

Figure 15.23 D1168 dihydroethidium (hydroethidine).

Other Viability/Cytotoxicity Assay Methods

A viable cell contains an ensemble of ion pumps and channels that maintain both intracellular ion concentrations and transmembrane potentials. Active maintenance of ion gradients ceases when the cell dies, and this loss of activity can be assessed using potentiometric dyes, acidotropic probes, Ca^{2+} indicators [115] (Chapter 19) and pH indicators [115] (Chapter 20).

Potentiometric Dyes

Molecular Probes makes a variety of dyes for detecting transmembrane potential gradients (Chapter 22), including several cationic probes that accumulate in the mitochondria of metabolically active cells (Section 12.2). The mitochondrion-selective rhodamine 123 [115] (R302; FluoroPure™ Grade, R22420) has been used to assess the viability of lymphocytes,[153] human fibroblasts,[154] Simian virus–transformed human cells [155] and bacteria;[156] however, rhodamine 123 is not taken up well by gram-negative bacteria.[156] Rhodamine 123 has also been used in combination with propidium iodide (P1304MP; P3566; FluoroPure™ Grade, P21493) for two-color flow cytometric viability assessment.[157]

The methyl and ethyl esters of tetramethylrhodamine (T668, T669) accumulate in the mitochondria of healthy cells in an amount related to the membrane potential. The dyes are nontoxic and highly fluorescent and do not form aggregates or display binding-dependent changes in their fluorescence efficiency, permitting continuous monitoring of cell heath.[158]

Other potential-sensitive dyes that have proven useful in viability studies include several fast-response styryl dyes and slow-response oxonol and carbocyanine dyes. The fast-response styryl dyes such as di-4-ANEPPS (D1199, Section 22.2) give relatively large fluorescence response to potential changes. Di-4-ANEPPS was used for rapid measurement of toxicity in frog embryos.[159] The symmetrical bis-oxonol dyes [115] (B413, B438; Section 22.3) have been used for viability assessment by flow cytometry [160–162] and imaging. These slow-response dyes have also been employed to determine antibiotic susceptibility of bacteria by flow cytometry,[163,164] and our *Bac*Light™ Bacterial Membrane Potential Kit (B34950, Section 15.3) provides the carbocyanine dye $DiOC_2(3)$ along with the proton ionophore CCCP for detecting membrane potential in both gram-positive and gram-negative bacteria.

The green-fluorescent cyanine dye JC-1 (5,5′,6,6′-tetrachloro-1,1′,3,3′-tetraethylbenzimidazolylcarbocyanine iodide, T3168; Figure 22.13) exists as a monomer at low concentrations or at low membrane potential; however, at higher concentrations (aqueous solutions above 0.1 µM) or higher potentials, JC-1 forms red-fluorescent "J-aggregates" (Figure 12.19, Figure 12.20, Figure 22.14) that exhibit a broad excitation spectrum and an emission maximum at ~590 nm (Figure 22.15). JC-1 has been used to investigate apoptosis,[72,165,166] as well as mitochondrial poisoning, uncoupling and anoxia.[167] The ability to make ratiometric emission measurements with JC-1 makes this probe particularly useful for monitoring changes in cell health. We have also discovered another mitochondrial marker, JC-9 (3,3′-dimethyl-β-naphthoxazolium iodide, D22421; Figure 22.18), with similar potential-dependent spectroscopic properties.

Acidotropic Stains

Membrane-bound proton pumps are used to maintain low pH within the cell's acidic organelles. Our complete selection of stains for lysosomes and other acidic organelles, including LysoTracker® and LysoSensor™ probes, is described in Section 12.3.

The lysosomal stain neutral red (N3246), which was first used for viability measurements by Ehrlich in 1894, has been employed in numerous cytotoxicity, cell proliferation and adhesion assays.[168–173] Although usually used as a chromophoric probe, neutral red also fluoresces at ~640 nm in viable cells and has been detected using a fluorescence microplate reader.[174] Furthermore, the fluorescence of neutral red and BCECF AM (or SYTOX® Green nucleic acid stain) can be measured simultaneously using a single excitation wavelength of 488 nm,[174] suggesting that neutral red may be an effective probe for multicolor flow cytometric determination of cell viability. Our neutral red is highly purified to reduce contaminants that might interfere with these observations.

Acridine orange (A1301, A3568) concentrates in acidic organelles in a pH-dependent manner. The metachromatic green or red fluorescence of acridine orange has been used to assess islet viability [175] and bacterial spore viability [176] and to monitor physiological activity in *Escherichia coli*.[177]

LysoTracker® Green DND-26 (L7526, Section 12.3) was used in a fluorometric assay of cryopreserved sperm to demonstrate both acrosomal integrity and sperm viability.[178] Of several methods used, LysoTracker® Green DND-26 staining was the quickest and easiest to use and gave excellent correlation with the SYBR® 14 staining method used in our LIVE/DEAD® Sperm Viability Kit (L7011, see below). When observed with a fluorescence microscope, sperm appeared to lose their green-fluorescent LysoTracker® Green DND-26 staining and instead exhibit red-fluorescent propidium iodide staining within about 30 seconds after motility ceased.[179,180]

Fluorescent Glucose Analogs

Measurements of glucose uptake can be used to assess viability in a variety of organisms. 2-NBD-deoxyglucose (2-NBDG, N13195) has been used to monitor glucose uptake in living pancreatic β-cells,[181] the yeast *Candida albicans* [182] and the bacterium *Escherichia coli*.[183–185] Molecular Probes also offers the fluorescent nonhydrolyzable glucose analog 6-NBD-deoxyglucose (6-NBDG, N23106). Using this probe, researchers have studied glucose uptake and transport in isolated cells [186–188] and intact tissues.[189] Although sensitive to its environment, NBD fluorescence typically displays excitation/emission maxima of ~465/540 nm and can be visualized using optical filters designed for fluorescein.

Fluorescent Phosphatase Substrate

ELF® 97 phosphate (E6588, E6589; Section 6.3) is intrinsically membrane impermeant; thus, it can be utilized as a marker for membrane integrity in which the intracellular phosphatase activity of membrane-compromised cells is detected.[190] The intense green fluorescence of the ELF® 97 alcohol precipitate (Figure 6.17) and its high photostability (Figure 6.16) permit facile localization of single cells in tissues.

Fluorescent Antibiotics and Related Probes

Fluorescent Polymyxins

Polymyxin B is a cyclic cationic peptide antibiotic that binds to the lipopolysaccharide (LPS) component of the outer membrane of gram-negative bacteria and increases its permeability to lysozyme and hydrophobic compounds. Fluorescent BODIPY® FL (P13235), Oregon Green® 514 (P13236), Texas Red®-X (P13237) and dansyl (P13238) derivatives of polymyxin B are available from Molecular Probes. Dansyl polymyxin B, which fluoresces weakly when free in solution, becomes highly fluorescent (excitation/emission ~340/485 nm) upon binding to intact cells or LPS.[191] The binding of dansyl polymyxin B to LPS can be displaced by a variety of polycationic antibiotics, as well as by Mg^{2+}. Consequently, dansyl polymyxin B displacement experiments can be used to assess the binding of various compounds, such as antibiotics and macrophage cationic proteins, to LPS and intact bacterial cells.[192–194] Dansyl polymyxin has also been used to localize regions of high anionic lipid content in both sperm[195] and aggregated human platelets,[196] and to analyze the morphology of lipid bilayers in preparations of acetylcholine receptor clusters from rat myotubules.[197] Green-fluorescent BODIPY® FL and Oregon Green® 514 polymyxin B and red-fluorescent Texas Red®-X polymyxin B provide additional color options for these experiments. Our fluorescent LPS are described in Section 13.3 and Section 16.1.

Fluorescent Penicillin Analogs

BOCILLIN™ FL penicillin and BOCILLIN™ 650/665 penicillin (B13233, B13234) are green- and infrared-fluorescent penicillin analogs, respectively, that bind selectively and with high affinity to penicillin-binding proteins present on the cytoplasmic membranes of eubacteria.[198,199] When electrophoresed under nonreducing conditions, the dye-labeled penicillin-binding proteins are easily visible in the gel with sensitivity in the low nanograms[200] (Figure 9.78). BOCILLIN™ FL penicillin, synthesized from penicillin V and the BODIPY® FL dye (spectrally similar to fluorescein), has been used to determine the penicillin-binding protein profiles of *Escherichia coli, Pseudomonas aeruginosa* and *Streptococcus pneumoniae*, and these binding profiles are found to be similar to those reported by researchers using radioactively labeled penicillin V.[198] Fluorescently labeled penicillin has also been used for direct labeling and rapid detection of whole *E. coli* and *Bacillus licheniformis*[201] and of *Enterobacter pneumoniae*.[202] The β-lactam sensor-transducer (BlaR), an integral membrane protein from *Staphylococcus aureus*, covalently and stoichiometrically reacts with β-lactam antibiotics, including BOCILLIN™ FL penicillin, by acylation of its active-site serine residue.[203]

BODIPY® FL Vancomycin

BODIPY® FL vancomycin (V34850), which contains a single BODIPY® FL dye per vancomycin molecule, is a green-fluorescent analog of this important antibiotic, which is active against gram-positive bacteria, including enterococci. Although its biological activity has not yet been reported, BODIPY® FL vancomycin may be useful for detecting vancomycin binding sites and transport, for fluorescence polarization assays (see Note 1.5 "Technical Focus: Fluorescence Polarization (FP)" in Section 1.4) of vancomycin concentration in serum[204–206] and for the study and detection of vancomycin-resistant enterococci[207] (VRE, Section 15.6).

Antimalarial Agents

The phosphonate antibiotics FR-31564 (fosmidomycin, F23103) and FR-900098 (F23104) are effective antimalarial agents that function by blocking a mevalonate-independent methylerythritol phosphate (MEP) pathway of isoprene synthesis.[208–211] The antibiotic activity of fosmidomycin is potentiated by glucose 1-phosphate.[212,213] Both products are also active against several gram-negative bacteria.[214]

References

1. J Immunol Methods 243, 155 (2000); **2.** Biochem Biophys Res Commun 172, 262 (1990); **3.** EMBO J 5, 51 (1986); **4.** J Immunol Methods 177, 101 (1994); **5.** J Immunol Methods 172, 227 (1994); **6.** J Immunol Methods 172, 115 (1994); **7.** Hum Immunol 37, 264 (1993); **8.** Biophys J 18, 3 (1977); **9.** J Cell Biol 125, 1077 (1994); **10.** Cornea 15, 599 (1996); **11.** Biophys J 68, 1207 (1995); **12.** Cytometry 19, 366 (1995); **13.** Cytometry 12, 666 (1991); **14.** J Immunol Methods 139, 281 (1991); **15.** Biophys J 68, 2608 (1995); **16.** Biochemistry 37, 2243 (1998); **17.** Appl Environ Microbiol 66, 4486 (2000); **18.** Science 251, 81 (1991); **19.** J Immunol Methods 108, 255 (1988); **20.** J Immunol Methods 172, 255 (1994); **21.** Cytometry 11, 244 (1990); **22.** J Immunol Methods 122, 15 (1989); **23.** Trop Med Parasitol 46, 45 (1995); **24.** Anal Biochem 177, 364 (1989); **25.** Cryobiology 14, 322 (1977); **26.** Vox Sang 27, 13 (1974); **27.** Proc Natl Acad Sci U S A 55, 134 (1966); **28.** J Immunol Methods 157, 117 (1993); **29.** Cancer Res 49, 3776 (1989); **30.** J Histochem Cytochem 33, 77 (1985); **31.** Cytometry 7, 70 (1986); **32.** Biochemistry 18, 2210 (1979); **33.** Immunol Lett 2, 187 (1981); **34.** J Immunol Methods 33, 33 (1980); **35.** Biochemistry 34, 1606 (1995); **36.** Cytometry 13, 739 (1992); **37.** J Immunol Methods 130, 251 (1990); **38.** Proc SPIE-Int Soc Opt Eng 3755, 24 (1999); **39.** J Immunol Methods 100, 261 (1987); **40.** Cytometry 15, 213 (1994); **41.** Appl Environ Microbiol 60, 1467 (1994); **42.** Biol Reprod 34, 127 (1986); **43.** J Immunol Methods 86, 7 (1986); **44.** Anticancer Res 14, 927 (1994); **45.** J Immunol Methods 155, 19 (1992); **46.** J Cell Biol 128, 779 (1995); **47.** Methods Enzymol 194, 644 (1991); **48.** Methods Cell Biol 31, 357 (1989); **49.** J Cell Biol 111, 3129 (1990); **50.** J Immunol Methods 133, 87 (1990); **51.** FEBS Lett 200, 203 (1986); **52.** Biotechniques 3, 270 (1985); **53.** Appl Environ Microbiol 61, 3415 (1995); **54.** J Vasc Res 32, 371 (1995); **55.** Connect Tissue Res 33, 233 (1996); **56.** Anal Biochem 269, 410 (1999); **57.** J Cell Biol 135, 1593 (1996); **58.** Biotechnol Intl 1, 291 (1997); **59.** Appl Environ Microbiol 63, 2421 (1997); **60.** Appl Environ Microbiol 60, 3284 (1994); **61.** Physiol Rev 82, 1013 (2002); **62.** Anal Biochem 221, 78 (1994); **63.** Cytometry 37, 14 (1999); **64.** Appl Environ Microbiol 67, 2326 (2001); **65.** Appl Environ Microbiol 61, 3623 (1995); **66.** Limnol Oceanogr 40, 1050 (1995); **67.** J Immunol Methods 185, 249 (1995); **68.** J Microbiol Methods 42, 3 (2000); **69.** J Neurosci 6, 1492 (1986); **70.** J Immunol Methods 52, 91 (1982); **71.** Appl Environ Microbiol 61, 2521 (1995); **72.** Neuron 15, 961 (1995); **73.** Anal Biochem 220, 149 (1994); **74.** J Immunol Methods 149, 133 (1992); **75.** J Immunol Methods 134, 201 (1990); **76.** Nucleic Acids Res 23, 1215 (1995); **77.** Nucleic Acids Res 20, 2803 (1992); **78.** Biochemistry 17, 5078 (1978); **79.** Biochemistry 17, 5071 (1978); **80.** Proc Natl Acad Sci U S A 87, 3851 (1990); **81.** J Immunol Methods 178, 71 (1995); **82.** Cytometry 20, 181 (1995); **83.** J Neurosci 15, 6239 (1995); **84.** J Neurosci 14, 2260 (1994); **85.** J Appl Physiol 85, 2370 (1998); **86.** Biotechniques 29, 874 (2000); **87.** Manual of Clinical Laboratory Immunology, Rose NR, Ed. pp. 933–941 (1992); **88.** Cytometry 12, 133 (1991); **89.** Appl Environ Microbiol 64, 2681 (1998); **90.** J Physiol 502, 105 (1997); **91.** Cytometry 32, 66 (1998); **92.** Cytometry 29, 58 (1997); **93.** J Cell Biol 126, 1375 (1994); **94.** Histochem J 17, 131 (1985); **95.** Cytometry 13, 204 (1992); **96.** Appl Environ Microbiol 56, 3785 (1990); **97.** J Dairy Res 57, 239 (1990); **98.** Hum Reprod 9, 1688 (1994); **99.** Fertil Steril 56, 743 (1991); **100.** Steroids 38, 281 (1981); **101.** Clin Chim Acta 70, 79 (1976); **102.** Clin Chem 29, 171 (1983); **103.** J Neurosci Methods 70, 195 (1996); **104.** Invest Ophthalmol Vis Sci 38, 1929 (1997); **105.** J Immunol Methods 170, 211 (1994); **106.** Antimicrob Agents Chemother 41, 1004 (1997); **107.** Gynecol Oncol 58, 101 (1995); **108.** J Immunol Methods 213, 157 (1998); **109.** J Clin Lab Anal 9, 89 (1995); **110.** J Immunol Methods 175, 181 (1994); **111.** J Neurosci Res 45, 216 (1996); **112.** Arch Toxicol 68, 582 (1994); **113.** Brain Res 635, 113 (1994);

References — continued

114. Chem Res Toxicol 5, 227 (1992); **115.** Principles and Methods of Toxicology, 3rd Ed., Hayes AW, Ed. pp. 1231–1258 (1994); **116.** Biochemistry 34, 7194 (1995); **117.** Cell 75, 241 (1993); **118.** J Immunol 130, 1910 (1983); **119.** J Pharmacol Exp Ther 300, 9 (2002); **120.** J Biol Chem 274, 19323 (1999); **121.** Cytometry 18, 147 (1994); **122.** Methods Enzymol 233, 539 (1994); **123.** Naturwissenschaften 75, 354 (1988); **124.** J Med Chem 30, 1757 (1987); **125.** J Cell Physiol 156, 428 (1993); **126.** Biochem Biophys Res Commun 175, 387 (1991); **127.** FEMS Microbiol Lett 122, 187 (1994); **128.** J Immunol Methods 170, 117 (1994); **129.** J Immunol Methods 140, 23 (1991); **130.** J Appl Physiol 76, 539 (1994); **131.** J Leukoc Biol 54, 300 (1993); **132.** J Biochem (Tokyo) 106, 355 (1989); **133.** Biochem Biophys Res Commun 155, 106 (1988); **134.** J Cell Physiol 151, 466 (1992); **135.** Free Radic Biol Med 28, 1266 (2000); **136.** J Immunol Methods 179, 95 (1995); **137.** J Infect Dis 172, 1153 (1995); **138.** J Appl Bacteriol 74, 433 (1993); **139.** J Immunol Methods 160, 89 (1993); **140.** J Immunol Methods 157, 203 (1993); **141.** J Immunol Methods 142, 257 (1991); **142.** J Cell Biol 128, 201 (1995); **143.** Cancer Res 54, 3620 (1994); **144.** Cell 77, 817 (1994); **145.** J Immunol Methods 164, 255 (1993); **146.** Biotechniques 25, 622 (1998); **147.** J Immunol Methods 159, 81 (1993); **148.** J Immunol Methods 147, 153 (1992); **149.** J Natl Cancer Inst 81, 577 (1989); **150.** Cancer Res 48, 4827 (1988); **151.** Clin Chim Acta 221, 197 (1993); **152.** J Leukoc Biol 53, 404 (1993); **153.** Clin Bull 11, 47 (1981); **154.** J Cell Biol 91, 392 (1981); **155.** Somatic Cell Genet 9, 375 (1983); **156.** J Appl Bacteriol 72, 410 (1992); **157.** Cancer Res 42, 799 (1982); **158.** Biophys J 53, 785 (1988); **159.** Bull Environ Contam Toxicol 51, 557 (1993); **160.** Cytometry 15, 343 (1994); **161.** J Immunol Methods 161, 119 (1993); **162.** Jpn J Pharmacol 57, 419 (1991); **163.** J Appl Bacteriol 78, 309 (1995); **164.** J Microsc 176, 8 (1994); **165.** J Cell Biol 130, 157 (1995); **166.** Exp Cell Res 214, 323 (1994); **167.** Cardiovasc Res 27, 1790 (1993); **168.** Clin Chem 41, 1906 (1995); **169.** Cell Biol Toxicol 10, 329 (1994); **170.** Anal Biochem 213, 426 (1993); **171.** Biotech Histochem 68, 29 (1993); **172.** ATLA 18, 129 (1990); **173.** Biotechnology (N Y) 8, 1248 (1990); **174.** In Vitro Toxicol 3, 219 (1990); **175.** In Vitro Cell Dev Biol 24, 266 (1988); **176.** Biotech Histochem 67, 27 (1992); **177.** J Microbiol Methods 13, 87 (1991); **178.** Biol Reprod 56, 991 (1997); **179.** Development 121, 825 (1995); **180.** J Immunol Methods 119, 45 (1989); **181.** J Biol Chem 275, 22278 (2000); **182.** Appl Microbiol Biotechnol 46, 400 (1996); **183.** J Microbiol Methods 42, 87 (2000); **184.** Biochim Biophys Acta 1289, 5 (1996); **185.** Biosci Biotechnol Biochem 60, 1899 (1996); **186.** Cytometry 27, 262 (1997); **187.** Biochemistry 34, 15395 (1995); **188.** Biochim Biophys Acta 1111, 231 (1992); **189.** Histochem J 26, 207 (1994); **190.** J Biol Chem 278, 36250 (2003); **191.** Antimicrob Agents Chemother 29, 496 (1986); **192.** Antimicrob Agents Chemother 37, 453 (1993); **193.** Antimicrob Agents Chemother 35, 1309 (1991); **194.** Infect Immun 56, 693 (1988); **195.** Proc Natl Acad Sci U S A 77, 6601 (1980); **196.** Thromb Res 50, 605 (1988); **197.** Exp Cell Res 195, 79 (1991); **198.** Antimicrob Agents Chemother 43, 1124 (1999); **199.** J Biol Chem 275, 17693 (2000); **200.** Electrophoresis 22, 960 (2001); **201.** Biochem J 291, 19 (1993); **202.** Biochem J 300, 141 (1994); **203.** J Biol Chem 278, 18419 (2003); **204.** Ther Drug Monit 20, 202 (1998); **205.** J Antimicrob Chemother 39, 355 (1997); **206.** Ther Drug Monit 20, 191 (1998); **207.** N Engl J Med 344, 1427 (2001); **208.** Parasitol Res 90 Suppl 2, S71 (2003); **209.** Proc Natl Acad Sci U S A 101, 7451 (2004); **210.** Science 285, 1502 (1999); **211.** Science 285, 1573 (1999); **212.** Eur J Clin Microbiol 6, 386 (1987); **213.** Infection 15, 465 (1987); **214.** J Antibiot (Tokyo) 33, 44 (1980).

Data Table — 15.2 Viability and Cytotoxicity Assay Reagents

Cat #	MW	Storage	Soluble	Abs	EC	Em	Solvent	Notes
A1301	301.82	L	H_2O, EtOH	500	53,000	526	H_2O/DNA	1, 2
A3568	301.82	RR,L	H_2O	500	53,000	526	H_2O/DNA	1, 2, 3
B1150	~615	F,D	DMSO	<300		none		4, 5
B1170	~615	F,D	DMSO	<300		none		4, 5
B3051	~615	F,D	DMSO	<300		none		3, 4, 5
B13233	661.46	F,D,L	H_2O, DMSO	504	68,000	511	MeOH	
B13234	653.44	F,D,L	DMSO	646	78,000	659	MeOH	
C195	460.40	F,D	DMSO	<300		none		6
C369	529.29	F,D	DMSO	<300		none		7
C400	531.30	F,D	DMSO, EtOH	290	5,600	none	MeCN	8
C1354	532.46	F,D	DMSO	<300		none		9
C1361	460.40	F,D	DMSO	<300		none		6
C1362	460.40	F,D	DMSO	<300		none		6
C1429	465.41	F,D,L	DMSO	322	13,000	437	DMSO	10
C1430	994.87	F,D	DMSO	<300		none		11
C2925	464.86	F,D	DMSO	<300		none		6
C2938	675.43	F,D,AA	DMSO	291	5,700	none	MeOH	8
C3099	994.87	F,D	DMSO	<300		none		3, 11
C3100MP	994.87	F,D	DMSO	<300		none		11
C6826	499.95	F,D	DMSO	<350		none		12
C6827	577.80	F,D,AA	DMSO	287	9,100	none	MeOH	8
C7025	464.86	F,D	DMSO	<300		none		6
C13196	560.52	F,D	DMSO	<300		none		13
C34851	789.55	F,D,L	DMSO	576	90,000	589	DMSO	14
C34852	994.87	F,D	DMSO	<300		none		11
C34853	465.41	F,D	DMSO	322	13,000	437	DMSO	10
D399	487.29	F,D	DMSO, EtOH	258	11,000	none	MeOH	8
D632	346.38	F,D,L,AA	DMF, DMSO	289	7,100	none	MeOH	15, 16
D633	444.57	F,D,L,AA	DMF, DMSO	296	11,000	none	MeOH	15, 16
D1168	315.42	FF,L,AA	DMF, DMSO	355	14,000	see Notes	MeCN	15, 17
D11347	315.42	FF,L,AA	DMF, DMSO	355	14,000	see Notes	MeCN	15, 17
D22421	532.38	D,L	DMSO, DMF	522	143,000	535	$CHCl_3$	18
D23107	315.42	FF,D,L,AA	DMSO	355	14,000	see Notes	MeCN	17, 19
D23805	1068.95	F,D	DMSO	285	5,800	none	MeCN	20
D23806	346.38	F,D,L,AA	DMSO	289	7,100	none	MeOH	16, 19
E1169	856.77	F,D,L	DMSO	528	7,000	617	H_2O/DNA	1, 21, 22
E1305	394.31	L	H_2O, DMSO	518	5,200	605	H_2O/DNA	1, 23
E1374	420.31	F,LL	DMF, EtOH	462	5,400	625	pH 7	24
E3565	394.31	RR,L	H_2O	518	5,200	605	H_2O/DNA	1, 3, 23

Data Table — 15.2 Viability and Cytotoxicity Assay Reagents — continued

Cat #	MW	Storage	Soluble	Abs	EC	Em	Solvent	Notes
E3599	1292.71	F,D,L	DMSO	535	8,000	624	H_2O/DNA	1, 3, 21, 22
F1303	416.39	F,D	DMSO	<300		none		6
F7030	528.84	F,D,L	DMSO	508	71,000	none	pH 7	3, 25
F13150	387.33	F,D,L	DMSO	465	81,000	none	pH 7	3, 26
F23103	205.08	F,D,L	H_2O	<300		none		
F23104	219.11	F,D,L	H_2O	<300		none		
H7593	497.42	L	DMSO	518	3,900	600	H_2O/DNA	1, 27
I6496	505.70	D	H_2O, DMSO	249	38,000	none	MeOH	
L8455	177.16	D,L	DMF	355	7,500	411	MeOH	28
M6494	414.32	D,L	H_2O, DMSO	375	8,300	none	MeOH	29, 30
N3246	288.78	D,L	H_2O, EtOH	541	39,000	640	see Notes	31
N6495	817.65	D,L	H_2O, DMSO	256	64,000	none	MeOH	29
N13195	342.26	F,L	H_2O	466	20,000	540	MeOH	32
N23106	342.26	F,L	DMSO	475	25,000	552	H_2O	32
O6151	496.38	F,D	DMSO	<300		none		33
P1304MP	668.40	L	H_2O, DMSO	535	5,400	617	H_2O/DNA	1, 34
P3566	668.40	RR,L	H_2O	535	5,400	617	H_2O/DNA	1, 3, 34
P12880	625.46	F,D	DMSO	<300		none		35
P21493	668.40	L	H_2O, DMSO	535	5,400	617	H_2O/DNA	36
R302	380.83	F,D,L	MeOH, DMF	507	101,000	529	MeOH	
R12204	251.17	L	H_2O, MeOH	604	60,000	none	MeOH	37
R14060	434.41	F,D,L,AA	DMSO	239	52,000	none	MeOH	15, 38
R22420	380.83	F,D,L	MeOH, DMF	507	101,000	529	MeOH	36
S1129	518.43	F,D	DMSO	<300		none		39
S7020	~600	F,D,L	DMSO	504	67,000	523	H_2O/DNA	1, 3, 40, 41
S7575	~400	F,D,L	DMSO	488	74,000	509	H_2O/DNA	1, 3, 40, 41
S11348	~400	F,D,L	DMSO	445	38,000	470	H_2O/DNA	1, 3, 40, 41
S11368	~500	F,D,L	DMSO	547	79,000	570	H_2O/DNA	1, 3, 40, 41
S32703	~800	F,D,L	DMSO	491	107,000	532	H_2O/RNA	1, 3, 40, 41
S32704	~350	F,D,L	DMSO	484	67,000	505	H_2O/DNA	1, 3, 40, 41
S32705	~450	F,D,L	DMSO	497	53,000	534	H_2O/DNA	1, 3, 40, 41
S32706	~500	F,D,L	DMSO	495	61,000	537	H_2O/DNA	1, 3, 40, 41
S32707	~450	F,D,L	DMSO	528	48,000	556	H_2O/DNA	1, 3, 40, 41
S34854	~400	F,D,L	DMSO	483	65,000	503	H_2O/DNA	1, 3, 40, 41
S34855	~400	F,D,L	DMSO	480	66,000	502	H_2O/DNA	1, 3, 40, 41
T668	500.93	F,D,L	DMSO, MeOH	549	115,000	573	MeOH	
T669	514.96	F,D,L	DMSO, EtOH	549	109,000	574	MeOH	
T3168	652.23	D,L	DMSO, DMF	514	195,000	529	MeOH	42
V34850	1723.35	F,D,L	H_2O, DMSO	504	68,000	511	MeOH	
X6493	674.53	F,D	H_2O, DMSO	286	15,000	none	MeOH	43

For definitions of the contents of this data table, see "Navigating *The Handbook*" in the introductory pages.

Notes

1. Spectra represent aqueous solutions of nucleic acid-bound dye. EC values are derived by comparing the absorbance of the nucleic acid-bound dye with that of free dye in a reference solvent (H_2O or MeOH).
2. Acridine orange bound to RNA has Abs ~460 nm, Em ~650 nm (Methods Cell Biol 41, 401 (1994); Cytometry 2, 201 (1982)).
3. This product is supplied as a ready-made solution in the solvent indicated under "Soluble."
4. MW value is approximate. BCECF, AM is a mixture of molecular species. Lot-specific average MW values are printed on product labels.
5. BCECF AM is colorless and nonfluorescent until converted to BCECF (B1151) by acetoxymethyl ester hydrolysis.
6. Acetate hydrolysis of this compound yields a fluorescent product with similar pH-dependent spectral characteristics to C1904.
7. C369 is converted to a fluorescent product (C368) after acetate hydrolysis.
8. Dihydrofluorescein diacetates are colorless and nonfluorescent until both of the acetate groups are hydrolyzed and the products are subsequently oxidized to fluorescein derivatives. The materials contain less than 0.1% of oxidized derivative when initially prepared. The oxidation products of C400, C2938, C6827, D399 and D2935 are 2′,7′-dichlorofluorescein derivatives with spectra similar to C368.
9. Hydrolysis of the acetate and acetoxymethyl ester groups of C1354 yields C1359.
10. Acetoxymethyl ester hydrolysis of calcein blue, AM yields the corresponding iminodiacetic acid. The iminodiacetic acid product is water-soluble and has similar spectroscopic properties to 7-hydroxy-4-methylcoumarin (H189).
11. Calcein AM is converted to fluorescent calcein (C481) after acetoxymethyl ester hydrolysis.
12. C6826 and S22801 are converted to fluorescent products with spectra similar to C1270 after acetate hydrolysis.
13. C13196 is converted to a fluorescent product (C652) after acetate hydrolysis.
14. Calcein red-orange, AM is converted to the corresponding nitrilotriacetic acid after acetoxymethyl ester hydrolysis. The nitrilotriacetic acid product is water-soluble and has similar spectroscopic properties to the AM ester form.
15. This compound is susceptible to oxidation, especially in solution. Store solutions under argon or nitrogen. Oxidation may be induced by illumination.
16. D632, D23806 and D633 are essentially colorless and nonfluorescent until oxidized. Oxidation products are R302 (from D632 and D23806) and R634 (from D633).
17. Dihydroethidium has blue fluorescence (Em ~420 nm) until oxidized to ethidium (E1305). The reduced dye does not bind to nucleic acids (FEBS Lett 26, 169 (1972)).
18. JC-9 exhibits long-wavelength J-aggregate emission at ~635 nm in aqueous solutions and polarized mitochondria.
19. This product is supplied as a ready-made solution in DMSO with sodium borohydride added to inhibit oxidation.
20. D23805 is colorless and nonfluorescent until the AM ester groups are hydrolyzed and the resulting leuco dye is subsequently oxidized. The final product is calcein (C481).
21. Although this compound is soluble in water, preparation of stock solutions in water is not recommended because of possible adsorption onto glass or plastic.
22. E1169 in H_2O: Abs = 493 nm (EC = 9100 $cm^{-1}M^{-1}$). E3599 in H_2O: Abs = 498 nm (EC = 10,800 $cm^{-1}M^{-1}$). Both compounds are very weakly fluorescent in H_2O. QY increases >40-fold on binding to dsDNA.
23. Ethidium bromide in H_2O: Abs = 480 nm (EC = 5600 $cm^{-1}M^{-1}$), Em = 620 nm (weakly fluorescent). Fluorescence is enhanced >10-fold on binding to dsDNA.

24. E1374 spectral data are for the free dye. Fluorescence is weak, but intensity increases ~15-fold on binding to DNA. After photocrosslinking to DNA, Abs = 504 nm (EC ~4000 $cm^{-1}M^{-1}$), Em = 600 nm (Nucleic Acids Res 5, 4891 (1978); Biochemistry 19, 3221 (1980)).
25. F7030 is fluorescent when bound to DNA (Em = 538 nm). Uptake and processing of the dye by live yeast results in red-shifted fluorescence (Em ~590 nm).
26. F13150 is fluorescent when bound to DNA (Em = 510 nm). Uptake and processing of the dye by live yeast results in red-shifted fluorescence (Em ~550 nm).
27. H7593 in H_2O: Abs = 482 nm (EC = 5500 $cm^{-1}M^{-1}$), Em = 625 nm (weakly fluorescent).
28. This compound emits chemiluminescence upon oxidation in basic aqueous solutions. Emission peaks are at 425 nm (L8455) and 470 nm (L6868).
29. Enzymatic reduction products are water-insoluble formazans with Abs = 505 nm (M6494) and 605 nm (N6495) after solubilization in DMSO or DMF. See literature sources for further information (Histochemistry 76, 381 (1982); Prog Histochem Cytochem 9, 1 (1976)).
30. M6494 also has Abs = 242 nm (EC = 21,000 $cm^{-1}M^{-1}$) in MeOH.
31. Spectra of N3246 are pH-dependent (pK_a ~6.7). Data reported are for 1:1 (v/v) EtOH/1% acetic acid.
32. Fluorescence of NBD and its derivatives in water is relatively weak. QY and τ increase and Em decreases in aprotic solvents and other nonpolar environments relative to water (Biochemistry 16, 5150 (1977); Photochem Photobiol 54, 361 (1991)).
33. Acetate hydrolysis of this compound yields a fluorescent product with similar spectral characteristics to O6146.
34. Propidium iodide in H_2O: Abs = 493 nm (EC = 5900 $cm^{-1}M^{-1}$), Em = 636 nm (weakly fluorescent). Fluorescence is enhanced >10-fold on binding to dsDNA.
35. P12880 is converted to a fluorescent product (P12925) after acetate hydrolysis.
36. This product is specified to equal or exceed 98% analytical purity by HPLC.
37. Enzymatic reduction of resazurin yields resorufin (R363).
38. R14060 is colorless and nonfluorescent until oxidized. The spectral characteristics of the oxidation product (2,3,4,5,6-pentafluorotetramethylrosamine) are similar to those of T639.
39. S1129 is converted to a fluorescent product (F1130) after acetate hydrolysis.
40. This product is essentially nonfluorescent except when bound to DNA or RNA.
41. MW: The preceding ~ symbol indicates an approximate value, not including counterions.
42. JC-1 forms J-aggregates with Abs/Em = 585/590 nm at concentrations above 0.1 µM in aqueous solutions (pH 8.0) (Biochemistry 30, 4480 (1991)).
43. Enzymatic reduction product is a water-soluble formazan, Abs = 475 nm.

Product List — 15.2 Viability and Cytotoxicity Assay Reagents

Cat #	Product Name	Unit Size
A1301	acridine orange	1 g
A3568	acridine orange *10 mg/mL solution in water*	10 mL
B1150	2′,7′-bis-(2-carboxyethyl)-5-(and-6)-carboxyfluorescein, acetoxymethyl ester (BCECF, AM)	1 mg
B1170	2′,7′-bis-(2-carboxyethyl)-5-(and-6)-carboxyfluorescein, acetoxymethyl ester (BCECF, AM) *special packaging*	20 x 50 µg
B3051	2′,7′-bis-(2-carboxyethyl)-5-(and-6)-carboxyfluorescein, acetoxymethyl ester (BCECF, AM) *1 mg/mL solution in dry DMSO*	1 mL
B13233	BOCILLIN™ FL penicillin, sodium salt	1 mg
B13234	BOCILLIN™ 650/665 penicillin, sodium salt	1 mg
C1430	calcein, AM	1 mg
C3099	calcein, AM *1 mg/mL solution in dry DMSO*	1 mL
C3100MP	calcein, AM *special packaging*	20 x 50 µg
C1429	calcein blue, AM	1 mg
C400	5-(and-6)-carboxy-2′,7′-dichlorodihydrofluorescein diacetate (carboxy-H_2DCFDA) *mixed isomers*	25 mg
C2938	6-carboxy-2′,7′-dichlorodihydrofluorescein diacetate, di(acetoxymethyl ester)	5 mg
C369	5-(and-6)-carboxy-2′,7′-dichlorofluorescein diacetate (carboxy-DCFDA) *mixed isomers*	100 mg
C1361	5-carboxyfluorescein diacetate (5-CFDA) *single isomer*	100 mg
C1362	6-carboxyfluorescein diacetate (6-CFDA) *single isomer*	100 mg
C195	5-(and-6)-carboxyfluorescein diacetate (5(6)-CFDA) *mixed isomers*	100 mg
C1354	5-carboxyfluorescein diacetate, acetoxymethyl ester (5-CFDA, AM)	5 mg
C13196	5-(and-6)-carboxynaphthofluorescein diacetate	10 mg
C34853	CellTrace™ calcein blue, AM *special packaging*	20 x 50 µg
C34852	CellTrace™ calcein green, AM *special packaging*	20 x 50 µg
C34851	CellTrace™ calcein red-orange, AM *special packaging*	20 x 50 µg
C2925	CellTracker™ Green CMFDA (5-chloromethylfluorescein diacetate)	1 mg
C7025	CellTracker™ Green CMFDA (5-chloromethylfluorescein diacetate) *special packaging*	20 x 50 µg
C6827	5-(and-6)-chloromethyl-2′,7′-dichlorodihydrofluorescein diacetate, acetyl ester (CM-H_2DCFDA) *mixed isomers* *special packaging*	20 x 50 µg
C6826	5-(and-6)-chloromethyl SNARF®-1, acetate *mixed isomers* *special packaging*	20 x 50 µg
D399	2′,7′-dichlorodihydrofluorescein diacetate (2′,7′-dichlorofluorescin diacetate; H_2DCFDA)	100 mg
D23805	dihydrocalcein, AM *special packaging*	20 x 50 µg
D1168	dihydroethidium (hydroethidine)	25 mg
D11347	dihydroethidium (hydroethidine) *special packaging*	10 x 1 mg
D23107	dihydroethidium (hydroethidine) *5 mM stabilized solution in DMSO*	1 mL
D632	dihydrorhodamine 123	10 mg
D23806	dihydrorhodamine 123 *5 mM stabilized solution in DMSO*	1 mL
D633	dihydrorhodamine 6G	25 mg
D22421	3,3′-dimethyl-α-naphthoxacarbocyanine iodide (JC-9; DiNOC$_1$(3))	5 mg
E1305	ethidium bromide	1 g
E3565	ethidium bromide *10 mg/mL solution in water*	10 mL

For current prices or to order online, visit probes.invitrogen.com

Product List — 15.2 Viability and Cytotoxicity Assay Reagents — continued

Cat #	Product Name	Unit Size
E1169	ethidium homodimer-1 (EthD-1)	1 mg
E3599	ethidium homodimer-2 (EthD-2) *1 mM solution in DMSO*	200 µL
E1374	ethidium monoazide bromide (EMA)	5 mg
F1303	fluorescein diacetate (FDA)	1 g
F23103	fosmidomycin, sodium salt (FR-31564)	25 mg
F23104	FR-900098	25 mg
F7030	FUN® 1 cell stain *10 mM solution in DMSO*	100 µL
F13150	FUN® 2 cell stain *10 mM solution in DMSO*	100 µL
H7593	hexidium iodide	5 mg
I6496	4-iodonitrotetrazolium violet (INT; 2-(4-iodophenyl)-3-(4-nitrophenyl)-5-phenyltetrazolium chloride)	1 g
L8455	luminol (3-aminophthalhydrazide)	25 g
M6494	MTT (3-(4,5-dimethylthiazol-2-yl)-2,5-diphenyltetrazolium bromide)	1 g
N3246	neutral red *high purity*	25 mg
N13195	2-(*N*-(7-nitrobenz-2-oxa-1,3-diazol-4-yl)amino)-2-deoxyglucose (2-NBDG)	5 mg
N23106	6-(*N*-(7-nitrobenz-2-oxa-1,3-diazol-4-yl)amino)-6-deoxyglucose (6-NBDG)	5 mg
N6495	nitro blue tetrazolium chloride (NBT)	1 g
N7565	Nucleic Acid Stains Dimer Sampler Kit	1 kit
O6151	Oregon Green® 488 carboxylic acid diacetate (carboxy-DFFDA) *6-isomer*	5 mg
P12880	5-(pentafluorobenzoylamino)fluorescein diacetate (PFB-FDA)	5 mg
P13235	polymyxin B, BODIPY® FL conjugate, trifluoroacetic acid salt *mixed species*	100 µg
P13238	polymyxin B, dansyl conjugate, trifluoroacetic acid salt *mixed species*	100 µg
P13236	polymyxin B, Oregon Green® 514 conjugate, trifluoroacetic acid salt *mixed species*	100 µg
P13237	polymyxin B, Texas Red®-X conjugate, trifluoroacetic acid salt *mixed species*	100 µg
P1304MP	propidium iodide	100 mg
P21493	propidium iodide *FluoroPure™ grade*	100 mg
P3566	propidium iodide *1.0 mg/mL solution in water*	10 mL
R14060	RedoxSensor™ Red CC-1 *special packaging*	10 x 50 µg
R12204	resazurin, sodium salt	10 mg
R302	rhodamine 123	25 mg
R22420	rhodamine 123 *FluoroPure™ grade*	25 mg
S1129	5-sulfofluorescein diacetate, sodium salt (SFDA)	25 mg
S11350	SYTO® Blue Fluorescent Nucleic Acid Stain Sampler Kit *SYTO® dyes 40-45* *50 µL each*	1 kit
S34854	SYTO® 9 green fluorescent nucleic acid stain *5 mM solution in DMSO*	100 µL
S32704	SYTO® 10 green fluorescent nucleic acid stain *5 mM solution in DMSO*	100 µL
S7575	SYTO® 13 green fluorescent nucleic acid stain *5 mM solution in DMSO*	250 µL
S32705	SYTO® 26 green fluorescent nucleic acid stain *5 mM solution in DMSO*	100 µL
S32706	SYTO® 27 green fluorescent nucleic acid stain *5 mM solution in DMSO*	100 µL
S34855	SYTO® BC green fluorescent nucleic acid stain *5 mM solution in DMSO*	100 µL
S7572	SYTO® Green Fluorescent Nucleic Acid Stain Sampler Kit #1 *SYTO® dyes 11-16* *50 µL each*	1 kit
S7554	SYTO® Green Fluorescent Nucleic Acid Stain Sampler Kit #2 *SYTO® dyes 20-25* *50 µL each*	1 kit
S32707	SYTO® 86 orange fluorescent nucleic acid stain *5 mM solution in DMSO*	100 µL
S11360	SYTO® Orange Fluorescent Nucleic Acid Stain Sampler Kit *SYTO® dyes 80-85* *50 µL each*	1 kit
S11340	SYTO® Red Fluorescent Nucleic Acid Stain Sampler Kit *SYTO® dyes 17 and 59-64* *50 µL each*	1 kit
S32703	SYTO® RNASelect™ green fluorescent cell stain *5 mM solution in DMSO*	100 µL
S11348	SYTOX® Blue nucleic acid stain *5 mM solution in DMSO*	250 µL
S7020	SYTOX® Green nucleic acid stain *5 mM solution in DMSO*	250 µL
S11368	SYTOX® Orange nucleic acid stain *5 mM solution in DMSO*	250 µL
T3168	5,5′,6,6′-tetrachloro-1,1′,3,3′-tetraethylbenzimidazolylcarbocyanine iodide (JC-1; $CBIC_2(3)$)	5 mg
T669	tetramethylrhodamine, ethyl ester, perchlorate (TMRE)	25 mg
T668	tetramethylrhodamine, methyl ester, perchlorate (TMRM)	25 mg
V34850	vancomycin, BODIPY® FL conjugate (BODIPY® FL vancomycin)	100 µg
X6493	XTT (2,3-bis-(2-methoxy-4-nitro-5-sulfophenyl)-2*H*-tetrazolium-5-carboxanilide)	100 mg

For current prices or to order online, visit probes.invitrogen.com

15.3 Viability and Cytotoxicity Assay Kits for Diverse Cell Types

This section contains a thorough description of each of our viability and cytotoxicity kits. Many of these assay kits have been developed and patented by Molecular Probes' scientists and are exclusively available from Molecular Probes and its distributors. Fluorometric assays of cell viability and cytotoxicity are easy to perform with the use of a fluorescence microscope, fluorometer, fluorescence microplate reader or flow cytometer,[1] and they offer many advantages over traditional colorimetric and radioactivity-based assays. Also discussed in this section are our unique single-step kits for assessing gram sign and for simultaneously determining gram sign and viability of bacteria.

Viability Assay Kits for Animal Cells

To facilitate use of our unique cell viability and cytotoxicity assay technology, Molecular Probes has developed several important products (Table 15.2) that combine fluorescent reagents to yield, in most cases, two-color discrimination of the population of live cells from the dead-cell population by simply adding the reagents, incubating for a brief period and observing the results without any wash steps required. These facile assays are ideal for high-throughput screening applications and, in most cases, for imaging, fluorometry and flow cytometry. Our unique LIVE/DEAD® Reduced Biohazard Kits permit

Table 15.2 — Molecular Probes' assay kits for cell viability, cell counting and bacterial gram staining

Cat #	Kit Name	Kit Components	# Assays	Assay Principle
L3224	LIVE/DEAD® Viability/ Cytotoxicity Kit	• Calcein AM • Ethidium homodimer-1 • A detailed protocol	1000 microscopy assays, 1000 microplate assays or 300 flow cytometry assays	Membrane-permeant calcein AM is cleaved by esterases in live cells to yield cytoplasmic green fluorescence, and membrane-impermeant ethidium homodimer-1 labels nucleic acids of membrane-compromised cells with red fluorescence.
L7013	LIVE/DEAD® Reduced Biohazard Cell Viability Kit #1	• SYTO® 10 nucleic acid stain • DEAD Red™ nucleic acid stain • A detailed protocol	100 microscopy assays or 100 flow cytometry assays	Membrane-permeant SYTO® 10 dye labels the nucleic acids of live cells with green fluorescence, and membrane-impermeant DEAD Red™ dye labels nucleic acids of membrane-compromised cells with red fluorescence. Subsequent fixation inactivates pathogens without distorting the staining pattern.
L23101	LIVE/DEAD® Reduced Biohazard Cell Viability Kit #2	• Green-fluorescent reactive dye • DMSO • A detailed protocol	200 flow cytometry assays	Live cells react with the green-fluorescent reactive dye only on their surface to yield weakly fluorescent cells. Cells with compromised membranes react with the dye throughout their volume, yielding brightly stained cells. Subsequent fixation inactivates pathogens without distorting the staining pattern.
L23102	LIVE/DEAD® Reduced Biohazard Cell Viability Kit #3	• Red-fluorescent reactive dye • DMSO • A detailed protocol	200 flow cytometry assays	Live cells react with the red-fluorescent reactive dye only on their surface to yield weakly fluorescent cells. Cells with compromised membranes react with the dye throughout their volume, yielding brightly stained cells. Subsequent fixation inactivates pathogens without distorting the staining pattern.
L23105	LIVE/DEAD® Reduced Biohazard Cell Viability Kit #4	• Blue-fluorescent reactive dye • DMSO • A detailed protocol	200 flow cytometry assays	Live cells react with the blue-fluorescent reactive dye only on their surface to yield weakly fluorescent cells. Cells with compromised membranes react with the dye throughout their volume, yielding brightly stained cells. Subsequent fixation inactivates pathogens without distorting the staining pattern.
L7010	LIVE/DEAD® Cell-Mediated Cytotoxicity Kit	• $DiOC_{18}(3)$ • Propidium iodide • A detailed protocol	2000 microscopy assays or 200 flow cytometry assays	Target cells are preincubated with the green-fluorescent membrane stain $DiOC_{18}(3)$ and then mixed with effector cells in the presence of the red-fluorescent, membrane-impermeant dye, propidium iodide. Live and dead target cells retain their green-fluorescent membrane stain; target and effector cells with compromised membranes exhibit red-fluorescent nucleic acid staining; live effector cells are nonfluorescent.
L7011	LIVE/DEAD® Sperm Viability Kit	• SYBR® 14 nucleic acid stain • Propidium iodide • A detailed protocol	1000 microscopy assays or 200 flow cytometry assays	Membrane-permeant SYBR® 14 nucleic acid stain labels live sperm with green fluorescence, and membrane-impermeant propidium iodide labels the nucleic acids of membrane-compromised sperm with red fluorescence.
L34951	LIVE/DEAD® Cell Vitality Assay Kit	• Dodecylresazurin (C_{12}-resazurin) • SYTOX® Green nucleic acid stain • DMSO • Phosphate-buffered saline • A detailed protocol	1000 flow cytometry assays	Metabolically active cells reduce C_{12}-resazurin to red-fluorescent C_{12}-resorufin, and cells with compromised membranes (usually late-apoptotic and necrotic cells) are labeled with the green-fluorescent SYTOX® Green nucleic acid stain.

Table 15.2 — Molecular Probes' assay kits for cell viability, cell counting and bacterial gram staining — continued

Cat #	Kit Name	Kit Components	# Assays	Assay Principle
V23110	Vybrant® Cell Metabolic Assay Kit	• Dodecylresazurin (C_{12}-resazurin) • DMSO • Resorufin • A detailed protocol	200 flow cytometry assays or 1000 microplate assays	Nonfluorescent C_{12}-resazurin is reduced to fluorescent C_{12}-resorufin by viable cells; the resulting signal is proportional to the number of cells present.
V23111	Vybrant® Cytotoxicity Assay Kit	• Resazurin • DMSO • Reaction mixture • Reaction buffer • Lysis buffer • A detailed protocol	1000 microplate assays	Damaged and dying cells release glucose 6-phosphate into the surrounding medium, which is detected by an enzymatic process that leads to the reduction of resazurin into red-fluorescent resorufin.
L7009	LIVE/DEAD® Yeast Viability Kit	• FUN® 1 cell stain • Calcofluor White M2R • A detailed protocol	>1000 microscopy assays or 1000 microplate assays	Plasma membrane integrity and metabolic function of fungi are required to convert the yellow-green–fluorescent intracellular staining of FUN® 1 into red-orange–fluorescent intravacuolar structures; Calcofluor White M2R labels cell-wall chitin with blue fluorescence regardless of metabolic state.
L7012 L7007 L13152	LIVE/DEAD® *Bac*Light™ Bacterial Viability Kit	• SYTO® 9 nucleic acid stain • Propidium iodide • *Bac*Light™ mounting oil • A detailed protocol	For Kit L7007 and L7012: >1000 microscopy assays, 1000 microplate assays or 200 flow cytometry assays For Kit L13152: each of the 10 applicator pairs allows ~1000 microscopy assays, 50 microplate assays or 10 flow cytometry assays	Membrane-permeant SYTO® 9 labels live bacteria with green fluorescence; membrane-impermeant propidium iodide labels membrane-compromised bacteria with red fluorescence. In Kit L7007, the stains are supplied in a mixed, two-component formulation, whereas in Kit L7012 the stains are provided as separate solutions. In Kit L13152, the separate dyes are dry and premeasured into pairs of polyethylene transfer pipets.
L34856	LIVE/DEAD® *Bac*Light™ Bacterial Viability and Counting Kit	• SYTO® 9 nucleic acid stain • Propidium iodide • Microsphere standard • A detailed protocol	100 flow cytometry assays	Membrane-permeant SYTO® 9 labels live bacteria with green fluorescence; membrane-impermeant propidium iodide labels membrane-compromised bacteria with red fluorescence. The calibrated suspension of polystyrene microspheres serves as a standard for the volume of suspension analyzed and is clearly distinguishable from stained bacteria in a fluorescence versus side scatter cytogram.
B34950	*Bac*Light™ Bacterial Membrane Potential Kit	• $DiOC_2(3)$ in DMSO • CCCP in DMSO • Phosphate-buffered saline (PBS) • A detailed protocol	100 flow cytometry assays	At low concentrations, $DiOC_2(3)$ exhibits green fluorescence in all bacterial cells, but it becomes more concentrated in healthy cells that are maintaining a membrane potential, causing the dye to self-associate and the fluorescence emission to shift to red. The red- and green-fluorescent bacterial populations are easily distinguished using a flow cytometer. CCCP is included in the kit for use as a control because it eradicates the proton gradient, eliminating bacterial membrane potential.
V7023	ViaGram™ Red+ Bacterial Gram Stain and Viability Kit	• DAPI • SYTOX® Green nucleic acid stain • Texas Red®-X conjugate of wheat germ agglutinin (WGA) • Sodium bicarbonate • *Bac*Light™ mounting oil • A detailed protocol	200 microscopy assays	Membrane-permeant DAPI labels live bacteria with blue fluorescence; membrane-impermeant SYTOX® Green nucleic acid stain labels bacteria with compromised membranes with green fluorescence. Simultaneous Texas Red®-X WGA staining produces red-fluorescent surface labeling of gram-positive bacteria.
L7005	LIVE *Bac*Light™ Bacterial Gram Stain Kit	• SYTO® 9 nucleic acid stain • Hexidium iodide • *Bac*Light™ mounting oil • A detailed protocol	>1000 microscopy assays, 1000 microplate assays or 200 flow cytometry assays	When gram-negative and gram-positive bacteria are simultaneously stained with the membrane-permeant SYTO® 9 dye and hexidium iodide, gram-negative bacteria fluoresce green and gram-positive bacteria fluoresce red.
B7277	Bacteria Counting Kit (Section 15.4)	• SYTO® BC bacteria stain • Suspended microsphere standard • A detailed protocol	100 flow cytometry assays	The membrane-permeant SYTO® BC stain labels both gram-positive and gram-negative bacteria with green fluorescence; the calibrated suspension of polystyrene microspheres serves as a standard for the volume of suspension analyzed.
A22066	ATP Determination Kit	• Luciferin • Luciferase • ATP • Dithiothreitol (DTT) • Reaction buffer • A detailed protocol	1000 microplate assays	Luciferase catalyzes the chemiluminescent reaction of luciferin, ATP and oxygen, producing a photon and other chemical by-products. Stores of ATP are higher in viable cells; therefore, the signal strength correlates with population viability.

discrimination of the live and dead populations with the analysis performed subsequent to fixation to kill possible pathogens in the sample. Some of our specialized assay kits enable sensitive assays for cell-mediated cytotoxicity, tumor necrosis factor and general cell cytotoxicity through analysis of glucose 6-phosphate dehydrogenase or ATP leakage from cells in bodily fluids. In addition, use of our single-step LIVE *Bac*Light™ Bacterial Gram Stain Kit or ViaGram™ Red⁺ Bacterial Gram Stain and Viability Kit (L7005, V7023, see below) overcomes many of the problems inherent in the otherwise labor-intensive, fixation-dependent gram-stain procedure.

LIVE/DEAD® Viability/Cytotoxicity Kit for Animal Cells

Molecular Probes' patented LIVE/DEAD® Viability/Cytotoxicity Kit (L3224) for animal cells provides an exceptionally easy fluorescence-based method for determining viability of adherent or nonadherent cells and for assaying cytotoxicity. The kit comprises two probes: calcein AM and ethidium homodimer-1. Calcein AM (Figure 15.2) is a fluorogenic esterase substrate that is hydrolyzed to a green-fluorescent product (calcein, Figure 14.32); thus, green fluorescence is an indicator of cells that have esterase activity as well as an intact membrane to retain the esterase products. Ethidium homodimer-1 (Figure 8.18) is a high-affinity, red-fluorescent nucleic acid stain that is only able to pass through the compromised membranes of dead cells.[2] The LIVE/DEAD® viability/cytotoxicity assay offers several advantages:

- **Simplicity.** The reagents are simultaneously added to the cell suspension, which is then incubated for 30–45 minutes. No wash steps are required before analysis.
- **Specificity and reliability.** Green-fluorescent cells are live; red-fluorescent cells are dead (Figure 15.16, Figure 15.24).
- **Versatility.** The LIVE/DEAD® viability/cytotoxicity assay is compatible with adherent cells such as astrocytes,[3] nonadherent cells and certain tissues.[4–6] Results can be analyzed by fluorescence microscopy using standard fluorescein longpass filter sets (Table 23.9), as well as by flow cytometry (Figure 15.25) or fluorometry. The fluorescence emissions of the two probes are easily resolved (Figure 15.15).
- **Simple quantitation.** Flow cytometric measurements yield only two populations; there are rarely any doubly stained cells (Figure 15.25). Quantitative assays of bulk cells can be made using a fluorescence microplate reader or fluorometer.
- **Suitability for high-throughput screening.** The ease, reliability and low cost of the LIVE/DEAD® Viability/Cytotoxicity Kit make it an economical assay for high-throughput screening of cytotoxic agents.

Several laboratories have established the validity of the LIVE/DEAD® viability/cytotoxicity assay for use with animal cells. Published applications have included measuring the toxic effects of tumor necrosis factor[7] (TNF), β-amyloid protein,[8] adenovirus E1A proteins,[9] tetrodotoxin (TTX) binding to Na^+ channels,[10] methamphetamines,[11] mitogenic sphingolipids[12] and photodynamic therapy.[13] The assay has also been adapted to quantitate lymphocyte-mediated cytotoxicity by flow cytometry,[14] cell-mediated cytotoxicity by fluorescence microscopy[15] and the viability of boar sperm by fluorescence microscopy.[16]

The LIVE/DEAD® Viability/Cytotoxicity Kit is intended for use with animal cells that can be analyzed within about an hour of adding the dyes to the cells. The kit components, number of assays and assay principles are summarized in Table 15.2. This kit's two viability probes — calcein AM (C1430, C3099, C3100MP) and ethidium homodimer-1 (E1169) — are also available separately (see Section 15.2) and may be used in combination with other probes for discrimination of live and dead cells. When assays need to be conducted over longer periods or when hazardous samples are being analyzed, we recommend our LIVE/DEAD® Reduced Biohazard Cell Viability Kit #1 (L7013, see below).

LIVE/DEAD® Reduced Biohazard Cell Viability Kit #1

Rigorous precautions are necessary during analysis of biohazardous specimens.[17,18] Therefore, fixation procedures that inactivate cells yet produce minimal distortion of their characteristics are highly advantageous.[19] The LIVE/DEAD® Reduced Biohazard Cell Viability Kit #1 (L7013) provides a unique two-color fluorescence assay for animal cell viability that is designed to reduce the risk associated with handling potential biohazards such as viral, bacterial or protozoan pathogens.

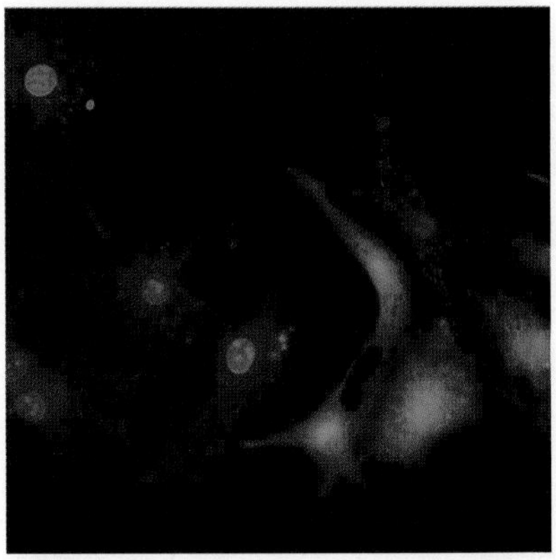

Figure 15.24 A mixture of live and ethanol-killed bovine pulmonary artery endothelial cells stained with the reagents in our LIVE/DEAD® Cell Viability/Cytotoxicity Assay Kit (L3224). Live cells fluoresce bright green, whereas dead cells with compromised membranes fluoresce red-orange.

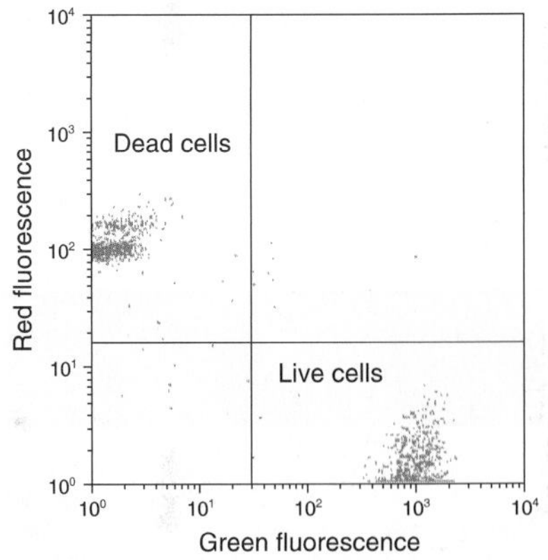

Figure 15.25 Flow cytometric viability assay using Molecular Probes' LIVE/DEAD® Viability/Cytotoxicity Kit (L3224). A 1:1 mixture of live and ethanol-fixed human B cells was stained with calcein AM and ethidium homodimer-1 according to the kit protocol. After 5 minutes, flow cytometric analysis was carried out with excitation at 488 nm. The resulting bivariate frequency distribution shows the clear separation of the green-fluorescent (530 nm) live-cell population from the red-fluorescent (585 nm) dead-cell population.

Viability analysis with the LIVE/DEAD® Reduced Biohazard Cell Viability Kit #1 is provided by our patented cell-permeant, green-fluorescent SYTO® 10 and cell-impermeant, red-fluorescent DEAD Red™ (ethidium homodimer-2) nucleic acid stains. The dye concentrations and their relative affinities are balanced so that a cell population exposed simultaneously to both dyes becomes differentially stained — live cells fluoresce green and dead cells fluoresce red (Figure 15.26, Figure 15.27). This assay is simple and fast and can be carried out using a fluorescence microscope, flow cytometer or fluorescence microplate reader. Moreover, the staining pattern of a cell population is retained for several hours after fixation (Figure 15.28).

Our LIVE/DEAD® Reduced Biohazard Cell Viability Kit #1 has several unique features:

- **Reduced handling risks.** This kit allows viability staining to take place while the potentially pathogenic sample is well contained. Subsequent treatment with 4% glutaraldehyde (or less effectively with formaldehyde) permits safer handling during analysis, without disrupting the distinctive staining pattern. Glutaraldehyde is known to inactivate cells and viruses while preserving their overall morphology.[20] In addition, the high sensitivity and specificity of the assay mean that sample sizes can be very small, further reducing potential biohazards.
- **Specificity and reliability.** Live cells initially fluoresce green, and dead cells fluoresce red. With time, this discrimination is reduced but can still be detected, even after 24 hours (Figure 15.28).
- **Independence from enzymatic activity.** Because it relies on two nucleic acid stains that differ in their membrane permeability, this assay equates loss of cell viability with loss of membrane integrity. Consequently, the assay is totally independent of variations in enzymatic activity or electrical potential of the cell.
- **Versatility.** The analysis is readily quantitated with a fluorescence microscope or flow cytometer (Figure 15.28). This kit's protocol includes methods for analyzing the viability of nonadherent cells, as well as adherent cells on coverslips.
- **Convenience.** Cells can be stained and fixed at various times during the experiment, and the results can be analyzed several hours later, without loss of the discrimination pattern.

The kit components, number of assays and assay principles are summarized in Table 15.2.

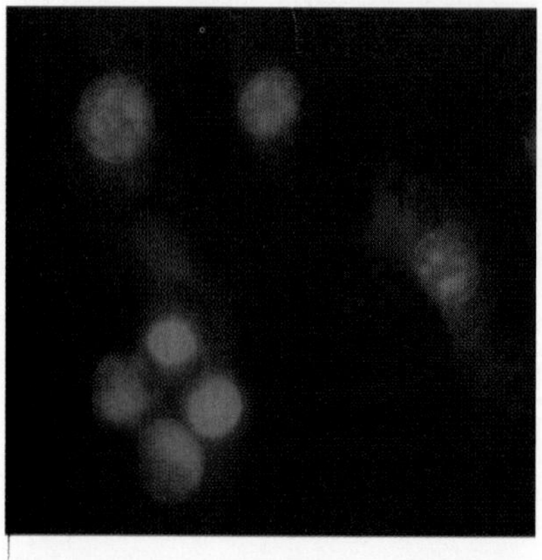

Figure 15.26 A mixed population of trinitrophenyl-sensitized and nonsensitized bovine pulmonary artery endothelial cells that have been probed with anti–dinitrophenyl-KLH antibody (A6430), incubated with rabbit complement and then stained using the LIVE/DEAD® Reduced Biohazard Viability/Cytotoxicity Kit #1 (L7013). With this kit, the membrane-permeant SYTO® 10 dye labels the nucleic acids of live cells with green fluorescence, and the membrane-impermeant DEAD Red™ dye labels nucleic acids of membrane-compromised cells with red fluorescence. Subsequent aldehyde-based fixation inactivates pathogens without distorting the original staining pattern. This multiple-exposure image was acquired with bandpass optical filters appropriate for fluorescein and Texas Red® dyes.

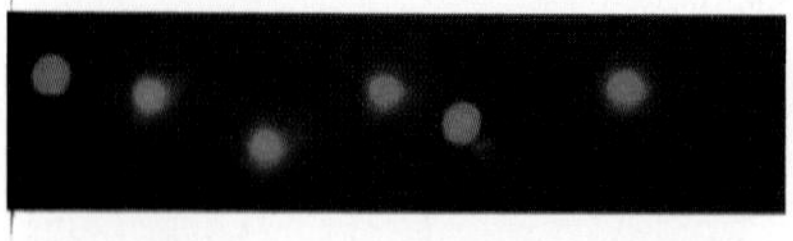

Figure 15.27 A mixture of live and dead goat lymphocytes stained with the LIVE/DEAD® Reduced Biohazard Viability/Cytotoxicity Kit (L7013) and subsequently fixed with 4% glutaraldehyde. This image was photographed in a single exposure through an Omega Optical triple bandpass filter set.

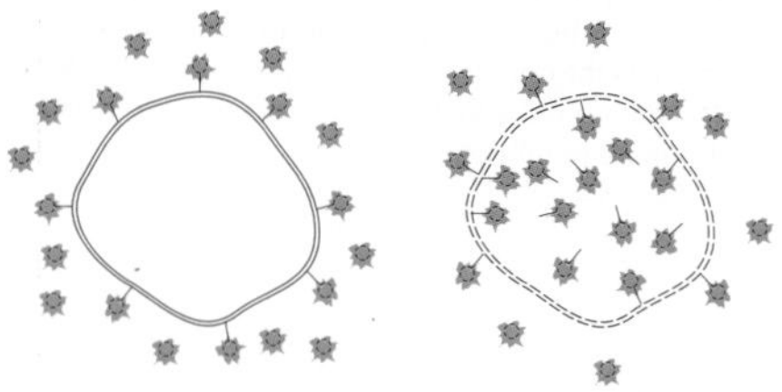

Figure 15.29 Principle of our LIVE/DEAD® Reduced Biohazard Cell Viability Kit #2 (L23101). Live cells (left) react with the kit's green-fluorescent reactive dye only on their surface to yield weakly fluorescent cells. Cells with compromised membranes (right) react with the dye throughout their volume, yielding brightly stained cells. In both cases, the excess reactive dye is subsequently washed away. Our LIVE/DEAD® Reduced Biohazard Cell Viability Kit #3 (L23102) is identical to Kit #2, except that it employs a red-fluorescent reactive dye and our LIVE/DEAD® Reduced Biohazard Cell Viability Kit #4 (L23105) utilizes a blue-fluorescent reactive dye.

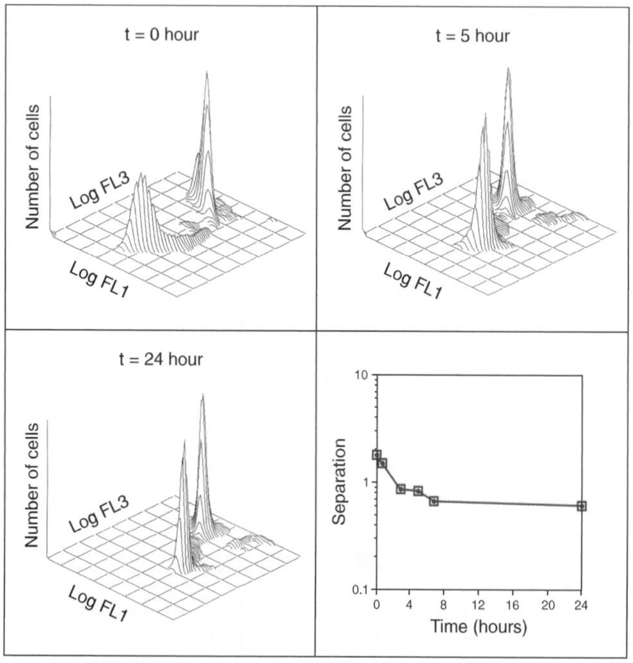

Figure 15.28 Flow cytometric analysis of a mixed population of live and complement-treated goat lymphocytes stained using the reagents and protocols provided in our LIVE/DEAD® Reduced Biohazard Cell Viability Kit #1 (L7013) and monitored over a 24-hour period. The panels (left to right, top to bottom) represent the distribution of SYTO® 10 green fluorescence and DEAD Red™ red fluorescence in lymphocytes at 0, 5 and 24 hours after fixation. Data are on a logarithmic scale. The lower right panel is a plot of the separation between the live- and dead-population peaks as a function of time.

LIVE/DEAD® Reduced Biohazard Cell Viability Kits #2, #3 and #4

Molecular Probes' LIVE/DEAD® Reduced Biohazard Cell Viability Kits #2, #3 and #4 (L23101, L23102, L23105) use a novel method to evaluate the viability of mammalian cells by flow cytometry. These assays are based on the reaction of a fluorescent reactive dye with cellular amines. The reactive dye can penetrate the compromised membranes of necrotic cells and react with free amines both in the cell interior and on the cell surface, yielding intense fluorescent staining. In contrast, only the cell-surface amines of viable cells are available to react with the dye, resulting in relatively dim staining (Figure 15.29). The difference in intensity between the live- and dead-cell populations is typically greater than 100-fold (Figure 15.30). Apoptotic cells may have intermediate fluorescence intensities. The discrimination is completely preserved following fixation of the sample by formaldehyde, under conditions that inactivate pathogens. Moreover, these single-color assays use only one channel of a flow cytometer, leaving the other channels available for multicolor experiments. The assays can also be used to detect dead cells by microscopy; however, the difference in fluorescence intensity of the live and dead cells can be appreciable, making it relatively difficult to simultaneously photograph the two populations.

The LIVE/DEAD® Reduced Biohazard Cell Viability Kits #2, #3 and #4 are essentially identical, except that Kit #2 contains a green-fluorescent reactive dye, Kit #3 contains a red-fluorescent reactive dye and Kit #4 contains a blue-fluorescent reactive dye. Cells labeled by the reactive dyes in either Kit #1 or Kit #2 can be excited by the 488 nm spectral line of an argon-ion laser. The green fluorescence is typically detected in the flow cytometer at 530 ± 15 nm and the red fluorescence at 630 ± 11 nm. Cells labeled with the blue-fluorescent reactive dye in Kit #4 must be excited by ultraviolet light; however, this leaves the entire visible spectrum available for additional green- or red-fluorescent probes. The kit components, number of assays and assay principles are summarized in Table 15.2.

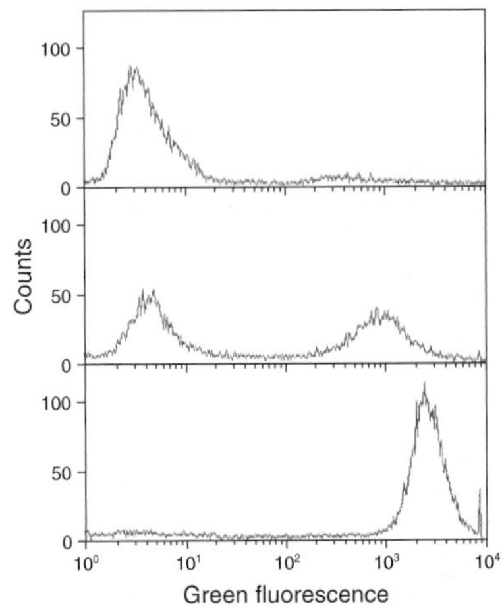

Figure 15.30 Live and dead cells distinguished by flow cytometry using the LIVE/DEAD® Reduced Biohazard Cell Viability Kit #2 (L23101). The LIVE/DEAD® Reduced Biohazard Cell Viability Kit #2 was used to differentially stain live and dead Jurkat cells taken from a healthy culture (top panel), an aged culture (middle panel) and a heat-killed culture (bottom panel). Following the staining reaction, the cells were fixed in 3.7% formaldehyde and analyzed by flow cytometry. Nearly identical results were obtained using unfixed cells (data not shown).

LIVE/DEAD® Cell-Mediated Cytotoxicity Kit

Cytotoxicity triggered by a natural defense mechanism may be much slower than cell lysis triggered by a cytotoxic reagent. Our LIVE/DEAD® Cell-Mediated Cytotoxicity Kit (L7010) is intended for cytotoxicity assessments extending over time periods that are too long for effective use of cytoplasmic markers, such as calcein, which may leak out or become sequestered. This kit is based directly on procedures developed by Kroesen and colleagues for measuring natural killer (NK) cell–mediated, lymphokine-activated killer (LAK) cell–mediated and T cell–mediated cytotoxicity by fluorescence microscopy.[21] The assay has also been adapted for rapid flow cytometric analysis of NK cell activity.[22–24]

Analysis of cell-mediated cytotoxicity using this kit is easy. In order to distinguish target cells, cultures are labeled overnight with $DiOC_{18}(3)$, a green-fluorescent membrane stain (Section 14.4). Target cells are then washed free of excess $DiOC_{18}(3)$ and combined in various proportions with effector cells. After a suitable incubation period, propidium iodide, a red-fluorescent, membrane-impermeant nucleic acid stain, is added. Propidium iodide labels dead effector cells as well as dead target cells once their plasma membranes are compromised. Because the target cells retain the green-fluorescent membrane stain, both live and dead effector cells and live and dead target cells can readily be discriminated with a fluorescence microscope. Dead target cells exhibit both green-fluorescent membrane staining and red-fluorescent nuclear staining, whereas dead effector cells show only red-fluorescent nuclear staining. Live target cells have only green-fluorescent membrane staining, and live effector cells are unstained. The kit components, number of assays and assay principles are summarized in Table 15.2.

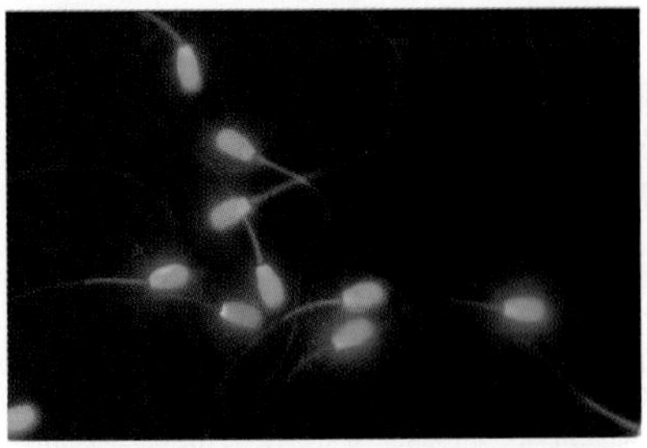

Figure 15.31 A mixture of live and dead bovine sperm cells stained with the dyes provided in our LIVE/DEAD® Sperm Viability Kit (L7011). Live sperm with intact membranes are labeled with our proprietary cell-permeant nucleic acid stain, SYBR® 14, and fluoresce green. Dead sperm, which have been killed by unprotected freeze-thawing, are labeled with propidium iodide (P1304MP, P3566, P21493) and fluoresce red-orange. The image was contributed by Duane L. Garner, School of Veterinary Medicine, University of Nevada, Reno, and Lawrence A. Johnson, USDA Agricultural Research Service.

LIVE/DEAD® Sperm Viability Kit

The LIVE/DEAD® Sperm Viability Kit (L7011), developed in collaboration with Duane L. Garner, provides a novel fluorescence-based method for analyzing the viability of sperm in different species.[25–28] The LIVE/DEAD® Sperm Viability Kit contains a patented membrane-permeant nucleic acid stain developed at Molecular Probes, the SYBR® 14 stain, along with the conventional dead-cell stain propidium iodide. Using this combination of dyes, researchers can rapidly distinguish live and dead cells with visible-light excitation (Figure 15.31), thus avoiding the harmful effects of UV exposure and allowing flow cytometric analysis of sperm viability to be performed using an argon-ion laser excitation source. When semen is incubated briefly with these two stains, live sperm with intact membranes fluoresce bright green, whereas sperm cells with damaged membranes fluoresce red. Garner and colleagues assessed bovine sperm viability with flow cytometry and with fluorescence microscopy; both techniques allowed live and dead cells to be visualized simultaneously.[28,29] Furthermore, it was reported that neither the ability to fertilize oocytes nor the development of the embryos was affected by SYBR® 14 staining of porcine sperm.[25] The effect of two-photon illumination on the viability of human sperm stained with these reagents has also been analyzed.[30] This assay is particularly useful for evaluating the viability of cryopreserved sperm.[31–35]

The dyes provided in the LIVE/DEAD® Sperm Viability Kit stain cells more rapidly than conventional stains (within 5–10 minutes), and both label DNA, thereby avoiding the ambiguity that may arise from targeting separate cellular components. The membrane-permeant SYBR® 14 stain provided in the LIVE/DEAD® Sperm Viability Kit should also serve as a valuable tool for labeling and tracking live sperm, thus facilitating analysis of their motility and abundance in semen samples. Reliable viability measurements with bovine,[28] porcine, ovine, murine,[26] goat, turkey[27] and human sperm[26,30] have been published. The kit components, number of assays and assay principles are summarized in Table 15.2.

Conventional sperm viability assays have employed mixtures of two or three dyes, including fluorescein diacetate derivatives, rhodamine 123 and reduced nucleic acid stains such as dihydroethidium[27,36–39] (hydroethidine, D1168, D11347, D23107; Section 15.2). Acridine orange (A1301, A3568), which fluoresces at different wavelengths when bound to DNA and RNA,[40,41] and the UV light–excitable nucleic acid stains Hoechst 33258 (H1398, H3569, H21491) and Hoechst 33342[42–44] (H1399, H3570, H21492) are frequently used to determine sperm viability and DNA content and to trace sperm–oocyte fusion.[45,46] These alternative viability probes are described in Section 8.1.

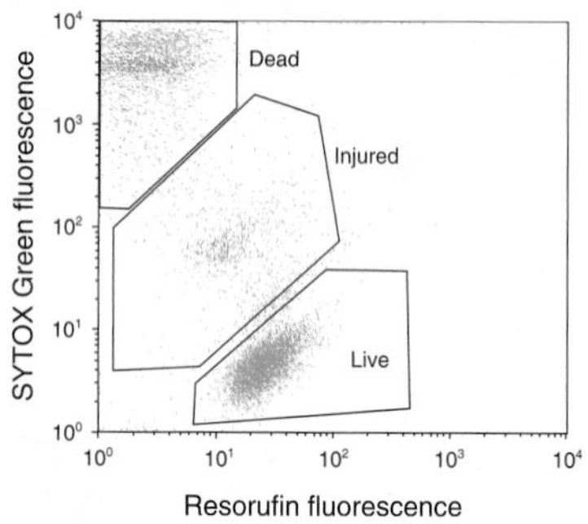

Figure 15.32 Flow cytometric analysis of Jurkat cells using the LIVE/DEAD® Cell Vitality Assay Kit (L34951). Jurkat human T-cell leukemia cells were first exposed to 10 µM camptothecin for 4 hours at 37°C, 5% CO_2. The cells were then treated with the reagents in the LIVE/DEAD® Cell Vitality Assay Kit as specified in the kit protocol and analyzed by flow cytometry. This dot plot of SYTOX® Green fluorescence versus resorufin fluorescence shows resolution of live-, injured- and dead-cell populations.

LIVE/DEAD® Cell Vitality Assay Kit

The LIVE/DEAD® Cell Vitality Assay Kit (L34951) provides a simple two-color fluorescence assay that distinguishes metabolically active cells from injured cells and dead cells. The assay is based on the reduction of C_{12}-resazurin to red-fluorescent C_{12}-resorufin in metabolically active cells and the uptake of the cell-impermeant SYTOX® Green nucleic acid stain in cells with compromised plasma membranes (usually late apoptotic and necrotic cells). Dead cells emit mostly green fluorescence, whereas healthy, metabolically active cells emit mostly red fluorescence (Figure 15.32). The injured cells have lower metabolic activity and, consequently, reduced red-fluorescent emission. Because they possess intact membranes, however, injured cells accumulate little SYTOX® Green dye and, therefore, emit very little green fluorescence.

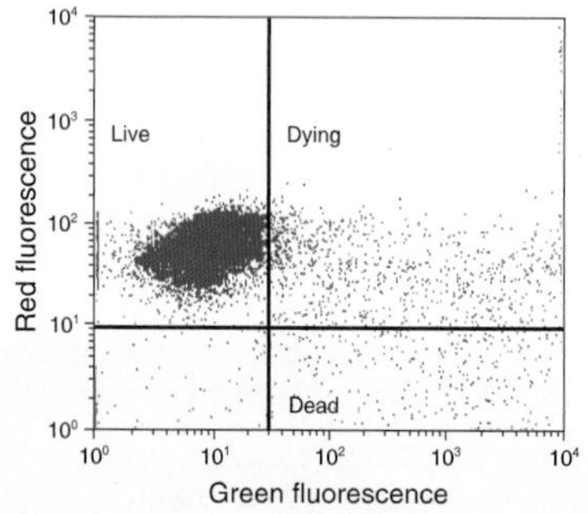

Figure 15.33 Flow cytometric analysis of Jurkat cells stained with C_{12}-resazurin. Cells were loaded with 0.1 µM C_{12}-resazurin, a component of the Vybrant® Cell Metabolic Assay Kit (V23110), and 1 mM SYTOX® Green (S7020). After a 15-minute incubation, the cells were analyzed. Healthy (live) cells reduce C_{12}-resazurin into red-fluorescent C_{12}-resorufin and exclude the cell impermeant green-fluorescent SYTOX® Green. Dead cells show little reduction of the C_{12}-resazurin, but strong staining by SYTOX® Green. Cells indicated in the figure as dying are of indeterminate viability, showing both reduction of C_{12}-resazurin and compromised membrane integrity.

Nonfluorescent resazurin, which can be reduced by viable cells to red-fluorescent resorufin, has been extensively used to detect the metabolic activity of many different cell types, from bacteria to higher eukaryotes.[47–49] Resazurin is nontoxic and stable in culture media, allowing researchers to continuously monitor proliferating cells[50] and to investigate cytotoxicity in both conventional[51] and high-throughput applications.[52] The LIVE/DEAD® Cell Vitality Assay Kit includes a lipophilic version of resazurin, C_{12}-resazurin, which is more permeable to live cells and, after reduction to C_{12}-resorufin, is far better retained than the nonlipophilic resorufin. These characteristics result in brighter signals and better detection limits. The kit components, number of assays and assay principles are summarized in Table 15.2.

Vybrant® Cell Metabolic Assay Kit

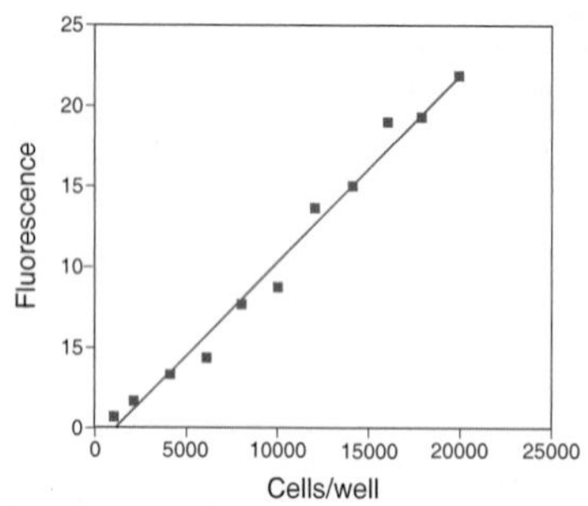

Figure 15.34 Detection limit of C_{12}-resazurin and linear response with increasing cell number using our Vybrant® Cell Metabolic Assay Kit (V23110). Jurkat cells were loaded with 5 µM C_{12}-resazurin for 15 minutes. The resulting signal was measured in a fluorescence microplate reader with excitation/emission at 530/590 nm. For comparison, the detection limit for alamarBlue (resazurin) in a similar experiment was ~8000 cells/well (data not shown).

One potential drawback in the use of resazurin as a substrate that can detect metabolic activity in live cells (R12204, Section 15.2) is the relatively poor uptake of the substrate and poor cellular retention of the reduced by-product, resorufin. Molecular Probes' scientists have found that the lipophilic dodecylresazurin (C_{12}-resazurin), included as a component in the Vybrant® Cell Metabolic Assay Kit (V23110), surpasses resazurin alone in cell permeability and its reduction product (C_{12}-resorufin) is very well retained, permitting single-cell analysis of the substrate's turnover by flow cytometry (Figure 15.33). This enhanced uptake, turnover and retention of C_{12}-resazurin by metabolically active cells translates into much brighter signals and far better detection limits when compared with assays using resazurin alone (Figure 15.34).

C_{12}-resazurin can be used in any viability/cytotoxicity assay that employs resazurin — also known as alamarBlue — for both conventional and high-throughput applications. C_{12}-resorufin, which is the reduction product of C_{12}-resazurin, has the same absorption/emission maxima as unmodified resorufin (~571/585 nm, Figure 10.6); therefore, no changes in instrumentation are required in order to use the kit in place of a resazurin-based assay. The Vybrant® Cell Metabolic Assay Kit (V23110) contains:

- Dodecylresazurin (C_{12}-resazurin)
- DMSO
- Resorufin
- A detailed protocol for the assay

Each kit contains sufficient reagents for 500–1000 assays in a fluorescence microplate or about 10,000 flow cytometry assays.

Vybrant® Cytotoxicity Assay Kit

The LIVE/DEAD® kits generally assay cell death via probes that gain entry to the interior of the cell as a result of plasma membrane damage. In contrast, the Vybrant® Cytotoxicity Assay Kit (V23111) monitors the release of the cytosolic enzyme glucose 6-phosphate dehydrogenase (G6PD) from damaged cells into the surrounding medium. G6PD is a ubiquitous enzyme that is part of the pentose phosphate pathway and is crucial for cellular antioxidant defenses via its production of NADPH.[53,54] Detection of G6PD is by a two-step enzymatic process that leads to the reduction of resazurin into the red-fluorescent resorufin (Figure 15.35). The resulting signal is proportional to the amount of G6PD released into the cell medium, which correlates with the number of dead cells in the sample (Figure 15.36).

The Vybrant® Cytotoxicity Assay Kit contains all enzymes and substrates needed to detect the release of G6PD from damaged and dying cells. The assay can be completed in less than an hour and is effective with as few as 500 cells per sample. Resorufin, the end product of the G6PD cytotoxicity assay, has absorption and emission maxima at ~571 nm and 585 nm, respectively (Figure 10.6), placing the fluorescent signal beyond the autofluorescence of most biological samples. In addition, the levels of G6PD in serum commonly used for cell culture are lower than those of lactate dehydrogenase (LDH), an enzyme often used in similar assays, thus resulting in lower background signals (Figure 15.37). The Vybrant® Cytotoxicity Assay Kit (V23111) contains:

- Resazurin
- DMSO
- Reaction mixture (diaphorase, glucose 6-phosphate and $NADP^+$)
- Reaction buffer
- Cell-lysis buffer
- A detailed protocol for the assay

Sufficient reagents are provided for about 1000 assays in a fluorescence microplate reader.

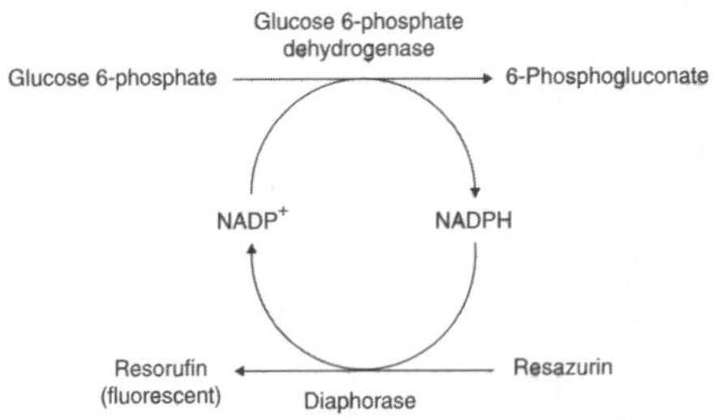

Figure 15.35 Principle of the coupled enzymatic assay for detection of glucose 6-phosphate dehydrogenase activity. Oxidation of glucose 6-phosphate by glucose 6-phosphate dehydrogenase results in the generation of NADPH, which in turn leads to the reduction of resazurin by diaphorase to yield fluorescent resorufin.

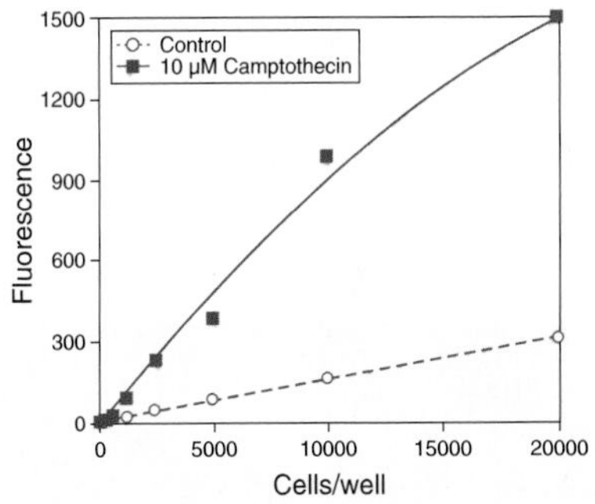

Figure 15.36 Detection of dead and dying cells using the Vybrant® Cytotoxicity Assay Kit (V23111). Jurkat cells were treated with 10 µM camptothecin for six hours, then assayed for glucose 6-phosphate dehydrogenase release. An untreated control sample is shown for comparison. The fluorescence was measured in a microplate reader (excitation/emission ~530/590 nm). A background of 55 fluorescence units was subtracted from each value.

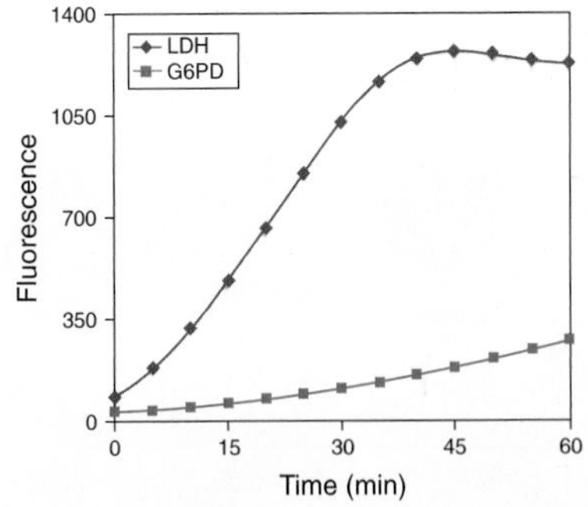

Figure 15.37 10% bovine serum was assayed for the presence of lactate dehydrogenase (LDH, blue) and glucose 6-phosphate dehydrogenase (G6PD, red). G6PD was assayed using the Vybrant® Cytotoxicity Assay Kit (V23111); LDH was detected using a similar method, in which LDH reduces lactate to generate NADH. The result clearly shows that, over the time course of the experiment, the serum generates a much lower signal in the G6PD assay than in the LDH assay.

Viability Assay Kits for Yeast and Bacteria

LIVE/DEAD® Yeast Viability Kit

Our LIVE/DEAD® Yeast Viability Kit (L7009) provides an extremely simple and sensitive assay for discriminating viable yeast and fungi in complex mixtures or in pure cultures.[55–57] This kit contains our unique two-color fluorescent viability probe, the FUN® 1 dye, which has low intrinsic fluorescence, moderate affinity for nucleic acids and exceptional membrane permeability. Also included is the UV light–excitable counterstain Calcofluor White M2R, which labels the cell walls of yeast and fungi fluorescent blue, regardless of the cells' metabolic state.[58–60]

The patented FUN® 1 viability probe displays some extraordinary spectral properties when used to stain metabolically active yeast and fungal cells, exploiting normal endogenous biochemical processing mechanisms that appear to be well conserved among different fungal species. The FUN® 1 stain passively diffuses into a variety of cell types and initially stains the cytoplasm with a diffusely distributed green fluorescence. However, in several common species of yeast and fungi, subsequent processing of the dye by live cells results in the formation of distinct vacuolar structures with compact form that exhibit a striking red fluorescence, accompanied by a reduction in the green cytoplasmic fluorescence[57,61] (Figure 15.38). Formation of the red-fluorescent intravacuolar structures requires both plasma membrane integrity and metabolic capability. Dead cells fluoresce bright yellow-green, with no discernable red structures.

FUN® 1 stain can be used alone or together with Calcofluor White M2R to determine the metabolic activity of single fungal cells by manual or automated fluorescence microscopy (Figure 15.39, Figure 15.40, Figure 15.41, Figure 15.42). Both live and dead cells may be viewed simultaneously by fluorescence microscopy using a standard fluorescein longpass optical filter set (Table 23.9). FUN® 1 dye staining can also be used to assay the viability of suspensions of fungal cells using a fluorescence microplate reader or a fluorometer. The FUN® 1 reagent has been extensively used for flow cytometric analysis of yeast, including of their susceptibility to antifungal agents.[62–66]

The LIVE/DEAD® Yeast Viability Kit has been tested on several fungal species, including *Candida albicans*, *Candida pseudotropicalis* and several strains of *Saccharomyces cerevisiae*, under a variety of experimental conditions. Formation of the red-fluorescent structures was observed not only in logarithmically growing cells but also in nonculturable cells with residual metabolic activity. The LIVE/DEAD® Yeast Viability Kit should be particularly useful for detecting very low numbers of live or dead fungal cells, even in complex mixtures such as blood (Figure 15.43). The kit components, number of assays and assay principles are summarized in Table 15.2. The FUN® 1 cell stain, as well as the shorter-wavelength FUN® 2 analog, are also available separately (F7030, F13150; Section 15.2).

LIVE/DEAD® BacLight™ Bacterial Viability Kits

Molecular Probes' original LIVE/DEAD® Viability/Cytotoxicity Kit (L3224, see above) is a proven tool for assessing viability of animal cells but is generally not suitable for use with bacterial and yeast cells.[67] Consequently, we have developed the LIVE/DEAD® *BacLight*™ Bacterial Viability Kits (L7007, L7012, L13152), which provide two different nucleic acid stains — the SYTO® 9 dye and propidium iodide — to rapidly distinguish live bacteria with intact plasma membranes from dead bacteria with compromised membranes[55,57,68] (Figure 15.44, Figure 15.17). This assay has several significant features:

- **Ease of use.** The reagents are simultaneously added to the bacterial suspension, which is then incubated for 5–10 minutes. No wash steps are required before analysis.
- **Specificity.** Live bacteria fluoresce green and dead bacteria fluoresce red. Live and dead bacteria can be distinguished and quantitated in minutes, even in a mixed population of bacterial species (Figure 15.45).
- **Reliability.** The LIVE/DEAD® *BacLight*™ Bacterial Viability Kits yield consistent results in tests on a variety of eubacterial genera (Table 15.3). It can also be used to assess the viabil-

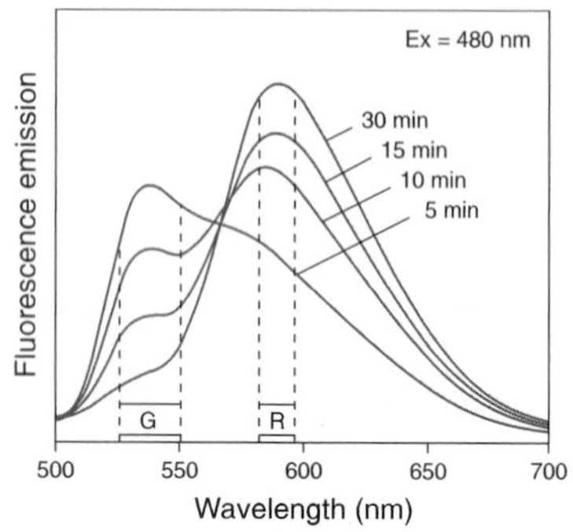

Figure 15.38 Fluorescence emission spectra of a *Saccharomyces cerevisiae* suspension that has been stained with the FUN® 1 cell stain, which is available separately (F7030) or in our LIVE/DEAD® Yeast Viability Kit (L7009). After the FUN® 1 reagent was added to the medium, the fluorescence emission spectrum (excited at 480 nm) was recorded in a spectrofluorometer at the indicated times during a 30-minute incubation period. The shift from green (G) to red (R) fluorescence reflects the processing of FUN® 1 by metabolically active yeast cells.

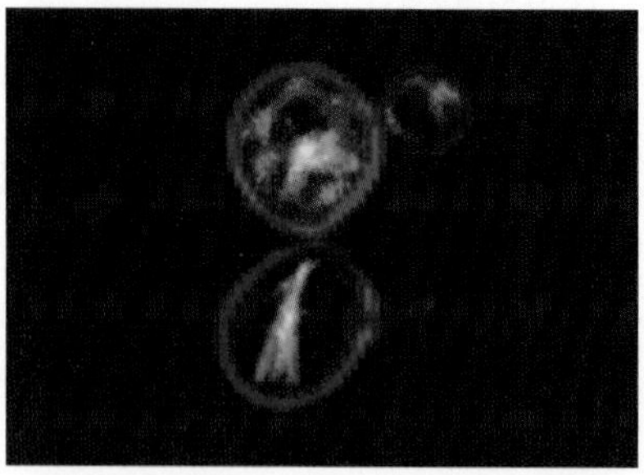

Figure 15.39 *Saccharomyces cerevisiae* stained with the FUN® 1 cell stain, which generates red-fluorescent intravacuolar structures, and with Calcofluor White M2R, a blue-fluorescent cell wall stain. Both probes are provided in our LIVE/DEAD® Yeast Viability Kit (L7009); FUN® 1 cell stain is also available separately (F7030).

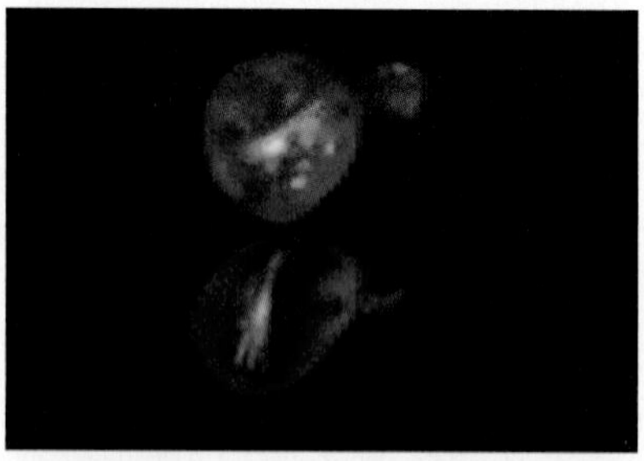

Figure 15.40 *Saccharomyces cerevisiae* stained with FUN® 1 cell stain, which generates red-fluorescent intravacuolar structures, and with Calcofluor White M2R, a blue-fluorescent cell wall stain. Both probes are provided in our LIVE/DEAD® Yeast Viability Kit (L7009); FUN® 1 cell stain is also available separately (F7030). A series of z-section images was acquired with a Deltavision widefield optical sectioning microscope (Applied Precision, Inc.). A three-dimensional projection movie was generated from a deconvolved z-image stack.

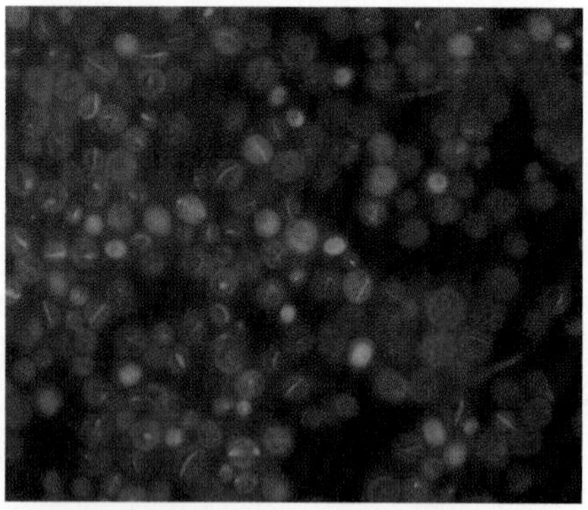

Figure 15.41 A culture of *Saccharomyces cerevisiae* incubated in medium containing the FUN® 1 viability indicator (F7030) and the counterstain Calcofluor White M2R, both of which are provided in our LIVE/DEAD® Yeast Viability Kit (L7009). Metabolically active yeast process the FUN® 1 dye, forming numerous red-fluorescent cylindrical structures within their vacuoles. Calcofluor stains the cell walls fluorescent blue, regardless of the yeast's metabolic state. The yeast were photographed in a single exposure through an Omega Optical triple bandpass filter set.

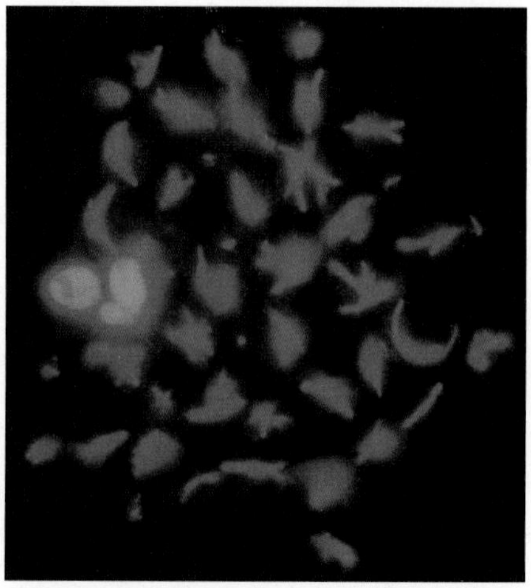

Figure 15.42 *Saccharomyces cerevisiae* stained with the FUN® 1 dye, available separately (F7030) or in our LIVE/DEAD® Yeast Viability Kit (L7009). Metabolically active yeast process the FUN® 1 dye, forming numerous red fluorescent cylindrical structures within their vacuoles.

ity of *Eurioplasma eurilytica* and *Mycoplasma hominus* mycoplasma as well as cysts of the protozoan parasite *Giardia muris* [69] (Figure 15.46).

- **Validity.** Viability measurements in fresh cultures of bacteria typically correlate well with enumeration techniques involving growth in liquid or solid media. However, variable results have been found using the LIVE/DEAD® *Bac*Light™ reagents to assess viability in some marine bacteria from environmental samples.
- **Versatility.** Bacteria can be stained in suspension or immobilized on microscope slides or filter membranes. Protocols are provided for bacterial viability analysis using a fluorescence microscope, fluorometer (Figure 15.47) or fluorescence microplate reader.

The intensities of the fluorescence signals produced by the SYTO® 9 and propidium iodide nucleic acid stains can be adjusted by mixing different proportions of the dye solutions provided in the LIVE/DEAD® *Bac*Light™ Kits. We have balanced the dye concentrations so that, for most bacteria, equal volumes of the two solutions provided give balanced staining of most species. The background remains virtually nonfluorescent, allowing live and dead cells to be easily differentiated in any fluorescence microscope equipped with a longpass fluorescein or comparable optical filter set (Table 23.9). Under certain conditions, bacteria with compromised membranes may recover and reproduce, even though such bacteria may be scored as dead in this assay. Conversely, some bacteria with intact membranes may be unable to reproduce in nutrient medium, yet be scored as live.[70] Combining several different measures of viability, such as membrane permeability, enzyme activity and redox potential, offers a more thorough assessment of bacterial viability and eliminates the inherent limitations of any single viability assay.

The LIVE/DEAD® *Bac*Light™ viability assay has been used to estimate total and viable bacteria in drinking water,[71] to quantitate total and viable concentrations of aerosolized *Pseudomonas fluorescens* by fluorescence microscopy [72] and to measure the reliability of disinfection agents on reducing the viability of *Cryptosporidium parvum* and *Giardia muris* cysts.[69,73,74] The number of live natural planktonic bacteria, as determined with the LIVE/DEAD® *Bac*Light™ Bacterial Viability Kit, reportedly correlated well with the number of bacteria with high DNA content (HDNA), as determined with SYTO® 13 green-fluorescent nucleic acid stain (S7575), leading to the recommendation that %HDNA be used as an index of the percentage of actively growing bacterial cells in marine plankton samples.[75] The reagents in the LIVE/DEAD® *Bac*Light™ Bacterial Viability Kit have been utilized in a high-throughput fluorescence-based screen for bacterial mechanosensitive ion-channel (MscL) activity that replaces otherwise tedious and difficult assays.[76]

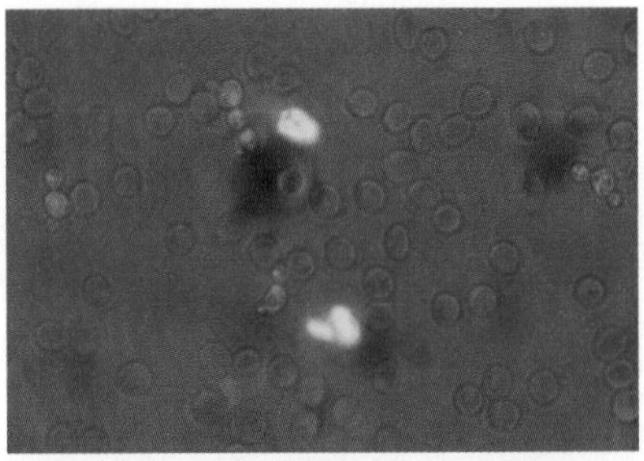

Figure 15.43 *Saccharomyces cerevisiae* in blood stained with the FUN® 1 dye, which is available separately (F7030) or in our LIVE/DEAD® Yeast Viability Kit (L7009). Metabolically active yeast process the FUN® 1 dye, forming numerous red-fluorescent cylindrical structures within their vacuoles. When stained with the FUN® 1 dye, leukocytes fluoresce yellow; fluorescence from red blood cells is not observed because it is quenched by the heme.

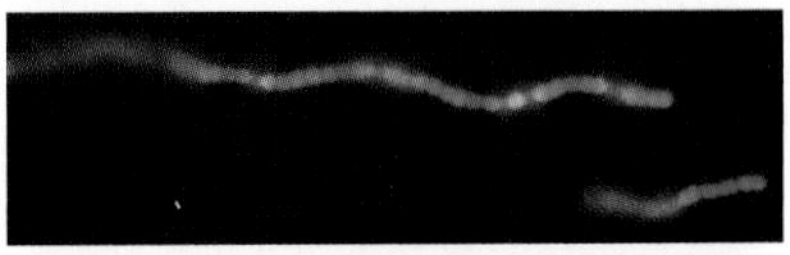

Figure 15.44 Use of our LIVE/DEAD® *Bac*Light™ Bacterial Viability Kit (L7007, L7012, L13152) to identify individual live and dead bacteria along a chain of *Streptococcus pyogenes*. This image was photographed in a single exposure through an Omega Optical triple bandpass filter set.

Table 15.3 — Some organisms that have been successfully stained with our LIVE/DEAD® *Bac*Light™ Bacterial Viability Kits (L7007, L7012, L13152)

Bacteria	
Gram-Positive	**Gram-Negative**
Bacillus cereus	*Agrobacterium tumefaciens*
Bacillus subtilis	*Edwardsiella ictaluri*
Clostridium perfringens	*Escherichia coli*
Lactobacillus sp.	*Deleya aquamarina*
Micrococcus luteus	*Helicobacter pylori*
Mycobacterium phlei	*Klebsiella pneumoniae*
Propionibacterium sp.	*Legionella pneumophila*
Staphylococcus aureus	*Pseudomonas aeruginosa*
Streptococcus pyogenes	*Pseudomonas syringae*
	Salmonella oranienburg
	Serratia marcescens
	Shigella sonnei
	Zymomonas sp.
Mycoplasma	
Eurioplasma eurilytica	
Mycoplasma hominus	
Protozoa	
Giardia muris cysts	

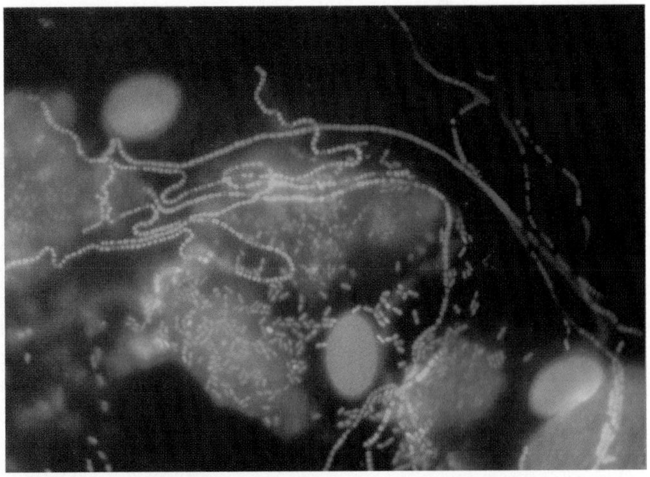

Figure 15.45 Live and dead bacteria visualized on freshly isolated human cheek epithelial cells using our LIVE/DEAD® *Bac*Light™ Bacterial Viability Kit (L7007, L7012, L13152). When incubated with the SYTO® 9 and propidium iodide nucleic acid stains provided in this kit, live bacteria with intact cell membranes fluoresce green and dead bacteria with compromised membranes fluoresce red. This image was photographed in a single exposure through an Omega Optical triple bandpass filter set.

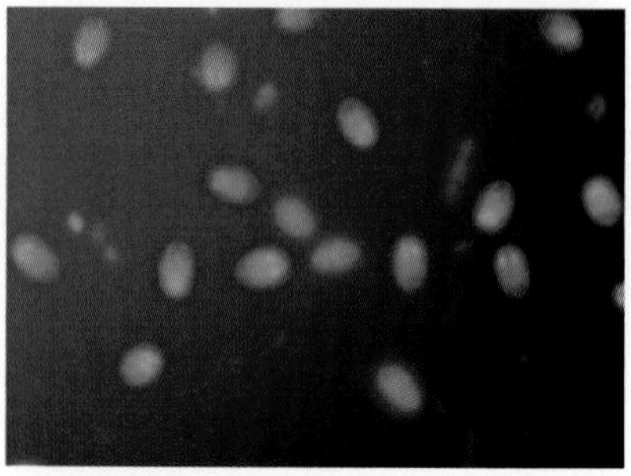

Figure 15.46 *Giardia muris* cysts stained with the reagents in the LIVE/DEAD® *Bac*Light™ Bacterial Viability Kit (L7007, L7012). When incubated with the SYTO® 9 and propidium iodide nucleic acid stains provided in this kit, live bacteria with intact cell membranes fluoresce green and dead bacteria with compromised membranes fluoresce red.

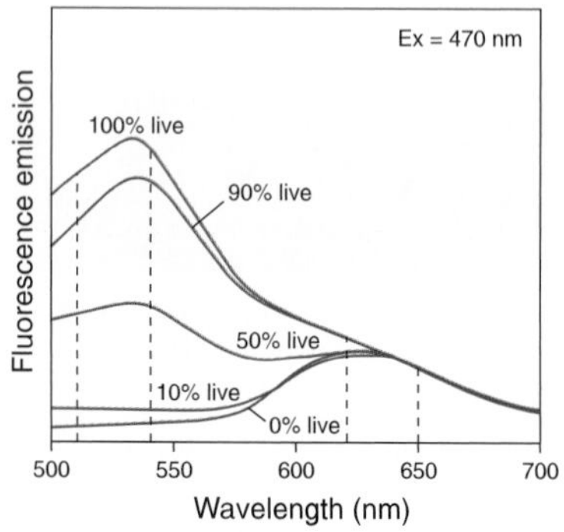

Figure 15.47 Analysis of relative viability of *Escherichia coli* suspensions by fluorescence spectroscopy. Emission spectra of suspensions of various proportions of live and isopropyl alcohol–killed *E. coli* were obtained from samples stained with the LIVE/DEAD® *Bac*Light™ Bacterial Viability Kit (L7007, L7012, L13152). Note that although the green-fluorescent dye (SYTO® 9) enters all cells regardless of viability state, its signal is significantly quenched in dead cells.

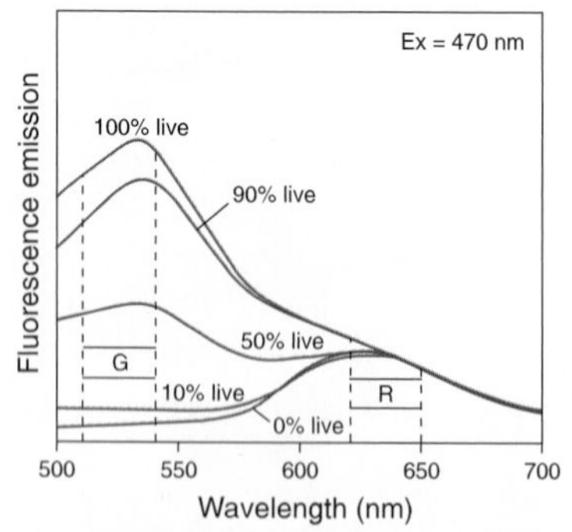

Figure 15.48 Viability analysis of bacterial suspensions comprising various proportions of live and isopropyl alcohol–killed *Escherichia coli* using the reagents in Molecular Probes' LIVE/DEAD® *Bac*Light™ Bacterial Viability Kit (L7007, L7012, L13152). Live and dead bacteria are stained fluorescent green (G) by SYTO® 9 and fluorescent red (R) by propidium iodide, respectively. Bacterial suspensions that have been incubated in the two stains simultaneously and then excited at 470 nm exhibit a fluorescence spectral shift from red to green as the percentage of live bacteria in the sample is increased.

Our original packaging of the LIVE/DEAD® *Bac*Light™ Bacterial Viability Kit (L7007), in which the dyes were mixed at different proportions in two solutions, is still available for customers who have already developed protocols using that formulation. However, we recommend use of the newer LIVE/DEAD® *Bac*Light™ Bacterial Viability Kit (L7012), which is more flexible because it provides separate solutions of the SYTO® 9 and propidium iodide nucleic acid stains, thus facilitating calibration of bacterial fluorescence at each of the two emission wavelengths in quantitative assays. Kit L7007 was designed primarily for use in fluorescence microscopy; Kit L7012 is equally well suited for use in fluorescence microscopy and is better suited than Kit L7007 for use in quantitative analysis with a fluorometer (Figure 15.48), fluorescence microplate reader, flow cytometer or other instrumentation.

For added convenience, our LIVE/DEAD® *Bac*Light™ Bacterial Viability Kit (L13152) provides the separate stains dry and premeasured into pairs of polyethylene transfer pipettes (Figure 15.49). Kit L13152 has several advantages:

- The stains are dry, without DMSO or other potentially harmful solvents, allowing viability determination of solvent-sensitive microorganisms — just dissolve the dyes in virtually any aqueous medium and then add them to the cells.
- The stains are premeasured and supplied in sealed polyethylene transfer pipettes, eliminating the need for pipetting microliter volumes — perfect for educational settings, where there is a need to simplify handling and minimize equipment expenditures.
- This stain formulation does not require refrigeration and is chemically stable, even in poor conditions — storage at 37°C for more than six months produces no detectable changes, making the assay well suited to field testing and other situations where storage or use conditions are less than optimal.

Each of our LIVE/DEAD® *Bac*Light™ Bacterial Viability Kits includes a procedure for mounting bacteria stained with the reagents in the LIVE/DEAD® *Bac*Light™ Bacterial Viability Kit on filter membranes and a proprietary mounting oil that we have found to be useful for the direct epifluorescence filter technique [77] (DEFT). The kit components, number of assays and assay principles are summarized in Table 15.2. The SYTO® 9 nucleic acid stain is also available separately (S34854, Section 15.2).

LIVE/DEAD® BacLight™ Bacterial Viability and Counting Kit

Accurate detection and enumeration of the live and dead bacteria in a sample is an important aspect of many experimental procedures in biotechnology. Because of the marked differences in morphology, cytology and physiology among the many bacterial genera, a universally applicable direct-count viability assay has been very difficult to attain. Conventional direct-count assays of bacterial viability are based on metabolic characteristics or membrane integrity. However, methods relying on metabolic characteristics often only work for a limited subset of bacterial groups,[78] and methods for assessing bacterial membrane integrity commonly have high levels of background fluorescence.[79] Both types of determinations suffer from being very sensitive to growth and staining conditions.[80,81] Molecular Probes' LIVE/DEAD® *Bac*Light™ Bacterial Counting and Viability Kit (L34856) allows researchers to reliably distinguish and quantitate live and dead bacteria with the aid of a flow cytometer, even in a mixed population containing a range of bacterial types.

This kit utilizes a mixture of two nucleic acid stains — the green-fluorescent SYTO® 9 dye and red-fluorescent propidium iodide — for viability determinations, as well as a calibrated suspension of beads for accurate sample volume measurements. The SYTO® 9 and propidium iodide stains differ both in their spectral characteristics and in their ability to penetrate healthy bacterial cells. When used alone, the SYTO® 9 stain generally labels all bacteria in a population — those with intact membranes and those with damaged membranes. In contrast, propidium iodide penetrates only bacteria with damaged membranes, causing a reduction in the SYTO® 9 stain fluorescence when both dyes are present. With an appropriate mixture of the SYTO® 9 and propidium iodide stains, bacteria with intact cell membranes fluoresce bright green, whereas bacteria with damaged membranes exhibit significantly less green fluorescence and they often also fluoresce red. The cell type and the gram character influence the amount of red-fluorescent staining exhibited by dead bacteria. Both the SYTO® 9 and propidium iodide stains are efficiently excited by the 488 nm spectral line of the argon-ion laser found in most flow cytometers, and their nucleic acid complexes can be detected in the green and red channels, respectively; the background remains virtually nonfluorescent.

The calibrated suspension of microspheres serves as a reference standard for sample volume. The size and fluorescence of the beads in this microsphere standard have been carefully chosen to ensure that they will be clearly distinguishable from any stained bacteria in a fluorescence versus side scatter cytogram. A bacterial culture is simply stained with the optimal mixture of SYTO® 9 dye and propidium iodide, and then a fixed number of microspheres are added before analyzing the sample on a flow cytometer. Live and dead bacteria and the microspheres are all easily distinguished in a plot of fluorescence versus side scatter (Figure 15.50). The concentration of both the live bacteria and the dead bacteria can then be determined from the ratio of bacteria events to microsphere events in the cytogram (Figure 15.51).

The kit components, number of assays and assay principles are summarized in Table 15.2. The SYTO® 9 nucleic acid stain is also available separately (S34854, Section 15.2).

BacLight™ Bacterial Membrane Potential Kit

The *Bac*Light™ Bacterial Membrane Potential Kit (B34950) provides a fluorescent membrane-potential indicator dye, $DiOC_2(3)$, along with a proton ionophore (CCCP) and premixed buffer. At low concentrations, $DiOC_2(3)$ exhibits green fluorescence in all bacterial cells, but it becomes more concentrated in healthy cells that are maintaining a membrane potential, causing the dye to self-associate and the fluorescence emission to shift to red. The red- and green-fluorescent bacterial populations are easily distinguished using a flow cytometer. CCCP is included in the kit for use as a control because it eradicates the proton gradient, eliminating bacterial membrane potential.[82,83]

Using the *Bac*Light™ Bacterial Membrane Potential Kit, we have detected membrane potentials in all bacteria tested (including logarithmically growing cultures of *Micrococcus luteus, Staphylococcus aureus, Bacillus cereus, Staphylococcus warnerii, Escherichia coli* and *Salmonella choleraesuis*), although the magnitude varies with species (Figure 22.19). For many gram-positive species, such as *M. luteus* and *S. aureus*, the $DiOC_2(3)$ red:green ratio has been shown to vary with the intensity of the proton gradient (Figure 22.20). In gram-negative bacteria, such as *E. coli* and *S. choleraesuis*, a $DiOC_2(3)$ response is observed in the presence of a membrane potential but the response does not appear to be proportional to proton gradient intensity.

Each *Bac*Light™ Bacterial Membrane Potential Kit contains:

- $DiOC_2(3)$ in dimethylsulfoxide (DMSO)
- CCCP in DMSO
- Phosphate-buffered saline (PBS)
- A detailed protocol

Using the recommended reagent dilutions and volumes, this kit provides sufficient $DiOC_2(3)$ to perform approximately 100 individual assays by flow cytometry; sufficient CCCP is provided for 30 depolarized control samples. The *Bac*Light™ Bacterial Membrane Potential Kit is designed to assay bacterial concentrations between 10^5 and 10^7 organisms per mL. Stained cells are efficiently excited by the 488 nm spectral line of the argon-ion laser, and fluorescence is detected using emission filters suitable for fluorescein and the Texas Red® dye. $DiOC_2(3)$ staining can be combined with the impermeant DNA-binding dye TO-PRO®-3 (T3605, Section 8.1) to distinguish depolarized cells from cells with damaged membranes.[82] The TO-PRO®-3 dye must be excited with a red laser such as the 633 nm spectral line of the He–Ne laser. Note that $DiOC_2(3)$ and CCCP are inhibitors

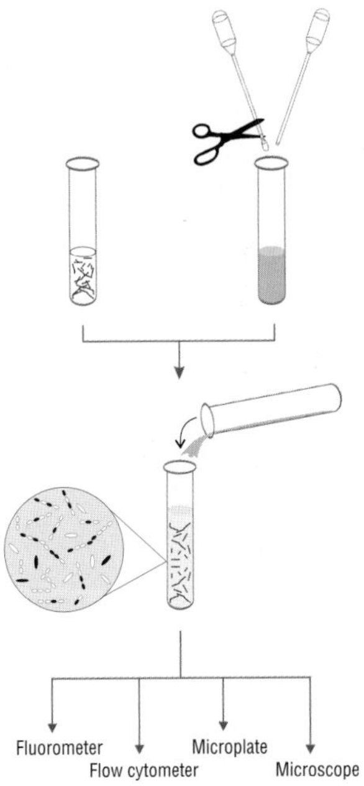

Figure 15.49 The convenient and versatile procedure for using the specially packaged LIVE/DEAD® *BacLight*™ Bacterial Viability Kit (L13152). Simply dissolve the premeasured dyes in buffer, mix with the bacterial sample and observe the fluorescence.

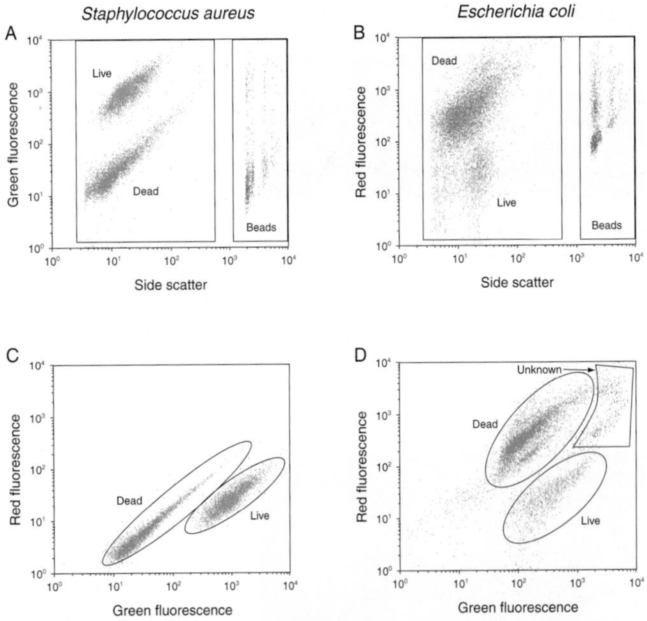

Figure 15.50 Analysis of bacterial cultures using the LIVE/DEAD® *BacLight*™ Bacterial Viability and Counting Kit (L34856). Suspensions of live (untreated) and dead (alcohol-treated) *Staphylococcus aureus* (Panels A and C) and *Escherichia coli* (Panels B and D) were stained with the SYTO® 9 nucleic acid stain and propidium iodide and then analyzed by flow cytometry according to the kit protocol. The green or red fluorescence versus side scatter cytogram (Panel A or B) was used to gate the bacterial population and the bead population (left and right boxes, respectively). Events in the bacteria region of each cytogram are also displayed in red fluorescence versus green fluorescence cytograms (Panels C and D). Live and dead bacteria/mL can be calculated from either the fluorescence versus side scatter cytogram or the green fluorescence versus red fluorescence cytogram, depending on which one shows the best separation of the live and dead populations. The position of the live and dead populations in these cytograms may be dependent on cell type and gram character. Some samples may exhibit events that fall outside the defined regions and should be evaluated appropriately (e.g., see Panel D).

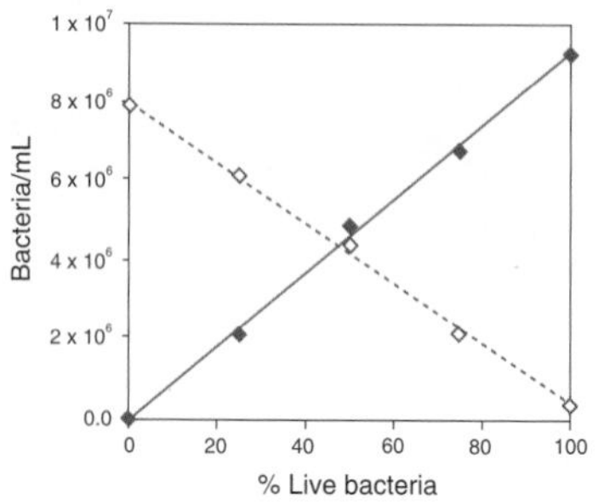

Figure 15.51 Best-fit linear regression analysis generated using the LIVE/DEAD® *Bac*Light™ Bacterial Viability and Counting Kit (L34856). Suspensions of live (untreated, solid line (r^2=0.9982)) and dead (alcohol-treated, dashed line (r^2=0.9974)) *Staphylococcus aureus* were mixed at various live:dead ratios. Mixtures were stained according to the kit protocol and analyzed in triplicate by flow cytometry. Values of bacteria/mL were calculated according to the equation provided in the kit protocol; the mean values are shown above. This experiment may be performed to determine optimal dye concentrations, to practice the cell-staining procedure or to generate a standard curve for unknown samples.

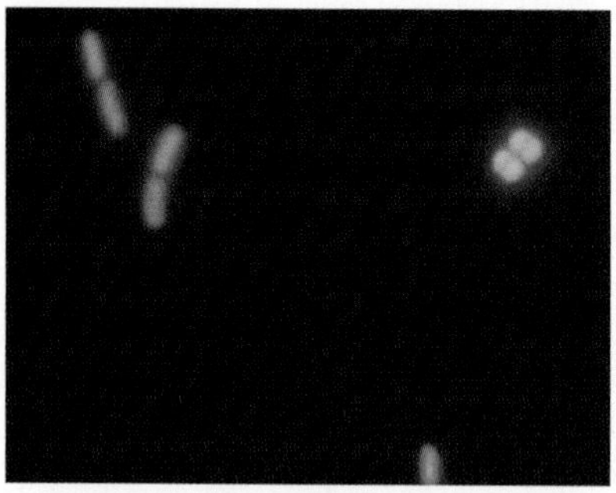

Figure 15.52 Live *Micrococcus luteus* and *Salmonella oranienburg* bacteria stained with the LIVE *Bac*Light™ Bacterial Gram Stain Kit (L7005). Gram-positive *M. luteus* cells fluoresce orange, whereas gram-negative *S. oranienburg* cells fluoresce green. This image was photographed in a single exposure through an Omega Optical triple bandpass filter set.

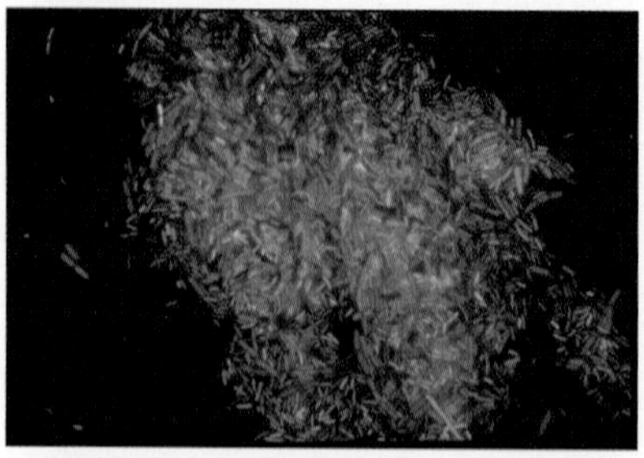

Figure 15.53 A mixed population of *Bacillus cereus* and *Pseudomonas aeruginosa* stained with the dye mixture provided in our LIVE *Bac*Light™ Gram Stain Kit (L7005). When live bacteria are incubated with this kit's cell-permeant nucleic acid stains, gram-positive organisms fluoresce orange and gram-negative organisms fluoresce green. The bacteria were photographed through an Omega Optical triple bandpass filter set.

of respiration.[84] Although these dyes do not alter assay results over the recommended staining periods, both $DiOC_2(3)$ and CCCP are toxic to bacterial cells, rendering the cells nonculturable after even brief exposure.

LIVE BacLight™ Bacterial Gram Stain Kit

Our patented LIVE *Bac*Light™ Bacterial Gram Stain Kit (L7005) is based on differential nucleic acid staining of *live* gram-negative and gram-positive bacteria. The gram stain is one of the most important and widely used differential stains for the taxonomic classification of bacteria in both clinical and research settings. The original method involves several steps, including heat fixation of the bacteria, a two-step staining protocol, alcohol extraction and counterstaining. Over the years, several improved gram-staining techniques have been developed, but most still involve cell-fixation or cell-permeabilization steps that kill the bacteria being tested. Our single-step LIVE *Bac*Light™ Bacterial Gram Stain Kits can overcome many of the problems inherent in these labor-intensive, fixation-dependent procedures.

Unlike conventional gram stain procedures, the LIVE *Bac*Light™ Bacterial Gram Stain Kit allows researchers to rapidly classify bacteria as either gram-negative or gram-positive in minutes using a single staining solution, no fixatives and no wash steps. The LIVE *Bac*Light™ Bacterial Gram Stain Kit contains our green-fluorescent SYTO® 9 and red-fluorescent hexidium iodide nucleic acid stains. These two dyes differ in both their spectral characteristics and in their ability to label live gram-negative and gram-positive bacteria. When a mixed population of live gram-negative and gram-positive bacteria is simultaneously stained with the membrane-permeant SYTO® 9 dye in combination with hexidium iodide, gram-negative bacteria fluoresce green, and the gram-positive bacteria fluoresce red-orange (Figure 15.52, Figure 15.53). Dead bacteria do not exhibit predictable staining patterns. Gram-negative and gram-positive organisms can be easily differentiated in any fluorescence microscope equipped with a standard fluorescein long-pass optical filter set or by flow cytometry.[85] The assay provides a sensitive indicator system for analyzing low numbers of bacteria in the presence of background material because the unbound reagents exhibit low fluorescence when not bound to nucleic acids. The LIVE *Bac*Light™ Bacterial Gram Stain Kit should be a useful tool for measuring dynamic changes in the composition of bacterial populations.

Our LIVE *Bac*Light™ Bacterial Gram Stain Kit provides separate solutions of the SYTO® 9 and hexidium iodide nucleic acid stains, thus facilitating calibration of bacterial fluorescence at each of the two emission wavelengths in quantitative assays. The kit is well suited for use in fluorescence microscopy, as well as for use in quantitative analysis with a fluorometer (Figure 15.54), fluorescence microplate reader, flow cytometer[86] or other instrumentation. The kit includes a procedure for mounting bacteria stained with the LIVE *Bac*Light™ Bacterial Gram Stain Kit on filter membranes, as well as the proprietary *Bac*Light™ mounting oil that we have found to be useful for the direct epifluorescence filter technique[77] (DEFT). The kit components, number of assays and assay principles are summarized in Table 15.2. Hexidium iodide (H7593), the gram-positive bacteria–selective nucleic acid stain, and the SYTO® 9 nucleic acid stain (S34854) are both available separately (Section 15.2). The validity of using hexidium iodide in combination with the SYTO® 13 green-fluorescent nucleic acid stain to correctly predict the gram sign of 45 clinically relevant organisms, including several known to be gram variable, has been demonstrated.[85]

ViaGram™ Red⁺ Bacterial Gram Stain and Viability Kit

Molecular Probes' ViaGram™ Red$^+$ Bacterial Gram Stain and Viability Kit (V7023) provides an easy three-color fluorescent staining protocol that differentially stains many gram-negative and gram-positive bacterial species and, at the same time, discriminates live from dead cells based on plasma membrane integrity. This kit contains three reagents: two nucleic acid stains for viability determination — the blue-fluorescent cell-permeant DAPI and the green-fluorescent cell-impermeant SYTOX® Green nucleic acid stain — as well as the red-fluorescent Texas Red®-X wheat germ agglutinin (WGA) for gram sign determination. Bacteria with intact cell membranes stain fluorescent blue with DAPI, whereas bacteria with damaged membranes stain fluorescent green with the SYTOX® Green nucleic acid stain. The background remains virtually nonfluorescent. The Texas Red®-X WGA component selectively binds to the surface of gram-positive bacteria, providing a red-fluorescent cell-surface stain that effectively distinguishes them from gram-negative bacteria, even in the presence of the viability stains. Thus, with three fluorescent colors, the four possible combinations of live or dead, gram-negative and gram-positive cells are discriminated with a fluorescence microscope (Figure 15.55, Figure 15.56). This kit also includes a procedure for mounting bacteria on filter membranes and the *Bac*Light™ mounting oil, which we have found to be useful for the direct epifluorescence filter technique[77] (DEFT). The kit components, number of assays and assay principles are summarized in Table 15.2.

Wheat Germ Agglutinin Sampler Kit

Fluorescent lectins have proven useful in microbiology applications. Fluorescent wheat germ agglutinin (WGA) conjugates selectively stain chitin in fungal cell walls,[87] as well as the surface of gram-positive but not of gram-negative bacteria.[88] Fluorescent WGA has also been shown to bind to sheathed microfilariae and has been used to detect filarial infection in blood smears.[89] Our Wheat Germ Agglutinin Sampler Kit (W7024) provides 1 mg samples of four of our brightest fluorescent WGA conjugates, spanning the spectrum from blue to red. Included in this kit are conjugates of the blue-fluorescent Alexa Fluor® 350, green-fluorescent Oregon Green® 488, orange-fluorescent tetramethylrhodamine and red-fluorescent Texas Red®-X dyes (Table 7.23). See Section 7.7 for more information on lectins, including additional WGA and concanavalin A (Con A) conjugates.

ATP Determination

The presence of adenosine 5′-triphosphate (ATP) is a useful marker of "life." Various quantitative methods have been developed for detecting ATP that is released during cell secretion or lysis; however, chemiluminescent detection of ATP using luciferase is the most sensitive assay and can be used for the essentially real-time measurement of ATP release from cells.[90–93] The luciferin–luciferase bioluminescence assay is extremely sensitive; most luminometers can detect as little as 1 picomole of pre-existing ATP or ATP as it is generated in kinetic systems. This sensitivity has led to its widespread use for detecting ATP in various enzymatic reactions, as well as for measuring viable cell number[94] and for detecting low-level bacterial contamination in samples such as blood, milk, urine, soil and sludge.[95–99] The luciferin–luciferase bioluminescence assay has also been used to determine cell proliferation and cytotoxicity in both bacterial[100,101] and mammalian cells,[102,103] and to distinguish cytostatic versus cytocidal potential of anticancer drugs on malignant cell growth.[104]

Molecular Probes offers a convenient ATP Determination Kit (A22066) for the sensitive bioluminescence-based detection of ATP with recombinant firefly luciferase and its substrate, luciferin. This assay is based on luciferase's requirement for ATP to produce light. In the presence of Mg^{2+}, luciferase catalyzes the reaction of luciferin, ATP and O_2 to form oxyluciferin, AMP, CO_2, pyrophosphate and ~560 nm light (Figure 15.57).

The ATP Determination Kit (A22066) contains:

- Luciferin
- Luciferase
- ATP
- Dithiothreitol (DTT)
- A concentrated reaction buffer
- A detailed protocol for ATP quantitation

Unlike many other commercially available ATP detection kits, our ATP Determination Kit provides the luciferase and luciferin packaged separately, which enables researchers to optimize the reaction conditions for their particular instruments and samples. The ATP Determination Kit provides sufficient reagents to perform 200 ATP assays using 0.5 mL sample volumes or 500 ATP assays using 0.2 mL sample volumes.

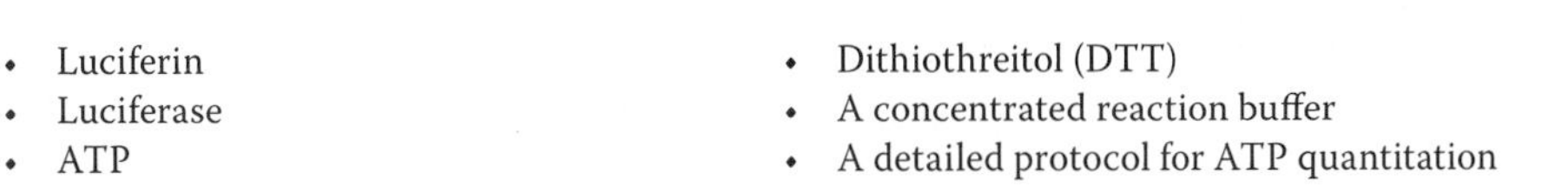

Figure 15.57 Reaction scheme for bioluminescence generation via luciferase-catalyzed conversion of luciferin (L2911, L2912, L2916) to oxyluciferin.

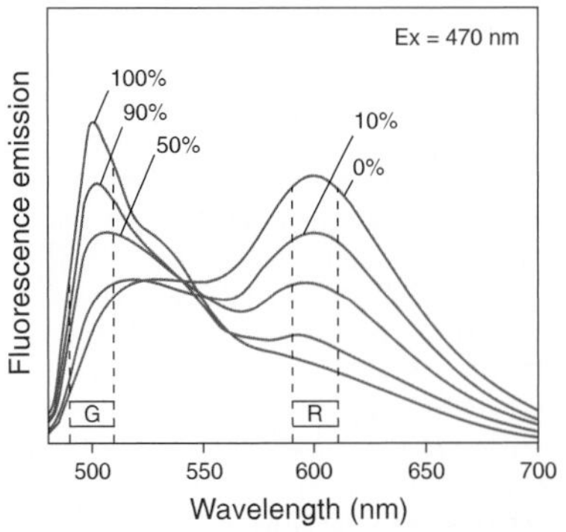

Figure 15.54 Analysis of the percentage of gram-negative *Escherichia coli* in mixed suspensions containing gram-positive *Staphylococcus aureus* using the reagents in Molecular Probes' LIVE *BacLight*™ Bacterial Gram Stain Kit (L7005). Live gram-negative and gram-positive bacteria are stained fluorescent green (G) by SYTO® 9 and fluorescent red (R) by hexidium iodide, respectively. Bacterial suspensions that have been incubated in the two stains simultaneously and then excited at 470 nm exhibit a fluorescence spectral shift from red to green as the percentage of gram-negative bacteria in the sample is increased.

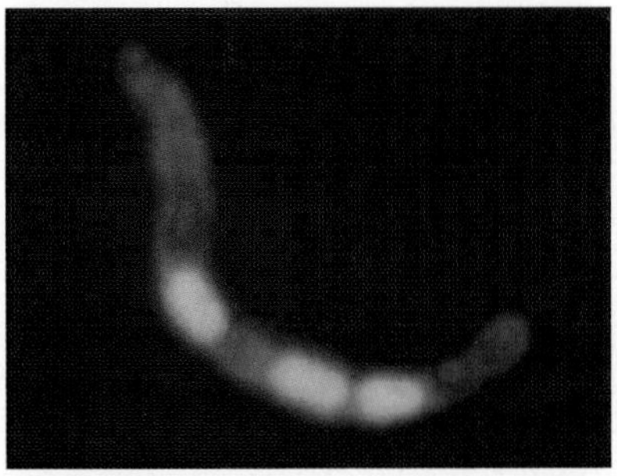

Figure 15.55 *Bifidobacterium sp.* bacteria stained with the ViaGram™ Red+ Bacterial Gram Stain and Viability Kit (V7023). While all cells exhibit a red-fluorescent surface stain (gram-positive), live cells exhibit blue-fluorescent internal staining and dead cells with compromised membranes exhibit yellow-green–fluorescent internal staining. This image was obtained by taking multiple exposures through bandpass optical filter sets appropriate for DAPI, fluorescein and Texas Red® dye.

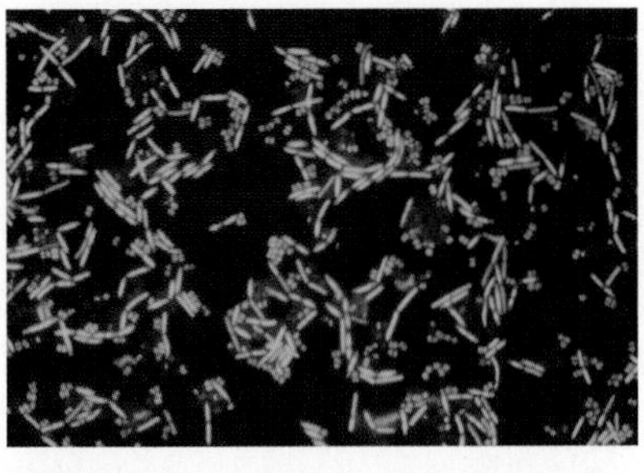

Figure 15.56 A mixed population of live and isopropyl alcohol–killed *Micrococcus luteus* and *Bacillus cereus* simultaneously stained with DAPI (D1306, D3571, D21490) and SYTOX® Green nucleic acid stain (S7020), the viability determination components of the ViaGram™ Red+ Bacterial Gram Stain and Viability Kit (V7023). Bacteria with intact cell membranes are stained exclusively with the cell-permeant DAPI nuclear stain and exhibit blue fluorescence, whereas cells with damaged membranes are stained with both fluorophores and exhibit green fluorescence. This image was acquired with a UV longpass optical filter set.

References

1. J Immunol Methods 243, 155 (2000); **2.** Principles and Methods of Toxicology, 3rd Ed., Hayes AW, Ed. pp. 1231–1258 (1994); **3.** J Neurosci 15, 5389 (1995); **4.** Biol Bull 189, 218 (1995); **5.** Ophthalmologe 92, 452 (1995); **6.** J Cell Sci 106, 685 (1993); **7.** Cytometry 20, 181 (1995); **8.** J Biol Chem 270, 23895 (1995); **9.** J Biol Chem 270, 7791 (1995); **10.** J Neurosci 14, 2464 (1994); **11.** J Neurosci 14, 2260 (1994); **12.** J Biol Chem 269, 6803 (1994); **13.** Photochem Photobiol 63, 111 (1996); **14.** J Immunol Methods 177, 101 (1994); **15.** Hum Immunol 37, 264 (1993); **16.** Theriogenology 43, 595 (1995); **17.** Practical Flow Cytometry, 3rd Ed., Shapiro HM, Ed. pp. 250–251 (1995); **18.** Methods Cell Biol 42 Pt B, 359 (1994); **19.** Methods Cell Biol 42 Pt B, 295 (1994); **20.** Manual of Clinical Microbiology, 5th Ed., Balows A, Ed. pp. 183–200 (1991); **21.** J Immunol Methods 156, 47 (1992); **22.** J Immunol Methods 185, 209 (1995); **23.** J Immunol Methods 166, 45 (1993); **24.** J Immunol Methods 204, 135 (1997); **25.** Theriogenology 45, 1103 (1996); **26.** Biol Reprod 53, 276 (1995); **27.** Poult Sci 74, 1191 (1995); **28.** J Androl 15, 620 (1994); **29.** Theriogenology 45, 923 (1996); **30.** Nature 377, 20 (1995); **31.** Biol Reprod 56, 143 (1997); **32.** Biol Reprod 57, 1401 (1997); **33.** Reprod Dom Anim 32, 279 (1997); **34.** Biol Reprod 58, 786 (1998); **35.** Biol Reprod 56, 991 (1997); **36.** Theriogenology 39, 1009 (1993); **37.** Gamete Res 22, 355 (1989); **38.** Biol Reprod 34, 127 (1986); **39.** J Histochem Cytochem 30, 279 (1982); **40.** Methods Cell Biol 33, 401 (1990); **41.** J Histochem Cytochem 25, 46 (1977); **42.** J Androl 12, 112 (1991); **43.** Cytometry 8, 642 (1987); **44.** Cytometry 1, 132 (1980); **45.** Biol Reprod 50, 987 (1994); **46.** J Reprod Fertil 96, 581 (1992); **47.** J Neurosci Methods 70, 195 (1996); **48.** Appl Environ Microbiol 56, 3785 (1990); **49.** J Dairy Res 57, 239 (1990); **50.** J Immunol Methods 210, 25 (1997); **51.** J Immunol Methods 213, 157 (1998); **52.** Antimicrob Agents Chemother 41, 1004 (1997); **53.** J Biol Chem 275, 40042 (2000); **54.** Nucleic Acids Res 14, 2511 (1986); **55.** FEMS Microbiol Lett 133, 1 (1995); **56.** J Cell Biol 126, 1375 (1994); **57.** Biotechnol Intl 1, 291 (1997); **58.** J Cell Biol 123, 1821 (1993); **59.** J Cell Biol 114, 111 (1991); **60.** J Cell Biol 114, 101 (1991); **61.** Appl Environ Microbiol 63, 2897 (1997); **62.** J Clin Microbiol 39, 2458 (2001); **63.** J Clin Microbiol 35, 5 (1997); **64.** Cytometry 31, 307 (1998); **65.** Mycoses 39, 45 (1996); **66.** Yeast 14, 147 (1998); **67.** J Microbiol Methods 17, 1 (1993); **68.** Cytometry 29, 58 (1997); **69.** Int J Parasitol 26, 637 (1996); **70.** Microbiol Rev 51, 365 (1987); **71.** J Microbiol Methods 37, 77 (1999); **72.** Appl Environ Microbiol 62, 2264 (1996); **73.** Proc Water Qual Technol Conf pp. 1277–1285 (1998); **74.** Int J Parasitol 27, 787 (1997); **75.** Appl Environ Microbiol 65, 4475 (1999); **76.** Biochim Biophys Acta 1514, 165 (2001); **77.** Appl Environ Microbiol 39, 423 (1980); **78.** J Appl Bacteriol 72, 410 (1992); **79.** Lett Appl Microbiol 13, 58 (1991); **80.** J Microbiol Methods 13, 87 (1991); **81.** Current Microbiol 4, 321 (1980); **82.** Antimicrob Agents Chemother 44, 827 (2000); **83.** Cytometry 35, 55 (1999); **84.** Glia 4, 611 (1991); **85.** Appl Environ Microbiol 64, 2681 (1998); **86.** Appl Environ Microbiol 64, 515 (1998); **87.** Invest Ophthalmol Vis Sci 27, 500 (1986); **88.** US 5,137,810; **89.** Int J Parasitol 20, 1099 (1990); **90.** Am J Physiol 275, C1391 (1998); **91.** J Biolumin Chemilumin 11, 149 (1996); **92.** Neuroscience 66, 915 (1995); **93.** FEBS Lett 185, 323 (1985); **94.** J Biolumin Chemilumin 10, 29 (1995); **95.** Anal Biochem 175, 14 (1988); **96.** Bio/Technology 6, 634 (1988); **97.** J Clin Microbiol 20, 644 (1984); **98.** J Clin Microbiol 18, 521 (1983); **99.** Methods Enzymol 57, 3 (1978); **100.** Biotechnol Bioeng 42, 30 (1993); **101.** J Biolumin Chemilumin 6, 193 (1991); **102.** Biochem J 295, 165 (1993); **103.** J Immunol Methods 160, 81 (1993); **104.** J Natl Cancer Inst 77, 1039 (1986).

Product List — 15.3 Viability and Cytotoxicity Assay Kits for Diverse Cell Types

Cat #	Product Name	Unit Size
A22066	ATP Determination Kit *special packaging* *200-1000 assays*	1 kit
B34950	*Bac*Light™ Bacterial Membrane Potential Kit *for flow cytometry* *100 assays*	1 kit
L7005	LIVE *Bac*Light™ Bacterial Gram Stain Kit *for microscopy and quantitative assays* *1000 assays*	1 kit
L34856	LIVE/DEAD® *Bac*Light™ Bacterial Viability and Counting Kit *for flow cytometry* *100 assays*	1 kit
L13152	LIVE/DEAD® *Bac*Light™ Bacterial Viability Kit *10 applicator sets* *500 assays*	1 kit
L7007	LIVE/DEAD® *Bac*Light™ Bacterial Viability Kit *for microscopy* *1000 assays*	1 kit
L7012	LIVE/DEAD® *Bac*Light™ Bacterial Viability Kit *for microscopy and quantitative assays* *1000 assays*	1 kit
L7010	LIVE/DEAD® Cell-Mediated Cytotoxicity Kit *for animal cells* *2000 assays*	1 kit
L34951	LIVE/DEAD® Cell Vitality Assay Kit *C_{12}-resazurin/SYTOX® Green* *1000 assays*	1 kit
L7013	LIVE/DEAD® Reduced Biohazard Cell Viability Kit #1 *green and red fluorescence* *100 assays*	1 kit
L23101	LIVE/DEAD® Reduced Biohazard Cell Viability Kit #2 *green fluorescence* *200 assays*	1 kit
L23102	LIVE/DEAD® Reduced Biohazard Cell Viability Kit #3 *red fluorescence* *200 assays*	1 kit
L23105	LIVE/DEAD® Reduced Biohazard Cell Viability Kit #4 *blue fluorescence* *200 assays*	1 kit
L7011	LIVE/DEAD® Sperm Viability Kit *200-1000 assays*	1 kit
L3224	LIVE/DEAD® Viability/Cytotoxicity Kit *for animal cells* *1000 assays*	1 kit
L7009	LIVE/DEAD® Yeast Viability Kit *1000 assays*	1 kit
V7023	ViaGram™ Red+ Bacterial Gram Stain and Viability Kit *200 assays*	1 kit
V23110	Vybrant® Cell Metabolic Assay Kit *with C_{12}-resazurin* *500-1000 assays*	1 kit
V23111	Vybrant® Cytotoxicity Assay Kit *G6PD release assay* *1000 assays*	1 kit
W7024	Wheat Germ Agglutinin Sampler Kit *four fluorescent conjugates, 1 mg each*	1 kit

For current prices or to order online, visit probes.invitrogen.com

15.4 Assays for Cell Enumeration, Cell Proliferation and Cell Cycle

Cell proliferation and the characterization of agents that either promote or retard cell proliferation are extremely important areas of cell biology and drug-discovery research. Molecular Probes offers both traditional reagents for assessing cell proliferation and cell cycle — in particular the Hoechst nucleic acid stains and probes for 5-bromo-2′-deoxyuridine (BrdU) incorporation during cell division — as well as some exceptional tools that we have developed, including our CyQUANT® GR, TOTO®-1, SYTOX® Green and SYTO® dyes. For simply detecting the presence of cells or enumerating them, fluorescent stains that identify cells by their characteristic morphology or light-scattering properties may be sufficient. For example, some of our SYTO® dyes have been employed to detect microorganisms that could be used as biological weapons.[1] The sensitivity of some of our fluorescent dyes even permits the detection and quantitation of viruses under certain circumstances.

Cell Enumeration and Cell Proliferation Assays for Animal Cells

Reagents for counting cells and quantitating cell proliferation are valuable research and diagnostic tools. Currently there is no fluorescent reagent that can be specifically incorporated into cells during cell division and directly detected on a single-cell basis. Consequently, most cell proliferation assays estimate the number of cells either by incorporating ^{3}H-thymidine or 5-bromo-2′-deoxyuridine (BrdU, a thymidine analog; B23151) into cells during proliferation or by measuring total nucleic acid or protein content of lysed cells.[2,3] Several of our nucleic acid stains (Section 8.1) and nucleotides (Section 8.1) have proven useful in BrdU-labeling protocols. Our CyQUANT® Cell Proliferation Assay Kit (C7026) uses the CyQUANT® GR reagent to measure changes in nucleic acid content that occur during cell proliferation. Our Bacteria Counting Kit provides a simple method for enumerating bacteria in samples.

Proliferation Assays Using Bromodeoxyuridine Incorporation

Incorporation of 5-bromo-2′-deoxyuridine (BrdU, B23151) into newly synthesized DNA permits indirect detection of rapidly proliferating cells with fluorescently labeled anti-BrdU antibodies or certain nucleic acid stains, thereby facilitating the identification of cells that have progressed through the S-phase of the cell cycle during the BrdU labeling period.[3–5] In conjunction with Phoenix Flow Systems, Molecular Probes offers fluorescent conjugates of the mouse monoclonal anti-BrdU antibody PRB-1 labeled with our brightest and most photostable dyes — the Alexa Fluor® 488 (A21303), Alexa Fluor® 532 (A21307), Alexa Fluor® 546 (A21308), Alexa Fluor® 594 (A21304), Alexa Fluor® 647 (A21305) and Alexa Fluor® 660 (A21306) dyes. This anti-BrdU antibody is also available as a biotin-XX conjugate (A21301MP), as well as unlabeled (A21300). The unlabeled mouse anti-BrdU can be detected with our anti-mouse secondary antibodies (Table 7.1) by either flow cytometry (Figure 15.58) or imaging (Figure 15.59). In addition to its use for detecting BrdU-labeled DNA, monoclonal PRB-1 recognizes 5-bromouridine (BrU) incorporated into RNA, and the same anti-BrdU conjugates can be used for the specific staining of RNA in cells that have incorporated BrU. It should be possible to amplify the detection of very low degrees of BrdU incorporation by using the biotin-XX conjugate of anti-BrdU (A21301MP) in conjunction with one of our streptavidin-based tyramide signal amplification (TSA) kits, which are described in Section 6.2. The unlabeled anti-BrdU antibody may also be used (A21300) with any of the Zenon® Mouse IgG_1 Labeling Kits (Section 7.3, Table 7.13, Figure 15.60).

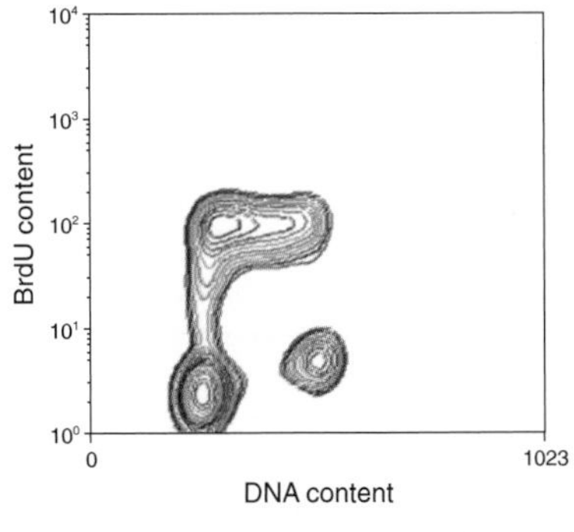

Figure 15.58 Detection of proliferation in Wil2S Lymphoma B cells. Cells were treated with 10 µM 5-bromo-2′-deoxyuridine (BrdU, B23151) in culture medium for one hour, then pelleted and fixed with cold 70% ethanol. After treatment with RNase and 4 M HCl (to denature the DNA), the cells were labeled with anti-BrdU (A21300) and detected using green-fluorescent Alexa Fluor® 488 goat anti–mouse IgG antibody (A11001). In addition, the cells were labeled with red-fluorescent propidium iodide (P1304MP, P3566, P21493) to assess the total cellular DNA content. The cells were analyzed by flow cytometry using 488 nm excitation; the fluorescent signals were collected at ~525 nm for the Alexa Fluor® 488 dye and at ~675 nm for propidium iodide. Increased BrdU incorporation is indicative of actively proliferating cells.

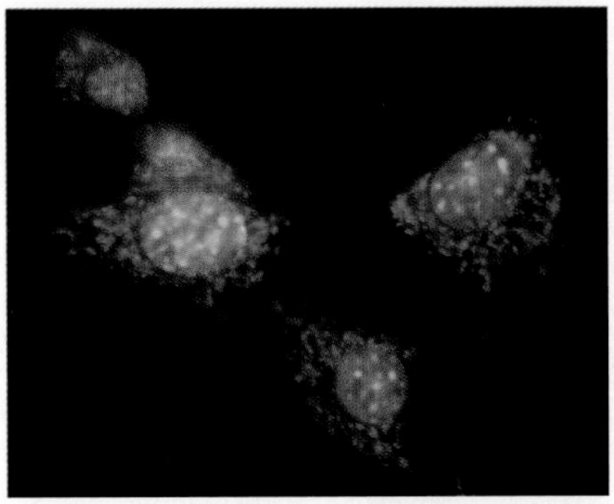

Figure 15.59 3T3 cells showing incorporation of BrdU. Cells were pulsed with BrdU (B23151) for 30 minutes before fixation. BrdU incorporated into the DNA of proliferating cells was detected with an anti-BrdU antibody (A21300) and green-fluorescent Alexa Fluor® 488 goat anti–mouse IgG_1 isotype-specific secondary antibody (A21121); the BrdU staining pattern is co-localized with the nuclear staining of blue-fluorescent DAPI (D1306, D21490). Mitochondria were labeled with anti-COX, Complex IV, subunit I (A6403), and red-fluorescent Alexa Fluor® 594 goat anti–mouse IgG_{2a} isotype-specific antibody (A21135). Coverslips were mounted with Prolong® antifade mounting medium (P7481).

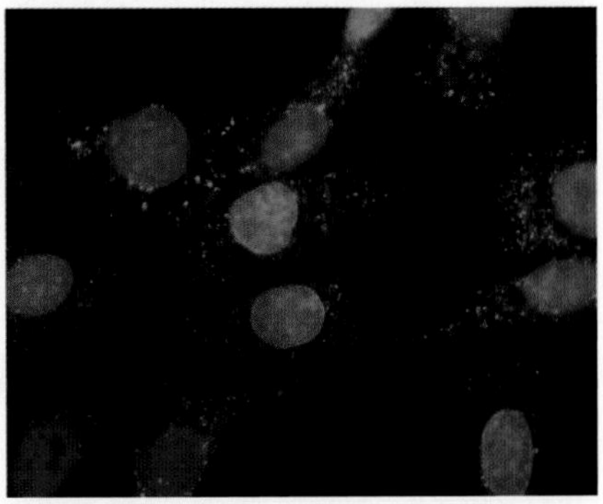

Figure 15.60 Detection of cell proliferation by BrdU incorporation. 3T3 cells were pulsed with BrdU (B23151) for 30 minutes before fixation. BrdU incorporated into the DNA of proliferating cells was detected with an anti-BrdU antibody (A21300) that was labeled with the Zenon® Alexa Fluor® 488 Mouse IgG_1 Labeling Kit (Z25002). The sample was mounted with Prolong® antifade mounting medium (P7481).

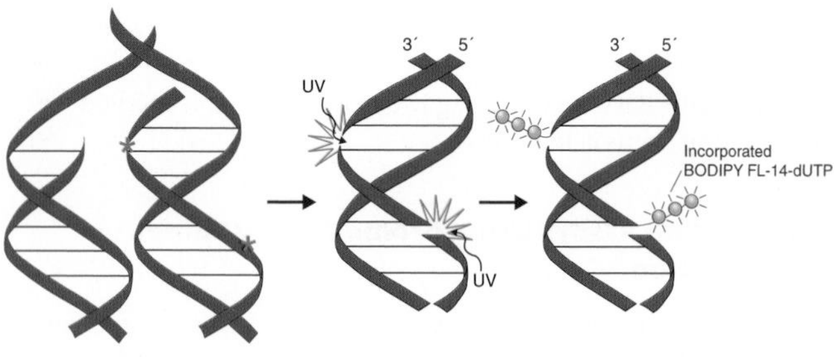

Figure 15.61 Schematic diagram showing the sequence of events in the strand break induction by photolysis (SBIP) technique (Cytometry 20, 172 (1995)). (**A**) Proliferating cells that have incorporated BrdU (*) into newly synthesized DNA are (**B**) exposed to UV light in order to induce DNA strand breaks. If the cells are stained with Hoechst 33258 prior to UV illumination, the photolysis efficiency is increased. (**C**) Once the cells are fixed, the 3′-hydroxyl ends exposed at these strand breaks can be directly labeled *in situ* using mammalian terminal deoxynucleotidyl transferase (TdT) and our ChromaTide® BODIPY® FL-14-dUTP (C7614).

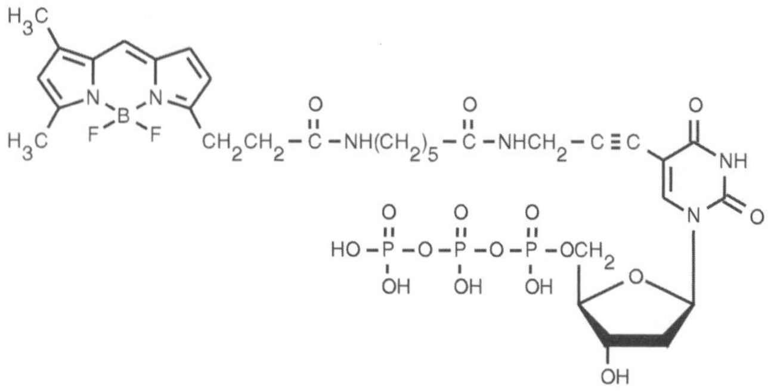

Figure 15.62 C7614 ChromaTide® BODIPY® FL-14-dUTP.

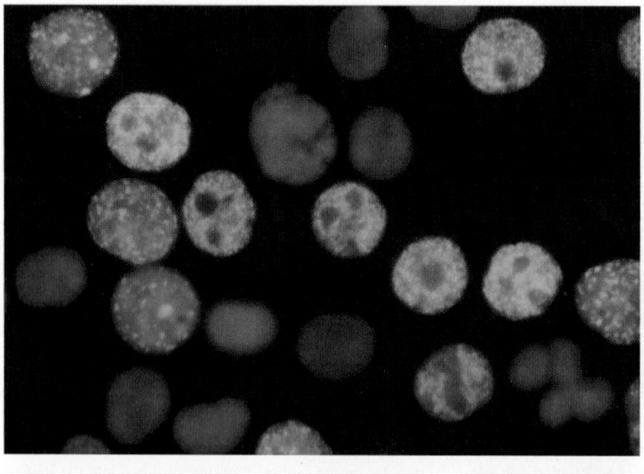

Figure 15.63 Detection of BrdU-incorporating cells using the SBIP (Strand Breaks Induced by Photolysis) technique. Exponentially growing human promyelocytic leukemia (HL60) cells were incubated with 20 µM BrdU (B23151) for 40 minutes and then with 20 µg/mL Hoechst 33258 (H1398, H3569, H21491) in the presence of 2% DMSO for an additional 20 minutes. After this incubation, the cells were exposed to 300 nm UV light for 5 minutes to selectively photolyze DNA that contained the incorporated BrdU, and then fixed in 70% ethanol. Subsequent incubation of the permeabilized cells with the ChromaTide® BODIPY® FL-14-dUTP (C7614) in the presence of exogenous terminal deoxynucleotidyl transferase resulted in incorporation of the fluorophore into DNA strand breaks, thereby labeling the S-phase cells. The DNA was counterstained with the red-fluorescent nucleic acid stain propidium iodide (P1304MP, P3566, P21493); therefore, the BODIPY® FL dye–labeled DNA appears yellow. The image was contributed by Zbigniew Darzynkiewicz, Cancer Research Institute, New York Medical College.

Because fluorescence of the Hoechst 33258 (H1398; H3569; FluoroPure™ Grade, H21491) and Hoechst 33342 (H1399; H3570; FluoroPure™ Grade, H21492) dyes bound to DNA is *quenched* at sites where BrdU is incorporated, Hoechst dye fluorescence can also be used to detect BrdU incorporation in single cells.[2,6–9] This technique has been employed to quantitate the noncycling cell fraction, as well as the fraction of cells that are in G_1 and G_2 of two subsequent cycles.[10] The addition of ethidium bromide (E1305, E3565; Section 8.1) as a counterstain that is *insensitive* to BrdU incorporation allows the resolution of G_1, S and G_2 compartments of up to three consecutive cell cycles.[11,12]

Unlike the fluorescence of Hoechst dyes, the fluorescence of TO-PRO®-3 (T3605) and LDS 751 (L7595) is considerably *enhanced* by the presence of bromodeoxyuridine in DNA. In conjunction with propidium iodide (P1304MP, P3566, P21493; Section 8.1), these nucleic acid stains have been used to discriminate BrdU-labeled cells from nonproliferating cells by flow cytometry[13,14] and with an imaging system for automated cell proliferation.[15]

Proliferation Assays Using ChromaTide® Nucleotides

In the strand break induction by photolysis (SBIP) technique, proliferating cells that have incorporated BrdU into newly synthesized DNA are subjected to Hoechst 33258 staining, followed by UV photolysis to induce DNA strand breaks[16] (Figure 15.61). Once the cells are fixed, strand breaks can be detected *in situ* using mammalian terminal deoxynucleotidyl transferase (TdT), which covalently adds labeled nucleotides to the 3′-hydroxyl ends of these DNA fragments.[17–20] Break sites have traditionally been labeled with biotinylated or haptenylated dUTP conjugates (Section 8.2) in conjunction with antibodies to the hapten (Section 7.4) or conjugates of streptavidin[20,21] (Section 7.6). However, a single-step procedure has been described that uses our ChromaTide® BODIPY® FL-14-dUTP (C7614, Figure 15.62) as a TdT substrate for directly detecting DNA strand breaks both in BrdU-labeled cells following SBIP and in apoptotic cells[16,22–25] (Section 15.5; Figure 15.63, Figure 15.84). The single-step BODIPY® FL dye–based assay has several advantages over indirect detection of biotinylated or haptenylated nucleotides. With direct detection procedures, no secondary detection reagents are required; fewer protocol steps translate into less chance for error and more immediate results. Moreover, the yield of cells with direct detection procedures is reported to be about three times greater than that of multistep procedures employing biotin- or digoxigenin-conjugated dUTP. Although both BODIPY® FL dye– and fluorescein-labeled nucleotides can be detected with fluorescence microscopy or flow cytometry, the BODIPY® FL dye–labeled nucleotides provide ~40% stronger signal than fluorescein-labeled nucleotides when assaying strand breaks in apoptotic versus nonapoptotic cells. In addition, fading of the fluorescence of the incorporated BODIPY® FL dUTP is less than that of the corresponding fluorescein dUTP analog.[22] Unlike traditional proliferation assays based on BrdU incorporation, no DNA heat- or acid-denaturation steps are required with SBIP in order to visualize the labeled strand breaks, allowing simultaneous detection of the morphology of nuclear proteins and other cellular constituents by immunocytochemical analysis. The narrow emission spectrum of the BODIPY® FL dye–labeled nucleotides is especially useful for multicolor labeling experiments.

An elegant technique permits tracking of labeled chromosomes through mitosis by metabolic incorporation of microinjected fluorescent nucleotides, including our fluorescein-12-dUTP, Oregon Green® 488-5-dUTP and BODIPY® TR-14-dUTP (C7604, C7630, C7618; Section 8.2), by endogenous cellular enzymes into DNA. The procedure does not interfere with subsequent progress through the cell cycle, and fluorescent strands of DNA can be followed as they assemble into chromosomes and segregate into daughters and granddaughters.[26–28] Presumably, injection of 5′-bromo-2′-deoxyuridine 5′-triphosphate (BrdUTP, B21550) followed by detection of the incorporated BrdU with one of our Alexa Fluor® conjugates of anti-BrdU would also be suitable for studying mitosis. The corresponding ribonucleotide (BrUTP, B21551) that has been microinjected into cells is incorporated into RNA of a nucleolar compartment,[29,30] a process that should also be detectable with fluorescent anti-BrdU conjugates.

ABSOLUTE-S SBIP Cell Proliferation Assay Kit

Many conventional BrdU-based protocols for assaying cell proliferation require DNA denaturation in order for the BrdU epitope to become accessible to the anti-BrdU antibody. The DNA denaturation is typically accomplished by heat (>90°C) or strong acid (2–4 M HCl). Such harsh treatments often make it difficult to perform multiparameter analysis because other cellular structures and antigens are not well preserved during these treatments.[31]

In conjunction with Phoenix Flow Systems, Molecular Probes offers the ABSOLUTE-S SBIP Cell Proliferation Assay Kit (A23150), which utilizes the strand break induction by photolysis (SBIP) methodology described above and does not require DNA denaturation at any step. In the ABSOLUTE-S assay, cells are first incubated in the presence of the BrdU photolyte, which is incorporated into cellular DNA during replication. Next, the photolyte enhancer is added to the cell culture to sensitize the BrdU-labeled DNA to photolysis. Once this treatment is complete, the cells are irradiated by UV light to induce DNA strand breaks at the sites where BrdU is incorporated. Additional BrdU is then added at the break sites using the TUNEL (terminal deoxynucleotidyltransferase dUTP nick-end labeling) technique. Finally, BrdU is detected using an Alexa Fluor® 488 dye–labeled anti-BrdU monoclonal antibody (Figure 15.64). This kit also provides propidium iodide for determining total cellular DNA content, as well as fixed control cells for assessing assay performance.

The ABSOLUTE-S Kit includes complete protocols for use in flow cytometry applications, though it may also be adapted for use with fluorescence microscopy. Each kit contains:

- BrdU photolyte, for labeling the cellular DNA during replication
- Photolyte enhancer, for sensitizing the BrdU-labeled DNA to UV photolysis
- Terminal deoxynucleotidyl transferase (TdT), for catalyzing the addition of BrdUTP at the break sites
- 5-Bromo-2′-deoxyuridine 5′-triphosphate (BrdUTP)
- Alexa Fluor® 488 dye–labeled anti-BrdU mouse monoclonal antibody PRB-1, for detecting BrdU labels
- Propidium iodide/RNase staining buffer, for quantitating total cellular DNA
- Reaction, wash and rinse buffers
- Reaction control cells (a fixed human lymphoma cell line)
- Photolysis control cells (a fixed human lymphoma cell line)
- A detailed protocol

Sufficient reagents are provided for approximately 60 assays of 1 mL samples, each containing 1–2 × 10^6 cells/mL.

Proliferation Assay Using the Succinimidyl Ester of Carboxyfluorescein Diacetate and Related Probes

The succinimidyl ester of carboxyfluorescein diacetate (5(6)-CFDA, SE or CFSE, C1157) is currently the most widely used probe for generation analysis of cells, although our succinimidyl ester of Oregon Green® 488 carboxylic acid diacetate (O34550, see below) offers several important advantages over this fluorescein derivative. CFDA SE spontaneously and irreversibly couples to both intracellular and cell-surface proteins by reaction with lysine side chains and other available amine groups. When cells divide, CFDA SE labeling is distributed equally between the daughter cells, which are therefore half as fluorescent as the parents. As a result, each successive generation in a population of proliferating cells is marked by a halving of cellular fluorescence intensity (excitation/emission maxima ~495/525 nm) that is readily detected by a flow cytometer (Figure 15.65), fluorescence microscope or fluorescence microplate reader. CFDA SE is available as a single vial containing 25 mg (C1157). CFDA SE is also available conveniently packaged for cell tracing applications in our Vybrant® CFDA SE Cell Tracer Kit (V12883, Figure 15.65) and for cell proliferation studies in our CellTrace™ Cell Proliferation Kit (C34554, Figure 15.66). The fluorescent CFDA SE

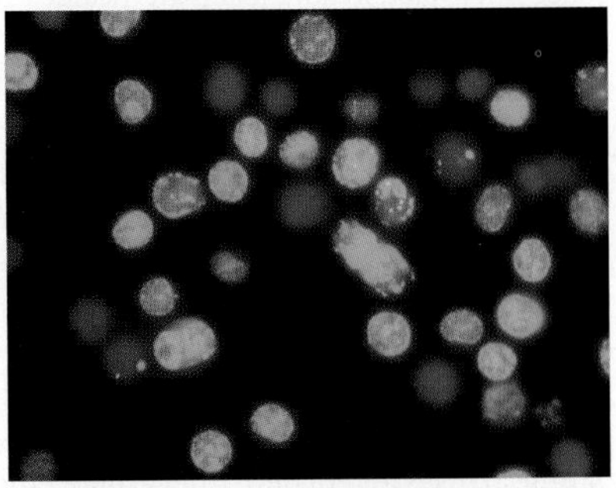

Figure 15.64 Human lymphoma cells were allowed to proliferate and then stained using the ABSOLUTE-S SBIP Cell Proliferation Assay Kit (A23150). Proliferating cells that have incorporated 5-bromo-2′-deoxyuridine (BrdU) stain green, while necrotic cells stain red.

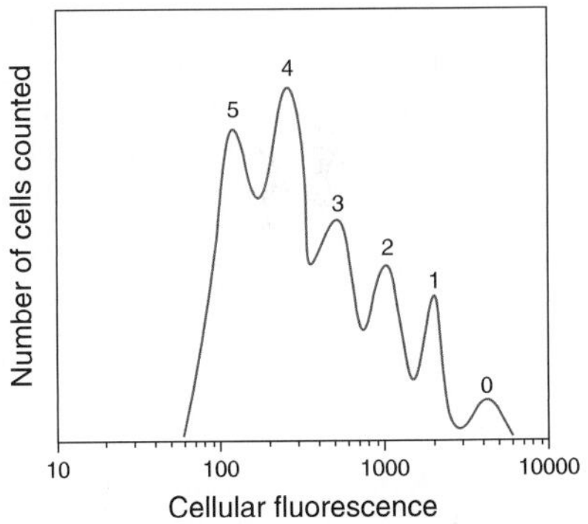

Figure 15.65 Tracking of asynchronous cell division using 5-(and 6-)carboxyfluorescein diacetate, succinimidyl ester (5(6)-CFDA SE or CFSE; C1157; V12883) labeling and flow cytometry. Cell division results in sequential halving of the initial fluorescence, resulting in a cellular fluorescence histogram. The peaks labeled 0, 1, 2, 3, 4 and 5 represent successive generations.

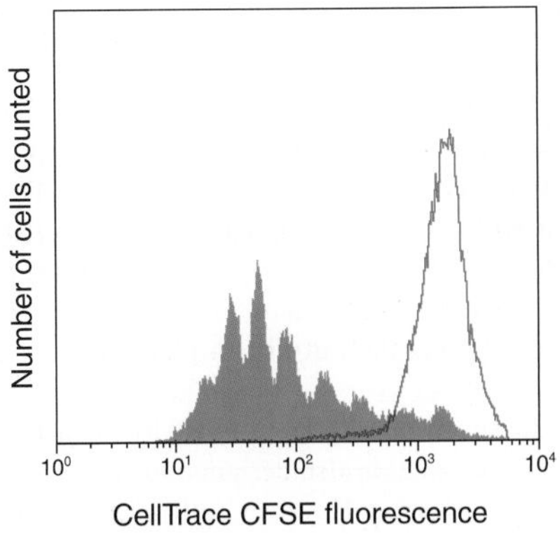

Figure 15.66 Following cell proliferation in human peripheral blood lymphocytes using the CellTrace™ CFSE Cell Proliferation Kit C34554). Human peripheral blood lymphocytes were harvested and stained with CellTrace™ CFSE (carboxyfluorescein diacetate, succinimidyl ester; 5(6)-CFDA, SE) on Day 0. A portion of the population was arrested at the parent generation using mitomycin C (red peak). The remainder of the sample was stimulated with phytohemagglutinin and allowed to proliferate for 5 days. Solid green peaks represent successive generations.

product has excitation/emission maxima of ~492/517 nm and can be detected using a fluorescence microscope, flow cytometer or fluorescence microplate reader. Each kit includes 10 single-use vials of CFDA SE (500 µg each in Kit V12883, 50 µg each in Kit C34554), as well as high-quality anhydrous DMSO and a complete protocol.

CFDA SE produces more homogenous cellular labeling and, consequently, much better intergenerational resolution than other cell-tracking dyes such as the membrane marker PKH26. Using flow cytometric analysis of CFDA SE labeling, researchers can reliably resolve 8 to 10 successive generations of lymphocytes.[32,33] In transplanted cells the signal of CFDA SE can be traced *in vivo* for weeks.[34,35] The potential of this important technique is discussed in a collection of nine articles and reviews appearing in the December 1999 issue of Immunology and Cell Biology.[36] The feasibility of using cell-permeant fluorescent tracers to follow cell division of natural killer (NK) cells, B cells, T cells, thymocytes, lymphocytes, fibroblasts and hematopoietic cells has been demonstrated with CFDA SE.[33,37–46] For instance, researchers have used CFDA SE labeling to show that transplantable hematopoietic cells proliferate *in vitro* in response to stimulation by a growth factor cocktail.[47] These studies helped provide direct evidence that the hematopoietic potential of cultured stem cells is limited by homing activity and not by proliferative capacity. Because the first division results in the largest change in fluorescence intensity, this method is particularly useful for detecting subsets of cells within a population that are resistant to cell division. The method is not limited to mammalian cells; it has also been applied to determine the number of cell divisions in stained *Lactobacillus plantarum*.[48]

Like CFDA SE, our succinimidyl ester of Oregon Green® 488 carboxylic acid diacetate (carboxy-DFFDA, SE; O34550) should be a useful tool for following proliferating cells. This Oregon Green® 488 probe can passively diffuse into cells, where it is colorless and nonfluorescent until its acetate groups are cleaved by intracellular esterases to yield the highly green-fluorescent, amine-reactive fluorophore. Upon reaction with amine-containing residues of intracellular proteins, this probe can form dye–protein adducts that are well retained in cells. Unlike fluorescein derivatives, however, Oregon Green® 488 derivatives exhibit bright green fluorescence (excitation/emission maxima ~496/524 nm) that is not pH dependent at typical cellular pH values. Moreover, Oregon Green® 488 probes are usually brighter and more photostable than fluorescein probes.

The intracellular conjugates of 5-(and 6-)carboxyeosin diacetate succinimidyl ester (C22803) have absorption and emission spectra at longer wavelengths than CFDA SE, which may make this probe useful in combination with CFDA SE for studies of proliferation of mixed-cell populations. Eosin conjugates are more effective singlet-oxygen generators than are simple fluorescein derivatives, potentially resulting in their utility for photoablation of cells.

The succinimidyl ester of SNARF®-1 carboxylic acid acetate (S22801, Figure 14.22) is also designed to serve as a cell tracer and indicator of cell division. However, unlike the green-fluorescent CFDA SE–labeled cells, cells labeled with the succinimidyl ester of SNARF®-1 carboxylic acid, acetate exhibit red fluorescence when excited near 488 nm. Although the fluorescence intensity of this SNARF® derivative in cells may be weaker than that of cells labeled with CFDA SE, its red fluorescence is easily distinguished from the green fluorescence of CFDA SE–labeled cells. The SNARF® dyes have been predominantly used as indicators of intracellular pH (Chapter 20).

Vybrant® DiI Cell-Labeling Solution

Analysis by mass spectrometry and HPLC indicates that the dye we use in our Vybrant® DiI cell-labeling solution (V22885) is identical to the dye called PKH 26. DiI (PKH 26) is a red-fluorescent lipophilic tracer that, in addition to being extensively used for cell tracing (Section 14.4), has been utilized for generational analysis of cells undergoing division.[36,49–52] Unlike the PKH 26 dye, which requires a special cell-labeling medium and low ionic strength for successful cell loading, our Vybrant® DiI cell-labeling solution is simply added to cells in normal growth medium. Dividing cells distribute the lipophilic tracer approximately equally between daughter cells. It is usually possibly to follow at least three or four generations of cells by flow cytometry, although asynchronous division times can quickly complicate the measurements. The dyes in our Vybrant® DiO, Vybrant® DiD and Vybrant® CM-DiI labeling solutions (V22886, V22887, V22888) may have similar utility for tracing cells through cell division. CM-DiI contains a thiol-reactive chloromethyl that allows the dye to covalently bind to cellular thiols. Thus, unlike other membrane stains, this label is well retained in some cells throughout fixation and permeabilization steps; see Section 14.4 for more information.

CyQUANT® Cell Proliferation Assay Kit

The quantity of DNA and RNA in a cell is tightly regulated. Therefore, changes in nucleic acid content can serve as a sensitive indicator of overall cell proliferation, as well as of cytotoxic events or pathological abnormalities that affect cell proliferation. Our CyQUANT® Cell Proliferation Assay Kit (C7026) provides an excellent method both for enumerating cells in a population and for measuring their proliferative activity. This assay is an important development for the rapid and quantitative screening of agents that affect cell proliferation. The CyQUANT® assay is based on the use of our patented green-fluorescent CyQUANT® GR dye, which exhibits strong fluorescence enhancement when bound to cellular nucleic acids.[53] The assay protocol is simple: the culture medium is removed (nonadherent cells require brief centrifugation); the cells are frozen, thawed and lysed by addition of the CyQUANT® cell buffer containing detergent and the CyQUANT® GR dye; and fluorescence is then measured directly in a fluorometer or fluorescence microplate reader (Figure 15.67). No washing steps, growth medium changes or long incubations are required. The CyQUANT® cell proliferation assay has a number of significant advantages over other proliferation assays:

- **Sensitivity and linearity.** The CyQUANT® assay is linear from 50 or fewer cells to at least 50,000 cells in 200 µL volumes (Figure 15.68); increasing the dye concentration extends the linear range to at least 250,000 cells. Methods that employ Hoechst 33258[54] (H1398, H3569; FluoroPure™ Grade, H21491) or Hoechst 33342[55] (H1399; H3570; FluoroPure™ Grade, H21492) to measure cell number and proliferation are much less sensitive — detection limits of 500 cells for Hoechst 33258[54] or 2500 cells for Hoechst 33342[55] — and have much smaller effective ranges.
- **No radioactivity.** Unlike assays that measure ^{3}H-thymidine incorporation, the CyQUANT® assay does not require radioisotopes and thus does not have the hazards or the expense associated with use, storage and disposal of radioisotopes.
- **Quick and easy protocol.** The CyQUANT® assay is a single-step procedure that requires no lengthy incubation steps and can be completed within an hour (Figure 15.67).
- **Specificity and reliability.** The assay is specific for total nucleic acids, with essentially no interference from other cell components. No wash steps are required because cellular growth media do not

significantly interfere with CyQUANT® GR fluorescence. The CyQUANT® assay is reliable for cell quantitation, even without treatment to eliminate cellular RNA. However, addition of RNase or DNase permits the easy quantitation of DNA or RNA, respectively, in the sample.

- **Convenience.** Unlike assays that use tetrazolium salts, ^{3}H-thymidine, BrdU, neutral red or methylene blue,[55–58] the CyQUANT® procedure is not dependent on cellular metabolism. Thus, cells can be frozen and stored prior to assaying, with no reduction in signal, or they can be assayed immediately after collection. Time-course assays are simplified because data obtained from stored samples taken at widely different time intervals can be assayed together with a single standard curve determination.

We have found the CyQUANT® Cell Proliferation Assay Kit to be useful for assaying widely disparate cell types, including:

- Human neonatal fibroblasts, keratinocytes, melanocytes, umbilical vein endothelial cells (HUVEC) and dermal microvascular endothelial cells (DMVEC)
- Murine fibroblasts (NIH 3T3 and CRE BAG 2 cells) and myeloma (P3X63A68) cells
- Madin–Darby canine kidney (MDCK) cells
- Chinook salmon embryo (CHSE) cells
- Rat basophilic leukemia (RBL) and glioma (C6) cells

In addition to quantitating proliferation, the CyQUANT® GR reagent may supplant ^{51}Cr-release studies for monitoring T-cell cytolysis and other cytolytic events.[59] Furthermore, determination of total cell number using the CyQUANT® GR reagent is potentially useful for quantitating cell adhesion (see "Cell Adhesion" in Section 15.6) and for determining the total number of cells in a tissue. Each CyQUANT® Cell Proliferation Assay Kit (C7026) includes:

- CyQUANT® GR reagent
- Cell-lysis buffer
- A DNA standard for calibration
- A detailed protocol

The kit supplies sufficient materials for performing 1000 assays based on a 200 µL sample volume or a proportionately lower number of assays with a larger sample volume. The CyQUANT® cell-lysis buffer (a 20X concentrate, C7027) is also available separately and has been formulated to produce efficient lysis, to protect nucleic acids from nuclease activity and to dissociate proteins that may interfere with dye binding to nucleic acids. It may prove generally useful in the development of other assays that require cell lysis.

Vybrant® MTT Cell Proliferation Assay Kit

Molecular Probes' convenient Vybrant® MTT Cell Proliferation Assay Kit (V13154) simplifies the task of counting cells with a microplate absorbance reader. The colorimetric MTT assay, developed by Mossman, is based on the conversion of the water-soluble MTT to an insoluble purple formazan.[60,61] This formazan is then solubilized and its concentration determined by optical density at 570 nm. The Vybrant® MTT Cell Proliferation Assay Kit provides a sensitive assay with excellent linearity up to approximately 10^6 cells per well. Each kit includes:

- MTT
- Sodium dodecyl sulfate (SDS)
- A detailed protocol

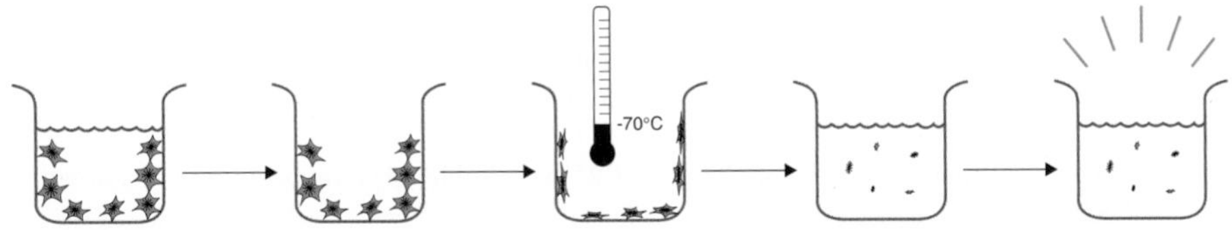

Figure 15.67 The simple procedure for using Molecular Probes' CyQUANT® Cell Proliferation Assay Kit (C7026).

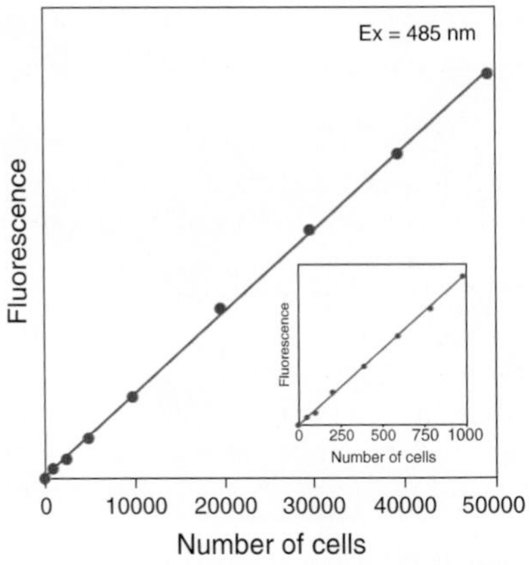

Figure 15.68 Quantitation of NIH 3T3 fibroblasts using Molecular Probes' CyQUANT® Cell Proliferation Assay Kit (C7026). Fluorescence measurements were made using a microplate reader with excitation at 485 nm and emission detection at 530 nm. The linear range of the assay under these conditions is from 50 to 50,000 cells per 200 µL sample. The inset shows the linearity that can be obtained at very low numbers of cells.

This kit provides sufficient materials for ~1000 assays using standard 96-well microplates. Numerous variations and modifications of the MTT assay have been published.[62–64] In addition to dehydrogenases, MTT is reduced by glutathione *S*-transferase[65] (GST). Therefore, MTT may not always be a reliable cell viability probe in cells treated with compounds that affect GST activity.

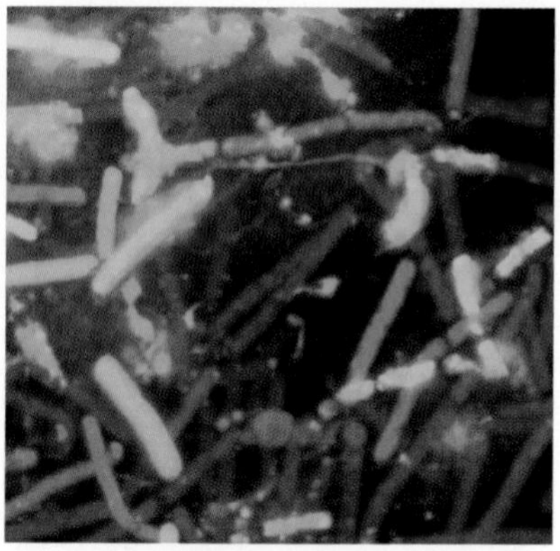

Figure 15.69 A mixture of live and heat-killed *Bacillus cereus* cells simultaneously stained with the cell-permeant SYTO® 59 red-fluorescent nucleic acid stain (S11341) and the cell-impermeant SYTOX® Green nucleic acid stain (S7020), each at a concentration of 5 µM. Bacteria with intact cell membranes stain fluorescent red, whereas bacteria with damaged membranes stain fluorescent green. This maximum-projection image was generated from a series of 10 images taken at 0.2 µm increments through the specimen with a Leica confocal laser-scanning microscope.

FluoReporter® Blue Fluorometric Nucleic Acid Assay Kit

The FluoReporter® Blue Fluorometric dsDNA Quantitation Kit (F2962) provides the protocols developed by Rago and colleagues[66] for analyzing cellular DNA with the blue-fluorescent Hoechst 33258 nucleic acid stain. The kit enables researchers to detect ~10 ng of isolated calf thymus DNA or ~1000 mouse NIH 3T3 cells in a 200 µL sample (substantially lower levels are detectable using our CyQUANT® Cell Proliferation Assay Kit described above).

With this kit, quantitation of cellular DNA is rapid, and all manipulations can be carried out in microplate wells. The cells are lysed by freezing them in distilled water, which circumvents the requirement for extraction procedures used in other Hoechst 33258 dye–based protocols.[57,67–70] The diluted dye solution is then added to the lysed cells, and fluorescence is measured. Kit components include:

- Hoechst 33258 in DMSO/H_2O
- TNE buffer
- A detailed protocol

Each kit provides sufficient reagents for assaying approximately 2000 samples using a fluorescence microplate reader.

Detection and Enumeration Assays for Microorganisms and Viruses

Detecting Bacteria, Yeast and Plankton Using Nucleic Acid Stains

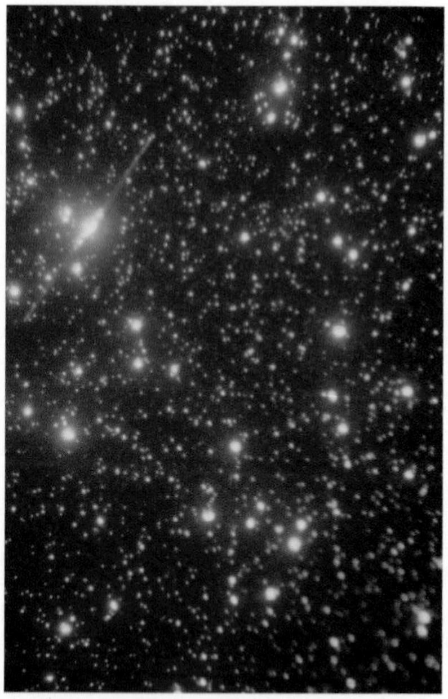

Figure 15.70 An environmental sample containing marine viruses (smallest dots), bacteria (larger, brighter dots) and a diatom (long thin cell with prominent nucleus) stained with SYBR® Green I nucleic acid stain (S7563, S7567, S7585). Image contributed by Jed Fuhrman, University of Southern California.

We recommend our patented SYTO® nucleic acid stains (see the complete list in Table 8.3) for simple detection of the presence of bacteria, yeast, mammalian cells and other nucleic acid–containing cells (Figure 8.132, Figure 8.133, Figure 15.69, Figure 16.26). The SYTO® dyes are essentially nonfluorescent except when bound to nucleic acids, where they become highly fluorescent, often with quantum yields exceeding 0.5. Consequently, it is usually not necessary to remove unbound stains before analysis. SYTO® dyes are available with blue, green, orange or red fluorescence. The SYTO® dyes rapidly penetrate the membranes of almost all cells, including bacteria and yeast. The various cell types can often be identified by their characteristic morphology or, in the case of flow cytometric applications, by their light-scattering properties. The SYTO® 11 and SYTO® 13 green-fluorescent nucleic acid stains (and probably most other SYTO® dyes) show exceptional ability to penetrate tissues for at least 100 µm, including untreated, unfixed human brain tissue, where they were used to enumerate cells by confocal laser-scanning microscopy.[71] Simultaneous labeling with a green-fluorescent SYTO® dye and a red-fluorescent nucleic acid stain — most often propidium iodide, ethidium homodimer-1 or -2, TOTO®-3 or TO-PRO®-3 (Table 8.2, Table 8.4) — is frequently used to assess cell viability (Section 15.2). Although some of the SYTO® dyes show higher quantum yields on DNA or RNA, they should not be considered specific stains for either of these nucleic acids. Our orange-fluorescent SYTO® dyes (SYTO® dyes numbered 80–86, Section 8.1) complement our blue-fluorescent, green-fluorescent and red-fluorescent SYTO® dyes (Table 8.3) and are likely to have applications similar to those of the other SYTO® dyes. The orange-fluorescent SYTO® dyes are available individually or in the SYTO® Orange Fluorescent Nucleic Acid Stain Sampler Kit (S11360), which contains 50 µL samples of six of the seven orange-fluorescent SYTO® nucleic acid stains.

The SYTO® dyes (Table 8.3) and some of our SYBR® dyes (Table 8.1) have been used in a broad range of cell quantitation assays:

- The SYTO® 15 and SYTO® 25 nucleic acid stains (S7577, S7560; Section 8.1), both of which fluoresce green only when bound to nucleic acids, are being used in combination for general detection of bacteria that may be used as biological warfare agents.[1] Use of two (or more) SYTO® dyes of the same color ensures a higher probability of detecting all bacteria since the permeability of the SYTO® dyes through the cell membrane is somewhat species dependent.

- Our SYTO® 13 green-fluorescent nucleic acid stain (S7575, Section 8.1) and various other SYTO® dyes, as well as our SYBR® Green II RNA gel stain (S7564, S7568, S7586; Section 8.1), have all been recommended for counting both live and dead bacteria by flow cytometry.[72,73] SYTO® 13 has also been utilized to sort marine bacteria based on their size and growth rates.[74–76]
- The SYTO® 9 dye (S34854, Section 8.1), which is also a component of our Cell Culture Contamination Detection Kit (C7028, see below), has been used for the quantitation of bacterial biomass in biofilms and of lactic acid bacteria in wine.[77,78]
- SYBR® Green I nucleic acid gel stain (S7563, S7567, S7585; Section 8.3) and SYTO® 13 (S7575) have been used to enumerate marine picoplankton (Figure 15.70), virioplankton and marine bacterial populations[79–82] and to analyze their cell cycles by flow cytometry.[83] In a novel application, SYBR® Green I was used to label marine viruses for use as fluorescent tracers in seawater samples in what is mathematically similar to an "isotope dilution" study.[84] SYBR® Green I has also been used to quantitate fungal mycelia.[85]
- The SYTO® 16 dye (S7578, Section 8.1) was selected as the best probe among the SYTO® 11 to SYTO® 16 series of green-fluorescent nucleic acid stains for assessing the growth and cell cycle–related properties of slow-growing mycobacteria, including *Mycobacterium avium*.[86]
- The red-fluorescent SYTO® 17 dye (S7579, Section 8.1) has been used to stain three different *Leishmania* species in order to estimate the percentage of *Leishmania*-infected human macrophage U-937 cells by flow cytometry.[87]
- SYTO® 21 stain (S7556, Section 8.1), which has green fluorescence when bound to nucleic acids, used in combination with propidium iodide, has been used to assess the damage caused by mechanical impact on neurons.[88]
- The red-fluorescent SYTO® 59 stain (S11341, Section 8.1) and the green-fluorescent SYTO® 9 dye (S34854, Section 8.1) have been used separately to determine the viability and infectivity of *Cryptosporidium parvum* oocysts.[89]
- The SYTO® 16 and SYTO® 59 dyes have been used to stain leukocytes, which were then reinjected into rats to follow retinal and choroidal blood flow.[90]

Furthermore, our patented SYTOX® Green nucleic acid stain (S7020) has proven useful for detecting live *Pseudomonas aeruginosa* on a sensing film that contains a hydroxy-terminated polyamidoamine (PAMAM-OH) dendrimer.[91] Although it is usually excluded from live cells, the SYTOX® Green stain is reportedly permeable to *P. aeruginosa* cells in the presence of the PAMAM-OH dendrimer and shows significant fluorescence enhancement upon binding bacterial nucleic acids, as detected with a miniature fiber-optic spectrophotometer. This optical biosensor can potentially be used in a portable instrument to detect live bacteria in environmental samples.

In addition to its use for cell-cycle analysis (see below) and other applications, DAPI (D1306; D3571; FluoroPure™ Grade, D21490) is frequently employed for DNA content–based counting of bacterial cells[92–94] and for detecting malarial infections by fluorescence microscopy.[95]

BacLight™ *Bacterial Stains*

The *Bac*Light™ Green and *Bac*Light™ Red bacterial stains (B35000, B35001) are fluorescent, non-nucleic acid labeling reagents for detecting and monitoring bacteria. Bacteria stained with the *Bac*Light™ Green and *Bac*Light™ Red bacterial stains exhibit bright green (excitation/emission maxima ~480/516 nm) and red (excitation/emission maxima ~581/644 nm) fluorescence, respectively, and can be resolved simultaneously using the appropriate flow cytometry channels. Although these dyes were specifically chosen for flow cytometry applications, bacteria stained with these *Bac*Light™ reagents can also be visualized by fluorescence microscopy with only minor, if any, adjustments in the staining concentrations. Furthermore, the *Bac*Light™ bacterial staining patterns are compatible with formaldehyde or alcohol fixation methods.

These *Bac*Light™ bacterial stains efficiently label a variety of different bacteria species. The intensity of the staining appears to depend on several factors, including gram character, outer membrane composition and overall membrane integrity. In the species we tested, gram-positive bacteria generally exhibited brighter fluorescence than gram-negative bacteria, and cells with compromised membranes accumulated more dye than intact cells (Figure 15.71). Because they are compatible with various labeling schemes, the *Bac*Light™ bacterial stains can also be combined with other fluorescent probes — including nucleic acid stains, lectin conjugates and antibody conjugates — for multiparameter analyses.

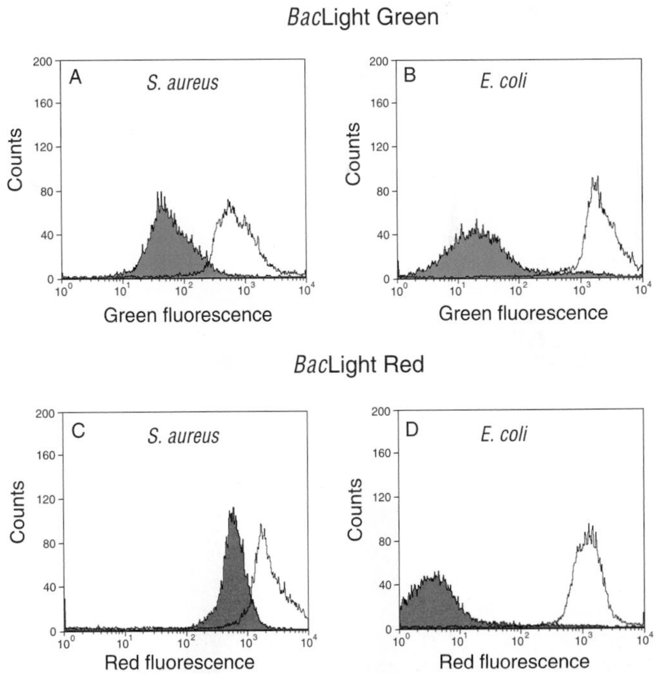

Figure 15.71 Flow cytometry histograms showing fluorescence of live and dead gram-positive and gram-negative bacteria stained with the *Bac*Light™ bacterial stains. Untreated and alcohol-treated gram-positive (*Staphylococcus aureus*, (A and C)) and gram-negative (*Escherichia coli*, (B and D)) bacteria were each stained separately with 100 nM of either the *Bac*Light™ Green (A and B) or the *Bac*Light™ Red (C and D) bacterial stains (B35000, B35001) in 0.85% NaCl buffer and then analyzed by flow cytometry. The histograms for the untreated (colored histogram curve) and alcohol-treated (uncolored histogram curve) bacteria samples were overlaid for each species and *Bac*Light™ bacterial stain.

Bacteria Counting Kit

Accurate enumeration of low numbers of bacteria in samples must be performed daily in many quality-control laboratories. To facilitate this determination by flow cytometry (Figure 15.72), Molecular Probes has developed the Bacteria Counting Kit (B7277), which provides:

- The cell-permeant, green-fluorescent SYTO® BC nucleic acid stain to label bacteria
- Fluorescent polystyrene microspheres to calibrate the volume of bacterial suspension analyzed
- A detailed protocol

The patented SYTO® BC dye, which is also available separately (S34855, Section 8.1), is a high-affinity nucleic acid stain that easily penetrates both gram-negative and gram-positive bacteria, producing an exceptionally bright green-fluorescent signal. The calibrated suspension of polystyrene microspheres contains beads that exhibit a uniform density, low-level fluorescence and optimal size to clearly separate the light scattering of the microspheres from that of most bacteria.

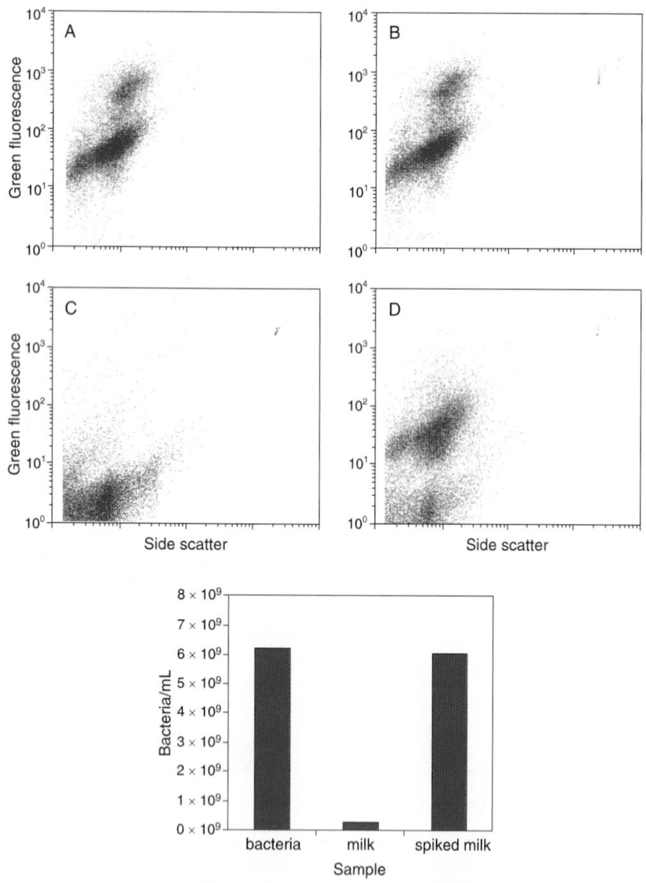

Figure 15.72 Detection and counting of bacteria in milk using the Bacteria Counting Kit (B7277). Equal numbers of bacteria were suspended in 150 mM NaCl or a mixture of milk and 150 mM NaCl and assayed using the protocol provided with the kit. As shown in the lower bar chart, the presence of milk does not affect the outcome of the assay. The upper panels plot green fluorescence versus side scatter for: A–B) bacteria alone; C) milk alone; D) bacteria mixed with milk (spiked milk). Panels B–D also contain reference beads, which appear in the upper right corner of the respective plots.

The Bacteria Counting Kit is particularly valuable for monitoring antibiotic sensitivity because it provides a convenient and accurate means for assessing changes in a bacterial population over time. A sample of the population is simply diluted, stained briefly with the SYTO® BC dye, mixed with a fixed number of microspheres and analyzed on a flow cytometer. Signals from both the stained bacteria and the beads are easily detected in the green fluorescence channel of most flow cytometers and can be distinguished on a plot of forward scatter versus fluorescence (Figure 15.73). The density of the bacteria in the sample can be determined from the ratio of bacterial signals to microsphere signals in the cytogram. The Bacteria Counting Kit can be used with a variety of gram-negative and gram-positive species of bacteria and provides sufficient reagents for approximately 100 flow cytometry assays.

The fluorescent microspheres in our Bacteria Counting Kit have also been recommended for the enumeration of yeast.[96] We offer a wide selection of labeled beads (Section 6.5, Section 23.1, Section 23.2) that may also prove useful for yeast quantitation and viability assays by flow cytometry.[97]

Cell Culture Contamination Detection Kit

Molecular Probes' Cell Culture Contamination Detection Kit (C7028) uses a simple and effective procedure for visually screening cell cultures for contamination by yeast (and other fungi) or by gram-negative or gram-positive bacteria. This kit not only serves to detect the contaminants, but also identifies the contaminant type, enabling the researcher to choose an appropriate course of action.

A sample of the suspected culture is subjected to two slide-staining protocols. One sample slide is stained with Calcofluor White M2R, a UV light–excitable, blue-fluorescent stain specific for fungal cell walls. A second slide is stained with our patented SYTO® 9 nucleic acid stain to identify all bacteria irrespective of gram sign, and also with the Texas Red®-X conjugate of wheat germ agglutinin (WGA), which selectively stains gram-positive bacteria.[98,99] Gram-positive bacteria on the second slide typically exhibit a green-fluorescent interior with red-fluorescent cell-surface staining, whereas gram-negative bacteria show only green-fluorescent interior staining. Staining and examination of the slides under a fluorescence microscope can be performed in less than one hour. Each Cell Culture Contamination Detection Kit contains:

- The green-fluorescent SYTO® 9 nucleic acid stain
- The blue-fluorescent Calcofluor White M2R fungal cell wall stain
- The red-fluorescent Texas Red®-X WGA, for positive identification of gram-positive bacteria
- Buffer for reconstituting Texas Red®-X WGA
- A detailed protocol

This kit provides sufficient material for approximately 200 contamination detection assays. The SYTO® 9 nucleic acid stain, which is also available separately (S34854, Section 15.2), has been used to detect lactic acid–producing bacteria in wine.[77]

MycoFluor™ Mycoplasma Detection Kit

Mycoplasma infections are generally difficult or impossible to detect during routine work with cultured cells because these intracellular pathogens cannot be observed by standard light microscopy. However, mycoplasma infections can be detected with the Hoechst dyes [100,101] (Figure 15.74) or with DAPI [102,103] (Section 8.1). Hoechst 33258, either alone [104] or in combination with merocyanine 540 [105] (M24571, Section 18.2), has been utilized to eradicate mycoplasma infections from cell cultures. It is not surprising then that mycoplasma infections are relatively common. Estimates of contaminated cultures in the United States range from 5% to 35%, whereas the contamination rate is postulated to be much higher in those countries where systematic detection and elimination are not practiced.[106] Not only do mycoplasma cause physiological and morphological distortions that can affect experimental results, but contamination can quickly spread to other cell lines.

The MycoFluor™ Mycoplasma Detection Kit (M7006) provides an extremely rapid and sensitive fluorescence microscopy–based assay for the visual identification of mycoplasma infection in laboratory cell cultures and media. In order to detect mycoplasma, the fluorescent MycoFluor™ reagent is added directly to the culture medium, with or without cells present, and the stained sample is then examined under a fluorescence microscope. The test for the presence of mycoplasma in live or fixed cell cultures takes about 15 minutes from when the reagent is added until when the sample is viewed with a fluorescence microscope equipped with DAPI optical filters (Table 23.9). The detection of mycoplasma in cell media requires about 30 minutes, depending on the amount of centrifugation required to concentrate potential contaminants.

Also provided with this kit are mycoplasma MORFS (Microscopic Optical Replicas for Fluorescence assays), which serve as inert positive controls that mimic the size, shape and fluorescence intensity of mycoplasma stained with the blue-fluorescent MycoFluor™ reagent and viewed by fluorescence microscopy. The optical properties of the mycoplasma MORFS enable the researcher to discriminate between stained mycoplasma and other fluorescent material without introducing infectious biological agents into the laboratory environment. No previous experience with mycoplasma testing is required.

Each MycoFluor™ Mycoplasma Detection Kit supplies sufficient materials for at least 100 tests of live cells, fixed cells or culture media. Kit contents include:

- Concentrated MycoFluor™ reagent
- A suspension of mycoplasma MORFS
- Coverslip sealant
- A cotton swab
- Reference micrographs
- A detailed protocol

Alternatively, the LIVE/DEAD® *BacLight*™ Bacterial Viability Kits (L7007, L7012, L13152; Section 15.3) may be useful for detecting mycoplasma infections. Researchers have determined that the reagents in our LIVE/DEAD® *BacLight*™ Kits can be used for viability determinations in *Eurioplasma eurilytica* and *Mycoplasma hominus* mycoplasma and in the cysts of the protozoan parasite *Giardia muris* [107] (Figure 15.46).

Detecting Viruses Using Nucleic Acid Stains

Because of their small size, direct detection of viruses by fluorescence requires highly sensitive reagents or, much more commonly, an amplification scheme. However, direct enumeration of marine viral abundance in seawater using SYBR® Green I nucleic acid gel stain [108–110] (S7563, S7567, S7585; Section 8.3; Figure 15.70), YO-PRO®-1 (Y3603, Section 8.1) and DAPI [111] (D1306; D3571; FluoroPure™ Grade, D21490) has been reported.

The slow off-rate of our dimeric nucleic acid stains, such as TOTO®-1 and YOYO®-1 (T3600, Y3601), has permitted their use for labeling nucleic acids, including viral RNA,[112] prior to microinjection into live cells to follow their trafficking. Similar staining techniques may permit tracing of viral uptake and transport by live cells.

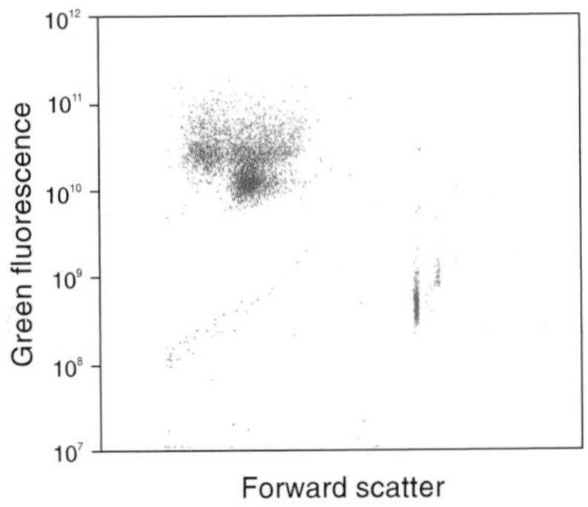

Figure 15.73 Flow cytometric enumeration of *Bacillus cereus* using Molecular Probes' Bacteria Counting Kit (B7277). Bacteria stained with the SYTO® BC bacterial cell stain and mixed with known concentrations of weakly fluorescent 6 µm polystyrene microsphere standards produce a bivariate frequency distribution for forward light scatter versus green fluorescence intensity that allows the bacterial population number to be determined by reference to the clearly separated microsphere standard population, indicated by red data points.

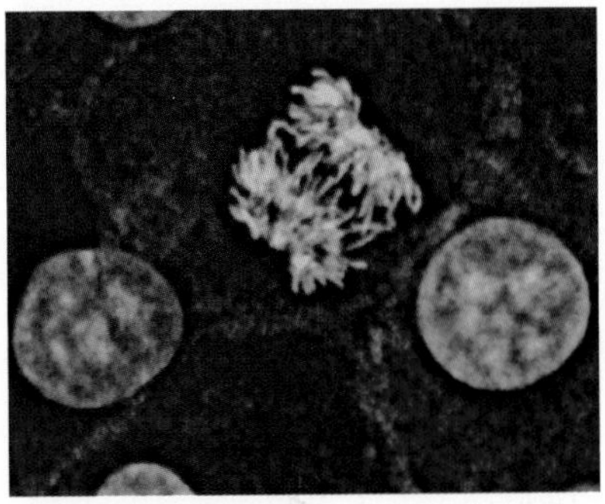

Figure 15.74 A mycoplasma-contaminated African green monkey fibroblast cell line was stained with cell-permeant, blue-fluorescent Hoechst 33342 nucleic acid stain (H1399, H3570, H21492), simultaneously illustrating both cell nuclei and mycoplasma. The image was acquired using filters appropriate for DAPI. Image contributed by Heiti Paves, Laboratory of Molecular Genetics, National Institute of Chemical Physics and Biophysics, Estonia.

Nucleic Acid Probes for Cell-Cycle Analysis

The cell-cycle distribution and proliferative state of a cell population are important parameters when studying oncogene and tumor suppressor gene mechanisms and other live-cell functions. The cell-cycle distribution within a population can be analyzed with nucleic acid stains that, upon binding to the DNA, exhibit fluorescence emission proportional to the DNA content of the cell. Subsequent analysis by flow cytometry yields a histogram of DNA content per cell that allows determination of the fraction of cells in the G_1, S and G_2 phases of the cell cycle. This analy-

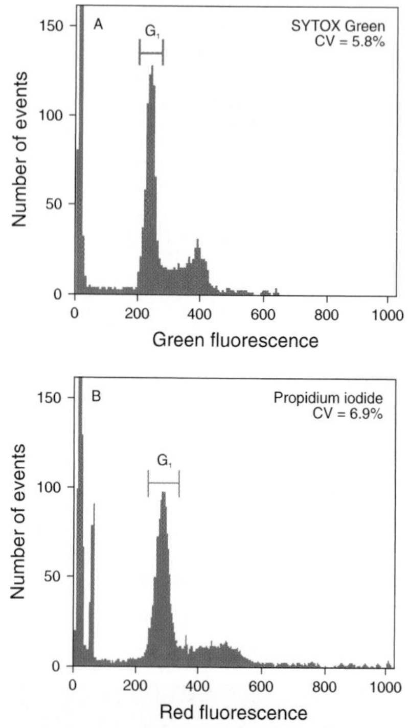

Figure 15.75 Comparison of DNA content histograms obtained with **A)** SYTOX® Green nucleic acid stain (S7020) and **B)** propidium iodide (P1304MP, P3566, P21493). Human B cells were suspended in permeabilizing buffer (100 mM Tris, pH 7.4, 154 mM NaCl, 1 mM $CaCl_2$, 0.5 mM $MgCl_2$, 0.1% Nonidet P-40) and then stained for 15 minutes with 0.5 µM SYTOX® Green or 5 µM propidium iodide. Flow cytometric analysis of the stained cells was carried out with excitation at 488 nm. SYTOX® Green staining produces a significantly narrower G_1 phase peak, indicated by the smaller coefficient of variation (CV).

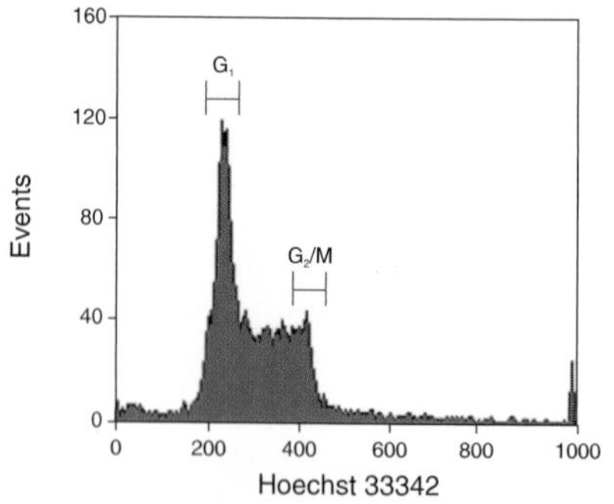

Figure 15.76 DNA content histogram for WIL2S cells. The cells were fixed in ethanol, treated with RNase and stained with 2 µg/mL Hoechst 33342 (H1399, H3570, H21492). Flow cytometric analysis of the stained cells was carried out using excitation at 350 nm.

sis is typically performed either on live cells using a cell-permeant nucleic acid stain [113,114] or on detergent-treated or fixed cells using a cell-impermeant nucleic acid stain.[6,115–117]

SYTOX® Green and SYTO® Nucleic Acid Stains

We have determined that our patented SYTOX® Green nucleic acid stain (S7020) is particularly useful for cell-cycle analysis on RNase-treated fixed cells (Figure 15.75). In particular, the SYTOX® Green dye produces lower coefficients of variation than propidium iodide, leading to improved resolution of cell phase. Figure 15.75 shows a comparison of DNA content histograms obtained with SYTOX® Green nucleic acid stain and propidium iodide after flow cytometric analysis.

Our patented SYTO® nucleic acid stains (S7554, S7572, S11340, S11350, S11360; Section 8.1; Figure 8.133) passively diffuse through cell membranes and may also be useful for cell-cycle analysis. Viable adherent cells stained with the SYTO® 16 green-fluorescent nucleic acid stain were analyzed with a microscope-based laser-scanning cytometer that measures multiple-wavelength fluorescence and light scattering for each cell on a microscope slide.[118] Although the DNA distribution was broader than that obtained with propidium iodide–stained fixed cells, data obtained with the SYTO® 16 dye provided sufficient resolution to distinguish mitotic cells from the G_{1a} population. SYTO® 16 staining has also been used to detect and count cells containing intracellular parasites.[119]

TOTO® and YOYO® Dimeric Cyanine Dyes

Most of our high-sensitivity cyanine dyes in the patented TOTO® and TO-PRO® series (Table 8.2) have been reported to be useful for staining nucleic acids in fixed-cell preparations. Staining with TOTO®-1 and YOYO®-1 dimeric cyanine dyes (T3600, Y3601) allows extremely sensitive flow cytometric analysis of aldehyde-fixed marine prokaryotes [120,121] and eukaryotes,[122] as well as of RNase-treated nuclei and isolated human chromosomes.[123] It is possible to detect single TOTO®-1 dye–stained fragments of a restriction digest by capillary flow cytometry in a bacterial profiling application.[124] It was reported that YOYO®-1 dye–stained nuclei exhibited over 1000 times the fluorescence signal obtained with mithramycin, and histograms of both TOTO®-1 dye– and YOYO®-1 dye–stained nuclei provided coefficients of variation that were at least as low as those found with propidium iodide or mithramycin.[6,123] Moreover, when nuclei were simultaneously stained with the YOYO®-1 dye and Hoechst 33258, the ratio of the fluorescence of these two dyes varied as a function of cell cycle, suggesting that the cyanine dyes might be useful for examining cell cycle–dependent changes that occur in chromatin structure. TOTO®-1 and YOYO®-1 dyes have also been used for quantitative cytometric assessment of nuclei in formaldehyde-fixed paraffin tissue sections and reportedly produced an intense, photostable fluorescent signal that correlated well with the DNA content of diploid, tetraploid and octaploid liver nuclei.[125] The longer-wavelength TOTO®-3 dye (T3604) may be useful in many of the same applications as its TOTO®-1 and YOYO®-1 analogs. Furthermore, this dye can be excited using low-cost sources such as red He–Ne and diode lasers.[126] We offer sample sizes of all eight dimeric cyanine dyes in our Nucleic Acid Stains Dimer Sampler Kit (N7565, Section 8.1). Properties of the TOTO® series of dimeric cyanine dyes are described in detail in Section 8.1 and Table 8.2.

Hoechst 33258, Hoechst 33342 and DAPI

The nucleic acid stains most frequently used for cell-cycle analysis — Hoechst 33258 (H1398; H3569; FluoroPure™ Grade, H21491), Hoechst 33342 (H1399; H3570; FluoroPure™ Grade, H21492) and DAPI (D1306, D3571; FluoroPure™ Grade, D21490) — bind to the minor groove of DNA at AT-rich sequences. Hoechst 33342, which more rapidly permeates cells than Hoechst 33258, is commonly used for determining the DNA content of viable cells without detergent treatment or fixation [113,114] (Figure 15.76). The Hoechst dyes and DAPI can be excited with a mercury-arc lamp, the UV spectral lines of the argon-ion laser or the 325 nm spectral line of the He–Cd laser. These blue-fluorescent nucleic acid stains preferentially bind to AT-rich sequences and also exhibit higher quantum yields when bound to AT-rich nucleic acids, thus introducing a strong bias into the measurements of nuclear DNA content.[127,128] As a consequence, data obtained with Hoechst 33342 and DAPI correlate very well with each other but less well with data obtained with propidium iodide, a red-fluorescent, cell-impermeant nucleic acid stain [129] (P1304MP, P3566, P21493; Section 8.1). Hoechst 33342 is used in the high-speed sorting of X chromosome– and Y chromosome–bearing sperm based on their DNA content.[130,131]

Ethidium Bromide and Its Analogs

Ethidium bromide (E1305, E3565), ethidium homodimer-1 (E1169), propidium iodide (P1304MP, P3566, P21493) and hexidium iodide (H7593), all of which are discussed in Section 8.1, are phenanthridinium derivatives that intercalate between the bases of the DNA in fixed cells to yield red fluorescence. Because these base-intercalating dyes are not specific for DNA, cell-cycle analysis usually requires treatment of fixed samples with RNase (50–100 µg/mL) to eliminate fluorescence resulting from dye binding to RNA.[6]

Acridine Orange

Acridine orange (A1301, A3568) emits green fluorescence when bound to double-stranded nucleic acids and red fluorescence when bound to single-stranded nucleic acids. This property has been exploited in methods for simultaneously analyzing the DNA and RNA content of a cell culture.[132,133] Acridine orange–based assays have enabled researchers to monitor early events during lymphocyte activation by flow cytometry,[133] as well as to study the steps leading to differentiation of keratinocytes in cell culture.[134] After staining with acridine orange, bacteria actively growing in a rich medium exhibit orange fluorescence, making them easily distinguished from bacteria in stationary phase, which have green fluorescence.[135]

7-Aminoactinomycin D

7-AAD (7-aminoactinomycin D, A1310; Figure 15.77) is a fluorescent intercalator that undergoes a spectral shift upon association with DNA. 7-AAD/DNA complexes can be excited by the argon-ion laser and emit beyond 610 nm (Figure 8.16), permitting use of 7-AAD in combination with any green-fluorescent probe. This visible light–excitable nucleic acid stain is suitable for cell-cycle analysis,[136,137] although the precision of the distributions obtained is generally inferior to those generated with other dyes.[137–139] 7-AAD appears to be generally excluded from live cells; however, it has been reported to label the nuclear region of live cultured mouse L cells and salivary gland polytene chromosomes of *Chironomus thummi thummi* larvae [140] and appears to be taken up by most apoptotic cells (Section 15.5). Nondifferentiated cells are also reported to bind 7-AAD better than differentiated cells,[141] which may make the dye a useful marker for malignant hematopoietic cells.[142] 7-AAD binds selectively to GC-rich regions of DNA,[143] yielding a distinct banding pattern in polytene chromosomes and chromatin.[140,144] This sequence selectivity has been exploited for chromosome-banding studies [145] (Section 8.6).

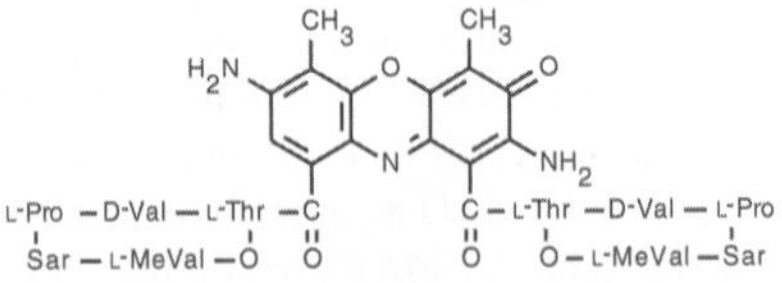

Figure 15.77 A1310 7-aminoactinomycin D (7-AAD).

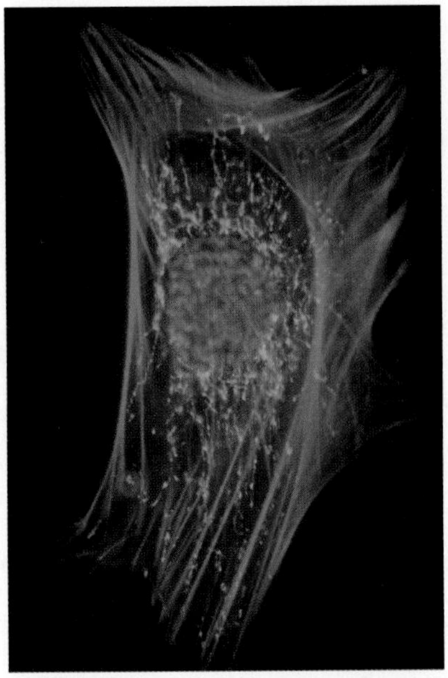

Figure 15.78 A muntjac cell stained with antibodies against cytoskeletal, nuclear and mitochondrial proteins. Fixed, permeabilized cells were stained with Alexa Fluor® 350 phalloidin (A22281) to label F-actin in the cytoskeleton. The anti–cdc6 peptide antibody (A21286) labeled with the Zenon® Alexa Fluor® 568 Mouse IgG_1 Labeling Kit (Z25006) was used to stain the nuclear region, and an anti–OxPhos Complex V inhibitor protein antibody (A21355) labeled with the Zenon® Alexa Fluor® 488 Mouse IgG_1 Labeling Kit (Z25002) was used to stain the mitochondria.

Antibodies to Proliferation Markers and Cell-Cycle Control Proteins

Anti–cdc6 Peptide Antibody

The cdc6 protein, which was originally described in budding yeast, functions during eukaryotic replication initiation and is essential for DNA synthesis.[146] This 30,000-dalton protein exhibits DNA-binding properties and is thought to be involved in the assembly of minichromosome maintenance proteins onto replicating DNA.[147] cdc6 is a nuclear protein that is expressed *only* in actively replicating cells, making it an excellent marker for cell proliferation.[148,149] Quiescent cells in G_0 do not express the protein.[150] Polyclonal antibodies to cdc6 have been shown to have potential clinical applications in the assessment of tumor prognosis[151] and have been used to detect abnormal cells in Papanicolau (Pap) cervical smears with very high specificity and sensitivity.[150]

Molecular Probes offers the anti–cdc6 peptide mouse monoclonal antibody 37F4 (A21286), which is suited for immunohistochemical applications. The antibody was generated by immunizing mice with a peptide (Leu-Ser-Pro-Arg-Lys-Arg-Leu-Gly-Asp-Asp-Asn-Leu-Cys) based on a segment of the amino acid sequence of human cdc6. Molecular Probes scientists have found that this anti–cdc6 peptide antibody is an excellent marker for the nucleus, and can replace traditional nucleic acid counterstains in multicolor applications (Figure 7.66, Figure 7.85, Figure 15.78). Moreover, this antibody can be used to visualize chromatin throughout mitosis (Figure 7.86, Figure 7.87, Figure 7.88, Figure 7.89, Figure 7.90).

Anti–Human mRNA-Binding Protein HuR Antibody (Anti-HuR Antibody)

The mRNA-binding protein HuR is expressed in a wide variety of proliferating cells.[152] HuR binds to AU-rich elements (ARE) in the 3′-untranslated region of transcripts, specifically to those areas located in the 3′-UTRs of mRNAs that encode growth-regulating proteins such as c-fos, c-myc, cyclin A, cyclin B1 and NOS II.[153–156] HuR mediates the hypoxic regulation of VEGF mRNA stability and UV light–induced regulation of p21WAF1 expression,[157] and is likely to regulate the mRNA expression of many other cytokines and transcription factors. Our mouse anti–human HuR antibody (A21277) was generated against a unique peptide from the N-terminus of HuR. Anti-HuR is suitable for immunohistochemical assays of paraffin-embedded tissue, as well as for Western blots. It can also be used in supershift assays to confirm that HuR is present in an mRNA/protein complex. Anti-HuR could prove very useful to investigators who wish to determine whether HuR regulates the expression of their mRNA. Although we have not investigated species specificity, the peptide sequence is well conserved; we therefore expect the antibody to crossreact with HuR of most species.

Antibodies against D Cyclins and Cyclin-Dependent Kinase Inhibitors

Progression of the cell cycle through G_1-phase and into S-phase is controlled in part by a series of serine/threonine kinase complexes, consisting of a cyclin regulatory subunit and catalytic subunit referred to as a cyclin-dependent kinase [158] (cdk). Binding of the cyclin to the cdk serves to activate the complex, which promotes cell-cycle progression by phosphorylation of specific target proteins. At least five proteins have been identified as G_1-phase cyclins (C, D1, D2, D3, E),[159] of which the three D cyclins form a closely related group.[160] Cyclin C has been shown to associate with cdk8,[161] while cyclin E activates cdk2.[162] The D1 and D2 cyclins can associate with both cdk4 and cdk6; activity of these complexes has been detected as early as mid-G_1 phase.[163] Cyclin D3 can also activate cdk4 and cdk6, but D3-associated cdk activity is found only at the G_1/S transition.[164]

The D cyclins, in particular, play an important role in regulatory decisions controlling the progression of the cell cycle; overexpression of these regulatory proteins is associated with a wide variety of proliferative diseases including breast [165,166] and gastric [167,168] cancers. For the detection of these important cell-cycle control proteins, Molecular Probes offers a monoclonal antibody against each individual D cyclin — mouse IgG_{2a} monoclonal DCS-6 anti–cyclin D1 (A21320), mouse IgG_{2b} monoclonal DCS-5.2 anti–cyclin D2 (A21321) and mouse IgG_1 monoclonal DCS-22 anti–cyclin D3 (A21322). Each of these antibodies is suitable for use in both Western blotting and immunohistochemical applications.

Active cyclin/cdk complexes can be inhibited by a number of different proteins, resulting in arrest of the cell cycle. In many cases these inhibitor proteins are activated by DNA damage, halting the progression through the cell cycle until repairs can be made.[169] Arrest in the G_1-phase is a result of activated Rb protein, which must be phosphorylated by a cdk in order to deactivate the protein and allow progression of the cell cycle.[170] Induction of the cdk inhibitor p21WAF1/CIP1 prevents phosphorylation of Rb, thereby maintaining arrest in G_1.[171]

Studies have shown that the absence of p21WAF1/CIP1 is associated with transformed cells but not tumor-derived cell lines.[172] Our mouse IgG_{2a} monoclonal DCS-60 anti-p21WAF1/CIP1 (A21319) should be a useful tool for analyzing protein abundance and cellular localization of this important cell-cycle inhibitor.[173]

Endostatin Protein and Angiostatin Protein for Angiogenesis Research

In physiological conditions, angiogenesis occurs primarily in embryo development, during wound healing and in response to ovulation.[174] The normal regulation of angiogenesis is governed by a fine balance between factors that induce the formation of blood vessels and those that halt or inhibit the process. When this balance is destroyed, it usually results in pathological angiogenesis or the abnormal rapid proliferation of blood vessels. Pathological angiogenesis is implicated in over 70 diseases, including cancer, psoriasis and age-related macular degeneration.[175] The angiogenic process can be summarized as follows:

- Angiogenic growth factors either directly or indirectly activate endothelial cells.
- Urokinase-type (uPA) and tissue-type (tPA) plasminogen activators convert plasminogen into plasmin, which can degrade extracellular matrix components (ECM) surrounding the existing blood vessel.
- Plasmin can also stimulate the endothelial cells to secrete matrix metalloproteases (MMPs) that proteolytically degrade the ECM.
- Protein fragments produced by the digestion of the blood-vessel walls further stimulate the endothelial cells to migrate into the interstitial space, as well as to proliferate.
- Cell adhesion molecules, including integrins, cadherins and selectins, assist the endothelial cells in forming a new capillary tube.
- Pericytes and smooth muscle cells stabilize the newly formed blood vessels, and blood flow begins.

Considerable research has been performed on the complex enzymatic and signal transduction cascades that need to be regulated in order to inhibit angiogenesis and to prevent diseases that are characterized by excessive vessel growth, such as cancer and arthritis. The ability to stimulate angiogenesis for the treatment of coronary heart disease and critical limb ischemia has also been studied.[176] In cooperation with EntreMed, Molecular Probes offers both recombinant Angiostatin protein (A23375) and Endostatin protein (E23377) for research purposes.

Angiostatin

Angiostatin protein (A23375), a kringle-containing internal fragment of plasminogen, is a potent inhibitor of angiogenesis *in vivo* [177] and a selective inhibitor of endothelial cell proliferation, migration and tube formation *in vitro*.[178,179] Angiostatin can be generated by many different enzymes, including several matrix metalloproteases (MMPs) [180] and urokinase.[181,182] Endothelial cells adhere to angiostatin in an integrin-dependent manner,[183] and endothelial cell-surface F_1F_0 ATP synthase is inhibited by angiostatin.[184] Although the signaling mechanisms of angiostatin remain poorly understood, recent research has shown that this angiogenesis inhibitor increases intracellular Ca^{2+} concentrations,[185] ceramide and free radical production.[186]

Endostatin

The angiogenesis inhibitor Endostatin protein (E23377) is an endogenous 20,000-dalton carboxyl-terminal fragment of collagen XVIII (Figure 16.14). Although the mechanism of its action is currently unknown, research has found that endostatin appears to trigger suppression of both apoptosis factors and cell proliferation genes, resulting in a potent antimigratory effect.[187] Endostatin has been shown to bind to glypicans or transmembrane heparan sulfate proteoglycans on the cell surface.[188] Once endocytosed, endostatin has demonstrated an affinity for tropomyosin,[189] a protein that stabilizes the pointed end of actin filaments by slowing depolymerization.[190] Indirectly, endostatin appears to induce an increase in intracellular Ca^{2+} and cAMP concentrations.[187]

References

1. Biophotonics Int 5, 34 (1998); **2.** Exp Cell Res 173, 256 (1987); **3.** Science 218, 474 (1982); **4.** Methods Cell Biol 41, 297 (1994); **5.** Proc Natl Acad Sci U S A 80, 5573 (1983); **6.** Methods Cell Biol 41, 195 (1994); **7.** J Histochem Cytochem 25, 913 (1977); **8.** Proc Natl Acad Sci U S A 70, 3395 (1973); **9.** Cytometry 41, 89 (2000); **10.** Proc Natl Acad Sci U S A 80, 2951 (1983); **11.** Methods Cell Biol 41, 327 (1994); **12.** Exp Cell Res 174, 319 (1988); **13.** Cytometry 37, 221 (1999); **14.** Cytometry 17, 310 (1994); **15.** Cytometry 45, 13 (2001); **16.** Cytometry 20, 172 (1995); **17.** Cytometry 20, 257 (1995); **18.** Cytometry 20, 245 (1995); **19.** J Histochem Cytochem 41, 7 (1993); **20.** J Cell Biol 119, 493 (1992); **21.** Cancer Res 54, 4289 (1994); **22.** Exp Cell Res 222, 28 (1996); **23.** Cell Prolif 28, 571 (1995); **24.** Cell Biology: A Laboratory Handbook, 2nd Ed., Vol. 1, Celis JE, Ed. pp. 341–350 (1998); **25.** Cytometry 27, 1 (1997); **26.** J Biol Chem 275, 16788 (2000); **27.** Dev Biol 206, 232 (1999); **28.** J Cell Biol 144, 813 (1999); **29.** Histochem Cell Biol 113, 181 (2000); **30.** Mol Biol Cell 10, 211 (1999); **31.** Cell Biology: A Laboratory Handbook, 2nd Ed., Vol I, Celis J, Ed. pp. 261–274 (1998); **32.** Immunol Cell Biol 77, 509 (1999); **33.** J Immunol Methods 171, 131 (1994); **34.** J Immunol Methods 133, 87 (1990); **35.** Transplant Proc 24, 2820 (1992); **36.** Immunol Cell Biol 77, 499 (1999); **37.** J Exp Med 189, 265 (1999); **38.** J Immunol 162, 735 (1999); **39.** Cell Immunol 188, 1 (1998); **40.** Cytometry 34, 143 (1998); **41.** Eur J Immunol 28, 1040 (1998); **42.** J Immunol 161, 5260 (1998); **43.** J Immunol 160, 3666 (1998); **44.** Br J Haematol 98, 528 (1997); **45.** J Biol Chem 274, 3541 (1999); **46.** J Exp Med 184, 277 (1996); **47.** Blood 94, 2161 (1999); **48.** Lett Appl Microbiol 25, 295 (1997); **49.** J Immunol Methods 230, 99 (1999); **50.** Blood 94, 2595 (1999); **51.** Leuk Res 17, 873 (1993); **52.** Anticancer Res 18, 4243 (1998); **53.** J Immunol Methods 254, 85 (2001); **54.** Anal Biochem 207, 186 (1992); **55.** J Immunol Methods 142, 199 (1991); **56.** Anal Biochem 213, 426 (1993); **57.** In Vitro Toxicol 3, 219 (1990); **58.** Exp Cell Res 124, 329 (1979); **59.** Biochimie 76, 452 (1994); **60.** J Neurochem 69, 581 (1997); **61.** J Immunol Methods 65, 55 (1983); **62.** J Immunol Methods 168, 253 (1994); **63.** Cancer Res 47, 943 (1987); **64.** J Immunol Methods 93, 157 (1986); **65.** Biotechniques 25, 622 (1998); **66.** Anal Biochem 191, 31 (1990); **67.** J Immunol Methods 162, 41 (1993); **68.** Cancer Res 49, 565 (1989); **69.** Anal Biochem 131, 538 (1983); **70.** Anal Biochem 102, 344 (1980); **71.** Cytometry 32, 66 (1998); **72.** J Microbiol Methods 32, 45 (1998); **73.** Appl Environ Microbiol 64, 1725 (1998); **74.** Microb Ecol 40, 148 (2000); **75.** Microb Ecol 38, 180 (1999); **76.** Aquat Microbial Ecol 16, 251 (1999); **77.** Lett Appl Microbiol 28, 23 (1999); **78.** J Microbiol Methods 32, 253 (1998); **79.** J Microbiol Methods 55, 841 (2003); **80.** Cytometry 44, 236 (2001); **81.** Microbios 101, 23 (2000); **82.** Appl Environ Microbiol 65, 4475 (1999); **83.** Appl Environ Microbiol 63, 186 (1997); **84.** Appl Environ Microbiol 66, 3790 (2000); **85.** Biotechniques 31, 42 (2001); **86.** Lett Appl Microbiol 25, 437 (1997); **87.** J Microbiol Methods 37, 123 (1999); **88.** J Neurotrauma 16, 1197 (1999); **89.** Appl Environ Microbiol 66, 406 (2000); **90.** Ophthalmic Surg Lasers 30, 140 (1999); **91.** Anal Chem 73, 467 (2001); **92.** J Microbiol Methods 20, 255 (1994); **93.** J Microbiol Methods 19, 89 (1994); **94.** Microbiol Rev 58, 603 (1994); **95.** J Parasitol 65, 421 (1979); **96.** Yeast 14, 147 (1998); **97.** J Immunol Methods 211, 51 (1998); **98.** Appl Environ Microbiol 56, 2245 (1990); **99.** J Clin Microbiol 10, 669 (1979); **100.** J Immunol Methods 38, 315 (1980); **101.** Exp Cell Res 104, 255 (1977); **102.** Leukemia 6, 335 (1992); **103.** J Immunol Methods 149, 43 (1992); **104.** Cytogenet Cell Genet 36, 584 (1983); **105.** J Immunol Methods 168, 245 (1994); **106.** Nature 339, 487 (1989); **107.** Int J Parasitol 26, 637 (1996); **108.** Appl Environ Microbiol 65, 45 (1999); **109.** Aquat Microbial Ecol 14, 113 (1998); **110.** Nature 399, 541 (1999); **111.** Aquat Microbial Ecol 13, 225 (1997); **112.** Proc Natl Acad Sci U S A 93, 12643 (1996); **113.** Arch Pathol Lab Med 113, 591 (1989); **114.** J Histochem Cytochem 25, 585 (1977); **115.** Methods Cell Biol 41, 231 (1994); **116.** Methods Cell Biol 41, 219 (1994); **117.** Methods Cell Biol 41, 211 (1994); **118.** Cytometry 23, 272 (1996); **119.** Cytometry 41, 223 (2000); **120.** Appl Environ Microbiol 62, 1649 (1996); **121.** Limnol Oceanogr 40, 1485 (1995); **122.** Mar Ecol Prog Ser 185, 301 (1999); **123.** Cytometry 15, 129 (1994); **124.** Cytometry 35, 169 (1999); **125.** Cytometry 17, 191 (1994); **126.** Cytometry 15, 267 (1994); **127.** Biochemistry 29, 9029 (1990); **128.** J Histochem Cytochem 24, 24 (1976); **129.** Cytometry 13, 389 (1992); **130.** Cytometry 33, 476 (1998); **131.** Cytometry 25, 191 (1996); **132.** Methods Cell Biol 41, 401 (1994); **133.** Proc Natl Acad Sci U S A 73, 2881 (1976); **134.** J Cell Physiol 143, 279 (1990); **135.** J Microbiol Methods 13, 87 (1991); **136.** Cytometry 39, 108 (2000); **137.** J Immunol 136, 2769 (1986); **138.** Cytometry 13, 60 (1992); **139.** Cytometry 12, 279 (1991); **140.** Histochem J 17, 131 (1985); **141.** Cytometry 5, 355 (1984); **142.** Cancer Res 52, 5007 (1992); **143.** Biopolymers 18, 1749 (1979); **144.** Cytometry 20, 296 (1995); **145.** Chromosoma 68, 287 (1978); **146.** Biochim Biophys Acta 1280, 115 (1996); **147.** Curr Opin Cell Biol 10, 742 (1998); **148.** J Cell Sci 113, 1929 (2000); **149.** Oncogene 17, 1777 (1998); **150.** Proc Natl Acad Sci U S A 95, 14932 (1998); **151.** Clin Cancer Res 5, 2121 (1999); **152.** J Neuroimmunol 92, 152 (1998); **153.** EMBO J 17, 3461 (1998); **154.** EMBO J 19, 2340 (2000); **155.** J Biol Chem 275, 26040 (2000); **156.** EMBO J 17, 3448 (1998); **157.** Mol Cell Biol 20, 760 (2000); **158.** Cell 73, 1059 (1993); **159.** Mol Cell Biol 15, 2600 (1995); **160.** Genomics 13, 575 (1992); **161.** Oncogene 20, 551 (2001); **162.** Science 257, 1958 (1992); **163.** Mol Cell Biol 14, 2077 (1994); **164.** Mol Cell Biol 14, 2066 (1994); **165.** Int J Cancer 57, 353 (1994); **166.** Proc Natl Acad Sci U S A 90, 1112 (1993); **167.** Histopathology 36, 151 (2000); **168.** Pathol Int 48, 717 (1998); **169.** Cancer Res 55, 2910 (1995); **170.** Trends Biochem Sci 22, 14 (1997); **171.** Proc Natl Acad Sci U S A 92, 9019 (1995); **172.** J Mol Med 73, 509 (1995); **173.** Hybridoma 19, 63 (2000); **174.** Nat Med 1, 27 (1995); **175.** Int J Biochem Cell Biol 33, 357 (2001); **176.** Pharmacol Rev 52, 237 (2000); **177.** Cancer Res 60, 2660 (2000); **178.** Cancer Metastasis Rev 19, 97 (2000); **179.** Biochem Biophys Res Commun 278, 821 (2000); **180.** Proc Natl Acad Sci U S A 97, 2202 (2000); **181.** Proc Natl Acad Sci U S A 94, 10868 (1997); **182.** J Biol Chem 273, 31480 (1998); **183.** J Biol Chem 276, 39562 (2001); **184.** Proc Natl Acad Sci U S A 98, 6656 (2001); **185.** Am J Physiol Cell Physiol 280, C1140 (2001); **186.** EMBO Rep 2, 536 (2001); **187.** FASEB J 15, 1044 (2001); **188.** Mol Cell 7, 811 (2001); **189.** J Biol Chem 276, 25190 (2001); **190.** Biochemistry 28, 1048 (1989).

Data Table — 15.4 Assays for Cell Enumeration, Cell Proliferation and Cell Cycle

Cat #	MW	Storage	Soluble	Abs	EC	Em	Solvent	Notes
A1301	301.82	L	H_2O, EtOH	500	53,000	526	H_2O/DNA	1, 2
A1310	1270.45	F,L	DMF, DMSO	546	25,000	647	H_2O/DNA	1
A3568	301.82	RR,L	H_2O	500	53,000	526	H_2O/DNA	1, 2, 3
B21550	612.99	FF,L	H_2O	<300		none		3
B21551	628.98	FF,L	H_2O	<300		none		3
B23151	307.10	F,L	DMSO	<300		none		
B35000	671.88	F,D,L	DMSO	490	119,000	516	MeOH	
B35001	724.00	F,D,L	DMSO	588	81,000	645	MeOH	
C1157	557.47	F,D	DMF, DMSO	<300		none		4
C7614	~908	FF,L	H_2O	504	68,000	513	pH 8	3, 5
C22803	873.05	F,D	DMSO	<300		none		6
D1306	350.25	L	H_2O, DMF	358	21,000	461	H_2O/DNA	1, 7
D3571	457.49	L	H_2O, MeOH	358	20,000	461	H_2O/DNA	
D21490	350.25	L	H_2O, DMF	358	21,000	461	H_2O/DNA	1, 7, 8
H1398	623.96	L	H_2O, DMF	352	40,000	461	H_2O/DNA	1, 9
H1399	615.99	L	H_2O, DMF	350	45,000	461	H_2O/DNA	1, 9
H3569	623.96	RR,L	H_2O	352	40,000	461	H_2O/DNA	1, 3, 9
H3570	615.99	RR,L	H_2O	350	45,000	461	H_2O/DNA	1, 3, 9
H21491	623.96	L	H_2O, DMF	352	40,000	461	H_2O/DNA	1, 8, 9
H21492	615.99	L	H_2O, DMF	350	45,000	461	H_2O/DNA	1, 8, 9
L7595	471.98	L	DMSO, EtOH	543	46,000	712	H_2O/DNA	1
O34550	593.45	F,D,L	DMSO	<300		none		10
S7020	~600	F,D,L	DMSO	504	67,000	523	H_2O/DNA	1, 3, 11, 12
S22801	592.56	F,D	DMSO	<350		none		13
T3600	1302.78	F,D,L	DMSO	514	117,000	533	H_2O/DNA	1, 3, 11, 14
T3604	1354.85	F,D,L	DMSO	642	154,000	660	H_2O/DNA	1, 3, 11, 14
T3605	671.42	F,D,L	DMSO	642	102,000	661	H_2O/DNA	1, 3, 11, 14
V22885	933.88	L	see Notes	549	148,000	565	MeOH	15
V22886	881.72	L	see Notes	484	154,000	501	MeOH	15
V22887	1052.08	L	see Notes	644	193,000	663	MeOH	15
V22888	1051.50	F,L	see Notes	553	134,000	570	MeOH	15
Y3601	1270.65	F,D,L	DMSO	491	99,000	509	H_2O/DNA	1, 3, 11, 14

For definitions of the contents of this data table, see "Navigating *The Handbook*" in the introductory pages.

Notes

1. Spectra represent aqueous solutions of nucleic acid-bound dye. EC values are derived by comparing the absorbance of the nucleic acid–bound dye with that of free dye in a reference solvent (H_2O or MeOH).
2. Acridine orange bound to RNA has Abs ~460 nm, Em ~650 nm (Methods Cell Biol 41, 401 (1994); Cytometry 2, 201 (1982)).
3. This product is supplied as a ready-made solution in the solvent indicated under "Soluble."
4. Acetate hydrolysis of this compound yields a fluorescent product with similar pH-dependent spectral characteristics to C1904.
5. The molecular weight (MW) of this product is approximate because the degree of hydration and/or salt form has not been conclusively established.
6. Acetate hydrolysis of C22803 yields a fluorescent product with spectra similar to 5-carboxyeosin, Abs = 519 nm (EC = 100,000 $cm^{-1}M^{-1}$), Em = 542 nm in pH 9 buffer.
7. DAPI in H_2O: Abs = 344 nm (EC = 23,000 $cm^{-1}M^{-1}$), Em = 450 nm. QY increases ~20-fold on binding to dsDNA (Ital J Biochem 31, 90 (1982)).
8. This product is specified to equal or exceed 98% analytical purity by HPLC.
9. MW is for the hydrated form of this product.
10. Acetate hydrolysis of this compound yields a fluorescent product with similar spectral characteristics to O6146.
11. This product is essentially nonfluorescent except when bound to DNA or RNA.
12. MW: The preceding ~ symbol indicates an approximate value, not including counterions.
13. C6826 and S22801 are converted to fluorescent products with spectra similar to C1270 after acetate hydrolysis.
14. Although this compound is soluble in water, preparation of stock solutions in water is not recommended because of possible adsorption onto glass or plastic.
15. This product is supplied as a ready-made staining solution.

Product List — 15.4 Assays for Cell Enumeration, Cell Proliferation and Cell Cycle

Cat #	Product Name	Unit Size
A23150	ABSOLUTE-S™ SBIP Cell Proliferation Assay Kit *with Alexa Fluor® 488 anti-BrdU* *50 assays*	1 kit
A1301	acridine orange	1 g
A3568	acridine orange *10 mg/mL solution in water*	10 mL
A1310	7-aminoactinomycin D (7-AAD)	1 mg
A23375	Angiostatin® protein (human, recombinant) *1 mg/mL*	250 µL
A21300	anti-bromodeoxyuridine, mouse IgG_1, monoclonal PRB-1 (anti-BrdU)	350 µL
A21303	anti-bromodeoxyuridine, mouse IgG_1, monoclonal PRB-1, Alexa Fluor® 488 conjugate (anti-BrdU, Alexa Fluor® 488 conjugate)	350 µL
A21307	anti-bromodeoxyuridine, mouse IgG_1, monoclonal PRB-1, Alexa Fluor® 532 conjugate (anti-BrdU, Alexa Fluor® 532 conjugate)	350 µL
A21308	anti-bromodeoxyuridine, mouse IgG_1, monoclonal PRB-1, Alexa Fluor® 546 conjugate (anti-BrdU, Alexa Fluor® 546 conjugate)	350 µL
A21304	anti-bromodeoxyuridine, mouse IgG_1, monoclonal PRB-1, Alexa Fluor® 594 conjugate (anti-BrdU, Alexa Fluor® 594 conjugate)	350 µL
A21305	anti-bromodeoxyuridine, mouse IgG_1, monoclonal PRB-1, Alexa Fluor® 647 conjugate (anti-BrdU, Alexa Fluor® 647 conjugate)	350 µL
A21306	anti-bromodeoxyuridine, mouse IgG_1, monoclonal PRB-1, Alexa Fluor® 660 conjugate (anti-BrdU, Alexa Fluor® 660 conjugate)	350 µL
A21301MP	anti-bromodeoxyuridine, mouse IgG_1, monoclonal PRB-1, biotin-XX conjugate (anti-BrdU, biotin conjugate)	350 µL
A21286	anti–cdc6 peptide (human), mouse IgG_{2a}, monoclonal 37F4 *for immunohistochemistry*	100 µg
A21320	anti-cyclin D1, mouse IgG_{2a}, monoclonal DCS-6	100 µg
A21321	anti-cyclin D2, mouse IgG_{2b}, monoclonal DCS-5.2	100 µg
A21322	anti-cyclin D3, mouse IgG_1, monoclonal DCS-22	100 µg
A21319	anti-p21WAF1/CIP1, mouse IgG_{2a}, monoclonal DCS-60	100 µg
B35000	*Bac*Light™ Green bacterial stain *special packaging*	20 x 50 µg
B35001	*Bac*Light™ Red bacterial stain *special packaging*	20 x 50 µg
B7277	Bacteria Counting Kit *for flow cytometry*	1 kit
B23151	5-bromo-2′-deoxyuridine (BrdU)	100 mg
B21550	5-bromo-2′-deoxyuridine 5′-triphosphate (BrdUTP) *10 mM in TE buffer*	25 µL
B21551	5-bromouridine 5′-triphosphate (BrUTP) *10 mM in TE buffer*	25 µL
C22803	5-(and-6)-carboxyeosin diacetate, succinimidyl ester *mixed isomers*	5 mg
C1157	5-(and-6)-carboxyfluorescein diacetate, succinimidyl ester (5(6)-CFDA, SE; CFSE) *mixed isomers*	25 mg
C7028	Cell Culture Contamination Detection Kit *200 assays*	1 kit
C34554	CellTrace™ CFSE Cell Proliferation Kit *for flow cytometry*	1 kit
C7614	ChromaTide® BODIPY® FL-14-dUTP *1 mM in TE buffer*	25 µL
C7027	CyQUANT® cell lysis buffer *20X concentrate*	50 mL
C7026	CyQUANT® Cell Proliferation Assay Kit *for cells in culture* *1000 assays*	1 kit
D1306	4′,6-diamidino-2-phenylindole, dihydrochloride (DAPI)	10 mg
D21490	4′,6-diamidino-2-phenylindole, dihydrochloride (DAPI) *FluoroPure™ grade*	10 mg
D3571	4′,6-diamidino-2-phenylindole, dilactate (DAPI, dilactate)	10 mg
E23377	Endostatin™ protein (human, recombinant) *1 mg/mL*	250 µL
F2962	FluoReporter® Blue Fluorometric dsDNA Quantitation Kit *200-2000 assays*	1 kit
H1398	Hoechst 33258, pentahydrate (bis-benzimide)	100 mg
H3569	Hoechst 33258, pentahydrate (bis-benzimide) *10 mg/mL solution in water*	10 mL
H21491	Hoechst 33258, pentahydrate (bis-benzimide) *FluoroPure™ grade*	100 mg
H1399	Hoechst 33342, trihydrochloride, trihydrate	100 mg
H3570	Hoechst 33342, trihydrochloride, trihydrate *10 mg/mL solution in water*	10 mL
H21492	Hoechst 33342, trihydrochloride, trihydrate *FluoroPure™ grade*	100 mg
L7595	LDS 751	10 mg
M7006	MycoFluor™ Mycoplasma Detection Kit	1 kit
O34550	Oregon Green® 488 carboxylic acid diacetate, succinimidyl ester (carboxy-DFFDA, SE) *mixed isomers*	1 mg
S22801	SNARF®-1 carboxylic acid, acetate, succinimidyl ester *special packaging*	10 x 50 µg
S7020	SYTOX® Green nucleic acid stain *5 mM solution in DMSO*	250 µL
T3605	TO-PRO®-3 iodide (642/661) *1 mM solution in DMSO*	1 mL
T3600	TOTO®-1 iodide (514/533) *1 mM solution in DMSO*	200 µL
T3604	TOTO®-3 iodide (642/660) *1 mM solution in DMSO*	200 µL
V12883	Vybrant® CFDA SE Cell Tracer Kit	1 kit
V22888	Vybrant® CM-DiI cell-labeling solution	1 mL
V22887	Vybrant® DiD cell-labeling solution	1 mL
V22885	Vybrant® DiI cell-labeling solution	1 mL
V22886	Vybrant® DiO cell-labeling solution	1 mL
V13154	Vybrant® MTT Cell Proliferation Assay Kit *1000 assays*	1 kit
Y3601	YOYO®-1 iodide (491/509) *1 mM solution in DMSO*	200 µL

For current prices or to order online, visit probes.invitrogen.com

15.5 Assays for Apoptosis

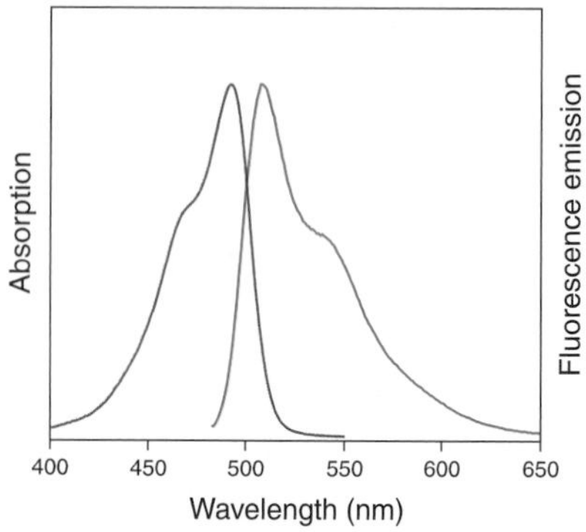

Figure 15.79 Absorption and fluorescence emission spectra of YO-PRO®-1 bound to DNA.

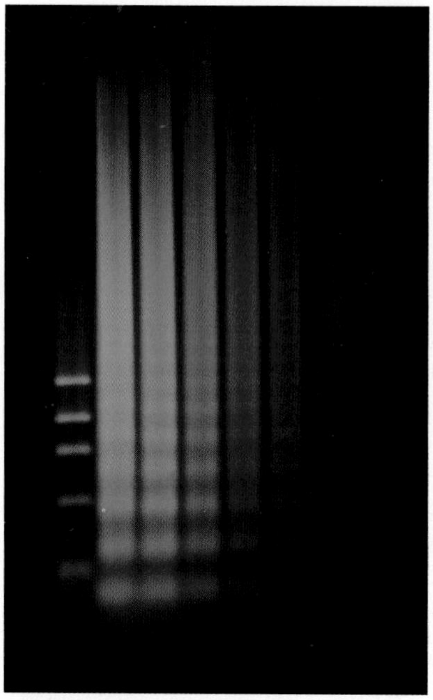

Figure 15.80 DNA extracts from camptothecin-treated HL-60 cells separated on an agarose gel and stained with SYBR® Green I nucleic acid gel stain (S7563, S7567, S7585). The 200 to 5000 bp DNA fragments characteristic of apoptotic cells (which appear as "ladders") are clearly visualized with this sensitive nucleic acid stain. Cell preparations were gifts of Zbigniew Darzynkiewicz, Cancer Research Institute, New York Medical College.

Apoptosis (programmed cell death) is the genetically controlled ablation of cells during normal development.[1] Inappropriately regulated apoptosis is implicated in disease states such as Alzheimer's disease, stroke and cancer.[2–4] Apoptosis is distinct from necrosis in both the biochemical and the morphological changes that occur.[5–8] In contrast to necrotic cells, apoptotic cells are characterized morphologically by compaction of the nuclear chromatin, shrinkage of the cytoplasm and production of membrane-bound apoptotic bodies. Biochemically, apoptosis is distinguished by fragmentation of the genome and cleavage or degradation of several cellular proteins.

As with cell viability, no single parameter fully defines cell death in all systems; therefore, it is often advantageous to use several different approaches when studying apoptosis. Several methods have been developed to distinguish live cells from early and late apoptotic cells and from necrotic cells; these are described below and in a number of review articles and seminal publications.[5,9–15] Anti-cancer drug candidates failing to induce apoptosis are likely to have decreased clinical efficacy,[16] making apoptosis assays important tools for high-throughput drug screening. Apoptotic cells are typically eliminated by phagocytosis; thus, apoptotic cells that have been selectively labeled with a fluorescent dye can potentially be used as tracers for phagocytosis,[17] a cell process that is discussed in Section 16.1.

Apoptosis Assays Using Nucleic Acid Stains

DNA Stains for Detecting Apoptotic Cells

The characteristic breakdown of the nucleus during apoptosis comprises collapse and fragmentation of the chromatin, degradation of the nuclear envelope and nuclear blebbing, resulting in the formation of micronuclei. Therefore, nucleic acid stains can be useful tools for identifying even low numbers of apoptotic cells in cell populations. Several nucleic acid stains, all of which are listed in Section 8.1, have been used to detect apoptotic cells by fluorescence imaging or flow cytometry.[18]

- Our YO-PRO®-1 (Y3603) nucleic acid stain is the basis of an important assay for apoptotic cells that is compatible with both fluorescence microscopy and flow cytometry.[19] Selective uptake of YO-PRO®-1 by apoptotic cells of a dexamethasone-treated population of thymocytes, an irradiated peripheral blood mononuclear cell population and a growth factor–depleted tumor B cell line was confirmed by cell sorting.[20] Unlike Hoechst 33342 staining, YO-PRO®-1 staining had no effect on the ability of stained T cells to proliferate. Moreover, the visible-light absorption of the YO-PRO®-1 stain (Figure 15.79) eliminates the need for UV excitation capabilities in flow cytometry. YO-PRO®-1 is the key reagent in our Vybrant® Apoptosis Assay Kits #4 and #7 (V13243, V23201, see below), which provide the reagents and tested protocols for combination flow cytometric apoptosis and necrosis assays.
- Some of our cell-permeant, green-fluorescent SYTO® dyes, including the SYTO® 13 and SYTO® 16 nucleic acid stains (S7575, S7578), are proving useful for distinguishing apoptotic neuronal cells[21] and apoptotic thymocytes.[22] Our SYTO® Fluorescent Nucleic Acid Stain Sampler Kits (S7554, S7572, S11340, S11350, S11360; Section 8.1) provide fluorescent SYTO® dyes covering the entire visible spectrum (Table 8.3) that may be screened for their utility in monitoring apoptosis. In addition, apoptotic cells in a follicular lymphoma cell line could be discriminated earlier with our SYTO® 17 red-fluorescent nucleic acid stain (S7579) than with either fluorescein-labeled annexin V or propidium iodide.[23]
- Hoechst 33342 (H1399, H3570; FluoroPure™ Grade, H21492) is readily taken up by cells during the initial stages of apoptosis, whereas cell-impermeant dyes such as propidium iodide (P1304MP, P3566, P21493; Section 8.1) and ethidium bromide[24–26] (E1305, E3565; Section 8.1) are excluded. Later stages of apoptosis are accompanied by an increase in membrane permeability, which allows propidium iodide to enter cells. Thus, a combination of Hoechst 33342 and propidium iodide has been extensively used for simultaneous flow cytometric and fluorescence imaging analysis of the stages of apoptosis and cell-cycle

distribution.[24,25,27–29] Our Vybrant® Apoptosis Assay Kit #5 (V13244, see below) is based on these reagents, and our Vybrant® Apoptosis Assay Kit #7 (V23201, see below) adds the YO-PRO®-1 nucleic acid to selectively determine the apoptotic cell population in a three-color experiment.

- The rate of Hoechst 33342 uptake in partially apoptotic cell populations is correlated with low intracellular pH, as measured with our carboxy SNARF®-1 pH indicator [30] (C1271, C1272; Section 20.2).
- Hoechst 33342, which selectively stains nuclei of apoptotic cells blue fluorescent, has also been used in combination with calcein AM (C1430, C3099, C3100MP; Section 15.2), which stains all cells that have intact membranes — even apoptotic cells — green fluorescent.[31,32] Presumably the dead-cell population could be selectively detected using propidium iodide to make this a three-color assay.
- 7-Aminoactinomycin D (7-AAD, A1310) has been used alone or in combination with Hoechst 33342 to separate populations of live cells, early apoptotic cells and late apoptotic cells by flow cytometry.[33–37] The staining pattern of 7-AAD is retained following cell fixation, and its unusually large Stokes shift is advantageous when simultaneously staining with cell-surface labels. 7-AAD staining has also been used to detect apoptotic cells by their characteristic morphology using fluorescence microscopy.[38] 7-AAD has also been used in combination with the green-fluorescent SYTO® 16 nucleic acid stain (S7578) to detect early stages of apoptosis that could not be detected by 7-AAD alone.[39]
- The cell-permeant nucleic acid stain LDS 751 (L7595) has been used to discriminate intact nucleated cells from nonnucleated cells and cells with damaged nuclei,[40,41] as well as to differentiate apoptotic cells from nonapoptotic cells.[22,42]
- Acridine orange (A1301, A3568) exhibits metachromatic fluorescence that is sensitive to DNA conformation, making it a useful probe for detecting apoptotic cells.[43] When analyzed by flow cytometry, apoptotic cells stained by acridine orange show reduced green fluorescence and enhanced red fluorescence in comparison to normal cells.[44]
- DAPI (D1306, D21490; Section 8.1) and sulforhodamine 101 (S359, Section 14.3) can be used together in fixed apoptotic cells to reveal concomitant breakdown of proteins and DNA.[5,44–46]
- The excited-state lifetime of ethidium homodimer-2 (E3599, Section 8.1) has been shown to be different in populations of aldehyde-fixed apoptotic and nonapoptotic cells.[47]
- Ethidium monoazide (E1374, Section 15.2) passes through the partially compromised membrane of apoptotic cells; photolysis results in covalent labeling of intracellular nucleic acids that persists through fixation and permeabilization.[48]

DNA fragmentation can also be detected *in vitro* using electrophoresis. DNA extracted from apoptotic cells, separated by gel electrophoresis and stained with ethidium bromide reveals a characteristic ladder pattern of low molecular weight DNA fragments.[45,49–52] Ethidium bromide has been used for a dot-blot assay to detect apoptotic DNA fragments.[53] Our ultrasensitive SYBR® Green I nucleic acid stain (S7567, Section 8.4) and SYBR® DX DNA blot stain (S7550, Section 8.5) allow the detection of even fewer apoptotic cells in these applications (Figure 15.80). Electrophoresis of apoptotic cells in an agarose gel matrix results in the formation of distinctive "comets" of DNA leaking from apoptotic cells (but not normal cells; see the paragraph, Comet (Single-Cell Gel Electrophoresis) Assay to Detect Damaged DNA, below) (Figure 15.83).

Vybrant® Apoptosis Assay Kit #4

Our Vybrant® Apoptosis Assay Kit #4 (V13243) detects apoptosis based on changes that occur in the permeability of cell membranes (Table 15.4). This kit contains ready-to-use solutions of both the YO-PRO®-1 and propidium iodide nucleic acid stains. Our patented YO-PRO®-1 nucleic acid stain selectively passes through the plasma membranes of apoptotic cells and labels them with moderate green fluorescence.[20,31,54–56] Necrotic cells are stained with the red-fluorescent propidium iodide, a DNA-selective dye that is membrane impermeant but that easily passes through the compromised plasma membranes of necrotic cells. Live cells are not appreciably stained by either YO-PRO®-1 or propidium iodide. The dyes included in the Vybrant® Apoptosis Assay Kit #4 are effectively excited by the 488 nm spectral line of the argon-ion laser and are useful for both flow cytometry (Figure 15.81) and fluorescence microscopy (Figure 15.82). We have optimized our Vybrant® Apoptosis Assay Kits using Jurkat cells, a human T-cell leukemia

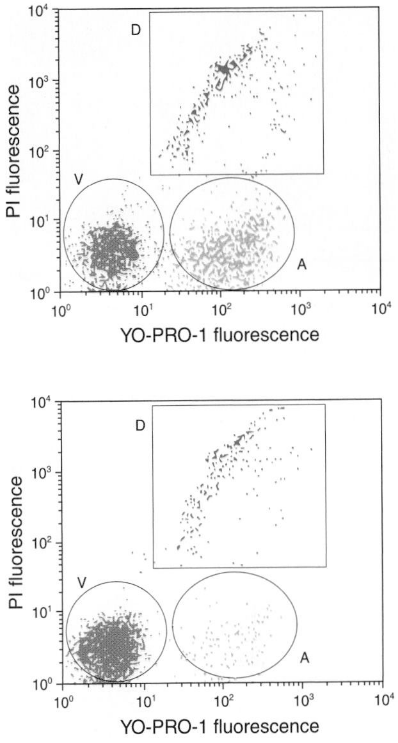

Figure 15.81 Flow cytometric analysis of Jurkat cells using the Vybrant® Apoptosis Assay Kit #4 (V13243). Jurkat human T-cell leukemia cells were first exposed to 10 µM camptothecin for four hours (top panel) or left untreated (as control, bottom panel). Cells were then treated with the reagents in the Vybrant® Apoptosis Assay Kit #4 and analyzed by flow cytometry. Note that the camptothecin-treated cells (top panel) have a significantly higher percentage of apoptotic cells (indicated by "A") than the basal level of apoptosis seen in the control cells (bottom panel). V = viable cells, D = dead cells.

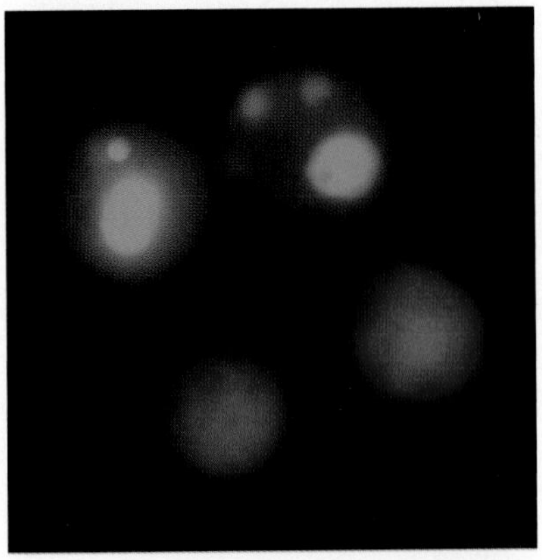

Figure 15.82 Apoptosis induced in Jurkat cells with 10 µM camptothecin. The cells were then treated with the reagents in the Vybrant® Apoptosis Assay Kit #4 (V13243). Apoptotic cell nuclei were labeled with YO-PRO®-1 dye (green) (Y3603). Necrotic cells were detected with propidium iodide (red) (P1304MP, P3566, P21493).

clone, treated with camptothecin to induce apoptosis. Some modifications may be required for use with other cell types. The kit components, number of assays and assay principles are summarized in Table 15.4.

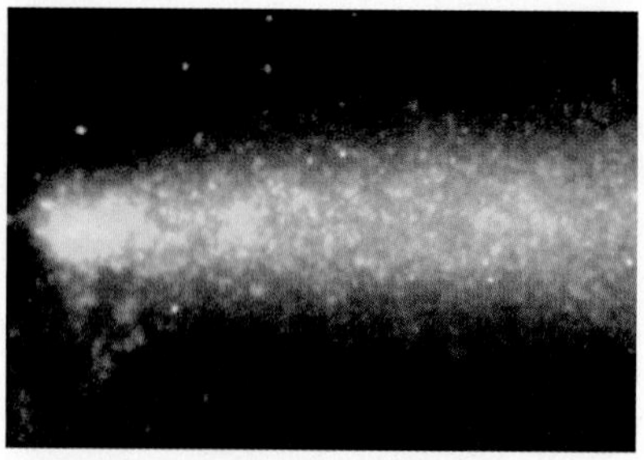

Figure 15.83 Comet assay with SYBR® Green I nucleic acid gel stain (S7563, S7567, S7585). DNA fragmentation associated with oxidative DNA damage was visualized using Trevigen's CometAssay kit. HL-60 cells were treated with H_2O_2 and immobilized onto a Trevigen CometSlide for analysis. The cells were gently lysed, washed and treated with endonuclease. Slides were subjected to electrophoresis in alkaline electrophoresis buffer and stained with SYBR® Green I stain.

Vybrant® Apoptosis Assay Kits #5 and #7

The Vybrant® Apoptosis Assay Kit #5 (V13244) provides a rapid and convenient assay for apoptosis based upon fluorescence detection of the compacted state of the chromatin in apoptotic cells. This kit contains ready-to-use solutions of the blue-fluorescent Hoechst 33342 dye (excitation/emission maxima ~350/461 nm when bound to DNA), which stains the condensed chromatin of apoptotic cells more brightly than the chromatin of nonapoptotic cells, and the red-fluorescent propidium iodide (excitation/emission maxima ~535/617 nm when bound to DNA), which is permeant only to dead cells with compromised membranes (Table 15.4). The staining pattern resulting from the simultaneous use of these dyes makes it possible to distinguish normal, apoptotic and dead cell populations by flow cytometry or fluorescence microscopy.[5,27,57] The 351 nm spectral line of an argon-ion laser or other suitable UV source is required for excitation of the Hoechst 33342 dye, whereas propidium iodide can be excited with the 488 nm spectral line of an argon-ion laser. We have optimized this assay using Jurkat cells, a human T-cell leukemia clone, treated with camptothecin to induce apoptosis. Some modifications may be required for use with other cell types. The kit components, number of assays and assay principles are summarized in Table 15.4.

The Vybrant® Apoptosis Assay Kit #7 combines the detection principles used in our Vybrant® Apoptosis Assay Kits #4 (see above) and #5. Three nucleic acid stains — Hoechst 33342, YO-PRO®-1 and propidium iodide — are utilized to identify by flow cytometry the blue-fluorescent live-cell population, the green-fluorescent apoptotic population and the red-fluorescent dead-cell population. The stains are provided as separate solutions to facilitate optimization of the assay for the cell line under study and the equipment available. However, once optimized, the assay can be completed using simultaneous staining with a mixture of the three nucleic acid stains and either UV excitation of all three dyes or a combination of UV excitation for the Hoechst 33342 dye and excitation by the 488 nm spectral line of the argon-ion laser. Differences in the intensity of the dye staining may make it difficult to simultaneously photograph the live, apoptotic and dead cells by microscopy. The kit components, number of assays and assay principles are summarized in Table 15.4.

Comet (Single-Cell Gel Electrophoresis) Assay to Detect Damaged DNA

The Comet assay, or single-cell gel electrophoresis assay, is used for rapid detection and quantitation of DNA damage from single cells.[58,59] The Comet assay is based on the alkaline lysis of labile DNA at sites of damage. Cells are immobilized in a thin agarose matrix on slides and gently lysed. When subjected to electrophoresis, the unwound, relaxed DNA migrates out of the cells. After staining with a nucleic acid stain, cells that have accumulated DNA damage appear as fluorescent comets, with tails of DNA fragmentation or unwinding (Figure 15.83). In contrast, cells with normal, undamaged DNA appear as round dots, because their intact DNA does not migrate out of the cell. The ease and sensitivity of the Comet assay has provided a fast and convenient way to measure damage to human sperm DNA,[60] evaluate DNA replicative integrity,[61] monitor the sensitivity of tumor cells to radiation damage[62] and assess the sensitivity of molluscan cells to toxins in the environment.[63] The Comet assay can also be used in combination with FISH (Section 8.5) to identify specific sequences with damaged DNA.[62]

Comet assays have traditionally been performed using ethidium bromide to stain the DNA.[58] However, our YOYO®-1 dye was found to increase the sensitivity of the assay eightfold as compared with ethidium bromide.[59] Use of the SYBR® Gold and SYBR® Green I stains[64] improves the sensitivity of this assay (Figure 15.83).

Detecting DNA Strand Breaks with ChromaTide® Nucleotides

DNA fragmentation that occurs during apoptosis produces DNA strand breaks. TUNEL (terminal deoxynucleotidyl transferase dUTP nick-end labeling) assays are widely used for detecting DNA nicks in apoptotic cells. Once the cells are fixed, DNA strand breaks can be detected *in situ*

Table 15.4 — Summary of Molecular Probes' Vybrant® Apoptosis Assay Kits

Cat #	Kit Name	Probe(s) for Apoptotic Cells (Abs/Em) *	Probe for Necrotic or Live Cells (Abs/Em) *	Number of Assays	Kit Features
V13240	Vybrant® Apoptosis Assay Kit #1	Alexa Fluor® 488 annexin V (495/519)	SYTOX® Green nucleic acid stain (504/523)	50 flow cytometry assays, each containing 2×10^5 to 1×10^6 cells in a 1 mL volume	Because the Alexa Fluor® 488 annexin V–based assay in Kit #1 uses only the green fluorescence channel on the flow cytometer, other parameters can be measured simultaneously using fluorescent probes that have different emission spectra.
V13241	Vybrant® Apoptosis Assay Kit #2	Alexa Fluor® 488 annexin V (495/519)	Propidium iodide (535/617)	50 flow cytometry assays, each containing 2×10^5 to 1×10^6 cells in a 1 mL volume	In Kit #2, apoptotic cells are labeled with annexin V conjugated to our exceptionally bright and photostable green-fluorescent Alexa Fluor® 488 dye. Necrotic cells are labeled with red-fluorescent propidium iodide.
V13242	Vybrant® Apoptosis Assay Kit #3	FITC annexin V (494/519)	Propidium iodide (535/617)	50 flow cytometry assays, each containing 2×10^5 to 1×10^6 cells in a 1 mL volume	Kit #3 is similar to Kit #2 except that it contains the fluorescein conjugate of annexin V.
V13243	Vybrant® Apoptosis Assay Kit #4	YO-PRO®-1 dye (491/509)	Propidium iodide (535/617)	200 flow cytometry assays, each containing 2×10^5 to 1×10^6 cells in a 1 mL volume	Kit #4 detects changes in cell membrane permeability with YO-PRO®-1 dye, a green-fluorescent nucleic acid stain that is permeant to apoptotic cells but not to live cells. Necrotic cells are labeled with red-fluorescent propidium iodide.
V13244	Vybrant® Apoptosis Assay Kit #5	Hoechst 33342 (346/480)	Propidium iodide (535/617)	200 flow cytometry assays, each containing 2×10^5 to 1×10^6 cells in a 1 mL volume	Kit #5 uses Hoechst 33342 in combination with propidium iodide to distinguish between the condensed chromatin of apoptotic cells and the looser chromatin structure in live cells.
V23200	Vybrant® Apoptosis Assay Kit #6	Biotin-X annexin V and Alexa Fluor® 350 streptavidin (345/442)	Propidium iodide (535/617)	50 flow cytometry assays, each containing 2×10^5 to 1×10^6 cells in a 1 mL volume	In Kit #6, apoptotic cells are labeled with the biotin-X conjugate of annexin V in conjunction with blue-fluorescent Alexa Fluor® 350 streptavidin. Necrotic cells are labeled with red-fluorescent propidium iodide.
V23201	Vybrant® Apoptosis Assay Kit #7	Hoechst 33342 (346/480) and YO-PRO®-1 dye (491/509)	Propidium iodide (535/617)	200 flow cytometry assays, each containing 2×10^5 to 1×10^6 cells in a 1 mL volume	Kit #7 is a combination of Kits #4 and #5. All three dyes can be excited by a UV laser, or by a combination of UV and 488 nm excitation.
V35112	Vybrant® Apoptosis Assay Kit #8	R-phycoerythrin (R-PE) annexin V (496/578)	SYTOX® Green nucleic acid stain (504/523)	50 flow cytometry assays, each containing 2×10^5 to 1×10^6 cells in a 1 mL volume	In Kit #8, apoptotic cells are labeled with annexin V conjugated to the intensely orange-fluorescent R-phycoerythrin (R-PE). Necrotic cells are labeled with the green-fluorescent SYTOX® Green nucleic acid stain. Both probes can be excited by the 488 nm spectral line of the argon-ion laser.
V35113	Vybrant® Apoptosis Assay Kit #9	Allophycocyanin annexin V (650/660)	SYTOX® Green nucleic acid stain (504/523)	50 flow cytometry assays, each containing 2×10^5 to 1×10^6 cells in a 1 mL volume	Kit #9 is similar to Kit #8 except that it contains the allophycocyanin conjugate of annexin V. Apoptotic cells are labeled with the intensely far-red–fluorescent allophycocyanin annexin V. Necrotic cells are labeled with green-fluorescent SYTOX® Green nucleic acid stain. These populations can easily be distinguished using a flow cytometer equipped with both the 488 nm spectral line of the argon-ion laser and the 633 nm spectral line of the He–Ne laser for excitation.
V35114	Vybrant® Apoptosis Assay Kit #10	Allophycocyanin annexin V (650/660)	SYTOX® Green nucleic acid stain (504/523)	50 flow cytometry assays, each containing 2×10^5 to 1×10^6 cells in a 1 mL volume	Kit #10 is identical to Kit #9 except that it also contains C_{12}-resazurin, which is reduced by viable cells to the orange-fluorescent C_{12}-resorufin (Abs/Em = 571/585 nm). Apoptotic, necrotic and live cell populations can easily be distinguished using a flow cytometer equipped with both the 488 nm spectral line of the argon-ion laser and the 633 nm spectral line of the He–Ne laser for excitation.
V35116	Vybrant® Apoptosis Assay Kit #11	Alexa Fluor® 488 annexin V (495/519)	MitoTracker® Red CMXRos (578/599)	50 flow cytometry assays, each containing 2×10^5 to 1×10^6 cells in a 1 mL volume	In Kit #11, apoptotic cells are labeled with annexin V conjugated to our exceptionally bright and photostable green-fluorescent Alexa Fluor® 488 dye. Live cells are labeled with MitoTracker® Red CMXRos, which exhibits bright red fluorescence in the presence of a mitochondrial transmembrane potential. Apoptotic and live cell populations can easily be distinguished using a flow cytometer and the 488 nm spectral line of the argon-ion laser.

* Approximate absorption and emission maxima, in nm

using mammalian terminal deoxynucleotidyl transferase (TdT), which covalently adds labeled nucleotides to the 3′-hydroxyl ends of these DNA fragments in a template-independent fashion.[18,65–68] Break sites have traditionally been labeled with biotinylated dUTP, followed by subsequent detection with an avidin or streptavidin conjugate[69–72] (Section 7.6, Table 7.22). However, a more direct approach for detecting DNA strand breaks in apoptotic cells is possible via the use of our ChromaTide® BODIPY® FL-14-dUTP (C7614) as a TdT substrate[73,74] (Figure 15.84).

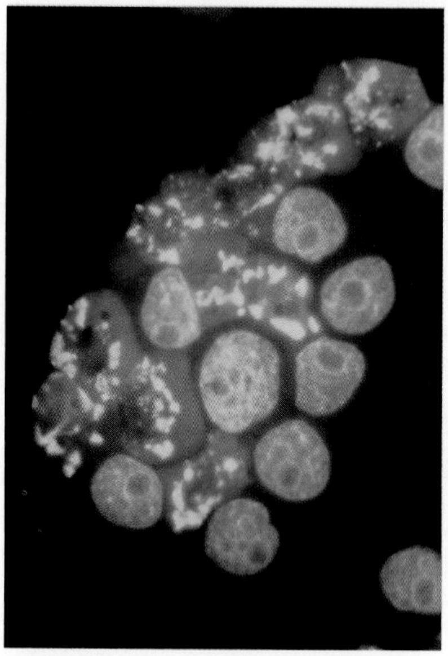

Figure 15.84 HL-60 cells treated with camptothecin for three hours. The DNA strand nicks characteristic of apoptosis were detected with the TUNEL (terminal deoxynucleotidyl transferase–mediated dUTP nick end-labeling) assay using the fluorescently labeled nucleotide, ChromaTide® BODIPY® FL-14-dUTP (C7614). Image contributed by Zbigniew Darzynkiewicz, Cancer Research Institute, New York Medical College.

The single-step BODIPY® FL dye–based assay has several advantages over indirect detection of biotinylated or haptenylated nucleotides, including fewer protocol steps and increased cell yields. BODIPY® FL dye–labeled nucleotides have also proven superior to fluorescein-labeled nucleotides for detection of DNA strand breaks in apoptotic cells because they provide stronger signals, a narrower emission spectrum and less photobleaching[73] (Figure 15.84). Moreover, it has been reported that ChromaTide® BODIPY® FL-14-dUTP incorporated into the granules of the condensed chromatin structure of late-apoptotic cells — cells characterized by extensive nuclear fragmentation — exhibits yellow fluorescence, whereas uncondensed areas of the nuclei or early-apoptotic cells exhibit green fluorescence. This spectral shift, which is characteristic of the BODIPY® fluorophores, is most likely a consequence of stacking of the BODIPY® FL fluorophores (Figure 13.6) and could be very useful for identifying the stages of apoptosis on a single-cell basis. Our ChromaTide® Texas Red®-12-dUTP (C7631) has been used similarly for a TdT-mediated apoptosis assay.[75] Presumably a number of the ChromaTide® dUTP nucleotides listed in Table 8.7 could be used for the direct or indirect TUNEL assay; we have not yet tried the ChromaTide® dCTP nucleotides in this assay. Furthermore, our anti-dye antibodies (Section 7.4) can amplify the signal of many of the dyes used to prepare the ChromaTide® nucleotides.

In situ DNA modifications by labeled nucleotides have been used to detect DNA fragmentation in what may be apoptotic cells in autopsy brains of Huntington's and Alzheimer's disease patients.[76–79] DNA fragmentation is also associated with amyotrophic lateral sclerosis.[80] Analogous to TdT's ability to label double-strand breaks, the *E. coli* repair enzyme DNA polymerase I can be used to detect single-strand nicks,[81,82] which appear as a relatively early step in some apoptotic processes.[83–85] Because our ChromaTide® BODIPY® FL-14-dUTP (C7614) and ChromaTide® fluorescein-12-dUTP[86,87] (C7604) are incorporated into DNA by *E. coli* DNA polymerase I, it is likely that they may also be effective for *in situ* labeling with the nick translation method.

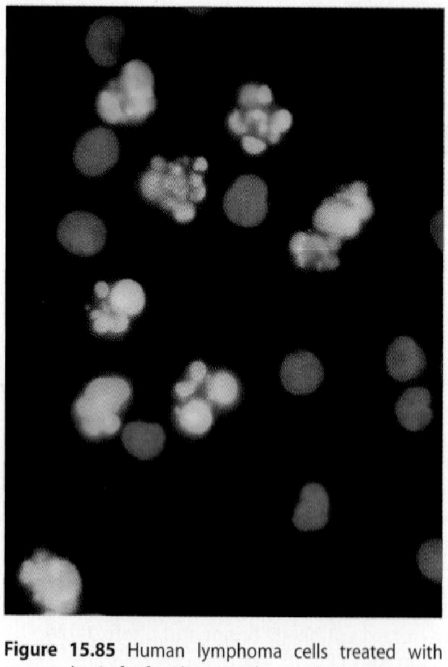

Figure 15.85 Human lymphoma cells treated with camptothecin for four hours and stained using the APO-BrdU TUNEL Assay Kit (A23210). Cells containing DNA strand nicks characteristic of apoptosis are detected by TUNEL and fluoresce green, while necrotic cells are stained with red-fluorescent propidium iodide.

APO-BrdU TUNEL Assay Kit

Because DNA fragmentation is one of the most reliable methods for detecting apoptosis,[83] we have collaborated with Phoenix Flow Systems to offer the APO-BrdU TUNEL Assay Kit (A23210), which provides all the materials necessary to label and detect the DNA strand breaks of apoptotic cells.[88] When DNA strands are cleaved or nicked by nucleases, a large number of 3′-hydroxyl ends are exposed. In the APO-BrdU assay, these ends are labeled with BrdUTP and terminal deoxynucleotidyl transferase (TdT) using the TUNEL technique described above. Once incorporated into the DNA, BrdU is detected using an Alexa Fluor® 488 dye–labeled anti-BrdU monoclonal antibody (Figure 15.85). This kit also provides propidium iodide for determining total cellular DNA content, as well as fixed control cells for assessing assay performance.

The APO-BrdU TUNEL Assay Kit includes complete protocols for use in flow cytometry applications, though it may also be adapted for use with fluorescence microscopy. Each kit contains:

- Terminal deoxynucleotidyl transferase (TdT), for catalyzing the addition of BrdUTP at the break sites
- 5-Bromo-2′-deoxyuridine 5′-triphosphate (BrdUTP)
- Alexa Fluor® 488 dye–labeled anti-BrdU mouse monoclonal antibody PRB-1, for detecting BrdU labels
- Propidium iodide/RNase staining buffer, for quantitating total cellular DNA
- Reaction, wash and rinse buffers
- Positive control cells (a fixed human lymphoma cell line)
- Negative control cells (a fixed human lymphoma cell line)
- Detailed protocols

Sufficient reagents are provided for approximately 60 assays of 1 mL samples, each containing 1–2 × 10^6 cells/mL.

Apoptosis Assays Using Annexin V Conjugates

Annexin V Conjugates

Molecular Probes is collaborating with Nexins Research BV — the original developer of fluorescent phosphatidylserine-binding proteins — to provide what we feel are the best and brightest annexin V conjugates available. The human vascular anticoagulant annexin V is a 35–36 kilodalton, Ca^{2+}-dependent phospholipid-binding protein that has a high affinity for phosphatidylserine[89–91] (PS). In normal viable cells, PS is located on the cytoplasmic surface of the cell membrane. However, in apoptotic cells, PS is translocated from the inner to the outer leaflet of the plasma membrane, exposing PS to the external cellular environment where it can be detected by annexin V conjugates.[92] In leukocyte apoptosis, PS on the outer surface of the cell marks the cell for recognition and phagocytosis by macrophages.[93,94]

Highly fluorescent annexin V conjugates provide quick and reliable detection methods for studying the externalization of phosphatidylserine,[12–14,95,96] an indicator of intermediate stages of apoptosis. Nuclear fragmentation, mitochondrial membrane potential flux and caspase-3 activation apparently precede phosphatidylserine "flipping" during apoptosis, whereas permeability to propidium iodide and cytoskeletal collapse occur later. The difference in fluorescence intensity between apoptotic and nonapoptotic cells stained by our fluorescent annexin V conjugates, as measured by flow cytometry, is typically about 100-fold (Figure 15.86). Annexin V conjugates are very useful for flow cytometry, confocal or epifluorescence microscopy and, like antibody staining, can be used in combination with other dyes, including nucleic acid stains, to accurately assess mixed populations of apoptotic and nonapoptotic cells.[97] Our annexin V conjugates are available as stand-alone reagents, each suitable for 50–100 flow cytometry assays or many more imaging assays, or in several variations of our Vybrant® Apoptosis Assay Kits (Table 15.4). Our annexin V conjugates include:

- Alexa Fluor® 488 annexin V[98] (A13201, Figure 15.87), a green-fluorescent conjugate (excitation/emission maxima ~495/519 nm) that has spectral characteristics similar to fluorescein conjugates, but exhibits fluorescence that is brighter, much more photostable and less pH dependent (Figure 1.9, Figure 1.10, Figure 1.11, Figure 1.53). Alexa Fluor® 488 annexin V is used in both our Vybrant® Apoptosis Assays Kits #1 and #2 (V13240, V13241; see below), which contain all of the reagents and an easy-to-follow protocol for flow cytometric detection and quantitation of apoptotic cells.
- Fluorescein (FITC) annexin V (A13199), a green-fluorescent conjugate that has been extensively used by a number of laboratories to detect apoptotic cells populations.[13,14,23,95,97] Fluorescein annexin V is frequently used in combination with propidium iodide to detect necrotic cells, as in our Vybrant® Apoptosis Assay Kit #3 (V13242, see below).
- Oregon Green® 488 annexin V (A13200), a green-fluorescent conjugate that is spectrally similar to the fluorescein annexin V conjugate but is brighter and more photostable (Figure 1.46).
- R-phycoerythrin annexin V (A35111), a highly fluorescent phycobiliprotein conjugate with absorption maxima at 496 nm, 546 nm and 565 nm and an emission maximum at 578 nm.
- Alexa Fluor® 568 annexin V (A13202), a red-orange–fluorescent annexin V conjugate (excitation/emission maxima ~578/603 nm) with exceptionally bright and photostable fluorescence. We have determined that this conjugate can be used for simultaneous staining with green-fluorescent probes, such as our green-fluorescent Alexa Fluor® 488 anti–CD 4 conjugate (A21335, Section 7.5), for multiparameter experiments.
- Alexa Fluor® 594 annexin V[99,100] (A13203), a red-fluorescent annexin V conjugate with spectra similar to those of Texas Red® conjugates (excitation/emission maxima ~590/617 nm) that can be used with green-fluorescent probes for multiparameter experiments. The Alexa Fluor® 594 conjugate is readily excited by the 568 nm spectral line used in many confocal laser-scanning microscopes and has fluorescence that is well separated from the emission of green-fluorescent probes.
- Alexa Fluor® 647 annexin V (A23204), which permits use of long-wavelength excitation sources for detection of apoptotic cells by either flow cytometry or microscopy.
- Allophycocyanin annexin V (A35110), a highly fluorescent phycobiliprotein conjugate with absorption/emission maxima of 650/660 nm.
- Alexa Fluor® 350 annexin V (A23202) can be excited in the ultraviolet and has bright blue fluorescence. Alternatively, the reagents in our Vybrant® Apoptosis Assay Kit #6 (V23200) can be used in this spectral region.
- Biotin-X annexin V[101,102] (A13204), which can be detected by any of our fluorescent avidin or streptavidin conjugates (Section 7.6, Table 7.22), gives the researcher the ultimate in color se-

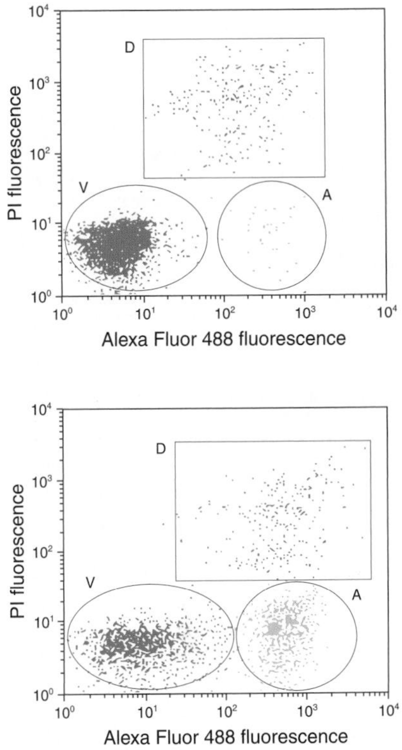

Figure 15.86 Flow cytometric analysis of Jurkat cells using the Vybrant® Apoptosis Assay Kit #2 (V13241). Jurkat human T-cell leukemia cells were first exposed to 10 µM camptothecin for four hours (bottom panel) or left untreated (as control, top panel). Cells were then treated with the reagents in the Vybrant® Apoptosis Assay Kit #2 and analyzed by flow cytometry. Note that the camptothecin-treated cells (bottom panel) have a significantly higher percentage of apoptotic cells (indicated by an "A") than the basal level of apoptosis seen in the control cells (top panel). V = viable cells, D = dead cells.

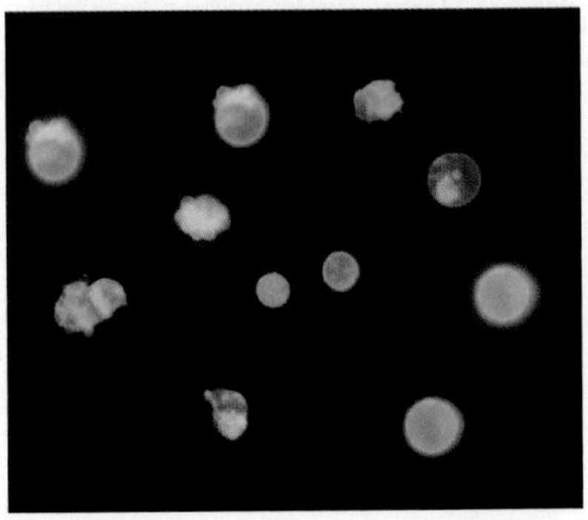

Figure 15.87 Jurkat human T-cell leukemia cells treated with 1 µM camptothecin. The externalized phosphatidylserine, a characteristic of early-stage apoptotic cells, was detected with Alexa Fluor® 488 annexin V (A13201). The late-stage apoptotic and necrotic cells were stained with propidium iodide (P1304MP, P3566, P21493). The image was acquired using bandpass filters appropriate for fluorescein.

lection for multiparameter experiments. Biotin-X annexin V also permits detection of apoptotic cells by electron microscopy[103] and should permit separation of apoptotic cells with our Captivate™ ferrofluid streptavidin conjugate (C21476, Section 7.6), optionally in combination with the Captivate™ microscope-mounted magnetic yoke assembly (C24700, Section 23.3, Figure 23.56).

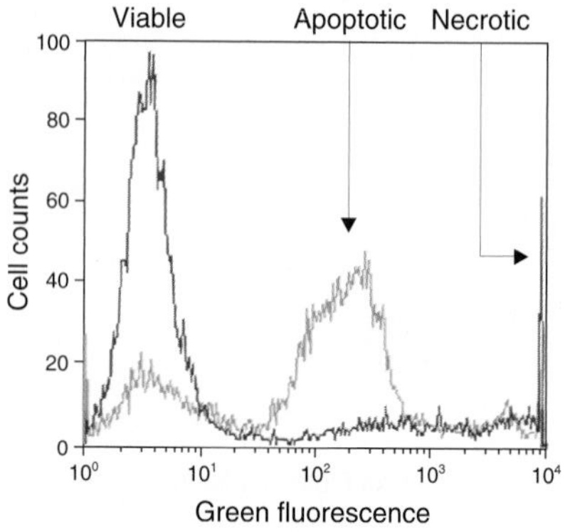

Figure 15.88 Flow cytometric analysis of Jurkat cells using the Vybrant® Apoptosis Assay Kit #1 (V13240). Jurkat human T-cell leukemia cells were first exposed to 10 µM camptothecin for four hours (green line) or left untreated (as control, blue line). Cells were then treated with the reagents in the Vybrant® Apoptosis Assay Kit #1 and analyzed by flow cytometry. Note that the camptothecin-treated cells (green line) have a significantly higher percentage of apoptotic cells (intermediate green fluorescence) than the basal level of apoptosis seen in the control cells (blue line).

Vybrant® Apoptosis Assay Kit #1

With the Vybrant® Apoptosis Assay Kit #1 (V13240), apoptotic cells are detected based on the externalization of phosphatidylserine. This kit contains recombinant annexin V conjugated to the Alexa Fluor® 488 dye, our brightest and most photostable green fluorophore, to provide maximum sensitivity. In addition, the kit includes a ready-to-use solution of the SYTOX® Green nucleic acid stain. The SYTOX® Green dye is impermeant to live cells and apoptotic cells but stains necrotic cells with intense green fluorescence by binding to cellular nucleic acids. After staining a cell population with Alexa Fluor® 488 annexin V and SYTOX® Green dye in the provided binding buffer, apoptotic cells show green fluorescence, dead cells show a higher level of green fluorescence and live cells show little or no fluorescence (Figure 15.88). These populations can easily be distinguished using a flow cytometer with the 488 nm spectral line of an argon-ion laser for excitation. Both Alexa Fluor® 488 annexin and the SYTOX® Green dye emit a green fluorescence that can be detected in the green channel, freeing the other channels for the detection of additional probes in multicolor labeling experiments. We have optimized the Vybrant® Apoptosis Assay Kits using Jurkat cells, a human T-cell leukemia clone, treated with camptothecin to induce apoptosis. Some modifications may be required for use with other cell types. The kit components, number of assays and assay principles are summarized in Table 15.4.

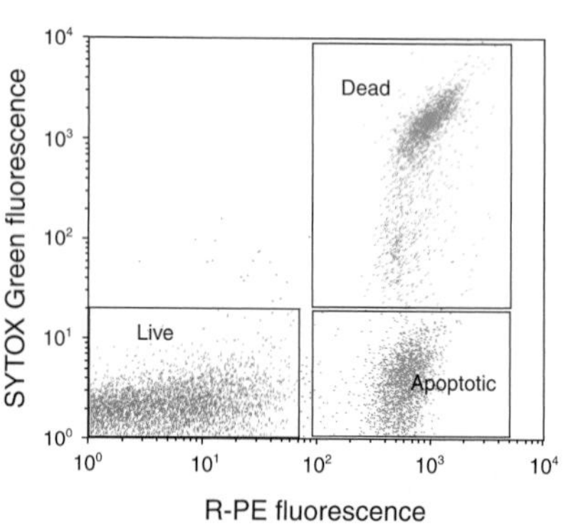

Figure 15.89 Flow cytometric analysis of Jurkat cells using the Vybrant® Apoptosis Assay Kit #8 (V35112). Jurkat human T-cell leukemia cells were first exposed to either 10 µM camptothecin or 2 mM hydrogen peroxide for 4 hours at 37°C, 5% CO_2. The cells were then combined, treated with the reagents in the Vybrant® Apoptosis Assay Kit #8 and analyzed by flow cytometry. The SYTOX® Green fluorescence versus R-phycoerythrin (R-PE) annexin fluorescence dot plot shows resolution of live, apoptotic and dead cell populations.

Vybrant® Apoptosis Assay Kit #2

Like the Vybrant® Apoptosis Kit #1, our Vybrant® Apoptosis Assay Kit #2 (V13241) detects the externalization of phosphatidylserine in apoptotic cells[88] (Table 15.4). The Vybrant® Apoptosis Assay Kit #2 provides a sensitive two-color assay that employs our green-fluorescent Alexa Fluor® 488 annexin and a ready-to-use solution of the red-fluorescent propidium iodide nucleic acid stain. Propidium iodide is impermeant to live cells and apoptotic cells but stains necrotic cells with red fluorescence, binding tightly to the nucleic acids in the cell. After staining a cell population with Alexa Fluor® 488 annexin V and propidium iodide in the provided binding buffer, apoptotic cells show green fluorescence, dead cells show red and green fluorescence and live cells show little or no fluorescence (Figure 15.86). These populations can easily be distinguished using a flow cytometer with the 488 nm spectral line of an argon-ion laser for excitation. We have optimized this assay using Jurkat cells, a human T-cell leukemia clone, treated with camptothecin to induce apoptosis. Some modifications may be required for use with other cell types. The Vybrant® Apoptosis Assay Kit #2 is designed for use with either flow cytometers or fluorescence microscopes. The kit components, number of assays and assay principles are summarized in Table 15.4.

Vybrant® Apoptosis Assay Kit #3

The Vybrant® Apoptosis Assay Kit #3 (V13242) is very similar to the Vybrant® Apoptosis Assay Kit #2, except that it contains fluorescein (FITC) annexin V in place of the Alexa Fluor® 488 conjugate found in Kit #2 (Table 15.4). The kit components, number of assays and assay principles are summarized in Table 15.4.

Vybrant® Apoptosis Assay Kit #6

The Vybrant® Apoptosis Assay Kit #6 (V23200) is very similar to the Vybrant® Apoptosis Assay Kit #2, except that it contains biotin-X annexin V and Alexa Fluor® 350 streptavidin in place of the Alexa Fluor® 488 conjugate found in Kit #2 (Table 15.4). After staining a cell population with biotin-X annexin V in the provided binding buffer, Alexa Fluor® 350 streptavidin is added to fluorescently label the bound annexin V. Finally, propidium iodide is added to detect necrotic cells. Apoptotic cells show blue fluorescence, dead cells show red and blue fluorescence and live cells show little or no fluorescence. These populations can easily be distinguished using a flow cytometer with UV excitation for the Alexa Fluor® 350 fluorophore and 488 nm excitation for the propidium iodide. With the Vybrant® Apoptosis Assay Kit #6, fluorescence in the green channel is minimal. In the same experiment for apoptosis detection, the researcher can apply a green-fluorescent probe, for example an antibody labeled with the Alexa Fluor® 488 dye or with fluorescein. The kit components, number of assays and assay principles are summarized in Table 15.4.

Vybrant® Apoptosis Assay Kits #8 and #9

The Vybrant® Apoptosis Assay Kits #8 and #9 (V35112, V35113) are very similar to the Vybrant® Apoptosis Assay Kit #1, except that they contain either R-phycoerythrin (R-PE) annexin V (Vybrant® Kit #8) or allophycocyanin annexin V (Vybrant® Kit #9) instead of Alexa Fluor® 488 annexin V. R-PE is an extremely fluorescent phycobiliprotein that can easily be excited with the 488 nm spectral line of the argon-ion laser on a standard flow cytometer and exhibits an emission maximum at 578 nm. Also intensely fluorescent, allophycocyanin can be efficiently excited with the 633 nm spectral line of the He–Ne laser on a standard flow cytometer and exhibits an emission maximum at 660 nm. In addition to the phycobiliprotein-conjugated annexin V, these kits include the SYTOX® Green nucleic acid stain, which is impermeant to live cells and apoptotic cells but stains necrotic cells with intense green fluorescence. After staining a cell population with R-PE annexin V and SYTOX® Green stain, apoptotic cells show orange fluorescence with very little green fluorescence, late apoptotic cells show a higher level of green and orange fluorescence and live cells show little or no fluorescence (Figure 15.89); these populations can easily be distinguished using a flow cytometer with the 488 nm spectral line of an argon-ion laser for excitation. After staining a cell population with allophycocyanin annexin V and the SYTOX® Green stain, apoptotic cells show far-red fluorescence with very little green fluorescence, late apoptotic cells show a higher level of green and far-red fluorescence and live cells show little or no fluorescence (Figure 15.90); these populations can easily be distinguished using a flow cytometer with both the 488 nm spectral line of an argon-ion laser and the 633 nm spectral line of a He–Ne laser for excitation. The kit components, number of assays and assay principles are summarized in Table 15.4.

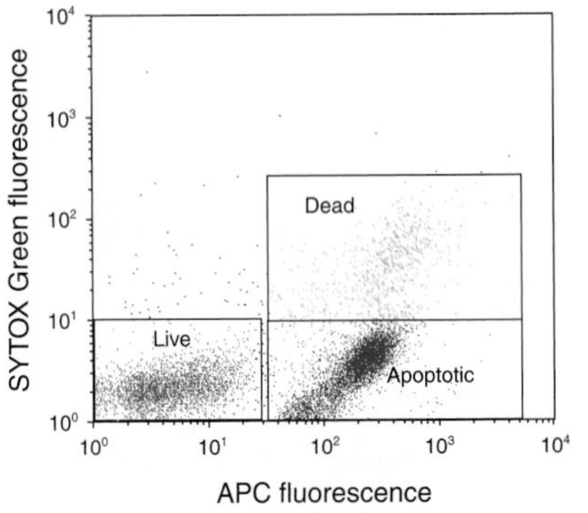

Figure 15.90 Flow cytometric analysis of Jurkat cells using the Vybrant® Apoptosis Assay Kit #9 (V35113). Jurkat human T-cell leukemia cells were first exposed to 10 µM camptothecin at 37°C, 5% CO_2. The cells were then treated with the reagents in the Vybrant® Apoptosis Assay Kit #9 and analyzed by flow cytometry. The SYTOX® Green fluorescence versus allophycocyanin (APC) annexin fluorescence dot plot shows resolution of live, apoptotic and dead cell populations.

Vybrant® Apoptosis Assay Kit #10

The Vybrant® Apoptosis Assay Kit #10 (V35114 is an enhanced version of the Vybrant® Apoptosis Assay Kit #9 because it also contains C_{12}-resazurin. Nonfluorescent C_{12}-resazurin is reduced by viable cells to orange-fluorescent C_{12}-resorufin. Resazurin (also called alamarBlue) has been used extensively to detect the metabolic activity of many different cell types, from bacteria to higher eukaryotes.[104–106] After staining a cell population with allophycocyanin annexin V, C_{12}-resazurin and the SYTOX® Green stain, apoptotic cells show far-red fluorescence, intermediate orange fluorescence and no green fluorescence; late apoptotic cells show intense far-red and green fluorescence and little orange fluorescence; live cells show little or no green or far-red fluorescence but significant orange fluorescence (Figure 15.91). These populations can easily be distinguished using a flow cytometer with both the 488 nm spectral line of an argon-ion laser and the 633 nm spectral line of a He–Ne laser for excitation. The kit components, number of assays and assay principles are summarized in Table 15.4.

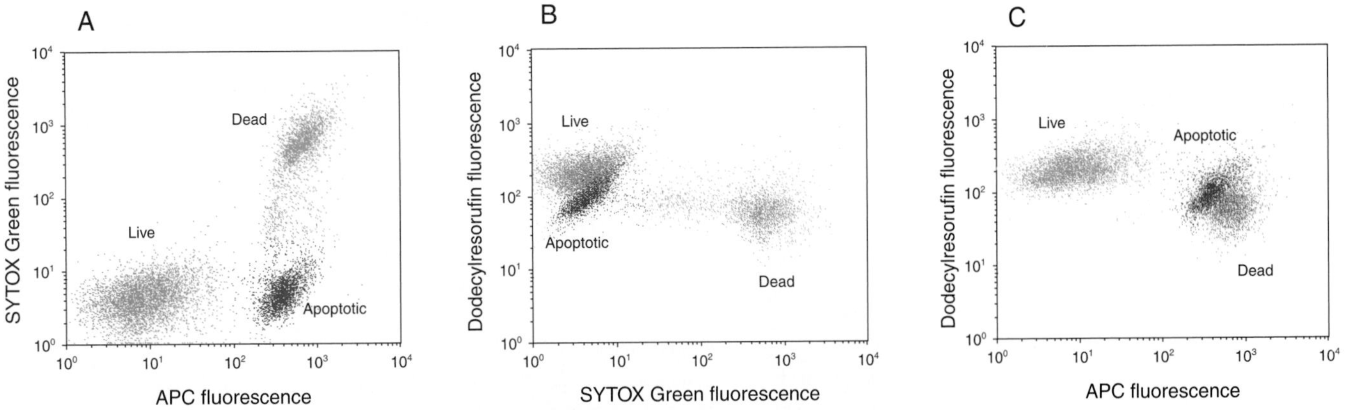

Figure 15.91 Flow cytometric analysis of Jurkat cells using the Vybrant® Apoptosis Assay Kit #10 (V35114). Jurkat human T-cell leukemia cells were first exposed to either 10 µM camptothecin or 2 mM hydrogen peroxide for 4 hours at 37°C, 5% CO_2. The cells were then combined, treated with the reagents in the Vybrant® Apoptosis Assay Kit #10 and analyzed by flow cytometry. The SYTOX® Green fluorescence versus allophycocyanin (APC) annexin fluorescence dot plot (A) shows resolution of live, apoptotic and dead cell populations. The cell populations can be evaluated for metabolic activity using the dodecylresorufin fluorescence versus SYTOX® Green fluorescence and dodecylresorufin fluorescence versus allophycocyanin fluorescence dot plots (B and C).

Vybrant® Apoptosis Assay Kit #11

The Vybrant® Apoptosis Assay Kit #11 (V35116) provides a rapid and convenient assay for two hallmarks of apoptosis — phosphatidylserine externalization and changes in mitochondrial membrane potential. Recombinant annexin V conjugated to the Alexa Fluor® 488 dye, our brightest and most photostable green fluorophore, provides maximum sensitivity for detecting phosphatidylserine externalization in apoptotic cells. Live cells are labeled with MitoTracker® Red CMXRos, which exhibits bright red fluorescence in the presence of a mitochondrial transmembrane potential. After staining a cell population with Alexa Fluor® 488 annexin V and MitoTracker® Red CMXRos dye in the provided binding buffer, live cells exhibit very little green fluorescence and bright red fluorescence, whereas apoptotic cells exhibit bright green fluorescence and decreased red fluorescence (Figure 15.92). These populations can easily be distinguished using a flow cytometer, and the 488 nm line of an argon-ion laser can be used to excite both dyes. The kit components, number of assays and assay principles are summarized in Table 15.4.

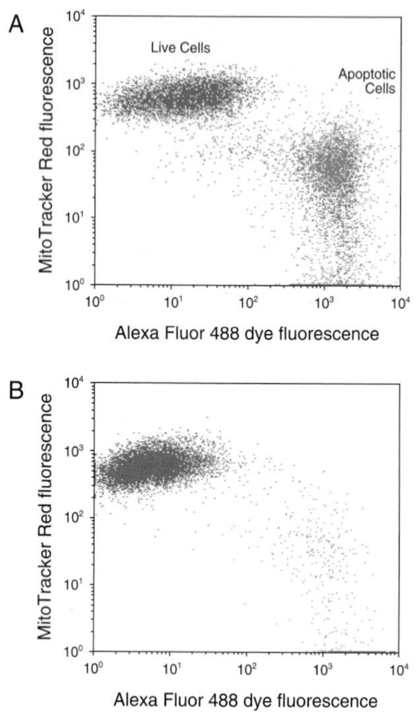

Figure 15.92 Flow cytometric analysis of Jurkat cells using the Vybrant® Apoptosis Assay Kit #11 (V35116). Jurkat human T-cell leukemia cells in complete medium were first exposed to 10 µM camptothecin for 4 hours (A) or left untreated (B). Both cell populations were then treated with the reagents in the Vybrant® Apoptosis Assay Kit #11 and analyzed by flow cytometry. Note that the apoptotic cells show higher reactivity for annexin V and lower MitoTracker® Red dye fluorescence than do live cells.

Apoptosis Assays Based on Protease Activity

Caspases

A distinctive feature of the early stages of apoptosis is the activation of caspase enzymes, the name applied to *c*ysteine–*asp*artic acid specific prote*ases*. Caspases are a key component of the apoptotic machinery of cells, participating in an enzyme cascade that results in cellular disassembly.[107] The recognition site for caspases is marked by three to four amino acids followed by an aspartic acid residue, with the cleavage occurring after the aspartate.[108] These proteases are typically synthesized as inactive precursors. Inhibitor release or cofactor binding activates the caspase through cleavage at internal aspartates through autocatalysis or by the action of another protease.[109]

Caspase-3 Substrates

Caspase-3 is a key effector in the apoptosis pathway, amplifying the signal from initiator caspases (such as caspase-8) and signifying full commitment to cellular disassembly. In addition to cleaving other caspases in the enzyme cascade, caspase-3 has been shown to cleave poly(ADP-ribose) polymerase (PARP), DNA-dependent protein kinase, protein kinase Cδ and actin.[110,111] Molecular Probes offers a selection of fluorogenic caspase substrates (Table 15.5), including Z-DEVD-AFC[112,113] (A22121), which contains containing the caspase-3 recognition site Asp-Glu-Val-Asp (DEVD) and undergoes an ~65 nm red-shift to exhibit a peak emission of ~500 nm upon cleavage. In addition, the bis-L-aspartic acid amide of R110 (D_2-R110, R22122), which contains rhodamine 110 (R110) flanked by aspartic acid residues, may serve as a substrate for a

Table 15.5 — Fluorogenic substrates for caspase activity

Peptide Sequence	Target for Caspases *	Fluorophore †		
		R110	AMC	AFC
YVAD	1, 4	R33750		
VDVAD	2	R33755		
DEVD	3, 6, 7, 8, 10	E13184 ‡ R22120 § R35100 **	E13183 ‡	A22121
VEID	6	R33754		
IETD	8, granzyme B	R22125 R22126 §	A22127	A22128
LEHD	9, 4, 5	R33751		
LEED	13	R33753		
AAD	granzyme B	R33752		
Aspartic acid	generic	R22122		

* Caspase substrates can often be cleaved by multiple enzymes. The caspase most often associated with the given peptide sequence is listed first. † R110 = rhodamine 110; AMC = 7-amino-4-methylcoumarin; AFC = 7-amino-4-trifluoromethylcoumarin. The absorption and emission maxima for the cleaved fluorophores at pH 7 are: 496/520 nm for R110, 342/441 nm for AMC and 380/500 nm for AFC. ‡ EnzChek® Caspase-3 Assay Kit. § Bulk packaging. ** RediPlate™ 96 EnzChek® Caspase-3 Assay Kit.

variety of apoptosis-related proteases, including caspase-3 and caspase-7 and does not appear to require any invasive techniques such as osmotic shock to gain entrance into the cytoplasm (Figure 15.93). It may serve as a substrate for a variety of apoptosis-related proteases, including caspase-3 and caspase-7.[114]

Caspase-8 Substrates

Caspase-8 plays a critical role in the early cascade of apoptosis, acting as an initiator of the caspase activation cascade. Activation of the enzyme itself is accomplished through direct interaction with the death domains of cell-surface receptors for apoptosis-inducing ligands.[115,116] The activated protease has been shown to be involved in a pathway that mediates the release of cytochrome *c* from the mitochondria[117] and is also known to activate downstream caspases, such as caspase-3.[118] Three fluorogenic substrates containing the caspase-8 recognition sequence Ile-Glu-Thr-Asp (IETD) are available (Table 15.5); Z-IETD-AMC and Z-IETD-AFC (A22127, A22128; blue fluorescent after cleavage) and Z-IETD-R110 (R22125, R22126; green fluorescent after cleavage).

Other Caspase and Granzyme B Substrates

In addition to our R110-derived caspase-3 and -8 substrates, we offer R110-based substrates for caspase-1, -2, -6, -9 and -13, as well as substrates for granzyme B (Table 15.5). Granzyme B, a serine protease contained within cytotoxic T lymphocytes and natural killer cells, is thought to induce apoptosis in target cells by activating caspases and causing mitochondrial cytochrome *c* release.[119]

EnzChek® Caspase-3 Assay Kits

The EnzChek® Caspase-3 Assay Kits #1 and #2 provide a simple and direct assay of caspase-3 (Figure 15.94) and other DEVD-specific protease activities (e.g., caspase-7). Each kit contains:

- Z-DEVD-AMC[120,121] (in Kit E13183) or Z-DEVD-R110[114,122,123] (in Kit E13184)
- Dimethylsulfoxide (DMSO)
- Concentrated cell-lysis buffer
- Concentrated reaction buffer
- Dithiothreitol (DTT)
- Ac-DEVD-CHO, a reversible aldehyde-based inhibitor
- 7-Amino-4-methylcoumarin (AMC) (in Kit E13183) or rhodamine 110 (in Kit E13184) reference standard to quantitate the amount of fluorophore released in the reaction
- Detailed protocols

Our EnzChek® Caspase-3 Assay Kit #1 (E13183) contains the 7-amino-4-methylcoumarin (AMC)–derived substrate Z-DEVD-AMC (Figure 15.95) (where Z represents a benzyloxycarbonyl group). This substrate, which is weakly fluorescent in the UV spectral range (excitation/emission maxima ~330/390 nm), yields the blue–fluorescent product AMC (A191, Section 10.1, Figure 10.4), which has excitation/emission maxima of 342/441 nm upon proteolytic cleavage.

The EnzChek® Caspase-3 Assay Kit #2 (E13184) contains the R110-derived substrate, Z-DEVD-R110[114,123] (Figure 15.96). This substrate is a bisamide derivative of R110, containing DEVD peptides covalently linked to each of R110's amino groups, thereby suppressing both the dye's visible absorption and fluorescence. Upon enzymatic cleavage by caspase-3 (or a closely related protease), the nonfluorescent bisamide substrate is converted in a two-step process first to the fluorescent monoamide and then to the even more fluorescent R110 (R6479, Section 10.1, Figure

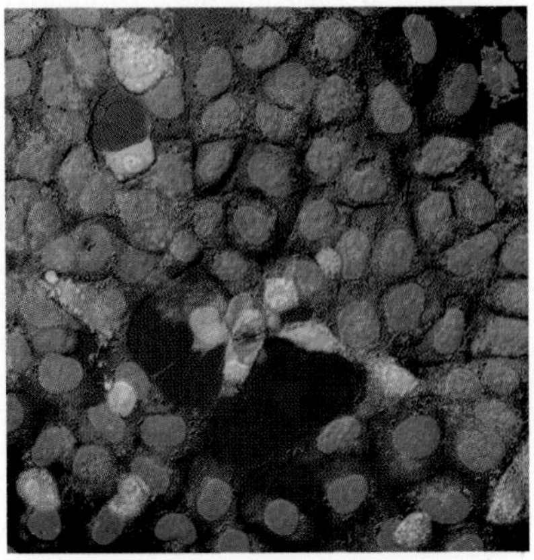

Figure 15.93 Detection of apoptosis in SK-N-MC neuroblastoma cells. Following a six-hour exposure to hydrogen peroxide, cells were labeled with Hoechst 33342 (H1399, H3570, H21492), tetramethylrhodamine ethyl ester (TMRE, T669) and rhodamine 110, bis-L-aspartic acid amide (R22122) for 15 minutes. Apoptotic cells show green cytosolic fluorescence resulting from cleavage of the rhodamine 110, bis-L-aspartic acid amide substrate by active caspase-3. The staining pattern of the Hoechst 33342 dye reveals that the majority of the rhodamine 110–positive cells also contain condensed or fragmented nuclei characteristic of apoptosis. Furthermore, the rhodamine 110–positive cells are also characterized by an absence of polarized mitochondria, as indicated by their failure to load the positively charged mitochondrial indicator TMRE. The image was contributed by A.K. Stout and J.T. Greenamyre, Emory University.

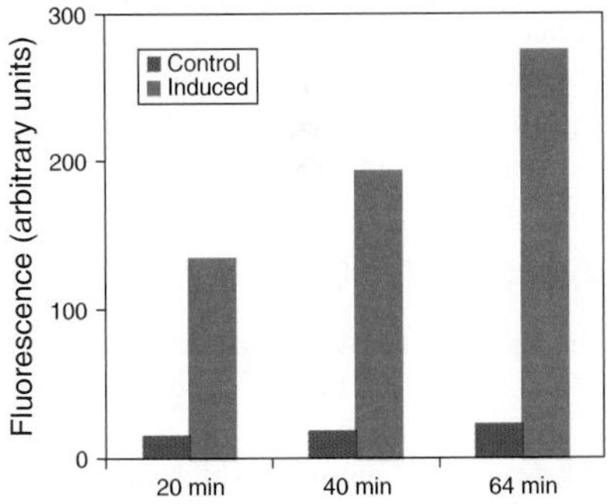

Figure 15.94 Detection of protease activity in Jurkat cells using the EnzChek® Caspase-3 Assay Kit #1 with Z-DEVD-AMC substrate (E13183). Cells were either treated with 10 µM camptothecin for four hours at 37°C to induce apoptosis (induced) or left untreated (control). Both induced and control cells were then harvested, lysed and assayed. Reactions were carried out at room temperature, and fluorescence was measured in a fluorescence microplate reader using excitation at 360 ± 20 nm with emission detection at 460 ± 20 nm after the indicated amount of time.

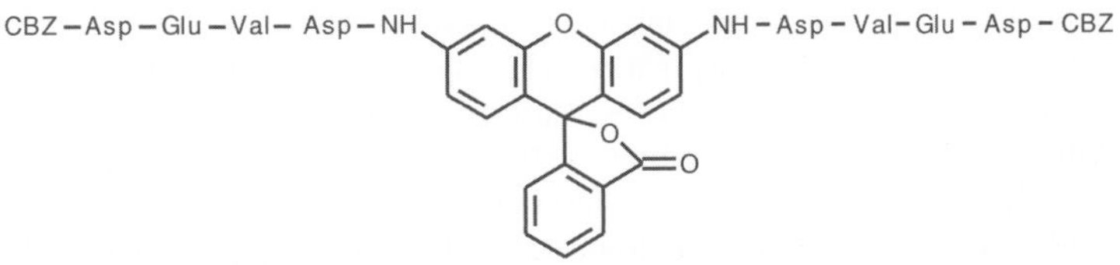

Figure 15.96 E13184 EnzChek® Caspase-3 Assay Kit #2.

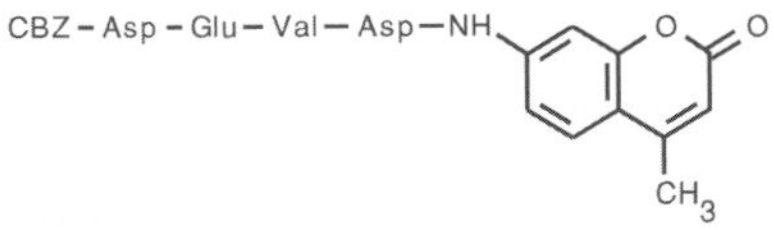

Figure 15.95 E13183 EnzChek® Caspase-3 Assay Kit #1.

10.5, Figure 10.52). Both of these hydrolysis products exhibit spectral properties similar to those of fluorescein, with excitation/emission maxima of 496/520 nm. The Z-DEVD-R110 substrate (R22120) is also available separately in a 20 mg unit size for high-throughput screening applications.

Either kit can be used to continuously measure the activity of caspase-3 and closely related proteases in cell extracts and purified enzyme preparations using a fluorescence microplate reader or fluorometer. The reversible aldehyde-based inhibitor Ac-DEVD-CHO can be used to confirm that the observed fluorescence signal in both induced and control cell populations is due to the activity of caspase-3–like proteases.[111] Each kit contains sufficient reagents for about 500 assays using 100 µL volumes.

Our EnzChek® Caspase-3 Assay Kit #2 is also available as a convenient RediPlate™ 96 EnzChek® Caspase-3 Assay Kit (R35100), which includes one 96-well microplate, contained in a resealable foil packet to ensure the integrity of the fluorogenic components, plus all necessary buffers and reagents for performing the assay (Figure 10.54). In this kit, the reversible aldehyde-based inhibitor Ac-DEVD-CHO is supplied in a separate vial for confirming the activity of caspase-3–like proteases.[111] The enzyme sample to be assayed is added to the microplate in a suitable buffer, along with any compounds to be tested. Then, after incubation, the resultant fluorescence is quantitated on a fluorescence microplate reader equipped with filters appropriate for the green-fluorescent R110, with excitation/emission maxima of 496/520 nm. The microplate consists of twelve removable strips, each with eight wells, allowing researchers to perform only as many assay as required for the experiment (Figure 8.60). Eleven of the strips (88 wells) are preloaded with the Z-DEVD-R110 substrate. The remaining strip, marked with blackened tabs, contains a dilution series of free R110 that may be used as a fluorescence reference standard. Table 10.3 summarizes our other RediPlate™ 96 and RediPlate™ 384 Assay Kits for protease activity (Section 10.4), phosphatase activity (Section 10.3) and dsDNA quantitation (Section 8.3). Significant discounts apply to purchases of multiple units of all of our RediPlate™ products.

Vybrant® FAM Caspase Assay Kits

The Vybrant® FAM Caspase Assay Kits employ a novel approach for caspase detection that is based on a fluorescent caspase inhibitor (FLICA methodology). The FLICA inhibitor comprises a fluoromethyl ketone (FMK) moiety, which can react covalently with a cysteine, a caspase-selective amino acid sequence and a fluorescent carboxyfluorescein (FAM) reporter group. Essentially an affinity label, the FLICA inhibitor is thought to interact with the enzymatic reactive center of an activated caspase via the recognition sequence, and then to attach covalently to a cysteine through the reactive FMK moiety.[124] Importantly, the FLICA inhibitor is cell permeant and not cytotoxic; unbound FLICA molecules diffuse out of the cell and are washed away. The remaining green-fluorescent signal (excitation/emission maxima ~488/530 nm) can be used as a direct measure of the amount of active caspase that was present at the time the inhibitor was added. FLICA reagents have been used widely to study apoptosis with flow cytometry and microscopy.[125–129] Recent work indicates that cellular fluorescence from the bound FLICA reagent is strongly linked to caspase activity in apoptotic cells; however, the interaction of the FLICA reagent with other cellular sites may contribute to signal intensity in nonapoptotic cells.[130] Appropriate controls should be included in any experimental design.

We offer three different Vybrant® FAM Caspase Assay Kits designed to target different caspases. The Vybrant® FAM Caspase-3 and -7 Assay Kit (V35118) provides a FLICA inhibitor containing the caspase-3 and -7 recognition sequence DEVD; the Vybrant® FAM Caspase-8 Assay Kit (V35119) provides a FLICA inhibitor containing the caspase-8 recognition sequence Leu-Glu-Thr-Asp (LETD); and the Vybrant® FAM Poly Caspases Assay Kit (V35117) provides a FLICA inhibitor containing the caspase recognition sequence Val-Ala-Asp (VAD), which is recognized by caspase-1, -3, -4, -5, -6, -7, -8 and -9. In addition to the selective FLICA reagent, these kits contain the Hoechst 33342 and propidium iodide nucleic acid stains to permit simultaneous evaluation of caspase activation, membrane permeability and cell cycle. Each Vybrant® FAM Caspase Assay Kit includes:

- FAM-DEVD-FMK caspase-3 and -7 reagent (in Kit V35118), FAM-LETD-FMK caspase-8 reagent (in Kit V35119) or FAM-VAD-FMK poly caspases reagent (in Kit V35117)
- Hoechst 33342
- Propidium iodide
- Dimethylsulfoxide (DMSO)
- Apoptosis fixative solution
- Concentrated apoptosis wash buffer
- Detailed protocols for flow cytometry assays

Sufficient reagents are provided for 25 assays, based on labeling volumes of 300 µL. These Vybrant® FAM Caspase Assay Kits can be used in combination with other fluorescent probes, such as the far-red–fluorescent allophycocyanin annexin V (A35110), for a multiparameter study of apoptosis.

Cathepsins and Calpains

The role of intracellular cathepsins and calpains in apoptosis is unclear, although an upstream role of cathepsin B in activation of some caspases[131,132] and cathepsins during apoptosis has been established.[133] Pepstatin A, which is a selective inhibitor of carboxyl (acid) proteases such as cathepsin D, has been reported to inhibit apoptosis in microglia, lymphoid cells and HeLa cells.[134–136] Consequently, our cell-permeant BODIPY® FL pepstatin derivative (P12271), which we have shown to inhibit cathepsin D *in vitro* (IC_{50} ~10 nM) and to target cathepsin D within lysosomes of live and fixed cells, may be of some utility in following the translocation of cathepsin D that may occur during apoptotic events.[137,138]

Calpains are a family of ubiquitous calcium-activated thiol proteases that are implicated in a variety of cellular functions including exocytosis, cell fusion, apoptosis and cell proliferation.[136,139] Caspase-dependent downstream processing of calpain has been reported, suggesting that calpain may play a role in the degradation phase of apoptosis that is distinct from that of caspases.[140–142] One mechanism of caspase dependence appears to be processing of the endogenous calpain inhibitor calpastin by caspases.[143] However, calpain activation has also been reported to be upstream of caspases in radiation-induced apoptosis.[144] Our *t*-BOC-Leu-Met-CMAC fluorogenic substrate (A6520) has been used to measure calpain activity in hepatocytes following the addition of extracellular ATP[145] and may be of utility in detecting caspase-activated processing of procalpain in live single cells. Peptidase substrates based on our CMAC fluorophore (7-amino-4-chloromethylcoumarin, C2110; Section 10.1) passively diffuse into several types of cells, where the thiol-reactive chloromethyl group is enzymatically conjugated to glutathione by intracellular glutathione *S*-transferase or reacts with protein thiols, thus transforming the substrate into a membrane-impermeant probe. Subsequent peptidase cleavage results in a bright blue-fluorescent glutathione conjugate (Section 10.4).

Apoptosis Assays Using Mitochondrial Stains

A distinctive feature of the early stages of programmed cell death is the disruption of active mitochondria.[146–148] This mitochondrial disruption includes changes in the membrane potential and alterations to the oxidation–reduction potential of the mitochondria. Changes in the membrane potential are presumed to be due to the opening of the mitochondrial permeability transition pore, allowing passage of ions and small molecules. The resulting equilibration of ions leads in turn to the decoupling of the respiratory chain and then the release of cytochrome *c* into the cytosol.[149,150]

Mitochondrial Stains for Detecting Apoptosis

Molecular Probes has available several unique reagents for studying changes in the mitochondria during apoptosis.

- The green-fluorescent dye JC-1 [151–154] (5,5′,6,6′-tetrachloro-1,1′,3,3′-tetraethylbenzimidazolylcarbocyanine iodide, T3168; Figure 22.13) exists as a monomer at low concentrations or at low membrane potential. However, at higher concentrations — aqueous solutions above 0.1 µM — or at higher membrane potentials, JC-1 forms red-fluorescent "J-aggregates" (Figure 12.19, Figure 12.20, Figure 22.14) that exhibit a broad excitation spectrum and an emission maximum at ~590 nm (Figure 22.15). Thus, the emission of this cyanine dye has been widely used to follow the changes in mitochondrial membrane potential that occur as a result of apoptosis [155–157] (MitoProbe™ JC-1 Assay Kit, M34152; see below). JC-1 has been used successfully to follow mitochondrial dysfunction in apoptotic hippocampal neurons [158] and opening of the mitochondrial permeability transition pore [159,160] (MTP).
- Our JC-9 dye (3,3′-dimethyl-α-naphthoxacarbocyanine iodide, D22421, Figure 22.17) undergoes a similar potential-dependent spectral shift from a green-fluorescent product to a red-fluorescent aggregate (Figure 22.18) and is likely to be similarly useful for detecting apoptotic cells by both imaging and flow cytometry. Unlike JC-1, the green fluorescence of JC-9 is essentially invariant with membrane potential while the red fluorescence is significantly increased at hyperpolarized membrane potentials.
- MitoTracker® Red CMXRos (M7512, Figure 12.4) provides quick, easy and reliable detection of the loss of mitochondrial membrane potential that occurs during apoptosis.[161–165] Our patented MitoTracker® Red CMXRos probe can be fixed using aldehyde-based fixatives and can thus be detected through subsequent immunocytochemistry, DNA end-labeling, *in situ* hybridization or counterstaining steps.[166] The changes in mitochondrial membrane potential in osteosarcoma cells observed using MitoTracker® Red CMXRos were instrumental in demonstrating the ability of these cells to undergo reversible apoptosis without entering cell death.[167] Ratiometric measurements that compare the fluorescence of the membrane potential–dependent MitoTracker® Red CMXRos label to that of the membrane potential–independent MitoTracker® Green FM dye (M7514, Section 12.2) result in improved discrimination of apoptotic and nonapoptotic cell populations.[161]
- Rhodamine 123 (R302; FluoroPure™ Grade, R22420) is a cell-permeant, cationic, fluorescent dye that is readily sequestered by active mitochondria without inducing cytotoxic effects.[168] Uptake and equilibration of rhodamine 123 is rapid — a few minutes — as compared with other membrane potential–sensitive dyes, which may take 30 minutes or longer.[169] Although not aldehyde-fixable, rhodamine 123 allows for quick and easy detection of apoptotic cells.[170,171]
- Most carbocyanine dyes with short (C_1–C_6) alkyl chains stain mitochondria of live cells when used at low concentrations (~0.5 µM or ~0.1 µg/mL) (MitoProbe™ $DiIC_1(5)$ and $DiOC_2(3)$ Assay Kits; M34151, M34150; see below). $DiOC_6(3)$ (D273) is a green-fluorescent cationic dye that accumulates in active mitochondria and is useful in following changes in the membrane potential of the mitochondria that occur during programmed cell death. This dye has been used in flow cytometric analysis to study mitochondrial changes in apoptotic human myeloid leukemia cells.[172]
- The accumulation of both the methyl and ethyl esters of tetramethylrhodamine (TMRM, T668; TMRE, T669) in mitochondria and endoplasmic reticulum is driven by membrane potential.[173,174] TMRM has been used to study the temporal relationship between cytochrome *c* release from mitochondria and reduced mitochondrial membrane potential in apoptotic pheochromocytoma-6 cells [175] and to investigate the mitochondrial permeability transition pore.[176–178]
- Calcein, a green-fluorescent dye that is formed inside cells that are loaded using calcein AM (C1430, C3099, C3100MP; Section 15.2, Figure 15.2), can be taken up into the matrix of mitochondria due to opening of the mitochondrial permeability transition pore (MTP). The MTP allows relatively large molecules (less than 620 daltons) to pass from the cytosol into the mitochondrial matrix.[179] The transport of calcein through the MTP has been used to study the role of the MTP in apoptosis.[176,177,180]
- Nonyl acridine orange (A1372) is reported to bind to cardiolipin in the inner mitochondrial membrane. Its fluorescence decreases as cardiolipin becomes oxidized or otherwise altered during apoptosis.[171,181–183]
- Our SYTO® 16 green-fluorescent nucleic acid stain (S7578) shows decreased fluorescence in apoptotic cells that may be due to changes in mitochondrial DNA conformation. It is optimally excited by the 488 nm spectral line of the argon-ion laser, making it useful for both flow cytometry and confocal laser-scanning microscopy.[22,164]

SelectFX™ Alexa Fluor® 488 Cytochrome c Apoptosis Detection Kit

The SelectFX™ Alexa Fluor® 488 Cytochrome *c* Apoptosis Detection Kit (S35115) provides all the reagents required to detect cytochrome *c* in fixed cells. Because cytochrome *c* is released from mitochondria into the cytosol during apoptosis, its localization can serve as a marker of apoptosis. This kit employs an anti–cytochrome *c* primary antibody and an Alexa Fluor® 488 dye–labeled secondary antibody. The Alexa Fluor® 488 dye exhibits bright green fluorescence that is compatible with filters and instrument settings appropriate for fluorescein. Each kit contains:

- Mouse IgG_1 anti–cytochrome *c* antibody
- Highly cross-adsorbed Alexa Fluor® 488 goat anti–mouse IgG antibody
- Concentrated fixative solution
- Concentrated phosphate-buffered saline (PBS)

- Concentrated permeabilization solution
- Concentrated blocking solution
- Detailed protocols for mammalian cell preparation and staining

The SelectFX™ Alexa Fluor® 488 Cytochrome *c* Apoptosis Detection Kit can be used in conjunction with probes for other cell targets to achieve multicolor cell staining.

MitoProbe™ Transition Pore Assay Kit for Flow Cytometry

The mitochondrial permeability transition pore, a nonspecific channel formed by components from the inner and outer mitochondrial membranes, appears to be involved in the release of mitochondrial components during apoptotic and necrotic cell death. In a healthy cell, the inner mitochondrial membrane is responsible for maintaining the electrochemical gradient that is essential for respiration and energy production. As Ca^{2+} is taken up and released by mitochondria, a low-conductance permeability transition pore appears to flicker between open and closed states.[184] During cell death, the opening of the mitochondrial permeability transition pore dramatically alters the permeability of mitochondria. Continuous pore activation results from mitochondrial Ca^{2+} overload, oxidation of mitochondrial glutathione, increased levels of reactive oxygen species in mitochondria and other pro-apoptotic conditions.[185] Cytochrome *c* release from mitochondria and loss of mitochondrial membrane potential are observed subsequent to continuous pore activation.

The MitoProbe™ Transition Pore Assay Kit (M34153), based on published experimentation for mitochondrial transition pore opening,[180,186] provides a more direct method of measuring mitochondrial permeability transition pore opening than assays relying on mitochondrial membrane potential alone (Figure 15.97). This assay employs the acetoxymethyl (AM) ester of calcein, a colorless and nonfluorescent esterase substrate, and $CoCl_2$, a quencher of calcein fluorescence, to selectively label mitochondria. Cells are loaded with calcein AM, which passively diffuses into the cells and accumulates in cytosolic compartments, including the mitochondria. Once inside cells, calcein AM is cleaved by intracellular esterases to liberate the very polar fluorescent dye calcein, which does not cross the mitochondrial or plasma membranes in appreciable amounts over relatively short periods of time. The fluorescence from cytosolic calcein is quenched by the addition of $CoCl_2$, while the fluorescence from the mitochondrial calcein is maintained. As a control, cells that have been loaded with calcein AM and $CoCl_2$ can also be treated with a Ca^{2+} ionophore such as ionomycin (I24222, Section 19.8) to allow entry of excess Ca^{2+} into the cells, which triggers mitochondrial pore activation and subsequent loss of mitochondrial calcein fluorescence. This ionomycin response can be blocked with cyclosporine A, a compound reported to prevent mitochondrial transition pore formation by binding cyclophilin D.

The MitoProbe™ Transition Pore Assay Kit has been tested with Jurkat cells, MH1C1 cells and bovine pulmonary artery endothelial cells (BPAEC). Each MitoProbe™ Transition Pore Assay Kit provides:

- Calcein AM
- $CoCl_2$
- Ionomycin
- Dimethylsulfoxide (DMSO)
- A detailed protocol

Sufficient reagents are provided for 100 assays, based on labeling volumes of 1 mL.

MitoProbe™ JC-1 Assay Kit for Flow Cytometry

The MitoProbe™ JC-1 Assay Kit (M34152) provides the cationic dye JC-1 and a mitochondrial membrane potential disrupter, CCCP (carbonyl cyanide 3-chlorophenylhydrazone), for the study of mitochondrial membrane potential. JC-1 (Figure 22.13) exhibits potential-dependent accumulation in mitochondria, indicated by a fluorescence emission shift from green (~529 nm) to red (~590 nm), due to concentration-dependent formation of red-fluorescent J-aggregates.[152,153,187] Consequently, mitochondrial depolarization is indicated by a decrease in the red/green fluorescence intensity ratio, which is dependent only on the membrane potential and not on other factors such as mitochondrial size, shape and density, which may influence single-component fluorescence measurements. Use of fluorescence ratio detection therefore allows researchers to make

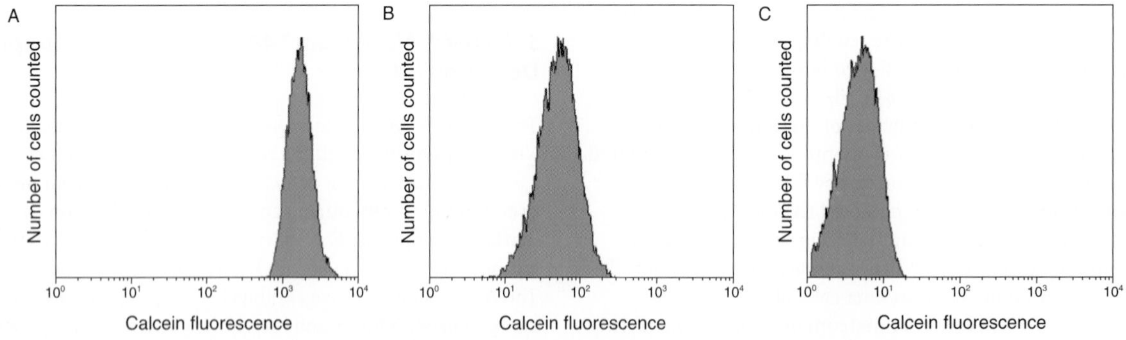

Figure 15.97 Flow cytometric analysis of Jurkat cells using the MitoProbe™ Transition Pore Assay Kit (M34153). Jurkat cells were incubated with the reagents in the MitoProbe™ Transition Pore Assay Kit and analyzed by flow cytometry. In the absence of $CoCl_2$ and ionomycin, fluorescent calcein is present in the cytosol as well as the mitochondria, resulting in a bright signal (panel A). In the presence of $CoCl_2$, calcein in the mitochondria emits a signal, but the cytosolic calcein fluorescence is quenched; the overall fluorescence is reduced, as compared with calcein alone (panel B). When ionomycin, a Ca^{2+} ionophore, and $CoCl_2$ are added to the cells at the same time that calcein AM is added, the fluorescent signals from both the cytosol and mitochondria are largely abolished (panel C). The change in fluorescence between panels B and C indicates the continuous activation of mitochondrial permeability transition pores.

comparative measurements of membrane potential and to determine the percentage of mitochondria within a population that respond to an applied stimulus. Subtle heterogeneity in cellular responses can be discerned in this way.[153,188] For example, four distinct patterns of mitochondrial membrane potential change in response to glutamate receptor activation in neurons have been identified using confocal ratio imaging of JC-1 fluorescence.[189]

JC-1 can be used as an indicator of mitochondrial potential in a variety of cell types, including myocytes [187] and neurons,[189] as well as in intact tissues [190] and isolated mitochondria.[188] JC-1 is more specific for mitochondrial versus plasma membrane potential and more consistent in its response to depolarization than some other cationic dyes such as $DiOC_6(3)$ and rhodamine 123.[155] The most widely implemented application for JC-1 is the detection of mitochondrial depolarization occurring in apoptosis [155,182,191,192] (Figure 15.98). Each MitoProbe™ JC-1 Assay Kit provides:

- JC-1
- Dimethylsulfoxide (DMSO)
- CCCP
- Concentrated phosphate-buffered saline (PBS)
- A detailed protocol

Sufficient reagents are provided for 100 assays, based on a labeling volume of 1 mL.

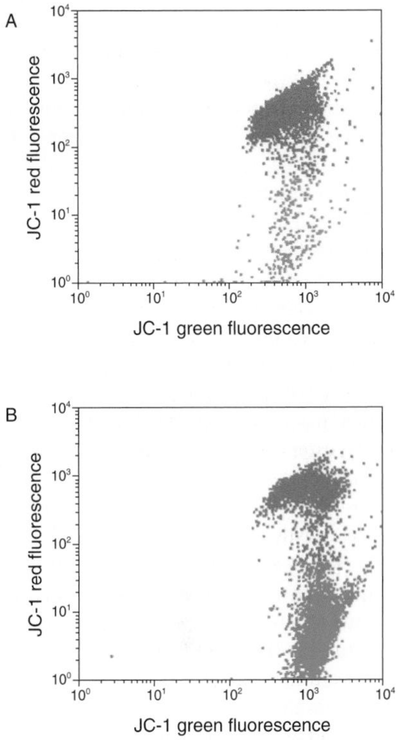

Figure 15.98 Flow cytometric analysis of Jurkat cells using the MitoProbe™ JC-1 Assay Kit (M34152). Jurkat cells were stained with 2 µM JC-1 for 15 minutes at 37°C, 5% CO_2, and then washed with phosphate-buffered saline (PBS) and analyzed on a flow cytometer using 488 nm excitation with 530 nm and 585 nm bandpass emission filters. Untreated cultured cells are shown in panel A. Panel B shows cells induced to apoptosis with 10 µM camptothecin for 4 hours at 37°C.

MitoProbe™ $DiIC_1(5)$ and MitoProbe™ $DiOC_2(3)$ Assay Kits for Flow Cytometry

Cationic carbocyanine dyes have been shown to accumulate in cells in response to membrane potential,[193] and membrane potential changes have been studied in association with apoptosis.[194,195] The MitoProbe™ $DiIC_1(5)$ and MitoProbe™ $DiOC_2(3)$ Assay Kits (M34151, M34150) provide solutions of the far-red–fluorescent $DiIC_1(5)$ (1,1′,3,3,3′,3′-hexamethylindodicarbocyanine iodide) and green-fluorescent $DiOC_2(3)$ (3,3′-diethyloxacarbocyanine iodide) carbocyanine dyes, respectively, along with a mitochondrial membrane potential disrupter, CCCP, for the study of mitochondrial membrane potential. These $DiIC_1(5)$ and $DiOC_2(3)$ carbocyanine dyes penetrate the cytosol of eukaryotic cells and, at concentrations below 100 nM, accumulate primarily in mitochondria with active membrane potentials. In the case of $DiOC_2(3)$, this accumulation is accompanied by a shift from green to red emission due to dye stacking (Figure 22.11), allowing the use of a ratiometric parameter (red/green fluorescence ratio) that corrects for size differences when measuring membrane potential in bacteria.[196,197] $DiIC_1(5)$ and $DiOC_2(3)$ stain intensities decrease when cells are treated with reagents that disrupt mitochondrial membrane potential, such as CCCP. Each MitoProbe™ $DiIC_1(5)$ and MitoProbe™ $DiOC_2(3)$ Assay Kit provides:

- $DiIC_1(5)$ (in Kit M34151) or $DiOC_2(3)$ (in Kit M34150)
- CCCP
- Detailed protocols for labeling cells with the short-chain carbocyanine dye, as well as with annexin V conjugates (not included)

Cells stained with $DiIC_1(5)$ can be visualized by flow cytometry with red excitation and far-red emission filters; cells stained with $DiOC_2(3)$ can be visualized by flow cytometry with blue excitation and green and red emission filters. $DiIC_1(5)$ can be paired with other reagents, such as propidium iodide and the green-fluorescent Alexa Fluor® 488 annexin V (both provided in the Vybrant® Apoptosis Assay Kit #2, V13241), for multiparameter study of vitality and apoptosis. $DiOC_2(3)$ can be paired with other reagents, such as the far-red–fluorescent allophycocyanin annexin V (A35110), for multiparameter study of vitality and apoptosis (Figure 15.99). Combining these short-chain carbocyanine dyes with annexin V conjugates results in superior resolution of subpopulations when compared with results obtained with other commonly used dyes.

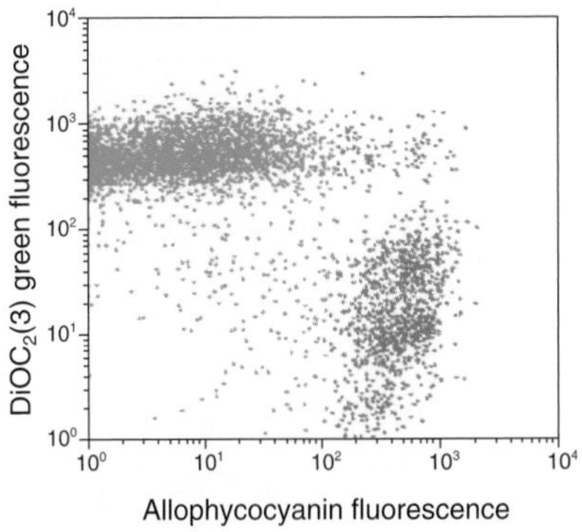

Figure 15.99 Flow cytometric analysis of camptothecin-treated Jurkat cells stained with $DiOC_2(3)$ (D14730, M34150) and allophycocyanin annexin V (A35110). Jurkat cells were incubated for 4 hours with camptothecin at 37°C, 5% CO_2, then stained with 50 nM $DiOC_2(3)$ and allophycocyanin annexin V. Cells were analyzed on a flow cytometer using 488 nm and 633 nm excitations with 530 nm and 660 nm bandpass emission filters.

Apoptosis Assays Using Free Radical Probes

The *bcl-2* proto-oncogene product is reported to play a role in preventing apoptosis through its antioxidant properties.[16,198,199] Following an apoptotic signal, cells sustain progressive lipid peroxidation — as detected with *cis*-parinaric acid (P36005) — that can be suppressed by *bcl-2* overexpression.[199] *cis*-Parinaric acid was also used to assess lipid peroxidation in Down syndrome neurons, which exhibit increased levels of intracellular reactive oxygen species that lead to a reduction in levels of intracellular reduced glutathione and apoptosis.[200,201] The reagent diphenyl-1-pyrenylphosphine (DPPP, D7894) is essentially nonfluorescent until it is oxidized by hydroperoxides to a phosphine oxide.[202–205] Its lipid solubility makes DPPP similarly useful for detecting hydroperoxides in the membranes of live cells.[206]

Induction of apoptosis in human natural killer (NK) cells by monocytes is blocked by catalase, a scavenger of hydrogen peroxide, and by sodium azide, a myeloperoxidase inhibitor, whereas scavengers of superoxide and hydroxyl radicals do not prevent apoptosis.[207] The most common fluorogenic probe for detecting reactive oxygen species is 2′,7′-dichlorodihydrofluorescein diacetate (H_2DCFDA, D399), which has been used to examine the effect of caspase-3 inhibitors on hydrogen peroxide production during apoptosis,[208] in apoptotic embryos[209] and in chemosensitive or chemoresistant cancer cells.[16] H_2DCFDA can detect so-called "necrotic zones" containing cells under oxidative stress in tissues;[210] however, for this application we recommend our 5-(and 6-)chloromethyl-2′,7′-dichlorodihydrofluorescein diacetate, acetyl ester (CM-H_2DCFDA, C6827; Figure 14.20), which has greater cell-membrane permeability and better cell retention of its green-fluorescent oxidation product. The acetoxymethyl ester of 2′,7′-dichlorodihydrofluorescein diacetate (C2938, Figure 15.100) is also more permeant to live cells and tissues and has been used to detect hydrogen peroxide in transplanted myoblasts.[211] As would be expected, the other major probes for reactive oxygen species — dihydrorhodamine 123 (D632, D23806; Figure 15.22) and dihydroethidium (hydroethidine; D1168, D11347, D23107), each of which is colorless and nonfluorescent until oxidized to the mitochondrial probe rhodamine 123 or to the nucleic acid stain ethidium — are also useful for detecting apoptotic cells in culture, and likely in tissues.[42,182] Another scavenger of reactive oxygen species, dihydrocalcein AM (D23805, Figure 15.4) yields the green-fluorescent dye calcein (Figure 14.32) upon intracellular oxidation; the cell retention of calcein is superior to that of most other dyes (Figure 15.3). The principal oxidant of these probes is reportedly peroxynitrite, which is generated from nitric oxide[212] (Section 18.3), although superoxide has also been implicated.[213,214]

Probes such as 10-acetyl-3,7-dihydroxyphenoxazine (the Amplex® Red reagent, A12222, A22177; Section 18.2) and the Amplex® UltraRed reagent (A36006) react with hydrogen peroxide in the presence of a peroxidase to form red-fluorescent resorufin derivatives and may therefore be useful for correlating hydrogen peroxide production in cells with apoptosis. All of our probes for detecting reactive oxygen species are described in Chapter 18.

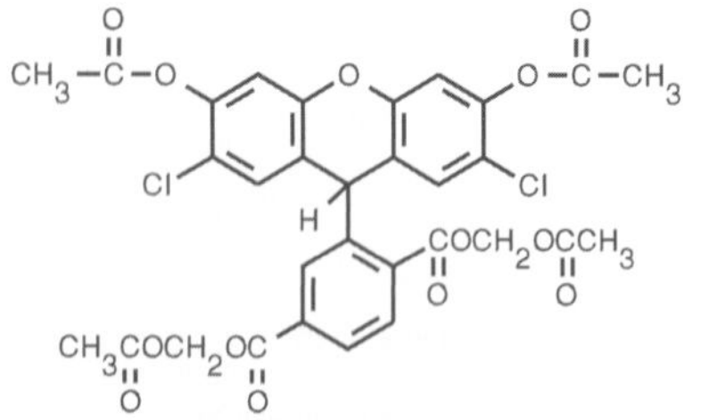

Figure 15.100 C2938 6-carboxy-2′,7′-dichlorodihydrofluorescein diacetate, di(acetoxymethyl ester).

Apoptosis Assays Using Ion Indicators

Significant changes in intracellular pH, Na^+, K^+ and Ca^{2+} concentrations accompany apoptosis. The role of acidification in apoptosis has been investigated using carboxy SNARF®-1 AM acetate[215–217] (C1271, C1272; Section 20.2) and BCECF AM[218] (B1150, B1170, B3051; Section 20.2) cell-permeant pH indicators.[216] Low intracellular pH, as measured with the carboxy SNARF®-1 pH indicator, and uptake of Hoechst 33342 have been shown to be correlated in partially apoptotic cell populations.[30] Plasma membrane depolarization and inactivation of the Na^+/K^+-ATPase early in apoptosis leads to an increase in intracellular Na^+ levels, as detected with SBFI AM (S1263, Section 21.1), and an inhibition of K^+ uptake, as detected with $^{86}Rb^+$ studies.[219] Changes in intracellular Ca^{2+} levels may influence gene expression, as well as nuclease, protease and kinase activity.[220–227] Our extensive selection of Ca^{2+} indicators, caged Ca^{2+} reagents, Ca^{2+} ionophores and Ca^{2+} chelators (Chapter 19) may help to sort out the mechanism of Ca^{2+} action in apoptosis.

Apoptosis Assays Using Esterase Substrates

Alterations in membrane permeability that occur during apoptosis have been monitored using nucleic acid stains (see above). These membrane changes may also affect the uptake and retention of our various general esterase substrates (Table 15.1) and substrates for other intracellular enzymes (Chapter 10). Results from staining apoptotic thymocytes with esterase substrates, however, showed significant variation depending on which probe was used.[24,57] Some of this variation undoubtedly resulted from differences in the pH sensitivity of the probes; thus, calcein AM (C1430, C3099, C3100MP; Section 15.2), which has low pH sensitivity in the physiological pH range, may be the best reagent for detecting membrane permeability changes that accompany apoptosis. Calcein AM has been extensively used to detect the permeability transition of the mitochondrial membrane that apparently accompanies late stages of apoptosis[167,179,228,229] (MitoProbe™ Transition Pore Assay Kit, M34153; see above). Calcein AM has been recommended as a better marker for early apoptotic events than annexin V conjugates in NIH 3T3 fibroblasts.[230] Confocal laser-scanning microscopy of calcein AM–labeled cells shows a large increase in nuclear fluorescence and cell shrinkage during the early stages of chromatin condensation and nuclear fragmentation.[230] Calcein AM staining also measures other important characteristics of apoptotic cells, including membrane blebbing and preservation of membrane integrity.

An Apoptosis Assay that Measures the ATP:ADP Ratio

Apoptotic cells are reported to have a relatively low ratio of ATP to ADP, apparently indicating decreased resynthesis of ATP in the mitochondria.[231–233] A very sensitive chemiluminescent assay that measures the average ATP:ADP ratio of cultured apoptotic cells based on the principles of our luciferin/luciferase-based ATP Determination Kit (A22066; Section 10.3, Section 15.2) has been described.[234]

References

1. J Immunol 132, 38 (1984); **2.** Science 281, 1302 (1998); **3.** Blood 85, 359 (1995); **4.** Genes Dev 8, 2817 (1994); **5.** Cytometry 27, 1 (1997); **6.** FASEB J 9, 1277 (1995); **7.** Am J Pathol 146, 3 (1995); **8.** Cell 74, 777 (1993); **9.** J Pharm Sci 87, 1368 (1998); **10.** Methods Cell Biol 41, 15 (1994); **11.** Cytometry 35, 80 (1999); **12.** Cell Mol Life Sci 53, 527 (1997); **13.** J Immunol Methods 184, 39 (1995); **14.** Blood 84, 1415 (1994); **15.** Cytometry 27, 136 (1997); **16.** Ann Surg Oncol 5, 287 (1998); **17.** Cytometry 27, 145 (1997); **18.** Methods Mol Biol 91, 217 (1998); **19.** J Immunol 160, 1875 (1998); **20.** J Immunol Methods 185, 249 (1995); **21.** Neuron 15, 961 (1995); **22.** Cytometry 21, 265 (1995); **23.** Cytometry 43, 134 (2001); **24.** Cytometry 14, 595 (1993); **25.** Anal Biochem 204, 351 (1992); **26.** Cytometry 13, 137 (1992); **27.** Cytometry 17, 59 (1994); **28.** Cytometry 16, 41 (1994); **29.** Hepatology 29, 51 (1999); **30.** Cytometry 25, 349 (1996); **31.** Blood 87, 4959 (1996); **32.** Exp Cell Res 220, 283 (1995); **33.** Br J Haematol 104, 530 (1999); **34.** Br J Haematol 104, 131 (1999); **35.** Cytometry 15, 12 (1994); **36.** J Immunol Methods 170, 145 (1994); **37.** J Immunol Methods 209, 111 (1997); **38.** Nature 378, 736 (1995); **39.** Bone Marrow Transplant 27, 487 (2001); **40.** J Immunol Methods 123, 103 (1989); **41.** Cytometry 9, 477 (1988); **42.** Cytometry 28, 253 (1997); **43.** Development 117, 29 (1993); **44.** Cytometry 13, 795 (1992); **45.** Anal Biochem 218, 314 (1994); **46.** Cancer Res 44, 83 (1984); **47.** J Histochem Cytochem 45, 165 (1997); **48.** Cytometry 25, 182 (1996); **49.** Nucleic Acids Res 22, 5506 (1994); **50.** Biotechniques 15, 1032 (1993); **51.** Cancer Res 51, 4671 (1991); **52.** Am J Pathol 136, 593 (1990); **53.** Anal Biochem 221, 431 (1994); **54.** J Cell Biol 150, 145 (2000); **55.** Cancer Res 57, 3804 (1997); **56.** J Exp Med 182, 1759 (1995); **57.** Exp Cell Res 211, 322 (1994); **58.** Exp Cell Res 175, 184 (1988); **59.** Int J Radiat Biol 66, 23 (1994); **60.** Mol Hum Reprod 2, 613 (1996); **61.** Irish J Med Sci 166, 177 (1997); **62.** Mutagenesis 13, 1 (1998); **63.** Mutat Res 399, 87 (1998); **64.** Biotechniques 27, 846 (1999); **65.** Cytometry 20, 257 (1995); **66.** Cytometry 20, 245 (1995); **67.** J Histochem Cytochem 41, 7 (1993); **68.** J Cell Biol 119, 493 (1992); **69.** J Histochem Cytochem 44, 959 (1996); **70.** Biotechniques 19, 800 (1995); **71.** Exp Neurol 133, 225 (1995); **72.** Jpn J Cancer Res 85, 939 (1994); **73.** Exp Cell Res 222, 28 (1996); **74.** Cytometry 20, 172 (1995); **75.** Biotechniques 27, 1130 (1999); **76.** Science 281, 1303 (1998); **77.** Neuroreport 6, 1053 (1995); **78.** Exp Neurol 133, 265 (1995); **79.** J Neurosci 15, 3775 (1995); **80.** Acta Neuropathol (Berl) 88, 207 (1994); **81.** Cancer Res 53, 1945 (1993); **82.** Int J Oncol 1, 639 (1992); **83.** Trends Cell Biol 5, 21 (1995); **84.** Jpn J Cancer Res 84, 566 (1993); **85.** Nucleic Acids Res 21, 4206 (1993); **86.** Cytometry 32, 95 (1998); **87.** Toxicol Appl Pharmacol 148, 176 (1998); **88.** Proc Natl Acad Sci U S A 99, 10706 (2002); **89.** J Biol Chem 265, 4923 (1990); **90.** FEBS Lett 203, 99 (1986); **91.** Biosci Rep 7, 289 (1987); **92.** Cytometry 31, 1 (1998); **93.** J Immunol 148, 2207 (1992); **94.** J Immunol 151, 4274 (1993); **95.** Cytometry 37, 197 (1999); **96.** J Neurosci Res 48, 563 (1997); **97.** Cytometry 37, 191 (1999); **98.** J Biol Chem 275, 23807 (2000); **99.** J Biol Chem 276, 1127 (2001); **100.** J Biol Chem 275, 25336 (2000); **101.** Methods Cell Biol 63, 107 (2001); **102.** J Biol Chem 275, 12737 (2000); **103.** Eur J Histochem 41, 211 (1997); **104.** J Neurosci Methods 70, 195 (1996); **105.** Appl Environ Microbiol 56, 3785 (1990); **106.** J Dairy Res 57, 239 (1990); **107.** Cell Death Differ 6, 1067 (1999); **108.** J Biol Chem 272, 17907 (1997); **109.** Science 281, 1312 (1998); **110.** Trends Biochem Sci 22, 388 (1997); **111.** Nature 376, 37 (1995); **112.** J Immunol 165, 6559 (2000); **113.** Cell 104, 791 (2001); **114.** Biochemistry 38, 13906 (1999); **115.** Cell Death Differ 6, 821 (1999); **116.** Science 281, 1305 (1998); **117.** J Biol Chem 274, 17484 (1999); **118.** Exp Cell Res 250, 203 (1999); **119.** J Biol Chem 276, 6974 (2001); **120.** Biochemistry 39, 16056 (2000); **121.** Oncogene 17, 1295 (1998); **122.** J Biol Chem 275, 288 (2000); **123.** Bioorg Med Chem Lett 9, 3231 (1999); **124.** Cell Death Differ 6, 1081 (1999); **125.** Exp Cell Res 259, 308 (2000); **126.** Biotechniques 31, 608 (2001); **127.** Leukemia 16, 1589 (2002); **128.** Cytometry 47, 143 (2002); **129.** J Immunol Methods 265, 111 (2002); **130.** Cytometry 55A, 50 (2003); **131.** Kidney Int 31, 112 (1987); **132.** FEBS Lett 438, 150 (1998); **133.** J Biomed Mater Res 22, 837 (1988); **134.** Mol Cells 7, 742 (1997); **135.** Brain Res 746, 220 (1997); **136.** Infect Immun 62, 5126 (1994); **137.** J Biochem Biophys Methods 42, 137 (2000); **138.** Biophotonics Int 5, 34 (1998); **139.** Biochem Biophys Res Commun 236, 549 (1997); **140.** Cancer Res 58, 1901 (1998); **141.** Proc Natl Acad Sci U S A 96, 3200 (1999); **142.** J Cell Physiol 159, 229 (1994); **143.** Methods Enzymol 294, 117 (1999); **144.** Cell Death Differ 5, 1051 (1998); **145.** J Biol Chem 268, 23593 (1993); **146.** Science 292, 624 (2001); **147.** Science 289, 1150 (2000); **148.** Trends Cell Biol 10, 369 (2000); **149.** Biochim Biophys Acta 1366, 151 (1998); **150.** Science 281, 1309 (1998); **151.** Methods Enzymol 260, 406 (1995); **152.** Biochemistry 30, 4480 (1991); **153.** Proc Natl Acad Sci U S A 88, 3671 (1991); **154.** Mol Reprod Dev 53, 222 (1999); **155.** FEBS Lett 411, 77 (1997); **156.** Cytometry 29, 97 (1997); **157.** Leukemia 11, 1147 (1997); **158.** J Neurochem 70, 66 (1998); **159.** J Biol Chem 275, 12175 (2000); **160.** J Exp Med 191, 33 (2000); **161.** Cytometry 35, 311 (1999); **162.** Cytometry 25, 333 (1996); **163.** Science 281, 2027 (1998); **164.** Cytometry 27, 358 (1997); **165.** J Histochem Cytochem 44, 1363 (1996); **166.** J Cell Biol 141, 1243 (1998); **167.** Exp Cell Res 246, 26 (1999); **168.** Proc Natl Acad Sci U S A 77, 990 (1980); **169.** Int Rev Cytol 122, 1 (1990); **170.** Immunol Lett 61, 157 (1998); **171.** Cytometry 24, 106 (1996); **172.** J Biol Chem 272, 21388 (1997); **173.** Biophys J 56, 1053 (1989); **174.** Biophys J 53, 785 (1988); **175.** J Biol Chem 274, 5654 (1999); **176.** Am J Physiol 272, C1286 (1997); **177.** Am J Physiol 273, C1783 (1997); **178.** Biochem J 307, 99 (1995); **179.** Biochim Biophys Acta 1366, 177 (1998); **180.** Biophys J 76, 725 (1999); **181.** Biochem Biophys Res Commun 269, 542 (2000); **182.** J Cell Biol 138, 449 (1997); **183.** Nature 389, 300 (1997); **184.** Am J Physiol Cell Physiol 279, C852 (2000); **185.** Biochem J 341 (Pt 2), 233 (1999); **186.** Biofactors 8, 263 (1998); **187.** J Physiol 486, 1 (1995); **188.** Exp Cell Res 222, 84 (1996); **189.** J Neurosci 16, 5688 (1996); **190.** Methods 18, 104 (1999); **191.** Exp Cell Res 245, 170 (1998); **192.** J Neurosci 18, 932 (1998); **193.** Proc Natl Acad Sci U S A 76, 5728 (1979); **194.** Methods Cell Biol 63, 467 (2001); **195.** Exp Cell Res 214, 323 (1994); **196.** Methods 21, 271 (2000); **197.** Cytometry 35, 55 (1999); **198.** Science 281, 1322 (1998); **199.** Cell 75, 241 (1993); **200.** Nature 378, 776 (1995); **201.** J Immunol 155, 5133 (1995); **202.** J Chromatogr 628, 31 (1993); **203.** J Chromatogr 622, 153 (1993); **204.** J Chromatogr 596, 197 (1992); **205.** Anal Lett 21, 965 (1988); **206.** FEBS Lett 474, 137 (2000); **207.** J Immunol 156, 42 (1996); **208.** J Cell Biol 273, 26900 (1998); **209.** Hum Reprod 13, 998 (1998); **210.** Exp Cell Res 238, 136 (1998); **211.** J Immunol 159, 2522 (1997); **212.** FEBS Lett 416, 175 (1997); **213.** Neuroscience 86, 1109 (1998); **214.** J Biol Chem 270, 16487 (1995); **215.** J Immunol Methods 221, 43 (1998); **216.** Proc Natl Acad Sci U S A 93, 654 (1996); **217.** J Biol Chem 270, 3203 (1995); **218.** J Biol Chem 270, 6235 (1995); **219.** J Biol Chem 276, 4304 (2001); **220.** Biochem Biophys Res Commun 214, 1130 (1995); **221.** J Neurosci 15, 1172 (1995); **222.** Biochim Biophys Acta 1223, 247 (1994); **223.** Cell Calcium 16, 279 (1994); **224.** Exp Cell Res 212, 84 (1994); **225.** FASEB J 8, 237 (1994); **226.** J Immunol 151, 5198 (1993); **227.** Exp Cell Res 197, 43 (1991); **228.** J Cell Biol 105, 2959 (1987); **229.** Biophys J 74, 2129 (1998); **230.** J Histochem Cytochem 46, 895 (1998); **231.** Neuroscience 86, 279 (1998); **232.** Exp Cell Res 226, 264 (1996); **233.** Blood 84, 1613 (1994); **234.** J Immunol Methods 240, 79 (2000).

Data Table — 15.5 Assays for Apoptosis

Cat #	MW	Storage	Soluble	Abs	EC	Em	Solvent	Notes
A1301	301.82	L	H_2O, EtOH	500	53,000	526	H_2O/DNA	1, 2
A1310	1270.45	F,L	DMF, DMSO	546	25,000	647	H_2O/DNA	1
A1372	472.51	L	DMSO, EtOH	495	84,000	519	MeOH	
A3568	301.82	RR,L	H_2O	500	53,000	526	H_2O/DNA	
A6520	554.10	F,D	DMSO	330	13,000	403	MeOH	3, 4
A6551	425.57	FF,D,AA	DMSO	286	8,000	none	MeOH	5
A22121	821.72	F,D	DMSO	339	7,900	435	MeOH	4, 6
A22127	767.79	F,D	DMSO	326	17,000	392	MeOH	3, 4
A22128	821.76	F,D	DMSO	340	8,200	434	MeOH	4, 6
C2938	675.43	F,D,AA	DMSO	291	5,700	none	MeOH	7
C6827	577.80	F,D,AA	DMSO	287	9,100	none	MeOH	7
C7604	~993	FF,L	H_2O	496	68,000	523	pH 8	8, 9
C7614	~908	FF,L	H_2O	504	68,000	513	pH 8	8, 9
D273	572.53	D,L	DMSO	484	154,000	501	MeOH	

Data Table — 15.5 Assays for Apoptosis — continued

Cat #	MW	Storage	Soluble	Abs	EC	Em	Solvent	Notes
D399	487.29	F,D	DMSO, EtOH	258	11,000	none	MeOH	7
D632	346.38	F,D,L,AA	DMF, DMSO	289	7,100	none	MeOH	10, 11
D1168	315.42	FF,L,AA	DMF, DMSO	355	14,000	see Notes	MeCN	10, 12
D7894	386.43	F,D,LL	MeCN	358	29,000	none	MeOH	13
D11347	315.42	FF,L,AA	DMF, DMSO	355	14,000	see Notes	MeCN	10, 12
D22421	532.38	D,L	DMSO, DMF	522	143,000	535	$CHCl_3$	14
D23107	315.42	FF,D,L,AA	DMSO	355	14,000	see Notes	MeCN	12, 15
D23805	1068.95	F,D	DMSO	285	5,800	none	MeCN	16
D23806	346.38	F,D,L,AA	DMSO	289	7,100	none	MeOH	11, 15
E13183	767.74	F,D,L	DMSO	325	16,000	395	pH 7	3, 4, 17
E13184	1515.46	F,D,L	DMSO	232	52,000	none	MeOH	17, 18
H1399	615.99	L	H_2O, DMF	350	45,000	461	H_2O/DNA	1, 19
H3570	615.99	RR,L	H_2O	350	45,000	461	H_2O/DNA	1, 9, 19
H21492	615.99	L	H_2O, DMF	350	45,000	461	H_2O/DNA	1, 19, 20
L7595	471.98	L	DMSO, EtOH	543	46,000	712	H_2O/DNA	1
M7512	531.52	F,D,L	DMSO	578	116,000	599	MeOH	
P12271	1044.14	F,D,L	DMSO	504	86,000	511	MeOH	
P36005	276.42	FF,LL,AA	EtOH	304	77,000	416	MeOH	9, 21
R302	380.83	F,D,L	MeOH, DMF	507	101,000	529	MeOH	
R22120	1515.46	F,D	DMSO, DMF	232	52,000	none	MeOH	18
R22122	788.57	F,D	DMSO, DMF	232	55,000	none	MeOH	18
R22125	1515.55	F,D	DMSO, DMF	232	52,000	none	MeOH	18
R22126	1515.55	F,D	DMSO, DMF	232	52,000	none	MeOH	18
R22420	380.83	F,D,L	MeOH, DMF	507	101,000	529	MeOH	20
R33750	1495.56	F,D	DMSO, DMF	230	76,000	none	MeOH	18
R33751	1587.62	F,D	DMSO, DMF	232	57,000	none	MeOH	18
R33752	1113.10	F,D	DMSO, DMF	232	57,000	none	MeOH	18
R33753	1571.57	F,D	DMSO, DMF	232	57,000	none	MeOH	18
R33754	1511.60	F,D	DMSO, DMF	232	57,000	none	MeOH	18
R33755	1597.65	F,D	DMSO, DMF	232	57,000	none	MeOH	18
S7575	~400	F,D,L	DMSO	488	74,000	509	H_2O/DNA	1, 9, 22, 23
S7578	~450	F,D,L	DMSO	488	42,000	518	H_2O/DNA	1, 9, 22, 23
S7579	~650	F,D,L	DMSO	621	88,000	634	H_2O/DNA	1, 9, 22, 23
T668	500.93	F,D,L	DMSO, MeOH	549	115,000	573	MeOH	
T669	514.96	F,D,L	DMSO, EtOH	549	109,000	574	MeOH	
T3168	652.23	D,L	DMSO, DMF	514	195,000	529	MeOH	24
Y3603	629.32	F,D,L	DMSO	491	52,000	509	H_2O/DNA	1, 9, 22, 25

For definitions of the contents of this data table, see "Navigating *The Handbook*" in the introductory pages.

Notes

1. Spectra represent aqueous solutions of nucleic acid-bound dye. EC values are derived by comparing the absorbance of the nucleic acid-bound dye with that of free dye in a reference solvent (H_2O or MeOH).
2. Acridine orange bound to RNA has Abs ~460 nm, Em ~650 nm (Methods Cell Biol 41, 401 (1994); Cytometry 2, 201 (1982)).
3. Peptidase cleavage of this substrate yields 7-amino-4-methylcoumarin (A191).
4. Fluorescence of the unhydrolyzed substrate is very weak.
5. Peroxidase-catalyzed reaction of A6551 with H_2O_2 produces fluorescent 2-dodecylresorufin (Abs = 578 nm (EC = 69,000 $cm^{-1}M^{-1}$), Em = 597 nm in MeOH).
6. Enzymatic cleavage of this substrate yields 7-amino-4-trifluoromethylcoumarin: Abs = 380 nm (EC = 13,000 $cm^{-1}M^{-1}$), Em = 500 nm in pH 7 buffer.
7. Dihydrofluorescein diacetates are colorless and nonfluorescent until both of the acetate groups are hydrolyzed and the products are subsequently oxidized to fluorescein derivatives. The materials contain less than 0.1% of oxidized derivative when initially prepared. The oxidation products of C400, C2938, C6827, D399 and D2935 are 2′,7′-dichlorofluorescein derivatives with spectra similar to C368.
8. The molecular weight (MW) of this product is approximate because the degree of hydration and/or salt form has not been conclusively established.
9. This product is supplied as a ready-made solution in the solvent indicated under "Soluble."
10. This compound is susceptible to oxidation, especially in solution. Store solutions under argon or nitrogen. Oxidation may be induced by illumination.
11. D632, D23806 and D633 are essentially colorless and nonfluorescent until oxidized. Oxidation products are R302 (from D632 and D23806) and R634 (from D633).
12. Dihydroethidium has blue fluorescence (Em ~420 nm) until oxidized to ethidium (E1305). The reduced dye does not bind to nucleic acids (FEBS Lett 26, 169 (1972)).
13. Oxidation of D7894 occurs rapidly in solution when illuminated. The oxidation product is strongly fluorescent. Em = 379 nm.
14. JC-9 exhibits long-wavelength J-aggregate emission at ~635 nm in aqueous solutions and polarized mitochondria.
15. This product is supplied as a ready-made solution in DMSO with sodium borohydride added to inhibit oxidation.
16. D23805 is colorless and nonfluorescent until the AM ester groups are hydrolyzed and the resulting leuco dye is subsequently oxidized. The final product is calcein (C481).
17. Data represent the substrate component of this kit.
18. Peptidase cleavage of this substrate yields rhodamine 110 (R6479).
19. MW is for the hydrated form of this product.
20. This product is specified to equal or exceed 98% analytical purity by HPLC.
21. *Cis*-parinaric acid is readily oxidized to nonfluorescent products. Use under N_2 or Ar except when oxidation is intended. Stock solutions should be prepared in deoxygenated solvents. *Cis*-parinaric acid is appreciably fluorescent in lipid environments and organic solvents but is nonfluorescent in water.
22. This product is essentially nonfluorescent except when bound to DNA or RNA.
23. MW: The preceding ~ symbol indicates an approximate value, not including counterions.
24. JC-1 forms J-aggregates with Abs/Em = 585/590 nm at concentrations above 0.1 µM in aqueous solutions (pH 8.0) (Biochemistry 30, 4480 (1991)).
25. Although this compound is soluble in water, preparation of stock solutions in water is not recommended because of possible adsorption onto glass or plastic.

Product List — 15.5 Assays for Apoptosis

Cat #	Product Name	Unit Size
A6551	10-acetyl-3,7-dihydroxy-2-dodecylphenoxazine *special packaging*	10 x 100 µg
A1301	acridine orange	1 g
A3568	acridine orange *10 mg/mL solution in water*	10 mL
A1372	acridine orange 10-nonyl bromide (nonyl acridine orange)	100 mg
A1310	7-aminoactinomycin D (7-AAD)	1 mg
A6520	7-amino-4-chloromethylcoumarin, *t*-BOC-L-leucyl-L-methionine amide (CMAC, *t*-BOC-Leu-Met)	5 mg
A22127	7-amino-4-methylcoumarin, *N*-CBZ-L-isoleucyl-L-glutamyl-L-threonyl-L-aspartic acid amide (Z-IETD-AMC)	5 mg
A22121	7-amino-4-trifluoromethylcoumarin, *N*-CBZ-L-aspartyl-L-glutamyl-L-valyl-L-aspartic acid amide (Z-DEVD-AFC)	5 mg
A22128	7-amino-4-trifluoromethylcoumarin, *N*-CBZ-L-isoleucyl-L-glutamyl-L-threonyl-L-aspartic acid amide (Z-IETD-AFC)	5 mg
A23202	annexin V, Alexa Fluor® 350 conjugate *100 assays*	500 µL
A13201	annexin V, Alexa Fluor® 488 conjugate *100 assays*	500 µL
A13202	annexin V, Alexa Fluor® 568 conjugate *100 assays*	500 µL
A13203	annexin V, Alexa Fluor® 594 conjugate *100 assays*	500 µL
A23204	annexin V, Alexa Fluor® 647 conjugate *100 assays*	500 µL
A35110	annexin V, allophycocyanin conjugate (APC annexin V) *50 assays*	250 µL
A13204	annexin V, biotin-X conjugate *100 assays*	500 µL
A13199	annexin V, fluorescein conjugate (FITC annexin V) *100 assays*	500 µL
A13200	annexin V, Oregon Green® 488 conjugate *100 assays*	500 µL
A35111	annexin V, R-phycoerythrin conjugate (R-PE annexin V) *50 assays*	250 µL
A23210	APO-BrdU™ TUNEL Assay Kit *with Alexa Fluor® 488 anti-BrdU* *60 assays*	1 kit
C2938	6-carboxy-2',7'-dichlorodihydrofluorescein diacetate, di(acetoxymethyl ester)	5 mg
C6827	5-(and-6)-chloromethyl-2',7'-dichlorodihydrofluorescein diacetate, acetyl ester (CM-H_2DCFDA) *mixed isomers* *special packaging*	20 x 50 µg
C7614	ChromaTide® BODIPY® FL-14-dUTP *1 mM in TE buffer*	25 µL
C7604	ChromaTide® fluorescein-12-dUTP *1 mM in TE buffer*	25 µL
D399	2',7'-dichlorodihydrofluorescein diacetate (2',7'-dichlorofluorescin diacetate; H_2DCFDA)	100 mg
D273	3,3'-dihexyloxacarbocyanine iodide ($DiOC_6(3)$)	100 mg
D23805	dihydrocalcein, AM *special packaging*	20 x 50 µg
D1168	dihydroethidium (hydroethidine)	25 mg
D11347	dihydroethidium (hydroethidine) *special packaging*	10 x 1 mg
D23107	dihydroethidium (hydroethidine) *5 mM stabilized solution in DMSO*	1 mL
D632	dihydrorhodamine 123	10 mg
D23806	dihydrorhodamine 123 *5 mM stabilized solution in DMSO*	1 mL
D22421	3,3'-dimethyl-α-naphthoxacarbocyanine iodide (JC-9; $DiNOC_1(3)$)	5 mg
D7894	diphenyl-1-pyrenylphosphine (DPPP)	5 mg
E13183	EnzChek® Caspase-3 Assay Kit #1 *Z-DEVD-AMC substrate* *500 assays*	1 kit
E13184	EnzChek® Caspase-3 Assay Kit #2 *Z-DEVD-R110 substrate* *500 assays*	1 kit
H1399	Hoechst 33342, trihydrochloride, trihydrate	100 mg
H3570	Hoechst 33342, trihydrochloride, trihydrate *10 mg/mL solution in water*	10 mL
H21492	Hoechst 33342, trihydrochloride, trihydrate *FluoroPure™ grade*	100 mg
L7595	LDS 751	10 mg
M34151	MitoProbe™ $DiIC_1(5)$ Assay Kit *for flow cytometry* *100 assays*	1 kit
M34150	MitoProbe™ $DiOC_2(3)$ Assay Kit *for flow cytometry* *100 assays*	1 kit
M34152	MitoProbe™ JC-1 Assay Kit *for flow cytometry* *100 assays*	1 kit
M34153	MitoProbe™ Transition Pore Assay Kit (MTP by Flow) *for flow cytometry* *100 assays*	1 kit
M7512	MitoTracker® Red CMXRos *special packaging*	20 x 50 µg
P36005	*cis*-parinaric acid *3 mM in ethanol*	10 mL
P12271	pepstatin A, BODIPY® FL conjugate	25 µg
R35100	RediPlate™ 96 EnzChek® Caspase-3 Assay Kit *Z-DEVD-R110 substrate* *one 96-well microplate*	1 kit
R22122	rhodamine 110, bis-(L-aspartic acid amide), trifluoroacetic acid salt	1 mg
R22120	rhodamine 110, bis-(*N*-CBZ-L-aspartyl-L-glutamyl-L-valyl-L-aspartic acid amide) (Z-DEVD-R110) *bulk packaging*	20 mg
R22125	rhodamine 110, bis-(*N*-CBZ-L-isoleucyl-L-glutamyl-L-threonyl-L-aspartic acid amide) (Z-IETD-R110)	2 mg
R22126	rhodamine 110, bis-(*N*-CBZ-L-isoleucyl-L-glutamyl-L-threonyl-L-aspartic acid amide) (Z-IETD-R110) *bulk packaging*	20 mg
R33752	rhodamine 110, bis-(*N*-CBZ-L-alanyl-L-alanyl-L-aspartic acid amide) (Z-AAD-R110)	2 mg
R33753	rhodamine 110, bis-(*N*-CBZ-L-leucyl-L-glutamyl-L-glutamyl-L-aspartic acid amide) (Z-LEED-R110)	2 mg
R33751	rhodamine 110, bis-(*N*-CBZ-L-leucyl-L-glutamyl-L-histidinyl-L-aspartic acid amide) (Z-LEHD-R110)	2 mg
R33750	rhodamine 110, bis-(*N*-CBZ-L-tyrosinyl-L-valyl-L-alanyl-L-aspartic acid amide) (Z-YVAD-R110)	2 mg
R33755	rhodamine 110, bis-(*N*-CBZ-L-valyl-L-aspartyl-L-valyl-L-alanyl-L-aspartic acid amide) (Z-VDVAD-R110)	2 mg
R33754	rhodamine 110, bis-(*N*-CBZ-L-valyl-L-glutamyl-L-isoleucyl-L-aspartic acid amide) (Z-VEID-R110)	2 mg
R302	rhodamine 123	25 mg
R22420	rhodamine 123 *FluoroPure™ grade*	25 mg

For current prices or to order online, visit probes.invitrogen.com

Product List — 15.5 Assays for Apoptosis — continued

Cat #	Product Name	Unit Size
S35115	SelectFX™ Alexa Fluor® 488 Cytochrome *c* Apoptosis Detection Kit *for fixed cells*	1 kit
S7575	SYTO® 13 green fluorescent nucleic acid stain *5 mM solution in DMSO*	250 µL
S7578	SYTO® 16 green fluorescent nucleic acid stain *1 mM solution in DMSO*	250 µL
S7579	SYTO® 17 red fluorescent nucleic acid stain *5 mM solution in DMSO*	250 µL
T3168	5,5′,6,6′-tetrachloro-1,1′,3,3′-tetraethylbenzimidazolylcarbocyanine iodide (JC-1; $CBIC_2(3)$)	5 mg
T669	tetramethylrhodamine, ethyl ester, perchlorate (TMRE)	25 mg
T668	tetramethylrhodamine, methyl ester, perchlorate (TMRM)	25 mg
V35112	Vybrant® Apoptosis Assay Kit #8 *R-phycoerythrin annexin V/SYTOX® Green* *50 assays*	1 kit
V35113	Vybrant® Apoptosis Assay Kit #9 *allophycocyanin annexin V/SYTOX® Green* *50 assays*	1 kit
V35114	Vybrant® Apoptosis Assay Kit #10 *allophycocyanin annexin V/C_{12}-resazurin/SYTOX® Green* *50 assays*	1 kit
V35116	Vybrant® Apoptosis Assay Kit #11 *Alexa Fluor® 488 annexin V/MitoTracker® Red CMXRos* *50 assays*	1 kit
V13240	Vybrant® Apoptosis Assay Kit #1 *Alexa Fluor® 488 annexin V/SYTOX® Green* *50 assays*	1 kit
V13241	Vybrant® Apoptosis Assay Kit #2 *Alexa Fluor® 488 annexin V/propidium iodide* *50 assays*	1 kit
V13242	Vybrant® Apoptosis Assay Kit #3 *FITC annexin V/propidium iodide* *50 assays*	1 kit
V13243	Vybrant® Apoptosis Assay Kit #4 *YO-PRO®-1/propidium iodide* *200 assays*	1 kit
V13244	Vybrant® Apoptosis Assay Kit #5 *Hoechst 33342/propidium iodide* *200 assays*	1 kit
V23200	Vybrant® Apoptosis Assay Kit #6 *biotin-X annexin V/Alexa Fluor® 350 streptavidin/propidium iodide* *50 assays*	1 kit
V23201	Vybrant® Apoptosis Assay Kit #7 *Hoechst 33342/YO-PRO®-1/propidium iodide* *200 assays*	1 kit
V35118	Vybrant® FAM Caspase-3 and -7 Assay Kit *for flow cytometry* *25 assays*	1 kit
V35119	Vybrant® FAM Caspase-8 Assay Kit *for flow cytometry* *25 assays*	1 kit
V35117	Vybrant® FAM Poly Caspases Assay Kit *for flow cytometry* *25 assays*	1 kit
Y3603	YO-PRO®-1 iodide (491/509) *1 mM solution in DMSO*	1 mL

For current prices or to order online, visit probes.invitrogen.com

15.6 Probes for Cell Adhesion, Chemotaxis, Multidrug Resistance and Glutathione

Cell Adhesion Assays

The fundamental role of cell–cell and cell–matrix adhesion in the morphology and development of organisms, organs and tissues has made identification of molecular mediators of cell adhesion an important research focus in cell biology and immunology.[1–3] The useful review by Löster and Hortstkorte describes a number of different assays that can detect cell adhesion.[4] In a typical fluorescence-based cell adhesion assay, unlabeled cell monolayers in multiwell plates are incubated with fluorescently labeled cells and then washed to separate the adherent and nonadherent populations. Cell adhesion can then be determined simply by correlating the retained fluorescence with cell number. An ideal fluorescent marker will retain proportionality between fluorescence and cell number and introduce minimal interference with the cell adhesion process. Because adhesion is a cell-surface phenomenon, cytoplasmic markers that can be passively loaded are preferable to compounds that label cell-surface molecules, provided they are retained in the cell for the duration of the experiment or their leakage rate can be independently measured. Adhesion of fluorescent dye–labeled cells to matrices such as bone[5] can be directly observed by fluorescence microscopy using cells loaded with the permeant live-cell tracers described in Section 14.2 and Section 15.2 or the lipophilic dyes in Section 14.4. Alternatively, high molecular weight, cell-impermeant, fluorescent dextrans (Section 14.5) have been used to define the area *outside* of adherent cells, with the adherent cells themselves remaining unstained.[6] This same "negative-staining" method can also be used to assess cell spreading and progress toward confluency.

Cell Adhesion Assays Using Enzyme Substrates

Essentially all of the esterase substrates in Table 15.1 useful for monitoring cell viability can also be used for studying cell adhesion. As with cell viability studies, calcein AM (C1430, C3099, C3100MP; Figure 15.2) appears to best satisfy the criteria for assaying cell adhesion[7–9] and to have the least effect on cell viability and other cell functions.[7] The results obtained with leukocyte adhesion assays using calcein AM correlate well with those obtained with ^{51}Cr assays,[10,11] but the calcein AM protocols are more rapid and avoid the special handling required for use of radioactive material. Calcein AM has been used in numerous cell adhesion assays, including those designed to measure:

- Binding of labeled Jurkat cells to vascular cell adhesion molecule-1 (VCAM1) in cell membrane preparations[12]
- Effects of E-selectin–binding peptides[13] and integrins[14] on neutrophil adhesion
- Integrin-mediated cell adhesion in transfected K562 cells[15,16] and BSC-1 cells[17]
- Leukocyte[7,11,18] and neutrophil[18–20] adhesion to endothelial cells
- Monocyte adhesion in HIV-infected cells[21]

Other fluorogenic esterase substrates that have been used to assess cell adhesion include BCECF AM[5,22–29] (B1150, B1170, B3051), carboxyfluorescein diacetate[7,30–32] (5(6)-CFDA, C195; Section 15.2), fluorescein diacetate[33] (F1303, Section 15.2), the succinimidyl ester of carboxyfluorescein diacetate[14] (5(6)-CFDA, SE; CFSE; C1157; Section 15.2) and CellTracker™ Green CMFDA[23] (C2925, C7025). Because of the possibility of slow leakage of calcein from calcein AM–labeled cells, CellTracker™ Green CMFDA and 5(6)-CFDA SE are recommended for quantitative adhesion or aggregation assays that require incubation for more than about an hour.[14,34,35] Use of a combination of a green-fluorescent dye (usually calcein AM, BCECF AM or CMFDA) and a red-fluorescent dye (especially chloromethyl SNARF®-1 acetate (C6826, Figure 14.21), SNARF®-1 carboxylic acid, acetate, succinimidyl ester (S22801, Section 15.4) or carboxynaphthofluorescein diacetate (C13196, Section 15.2)) enables two-color measurements of adhesion or cell–cell aggregation in mixed cell cultures.[36] Calcein AM has also been used in a quantitative microplate assay of spreading of adherent cells on artificial or biological surfaces.[18]

In their review,[4] Löster and Hortstkorte describe the use of a number of other fluorogenic substrates for quantitating cell adhesion; among these are fluorescein diphosphate (F2999, Section 10.3) and ELF® 97 phosphate (Section 6.3) for lysosomal and membrane phosphatases and various substrates for glycosidases (Section 10.2), oxidases and peroxidase (Section 10.5).

Vybrant® Cell Adhesion Assay Kit

The Vybrant® Cell Adhesion Assay Kit (V13181) utilizes calcein AM to provide a fast and sensitive method for measuring cell–cell or cell–substratum adhesion.[7,13,14] Calcein AM is nonfluorescent but, once loaded into cells, is cleaved by endogenous esterases to produce calcein, a highly fluorescent and well-retained dye. Calcein provides a bright green-fluorescent, pH-independent, cytoplasmic cell marker that does not appear to affect the cell adhesion process.[9]

The Vybrant® Cell Adhesion Assay Kit is designed for use with a fluorescence microplate reader. To perform this assay, samples of calcein AM–labeled cells are added to monolayers of unlabeled cells in a microplate. Following incubation to allow the labeled cells to adhere to the unlabeled cells, the samples are washed to remove any nonadhering labeled cells (Figure 15.101). The calcein fluorescence in this sample, as compared with that of an unlabeled control sample, can then be used to calculate the number of adherent cells. The absorption/emission maxima of calcein (~494/517 nm) are ideally suited

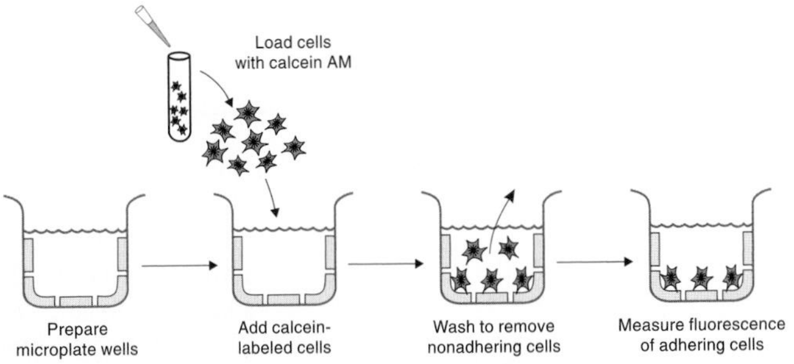

Figure 15.101 Principle of the Vybrant® Cell Adhesion Assay Kit (V13181). Microplate wells may be left untreated or precoated with extracellular matrix proteins, antibodies or other reagents.

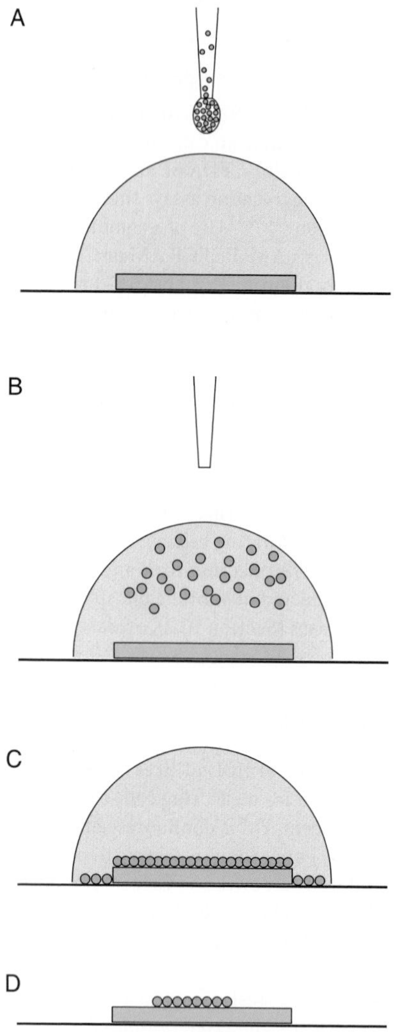

Figure 15.102 Schematic view of the microsphere-adhesion assay. Membrane-coated microspheres are added to a living tissue slice in a drop of medium (panel A). The microspheres disperse through the medium and eventually cover the tissue slice (panels B and C). After incubation, nonadherent microspheres are removed by extensive washing, and the sample is ready for analysis by fluorescence microscopy (panel D).

for detection by instruments equipped with standard fluorescein optical filters (Table 23.9). This simple fluorescence-based cell adhesion assay avoids problems associated with assays that utilize radioisotopes, which generate hazardous waste, and with assays that rely on the use of covalently coupled cell-surface labels, which can potentially alter cell function.

In addition to calcein AM, the Vybrant® Cell Adhesion Assay Kit also includes SYTOX® Green nucleic acid stain, an easy-to-use dead-cell indicator for assessing overall health of cells prior to performing the cell adhesion assay. As a fluorescent substitute for trypan blue, this high-affinity nucleic acid stain easily penetrates cells that have compromised membranes but will not cross the membranes of live cells. Upon binding to nucleic acids, the SYTOX® Green dye exhibits a >500-fold fluorescence enhancement and can be observed with standard fluorescein optical filters (excitation/emission ~504/523 nm).

The Vybrant® Cell Adhesion Assay Kit contains:

- Calcein AM
- The SYTOX® Green nucleic acid stain, an easy-to-use green-fluorescent indicator of the overall health of cells prior to performing the cell adhesion assay
- A detailed protocol

When used at the concentration suggested in the protocol, this kit provides sufficient reagents to perform about 1000 assays using a fluorescence microplate reader.

Cell Adhesion Assays Using the CyQUANT® Cell Proliferation Assay Kit

Our CyQUANT® Cell Proliferation Assay Kit (C7026, Section 15.4) can also serve as an important tool for quantitating both cell–cell and cell–surface adhesion. The CyQUANT® assay detects total nucleic acids in cells, with a linear response between fewer than 50 to at least 50,000 cells (Figure 15.68). To quantitate cell–surface adhesion, cells are simply permitted to adhere to the surface, gently washed to remove nonadherent cells, frozen and lysed with buffer containing the CyQUANT® GR reagent and then analyzed to determine total nucleic acids in the adherent cells. As a control, the fluorescence of the total number of cells added to the well before the wash step can be determined by the same assay method to yield the percentage of adherent cells. It should also be possible to extend the CyQUANT® assay to studies of cell–cell adhesion by quantitating both the number of surface-adhering cells originally plated and the number of total cells after a second cell line has been introduced and allowed to adhere. A similar assay for cell adhesion based on DAPI (D1306, D3571, D21490; Section 8.1) has been reported.[37]

Microsphere Adhesion Assays

In a novel method for studying adhesion in live neural tissue slices, including hippocampal slices, fluorescent 4 µm microspheres (F8858, F8859; Section 6.5) are coated with isolated cell membranes from dissociated live cells. The membrane-coated microspheres are then seeded on live tissue slices, and after a short incubation time, the nonadherent microspheres are eliminated by washing (Figure 15.102). The pattern of tissue labeling of adherent microspheres can then be visualized by epifluorescence microscopy.[38] A flow cytometry–based microsphere adhesion assay has also been developed to determine integrin-specific adhesion, as well as to analyze integrin-mediated adhesion defects in B-lineage acute lymphoblastic leukemia.[39,40] FluoSpheres® microspheres of different colors (or sizes or intensities) (Section 6.5) can be used for simultaneous labeling of different adhesion factors.

Fluorescent Fibrinogen

Fibrinogen is a key component in the blood clotting process and can support both platelet–platelet and platelet–surface interactions by binding to the glycoprotein IIb-IIIa (GPIIb-IIIa) receptor[41–44] (also called integrin $\alpha_{IIb}\beta_3$). Although the mechanism is not well understood, activation of GPIIb-IIIa is required for fibrinogen binding, which leads to platelet activation, adhesion, spreading and microfilament reorganization of human endothelial cells *in vitro*.[41,44–46] Soluble fibrinogen binds to its receptor with a Ca^{2+}-dependent apparent K_d of 0.18 µM.[47] This binding is apparently mediated by the tripeptide sequence Arg–Gly–Asp (RGD), found both in fibrinogen and fibronectin, as well as some other proteins.[44,48–50]

Fluorescently labeled fibrinogen has proven to be a valuable tool for investigating platelet activation and subsequent fibrinogen binding. Fluorescein fibrinogen has been used to identify activated platelets by flow cytometry.[45,51–53] The binding of fluorescein fibrinogen to activated platelets has been shown to be saturable and can be inhibited completely by underivatized fibrinogen.[52] The preferential binding and accumulation of fluorescein fibrinogen at the endothelial border of venular blood vessels has been studied by quantitative fluorescence microscopy.[54]

Molecular Probes offers five conjugates of human fibrinogen in four different fluorescent colors. The Alexa Fluor® 488 human fibrinogen conjugate (F13191) and the Oregon Green® 488 human fibrinogen conjugate (F7496) have spectral characteristics (Figure 7.21, Figure 7.5) similar to fluorescein conjugates. However, the fluorescence of Oregon Green® 488 and Alexa Fluor® 488 protein conjugates is much more photostable and less pH dependent than that of fluorescein conjugates (Figure 1.12, Figure 1.46, Figure 1.53). The red-orange–fluorescent (Figure 7.9) Alexa Fluor® 546 human fibrinogen conjugate (F13192) is brighter and more photostable than the spectrally similar tetramethylrhodamine fibrinogen conjugates. Similarly, the red-fluorescent (Figure 7.12) Alexa Fluor® 594 human fibrinogen conjugate (F13193) and far-red–fluorescent (Figure 7.16) Alexa Fluor® 647 human fibrinogen conjugate (F35200) are brighter than Texas Red® and Cy5 conjugates, respectively, yet have similar excitation and emission maxima. These highly fluorescent fibrinogen conjugates are useful for investigating platelet activation and subsequent fibrinogen binding using fluorescence microscopy or flow cytometry (Figure 15.103).

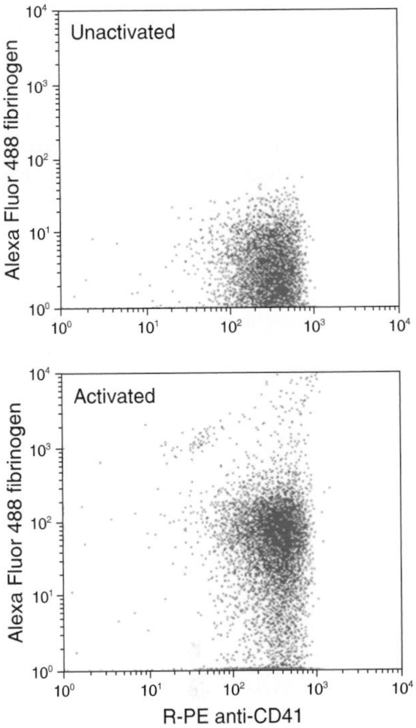

Figure 15.103 Interaction of fluorescently labeled fibrinogen with activated platelets. Whole blood was first incubated with an R-phycoerythrin (R-PE)–labeled anti-CD41 antibody to label the platelets. 20 µM adenosine 5′-diphosphate (ADP) was added in order to activate the platelets, then 2 µg/mL Alexa Fluor® 488 fibrinogen (F13191) was added and incubated with the sample for 5 minutes. Cells were analyzed by flow cytometry using excitation at 488 nm. Both activated and unactivated platelets show binding of the anti-CD41 antibody; however, only the activated platelets show strong binding by fibrinogen. A total of 5000 platelets are shown in each experiment.

Fluorescent Gelatin and Type IV Collagen

Collagen is a major component of the extracellular matrix and, in vertebrates, constitutes approximately 25% of total cellular protein. This important protein not only serves a structural role, but also is important in cell adhesion and migration. Specific collagen receptors, fibronectin and a number of other proteins involved in cell–cell and cell–surface adhesion have been demonstrated to bind collagen and gelatin[55,56] (denatured collagen). Molecular Probes prepares fluorescent conjugates of gelatin and type IV collagen, the principal collagen in basement membranes. These reagents are designed for researchers studying collagen-binding proteins and collagen metabolism, as well as gelatinases and collagenases (Section 10.4), which are metalloproteins that digest gelatin and collagen. We offer two green-fluorescent gelatin conjugates — fluorescein gelatin (G13187) and Oregon Green® 488 gelatin (G13186). When compared with the fluorescein conjugate, the Oregon Green® 488 conjugate exhibits almost identical fluorescence spectra but its fluorescence is much more photostable and less pH dependent. For researchers requiring a more specific substrate, we also offer the Oregon Green® 488 conjugate of human type IV collagen (C13185) and yellow-green–fluorescent collagen-coated FluoSpheres® microspheres (F20892, F20893; Section 16.1). By analogy to the results previously obtained with fluorescein conjugates of these proteins, these highly fluorescent gelatin and collagen conjugates are potentially useful for:

- Following integrin-mediated phagocytosis[57]
- Localizing surface fibronectin on cultured cells[58]
- Studying fibronectin–gelatin interactions in solution using fluorescence polarization[56,59]
- Visualizing gelatinase activity using *in situ* gel zymography[60]

Anti-Fibronectin Antibody

Fibronectin is a large glycoprotein that is found in both plasma[61] and in the extracellular matrix.[62] The protein is coded by a single gene, but alternate RNA splicing gives rise to several fibronectin isoforms that play important roles in cellular adhesion and migration, blood clotting and phagocytosis.[63] The apparent function of fibronectin is to mediate cell attachment via interactions with both cell-surface receptors and components of the extracellular matrix such as heparin, fibrinogen and collagen.[64] Molecular Probes offers a chicken IgY anti-fibronectin (human) antibody (A21316) for detecting fibronectin in Western blotting and immunohistochemistry applications (Figure 15.104), as well as several fluorescent anti–chicken IgG secondary antibodies that recognize this antibody (Section 7.2, Table 7.1).

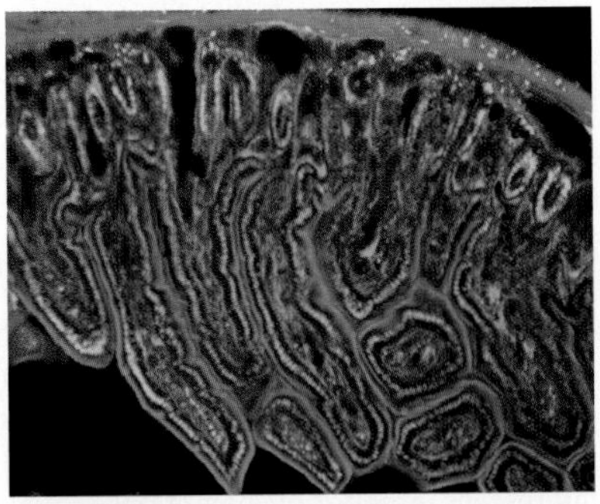

Figure 15.104 Mouse intestine cryosection showing basement membranes labeled with our chicken IgY anti-fibronectin antibody (A21316) and the Alexa Fluor® 488 goat anti–chicken IgG (A11039, green). Goblet cells and crypt cells were labeled with Alexa Fluor® 594 wheat germ agglutinin (W11262, red). The microvillar brush border and smooth muscle layers were visualized with Alexa Fluor® 680 phalloidin (A22286, pseudocolored purple). The section was counterstained with DAPI (D1306, D3571, D21490, blue).

Chemotaxis Assays

Direct Detection of Chemotaxis Using Cell Counting

Chemotaxis, defined as directed cell motion toward an extracellular gradient, plays an important role during fertilization, inflammation, wound healing and hematopoiesis.[65] Measurement of chemotaxis usually has relied on determination of the number of viable cells that have migrated through a special "chemotaxis chamber." A 96-well disposable chemotaxis chamber is reported to be suitable for fluorescence-based assays that are faster, less labor intensive and more sensitive than visually detected migration assays.[66] The probes used to follow chemotaxis in live cells typically are the same esterase substrates that are useful for assaying cell viability and cell adhesion (Table 15.1). The primary esterase substrates used for this purpose are calcein AM[67–71] (C1430, C3099, C3100MP), BCECF AM[7,24] (B1150, B1170, B3051) and CellTracker™ Green CMFDA[72] (C2925, C7025). Calcein AM does not interfere with lymphocyte proliferation or with granulocyte or neutrophil chemotaxis or superoxide production,[7,68] and, unlike BCECF AM, calcein AM does not affect chemotaxis in leukocytes.[69]

Because chemotaxis involves translocation of whole cells, assays that simply count cell numbers — as with our CyQUANT® GR reagent, part of our CyQUANT® Cell Proliferation Assay Kit (C7026, Section 15.4) — are also quite reliable for following chemotaxis.[73]

The green-fluorescent SYTO® 13 and orange-fluorescent SYTO® 15 dyes (S7575, S7577; Section 8.1) have been used to track the co-migration of separately stained populations of neutrophils using opposing gradients of leukotriene B_4 and interleukin 8 as the chemoattractants.[74]

Probes for Chemotaxis Receptors

Molecular Probes prepares the fluorescein conjugate of the chemotactic hexapeptide *N*-formyl-Nle-Leu-Phe-Nle-Tyr-Lys (F1314), which binds to the fMLF receptor[75,76] (Section 16.1). Molecular Probes also offers fluorescein-labeled casein (C2990). Using fluorescein-labeled casein, researchers have demonstrated casein-specific chemotaxis receptors in human neutrophils and monocytes with flow cytometry.[77,78] Neutrophils activated with phorbol myristate acetate have been shown to undergo a dose-dependent increase in binding of fluorescein-labeled casein.[79]

BODIPY® FL Cytochalasin B: A Chemotaxis Inhibitor

Cytochalasin B is a common inhibitor of chemotaxis through its effect on actin polymerization. Although we have not evaluated the probe for the application, our green-fluorescent BODIPY® FL conjugate of cytochalasin B (C12376, Section 11.1) may have utility as a fluorescent inhibitor of chemotaxis.

Multidrug Resistance Assays

Multidrug resistance (MDR) is a phenomenon representing a complex group of biological processes that are of growing interest in both clinical and experimental oncology.[80–82] The MDR phenotype is characterized by the acquired resistance of tumor cells to structurally and functionally dissimilar anticancer drugs. Among the many mechanisms contributing to this multidrug resistance are the following:

- Amplification of genes encoding drug-metabolizing enzymes
- Elevated levels of glutathione and glutathione-conjugating enzymes
- Mutated DNA topoisomerases
- Overexpression of plasma membrane ATP-dependent drug efflux pumps

Based on substrate and inhibitor profiles, at least four different plasma membrane ATP-dependent drug efflux pumps have been identified.[83,84] The activity of the verapamil-sensitive P-glycoprotein (Pgp) encoded by the *MDR1* gene leads to extrusion of anthracyclins, epipodophyllotoxins, *Vinca* alkaloids, coelenterazine and other cytostatic drugs.[85,86] Many tumor cells do not express Pgp but export daunorubicin via a second, energy-dependent drug export mechanism.[87] A third, energy-dependent drug exporting mechanism has been described that is associated with a MDR-associated protein[88] (MRP), which shows high selectivity toward glutathione *S*-conjugates and is inhibited by *Vinca* alkaloids and probenecid.[89,90] A fourth vanadate- and verapamil-resistant but probenecid-sensitive glutathione *S*-conjugate–exporting system in mouse and rat fibroblasts has also been reported.[91] Obviously, the mechanisms of MDR are complex and, in some cases, have overlapping selectivity for the substrates.[84] Molecular Probes offers the Vybrant® Multidrug Resistance Assay Kit, along with a variety of useful fluorescent probes for monitoring various aspects of the MDR phenotype.

MDR Assays Using Acetoxymethyl Esters

The discovery that acetoxymethyl (AM) ester derivatives of fluorescent calcium indicators such as indo-1 AM and fluo-3 AM (I1203, F1241, F23915; Section 19.3) or other dyes such as calcein AM (C1430, C3099, C3100MP), are rapidly extruded from cells expressing Pgp[92] presented a new class of highly sensitive probes for functional assays of the *MDR1*-encoded Pgp. Calcein AM — but not calcein — is an activator of Pgp in isolated membranes with a $K_d \leq 1\ \mu M$.[93] Cells expressing the *MDR1*-encoded Pgp rapidly remove the nonfluorescent probe calcein AM, resulting in decreased accumulation of the highly fluorescent calcein in the cytoplasmic compartment.[90,93–95] Calcein AM is also a substrate for the MDR-associated protein (MRP), although in this case the hydrophilic free calcein anion is also exported.[96–98] Because calcein itself is not a substrate for the *MDR1*-encoded Pgp, MDR can be quantitatively assessed by measuring the net accumulation of intracellular fluorescence.[99] Cellular depletion of glutathione does not affect the extrusion of calcein AM by the *MDR1*-encoded Pgp.[96] Fluorescence of intracellular calcein can be distinguished from that of calcein that has leaked into the medium by adding Co^{2+} to totally quench the fluorescence of the extracellular dye.[98] The patented calcein AM assay for Pgp-related MDR is suitable for either flow cytometry[100] or fluorometry and is more rapid and significantly more sensitive than conventional assays based on doxorubicin accumulation.[101] Reduced accumulation of calcein in MDR cells can also be observed in single cells by fluorescence microscopy.[94,97]

Vybrant® Multidrug Resistance Assay Kit

The Vybrant® Multidrug Resistance Assay Kit (V13180), which is based on the fluorescence microplate–based method developed by Tiberghien and Loor,[95] provides a rapid and simple method for large-scale screening of MDR inhibitors. This assay utilizes the fluorogenic dye calcein AM as a substrate for efflux activity of Pgp. Calcein AM is a nonfluorescent, highly lipid-soluble dye (Figure 15.2) that can rapidly penetrate the plasma membrane of normal cells. Once inside the cell, ester bonds are cleaved by endogenous esterases, transforming calcein AM into the hydrophilic and intensely fluorescent dye, calcein. Calcein is well retained in the cytosol and, unlike other fluorescent Pgp substrates such as BCECF or fura-2, its fluorescence is neither pH nor calcium dependent. MDR cells expressing high levels of Pgp rapidly extrude nonfluorescent calcein AM from the plasma membrane, reducing accumulation of fluorescent calcein in the cytosol [90,93,94,99] (Figure 15.105). The amount of Pgp activity is inversely proportional to the accumulation of intracellular calcein fluorescence. This assay is designed for use with fluorescence microplate readers and is particularly useful for rapid and sensitive screening of candidate Pgp inhibitors in MDR cell lines. The absorption/emission maxima of calcein (494/517 nm) are ideally suited for detection by instruments equipped with standard fluorescein filters. The Vybrant® Multidrug Resistance Assay Kit (V13180) contains:

- Calcein AM
- Cyclosporin A, a competitive inhibitor of drug binding to Pgp
- Verapamil, a calcium channel blocker that noncompetitively inhibits Pgp activity
- A detailed protocol

When used at the concentration recommended in the protocol, this kit provides sufficient calcein AM to perform about 10,000 assays using a fluorescence microplate reader.

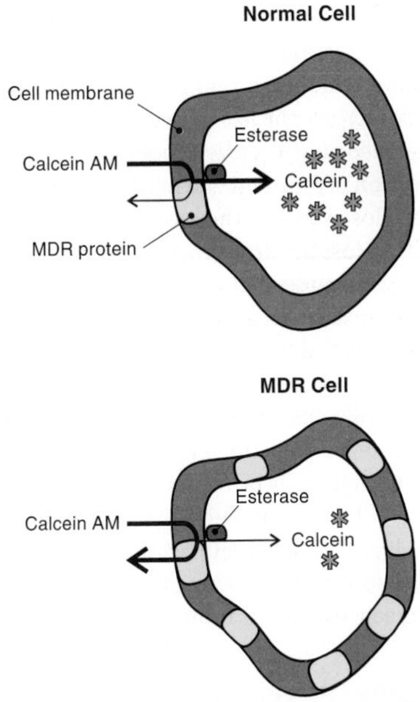

Figure 15.105 Principle of the Vybrant® Multidrug Resistance Assay Kit (V13180). In normal cells, nonfluorescent calcein AM readily diffuses across the cell membrane. Fluorescent calcein accumulates in the cytoplasm after cleavage of calcein AM by endogenous esterases. In MDR cells, overexpression of MDR transporter proteins increases expulsion of calcein AM from the cell membrane before enzymatic hydrolysis of its AM esters, thus reducing accumulation of intracellular calcein.

Diagnostic Assay for Multidrug Resistance

Multidrug resistance has been identified in many different cancer cell lines, and is a well-characterized cause of chemotherapeutic failure.[102–104] Whereas the Vybrant® Multidrug Resistance Assay Kit provides a microplate assay for screening MDR inhibitors, the calcein AM extrusion assay may also be used for the functional determination of multidrug resistance in tumor cells. The MultiDrugQuant Assay Kit, available from Solvo Biotechnology (www.solvobiotech.com), provides a quantitative, flow cytometric method for measuring the transport activity of both MDR1 and MRP1 multidrug resistance proteins. This kit is based on the assay developed by Sarkadi and co-workers, which has been shown to predict therapy response and survival of patients with acute myeloid leukemia.[105]

MDR Assays Using Glutathione-Reactive Probes

Presence of the MDR-associated protein (MRP) is responsible for selective ATP-dependent extrusion of glutathione conjugates of a variety of chemically unrelated cytotoxic compounds. Consequently, a wide variety of the thiol-reactive fluorescent dyes described in Chapter 2 should have utility for following MRP-mediated transport. By using a combination of calcein AM and the thiol-reactive dye pyrene maleimide (P28, Section 2.3), it has been shown that MRP expression results in extrusion via two MDR pathways, and that the mechanisms are mutually exclusive.[96] The principal probes that have been used to follow the transport of glutathione adducts are the same probes used to measure intracellular levels of glutathione (see below): monochlorobimane [106–109] (M1381MP) and CellTracker™ Green CMFDA [108,110,111] (C2925, C7025).

MDR Assays Using Mitochondrial Probes

In the classical functional assay for MDR, doxorubicin efflux is measured.[112–114] The principal weakness of this assay is its low sensitivity, which has stimulated the search for other fluorochromes to monitor drug efflux. MDR cells overexpressing the Pgp have been identified using various mitochondrial probes (Section 12.2), including rhodamine 123 (R302, R22420), acridine orange 10-nonyl bromide (nonyl acridine orange, A1372) and rhodamine 6G [83,115–122] (R634). Furthermore, it has been reported that the fluorescence excitation spectrum of rhodamine 123 is different in drug-resistant and drug-sensitive cells.[123,124]

The potential-sensitive carbocyanine dyes, including dipentyl-, dihexyl- and diheptyloxacarbocyanines (D272, D273, D378; Section 22.3), also have advantages over the common doxorubicin assay for MDR.[112,125] Not only are these carbocyanine dyes more fluorescent, permitting use of lower dye concentrations, but their fluorescence increases upon binding to cell membranes,[126] unlike the fluorescence of doxorubicin, which is substantially quenched inside cells.[127] The ratiometric, potential-sensitive di-4-ANEPPS probe (D1199, Section 22.2) has been used to demonstrate that MDR cells have decreased electrical potentials.[128]

MDR Assays Using Nucleic Acid Stains

MDR cells have also been identified by their decreased accumulation of nucleic acid–binding dyes such as Hoechst 33258 (H1398, H3569, H21491; Section 8.1), Hoechst 33342 (H1399, H3570, H21492; Section 8.1) and ethidium bromide [122,129,130] (E1305, E3565; Section 8.1). A report describes the use of two membrane-permeant nucleic acid stains developed at Molecular Probes (SY-38 and SY-3150) for improved detection of Pgp-dependent MDR by flow cytometry.[131] These dyes more closely mimic the kinetics of uptake and accumulation of many of the cytostatic drugs that are eliminated from tumor cells by the energy-dependent efflux mechanisms. Although these specific nucleic acid stains are not available from Molecular Probes, their chemical structures and fluorescence properties are similar to those of several of our SYTO® dyes (Section 8.1, Table 8.3), including the SYTO® 16 green-fluorescent nucleic acid stain, which was shown to be a useful substrate for detecting Pgp-mediated resistance by flow cytometry and in single cells by confocal laser-scanning microscopy.[132] Our five SYTO® Fluorescent Nucleic Acid Stain Sampler Kits (S7554, S7572, S11340, S11350, S11360; Section 8.1) provide samples of SYTO® dyes with fluorescence covering the entire visible spectrum; these dyes may be screened for their utility in detecting MDR cells.

BODIPY® FL Verapamil

The Ca^{2+}-channel blocker verapamil is one of several molecules known to inhibit Pgp-mediated drug efflux.[133] Molecular Probes offers the green-fluorescent BODIPY® FL verapamil probe (B7431, Figure 16.38) for the study of Pgp function and localization. Verapamil appears to inhibit drug efflux by acting as a substrate for Pgp, thereby overwhelming the transporter's capacity to expel other drugs. Our BODIPY® FL conjugate of verapamil, with spectral properties similar to fluorescein, also serves as a substrate for Pgp. This fluorescent verapamil derivative preferentially accumulates in the lysosomes of normal, drug-sensitive NIH 3T3 cells but is rapidly transported out of MDR cells, as revealed by fluorescence microscopy.[134–138] The outward transport of BODIPY® FL verapamil from MDR cells is inhibited by underivatized verapamil, as well as by excess vinblastine.[136]

BODIPY® Dihydropyridines

Like verapamil, dihydropyridines are known to inhibit drug efflux. Consequently, our fluorescent dihydropyridines [139,140] labeled with either the green-fluorescent DM-BODIPY® (D7443, Section 16.3) or the orange-fluorescent ST-BODIPY® (S7445, Section 16.3) fluorophores may be useful MDR probes.

BODIPY® FL Paclitaxel

BODIPY® FL paclitaxel (BODIPY® FL Taxol, P7500; Section 11.2) is a substrate for Pgp-mediated transport that has been used as a probe for tumor spheroids.[141]

BODIPY® FL Vinblastine

The antimitotic agent vinblastine inhibits the Pgp-mediated efflux of a number of drugs and other probes from multidrug-resistant cells. Our BODIPY® FL conjugate of vinblastine (V12390) is useful as a highly fluorescent vinblastine analog.[142] A biologically active coumarin dye–labeled vinblastine has previously been described.[143]

BODIPY® Prazosin and BODIPY® Forskolin

Photoaffinity analogs of prazosin, an α_1-adrenergic receptor antagonist,[144,145] and forskolin, an adenylate cyclase activator, have been shown to selectively photolabel isolated Pgp.[146–149] Our green-fluorescent BODIPY® FL prazosin (B7433, Figure 16.30) and BODIPY® FL forskolin (B7469, Figure 17.13) and red-fluorescent BODIPY® 558/568 prazosin (B7434) are potentially useful tools for probing MDR mechanisms.

MDR Assays Using Ion Indicators

Using fluorescent pH indicators, researchers have demonstrated that MDR cells exhibit increased intracellular pH, increased acid secretion or increased intracellular pH evoked by alkalinization of the medium.[127,128,150–153] Molecular Probes' extensive selection of fluorescent pH indicators is described in Chapter 20. However, as mentioned above, neutral AM esters (and acetates) are partially pumped out of some MDR cells before they hydrolyze to the indicator.

Methotrexate Resistance and Gene Amplification

Tumor cells often undergo gene amplification that leads to overexpression of dihydrofolate reductase (DHFR). This increased DHFR expression (Figure 15.106) confers enhanced tolerance to the cytotoxic effects of methotrexate.[80,122] For the study of antimetabolite resistance and spontaneous gene amplification, we offer four fluorescent methotrexate conjugates. In addition to green-fluorescent fluorescein methotrexate (M1198MP), which has been used to visualize biochemical networks in living cells,[154] we provide Alexa Fluor® 488 methotrexate (M23271) and BODIPY® FL methotrexate (M23272), both of which exhibit fluorescein-like spectral characteristics, as well as the red-fluorescent Texas Red®-X methotrexate (M23273). The quantitative binding of fluorescein methotrexate (M1198MP) to dihydrofolate reductase (DHFR) enables researchers to isolate cells based on DHFR expression.[155–158] Our fluorescein cadaverine adduct, which was originally described by Gapski and colleagues,[159] appears to be equivalent to fluorescein lysine methotrexate in its applications.[155]

Glutathione Determination

The tripeptide glutathione (γ-L-glutamyl-L-cysteinylglycine) is the most abundant (up to 10 mM in the cytoplasm and about 1 mM in blood [160]) and important nonprotein thiols in mammalian cells. Glutathione plays a central role in protecting cells of all organs, including the brain,[161] against damage produced by free radicals, oxidants and electrophiles. A distinct mechanism of MDR involves the overexpression of energy-dependent membrane pumps dedicated to removal of glutathione *S*-conjugates from the cytoplasm by a multidrug resistance–associated protein [88,162] (MRP). An increased rate of efflux of glutathione from Jurkat T lymphocytes during anti-FAS/APO-1 antibody–induced apoptosis has been reported.[163]

Several fluorescent reagents have been proposed for determining cellular levels of glutathione and glutathione *S*-transferase (GST), which catalyzes the formation of glutathione *S*-conjugates, but no probe is without drawbacks in quantitative studies of live cells. The high but variable levels of intracellular glutathione and the multitude of GST isozymes make kinetic measurements under saturating substrate conditions difficult or impossible.[164,165] Isozymes of GST vary both in abundance and activity, further complicating the analysis.[166] Moreover, the fluorescent reagents designed to measure glutathione may react with intracellular thiols other than glutathione, including proteins in glutathione-depleted cells.[167] Therefore, precautions must be taken in applying the reagents mentioned here to quantitate either glutathione or GST in cells. A useful strategy is to test a variety of glutathione-sensitive dyes — those requiring glutathione S-transferase activity, as well as GST-independent fluorophores — under controlled experimental conditions in which glutathione is depleted.[168]

Glutathione Determination with Monochlorobimane

Cell-permeant monochlorobimane (mBCl, M1381MP), which is essentially nonfluorescent until conjugated to thiols, has long been the preferred thiol-reactive probe for quantitating glutathione levels in cells and for measuring GST activity.[169,170] Because the blue-fluorescent glutathione adduct of monochlorobimane eventually accumulates in the nucleus, it is not a reliable indicator of the nuclear and cytoplasmic distribution of cellular glutathione.[171] Tissue glutathione levels can also be measured fluorometrically by adding both monochlorobimane and glutathione S-transferase to tissue homogenates.[172]

Monochlorobimane is reported to react more selectively with glutathione in whole cells than does monobromobimane (M1378, M20381; Section 2.3; Figure 2.31) and has proven useful for assaying drug resistance by flow cytometry[165,170,173] and by fluorescence microscopy.[174,175] Moreover, HPLC analysis has shown that glutathione is the only low molecular weight thiol in hepatocytes that reacts with monochlorobimane.[176] Results from glutathione determination with monochlorobimane have been shown to match those from an independent glutathione-specific assay using glutathione reductase.[177,178] However, although monochlorobimane was shown to be highly selective for glutathione in rodent cells, it was reported to inadequately label glutathione in human cells because of its low affinity for human glutathione S-transferases.[165] The reducing agent tris-(2-carboxyethyl)phosphine (TCEP, T2556; Section 2.1) has been used in place of dithiothreitol (DTT, D1532; Section 2.1) in a simplified monobromobimane-based assay for glutathione[179] and thus may also prove useful for monochlorobimane-based assays. In this monobromobimane-based glutathione assay, an extraction step is reportedly necessary to remove a fluorescent, reductive-dehalogenation side product of TCEP and monobromobimane.[180]

Monochlorobimane has been used to detect a vanadate- and verapamil-resistant but probenecid-sensitive glutathione S-conjugate exporting system in mouse and rat fibroblasts.[91] Probenecid inhibits the ATP-dependent organic anion pump and blocks the loss of the fluorescent bimane–glutathione adduct from rat fibroblasts.[181] Monochlorobimane has also been employed to sort cells based on their expression of recombinant GST.[182]

Glutathione Determination with Visible Light–Excitable Thiol-Reactive Probes

Molecular Probes' patented CellTracker™ Green CMFDA (5-chloromethylfluorescein diacetate, C2925, C7025; Figure 14.6) is a useful alternative to the UV light–excitable monochlorobimane for determining levels of intracellular glutathione.[183,184] CellTracker™ Green CMFDA can be excited by the argon-ion laser, and is compatible with flow cytometry and confocal laser-scanning microscopy applications. CellTracker™ Green CMFDA's enzymatic product has a much higher absorbance and fluorescence quantum yield than that of monochlorobimane. In conjunction with Hoechst 33342 (H1399, H3570, H21492; Section 8.1), CellTracker™ Green CMFDA has also been shown to be effective for analyzing intracellular thiol levels as a function of cell cycle using flow cytometry,[183,185] for following transport of the glutathione adduct to secretory vesicles in multidrug-resistant cells[108] and for detecting apoptotic cells, which have reduced levels of intracellular reduced glutathione.[186] Selectivity of CellTracker™ Green CMFDA for glutathione (versus thiolated proteins) was shown by the isolation of >95% of the intracellular fluorescent products as a mixture of the glutathione adduct and the unconjugated hydrolysis product, chloromethylfluorescein.[165] However, in these experiments, the high fluorescence of unconjugated chloromethylfluorescein resulted in significantly increased background levels. Because glutathione-depleting chemicals may also cause cell death, it has been recommended that calcein AM be used to independently assess cell viability in assays that use CellTracker™ Green CMFDA to measure changes in the level of intracellular glutathione.[184] Presumably propidium iodide (P1304MP, P3566, P21493; Section 8.1) could also be used simultaneously with CellTracker™ Green CMFDA to discriminate the red-fluorescent dead cells and green-fluorescent live cells.

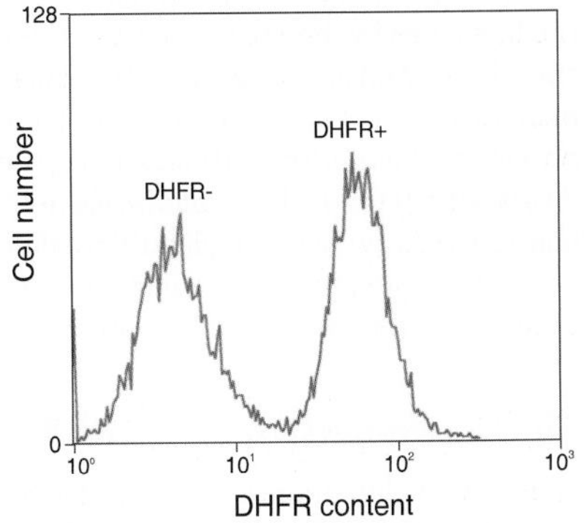

Figure 15.106 Analysis of dihydrofolate reductase (DHFR) content in CHO cells. A mixture of DHFR+ and DHFR- cells was stained with 1 µM fluorescein methotrexate (M1198MP) for 2 hours at 37°C. Following incubation with fluorescein methotrexate, cells were trypsinized, washed in phosphate-buffered saline and analyzed by flow cytometry using 488 nm excitation. Emission was collected at 525 nm.

Like CMFDA, chloromethyl SNARF®-1 acetate (C6826, Figure 14.19) forms adducts with intracellular thiols that are well retained by viable cells (Figure 14.21). The glutathione adduct of chloromethyl SNARF®-1 can be excited by the 488 nm spectral line of the argon-ion laser yet emits beyond 630 nm (Figure 20.11), which may prove advantageous in multicolor applications or when assaying autofluorescent samples. A number of our other CellTracker™ (Section 14.2) and MitoTracker® (Section 12.2) probes have thiol-reactive chloromethyl moieties and may be similarly useful for glutathione determination. All of these probes form glutathione *S*-conjugates that are likely to be transported from the cytoplasm by an MDR-associated protein[88,162] (MRP).

Glutathiolation Detection with BioGEE

Biotinylated glutathione ethyl ester (BioGEE, G36000; Figure 15.107) is a cell-permeant, biotinylated glutathione analog for detecting glutathiolation. Under conditions of oxidative stress, cells may transiently incorporate glutathione into proteins. Stressed cells incubated with BioGEE will also incorporate this biotinylated glutathione derivative into proteins, facilitating the identification of oxidation-sensitive proteins.[187] Once these cells are fixed and permeabilized, glutathiolation levels can be detected with a fluorescent streptavidin conjugate (Table 7.22, Section 7.6) using either flow cytometry or fluorescence microscopy. Proteins glutathiolated with BioGEE can also be extracted and analyzed by mass spectrometry or by Western blotting methods (Section 9.3) in conjunction with fluorophore- or enzyme-labeled streptavidin conjugates (Section 7.6, Table 7.22).

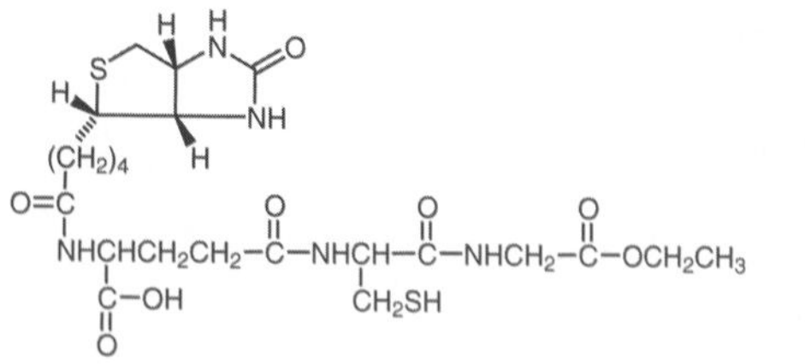

Figure 15.107 G36000 glutathione ethyl ester, biotin amide (BioGEE).

PFB Aminofluorescein: A Specific Substrate for Glutathione S-Transferase

We have shown that our patented 5-(pentafluorobenzoylamino)fluorescein (PFB-F, P12925) is the most selective substrate known for at least some glutathione *S*-transferase (GST) isozymes *in vitro*.[188] In our experiments, PFB-F does not react with thiol-containing proteins such as β-galactosidase, and its reaction rate with glutathione in the absence of GST is extremely low. The reaction of PFB-F with glutathione is quite specific — there is virtually no reaction with oxidized glutathione, cysteine, other low molecular weight thiols or with glutathione conjugates. Oxidized glutathione (or total glutathione) can be determined as glutathione following reduction with a reagent such as TCEP (T2556, Section 2.1). The highly fluorescent, unreacted PFB-F and its glutathione conjugate can be readily separated by TLC or HPLC. Because the assay requires a separation step, PFB-F is not an effective probe for quantitating glutathione in single intact cells. However, the method can be used to quantitate the average level of either glutathione or glutathione *S*-transferase in as few as 200–500 cells using thin-layer chromatography and a fluorescence scanner.[188]

Glutathione Determination With o-Phthaldialdehyde and Naphthalene-2,3-dicarboxaldehyde

The reagent *o*-phthaldialdehyde (OPA, P2331MP) reacts with both the thiol and the amine functions of glutathione, yielding a cyclic derivative that is fluorescent. The spectra of the glutathione adduct of OPA (excitation/emission maxima of 350/420 nm) are shifted from those of its protein adducts.[189] This effect has occasionally been used to estimate glutathione levels in cells.[165,190] OPA has also been used as a derivatization reagent for the chromatographic determination of glutathione in cells, blood and tissues.[191,192]

The membrane-permeant naphthalene-2,3-dicarboxaldehyde (NDA, N1138) has been used to determine glutathione levels in single cells. Cells were treated with the NDA reagent and then analyzed by capillary electrophoresis;[193] glutathione labeling was reported to be complete within two minutes. The glutathione adduct of NDA can be excited by the 458 nm spectral line of the argon-ion laser.

References

1. Pharmacol Rev 50, 197 (1998); **2.** Cell 84, 345 (1996); **3.** Annu Rev Biochem 60, 155 (1991); **4.** Micron 31, 41 (2000); **5.** Anal Biochem 267, 37 (1999); **6.** Cytometry 33, 41 (1998); **7.** J Immunol Methods 172, 115 (1994); **8.** Cell Biol Toxicol 10, 329 (1994); **9.** J Immunol Methods 178, 41 (1995); **10.** Biotechniques 23, 1056 (1997); **11.** J Immunol Methods 163, 181 (1993); **12.** J Immunol Methods 175, 59 (1994); **13.** J Biol Chem 270, 21129 (1995); **14.** J Immunol Methods 172, 25 (1994); **15.** J Cell Biol 130, 745 (1995); **16.** J Cell Biol 127, 1129 (1994); **17.** Proc Natl Acad Sci U S A 90, 5700 (1993); **18.** Anal Biochem 219, 288 (1994); **19.** J Immunol 157, 3617 (1996); **20.** J Biol Chem 269, 10008 (1994); **21.** J Immunol 156, 1638 (1996); **22.** J Biol Chem 275, 7052 (2000); **23.** J Cell Biol 133, 445 (1996); **24.** Mol Biol Cell 6, 661 (1995); **25.** J Biol Chem 269, 1033 (1994); **26.** J Cell Biol 125, 1395 (1994); **27.** J Biol Chem 268, 8835 (1993); **28.** J Cell Biol 123, 245 (1993); **29.** Biochem Biophys Res Commun 172, 262 (1990); **30.** J Cell Biol 124, 609 (1994); **31.** Dev Biol 135, 133 (1989); **32.** J Cell Biol 109, 3465 (1989); **33.** J Immunol Methods 157, 117 (1993); **34.** Neuron 17, 1089 (1996); **35.** Neuron 17, 353 (1996); **36.** J Cell Biol 135, 1593 (1996); **37.** J Immunol Methods 165, 93 (1993); **38.** Biotechniques 26, 466 (1999); **39.** J Immunol 165, 442 (2000); **40.** Blood 94, 754 (1999); **41.** J Biol Chem 270, 28812 (1995); **42.** Thromb Res 77, 543 (1995); **43.** Biochem J 270, 149 (1990); **44.** Biochem Pharmacol 36, 4035 (1987); **45.** J Biol Chem 270, 11358 (1995); **46.** J Cell Biol 104, 1403 (1987); **47.** J Biol Chem 258, 12582 (1983); **48.** J Biol Chem 273, 6821 (1998); **49.** Science 231, 1559 (1986); **50.** Proc Natl Acad Sci U S A 82, 8057 (1985); **51.** J Biol Chem 275, 7795 (2000); **52.** Cytometry 17, 287 (1994); **53.** J Lab Clin Med 123, 728 (1994); **54.** Ann N Y Acad Sci 416, 426 (1983); **55.** J Cell Sci 101, 873 (1992); **56.** Arch Biochem Biophys 227, 358 (1983); **57.** Biophys J 71, 2319 (1996); **58.** J Cell Biol 87, 14 (1980); **59.** Biochemistry 32, 8168 (1993); **60.** FASEB J 9, 974 (1995); **61.** J Biol Chem 245, 5728 (1970); **62.** J Exp Med 147, 1054 (1978); **63.** Molecular Biology of the Cell, 3rd Ed., Alberts B, Bray D, Lewis J, Raff M, Roberts K, Watson JD pp. 986–988 (1994); **64.** Annu Rev Cell Biol 1, 67 (1985); **65.** Annu Rev Cell Biol 4, 649 (1988); **66.** J Immunol Methods 213, 41 (1998); **67.** Anal Biochem 280, 11 (2000); **68.** Biophys J 68, 1207 (1995); **69.** Cytometry 19, 366 (1995); **70.** J Immunol 156, 679 (1996); **71.** Immunol Invest 25, 49 (1996); **72.** Am J Physiol 274, C182 (1998); **73.** Biotechniques 29, 81 (2000); **74.** J Cell Biol 147, 577 (1999); **75.** Biochemistry 29, 313 (1990); **76.** J Biol Chem 265, 16725 (1990); **77.** Inflammation 7, 363 (1983); **78.** Inflammation 2, 115 (1977); **79.** J Immunol 139, 3028 (1987); **80.** Cancer Res 54, 666 (1994); **81.** Proc Natl Acad Sci U S A 91, 3497 (1994); **82.** Annu Rev Biochem 62, 385 (1993); **83.** Biochemistry 34, 32 (1995); **84.** Cytometry 29, 279 (1997); **85.** Proc Natl Acad Sci U S A 101, 1702 (2004); **86.** Biochim Biophys Acta 1288, F37 (1996); **87.** Cancer Res 52, 17 (1992); **88.** Proc Natl Acad Sci U S A 91, 13033 (1994); **89.** Biochem Pharmacol 52, 967 (1996); **90.** FEBS Lett 368, 385 (1995); **91.** Cytometry (Suppl 6) 8, abstract #35A (1993); **92.** Cytometry 17, 343 (1994); **93.** J Biol Chem 268, 21493 (1993); **94.** J Biol Chem 271, 13668 (1996); **95.** Anticancer Drugs 7, 568 (1996); **96.** FEBS Lett 383, 99 (1996); **97.** Anticancer Res 18, 2981 (1998); **98.** Biochemistry 37, 2243 (1998); **99.** Biochim Biophys Acta 1191, 384 (1994); **100.** Br J Cancer 73, 849 (1996); **101.** Eur J Cancer 29A, 1024 (1993); **102.** J Intern Med 247, 521 (2000); **103.** J Clin Oncol 16, 3674 (1998); **104.** Science 258, 1650 (1992); **105.** Br J

References — continued

Haematol 112, 308 (2001); **106.** J Pharm Biomed Anal 18, 585 (1998); **107.** Int J Radiat Biol 74, 647 (1998); **108.** Int J Cancer 76, 55 (1998); **109.** Int J Radiat Oncol Biol Phys 16, 1315 (1989); **110.** J Biol Chem 271, 30587 (1996); **111.** J Cell Sci 111, 1137 (1998); **112.** Cytometry 8, 306 (1987); **113.** Cancer Res 43, 5126 (1983); **114.** Cancer Res 40, 3895 (1980); **115.** Anticancer Res 15, 121 (1995); **116.** Cytometry 17, 50 (1994); **117.** J Biol Chem 269, 7145 (1994); **118.** Mol Pharmacol 45, 1145 (1994); **119.** Proc Natl Acad Sci U S A 91, 4654 (1994); **120.** FEBS Lett 329, 63 (1993); **121.** Blood 78, 1385 (1991); **122.** Cancer Res 51, 4665 (1991); **123.** Exp Cell Res 196, 323 (1991); **124.** Cancer Commun 1, 145 (1989); **125.** J Cell Physiol 126, 266 (1986); **126.** Biochemistry 34, 3858 (1995); **127.** Biochemistry 31, 12555 (1992); **128.** Biochemistry 32, 11042 (1993); **129.** Anticancer Res 13, 1557 (1993); **130.** Cell Biochem Funct 10, 9 (1992); **131.** Cytometry 20, 218 (1995); **132.** Br J Cancer 76, 1029 (1997); **133.** Cancer Res 47, 1421 (1987); **134.** Biochem Biophys Res Commun 212, 494 (1995); **135.** Biochim Biophys Acta 1237, 31 (1995); **136.** Mol Pharmacol 40, 490 (1991); **137.** Blood 91, 4106 (1998); **138.** Biochemistry 38, 6630 (1999); **139.** Biochemistry 33, 11875 (1994); **140.** Proc Natl Acad Sci U S A 89, 3586 (1992); **141.** Br J Cancer 89, 1581 (2003); **142.** Anticancer Res 17, 3321 (1997); **143.** Biochemistry 33, 12665 (1994); **144.** Cardiology 73, 164 (1986); **145.** Life Sci 27, 1525 (1980); **146.** J Biol Chem 268, 11417 (1993); **147.** Biochem Pharmacol 43, 89 (1992); **148.** J Biol Chem 266, 20744 (1991); **149.** J Biol Chem 264, 15483 (1989); **150.** Biochemistry 33, 7229 (1994); **151.** J Histochem Cytochem 38, 685 (1990); **152.** Br J Cancer 61, 568 (1990); **153.** J Natl Cancer Inst 81, 706 (1989); **154.** Proc Natl Acad Sci U S A 98, 7678 (2001); **155.** J Biol Chem 257, 14162 (1982); **156.** Cancer Res 50, 4946 (1990); **157.** Proc Natl Acad Sci U S A 80, 3711 (1983); **158.** J Biol Chem 253, 5852 (1978); **159.** J Med Chem 18, 526 (1975); **160.** Clin Chem 42, 64 (1996); **161.** Prog Neurobiol 62, 649 (2000); **162.** J Biol Chem 269, 29085 (1994); **163.** J Biol Chem 271, 15420 (1996); **164.** Anal Biochem 217, 41 (1994); **165.** Cytometry 15, 349 (1994); **166.** Cancer Res 51, 1783 (1991); **167.** Cytometry 12, 366 (1991); **168.** Glia 30, 329 (2000); **169.** Ann N Y Acad Sci 677, 341 (1993); **170.** Cancer Res 46, 6105 (1986); **171.** Biochem J 294, 631 (1993); **172.** Anal Biochem 286, 35 (2000); **173.** J Biol Chem 263, 14107 (1988); **174.** Principles and Methods of Toxicology, 3rd Ed., Hayes AW, Ed. pp. 1231–1258 (1994); **175.** Cytometry 19, 226 (1995); **176.** Anal Biochem 190, 212 (1990); **177.** Cancer Res 51, 4287 (1991); **178.** J Clin Lab Anal 4, 324 (1990); **179.** Anal Biochem 272, 107 (1999); **180.** Anal Biochem 318, 325 (2003); **181.** Cytometry 23, 78 (1996); **182.** Cytometry 12, 651 (1991); **183.** Cytometry 12, 184 (1991); **184.** Toxicol in Vitro 10, 341 (1996); **185.** Cytometry 14, 747 (1993); **186.** J Immunol 158, 4612 (1997); **187.** Biochemistry 39, 11121 (2000); **188.** Anal Biochem 269, 410 (1999); **189.** Anal Biochem 14, 434 (1966); **190.** Exp Cell Res 163, 518 (1986); **191.** Clin Chem 41, 448 (1995); **192.** Chromatographia 36, 130 (1993); **193.** Anal Chem 67, 4261 (1995).

Data Table — 15.6 Probes for Cell Adhesion, Chemotaxis, Multidrug Resistance and Glutathione

Cat #	MW	Storage	Soluble	Abs	EC	Em	Solvent	Notes
B1150	~615	F,D	DMSO	<300		none		1, 2
B1170	~615	F,D	DMSO	<300		none		1, 2
B3051	~615	F,D	DMSO	<300		none		1, 2, 3
B7431	769.18	F,D,L	DMSO, EtOH	504	74,000	511	MeOH	
B7433	563.41	F,D,L	DMSO, EtOH	504	77,000	511	MeOH	
B7434	617.48	F,D,L	DMSO, EtOH	560	76,000	569	MeOH	
B7469	784.70	F,D,L	DMSO	504	79,000	511	MeOH	
C1430	994.87	F,D	DMSO	<300		none		4
C2925	464.86	F,D	DMSO	<300		none		5
C3099	994.87	F,D	DMSO	<300		none		3, 4
C3100MP	994.87	F,D	DMSO	<300		none		4
C6826	499.95	F,D	DMSO	<350		none		6
C7025	464.86	F,D	DMSO	<300		none		5
F1314	1213.41	F,L	pH >6, DMF	494	72,000	517	pH 9	
G36000	561.67	F,D	DMSO	<300		none		
M1198MP	979.08	F,L	pH >6, DMF	496	67,000	516	pH 9	
M1381MP	226.66	F,L	DMSO	380	6,000	see Notes	MeOH	7
M23271	1055.06	F,D,L	DMSO	494	78,000	518	pH 7	
M23272	812.68	F,D,L	DMSO	505	91,000	511	MeOH	
M23273	1257.49	F,D,L	DMSO	587	101,000	603	MeOH	
N1138	184.19	L	DMF, MeCN	419	9,400	493	see Notes	8
P2331MP	134.13	L	EtOH	334	5,700	455	pH 9	9
P12925	541.39	F,D,L	DMSO, EtOH	492	80,000	516	pH 10	10
V12390	1043.02	F,D,L	DMSO, DMF	503	83,000	510	MeOH	

For definitions of the contents of this data table, see "Navigating *The Handbook*" in the introductory pages.

Notes

1. MW value is approximate. BCECF, AM is a mixture of molecular species. Lot-specific average MW values are printed on product labels.
2. BCECF AM is colorless and nonfluorescent until converted to BCECF (B1151) by acetoxymethyl ester hydrolysis.
3. This product is supplied as a ready-made solution in the solvent indicated under "Soluble."
4. Calcein AM is converted to fluorescent calcein (C481) after acetoxymethyl ester hydrolysis.
5. Acetate hydrolysis of this compound yields a fluorescent product with similar pH-dependent spectral characteristics to C1904.
6. C6826 and S22801 are converted to fluorescent products with spectra similar to C1270 after acetate hydrolysis.
7. Bimanes are almost nonfluorescent until reacted with thiols. For monobromobimane conjugated to glutathione, Abs = 394 nm, Em = 490 nm (QY ~0.1–0.3) in pH 8 buffer (Methods Enzymol 143, 76 (1987); Methods Enzymol 251, 133 (1995)).
8. Spectral data are for the reaction product with glycine in the presence of cyanide, measured in pH 7.0 buffer/MeCN (40:60) (Anal Chem 59, 1102 (1987)). Unreacted reagent in MeOH: Abs = 279 nm (EC = 5500 $cm^{-1}M^{-1}$), Em = 330 nm.
9. Spectral data are for the reaction product of P2331MP with alanine and 2-mercaptoethanol. The spectra and stability of the adduct depend on the amine and thiol reactants (Biochim Biophys Acta 576, 440 (1979)). Unreacted reagent in H_2O: Abs = 257 nm (EC = 1000 $cm^{-1}M^{-1}$).
10. Absorption and fluorescence of fluorescein derivatives are pH-dependent. Extinction coefficients and fluorescence quantum yields decrease markedly at pH <7.

Product List — 15.6 Probes for Cell Adhesion, Chemotaxis, Multidrug Resistance and Glutathione

Cat #	Product Name	Unit Size
A21316	anti-fibronectin (human), chicken IgY fraction *1 mg/mL*	0.5 mL
B1150	2',7'-bis-(2-carboxyethyl)-5-(and-6)-carboxyfluorescein, acetoxymethyl ester (BCECF, AM)	1 mg
B1170	2',7'-bis-(2-carboxyethyl)-5-(and-6)-carboxyfluorescein, acetoxymethyl ester (BCECF, AM) *special packaging*	20 x 50 µg
B3051	2',7'-bis-(2-carboxyethyl)-5-(and-6)-carboxyfluorescein, acetoxymethyl ester (BCECF, AM) *1 mg/mL solution in dry DMSO*	1 mL
B7469	BODIPY® FL forskolin	100 µg
B7433	BODIPY® FL prazosin	100 µg
B7431	BODIPY® FL verapamil, hydrochloride	1 mg
B7434	BODIPY® 558/568 prazosin	100 µg
C1430	calcein, AM	1 mg
C3099	calcein, AM *1 mg/mL solution in dry DMSO*	1 mL
C3100MP	calcein, AM *special packaging*	20 x 50 µg
C2990	casein, fluorescein conjugate	25 mg
C2925	CellTracker™ Green CMFDA (5-chloromethylfluorescein diacetate)	1 mg
C7025	CellTracker™ Green CMFDA (5-chloromethylfluorescein diacetate) *special packaging*	20 x 50 µg
C6826	5-(and-6)-chloromethyl SNARF®-1, acetate *mixed isomers* *special packaging*	20 x 50 µg
C13185	collagen, type IV from human placenta, Oregon Green® 488 conjugate	1 mg
F13191	fibrinogen from human plasma, Alexa Fluor® 488 conjugate	5 mg
F13192	fibrinogen from human plasma, Alexa Fluor® 546 conjugate	5 mg
F13193	fibrinogen from human plasma, Alexa Fluor® 594 conjugate	5 mg
F35200	fibrinogen from human plasma, Alexa Fluor® 647 conjugate	5 mg
F7496	fibrinogen from human plasma, Oregon Green® 488 conjugate	5 mg
F1314	formyl-Nle-Leu-Phe-Nle-Tyr-Lys, fluorescein derivative	1 mg
G13187	gelatin from pig skin, fluorescein conjugate	5 mg
G13186	gelatin from pig skin, Oregon Green® 488 conjugate	5 mg
G36000	glutathione ethyl ester, biotin amide (BioGEE) *glutathiolation detection reagent* *special packaging*	10 x 100 µg
M23271	methotrexate, Alexa Fluor® 488, inner salt (Alexa Fluor® 488 methotrexate) *mixed isomers*	500 µg
M23272	methotrexate, BODIPY® FL (BODIPY® FL methotrexate)	500 µg
M1198MP	methotrexate, fluorescein, triammonium salt (fluorescein methotrexate)	1 mg
M23273	methotrexate, Texas Red®-X, ammonium salt (Texas Red®-X methotrexate)	500 µg
M1381MP	monochlorobimane (mBCl)	25 mg
N1138	naphthalene-2,3-dicarboxaldehyde (NDA)	100 mg
P12925	5-(pentafluorobenzoylamino)fluorescein (PFB-F)	5 mg
P2331MP	*o*-phthaldialdehyde (OPA) *high purity*	1 g
V12390	vinblastine, BODIPY® FL conjugate (BODIPY® FL vinblastine)	100 µg
V13181	Vybrant® Cell Adhesion Assay Kit	1 kit
V13180	Vybrant® Multidrug Resistance Assay Kit	1 kit

For current prices or to order online, visit probes.invitrogen.com

Chapter 16

Probes for Endocytosis, Receptors and Ion Channels

16.1 Probes for Following Receptor Binding, Endocytosis and Exocytosis

The plasma membrane defines the inside and outside of the cell. It not only encloses the cytosol to maintain the intracellular environment but also serves as a formidable barrier to the extracellular environment. Because cells require input from their surroundings — in the form of hydrated ions, small polar molecules, large biomolecules and even other cells — they have developed strategies for overcoming this barrier. Many of these mechanisms involve initial formation of receptor–ligand complexes, often followed by transport of the ligand across the cell's membrane. A useful compendium of human diseases that affect intracellular transport processes has been published.[1]

This section focuses on probes for following receptor binding, endocytosis and exocytosis.[2] Section 16.2 contains probes for neurotransmitter receptors, which are transmembrane proteins that allow the cell to respond to its environment by selectively binding ligands and then transmitting this signal across the plasma membrane (Figure 17.1). Section 16.3 discusses probes for ion channels and carriers, which mediate some signal transduction processes but also allow the cell to maintain or modify its electrolyte balance and control its osmotic properties.

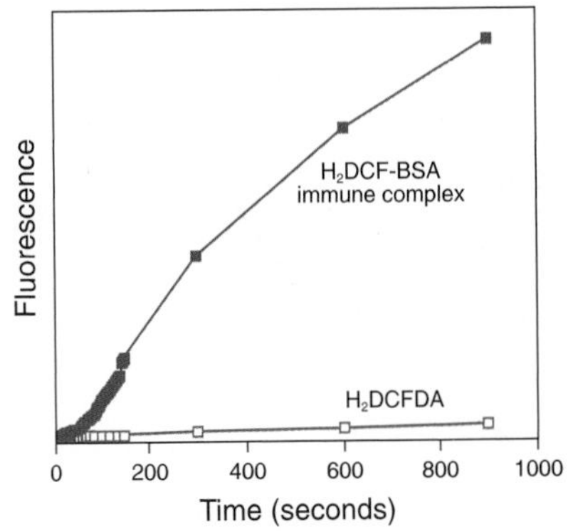

Figure 16.1 Fluorescence emission of human neutrophils challenged either with Molecular Probes' Fc OxyBURST® Green assay reagent (H_2DCF-BSA immune complexes, F2902) or with unlabeled immune complexes in the presence of dichlorodihydrofluorescein diacetate (H_2DCFDA, D399; Section 18.2). The Fc OxyBURST® Green assay reagent generates significantly more fluorescence than does the more commonly used H_2DCFDA. Flow cytometry data provided by Elizabeth Simons, Boston University (J Immunol Methods 130, 223 (1990)).

Ligands for Studying Receptor-Mediated Endocytosis

Molecular Probes offers a variety of fluorescent and fluorogenic ligands that bind to membrane receptors and, in many cases, are internalized upon binding to their specific cell receptor. In some cases, the bound ligand is released intracellularly and the receptor is then recycled to the plasma membrane. Receptor binding may also result in signal transduction (Chapter 17), Ca^{2+} mobilization (Chapter 19), intracellular pH changes (Chapter 20) and formation of reactive oxygen species (ROS, Chapter 18).

Fc OxyBURST® Green Assay Reagent: Fluorogenic Immune Complex

Our OxyBURST® technology utilizes conjugates of dihydrofluorescein dyes as fluorogenic substrates that can easily detect receptor-mediated uptake of biomolecules during phagocytosis.

When soluble or surface-bound IgG immune complexes interact with Fc receptors on phagocytic cells, a number of host defense mechanisms are activated, including phagocytosis and activation of an NADPH oxidase–mediated oxidative burst.[3] Dichlorodihydrofluorescein diacetate (H_2DCFDA, D399; Section 18.2; Figure 18.7), a cell-permeant fluorogenic probe that localizes in the cytosol, has frequently been used to monitor this oxidative burst;[4] however, its fluorescence response is limited by the diffusion rate of the reactive oxygen species into the cytosol from the phagovacuole where it is generated. In contrast, our Fc OxyBURST® assay reagents permit direct measurement of the kinetics of Fc receptor–mediated internalization and the subsequent oxidative burst in the phagovacuole, yielding signals that are many times brighter than those generated by H_2DCFDA.

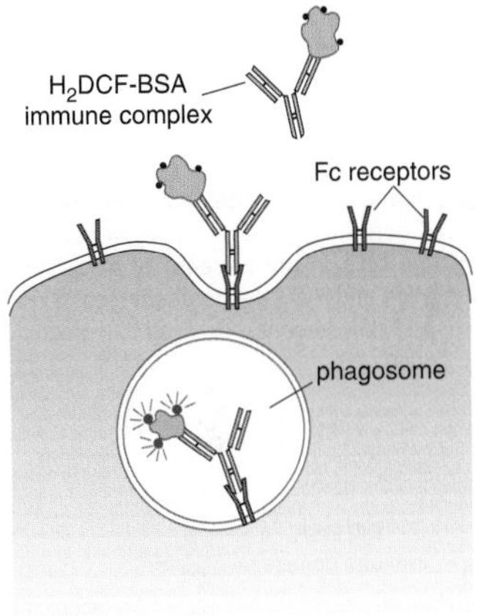

Figure 16.2 Fc OxyBURST® reagent (F2902) for fluorescent detection of the Fc receptor–mediated phagocytosis pathway. Dichlorodihydrofluorescein (H_2DCF) is covalently attached to bovine serum albumin (BSA), then complexed with a rabbit polyclonal anti-BSA antibody (A11133). Upon binding to an Fc receptor, the nonfluorescent immune complex is internalized and subsequently oxidized to the fluorescent DCF.

Molecular Probes' Fc OxyBURST® Green assay reagent (F2902) was developed in collaboration with Elizabeth Simons of Boston University to monitor the oxidative burst in phagocytic cells using fluorescence instrumentation. The Fc OxyBURST® Green assay reagent comprises bovine serum albumin (BSA) that has been covalently linked to dichlorodihydrofluorescein (H_2DCF) and then complexed with a purified rabbit polyclonal anti-BSA antibody (our A11133). When these immune complexes bind to Fc receptors, the nonfluorescent H_2DCF molecules are internalized within the phagovacuole and subsequently oxidized to green-fluorescent 2′,7′-dichlorofluorescein (DCF; Figure 16.1, Figure 16.2). Unlike H_2DCFDA, the Fc OxyBURST® Green assay reagent does not require intracellular esterases for activation, making this reagent particularly suitable for detecting the oxidative burst in cells with low esterase activity such as monocytes.[5] The Fc OxyBURST® Green assay reagent reportedly produces >8 times more fluorescence than does H_2DCFDA at 60 seconds and >20 times more at 15 minutes following internalization of the immune complex.[6]

Various reports have described the use of the Fc OxyBURST® Green assay reagent to study the oxidative burst in phagovacuoles.[7,8] Neutrophils from patients with chronic granulomatous disease, a genetic deficiency known to disable NADPH oxidase–mediated oxidative bursts, were observed to bind but not oxidize the Fc OxyBURST® Green assay reagent[6] (Figure 16.3). Using microfluorometry to detect the Fc OxyBURST® Green response, researchers were able to simultaneously monitor oxidative activity and membrane currents in voltage-clamped human mononuclear cells.[9] The Fc OxyBURST® Green assay reagent has also been employed to assess the effect of manganese-based superoxide dismutase mimetics on superoxide generation in human neutrophils.[10]

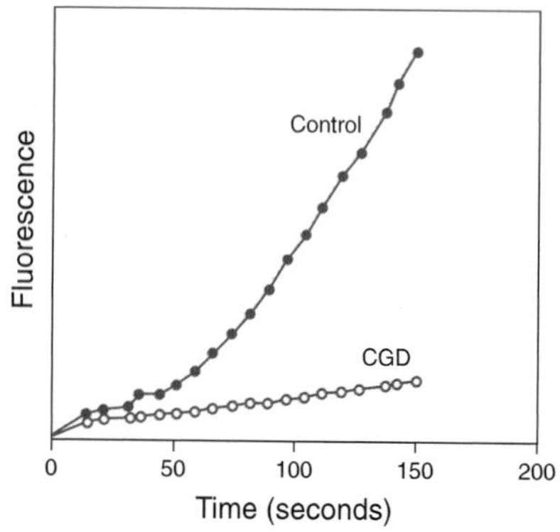

Figure 16.3 Oxidative bursts of human neutrophils from a healthy donor (control) compared with those from a patient with chronic granulomatous disease (CGD), as detected using the Fc OxyBURST® Green assay reagent (F2902). Flow cytometry data provided by Elizabeth Simons, Boston University (J Immunol Methods 130, 223 (1990)).

OxyBURST® Green H_2HFF BSA Reagent

The OxyBURST® Green H_2HFF BSA reagent[11] (O13291) is similar to the Fc OxyBURST® reagent, except that it is prepared by reacting the succinimidyl ester of a reduced form of our Oregon Green® 488 dye with BSA. The absorption maximum of the oxidation product of this reagent (~492 nm) matches the 488 nm spectral line of the argon-ion laser better than does that of the Fc OxyBURST® Green assay reagent (~495 nm). We have utilized the OxyBURST® Green H_2HFF BSA reagent in combination with horseradish peroxidase to detect leakage of hydrogen peroxide from cells (Figure 16.4). The OxyBURST® Green H_2HFF BSA reagent can also be complexed with anti-BSA (see below) to form an immune complex that can be utilized like the Fc OxyBURST® Green assay reagent (F2902, see above).

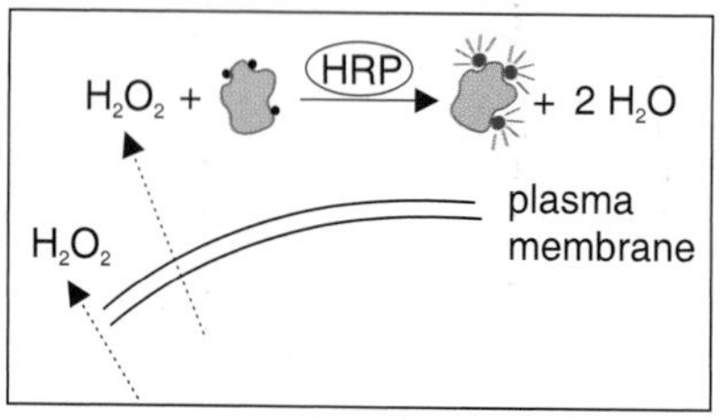

Figure 16.4 OxyBURST® Green H_2HFF BSA reagent (O13291) detecting leakage of hydrogen peroxide (H_2O_2) from cells. In the presence of horseradish peroxidase (HRP) and H_2O_2, the nonfluorescent OxyBURST® Green H_2HFF BSA reagent is oxidized to a green-fluorescent product.

All of the OxyBURST® reagents are slowly oxidized by molecular oxygen and are also susceptible to oxidation catalyzed by illumination in a fluorescence microscope. These reagents are reasonably stable in solution for at least six months when stored under nitrogen or argon in the dark at 4°C. We also offer a purified rabbit polyclonal anti-BSA antibody (A11133), which can bind any of our BSA conjugates (Section 14.7) or fluorogenic DQ™ BSA conjugates (D12050, D12051; Section 10.4) to create immune complexes for analyzing the Fc receptor–mediated phagocytosis pathway. In the case of the anti-BSA complex with DQ™ BSA, initial binding and internalization of the probe is followed by hydrolysis to fluorescent peptides by proteases in the phagovacuole (Figure 16.5).

Amine-Reactive OxyBURST® Green Reagent

As an alternative to our Fc OxyBURST® Green assay reagent and OxyBURST® Green H_2HFF BSA, Molecular Probes offers amine-reactive OxyBURST® Green H_2DCFDA succinimidyl ester (2′,7′-dichlorodihydrofluorescein diacetate, SE; D2935; Figure 16.6), which can be used to prepare oxidation-sensitive conjugates of a wide variety of biomolecules and particles, including antibodies, antigens, peptides, proteins, dextrans, bacteria, yeast and polystyrene microspheres.[6,12] Following conjugation to amines, the two acetates of the OxyBURST® Green H_2DCFDA reagent can be removed by treatment with hydroxylamine at near-neutral pH to yield the dichlorodihydrofluorescein conjugates. The OxyBURST® Green H_2DCFDA conjugates are nonfluorescent until they are oxidized to the corresponding fluorescein derivatives. Thus, like our Fc OxyBURST® Green assay reagent, they provide a means of detecting the oxidative burst in phagocytic cells. In one application, OxyBURST® Green H_2DCFDA succinimidyl ester was conjugated to an antibody that binds specifically to YAC tumor cells. YAC cells opsonized with this customized OxyBURST® reagent were then used in a fluorescence microscopy study to show that Fc receptor–activated neutrophils appear to deliver reactive oxygen species to the surface of their target cells.[12]

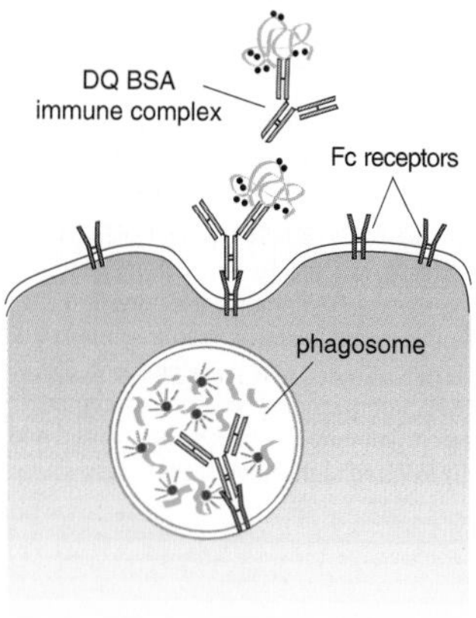

Figure 16.5 Immune complex of DQ™ BSA conjugate (D12050, D12051) with an anti–bovine serum albumin (BSA) antibody (A11133) for the fluorescent detection of the Fc receptor–mediated phagocytosis pathway. The DQ™ BSA is a derivative of BSA that is labeled to such a high degree with either the green-fluorescent BODIPY® FL or red-fluorescent BODIPY® TR-X dye that the fluorescence is self-quenched. Upon binding to an Fc receptor, the nonfluorescent immune complex is internalized and the protein is subsequently hydrolyzed to fluorescent peptides within the phagovacuole.

Several other reagents — dihydrofluoresceins, dihydrorhodamines, dihydroethidium and chemiluminescent probes — that have been used to detect the reactive oxygen species (ROS) produced during phagocytosis are described in Section 18.2.

Fluorescent Low-Density Lipoprotein Complexes

The human LDL complex, which delivers cholesterol to cells by receptor-mediated endocytosis, comprises a core of about 1500 molecules of cholesteryl ester and triglyceride, surrounded by a 20 Å–thick shell of phospholipids, unesterified cholesterol and a single copy of apoprotein B 100[13] (MW ~500,000 daltons). Once internalized, LDL dissociates from its receptor and eventually appears in lysosomes.[14] Molecular Probes offers unlabeled LDL (L3486), which has been reported to be an effective vehicle for selectively delivering antitumor drugs to cancer cells.[15] We also prepare two classes of labeled LDL probes — those containing an unmodified apoprotein, used to study the mechanisms of normal cholesterol delivery and internalization, and those with an acetylated apoprotein, used to study endothelial, microglial and other cell types that express receptors that specifically bind this modified LDL (see below).

Molecular Probes offers LDL labeled with either DiI (DiI LDL, L3482) or the BODIPY® FL fluorophore (BODIPY® FL LDL, L3483), highly fluorescent lipophilic dyes that diffuse into the hydrophobic portion of the LDL complex without affecting the LDL-specific binding of the apoprotein. The contrasting fluorescence of DiI LDL and fluorescein transferrin (T2871) permits their simultaneous use to follow the lysosomally directed pathway and the recycling pathways, respectively.[16] As compared with DiI LDL, BODIPY® FL LDL is more efficiently excited by the 488 nm spectral line of the argon-ion laser, making it better suited for flow cytometry and confocal laser-scanning microscopy studies. Like our BODIPY® FL C_5-ceramide (D3521, Section 12.4), BODIPY® FL LDL fluoresces somewhat in the red region, particularly at high concentration or as aggregates (Figure 13.6), sometimes precluding its use for multicolor labeling with red fluorophores. Both BODIPY® FL LDL and DiI LDL have been used to investigate the binding specificity and partitioning of LDL throughout the *Schistosoma mansoni* parasite[17] (Figure 16.7). Fluorescent LDL complexes have also proven useful in a variety of experimental systems to:

- Count the number of cell-surface LDL receptors, analyze their motion and clustering and follow their internalization[18–20]
- Demonstrate that fibroblasts grown continuously in the presence of DiI LDL (L3482) proliferate normally and exhibit normal morphology,[21] making DiI LDL a valuable alternative to ^{125}I-labeled LDL for quantitating LDL receptor activity[22]
- Identify LDL receptor–deficient Chinese hamster ovary (CHO) cell mutants[23]
- Investigate the expression of LDL receptors in granulosa and luteal cells in primate and porcine ovarian follicles[24–26]
- Track the mobility of LDL receptors in an electric field[27–29]

We prepare our fluorescent LDL products from fresh human plasma at the end of every odd-numbered month and ship them within two weeks of their preparation. If stored refrigerated and protected from light, our LDL products are stable for at least four to six weeks from the date of shipment; these products must not be frozen. Because preparation of these complexes involves several variables, some batch-to-batch variability in degree of labeling and fluorescence yield is expected.

Fluorescent Acetylated LDL Complexes

If the lysine residues of LDL's apoprotein have been acetylated, the LDL complex no longer binds to the LDL receptor,[30] but rather is taken up by macrophage and endothelial cells that possess "scavenger" receptors specific for the modified LDL.[31,32] Once the acetylated LDL (AcLDL) complexes accumulate within these cells, they assume an appearance similar to that of foam cells found in atherosclerotic plaques.[33–35] Molecular Probes offers unlabeled AcLDL (L35354), as well as AcLDL labeled with DiI (DiI AcLDL, L3484; Figure 16.8), the Alexa Fluor® 488 fluorophore (Alexa Fluor® 488 AcLDL, L23380), the Alexa Fluor® 594 fluorophore (Alexa Fluor® 594 AcLDL, L35353) and the BODIPY® FL fluorophore (BODIPY® FL AcLDL, L3485). Fluorescent dye conjugates of high-density lipoproteins, including one prepared using our Alexa Fluor® 488 succinimidyl ester (A20000, A20100; Section 1.3), are taken up via the same receptor.[36]

Using DiI AcLDL, researchers have discovered that the scavenger receptors on rabbit fibroblasts and smooth muscle cells appear to be up-regulated through activation of the protein kinase C pathway.[37] DiI AcLDL has also been used to show that Chinese hamster ovary (CHO) cells express AcLDL receptors that are distinct from macrophage scavenger receptors.[38,39] Ultrastructural localization of endocytic compartments that maintain a connection to the extracellular space has been achieved by photoconversion of DiI AcLDL in the presence of diaminobenzidine[40] (see Note 14.2 "Product Highlight: Fluorescent Probes for Photoconversion of Diaminobenzidine Reagents" in Section 14.3). A quantitative assay for LDL- and scavenger-receptor activity in adherent and nonadherent cultured cells that avoids the use of both radioactivity and organic solvents has been described.[41]

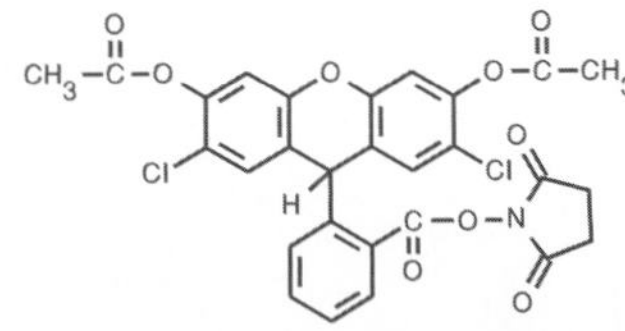

Figure 16.6 D2935 2',7'-dichlorodihydrofluorescein diacetate, succinimidyl ester (OxyBURST® Green H_2DCFDA, SE).

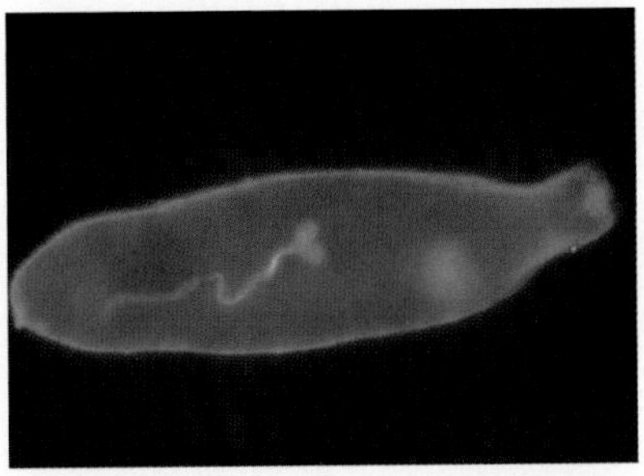

Figure 16.7 DiI LDL (L3482) bound to the surface and internalized in the gut of the parasite *Schistosoma mansoni*. The distribution of LDL in the parasite is used to study a putative mechanism by which the parasite may avoid host immune recognition. Image contributed by John P. Caulfield, Harvard School of Public Health.

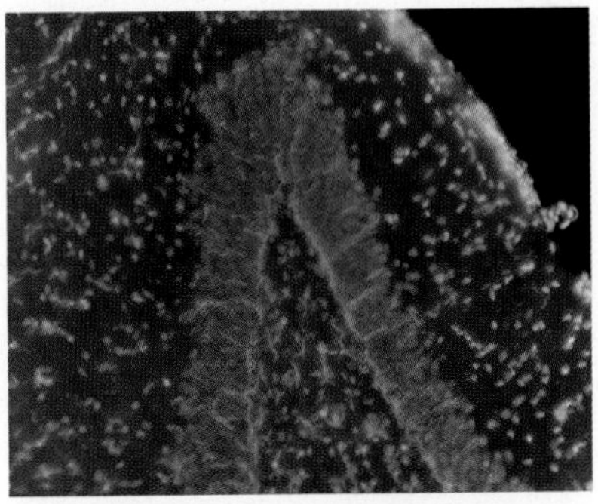

Figure 16.8 Microglial cells in a rat hippocampus cryosection labeled with red-orange–fluorescent DiI acetylated low-density lipoprotein (L3484) and stained using blue-fluorescent DAPI (D1306, D3571, D21490).

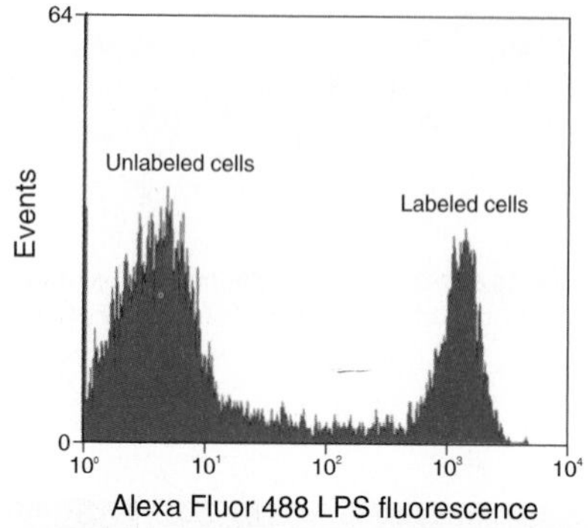

Figure 16.9 Flow cytometric analysis of blood using an Alexa Fluor® 488 lipopolysaccharide (LPS). Human blood was incubated with Alexa Fluor® 488 LPS from *Escherichia coli* (L23351) and anti-CD14 antibody on ice for 20 minutes. The red blood cells were lysed and the sample was analyzed on a flow cytometer equipped with a 488 nm Ar–Kr excitation source and a 525 ± 12 nm bandpass emission filter. Monocytes were identified based on their light scatter and CD14 expression.

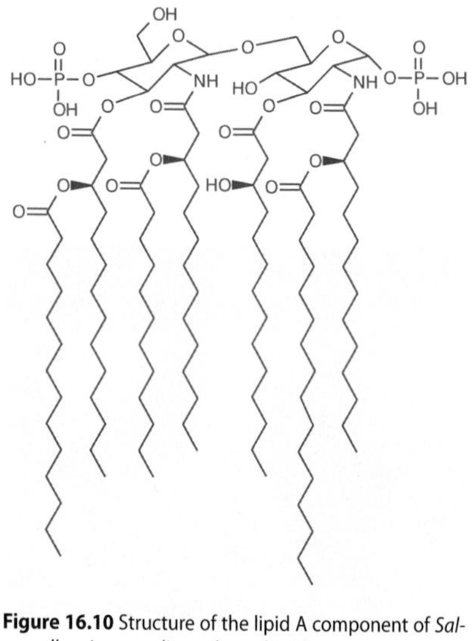

Figure 16.10 Structure of the lipid A component of *Salmonella minnesota* lipopolysaccharide.

It has now become routine to identify endothelial cells and microglial cells in primary cell culture by their ability to take up DiI-labeled acetylated LDL;[42–45] DiI AcLDL is taken up by microglia but not by astrocytes.[46] DiI AcLDL was employed in order to confirm endothelial cell identity in investigations of shear stress[47] and P-glycoprotein expression,[48] as well as to identify blood vessels in a growing murine melanoma.[49] In addition, patch-clamp techniques have been used to investigate membrane currents in mouse microglia, which were identified both in culture and in brain slices by their staining with DiI AcLDL.[50,51] For some applications, our Alexa Fluor® 488, Alexa Fluor® 594 or BODIPY® FL AcLDL may be the preferred probes because the dyes are covalently bound to the modified apoprotein portion of the LDL complex and are therefore not extracted during subsequent manipulations of the cells. Furthermore, the Alexa Fluor® 488 AcLDL conjugate has spectral characteristics similar to fluorescein (Figure 7.51); however, the Alexa Fluor® 488 dye produces brighter and more photostable conjugates that researchers may find useful for analyses with instruments equipped with the 488 nm argon-ion laser excitation sources, including flow cytometers and confocal laser-scanning microscopes. The bright and photostable red-fluorescent Alexa Fluor® 594 AcLDL conjugate is useful for multilabeling experiments with green-fluorescent probes and can be efficiently excited by the 594 nm spectral line of the orange He–Ne laser.

Fluorescent Conjugates of Lipopolysaccharides

Molecular Probes offers fluorescent conjugates of lipopolysaccharides (LPS) from *Escherichia coli* and *Salmonella minnesota* (Table 16.1) with our BODIPY® FL fluorophore and three of our Alexa Fluor® dyes. LPS or endotoxins are complex macromolecules present on the outer cell walls of gram-negative bacteria. Recognition of LPS by binding to the CD14 cell-surface receptor of phagocytes (Figure 16.9) is the key initiation step in the mammalian immune response to infection by gram-negative bacteria. The structural core of LPS, and the primary determinant of its biological activity, is the *N*-acetylglucosamine derivative, lipid A (Figure 16.10). Two plasma proteins — LPS-binding protein (LBP) and soluble CD14 (sCD14) — play primary roles in transporting LPS and mediating cellular responses.[52–57] If the fatty acid residues are removed from the lipid A component, the toxicity of the LPS can be reduced significantly. However, the mono- or diphosphoryl forms of lipid A are inherently toxic. In many gram-negative bacterial infections, LPS are responsible for clinically significant symptoms like fever, low blood pressure and tissue edema, which can lead to disseminated intravascular coagulation, organ failure and death. Studies also clearly indicate that LPS induce various signal transduction pathways, including those involving protein kinase C[58,59] and protein myristylation,[60] and stimulate a variety of immunochemical responses, including B lymphocyte[61] and G-protein activation.[62]

Our fluorescent BODIPY® FL and Alexa Fluor® LPS conjugates, which are labeled with succinimidyl esters of these dyes, allow researchers to follow LPS binding, transport and cell internalization processes[63] (Figure 16.9). Lipopolysaccharide internalization activates endotoxin-dependent signal transduction in cardiomyocytes.[64] The Alexa Fluor® 488 LPS conjugates (L23351, L23356) selectively label microglia in a mixed culture containing oligodendrocyte precursors, astrocytes and microglia.[65] A biologically active conjugate of galactose oxidase–oxidized *S. minnesota* LPS and our Alexa Fluor® 488 hydrazide (A10436, A10440; Section 14.3) has been used to elucidate molecular mechanisms of septic shock.[66] Aggregation of the BODIPY® FL derivative of *S. minnesota* strain R595 (L23355) in aqueous solution is reported to result in a spectral shift of the BODIPY® FL dye's emission maximum to ~620 nm. Addition of LBP results in a relatively small fluorescence increase, indicating that the LPS remain aggregated upon binding. Subsequent addition of sCD14 results in a large increase in fluorescence intensity and a shift in emis-

Table 16.1 — Fluorescent lipopolysaccharide conjugates

Fluorophore	Abs *	Em *	*Escherichia coli*	*Salmonella minnesota*
Alexa Fluor® 488	495	519	L23351	L23356
BODIPY® FL	503	513 †	L23350	L23355
Alexa Fluor® 568	578	603	L23352	L23357
Alexa Fluor® 594	590	617	L23353	L23358

* Approximate absorption (Abs) and fluorescence emission (Em) maxima for conjugates, in nm. † At high concentrations, such as in micelles or aggregates, the emission maximum for the BODIPY® FL dye may shift from ~513 nm to ~620 nm. (J Immunol 158, 3925 (1997); J Biol Chem 271, 4100 (1996)).

sion maximum to ~510 nm, indicating LBP-mediated transfer of LPS monomers to sCD14.[54] In one study, a BODIPY® FL derivative of LPS from *E. coli* strain LCD25 (L23350) was used to measure the transfer rate of LPS from monocytes to high-density lipoprotein[67] (HDL). Another study utilized a BODIPY® FL derivative of LPS from *S. minnesota* to demonstrate transport to the Golgi apparatus in neutrophils,[52,53] although this could have been due to probe metabolism. It has been reported that organelles other than the Golgi are labeled by some fluorescent or nonfluorescent LPS.[68,69] Cationic lipids are reported to assist the translocation of fluorescent lipopolysaccharides into live cells;[70] cell surface–bound fluorescent LPS can be quenched by trypan blue[67] (Figure 16.24). Molecular Probes' fluorescent LPS can potentially be combined with other fluorescent indicators, such as Ca^{2+}-, pH- or organelle-specific stains, to monitor intracellular localization, as well as real-time changes in cellular response to LPS. We also offer the Pro-Q® Emerald 300 Lipopolysaccharide Gel Stain Kit (P20495, Section 3.2, Figure 3.20, Figure 3.21), which permits ultrasensitive analysis of unlabeled lipopolysaccharides in gel electrophoretograms (Figure 3.19, Figure 3.20, Figure 3.21).

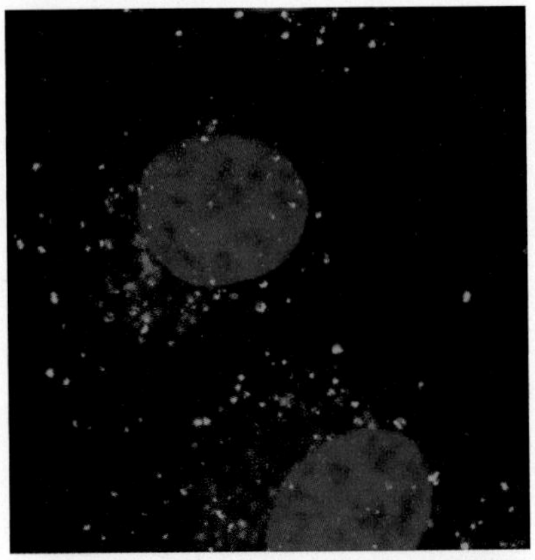

Figure 16.11 Early endosomes in live HeLa cells identified after a 10-minute incubation with green-fluorescent Alexa Fluor® 488 epidermal growth factor (E13345). The cells were subsequently fixed with paraformaldehyde and labeled with an antibody to the late endosomal protein, RhoB. That antibody was visualized with a red-orange–fluorescent secondary antibody. Nuclei were stained with TO-PRO®-3 iodide (T3605, pseudocolored blue). The image was contributed by Harry Mellor, University of Bristol.

Epidermal Growth Factor Derivatives

Epidermal growth factor (EGF, E3476) is a 53–amino acid polypeptide hormone (MW 6045 daltons) that stimulates division of epidermal and other cells.[71–73] The EGF receptors include the HER-2/neu receptor (where "HER-2" is an acronym for human epidermal growth factor receptor-2 and "neu" refers to an original mouse origin); HER-2/neu overexpression has evolved as a prognostic/predictive factor in some solid tumors. Binding of EGF to its 170,000-dalton receptor protein results in the activation of kinases, phospholipases and Ca^{2+} mobilization and precipitates a wide variety of cellular responses related to differentiation, mitogenesis, organ development and cell motility.

Molecular Probes offers unlabeled mouse submaxillary gland EGF (E3476), as well as EGF labeled with biotin-XX, fluorescein, Oregon Green® 514 and tetramethylrhodamine (E3477, E3478, E7498, E3481), all containing a single biotin or fluorophore on the N-terminal amino acid. The long spacer arm in our biotin-XX EGF enhances the probe's affinity for the EGF receptor.[74] The dissociation constant of the EGF conjugates in DMEM-HEPES medium is in the low nanomolar range for human epidermoid carcinoma (A431) cells,[75] a value that approximates that of the unlabeled EGF.

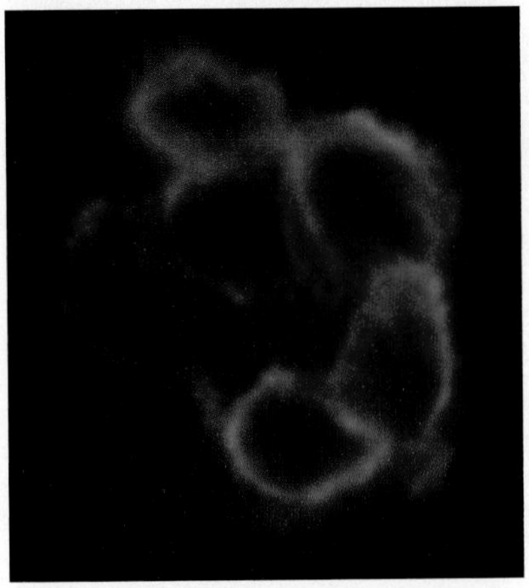

Figure 16.12 Lightly fixed human epidermoid carcinoma cells (A431) stained with biotinylated epidermal growth factor (EGF) complexed to Texas Red® streptavidin (E3480). An identical cell preparation stained in the presence of a 100-fold excess of unlabeled EGF (E3476) showed no fluorescent signal.

Fluorescently labeled EGF has enabled scientists to use fluorescence resonance energy transfer techniques to assess EGF receptor–receptor and receptor–membrane interactions[76–78] (see Note 1.2 "Technical Focus: Fluorescence Resonance Energy Transfer (FRET)" in Section 1.3). Using fluorescein EGF as the donor and tetramethylrhodamine EGF as the acceptor, researchers examined temperature-dependent lateral and transverse distribution of EGF receptors in A431 cell plasma membranes.[78] When fluorescein EGF binds to A431 cells, it apparently undergoes a biphasic quenching, which can be attributed first to changes in rotational mobility upon binding and then to receptor–ligand internalization. By monitoring this quenching in real time, the rate constants for the interaction of fluorescein EGF with its receptor were determined.[79]

Although fluorescently labeled EGF can be used to follow lateral mobility and endocytosis of the EGF receptor,[80,81] the visualization of fluorescent EGF may require low-light imaging technology, especially in cells that express low levels of the EGF receptor.[82] In cells with few EGF receptors, it can be difficult to detect signal over background fluorescence unless signal amplification methods are employed (Figure 6.10). Oregon Green® 514 dye–labeled EGF is one of our most fluorescent and photostable EGF conjugates. We also prepare biotinylated EGF precomplexed to Alexa Fluor® 488 streptavidin (E13345, Figure 16.11), Alexa Fluor® 555 streptavidin (E35350), Alexa Fluor® 647 streptavidin (E35351) or Texas Red® streptavidin[83,84] (E3480). These products yield severalfold brighter signals per EGF receptor when compared with the direct conjugates. We have found that EGF receptors can easily be detected with these complexes without resorting to low-light imaging technology (Figure 16.12). We have also used our avidin- and streptavidin-coated FluoSpheres® and TransFluoSpheres® microspheres (Section 6.5) for the sensitive detection of EGF receptors by flow cytometry.[85]

In addition, we offer biotin-XX EGF, which contains a long spacer arm that facilitates binding of fluorescent or enzyme-conjugated streptavidins (Section 7.6). Using biotinylated EGF and phycoerythrin-labeled secondary reagents (Section 6.4), researchers were able to detect as few as 10,000 EGF cell-surface receptors by confocal laser-scanning microscopy.[86] We have used our ELF® 97 Cytological Labeling Kit (E6603, Section 6.3) in conjunction with biotinylated EGF to detect low-abundance EGF receptors (Figure 6.26). Tyramide signal amplification (TSA) technology (Section 6.2) is particularly valuable for detection and localization of low-abundance EGF receptors by both imaging and flow cytometry (Figure 6.10).

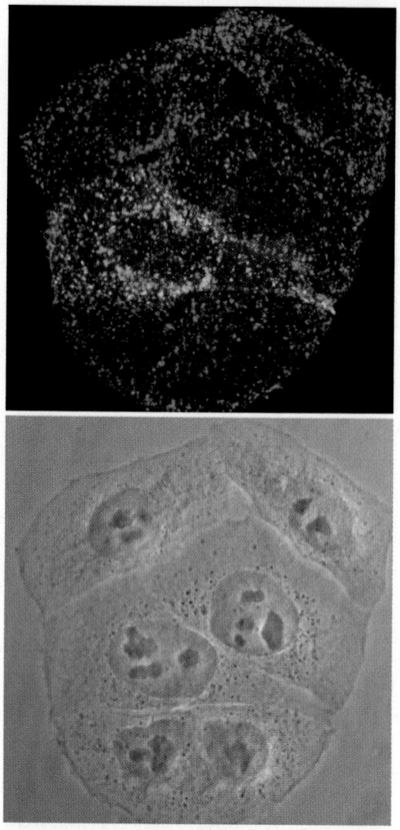

Figure 16.13 Live HeLa cells incubated with Alexa Fluor® 594 transferrin (T13343) for 10 minutes to label early endosomes. The cells were subsequently fixed with paraformaldehyde and labeled with an antibody to the endosomal protein RhoD. That antibody was visualized with a green-fluorescent secondary antibody. Yellow fluorescence indicates regions of co-localization. To illustrate the staining pattern, the cells were imaged by both fluorescence (top panel) and differential interference contrast (DIC) microscopy (bottom panel). The image was contributed by Harry Mellor, University of Bristol.

Transferrin Conjugates

Transferrin is a monomeric serum glycoprotein (MW ~80,000 daltons) that binds up to two Fe^{3+} atoms for delivery to vertebrate cells through receptor-mediated endocytosis.[87–89] Once iron-carrying transferrin proteins are inside endosomes, the acidic environment favors dissociation of the sequestered iron from the transferrin–receptor complex. Following the release of iron, the apotransferrin is recycled to the plasma membrane, where it is released from its receptor to scavenge more iron.[90,91] Labeled transferrin conjugates can therefore be used with fluorescent LDL to distinguish the lysosomally directed and recycling endosomal pathways.[14,16]

Molecular Probes' fluorescent di-ferric (Fe^{3+}) human transferrin conjugates include those of the fluorescein, BODIPY® FL,[92] Oregon Green® 488,[93] Alexa Fluor® 488,[94–97] Alexa Fluor® 546, Alexa Fluor® 555, Alexa Fluor® 568, Alexa Fluor® 594[98–100] (Figure 16.13), Alexa Fluor® 647, tetramethylrhodamine and Texas Red® fluorophores (Table 16.2). Fluorescently labeled transferrin has greatly aided the investigation of endocytosis.[101–103] The Alexa Fluor® conjugates of transferrin[95–100,104,105] are highly recommended because of their brightness, enhanced photostability and lack of sensitivity to pH (Section 1.3). The pH sensitivity of fluorescein-labeled transferrin has been exploited to investigate events occurring during endosomal acidification.[106–109] Fluorescent transferrins have also been used to:

- Analyze the role of the γ-chain of type III IgG receptors in antigen–antibody complex internalization[110]
- Define the nature of several mutations that affect the endosomal pathway[111–113]
- Demonstrate that the fungal metabolite brefeldin A (B7450, Section 12.4) induces an increase in tubulation of transferrin receptors in BHK-21 cells[114] and in the perikaryal–dendritic region of cultured hippocampal neurons[115]
- Observe receptor trafficking in living cells by confocal laser-scanning microscopy and show that recycling transferrin receptors are distributed on the surface of the leading lamella in migrating fibroblasts[116]
- Show that the endosomal compartment of living epidermoid carcinoma cells is an extensive network of tubular cisternae[117]

Uptake of a horseradish peroxidase (HRP) conjugate of transferrin by endosomes has been detected using tyramide signal amplification (TSA, Section 6.2) by catalytic deposition of biotin tyramide and use of fluorescent streptavidin conjugates[118] (Section 7.6).

Table 16.2 — Transferrin conjugates

Cat #	Label	Abs *	Em *
T23363	biotin-XX	NA	NA
T2871	fluorescein	494	518
T13342	Alexa Fluor® 488	495	518
T13341	Oregon Green® 488	496	524
T2873	BODIPY® FL	505	513
T2872	tetramethylrhodamine	555	580
T23364	Alexa Fluor® 546	556	575
S32352	Alexa Fluor® 555	555	565
T23365	Alexa Fluor® 568	578	603
T13343	Alexa Fluor® 594	589	616
T2875	Texas Red®	595	615
T23362	Alexa Fluor® 633	632	647
T23366	Alexa Fluor® 647	650	665

* Approximate absorption (Abs) and fluorescence emission (Em) maxima for conjugates, in nm. NA = Not applicable.

In addition to its fluorescent and biotinylated transferrin conjugates, Molecular Probes carries a mouse IgG_1 monoclonal anti–human transferrin receptor antibody (A11130). It should be possible to combine this antibody with any of our Zenon® Mouse IgG_1 Labeling Kits (Section 7.3, Table 7.13) for rapid preparation of labeling complexes (Figure 7.59). Antibodies against transferrin receptors have been used for indirect immunofluorescent staining of the transferrin receptor,[119–121] transport of molecules across the blood–brain barrier,[122] the characterization of transferrin in recycling compartments,[119] enzyme-linked immunosorbent assays (ELISAs) [121] and antibody competition with transferrin uptake.[123]

Fluorescent Fibrinogen

Fibrinogen is a key component in the blood clotting process and can support both platelet–platelet and platelet–surface interactions by binding to the glycoprotein IIb-IIIa (GPIIb-IIIa) receptor (also called integrin $\alpha_{IIb}\beta_3$) of activated platelets.[124–128] Although not well understood, activation of GPIIb-IIIa is required for fibrinogen binding, which leads to platelet activation, adhesion, spreading and microfilament reorganization of human endothelial cells *in vitro*.[124,127,129,130] Bone marrow transplant patients have significantly higher levels of fibrinogen binding, as compared with controls.[131] Soluble fibrinogen binds to its receptor with a Ca^{2+}-dependent apparent K_d of 0.18 µM.[132] This binding is apparently mediated by the tripeptide sequence Arg–Gly–Asp (RGD), found in both fibrinogen and fibronectin.[127,133,134]

Fluorescently labeled fibrinogen has proven to be a valuable tool for investigating platelet activation and subsequent fibrinogen binding. Fluorescein fibrinogen has been used to identify activated platelets by flow cytometry.[129,135–138] The binding of fluorescein fibrinogen to activated platelets has been shown to be saturable and can be inhibited completely by underivatized fibrinogen.[137,138] The preferential binding and accumulation of fluorescein fibrinogen at the endothelial border of venular blood vessels has been studied by quantitative fluorescence microscopy.[139] A biotinylated fibrinogen derivative is rapidly internalized by activated platelets.[140]

Molecular Probes offers five conjugates of human fibrinogen in four different fluorescent colors. The Alexa Fluor® 488 human fibrinogen conjugate (F13191) and the Oregon Green® 488 human fibrinogen conjugate (F7496) have spectral characteristics (Figure 7.5, Figure 7.21) similar to fluorescein conjugates. However, the fluorescence of Oregon Green® 488 and Alexa Fluor® 488 protein conjugates is much more photostable and less pH dependent than that of fluorescein conjugates (Figure 1.12, Figure 1.46, Figure 1.53). The red-orange–fluorescent (Figure 7.9) Alexa Fluor® 546 human fibrinogen conjugate (F13192) is brighter and more photostable than the spectrally similar tetramethylrhodamine fibrinogen conjugates. Similarly, the red-fluorescent (Figure 7.12) Alexa Fluor® 594 human fibrinogen conjugate (F13193) and far-red–fluorescent (Figure 7.16) Alexa Fluor® 647 human fibrinogen conjugate (F35200) are brighter than Texas Red® and Cy5 conjugates, respectively, yet have similar excitation and emission maxima. These highly fluorescent fibrinogen conjugates are useful for investigating platelet activation and subsequent fibrinogen binding using fluorescence microscopy or flow cytometry (Figure 15.103).

Endostatin Protein

The angiogenesis inhibitor, endostatin, is an endogenous 20,000-dalton carboxyl-terminal fragment of collagen XVIII (Figure 16.14) that induces regression of tumors in mice. Although its complete mechanism of action is unknown, research has found that endostatin appears to trigger suppression of both apoptosis factors and cell proliferation genes, including *c-myc* gene expression, resulting in a potent antimigratory effect.[141] On the cell surface, endostatin has been shown to bind to glypicans or transmembrane heparan sulfate proteoglycans.[142,143] Once endocytosed, the protein has been demonstrated to bind to tropomyosin,[144] a protein that stabilizes the pointed end of actin filaments by slowing depolymerization.[145] Indirectly, endostatin appears to induce increases in cytosolic Ca^{2+} and cAMP.[141] Molecular Probes offers recombinant Endostatin protein (E23377) for research purposes; recombinant Angiostatin protein, another protein useful for angiogenesis research, is also available (A23375, Section 15.4).

Fluorescent Gelatin and Type IV Collagen

Collagen is a major component of the extracellular matrix and, in vertebrates, constitutes approximately 25% of total protein. This important protein not only serves a structural role, but also is important in cell adhesion and migration. Specific collagen receptors, fibronectin and a number of other proteins involved in cell–cell and cell–surface adhesion have been demonstrated to bind collagen and gelatin [146,147] (denatured collagen).

Molecular Probes prepares fluorescent conjugates of gelatin and type IV collagen, the principal collagen in basement membranes. These reagents are designed for researchers studying collagen-binding proteins and collagen metabolism, as well as gelatinases and collagenases, which are metalloproteins that digest gelatin and collagen. We offer two green-fluorescent gelatin conjugates — fluorescein gelatin and Oregon Green® 488 gelatin (G13187, G13186). When compared with the fluorescein conjugate, the Oregon Green® 488 conjugate exhibits almost identical fluorescence spectra but its fluorescence is much more photostable and much less pH dependent (Figure 1.12). For researchers requiring a more specific substrate, we also offer the Oregon Green® 488 conjugate of human type IV collagen (C13185). These highly fluorescent gelatin and collagen conjugates have been shown to be useful for:

- Following integrin-mediated phagocytosis [148]
- Localizing surface fibronectin on cultured cells [149]

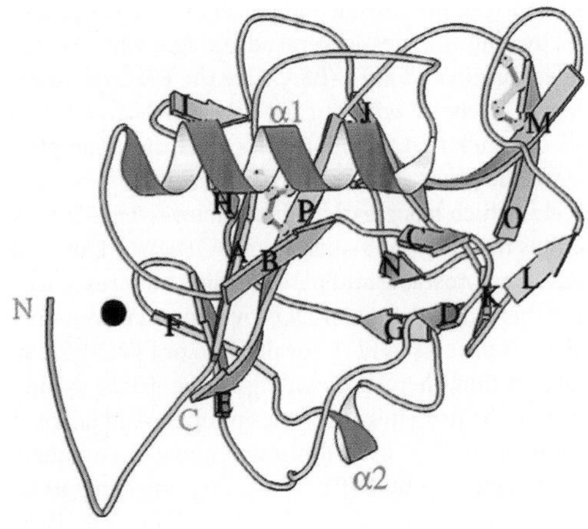

Figure 16.14 Crystal structure of recombinant human Endostatin protein (E23377). Image courtesy of EntreMed, Inc.

- Studying fibronectin–gelatin interactions in solution using fluorescence polarization [147,150] (see Note 1.5 "Technical Focus: Fluorescence Polarization (FP)" in Section 1.4)

Molecular Probes has also developed fluorogenic gelatinase and collagenase substrates — DQ™ gelatin and DQ™ collagen — that are described in Section 10.4. In addition, we offer fluorescent microspheres coated with collagen, which are described below. Molecular Probes also has available highly purified rabbit polyclonal antibodies to matrix metalloproteinases, including MMP-1 (interstitial collagenase), MMP-2 (gelatinase A or type IV collagenase), MMP-3 (stromelysin) and MMP-9 (gelatinase B or type V collagenase). See Section 7.5 and Table 7.21 for more information on these antibodies.

DQ™ Ovalbumin: A Probe for Antigen Processing and Presentation

Although antigen processing and presentation have been extensively studied, the exact sequence and detailed pathways for generating antigenic peptides have yet to be elucidated. In general, the immunogenic protein is internalized by a macrophage, denatured, reduced and proteolyzed, and then the resulting peptides associate with MHC class II molecules that are expressed at the cell surface.[151] Ovalbumin is efficiently processed through mannose receptor–mediated endocytosis by antigen-presenting cells and is widely used for studying antigen processing.[152–154] Molecular Probes' self-quenched ovalbumin conjugate, DQ™ ovalbumin [155] (D12053), is designed specifically for the study of macrophage-mediated antigen processing in flow cytometry and microscopy assays.

Traditionally, fluorescein-labeled bovine serum albumin (FITC-BSA) has been used as a fluorogenic protein antigen for studying the real-time kinetics of antigen processing in live macrophages by flow cytometry,[156] two-photon fluorescence lifetime imaging microscopy (FLIM) [157] and fluorescence polarization.[156,158,159] FITC-ovalbumin has been employed to study antigen uptake in HIV-1–infected monocytic cells.[160] The FITC-ovalbumin and FITC-BSA used in these experiments were heavily labeled with fluorescein such that the intact conjugates were relatively nonfluorescent due to self-quenching. Upon denaturation and proteolysis, however, these FITC conjugates became highly fluorescent, allowing researchers to monitor intracellular trafficking and the processing of ovalbumin and BSA in macrophages.

For studies of antigen processing and presentation, Molecular Probes' DQ™ ovalbumin offers several advantages when compared with FITC-ovalbumin and FITC-BSA. Like the FITC conjugates, DQ™ ovalbumin is labeled with our pH-insensitive, green-fluorescent BODIPY® FL dye such that the fluorescence is almost completely quenched until the probe is digested by proteases (Figure 16.15). Unlike fluorescein, which has greatly reduced fluorescence intensity at acidic pH and is not very photostable, our BODIPY® FL dye exhibits bright, relatively photostable and pH-insensitive fluorescence from pH 3 to 9. Furthermore, the intact DQ™ ovalbumin is more highly quenched than unprocessed FITC-ovalbumin or FITC-BSA at a lower degree of substitution, thereby providing a lower background signal while preserving the protein's antigenic epitopes. And lastly, if the digested fragments of DQ™ ovalbumin accumulate in organelles at a high concentration, the BODIPY® FL fluorophore can potentially form excimers, resulting in a shift of the fluorophore's emission maximum from 515 nm (green) to ~620 nm (red). Although we offer the green-fluorescent DQ™ Green BSA and red-fluorescent DQ™ Red BSA (D12050, D12051; Section 10.4), which are also self-quenched BODIPY® FL and BODIPY® TR conjugates, we highly recommend DQ™ ovalbumin (D12053) for studying antigen processing and presentation because ovalbumin is internalized via the mannose receptor–mediated endocytosis pathway and is thus processed more efficiently by antigen-presenting cells than is BSA.[161] Antigen processing of DQ™ ovalbumin by both eosinophils [162] and immature dendritic cells [155] has been reported.

Fluorescent Casein

Using fluorescein-labeled casein (C2990), researchers have demonstrated casein-specific chemotaxis receptors in human neutrophils and monocytes with flow cytometry.[163] Neutrophils activated with phorbol myristate acetate have been shown to undergo a dose-dependent increase in binding of fluorescein-labeled casein.[164] It has also been demonstrated that fluorescein-labeled casein reversibly binds to specific receptors on human monocytes but does not bind to lymphocytes *in vitro*.[163]

EnzChek® Protease Assay Kits

Our patented EnzChek® Protease Assay Kits (E6638, E6639), which provide convenient fluorescence-based assays for protease activity, contain either green-fluorescent BODIPY® FL casein or red-fluorescent BODIPY® TR-X casein.[165] These casein-based substrates are heavily labeled and therefore highly quenched conjugates; they typically exhibit <3% of the fluorescence of the corresponding free dyes. Protease-catalyzed hydrolysis relieves this quenching, yielding brightly fluorescent BODIPY® FL– or BODIPY® TR-X–labeled peptides (Figure 16.15). In addition to their utility for detecting protease contamination in culture medium and other experimental samples, BODIPY® FL casein and BODIPY® TR-X casein appear to have significant potential as nontoxic and pH-insensitive general markers for phagocytic cells in culture. In unpublished work, we have shown that uptake of these quenched conjugates by neutrophils is accompanied by hydrolysis of the labeled proteins by intracellular proteases and the generation of fluorescent products that are well retained in cells. Once formed, small BODIPY® FL– or BODIPY® TR-X–labeled peptides may diffuse into other organelles or pass through gap junctions. This phagocytosis assay is readily performed in a fluorescence microplate reader or a flow cytometer; localization of the fluorescent products can be determined by fluorescence microscopy. Our RediPlate™ 96 (R22130, R22132) and RediPlate™ 384 (R22131, R22133) versions of these substrates (Section 10.4) are ideal for high-throughput screening of potential protease inhibitors.

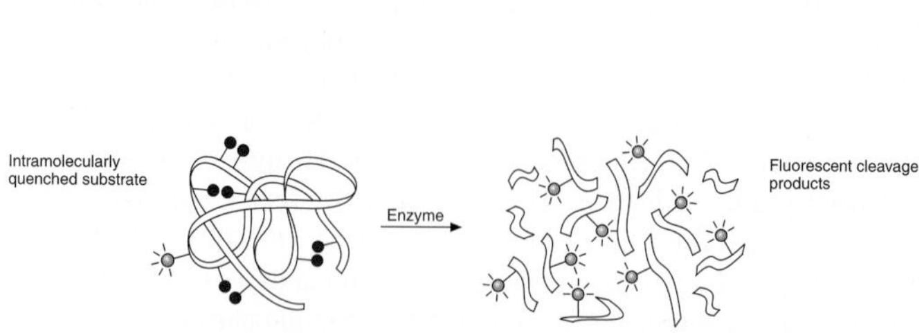

Figure 16.15 Principle of enzyme detection via the disruption of intramolecular self-quenching. Enzyme-catalyzed hydrolysis of the heavily labeled and almost totally quenched substrates provided in our EnzChek® Protease Assay Kits (E6638, E6639), EnzChek® Amylase Assay Kit (E11954), EnzChek® Gelatinase/Collagenase Assay Kit (E12055), EnzChek® Elastase Kit (E12056), EnzChek® Lysozyme Assay Kit (E22013) — as well as the stand-alone quenched substrates DQ™ BSA (D12050, D12051), DQ™ collagen (D12052, D12060), DQ™ ovalbumin (D12053) and DQ™ gelatin (D12054) — relieves the intramolecular self-quenching, yielding brightly fluorescent reaction products.

Alexa Fluor® 488 Histones

The Alexa Fluor® 488 conjugate of the lysine-rich calf thymus histone H1 (H13188) should be a useful probe for yeast nuclear protein transport assays [166] and for the study of nuclei in live cells in experiments similar to those described in the literature.[167,168] Unlike fluorescein conjugates of histones, Alexa Fluor® 488 histones have pH-insensitive fluorescence and exceptional photostability (Figure 1.12, Figure 1.46).

Probes for the Acrosome Reaction

Soybean trypsin inhibitor (SBTI) inhibits the catalytic activity of serine proteases and binds to acrosin, an acrosomal serine protease associated with binding of spermatozoa to the zona pellucida.[169] Our Alexa Fluor® 488 dye–labeled trypsin inhibitor from soybean (T23011) is useful for monitoring the surface expression of acrosin during the acrosome reaction of spermatogenesis.[170] The conjugate has been reported to have no effect on sperm mobility, survival or zona binding capability, allowing simultaneous assessment of acrosomal status and motility.[170] A fluorescent peanut lectin has been combined with ethidium homodimer-1 (EthD-1, E1169; Section 15.2) for a combined acrosome reaction assay and vital staining.[171] Our Alexa Fluor® 488, Alexa Fluor® 568, Alexa Fluor® 594 and Alexa Fluor® 647 conjugates of PNA (L21409, L32458, L32459, L32460) may have similar utility as acrosomal stains. Wheat germ agglutinin (WGA) and *Phaseolus vulgaris* lectin conjugates (Section 7.7) are also known to bind to acrosomal structures of spermatids.[172,173]

BODIPY® FL Hyaluronic Acid

Hyaluronic acid, a major glycosaminoglycan (GAG) constituent of the extracellular matrix, participates in the adhesion, motility, proliferation, and differentiation of cells, and is involved in inflammation and cancer.[174] The numerous biological effects of this relatively simple, unbranched polysaccharide are exerted through interactions with proteins, including the cell-surface receptors CD44 and RHAMM [175,176] (receptor for hyaluronic acid–mediated motility). CD44, a 90,000-dalton transmembrane adhesion glycoprotein, is frequently overexpressed by tumor cells.[177,178] A BODIPY® FL dye–labeled hyaluronic acid derivative similar to that described by Luo and Prestwich [179] is available from Molecular Probes (H23379). Receptor-mediated internalization of BODIPY® FL dye–conjugated hyaluronic acid by human ovarian cancer cells has been visualized by confocal laser-scanning microscopy,[179] providing a foretaste of its anticipated broad utility for direct detection of hyaluronic acid–protein interactions.

Fluorescent Cholera Toxin Subunit B: Markers of Lipid Rafts

Fluorescent cholera toxins, which bind to galactosyl moieties, are markers of lipid rafts — regions of cell membranes high in ganglioside G_{M1} that are thought to be important in cell signaling [180–182] (see Note 7.5 "Technical Focus: Cholera Toxin Subunits A and B" in Section 7.7). Lipid rafts are detergent-insoluble, sphingolipid- and cholesterol-rich membrane microdomains that form lateral assemblies in the plasma membrane.[183–189] Lipid rafts also sequester glycophosphatidylinositol (GPI)-linked proteins and other signaling proteins and receptors, which may be regulated by their selective interactions with these membrane microdomains.[180,190–194] Recent research has demonstrated that lipid rafts play a role in a variety of cellular processes — including the compartmentalization of cell-signaling events,[195–202] the regulation of apoptosis [203–205] and the intracellular trafficking of certain membrane proteins and lipids [206–208] — as well as in the infectious cycles of several viruses and bacterial pathogens.[209–214]

The Vybrant® Lipid Raft Labeling Kits (V34403, V34404, V34405; Section 17.4) provide the key reagents for fluorescently labeling lipid rafts *in vivo* with our bright and extremely photostable Alexa Fluor® dyes (Figure 13.33, Figure 17.41). Live cells are first labeled with the green-fluorescent Alexa Fluor® 488, orange-fluorescent Alexa Fluor® 555 or red-fluorescent Alexa Fluor® 594 conjugate of cholera toxin subunit B (CT-B). This CT-B conjugate binds to the pentasaccharide chain of plasma membrane ganglioside G_{M1}, which selectively partitions into lipid rafts.[180–182] An antibody that specifically recognizes CT-B is then used to crosslink the CT-B–labeled lipid rafts into distinct patches on the plasma membrane, which are easily visualized by fluorescence microscopy.[215,216] Each Vybrant® Lipid Raft Labeling Kit contains sufficient reagents to label 50 live-cell samples in a 2 mL assay, including:

- Recombinant cholera toxin subunit B (CT-B) labeled with the Alexa Fluor® 488 (in Kit V34403), Alexa Fluor® 555 (in Kit V34404) or Alexa Fluor® 594 (in Kit V34405) dye
- Anti–cholera toxin subunit B antibody (anti–CT-B)
- Concentrated phosphate-buffered saline (PBS)
- A detailed labeling protocol

Cholera toxin subunit B and its conjugates are also emerging as superior tracers for retrograde labeling of neurons.[217,218] Researchers have used cholera toxin subunit B in a variety of applications, including tracing of rat forebrain afferents,[219] projections of the parabrachial region [220] and neurons of the urinary bladder wall.[221] Cholera toxin subunit B conjugates bind to the pentasaccharide chain of ganglioside G_{M1} on neuronal cell surfaces and are actively taken up and transported; alternatively, they can be injected by iontophoresis. Unlike the carbocyanine-based neuronal tracers such as DiI (D282, D3911, V22885; Section 14.4), cholera toxin subunit B conjugates can be used on tissue sections that will be fixed and frozen.[222]

All of Molecular Probes' cholera toxin subunit B conjugates are prepared from recombinant cholera toxin subunit B, which is completely free of the toxic subunit A, thus eliminating any concern for toxicity or ADP-ribosylating activity. Our Alexa Fluor® 488 (C22841, C34775), Alexa Fluor® 555 (C22843, C34776), Alexa Fluor® 594 (C22842, C34777) and Alexa Fluor® 647 (C34778) conjugates of cholera toxin subunit B combine this versatile tracer with the superior brightness of our Alexa Fluor® dyes to provide sensitive and selective receptor labeling and neuronal tracing. We also offer biotin-XX (C34779) and horseradish peroxidase (C34780) conjugates of cholera toxin subunit B for use with sensitive secondary detection methods such as diaminobenzidine (DAB) and tyramide signal amplification (TSA).

Fluorescent α-Crystallin

α-Crystallin is a large, polydisperse heat-shock protein that accounts for up to 50% of the total protein content in vertebrate lenses. This protein complex consists of many copies of two types of homologous subunits, αA and αB crystallin, and has an average molecular mass of ~800,000 daltons.[223] In the eye, α-crystallin helps to maintain the proper refractive index of the lens, which it may do in part by acting as a molecular chaperone to prevent denaturation of other lens proteins.[223–225] Fluorescent α-crystallin conjugates have been used to characterize the interaction of this protein with fiber cell plasma membranes, which increases with age or the onset of cataracts.[226,227]

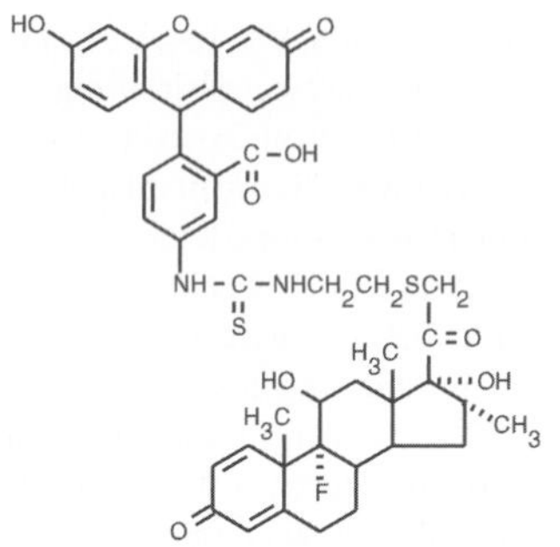

Figure 16.16 D1383 dexamethasone fluorescein.

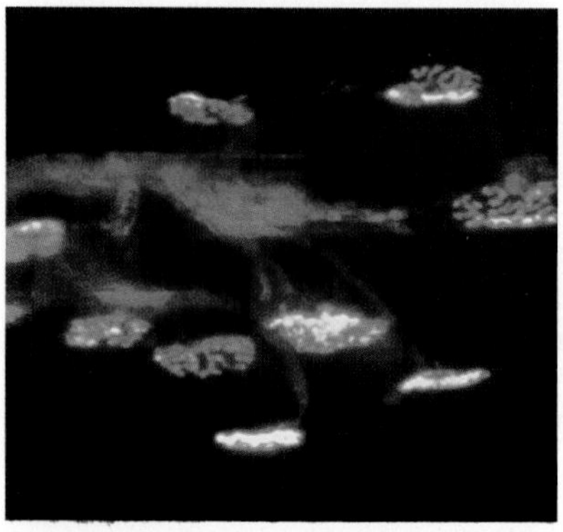

Figure 16.17 Live nerve terminals of motorneurons that innervate a rat lumbrical muscle stained with the activity-dependent dye, FM® 1-43 (T3163, T35356) and observed under low magnification. The dye molecules, which insert into the outer leaflet of the surface membrane, are captured in recycled synaptic vesicles of actively firing neurons. The image was contributed by William J. Betz, University of Colorado School of Medicine.

To facilitate these investigations, Molecular Probes offers a green-fluorescent conjugate of α-crystallin using our outstanding Alexa Fluor® 488 dye (C23010), which yields bright, photostable and pH-insensitive fluorescence between pH 4 and pH 10 (Figure 1.12).

Fluorescent Chemotactic Peptide

A variety of white blood cells containing the formyl-Met-Leu-Phe (fMLF) receptor respond to bacterial *N*-formyl peptides by migrating to the site of bacterial invasion and then initiating an activation pathway to control the spread of infection. Activation involves Ca^{2+} mobilization,[228,229] transient acidification,[230,231] actin polymerization,[232] phagocytosis[233] and production of oxidative species.[234] Molecular Probes offers the fluorescein conjugate of the hexapeptide formyl-Nle-Leu-Phe-Nle-Tyr-Lys (F1314), which has been extensively employed to investigate the fMLF receptor.[235–239] This probe is well suited for instruments that employ the argon-ion laser, including confocal laser-scanning microscopes and flow cytometers. The fluorescein-labeled chemotactic peptide has been used to study G-protein coupling and receptor structure,[240,241] expression,[242,243] distribution[244–246] and internalization.[247] For studies of fMLF receptor internalization, the fluorescence of extracellular labeled *N*-formyl hexapeptides can be quenched by adding the anti-fluorescein/Oregon Green® antibody (Section 7.4, Table 7.18). Alternatively, reducing the pH of the external medium or adding trypan blue (Figure 16.24) can quench extracellular fluorescence of the pH-sensitive fluorescein conjugate.

Fluorescent Insulin

Molecular Probes has prepared a high-purity, zinc-free fluorescein isothiocyanate conjugate of human insulin (FITC insulin, I13269). Unlike most commercially available preparations, our FITC insulin is purified by HPLC and consists of a singly labeled species of insulin that has been specifically modified at the N-terminus of the B-chain. Because the degree and position of labeling can alter the biological activity of insulin, we have isolated the singly labeled species that has been shown to retain its biological activity in an autophosphorylation assay.[248] Our FITC insulin preparation should be useful for studying the insulin receptor, as well as for conducting insulin-binding assays using fluorescence polarization and flow cytometry techniques.

Fluorescein-Labeled α-MSH Analog

[Nle^4, D-Phe^7]-α-MSH is an analog of the tridecapeptide α-melanocyte-stimulating hormone (α-MSH, melanotropin) with more potent and prolonged biological activity than native α-MSH.[249] α-MSH is active in fetal development, learning and memory processes, and its receptors are important markers for the detection of melanomas. To facilitate further investigation of these processes, we offer an N-terminal fluorescein–labeled analog of [Nle^4, D-Phe^7]-α-MSH[250] (M13440).

Fluorescent Dexamethasone Probe for Glucocorticoid Receptors

The synthetic steroid hormone dexamethasone binds to the glucocorticoid receptor, producing a steroid–receptor complex that then localizes in the nucleus and regulates gene transcription. In hepatoma tissue culture (HTC) cells, tetramethylrhodamine-labeled dexamethasone has been shown to have high affinity for the glucocorticoid receptor in a cell-free system and to induce tyrosine aminotransferase (TAT) expression in whole cells, albeit at a much lower rate than unmodified dexamethasone.[251] This labeled dexamethasone also allowed the first observations of the fluorescent steroid–receptor complex in the HTC cell cytosol.[251] Molecular Probes' fluorescein dexamethasone (D1383, Figure 16.16) should be similarly useful for studying the mechanism of glucocorticoid receptor activation.

Methods for Detecting Internalized Fluorescent Ligands

Many of the fluorescent ligands described in this section first bind to cell surface receptors, then are internalized and, in some cases, recycled to the cell's surface. Consequently, it can be difficult to assess whether the fluorescent signal is emanating from the cell surface, the cell interior or, as is more typical, a combination of the two sites. Furthermore, the fluorophore's sensitivity to environmental factors — principally intracellular pH — can affect the signal of the fluorescent ligand. Fortunately, there are means by which these signals can be separated and, in some cases, quantitated. These include:

- Use of antibodies to the Alexa Fluor® 488, BODIPY® FL, fluorescein/Oregon Green®, tetramethylrhodamine, Texas Red® and Alexa Fluor® 405/Cascade Blue® dyes (Section 7.4, Table 7.18) to quench most of the fluorescence of surface-bound or exocytosed probes. In addition, these anti-fluorophore antibodies enable researchers to develop their cell or tissue preparations for electron microscopy using standard horseradish peroxidase/diaminobenzidine [252] or colloidal gold [253] methodology or our NANOGOLD and Alexa Fluor® FluoroNanogold 1.4 nm gold cluster antibody and streptavidin conjugates (Section 7.2, Section 7.6) followed by silver enhancement with the LI Silver (LIS) Enhancement Kit (L24919, Section 7.2, Figure 7.57).
- Use of a dye such as trypan blue to quench external fluorescent signals but not internalized signals [254,255] (Figure 16.24) — a method employed in our Vybrant® Phagocytosis Assay Kit (V6694).
- Rapid acidification of the medium to quench the fluorescence of pH-sensitive fluorophores such as fluorescein on the cell's surface, thus enabling the selective detection of the endocytosed probe.
- Tagging of proteins, polysaccharides, cells, bacteria, yeast, fungi [256] and other materials to be endocytosed with a pH-sensitive dye — such as one of our SNARF® or Oregon Green® dyes (Chapter 20) — that undergoes a spectral shift (Figure 20.13, Figure 20.20) or intensity change in the acidic pH range found in phagovacuoles and early endosomes.
- Use of heavily labeled proteins such as our DQ™ BSA and DQ™ gelatin probes that undergo intracellular proteolysis to highly fluorescent peptides [257] (Section 10.4).
- Use of the optical sectioning capabilities of confocal laser-scanning microscopes, or the multiphoton capabilities of certain microscopes (Figure 1.47), to make direct measurements of internalized probes.

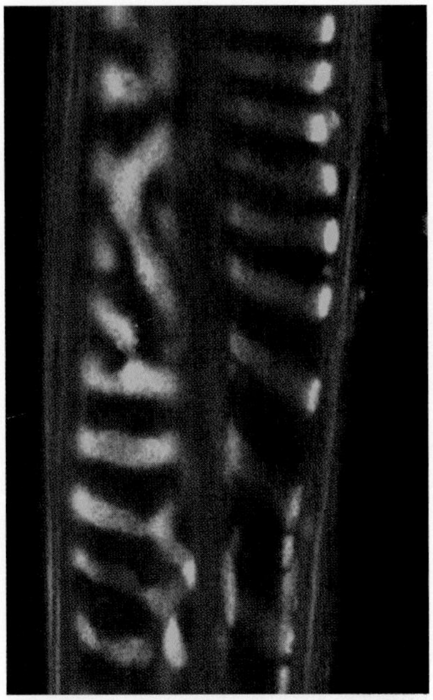

Figure 16.18 A feline mesenteric Pacinian corpuscle labeled with the vital stain FM® 1-43 (T3163, T35356). The image was contributed by Michael Chua, University of North Carolina at Chapel Hill.

Membrane Markers of Endocytosis and Exocytosis

FM® 1-43

Molecular Probes' membrane probes FM® 1-43, FM® 2-10, FM® 4-64, FM® 5-95 and the aldehyde-fixable FM® 1-43FX are excellent reagents both for identifying actively firing neurons and for investigating the mechanisms of activity-dependent vesicle cycling in widely different species.[258–262] FM® dyes may also be useful as general-purpose probes for investigating endocytosis and for simply identifying cell membrane boundaries. These water-soluble dyes, which are nontoxic to cells and virtually nonfluorescent in aqueous medium, are believed to insert into the outer leaflet of the surface membrane where they become intensely fluorescent. In a neuron that is actively releasing neurotransmitters, these dyes become internalized within the recycled synaptic vesicles and the nerve terminals become brightly stained (Figure 16.17, Figure 16.18). The nonspecific staining of cell-surface membranes can simply be washed off prior to viewing. The amount of FM® 1-43 taken up per vesicle by endocytosis equals the amount of dye released upon exocytosis, indicating that the dye does not transfer from internalized vesicles to an endosome-like compartment during the recycling process.[263] This feature permits quantitative fluorescence measurements to be made. Like most styryl dyes, the absorption and fluorescence emission spectra of FM® 1-43 (absorption/emission maxima = 510/626 nm in methanol) are significantly shifted in the membrane environment (Figure 14.65); FM® 1-43 is efficiently excited with standard fluorescein optical filters (Table 23.9) but poorly excited with standard tetramethylrhodamine optical filters. We offer FM® 1-43 in a 1 mg vial (T3163) or specially packaged in 10 vials of 100 µg each (T35356).

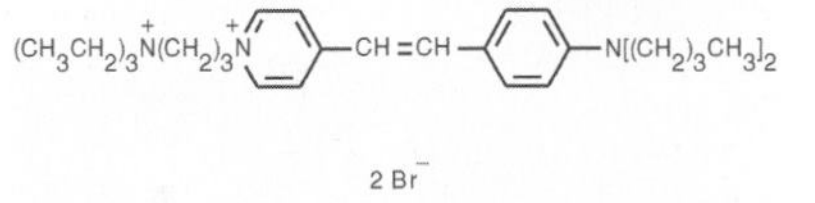

Figure 16.19 T3163 *N*-(3-triethylammoniumpropyl)-4-(4-(dibutylamino)styryl)pyridinium dibromide (FM® 1-43).

Betz and his colleagues, who were the first to employ the styrylpyridinium dye FM® 1-43 (Figure 16.19) to observe vesicle cycling in living nerve terminals,[264–266] have used this important probe to examine the effects of okadaic acid on synaptic vesicle clustering.[267] FM® 1-43 has been used to investigate synaptosomal recycling in a range of species including frog, rat and mouse.[262,265,266,268–271] It has also been shown that FM® 1-43 can be used in *Drosophila* larvae, thereby facilitating the analysis of mutations in synaptic vesicle recycling.[272] FM® 1-43 was employed in a study showing that synaptosomal endocytosis is independent of both extracellular Ca^{2+} and membrane potential in dissociated hippocampal neurons,[270] as well as in a spectrofluorometric assay demonstrating that nitric oxide–stimulated vesicle release is independent of Ca^{2+} in isolated rat hippocampal nerve terminals.[273] In addition, FM® 1-43 has been used in combination with fura-2 (Section 19.2) to simultaneously measure intracellular Ca^{2+} and membrane turnover.[274] In an alternative approach, sulforhodamine 101 (S359, Section 14.3), a red-fluorescent dye that is not taken up by synaptic vesicles, has been used to reduce nonsynaptic fluorescence in FM® 1-43 dye–labeled rat hippocampal slices.[275] FM® 1-43 dye–mediated photoconversion has been used to visualize recycling vesicles in hippocampal neurons.[276]

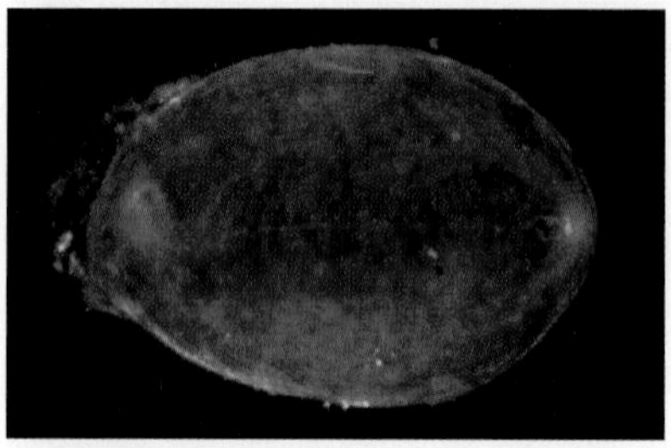

Figure 16.20 Feline muscle spindle, a specialized sensory receptor unit that detects muscle length and changes in muscle length and velocity, was labeled with the vital stain FM® 2-10 (T7508). Image contributed by Michael Chua, University of North Carolina at Chapel Hill.

FM® 1-43FX

FM® 1-43FX is an FM® 1-43 analog that has been modified to contain an aliphatic amine. This modification makes the probe fixable with aldehyde-based fixatives, including formaldehyde and glutaraldehyde. FM® 1-43FX has been used to study synaptic vesicle cycling in cone photoreceptor terminals[258] and to investigate the functional maturation of glutamatergic synapses.[277] FM® 1-43FX is available specially packaged in 10 vials of 100 µg each (F35355).

Other Analogs of FM® 1-43

A comparison of mammalian motor nerve terminals stained with either FM® 1-43 or the more hydrophilic analog FM® 2-10 (T7508, Figure 16.20) revealed that lower background staining by FM® 2-10 and its faster destaining rate may make it the preferred probe for quantitative applications.[261,262] However, staining with FM® 2-10 requires much higher dye concentrations[262] (100 µM compared with 2 µM for FM® 1-43). FM® 4-64 (T3166, T13320; Figure 14.66) and RH 414 (T1111) — both more hydrophobic than FM® 1-43 — may also be useful as probes for investigating endocytosis. Because small differences in the polarity of these probes can play a large role in their rates of uptake and their retention properties, we have introduced FM® 5-95 (T23360), a slightly less lipophilic analog of FM® 4-64 with essentially identical spectroscopic properties. FM® 4-64 exhibits long-wavelength red fluorescence that can be distinguished from the green fluorescence of FM® 1-43 with the proper optical filter sets (Table 23.9), thus permitting two-color observation of membrane recycling in real time;[278,279] Membranes stained with RH 414 typically exhibit orange fluorescence when observed through a longpass optical filter that permits passage of light beyond 510 nm.[265,266,280]

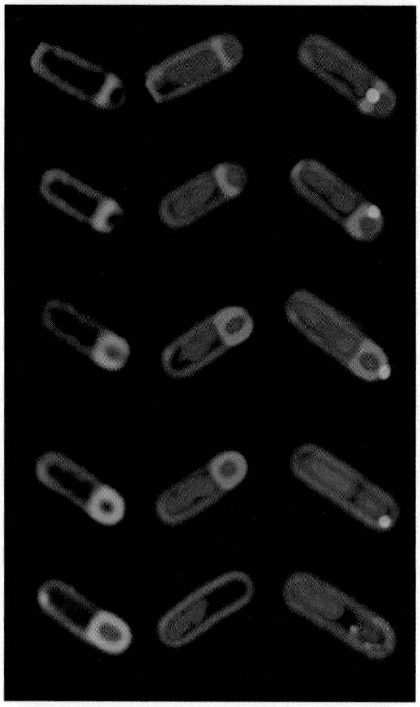

Figure 16.21 Correlated fluorescence imaging of membrane migration, protein translocation and chromosome localization during *Bacillus subtilis* sporulation. Membranes were stained with red-fluorescent FM® 4-64 (T3166, T13320). Chromosomes were localized with the blue-fluorescent nuclear counterstain, DAPI (D1306, D3571, D21490). The small, green-fluorescent patches (right column) indicate the localization of a GFP fusion to SpoIIIE, a protein essential for both initial membrane fusion and forespore engulfment. Progression of the engulfment is shown from top to bottom. Green fluorescence in the middle and left columns demonstrates fully engulfed sporangia stained with MitoTracker® Green FM (M7514). Full details of the experimental methods and interpretation are published in Proc Natl Acad Sci U S A 96, 14553 (1999). Image contributed by Kit Pogliano and Marc Sharp, University of California at San Diego. Reproduced from the 7 December 1999 issue of *Proc Natl Acad Sci U S A*, with permission.

Using time-lapse video fluorescence microscopy, Heuser and colleagues were able to follow the internalization of FM® 4-64 from the *Dictyostelium* plasma membrane into the contractile vacuole and to observe up to 10 contractile vacuole cycles before the dye redistributed to the endosomes.[281] In addition, FM® 4-64 staining has been used to visualize membrane migration and fusion during *Bacillus subtilis* sporulation — movements that can be correlated with the translocation of green-fluorescent protein–labeled proteins[282] (Figure 14.66, Figure 16.21). FM® 4-64 has also been reported to selectively stain yeast vacuolar membranes and is proving to be an important tool for visualizing vacuolar organelle morphology and dynamics and for studying the endocytic pathway and vacuole fusion in yeast[283–288] (Section 12.3). FM® 4-64 is an endosomal marker and vital stain that persists through cell division[289,290] and is a stain for functional presynaptic boutons.[291]

4-Di-1-ASP and 4-Di-2-ASP

Some cationic mitochondrial dyes such as 4-Di-1-ASP (D288) and 4-Di-2-ASP (D289) stain presynaptic nerve terminals independent of neuronal activity.[292–294] The photostable 4-Di-2-ASP dye, which is nontoxic to cells, has been employed to stain living nerve terminals in rabbit corneal epithelium,[295] in rat epidermis[292] and at mouse, snake and frog neuromuscular junctions,[296–299] as well as to visualize the innervation of the human choroid[300] and whole mounts of the gastrointestinal tract.[301] 4-Di-2-ASP staining of neuromuscular junctions reportedly persists for several months in living mice.[299] Methods for using 4-Di-2-ASP to image neuronal cells in live animals have been described[302] (Figure 16.22).

TMA-DPH and TMAP-DPH

Also useful as a lipid marker for endocytosis and exocytosis is the cationic linear polyene TMA-DPH (T204, Figure 13.50), which readily incorporates in the plasma membrane of live cells.[303,304] TMA-DPH is virtually nonfluorescent in water and is reported to bind to cells in proportion to the available membrane surface.[305] Its fluorescence intensity is therefore sensitive to physiological processes that cause a net change in membrane surface area, making it an excellent probe for monitoring events such as changes in cell volume and exocytosis.[305–308] During endocytosis, TMA-DPH progresses from the cell periphery to perinuclear regions with little loss in fluorescence intensity.[309] TMA-DPH can be extracted from plasma membranes by washing with medium, thus providing a method for isolating cells that have only the internalized probe and monitoring endocytosis.[310–312] To provide supporting evidence for the maturation model for endocytosis, researchers used TMA-DPH in fluorescence anisotropy–based assays to investigate membrane fluidity in the plasma membrane and in successive endocytic compartments of L929 cells.[309] A protocol has been published that uses TMA-DPH for labeling and flow-sorting of early endosomes.[313]

We also offer TMAP-DPH (P3900), which has a three-carbon spacer between the DPH fluorophore and the trimethylammonium substituent (Figure 16.23); the partitioning properties of TMAP-DPH probe in multilamellar liposomes and use of the probe to assess membrane fluidity have been described.[314–317] Measurements of the fluorescence lifetime of membrane-bound TMAP-DPH can be used to probe for hydration of lipid bilayers.[318,319]

Anti–Synapsin I Antibody

Synapsin I is an actin-binding protein that is localized exclusively to synaptic vesicles and thus serves as an excellent marker for synapses in brain and other neuronal tissues.[320,321] Synapsin I inhibits neurotransmitter release, an effect that is abolished upon its phosphorylation by Ca^{2+}/calmodulin–dependent protein kinase II[322] (CaM kinase II). Antibodies directed against synapsin I have proven valuable in molecular and neurobiology research, for example, to estimate synaptic density and to follow synaptogenesis.[270,323–325]

Molecular Probes offers a rabbit polyclonal anti–bovine synapsin I antibody as an affinity-purified IgG fraction (A6442). This antibody was isolated from rabbits immunized against bovine brain synapsin I but is also active against human, rat and mouse forms of the antigen; it has little or no activity against synapsin II. The affinity-purified rabbit polyclonal antibody was fractionated from the serum using column chromatography in which bovine synapsin I was covalently bound to the column matrix. Affinity-purified anti–synapsin I antibody is suitable for immunohistochemistry (Figure 17.12), Western blots, enzyme-linked immunoadsorbent assays and immunoprecipitations. Our Zenon® Rabbit IgG Labeling Kits (Section 7.3, Table 7.13) can be used to prepare fluorescent dye–, biotin- or enzyme-labeled complexes of this antibody.

High Molecular Weight Polar Markers

BioParticles® Fluorescent Bacteria and Yeast

Molecular Probes' BioParticles® product line consists of a series of fluorescently labeled, heat- or chemically killed bacteria and yeast in a variety of sizes, shapes and natural antigenicities. These fluorescent BioParticles® products have been employed to study phagocytosis by fluorescence microscopy,[326] quantitative spectrofluorometry[327] and flow cytometry.[328–331] We offer *Escherichia coli* (K-12 strain), *Staphylococcus aureus* (Wood strain without protein A) and zymosan (*Saccharomyces cerevisiae*) BioParticles® covalently labeled with a variety of fluorophores, including fluorescein, Alexa Fluor® 488, BODIPY® FL, tetramethylrhodamine and Texas Red® dyes (Table 16.3). Special care has been taken to remove any free dye after conjugation. Our Alexa Fluor® 488 conjugate of the *E. coli* BioParticles® bacteria (E13231) has exceptionally bright and photostable green fluorescence. Unlike the fluorescence of fluorescein-labeled BioParticles® fluorescent bacteria and yeast (Figure 20.2), which is partially quenched in acidic environments, fluorescence of the Alexa Fluor® 488, BODIPY® FL, tetramethylrhodamine and Texas Red® conjugates is uniformly intense between pH 3 and 10. This property may be particularly useful in quantitating fluorescent bacteria and zymosan within acidic phagocytic vacuoles. BioParticles® products, which are freeze-dried and ready for reconstitution in a buffer of choice, come with a general

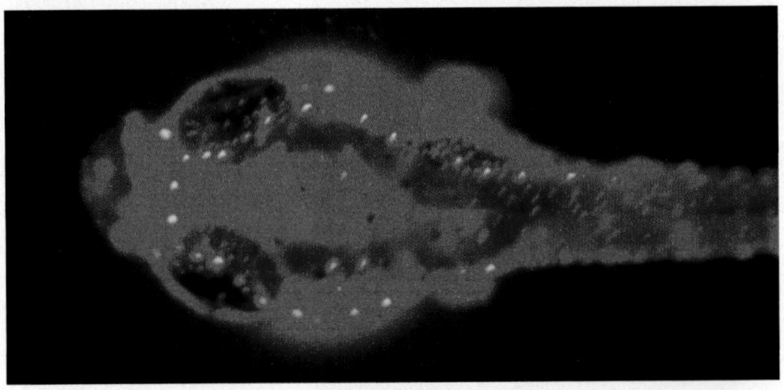

Figure 16.22 Neuromasts, the external mechanosensory organs of fish, stained selectively with the vital fluorescent probe 4-Di-2-ASP (D289) in a living larva of the Siamese fighting fish *Betta splendans* at ten days postfertilization. In this dorsal view, staining was accomplished by putting live fish into a dilute aqueous solution of the dye. Image contributed by Paula Mabee, San Diego State University.

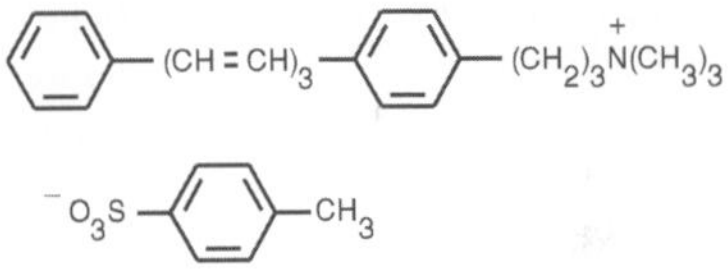

Figure 16.23 P3900 *N*-((4-(6-phenyl-1,3,5-hexatrienyl)phenyl)propyl)trimethylammonium *p*-toluenesulfonate (TMAP-DPH).

Table 16.3 — Molecular Probes' selection of BioParticles® fluorescent bacteria and yeast

Label (Abs/Em Maxima)	*Escherichia coli* (K-12 strain)	*Staphylococcus aureus* (Wood strain without protein A)	Zymosan A (*Saccharomyces cerevisiae*)
Fluorescein (494/518)	E2861	S2851	Z2841
Alexa Fluor® 488 (495/519)	E13231	S23371	Z23373
BODIPY® FL (505/513)	E2864	S2854	Z2844
Tetramethyl-rhodamine (555/580)	E2862		
Alexa Fluor® 594 (590/617)	E23370	S23372	Z23374
Texas Red® dye (595/615)	E2863		Z2843
Unlabeled		S2859	Z2849

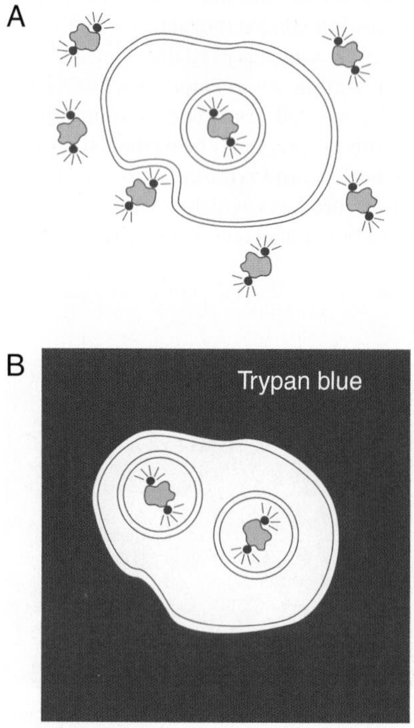

Figure 16.24 Principle of the Vybrant® Phagocytosis Assay Kit (V6694) for the simple quantitation of phagocytosis. (A) Briefly, phagocytic cells are incubated with the green-fluorescent BioParticles® fluorescein-labeled *Escherichia coli* (E2861). (B). The fluorescence from any noninternalized BioParticles® is then quenched by the addition of trypan blue, and the samples are subsequently assayed with a fluorescence microplate reader equipped with filters for the detection of fluorescein (FITC).

protocol for measuring phagocytosis. We also offer opsonizing reagents for use with each particle type as described below.

Fluorescent bacteria and yeast particles are proven tools for studying a variety of parameters influencing phagocytosis; for example, they have been used to:

- Detect the phagocytosis of yeast by murine peritoneal macrophage [332] and human neutrophils [327]
- Determine the effects of different opsonization procedures on the efficiency of phagocytosis of pathogenic bacteria [333] and yeast [327]
- Investigate the kinetics of phagocytosis degranulation and actin polymerization in stimulated leukocytes [327]
- Measure phagocytosis and, in conjunction with dihydroethidium (hydroethidine, D1168, D11347, D23107; Section 18.2), oxidative bursts in leukocytes using flow cytometry [334,335]
- Quantitate the effects of anti-inflammatory drugs on phagocytosis [327]
- Show that *Dictyostelium discoideum* depleted of clathrin heavy chains are still able to undergo phagocytosis of fluorescent zymosans [336]
- Study molecular defects in phagocytic function [337]

Trypan blue and other quenchers can quench the fluorescence of BioParticles® fluorescent bacteria and yeast that are bound to the surface but not internalized [254,255,328] (Figure 16.24). Phagocytosis of viable *Candida albicans* that were loaded with 5-(and 6-)carboxy SNARF®-1, acetoxymethyl ester, acetate (C1271, C1272; Section 20.2), a cell-permeant pH indicator, has been quantitated on a single-cell level by flow cytometry without interfering cell autofluorescence.[338] In addition to cellular applications, our fluorescent BioParticles® products may be effective as flow cytometry calibration references when sorting bacteria and yeast mutants. These small particles may also be useful references for light scattering studies because their sizes and shapes differ in characteristic ways.

Vybrant® Phagocytosis Assay Kit

Our Vybrant® Phagocytosis Assay Kit (V6694) provides a convenient set of reagents for quantitating phagocytosis and assessing the effects of certain drugs or conditions on this cellular process. In this assay, cells of interest are incubated first with green-fluorescent *E. coli* BioParticles®, which are internalized by phagocytosis, and then with trypan blue, which quenches the fluorescence of any extracellular BioParticles® conjugate (Figure 16.24). The methodology provided by this kit was developed using the adherent murine macrophage cell line J774;[255] however, researchers can likely adapt this assay to other phagocytic cell types. Each kit provides sufficient reagents for 250 tests using a 96-well microplate format and contains:

- BioParticles® fluorescein-labeled *Escherichia coli*
- Hanks' balanced salt solution (HBSS)
- Trypan blue
- Step-by-step instructions for performing the phagocytosis assay

Opsonizing Reagents and Nonfluorescent BioParticles®

Many researchers may want to use autologous serum to opsonize their fluorescent zymosan and bacterial particles; however, we also offer special opsonizing reagents (E2870, S2860, Z2850) for enhancing the uptake of each type of particle, along with a protocol for opsonization. These reagents are derived from purified rabbit polyclonal IgG antibodies that are specific for the *E. coli*, *S. aureus* or zymosan particles. Reconstitution of the lyophilized opsonizing reagents requires only the addition of water, and one unit of opsonizing reagent is sufficient to opsonize ~10 mg of the corresponding BioParticles® product.

In addition, Molecular Probes offers nonfluorescent zymosan (Z2849) and *S. aureus* (S2859) BioParticles® products. These nonfluorescent BioParticles® products are useful either as controls or for custom labeling with the reactive dye or indicator of interest.

Fluorescent Polystyrene Microspheres

Fluorescent polystyrene microspheres with diameters between 0.5 and 2.0 µm have been used to investigate phagocytic processes in rat and human neutrophils,[339,340] human trabecular meshwork cells,[341] mouse peritoneal macrophages,[342,343] ciliated protozoa[344,345] and *Dictyostelium discoideum*.[346] The phagocytosis of fluorescent microspheres has been quantitated both with image analysis[343] and with flow cytometry.[342,344,345] Section 6.5 includes a detailed description of our full line of FluoSpheres® (Table 6.7) and TransFluoSpheres® (Table 6.9) fluorescent microspheres. Because of their low nonspecific binding, carboxylate-modified microspheres appear to be best for applications involving phagocytosis. For phagocytosis experiments involving multicolor detection, we particularly recommend our 1.0 µm TransFluoSpheres® fluorescent microspheres (T8880, T8883; Section 6.5), which have greater Stokes shifts than do the FluoSpheres® microspheres. Various opsonizing reagents, such as rabbit serum or fetal calf serum, have been used with the microspheres to facilitate phagocytosis. Methods for coating fluorescent microspheres with the CR1 complement receptor have also been described.[347] Numerous references in our extensive microspheres bibliography (M8997) describe the use of fluorescent microspheres for phagocytosis studies; continuously updated copies are available upon request from our Technical Assistance Department or through our web site (probes.invitrogen.com).

Fluorescent Microspheres Coated with Collagen

Fibroblasts phagocytose and then intracellularly digest collagen. These activities play an important role in the remodeling of the extracellular matrix during normal physiological turnover of connective tissues, in development, in wound repair and possibly in aging and various disorders. A well-established procedure for observing collagen phagocytosis by either flow cytometry or fluorescence microscopy involves the use of collagen-coated fluorescent microspheres, which attach to the cell surface and become engulfed by fibroblasts.[348–350] Molecular Probes offers yellow-green–fluorescent FluoSpheres® collagen I–labeled microspheres in either 1.0 µm or 2.0 µm diameters (F20892, F20893) for use in these applications. In the production of these microspheres, collagen I from calf skin is attached covalently to the microsphere's surface.

Fluorescent Dextrans

Fluorescent dextrans can be used to monitor the uptake and internal processing of exogenous materials by endocytosis.[351–356] Molecular Probes offers dextrans with nominal molecular weights ranging from 3000 to 2,000,000 daltons, many of which can be used as pinocytosis or phagocytosis markers (see Section 14.5 and Table 14.4 for further discussion and a complete product list). Discrimination of internalized fluorescent dextrans from dextrans in the growth medium is facilitated by use of reagents that quench the fluorescence of the external probe. For example, most of our anti-fluorophore antibodies (Section 7.4, Table 7.18) strongly quench the fluorescence of the corresponding dyes. In addition, although we are not aware of any publications that have used our Ca^{2+} indicator–conjugated dextrans as probes for uptake by cells, it should be possible to follow endocytosis of dextran conjugates of fura-2, indo-1, Calcium Green™, fluo-4, rhod and X-rhod (Section 19.4) by using Mn^{2+} to quench the fluorescence of the residual extracellular dextrans without affecting intracellular dextrans. Using fluorescent dextran probes, researchers have investigated:

- Effects of the calmodulin antagonist W-13 on transcytosis and vesicular morphology in Madin–Darby canine kidney (MDCK) cells[357]
- Endocytic vesicles in *Plasmodium falciparum*[358]
- Endocytosis-defective Chinese hamster ovary (CHO) cells[359] and *Dictyostelium discoideum*[346,360–362]
- Fusion competence of lysosomes in parasite-infected cells[363]
- Kinetics of pinocytosis in mouse L cells by flow cytometry[364] and the suppression of pinocytosis in mouse peritoneal macrophages by interferon[365]
- Membrane changes in prostatic adenocarcinoma[366] and basophilic leukemia cells[367,368]
- Methods to enhance receptor-mediated gene delivery[351]
- Vacuolar morphology in *Saccharomyces cerevisiae* both during the cell cycle[369–371] and in mutant cell lines[372]

Intracellular fusion of endosomes has been monitored with a BODIPY® FL avidin conjugate by following the fluorescence enhancement that occurs when it complexes with a biotinylated dextran.[373] We have found our Oregon Green® 514 streptavidin (S6369, Section 7.6) to have an over 15-fold increase in fluorescence intensity upon binding free biotin, which may make it the preferred probe for this application (Figure 16.25).

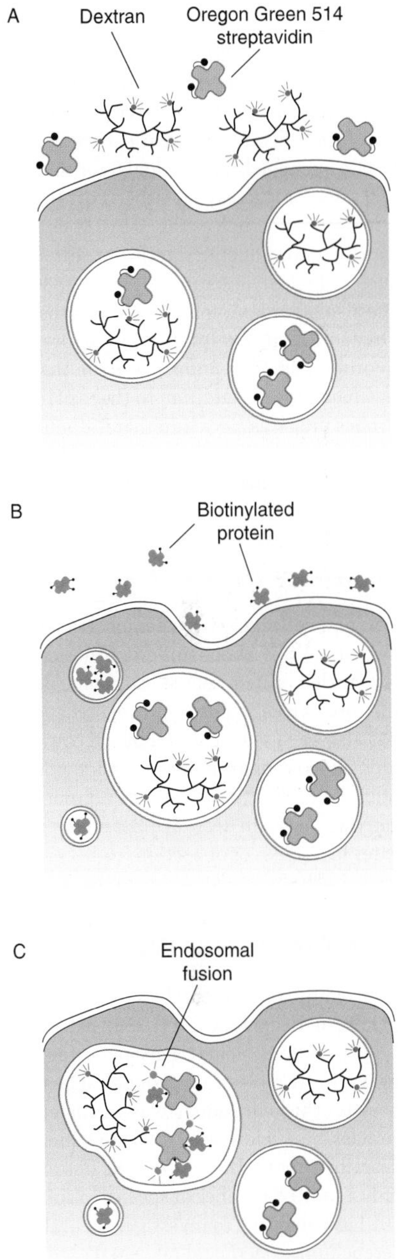

Figure 16.25 Detection of endosomal fusion. (A) Cells are first incubated with a combination of a high molecular weight, red-fluorescent dextran (D1829, D1830, D1864) and the green-fluorescent Oregon Green® 514 streptavidin (S6369), which intrinsically has low fluorescence. (B) The cells are then incubated with a biotinylated probe, e.g., biotinylated transferrin (T23363) and the excess conjugate is washed. (C) Endosomal fusion is monitored by an increase in fluorescence by the Oregon Green® 514 dye as it is displaced by the biotinylated protein. The red-fluorescent dextran's fluorescence remains constant and allows for ratiometric measurements of the fused endosomes.

pH Indicator Dextrans

The fluorescein dextrans (pK_a ~6.4) are frequently used to investigate endocytic acidification.[355,374–378] Fluorescence of fluorescein-labeled dextrans is strongly quenched upon acidification (Figure 20.2); however, fluorescein's lack of a spectral shift in acidic solution makes it difficult to discriminate between an internalized probe that is quenched and residual fluorescence of the external medium. Dextran conjugates that either shift their emission spectra in acidic environments, such as the SNARF® dextrans (D3303, D3304; Section 20.4), or undergo significant shifts of their excitation spectra, such as BCECF dextrans (D1878, D1880; Section 20.4), are preferred. We also offer dextrans labeled with the ratiometric, pH-sensitive, Oregon Green® 488 (pK_a ~4.7) and Oregon Green® 514 (pK_a ~4.7) fluorophores. More information on these pH indicators can be found in Chapter 20. In addition to these pH indicator dextrans, Molecular Probes prepares a dextran that is double-labeled with fluorescein and tetramethylrhodamine (D1950, D1951; Section 20.4), which has been used as a ratiometric indicator (Figure 20.32) to measure endosomal acidification in Swiss 3T3 fibroblasts[379] and Hep G2 cells.[380]

Vitamin-Conjugated Probes

Low and colleagues have demonstrated that modification of proteins by biotin,[381,382] riboflavin[383] or folic acid[384–386] can facilitate uptake of the labeled protein into at least some plant cells (soybeans) and many mammalian cells, apparently via receptor-mediated endocytosis. It has also been reported that biotin covalently attached to cell surfaces induces existing receptors to endocytose avidin bioconjugates into nucleated cells[387] (but not into nonnucleated cells). Our biotin conjugates are listed in Section 4.3, and our avidin and streptavidin conjugates in Table 7.22 of Section 7.6.

Low Molecular Weight Polar Markers

Hydrophilic fluorescent dyes — including sulforhodamine 101 (S359), lucifer yellow CH (L453), calcein (C481), 8-hydroxypyrene-1,3,6-trisulfonic acid (HPTS, pyranine; H348) and Cascade Blue® hydrazide (C687) — are thought to be taken up by actively firing neurons through endocytosis-mediated recycling of the synaptic vesicles.[388,389] However, unlike the fluorescent FM® membrane probes described above, the hydrophilic fluorophores appear to work for only a limited number of species in this application. Sulforhodamine 101 has been used to investigate neural activity in turtle brainstem cerebellum,[390] neonatal rat spinal cord[391,392] and developing snake neuromuscular junctions.[393] The ratiometric pH indicator (Figure 20.23) pyranine has been employed to measure organelle acidification in the endosomal–lysosomal pathway.[394] The same dyes have frequently been used as fluid-phase markers of pinocytosis.[395–400] Pyranine has blue fluorescence in acidic solutions and yellow fluorescence in neutral to basic solutions. Our highly water-soluble Alexa Fluor® hydrazides and Alexa Fluor® hydroxylamines (Section 14.3, Table 3.1) provide superior spectral properties and can be fixed in cells by aldehyde-based fixatives.

Carbohydrates

Fluorescent Glucose Analogs

Measurements of glucose uptake can be used to assess transport and viability in a variety of organisms. 2-NBD-deoxyglucose (2-NBDG, N13195) has been used to monitor glucose uptake in pancreatic cells,[401] the yeast *Candida albicans*[402] and the bacteria *Escherichia coli*.[403–405] Molecular Probes also offers the fluorescent glucose analog 6-NBD-deoxyglucose (6-NBDG, N23106). Using this probe, researchers have studied glucose uptake and transport in isolated cells[406–408] and intact tissues.[409] NBD fluorescence is environment sensitive, but typically displays excitation/emission maxima of ~465/540 nm and can be visualized using optical filters designed for fluorescein (Table 23.9).

ManLev and ManLev Tetraacetate

The oligosaccharide components of cell-surface glycoproteins play a role in the interactions that regulate many important biological processes, from cell–cell adhesion to signal transduction. Because modification of these surface groups affects the behavior of the cell,[410] strategies that introduce alternative surface groups to the cell[411] provide researchers with novel methods for tagging specific cell populations.

Sialic acids are the most abundant terminal components of oligosaccharides on mammalian cell-surface glycoproteins and are synthesized from the six-carbon precursor *N*-acetylmannosamine.[412] When cells in culture are incubated with 25 mM *N*-levulinoyl-D-mannosamine (ManLev, L20492; Figure 3.9) or — much more efficiently — with 25 µM ManLev tetraacetate (L20493), this ketone-containing monosaccharide serves as a substrate in the oligosaccharide synthesis pathway, resulting in ketone-tagged cell-surface oligosaccharides.[413–418] Because ketones are rare in cells, reaction with 2 mM biotinylated aldehyde-reactive probe (ARP, A10550; Section 4.2; Figure 3.10) followed by a fluorescent avidin or streptavidin conjugate (Section 7.6, Table 7.22) provides a means of identifying and tracing tagged cells by either imaging (Figure 3.11) or flow cytometry. We find that the biotin hydroxylamine ARP is much more reactive than biotin hydrazides; fluorescent hydrazides and hydroxylamines usually are not suitable for this detection because the concentrations that are required can result in their internalization in live cells by pinocytosis.

Probes for Investigating Secretion and Degranulation

Intracellular calcium plays an important role in stimulus–secretion coupling, making Molecular Probes' fluorescent Ca^{2+} indicators (Chapter 19) among the commonly used tools for investigating secretion. For example, researchers used our Fura Red™ calcium indicator to show that Ca^{2+} spikes occurring in the granular areas of rat pancreatic acinar cells could be correlated with secretion.[419] In addition, we offer probes that modify intracellular Ca^{2+} levels by a variety of mechanisms. For example, thapsigargin (T7458, Section 17.2), which inhibits Ca^{2+}-ATPase–mediated uptake of Ca^{2+} into the endoplasmic reticulum, has been used to further define the role of intracellular Ca^{2+} in stimulus–secretion coupling in a number of cell types.[420–422]

Fluorogenic and chromogenic substrates for enzymes that are released during secretion or degranulation — such as glucosaminidase, galactosidase, glucuronidase and acid phosphatase (see Chapter 10) — may also be useful for detecting secretion. Many probes described in this and other chapters have been used to detect, induce or block secretion or degranulation, including:

- BODIPY® FL casein and BODIPY® TR-X casein,[165] substrates in our EnzChek® Protease Assay Kits (E6638, E6639), and DQ™ Green BSA and DQ™ Red BSA (D12050, D12051), which can detect secretion of proteases from cells, including in agar plates,[423] and may be useful for selecting enzyme-secreting mutants
- Our EnzChek® Elastase Assay Kit (E12056, Section 10.4), which may be useful for the continuous assay of elastase loss from cells during secretion or degranulation[424]
- Luciferin (L2911, L2912, L2916; Section 10.5), which has been used to detect ATP secretion from bovine adrenal chromaffin cells[425]
- The Amplex® Red Hydrogen Peroxide/Peroxidase Assay Kit[426–428] (A22188, Section 18.2), the OxyBURST® Green H_2HFF BSA reagent (O13291) and other reagents described in Section 18.2 for detecting the production of extracellular reactive oxygen species (ROS)
- TMA-DPH (T204), which partially transfers from the plasma membrane to the mast cell granule membrane during secretion, and acridine orange (A1301, A3568; Section 12.3), which stains mast cell granules[307,429]
- Anion-channel blockers such as DIDS and SITS (D337, A339; Section 16.3), which block secretion[430–432]
- Brefeldin A (B7450, Section 12.4), which blocks transport of NBD C_6-ceramide and BODIPY® FL C_5-ceramide (N1154, N22651, D3521, B22650; Section 12.4) through the Golgi apparatus[433,434]
- BODIPY® FL C_5-ceramide and its BSA complex (D3521, B22650; Section 12.4), which are normally transported from the Golgi apparatus to the cell surface and thus permit isolation of mutant mammalian cells with defects in the secretory pathway[433]
- Cyclic ADP-ribose (C7619, Section 17.2), which induces insulin secretion in pancreatic islets[435]
- Nitric oxide donors, including SNAP (N7892, N7927; Section 18.3), which have been shown to either inhibit[436] or stimulate[437] secretion
- Fluorescent analogs of polymyxin B (Section 17.3), an antibiotic that induces dose-dependent histamine and serotonin release from mast cells[438–441]

References

1. Traffic 1, 836 (2000); **2.** Subcellular Biochemistry, Vol. 19: Endocytic Components: Identification and Characterization, J.J.M. pp. 95–123 (1993); **3.** J Immunol Methods 232, 23 (1999); **4.** J Immunol 130, 1910 (1983); **5.** J Leukoc Biol 43, 304 (1988); **6.** J Immunol Methods 130, 223 (1990); **7.** Biophys J 75, 2577 (1998); **8.** J Leukoc Biol 64, 98 (1998); **9.** J Biol Chem 270, 8328 (1995); **10.** J Biol Chem 269, 18535 (1994); **11.** Proc Natl Acad Sci U S A 100, 13326 (2003); **12.** J Cell Physiol 156, 428 (1993); **13.** Proc Natl Acad Sci U S A 74, 837 (1977); **14.** J Cell Biol 121, 1257 (1993); **15.** Bioconjug Chem 5, 105 (1994); **16.** J Cell Sci 107, 2177 (1994); **17.** Am J Pathol 138, 1173 (1991); **18.** Biophys J 66, 1301 (1994); **19.** Biophys J 67, 1280 (1994); **20.** Methods Enzymol 98, 241 (1983); **21.** In Vitro Cell Dev Biol 27A, 633 (1991); **22.** J Lipid Res 34, 325 (1993); **23.** J Biol Chem 269, 20958 (1994); **24.** Biol Reprod 50, 204 (1994); **25.** Endocrinology 129, 3247 (1991); **26.** Biol Reprod 47, 355 (1992); **27.** J Cell Biol 101, 148 (1985); **28.** Proc Natl Acad Sci U S A 81, 5454 (1984); **29.** J Cell Biol 90, 595 (1981); **30.** J Biol Chem 253, 9053 (1978); **31.** J Supramol Struct 13, 67 (1980); **32.** J Cell Biol 82, 597 (1979); **33.** Annu Rev Biochem 52, 223 (1983); **34.** Arteriosclerosis 3, 2 (1983); **35.** Arteriosclerosis 1, 177 (1981); **36.** J Biol Chem 275, 9120 (2000); **37.** J Biol Chem 265, 12722 (1990); **38.** J Biol Chem 270, 1921 (1995); **39.** J Biol Chem 269, 21003 (1994); **40.** J Cell Biol 129, 133 (1995); **41.** Biochim Biophys Acta 1303, 193 (1996); **42.** Eur J Cell Biol 60, 48 (1993); **43.** J Cell Biol 122, 923 (1993); **44.** J Cell Biol 122, 417 (1993); **45.** J Cell Biol 99, 2034 (1984); **46.** J Neurosci 6, 2163 (1986); **47.** Exp Cell Res 198, 31 (1992); **48.** J Biol Chem 267, 20383 (1992); **49.** Histochem J 17, 1309 (1985); **50.** J Neurosci 13, 4412 (1993); **51.** J Neurosci 13, 4403 (1993); **52.** J Exp Med 190, 523 (1999); **53.** J Exp Med 190, 509 (1999); **54.** J Biol Chem 271, 4100 (1996); **55.** J Exp Med 181, 1743 (1995); **56.** J Exp Med 180, 1025 (1994); **57.** J Exp Med 179, 269 (1994); **58.** J Biol Chem 259, 10048 (1984); **59.** J Exp Med 183, 1899 (1996); **60.** Proc Natl Acad Sci U S A 83, 5817 (1986); **61.** Adv Immunol 28, 293 (1979); **62.** Eur J Immunol 19, 125 (1989); **63.** Blood 95, 198 (2000); **64.** Circ Res 88, 491 (2001); **65.** J Neurosci 22, 2478 (2002); **66.** Cytometry 41, 316 (2000); **67.** J Biol Chem 274, 34116 (1999); **68.** Electron Microsc Rev 5, 381 (1992); **69.** J Periodontol 56, 553 (1985); **70.** Biotechniques 28, 510 (2000); **71.** Cell 61, 203 (1990); **72.** J Biol Chem 265, 7709 (1990); **73.** Annu Rev Biochem 56, 881 (1987); **74.** J Biol Chem 273, 28004 (1998); **75.** EMBO J 5, 1181 (1986); **76.** J Fluorescence 4, 295 (1994); **77.** J Biol Chem 268, 23860 (1993); **78.** J Membr Biol 118, 215 (1990); **79.** Biochemistry 32, 12039 (1993); **80.** J Cell Biol 109, 2105 (1989); **81.** J Cell Biol 106, 1903 (1988); **82.** Proc Natl Acad Sci U S A 75, 2135 (1978); **83.** Mol Biol Cell 11, 747 (2000); **84.** Mol Biol Cell 9, 809 (1998); **85.** J Immunol Methods 219, 57 (1998); **86.** J Histochem Cytochem 40, 1353 (1992); **87.** Cell 49, 423 (1987); **88.** Trends Biochem Sci 12, 350 (1987); **89.** Biochimie 68, 375 (1986); **90.** J Cell Biol 108, 1291 (1989); **91.** Cell 37, 789 (1984); **92.** Blood 95, 721 (2000); **93.** Scand J Immunol 53, 393 (2001); **94.** J Biol Chem 276, 9649 (2001); **95.** J Biol Chem 274, 22303 (1999); **96.** J Biol Chem 274, 26233 (1999); **97.** Mol Biol Cell 10, 3835 (1999); **98.** Cancer Res 61, 7763 (2001); **99.** J Biol Chem 276, 13096 (2001); **100.** Mol Biol Cell 10, 4403 (1999); **101.** J Cell Biol 125, 253 (1994); **102.** J Cell Biol 121, 61 (1993); **103.** J Biol Chem 263, 8844 (1988); **104.** J Biol Chem 275, 15271 (2000); **105.** J Biol Chem 275, 29636 (2000); **106.** Biochemistry 31, 5820 (1992); **107.** J Bioenerg Biomembr 23, 147 (1991); **108.** J Biol Chem 266, 3469 (1991); **109.** J Biol Chem 265, 6688 (1990); **110.** Nature 358, 337 (1992); **111.** J Cell Biol 123, 1119 (1993); **112.** J Cell Biol 122, 1231 (1993); **113.** J Cell Biol 122, 565 (1993); **114.** J Cell Biol 118, 267 (1992); **115.** J Cell Biol 122, 1207 (1993); **116.** J Cell Biol 125, 1265 (1994); **117.** Nature 346, 335 (1990); **118.** Eur J Cell Biol 79, 394 (2000); **119.** J Biol Chem 272, 13929 (1997); **120.** J Cell Biol 135, 1749 (1996); **121.** Mol Biol Cell 7, 355 (1996); **122.** Pharmacol Toxicol 71, 3 (1992); **123.** Nature 391, 499 (1998); **124.** J Biol Chem 270, 28812 (1995); **125.** Thromb Res 77, 543 (1995); **126.** Biochem J 270, 149 (1990); **127.** Biochem Pharmacol 36, 4035 (1987); **128.** Biochemistry 33, 266 (1994); **129.** J Biol Chem 270, 11358 (1995); **130.** J Cell Biol 104, 1403 (1987); **131.** Eur J Med Res 3, 465 (1998); **132.** J Biol Chem 258, 12582 (1983); **133.** Science 231, 1559 (1986); **134.** Proc Natl Acad Sci U S A 82, 8057 (1985); **135.** J Cell Biol 147, 1419 (1999); **136.** Br J Haematol 93, 204 (1996); **137.** J Lab Clin Med 123, 728 (1994); **138.** Cytometry 17, 287 (1994); **139.** Ann N Y Acad Sci 416, 426 (1983); **140.** Blood 87, 602 (1996); **141.** FASEB J 15, 1044 (2001); **142.** Proc Natl Acad Sci U S A 98, 12509 (2001); **143.** Mol Cell 7, 811 (2001); **144.** J Biol Chem 276, 25190 (2001); **145.** Biochemistry 28, 1048 (1989); **146.** J Cell Sci 101, 873 (1992); **147.** Arch Biochem Biophys 227, 358 (1983); **148.** Biophys J 71, 2319 (1996); **149.** J Cell Biol 87, 14 (1980); **150.** Biochemistry 32, 8168 (1993); **151.** Immunology, 3rd Ed., Roitt IM, Brostoff J, Male DK pp. 6–14 (1993); **152.** Eur J Immunol 25, 1823 (1995); **153.** J Immunol 149, 2894 (1992); **154.** J Immunol 145, 417 (1990); **155.** Proc Natl Acad Sci U S A 96, 15056 (1999); **156.** Biol Cell 87, 95 (1996); **157.** J Microsc 185, 339 (1997); **158.** Biol Cell 90, 169 (1998); **159.** Cytometry 28, 25 (1997); **160.** J Immunol 159, 2177 (1997); **161.** Exp Cell Res 215, 17 (1994); **162.** J Immunol 167, 3146 (2001); **163.** Inflammation 7, 363 (1983); **164.** J Immunol 139, 3028 (1987); **165.** Anal Biochem 251, 144 (1997); **166.** J Cell Biol 123, 785 (1993); **167.** J Cell Biol 109, 505 (1989); **168.** Biotechniques 17, 730 (1994); **169.** Mol Reprod Dev 53, 350 (1999); **170.** Zygote 8, 127 (2000); **171.** J Androl 19, 542 (1998); **172.** Mol Reprod Dev 40, 164 (1995); **173.** Res Vet Sci 69, 113 (2000); **174.** Curr Opin Cell Biol 12, 581 (2000); **175.** Proteins 39, 103 (2000); **176.** Trends Mol Med 7, 213 (2001); **177.** Bioconjug Chem 10, 755 (1999); **178.** Clin Cancer Res 1,

References — continued

333 (1995); **179.** Bioconjug Chem 12, 1085 (2001); **180.** J Cell Biol 147, 447 (1999); **181.** Biochemistry 35, 16069 (1996); **182.** Mol Microbiol 13, 745 (1994); **183.** J Cell Biol 162, 365 (2003); **184.** J Lipid Res 44, 655 (2003); **185.** Eur J Biochem 269, 737 (2002); **186.** Science 290, 1721 (2000); **187.** Mol Membr Biol 16, 145 (1999); **188.** Trends Cell Biol 9, 87 (1999); **189.** Annu Rev Cell Dev Biol 14, 111 (1998); **190.** Proc Natl Acad Sci U S A 100, 5813 (2003); **191.** J Immunol 170, 1329 (2003); **192.** J Membr Biol 189, 35 (2002); **193.** Proc Natl Acad Sci U S A 98, 9098 (2001); **194.** Mol Biol Cell 10, 3187 (1999); **195.** Biochim Biophys Acta 1610, 247 (2003); **196.** Annu Rev Immunol 21, 457 (2003); **197.** Mol Immunol 38, 1247 (2002); **198.** Nat Rev Immunol 2, 96 (2002); **199.** Biol Res 35, 127 (2002); **200.** Nat Rev Mol Cell Biol 1, 31 (2000); **201.** J Exp Med 190, 1549 (1999); **202.** J Cell Biol 143, 637 (1998); **203.** Immunity 18, 655 (2003); **204.** J Biol Chem 277, 39541 (2002); **205.** Biochem Biophys Res Commun 297, 876 (2002); **206.** Biol Chem 383, 1475 (2002); **207.** J Cell Biol 153, 529 (2001); **208.** J Cell Sci 114, 3957 (2001); **209.** J Virol 77, 9542 (2003); **210.** Exp Cell Res 287, 67 (2003); **211.** Traffic 3, 705 (2002); **212.** J Clin Virol 22, 217 (2001); **213.** Curr Biol 10, R823 (2000); **214.** J Virol 74, 3264 (2000); **215.** J Cell Biol 141, 929 (1998); **216.** J Biol Chem 269, 30745 (1994); **217.** Brain Res 243, 215 (1982); **218.** Brain Res 231, 33 (1982); **219.** Neuroscience 82, 443 (1998); **220.** Brain Res 816, 364 (1999); **221.** Neuroscience 87, 275 (1998); **222.** J Neurosci 22, 9419 (2002); **223.** J Biol Chem 271, 29060 (1996); **224.** Eye 13, 403 (1999); **225.** Proc Natl Acad Sci U S A 97, 3260 (2000); **226.** Biochemistry 39, 15791 (2000); **227.** J Biol Chem 275, 6664 (2000); **228.** J Leukoc Biol 49, 369 (1991); **229.** Trends Biochem Sci 15, 69 (1990); **230.** J Leukoc Biol 53, 673 (1993); **231.** Biochem Biophys Res Commun 122, 755 (1984); **232.** Physiol Rev 67, 285 (1987); **233.** J Cell Biol 82, 517 (1979); **234.** J Biol Chem 265, 13449 (1990); **235.** Biochemistry 29, 313 (1990); **236.** J Biol Chem 265, 16725 (1990); **237.** J Cell Biol 109, 1133 (1989); **238.** Proc Natl Acad Sci U S A 78, 7540 (1981); **239.** Science 205, 1412 (1979); **240.** J Biol Chem 270, 10686 (1995); **241.** J Biol Chem 269, 326 (1994); **242.** J Immunol Methods 149, 159 (1992); **243.** Biochemistry 29, 11123 (1990); **244.** J Cell Biol 121, 1281 (1993); **245.** J Cell Sci 100, 473 (1991); **246.** Biochem Soc Trans 18, 219 (1990); **247.** J Biol Chem 259, 5661 (1984); **248.** Anal Chem 69, 4994 (1997); **249.** Proc Natl Acad Sci U S A 77, 5754 (1980); **250.** J Pharm Sci 74, 237 (1985); **251.** J Steroid Biochem 23, 267 (1985); **252.** Histochemistry 84, 333 (1986); **253.** J Cell Biol 111, 249 (1990); **254.** J Insect Physiol 40, 1045 (1994); **255.** J Immunol Methods 162, 1 (1993); **256.** Infect Immun 67, 885 (1999); **257.** Eur J Cell Biol 75, 192 (1998); **258.** Neuron 41, 755 (2004); **259.** J Biol Chem 275, 15279 (2000); **260.** J Neurochem 73, 2227 (1999); **261.** Annu Rev Neurosci 22, 1 (1999); **262.** Proc R Soc Lond B Biol Sci 255, 61 (1994); **263.** Nature 392, 497 (1998); **264.** Annu Rev Physiol 60, 347 (1998); **265.** J Neurosci 12, 363 (1992); **266.** Science 255, 200 (1992); **267.** J Cell Biol 124, 843 (1994); **268.** Neuron 14, 983 (1995); **269.** Neuron 14, 773 (1995); **270.** Neuron 11, 713 (1993); **271.** J Physiol 460, 287 (1993); **272.** Neuron 13, 363 (1994); **273.** Neuron 12, 1235 (1994); **274.** Cell Calcium 18, 440 (1995); **275.** Neuron 24, 803 (1999); **276.** Proc Natl Acad Sci U S A 98, 12748 (2001); **277.** Neuron 29, 469 (2001); **278.** J Cell Biol 131, 679 (1995); **279.** J Neurosci 15, 8246 (1995); **280.** J Neurosci 15, 6327 (1995); **281.** J Cell Biol 121, 1311 (1993); **282.** Proc Natl Acad Sci U S A 96, 14553 (1999); **283.** J Cell Biol 149, 397 (2000); **284.** J Cell Biol 146, 85 (1999); **285.** Science 285, 1084 (1999); **286.** Proc Natl Acad Sci U S A 94, 5582 (1997); **287.** Proc Natl Acad Sci U S A 94, 5662 (1997); **288.** J Cell Biol 128, 779 (1995); **289.** Science 282, 1516 (1998); **290.** J Cell Biol 141, 625 (1998); **291.** Neuron 17, 91 (1996); **292.** Cell Tissue Res 255, 125 (1989); **293.** J Neurosci 7, 1207 (1987); **294.** Nature 310, 53 (1984); **295.** J Neurosci 13, 4511 (1993); **296.** J Neurosci 14, 5672 (1994); **297.** J Neurosci 14, 3319 (1994); **298.** J Neurosci 14, 796 (1994); **299.** J Neurosci 7, 1215 (1987); **300.** Ophthalmic Res 26, 290 (1994); **301.** J Auton Nerv Syst 38, 77 (1992); **302.** Trends Neurosci 10, 398 (1987); **303.** J Cell Biol 127, 725 (1994); **304.** Cell Biophys 5, 129 (1983); **305.** Biochemistry 25, 2149 (1986); **306.** Biol Cell 79, 265 (1993); **307.** Biochim Biophys Acta 1067, 71 (1991); **308.** Biochim Biophys Acta 901, 138 (1987); **309.** J Cell Biol 125, 783 (1994); **310.** Biol Cell 71, 293 (1991); **311.** Biochim Biophys Acta 1030, 73 (1990); **312.** Cell Biophys 14, 17 (1989); **313.** Cell Biology: A Laboratory Handbook, 2nd Ed., Vol. 2, Celis JE, Ed. pp. 63–69 (1998); **314.** Mol Cell Biochem 206, 33 (2000); **315.** Ann N Y Acad Sci 786, 274 (1996); **316.** Chem Phys Lipids 66, 135 (1993); **317.** J Fluorescence 3, 145 (1993); **318.** Biophys J 72, 1264 (1997); **319.** Biochemistry 36, 10630 (1997); **320.** Science 226, 1209 (1984); **321.** J Cell Biol 96, 1337 (1983); **322.** Molecular and Cellular Mechanisms of Neurotransmitter Release, Stjarne L, et al., Eds. pp. 31–45 (1994); **323.** J Neurosci 12, 1736 (1992); **324.** J Neurosci 11, 1617 (1991); **325.** J Neurosci 9, 2151 (1989); **326.** J Immunol Methods 142, 31 (1991); **327.** J Immunol Methods 112, 99 (1988); **328.** Cytometry 17, 173 (1994); **329.** J Clin Microbiol 30, 2071 (1992); **330.** J Immunol Methods 121, 203 (1989); **331.** J Immunol 133, 3303 (1984); **332.** J Immunol Methods 123, 259 (1989); **333.** J Immunol Methods 116, 235 (1989); **334.** J Immunol Methods 170, 117 (1994); **335.** Cytometry 12, 687 (1991); **336.** J Cell Biol 118, 1371 (1992); **337.** Diagn Clin Immunol 5, 62 (1987); **338.** Am J Physiol 267, L211 (1994); **339.** J Immunol Methods 88, 175 (1986); **340.** Biochem J 266, 669 (1990); **341.** Invest Ophthalmol Vis Sci 30, 2499 (1989); **342.** Cell Immunol 156, 508 (1994); **343.** J Leukoc Biol 48, 403 (1990); **344.** Cytometry 13, 423 (1992); **345.** Cytometry 11, 875 (1990); **346.** J Cell Biol 126, 1433 (1994); **347.** Cytometry 12, 677 (1991); **348.** Exp Cell Res 237, 383 (1997); **349.** J Cell Physiol 155, 461 (1993); **350.** J Cell Biol 98, 1947 (1984); **351.** J Biol Chem 269, 12918 (1994); **352.** Am J Physiol 258, C309 (1990); **353.** J Cell Physiol 131, 200 (1987); **354.** Proc Natl Acad Sci U S A 82, 8523 (1985); **355.** Exp Cell Res 150, 36 (1984); **356.** Proc Natl Acad Sci U S A 80, 3334 (1983); **357.** J Biol Chem 269, 19005 (1994); **358.** J Cell Biol 101, 2302 (1985); **359.** J Biol Chem 268, 25357 (1993); **360.** J Cell Biol 127, 387 (1994); **361.** J Cell Biol 126, 343 (1994); **362.** J Cell Biol 118, 1271 (1992); **363.** Science 249, 641 (1990); **364.** Eur J Biol 34, 96 (1984); **365.** J Cell Biol 98, 1328 (1984); **366.** Cytometry 14, 826 (1993); **367.** J Cell Biol 101, 2156 (1985); **368.** J Cell Biol 101, 2145 (1985); **369.** J Cell Biol 107, 115 (1988); **370.** Science 241, 589 (1988); **371.** J Cell Biol 105, 1539 (1987); **372.** J Cell Biol 107, 1369 (1988); **373.** Biophys J 71, 487 (1996); **374.** FASEB J 8, 573 (1994); **375.** Proc Natl Acad Sci U S A 91, 4811 (1994); **376.** J Biol Chem 268, 6742 (1993); **377.** J Cell Sci 105, 861 (1993); **378.** Exp Cell Res 150, 29 (1984); **379.** J Cell Biol 119, 99 (1992); **380.** J Cell Biol 130, 821 (1995); **381.** Plant Physiol 93, 1492 (1990); **382.** Plant Physiol 98, 673 (1992); **383.** Biochim Biophys Acta 1426, 195 (1999); **384.** Biochim Biophys Acta 1312, 237 (1996); **385.** Proc Natl Acad Sci U S A 88, 5572 (1991); **386.** J Cell Sci 106, 423 (1993); **387.** Bioconjug Chem 10, 1044 (1999); **388.** Nature 314, 357 (1985); **389.** Science 225, 851 (1984); **390.** J Neurosci 12, 3187 (1992); **391.** J Comp Neurol 396, 521 (1998); **392.** J Physiol 478, 265 (1994); **393.** Neuron 11, 801 (1993); **394.** Proc Natl Acad Sci U S A 92, 3156 (1995); **395.** Cell Biology: A Laboratory Handbook, 2nd Ed., Vol. 2, Celis JE, Ed. pp. 495–500 (1998); **396.** Am J Physiol 275, R697 (1998); **397.** Microvasc Res 39, 1 (1990); **398.** Am J Vet Res 49, 663 (1988); **399.** J Membr Biol 93, 237 (1986); **400.** Proc Natl Acad Sci U S A 84, 1921 (1987); **401.** J Biol Chem 275, 22278 (2000); **402.** Appl Microbiol Biotechnol 46, 400 (1996); **403.** J Microbiol Methods 42, 87 (2000); **404.** Biochim Biophys Acta 1289, 5 (1996); **405.** Biosci Biotechnol Biochem 60, 1899 (1996); **406.** Cytometry 27, 262 (1997); **407.** Biochemistry 34, 15395 (1995); **408.** Biochim Biophys Acta 1111, 231 (1992); **409.** Histochem J 26, 207 (1994); **410.** Cell 1, 147 (1974); **411.** Biotechniques 31, 384 (2001); **412.** Glycobiology 1, 187 (1991); **413.** Nat Biotechnol 19, 553 (2001); **414.** Methods Enzymol 327, 260 (2000); **415.** Glycobiology 11, 11R (2001); **416.** Glycobiology 10, 1049 (2000); **417.** Science 276, 1125 (1997); **418.** J Biol Chem 273, 31168 (1998); **419.** EMBO J 12, 3017 (1993); **420.** Biochim Biophys Acta 1220, 199 (1994); **421.** J Neurochem 59, 2224 (1992); **422.** Cell Regul 2, 27 (1991); **423.** Biophys J 74, 90 (1998); **424.** J Leukoc Biol 41, 8 (1987); **425.** J Neurochem 49, 1266 (1987); **426.** Anal Biochem 253, 162 (1997); **427.** J Clin Microbiol 29, 1836 (1991); **428.** FASEB J 13, 69 (1999); **429.** J Histochem Cytochem 31, 737 (1983); **430.** Endocrinology 125, 1231 (1989); **431.** Exp Cell Res 140, 15 (1982); **432.** Proc Natl Acad Sci U S A 77, 2721 (1980); **433.** Mol Biol Cell 6, 135 (1995); **434.** J Biol Chem 268, 2341 (1993); **435.** Science 259, 370 (1993); **436.** Biochem Biophys Res Commun 195, 1354 (1993); **437.** Am J Physiol 265, G418 (1993); **438.** J Neurosci Methods 75, 103 (1997); **439.** Anal Chem 68, 2897 (1996); **440.** Agents Actions 14, 379 (1984); **441.** Cell Biophys 4, 245 (1982).

Data Table — 16.1 Probes for Following Receptor Binding, Endocytosis and Exocytosis

Cat #	MW	Storage	Soluble	Abs	EC	Em	Solvent	Notes
C481	622.54	L	pH >5	494	77,000	517	pH 9	1
C687	596.44	L	H_2O	399	30,000	421	H_2O	2, 3
D288	366.24	L	DMF	475	45,000	605	MeOH	4
D289	394.30	L	H_2O, DMF	488	48,000	607	MeOH	4
D1383	840.98	L	pH >6, DMF	494	76,000	519	pH 9	
D2935	584.37	F,D,AA	DMF	258	11,000	none	MeOH	5
E3476	~6100	FF,D	H_2O	<300		none		
E3477	~6600	FF,D	H_2O	<300		none		6
E3478	~6500	FF,D,L	H_2O	495	84,000	517	pH 8	6, 7
E3480	see Notes	FF,D,L	H_2O	596	ND	612	pH 7	8, 9
E3481	~6800	FF,D,L	H_2O	555	85,000	581	pH 7	6, 7
E7498	~6600	FF,D,L	H_2O	511	85,000	528	pH 9	6, 7
E13345	see Notes	FF,D,L	H_2O	497	ND	520	pH 8	8, 10
E35350	see Notes	FF,D,L	H_2O	554	ND	568	pH 7	8, 11
E35351	see Notes	FF,D,L	H_2O	653	ND	671	pH 7	8, 12
F1314	1213.41	F,L	pH >6, DMF	494	72,000	517	pH 9	
F2902	see Notes	RR,L,AA	H_2O	<300		none		13, 14, 15
F35355	560.09	D,L	H_2O, DMSO	510	50,000	626	MeOH	4
H348	524.37	D,L	H_2O	454	24,000	511	pH 9	16
L453	457.24	L	H_2O	428	12,000	536	H_2O	17
L3482	see Notes	RR,L,AA	see Notes	554	ND	571	see Notes	8, 18, 19, 20
L3483	see Notes	RR,L,AA	see Notes	515	ND	520	see Notes	8, 18, 19, 20
L3484	see Notes	RR,L,AA	see Notes	554	ND	571	see Notes	8, 18, 19, 20
L3485	see Notes	RR,L,AA	see Notes	510	ND	518	see Notes	8, 18, 19, 20
L20492	277.27	F,DD	H_2O	<300		none		
L20493	445.42	F,DD	DMSO	<300		none		13
L23380	see Notes	RR,L,AA	see Notes	495	ND	519	see Notes	8, 18, 19, 20
M13440	1963.13	F,D,L	H_2O	494	78,000	524	pH 9	21
N13195	342.26	F,L	H_2O	466	20,000	540	MeOH	22
N23106	342.26	F,L	DMSO	475	25,000	552	H_2O	22
P3900	503.70	D,L	DMF, DMSO	354	85,000	429	MeOH	23
P13290	627.48	F,D,AA	DMSO	259	22,000	none	MeOH	24
S359	606.71	L	H_2O	586	108,000	605	H_2O	
T204	461.62	D,L	DMF, DMSO	355	75,000	430	MeOH	23
T1111	581.48	D,L	DMSO, EtOH	532	55,000	716	MeOH	4, 25
T3163	611.55	D,L	H_2O, DMSO	510	56,000	626	MeOH	4, 26
T3164	639.60	DD,L	H_2O, DMSO	510	52,000	625	MeOH	4
T3166	607.51	D,L	H_2O, DMSO	558	48,000	734	$CHCl_3$	27
T7508	555.44	D,L	H_2O, DMSO	506	50,000	620	MeOH	4
T13320	607.51	D,L	H_2O, DMSO	558	46,000	734	$CHCl_3$	27
T13361	889.98	F,D,L	H_2O	493	78,000	517	pH 9	21
T23360	565.43	D,L	H_2O, DMSO	560	43,000	734	$CHCl_3$	27
T35356	611.55	D,L	H_2O, DMSO	510	56,000	626	MeOH	4, 26

For definitions of the contents of this data table, see "Navigating *The Handbook*" in the introductory pages.

Notes

1. C481 fluorescence is strongly quenched by micromolar concentrations of Fe^{3+}, Co^{2+}, Ni^{2+} and Cu^{2+} at pH 7 (Am J Physiol 268, C1354 (1995); J Biol Chem 274, 13375 (1999)).
2. The Alexa Fluor® 405 and Cascade Blue® dyes have a second absorption peak at about 376 nm with EC ~80% of the 395–400 nm peak.
3. Maximum solubility in water is ~1% for C687, ~1% for C3221 and ~8% for C3239.
4. Abs and Em of styryl dyes are at shorter wavelengths in membrane environments than in reference solvents such as methanol. The difference is typically 20 nm for absorption and 80 nm for emission, but varies considerably from one dye to another. Styryl dyes are generally nonfluorescent in water.
5. Dihydrofluorescein diacetates are colorless and nonfluorescent until both of the acetate groups are hydrolyzed and the products are subsequently oxidized to fluorescein derivatives. The materials contain less than 0.1% of oxidized derivative when initially prepared. The oxidation products of C400, C2938, C6827, D399 and D2935 are 2′,7′-dichlorofluorescein derivatives with spectra similar to C368.
6. α-Bungarotoxin, EGF and phallotoxin conjugates have approximately 1 label per peptide.
7. The value of EC listed for this EGF conjugate is for the labeling dye in free solution. Use of this value for the conjugate assumes a 1:1 dye:peptide labeling ratio and no change of EC due to dye-peptide interactions.
8. ND = not determined.
9. E3480 is a complex of E3477 with Texas Red® streptavidin, which typically incorporates 3 dyes/streptavidin (MW ~52,800).
10. E13345 is a complex of E3477 with Alexa Fluor® 488 streptavidin, which typically incorporates 5 dyes/streptavidin (MW ~52,800).
11. E35350 is a complex of E3477 with Alexa Fluor® 555 streptavidin, which typically incorporates 3 dyes/streptavidin (MW ~52,800).
12. E35351 is a complex of E3477 with Alexa Fluor® 647 streptavidin, which typically incorporates 3 dyes/streptavidin (MW ~52,800).
13. This product is supplied as a ready-made solution in the solvent indicated under "Soluble."
14. F2902 is essentially colorless and nonfluorescent until oxidized. A small amount (~5%) of oxidized material is normal and acceptable for the product as supplied. The oxidation product is fluorescent (Abs = 495 nm, Em = 524 nm) (J Immunol Methods 130, 223 (1990)).
15. This product consists of a dye–bovine serum albumin conjugate (MW ~66,000) complexed with IgG in a ratio of approximately 1:4 mol:mol (BSA:IgG)
16. H348 spectra are pH-dependent.
17. Maximum solubility in water is ~8% for L453, ~6% for L682 and ~1% for L1177.
18. LDL complexes must be stored refrigerated BUT NOT FROZEN. The maximum shelf-life under the indicated storage conditions is 4–6 weeks.
19. This LDL complex incorporates multiple fluorescent labels. The number of dyes per apoprotein B (MW ~500,000) is indicated on the product label.

20. LDL complexes are packaged under argon in 10 mM Tris, 150 mM NaCl, 0.3 mM EDTA, pH 8.3 containing 2 mM azide. Spectral data reported are measured in this buffer.
21. The value of EC listed for this peptide conjugate is that of the labeling dye in free solution. Use of this value for the conjugate assumes a 1:1 dye:peptide labeling ratio and no change of EC due to dye–peptide interactions.
22. Fluorescence of NBD and its derivatives in water is relatively weak. QY and τ increase and Em decreases in aprotic solvents and other nonpolar environments relative to water (Biochemistry 16, 5150 (1977); Photochem Photobiol 54, 361 (1991)).
23. Diphenylhexatriene (DPH) and its derivatives are essentially nonfluorescent in water. Absorption and emission spectra have multiple peaks. The wavelength, resolution and relative intensity of these peaks are environment dependent. Abs and Em values are for the most intense peak in the solvent specified.
24. Acetate hydrolysis and subsequent oxidation of P13290 generate P12925.
25. RH 414 Abs ~500 nm, Em ~635 nm when bound to phospholipid bilayer membranes.
26. FM® 1-43 Abs = 479 nm, Em = 598 nm bound to phospholipid bilayer membranes. Em = 565 nm bound to synaptosomal membranes (Neuron 12, 1235 (1994)).
27. FM® 4-64 and FM® 5-95 are nonfluorescent in water. For two-color imaging in GFP-expressing cells, these dyes can be excited at 568 nm with emission detection at 690–730 nm (Am J Physiol Cell Physiol 281, C624 (2001)).

Product List — 16.1 Probes for Following Receptor Binding, Endocytosis and Exocytosis

Cat #	Product Name	Unit Size
A6442	anti-synapsin I (bovine), rabbit IgG fraction *affinity purified*	10 µg
A11130	anti-transferrin receptor (human), mouse IgG_1, monoclonal 236-15375	50 µg
C481	calcein *high purity*	100 mg
C687	Cascade Blue® hydrazide, trisodium salt	10 mg
C2990	casein, fluorescein conjugate	25 mg
C22841	cholera toxin subunit B (recombinant), Alexa Fluor® 488 conjugate	500 µg
C34775	cholera toxin subunit B (recombinant), Alexa Fluor® 488 conjugate	100 µg
C22843	cholera toxin subunit B (recombinant), Alexa Fluor® 555 conjugate	500 µg
C34776	cholera toxin subunit B (recombinant), Alexa Fluor® 555 conjugate	100 µg
C22842	cholera toxin subunit B (recombinant), Alexa Fluor® 594 conjugate	500 µg
C34777	cholera toxin subunit B (recombinant), Alexa Fluor® 594 conjugate	100 µg
C34778	cholera toxin subunit B (recombinant), Alexa Fluor® 647 conjugate	100 µg
C34779	cholera toxin subunit B (recombinant), biotin-XX conjugate	100 µg
C34780	cholera toxin subunit B (recombinant), horseradish peroxidase conjugate	100 µg
C23010	α-crystallin from bovine eye lens, Alexa Fluor® 488 conjugate	1 mg
D1383	dexamethasone fluorescein	5 mg
D2935	2',7'-dichlorodihydrofluorescein diacetate, succinimidyl ester (OxyBURST® Green H_2DCFDA, SE)	5 mg
D289	4-(4-(diethylamino)styryl)-*N*-methylpyridinium iodide (4-Di-2-ASP)	1 g
D288	4-(4-(dimethylamino)styryl)-*N*-methylpyridinium iodide (4-Di-1-ASP)	1 g
D12050	DQ™ Green BSA *special packaging*	5 x 1 mg
D12053	DQ™ ovalbumin *special packaging*	5 x 1 mg
D12051	DQ™ Red BSA *special packaging*	5 x 1 mg
E23377	Endostatin™ protein (human, recombinant) *1 mg/mL*	250 µL
E3476	epidermal growth factor (EGF) *from mouse submaxillary glands*	100 µg
E3477	epidermal growth factor, biotin-XX conjugate (biotin EGF)	20 µg
E13345	epidermal growth factor, biotinylated, complexed to Alexa Fluor® 488 streptavidin (Alexa Fluor® 488 EGF complex)	100 µg
E35350	epidermal growth factor, biotinylated, complexed to Alexa Fluor® 555 streptavidin (Alexa Fluor® 555 EGF complex)	100 µg
E35351	epidermal growth factor, biotinylated, complexed to Alexa Fluor® 647 streptavidin (Alexa Fluor® 647 EGF complex)	100 µg
E3480	epidermal growth factor, biotinylated, complexed to Texas Red® streptavidin (Texas Red® EGF complex)	100 µg
E3478	epidermal growth factor, fluorescein conjugate (fluorescein EGF)	20 µg
E7498	epidermal growth factor, Oregon Green® 514 conjugate (Oregon Green® 514 EGF)	20 µg
E3481	epidermal growth factor, tetramethylrhodamine conjugate (rhodamine EGF)	20 µg
E2870	*Escherichia coli* BioParticles® opsonizing reagent	1 U
E13231	*Escherichia coli* (K-12 strain) BioParticles®, Alexa Fluor® 488 conjugate	2 mg
E23370	*Escherichia coli* (K-12 strain) BioParticles®, Alexa Fluor® 594 conjugate	2 mg
E2864	*Escherichia coli* (K-12 strain) BioParticles®, BODIPY® FL conjugate	10 mg
E2861	*Escherichia coli* (K-12 strain) BioParticles®, fluorescein conjugate	10 mg
E2862	*Escherichia coli* (K-12 strain) BioParticles®, tetramethylrhodamine conjugate	10 mg
E2863	*Escherichia coli* (K-12 strain) BioParticles®, Texas Red® conjugate	10 mg
F2902	Fc OxyBURST® Green assay reagent *25 assays* *3 mg/mL*	500 µL
F13191	fibrinogen from human plasma, Alexa Fluor® 488 conjugate	5 mg
F13192	fibrinogen from human plasma, Alexa Fluor® 546 conjugate	5 mg
F13193	fibrinogen from human plasma, Alexa Fluor® 594 conjugate	5 mg
F35200	fibrinogen from human plasma, Alexa Fluor® 647 conjugate	5 mg
F7496	fibrinogen from human plasma, Oregon Green® 488 conjugate	5 mg
F20892	FluoSpheres® collagen I-labeled microspheres, 1.0 µm, yellow-green fluorescent (505/515) *0.5% solids*	0.4 mL

For current prices or to order online, visit probes.invitrogen.com

Cat #	Product Name	Unit Size
F20893	FluoSpheres® collagen I-labeled microspheres, 2.0 µm, yellow-green fluorescent (505/515) *0.5% solids*	0.4 mL
F35355	FM® 1-43FX *fixable analog of FM® 1-43 membrane stain*	10 x 100 µg
F1314	formyl-Nle-Leu-Phe-Nle-Tyr-Lys, fluorescein derivative	1 mg
G13360	gastrin, Rhodamine Green™ conjugate	25 µg
H13188	histone H1 from calf thymus, Alexa Fluor® 488 conjugate	1 mg
H23379	hyaluronic acid, BODIPY® FL conjugate (BODIPY® FL hyaluronic acid)	500 µg
H348	8-hydroxypyrene-1,3,6-trisulfonic acid, trisodium salt (HPTS; pyranine)	1 g
I13269	insulin, human, recombinant from *E. coli*, fluorescein conjugate (FITC insulin) *monolabeled* *zinc free*	100 µg
L21409	lectin PNA from *Arachis hypogaea* (peanut), Alexa Fluor® 488 conjugate	1 mg
L32458	lectin PNA from *Arachis hypogaea* (peanut), Alexa Fluor® 568 conjugate	1 mg
L32459	lectin PNA from *Arachis hypogaea* (peanut), Alexa Fluor® 594 conjugate	1 mg
L32460	lectin PNA from *Arachis hypogaea* (peanut), Alexa Fluor® 647 conjugate	1 mg
L20492	*N*-levulinoyl-D-mannosamine (ManLev)	25 mg
L20493	*N*-levulinoyl-D-mannosamine, tetraacetate (ManLev tetraacetate) *5 mM solution in DMSO*	500 µL
L23351	lipopolysaccharides from *Escherichia coli* serotype 055:B5, Alexa Fluor® 488 conjugate	100 µg
L23352	lipopolysaccharides from *Escherichia coli* serotype 055:B5, Alexa Fluor® 568 conjugate	100 µg
L23353	lipopolysaccharides from *Escherichia coli* serotype 055:B5, Alexa Fluor® 594 conjugate	100 µg
L23350	lipopolysaccharides from *Escherichia coli* serotype 055:B5, BODIPY® FL conjugate	100 µg
L23356	lipopolysaccharides from *Salmonella minnesota*, Alexa Fluor® 488 conjugate	100 µg
L23357	lipopolysaccharides from *Salmonella minnesota*, Alexa Fluor® 568 conjugate	100 µg
L23358	lipopolysaccharides from *Salmonella minnesota*, Alexa Fluor® 594 conjugate	100 µg
L23355	lipopolysaccharides from *Salmonella minnesota*, BODIPY® FL conjugate	100 µg
L3486	low-density lipoprotein from human plasma (LDL) *2.5 mg/mL*	200 µL
L35354	low-density lipoprotein from human plasma, acetylated (AcLDL) *2.5 mg/mL*	200 µL
L23380	low-density lipoprotein from human plasma, acetylated, Alexa Fluor® 488 conjugate (Alexa Fluor® 488 AcLDL) *1 mg/mL*	200 µL
L35353	low-density lipoprotein from human plasma, acetylated, Alexa Fluor® 594 conjugate (Alexa Fluor® 594 AcLDL) *1 mg/mL*	200 µL
L3485	low-density lipoprotein from human plasma, acetylated, BODIPY® FL conjugate (BODIPY® FL AcLDL) *1 mg/mL*	200 µL
L3484	low-density lipoprotein from human plasma, acetylated, DiI complex (DiI AcLDL) *1 mg/mL*	200 µL
L3483	low-density lipoprotein from human plasma, BODIPY® FL complex (BODIPY® FL LDL) *1 mg/mL*	200 µL
L3482	low-density lipoprotein from human plasma, DiI complex (DiI LDL) *1 mg/mL*	200 µL
L453	lucifer yellow CH, lithium salt	25 mg
M13440	[Nle^4, D-Phe^7]-α-melanocyte-stimulating hormone, fluorescein conjugate ([Nle^4, D-Phe^7]-α-MSH, fluorescein conjugate)	25 µg
N13195	2-(*N*-(7-nitrobenz-2-oxa-1,3-diazol-4-yl)amino)-2-deoxyglucose (2-NBDG)	5 mg
N23106	6-(*N*-(7-nitrobenz-2-oxa-1,3-diazol-4-yl)amino)-6-deoxyglucose (6-NBDG)	5 mg
O13291	OxyBURST® Green H_2HFF BSA *special packaging*	5 x 1 mg
P13290	5-(pentafluorobenzoylamino)dihydrofluorescein diacetate (PFB-H_2FDA)	5 mg
P3900	*N*-((4-(6-phenyl-1,3,5-hexatrienyl)phenyl)propyl)trimethylammonium *p*-toluenesulfonate (TMAP-DPH)	5 mg
S2860	*Staphylococcus aureus* BioParticles® opsonizing reagent	1 U
S23371	*Staphylococcus aureus* (Wood strain without protein A) BioParticles®, Alexa Fluor® 488 conjugate	2 mg
S23372	*Staphylococcus aureus* (Wood strain without protein A) BioParticles®, Alexa Fluor® 594 conjugate	2 mg
S2854	*Staphylococcus aureus* (Wood strain without protein A) BioParticles®, BODIPY® FL conjugate	10 mg
S2851	*Staphylococcus aureus* (Wood strain without protein A) BioParticles®, fluorescein conjugate	10 mg
S2852	*Staphylococcus aureus* (Wood strain without protein A) BioParticles®, tetramethylrhodamine conjugate	10 mg
S2859	*Staphylococcus aureus* (Wood strain without protein A) BioParticles®, unlabeled	100 mg
S359	sulforhodamine 101	25 mg
T13342	transferrin from human serum, Alexa Fluor® 488 conjugate	5 mg
T23364	transferrin from human serum, Alexa Fluor® 546 conjugate	5 mg
T35352	transferrin from human serum, Alexa Fluor® 555 conjugate	5 mg
T23365	transferrin from human serum, Alexa Fluor® 568 conjugate	5 mg
T13343	transferrin from human serum, Alexa Fluor® 594 conjugate	5 mg
T23362	transferrin from human serum, Alexa Fluor® 633 conjugate	5 mg
T23366	transferrin from human serum, Alexa Fluor® 647 conjugate	5 mg
T23363	transferrin from human serum, biotin-XX conjugate	5 mg
T2873	transferrin from human serum, BODIPY® FL conjugate	5 mg
T2871	transferrin from human serum, fluorescein conjugate	5 mg
T13341	transferrin from human serum, Oregon Green® 488 conjugate	5 mg
T2872	transferrin from human serum, tetramethylrhodamine conjugate	5 mg
T2875	transferrin from human serum, Texas Red® conjugate	5 mg
T3163	*N*-(3-triethylammoniumpropyl)-4-(4-(dibutylamino)styryl)pyridinium dibromide (FM® 1-43)	1 mg
T35356	*N*-(3-triethylammoniumpropyl)-4-(4-(dibutylamino)styryl)pyridinium dibromide (FM® 1-43) *special packaging*	10 x 100 µg
T1111	*N*-(3-triethylammoniumpropyl)-4-(4-(4-(diethylamino)phenyl)butadienyl)pyridinium dibromide (RH 414)	5 mg
T3166	*N*-(3-triethylammoniumpropyl)-4-(6-(4-(diethylamino)phenyl)hexatrienyl)pyridinium dibromide (FM® 4-64)	1 mg

For current prices or to order online, visit probes.invitrogen.com

Product List — 16.1 Probes for Following Receptor Binding, Endocytosis and Exocytosis — continued

Cat #	Product Name	Unit Size
T13320	*N*-(3-triethylammoniumpropyl)-4-(6-(4-(diethylamino)phenyl)hexatrienyl)pyridinium dibromide (FM® 4-64) *special packaging*	10 x 100 µg
T7508	*N*-(3-triethylammoniumpropyl)-4-(4-(diethylamino)styryl)pyridinium dibromide (FM® 2-10)	5 mg
T3164	*N*-(3-triethylammoniumpropyl)-4-(4-(dipentylamino)styryl)pyridinium dibromide (FM® 1-84)	1 mg
T204	1-(4-trimethylammoniumphenyl)-6-phenyl-1,3,5-hexatriene *p*-toluenesulfonate (TMA-DPH)	25 mg
T23360	*N*-(3-trimethylammoniumpropyl)-4-(6-(4-(diethylamino)phenyl)hexatrienyl)pyridinium dibromide (FM® 5-95)	1 mg
T23011	trypsin inhibitor from soybean, Alexa Fluor® 488 conjugate	1 mg
T13361	tuftsin, fluorescein conjugate (FITC tuftsin)	100 µg
V6694	Vybrant® Phagocytosis Assay Kit *250 assays*	1 kit
Z2850	zymosan A BioParticles® opsonizing reagent	1 U
Z23373	zymosan A (*S. cerevisiae*) BioParticles®, Alexa Fluor® 488 conjugate	2 mg
Z23374	zymosan A (*S. cerevisiae*) BioParticles®, Alexa Fluor® 594 conjugate	2 mg
Z2844	zymosan A (*S. cerevisiae*) BioParticles®, BODIPY® FL conjugate	10 mg
Z2841	zymosan A (*S. cerevisiae*) BioParticles®, fluorescein conjugate	10 mg
Z2843	zymosan A (*S. cerevisiae*) BioParticles®, Texas Red® conjugate	10 mg
Z2849	zymosan A (*S. cerevisiae*) BioParticles®, unlabeled	100 mg

For current prices or to order online, visit probes.invitrogen.com

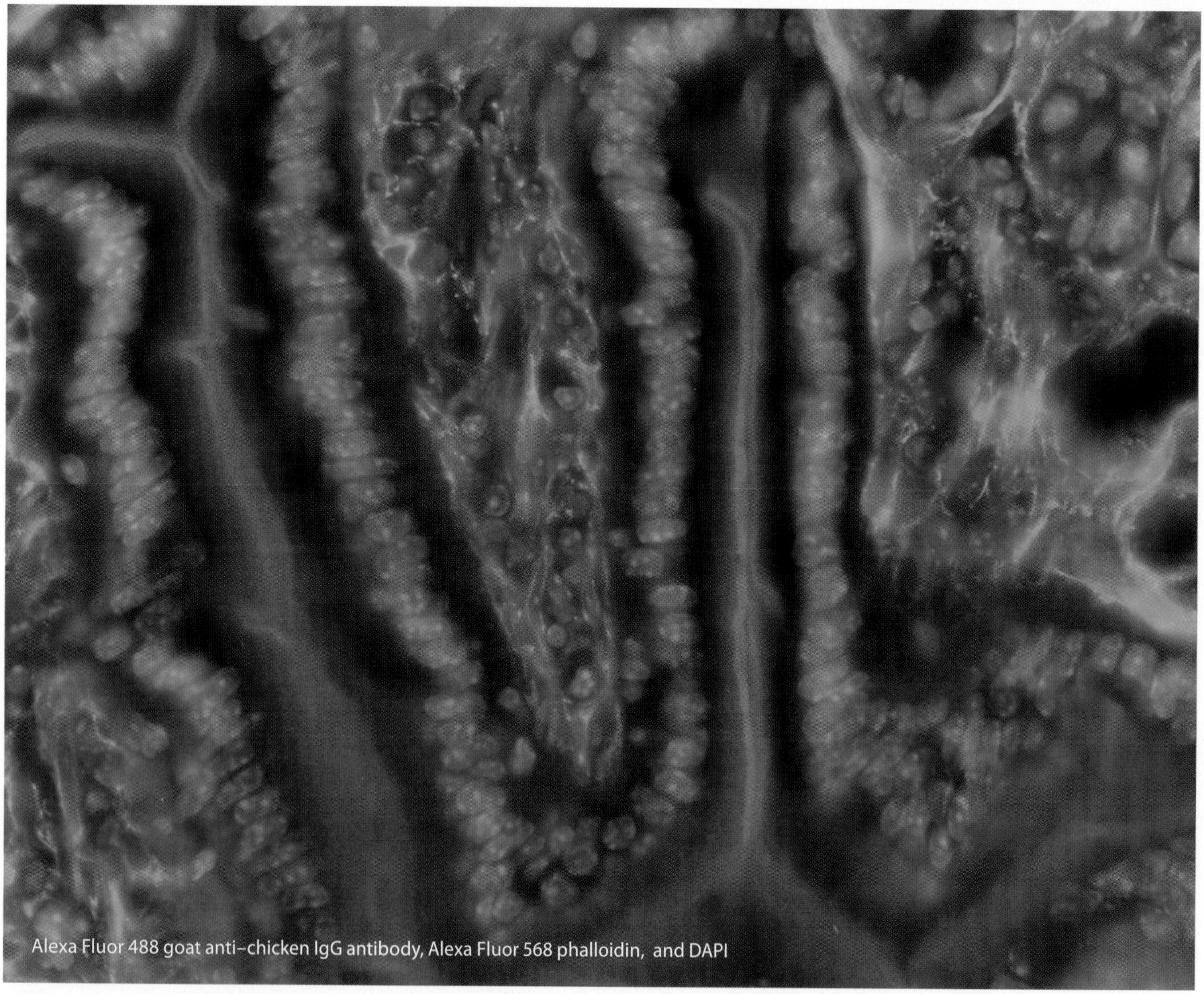

Alexa Fluor 488 goat anti-chicken IgG antibody, Alexa Fluor 568 phalloidin, and DAPI

16.2 Probes for Neurotransmitter Receptors

Because receptor-mediated signal transduction underlies much of what occurs in cellular biochemistry and physiology,[1,2] fluorescent receptor ligands can provide a sensitive means of identifying and localizing some of the most pivotal molecules in cell biology. Molecular Probes offers fluorescently labeled and unlabeled ligands for various cellular receptors, ion channels and ion carriers. Many of these site-selective fluorescent probes may be used on live or fixed cells, as well as in cell-free extracts. In particular, we would like to highlight those ligands conjugated to the green-fluorescent Alexa Fluor® 488, BODIPY® FL and Oregon Green® 514 dyes and the red-fluorescent Alexa Fluor® 594 and Texas Red® dyes, which provide extremely bright signals and superior photostability. The high sensitivity and selectivity of these fluorescent probes make them especially good candidates for measuring low-abundance receptors. Various methods for further amplifying detection of these receptors are discussed in Chapter 6 and Chapter 7.

This section is devoted to our probes for neurotransmitter receptors. Additional fluorescently labeled receptor ligands (including low-density lipoproteins, epidermal growth factors, transferrin and fibrinogen conjugates and chemotactic peptides) are described in Section 16.1, along with other probes for studying receptor-mediated endocytosis, as well as membrane markers of endocytosis and exocytosis. Section 16.3 describes a variety of probes for Ca^{2+}, Na^+, K^+ and Cl^- ion channels and carriers. Chapter 17, entitled "Probes for Signal Transduction," focuses on reagents for investigating events — such as calcium regulation; kinase, phosphatase and phospholipase activation; nucleotide binding and lipid trafficking — that occur downstream from the receptor–ligand interaction (Figure 17.1).

α-Bungarotoxin Probes for Nicotinic Acetylcholine Receptors

Fluorescent α-Bungarotoxins

Nicotinic acetylcholine receptors (nicotinic AChRs) are neurotransmitter-gated ion channels that produce an increase in Na^+ and K^+ permeability, depolarization and excitation upon activation by acetylcholine[3] (Figure 17.1). α-Bungarotoxin, a 74–amino acid peptide extracted from *Bungarus multicinctus* venom, binds with high affinity to the α-subunit of the nicotinic AChR of neuromuscular junctions.[4] Molecular Probes provides an extensive selection of fluorescent α-bungarotoxin conjugates (Table 16.4) to facilitate visualization of nicotinic AChRs with a variety of instrumentation. We attach approximately one fluorophore to each molecule of α-bungarotoxin, thus retaining optimal binding specificity. The labeled bungarotoxins are then chromatographically separated from unlabeled molecules to ensure adequate labeling of the product.

Alexa Fluor® 488 α-bungarotoxin (B13422) and Oregon Green® 514 α-bungarotoxin[5] (B7488) have fluorescence spectra (Figure 7.5, Figure 7.22) similar to those of fluorescein α-bungarotoxin (F1176, Figure 7.27) and are therefore suitable for use with standard fluorescein optical filter sets (Table 23.9). Our Alexa Fluor® 488 and Oregon Green® 514 dyes are brighter and more photostable than any other green-fluorescent dye (Figure 1.46), making their conjugates of α-bungarotoxin especially well suited to fluorescence and confocal laser-scanning microscopy. Tetramethylrhodamine α-bungarotoxin[6,7] (T1175) has been the preferred red-orange–fluorescent probe for staining the nicotinic AChR (Figure 16.26). However, our Alexa Fluor® 594 α-bungarotoxin (B13423) has a longer-wavelength emission maximum and therefore offers better spectral separation from

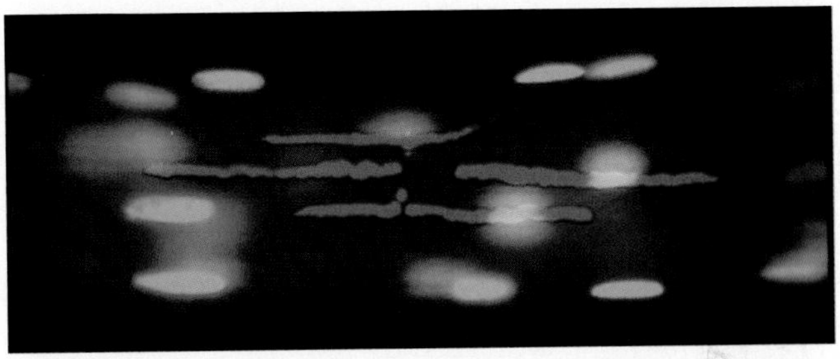

Figure 16.26 Pseudocolored photomicrograph of the synaptic region of fluorescently labeled living muscle fibers from the lumbricalis muscle of the adult frog *Rana pipiens*. Six hours after isolation of the muscle fibers, acetylcholine receptors were stained with red-fluorescent tetramethylrhodamine α-bungarotoxin (T1175) and myonuclei were stained with the green-fluorescent SYTO® 13 live-cell nucleic acid stain (S7575). Photo contributed by Christian Brösamle, Brain Research Institute, University of Zurich, and Damien Kuffler, Institute of Neurobiology, University of Puerto Rico.

Table 16.4 — Labeled and unlabeled α-bungarotoxins

Cat #	Label	Ex/Em (nm)	Notes	Size
F1176	Fluorescein	494/518	Original green-fluorescent conjugate	500 µg
B13422	Alexa Fluor® 488	495/519	Brightest and most photostable green-fluorescent conjugate	500 µg
B7488	Oregon Green® 514	512/530	Photostable green-fluorescent α-bungarotoxin	500 µg
T1175	Tetramethylrhodamine	553/577	An extensively used conjugate	500 µg
B13423	Alexa Fluor® 594	590/617	Excellent dye to combine with green-fluorescent probes	500 µg
B35450	Alexa Fluor® 647	650/668	Excellent dye to combine with green-fluorescent and orange-fluorescent probes	500 µg
B1196	Biotin-XX	NA	Visualized with secondary detection reagents (Section 7.6)	500 µg
B1601	Unlabeled	NA	Useful as a control, as well as for radioiodination and for preparation of new conjugates	1 mg

NA = Not applicable.

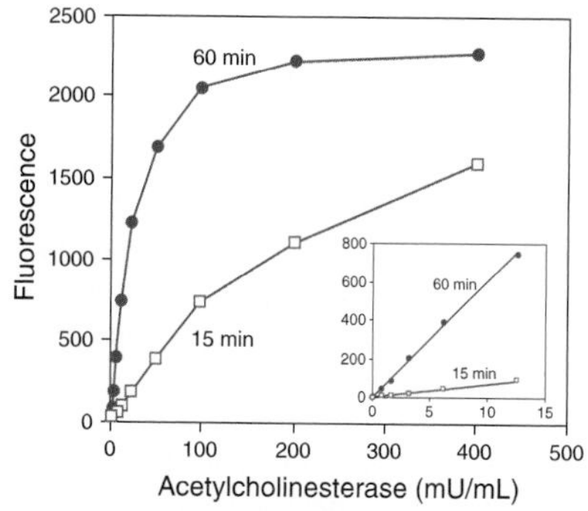

Figure 16.27 Detection of electric eel acetylcholinesterase activity using the Amplex® Red Acetylcholine/Acetylcholinesterase Assay Kit (A12217). Each reaction contained 50 µM acetylcholine, 200 µM Amplex® Red reagent, 1 U/mL HRP, 0.1 U/mL choline oxidase and the indicated amount of acetylcholinesterase in 1X reaction buffer. Reactions were incubated at room temperature. After 15 and 60 minutes, fluorescence was measured in a fluorescence microplate reader using excitation at 560 ± 10 nm and fluorescence detection at 590 ± 10 nm. The inset shows the sensitivity of the 15 min (□) and 60 min (●) assays at low levels of acetylcholinesterase activity (0–13 mU/mL).

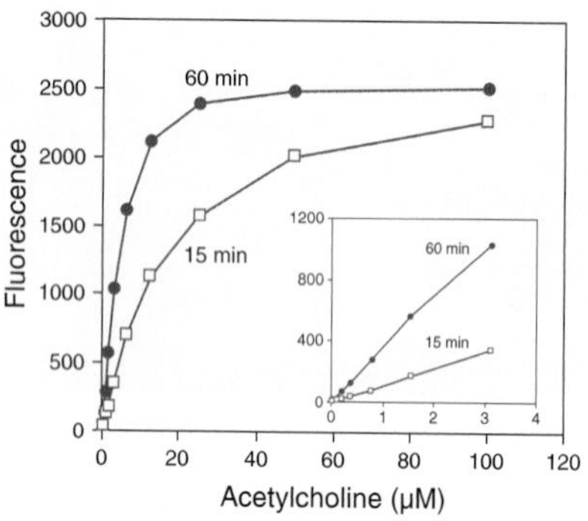

Figure 16.28 Detection of acetylcholine using the Amplex® Red Acetylcholine/Acetylcholinesterase Assay Kit (A12217). Each reaction contained 200 µM Amplex® Red reagent, 1 U/mL HRP, 0.1 U/mL choline oxidase, 0.5 U/mL acetylcholinesterase and the indicated amount of acetylcholine in 1X reaction buffer. Reactions were incubated at room temperature. After 15 and 60 minutes, fluorescence was measured with a fluorescence microplate reader using excitation at 560 ± 10 nm and fluorescence detection at 590 ± 10 nm. The inset shows the sensitivity of the 15 min (□) and 60 min (●) assays at low levels of acetylcholine (0–3 µM).

green-fluorescent dyes in multicolor experiments. Our longest-wavelength conjugate — Alexa Fluor® 647 α-bungarotoxin (B35450) — is spectrally separated from both green-fluorescent and orange-fluorescent dyes, allowing researchers to easily perform three- and four-color experiments. Furthermore, the Alexa Fluor® 647 dye is ideal for the 647 nm spectral line of the krypton-ion laser available with many confocal laser-scanning microscopes.

Fluorescent α-bungarotoxins have been used in a variety of informative investigations of the nicotinic AChR to:

- Correlate receptor clustering during neuromuscular development with tyrosine phosphorylation of the receptor.[8,9]
- Document nicotinic AChR cluster formation after myoblast fusion.[10]
- Quantitate nicotinic AChRs in a study that showed that several isotypes of agrin, a component of synaptic basal lamina, help trigger the nicotinic AChR aggregation that occurs during neuromuscular junction formation.[11]
- Detect reinnervation of adult muscle after nerve damage and to identify and visualize endplates.[12,13]

Biotinylated α-Bungarotoxin

Nicotinic AChRs can also be labeled with biotinylated α-bungarotoxin (B1196), which is then localized using fluorophore- or enzyme-labeled avidin, streptavidin or NeutrAvidin biotin-binding protein conjugates, or NANOGOLD and Alexa Fluor® FluoroNanogold streptavidin[9,14–16] (Section 7.6, Table 7.22). In addition, the biotinylated toxin can be employed for affinity isolation of the nicotinic AChR using streptavidin or CaptAvidin™ agarose (S951, C21386; Section 7.6) column[17] or with Captivate™ ferrofluid streptavidin (C21476, Section 7.6) for enzyme-linked immunosorbent assays (ELISAs) designed to detect anti–nicotinic AChR antibodies.[18]

Unlabeled α-Bungarotoxin

In addition to the fluorescent and biotinylated derivatives, we have unlabeled α-bungarotoxin (B1601), which has been shown to be useful for radioiodination.[4,19] Unlabeled α-bungarotoxin has also been employed for ELISA testing of nicotinic AChR binding,[20] as well as for investigating the function of the α-bungarotoxin–binding component (α-BgtBC) in vertebrate neurons.[21]

Amplex® Red Acetylcholine/Acetylcholinesterase Assay Kit

The action of acetylcholine (ACh) at neuromuscular junctions is regulated by acetylcholinesterase (AChE), the enzyme that hydrolyzes ACh to choline and acetate. The Amplex® Red Acetylcholine/Acetylcholinesterase Assay Kit (A12217) provides an ultrasensitive method for continuously monitoring AChE activity and for detecting ACh in a fluorescence microplate reader or fluorometer. Other potential uses for this kit include screening for AChE inhibitors and measuring the release of ACh from synaptosomes. The Amplex® Red Acetylcholine/Acetylcholinesterase Assay Kit can also be used for the ultrasensitive and specific assay of free choline, an "essential nutrient," in foods.[22]

In this assay, AChE activity is monitored indirectly using the Amplex® Red reagent, 10-acetyl-3,7-dihydroxyphenoxazine, a highly sensitive and stable fluorogenic probe for H_2O_2 that is useful in numerous assays for enzymes and other analytes (Section 10.5, Figure 10.65). First, AChE converts the acetylcholine substrate to choline. Choline is in turn oxidized by choline oxidase to betaine and H_2O_2, the latter of which, in the presence of horseradish peroxidase, reacts with the Amplex® Red reagent to generate the red-fluorescent product resorufin (R363, Section 10.1, Figure 10.59) with excitation/emission maxima of ~570/585 nm (Figure 10.6). Experiments with purified AChE from electric eel indicate that the Amplex® Red Acetylcholine/Acetylcholinesterase Assay Kit can detect AChE levels as low as 0.002 U/mL using a reaction time of only one hour (Figure 16.27). We have been able to detect acetylcholinesterase activity from a tissue sample with total protein content as low as 200 ng/mL or 20 ng/well in a microplate assay.[23] By providing an excess of AChE in the assay, the kit can also be used to detect acetylcholine levels as low as 0.3 µM, with a range of detection from 0.3 µM to ~100 µM acetylcholine (Figure 16.28). The Amplex® Red Acetylcholine/Acetylcholinesterase Assay Kit contains:

- Amplex® Red reagent
- Dimethylsulfoxide (DMSO)
- Horseradish peroxidase (HRP)
- H_2O_2 for use as a positive control
- Concentrated reaction buffer
- Choline oxidase from *Alcaligenes* sp.
- Acetylcholine (ACh)
- Acetylcholinesterase (AChE) from electric eel
- A detailed protocol

Each kit provides sufficient reagents for approximately 500 assays using a fluorescence microplate reader and a reaction volume of 200 µL per assay.

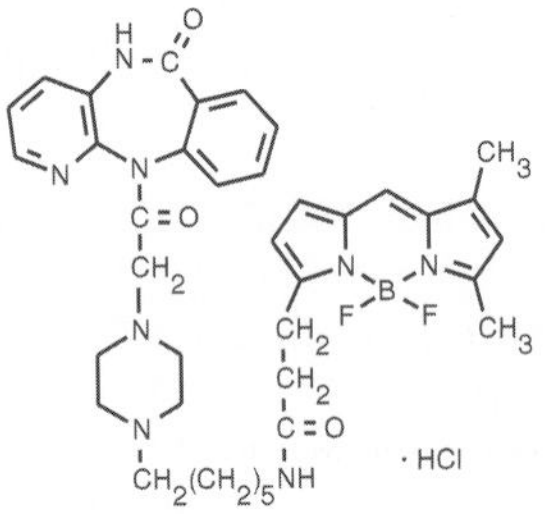

Figure 16.29 B7436 BODIPY® FL pirenzepine, hydrochloride.

Pirenzepine Probes for Muscarinic Acetylcholine Receptors

Unlike nicotinic AChRs, muscarinic acetylcholine receptors (muscarinic AChRs) are G-protein–coupled receptors that produce either excitatory or inhibitory responses and are not necessarily associated with changes in ion permeability (Figure 17.1). Fluorescent derivatives of pirenzepine are selective antagonists for the M_1 muscarinic AChR.[24–27] The green-fluorescent BODIPY® FL (B7436, Figure 16.29) and red-fluorescent BODIPY® 558/568 (B7437) derivatives retain pirenzepine's specificity for the M_1 muscarinic receptor and exhibit similar inhibition and displacement profiles. BODIPY® FL pirenzepine was employed to study the activity-dependent expression of the M_1 muscarinic receptor in cultured neurons derived from rat visual cortex.[24] Expression of the receptor increased in response to antagonist application and to chronic membrane depolarization. Conversely, receptor expression decreased when an agonist or the Na^+-channel blocker tetrodotoxin was applied.

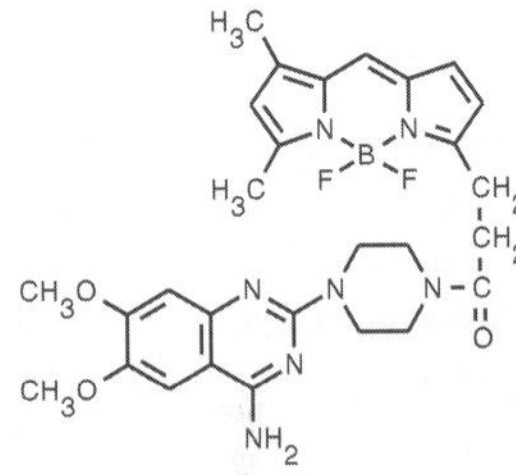

Figure 16.30 B7433 BODIPY® FL prazosin.

Prazosin Probes for α_1-Adrenergic Receptors

We have prepared the green-fluorescent BODIPY® FL (B7433, Figure 16.30) and red-fluorescent BODIPY® 558/568 (B7434) derivatives of prazosin, a high-affinity antagonist for the α_1-adrenergic receptor.[28,29] These derivatives can be used to localize the α_1-adrenergic receptor on cultured cortical neurons.[30,31] BODIPY® FL prazosin has been employed for flow cytometric detection of α_1-adrenergic receptors, including the α_{1a}, α_{1b} and α_{1d} receptor subtypes, on Chinese hamster ovary (CHO) cells.[32]

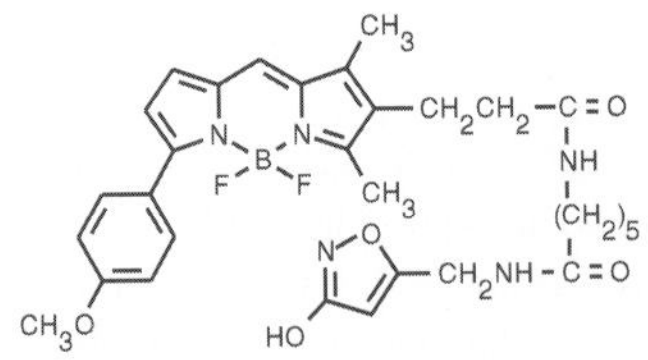

Figure 16.31 M23400 muscimol, BODIPY® TMR-X conjugate.

BODIPY® TMR-X Muscimol for the $GABA_A$ Receptor

Muscimol is a powerful agonist of the $GABA_A$ receptor and has been widely used to reversibly inactivate localized groups of neurons.[33,34] With the introduction of the BODIPY® TMR-X muscimol conjugate (M23400, Figure 16.31), researchers can avoid using radioactive methods to map the distribution of the drug in the central nervous system,[35] as well as to detect the presence of $GABA_A$ receptors on cell surfaces.[36]

Neuropeptide Probes for the Neurokinin Receptors

In response to the increased need for fluorescent peptide-analogs for imaging of receptor localization and endocytosis, characterization of ligand-binding interactions and pharmacological screening, we have introduced a variety of fluorescent peptides, including derivatives of substance P, neuromedin C and angiotensin II. All of our fluorescent neuropeptides have been characterized for purity by HPLC and mass spectrometry; however, in most cases, the receptor-binding properties of the ligands have not been completely characterized.

Substance P Analogs

Substance P is an agonist of the neurokinin 1 (NK1) receptor, a member of the seven-domain transmembrane G-protein–coupled receptor family.[37,38] Substance P is a tachykinin — one of a group of neuropeptides that are primarily involved in the mediation of inflammatory responses. Our HPLC-purified substance P analogs are labeled on the ε–amino group of Lys-3 using a single-isomer succinimidyl ester of one of four different fluorescent labels. Our NK1 receptor probes include the:

- Alexa Fluor® 488 (S13426) and Oregon Green® 488 (S13427) conjugates of substance P — The Alexa Fluor® 488 and Oregon Green® 488 dyes virtually match fluorescein's excitation and emission spectra but have the additional benefits of superior photostability and lower pH sensitivity.
- Fluorescein conjugate of substance P (S13424) — Our fluorescein-labeled substance P analog is very similar to one described by Tota and co-workers.[39,40]
- Tetramethylrhodamine conjugate of substance P (S13428) — Substance P labeled with the photostable, orange-fluorescent tetramethylrhodamine dye offers researchers another option for multicolor experiments.

A detailed study of the use of our fluorescent substance P analogs for binding, imaging and receptor activation has been published by Bennett and Simmons.[41] The Oregon Green® 488 and BODIPY® FL analogs were found to be the most useful probes for labeling the receptor without affecting its biological activity.

Fluorescent Neuromedin C Analogs

Neuromedin C consists of the C-terminal decapeptide fragment (residues 18–27) of gastrin-releasing peptide (GRP). Its normal function is stimulation of gastrin release in the stomach and amylase release in the pancreas, but it also appears as a mitogen in lung, breast and gastrointestinal cancer cells. Our fluorescent analog of neuromedin C is labeled on the N-terminal amino group with the exceptionally photostable Alexa Fluor® 488 dye (N13437). A fluorescein-labeled neuromedin C is known to be biologically active in amylase-release assays;[42] it has also been used to identify specific neuromedin C receptors in rat stomach tissue preparations.[42]

Fluorescent Angiotensin II Analogs

Angiotensin II (Asp-Arg-Val-Tyr-Ile-His-Pro-Phe) stimulates smooth muscle contraction and plays an important role in blood pressure control and in water and salt homeostasis. These effects are exerted via two G-protein–coupled receptor subtypes, referred to as AT1 and AT2. Our N-terminal–labeled fluorescein and Alexa Fluor® 488 analogs of angiotensin II (A13438, A13439) should be useful tools for imaging the distribution of these receptors.[43–45] It is not known at present whether these fluorescent analogs display selectivity for AT1 versus AT2 binding.

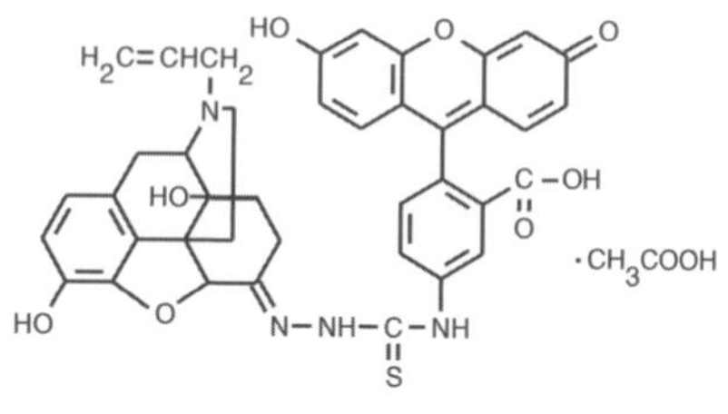

Figure 16.32 N1384 naloxone fluorescein.

Naloxone and Naltrexone Probes for μ-Opioid Receptors

The μ-opioid receptor plays a critical role in analgesia. Among the antagonists that have been used to define and characterize these receptors is naltrexone, a nonaddictive drug that has been used for the treatment of opioid addiction. The fluorescent derivatives naloxone fluorescein (Figure 16.32) and naltrexone fluorescein (N1384, N1385) have been reported to bind to the μ-opioid binding site with high affinity,[46–48] permitting their visualization in Chinese hamster ovary (CHO) cells containing transfected receptors.[49] Flow cytometric analysis of the binding of fluorescein naloxone to NMDA- and μ-opioid receptors (which was displaced by NMDA and met-enkephalin, respectively) has been used to deduce the effects of operant conditioning on visual cortex receptor pattern.[50]

Probes for Amino Acid Neurotransmitter Receptors

Caged Amino Acid Neurotransmitters

When illuminated with UV light or by multiphoton excitation,[51] caged amino acid neurotransmitters are converted into biologically active amino acids that rapidly initiate neurotransmitter action.[52–55] Thus, these caged probes provide a means of controlling the release — both spatially and temporally — of agonists for kinetic studies of receptor binding or channel opening.

The different caging groups confer special properties on these photoactivatable probes (Table 5.2). We synthesize several caged versions of L-glutamic acid[56–64] (C7122, G7055), as well as caged carbachol[65,66] (*N*-(CNB-caged) carbachol, C13654), caged γ-aminobutyric acid[60,67–70] (*O*-(CNB-caged) GABA, A7110) and caged *N*-methyl-D-aspartic acid (β-(CNB-caged) NMDA, M7114), all of which are biologically inactive before photolysis.[52] *O*-(CNB-caged) GABA (A7110) and γ-(CNB-caged) L-glutamic acid (G7055), which exhibit fast uncaging rates and high photolysis quantum yields, have been used to investigate the activation kinetics of GABA receptors[70] and glutamate receptors,[59] respectively. *N*-(CNB-caged) L-glutamic acid (C7122) does not hydrolyze in aqueous solution because it is caged on the amino group, thus enabling researchers to use very high concentrations without risk of light-independent glutamic acid production.[59,61]

Anti–NMDA Receptor Antibodies

N-methyl-D-aspartate (NMDA) receptors constitute cation channels of the central nervous system that are gated by the excitatory neurotransmitter L-glutamate.[71,72] Activation of NMDA receptors is essential for inducing long-term potentiation (LTP), a form of activity-dependent synaptic plasticity that is implicated in the learning process in animal behavioral models.[73] The biophysical properties of NMDA receptor channels contributing to LTP include Ca^{2+} permeability, voltage-dependent Mg^{2+} blocking and slow-gating kinetics.[74–77] NMDA receptor–channel activities play a role in neuronal development and in disorders such as epilepsy and ischemic neuronal cell death. As targets for ethanol, NMDA receptors may also function in the pathology of alcoholism.[78,79]

In vitro reconstitution experiments with the cloned NMDA receptor subunit 1 and any one of the four NMDA receptor subunits 2A, 2B, 2C and 2D revealed that the physical properties of the heteromeric NMDA receptor channel appear to be imparted by the particular NMDA receptor subunit 2.[80] NMDA receptor subunits 2A and 2B are detected predominantly in the hippocampus and cortex, whereas 2C is found mainly in the cerebellum. Thus, cellular expression profiles of the NMDA receptor subunits 2A, 2B, 2C and 2D may contribute to the biophysical properties of NMDA receptors in specific central neurons.

For neurobiologists, Molecular Probes offers affinity-purified rabbit polyclonal antibodies to NMDA receptor subunits 2A, 2B and 2C (A6473, A6474, A6475). The anti–NMDA receptor subunit 2A and 2B antibodies were generated against fusion proteins containing amino acid residues 1253–1391 of subunit 2A and 984–1104 of subunit 2B, respectively. These two antibodies are active against mouse, rat and human forms of the antigens and are specific for the subunit against which they were generated. In contrast, the anti–NMDA receptor subunit 2C antibody was generated against amino acid residues 25–130 of subunit 2C and recognizes the 140,000-dalton subunit 2C, as well as the 180,000-dalton subunit 2A and subunit 2B from mouse, rat and human. These three affinity-purified antibodies are suitable for immunohistochemistry (Figure 16.33), Western blots, enzyme-linked immunosorbent assays (ELISAs) and immunoprecipitations. Our Zenon® Rabbit IgG Labeling Kits (Section 7.3, Table 7.13) can be used to prepare fluorescent dye–, biotin- or enzyme-labeled complexes of these antibodies.

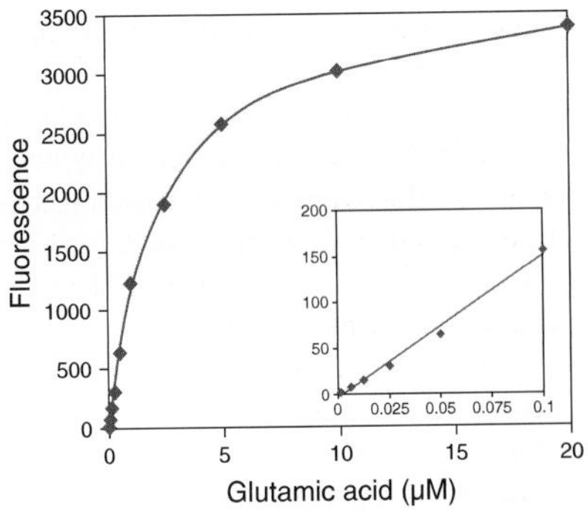

Figure 16.34 Detection of L-glutamic acid using the Amplex® Red Glutamic Acid/Glutamate Oxidase Assay Kit (A12221). Each reaction contained 50 µM Amplex® Red reagent, 0.125 U/mL HRP, 0.04 U/mL L-glutamate oxidase, 0.25 U/mL L-glutamate–pyruvate transaminase, 100 µM L-alanine and the indicated amount of L-glutamic acid in 1X reaction buffer. Reactions were incubated at 37°C. After 30 minutes, fluorescence was measured in a fluorescence microplate reader using excitation at 530 ± 12.5 nm and fluorescence detection at 590 ± 17.5 nm.

Amplex® Red Glutamic Acid/Glutamate Oxidase Assay Kit

The Amplex® Red Glutamic Acid/Glutamate Oxidase Assay Kit (A12221) provides an ultrasensitive method for continuously detecting glutamic acid[81] or for monitoring glutamate oxidase activity in a fluorescence microplate reader or a fluorometer.[82] In this assay, L-glutamic acid is oxidized by glutamate oxidase to produce α-ketoglutarate, NH_3 and H_2O_2. L-Alanine and L-glutamate–pyruvate transaminase are also included in the reaction. Thus, the L-glutamic acid is regenerated by transamination of α-ketoglutarate, resulting in multiple cycles of the initial reaction and a significant amplification of the H_2O_2 produced. Hydrogen peroxide reacts with the Amplex® Red reagent in a 1:1 stoichiometry in a reaction catalyzed by horseradish peroxidase (HRP) to generate the highly fluorescent product resorufin[83,84] (R363, Section 10.1, Figure 10.59). Because resorufin has absorption/emission maxima of ~571/ 585 nm (Figure 10.6), there is little interference from autofluorescence in most biological samples.

If the concentration of L-glutamic acid is limiting in this assay, then the fluorescence increase is proportional to the initial L-glutamic acid concentration. The Amplex® Red Glutamic Acid/

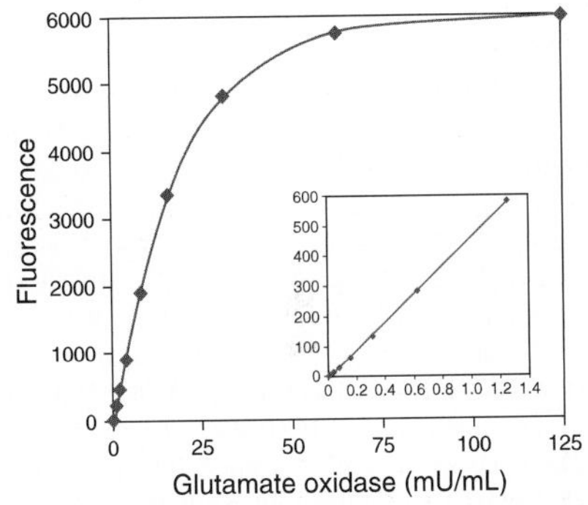

Figure 16.35 Detection of L-glutamate oxidase using the Amplex® Red Glutamic Acid/Glutamate Oxidase Assay Kit (A12221). Each reaction contained 50 µM Amplex® Red reagent, 0.125 U/mL HRP, 0.25 U/mL L-glutamate–pyruvate transaminase, 20 µM L-glutamic acid, 100 µM L-alanine and the indicated amount of *Streptomyces* L-glutamate oxidase in 1X reaction buffer. Reactions were incubated at 37°C. After 60 minutes, fluorescence was measured in a fluorescence microplate reader using excitation at 530 ± 12.5 nm and fluorescence detection at 590 ± 17.5 nm. The inset represents data from a separate experiment for lower L-glutamate oxidase concentrations and incubation time of 60 minutes (0–1.25 mU/mL).

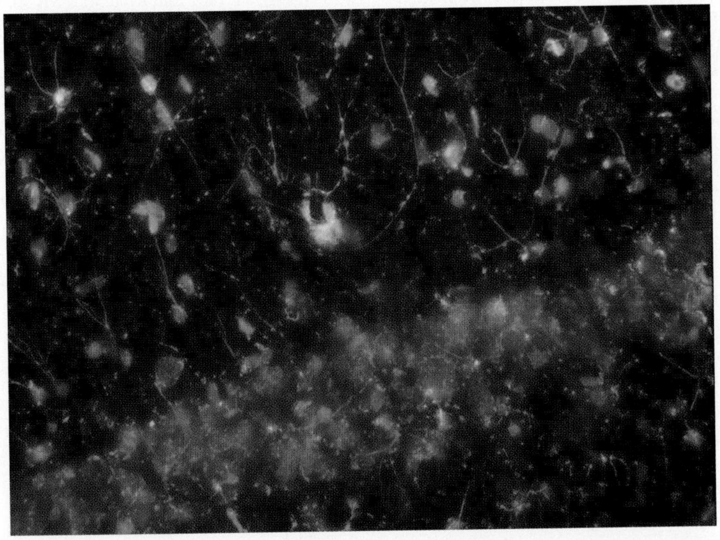

Figure 16.33 Rat brain cryosections labeled with anti-NMDA receptor, subunit 2A (rat), rabbit IgG fraction (A6473) and detected using Alexa Fluor® 488 goat anti–rabbit IgG antibody (A11008). The tissue was also labeled with Alexa Fluor® 594 anti–glial fibrillary acidic protein antibody (A21295) and counterstained with TOTO®-3 iodide (T3604), which was pseudocolored light blue in this image.

Glutamate Oxidase Assay Kit allows detection of as little as 10 nM L-glutamic acid in purified systems using a 30-minute reaction time (Figure 16.34). If the reaction is modified to include an excess of L-glutamic acid, then this kit can be used to continuously monitor glutamate oxidase activity. For example, purified L-glutamate oxidase from *Streptomyces* can be detected at levels as low as 40 µU/mL (Figure 16.35). The Amplex® Red reagent has been used to quantitate the activity of glutamate-producing enzymes in a high-throughput assay for drug discovery.[81] Each Amplex® Red Glutamic Acid/Glutamate Oxidase Assay Kit contains:

- Amplex® Red reagent
- Dimethylsulfoxide (DMSO)
- Horseradish peroxidase (HRP)
- H_2O_2
- Concentrated reaction buffer
- L-Glutamate oxidase from *Streptomyces* sp.
- L-Glutamate–pyruvate transaminase from pig heart
- L-Glutamic acid
- L-Alanine
- A detailed protocol

Each kit provides sufficient reagents for approximately 200 assays using a fluorescence microplate reader and a reaction volume of 100 µL per assay.

Probes for Other Receptors

Molecular Probes offers a diverse array of fluorescent derivatives of:

- Low-density lipoprotein (LDL)
- Epidermal growth factor (EGF)
- Transferrin
- Fibrinogen
- Gelatin and collagen
- Ovalbumin and bovine serum albumin
- Soybean trypsin inhibitor
- Casein
- BioParticles® *E. coli, S. aureus* and zymosan A conjugates
- Lipopolysaccharides
- Histone H1
- α-Crystallin from bovine eye lens
- Hyaluronic acid
- Subunit B of cholera toxin
- Chemotactic peptides
- Insulin

These ligands are all transported into the cell by receptor-mediated endocytosis. Additional information about these probes as well as probes for following endocytosis and exocytosis can be found in Section 16.1.

References

1. Pharmacol Rev 51, 7 (1999); **2.** Trends Neurosci 16, 233 (1993); **3.** Biochemistry 29, 11009 (1990); **4.** Meth Neurosci 8, 67 (1992); **5.** J Cell Biol 141, 1613 (1998); **6.** Proc Natl Acad Sci U S A 73, 4594 (1976); **7.** J Physiol 237, 385 (1974); **8.** J Cell Biol 120, 197 (1993); **9.** J Cell Biol 120, 185 (1993); **10.** Dev Dyn 201, 29 (1994); **11.** J Cell Biol 128, 625 (1995); **12.** J Neurosci 15, 520 (1995); **13.** J Cell Biol 124, 139 (1994); **14.** J Cell Biol 131, 441 (1995); **15.** J Biol Chem 268, 25108 (1993); **16.** Proc Natl Acad Sci U S A 77, 4823 (1980); **17.** J Cell Biol 125, 661 (1994); **18.** J Immunol Methods 107, 197 (1988); **19.** Biochemistry 18, 1875 (1979); **20.** Toxicon 29, 503 (1991); **21.** Neuron 8, 353 (1992); **22.** Science 281, 794 (1998); **23.** Proc SPIE-Int Soc Opt Eng 3926, 166 (2000); **24.** J Neurosci 14, 4147 (1994); **25.** J Neurosci 13, 4293 (1993); **26.** Endocrinology 131, 235 (1992); **27.** Biochem Cell Biol 75, 127 (1997); **28.** Cardiology 73, 164 (1986); **29.** Life Sci 27, 1525 (1980); **30.** Brain Res Dev Brain Res 102, 35 (1997); **31.** Soc Neurosci 20, 699, abstract #297.1 (1994); **32.** FEBS Lett 386, 141 (1996); **33.** J Neurosci Res 31, 166 (1992); **34.** Neural Plast 7, 19 (2000); **35.** Neurosci Lett 127, 160 (1991); **36.** Vis Neurosci 17, 11 (2000); **37.** Neuropeptides 32, 1 (1998); **38.** Neuropeptides 31, 537 (1997); **39.** J Gen Physiol 112, 577 (1998); **40.** Biochemistry 33, 13079 (1994); **41.** BMC Chem Biol 1, 1 (2001); **42.** Peptides 16, 255 (1995); **43.** Mol Endocrinol 11, 1266 (1997); **44.** Am J Physiol 273, R49 (1997); **45.** Circ Res 79, 765 (1996); **46.** Pharm Res 3, 56 (1986); **47.** Pharm Res 6, 266 (1985); **48.** Life Sci 33 Suppl 1, 423 (1983); **49.** J Neurosci Methods 97, 123 (2000); **50.** Biol Chem Hoppe Seyler 376, 483 (1995); **51.** Proc Natl Acad Sci U S A 97, 8635 (2000); **52.** Methods Enzymol 291, 30 (1998); **53.** Annu Rev Physiol 55, 755 (1993); **54.** Biological Applications of Photochemical Switches, Morrison H, Ed. pp. 243–305 (1993); **55.** Optical Microscopy: Emerging Methods and Applications, Herman B, Lemasters JJ, Eds. pp. 27–85 (1993); **56.** Nat Neurosci 1, 119 (1998); **57.** Neuroscience 86, 265 (1998); **58.** Science 279, 1203 (1998); **59.** Proc Natl Acad Sci U S A 91, 8752 (1994); **60.** J Org Chem 61, 1228 (1996); **61.** Abstr Soc Neurosci 21, 579, abstract #238.11 (1995); **62.** J Neurosci Methods 54, 205 (1994); **63.** Science 265, 255 (1994); **64.** Proc Natl Acad Sci U S A 90, 7661 (1993); **65.** Proc Natl Acad Sci U S A 97, 13895 (2000); **66.** Biochemistry 38, 7837 (1999); **67.** Methods Enzymol 291, 443 (1998); **68.** Neuron 15, 755 (1995); **69.** J Org Chem 55, 1585 (1990); **70.** J Am Chem Soc 116, 8366 (1994); **71.** Neuron 12, 529 (1994); **72.** Nature 354, 31 (1991); **73.** J Neurosci 9, 3040 (1989); **74.** Nature 346, 565 (1990); **75.** Nature 325, 529 (1987); **76.** Nature 321, 519 (1986); **77.** Nature 307, 462 (1984); **78.** Mol Pharmacol 45, 324 (1994); **79.** Neurosci Lett 152, 13 (1993); **80.** Science 256, 1217 (1992); **81.** Anal Biochem 284, 382 (2000); **82.** Anal Chim Acta 402, 47 (1999); **83.** Anal Biochem 253, 162 (1997); **84.** J Immunol Methods 202, 133 (1997).

Data Table — 16.2 Probes for Neurotransmitter Receptors

Cat #	MW	Storage	Soluble	Abs	EC	Em	Solvent	Notes
A7110	396.28	F,D,LL	H_2O	262	4,500	none	pH 7	1, 2
A13438	1404.50	F,D,L	H_2O, DMSO	494	78,000	522	pH 9	3
A13439	1586.64	F,D,L	H_2O, DMSO	491	78,000	516	pH 7	3
B1196	~8400	F,D	H_2O	<300		none		4
B1601	7984.14	F	H_2O	<300		see Notes		5
B3420	576.88	F,D,L	DMSO	504	77,000	511	MeOH	
B3460	598.54	F,D,L	DMF, DMSO	504	79,000	511	MeOH	
B7433	563.41	F,D,L	DMSO, EtOH	504	77,000	511	MeOH	
B7434	617.48	F,D,L	DMSO, EtOH	560	76,000	569	MeOH	
B7436	747.09	F,D,L	DMSO, EtOH	504	77,000	511	MeOH	
B7437	801.16	F,D,L	DMSO, EtOH	560	75,000	569	MeOH	
B7488	~8500	F,D,L	H_2O	512	85,000	530	pH 8	4, 6
B13422	~8500	F,D,L	H_2O	495	78,000	519	pH 8	4, 6
B13423	~8700	F,D,L	H_2O	593	92,000	617	pH 7	4, 6
B13650	619.42	F,D,LL	DMSO	262	6,600	none	pH 7	1, 2
B35450	~10000	F,D,L	H_2O	649	246,000	668	pH 7	4, 6
C7122	326.26	F,D,LL	H_2O	266	4,800	none	pH 7	1, 2
C13654	439.34	F,D,LL	H_2O	264	4,200	none	H_2O	1, 2
F1176	~8400	F,D,L	H_2O	494	84,000	518	pH 8	4, 6
G2504	378.77	F,D,LL	H_2O	346	5,900	none	H_2O	1
G7055	440.29	F,D,LL	H_2O, DMSO	262	5,100	none	pH 7	1, 2
M7114	440.29	F,D,LL	H_2O	264	5,100	none	pH 7	1, 2
M13652	517.37	F,D,LL	DMSO, MeOH	265	9,400	none	pH 7	1, 2
M23400	607.46	F,D,L	DMSO	543	60,000	572	MeOH	
N1384	790.84	D,L	EtOH, DMF	492	79,000	516	pH 9	
N1385	804.87	D,L	EtOH, DMF	493	87,000	516	pH 9	
N13436	1478.60	F,D,L	H_2O, DMSO	494	78,000	524	pH 9	3
N13437	1658.68	F,D,L	H_2O, DMSO	491	78,000	515	pH 7	3
R6922	775.08	F,D,L	DMSO, EtOH	629	83,000	659	MeOH	
S13424	1705.95	F,D,L	DMSO	494	78,000	524	pH 9	3
S13426	1908.06	F,D,L	DMSO	493	78,000	516	pH 7	3
S13427	1741.93	F,D,L	DMSO	496	86,000	520	pH 9	3
S13428	1760.08	F,D,L	DMSO	554	85,000	578	pH 7	3
T1175	~8400	F,D,L	H_2O	553	85,000	577	H_2O	4, 6

For definitions of the contents of this data table, see "Navigating *The Handbook*" in the introductory pages.

Notes

1. All photoactivatable probes are sensitive to light. They should be protected from illumination except when photolysis is intended.
2. This compound has weaker visible absorption at >300 nm but no discernible absorption peaks in this region.
3. The value of EC listed for this peptide conjugate is that of the labeling dye in free solution. Use of this value for the conjugate assumes a 1:1 dye:peptide labeling ratio and no change of EC due to dye–peptide interactions.
4. α-Bungarotoxin, EGF and phallotoxin conjugates have approximately 1 label per peptide.
5. This peptide exhibits intrinsic tryptophan fluorescence (Em ~350 nm) when excited at <300 nm.
6. The value of EC listed for this α-bungarotoxin conjugate is for the labeling dye in free solution. Use of this value for the conjugate assumes a 1:1 dye:peptide labeling ratio and no change of EC due to dye–peptide interactions.

Product List — 16.2 Probes for Neurotransmitter Receptors

Cat #	Product Name	Unit Size
A7110	γ-aminobutyric acid, α-carboxy-2-nitrobenzyl ester, trifluoroacetic acid salt (*O*-(CNB-caged) GABA)	5 mg
A12217	Amplex® Red Acetylcholine/Acetylcholinesterase Assay Kit *500 assays*	1 kit
A12221	Amplex® Red Glutamic Acid/Glutamate Oxidase Assay Kit *200 assays*	1 kit
A13439	angiotensin II, Alexa Fluor® 488 conjugate	25 µg
A13438	angiotensin II, fluorescein conjugate	25 µg
A6473	anti-NMDA receptor, subunit 2A (rat), rabbit IgG fraction *affinity purified*	10 µg
A6474	anti-NMDA receptor, subunit 2B (rat), rabbit IgG fraction *affinity purified*	10 µg
A6475	anti-NMDA receptor, subunit 2C (rat), rabbit IgG fraction *affinity purified*	10 µg
B13650	α,γ-bis-(α-carboxy-2-nitrobenzyl)-L-glutamic acid, trifluoroacetic acid salt (α,γ-bis-(CNB-caged) L-glutamic acid)	5 mg
B7436	BODIPY® FL pirenzepine, hydrochloride	100 µg
B3460	BODIPY® FL PPHT	200 µg
B7433	BODIPY® FL prazosin	100 µg
B3420	BODIPY® FL SCH 23390	1 mg
B7437	BODIPY® 558/568 pirenzepine, hydrochloride	100 µg
B7434	BODIPY® 558/568 prazosin	100 µg
B1601	α-bungarotoxin *from *Bungarus multicinctus**	1 mg
B13422	α-bungarotoxin, Alexa Fluor® 488 conjugate	500 µg
B13423	α-bungarotoxin, Alexa Fluor® 594 conjugate	500 µg
B35450	α-bungarotoxin, Alexa Fluor® 647 conjugate	500 µg
B1196	α-bungarotoxin, biotin-XX conjugate	500 µg
B7488	α-bungarotoxin, Oregon Green® 514 conjugate	500 µg
C13654	*N*-(α-carboxy-2-nitrobenzyl)carbamylcholine, trifluoroacetic acid salt (*N*-(CNB-caged) carbachol)	5 mg
C7122	*N*-(α-carboxy-2-nitrobenzyl)-L-glutamic acid (*N*-(CNB-caged) L-glutamic acid)	5 mg
F1176	fluorescein α-bungarotoxin (α-bungarotoxin, fluorescein conjugate)	500 µg
G7055	L-glutamic acid, γ-(α-carboxy-2-nitrobenzyl) ester, trifluoroacetic acid salt (γ-(CNB-caged) L-glutamic acid)	5 mg
G2504	L-glutamic acid, α-(4,5-dimethoxy-2-nitrobenzyl) ester, hydrochloride (α-(DMNB-caged) L-glutamic acid)	5 mg
M7114	*N*-methyl-D-aspartic acid, β-(α-carboxy-2-nitrobenzyl) ester, trifluoroacetic acid salt (β-(CNB-caged) NMDA)	1 mg
M13652	*N*-methyl-D-aspartic acid, β-(2,2′-dinitrobenzhydryl) ester, trifluoroacetic acid salt (β-(DNBH-caged) NMDA)	1 mg
M23400	muscimol, BODIPY® TMR-X conjugate	1 mg
N1384	naloxone fluorescein	5 mg
N1385	naltrexone fluorescein	5 mg
N13437	neuromedin C, Alexa Fluor® 488 conjugate	25 µg
N13436	neuromedin C, fluorescein conjugate	25 µg
R6922	RGA-30	5 mg
S13430	substance K, fluorescein conjugate (neurokinin-A, fluorescein conjugate)	25 µg
S13426	substance P, Alexa Fluor® 488 conjugate	25 µg
S13424	substance P, fluorescein conjugate	25 µg
S13427	substance P, Oregon Green® 488 conjugate	25 µg
S13428	substance P, tetramethylrhodamine conjugate	25 µg
T1175	tetramethylrhodamine α-bungarotoxin (α-bungarotoxin, tetramethylrhodamine conjugate)	500 µg

For current prices or to order online, visit probes.invitrogen.com

16.3 Probes for Ion Channels and Carriers

This section describes a variety of probes for Ca^{2+}, Na^{+}, K^{+} and Cl^{-} ion channels and carriers. Chapter 19, Chapter 20 and Chapter 21 contain our extensive selection of indicators for these physiologically important ions, providing a means of correlating ion channel activation with subsequent changes in intracellular ion concentration. Ion flux also affects the cell's membrane potential, which can be measured with the probes described in Chapter 22.

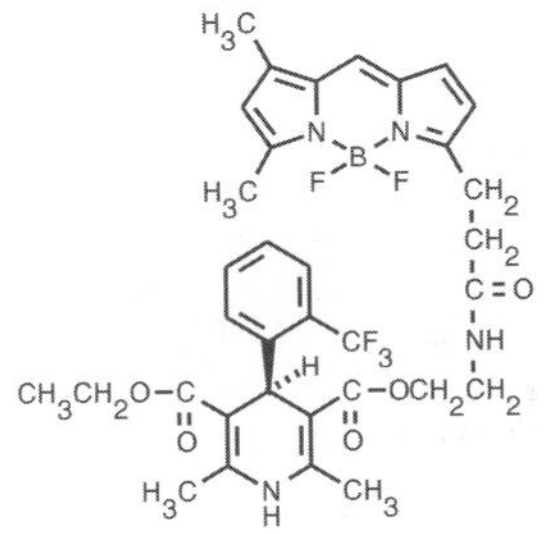

Figure 16.36 D7443 DM-BODIPY® (-)-dihydropyridine.

Probes for Ca^{2+} Channels and Carriers

In both excitable and nonexcitable cells, intracellular Ca^{2+} levels modulate a multitude of vital cellular processes — including gene expression, cell viability, cell proliferation, cell motility and cell shape and volume regulation — thereby playing a key role in regulating cell responses to external activating agents. These dynamic changes in intracellular Ca^{2+} levels are regulated by ligand-gated and G-protein–coupled ion channels in the plasma membrane, as well as by mobilization of Ca^{2+} from intracellular stores. One of the best-studied examples of Ca^{2+}-dependent signal transduction is the depolarization of excitable cells, such as those of neuronal, cardiac, skeletal and smooth muscle tissue, which is mediated by inward Ca^{2+} and Na^{+} currents. The Ca^{2+} current is attributed to the movement of ions through N-, L-, P- and T-type Ca^{2+} channels, which are defined both pharmacologically and by their biophysical properties, including conductance and voltage sensitivity. Molecular Probes offers fluorescent analogs of dihydropyridine and verapamil as ligands for N- and L-type Ca^{2+} channels. In addition, we offer unlabeled and fluorescent derivatives of ryanodine, a powerful modulator of the intracellular Ca^{2+} channels found in the sarcoplasmic reticulum and other subcellular organelles.

Fluorescent Dihydropyridines for L-Type Ca^{2+} Channels

The L-type Ca^{2+} channel is readily blocked by the binding of dihydropyridine to the channel's pore-forming α_1-subunit. To facilitate the study of channel number and distribution in single cells, Molecular Probes has developed fluorescent dihydropyridine derivatives. The high-affinity (–)-enantiomer of dihydropyridine is available labeled with either the green-fluorescent DM-BODIPY® (D7443, Figure 16.36) or the orange-fluorescent ST-BODIPY® (S7445) fluorophore. Knaus and colleagues have shown that these BODIPY® dihydropyridines bind to L-type Ca^{2+} channels with high affinity and inhibit the Ca^{2+} influx in GH_3 cells.[1] DM-BODIPY® dihydropyridine has been employed to investigate the molecular mechanism for dihydropyridine binding to L-type channels. Upon binding to the α_1-subunit, this ligand is reported to exhibit an increase in fluorescence quantum yield, as well as fluorescence resonance energy transfer (FRET) between its fluorophore and one or more of the channel's tryptophan residues[2] (see Note 1.2 "Technical Focus: Fluorescence Resonance Energy Transfer (FRET)" in Section 1.3). For neuronal L-type Ca^{2+} channels, the (–)-enantiomers of the DM-BODIPY® dihydropyridine and ST-BODIPY® derivatives each exhibit a K_i of 0.9 nM. Their affinities for skeletal muscle L-type Ca^{2+} channels are somewhat lower. Although DM-BODIPY® dihydropyridine exhibits a more intense fluorescence, the particularly high degree of stereoselectivity retained by the ST-BODIPY® derivatives has proven useful for the *in vivo* visualization of L-type Ca^{2+} channels.

The spatial distribution and density of L-type Ca^{2+} channels in cultured olfactory neurons were determined by confocal laser-scanning microscopy using the ratio of the site-selective fluorescent staining produced by the (–)-enantiomer of DM-BODIPY® dihydropyridine (D7443, Figure 16.36) to the uniform fluorescent membrane staining by RH 414[3] (T1111, Section 14.4). In this study, RH 414 staining served to control for optical artifacts and differences in membrane surface area (Figure 16.37). The DM-BODIPY® dihydropyridine and ST-BODIPY® dihydropyridine have also been used to label dihydropyridine receptors in *Fucus* zygotes and embryos[4,5] and to demonstrate the presence of L-type Ca^{2+} channels in peripheral blood–derived human dendritic cells[6] and smooth muscle cells.[7]

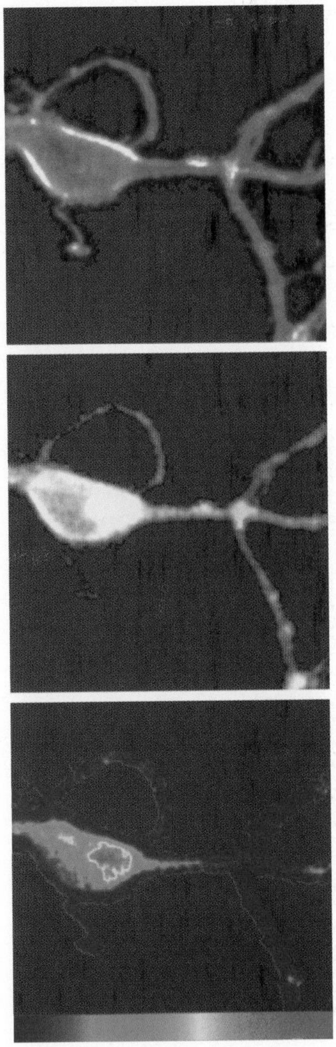

Figure 16.37 Cultured olfactory bulb neuron stained with RH 414 (T1111) and DM-BODIPY®(–)-dihydropyridine (D7443) (J Neurosci Methods 59, 183 (1995)). Top: image at >580 nm; Middle: image at 510–580 nm; Bottom: ratio of the middle image divided by the top image. Images were acquired with a Leica confocal laser-scanning microscope. The images were contributed by D. Schild, H. Geiling and J. Bischofberger, Physiologisches Institut, Universität Göttingen.

BODIPY® FL Verapamil

Like dihydropyridine, phenylalkylamines also bind to the α_1-subunit of L-type Ca^{2+} channels and block Ca^{2+} transport. Molecular Probes offers a green-fluorescent BODIPY® FL derivative (B7431, Figure 16.38) of verapamil, a phenylalkylamine known to inhibit P-glycoprotein–mediated drug efflux. Although we do not yet know the effect of BODIPY® FL verapamil on L-type Ca^{2+} channels, this fluorescent phenylalkylamine should be useful for investigating P-glycoprotein–mediated multidrug resistance.

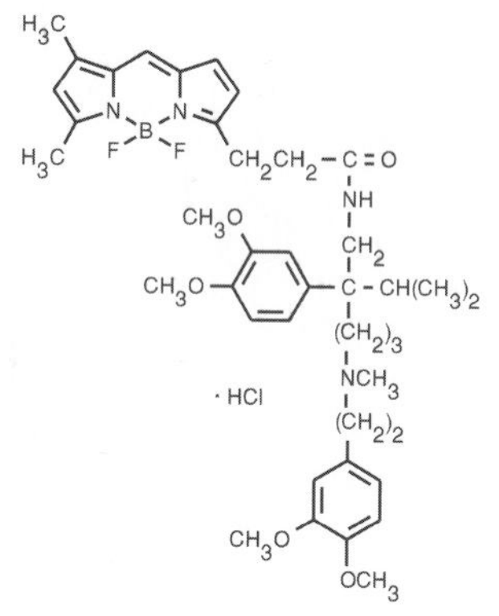
Figure 16.38 B7431 BODIPY® FL verapamil, hydrochloride.

The 170,000-dalton P-glycoprotein is typically overexpressed in tumor cells that have acquired resistance to a variety of anticancer drugs (Section 15.6). P-glycoprotein is thought to mediate the ATP-dependent efflux or sequestration of structurally unrelated molecules, including actinomycin D, anthracyclines, colchicine, epipodophyllotoxins and vinblastine. Verapamil appears to inhibit drug efflux by acting as a substrate of P-glycoprotein, thereby overwhelming the transporter's capacity to expel the drugs. BODIPY® FL verapamil also appears to serve as a substrate for P-glycoprotein. This fluorescent verapamil derivative preferentially accumulates in the lysosomes of normal, drug-sensitive NIH 3T3 cells but is rapidly transported out of multidrug-resistant cells, as revealed by fluorescence microscopy.[8]

Ryanodine Probes for Intracellular Ca^{2+} Channels

Ryanodine is a plant alkaloid that mobilizes Ca^{2+} from intracellular stores by activating a class of Ins 1,4,5-P_3–insensitive Ca^{2+} channels.[9] It alters the function of the Ca^{2+} channel in a complex manner: submicromolar concentrations lock the channel in a long-lived open state, whereas micromolar or greater concentrations inhibit Ca^{2+} release.[10,11] Ryanodine has been used to modulate the Ca^{2+} concentration in sea urchin eggs [12] and in parotid acinar cells.[13] In developing skeletal muscle, ryanodine receptors localize in discrete regions of the T tubules, binding at the junctional complex between the T tubules and the sarcoplasmic reticulum.[14]

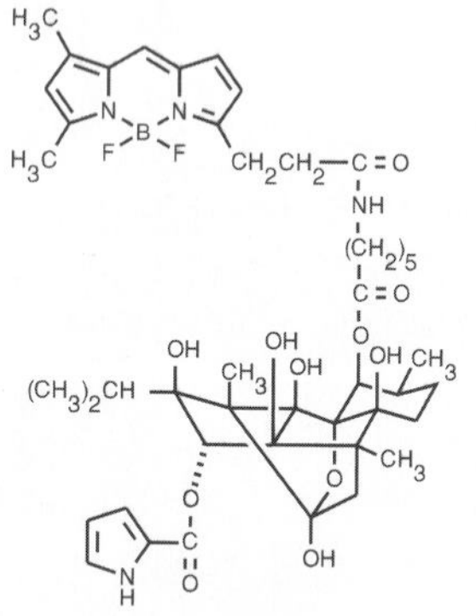
Figure 16.39 B7505 BODIPY® FL-X ryanodine.

Unlabeled "ryanodine" from most other commercial sources is typically a mixture of ryanodine and dehydroryanodine.[15,16] However, Molecular Probes offers an HPLC-purified grade of ryanodine (R7478) that is >95% pure. In addition to unlabeled ryanodine, we have prepared a monosubstituted BODIPY® FL-X derivative (B7505), which is a mixture of BODIPY® FL-X ryanodine and BODIPY® FL-X dehydroryanodine, most likely labeled at the 10 position of the ryanodine molecule (Figure 16.39). Structurally similar BODIPY® ryanodines were shown to have a dissociation constant near that of ryanodine.[15,17] BODIPY® FL-X ryanodine has been used to visualize ryanodine receptor distribution in live porcine endothelial cells,[18] in pancreatic β-cells,[19] in vascular myocytes,[20] in cardiomyocytes,[21] in frog sympathetic neurons [22,23] and in the rat parotid gland.[24]

Eosin Derivatives: Inhibitors of the Calcium Pump

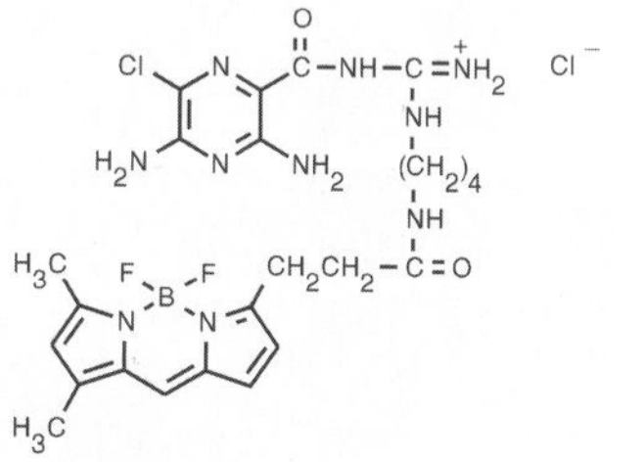
Figure 16.40 B6905 BODIPY® FL amiloride.

Eosin isothiocyanate (E18) is a potent reversible inhibitor of the erythrocyte calcium pump, with a half-maximal inhibitory concentration of <0.2 µM.[25] Eosin isothiocyanate also reacts irreversibly at the ATP-binding site in erythrocytes. Fluorescein isothiocyanate (F143, Section 1.4) is a weaker inhibitor of this calcium pump. The succinimidyl ester of carboxyeosin diacetate (C22803) is a cell membrane–permeant eosin derivative that inhibits the red cell plasma membrane Ca^{2+} pump.[26,27]

Probes for Na^+ Channels and Carriers

Amiloride Analogs: Probes for the Na^+ Channel and the Na^+/H^+ Antiporter

Amiloride is a compound known to inhibit the Na^+/H^+ antiporter of vertebrate cells by acting competitively at the Na^+-binding site.[28] The antiporter extrudes protons from cells using the inward Na^+ gradient as a driving force, resulting in intracellular alkalinization. In 1967, Cragoe and co-workers reported the synthesis of amiloride and several amiloride analogs, pyrazine diuretics that inhibit the Na^+ channel in urinary epithelia.[29] Since then, more than 1000 different amiloride analogs have been synthesized and many of these tested for their specificity and potency in inhibiting the Na^+ channel, Na^+/H^+ antiporter and Na^+/Ca^{2+} exchanger.[30] Unmodified amiloride inhibits the Na^+ channel with an IC_{50} of less than 1 µM. We offer BODIPY® FL amiloride (B6905), a green-fluorescent probe in which the BODIPY® fluorophore is attached at the R^3 position (Figure 16.40).

Additionally, amiloride is an important tool for studying the Na^+/H^+ antiporter. Structure–activity relationships have demonstrated that amiloride analogs with hydrophobic groups in the drug are the most potent and specific inhibitors for the Na^+/H^+ antiporter.[30–35] For example, our 5-(*N*-ethyl-*N*-isopropyl)amiloride (E3111, Figure 16.41) is 200-fold more potent than amiloride for inhibiting this antiporter.

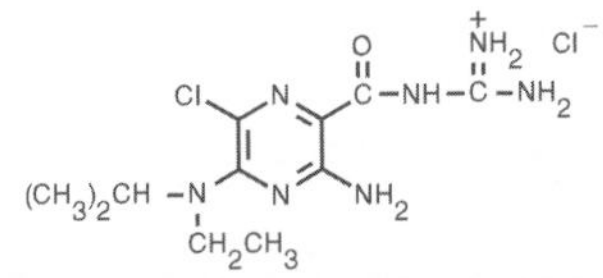

Figure 16.41 E3111 5-(*N*-ethyl-*N*-isopropyl)amiloride, hydrochloride.

Cardiac Glycosides, Including Ouabain Probes for Na^+/K^+-ATPase

Ouabain and digoxigenin are members of a class of glycosylated steroids collectively known as cardiac glycosides due to their therapeutic efficacy in the treatment of congestive heart failure. Ouabain achieves this effect by binding to the catalytic α-subunit of Na^+/K^+-ATPase and inhibiting its transport of Na^+ across the plasma membrane. 9-Anthroyl ouabain (A1322) — a fluorescent probe that binds to a variety of cells from different species — is useful for localizing Na^+/K^+-ATPase and for studying its membrane orientation, mobility and dynamics.[36] Anthroyl ouabain has also been employed to investigate Na^+/K^+-ATPase's active site, inhibition and conformational changes,[37–42] as well as to investigate the kinetics of cardiac glycoside binding.[43–48] BODIPY® FL ouabain (B23461, Figure 16.42) and BODIPY® FL digoxigenin (B23460, Figure 16.43) offer some potentially valuable properties for these applications. Because the BODIPY® FL fluorophore is nonpolar and relatively small, labeled ligands typically have superior receptor-binding properties over fluorescein- and NBD-labeled probes. BODIPY® FL digoxigenin has been used to screen and sort high-affinity functional clones of single-chain Fv antibodies from a phage display library by flow cytometry.[49–52]

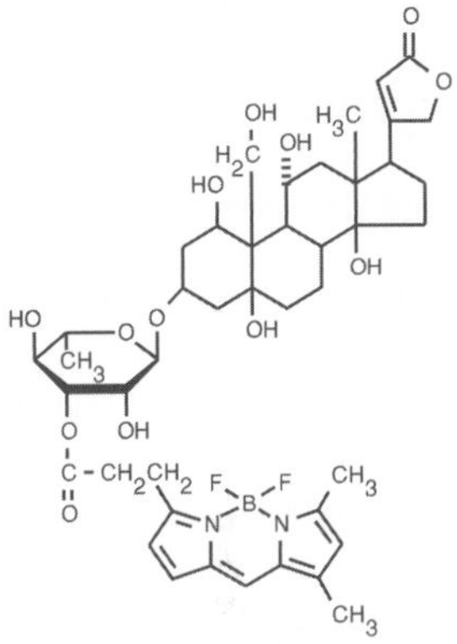

Figure 16.42 B23461 BODIPY® FL ouabain.

Probes for K^+ Channels and Carriers

Glibenclamide Probes for the ATP-Dependent K^+ Channel

Glibenclamide blocks the ATP-dependent K^+ channel, thereby eliciting insulin secretion.[53] In collaboration with Gabriel Haddad of Yale University, Molecular Probes has prepared the green-fluorescent BODIPY® FL glibenclamide and red-fluorescent BODIPY® TR glibenclamide (B7439, B13540; Figure 16.44) as probes for the ATP-dependent K^+ channel. Although the binding affinity of BODIPY® FL glibenclamide was lower than that of the unlabeled antagonist glibenclamide, Haddad and co-workers were able to visualize ATP-dependent K^+ channels in brain sections and cultured brain cells.[54] BODIPY® TR glibenclamide has been used to detect sulfonylurea receptors associated with ATP-dependent K^+ channels in bovine monocytes and in β-cells[55,56] and to label a novel mitochondrial ATP-sensitive potassium channel in brain.[57]

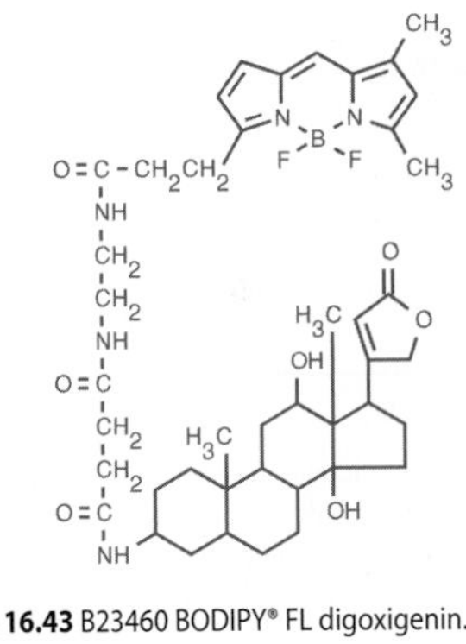

Figure 16.43 B23460 BODIPY® FL digoxigenin.

Apamin for Small-Conductance Ca^{2+}-Activated K^+ Channels

Apamin, an 18–amino acid peptide isolated from *Apis mellifera* bee venom,[58–61] primarily blocks small-conductance Ca^{2+}-activated K^+ channels in mammalian neurons and skeletal muscle.[62–67] For localizing these K^+ channels, Molecular Probes has introduced Alexa Fluor® 488 apamin (A13541) and BODIPY® FL apamin (A13542). This green-fluorescent apamin derivative may be useful as an alternative to radiolabeled apamin, which has been used to study the peptide's interaction with neuroblastoma cells.[67] Apamin also possesses potent convulsant activity and is known to cross the blood–brain barrier.[62]

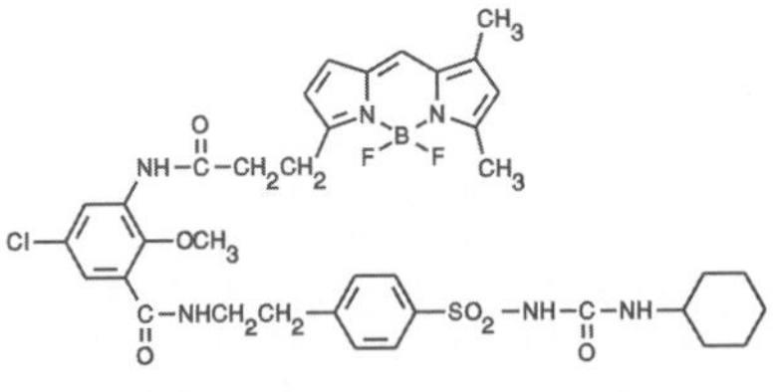

Figure 16.44 B7439 BODIPY® FL glibenclamide (BODIPY® FL glyburide).

Probes for Cl^- Channels and Carriers

Ivermectin Probes for Glutamate-Gated Cl^- Channels

Molecular Probes has developed a green-fluorescent derivative of the antiparasitic agent ivermectin — BODIPY® FL ivermectin (B13510). Ivermectin selectively binds to glutamate-gated Cl^- channels in invertebrate nerve and muscle cells. This binding leads to an increase in cell membrane permeability to Cl^- ions. Hyperpolarization of the cell results in paralysis and death of the parasite. BODIPY® FL ivermectin has allowed researchers to investigate epithelial transport in isolated proximal kidney tubules.[68] Similar fluorescent derivatives of ivermectin have been used to measure cellular uptake of ivermectin,[69] to study ivermectin-sensitive Cl^- channels [70,71] and to measure the concentration, mobility and distribution of ivermectin in the plasma membrane.[72,73]

Stilbene Disulfonates: Anion-Transport Inhibitors

Molecular Probes offers five stilbene disulfonates that have been employed to inhibit (frequently irreversibly) anion transport in a large number of mammalian cell types:[74]

- DBDS (D675)
- DIDS (D337)
- H_2DIDS (D338)
- DNDS (D673)
- SITS (A339)

DNDS and SITS were among the inhibitors used to characterize three different anion exchangers in the membranes of renal brush border cells and to compare these exchangers with the band-3 anion-transport protein of erythrocyte membranes.[75] Binding of DBDS to the band-3 anion-transport protein is accompanied by a large increase in the probe's fluorescence that can be used to detect competitive binding of other drugs at this site.[76,77]

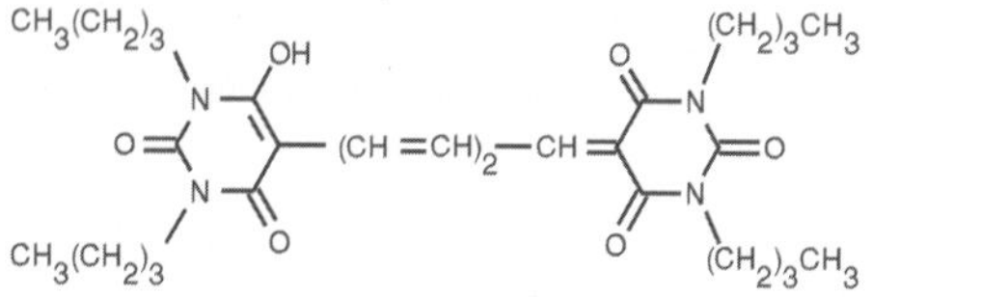

Figure 16.45 B436 bis-(1,3-dibutylbarbituric acid)pentamethine oxonol (DiBAC$_4$(5)).

These stilbene disulfonates can, in some cases, bind specifically to proteins that are not anion transporters. For example, DIDS, H_2DIDS and SITS complex specifically with the CD4 glycoprotein on T-helper lymphocytes and macrophages, blocking HIV type-1 growth at multiple stages of the virus life cycle.[78]

Our stilbene disulfonate probes, which are 95–99% pure by HPLC, have significantly higher purity and more defined composition than those available from other commercial sources.

Other Inhibitors for Anion Transporters

DiBAC$_4$(5)

The membrane potential–sensing dye bis-(1,3-dibutylbarbituric acid)pentamethine oxonol (DiBAC$_4$(5), B436; Figure 16.45) initially inhibits Cl^- exchange with an IC_{50} of 0.146 µM. However, this inhibition increases with time to an IC_{50} of 1.05 nM, making DiBAC$_4$(5) a more potent inhibitor than DIDS, which has an IC_{50} of 31 nM under similar conditions.[79]

Eosin Maleimide

Although usually selectively reactive with thiols, eosin-5-maleimide (E118, Section 2.2) is known to react with a specific lysine residue of the band-3 protein in human erythrocytes, inhibiting anion exchange in these cells and providing a convenient tag for observing band-3 behavior in the membrane.[80–82] Eosin-5-isothiocyanate (E18) has similar reactivity with band-3 proteins.[83,84]

References

1. Proc Natl Acad Sci U S A 89, 3586 (1992); **2.** Biochemistry 33, 11875 (1994); **3.** J Neurosci Methods 59, 183 (1995); **4.** J Cell Sci 109, 335 (1996); **5.** Biotechniques 19, 946 (1995); **6.** J Biol Chem 273, 7205 (1998); **7.** Am J Physiol 268, F251 (1995); **8.** Mol Pharmacol 40, 490 (1991); **9.** J Biol Chem 268, 13765 (1993); **10.** J Gen Physiol 92, 1 (1988); **11.** Am J Physiol 253, C364 (1987); **12.** Science 253, 1143 (1991); **13.** J Biol Chem 266, 14535 (1991); **14.** J Cell Biol 112, 289 (1991); **15.** J Biol Chem 269, 30243 (1994); **16.** J Labelled Compounds Radiopharmaceut 23, 215 (1986); **17.** Biochemistry 33, 6074 (1994); **18.** J Physiol 506, 109 (1998); **19.** J Biol Chem 274, 14147 (1999); **20.** J Biol Chem 275, 9596 (2000); **21.** Cell Calcium 28, 127 (2000); **22.** J Neurosci 20, 9059 (2000); **23.** J Gen Physiol 116, 697 (2000); **24.** Biochem J 340, 519 (1999); **25.** Am J Physiol 264, C1577 (1993); **26.** J Physiol 515, 109 (1999); **27.** Cell Calcium 22, 99 (1997); **28.** J Biol Chem 258, 3503 (1983); **29.** J Med Chem 10, 66 (1967); **30.** J Membr Biol 105, 1 (1988); **31.** Biochimie 70, 1285 (1988); **32.** Mol Pharmacol 30, 112 (1986); **33.** Biochemistry 23, 4481 (1984); **34.** J Biol Chem 259, 4313 (1984); **35.** Mol Pharmacol 25, 131 (1984); **36.** Biochemistry 16, 531 (1977); **37.** J Biol Chem 273, 28813 (1998); **38.** Cell Biol Int 18, 723 (1994); **39.** Physiol Res 43, 33 (1994); **40.** Biochemistry 25, 8133 (1986); **41.** J Biol Chem 260, 14484 (1985); **42.** J Biol Chem 257, 5601 (1982); **43.** Biochemistry 37, 6658 (1998); **44.** Biophys Chem 71, 245 (1998); **45.** Cell Tissue Res 260, 529 (1990); **46.** J Cell Biol 103, 1473 (1986); **47.** J Biol Chem 259, 11176 (1984); **48.** Biochemistry 19, 969 (1980); **49.** Nat Biotechnol 19, 537 (2001); **50.** Proc Natl Acad Sci U S A 97, 2029 (2000); **51.** Protein Eng 12, 613 (1999); **52.** Protein Eng 11, 825 (1998); **53.** Trends Pharmacol Sci 11, 417 (1990); **54.** G. Haddad, Yale University, personal communication; **55.** Diabetes 48, 2390 (1999); **56.** Pflugers Arch 434, 712 (1997); **57.** J Biol Chem 276, 33369 (2001); **58.** Biochemistry 31, 1476 (1992); **59.** Meth Neurosci 8, 15 (1992); **60.** FEBS Lett 197, 289 (1986); **61.** Science 177, 314 (1972); **62.** J Membr Biol 105, 95 (1988); **63.** FEBS Lett 275, 185 (1990); **64.** Nature 323, 718 (1986); **65.** J Biol Chem 259, 1491 (1984); **66.** EMBO J 1, 1039 (1982); **67.** Proc Natl Acad Sci U S A 79, 1308 (1982); **68.** Pharm Res 16, 1570 (1999); **69.** Vet Res Commun 16, 365 (1992); **70.** EMBO J 16, 5867 (1997); **71.** Neurosci Lett 230, 183 (1997); **72.** Parasitology 104, 549 (1992); **73.** J Parasitol 76, 340 (1990); **74.** Am J Physiol 262, C803 (1992); **75.** J Biol Chem 269, 21489 (1994); **76.** Biochim Biophys Acta 979, 193 (1989); **77.** Nature 282, 520 (1979); **78.** J Biol Chem 266, 13355 (1991); **79.** Am J Physiol 269, C1073 (1995); **80.** Biochemistry 34, 4880 (1995); **81.** Biophys J 66, 1726 (1994); **82.** Am J Physiol 264, C1144 (1993); **83.** Biochim Biophys Acta 897, 14 (1987); **84.** Biochim Biophys Acta 550, 328 (1979).

Data Table — 16.3 Probes for Ion Channels and Carriers

Cat #	MW	Storage	Soluble	Abs	EC	Em	Solvent	Notes
A339	498.45	F,DD	H_2O	336	47,000	436	pH 7	1
A1322	788.89	F,D,L	DMSO	362	7,500	471	MeOH	
A13541	~2600	F,D,L	DMSO	494	78,000	520	pH 8	2
A13542	~2500	F,D,L	DMSO	504	83,000	513	H_2O	2
B436	542.67	L	DMSO, EtOH	590	160,000	616	MeOH	3
B6905	611.29	F,D,L	DMSO, MeOH	504	61,000	511	MeOH	
B7431	769.18	F,D,L	DMSO, EtOH	504	74,000	511	MeOH	
B7439	783.10	F,D,L	DMSO, EtOH	504	76,000	511	MeOH	
B7505	880.79	FF,D,L	DMSO	504	79,000	511	MeOH	
B13510	~1150	F,D,L	DMSO	503	71,000	511	MeOH	
B13511	~1400	F,D,L	DMSO	589	62,000	617	MeOH	
B13540	915.23	F,D,L	DMSO, EtOH	587	60,000	615	MeOH	
B23460	805.77	F,D,L	$CHCl_3$, DMF	504	80,000	511	MeOH	
B23461	858.74	F,D,L	DMSO	503	80,000	510	MeOH	
C22803	873.05	F,D	DMSO	<300		none		
D337	498.47	F,DD	H_2O	341	61,000	415	H_2O	1
D338	500.48	F,DD	H_2O	286	41,000	none	MeOH	1
D673	474.32	L	H_2O	352	32,000	none	H_2O	
D675	622.57	L	H_2O	343	50,000	430	MeOH	
D7441	713.67	F,D,L	DMSO, EtOH	504	83,000	511	MeOH	
D7443	686.48	F,D,L,A	DMSO, EtOH	504	83,000	511	MeOH	
D7444	686.48	F,D,L,A	DMSO, EtOH	504	83,000	510	MeOH	
E18	704.97	F,DD,L	pH >6, DMF	521	95,000	544	pH 9	1
E3111	336.22	D,L	H_2O, MeOH	378	23,000	423	MeOH	
I6881	393.57	F,D,L	MeOH	367	18,000	ND	pH 7	4
R7478	493.55	F,D	MeOH, DMSO	<300		none		
S7445	760.57	F,D,L,A	DMSO, EtOH	565	143,000	570	MeOH	
W435	757.00	D,L	DMSO, EtOH	605	120,000	639	MeOH	5

For definitions of the contents of this data table, see "Navigating *The Handbook*" in the introductory pages.

Notes

1. Isothiocyanates are unstable in water and should not be stored in aqueous solution.
2. The value of EC listed for this peptide conjugate is that of the labeling dye in free solution. Use of this value for the conjugate assumes a 1:1 dye:peptide labeling ratio and no change of EC due to dye–peptide interactions.
3. Oxonols may require addition of a base to be soluble.
4. MW of I6881 is for the dihydrate form. MWs for other amiloride derivatives are based on the anhydrous compound.
5. Fluorescence excitation/emission maxima of W435 are 615/650 nm in cell suspensions (Biophys J 57, 835 (1990)).

Product List — 16.3 Probes for Ion Channels and Carriers

Cat #	Product Name	Unit Size
A339	4-acetamido-4′-isothiocyanatostilbene-2,2′-disulfonic acid, disodium salt (SITS)	100 mg
A1322	9-anthroyl ouabain	5 mg
A13541	apamin, Alexa Fluor® 488 conjugate	25 µg
A13542	apamin, BODIPY® FL conjugate	25 µg
B436	bis-(1,3-dibutylbarbituric acid)pentamethine oxonol (DiBAC$_4$(5))	25 mg
B6905	BODIPY® FL amiloride	25 µg
B23460	BODIPY® FL digoxigenin	100 µg
B7439	BODIPY® FL glibenclamide (BODIPY® FL glyburide)	100 µg
B13510	BODIPY® FL ivermectin *mixed isomers*	100 µg
B23461	BODIPY® FL ouabain	100 µg
B7431	BODIPY® FL verapamil, hydrochloride	1 mg
B7505	BODIPY® FL-X ryanodine	25 µg
B13540	BODIPY® TR glibenclamide (BODIPY® TR glyburide)	100 µg
B13511	BODIPY® TR-X ivermectin *mixed isomers*	100 µg
C22803	5-(and-6)-carboxyeosin diacetate, succinimidyl ester *mixed isomers*	5 mg
D675	4,4′-dibenzamidostilbene-2,2′-disulfonic acid, disodium salt (DBDS)	100 mg
D338	4,4′-diisothiocyanatodihydrostilbene-2,2′-disulfonic acid, disodium salt (H$_2$DIDS)	100 mg
D337	4,4′-diisothiocyanatostilbene-2,2′-disulfonic acid, disodium salt (DIDS)	100 mg
D673	4,4′-dinitrostilbene-2,2′-disulfonic acid, disodium salt (DNDS)	1 g
D7443	DM-BODIPY® (-)-dihydropyridine *high affinity enantiomer*	25 µg
D7444	DM-BODIPY® (+)-dihydropyridine *low affinity enantiomer*	25 µg
D7441	DM-BODIPY® PAA (BODIPY® FL phenylalkylamine)	25 µg
E18	eosin-5-isothiocyanate	100 mg
E3111	5-(*N*-ethyl-*N*-isopropyl)amiloride, hydrochloride	5 mg
I6881	6-iodoamiloride, hydrochloride, dihydrate	5 mg
R7478	ryanodine *free of dehydroryanodine*	1 mg
S7445	ST-BODIPY® (-)-dihydropyridine *high affinity enantiomer*	25 µg
W435	WW 781, triethylammonium salt	25 mg

For current prices or to order online, visit probes.invitrogen.com

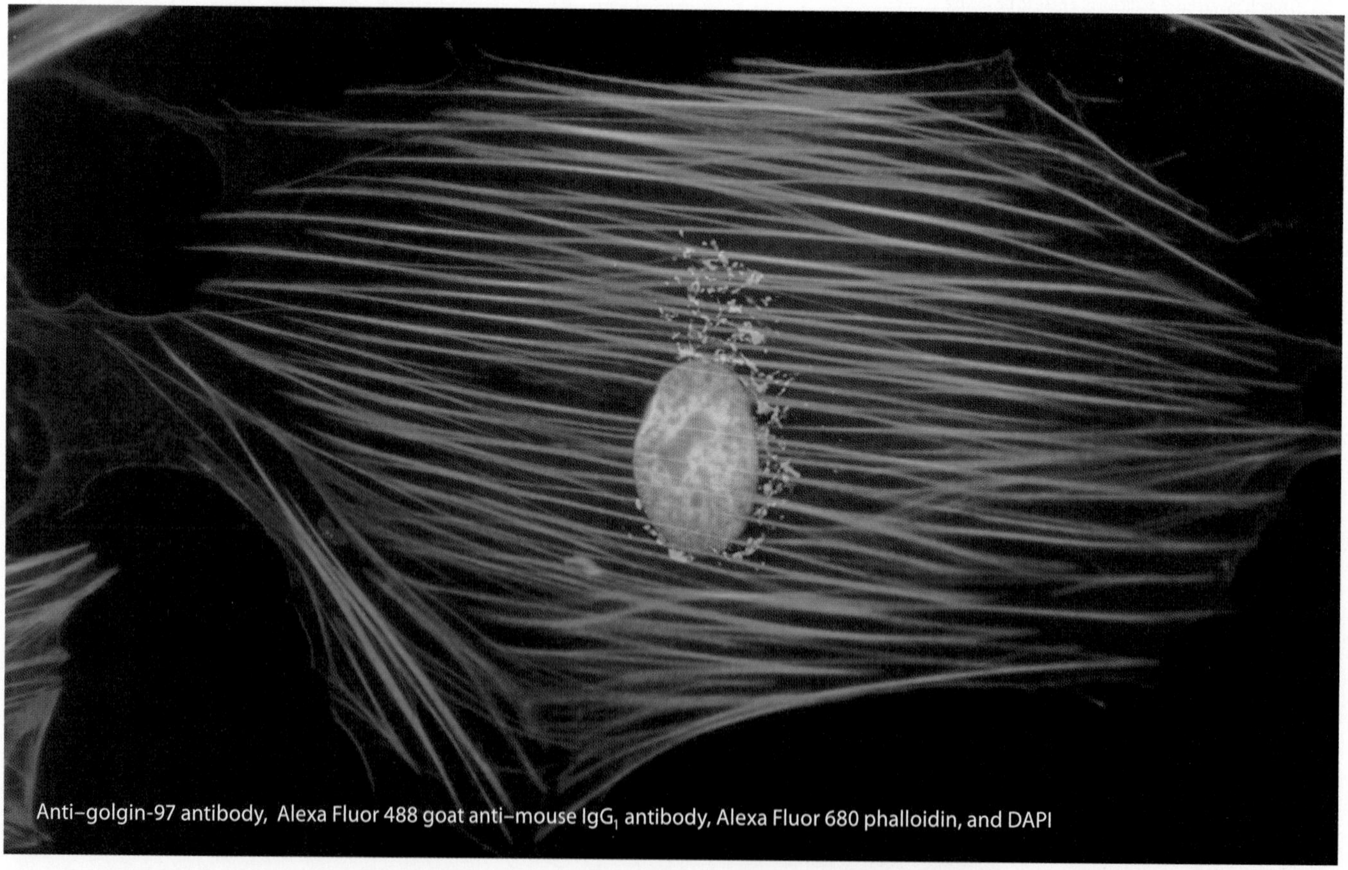

Anti–golgin-97 antibody, Alexa Fluor 488 goat anti–mouse IgG$_1$ antibody, Alexa Fluor 680 phalloidin, and DAPI

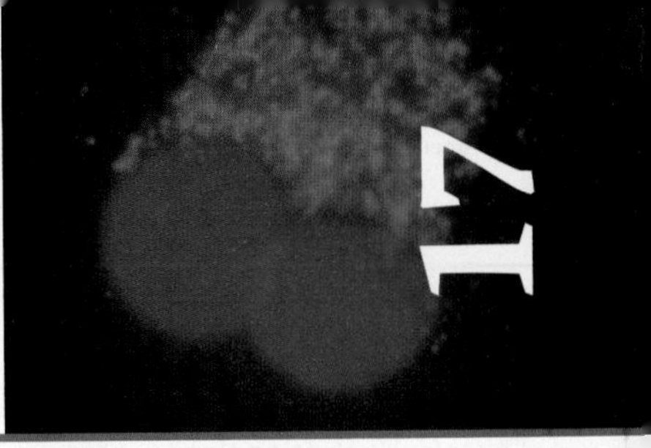

Chapter 17

Probes for Signal Transduction

17.1 Introduction to Signal Transduction

Cells respond to their environment through a complex and interdependent series of signal transduction pathways that frequently begin at the cell membrane. Many cellular receptors are transmembrane proteins with extracellular domains that selectively bind ligands. In response to ligand binding, the receptor's cytoplasmic domain may change conformation and transmit the signal across the membrane, or individual receptors may aggregate and interact with other membrane proteins in order to generate a response. Transmembrane signals trigger a cascade of events in the cell, which can include changes in intracellular Ca^{2+} levels, enzymatic activity and gene expression (Figure 17.1).

Molecular Probes offers several important reagents for studying signal transduction mechanisms, including Ca^{2+} regulation and the activities of other second messengers. This chapter focuses on probes for events occurring downstream from the receptor–ligand interaction. These products complement the probes for receptors and ion channels in Chapter 16, as well as the many ion indicators discussed in Chapter 19, Chapter 20 and Chapter 21. Chapter 18 describes our line of probes for nitric oxide research — including nitric oxide donors, nitric oxide synthase inhibitors and reagents for nitrite detection — as well as for other reactive oxygen species.

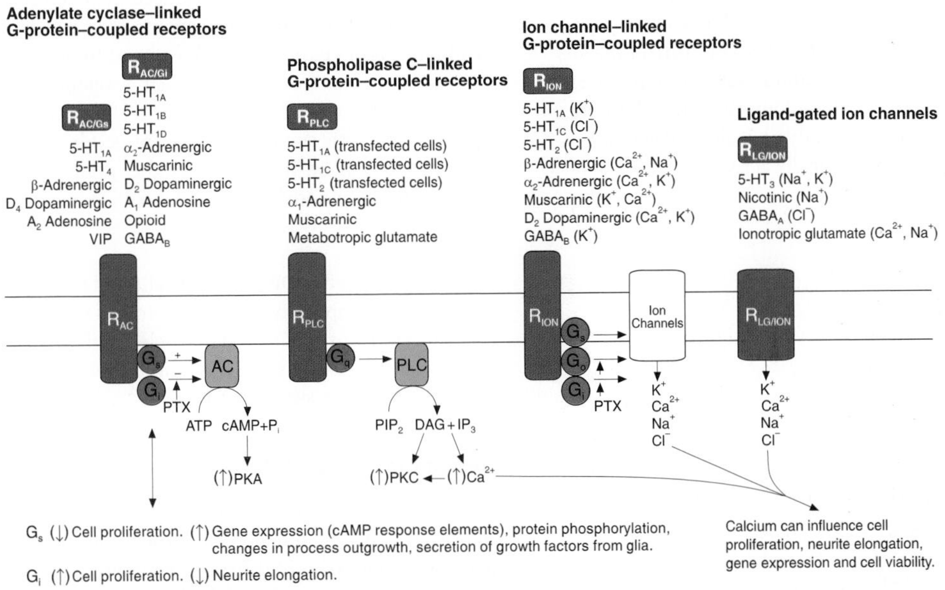

Figure 17.1 Neurotransmitter receptors linked to second messengers mediating growth responses in neuronal and nonneuronal cells. Abbreviations: $R_{AC/Gs}$ = Receptors coupled to G-proteins that stimulate adenylate cyclase (AC) activity, leading to cAMP formation and enhanced activity of protein kinase A (PKA). $R_{AC/Gi}$ = Receptors coupled to pertussis toxin (PTX)–sensitive G-proteins that inhibit adenylate cyclase activity. R_{PLC} = Receptors promoting the hydrolysis of phosphatidylinositol 4,5-diphosphate (PIP_2) to inositol 1,4,5-triphosphate (IP_3), which increases intracellular Ca^{2+}, and diacylglycerol (DAG), which activates protein kinase C (PKC). R_{ION} = Receptors indirectly promoting ion fluxes due to coupling to various G-proteins. $R_{LG/ION}$ = Receptors that promote ion fluxes directly because they are structurally linked to ion channels (members of the superfamily of ligand-gated ion channel receptors). Stimulation of proliferation is most often associated with activation of G-proteins negatively coupled to adenylate cyclase (G_i), or positively coupled to phospholipase C (G_q) or to pertussis toxin–sensitive pathways (G_o, G_i). In contrast, activation of neurotransmitter receptors positively coupled to cAMP usually inhibits cell proliferation and causes changes in cell shape indicative of differentiation. Reprinted and modified with permission from J.M. Lauder and Trends Neurosci 16, 233 (1993).

17.2 Calcium Regulation

Intracellular Ca^{2+} levels modulate a multitude of vital cellular processes — including gene expression, cell viability, cell proliferation, cell motility and cell shape and volume regulation — thereby playing a key role in regulating cell responses to external signals. These dynamic changes in Ca^{2+} levels are regulated by ligand-gated and G-protein–coupled ion channels in the plasma membrane and by mobilization of Ca^{2+} from intracellular stores. The generation of cytosolic Ca^{2+} spikes and oscillations typically involves the coordinated release and uptake of Ca^{2+} from these stores, mediated by intracellular Ca^{2+} channels and their response to several second messengers such as Ca^{2+} itself, cyclic ADP ribose and inositol triphosphate.[1–3] Molecular Probes has available several important reagents, described in this section, for studying Ca^{2+} regulation in live cells. Fluorescent nucleotides, including analogs of ATP, ADP, ATP-γ-*S*, AMPPNP, GTP, GDP, GTP-γ-*S* and GMPPNP, are described in Section 17.3. Our GTP analogs may be particularly useful in the assay of G-protein–coupled receptors. In Section 17.4 are described our phosphodiesterase substrates, including several unique fluorescent phosphatidylinositol derivatives, as well as monoclonal antibodies to phosphatidylinositol phosphates.

Inositol Triphosphate Pathway

D-myo-1,4,5-Inositol Triphosphate and Caged D-myo-1,4,5-Inositol Triphosphate

Molecular Probes offers the potassium salt of D-*myo*-inositol 1,4,5-triphosphate (Ins 1,4,5-P_3, I3716) for researchers investigating inositol triphosphate–dependent Ca^{2+} mobilization and signal transduction mechanisms.[4] Cytoplasmic Ins 1,4,5-P_3 is a potent intracellular second messenger that induces Ca^{2+} release from membrane-bound stores in many tissues.[1,4,5] Our Ins 1,4,5-P_3 is at least 99% pure, as determined by paper chromatography and by ^1H NMR and ^{31}P NMR.

NPE-caged Ins 1,4,5-P_3 can be used to generate rapid and precisely controlled release of Ins 1,4,5-P_3 in intact cells and is widely employed in studies of Ins 1,4,5-P_3–mediated second messenger pathways.[6,7] Our NPE-caged Ins 1,4,5-P_3 (I23580) is a mixture of the physiologically inert, singly esterified P^4 and P^5 esters (Figure 17.2) and does not contain the somewhat physiologically active P^1 ester. NPE-caged Ins 1,4,5-P_3 exhibits essentially no biological activity prior to photolytic release of the biologically active Ins 1,4,5-P_3.

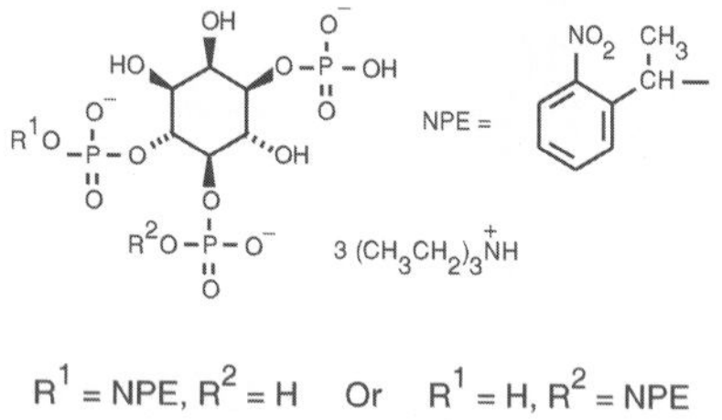

Figure 17.2 I23580 D-*myo*-inositol 1,4,5-triphosphate, $P_{4(5)}$-(1-(2-nitrophenyl)ethyl) ester, tris(triethylammonium) salt (NPE-caged Ins 1,4,5-P_3).

Fluorescent Heparin

Our fluorescein-labeled heparin (H7482) should be a useful tool for studying binding of this mucopolysaccharide in cells and tissues.[8] In addition to its well-known anticoagulant activity,[9] heparin binds to the Ins 1,4,5-P_3 receptor and inhibits the biological cascade of events mediated by Ins 1,4,5-P_3.[10] Heparin exhibits a number of other biological properties, including modulation of the structure, function and metabolism of many proteins and enzymes. This mucopolysaccharide binds to thrombin,[11] low-density lipoproteins,[12,13] lipoprotein lipase, circulatory serine proteases and proteinase inhibitors, as well as to blood vessel–associated proteins such as fibronectin[12,14–16] and laminin.[17] Heparin also interacts with heparin-binding growth factors (HBGFs) and, for HBGF-1, amplifies its mutagenic and neurotrophic activity.[18] Fluorescein-labeled heparin can be prepared by a variety of methods, which may influence its applications. Therefore, fluorescein heparin from Molecular Probes may not be identical to those used in all of the reported applications.[12,14–16,19–24]

Calcium-Induced Calcium Release

Cyclic ADP Ribose and Caged Cyclic ADP Ribose

Molecular Probes offers cyclic ADP ribose (cADP-ribose, C7619), a potent, microinjectable Ca^{2+}-mobilizing agent that functions as a second messenger in an Ins 1,4,5-P_3–independent pathway and is involved in Ca^{2+}-induced Ca^{2+} release in both mammalian cells[25–31] and plants.[32] cADP-ribose is a putative physiological regulator of certain isoforms of ryanodine-activated Ca^{2+} channels[33–36] that may act through a calmodulin-mediated mechanism.[37] cADP-ribose is reported to mobilize Ca^{2+} in dorsal root ganglion cells, pituitary cells and sea urchin eggs,[38–40] where it can also act synergistically with ryanodine to release Ca^{2+} from intracellular Ca^{2+} stores.[41] This Ca^{2+}-mobilizing agent is also produced in pancreatic islets by glucose stimulation[42,43] and has been shown to mediate glucose-induced insulin release in pancreatic cells[44,45] and to induce release of Ca^{2+} from stores in and around the nuclear envelope.[46] Researchers have investigated the role of cADP-ribose in agonist-evoked Ca^{2+} oscillations in pancreatic acinar cells.[47] In this study, cADP-ribose–induced Ca^{2+} spikes could be blocked with either ryanodine or heparin, implicating both ryanodine and Ins 1,4,5-P_3 receptors in the Ca^{2+} spike generation.

The application of cADP-ribose in cells and tissues can be controlled spatially and temporally by flash photolysis of our patented NPE-caged cADP-ribose (C7074). Photorelease of cADP-ribose from NPE-caged cADP-ribose results in initiation of Ca^{2+} release and the cortical reaction in sea urchin eggs.[48]

Deaza Cyclic ADP Ribose

3-Deaza-cyclic adenosine 5′-diphosphate ribose (3-deaza-cADP-ribose, D23650) is a stable, nonhydrolyzable analog of cADP-ribose that is reported to be 70 times more potent than cADP-ribose when used in similar applications.[25,49] Concentrations of 3-deaza-cADP-ribose as low as 0.3 nM induce calcium release in sea urchin egg homogenates. This release can be blocked by 8-amino-cADP-ribose (A7621).

Cyclic ADP Ribose Antagonist

Inhibition of cADP-ribose–induced Ca^{2+} mobilization can be achieved specifically and reversibly with the cADP-ribose antagonist 8-amino-cADP-ribose[27,28,50–52] (A7621). 8-Amino-cADP-ribose has been shown both to block binding of radiolabeled cADP-ribose to sea urchin egg microsomes and to inhibit cADP-ribose–mediated release of Ca^{2+} from egg homogenates, but it does not block caffeine- or ryanodine-induced Ca^{2+} release.

Ryanodine and Fluorescent Ryanodine

Ryanodine is a plant alkaloid that mobilizes Ca^{2+} from intracellular stores by activating a class of Ins 1,4,5-P_3–insensitive Ca^{2+} channels.[53] It alters the function of the Ca^{2+} channel in a complex manner: submicromolar concentrations lock the channel in a long-lived open state, whereas micromolar or greater concentrations inhibit Ca^{2+} release.[54,55] Ryanodine can be used to modulate the Ca^{2+} concentration in sea urchin eggs[39] and in parotid acinar cells.[56] In developing skeletal muscle, ryanodine receptors localize in discrete regions of the T tubules, binding at the junctional complex between the T tubules and the sarcoplasmic reticulum.[57]

Unlabeled "ryanodine" from most other commercial sources is an almost equimolar mixture of ryanodine and dehydroryanodine; however, Molecular Probes offers HPLC-purified ryanodine (R7478, Figure 17.3) that is >95% pure.

In addition to unlabeled ryanodine, we have prepared a monosubstituted BODIPY® FL-X derivative (B7505), which is a mixture of BODIPY® FL-X ryanodine and BODIPY® FL-X dehydroryanodine, most likely labeled at the 10 position of the ryanodine molecule (Figure 16.39). Structurally similar BODIPY® ryanodines were shown to have a dissociation constant near that of ryanodine.[58,59] BODIPY® FL-X ryanodine has been used to visualize ryanodine receptor distribution in live porcine endothelial cells,[60] in pancreatic β-cells,[61] in vascular myocytes,[62] in cardiomyocytes,[63] in frog sympathetic neurons [64,65] and in the rat parotid gland.[66]

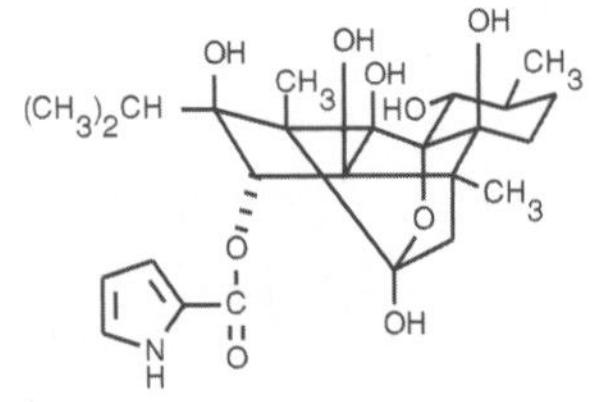

Figure 17.3 R7478 ryanodine.

Caged Ca^{2+} and Caged Ca^{2+} Chelators

Caged ions and caged chelators can be used to influence the ionic composition of both solutions and cells, particularly for ions such as Ca^{2+} that are present at low concentrations. The properties and uses of caged probes are described in Section 5.3.

NP-EGTA: A Caged Ca^{2+} Reagent

Ellis-Davies and Kaplan have developed a photolabile chelator — *o*-nitrophenyl EGTA (NP-EGTA) — that exhibits a high selectivity for Ca^{2+}, a dramatic 12,500-fold *decrease* in affinity for Ca^{2+} upon UV illumination (its K_d increases from 80 nM to >1 mM) and a high photochemical quantum yield[67,68] (~0.2). Furthermore, with a K_d for Mg^{2+} of 9 mM, NP-caged EGTA does not perturb physiological levels of Mg^{2+}. We offer the potassium salt (N6802) and the acetoxymethyl (AM) ester (N6803) of NP-EGTA. The NP-EGTA salt can be complexed with Ca^{2+} to generate a caged calcium complex that will rapidly deliver Ca^{2+} upon photolysis (Figure 17.4). The cell-permeant AM ester of NP-EGTA does not bind Ca^{2+} unless the AM esters are removed. It can potentially serve as a photolabile buffer in cells because, once converted to NP-EGTA by intracellular esterases, it will bind Ca^{2+} with high affinity until photolyzed with UV light. NP-EGTA has been used to measure the calcium buffering capacity of cells.[69] We have loaded similar chelators into cells with our Influx™ pinocytic cell-loading reagent (I14402, Section 19.8).

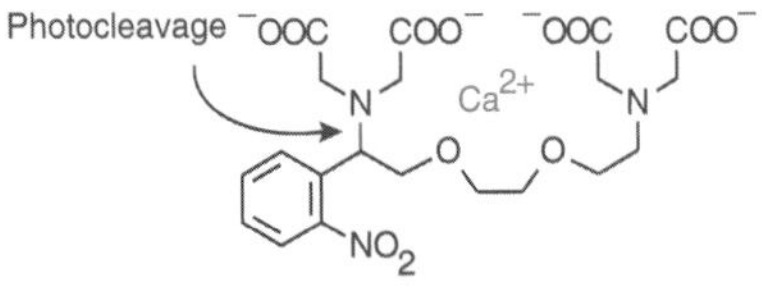

Figure 17.4 NP-EGTA (N6802) complexed with Ca^{2+}. Upon illumination, this complex is cleaved to yield free Ca^{2+} and two iminodiacetic acid photoproducts. The affinity of the photoproducts for Ca^{2+} is ~12,500-fold lower than that of NP-EGTA.

DMNP-EDTA: A Caged Ca^{2+} Reagent

The first caged Ca^{2+} reagent described by Ellis-Davies and Kaplan was 1-(4,5-dimethoxy-2-nitrophenyl) EDTA (DMNP-EDTA, D6814), which they named DM-Nitrophen [70,71] (now a trademark of Calbiochem-Novabiochem Corp.). Because its structure better resembles that of EDTA than EGTA, we named it as a caged EDTA derivative (Figure 17.5). Upon illumination, DMNP-EDTA's K_d for Ca^{2+} increases from 5 nM to 3 mM. Thus, photolysis of DMNP-EDTA complexed with Ca^{2+} results in a pulse of free Ca^{2+}. Furthermore, DMNP-EDTA has significantly higher affinity for Mg^{2+} (K_d = 2.5 µM) than does NP-EGTA [70] (K_d = 9 mM). The photolysis product's K_d for Mg^{2+} is ~3 mM, making DMNP-EDTA an effective caged Mg^{2+} source, in addition to its applications for photolytic Ca^{2+} release.[72,73] Photorelease of Ca^{2+} has been shown to occur in <180 microseconds, with even faster photorelease of Mg^{2+}.[74] A paper by Neher and Zucker discusses the uses and limitations of DMNP-EDTA.[73] In addition to high-purity DMNP-EDTA (D6814), we have prepared its membrane-permeant acetoxymethyl (AM) ester (D6815).

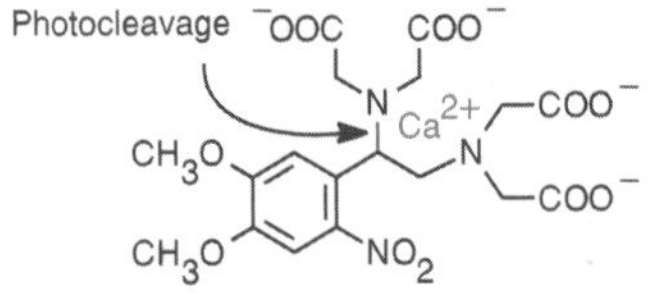

Figure 17.5 DMNP-EDTA (D6814) complexed with Ca^{2+}. Upon illumination, this complex is cleaved to yield free Ca^{2+} and two iminodiacetic acid photoproducts. The affinity of the photoproducts for Ca^{2+} is ~600,000-fold lower than that of DMNP-EDTA.

Diazo-2: A Photoactivatable Ca^{2+} Scavenger

In contrast to NP-EGTA and DMNP-EDTA, diazo-2 is a photoactivatable Ca^{2+} scavenger. Diazo-2 (Figure 5.20), which was introduced by Adams, Kao and Tsien,[75,76] is a relatively weak chelator (K_d for Ca^{2+} = 2.2 µM). However, following flash photolysis at ~360 nm, cytosolic free Ca^{2+} rapidly binds to the diazo-2 photolysis product, which has a high affinity for Ca^{2+} (K_d = 73 nM). Photolysis of diazo-2 has been used to *decrease* cytosolic Ca^{2+} in less than two milliseconds in tensed frog muscle cells [77] and rabbit arterial smooth muscle.[78] Microinjecting a relatively low concentration of fluo-3, fluo-4, or one of the Calcium Green™ or Oregon Green® 488 BAPTA indicators (Section 19.3), along with a known quantity of diazo-2, permits measurement of the

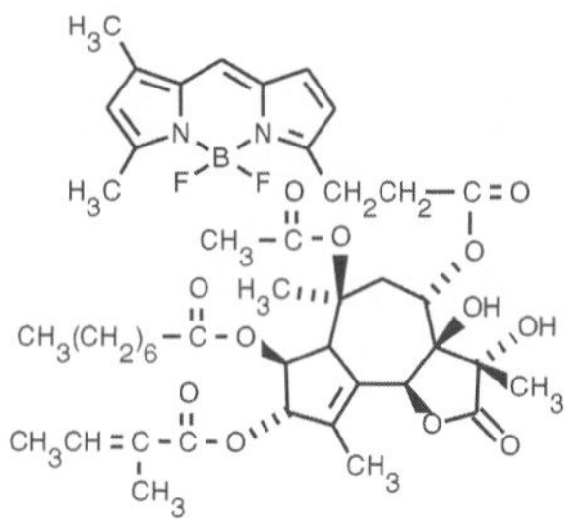

Figure 17.6 B7487 BODIPY® FL thapsigargin.

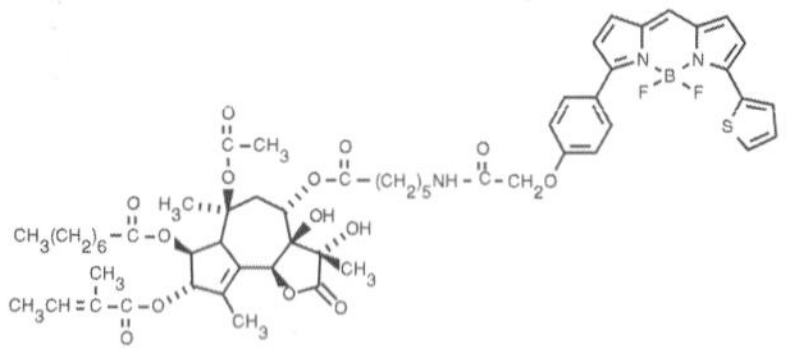

Figure 17.7 B13800 BODIPY® TR-X thapsigargin.

extent of depletion of cytosolic Ca^{2+} following photolysis.[76,79,80] Diazo-2 can be microinjected into cells as its potassium salt (D3034) or utilized as its cell membrane–permeant acetoxymethyl ester (diazo-2, AM; D3036). Diazo-2 also has been loaded into cells permeabilized with *Staphylococcus aureus* α-toxin[78] and can probably be loaded into cells using our Influx™ pinocytic cell-loading reagent (I14402, Section 19.8).

Other Probes for Calcium Regulation

Thapsigargin and Fluorescent Thapsigargin

Thapsigargin is a naturally occurring sesquiterpene lactone isolated from the umbelliferous plant *Thapsia garganica*.[81] This tumor promoter releases Ca^{2+} from intracellular stores by specifically inhibiting the endoplasmic reticulum Ca^{2+}-ATPase;[82,83] it does not directly affect plasma membrane Ca^{2+}-ATPases, Ins 1,4,5-P_3 production or protein kinase C activity.[84,85] Reports have described the effects of thapsigargin-induced Ca^{2+} signals on the transient suppression of c-*myb* mRNA levels,[86] as well as the regulation of such Ca^{2+} signals by sphingomyelinase and sphingosine.[87] Thapsigargin is available from Molecular Probes in 1 mg units (T7458) and specially packaged in 20 vials containing 50 µg each (T7459). We have prepared the green-fluorescent BODIPY® FL thapsigargin[63,88] (B7487, Figure 17.6) and red-fluorescent BODIPY® TR-X thapsigargin[89] (B13800, Figure 17.7). These membrane-permeant probes have spectral properties similar to those of fluorescein and the Texas Red® dye, respectively, and may be useful for localization of thapsigargin binding sites in live cells.

Luminescent Calcium Analog

The trivalent lanthanide terbium (III), which is supplied by Molecular Probes as its chloride salt (T1247), is a luminescent analog of Ca^{2+} that can be used to study structure–function relationships in Ca^{2+}-binding proteins such as calmodulin (C23693, Section 17.3), oncomodulin, lactalbumin and ATPases.[90–92] The long-lived luminescence of Tb^{3+} has also been use to probe Ca^{2+}-binding sites of alkaline phosphatase,[93] glutamine synthetase,[94] integrins,[90] protein kinase C[95] and Ca^{2+}-binding sites of ryanodine-sensitive Ca^{2+} channels.[96] Tb^{3+} reportedly binds most strongly to the I and II sites of calmodulin.[97]

References

1. Nat Rev Mol Cell Biol 2, 327 (2001); **2.** Annu Rev Physiol 56, 297 (1994); **3.** Nature 365, 388 (1993); **4.** Nature 341, 197 (1989); **5.** Annu Rev Biochem 56, 159 (1987); **6.** J Physiol 487, 343 (1995); **7.** Neuron 15, 755 (1995); **8.** Nature 372, 231 (1994); **9.** J Biol Chem 267, 8857 (1992); **10.** Biochem J 302, 155 (1994); **11.** J Biol Chem 273, 34730 (1998); **12.** Biochemistry 31, 5996 (1992); **13.** Biochim Biophys Acta 1167, 211 (1993); **14.** Biochemistry 27, 7565 (1988); **15.** Biochemistry 32, 12548 (1993); **16.** J Biol Chem 260, 7250 (1985); **17.** Anal Biochem 156, 320 (1986); **18.** Biochemistry 31, 6498 (1992); **19.** Cytometry 23, 59 (1996); **20.** Biol Pharm Bull 16, 939 (1993); **21.** Anal Biochem 160, 105 (1987); **22.** Biochim Biophys Acta 925, 57 (1987); **23.** Anal Biochem 130, 287 (1983); **24.** Carbohydr Res 105, 69 (1982); **25.** FASEB J 14, 680 (2000); **26.** Nature 398, 70 (1999); **27.** Physiol Rev 77, 1133 (1997); **28.** J Biol Chem 270, 25488 (1995); **29.** J Biol Chem 270, 9060 (1995); **30.** Cell Signal 6, 591 (1994); **31.** Mol Cell Biochem 138, 229 (1994); **32.** Science 278, 2126 (1997); **33.** J Biol Chem 270, 17917 (1995); **34.** Pflugers Arch 429, 426 (1995); **35.** Neuron 12, 1073 (1994); **36.** Nature 364, 76 (1993); **37.** Nature 370, 307 (1994); **38.** Biochemistry 34, 2815 (1995); **39.** Science 253, 1143 (1991); **40.** J Biol Chem 264, 1608 (1989); **41.** Dev Biol 163, 1 (1994); **42.** J Biol Chem 270, 30257 (1995); **43.** J Biol Chem 270, 30045 (1995); **44.** Biochimie 77, 356 (1995); **45.** Science 259, 370 (1993); **46.** Cell 80, 439 (1995); **47.** EMBO J 13, 2038 (1994); **48.** J Biol Chem 270, 7745 (1995); **49.** Biochim Biophys Acta 1472, 555 (1999); **50.** Am J Physiol 274, C1653 (1998); **51.** J Biol Chem 273, 2497 (1998); **52.** Biochemistry 35, 10922 (1996); **53.** J Biol Chem 268, 13765 (1993); **54.** J Gen Physiol 92, 1 (1988); **55.** Am J Physiol 253, C364 (1987); **56.** J Biol Chem 266, 14535 (1991); **57.** J Cell Biol 112, 289 (1991); **58.** J Biol Chem 269, 30243 (1994); **59.** Biochemistry 33, 6074 (1994); **60.** J Physiol 506, 109 (1998); **61.** J Biol Chem 274, 14147 (1999); **62.** J Biol Chem 275, 9596 (2000); **63.** Cell Calcium 28, 127 (2000); **64.** J Neurosci 20, 9059 (2000); **65.** J Gen Physiol 116, 697 (2000); **66.** Biochem J 340, 519 (1999); **67.** J Biol Chem 270, 23966 (1995); **68.** Proc Natl Acad Sci U S A 91, 187 (1994); **69.** Biochem Biophys Res Commun 250, 786 (1998); **70.** Proc Natl Acad Sci U S A 85, 6571 (1988); **71.** Science 241, 842 (1988); **72.** Methods Cell Biol 40, 31 (1994); **73.** Neuron 10, 21 (1993); **74.** Biochemistry 31, 8856 (1992); **75.** Biochim Biophys Acta 1035, 378 (1990); **76.** J Am Chem Soc 111, 7957 (1989); **77.** FEBS Lett 255, 1 (1989); **78.** Biophys J 69, 2611 (1995); **79.** Nature 371, 603 (1994); **80.** Biophys J 65, 2537 (1993); **81.** Acta Pharm Suec 15, 133 (1978); **82.** J Biol Chem 273, 12994 (1998); **83.** J Biol Chem 270, 11731 (1995); **84.** Proc Natl Acad Sci U S A 87, 2466 (1990); **85.** J Biol Chem 264, 12266 (1989); **86.** J Biol Chem 269, 8786 (1994); **87.** J Biol Chem 269, 5054 (1994); **88.** Biochem J 325, 239 (1997); **89.** J Biol Chem 274, 32535 (1999); **90.** Biochemistry 33, 12238 (1994); **91.** J Biol Chem 267, 13340 (1992); **92.** Photochem Photobiol 46, 1067 (1987); **93.** J Photochem Photobiol B 13, 289 (1992); **94.** Biochemistry 30, 3417 (1991); **95.** J Biol Chem 263, 4223 (1988); **96.** J Biol Chem 269, 24864 (1994); **97.** Biochem Biophys Res Commun 138, 1243 (1986).

Data Table — 17.2 Calcium Regulation

Cat #	MW	Storage	Soluble	Abs	EC	Em	Solvent	Notes
A7621	556.32	FF,D	H_2O	274	14,000	none	pH 7	
B7487	854.75	FF,D,L	DMSO	503	85,000	511	MeOH	
B7505	880.79	FF,D,L	DMSO	504	79,000	511	MeOH	
B13800	1100.04	FF,D,L	DMSO	589	62,000	616	MeOH	
C7074	690.45	FF,D,LL	H_2O	259	16,000	none	H_2O	1, 2
C7619	541.30	FF,D	H_2O	258	9,900	none	pH 7	
D3034	710.86	F,D,LL	pH >6	369	18,000	none	pH 7.2	1, 3, 4
D3036	846.75	F,D,LL	DMSO	342	22,000	none	MeOH	
D6814	473.39	D,LL	DMSO	348	4,200	none	pH 7.2	1, 4, 5
D6815	761.65	F,D,LL	DMSO	333	4,600	none	MeOH	6
D23650	540.32	F,D	H_2O	265	11,000	none	pH 7	
E6960	366.41	D	H_2O	337	17,000	613	H_2O	7, 8
H7482	~18,000	FF,D,L	H_2O	493	ND	514	pH 8	9, 10
I3716	648.64	F,D	H_2O	<250		none		
I23580	872.82	FF,D,LL	H_2O	264	4,200	none	H_2O	1, 2, 11
N6802	653.81	FF,D,LL	pH >6	260	3,500	none	pH 7.2	1, 2, 4, 12
N6803	789.70	FF,D,LL	DMSO	250	4,200	none	MeCN	6, 13
N7622	744.39	FF,D	H_2O	254	17,000	none	H_2O	
R7478	493.55	F,D	MeOH, DMSO	<300		none		
T1247	373.38	D	H_2O	270	4,700	545	H_2O	8, 14
T7458	650.76	F,D	DMSO, EtOH	<300		none		
T7459	650.76	F,D	DMSO, EtOH	<300		none		

For definitions of the contents of this data table, see "Navigating *The Handbook*" in the introductory pages.

Notes

1. All photoactivatable probes are sensitive to light. They should be protected from illumination except when photolysis is intended.
2. This compound has weaker visible absorption at >300 nm but no discernible absorption peaks in this region.
3. The Ca^{2+} dissociation constant of diazo-2 is 2200 nM before photolysis and 73 nM after ultraviolet photolysis. The absorption spectrum of the photolysis product is similar to that of B1204 (J Am Chem Soc 111, 7957 (1989)).
4. Abs and EC values determined in Ca^{2+}-free solution (100 mM KCl, 10 mM EGTA, 10 mM MOPS, pH 7.2).
5. $K_d(Ca^{2+})$ increases from 5 nM to 3 mM after ultraviolet photolysis. K_d values determined in 130 mM KCl, 10 mM HEPES, pH 7.1 (Proc Natl Acad Sci U S A 85, 6571 (1988)).
6. This product is intrinsically a liquid or an oil at room temperature.
7. Absorption and luminescence of E6960 are extremely weak unless it is chelated. Data are for the detergent-solubilized NTA (T411) chelate.
8. MW is for the hydrated form of this product.
9. ND = not determined.
10. This product is a multiply labeled bioconjugate. The number of labels per conjugate is indicated on the vial.
11. Ultraviolet photolysis of I23580 generates I3716.
12. $K_d (Ca^{2+})$ increases from 80 nM to 1 mM after ultraviolet photolysis. K_d values determined in 100 mM KCl, 40 mM HEPES, pH 7.2 (Proc Natl Acad Sci U S A 91, 187 (1994)).
13. N6803 is converted to N6802 via hydrolysis of its acetoxymethyl ester (AM) groups.
14. Absorption and luminescence of T1247 are extremely weak unless it is chelated. Data are for dipicolinic acid (DPA) chelate. The luminescence spectrum has secondary peak at 490 nm.

Product List — 17.2 Calcium Regulation

Cat #	Product Name	Unit Size
A7621	8-amino-cyclic adenosine 5′-diphosphate ribose (8-amino-cADP-ribose)	10 µg
B7487	BODIPY® FL thapsigargin	100 µg
B7505	BODIPY® FL-X ryanodine	25 µg
B13800	BODIPY® TR-X thapsigargin	25 µg
C7619	cyclic adenosine 5′-diphosphate ribose (cADP-ribose)	100 µg
C7074	cyclic adenosine 5′-diphosphate ribose, 1-(1-(2-nitrophenyl)ethyl) ester (NPE-caged cADP-ribose) *mixed isomers*	50 µg
D23650	3-deaza-cyclic adenosine 5′-diphosphate ribose (3-deaza-cADP-ribose)	5 µg
D3036	diazo-2, AM *cell permeant* *special packaging*	20 x 50 µg
D3034	diazo-2, tetrapotassium salt *cell impermeant*	1 mg
D6814	1-(4,5-dimethoxy-2-nitrophenyl)-1,2-diaminoethane-*N,N,N′,N′*-tetraacetic acid (DMNP-EDTA) *cell impermeant*	5 mg
D6815	1-(4,5-dimethoxy-2-nitrophenyl)-1,2-diaminoethane-*N,N,N′,N′*-tetraacetic acid, tetra(acetoxymethyl ester) (DMNP-EDTA, AM) *cell permeant* *special packaging*	20 x 50 µg
E6960	europium(III) chloride, hexahydrate *99.99%*	1 g
H7482	heparin, fluorescein conjugate	1 mg
I3716	D-*myo*-inositol 1,4,5-triphosphate, hexapotassium salt (Ins 1,4,5-P_3)	1 mg
I23580	D-*myo*-inositol 1,4,5-triphosphate, $P_{4(5)}$-(1-(2-nitrophenyl)ethyl) ester, tris(triethylammonium) salt (NPE-caged Ins 1,4,5-P_3)	25 µg
N7622	β-nicotinic acid adenine dinucleotide phosphate (NAADP)	10 µg
N6803	*o*-nitrophenyl EGTA, AM (NP-EGTA, AM) *cell permeant* *special packaging*	20 x 50 µg
N6802	*o*-nitrophenyl EGTA, tetrapotassium salt (NP-EGTA) *cell impermeant*	1 mg
R7478	ryanodine *free of dehydroryanodine*	1 mg
T1247	terbium(III) chloride, hexahydrate	1 g
T7458	thapsigargin	1 mg
T7459	thapsigargin *special packaging*	20 x 50 µg

For current prices or to order online, visit probes.invitrogen.com

17.3 Probes for Protein Kinases, Protein Phosphatases and Nucleotide-Binding Proteins

The cascade of events that culminates in cellular response to an internal signal or environmental stimulus requires numerous molecular participants, ranging from ions to enzymes. Signal transduction pathways frequently activate specific protein kinases, leading to the phosphorylation of particular cellular proteins and subsequent initiation of a multitude of diverse cellular responses. Binding and hydrolysis of nucleotides plays a major role in these activities, and our nucleotide analogs and assays for phosphate-producing enzymes are important tools for signal transduction research and high-throughput screening of compounds that affect signal transduction. Molecular Probes offers a selection of native and modified biomolecules to aid the researcher in dissecting this highly complex branch of the signal transduction process. In addition to the probes below, we have developed the P_iPer™ and EnzChek® assay kits for quantitation of inorganic phosphate and pyrophosphate that are extremely useful for following hydrolysis of nucleotides by various enzymes and of phosphate esters by protein phosphatases. These kits and other kits to measure ATP by chemiluminescence and protein phosphatase activity are described in Section 10.3.

Protein Kinase C

Protein kinase C (PKC) is a key player in many transmembrane signal transduction systems.[1–5] This Ca^{2+}-dependent serine/threonine protein kinase is activated in the presence of certain membrane-derived lipids such as diacylglycerols and phosphatidyl serines, phosphorylating a wide variety of substrates, including ion-channel proteins and cytoskeletal proteins. Molecular Probes offers a highly purified preparation of PKC holoenzyme (P7432), which is prepared from rat brain using ion-exchange and affinity chromatography.[6,7] These chromatographic techniques yield an enzyme preparation that is >95% pure by gel electrophoresis and contains the α-, β- and γ-isoforms (77,000–80,000 daltons). Purified PKC can be used to identify substrates, to determine the state of phosphorylation of PKC substrates and to serve as a positive control in PKC assays.[3,5]

Protein Kinase Inhibitors

A Fluorescent Bisindolylmaleimide: Fim-1

Bisindolylmaleimides selectively inhibit PKC by binding to the enzyme's catalytic domain. To monitor PKC activation and translocation from the cytoplasm to membranes, Chen and Poenie have developed fluorescent derivatives of bisindolylmaleimides.[8] Molecular Probes offers fim-1 (F7462, Figure 17.8), a fluorescein-conjugated bisindolylmaleimide, and fim-1 diacetate (F7453), its membrane-permeant derivative.

Fim-1 has been shown to be an effective inhibitor of PKC and to exhibit 16-fold selectivity for PKC over PKA. Enzyme kinetic analysis has demonstrated that fim-1 inhibits PKC by competing with ATP and not with phosphatidylserine or diacylglycerol, which is consistent with its binding at the catalytic domain rather than the regulatory domain.[8,9] Using fixed and permeabilized cells, Chen and Poenie have shown that the pattern of staining produced by fim-1 is very similar to that of an anti-PKC antibody, except that the fluorescent inhibitor also appeared to stain mitochondria; this mitochondrial staining is not yet understood.[8] Fim-1 has significant potential for monitoring PKC activity in live cells.[9–11]

Fluorescent Polymyxin B Analogs

Polymyxin B is a cyclic polycationic peptide antibiotic that binds to anionic lipids. It is also a selective inhibitor of protein kinase C[12–15] (IC_{50} ~35 µM). Other direct and indirect biological effects of polymyxin B include induction of apoptosis,[16–18] blocking the effect of endotoxins,[19,20] modulation of K^+-ATP channels,[21] inhibition of the effect of phorbol ester–stimulated superoxide release,[22] inhibition of sarcoplasmic reticulum Ca^{2+}-ATPase[23] and inhibition of insulin secretion.[24] Polymyxin B is also reported to be a potent inhibitor of calmodulin (C23693), with an IC_{50} of 80 nM in the presence of 500 µM Ca^{2+}.[25]

Our fluorescent polymyxin B analogs include those of the green-fluorescent BODIPY® FL and Oregon Green® 514 fluorophores (P13235, P13236) and the red-fluorescent Texas Red®-X dye (P13237), as well as the previously known dansyl polymyxin[26,27] (P13238).

Hypericin and Hypocrellins A and B

Hypericin (H7476, Figure 17.9), a natural pigment isolated from plants of the genus *Hypericum*,[28] is a potent, selective inhibitor of PKC (IC_{50} = 1.7 µg/mL = 3.4 µM) that should be useful for probing and manipulating PKC in live cells.[29,30] When compared with other PKC probes, this aromatic polycyclic dione offers several advantages, including bright red fluorescence emission and exceptional photosta-

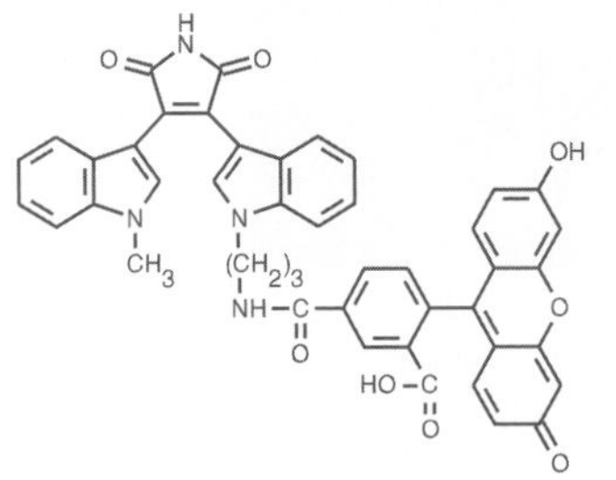

Figure 17.8 F7462 fim-1.

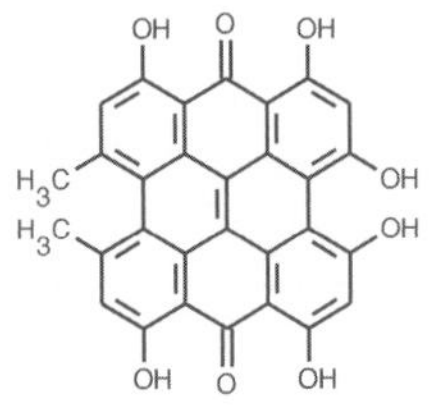

Figure 17.9 H7476 hypericin.

bility. Furthermore, hypericin exhibits light-induced inhibition of PKC,[28,29] thus providing the researcher with another level of control in manipulating and evaluating PKC activity and distribution. Hypericin has a variety of pharmacological properties, from antibacterial and antineoplastic activities to antiviral activities[30–33] and induction of apoptosis.[34,35] Hypericin is a potent photosensitizer, with a quantum yield of 0.75 for the generation of singlet oxygen.[36]

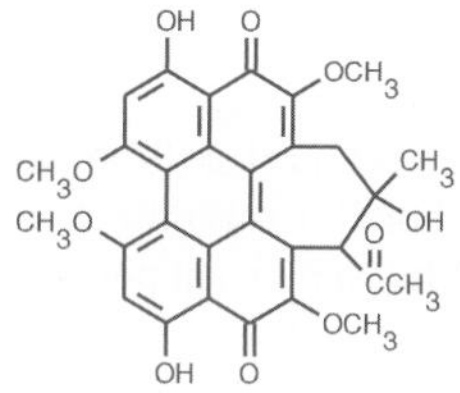

Figure 17.10 H7515 hypocrellin A.

We also offer the structurally similar reagents hypocrellin A (H7515, Figure 17.10) and hypocrellin B (H7516, Figure 17.11), which have been shown to be selective and potent inhibitors of PKC, with IC_{50} values of 3.6 and 9.0 µM, respectively.[37,38] Like hypericin, PKC inhibition by hypocrellins is light dependent. The extremely broad absorption spectra of hypocrellins make them readily excited by a variety of light sources.[39] These chemically stable, fluorescent photosensitizers have quantum yields for singlet-oxygen generation in excess of 0.7.[39,40] In addition to their utility as probes, they may serve as building blocks for preparing antiviral and anticancer agents.[38,41–43]

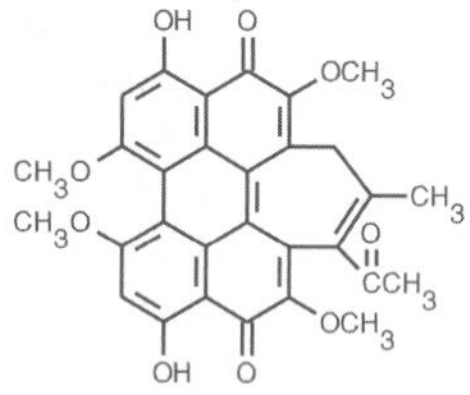

Figure 17.11 H7516 hypocrellin B.

Antibody against a CaM Kinase II Substrate, Synapsin I

Ca^{2+}/calmodulin-dependent kinase II (CaM kinase II) is a multifunctional kinase found in most, if not all, tissues. It regulates a number of cellular functions, including neurotransmitter synthesis and release, gene expression, carbohydrate metabolism, cytoskeletal function and Ca^{2+} homeostasis.[44–49] CaM kinase II, which phosphorylates the Ins 1,4,5-P_3 receptor,[50] is reported to be essential for the cADP-ribose–mediated Ca^{2+} mobilization that is required for insulin secretion by pancreatic β-islet cells.[51]

Synapsin I is a synaptic vesicle–associated protein that inhibits neurotransmitter release, a function that is abolished upon its phosphorylation by CaM kinase II.[52] Calmodulin (C23693) also influences synapsin's function indirectly by activating CaM kinases and directly by binding to synapsin and potentiating the effects of phosphorylation.[53–55] Unphosphorylated synapsin I is able to promote actin polymerization and bundling of actin filaments in the presence of synaptic vesicles.[56,57] Upon membrane polarization and activation of protein kinases, synapsin becomes phosphorylated, which reduces its affinity for actin and disrupts the actin network that has been constraining the synaptic vesicles. These synaptic vesicles then migrate to the presynaptic membrane, where they undergo membrane fusion and release the neurotransmitter.[58,59]

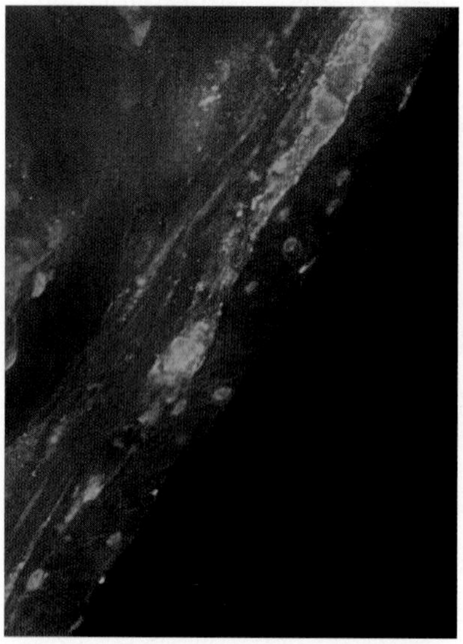

Figure 17.12 Peripheral neurons in mouse intestinal cryosections were labeled with rabbit anti–synapsin I antibody (A6442) and detected using Alexa Fluor® 488 goat anti–rabbit IgG antibody (A11008). This tissue was counterstained with DAPI (D1306, D3571, D21490).

Synapsin is localized exclusively to synaptic vesicles and thus serves as an excellent marker for synapses in brain and other neuronal tissue.[60,61] Antibodies directed against synapsin I have proven valuable in molecular and neurobiology research, for example to estimate synaptic density and to follow synaptogenesis.[62–64] Molecular Probes offers a rabbit polyclonal anti–bovine synapsin I as an affinity-purified IgG fraction (A6442). This antibody was isolated from rabbits immunized against bovine brain synapsin I, but it is also active against human, rat and mouse forms of the antigen; it has little or no activity against synapsin II. Affinity-purified anti–synapsin I antibody is suitable for immunohistochemistry (Figure 17.12), Western blots, enzyme-linked immunosorbent assays (ELISAs) and immunoprecipitation. Our Zenon® Rabbit IgG Labeling Kits (Section 7.3, Table 7.13) can be used to prepare fluorescent dye– or enzyme-labeled complexes of this antibody.

Calmodulin and Calmodulin Conjugates

Calmodulin (C23693) is a heat-stable, calcium-binding protein that is present in all eukaryotic cells. It mediates many of the regulatory functions of calcium ions.[65–67] Calmodulin has also been identified as a regulator for the activity of smooth muscle myosin light chain kinase[68,69] (MLCK). The feasibility of using fluorescently labeled calmodulin to study the *in vivo* behavior of the protein has been well documented in:

- Visualizing calmodulin localization in fertilized sea urchin eggs[70]
- Identifying calmodulin-binding sites on mitochondria in cultured 3T3 cells[71]
- Studying the dynamics of calmodulin in the mammalian mitotic spindle[72,73]
- Observing the distribution of calmodulin and tubulin in the meiotic apparatus of mouse oocytes[74]
- Examining the mechanism of localization of calmodulin to the mitotic apparatus during the first cell cycle of the sea urchin embryo[75]

In vitro, fluorescently labeled calmodulin has been used for:

- Following the binding of calmodulin to protein kinase substrates [76]
- Studying the interactions of myogenic basic helix-loop-helix transcription factors with calmodulin [77]
- Investigating the molecular mechanisms for calmodulin trapping by Ca^{2+}/calmodulin-dependent protein kinase II [78,79]
- Characterizing inhibitors of calmodulin activation of MLCK-catalyzed phosphorylation of the smooth muscle regulatory chain [80]

Our high-purity, unlabeled calmodulin from bovine brain (C23693) and Alexa Fluor® 488 and Alexa Fluor® 594 conjugates of calmodulin (C13844, C13845) should prove to be useful for both cellular and solution studies. The superior brightness and photostability of the Alexa Fluor® dyes (Section 1.3) will be particularly beneficial for localization studies by confocal laser-scanning microscopy. Our unlabeled calmodulin gives a single band on SDS-polyacrylamide gel electrophoresis and binds to and activates MLCK with a 1:1 stoichiometry and high affinity.

Antibody Beacon™ Tyrosine Kinase Assay Kit: Real-Time Measurement of Tyrosine Kinase Activity

Tyrosine kinases are critical players in signal transduction pathways; however, the fluorometric assay of all kinases has been difficult because phosphorylation of the target by the combination of ATP and a fluorescent peptide target does not lead to appreciable changes in the fluorescence of any product. Previous attempts to develop fluorometric assays for kinases have typically utilized synthetic peptides labeled with an environment-sensitive fluorescent dye, which, after considerable trial and error in substrate selection, may exhibit an adventitious but small fluorescence change (either up or down) results upon phosphorylation. Molecular Probes has discovered a unique and general method for the continuous assay of most or all tyrosine kinases that promises to be very useful for both routine laboratory use and high-throughput screening applications. Moreover, this method utilizes the natural, unlabeled target peptide or protein, which yields results that may be more relevant to the researcher.

The Antibody Beacon™ Tyrosine Kinase Assay Kit (A35725) provides a simple yet robust solution assay for measuring the activity of tyrosine kinases (Figure 10.48) and the effectiveness of potential inhibitors and modulators (Figure 10.49). The key to this tyrosine kinase assay is a small-molecule tracer ligand labeled with our bright green-fluorescent Oregon Green® 488 dye. When an anti-phosphotyrosine antibody binds this tracer ligand to form the Antibody Beacon™ detection complex, the fluorescence of the Oregon Green® 488 dye is efficiently quenched. In the presence of a phosphotyrosine-containing peptide, however, this Antibody Beacon™ detection complex is rapidly disrupted, releasing the tracer ligand and relieving its antibody-induced quenching. Upon its displacement by a phosphotyrosine residue, the Oregon Green® 488 dye–labeled tracer ligand exhibits an approximately fourfold enhancement in its fluorescence, enabling the detection of as little as 50 nM phosphotyrosine-containing peptide with excellent signal-to-background discrimination (Figure 10.50).

We have optimized each component of this kit in order to provide minimal background fluorescence, maximal displacement of the tracer ligand and a large fluorescence enhancement upon the ligand's release. Key benefits of the Antibody Beacon™ Tyrosine Kinase Assay Kit include:

- **Real-time measurements.** Unlike many other commercially available tyrosine kinase assays, the Antibody Beacon™ Tyrosine Kinase Assay Kit permits real-time monitoring of kinase activity (Figure 10.51). Not only is the Antibody Beacon™ detection complex rapidly dissociated in the presence of phosphotyrosine residues, but the assay components have been designed to be simultaneously combined, eliminating any delay in the measurements.
- **Simple detection protocol.** Tyrosine kinase activity is measured by a simple increase in fluorescence intensity; no special equipment, additional reagents, or extra steps are required. The absorption and emission spectra of the Oregon Green® 488 dye perfectly match those of fluorescein, making this assay readily compatible with any fluorescence microplate reader.
- **Use of natural substrates.** The Antibody Beacon™ tyrosine kinase assay utilizes unlabeled peptides or proteins (provided by the user) and is applicable to the assay of a wide variety of kinases.
- **Compatibility.** The anti-phosphotyrosine antibody provided in the Antibody Beacon™ Tyrosine Kinase Assay Kit is specific for phosphotyrosine residues; coexisting assay components such as ATP (up to 1 mM) and reducing agents such as dithiothreitol (DTT, up to 1 mM) do not interfere with this assay. This anti-phosphotyrosine antibody was selected from among several clones to produce the greatest fluorescence enhancement by the kinase-phosphorylated product.
- **Reliability.** This tyrosine kinase assay has a broad signal window, indicated by a Z′ factor [81] of >0.85.

The Antibody Beacon™ Tyrosine Kinase Assay Kit comes with all the reagents needed to perform this assay right out of the box, including:

- Oregon Green® 488 dye–labeled tracer ligand
- Anti-phosphotyrosine antibody
- Concentrated tyrosine kinase reaction buffer
- Two generic tyrosine kinase substrate solutions: a poly(Glu:Tyr) solution and a poly(Glu:Ala:Tyr) solution
- Dithiothreitol (DTT)
- Adenosine triphosphate (ATP)
- Phosphotyrosine-containing peptide, phospho-pp60 c-src (521–533), for use as a reference

Each kit provides sufficient reagents to perform ~400 assays using a 50 µL assay volume in a fluorescence microplate reader.

Pro-Q® Diamond Phosphoprotein/Phosphopeptide Microarray Stain Kit

The Pro-Q® Diamond Phosphoprotein/Phosphopeptide Microarray Stain Kit (P33706) provides a method for selective staining of phosphoproteins or phosphopeptides on microarrays, without the use of antibodies or radioactivity. This kit permits direct detection of phosphate groups attached to tyrosine, serine or threonine residues in a microarray environment and has been optimized for microarrays with acrylamide gel surfaces. Each Pro-Q® Diamond Phosphoprotein/Phosphopeptide Microarray Stain Kit provides:

- Pro-Q® Diamond phosphoprotein/phosphopeptide microarray stain
- Pro-Q® Diamond microarray destain solution
- Microarray staining gasket with seal tabs, 10 chambers
- Slide holder tube, 20 tubes
- Detailed protocols

The Pro-Q® Diamond Phosphoprotein/Phosphopeptide Microarray Stain Kit is ideal for identifying kinase targets in signal transduction pathways and for phosphoproteomics studies.

RediPlate™ EnzChek® Phosphatase Assay Kits for Signal Transduction

RediPlate™ 96 and RediPlate™ 384 EnzChek® Tyrosine Phosphatase Assay Kits

Protein tyrosine phosphatases (PTP) represent a large family of enzymes that play a very important role in intra- and intercellular signaling. PTPs work antagonistically with protein tyrosine kinases to regulate signal transduction pathways in response to a variety of signals, including hormones and mitogens.[82–84] Our RediPlate™ 96 and RediPlate™ 384 EnzChek® Tyrosine Phosphatase Assay Kits (R22067, R22068) provide researchers with a sensitive and convenient means to monitor PTP and screen PTP inhibitors for a variety of research areas (Figure 10.43), including:

- Insulin regulation[85–87]
- Cell proliferation and differentiation[88]
- Axonal outgrowth[89,90]
- Immune response and inflammation[91]
- Angiogenesis[92]

Our tyrosine phosphatase assay is based on our patented 6,8-difluoro-4-methylumbelliferyl phosphate (DiFMUP, D6567, D22065; Section 10.3), an acid and alkaline phosphatase substrate whose hydrolysis product (6,8-difluoro-7-hydroxy-4-methylcoumarin, DiFMU; D6566, Section 10.1, Figure 10.3) exhibits excitation/emission maxima of ~358/455 nm (Figure 10.2), a low pK_a (~4.9, Figure 1.96) and a high quantum yield (~0.89). Unlike other end-point tyrosine phosphatase assay kits, the EnzChek® tyrosine phosphatase assay is continuous, allowing researchers to easily measure fluorescence at various time points in order to follow the kinetics of the reaction. Furthermore, the assay is not affected by free phosphate and is compatible with most nonionic detergents, resulting in minimal sample processing before analysis. Most importantly, each assay well contains inhibitors to ensure that the assay is selective for tyrosine phosphatases; other phosphatases, including serine/threonine phosphatases, will not hydrolyze DiFMUP under our assay conditions (Figure 10.44). Unlike phosphopeptide-based assays, this DiFMUP-based assay can be used to monitor a variety of tyrosine phosphatases, including PTP-1B and CD-45. Tyrosine phosphatase inhibitors can be evaluated quantitatively in the assay for their effect on tyrosine phosphatase activity.

Each RediPlate™ 96 EnzChek® Tyrosine Phosphatase Assay Kit (R22067) or RediPlate™ 384 EnzChek® Tyrosine Phosphatase Assay Kit (R22068) includes one microplate of either 96 or 384 wells, respectively, contained in a resealable foil packet to ensure the integrity of the fluorogenic components, plus a vial of reaction buffer. The first row of wells in the microplate contains a dilution series of the 6,8-difluoro-7-hydroxy-4-methylcoumarin (DiFMU) reference standard for generating a standard curve, and the remaining wells are preloaded with the DiFMUP substrate. Additionally, each RediPlate™ 96 assay plate has removable lanes that allow researchers to perform only as many assays as required for the experiment (Figure 8.60). The RediPlate™ 384 EnzChek® Tyrosine Phosphatase Assay Kit includes a single 384-well plate for high-throughput screening of tyrosine phosphatase activity. Table 10.3 summarizes our other RediPlate™ 96 and RediPlate™ 384 Assay Kits for serine/threonine phosphatase activity (see below), dsDNA quantitation (Section 8.3) and protease activity (Section 10.4). Significant discounts apply to purchases of multiple units of any of our RediPlate™ products.

RediPlate™ 96 EnzChek® Serine/Threonine Phosphatase Assay Kit

The majority of protein phosphorylation occurs on serine and threonine residues, with <0.01–0.05% on tyrosine residues.[82] Serine/threonine phosphatases represent a large family of enzymes that have been implicated in the regulation of metabolism,[93] transcription,[94] translation,[95] differentiation,[96] cell cycle,[82] cytoskeletal dynamics,[97] oncogenesis[98,99] and signal transduction.[100,101] Molecular Probes' RediPlate™ 96 EnzChek® Serine/Threonine Phosphatase Assay Kit (R33700) provides a fast, simple and direct fluorescence-based assay for detecting serine/threonine phosphatases and their corresponding modulators and inhibitors (Figure 10.43).

As with the RediPlate™ EnzChek® Tyrosine Phosphatase Kits, the substrate incorporated in the RediPlate™ 96 EnzChek® Serine/Threonine Phosphatase Assay Kit is our patented DiFMUP, which upon hydrolysis generates DiFMU (D6566, Section 10.1, Figure 10.3) with excitation/emission maxima of 358/452 nm (Figure 10.2), a low pK_a (~4.9) and a high quantum yield (~0.89). Inhibitors are included in each assay well to ensure that the assay is selective for serine/threonine phosphatases; under the prescribed assay conditions, other phosphatases, including tyrosine phosphatases, do not significantly react with the substrate (Figure 10.45). Furthermore, unlike phosphopeptide-based assays, this DiFMUP-based assay can be used to monitor a variety of serine/threonine phosphatases including PP-1, PP-2A and PP-2B (Figure 10.45). Serine/threonine phosphatase inhibitors can be evaluated quantitatively in the assay for their effect on serine/threonine phosphatase activity (Figure 10.46). Additional advantages of this RediPlate™ assay include compatibility with nonionic detergents and insensitivity to free phosphate, resulting in minimal sample processing before analysis.

Each RediPlate™ 96 EnzChek® Serine/Threonine Phosphatase Assay Kit includes:

- One RediPlate™ 96 EnzChek® serine/threonine phosphatase assay 96-well microplate
- Concentrated reaction buffer
- $NiCl_2$
- $MnCl_2$
- Dithiothreitol
- A detailed assay protocol

To ensure the integrity of the fluorogenic components, the 96-well microplate is contained in a resealable foil packet and consists of twelve removable strips, each with eight wells (Figure 8.60). Eleven of the strips (88 wells) are preloaded with the fluorogenic substrate

DiFMUP. The remaining strip, marked with black tabs, contains a dilution series of the DiFMU reference standard for generating a standard curve. We also offer RediPlate™ 96 and RediPlate™ 384 Assay Kits for tyrosine phosphatase activity (see above), dsDNA quantitation (Section 8.3) and protease activity (Section 10.4), which are summarized in Table 10.3. Significant discounts apply to purchases of multiple units of any of our RediPlate™ products.

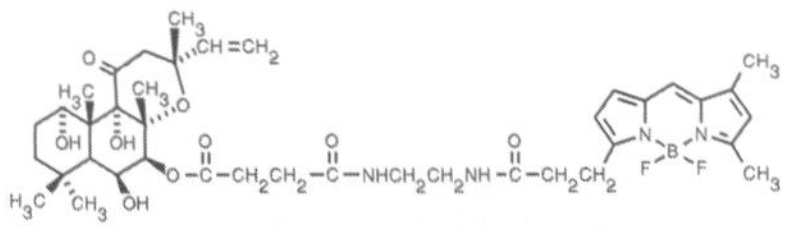

Figure 17.13 B7469 BODIPY® FL forskolin.

Adenylate Cyclase Probe: Fluorescent Forskolin

Forskolin, isolated from *Coleus forskohlii*, is a potent activator of adenylate cyclase, the enzyme that catalyzes the formation of cAMP from ATP. Cervical cells stained with our BODIPY® FL forskolin (B7469, Figure 17.13) exhibit a staining pattern identical to that seen with a fluorescent anti–adenylate cyclase antibody.[102] BODIPY® FL forskolin was successfully used to assess the localization of adenylate cyclase in both live tissues and cultured neurons.[103]

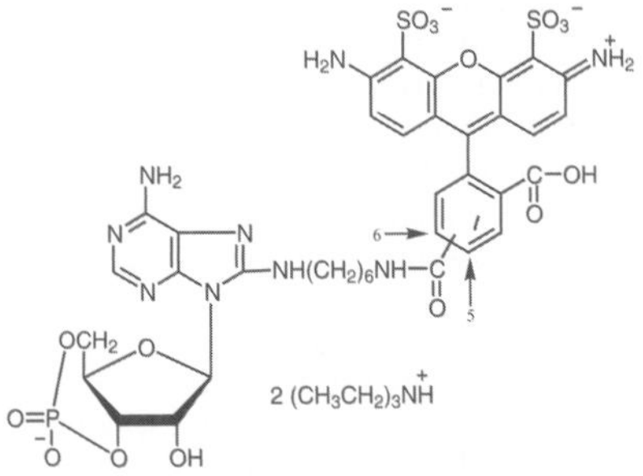

Figure 17.14 A35775 Alexa Fluor® 488 8-(6 aminoexyl)aminoadenosine 3',5'-cyclicmonophosphate, bis(triethylammonium) salt (Alexa Fluor® 488 cAMP).

Nucleotide Analogs

Nucleotide analogs that serve as substrates or inhibitors of enzymes, and nucleotide derivatives that selectively bind to regulatory sites of nucleotide-binding proteins, have been used as structural and mechanistic probes for isolated proteins, reconstituted membrane-bound enzymes, organelles such as mitochondria and tissues such as skinned muscle fibers. More recently, however, these analogs have also been utilized to probe for the effects of nucleotides on signal transduction and to screen for compounds that may affect signal transduction, such as G-protein inhibitors and activators (see Note 17.1 "Technical Focus: G-proteins and GTP Analogs for Binding Studies").

Molecular Probes prepares a variety of nucleotide analogs, including:

- Alexa Fluor® derivatives of cAMP for use as probes of type I cAMP-dependent protein kinases (PKA I),
- An Alexa Fluor® 647 conjugate of ATP (A22362)
- BODIPY® dye–labeled nucleotides for use as long-wavelength probes of nucleotide-binding sites, enzyme substrates and screening applications
- Blue-fluorescent and environment-sensitive *N*-methylanthraniloyl (MANT) nucleotides
- Classic, blue-fluorescent ethenoadenosine triphosphate (ε-ATP, E23691)
- Environment-sensitive trinitrophenyl (TNP) nucleotides
- Caged nucleotides, which are important probes for studying the kinetics and mechanism of nucleotide-binding proteins because they enable the researcher to control the release of an active nucleotide both spatially and temporally
- Photoaffinity nucleotides for site-selective covalent labeling
- Fluorescent ChromaTide® nucleotides and aha-dUTP nucleotides (Table 8.6, Table 8.7), whose principal utility is for biosynthetic incorporation into DNA or RNA (Section 8.2)

Alexa Fluor® Nucleotides

Alexa Fluor® cAMP Analogs

Our Alexa Fluor® cAMP analogs are 8-(6-aminohexyl)amino derivatives; similar analogs have been shown to exhibit a marked preference for binding to type I cAMP-dependent protein kinases (PKA I). We offer the green-fluorescent Alexa Fluor® 488 cAMP (A35775, Figure 17.14), orange-fluorescent Alexa Fluor® 555 cAMP (A35776) and far-red–fluorescent Alexa Fluor® 647 cAMP (A35777).

Alexa Fluor® 647 ATP

The Alexa Fluor® 647 conjugate of adenosine 5′-triphosphate (A22362) links this long-wavelength fluorophore to the ribose by a urethane bridge, as in the BODIPY® ATP conjugates. We have not fully characterized the use of this probe in the study of nucleotide-binding proteins.

Note 17.1 — Technical Focus

G-proteins and GTP Analogs for Binding Studies

Molecular Probes prepares a wide variety of nucleotide analogs for protein-binding studies, whose chemical and spectral properties are described in Section 17.3. These include various fluorescent, photoaffinity and caged versions of adenosine and guanosine triphosphates, diphosphates and cyclic monophosphates. The GTP analogs are among the most important probes for the study of "G-proteins" and G-protein–coupled receptors (GPCR). Heterotrimeric guanine nucleotide binding regulatory proteins transmit a variety of receptor signals to modulate diverse cellular responses,[1,2] including apoptosis.[3]

G-proteins are composed of α-, β- and γ-subunits. Upon receptor stimulus, the α-subunit of the heterotrimeric G-proteins exchanges GDP for GTP and dissociates from the β–γ-subunit complex. The GTP-bound G-protein will interact with various second messenger systems, either inhibiting (G_i) or stimulating (G_s) their activity. Stimulatory G-proteins are permanently activated by cholera toxin, inhibitory ones by pertussis toxin. The α-subunit has a slow intrinsic rate of GTP hydrolysis, and once the GTP is hydrolyzed it reassociates with the β–γ- complex. The GTP hydrolysis by G-proteins is regulated by interactions with so-called GTPase-activating proteins, or GAPs. There is a large family of GAPs for G-proteins known as regulators of G-protein signaling or RGS proteins.[4] G-proteins are turned off when the α-subunit hydrolyzes the GTP, either spontaneously or upon interaction with a GTPase-activating protein, permitting the heterotrimeric α–β–γ-complex to reassociate.

The GAPs are a diverse group of monomeric GTPases, including ARF, Ran, Ras, Rab, Rac, Rho and Sar, which play an important part in regulating many intracellular processes, such as cytoskeletal organization and secretion. There is less diversity among the β and γ subunits, but they may have direct activating effects in their own right. Most β- and γ-subunits are post-translationally modified by myristoylation or isoprenylation, which may alter their association with membranes.

Our GTP analogs include:

- Blue-fluorescent MANT-GTP (M12415) and nonhydrolyzable MANT-GMPPNP (M22353)
- Green-fluorescent BODIPY® FL guanosine 5′-triphosphate (BODIPY® FL GTP, G12411)
- Orange-fluorescent BODIPY® R6G guanosine 5′-triphosphate (BODIPY® R6G GTP, G22350)
- Red-fluorescent BODIPY® TR guanosine 5′-triphosphate (BODIPY® TR GTP, G22351)
- Nonhydrolyzable and green-fluorescent BODIPY® FL GMPPNP (B22355) and BODIPY® FL GTP-γ-*S* thioester (G22183)
- Environment-sensitive 2′-(or 3′-)*O*-(trinitrophenyl)guanosine 5′-triphosphate (TNP-GTP, T7600)
- BzBzGTP (2′-(or 3′-)*O*-(4-benzoylbenzoyl)guanosine 5′-triphosphate, B22357), a potential photoaffinity reagent for G-proteins
- *S*-(DMNPE-caged) GTP-γ-*S* (G1053) for photorelease of GTP-γ-*S*

References

1. Annu Rev Biochem 56, 615 (1987); **2.** Physiol Rev 79, 1373 (1999); **3.** J Biol Chem 275, 20726 (2000); **4.** J Biol Chem 273, 1269 (1998).

BODIPY® Nucleotides

BODIPY® Ribonucleotide Di- and Triphosphates

Molecular Probes continues to expand our line of BODIPY® dye–modified ribonucleotides. We currently offer:

- BODIPY® FL adenosine 5′-triphosphate (BODIPY® FL ATP, A12410)
- BODIPY® TR adenosine 5′-triphosphate (BODIPY® TR ATP, A22352)
- BODIPY® TR adenosine 5′-diphosphate (BODIPY® TR ADP, A22359)
- BODIPY® FL guanosine 5′-triphosphate (BODIPY® FL GTP, G12411)
- BODIPY® R6G guanosine 5′-triphosphate (BODIPY® R6G GTP, G22350)
- BODIPY® TR guanosine 5′-triphosphate (BODIPY® TR GTP, G22351)
- BODIPY® FL guanosine 5′-diphosphate (BODIPY® FL GDP, G22360)

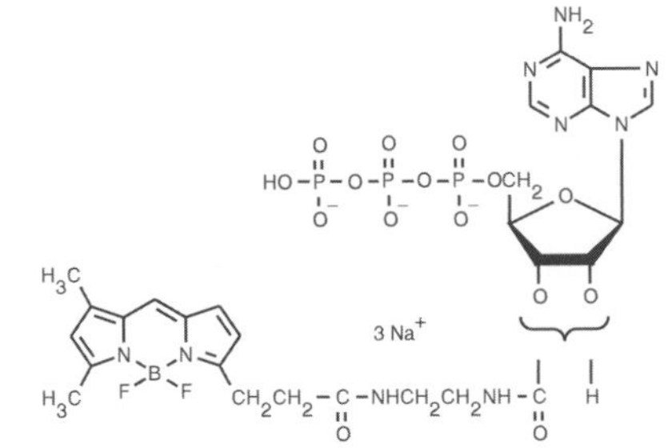

Figure 17.15 A12410 adenosine 5′-triphosphate, BODIPY® FL 2′-(or-3′)-*O*-(*N*-(2-aminoethyl)urethane), trisodium salt (BODIPY® FL ATP).

These mixed-isomer analogs comprise a BODIPY® fluorophore attached to the 2′ or 3′ position of the ribose ring via an aminoethylcarbamoyl linker (Figure 17.15). Interactions between the fluorophore and the purine base are evident from the spectroscopic properties of these nucleotide analogs. The fluorescence quantum yield of BODIPY® FL GTP, BODIPY® R6G GTP and BODIPY® TR GTP is significantly quenched in solution (Figure 17.16) and increases upon binding to at least some GTP-binding proteins.[104,105] Similar nucleotide analogs incorporating fluorophores such as fluorescein, tetramethylrhodamine and Cy3 have been developed previously, primarily for biophysical studies of nucleotide-binding proteins.[106] The BODIPY® dye–labeled nucleotides may be particularly useful for fluorescence polarization–based assays of ATP- or GTP-binding proteins.

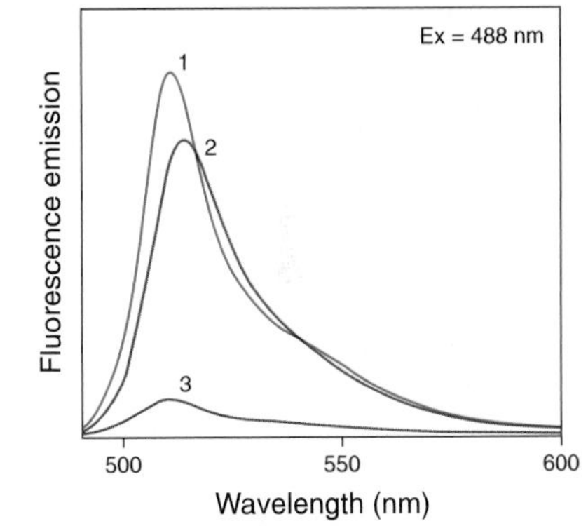

Figure 17.16 Fluorescence emission spectra of (1) free BODIPY® FL dye in phosphate-buffered saline, pH 7.2; (2) BODIPY® FL ATP (A12410); and (3) BODIPY® FL GTP (G12411). Samples were prepared with equal absorbance at the excitation wavelength (488 nm). The areas under the curves are therefore proportional to the relative fluorescence quantum yields, clearly showing the quenching effect caused by interaction of the BODIPY® FL fluorophore with the guanine base of GTP.

BODIPY® FL AMPPNP and BODIPY® FL GMPPNP

Among the most useful fluorescent nucleotides for protein-binding studies are those that stoichiometrically bind to ATP- or GTP-binding sites but are not metabolized.[107] To match those requirements, we offer BODIPY® FL AMPPNP (B22356) and BODIPY® FL GMPPNP (B22355). The fluorescence of BODIPY® FL GMPPNP is quenched ~90% relative to that of the free dye but may be recovered upon binding to G-proteins.[105]

BODIPY® ATP-γ-S and BODIPY® GTP-γ-S Thioesters and BODIPY® GTP-γ-NH Amide

For protein-binding studies that require nonhydrolyzable nucleotides, we offer the BODIPY® FL fluorophore linked through the γ-thiol of ATP-γ-*S* (A22184, Figure 17.17) and the BODIPY® FL, BODIPY® 515/530 and BODIPY® TR fluorophores linked through the γ-thiol of GTP-γ-*S*[104] (G22183, G35779, G35780). Like BODIPY® FL GMPPNP, the fluorescence of the BODIPY® GTP-γ-*S* thioesters is quenched ~90% relative to that of the free dye but is recovered upon protein binding to at least some G-proteins.[104] The green-fluorescent BODIPY® FL GTP-γ-*S* has been used to detect GTP-binding proteins separated by capillary electrophoresis.[108] BODIPY® 515/530 GTP-γ-*S* thioester also exhibits green fluorescence and has a greater fluorescence increase upon protein binding, as compared with the BODIPY® FL GTP-γ-*S* thioester. The BODIPY® TR GTP-γ-*S* thioester is a red-fluorescent analog with spectral properties similar to the Texas Red® dye.

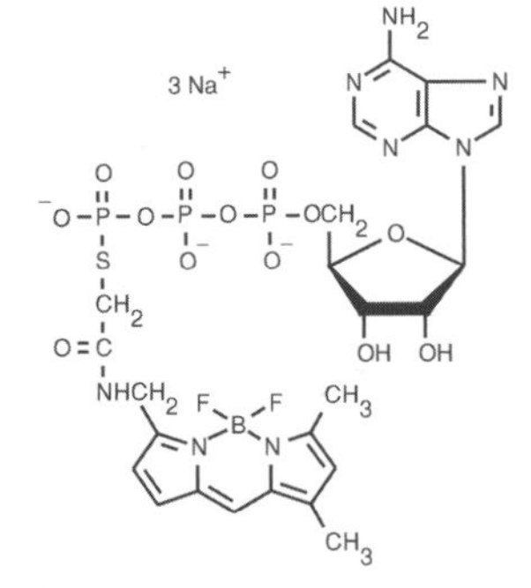

Figure 17.17 A22184 adenosine 5′-*O*-(3-thiotriphosphate), BODIPY® FL thioester, sodium salt (BODIPY® FL ATP-γ-S, thioester).

We also offer the green-fluorescent BODIPY® FL GTP-γ-*NH* amide (G35778) as another choice for protein-binding studies. Although this analog exhibits less fluorescence enhancement upon protein binding, it is reportedly the best of the three green-fluorescent GTP-γ analogs for directly monitoring nucleotide exchange.[109] The different linker lengths of the green-fluorescent GTP-γ analogs (six-carbon for BODIPY® FL GTP-γ-*NH* amide, four-carbon for BODIPY® FL GTP-γ-*S* and one-carbon for BODIPY® 515/530 GTP-γ-*S*) may be useful for understanding protein active-site geometries.

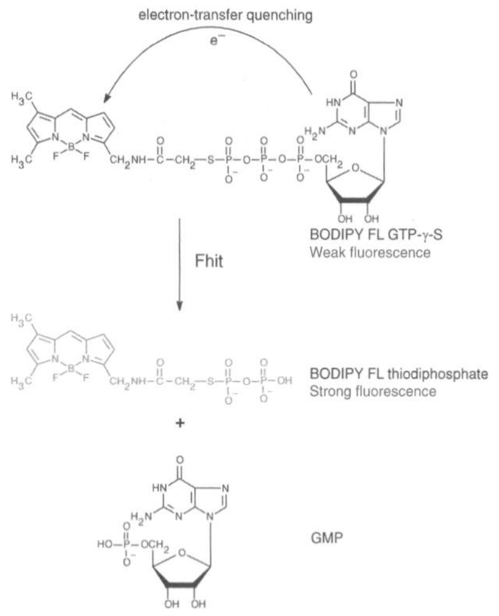

Figure 17.18 Principle of fluorescence-based detection of the diadenosine triphosphate hydrolase activity of Fhit using BODIPY® FL GTP-γ-*S* thioester (G22183) as a substrate analog.

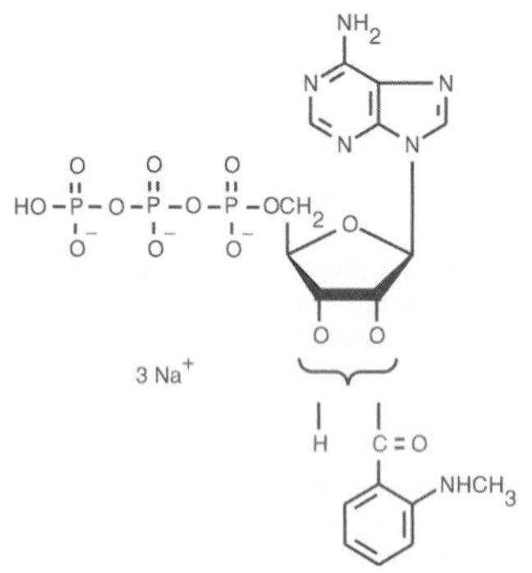

Figure 17.19 M12417 2′-(or-3′)-*O*-(*N*-methylanthraniloyl) adenosine 5′-triphosphate, trisodium salt (MANT-ATP).

In addition to their potential use for binding studies, our patented BODIPY® FL ATP-γ-*S* and BODIPY® FL GTP-γ-*S* thioesters are important substrates for Fhit (Figure 17.18), a member of the histidine triad superfamily of nucleotide-binding proteins that bind and cleave diadenosine polyphosphates.[110–112] Fhit, one of the most frequently inactivated proteins in lung cancer, functions as a tumor suppressor by inducing apoptosis.[111,113,114] These BODIPY® nucleotides should be especially useful for screening potential Fhit inhibitors and activators.

N-Methylanthraniloyl (MANT) Nucleotides

The blue-fluorescent MANT nucleotide analogs of ATP (Figure 17.19), AMPPNP, GTP, GMPPNP, ADP and GDP are modified on the ribose moiety, making these probes particularly useful for studying nucleotide-binding proteins that are sensitive to modifications of the purine base.[115,116] The compact nature of the MANT fluorophore and its attachment position on the ribose ring results in nucleotide analogs that induce minimal perturbation of nucleotide–protein interactions, as confirmed by X-ray crystal structures of MANT nucleotides bound to myosin[117] and H-ras p21.[118] Furthermore, because MANT fluorescence is sensitive to the environment of the fluorophore, nucleotide–protein interactions may be directly detectable. These properties (Table 17.1) make MANT nucleotides valuable probes of the structure and enzymatic activity of nucleotide-binding proteins.[106]

MANT-ATP, MANT-ADP and MANT-AMPPNP

Applications for MANT-ATP (M12417), MANT-ADP (M12416) and MANT-AMPPNP (M22354) include analysis of:

- Conformation of the myosin subfragment-1 nucleotide-binding site, as indicated by fluorescence quencher accessibility[119,120]
- Myosin ATPase activity in rabbit skeletal muscle[121]
- ATPase kinetics of kinesin[122–124] and other microtubule motor-proteins[125,126] using stopped-flow fluorescence measurements
- Interaction of P-glycoprotein ATP-binding sites with drug efflux–modulating steroids[127]
- Structural characteristics of the nucleotide-binding site of *Escherichia coli* DnaB helicase[128,129]

MANT-GTP, MANT-GDP and MANT-GMPPNP

Applications for MANT-GTP (M12415) and MANT-GDP (M12414) include analysis of:

- Nucleotide hydrolysis and dissociation kinetics of H-ras p21 and other low molecular weight GTP-binding proteins[115,130–133]
- Effects of nucleotide structural modifications on binding to H-ras p21[134]
- Activation of protein kinases by Rho subfamily GTP-binding proteins[135]
- Conformational changes during activation of heterotrimeric G-proteins[136]

Researchers have extensively used MANT-GMPPNP (M22353) to study the GTP-binding proteins Rab5 and Rab7,[137] Raf-1,[138] Rho[139,140] and Rac,[141,142] as well as Ras-related proteins.[115,130,143,144]

Table 17.1 — Spectroscopic properties of MANT-ATP in aqueous solution (pH 8)

Parameter	Value	Notes
Absorption maximum	356 nm	Stronger absorption at shorter wavelengths (λ_{max} = 255 nm)
Molar extinction coefficient (ε_{max})	5800 $cm^{-1}M^{-1}$	23,000 $cm^{-1}M^{-1}$ at 255 nm
Fluorescence emission maximum	448 nm	Shifts 10–20 nm shorter in nonpolar solvents and upon binding to most proteins
Fluorescence quantum yield	0.22	Increases in nonpolar solvents and upon binding to most proteins

Ethenoadenosine Nucleotides

The ethenoadenosine nucleotides — developed in 1972 by Leonard and collaborators [145,146] — bind like endogenous nucleotides to several proteins. The properties and applications of etheno nucleotides have been comprehensively reviewed by Leonard.[147,148] The etheno ATP analog (ε-ATP, E23691; Figure 17.20) can often mimic ATP in both binding and function. This probe has been used to replace ATP in actin polymerization reactions [149] and is frequently incorporated in place of the tightly bound actin nucleotide.[150] It also supports contraction of actomyosin, facilitates the measurement of nucleotide-exchange kinetics in actin [151] and carbamoyl-phosphate synthetase [152] and serves as a substrate for myosin, which converts it to ε-ADP.[153] ε-ATP is not a substrate for firefly luciferase;[154] however, when added to a reaction mixture containing luciferase, luciferin and ATP, ε-ATP enhances light production, probably by increasing the rate at which the enzyme releases the inhibitory product, oxyluciferin.[155]

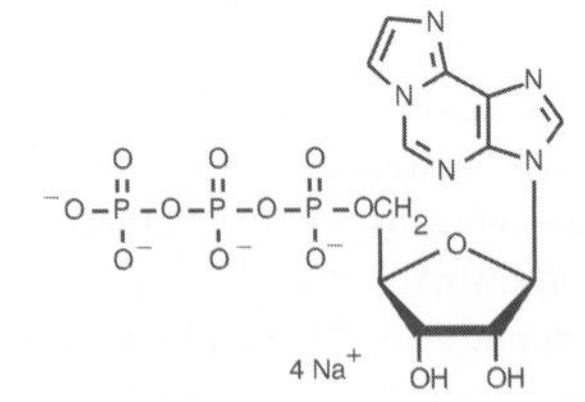

Figure 17.20 E23691 1,N^6-ethenoadenosine 5′-triphosphate (ε-ATP).

The etheno nucleotides usually bind to nucleotide-binding sites with high specificity. Because their blue fluorescence is not very environment-sensitive, however, protein binding is typically detected by fluorescence anisotropy (see Note 1.5 "Technical Focus: Fluorescence Polarization (FP)" in Section 1.4) or circular dichroism. The radiative lifetime of the ethenoadenosines is unusually long (>30 nanoseconds). Binding of etheno nucleotides to proteins is frequently accompanied by energy transfer from the protein's tryptophan residues to the nucleotide.[156] These nucleotides are also often used as fluorescence resonance energy transfer (FRET) donors to longer-wavelength dyes as a means of establishing distances within and between cytoskeletal and other proteins [157–159] (see Note 1.2 "Technical Focus: Fluorescence Resonance Energy Transfer (FRET)" in Section 1.3).

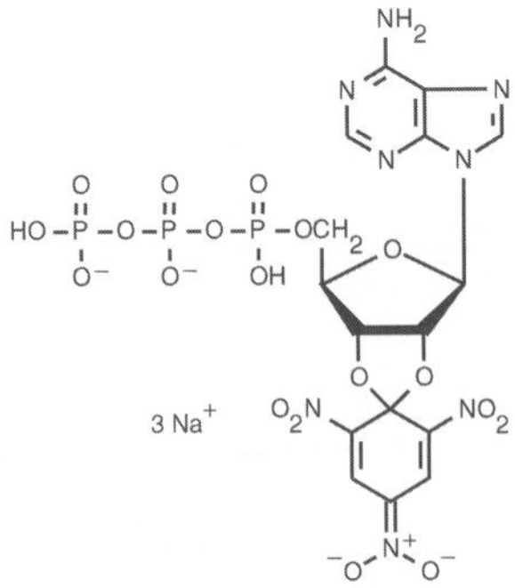

Figure 17.21 T7602 2′-(or-3′)-*O*-(trinitrophenyl)adenosine 5′-triphosphate, trisodium salt (TNP-ATP).

Trinitrophenyl (TNP) Nucleotides

Unlike the etheno derivatives, the free trinitrophenyl (TNP) nucleotides are essentially nonfluorescent in water. The TNP nucleotides undergo an equilibrium transition to a semiquinoid structure that has relatively long-wavelength spectral properties;[160,161] this form is only fluorescent when bound to the nucleotide-binding site of some proteins. The TNP derivative of ATP frequently exhibits a spectral shift and fluorescence enhancement upon protein binding and actually binds with higher affinity than ATP to several proteins. The broad, long-wavelength absorption of TNP nucleotides makes them useful for FRET studies [159,162,163] (see Note 1.2 "Technical Focus: Fluorescence Resonance Energy Transfer (FRET)" in Section 1.3). The TNP derivatives of ATP (TNP-ATP, T7602; Figure 17.21), ADP (TNP-ADP, T7601) and AMP (TNP-AMP, T7624) have been used as structural probes for a wide variety of proteins, including:

- Myosin [160]
- Tubulin [164]
- Na^+/K^+-ATPase [163]
- Gastric H^+/K^+-ATPase [165]
- Erythrocyte Ca^{2+}/Mg^{2+}-ATPase [166]
- F_1-ATPase [167–169]
- Sarcoplasmic reticulum ATPase [170–172]
- Adenylate kinase [173]
- Aspartokinase [174]
- Phosphoglycerate kinase [175]

Molecular Probes also prepares the TNP analog of GTP (T7600). This analog has been used as a spectroscopic probe for the GTP inhibitory site of liver glutamate dehydrogenase [176] and as an inhibitor of adenylate cyclase.[177]

We have found that chromatographically purified TNP nucleotides are unstable during lyophilization. Consequently, these derivatives are sold in aqueous solution and should be frozen immediately upon arrival.

Caged Nucleotides

Caged nucleotides are nucleotide analogs in which the terminal phosphate is esterified with a blocking group, rendering the molecule biologically inactive. Photolytic removal of the caging group by UV illumination results in a pulse of the nucleotide — often on a microsecond to millisecond time scale — at the site of illumination. Because photolysis ("uncaging") can be temporally controlled and confined to the area of illumination, the popularity of this technique is growing. Molecular Probes is supporting this development by synthesizing a variety of caged nucleotides, ligands for biological receptors, probes involved in signal transduction and fluorescent dyes. Our current selection of caged nucleotides includes the following probes:

- NPE-caged ATP (A1048)
- DMNPE-caged ATP (A1049)
- NPE-caged ADP (A7056)
- DMNB-caged c-AMP (D1037)
- DMNPE-caged GTP-γ-*S* (G1053)

Section 5.3 discusses our selection of caged probes and the properties of the different caging groups that we use (Table 5.2).

Researchers investigating the cytoskeleton have benefited greatly from recent advances in caging technology, primarily originating from the work of Trentham,[178,179] Kaplan [180,181] and their colleagues. NPE-caged ADP (A7056) is a useful probe for studying the effect of photolytic release of ADP in muscle fibers [182,183] and isolated sarcoplasmic reticulum.[184] Although it is sometimes difficult to properly abstract papers that describe experiments with caged ATP because they could be referring to either NPE-caged ATP (A1048), DMNPE-caged ATP (A1049) or earlier caged versions of this nucleotide, most researchers have used NPE-caged ATP. Caged ATP has been employed in a variety of experimental systems, including tissues, cells and isolated proteins:

- Skinned cardiac and skeletal muscle fibers [182,185–188]
- Submitochondrial particles [189]
- Isolated myosin subfragment-1 [190,191]
- F-actin [192]
- Sarcoplasmic reticulum Ca^{2+}-ATPase [193]
- ATP-regulated K^+ channels of pancreatic β-cells [194] and rat heart cells [195]

Because the caged nucleotides may be added to an experimental system at relatively high concentrations, use of the enzyme apyrase was recommended by Sleep and Burton [196] to eliminate any traces of ATP that may be present in the caged ATP probes.[185,197–199] Once the caged ATP solutions have been preincubated with apyrase, the enzyme can be removed by centrifugal filtration.[185,198]

These caged nucleotides are generally cell impermeant and must be microinjected into cells or loaded by other techniques (Table 14.1). Permeabilization of cells with staphylococcal α-toxin or the saponin ester β-escin is reported to make the membrane of smooth muscle cells permeable to low molecular weight (<1000 daltons) molecules, while retaining high molecular weight compounds.[200] α-Toxin permeabilization has permitted the introduction of caged nucleotides, including caged ATP (A1048) and caged GTP-γ-*S* (G1053), as well as of caged inositol 1,4,5-triphosphate (NPE-caged Ins 1,4,5-P_3; I23580; Section 17.2) into smooth muscle cells.[201] Caged inositol 1,4,5-triphosphate has also been successfully loaded in ECV304 cells using electroporation.[202]

Other Nucleotide Analogs

BzBzATP and BzBzGTP

Functional ion channels can be assembled from both homomeric and heteromeric combinations of the seven P2X receptor subunits so far identified ($P2X_{1–7}$). Due to the lack of specific agonists or antagonists for P2X receptors, it is difficult to determine which receptor subtypes mediate particular cellular responses. One of the most potent and widely used P2X receptor agonists, BzBzATP (2′-(or 3′-)*O*-(4-benzoylbenzoyl)adenosine 5′-triphosphate, B22358), is available from Molecular Probes,[203,204] along with the corresponding GTP derivative (B22357). Both BzBzATP and BzBzGTP have more general applications for site-directed irreversible modification of nucleotide-binding proteins via photoaffinity labeling.[205,206]

ATP γ-AmNS, dATP γ-AmNS and UTP γ-AmNS

We offer ATP γ-AmNS (A12412), its dATP analog (D22361) and UTP γ-AmNS (U23692), which have absorption/emission maxima of ~330/463 nm. ATP γ-AmNS, in which the aminonaphthalenesulfonate (AmNS) is attached to the terminal phosphate of ATP (Figure 17.22) or dATP as a phosphoramide, is a useful fluorescent probe for studying ATP-binding sites of *Escherichia coli* RNA polymerase [207] and the mitochondrial adenine-nucleotide carrier [208] and as a fluorescence resonance energy transfer (FRET) donor or acceptor.[209,210] The AmNS derivative of UTP binds to RNA polymerase [209,210] with micromolar affinity [211] and is a useful reagent for following RNA polymerase activity.[209]

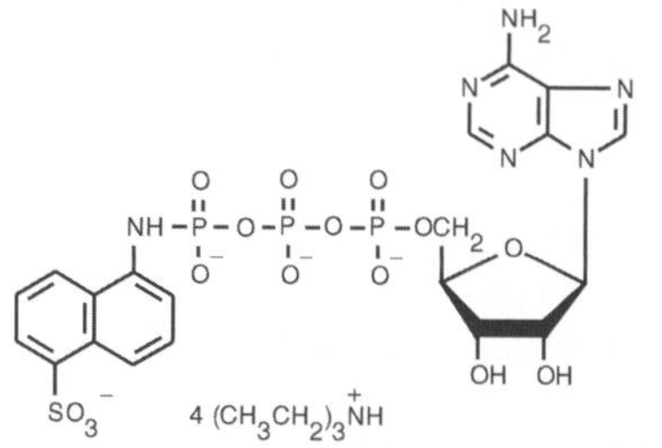

Figure 17.22 A12412 adenosine 5′-triphosphate, P^3-(5-sulfo-1-naphthylamide), tetra(triethylammonium) salt (ATP γ-AmNS).

References

1. Annu Rep Med Chem 29, 255 (1994); **2.** Eur J Biochem 208, 547 (1992); **3.** Science 258, 607 (1992); **4.** Eur J Biochem 195, 9 (1991); **5.** Annu Rev Cell Biol 2, 149 (1986); **6.** J Neurochem 52, 215 (1989); **7.** Eur J Biochem 164, 461 (1987); **8.** J Biol Chem 268, 15812 (1993); **9.** Exp Cell Res 234, 115 (1997); **10.** Eur J Neurosci 12, 215 (2000); **11.** Hear Res 94, 24 (1996); **12.** Am J Physiol 256, C886 (1989); **13.** J Neurochem 47, 1405 (1986); **14.** Nature 321, 698 (1986); **15.** J Neurosci 5, 2672 (1985); **16.** Neurochem Int 31, 261 (1997); **17.** Biosci Rep 12, 199 (1992); **18.** FEBS Lett 279, 19 (1991); **19.** J Neurosci Res 45, 216 (1996); **20.** Circ Shock 38, 85 (1992); **21.** Pflugers Arch 426, 31 (1994); **22.** J Leukoc Biol 47, 283 (1990); **23.** Biosci Rep 9, 573 (1989); **24.** Biochem Biophys Res Commun 136, 1001 (1986); **25.** Eur J Pharmacol 207, 17 (1991); **26.** Proc Natl Acad Sci U S A 77, 6601 (1980); **27.** J Gen Microbiol 12, 226 (1955); **28.** Med Res Rev 15, 111 (1995); **29.** Biochem Biophys Res Commun 165, 1207 (1989); **30.** Proc Natl Acad Sci U S A 86, 5963 (1989); **31.** Anticancer Res 18, 4651 (1998); **32.** Photochem Photobiol 68, 593 (1998); **33.** Pharmacol Ther 63, 1 (1994); **34.** FEBS Lett 440, 19 (1998); **35.** Cancer Res 58, 5777 (1998); **36.** Photochem Photobiol 59, 529 (1994); **37.** Photochem Photobiol 61, 529 (1995); **38.** Biochem Pharmacol 47, 373 (1994); **39.** J Photochem Photobiol A 64, 273 (1992); **40.** Photochem Photobiol 52, 609 (1990); **41.** Biochemistry 34, 15845 (1995); **42.** Photochem Photobiol 60, 253 (1994); **43.** Anticancer Drug Des 8, 129 (1993); **44.** J Biol Chem 270, 10043 (1995); **45.** Science 268, 239 (1995); **46.** J Biol Chem 269, 20872 (1994); **47.** Trends Neurosci 17, 406 (1994); **48.** Science 260, 181 (1993); **49.** Annu Rev Biochem 61, 559 (1992); **50.** Proc Natl Acad Sci U S A 88, 2232 (1991); **51.** J Biol Chem 270, 30257 (1995); **52.** Molecular and Cellular Mechanisms of Neurotransmitter Release, Stjarne L, et al., Eds. pp. 31–45 (1994); **53.** Biochemistry 34, 1912 (1995); **54.** Biochem Soc Trans 23, 65 (1995); **55.** Eur J Biochem 224, 229 (1994); **56.** J Cell Biol 128, 905 (1995); **57.** FEBS Lett 329, 301 (1993); **58.** Science 259, 780 (1993); **59.** J Cell Biol 108, 111 (1989); **60.** Science 226, 1209 (1984); **61.** J Cell Biol 96, 1337 (1983); **62.** J Neurosci 12, 1736 (1992); **63.** J Neurosci 11, 1617 (1991); **64.** J Neurosci 9, 2151 (1989); **65.** Physiol Rev 62, 1 (1982); **66.** Science 207, 19 (1980); **67.** Annu Rev Biochem 49, 489 (1980); **68.** J Biol Chem 253, 1338 (1978); **69.** Biochemistry 17, 253 (1978); **70.** Biomed Res 1, 502 (1980); **71.** Cell 23, 533 (1981); **72.** Exp Cell Res 149, 375 (1983); **73.** Cell Motil Cytoskeleton 9, 231 (1988); **74.** Cell Struct Funct 14, 241 (1989); **75.** In Vitro Toxicol 3, 219 (1990); **76.** Biochem Biophys Res Commun 108, 266 (1982); **77.** Biochemistry 34, 7834 (1995); **78.** J Biol Chem 273, 17579 (1998); **79.** J Biol Chem 271, 29619 (1996); **80.** Biochemistry 37, 6188 (1998); **81.** J Biomol Screen 4, 67 (1999); **82.** Oncogene 19, 6607 (2000); **83.** Trends Cell Biol 11, 258 (2001); **84.** Curr Opin Cell Biol 13, 182 (2001); **85.** Curr Opin Chem Biol 5, 416 (2001); **86.** J Mol Med 78, 473 (2000); **87.** Biochem Pharmacol 60, 877 (2000); **88.** Cell Res 10, 279 (2000); **89.** Curr Opin Neurobiol 11, 95 (2001); **90.** Neuroreport 11, R5 (2000); **91.** Biochem Biophys Res Commun 286, 721 (2001); **92.** Adv Exp Med Biol 476, 35 (2000); **93.** Proc Natl Acad Sci U S A 98, 13710 (2001); **94.** Biochem Biophys Res Commun 285, 1192 (2001); **95.** J Biol Chem 276, 14829 (2001); **96.** J Neurosci Methods 105, 87 (2001); **97.** Eur J Immunol 30, 3422 (2000); **98.** Proc Natl Acad Sci U S A 97, 3207 (2000); **99.** Eur J Biochem 263, 605 (1999); **100.** Eur J Biochem 269, 1060 (2002); **101.** Proc Natl Acad Sci U S A 98, 13613 (2001); **102.** Daisy McCann, McCann Associates, Inc., personal communication; **103.** Cell Tissue Res 293, 57 (1998); **104.** J Biol Chem 276, 29275 (2001); **105.** Anal Biochem 291, 109 (2001); **106.** Methods Enzymol 278, 363 (1997); **107.** J Biol Chem 279, 28402 (2004); **108.** Anal Chem 75, 4297 (2003); **109.** Proc Natl Acad Sci U S A 101, 2800 (2004); **110.** Proc Natl Acad Sci U S A 100, 1592 (2003); **111.** Curr Biol 10, 907 (2000); **112.** J Biol Chem 275, 4555 (2000); **113.** Am J Pathol 156, 419 (2000); **114.** J Natl Cancer Inst 92, 338 (2000); **115.** Proc Natl Acad Sci U S A 87, 3562 (1990); **116.** Biochim Biophys Acta 742, 496 (1983); **117.** J Mol Biol 274, 394 (1997); **118.** J Mol Biol 253, 132 (1995); **119.** Biophys J 68, 142S (1995); **120.** Biochemistry 29, 3309 (1990); **121.** J Gen Physiol 106, 957 (1995); **122.** Biochemistry 37, 792 (1998); **123.** J Biol Chem 272, 717 (1997); **124.** Biochemistry 34, 13233 (1995); **125.** Biochemistry 35, 2365 (1996); **126.** Biochemistry 34, 13259 (1995); **127.** Biochemistry 36, 15208 (1997); **128.** Biophys J 71, 2075 (1996); **129.** J Cell Biol 139, 63 (1997); **130.** Biochemistry 36, 4535 (1997); **131.** Biochemistry 34, 12543 (1995); **132.** Biochemistry 34, 639 (1995); **133.** Biochemistry 32, 7451 (1993); **134.** Biochemistry 34, 593 (1995); **135.** Biochemistry 36, 1173 (1997); **136.** J Biol Chem 269, 13771 (1994); **137.** J Biol Chem 271, 20470 (1996); **138.** J Biol Chem 275, 22172 (2000); **139.** Biochemistry 38, 985 (1999); **140.** J Biol Chem 271, 10004 (1996); **141.** J Biol Chem 272, 18834 (1997); **142.** J Biol Chem 271, 19794 (1996); **143.** Biochemistry 36, 12027 (1997); **144.** J Biol Chem 271, 6794 (1996); **145.** Biochem Biophys Res Commun 46, 597 (1972); **146.** Science 175, 646 (1972); **147.** Chemtracts Biochem Mol Biol 4, 251 (1993); **148.** Chemtracts Biochem Mol Biol 3, 273 (1992); **149.** Biochemistry 27, 3812 (1988); **150.** J Biol Chem 268, 8683 (1993); **151.** J Cell Biol 106, 1553 (1988); **152.** Biochemistry 27, 8050 (1988); **153.** J Biol Chem 259, 11920 (1984); **154.** Proc Natl Acad Sci USA 70, 1664 (1973); **155.** Am J Physiol 261, C1210 (1991); **156.** J Biol Chem 269, 31359 (1994); **157.** Eur J Biochem 217, 737 (1993); **158.** Eur J Biochem 205, 591 (1992); **159.** J Muscle Res Cell Motil 13, 132 (1992); **160.** Biochim Biophys Acta 453, 293 (1976); **161.** Biochim Biophys Acta 320, 635 (1973); **162.** Biochemistry 31, 3930 (1992); **163.** Biophys J 61, 553 (1992); **164.** Biophys Chem 48, 359 (1994); **165.** Biochemistry 29, 3179 (1990); **166.** Clin Chim Acta 156, 165 (1986); **167.** Biochim Biophys Acta 1188, 108 (1994); **168.** J Biol Chem 269, 15431 (1994); **169.** J Biol Chem 268, 6978 (1993); **170.** J Biol Chem 269, 11147 (1994); **171.** Biochemistry 32, 3414 (1993); **172.** J Biol Chem 268, 6917 (1993); **173.** Biochim Biophys Acta 719, 509 (1982); **174.** J Biol Chem 258, 12940 (1983); **175.** Biochem J 301, 885 (1994); **176.** J Biol Chem 260, 4784 (1985); **177.** Arch Biochem Biophys 245, 369 (1986); **178.** J Am Chem Soc 110, 7170 (1988); **179.** J Physiol 352, 575 (1984); **180.** Nature 288, 587 (1980); **181.** Biochemistry 17, 1929 (1978); **182.** Biophys J 68, 78S (1995); **183.** J Mol Biol 223, 185 (1992); **184.** Ann N Y Acad Sci 402, 478 (1982); **185.** Biophys J 67, 1933 (1994); **186.** Biophys J 67, 1925 (1994); **187.** Biophys J 67, 1141 (1994); **188.** J Muscle Res Cell Motil 14, 666 (1993); **189.** J Biol Chem 268, 25320 (1993); **190.** Biochemistry 33, 6038 (1994); **191.** Biochemistry 30, 11036 (1991); **192.** Biophys J 59, 1235 (1991); **193.** Biochemistry 34, 4864 (1995); **194.** Biochim Biophys Acta 1092, 347 (1991); **195.** Pflugers Arch 415, 510 (1990); **196.** Biophys J 67, 2436 (1994); **197.** J Biol Chem 270, 23966 (1995); **198.** Biophys J 66, 1115 (1994); **199.** J Biolumin Chemilumin 9, 29 (1994); **200.** Methods Cell Biol 31, 63 (1989); **201.** Annu Rev Physiol 52, 857 (1990); **202.** J Neurosci Methods 132, 81 (2004); **203.** J Physiol 519 Pt 3, 723 (1999); **204.** Mol Pharmacol 56, 1171 (1999); **205.** J Neurochem 61, 1657 (1993); **206.** Biochemistry 28, 3989 (1989); **207.** Arch Biochem Biophys 246, 564 (1986); **208.** Biochim Biophys Acta 767, 369 (1984); **209.** Biochemistry 31, 6447 (1992); **210.** J Biol Chem 262, 13147 (1987); **211.** Eur J Biochem 225, 737 (1994).

Data Table — 17.3 Probes for Protein Kinases, Protein Phosphatases and Nucleotide-Binding Proteins

Cat #	MW	Storage	Soluble	Abs	EC	Em	Solvent	Notes
A1048	700.30	FF,D,LL	H_2O	259	18,000	none	MeOH	1, 2, 3
A1049	760.35	FF,D,LL	H_2O	351	4,400	none	H_2O	1, 2
A7056	614.44	FF,D,LL	H_2O	259	15,000	none	MeOH	1, 2, 3
A12410	933.30	FF,L	H_2O	505	54,000	514	H_2O	4, 5
A12412	1117.18	FF,L	H_2O	323	4,200	461	pH 7	4, 5, 6
A22184	878.28	FF,L	H_2O	504	68,000	514	pH 7	4, 5
A22352	1065.43	FF,L	H_2O	591	55,000	620	pH 7	4, 5
A22359	963.47	FF,L	H_2O	592	57,000	621	pH 7	4, 5
A22362	~2050	FF,L	H_2O	648	246,000	667	pH 7	4, 5
A35775	1162.23	FF,L	H_2O	493	71,000	517	pH 7	4, 5
A35776	~1650	FF,L	H_2O	552	150,000	566	pH 7	4, 5
A35777	~1700	FF,L	H_2O	649	246,000	666	pH 7	4, 5
B7469	784.70	F,D,L	DMSO	504	79,000	511	MeOH	
B22355	948.31	FF,L	H_2O	504	68,000	510	H_2O	4, 5, 7
B22356	932.31	FF,L	H_2O	504	68,000	514	H_2O	4, 5
B22357	1034.97	FF,L	H_2O	257	24,000	none	pH 7	3, 4, 5, 8
B22358	1018.97	FF,L	H_2O	260	27,000	none	pH 7	
D1037	524.38	F,D,LL	DMSO	338	6,100	none	MeOH	1, 2
D7475	412.49	L	DMSO, DMF	459	8,600	see Notes	MeOH	9
D22361	784.34	FF,L	H_2O	323	4,200	461	pH 7	4, 5
E23691	619.13	FF	H_2O	265	5,000	411	pH 7	5
F7453	840.84	F,D,L	DMSO, DMF	464	9,100	none	MeOH	10
F7462	755.76	F,D,L	DMSO, DMF	494	76,000	524	pH 9	
G1053	799.54	FF,D,LL	H_2O	352	3,700	none	H_2O	1, 2
G12411	949.30	FF,L	H_2O	504	68,000	511	H_2O	4, 5, 7
G22183	894.28	FF,L	H_2O	504	68,000	510	pH 7	4, 5, 7
G22350	997.34	FF,L	H_2O	530	51,000	551	pH 7	4, 5, 7
G22351	1081.43	FF,L	H_2O	591	56,000	620	pH 7	4, 5, 7
G22360	1005.75	FF,L	H_2O	504	68,000	508	pH 7	4, 5, 7
G35778	905.29	FF,L	H_2O	505	68,000	512	pH 7	4, 5, 7
H7476	504.45	F,D,L	DMSO, DMF	591	37,000	594	EtOH	
H7515	546.53	F,D,L	DMSO	463	24,000	600	MeOH	11
H7516	528.51	F,D,L	DMSO	459	23,000	616	MeOH	11
M12414	620.32	FF,L	H_2O	356	5,700	447	pH 8	4, 5, 12
M12415	722.28	FF,L	H_2O	356	5,700	448	pH 7	4, 5, 12
M12416	604.32	FF,L	H_2O	356	5,800	448	pH 7	4, 5, 12
M12417	706.28	FF,L	H_2O	356	5,800	447	pH 7	4, 5, 12
M22353	721.29	FF,L	H_2O	357	5,700	447	pH 8	4, 5, 12
M22354	705.29	FF,L	H_2O	357	5,800	447	pH 8	4, 5, 12
R7454	939.11	D,L	DMSO, DMF	562	110,000	581	MeOH	
T7600	799.21	FF,L	H_2O	409	26,000	none	pH 8	4, 5, 13
T7601	682.26	FF,L	H_2O	408	26,000	none	pH 8	4, 5, 13
T7602	784.22	FF,L	H_2O	408	26,000	none	pH 8	4, 5, 13
T7624	579.29	F,L	H_2O	408	26,000	none	pH 8	4, 5, 13
U23692	1094.14	FF,L	H_2O	323	4,200	461	pH 7	4, 5

For definitions of the contents of this data table, see "Navigating *The Handbook*" in the introductory pages.

Notes

1. Caged nucleotide esters are free of contaminating free nucleotides when initially prepared. However, some decomposition may occur during storage.
2. All photoactivatable probes are sensitive to light. They should be protected from illumination except when photolysis is intended.
3. This compound has weaker visible absorption at >300 nm but no discernible absorption peaks in this region.
4. The molecular weight (MW) of this product is approximate because the degree of hydration and/or salt form has not been conclusively established.
5. This product is supplied as a ready-made solution in the solvent indicated under "Soluble."
6. QY = 0.63 in 50 mM Tris, pH 8.0. Fluorescence shifts to longer wavelengths (Em ~475 nm) on enzymatic cleavage of the α–β phosphoryl bond (Biochem Biophys Res Commun 81, 35 (1978); J Biol Chem 254, 12069 (1979)).
7. Fluorescence of BODIPY® dye–labeled guanosine derivatives is generally weak due to base-specific intramolecular quenching (Anal Biochem 291, 109 (2001)).
8. This product can be activated by long-wavelength ultraviolet light (>300 nm) for photoaffinity labeling of proteins.
9. D7475 is weakly fluorescent, Em = 660 nm in MeOH.
10. Acetate hydrolysis of F7453 yields F7462.
11. H7515 and H7516 have weaker absorption peaks at longer wavelengths: Abs = 581 nm (EC = 12,000 $cm^{-1}M^{-1}$) for H7515, Abs = 580 nm (EC = 9000 $cm^{-1}M^{-1}$) for H7516. Their quantum yields for singlet oxygen production (0.83 for H7515, 0.76 for H7516) are essentially independent of the irradiation wavelength between 430 and 580 nm (J Photochem Photobiol A 64, 273 (1992)).
12. Fluorescence quantum yields of MANT nucleotides are environment-dependent. In H_2O, QY is ~0.2 (Biochim Biophys Acta 742, 496 (1983)).
13. Trinitrophenyl nucleotides are in fact very weakly fluorescent in water (Em ~560 nm). Fluorescence is blue-shifted and more intense in organic solvents (DMSO, EtOH) and when bound to proteins (Em ~540 nm). Absorption spectrum also has a second, less-intense, peak at about 470 nm (Biochim Biophys Acta 719, 509 (1982)).

Product List — 17.3 Probes for Protein Kinases, Protein Phosphatases and Nucleotide-Binding Proteins

Cat #	Product Name	Unit Size
A22359	adenosine 5′-diphosphate, BODIPY® TR 2′-(or-3′)-O-(N-(2-aminoethyl)urethane), disodium salt (BODIPY® TR ADP) *5 mM in buffer*	100 µL
A7056	adenosine 5′-diphosphate, P^2-(1-(2-nitrophenyl)ethyl) ester, monopotassium salt (NPE-caged ADP)	5 mg
A22184	adenosine 5′-O-(3-thiotriphosphate), BODIPY® FL thioester, sodium salt (BODIPY® FL ATP-γ-S, thioester) *5 mM in buffer*	50 µL
A22362	adenosine 5′-triphosphate, Alexa Fluor® 647 2′-(or-3′)-O-(N-(2-aminoethyl)urethane), hexa(triethylammonium) salt (Alexa Fluor® 647 ATP) *5 mM in buffer*	100 µL
A12410	adenosine 5′-triphosphate, BODIPY® FL 2′-(or-3′)-O-(N-(2-aminoethyl)urethane), trisodium salt (BODIPY® FL ATP) *5 mM in buffer*	100 µL
A22352	adenosine 5′-triphosphate, BODIPY® TR 2′-(or-3′)-O-(N-(2-aminoethyl)urethane), trisodium salt (BODIPY® TR ATP) *5 mM in buffer*	100 µL
A1049	adenosine 5′-triphosphate, P^3-(1-(4,5-dimethoxy-2-nitrophenyl)ethyl) ester, disodium salt (DMNPE-caged ATP)	5 mg
A1048	adenosine 5′-triphosphate, P^3-(1-(2-nitrophenyl)ethyl) ester, disodium salt (NPE-caged ATP)	5 mg
A12412	adenosine 5′-triphosphate, P^3-(5-sulfo-1-naphthylamide), tetra(triethylammonium) salt (ATP γ-AmNS) *5 mM in buffer*	400 µL
A35775	Alexa Fluor® 488 8-(6-aminohexyl)aminoadenosine 3′,5′-cyclicmonophosphate, bis(triethylammonium) salt (Alexa Fluor® 488 cAMP) *5 mM in buffer*	100 µL
A35776	Alexa Fluor® 555 8-(6-aminohexyl)aminoadenosine 3′,5′-cyclicmonophosphate, tetra(triethylammonium) salt (Alexa Fluor® 555 cAMP) *5 mM in buffer*	100 µL
A35777	Alexa Fluor® 647 8-(6-aminohexyl)aminoadenosine 3′,5′-cyclicmonophosphate, tetra(triethylammonium) salt (Alexa Fluor® 647 cAMP) *5 mM in buffer*	100 µL
A35725	Antibody Beacon™ Tyrosine Kinase Assay Kit *400 assays*	1 kit
A6442	anti-synapsin I (bovine), rabbit IgG fraction *affinity purified*	10 µg
B22358	2′-(or-3′)-O-(4-benzoylbenzoyl)adenosine 5′-triphosphate, tris(triethylammonium) salt (BzBzATP) *5 mM in buffer*	2 mL
B22357	2′-(or-3′)-O-(4-benzoylbenzoyl)guanosine 5′-triphosphate, tris(triethylammonium) salt (BzBzGTP) *5 mM in buffer*	2 mL
B7469	BODIPY® FL forskolin	100 µg
B22356	2′-(or-3′)-O-(BODIPY® FL)-β:γ-imidoadenosine 5′-triphosphate, trisodium salt (BODIPY® FL AMPPNP) *5 mM in buffer*	50 µL
B22355	2′-(or-3′)-O-(BODIPY® FL)-β:γ-imidoguanosine 5′-triphosphate, trisodium salt (BODIPY® FL GMPPNP) *5 mM in buffer*	50 µL
C23693	calmodulin from bovine brain	1 mg
C13844	calmodulin from bovine brain, Alexa Fluor® 488 conjugate	200 µg
C13845	calmodulin from bovine brain, Alexa Fluor® 594 conjugate	200 µg
D22361	2′-deoxyadenosine 5′-triphosphate, P^3-(5-sulfo-1-naphthylamide) (dATP γ-AmNS) *5 mM in water*	400 µL
D1037	4,5-dimethoxy-2-nitrobenzyl adenosine 3′,5′-cyclicmonophosphate (DMNB-caged cAMP)	5 mg
D7475	2-(1-(3-dimethylaminopropyl)-indol-3-yl)-3-(indol-3-yl)maleimide (bisindolylmaleimide; GF 109203X)	~1 mg
E23691	1,N^6-ethenoadenosine 5′-triphosphate (ε-ATP) *5 mM in buffer*	2 mL
F7462	fim-1	1 mg
F7453	fim-1 diacetate	1 mg
G22360	guanosine 5′-diphosphate, BODIPY® FL 2′-(or-3′)-O-(N-(2-aminoethyl)urethane), bis(triethylammonium) salt (BODIPY® FL GDP) *5 mM in water*	100 µL
G35779	guanosine 5′-O-(3-thiotriphosphate), BODIPY® 515/530 thioester, sodium salt (BODIPY® 515/530 GTP-γ-S, thioester) *1 mM in buffer*	100 µL
G22183	guanosine 5′-O-(3-thiotriphosphate), BODIPY® FL thioester, sodium salt (BODIPY® FL GTP-γ-S, thioester) *5 mM in buffer*	50 µL
G35780	guanosine 5′-O-(3-thiotriphosphate), BODIPY® TR thioester, sodium salt (BODIPY® TR GTP-γ-S, thioester) *1 mM in buffer*	100 µL
G1053	guanosine 5′-O-(3-thiotriphosphate), $P^{3(S)}$-(1-(4,5-dimethoxy-2-nitrophenyl)ethyl) ester, triammonium salt (S-(DMNPE-caged) GTP-γ-S)	1 mg
G12411	guanosine 5′-triphosphate, BODIPY® FL 2′-(or-3′)-O-(N-(2-aminoethyl)urethane), trisodium salt (BODIPY® FL GTP) *5 mM in water*	100 µL
G22350	guanosine 5′-triphosphate, BODIPY® R6G 2′-(or-3′)-O-(N-(2-aminoethyl)urethane), trisodium salt (BODIPY® R6G GTP) *5 mM in water*	100 µL
G22351	guanosine 5′-triphosphate, BODIPY® TR 2′-(or-3′)-O-(N-(2-aminoethyl)urethane), trisodium salt (BODIPY® TR GTP) *5 mM in water*	100 µL
G35778	guanosine 5′-O-(3-iminotriphosphate), BODIPY® FL ethylamide, sodium salt (BODIPY® FL GTP-γ-NH, amide) *1 mM in buffer*	100 µL
H7476	hypericin	1 mg
H7515	hypocrellin A	1 mg
H7516	hypocrellin B	1 mg
M12416	2′-(or-3′)-O-(N-methylanthraniloyl)adenosine 5′-diphosphate, disodium salt (MANT-ADP) *5 mM in buffer*	400 µL
M12417	2′-(or-3′)-O-(N-methylanthraniloyl)adenosine 5′-triphosphate, trisodium salt (MANT-ATP) *5 mM in buffer*	400 µL
M12414	2′-(or-3′)-O-(N-methylanthraniloyl)guanosine 5′-diphosphate, disodium salt (MANT-GDP) *5 mM in buffer*	400 µL
M12415	2′-(or-3′)-O-(N-methylanthraniloyl)guanosine 5′-triphosphate, trisodium salt (MANT-GTP) *5 mM in buffer*	400 µL
M22354	2′-(or-3′)-O-(N-methylanthraniloyl)-β:γ-imidoadenosine 5′-triphosphate, trisodium salt (MANT-AMPPNP) *5 mM in buffer*	50 µL
M22353	2′-(or-3′)-O-(N-methylanthraniloyl)-β:γ-imidoguanosine 5′-triphosphate, trisodium salt (MANT-GMPPNP) *5 mM in buffer*	50 µL
P13235	polymyxin B, BODIPY® FL conjugate, trifluoroacetic acid salt *mixed species*	100 µg
P13238	polymyxin B, dansyl conjugate, trifluoroacetic acid salt *mixed species*	100 µg
P13236	polymyxin B, Oregon Green® 514 conjugate, trifluoroacetic acid salt *mixed species*	100 µg
P13237	polymyxin B, Texas Red®-X conjugate, trifluoroacetic acid salt *mixed species*	100 µg
P33706	Pro-Q® Diamond Phosphoprotein/Phosphopeptide Microarray Stain Kit	1 kit
P7432	protein kinase C *from rat brain* *6.7 ng/µL*	2 x 75 µL
R33700	RediPlate™ 96 EnzChek® Serine/Threonine Phosphatase Assay Kit *one 96-well microplate*	1 kit
R22067	RediPlate™ 96 EnzChek® Tyrosine Phosphatase Assay Kit *one 96-well microplate*	1 kit
R22068	RediPlate™ 384 EnzChek® Tyrosine Phosphatase Assay Kit *one 384-well microplate*	1 kit
R7454	rim-1	1 mg
T7601	2′-(or-3′)-O-(trinitrophenyl)adenosine 5′-diphosphate, disodium salt (TNP-ADP) *5 mg/mL in water*	2 mL
T7624	2′-(or-3′)-O-(trinitrophenyl)adenosine 5′-monophosphate, sodium salt (TNP-AMP) *5 mg/mL in buffer*	2 mL
T7602	2′-(or-3′)-O-(trinitrophenyl)adenosine 5′-triphosphate, trisodium salt (TNP-ATP) *5 mg/mL in buffer*	2 mL
T7600	2′-(or-3′)-O-(trinitrophenyl)guanosine 5′-triphosphate, trisodium salt (TNP-GTP) *5 mg/mL in water*	1 mL
U23692	uridine 5′-triphosphate, P^3-(5-sulfo-1-naphthylamide), tetra(triethylammonium) salt (UTP γ-AmNS) *5 mM in water*	400 µL

For current prices or to order online, visit probes.invitrogen.com

17.4 Probes for Lipid Metabolism and Signaling

Table 17.2 — Fluorescence-based phospholipase assays

PL *	Probes	Assay Principle	Detection Method
A_1, A_2	B7701	Intramolecular self-quenching	Fluorescence increase at ~515 nm [1]
A_1, A_2	B3781, B3782	Intramolecular excimer formation	Emission ratio 380/470 nm [2–4]
A_1, A_2	A3880	Free fatty acid sensor	Emission ratio 432/505 nm [5–7]
A_2	D23739	Intramolecular self-quenching	Fluorescence increase at ~515 nm [8]
A_2	N3786, N3787	Intermolecular self-quenching	Fluorescence increase at ~530 nm [9,10]
A_2	H361, H3810	Intermolecular excimer formation	Emission ratio 380/470 nm [11–13]
A_2	O7703	Release of a MeOH/H_2O–soluble fatty acid	Phase separation of a fluorescent product (P3840, Section 13.2) [14,15]
A_2	D3803	Release of a fluorescent fatty acid	TLC or fluorescence image scanner [16]
A_2, C, D	D3771	Formation of a fluorescent *O*-alkylglycerol derivative	TLC or HPLC [17,18]
A_2, C, D	H361	Quenching by a disulfide-polymerized lipid matrix	Fluorescence increase at ~380 nm [19,20]
C	A12218	Peroxidase-linked detection of phosphocholine	Conversion of the nonfluorescent Amplex® Red reagent to fluorescent resorufin [21–23]
D	A12219	Peroxidase-linked detection of choline	Conversion of the nonfluorescent Amplex® Red reagent to fluorescent resorufin [21,23,24]

* Phospholipase specificity: A_1, A_2, C or D (see Figure 17.23 for definitions). **1.** J Biol Chem 267, 21465 (1992); **2.** Biochemistry 32, 583 (1993); **3.** Anal Biochem 116, 553 (1981); **4.** Biochim Biophys Acta 1192, 132 (1994); **5.** Anal Biochem 229, 256 (1995); **6.** Biochem J 298, 23 (1994); **7.** J Biol Chem 267, 23495 (1992); **8.** Anal Biochem 276, 27 (1999); **9.** Lipids 24, 691 (1989); **10.** Biochem Biophys Res Commun 118, 894 (1984); **11.** Biochim Biophys Acta 917, 411 (1987); **12.** Chem Phys Lipids 53, 129 (1990); **13.** Anal Biochem 177, 103 (1989); **14.** Clin Chem 31, 714 (1985); **15.** Biochemistry 32, 5373 (1993); **16.** J Biol Chem 274, 19338 (1999); **17.** Anal Biochem 218, 136 (1994); **18.** Biochem J 307, 799 (1995); **19.** Anal Biochem 221, 152 (1994); **20.** J Biol Chem 270, 263 (1995); **21.** Proc Natl Acad Sci U S A 101, 9745 (2004); **22.** Mol Pharmacol 57, 1142 (2000); **23.** Proc SPIE-Int Soc Opt Eng 3926, 166 (2000); **24.** J Biol Chem 277, 45592 (2002).

Lipids and lipid metabolites are abundant in cells and have both a structural role and a role in cell regulation. Phospholipases, in particular, play an important part in cellular signaling processes via the generation of second messengers such as diacylglycerols, arachidonate and inositol 1,4,5-triphosphate [1–4] (Ins 1,4,5-P_3, I3716; Section 17.2). In addition, phospholipase A_2 activation is a key step in inflammation processes, making these enzymes important therapeutic targets, and phospholipase A_2 plays a major role in the pathogenesis of acute respiratory distress syndrome [5–7] (ARDS). Enzymatic processing of sphingolipids and phospholipids produces a wide range of physiological and pathological effects, including apoptosis, inflammatory responses, cell differentiation and proliferation.[8,9]

Phospholipases are classified according to the cleavage site on the phospholipid substrate (Figure 17.23). There are at least three types of fluorescence-based phospholipase detection methods:[10]

- Continuous methods, which permit direct fluorometric monitoring of enzymatic activity using self-quenching or excimer-forming probes
- Methods that continuously detect nonfluorescent product formation from natural phospholipids such as the fatty acid component with our ADIFAB reagent or choline with our Amplex® Red Phospholipase Assay Kits
- Discontinuous methods, which require resolution of fluorescent substrates and products by TLC, HPLC or other separation techniques

Table 17.2 summarizes Molecular Probes' products for fluorescence-based phospholipase assays. Other applications for our wide range of fluorescent phospholipids are described in Chapter 13.

Phospholipases A_1 and A_2

Molecular Probes exclusively supplies a variety of unique fluorescent and fluorogenic substrates for phospholipases. Several of these probes may also be useful for detection of intracellular and secreted phospholipases and phospholipid-binding proteins by monitoring changes in their fluorescence intensity or polarization properties.

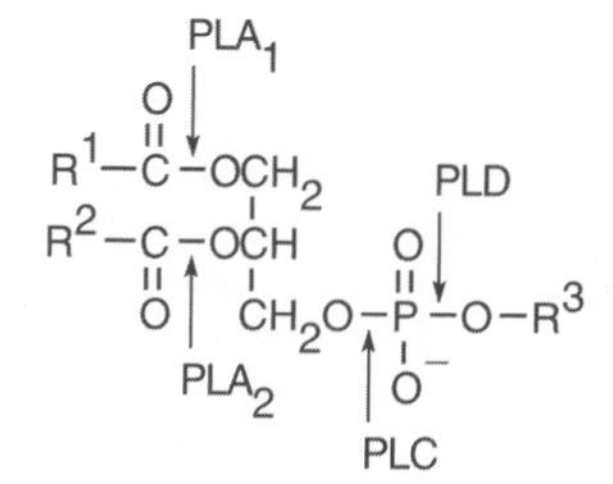

Figure 17.23 Cleavage specificities of phospholipases. R^1 and R^2 are typically saturated or unsaturated aliphatic groups. The polar head group R^3 can be choline, ethanolamine, glycerol, inositol, inositol phosphate, serine or other alcohols.

BODIPY® Dye Phospholipase A Substrates

Our patented phospholipase A substrate — bis-BODIPY® FL glycerophosphocholine (bis-BODIPY® FL C_{11}-PC, B7701) — has been specifically designed to allow continuous monitoring of phospholipase A action and to be spectrally compatible with argon-ion laser excitation sources.[11] When this probe is incorporated into cell membranes, the proximity of the BODIPY® FL fluorophores on adjacent phospholipid acyl chains causes fluorescence self-quenching (Figure 17.24). Separation of the fluorophores upon hydrolytic cleavage of one of the acyl chains by either phospholipase A_1 or A_2 results in increased fluorescence. Bis-BODIPY® FL C_{11}-PC has been developed in collaboration with Elizabeth Simons, who has successfully employed it for flow cytometric detection of phospholipase A activity in neutrophils. Using bis-BODIPY® FL C_{11}-PC and indo-1 simultaneously, researchers in the Simons lab at Boston University have demonstrated that a rise in intracellular Ca^{2+} precedes phospholipase A activation in immune complex–stimulated cells.[12] More recently, bis-BODIPY® FL C_{11}-PC has been used to detect phospholipase A_2 activation induced by tumor necrosis factor (TNF)[13] and for imaging G-protein–coupled phospholipase A activity associated with plant cell plasma membranes.[14]

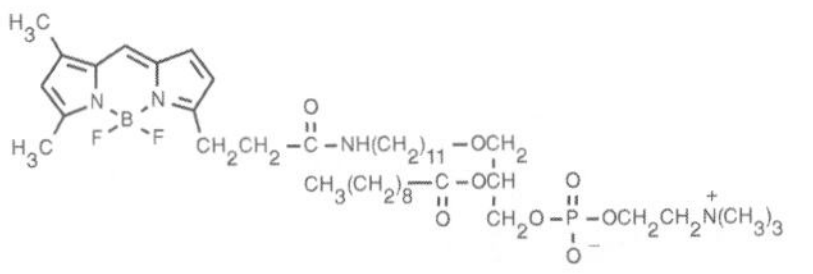

Figure 17.25 D3771 2-decanoyl-1-(*O*-(11-(4,4-difluoro-5,7-dimethyl-4-bora-3a,4a-diaza-*s*-indacene-3-propionyl)amino)undecyl)-*sn*-glycero-3-phosphocholine.

Specificity for phospholipase A_2 versus phospholipase A_1 can be obtained using phospholipids with nonhydrolyzable, ether-linked alkyl chains in the *sn*-1 position. A 1-*O*-alkyl–substituted phospholipid containing the BODIPY® FL fluorophore (D3771, Figure 17.25) is a useful substrate for a phospholipase A_2–specific chromatographic assay.[15] β-BODIPY® FL C_5-HPC (D3803) has been used to quantitatively delineate a discontinuous increase of Ca^{2+}-dependent cytosolic phospholipase A_2 ($cPLA_2$) activity during zebrafish embryogenesis. The analytical method developed for this study uses a fluorescence image scanner to quantitatively detect the free BODIPY® FL dye–labeled fatty acid generated by the action of $cPLA_2$[16] (Figure 17.26).

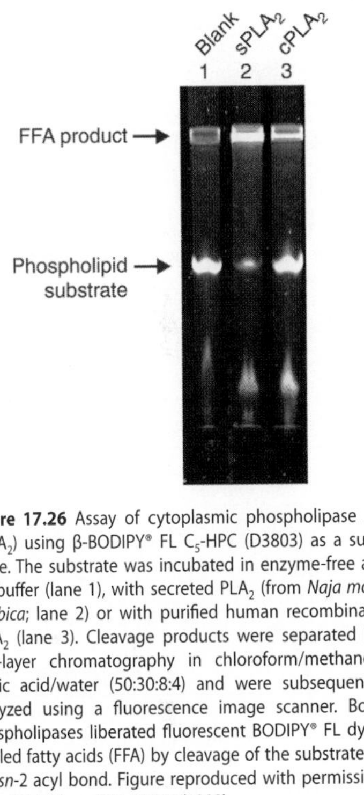

Figure 17.26 Assay of cytoplasmic phospholipase A_2 ($cPLA_2$) using β-BODIPY® FL C_5-HPC (D3803) as a substrate. The substrate was incubated in enzyme-free assay buffer (lane 1), with secreted PLA_2 (from *Naja mossambica*; lane 2) or with purified human recombinant $cPLA_2$ (lane 3). Cleavage products were separated by thin-layer chromatography in chloroform/methanol/acetic acid/water (50:30:8:4) and were subsequently analyzed using a fluorescence image scanner. Both phospholipases liberated fluorescent BODIPY® FL dye–labeled fatty acids (FFA) by cleavage of the substrate at the *sn*-2 acyl bond. Figure reproduced with permission from J Biol Chem 274, 19338 (1999).

PED6 Phospholipase A_2 Substrate

PED6 (D23739, Figure 13.14) is a fluorogenic substrate for phospholipase A_2 incorporating a BODIPY® FL dye–labeled *sn*-2 acyl chain and a dinitrophenyl quencher group[17] (Figure 17.24). Cleavage of the dye-labeled acyl chain by phospholipase A_2 eliminates the intramolecular quenching effect of the dinitrophenyl group, resulting in a corresponding fluorescence increase. Continuous kinetic assays show PED6 to be a good substrate for both secreted and cytosolic phospholipase A_2 and platelet-activating factor acetylhydrolase.[17] PED6 has been used by Steven Farber and co-workers for *in vivo* analysis of intestinal lipid metabolism in zebrafish larvae as a basis for identifying and screening mutant phenotypes[18,19] (Figure 17.27). PED6 is also useful for high-throughput screening of potential phospholipase A_2 inhibitors or activators.

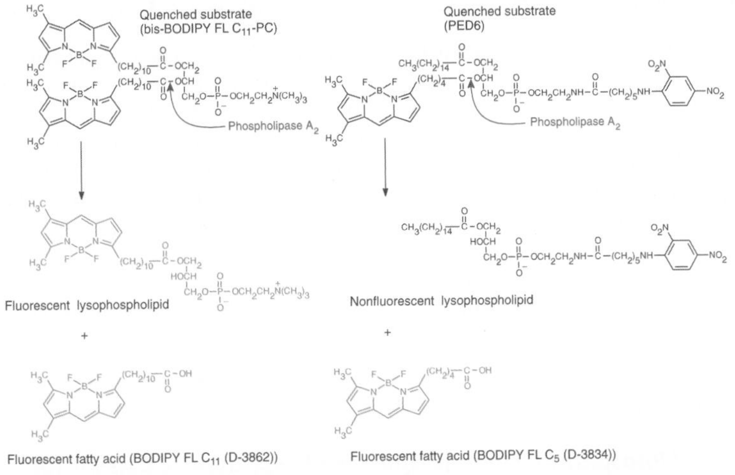

Figure 17.24 Mechanism of phospholipase activity–linked fluorescence enhancement responses of bis-BODIPY® FL C_{11}-PC (B7701) and PED6 (D23739). Note that enzymatic cleavage of bis-BODIPY® FL C_{11}-PC yields two fluorescent products, whereas cleavage of PED6 yields only one.

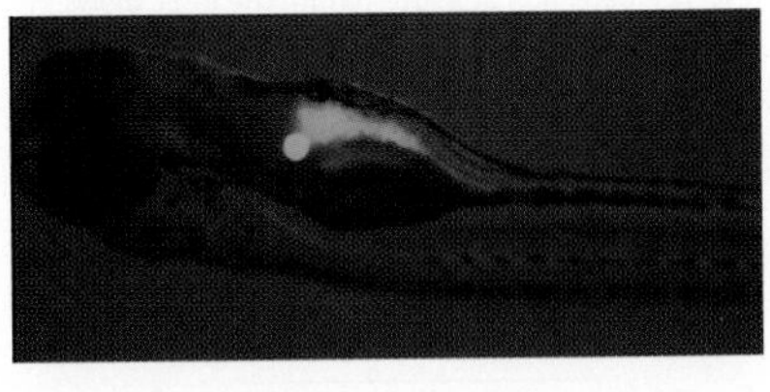

Figure 17.27 Imaging of lipid digestion pathways in zebrafish (*Danio rerio*) using the fluorogenic phospholipase A_2 substrate PED6 (D23739). A zebrafish larva (5 days post-fertilization) was incubated with 0.3 g/mL PED6 for two hours. Localized fluorescence in the gallbladder and intestinal lumen results from endogenous lipase activity and rapid transport of the substrate cleavage products through the intestinal and hepatobiliary systems. The image was provided by Steven A. Farber, Thomas Jefferson University.

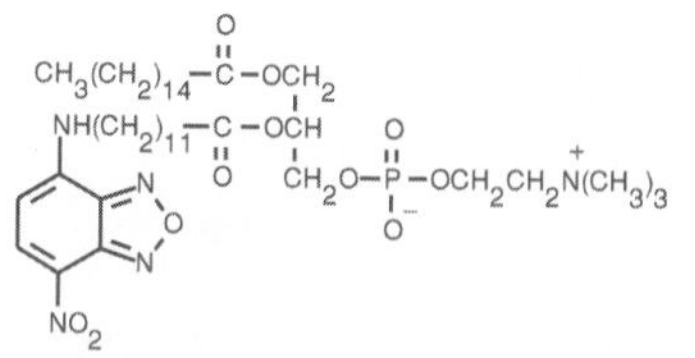

Figure 17.28 N3787 2-(12-(7-nitrobenz-2-oxa-1,3-diazol-4-yl)amino)dodecanoyl-1-hexadecanoyl-*sn*-glycero-3-phosphocholine (NBD C_{12}-HPC).

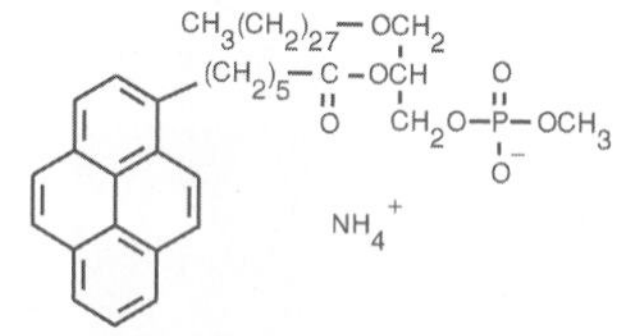

Figure 17.29 O7703 1-octacosanyl-2-(1-pyrenehexanoyl)-*sn*-glycero-3-phosphomethanol, ammonium salt (C_{28}-O-PHPM).

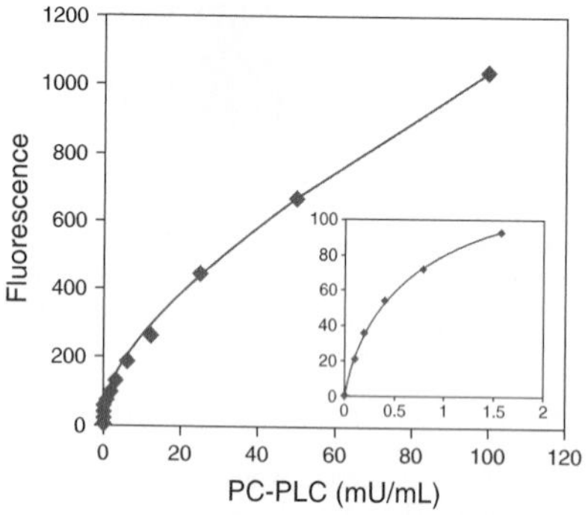

Figure 17.30 Detection of phosphatidylcholine-specific phospholipase C using the Amplex® Red Phosphatidylcholine-Specific Phospholipase C Assay Kit (A12218). Fluorescence was measured in a fluorescence microplate reader using excitation at 560 ± 10 nm and fluorescence detection at 590 ± 10 nm. The inset shows the sensitivity at very low enzyme concentrations.

Bis-Pyrenyl Phospholipase A Substrates

Our bis-pyrenyl phospholipase A probes (B3781, B3782) both emit at ~470 nm, indicating that their adjacent pyrene fluorophores (Figure 13.23) form excited-state dimers (Figure 13.8). Phospholipase A–mediated hydrolysis separates the fluorophores, which then emit as monomers at ~380 nm.[20] These substrates have proven to be effective phospholipase A_2 substrates in model membrane systems (Table 17.2); however, it has been reported that 1,2-bis-(1-pyrenebutanoyl)-*sn*-glycero-3-phosphocholine (B3781) is highly resistant to degradation by phospholipases in human skin fibroblasts.[21] 1,2-Bis-(1-pyrenebutanoyl)-*sn*-glycero-3-phosphocholine has been used in a sensitive, continuous assay for lecithin:cholesterol acyltransferase[22,23] (LCAT). These probes have several other reported applications, including investigations of protein kinase C (PKC) interactions with lipids,[24] DNA binding to liposomes[25,26] and lipid dynamics.[27–29]

Singly Labeled Pyrenyl and NBD Phospholipase A Substrates

Phospholipase A_2 activity has also been measured using phospholipids labeled with a single pyrene (H361, H3809, H3810) or NBD (N3786, N3787) fluorophore (Table 17.2). Because only the *sn*-2 phospholipid acyl chain is labeled (Figure 13.21, Figure 13.22, Figure 17.28), these probes can discriminate between phospholipase A_2 and phospholipase A_1 activity. To obtain a direct fluorescence response to enzymatic cleavage, sufficient phospholipid must be loaded into membranes to cause either intermolecular self-quenching (NBD-acyl phospholipids) or excimer formation[30] (pyreneacyl phospholipids). Pyrene-labeled acidic phospholipids — particularly the phosphoglycerol and phosphomethanol derivatives[31–38] (H3809, H3810) — are preferred as substrates by pancreatic and intestinal phospholipase A_2, whereas phosphocholines (H361, Figure 13.21) are preferred by phospholipase A_2 from snake venom.[38] A very sensitive continuous assay that uses a phosphomethanol derivative (H3810) to measure mammalian cytosolic phospholipase A_2 and human nonpancreatic phospholipase A_2 has been described.[39] 1-Octacosanyl-2-(1-pyrenehexanoyl)-*sn*-glycero-3-phosphomethanol (C_{28}-*O*-PHPM, O7703; Figure 17.29) was developed for monitoring phospholipase A_2 in serum because the bis-pyrenyl probes are not specific for phospholipase A_2 and can also produce false indications of activity due to interactions with serum proteins. The cleavage product of C_{28}-*O*-PHPM hydrolysis by phospholipase A_2 — 1-pyrenehexanoic acid (P3840, Section 13.2) — cannot be directly distinguished from the substrate based on its fluorescence. However, this product can be readily resolved by liquid/liquid partition of the dye into aqueous methanol from chloroform/heptane.[40–42] Pyrene-labeled phospholipids have been inserted into liposomes consisting of disulfide-linked polymerized phospholipids, which form a stable host matrix that is resistant to degradation by phospholipase A_2.[43,44] Pyrene fluorescence is quenched by interactions with the lipid matrix and increases upon cleavage of the probe by phospholipase. This versatile approach can be adapted for detection of phospholipase A_2 by using β-py-C_{10}-HPC (H361).

ADIFAB and DAUDA: A Different View of Phospholipase A Activity

The ADIFAB fatty acid indicator (A3880, Figure 17.42) functions as a fluorescent sensor for the free fatty acid cleavage products of phospholipases.[45–48] It does not require membrane loading and can be used to monitor hydrolysis of natural (rather than synthetic) substrates. Assaying lysophospholipase activity with ADIFAB yields sensitivity comparable to radioisotopic methods.[49] Richieri and Kleinfeld have described a methodology for using the ADIFAB reagent to measure the activity of phospholipase A_2 on cell and lipid-vesicle membranes. Their assay is capable of detecting hydrolysis rates as low as 10^{-12} mole/minute.[48] Displacement of dansylundecanoic acid (DAUDA, D94) from the rat intestinal fatty acid–binding protein I-FABP is the basis of another phospholipase A_2 assay method (Table 17.2) that is conceptually similar to the detection mechanism of ADIFAB.[50–52] There is more information about ADIFAB at the end of this section.

Phospholipase C

Amplex® Red Phosphatidylcholine-Specific Phospholipase C Assay Kit

The Amplex® Red Phosphatidylcholine-Specific Phospholipase C Assay Kit (A12218) provides a sensitive method for continuously monitoring phosphatidylcholine-specific phospholipase C (PC-PLC) activity *in vitro* using a fluorescence microplate reader or fluorometer.[53–55] In this enzyme-coupled assay, PC-PLC activity is monitored indirectly using the Amplex® Red reagent, a sensitive fluorogenic probe for H_2O_2 (Section 10.5, Figure 10.59). First, PC-PLC converts the phosphatidylcholine (lecithin) substrate to form phosphocholine and diacylglycerol. After the action of alkaline phosphatase, which hydrolyzes phosphocholine to inorganic phosphate and choline, choline is oxidized by choline oxidase to betaine and H_2O_2. Finally, H_2O_2, in the presence of horseradish peroxidase, reacts with the Amplex® Red reagent in a 1:1 stoichiometry to generate the highly fluorescent product, resorufin. Because resorufin has absorption and fluorescence emission maxima of approximately 571 nm and 585 nm, respectively, there is little interference from autofluorescence in most biological samples. Experiments with purified PC-PLC from *Bacillus cereus* (E6646, see below) indicate that the Amplex® Red Phosphatidylcholine-Specific Phospholipase C Assay Kit can detect PC-PLC levels as low as 0.2 mU/mL using a reaction time of one hour (Figure 17.30). One unit of PC-PLC is defined as the amount of enzyme that will liberate 1.0 micromole of water-soluble organic phosphorus from L-α-phosphatidylcholine per minute at pH 7.3 at 37°C. The Amplex® Red Phosphatidylcholine-Specific Phospholipase C Assay Kit is potentially useful for detecting PC-PLC activity in cell extracts and for screening PC-PLC inhibitors. Each kit includes:

- Amplex® Red reagent
- Dimethylsulfoxide (DMSO)
- Horseradish peroxidase (HRP)
- H_2O_2 for use as a positive control
- Concentrated reaction buffer
- Choline oxidase from *Alcaligenes* sp.
- Alkaline phosphatase from calf intestine
- L-α-Phosphatidylcholine (lecithin)
- Phosphatidylcholine-specific phospholipase C from *Bacillus cereus*
- A detailed protocol

Each kit provides sufficient reagents for approximately 500 assays using a fluorescence microplate reader and a reaction volume of 200 µL per assay.

D 609: A Selective Phospholipase C Inhibitor

D 609 (tricyclodecan-9-yl xanthogenate, T6615; Figure 17.31) is a selective inhibitor of phosphatidylcholine-specific phospholipase C. D 609 also is reported to have antiviral and antitumor activity. D 609 has a wide variety of indirect effects on cells, including stimulation of DNA synthesis,[56] blocking DNA fragmentation during apoptosis,[57] prevention of cell spreading[58] and enhancing the synthesis and secretion of interleukins.[59,60] D 609 is an important tool for differentiating the activities of the various PLC enzymes on phospholipids bearing different head groups and between the activities of PLC and phospholipase D[61] (PLD).

Bacillus cereus *PI-PLC*

Phosphatidylinositol-specific phospholipase C (PI-PLC, EC 3.1.4.10) from *Bacillus cereus* cleaves phosphatidylinositol (PI), yielding water-soluble D-*myo*-inositol 1,2-cyclic monophosphate and lipid-soluble diacylglycerol.[62] This enzyme also functions to release enzymes that are linked to glycosyl phosphatidylinositol (GPI) membrane anchors. Molecular Probes offers highly purified *B. cereus* PI-PLC (P6466), which has been used in studies of PI synthesis and export across the plasma membrane.[63] PI-PLC generates diacylglycerols for PKC-linked signal transduction studies[64] and provides an efficient means of releasing most GPI-anchored proteins from cell surfaces under conditions in which the cells remain viable.[65,66]

Phospholipase D

Amplex® Red Phospholipase D Assay Kit

The Amplex® Red Phospholipase D Assay Kit (A12219) provides a sensitive method for measuring phospholipase D (PLD) activity *in vitro* using a fluorescence microplate reader or fluorometer.[53,55,67] In this enzyme-coupled assay, PLD activity is monitored indirectly using the Amplex® Red reagent (Section 10.5). First, PLD cleaves the phosphatidylcholine (lecithin) substrate to yield choline and phosphatidic acid. Second, choline is oxidized by choline oxidase to betaine and H_2O_2. Finally, H_2O_2, in the presence of horseradish peroxidase, reacts with the Amplex® Red reagent to generate the highly fluorescent product, resorufin (excitation/emission maxima ~571/585 nm). This kit can be used to continuously assay PLD enzymes with near-neutral pH optima, whereas PLD enzymes with acidic pH optima can be assayed in a simple two-step procedure. Experiments with purified PLD from *Streptomyces chromofuscus* indicate that the Amplex® Red Phospholipase D Assay Kit can detect PLD levels as low as 10 mU/mL using a reaction time of one hour (Figure 17.32). One unit of PLD is defined as the amount of enzyme that will liberate 1.0 µmole of choline from L-α-phosphatidylcholine per minute at pH 8.0 at 30°C. The Amplex® Red Phospholipase D Assay Kit is potentially useful for detecting PLD activity in cell extracts or for screening PLD inhibitors. Each kit includes:

- Amplex® Red reagent
- Dimethylsulfoxide (DMSO)
- Horseradish peroxidase (HRP)
- H_2O_2 for use as a positive control

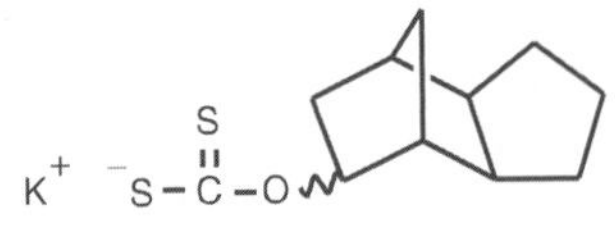

Figure 17.31 T6615 tricyclodecan-9-yl xanthogenate, potassium salt (D 609).

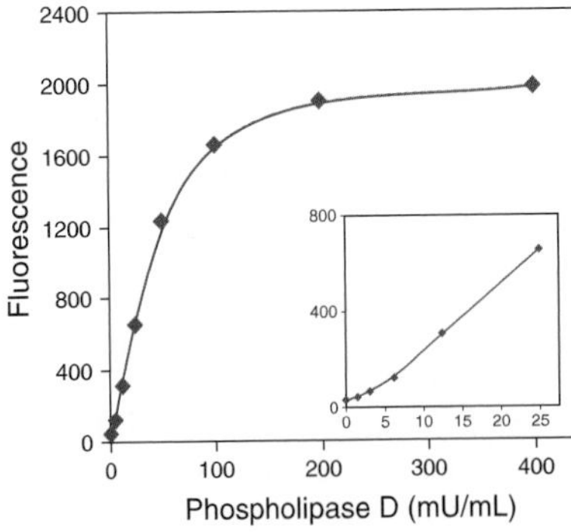

Figure 17.32 Quantitation of phospholipase D from *Streptomyces chromofuscus* using the Amplex® Red Phospholipase D Assay Kit (A12219). Fluorescence was measured with a fluorescence microplate reader using excitation at 530 ± 12.5 nm and fluorescence detection at 590 ± 17.5 nm. The inset shows the sensitivity at very low enzyme concentrations (0–25 mU/mL).

- Concentrated reaction buffer
- Choline oxidase from *Alcaligenes* sp.
- L-α-Phosphatidylcholine (lecithin)
- A detailed protocol

Each kit provides sufficient reagents for approximately 500 assays using a fluorescence microplate reader and a reaction volume of 200 µL per assay.

Fluorescent Substrates for Phospholipase D

The products of phospholipase A_2, C and D cleavage of 1-*O*-alkyl-2-decanoyl-*sn*-glycero-3-phosphocholine labeled with the BODIPY® FL fluorophore (D3771, Figure 17.25) can be separated and independently quantitated based on their differential migration on TLC or HPLC.[15,68,69] Our BODIPY® FL analog is preferred for this application because it is relatively photostable and the fluorescence properties of its different enzymatic products are all very similar.[70] Researchers have taken advantage of these features to detect and quantitate phospholipase D activity in vascular smooth muscle cells,[70,71] cultured mammalian cells[72] and yeast.[73,74]

Probes for Phosphoinositide-Mediated Cellular Functions

Phosphatidylinositol (PI or PtdIns) and its phosphorylated derivatives represent only a small fraction of eukaryotic cellular phospholipids but are functionally significant in a disproportionately large number of regulatory and signal transduction processes.[75–80] The most familiar of these processes is the phospholipase C–mediated generation of the ubiquitous second messengers inositol 1,4,5-triphosphate ($InsP_3$) and diacylglycerol (DAG) from phosphatidylinositol 4,5-diphosphate ($PtdIns(4,5)P_2$; Section 17.2; Figure 17.1). Because these events are transient and spatially compartmentalized, methods for visualizing changes in the cellular localization of phosphoinositides are essential for their complete characterization.[81] In collaboration with Echelon Biosciences, Inc. (www.echelon-inc.com), we have introduced an extensive collection of biologically active fluorescent phosphoinositides, anti-phosphoinositide antibodies and immobilized phosphoinositide arrays.

Fluorescent Phosphoinositides

We offer fluorescent analogs of phosphatidylinositol (PtdIns) and of its 3-, 4- and 5-phosphorylated derivatives (Table 17.3), together with Shuttle PIP carriers for delivering them into living cells.[82,83] All of the fluorescent analogs are labeled with a BODIPY® dye on the *sn*-1 acyl chain (Figure 17.33). This labeling pattern maximizes the separation of the dye from the inositol ring and ensures retention of biological activity.[83] Each phosphoinositide analog is available with three different BODIPY® dye label options (Table 17.3) for multicolor detection in combination with fluorescent Shuttle PIP carriers (see below), fluorescent Ca^{2+} indicators[83] or GFP chimeras. compared with alternative methods based on GFP–pleckstrin homology domain chimeras,[81] detection of intracellular phosphoinositides using these probes is not complicated by parallel detection of soluble inositol phosphates and is subject to less distributional bias.[83] A sensitive method for analyzing these fluorescent phosphoinositides and other products of lipid-modifying enzymes has been developed using a microfluidic chip device that separates lipids based on micellar electrokinetic capillary chromatography.[84]

Shuttle PIP Carriers

Shuttle PIP carriers are polybasic molecules that have been selected on the basis of their ability to facilitate intracellular delivery of phosphatidylinositol diphosphates and triphosphates into live cells in the form of electrostatically neutral complexes (Figure 17.34). Uptake of Shuttle PIP complexes of phosphoinositide by cells is a passive process (requiring only a few minutes of incubation) and has been demonstrated in mammalian (CHO, COS-7, MDCK, NIH 3T3) (Figure 17.35), yeast, plant and bacterial cell types.[83] Shuttle PIP carriers do not appear to be effective for intracellular delivery of phosphatidylinositol and its monophosphorylated derivatives. Unlabeled Shuttle PIP carriers (Shuttle PIP carrier-1 *histone H1*, S23731; Shuttle PIP carrier-2 *neomycin B sulfate*, S35900) are available, as well as the green-fluorescent Oregon Green® 488 and orange-fluorescent tetramethylrhodamine conjugates of Shuttle PIP carrier-1 (S23733, S23732). Labeled Shuttle PIP carriers are designed to enable visualization of the intracellular destinations of the carriers and their phosphoinositide cargoes in contrasting fluorescent colors.

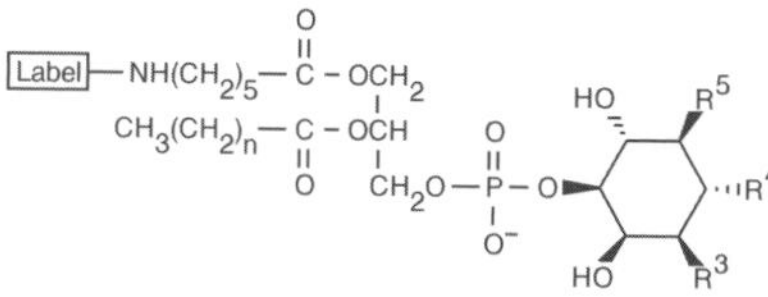

Figure 17.33 Structures of fluorescent phosphoinositides. The groups R^3, R^4 and R^5, the identities of the labels and the values of n are as described in Table 17.3.

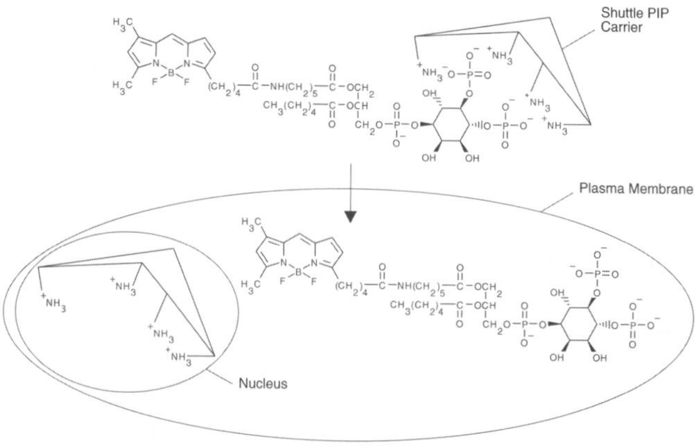

Figure 17.34 Intracellular delivery of fluorescent phosphoinositide analogs, represented by BODIPY® FL C_5, C_6-$PtdIns(4,5)P_2$ (B22627), via formation of electrostatically neutral complexes with polybasic Shuttle PIP carriers.

Table 17.3 — BODIPY® dye–labeled phosphoinositides

Phosphoinositide	Structure *				Cat #
	R^3	R^4	R^5	Label (Ex/Em) †	
PtdIns	OH	OH	OH	BODIPY® FL (505/513)	B22621
				BODIPY® TMR-X (542/574)	B22631
PtdIns(3)P	OPO_3^{2-}	OH	OH	BODIPY® TR-X (589/617)	B22641
				BODIPY® FL (505/513)	B22622, B22618
				BODIPY® TMR-X (542/574)	B22632
PtdIns(4)P	OH	OPO_3^{2-}	OH	BODIPY® TR-X (589/617)	B22642
				BODIPY® FL (505/513)	B22623, B22619
				BODIPY® TMR-X (542/574)	B22633
PtdIns(5)P	OH	OH	OPO_3^{2-}	BODIPY® TR-X (589/617)	B22643
				BODIPY® FL (505/513)	B22624, B22620
				BODIPY® TMR-X (542/574)	B22634
PtdIns(3,4)P_2	OPO_3^{2-}	OPO_3^{2-}	OH	BODIPY® TR-X (589/617)	B22644
				BODIPY® FL (505/513)	B22625
				BODIPY® TMR-X (542/574)	B22635
PtdIns(3,5)P_2	OPO_3^{2-}	OH	OPO_3^{2-}	BODIPY® TR-X (589/617)	B22645
				BODIPY® FL (505/513)	B22626
				BODIPY® TMR-X (542/574)	B22636
PtdIns(4,5)P_2	OH	OPO_3^{2-}	OPO_3^{2-}	BODIPY® TR-X (589/617)	B22646
				BODIPY® FL (505/513)	B22627
				BODIPY® TMR-X (542/574)	B22637
PtdIns(3,4,5)P_3	OPO_3^{2-}	OPO_3^{2-}	OPO_3^{2-}	BODIPY® TR-X (589/617)	B22647
				BODIPY® FL (505/513)	B22628
				BODIPY® TMR-X (542/574)	B22638

*The structural elements R^3, R^4, R^5, n and Label are defined in Figure 17.33. For B22618, B22619 and B22620, n = 14. For all other compounds, n = 4. † Fluorescence excitation (Ex) and emission (Em) maxima, in nm.

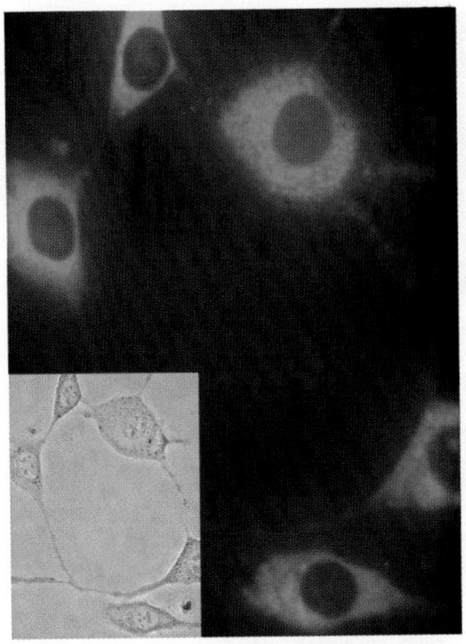

Figure 17.35 NIH 3T3 cells labeled with the green-fluorescent phosphatidylinositol analog BODIPY® FL C_5, C_6-PtdIns(4,5)P_2 (B22627), delivered as an electrostatically neutral complex with polybasic Shuttle PIP carrier-1 (S23731). The image was contributed by Paul Nielsen, Echelon Biosciences, Inc., Salt Lake City, Utah.

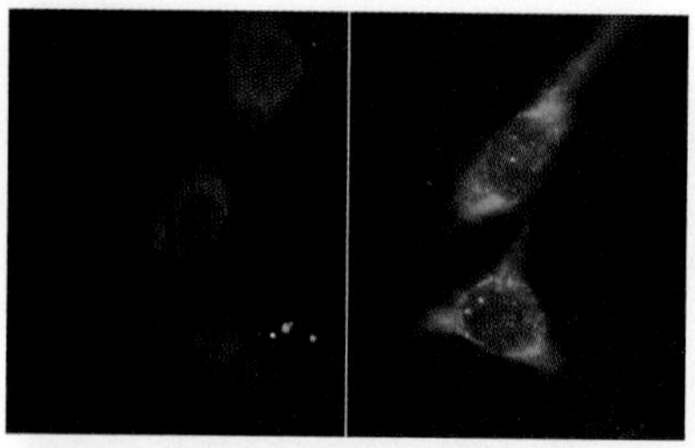

Figure 17.36 Localization of phosphatidylinositol 3,4,5-triphosphate in unstimulated (left panel) and insulin-stimulated (right panel) 3T3-L1 cells detected using anti–phosphatidylinositol 3,4,5-triphosphate, mouse IgM monoclonal RC6F8 (A21328) and visualized using biotinylated goat anti–mouse IgM in conjunction with Alexa Fluor® 488 streptavidin (S11223). Image courtesy of Echelon Research Laboratories, Inc.

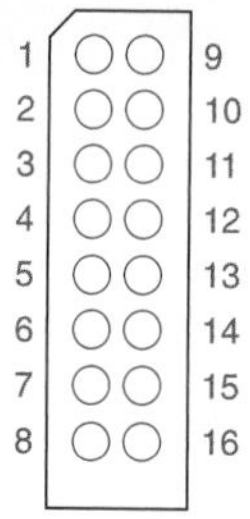

Spot #	PIP Strips * and PIP MicroStrips †	SphingoStrips *
1	Lysophosphatidic acid	Sphingosine
2	Lysophosphatidylcholine	Sphingosine 1-phosphate
3	Phosphatidylinositol (PtdIns)	Phytosphingosine
4	PtdIns(3)P	Ceramide
5	PtdIns(4)P	Sphingomyelin
6	PtdIns(5)P	Sphingosylphosphocholine
7	Phosphatidylethanolamine	Lysophosphatidic acid
8	Phosphatidylcholine	Myriocin
9	Sphingosine 1-phosphate	Monosialoganglioside G_{M1}
10	PtdIns(3,4)P_2	Disialoganglioside G_{D3}
11	PtdIns(3,5)P_2	Sulfatide
12	PtdIns(4,5)P_2	Sphingosylgalactoside (psychosine)
13	PtdIns(3,4,5)P_3	Cholesterol
14	Phosphatidic acid	Lysophosphatidylcholine
15	Phosphatidylserine	Phosphatidylcholine
16	Blank	Blank

* 100 picomoles of lipid per spot. † 20 picomoles of lipid per spot.

Figure 17.37 Layout of PIP Strips (P23750, P23751), PIP MicroStrips (P23752) and SphingoStrips (S23753). The dimensions of PIP Strips and SphingoStrips are 2 cm × 6 cm. The dimensions of PIP MicroStrips are 1.0 cm × 2.0 cm.

Table 17.4 — Phosphoinositide-coated agarose beads (PIP Beads)

Phosphoinositide	Cat # *
PtdIns	P23740
PtdIns(3)P	P23741
PtdIns(4)P	P23742
PtdIns(5)P	P23743
PtdIns(3,4)P_2	P23744
PtdIns(3,5)P_2	P23745
PtdIns(4,5)P_2	P23746
PtdIns(3,4,5)P_3	P23747

* All PIP Beads are offered as sedimented suspensions in PBS in 1 mL units (10 nanomoles of bound phosphoinositide per mL).

Phosphoinositide Cell-Labeling Kits

To facilitate initial evaluations, we have assembled a series of Phosphoinositide Cell-Labeling Kits (B22615, B22616, B22617), providing pre-tested combinations of fluorescent phosphoinositides and Shuttle PIP carriers. Each kit contains the following items:

- BODIPY® FL dye–labeled phosphoinositide
- Corresponding unlabeled phosphoinositide
- Unlabeled and tetramethylrhodamine-labeled versions of two different Shuttle PIP carriers
- An intracellular delivery protocol

Anti-Phosphoinositide Monoclonal Antibodies

Research has revealed the direct action of phosphatidylinositol 4,5-diphosphate (PtdIns(4,5)P_2) and phosphatidylinositol 3,4,5-triphosphate (PtdIns(3,4,5)P_3) on a diverse array of cellular functions, including actin assembly and cytoskeletal dynamics,[85,86] vesicular protein trafficking,[87] protein kinase localization and activation,[88] cell proliferation[89] and apoptosis.[90] We offer mouse monoclonal IgM antibodies to PtdIns(4,5)P_2 (A21327) and PtdIns(3,4,5)P_3 (A21328) for immunocytochemical localization of these important lipid metabolites[91] (Figure 17.36). Both antibodies have been shown to recognize their cognate phosphoinositides in murine and human cells with only slight crossreactivity with other phosphoinositides or phospholipids.

Arrays for Detection of Phosphoinositide–Protein Interactions

Protein domains that specifically bind phosphoinositides have emerged as major determinants in localizing proteins to their site of function.[92–95] These phosphoinositide-binding motifs, which include the C2 (PKC conserved region 2), PH (pleckstrin homology), FYVE (Fab1p/YOTP/Vac1p/EEA1), ENTH (epsin NH_2-terminal homology) and PX (Phox homology) domains, are found in proteins implicated in a diverse array of cellular processes, such as actin cytoskeletal organization, cell growth regulation, control of gene expression, protein transport, exocytosis and endocytosis. Through localized phosphoinositide biosynthesis within the cell, proteins containing these lipid-recognition domains can be directed to functionally appropriate sites. PIP Strips and PIP Arrays, developed by Echelon Biosciences, Inc., are designed for identification of proteins possessing phosphoinositide recognition domains and analysis of their lipid binding specificities. PIP Strips provide 100 picomole samples of 15 different phospholipids, and a blank sample, immobilized on nitrocellulose membranes (Figure 17.37). We offer PIP Strips in packages of two (P23750) or ten (P23751) strips. PIP Strips are also available in a miniaturized format (PIP MicroStrips, P23752), which have been designed to allow immersion inside a standard microcentrifuge tube. PIP Arrays provide eight different phospholipids arrayed in amounts from 100 to 1.6 picomoles (Figure 17.38), allowing assessment of the strength of a protein's binding, in addition to its lipid specificity. We offer PIP Arrays in packages of two (P23748) or five (P23749) arrays. Phosphoinositide-mediated binding of proteins to PIP Strips and PIP Arrays is typically analyzed by protein–lipid overlay assays.[96,97] Proteins may be detected using standard Western blot procedures in conjunction with our high-performance alkaline phosphatase– and horseradish peroxidase–mediated signal generation systems (Section 9.4).

Phosphoinositide-Coupled Agarose Beads

Through our collaboration with Echelon Biosciences, Inc., we offer phosphoinositide–coupled agarose beads (PIP Beads). PIP Beads are designed to allow isolation of phosphoinositide-binding proteins from cell lysates or expression libraries generated by *in vitro* transcription/translation reactions.[98] We offer PIP Beads coated with phosphatidylinositol (PtdIns) and each of its seven possible 3-, 4- and 5-phosphorylated derivatives (Table 17.4).

Sphingolipids

Sphingolipids include sphingomyelins, which are phospholipid analogs, as well as ceramides, glycosyl ceramides (cerebrosides), gangliosides and other derivatives (Figure 13.3). Several excellent reviews of the chemistry and biology of sphingolipids and glycosphingolipids and their role in the process of signal transduction are available.[9,99,100]

BODIPY® Sphingolipids

Ceramides (*N*-acylsphingosines), like diacylglycerols, are lipid second messengers that function in signal transduction processes.[9,101,102] The concentration-dependent spectral properties of Molecular Probes' BODIPY® FL C_5-ceramide (D3521, B22650; Figure 13.31), BODIPY® FL C_5-sphingomyelin [103–105] (D3522, Figure 13.32) and BODIPY® FL C_{12}-sphingomyelin [106] (D7711) make them particularly suitable for investigating sphingolipid transport and metabolism,[105,107–110] in addition to their applications as structural markers for the Golgi complex [111] (Section 12.4, Figure 12.51). BODIPY® FL C_5-ceramide can be visualized by fluorescence microscopy [112,113] (Figure 17.39, Figure 12.51, Figure 13.54) or by electron microscopy following diaminobenzidine (DAB) photoconversion to an electron-dense product.[114] (see Note 14.2 "Product Highlight: Fluorescent Probes for Photoconversion of Diaminobenzidine Reagents" in Section 14.3).

Our range of BODIPY® sphingolipids also includes the long-wavelength light–excitable BODIPY® TR ceramide [115,116] (D7540, Figure 17.40), as well as BODIPY® FL C_5-lactosylceramide [117–122] (D13951), BODIPY® FL C_5-ganglioside G_{M1} [123] (B13950, Figure 13.30) and three BODIPY® FL cerebrosides [109,124] (glycosylated ceramides; D7519, D7547, D7548). All of Molecular Probes' sphingolipids are prepared from D-*erythro*-sphingosine and therefore have the same stereochemical conformation as natural biologically active sphingolipids.[125]

Complexing fluorescent lipids with bovine serum albumin (BSA) facilitates cell labeling by eliminating the need for organic solvents to dissolve the lipophilic probe — the BSA-complexed probe can be directly dissolved in water.[126] We offer four BODIPY® sphingolipid–BSA complexes for the study of lipid metabolism and trafficking, including BODIPY® FL C_5-ceramide, BODIPY® TR C_5-ceramide, BODIPY® FL C_5-lactosylceramide and BODIPY® FL C_5-ganglioside G_{M1}, each complexed with defatted BSA (B22650, B34400, B34401, B34402).

BODIPY® FL C_5-ceramide has been used to investigate the linkage of sphingolipid metabolism to protein secretory pathways [127–129] and neuronal growth.[120,130] Internalization of BODIPY® FL C_5-sphingomyelin (D3522) from the plasma membrane of human skin fibroblasts results in a mixed population of labeled endosomes that can be distinguished based on the concentration-dependent green (~515 nm) or red (~620 nm) emission of the probe [105] (Figure 12.51). BODIPY® C_5-sphingomyelin has also been used to assess sphingomyelinase gene transfer and expression in hematopoietic stem and progenitor cells.[131] Our BODIPY® FL C_5-lactosylceramide, BODIPY® FL C_5-ganglioside G_{M1} and BODIPY® FL cerebrosides should be useful tools for the study of glycosphingolipid transport and signaling pathways in cells [132,133] and for diagnosis of lipid-storage disorders such as Niemann–Pick disease,[134] Gaucher's disease, G_{M1} gangliosidosis, Morquio's syndrome and type IV mucolipidosis [122,135–142] (ML-IV). Addition of BODIPY® FL C_5-lactosylceramide to the culture medium of cells from patients with sphingolipid-storage diseases (sphingolipidosis) results in fluorescent product accumulation in lysosomes, whereas this probe accumulates in the Golgi apparatus of normal cells and cells from patients with other storage diseases.[119,121] BODIPY® FL C_5-ganglioside G_{M1} has been shown to form cholesterol-enhanced clusters in membrane complexes with amyloid β-protein in a model of Alzheimer's disease amyloid fibrils.[143] Colocalization of fluorescent cholera toxin B conjugates (Section 7.7) and BODIPY® FL C_5-ganglioside G_{M1} observed by fluorescence microscopy provides a direct indication of the association of these molecules in lipid rafts [123] (Figure 13.33, Figure 17.41). Studies by Martin and Pagano have shown that the internalization routes for BODIPY® FL C_5-glucocerebroside (D7548) follow both endocytic and nonendocytic pathways and are quite different from those for BODIPY® FL C_5-sphingomyelin.[124]

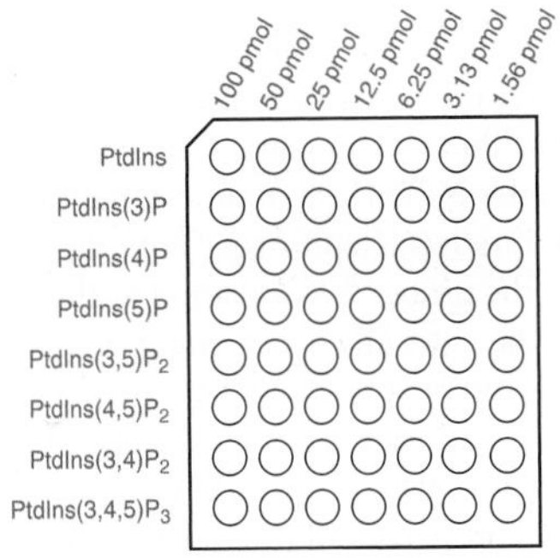

Figure 17.38 Layout of immobilized phosphoinositides on PIP Arrays (P23748, P23749). The dimensions of PIP Arrays are 4 cm × 4 cm.

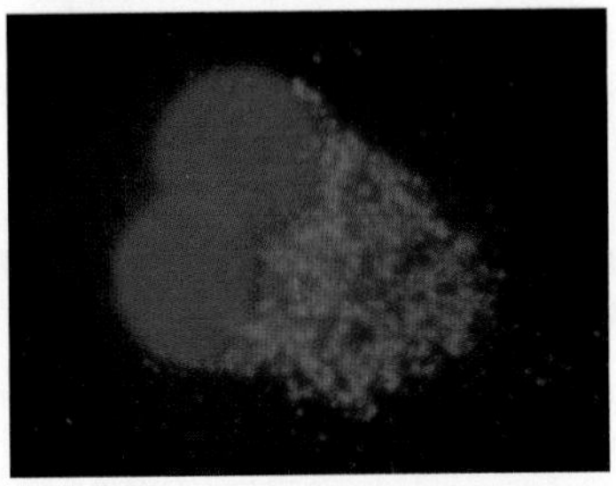

Figure 17.39 Nucleus and Golgi apparatus of a bovine pulmonary artery endothelial cell (BPAEC) labeled with Hoechst 33342 (H1399, H3569, H21492) and the BSA complex of BODIPY® FL C_5-ceramide (D3521, B22650), respectively.

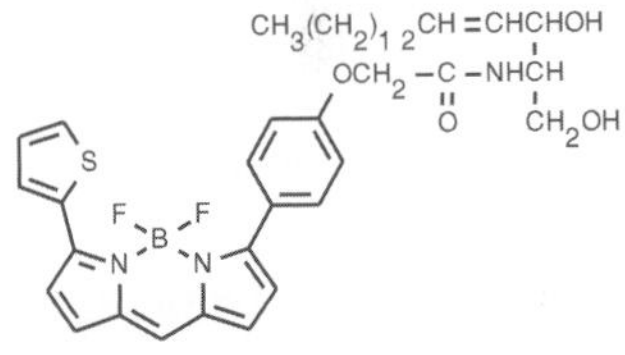

Figure 17.40 D7540 *N*-((4-(4,4-difluoro-5-(2-thienyl)-4-bora-3a,4a-diaza-*s*-indacene-3-yl)phenoxy)acetyl)sphingosine (BODIPY® TR ceramide).

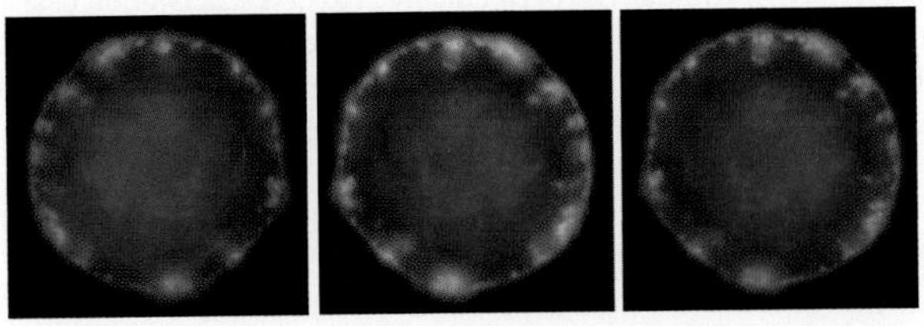

Figure 17.41 A J774 mouse macrophage cell sequentially stained with BODIPY® FL ganglioside G_{M1} (B13950) and then with Alexa Fluor® 555 dye–labeled cholera toxin subunit B (C22843, C34776; also available as a component of V34404). The cell was then treated with an anti–CT-B antibody (a component of V34404) to induce crosslinking. Alexa Fluor® 555 dye fluorescence (left panel, red) and BODIPY® FL dye fluorescence (right panel, green) were imaged separately and overlaid to emphasize the coincident staining (center panel, yellow). Nuclei were stained with blue-fluorescent Hoechst 33258 (H1398, H3569, H21491).

NBD Sphingolipids

NBD C_6-ceramide (N1154) and NBD C_6-sphingomyelin (N3524) analogs predate their BODIPY® counterparts and have been extensively used for following sphingolipid metabolism in cells [132,144,145] and in multicellular organisms.[146] As with BODIPY® FL C_5-ceramide, we also offer NBD C_6-ceramide complexed with defatted BSA (N22651) to facilitate cell loading without the use of organic solvents to dissolve the probe.[126] Koval and Pagano have prepared NBD analogs of both the naturally occurring D-*erythro* and the nonnatural L-*threo* stereoisomers of sphingomyelin and have compared their intracellular transport behavior in Chinese hamster ovary (CHO) fibroblasts.[147] NBD C_6-ceramide lacks the useful concentration-dependent optical properties of the BODIPY® FL analog and is less photostable; however, the fluorescence of NBD C_6-ceramide is apparently sensitive to the cholesterol content of the Golgi apparatus, a phenomenon that is not observed with BODIPY® FL C_5-ceramide. If NBD C_6-ceramide–containing cells are starved for cholesterol, the NBD C_6-ceramide that accumulates within the Golgi apparatus appears to be severely photolabile, but this NBD photobleaching can be reduced by stimulation of cholesterol synthesis. Thus, NBD C_6-ceramide may be useful in monitoring the cholesterol content of the Golgi apparatus in live cells.[148]

Arrays for Detection of Sphingolipid–Protein Interactions

Sphingolipid–protein interactions are involved in physiological and pathological processes, including signal transduction mediated by G-protein–coupled receptors (GPCRs),[149,150] induction of apoptosis [151] and amyloid fibril formation.[143] SphingoStrips, developed by Echelon Biosciences, Inc., are designed for identification of proteins possessing sphingolipid recognition domains and analysis of their lipid-binding specificities. SphingoStrips provide 100 picomole samples of 15 different lipids, and a blank sample, immobilized on nitrocellulose membranes (Figure 17.37), and are offered in packages of 10 strips (S23753). Membrane-bound proteins may be detected using standard Western blot procedures in conjunction with our high-performance alkaline phosphatase– and horseradish peroxidase–mediated signal generation systems (Section 9.4).

Vybrant® Lipid Raft Labeling Kits

The Vybrant® Lipid Raft Labeling Kits (V34403, V34404, V34405) are designed to provide convenient, reliable and extremely bright fluorescent labeling of lipid rafts in live cells. Lipid rafts are detergent-insoluble, sphingolipid- and cholesterol-rich membrane microdomains that form lateral assemblies in the plasma membrane.[152–158] Lipid rafts also sequester glycophosphatidylinositol (GPI)-linked proteins and other signaling proteins and receptors, which may be regulated by their selective interactions with these membrane microdomains.[123,159–163] Recent research has demonstrated that lipid rafts play a role in a variety of cellular processes — including the compartmentalization of cell-signaling events,[164–171] the regulation of apoptosis [172–174] and the intracellular trafficking of certain membrane proteins and lipids [175–177] — as well as in the infectious cycles of several viruses and bacterial pathogens.[178–183] Examining the formation and regulation of lipid rafts is a critical step in understanding these aspects of eukaryotic cell function.

The Vybrant® Lipid Raft Labeling Kits provide the key reagents for fluorescently labeling lipid rafts *in vivo* with our bright and extremely photostable Alexa Fluor® dyes (Figure 13.33, Figure 17.41). Live cells are first labeled with the green-fluorescent Alexa Fluor® 488, orange-fluorescent Alexa Fluor® 555 or red-fluorescent Alexa Fluor® 594 conjugate of cholera toxin subunit B (CT-B). This CT-B conjugate binds to the pentasaccharide chain of plasma membrane ganglioside G_{M1}, which selectively partitions into lipid rafts.[123,184,185] All of Molecular Probes' CT-B conjugates are prepared from recombinant CT-B and are completely free of the toxic subunit A, thus eliminating any concern for toxicity or ADP-ribosylating activity. An antibody that specifically recognizes CT-B is then used to crosslink the CT-B–labeled lipid rafts into distinct patches on the plasma membrane, which are easily visualized by fluorescence microscopy.[186,187] Each Vybrant® Lipid Raft Labeling Kit contains sufficient reagents to label 50 live-cell samples in a 2 mL assay, including:

- Recombinant cholera toxin subunit B (CT-B) labeled with the Alexa Fluor® 488 (in Kit V34403), Alexa Fluor® 555 (in Kit V34404) or Alexa Fluor® 594 (in Kit V34405) dye
- Anti–cholera toxin subunit B antibody (anti–CT-B)
- Concentrated phosphate-buffered saline (PBS)
- A detailed labeling protocol

Because they are compatible with various multilabeling schemes, the Vybrant® Lipid Raft Labeling Kits can also serve as important tools for identifying physiologically significant membrane proteins that associate with lipid rafts. Cells can be labeled with other live-cell probes during the lipid raft labeling protocol or immediately following the antibody crosslinking step, depending on the specific labeling requirements of the other probes. Alternatively, once the lipid rafts have been labeled and crosslinked, the cells can be fixed for long-term storage or fixed and permeabilized for subsequent labeling with antibodies or other probes that are impermeant to live cells.

Amplex® Red Sphingomyelinase Assay Kit

The Amplex® Red Sphingomyelinase Assay Kit (A12220) is designed for measuring sphingomyelinase activity in solution using a fluorescence microplate reader or fluorometer (Figure 13.35). This assay should be useful for screening sphingomyelinase activators or inhibitors or for detecting sphingomyelinase activity in cell and tissue extracts. The assay, which uses natural sphingomyelin as the principal substrate, employs an enzyme-coupled detection scheme in which phosphocholine liberated by the action of sphingomyelinase is cleaved by alkaline phosphatase to generate choline. Choline is, in turn, oxidized to betaine by choline oxidase, generating H_2O_2, which drives the conversion of the Amplex® Red reagent (A12222, A22177; Section 10.5) to red-fluorescent resorufin (Figure 10.6). This sensitive assay technique has been employed to detect activation of acid sphingomyelinase associated with ultraviolet radiation–induced apoptosis [188] and to characterize an insecticidal sphingomyelinase C produced by *Bacillus cereus*.[189] The Amplex® Red Sphingomyelinase Assay Kit contains:

- Amplex® Red reagent
- Dimethylsulfoxide (DMSO)
- Horseradish peroxidase (HRP)
- H_2O_2 for use as a positive control
- Concentrated reaction buffer
- Choline oxidase from *Alcaligenes* sp.
- Alkaline phosphatase from calf intestine
- Sphingomyelin

- Triton X-100
- Sphingomyelinase from *Staphylococcus* sp.
- A detailed protocol

Each kit provides sufficient reagents for approximately 500 assays using a fluorescence microplate reader and a reaction volume of 200 µL per assay.

ADIFAB: A Unique Free Fatty Acid Indicator

Elevated levels of free fatty acids (FFA) — which are associated with multiple pathological states, including cancer, diabetes and cardiac ischemia [190] — are generated by inflammatory responses, phospholipase A activity and cytotoxic phenomena.[191] Sensitive techniques are required to detect and quantitate free fatty acids because these important metabolites have low aqueous solubility and are usually found complexed to carriers. ADIFAB (A3880) is a dual-wavelength fluorescent FFA indicator that consists of a polarity-sensitive fluorescent probe (acrylodan, A433; Section 2.3) conjugated to I-FABP, a rat intestinal fatty acid–binding protein with a low molecular weight (15,000 daltons) and a high binding affinity for FFA [192–194] (Figure 17.42).

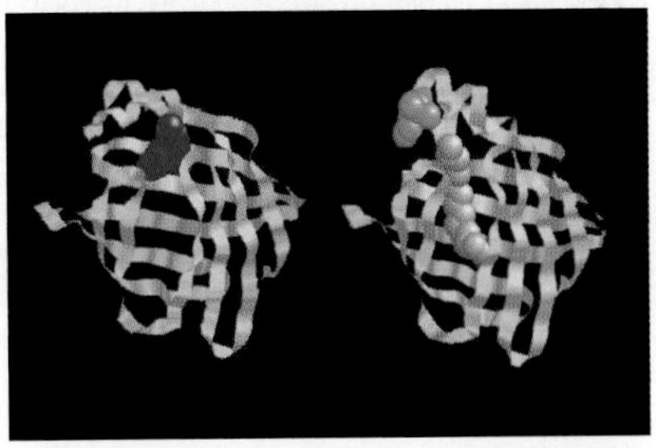

Figure 17.42 Ribbon representation of the ADIFAB free fatty acid indicator (A3880). In the left-hand image, the fatty acid binding site of intestinal fatty acid–binding protein (yellow) is occupied by a covalently attached acrylodan fluorophore (blue). In the right-hand image, a fatty acid molecule (gray) binds to the protein, displacing the fluorophore (green) and producing a shift of its fluorescence emission spectrum. Image contributed by Alan Kleinfeld, FFA Sciences LLC, San Diego.

As shown in Figure 17.43, titration of the ADIFAB reagent with oleic acid results in a shift of its fluorescence maximum from ~432 nm to ~505 nm. The ratio (R) of these signals (505 nm/432 nm) can be converted to an FFA concentration by using the FFA dissociation constant (K_d) and employing analysis procedures similar to those developed for Ca^{2+} indicators [195] (Chapter 19). Values of K_d vary considerably for different fatty acids; a typical value is 0.28 µM for oleic acid [194] (determined at 37°C). There is little, if any, interference from bile acids, glycerides, sterols or bilirubin. With appropriate precautions, which are described in the product information included with the material, ADIFAB can be used to determine FFA concentrations in the range 1 nM to >20 µM.

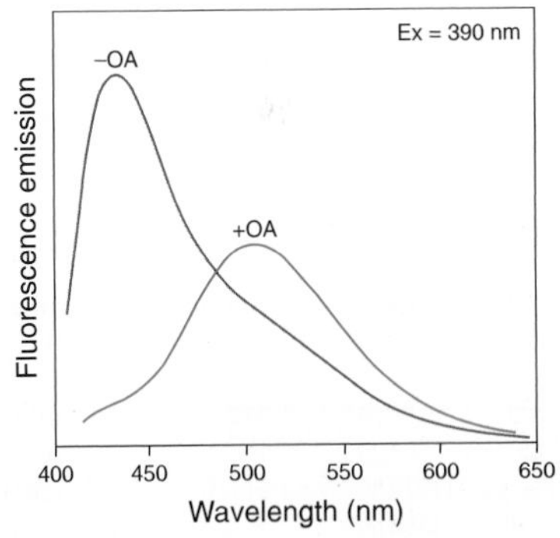

Figure 17.43 The free fatty acid–dependent spectral shift of ADIFAB (A3880). Spectra shown represent 0.2 µM ADIFAB in pH 8.0 buffer with (+OA) and without (–OA) addition of 4.7 µM *cis*-9-octadecenoic (oleic) acid (OA). The ratio of fluorescence emission intensities at 505 nm and 432 nm can be quantitatively related to free fatty acid concentrations.

ADIFAB was used to investigate the physical basis of *cis*-unsaturated fatty acid inhibition of cytotoxic T cells.[196] This effect is due to inhibition of a specific tyrosine phosphorylation event that normally accompanies antigen stimulation.[197,198] Measurements using ADIFAB have also revealed previously undetected differences in FFA binding affinities among fatty acid–binding proteins from different tissues [199,200] and have enabled quantitation of FFA levels in human serum as a potential diagnostic tool.[190,201]

References

1. Nat Rev Mol Cell Biol 2, 327 (2001); **2.** Curr Opin Struct Biol 10, 737 (2000); **3.** Physiol Rev 80, 1291 (2000); **4.** Biochim Biophys Acta 1212, 26 (1994); **5.** Biochim Biophys Acta 1488, 124 (2000); **6.** Mol Med Today 5, 244 (1999); **7.** FASEB J 8, 916 (1994); **8.** Annu Rev Physiol 60, 643 (1998); **9.** Biochemistry 40, 4893 (2001); **10.** Anal Biochem 219, 1 (1994); **11.** Br J Pharmacol 124, 1675 (1998); **12.** J Biol Chem 267, 21465 (1992); **13.** J Biol Chem 276, 12035 (2001); **14.** Biochim Biophys Acta 1448, 390 (1999); **15.** Anal Biochem 185, 80 (1990); **16.** J Biol Chem 274, 19338 (1999); **17.** Anal Biochem 276, 27 (1999); **18.** Science 292, 1385 (2001); **19.** Science 288, 1160 (2000); **20.** Anal Biochem 116, 553 (1981); **21.** Biochemistry 34, 2049 (1995); **22.** Biochim Biophys Acta 1486, 321 (2000); **23.** J Lipid Res 33, 1863 (1992); **24.** J Biol Chem 270, 1254 (1995); **25.** Chem Phys Lipids 72, 77 (1994); **26.** Chem Phys Lipids 66, 75 (1993); **27.** Biochemistry 38, 9328 (1999); **28.** Biophys J 66, 1981 (1994); **29.** Biophys J 64, 137 (1993); **30.** J Neurosci Methods 100, 127 (2000); **31.** Biochemistry 38, 7803 (1999); **32.** Biochemistry 36, 14325 (1997); **33.** Biophys J 70, 2185 (1996); **34.** Biochemistry 35, 4529 (1996); **35.** Biochemistry 35, 12164 (1996); **36.** J Biol Chem 270, 17327 (1995); **37.** Biochemistry 30, 8074 (1991); **38.** Biochim Biophys Acta 917, 411 (1987); **39.** Anal Biochem 232, 7 (1995); **40.** Clin Chem 31, 714 (1985); **41.** Biochem Biophys Res Commun 185, 185 (1992); **42.** J Biol Chem 266, 6302 (1991); **43.** Biochemistry 32, 13902 (1993); **44.** J Am Chem Soc 108, 7789 (1986); **45.** J Biol Chem 276, 22732 (2001); **46.** J Biol Chem 274, 11494 (1999); **47.** Biochemistry 38, 3867 (1999); **48.** Anal Biochem 229, 256 (1995); **49.** Biochem J 298, 23 (1994); **50.** Biochim Biophys Acta 1484, 195 (2000); **51.** Anal Biochem 212, 65 (1993); **52.** Biochem J 266, 435 (1990); **53.** Proc Natl Acad Sci U S A 101, 9745 (2004); **54.** Mol Pharmacol 57, 1142 (2000); **55.** Proc SPIE-Int Soc Opt Eng 3926, 166 (2000); **56.** Biochem Pharmacol 55, 915 (1998); **57.** Endothelium 5, 231 (1997); **58.** J Leukoc Biol 65, 127 (1999); **59.** J Cell Biochem 67, 103 (1997); **60.** J Biol Chem 272, 25099 (1997); **61.** Biochim Biophys Acta 1487, 201 (2000); **62.** J Mol Biol 275, 635 (1998); **63.** Biochim Biophys Acta 1224, 247 (1994); **64.** J Biol Chem 269, 4098 (1994); **65.** J Biol Chem 266, 1926 (1991); **66.** J Neurochem 57, 67 (1991); **67.** J Biol Chem 277, 45592 (2002); **68.** Anal Biochem 286, 277 (2000); **69.** J Biol Chem 272, 12909 (1997); **70.** Anal Biochem 218, 136 (1994); **71.** J Biol Chem 269, 23790 (1994); **72.** Mol Biol Cell 10, 3863 (1999); **73.** Biochem J 314, 15 (1996); **74.** Biochem J 307, 799 (1995); **75.** Biochem J 360, 513 (2001); **76.** Biochem J 355, 249 (2001); **77.** Cell 100, 603 (2000); **78.** J Biol Chem 274, 8347 (1999); **79.** J Biol Chem 274, 9907 (1999); **80.** Annu Rev Cell Dev Biol 14, 231 (1998); **81.** Trends Pharmacol Sci 21, 238 (2000); **82.** Biochem J 379, 527 (2004); **83.** Proc Natl Acad Sci U S A 97, 11286 (2000); **84.** Anal Biochem 314, 97 (2003); **85.** Chem Phys Lipids 98, 13 (1999); **86.** Chem Phys Lipids 101, 93 (1999); **87.** J Biol Chem 274, 9129 (1999); **88.** Annu Rev Biochem 68, 965 (1999); **89.** Proc Natl Acad Sci U S A 96, 4240

References — continued

(1999); **90.** J Cell Biol 151, 483 (2000); **91.** Biochem Soc Trans 27, 648 (1999); **92.** Science 294, 1881 (2001); **93.** Science 292, 2041 (2001); **94.** Nat Cell Biol 3, E179 (2001); **95.** Curr Opin Cell Biol 13, 146 (2001); **96.** Biochem J 351, 19 (2000); **97.** Biochem J 342, 7 (1999); **98.** J Biol Chem 274, 37893 (1999); **99.** Annu Rev Biochem 67, 27 (1998); **100.** Prog Lipid Res 36, 153 (1997); **101.** Trends Cell Biol 10, 408 (2000); **102.** J Biol Chem 269, 3125 (1994); **103.** Chem Phys Lipids 102, 55 (1999); **104.** Ann N Y Acad Sci 845, 152 (1998); **105.** Biophys J 72, 37 (1997); **106.** J Cell Biol 140, 39 (1998); **107.** Methods Enzymol 312, 293 (2000); **108.** Methods Enzymol 312, 523 (2000); **109.** Frontiers in Bioactive Lipids, Vanderhoek JV, Ed. pp. 203–213 (1996); **110.** J Cell Biol 134, 1031 (1996); **111.** J Cell Biol 113, 1267 (1991); **112.** Cytometry 14, 251 (1993); **113.** J Cell Biol 120, 399 (1993); **114.** Eur J Cell Biol 58, 214 (1992); **115.** Mol Biochem Parasitol 106, 21 (2000); **116.** Infect Immun 68, 5960 (2000); **117.** J Cell Biol 154, 535 (2001); **118.** Am J Physiol Lung Cell Mol Physiol 280, L938 (2001); **119.** Nat Cell Biol 1, 386 (1999); **120.** J Neurochem 73, 1375 (1999); **121.** Lancet 354, 901 (1999); **122.** Proc Natl Acad Sci U S A 95, 6373 (1998); **123.** J Cell Biol 147, 447 (1999); **124.** J Cell Biol 125, 769 (1994); **125.** Biophys J 77, 1498 (1999); **126.** Cell Biology: A Laboratory Handbook, 2nd Ed., Vol. 2, Celis JE, Ed. pp. 507–512 (1998); **127.** Mol Biol Cell 6, 135 (1995); **128.** J Biol Chem 268, 4577 (1993); **129.** Biochemistry 31, 3581 (1992); **130.** J Biol Chem 268, 14476 (1993); **131.** Blood 93, 80 (1999); **132.** Biochim Biophys Acta 1113, 277 (1992); **133.** Brain Res 597, 108 (1992); **134.** Anal Biochem 293, 204 (2001); **135.** Biochim Biophys Acta 1455, 85 (1999); **136.** Traffic 1, 807 (2000); **137.** J Biol Chem 268, 14861 (1993); **138.** Biochim Biophys Acta 915, 87 (1987); **139.** Clin Chim Acta 142, 313 (1984); **140.** Clin Chim Acta 124, 123 (1982); **141.** Biochem Biophys Res Comm 18, 221 (1965); **142.** Anal Biochem 136, 223 (1984); **143.** J Biol Chem 276, 24985 (2001); **144.** Adv Cell Mol Biol Membranes 1, 199 (1993); **145.** Biochim Biophys Acta 1082, 113 (1991); **146.** Parasitology 105, 81 (1992); **147.** J Cell Biol 108, 2169 (1989); **148.** Proc Natl Acad Sci U S A 90, 2661 (1993); **149.** J Biol Chem 275, 288 (2000); **150.** J Cell Biol 153, 429 (2001); **151.** Chem Biol 6, 221 (1999); **152.** J Cell Biol 162, 365 (2003); **153.** J Lipid Res 44, 655 (2003); **154.** Eur J Biochem 269, 737 (2002); **155.** Science 290, 1721 (2000); **156.** Mol Membr Biol 16, 145 (1999); **157.** Trends Cell Biol 9, 87 (1999); **158.** Annu Rev Cell Dev Biol 14, 111 (1998); **159.** Proc Natl Acad Sci U S A 100, 5813 (2003); **160.** J Immunol 170, 1329 (2003); **161.** J Membr Biol 189, 35 (2002); **162.** Proc Natl Acad Sci U S A 98, 9098 (2001); **163.** Mol Biol Cell 10, 3187 (1999); **164.** Biochim Biophys Acta 1610, 247 (2003); **165.** Annu Rev Immunol 21, 457 (2003); **166.** Mol Immunol 38, 1247 (2002); **167.** Nat Rev Immunol 2, 96 (2002); **168.** Biol Res 35, 127 (2002); **169.** Nat Rev Mol Cell Biol 1, 31 (2000); **170.** J Exp Med 190, 1549 (1999); **171.** J Cell Biol 143, 637 (1998); **172.** Immunity 18, 655 (2003); **173.** J Biol Chem 277, 39541 (2002); **174.** Biochem Biophys Res Commun 297, 876 (2002); **175.** Biol Chem 383, 1475 (2002); **176.** J Cell Biol 153, 529 (2001); **177.** J Cell Sci 114, 3957 (2001); **178.** J Virol 77, 9542 (2003); **179.** Exp Cell Res 287, 67 (2003); **180.** Traffic 3, 705 (2002); **181.** J Clin Virol 22, 217 (2001); **182.** Curr Biol 10, R823 (2000); **183.** J Virol 74, 3264 (2000); **184.** Biochemistry 35, 16069 (1996); **185.** Mol Microbiol 13, 745 (1994); **186.** J Cell Biol 141, 929 (1998); **187.** J Biol Chem 269, 30745 (1994); **188.** J Biol Chem 276, 11775 (2001); **189.** Eur J Biochem 271, 601 (2004); **190.** Am J Cardiol 78, 1350 (1996); **191.** J Immunol 147, 2809 (1991); **192.** J Biol Chem 270, 15076 (1995); **193.** Biochemistry 32, 7574 (1993); **194.** J Biol Chem 267, 23495 (1992); **195.** Mol Cell Biochem 192, 87 (1999); **196.** Biochemistry 32, 530 (1993); **197.** J Biol Chem 269, 9506 (1994); **198.** J Biol Chem 268, 17578 (1993); **199.** Biochemistry 39, 7197 (2000); **200.** J Biol Chem 269, 23918 (1994); **201.** J Lipid Res 36, 229 (1995).

Data Table — 17.4 Probes for Lipid Metabolism and Signaling

Cat #	MW	Storage	Soluble	Abs	EC	Em	Solvent	Notes
A3880	~15,350	FF,L,AA	H_2O	365	10,500	432	H_2O	1
A7509	341.53	F	DMSO, EtOH	<300		none		
B3781	797.88	FF,D,L	see Notes	342	75,000	471	EtOH	2, 3
B3782	966.20	FF,D,L	see Notes	340	62,000	473	EtOH	2, 4
B7701	1029.80	FF,D,L	see Notes	505	123,000	512	MeOH	2, 5
B13950	1582.50	F,D,L	DMSO, EtOH	505	80,000	512	MeOH	6
B22618	1371.47	F,D,L	DMSO	504	80,000	511	MeOH	7
B22619	1371.47	F,D,L	DMSO	504	80,000	511	MeOH	7
B22620	1371.47	F,D,L	DMSO	504	80,000	511	MeOH	7
B22621	948.84	F,D,L	DMSO	504	80,000	511	MeOH	7
B22622	1231.20	F,D,L	H_2O, DMSO	504	80,000	511	MeOH	7
B22623	1231.20	F,D,L	H_2O, DMSO	504	80,000	511	MeOH	7
B22624	1231.20	F,D,L	H_2O, DMSO	504	80,000	511	MeOH	7
B22625	1513.57	F,D,L	H_2O, DMSO	504	80,000	511	MeOH	7
B22626	1513.57	F,D,L	H_2O, DMSO	504	80,000	511	MeOH	7
B22627	1513.57	F,D,L	H_2O, DMSO	504	80,000	511	MeOH	7
B22628	1795.93	F,D,L	H_2O, DMSO	504	80,000	511	MeOH	7
B22631	1140.07	F,D,L	DMSO	544	60,000	570	MeOH	7
B22632	1422.43	F,D,L	H_2O, DMSO	544	60,000	570	MeOH	7
B22633	1422.43	F,D,L	H_2O, DMSO	544	60,000	570	MeOH	7
B22634	1422.43	F,D,L	H_2O, DMSO	544	60,000	570	MeOH	7
B22635	1704.79	F,D,L	H_2O, DMSO	544	60,000	570	MeOH	7
B22636	1704.79	F,D,L	H_2O, DMSO	544	60,000	570	MeOH	7
B22637	1704.79	F,D,L	H_2O, DMSO	544	60,000	570	MeOH	7
B22638	1987.16	F,D,L	H_2O, DMSO	544	60,000	570	MeOH	7
B22641	1166.08	F,D,L	DMSO	588	68,000	616	MeOH	7
B22642	1448.44	F,D,L	H_2O, DMSO	588	68,000	616	MeOH	7
B22643	1448.44	F,D,L	H_2O, DMSO	588	68,000	616	MeOH	7
B22644	1448.44	F,D,L	H_2O, DMSO	588	68,000	616	MeOH	7
B22645	1730.81	F,D,L	H_2O, DMSO	588	68,000	616	MeOH	7
B22646	1730.81	F,D,L	H_2O, DMSO	588	68,000	616	MeOH	7
B22647	1730.81	F,D,L	H_2O, DMSO	588	68,000	616	MeOH	7
B22648	2013.17	F,D,L	H_2O, DMSO	588	68,000	616	MeOH	7
B22650	~66,000	F,D,L	H_2O	505	91,000	511	MeOH	6, 8
B34400	~66,000	F,D,L	H_2O	589	65,000	616	MeOH	8
B34401	~66,000	F,D,L	H_2O	505	80,000	512	MeOH	6, 8
B34402	~66,000	F,D,L	H_2O	505	80,000	511	MeOH	6, 8
D94	434.59	F,L	DMSO, EtOH	335	4,800	519	MeOH	

Cat #	MW	Storage	Soluble	Abs	EC	Em	Solvent	Notes
D3521	601.63	FF,D,L	$CHCl_3$, DMSO	505	91,000	511	MeOH	6
D3522	766.75	FF,D,L	see Notes	505	77,000	512	MeOH	2, 6
D3771	854.86	FF,D,L	see Notes	506	71,000	512	EtOH	2
D3803	797.77	FF,D,L	see Notes	503	80,000	512	MeOH	2, 9
D7519	861.96	FF,D,L	DMSO, EtOH	505	85,000	511	MeOH	6
D7540	705.71	FF,D,L	$CHCl_3$, DMSO	589	65,000	616	MeOH	
D7546	759.42	FF,D,L	$CHCl_3$, DMSO	533	80,000	545	MeOH	
D7547	861.96	FF,D,L	DMSO, EtOH	505	85,000	511	MeOH	6
D7548	763.77	FF,D,L	DMSO, EtOH	505	85,000	511	MeOH	6
D7711	864.94	FF,D,L	DMSO	505	75,000	513	MeOH	6, 10
D13951	925.91	FF,D,L	DMSO, EtOH	505	80,000	511	MeOH	6
D23739	1136.13	FF,D,L	DMSO	505	92,000	511	MeOH	2, 11
H361	850.13	FF,D,L	see Notes	342	37,000	376	MeOH	2, 12, 13, 14
H3809	856.09	FF,D,L	see Notes	341	38,000	376	MeOH	2, 12, 13, 14
H3810	800.99	FF,D,L	see Notes	341	40,000	376	MeOH	2, 12, 13, 14
H3818	794.02	FF,D,L	see Notes	341	37,000	377	MeOH	2, 12, 13, 14
N1154	575.75	FF,D,L	$CHCl_3$, DMSO	466	22,000	536	MeOH	15
N3524	740.88	FF,D,L	see Notes	466	22,000	536	MeOH	2, 15
N3786	771.89	FF,D,L	see Notes	465	21,000	533	EtOH	2, 15, 16
N3787	856.05	FF,D,L	see Notes	465	22,000	534	EtOH	2, 15, 16
N22651	~66,000	F,D,L	H_2O	466	22,000	536	MeOH	8, 15
O7703	894.27	FF,D,L	$CHCl_3$, EtOH	341	37,000	376	MeOH	2, 13, 14
P58	1057.46	FF,D,L	see Notes	350	35,000	379	MeOH	2
T6615	266.46	F,D	DMSO, DMF	<300		none		

For definitions of the contents of this data table, see "Navigating *The Handbook*" in the introductory pages.

Notes

1. ADIFAB fatty acid indicator is a protein conjugate with a molecular weight of approximately 15,350. Em shifts from about 432 nm to 505 nm upon binding of fatty acids (Mol Cell Biochem 192, 87 (1999)).
2. Chloroform is the most generally useful solvent for preparing stock solutions of phospholipids (including sphingomyelins). Glycerophosphocholines are usually freely soluble in ethanol. Most other glycerophospholipids (phosphoethanolamines, phosphatidic acids and phosphoglycerols) are less soluble in ethanol, but solutions up to 1–2 mg/mL should be obtainable, using sonication to aid dispersion if necessary. Labeling of cells with fluorescent phospholipids can be enhanced by addition of cyclodextrins during incubation (J Biol Chem 274, 35359 (1999)).
3. Phospholipase A cleavage generates a fluorescent fatty acid (P1903MP) and a fluorescent lysophospholipid.
4. Phospholipase A cleavage generates a fluorescent fatty acid (P31) and a fluorescent lysophospholipid.
5. Phospholipase A cleavage results in increased fluorescence with essentially no wavelength shift. The cleavage products are D3862 and a fluorescent lysophospholipid.
6. Em for BODIPY® FL sphingolipids shifts to ~620 nm when high concentrations of the probe (>5 mol %) are incorporated in lipid mixtures (J Cell Biol 113, 1267 (1991)).
7. The absorption and fluorescence spectra of BODIPY® derivatives are relatively insensitive to the solvent.
8. This product is a lipid complexed with bovine serum albumin (BSA). Spectroscopic data are for the free lipid in MeOH.
9. Phospholipase A_2 cleavage generates a fluorescent fatty acid (D3834) and a nonfluorescent lysophospholipid.
10. This product is supplied as a ready-made solution in the solvent indicated under "Soluble."
11. Phospholipase A_2 cleavage results in increased fluorescence with essentially no wavelength shift. The cleavage products are D3834 and a dinitrophenylated lysophospholipid.
12. Alkylpyrene fluorescence lifetimes are up to 110 nanoseconds and are very sensitive to oxygen.
13. Pyrene derivatives exhibit structured spectra. The absorption maximum is usually about 340 nm with a subsidiary peak at about 325 nm. There are also strong absorption peaks below 300 nm. The emission maximum is usually about 376 nm with a subsidiary peak at 396 nm. Excimer emission at about 470 nm may be observed at high concentrations.
14. Phospholipase A_2 hydrolysis releases a fluorescent fatty acid; P31 from H361, H3809 and H3810 or P3840 from H3818 and O7703.
15. Fluorescence of NBD and its derivatives in water is relatively weak. QY and τ increase and Em decreases in aprotic solvents and other nonpolar environments relative to water (Biochemistry 16, 5150 (1977); Photochem Photobiol 54, 361 (1991)).
16. Phospholipase A_2 hydrolysis releases a fluorescent fatty acid; N316 from N3786 or N678 from N3787.

Product List — 17.4 Probes for Lipid Metabolism and Signaling

Cat #	Product Name	Unit Size
A7509	*N*-acetyl-D-erythro-sphingosine (acetyl ceramide; C_2-ceramide)	5 mg
A3880	ADIFAB fatty acid indicator	200 µg
A12218	Amplex® Red Phosphatidylcholine-Specific Phospholipase C Assay Kit *500 assays*	1 kit
A12219	Amplex® Red Phospholipase D Assay Kit *500 assays*	1 kit
A12220	Amplex® Red Sphingomyelinase Assay Kit *500 assays*	1 kit
A21327	anti-phosphatidylinositol 4,5-diphosphate, mouse IgM, monoclonal 2C11 (anti-PtdIns(4,5)P_2) *1 mg/mL*	100 µL
A21328	anti-phosphatidylinositol 3,4,5-triphosphate, mouse IgM, monoclonal RC6F8 (anti-PtdIns(3,4,5)P_3) *1 mg/mL*	100 µL
B7701	1,2-bis-(4,4-difluoro-5,7-dimethyl-4-bora-3a,4a-diaza-*s*-indacene-3-undecanoyl)-*sn*-glycero-3-phosphocholine (bis-BODIPY® FL C_{11}-PC)	100 µg
B3781	1,2-bis-(1-pyrenebutanoyl)-*sn*-glycero-3-phosphocholine	1 mg
B3782	1,2-bis-(1-pyrenedecanoyl)-*sn*-glycero-3-phosphocholine	1 mg
B22650	BODIPY® FL C_5-ceramide complexed to BSA	5 mg
B22621	BODIPY® FL C_5, C_6-phosphatidylinositol (BODIPY® FL C_5, C_6-PtdIns)	50 µg
B22618	BODIPY® FL C_5, C_{16}-phosphatidylinositol 3-phosphate (BODIPY® FL C_5, C_{16}-PtdIns(3)P)	50 µg
B22622	BODIPY® FL C_5, C_6-phosphatidylinositol 3-phosphate (BODIPY® FL C_5, C_6-PtdIns(3)P)	50 µg
B22619	BODIPY® FL C_5, C_{16}-phosphatidylinositol 4-phosphate (BODIPY® FL C_5, C_{16}-PtdIns(4)P)	50 µg
B22623	BODIPY® FL C_5, C_6-phosphatidylinositol 4-phosphate (BODIPY® FL C_5, C_6-PtdIns(4)P)	50 µg
B22620	BODIPY® FL C_5, C_{16}-phosphatidylinositol 5-phosphate (BODIPY® FL C_5, C_{16}-PtdIns(5)P)	50 µg
B22624	BODIPY® FL C_5, C_6-phosphatidylinositol 5-phosphate (BODIPY® FL C_5, C_6-PtdIns(5)P)	50 µg
B22625	BODIPY® FL C_5, C_6-phosphatidylinositol 3,4-diphosphate (BODIPY® FL C_5, C_6-PtdIns(3,4)P_2)	50 µg
B22615	BODIPY® FL C_5, C_6-Phosphatidylinositol 3,4-Diphosphate Cell-Labeling Kit	1 kit
B22626	BODIPY® FL C_5, C_6-phosphatidylinositol 3,5-diphosphate (BODIPY® FL C_5, C_6-PtdIns(3,5)P_2)	50 µg
B22627	BODIPY® FL C_5, C_6-phosphatidylinositol 4,5-diphosphate (BODIPY® FL C_5, C_6-PtdIns(4,5)P_2)	50 µg
B22616	BODIPY® FL C_5, C_6-Phosphatidylinositol 4,5-Diphosphate Cell-Labeling Kit	1 kit
B22628	BODIPY® FL C_5, C_6-phosphatidylinositol 3,4,5-triphosphate (BODIPY® FL C_5, C_6-PtdIns(3,4,5)P_3)	50 µg
B22617	BODIPY® FL C_5, C_6-Phosphatidylinositol 3,4,5-Triphosphate Cell-Labeling Kit	1 kit
B13950	BODIPY® FL C_5-ganglioside G_{M1}	25 µg
B34401	BODIPY® FL C_5-ganglioside G_{M1} complexed to BSA	1 mg
B34402	BODIPY® FL C_5-lactosylceramide complexed to BSA	1 mg
B22631	BODIPY® TMR-X C_6-phosphatidylinositol (BODIPY® TMR-X C_6-PtdIns)	50 µg
B22632	BODIPY® TMR-X C_6-phosphatidylinositol 3-phosphate (BODIPY® TMR-X C_6-PtdIns(3)P)	50 µg
B22633	BODIPY® TMR-X C_6-phosphatidylinositol 4-phosphate (BODIPY® TMR-X C_6-PtdIns(4)P)	50 µg
B22634	BODIPY® TMR-X C_6-phosphatidylinositol 5-phosphate (BODIPY® TMR-X C_6-PtdIns(5)P)	50 µg
B22635	BODIPY® TMR-X C_6-phosphatidylinositol 3,4-diphosphate (BODIPY® TMR-X C_6-PtdIns(3,4)P_2)	50 µg
B22636	BODIPY® TMR-X C_6-phosphatidylinositol 3,5-diphosphate (BODIPY® TMR-X C_6-PtdIns(3,5)P_2)	50 µg
B22637	BODIPY® TMR-X C_6-phosphatidylinositol 4,5-diphosphate (BODIPY® TMR-X C_6-PtdIns(4,5)P_2)	50 µg
B22638	BODIPY® TMR-X C_6-phosphatidylinositol 3,4,5-triphosphate (BODIPY® TMR-X C_6-PtdIns(3,4,5)P_3)	50 µg
B34400	BODIPY® TR C_5-ceramide complexed to BSA	5 mg
B22641	BODIPY® TR-X C_6-phosphatidylinositol (BODIPY® TR-X C_6-PtdIns)	50 µg
B22642	BODIPY® TR-X C_6-phosphatidylinositol 3-phosphate (BODIPY® TR-X C_6-PtdIns(3)P)	50 µg
B22643	BODIPY® TR-X C_6-phosphatidylinositol 4-phosphate (BODIPY® TR-X C_6-PtdIns(4)P)	50 µg
B22644	BODIPY® TR-X C_6-phosphatidylinositol 5-phosphate (BODIPY® TR-X C_6-PtdIns(5)P)	50 µg
B22645	BODIPY® TR-X C_6-phosphatidylinositol 3,4-diphosphate (BODIPY® TR-X C_6-PtdIns(3,4)P_2)	50 µg
B22646	BODIPY® TR-X C_6-phosphatidylinositol 3,5-diphosphate (BODIPY® TR-X C_6-PtdIns(3,5)P_2)	50 µg
B22647	BODIPY® TR-X C_6-phosphatidylinositol 4,5-diphosphate (BODIPY® TR-X C_6-PtdIns(4,5)P_2)	50 µg
B22648	BODIPY® TR-X C_6-phosphatidylinositol 3,4,5-triphosphate (BODIPY® TR-X C_6-PtdIns(3,4,5)P_3)	50 µg
D3771	2-decanoyl-1-(*O*-(11-(4,4-difluoro-5,7-dimethyl-4-bora-3a,4a-diaza-*s*-indacene-3-propionyl)amino)undecyl)-*sn*-glycero-3-phosphocholine	1 mg
D7546	*N*-(2,6-dibromo-4,4-difluoro-5,7-dimethyl-4-bora-3a,4a-diaza-*s*-indacene-3-pentanoyl)sphingosine (BODIPY® FL Br_2C_5-ceramide)	250 µg
D7519	*N*-(4,4-difluoro-5,7-dimethyl-4-bora-3a,4a-diaza-*s*-indacene-3-dodecanoyl)sphingosyl 1-β-D-galactopyranoside (BODIPY® FL C_{12}-galactocerebroside)	25 µg
D7547	*N*-(4,4-difluoro-5,7-dimethyl-4-bora-3a,4a-diaza-*s*-indacene-3-dodecanoyl)sphingosyl 1-β-D-glucopyranoside (BODIPY® FL C_{12}-glucocerebroside)	250 µg
D7711	*N*-(4,4-difluoro-5,7-dimethyl-4-bora-3a,4a-diaza-*s*-indacene-3-dodecanoyl)sphingosyl phosphocholine (BODIPY® FL C_{12}-sphingomyelin) *1 mg/mL in DMSO*	250 µL
D3803	2-(4,4-difluoro-5,7-dimethyl-4-bora-3a,4a-diaza-*s*-indacene-3-pentanoyl)-1-hexadecanoyl-*sn*-glycero-3-phosphocholine (β-BODIPY® FL C_5-HPC)	100 µg
D3521	*N*-(4,4-difluoro-5,7-dimethyl-4-bora-3a,4a-diaza-*s*-indacene-3-pentanoyl)sphingosine (BODIPY® FL C_5-ceramide)	250 µg
D7548	*N*-(4,4-difluoro-5,7-dimethyl-4-bora-3a,4a-diaza-*s*-indacene-3-pentanoyl)sphingosyl 1-β-D-glucopyranoside (BODIPY® FL C_5-glucocerebroside)	250 µg
D13951	*N*-(4,4-difluoro-5,7-dimethyl-4-bora-3a,4a-diaza-*s*-indacene-3-pentanoyl)sphingosyl 1-β-D-lactoside (BODIPY® FL C_5-lactosylceramide)	25 µg
D3522	*N*-(4,4-difluoro-5,7-dimethyl-4-bora-3a,4a-diaza-*s*-indacene-3-pentanoyl)sphingosyl phosphocholine (BODIPY® FL C_5-sphingomyelin)	250 µg
D7540	*N*-((4-(4,4-difluoro-5-(2-thienyl)-4-bora-3a,4a-diaza-*s*-indacene-3-yl)phenoxy)acetyl)sphingosine (BODIPY® TR ceramide)	250 µg
D94	11-((5-dimethylaminonaphthalene-1-sulfonyl)amino)undecanoic acid (DAUDA)	100 mg
D23739	*N*-((6-(2,4-dinitrophenyl)amino)hexanoyl)-2-(4,4-difluoro-5,7-dimethyl-4-bora-3a,4a-diaza-*s*-indacene-3-pentanoyl)-1-hexadecanoyl-*sn*-glycero-3-phosphoethanolamine, triethylammonium salt (PED6)	1 mg
H361	1-hexadecanoyl-2-(1-pyrenedecanoyl)-*sn*-glycero-3-phosphocholine (β-py-C_{10}-HPC)	1 mg

For current prices or to order online, visit probes.invitrogen.com

Cat #	Product Name	Unit Size
H3809	1-hexadecanoyl-2-(1-pyrenedecanoyl)-*sn*-glycero-3-phosphoglycerol, ammonium salt (β-py-C_{10}-PG)	1 mg
H3810	1-hexadecanoyl-2-(1-pyrenedecanoyl)-*sn*-glycero-3-phosphomethanol, sodium salt (β-py-C_{10}-HPM)	1 mg
H3818	1-hexadecanoyl-2-(1-pyrenehexanoyl)-*sn*-glycero-3-phosphocholine (β-py-C_6-HPC)	1 mg
N22651	NBD C_6-ceramide complexed to BSA	5 mg
N3787	2-(12-(7-nitrobenz-2-oxa-1,3-diazol-4-yl)amino)dodecanoyl-1-hexadecanoyl-*sn*-glycero-3-phosphocholine (NBD C_{12}-HPC)	5 mg
N3786	2-(6-(7-nitrobenz-2-oxa-1,3-diazol-4-yl)amino)hexanoyl-1-hexadecanoyl-*sn*-glycero-3-phosphocholine (NBD C_6-HPC)	5 mg
N1154	6-((*N*-(7-nitrobenz-2-oxa-1,3-diazol-4-yl)amino)hexanoyl)sphingosine (NBD C_6-ceramide)	1 mg
N3524	6-((*N*-(7-nitrobenz-2-oxa-1,3-diazol-4-yl)amino)hexanoyl)sphingosyl phosphocholine (NBD C_6-sphingomyelin)	1 mg
O7703	1-octacosanyl-2-(1-pyrenehexanoyl)-*sn*-glycero-3-phosphomethanol, ammonium salt (C_{28}-O-PHPM)	250 µg
P6466	phospholipase C, phosphatidylinositol-specific *from *Bacillus cereus* *100 U/mL*	50 µL
P23748	PIP Array™ membranes *set of 2*	1 set
P23749	PIP Array™ membranes *set of 5*	1 set
P23740	PIP Beads™, PtdIns-labeled *sedimented agarose bead suspension*	1 mL
P23741	PIP Beads™, PtdIns(3)P-labeled *sedimented agarose bead suspension*	1 mL
P23742	PIP Beads™, PtdIns(4)P-labeled *sedimented agarose bead suspension*	1 mL
P23743	PIP Beads™, PtdIns(5)P-labeled *sedimented agarose bead suspension*	1 mL
P23744	PIP Beads™, PtdIns(3,4)P_2-labeled *sedimented agarose bead suspension*	1 mL
P23745	PIP Beads™, PtdIns(3,5)P_2-labeled *sedimented agarose bead suspension*	1 mL
P23746	PIP Beads™, PtdIns(4,5)P_2-labeled *sedimented agarose bead suspension*	1 mL
P23747	PIP Beads™, PtdIns(3,4,5)P_3-labeled *sedimented agarose bead suspension*	1 mL
P23752	PIP MicroStrips™ membranes *set of 10*	1 set
P23750	PIP Strips™ membranes *set of 2*	1 set
P23751	PIP Strips™ membranes *set of 10*	1 set
P58	*N*-(1-pyrenesulfonyl)-1,2-dihexadecanoyl-*sn*-glycero-3-phosphoethanolamine, triethylammonium salt (pyS DHPE)	25 mg
S23731	Shuttle PIP™ carrier-1 *histone H1* *0.5 mM in water*	200 µL
S23733	Shuttle PIP™ carrier-1, Oregon Green® 488 conjugate *histone H1* *0.5 mM in water*	200 µL
S23732	Shuttle PIP™ carrier-1, tetramethylrhodamine conjugate *histone H1* *0.5 mM in water*	200 µL
S35900	Shuttle PIP™ carrier-2 *neomycin B sulfate*	2 x 50 nmol
S23753	SphingoStrips™ membranes *set of 10*	1 set
T6615	tricyclodecan-9-yl xanthogenate, potassium salt (D 609)	5 mg
V34403	Vybrant® Alexa Fluor® 488 Lipid Raft Labeling Kit *50 labelings*	1 kit
V34404	Vybrant® Alexa Fluor® 555 Lipid Raft Labeling Kit *50 labelings*	1 kit
V34405	Vybrant® Alexa Fluor® 594 Lipid Raft Labeling Kit *50 labelings*	1 kit

For current prices or to order online, visit probes.invitrogen.com

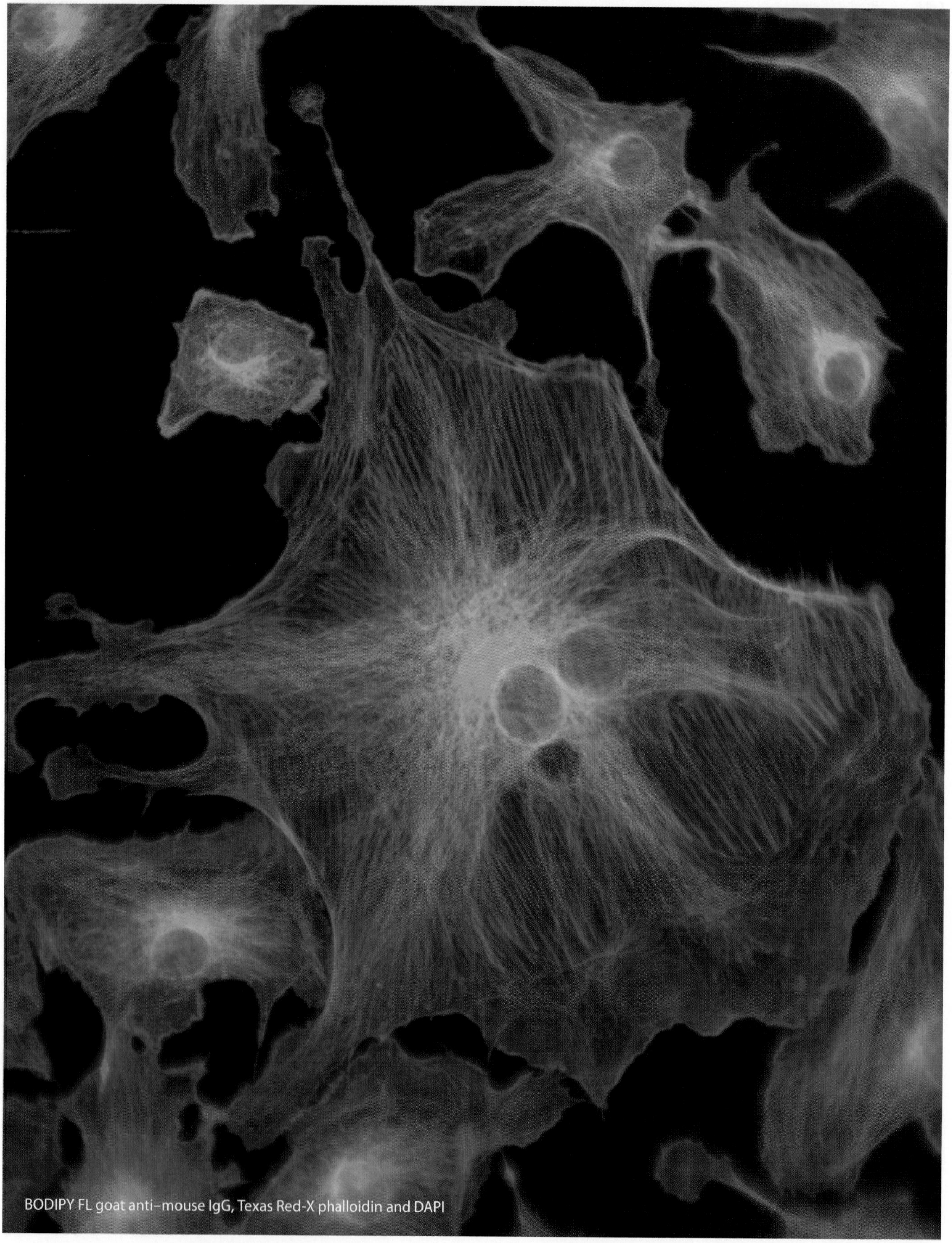

BODIPY FL goat anti–mouse IgG, Texas Red-X phalloidin and DAPI

Chapter 18

Probes for Reactive Oxygen Species, Including Nitric Oxide

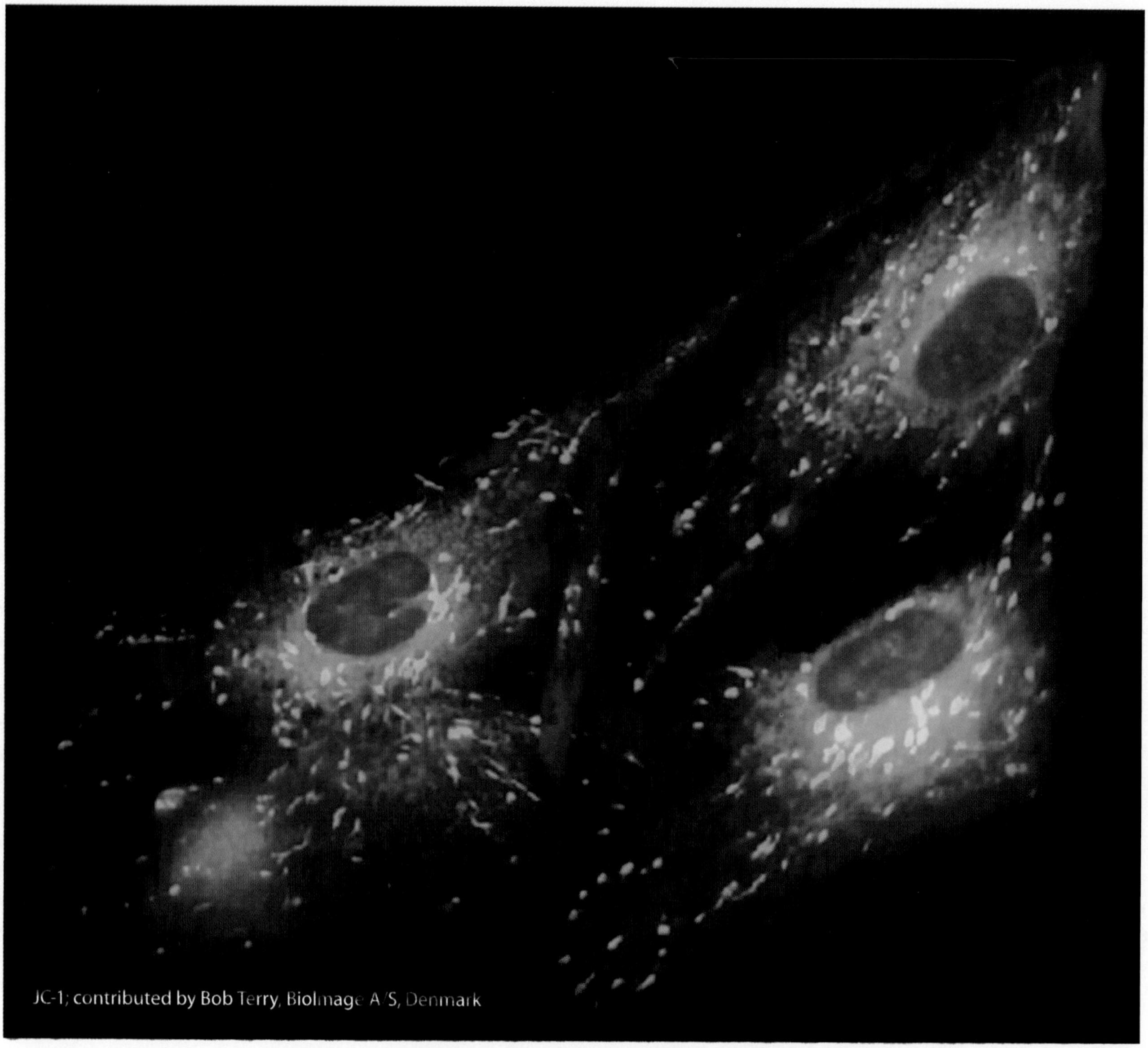

JC-1; contributed by Bob Terry, BioImage A/S, Denmark

18.1 Introduction to Reactive Oxygen Species

Molecular Probes has available several probes that either generate or detect various reactive oxygen species (Table 18.1), including singlet oxygen ($^1O_2$), superoxide ($\cdot O_2^-$), hydroxyl radical (HO·) and various peroxides (ROOR′) and hydroperoxides (ROOH). Section 18.2 focuses on these probes and their applications *in vitro* and *in vivo*. Produced during a number of physiological processes, such as Alzheimer's disease,[1] apoptosis (Section 15.5) and phagocytosis (Section 16.1), activated oxygen species react with a large variety of easily oxidizable

Table 18.1 — Reactive oxygen species

Reactive Oxygen Species	Structure	Detection Reagents	
Hydrogen peroxide	H_2O_2	• Carboxy-H_2DCFDA (C400) [1–3] • CM-H_2DCFDA (C6827) [4,5] • Dihydrocalcein AM (D23805) • Dihydrorhodamine 123 (D632, D23806) [6] • Dihydrorhodamine 6G (D633) [7]	• H_2DCFDA (D399) [8–11] • Lucigenin (L6868) [12,13] • Luminol (L8455) [14] • RedoxSensor™ Red CC-1 (R14060) [15]
Hydroxyl radical *	HO·	• 3′-(*p*-Aminophenyl) fluorescein (APF, A36003) • 3′-(*p*-Hydroxyphenyl) fluorescein (HPF, H36004) • CM-H_2DCFDA (C6827) [16]	• Proxyl fluorescamine (C7924) [17] • TEMPO-9-AC (A7923)
Hypochlorous acid	HOCl	• Aminophenyl fluorescein (APF, A36003) • Dihydrorhodamine 123 (D632, D23806) [18] • Luminol (L8455) [19–21]	
Nitric oxide	NO	• DAF-FM (D23841) [22,23] • DAF-FM diacetate (D23842, D23844) [22,23] • DAA (D23840) [24] • Luminol (L8455) [25]	
Peroxyl radical, including both alkylperoxyl and hydroperoxyl [26] radicals (wherein R = H)	ROO·	• BODIPY® FL EDA (D2390) [27] • BODIPY® 665/676 (B3932) [28] • H_2DCFDA (D399) [29–33] • Carboxy-H_2DCFDA (C400) [34] • CM-H_2DCFDA (C6827)	• DPPP (D7894) [35–37] • Luminol (L8455) [38–40] • *cis*-Parinaric acid (P36005) [41,42] • RedoxSensor™ Red CC-1 (R14060) [15]
Peroxynitrite anion †	$ONOO^-$	• 3′-(*p*-Aminophenyl) fluorescein (APF, A36003) • 3′-(*p*-Hydroxyphenyl) fluorescein (HPF, H36004) • H_2DCFDA (D399) [43,44] • Carboxy-H_2DCFDA (C400) • CM-H_2DCFDA (C6827)	• Coelenterazine (C2944) [45] • Dihydrorhodamine 123 (D632, D23806) [43,46–48] • Dihydrorhodamine 6G (D633) • Luminol (L8455) [43,49,50]
Singlet oxygen ‡	$^1O_2$	• Singlet Oxygen Sensor Green reagent (S36002) • *trans*-1-(2′-methoxyvinyl)pyrene (M7913) [51,52]	
Superoxide anion	$\cdot O_2^-$	• Coelenterazine (C2944) [53,54] • Dihydroethidium (D1168, D11347, D23107) [55,56] • Fc OxyBURST® Green assay reagent (F2902) [57,58] • OxyBURST® Green H_2DCFDA SE (D2935) [59,60] • OxyBURST® Green H_2HFF BSA (O13291) [61] • Lucigenin (L6868) [62,63] • Luminol (L8455) [64]	• MCLA (M23800) [65,66] • MTT (M6494) [67] • NBT (N6495) [68] • RedoxSensor™ Red CC-1 (R14060) [15] • TEMPO-9-AC (A7923) • XTT (X6493) [69]

* Hydroxyl radicals can also be photosensitized by malachite green isothiocyanate (M689) or generated by a *N*-(1,10-phenanthrolin-5-yl)iodoacetamide (P6879) metal–ligand complex. † 3-Nitrotyrosine, a product of this potent nitrating reagent, can be detected with an anti-nitrotyrosine antibody (A21285). ‡ Singlet oxygen can also be photosensitized by hypocrellin A (H7515), hypocrellin B (H7516), hypericin (H7476), rose bengal diacetate (R14000) and merocyanine 540 (M24571).

1. Biol Pharm Bull 23, 1153 (2000); **2.** J Neurosci 19, 9209 (1999); **3.** J Biol Chem 271, 21505 (1996); **4.** J Biol Chem 276, 21938 (2001); **5.** Proc Natl Acad Sci U S A 94, 11557 (1997); **6.** Biochim Biophys Acta 1454, 275 (1999); **7.** Proc Natl Acad Sci U S A 97, 8266 (2000); **8.** J Biol Chem 276, 514 (2001); **9.** J Immunol Methods 117, 53 (1989); **10.** Brain Res 635, 113 (1994); **11.** J Biol Chem 274, 37111 (1999); **12.** Analyst 3, 941 (1986); **13.** J Am Chem Soc 101, 5347 (1979); **14.** J Bone Miner Res 7, 1139 (1992); **15.** Free Radic Biol Med 28, 1266 (2000); **16.** Proc Natl Acad Sci U S A 98, 1643 (2001); **17.** Anal Chem 69, 4295 (1997); **18.** Nitric Oxide 1, 145 (1997); **19.** Biochim Biophys Acta 1097, 145 (1991); **20.** Luminescence 14, 239 (1999); **21.** Am J Physiol 263, G719 (1992); **22.** Anal Biochem 287, 203 (2000); **23.** Angew Chem Int Ed Engl 38, 3209 (1999); **24.** Neuroreport 9, 4051 (1998); **25.** Anal Chem 65, 1794 (1993); **26.** DNA Cell Biol 21, 251 (2002); **27.** J Biochem Biophys Methods 35, 23 (1997); **28.** J Agric Food Chem 48, 1150 (2000); **29.** Toxicol Meth 4, 224 (1994); **30.** J Biol Chem 275, 40028 (2000); **31.** Anal Biochem 134, 111 (1983); **32.** Am J Physiol 257, C347 (1989); **33.** Methods Enzymol 105, 352 (1984); **34.** J Biol Chem 273, 5294 (1998); **35.** J Chromatogr 628, 31 (1993); **36.** Anal Lett 20, 731 (1987); **37.** Methods Enzymol 186, 157 (1990); **38.** Free Radic Biol Med 18, 1 (1995); **39.** Biomed Chromatogr 4, 131 (1990); **40.** Lipids 33, 1235 (1998); **41.** J Biol Chem 272, 123282 (1997); **42.** Biochem Biophys Res Commun 244, 647 (1998); **43.** Free Radic Biol Med 30, 463 (2001); **44.** FEBS Lett 468, 89 (2000); **45.** Circ Res 84, 1203 (1999); **46.** FASEB J (2001); **47.** Arch Biochem Biophys 373, 302 (2000); **48.** FASEB J 14, 1061 (2000); **49.** J Biol Chem 271, 29223 (1996); **50.** Arch Biochem Biophys 310, 352 (1994); **51.** Biochem Biophys Res Commun 123, 869 (1984); **52.** Methods Enzymol 133, 569 (1986); **53.** Anal Biochem 206, 273 (1992); **54.** Free Radic Biol Med 29, 170 (2000); **55.** Circ Res 88, 824 (2001); **56.** J Biol Chem 276, 17621 (2001); **57.** J Leukoc Biol 62, 329 (1997); **58.** J Biol Chem 270, 8328 (1995); **59.** Immunology 83, 507 (1994); **60.** J Immunol Methods 130, 223 (1990); **61.** Biophys J 75, 2577 (1998); **62.** Free Radic Biol Med 28, 1232 (2000); **63.** J Biol Chem 273, 2015 (1998); **64.** J Immunol Methods 155, 151 (1992); **65.** Free Radic Res 32, 265 (2000); **66.** Anal Biochem 271, 53 (1999); **67.** Free Radic Res Commun 18, 369 (1993); **68.** Arch Biochem Biophys 342, 275 (1997); **69.** Plant Physiol 117, 491 (1998).

cellular components, including NADH, NADPH, dopa, ascorbic acid, histidine, tryptophan, tyrosine, cysteine, glutathione, proteins and nucleic acids.[2–6] Reactive oxygen species can also oxidize cholesterol and unsaturated fatty acids, causing membrane lipid peroxidation.[7,8] Using the Amplex® Red reagent (Section 18.2), researchers have discovered that antibodies can convert molecular oxygen to H_2O_2, which may be important in understanding a new chemical arm of the immune system, as well as the evolution of antibodies and the role they may play in human diseases.[9,10] Several reviews discuss the chemistry of the different reactive oxygen species and their lipid peroxidation products.[11–16] In addition, Tarpey, Wink and Grisham have published a comprehensive review describing methods for detecting reactive oxygen and reactive nitrogen species *in vitro* and *in vivo*.[17]

The importance of the nitric oxide radical (abbreviated NO) and other reactive oxygen species as biological messengers has been increasingly recognized during the last several years.[18–23] Section 18.3 is devoted to our probes for promoting, inhibiting or detecting nitric oxide production in a variety of experimental systems.

References

1. Prog Neurobiol 62, 633 (2000); **2.** Annu Rev Biochem 64, 97 (1995); **3.** Methods Enzymol 234, (Complete Volume) (1994); **4.** Methods Enzymol 233, (Complete Volume) (1994); **5.** Methods Enzymol 186, (Complete Volume) (1990); **6.** Methods Enzymol 105, (Complete Volume) (1984); **7.** J Biol Chem 268, 18502 (1993); **8.** Pharmacol Ther 53, 375 (1992); **9.** Science 293, 1806 (2001); **10.** Proc Natl Acad Sci U S A 97, 10930 (2000); **11.** Free Radic Biol Med 30, 463 (2001); **12.** Clin Chem 41, 1819 (1995); **13.** Free Radic Biol Med 19, 77 (1995); **14.** Free Radic Biol Med 18, 1033 (1995); **15.** Free Radic Biol Med 18, 775 (1995); **16.** Biochimie 76, 355 (1994); **17.** Am J Physiol Regul Integr Comp Physiol 286, R431 (2004); **18.** Curr Biol 7, R376 (1997); **19.** J Med Chem 38, 4343 (1995); **20.** Annu Rev Biochem 63, 175 (1994); **21.** Cell 78, 919 (1994); **22.** Am J Physiol 262, G379 (1992); **23.** Science 257, 494 (1992).

18.2 Generating and Detecting Reactive Oxygen Species

Molecular Probes prepares an assortment of probes for the generation of reactive oxygen species (ROS) — singlet oxygen, hydroxyl radicals, superoxide, hydroperoxides and peroxides (Table 18.1) — as well as for their fluorometric detection in solution. Although there are no equilibrium sensors that continuously monitor the level of reactive oxygen species, this section discusses a number of probes that trap or otherwise react with singlet oxygen, hydroxyl radicals or superoxide. The optical or electron spin properties of the resulting products are in some way a measure of the presence or quantity of the reactive oxygen species and, in certain cases, can report the kinetics and location of their formation.

Generating Singlet Oxygen

Singlet oxygen is responsible for much of the physiological damage caused by reactive oxygen species, including nucleic acid modification through selective reaction with deoxyguanosine.[1] The lifetime of singlet oxygen is sufficiently long (4.4 microseconds in water[2]) to permit significant diffusion in cells and tissues.[3] In the laboratory, singlet oxygen is usually generated in one of three ways: photochemically from dioxygen ($^3O_2$) using a photosensitizing dye;[4] chemically, either by thermal decomposition of a peroxide or dioxetane; or by microwave discharge through an oxygen stream. The generation of singlet oxygen can also be targeted to the mitochondria by several cationic dyes.[5] Singlet oxygen can be detected by its characteristic weak chemiluminescence at 1268 nm[6] or at 634 and 703 nm.[7]

Hypocrellins and Hypericin

Among the most efficient reagents for generating singlet oxygen are the photosensitizers hypocrellin A (H7515, Figure 17.10), hypocrellin B (H7516, Figure 17.11) and hypericin (H7476, Figure 17.9). These heat-stable dyes exhibit quantum yields for singlet oxygen generation in excess of 0.7, as well as high photostability, making them important agents for both anticancer and antiviral therapy.[8–14] Hypocrellins are also specific and potent inhibitors of protein kinase C[15,16] (Section 17.3), whereas hypericin is an effective inhibitor of both protein kinase C and tyrosine protein kinase[17] with antiretroviral activity.[18]

Because their chemical reactivities are well characterized,[19,20] hypocrellins and hypericin are amenable to conjugation to a variety of primary and secondary detection reagents. Not only do these photosensitizing dyes efficiently oxidize diaminobenzidine (DAB) to form an insoluble, electron-dense DAB oxidation product (see Note 14.2 "Product Highlight: Fluorescent Probes for Photoconversion of Diaminobenzidine Reagents" in Section 14.3), but they exhibit modest fluorescence quantum yields and broad UV and visible spectra. Thus, hypocrellin- and hypericin-labeled detection reagents are compatible with fluorescence, light or electron microscopy applications.[9,10]

Halogenated Fluoresceins

Halogenated derivatives of fluorescein dyes are known to be effective photosensitizers and singlet oxygen generators.[21] This property of eosin and other halogenated fluoresceins and their conjugates has been exploited to improve ultrastructural resolution (see Note 14.2 "Product Highlight: Fluorescent Probes for Photoconversion of Diaminobenzidine Reagents" in Section 14.3). Bioconjugates of eosin and erythrosin fluorophores can be prepared using the reactive derivatives described in Chapter 1, Chapter 2 and Chapter 3.

Rose Bengal Diacetate

Rose bengal diacetate (R14000) is an efficient, cell-permeant generator of singlet oxygen.[22] It is an iodinated xanthene derivative that has been chemically modified by the introduction of acetate groups (Figure 18.1). These modifications inactivate both its fluorescence and photosensitization properties, while increasing its ability to cross cell membranes. Once inside a live cell, esterases remove the acetate groups and restore rose bengal to its native structure. This intracellular localization allows rose bengal diacetate to be a very effective photosensitizer.

Merocyanine 540

Photolysis of merocyanine 540 (M24571) produces both singlet oxygen and other reactive oxygen species, including oxygen radicals.[23–26] Merocyanine 540 is commonly used as a photosensitizer in photodynamic therapy.[11,27–35]

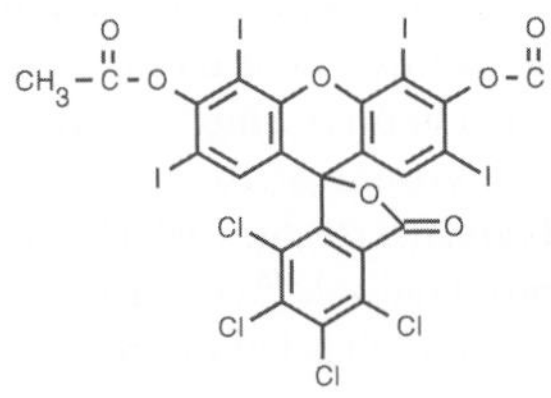

Figure 18.1 R14000 rose bengal diacetate.

Detecting Singlet Oxygen

Singlet Oxygen Sensor Green Reagent

Unlike other fluorescent and chemiluminescent singlet oxygen detection reagents, the Singlet Oxygen Sensor Green reagent (S36002) is highly selective for singlet oxygen ($^1O_2$); it shows no appreciable response to other ROS, including hydroxyl radical (HO·), superoxide (·O_2^-) and nitric oxide (NO) (Figure 18.2). Before reaction with singlet oxygen, this probe initially exhibits weak blue fluorescence with excitation peaks at 372 and 393 nm and emission peaks at 395 and 416 nm. In the presence of singlet oxygen, however, it emits a green fluorescence similar to that of fluorescein (excitation/emission maxima ~504/525 nm). We have observed that the fluorescent product of Singlet Oxygen Sensor Green reagent can degrade with time in some solutions and that Singlet Oxygen Sensor Green reagent can become fluorescent at alkaline pH in the absence of singlet oxygen. Nevertheless, with the proper controls the intensity of the green-fluorescent signal can be correlated with singlet oxygen concentration, without significant interference from other ROS. The Singlet Oxygen Sensor Green reagent is available as a cell-impermeant derivative (S36002) for detecting singlet oxygen in solution. It can also potentially serve to assess the efficacy of free radical scavengers, which are frequently used to improve the flavor and nutritional quality in foods.

trans-1-(2´-Methoxyvinyl)pyrene

trans-1-(2´-Methoxyvinyl)pyrene (M7913) can be used to detect picomole quantities of singlet oxygen in chemical and biological systems (Figure 18.3), making this compound perhaps the most sensitive singlet oxygen probe currently available.[36–38] Furthermore, this highly selective chemiluminescent probe does not react with other activated oxygen species such as hydroxyl radical, superoxide or hydrogen peroxide.

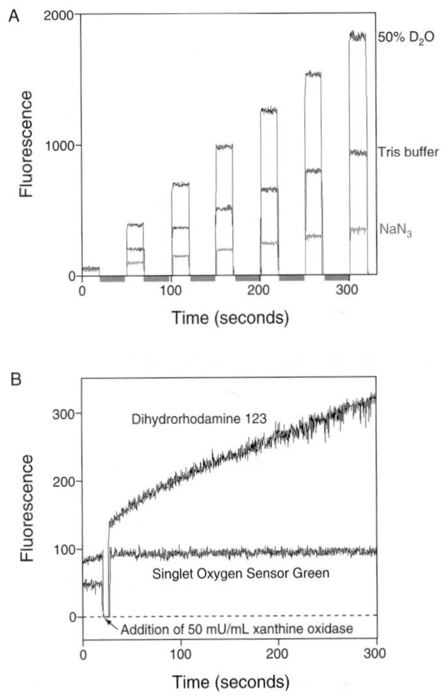

Figure 18.2 Fluorescence response and specificity of Singlet Oxygen Sensor Green reagent (S36002) to $^1O_2$. (A) Fluorescence measurements were made in a spectrofluorometer using excitation/emission wavelengths of 488/525 nm for solutions containing: 1 µM Singlet Oxygen Sensor Green reagent and 10 µM methylene blue in 100 mM pH 7.5 Tris buffer alone; the singlet oxygen scavenger sodium azide (NaN_3); or 50% D_2O, which increases the lifetime of $^1O_2$. Measurements were made for 20-second periods, with 30-second intervals (indicated by grey bars) between each measurement. During the 30-second intervals, the samples were exposed to laser radiation (630–680 nm, <5 mW), resulting in methylene blue–photosensitized generation of $^1O_2$. (B) Fluorescence measurements were made in a spectrofluorometer using excitation/emission wavelengths of 488/525 nm for solutions of 50 mM pH 7 Tris buffer with 1 mM xanthine containing either 1 µM Singlet Oxygen Sensor Green reagent or dihydrorhodamine 123. After ~20 seconds, 50 mU/mL of xanthine oxidase (XO) was added. XO catalzyes the oxidation of xanthine, producing uric acid and superoxide. Superoxide can spontaneously degrade to H_2O_2.

Generating Hydroxyl and Superoxide Radicals

Hydroxyl and superoxide radicals have been implicated in a number of pathological conditions, including ischemia, reperfusion and aging. The superoxide anion (Table 18.1) may also play a role in regulating normal vascular function. The hydroxyl radical is a very reactive oxygen species that has a lifetime of about 2 nanoseconds in aqueous solution and a radius of diffusion of about 20 Å. Thus, it induces peroxidation only when it is generated in close proximity to its target. The hydroxyl radical can be derived from superoxide in a reaction catalyzed by Fe^{2+} or other transition metals, as well as by the effect of

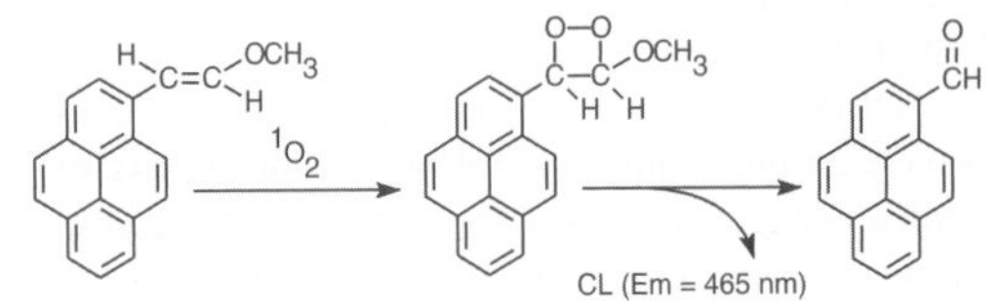

Figure 18.3 Reaction of *trans*-1-(2'-methoxyvinyl)pyrene (M7913) with singlet oxygen ($^1O_2$), yielding a dioxetane intermediate that generates chemiluminescence (CL) upon decomposition to 1-pyrenecarboxaldehyde.

ionizing radiation on dioxygen. Superoxide is most effectively generated from a hypoxanthine–xanthine oxidase generating system.[39–41] In one cell-based assay for hydroxyl radical formation, D-phenylalanine is specifically converted to D-tyrosine.[42] In phagocytic cells, H_2O_2 also produces *O,O´*-dityrosine, an oxidative crosslink product of appropriately situated tyrosine residues, which is formed through the intermediacy of phenoxyl radicals.[43] *O,O´*-Dityrosine is intrinsically fluorescent at a relatively high pH or can be detected using specific antibodies.

Malachite Green

Malachite green is a nonfluorescent photosensitizer that absorbs at long wavelengths (~630 nm). Its photosensitizing action can be targeted to particular cellular sites by conjugating malachite green isothiocyanate (M689, Figure 1.89) to specific antibodies.[44,45] Enzymes and other proteins within ~10 Å of the binding site of the malachite green–labeled antibody can then be selectively destroyed upon irradiation with long-wavelength light. Studies by Jay and colleagues have demonstrated that this photoinduced destruction of enzymes in the immediate vicinity of the chromophore is apparently the result of localized production of hydroxyl radicals, which have short lifetimes that limit their diffusion from the site of their generation.[46]

1,10-Phenanthroline Iodoacetamide

Conjugation of the iodoacetamide of 1,10-phenanthroline (P6879) to thiol-containing ligands confers the metal-binding properties of this important complexing agent on the ligand. For example, the covalent copper–phenanthroline complex of oligonucleotides or nucleic acid–binding molecules in combination with hydrogen peroxide acts as a chemical nuclease to selectively cleave DNA or RNA.[47–52] Hydroxyl radicals or other reactive oxygen species appear to be involved in this cleavage.[53,54]

Detecting Hydroxyl and Superoxide Radicals

Fluorogenic Spin Traps

Hydroxyl radicals have usually been detected after reaction with spin traps. We offer TEMPO-9-AC (A7923) and proxyl fluorescamine[55–58] (C7924), two fluorogenic probes for detecting hydroxyl radicals and superoxide. Each of these molecules contains a nitroxide moiety that effectively quenches its fluorescence. However, once TEMPO-9-AC or proxyl fluorescamine traps a hydroxyl radical or superoxide, its fluorescence is restored and the radical's electron spin resonance signal is destroyed, making these probes useful for detecting radicals either by fluorescence or by electron spin resonance spectroscopy. TEMPO-9-AC has been reported to detect glutathionyl radicals but not phenoxyl radicals.[59] Proxyl fluorescamine can also be used to detect the methyl radicals that are formed by the reaction of hydroxyl radicals with DMSO.[58] Radical-specific scavengers — such as the superoxide-specific *p*-benzoquinone and superoxide dismutase[60] or the hydroxyl radical–specific mannitol and dimethylsulfoxide (DMSO)[55,61,62] — can be used to identify the detected species.

Chemiluminescent and Chromogenic Reagents for Detecting Superoxide

In the absence of apoaequorin, the luminophore coelenterazine (C2944) produces chemiluminescence in response to superoxide generation in phorbol ester– or chemotactic peptide–stimulated neutrophils.[63] Unlike luminol, coelenterazine exhibits luminescence that does not depend on the activity of cell-derived myeloperoxidase and is not inhibited by azide.[63]

In addition to coelenterazine, we offer MCLA (M23800) for detecting superoxide. MCLA and coelenterazine are superior alternatives to lucigenin (L6868) for this application because lucigenin can reportedly sensitize superoxide production, leading to false-positive results.[64–68] An additional advantage of MCLA is that its pH optimum for luminescence generation is closer to the physiological near-neutral range than are the pH optima of luminol and lucigenin.[69]

Lucigenin (L6868) exhibits chemiluminescence that is reported to be sensitive to the superoxide anion.[70–74] Lucigenin has been employed to investigate superoxide generation in spermatozoa,[75] L929 cells,[76] chondrocytes contained within the matrix of live cartilage tissue,[77] and mitochondria of alveolar macrophages.[74] It has also been used to examine the role of the superoxide anion in reoxygenation injury in isolated rat hepatocytes.[78,79] We have purified our lucigenin to remove a blue-fluorescent impurity that is found in some commercial samples.

Nitro blue tetrazolium salt (NBT, N6495; Table 18.2) and other tetrazolium salts are chromogenic probes useful for superoxide determination.[80,81] These probes are also widely used for detecting redox potential of cells for viability, proliferation and cytotoxicity assays; see below for more information.

Detecting Hydrogen Peroxide, Hydroperoxides and Peroxyl Radicals

In peroxisomes, H_2O_2 is produced by several enzymes that use molecular oxygen to oxidize organic compounds. This H_2O_2 is then utilized by catalase to oxidize other substrates, including phenols, formic acid, formaldehyde and alcohol. In liver and kidney cells, these oxidation reactions are important for detoxifying a variety of compounds in the bloodstream.[82–85] However, H_2O_2 also plays a role in neurodegenerative and other disorders through induction of apoptosis,[86] oxidation of glutathione, modification of intracellular Ca^{2+} levels and mitochondrial potential and induction of DNA strand breaks.[87] In addition, H_2O_2 is released from cells during hypoxia.[88]

Peroxidation of unsaturated lipids plays an important role in cell membrane properties,[89] signal transduction pathways,[90,91] apoptosis and the deterioration of foods and other biological compounds.[92] Lipid oxidation may also be responsible for aging, as well as pathological processes such as drug-induced phototoxicity and atherosclerosis.[93] Lipid hydroperoxides have been reported to accumulate in oxidatively stressed individuals, including HIV-infected patients.[94] To directly assess the extent of lipid peroxidation, researchers either measure the amount of lipid hydroperoxides directly or detect the presence of secondary reaction products[95–97] (e.g., 4-hydroxy-2-nonenal or malonaldehyde; see below).

Peroxyl radicals are formed by the decomposition of various peroxides and hydroperoxides, including lipid hydroperoxides. The hydroperoxyl radical is also the protonated form of superoxide, and approximately 0.3% of the superoxide in the cytosol is present as this protonated radical.[98] Experimentally, peroxyl radicals, including alkylperoxyl (ROO·) and hydroperoxyl (HOO·) radicals, are generated from compounds such as 2,2′-azobis(2-amidinopropane) and from hydroperoxides such as cumene hydroperoxide. Free radical–mediated damage in cells is often the result of lipid peroxidation. A problem with investigating the link between lipid peroxidation and diseases such as atherosclerosis, diabetes and Parkinson's has been the lack of suitable methods to detect the relationship between lipid peroxidation and the onset of such diseases.[99]

Amplex® Red Reagent: Stable Substrate for Peroxidase Detection

In the presence of horseradish peroxidase (HRP), the Amplex® Red reagent (10-acetyl-3,7-dihydroxyphenoxazine, A12222, A22177; Figure 10.58) reacts with H_2O_2 with a 1:1 stoichiometry to produce highly fluorescent resorufin[100] (R363, Section 10.1, Figure 10.59). The Amplex® Red reagent has greater stability, yields less background and produces a red-fluorescent product that is more readily detected than the similar reduced methylene blue derivatives commonly used for colorimetric determination of lipid peroxides in plasma, sera, cell extracts and a variety of membrane systems.[31,101,102] Using the Amplex® Red reagent in conjunction with HRP, we have found that release of hydrogen peroxide to the medium by as few as 2000 phorbol ester–stimulated neutrophils can be detected in a fluorescence microplate reader.

The Amplex® Red reagent has been used to detect the release of H_2O_2 from activated human leukocytes,[100,103] to measure the activity of monoamine oxidase in cow brain tissue,[104] to demonstrate the extracellular production of H_2O_2 produced by UV light stimulation of human keratinocytes[105–107] and to measure L-glutamate in food samples.[108] Using the Amplex® Red reagent, researchers have discovered that antibodies can convert molecular oxygen to H_2O_2, which may be important in understanding a new chemical arm of the immune system, as well as the evolution of antibodies and the role they may play in human diseases.[109,110] The Amplex® Red reagent can be purchased separately in a single 5 mg vial (A12222) or packaged as a set of 10 vials, each containing 10 mg of the substrate, for high-throughput screening applications (A22177).

Amplex® UltraRed Reagent: Brighter and More Sensitive than the Amplex® Red Reagent

Our Amplex® UltraRed reagent (A36006) improves upon the performance of the Amplex® Red reagent, offering brighter fluorescence and enhanced sensitivity on a per-mole basis in horseradish peroxidase or horseradish peroxidase-coupled enzyme assays (Figure 10.62). Fluorescence of the oxidized Amplex® UltraRed reagent is also less sensitive to pH (Figure 10.63), and the substrate and its oxidation product exhibit greater stability that the Amplex® Red reagent in the presence of hydrogen peroxide (H_2O_2) or thiols such as dithiothreitol (DTT). Like the Amplex® Red reagent, the nonfluorescent Amplex® UltraRed reagent reacts with H_2O_2 in a 1:1 stoichiometric ratio to produce a brightly fluorescent and strongly absorbing reaction product (excitation/emission maxima ~568/581 nm) (Figure 10.64). Because the reaction product has long-wavelength spectra, there is little interference from the blue or green autofluorescence found in most biological samples.

The Amplex® UltraRed reagent can provide increased sensitivity in peroxidase-based enzyme-linked immunosorbent assays (ELISAs). With a high extinction coefficient and good quantum efficiency, the fluorescence-based Amplex® UltraRed reagent is more sensitive than

Table 18.2 — Tetrazolium salts for detecting redox potential in living cells and tissues

Cat #	Tetrazolium Salt	Color of Formazan	Water Solubility of Formazan	Applications
M6494 (MTT)	3-(4,5-Dimethylthiazol-2-yl)-2,5-diphenyltetrazolium bromide	purple	no	• Superoxide generation by fumarate reductase[1] and nitric oxide synthase[2] • Mitochondrial dehydrogenase activity[3] • Cell viability and proliferation[4–9] • Neuronal cell death[10] • Platelet activation[11] • Tumor cell adhesion[12] and invasion[13] • Multidrug resistance[14] • *In vitro* toxicity testing[15–17]
N6495 (NBT)	Nitro blue tetrazolium chloride	deep blue	no	• Superoxide generation by xanthine oxidase[18] • Neutrophil oxidative metabolism[19,20] • NADPH diaphorase activity[21–23] • Succinic dehydrogenase histochemistry[24]
X6493 (XTT)	2,3-Bis-(2-methoxy-4-nitro-5 sulfophenyl) -2*H*-tetrazolium-5-carboxanilide	orange	yes	• Antifungal susceptibility[25] • Drug sensitivity of cells[26] • Parasitic nematode viability[27] • Tumor cell cytotoxicity[28]

1. J Biol Chem 270, 19767 (1995); **2.** J Biol Chem 269, 12589 (1994); **3.** Cytometry 13, 532 (1992); **4.** Biotechniques 25, 622 (1998); **5.** J Immunol Methods 168, 253 (1994); **6.** Anal Biochem 214, 190 (1993); **7.** J Immunol Methods 164, 149 (1993); **8.** Anal Biochem 205, 8 (1992); **9.** J Immunol Methods 89, 271 (1986); **10.** J Cell Biol 128, 201 (1995); **11.** J Immunol Methods 159, 253 (1993); **12.** J Immunol Methods 164, 255 (1993); **13.** Cancer Res 54, 3620 (1994); **14.** Leuk Res 16, 1165 (1992); **15.** Biosci Biotechnol Biochem 56, 1472 (1992); **16.** J Immunol Methods 144, 141 (1991); **17.** J Immunol Methods 131, 165 (1990); **18.** J Reprod Fertil 97, 441 (1993); **19.** Clin Chim Acta 221, 197 (1993); **20.** J Leukoc Biol 53, 404 (1993); **21.** Neurosci Lett 155, 61 (1993); **22.** Proc Natl Acad Sci U S A 88, 7797 (1991); **23.** Proc Natl Acad Sci U S A 88, 2811 (1991); **24.** Histochemistry 76, 381 (1982); **25.** Antimicrob Agents Chemother 36, 1619 (1992); **26.** Cancer Res 48, 4827 (1988); **27.** Parasitology 107, 175 (1993); **28.** J Immunol Methods 147, 153 (1992).

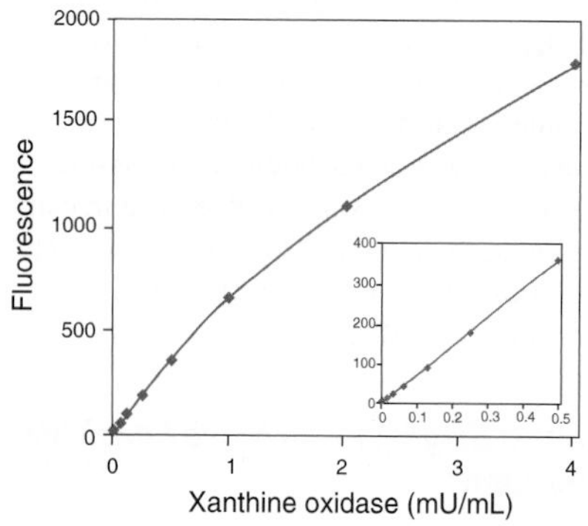

Figure 18.4 Detection of xanthine oxidase using the Amplex® Red reagent–based assay (A22182). Each reaction contained 50 µM Amplex® Red reagent, 0.2 U/mL horseradish peroxidase, 0.1 mM hypoxanthine and the indicated amount of xanthine oxidase in 1X reaction buffer. After 30 minutes, fluorescence was measured in a fluorescence microplate reader using excitation at 530 ± 12.5 nm and detection at 590 ± 17.5 nm. A background of 65 fluorescence units was subtracted from each data point. The inset shows the assay's sensitivity and linearity at low hypoxanthine concentrations.

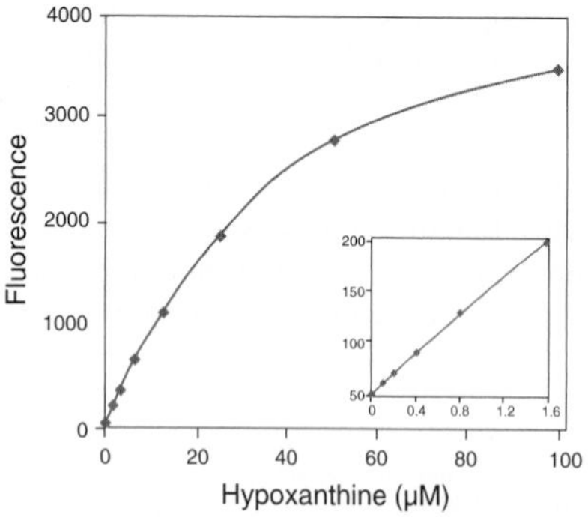

Figure 18.5 Detection of hypoxanthine using the Amplex® Red reagent–based assay (A22182). Each reaction contained 50 µM Amplex® Red reagent, 0.2 U/mL horseradish peroxidase, 20 mU/mL xanthine oxidase and the indicated amount of hypoxanthine in 1X reaction buffer. Reactions were incubated at 37°C. After 30 minutes, fluorescence was measured in a fluorescence microplate reader using excitation at 530 ± 12.5 nm and detection at 590 ± 17.5 nm. A background of 54 fluorescence units was subtracted from each data point. The inset shows the assay's sensitivity and linearity at low enzyme concentrations.

standard colorimetric reagents and provides a broader measurement range for ELISAs. In contrast to commonly used ELISA reagents such as ABTS and TMB, the Amplex® UltraRed reagent is exceptionally resistant to autooxidation, making it a superior alternative for peroxidase detection (Table 10.5). Like the Amplex® Red reagent, the versatile Amplex® UltraRed reagent can be detected using either fluorescence- or absorption-based instrumentation. The Amplex® UltraRed reagent, which should be suitable for any of the applications described for the Amplex® Red reagent (Section 10.5), is available as a set of five vials, each containing 1 mg of the substrate (A36006).

Amplex® Red Hydrogen Peroxide/Peroxidase Assay Kit

The Amplex® Red Hydrogen Peroxide/Peroxidase Assay Kit (A22188) provides a simple, sensitive, one-step assay for detecting H_2O_2 or the activity of horseradish peroxidase either by measuring fluorescence with a fluorescence-based microplate reader or a fluorometer (Figure 10.66) or by measuring absorption with an absorption-based microplate reader or a spectrophotometer. The Amplex® Red peroxidase substrate can detect the presence of active peroxidases and the release of H_2O_2 from biological samples, including cells and cell extracts [100,103,111–113] and is also useful for detecting H_2O_2 that is produced as a product of enzyme-coupled reactions.[105,114–116] The Amplex® Red Hydrogen Peroxide/Peroxidase Assay Kit contains:

- Amplex® Red reagent
- Dimethylsulfoxide (DMSO)
- Horseradish peroxide (HRP)
- H_2O_2 for use as a positive control
- Concentrated reaction buffer
- A detailed protocol

Each kit provides sufficient reagents for approximately 500 assays using a fluorescence- or absorption-based microplate reader and a reaction volume of 100 µL per assay. Several additional kits that utilize our Amplex® Red peroxidase substrate to detect H_2O_2 in coupled enzymatic reactions are described in Section 10.5.

Amplex® Red Xanthine/Xanthine Oxidase Assay Kit

Xanthine oxidase plays a key role in the production of free radicals, including superoxide, in the body. The Amplex® Red Xanthine/Xanthine Oxidase Assay Kit (A22182) provides an ultrasensitive method for detecting xanthine or hypoxanthine or for monitoring xanthine oxidase activity. In the assay, xanthine oxidase catalyzes the oxidation of purine nucleotides, hypoxanthine or xanthine, to uric acid and superoxide. In the reaction mixture, the superoxide spontaneously degrades to H_2O_2, which in the presence of HRP reacts stoichiometrically with the Amplex® Red reagent to generate the red-fluorescent oxidation product, resorufin. Resorufin has absorption and fluorescence emission maxima of approximately 571 nm and 585 nm (Figure 10.6), respectively, and because the extinction coefficient is high (54,000 $cm^{-1}M^{-1}$), the assay can be performed either fluorometrically or spectrophotometrically.

In healthy individuals, xanthine oxidase is present in appreciable amounts only in the liver and jejunum. However, in various liver disorders the enzyme is released into circulation. Therefore, determination of serum xanthine oxidase levels serves as a sensitive indicator of acute liver damage such as jaundice. The Amplex® Red xanthine/xanthine oxidase assay has been used as a marker of recovery from exercise stress.[117] Previously, researchers have utilized chemiluminescence or absorbance to monitor xanthine oxidase activity. The Amplex® Red Xanthine/Xanthine Oxidase Assay Kit permits the detection of xanthine oxidase in a purified system at levels as low as 0.1 mU/mL by fluorescence (Figure 18.4). This kit can also be used to detect as little as 200 nM hypoxanthine or xanthine (Figure 18.5), and, when coupled to the purine nucleotide phosphorylase enzyme, to detect inorganic phosphate.[118]

The Amplex® Red Xanthine/Xanthine Oxidase Assay Kit (A22182) contains:

- Amplex® Red reagent
- Dimethylsulfoxide (DMSO)
- Horseradish peroxidase (HRP)
- H_2O_2

- Concentrated reaction buffer
- Xanthine oxidase from buttermilk
- Hypoxanthine
- Xanthine
- A detailed protocol

Each kit provides sufficient reagents for approximately 400 assays using either a fluorescence- or absorption-based microplate reader and a reaction volume of 100 μL per assay.

cis-Parinaric Acid

Fluorescence quenching of the fatty acid analog *cis*-parinaric acid (P36005) has been used in several lipid peroxidation assays,[99,119–123] including quantitative determinations in live cells.[124–129] In a study investigating the membrane antioxidant properties of the *bcl-2* proto-oncogene product, researchers used *cis*-parinaric acid to detect lipid hydroperoxides together with 6-carboxy-2′,7′-dichlorodihydrofluorescein diacetate, di(acetoxymethyl ester) (C2938) to detect cytosolic reactive oxygen molecules.[130] Parinaric acid's extensive unsaturation (Figure 13.11) makes it quite susceptible to oxidation if not rigorously protected from air.[131] Consequently, we offer *cis*-parinaric acid in a 10 mL unit size of a 3 mM solution in deoxygenated ethanol (P36005); if stored protected from light under an inert argon atmosphere at -20°C, this stock solution should be stable for at least six months. During experiments, we advise handling parinaric acid samples under inert gas and preparing solutions using degassed buffers and solvents. Parinaric acid is also somewhat photolabile and undergoes photodimerization when exposed to intense illumination, resulting in loss of fluorescence.[132]

Diphenyl-1-Pyrenylphosphine

The direct fluorometric detection of hydroperoxides in lipids, serum, tissues and foodstuffs[133,134] is now possible using the reagent diphenyl-1-pyrenylphosphine (DPPP, D7894). DPPP is essentially nonfluorescent until oxidized to a phosphine oxide by peroxides; *in vitro*, DPPP remains nonfluorescent in the presence of hydroxyl radicals generated by the Cu^{2+}-ascorbated method.[135] DPPP has previously been used to detect picomole levels of hydroperoxides by HPLC.[136–139] Its solubility in lipids makes DPPP quite useful for detecting hydroperoxides in the membranes of live cells[135,140,141] and in low-density lipoprotein particles,[142] as well as for studying superoxide dismutase (SOD), which catalyzes the conversion of superoxide to hydrogen peroxide. In U937 cells, exposure to DPPP did not appreciably affect cell viability, proliferation or morphology for three days, and the fluorescent phosphine oxide was stable in the cell membranes for at least two days.[140]

BODIPY® Dyes: Peroxyl Radical Scavengers

A unique assay for peroxyl radicals uses some of our BODIPY® dyes, including the BODIPY® 581/591 fatty acid (D3861) and the BODIPY® 665/676 dye (B3932), to measure the antioxidant activity in an organic lipid environment or in a liposomal medium.[89,143,144] This assay is based on the loss or shift of the dye's fluorescence as the result of its interaction with peroxyl radicals, and on the retention of the fluorescent signal in the presence of antioxidants that intercept these free radicals. It has been proposed that this assay is suitable for a fluorescence microplate reader or flow cytometer to examine the effect of lipid peroxidation on a cell-by-cell basis.[144]

The oxidation sensitivity of the conjugated double bonds of the BODIPY® 581/591 fatty acid (Figure 18.6) has also been exploited in a ratiometric assay of lipid oxidation in live cells that is essentially independent of uneven dye loading, cell thickness and compartmentalization.[145–147] In this assay, the cell membranes of rat-1 fibroblasts and myocardial cells were labeled with the BODIPY® 581/591 fatty acid, and then cumene hydroperoxide was added to induce oxidation. Upon oxidation, the BODIPY® 581/591 fluorophore exhibited a shift in its fluorescence from red to green, which was observed using confocal laser-scanning microscopy. As compared with arachidonic acid, the fluorescence of this BODIPY® probe was reportedly twice as sensitive to oxidation. In a similar application, the BODIPY® 581/591 fatty acid was used to detect lipid peroxidation in equine spermatozoa after exposure to ferrous sulfate, sodium ascorbate, cumene hydroperoxide and cooled storage, and ratiometric measurements were made with either a fluorescence microplate reader or a flow cytometer.[148]

Peroxyl radicals have also been detected in erythrocyte and red blood cell membranes using BODIPY® FL EDA[121] (D2390, Section 3.3), a water-soluble BODIPY® dye, or BODIPY® FL hexadecanoic acid (D3821, Section 13.2). BODIPY® FL hexadecanoic acid exhibits the red shift common to the fluorescence of lipophilic BODIPY® dyes when they are concentrated (Figure 13.6), permitting ratiometric measurements of hydroxyl radical production and allowing the onset of lipid peroxidation in live cells to be monitored.[121]

Other Scavengers for Peroxyl Radicals

The fluorescence of several other probes is lost following interaction with peroxyl radicals. Lipophilic fluorescein dyes such as hexadecanoylaminofluorescein[99] (H110, Section 13.5) and fluorescein-labeled phosphatidylethanolamine (F362, Section 13.2) have been or potentially are useful for detecting peroxyl radical formation in membranes and in solution. Phycobiliproteins such as B-phycoerythrin,[149–154] R-phycoerythrin[99,152,155,156] and allophycocyanin[157] (P800, P801, A803, A819; Section 6.4) may be similarly useful. R-phycoerythrin has been used to detect and measure total plasma antioxidant capacity, including peroxyl radicals.[152,154,156,158]

Luminol

Although luminol (L8455) is not useful for detecting superoxide in live cells,[72] it is commonly employed to detect peroxidase- or metal ion–mediated oxidative events.[159–161] Used alone, luminol can detect oxidative events in cells rich in peroxidases, including granulocytes[162–165] and spermatozoa.[75] This probe has also been used in conjunction with horseradish peroxidase (HRP) to investigate reoxygenation injury in rat hepatocytes.[78,166] In these experiments,

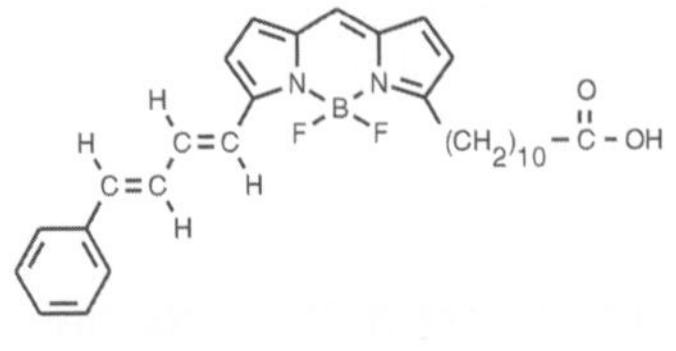

Figure 18.6 D3861 4,4-difluoro-5-(4-phenyl-1,3-butadienyl)-4-bora-3a,4a-diaza-s-indacene-3-undecanoic acid (BODIPY® 581/591 C_{11}).

it is thought that the primary species being detected is hydrogen peroxide. In addition, luminol has been employed to detect peroxynitrite,[167–169] a molecule thought to be generated in a variety of pathological conditions.[61] Phospholipid hydroperoxides have been determined directly by chemiluminescence-detected HPLC with luminol[170–172] (L8455) or a combination of luminol and cytochrome *c*.[173] This chemiluminescent probe has also been employed as a chemical sensor for dioxygen and nitrogen dioxide. It has been reported that luminol's chemiluminescence response to oxidative species may be competitively inhibited by biomolecules containing sulfhydryl and thioether groups.[174,175]

Detecting 4-Hydroxy-2-Nonenal

Formation of 4-hydroxy-2-nonenal from linoleic acid is a major cause of lipid peroxidation–induced liver toxicity. Several reagents for the direct fluorometric detection of aldehydes are described in Section 3.2. The modification of 4-hydroxy-2-nonenal or malonaldehyde with a fluorescent or chromophoric hydrazine or hydroxylamine reagent coupled with the separation and detection of the reaction product by a chromatography-based technique has rarely been reported but appears to be one of the most promising approaches for detecting these lipid peroxidation products.

Assaying Oxidative Activity in Live Cells with Leuco Dyes

Assaying oxidative activity in live cells with fluorogenic, chemiluminescent or chromogenic probes is complicated by the possibility of having multiple forms of reactive oxygen in the same cell. In addition, the nitric oxide radical (Section 18.3) may produce the same changes in the optical properties of the probe as do other reactive oxygen molecules. Blocking agents and enzyme inhibitors can sometimes help to sort out the species responsible for the probe's optical response. Quantitative analysis is also difficult because of: 1) the high intracellular concentration of glutathione, which can form thiyl or sulfinyl radicals or otherwise trap or reduce oxygen species;[39] 2) the variable concentration of metals, which can either catalyze or inhibit radical reactions; and 3) the presence of other free radical–quenching agents such as spermine.[176]

Fluorescein, rhodamine and various other dyes can be chemically reduced to colorless, nonfluorescent leuco dyes. These "dihydro" derivatives are readily oxidized back to the parent dye by some reactive oxygen species and thus can serve as fluorogenic probes for detecting oxidative activity in cells and tissues;[177–179] however, their oxidation may not easily discriminate between the various reactive oxygen species. It has been reported that dihydroethidium, dichlorodihydrofluorescein (H_2DCF) and dihydrorhodamine 123 react with intracellular hydrogen peroxide in a reaction mediated by peroxidase, cytochrome *c* or Fe^{2+}.[179–182] The leuco dyes also serve as fluorogenic substrates for peroxidase enzymes (Section 10.5). All of these reagents are slowly oxidized by air back to the parent fluorescent dyes, and in some cases light appears to accelerate their oxidation.

Dichlorodihydrofluorescein Diacetate and Its Analogs

The oxidation of the nonfluorescent 2′,7′-dichlorodihydrofluorescein diacetate (H_2DCFDA, D399; Figure 18.7), also known as dichlorofluo*rescin* diacetate, to the highly fluorescent 2′,7′-dichlorofluorescein (DCF) is commonly used to detect the generation of reactive oxygen intermediates in neutrophils and macrophages.[183–187] Cell-permeant H_2DCFDA may also be extremely useful for assessing the overall oxidative stress in toxicological phenomena.[178,179]

Oxidation of H_2DCFDA is reportedly not directly sensitive to singlet oxygen, but singlet oxygen can indirectly contribute to the formation of DCF through its reaction with cellular substrates that yield peroxy products and peroxyl radicals.[188] DCF itself can also act as a photosensitizer for H_2DCFDA oxidation, both priming and accelerating the formation of DCF.[188] In a cell-free system, H_2DCF has been shown to be oxidized to DCF by peroxynitrite anion ($ONOO^-$), horseradish peroxidase (in the absence of H_2O_2) and Fe^{2+} (in the absence of H_2O_2), and the oxidation by Fe^{2+} in the presence of H_2O_2 was reduced by the HO· radical scavenger formate and the iron chelator .[189]

A review by Tsuchiya and colleagues outlined methods for visualizing the generation of oxidative species in whole animals. For example, they suggest using propidium iodide (P1304MP, P3566; FluoroPure™ Grade, P21493; Section 8.1) with H_2DCFDA to simultaneously monitor oxidant production and cell injury.[190] H_2DCFDA has been used to visualize oxidative changes in carbon tetrachloride–perfused rat liver[191] and in venular endothelium during neutrophil activation,[192] as well as to examine the effect of ischemia and reperfusion in lung and heart tissue.[193,194] Using H_2DCFDA, researchers characterized hypoxia-dependent peroxide production in *Saccharomyces cerevisiae* as a possible model for ischemic tissue destruction.[195] A variety of toxicological phenomena in cultured cells have also been investigated with H_2DCFDA, including:

- Amyloid β protein–mediated increases in hydrogen peroxide in PC12 cells[196]
- Effects of calcium antagonists on oxidative metabolism in dissociated rat cerebellar and cortical neurons[197]
- Methamphetamine-induced oxidative stress in dopaminergic neurons[198]
- Effect of lipopolysaccharides on the level of oxygen metabolites in rat liver Kupffer cells[199]
- Nephrotoxin-induced oxidative stress in isolated proximal tubular cells[200]
- Nickel-induced increases in oxidant levels in Chinese hamster ovary (CHO) cells[201]
- Effect of transforming growth factor–β1 on the overall oxidized state of mouse osteoblastic cells[202]

In neutrophils, H_2DCFDA has proven useful for flow cytometric analysis of nitric oxide, forming a product that has spectral properties identical to those produced when it reacts with hydrogen peroxide.[203] In this study, H_2DCFDA's reaction with nitric oxide was blocked by adding the arginine analog N^G-methyl-L-arginine

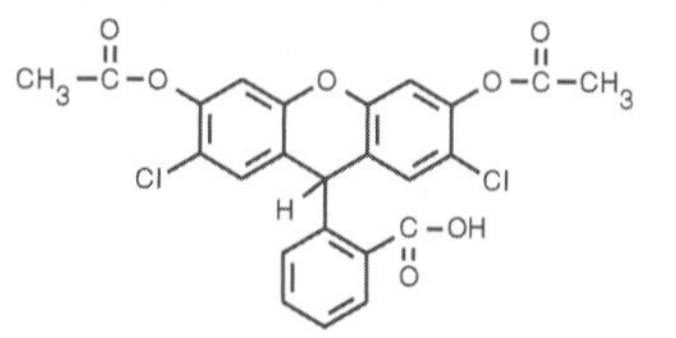

Figure 18.7 D399 2′,7′-dichlorodihydrofluorescein diacetate (2′,7′-dichlorofluorescin diacetate; H_2DCFDA).

(L-NMMA, M7898; Section 18.3) to the cell suspension.[203] 2′,7′-Dichlorofluorescein — the oxidation product of H_2DCF — can reportedly be further oxidized to a phenoxyl radical in a horseradish peroxidase–catalyzed reaction, and this reaction may complicate the interpretation of results obtained with this probe in cells undergoing oxidative stress.[204] H_2DCF is also photo-oxidized to fluorescent products by photoirradiation;[205] in a cell-free system, this photoreaction can be suppressed by addition of ascorbic acid.

Improved Versions of H_2DCFDA

Intracellular oxidation of H_2DCF tends to be accompanied by leakage of the product, 2′,7′-dichlorofluorescein,[206] which may make quantitation or detection of slow oxidation difficult. To enhance retention of the fluorescent product, Molecular Probes offers the carboxylated H_2DCFDA analog (carboxy-H_2DCFDA, C400), which has two negative charges at physiological pH, and its di(acetoxymethyl ester) (C2938, Figure 15.100, Figure 18.8), which should more easily pass through membranes during cell loading. Upon oxidation and cleavage of the acetate and ester groups by intracellular esterases, both analogs form carboxydichlorofluorescein (C368, Section 14.3), with additional negative charges that should impede its leakage out of the cell. Carboxy-H_2DCFDA (C400) has been used to assess the oxidative process in isolated perfused rat heart tissue[194] and in transfected *cos*-1 cells expressing native or mutagenized prostaglandin endoperoxide H synthase.[207] Its di(acetoxymethyl ester) (C2938) has been employed to investigate the role of the *bcl-2* proto-oncogene product in preventing apoptosis through its antioxidant properties.[130] Another probe for oxidative bursts and reactive oxygen species — 5-(and 6-)carboxy-2′,7′-difluorodihydrofluorescein diacetate (carboxy-H_2DFFDA, C13293) — exhibits improved photostability when compared with other fluorescein derivatives in common use.

Molecular Probes has also developed 5-(and 6-)chloromethyl-2′,7′-dichlorodihydrofluorescein diacetate, acetyl ester (CM-H_2DCFDA, C6827; Figure 18.9; Figure 18.10) — a chloromethyl derivative of H_2DCFDA that should exhibit much better retention in live cells. As with our other chloromethyl derivatives (see the description of our CellTracker™ probes in Section 14.2), we believe that CM-H_2DCFDA passively diffuses into cells, where its acetate groups are cleaved by intracellular esterases and its thiol-reactive chloromethyl group reacts with intracellular glutathione and other thiols. Subsequent oxidation yields a fluorescent adduct that is trapped inside the cell, thus facilitating long-term studies. Among its many applications, CM-H_2DCFDA has been used to:

- Measure intracellular reactive oxygen species in cardiac myocytes[208] in human embryonic kidney 293 (HEK293) cells stably transfected with the human vanilloid receptor 1 (VR1) cation channel[209]
- Detect insulin-stimulated production of H_2O_2 in insulin-sensitive hepatoma and adipose cells[210]
- Detect arsenic-induced production of oxyradicals by confocal laser-scanning microscopy[211]
- Explore the parallel induction of reactive oxygen species and Ca^{2+} transients in ouabain-treated myocytes[208,212]

The diacetate derivatives of the dichlorodihydrofluoresceins are quite stable. When used for intracellular applications, the acetates are cleaved by endogenous esterases, releasing the corresponding dichlorodihydrofluorescein derivative. If, however, these nonfluorescent diacetate derivatives are used for *in vitro* assays, they must first be hydrolyzed with mild base to form the colorless probe.

Aminophenyl Fluorescein and Hydroxyphenyl Fluorescein

3′-(*p*-Aminophenyl) fluorescein (APF, A36003) and 3′-(*p*-hydroxyphenyl) fluorescein (HPF, H36004), two new ROS indicators developed by Nagano,[213] offer greater selectivity and stability than does dichlorodihydrofluorescein diacetate (H_2DCFDA, also called dichlorofluores*cin* diacetate or DCF; D399). H_2DCFDA is probably the most commonly used reagent for detecting intracellular ROS species despite its lack of specificity and tendency to spontaneously photo-oxidize. The nonfluorescent H_2DCFDA becomes fluorescent in the presence of a wide variety of ROS including, but not limited to, peroxyl (ROO·) and hydroxyl (HO·) radicals and the peroxynitrite anion ($ONOO^-$). In contrast, APF and HPF show much more limited reactivity and

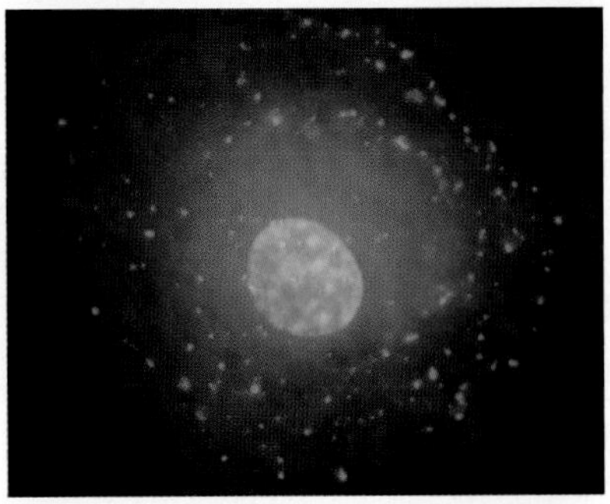

Figure 18.8 Bovine pulmonary artery endothelial cells were initially stained with the reactive oxygen species (ROS) indicator, 6-carboxy-2′,7′-dichlorodihydrofluorescein diacetate, di(acetoxymethyl ester) (C2938). After a 30-minute incubation, the cells were washed and then incubated simultaneously with FM® 5-95 (T23360) and Hoechst 33342 (H1399, H3570, H21492) in phosphate-buffered saline (PBS) for an additional five minutes before washing and mounting in PBS. The red-fluorescent FM® 5-95 appears to stain both the plasma membrane and early endosomes; the green-fluorescent, oxidized carboxydichlorofluorescein localizes to the cytoplasm; and the blue-fluorescent Hoechst 33342 dye stains the nucleus. The image was deconvolved using Huygens software (Scientific Volume Imaging).

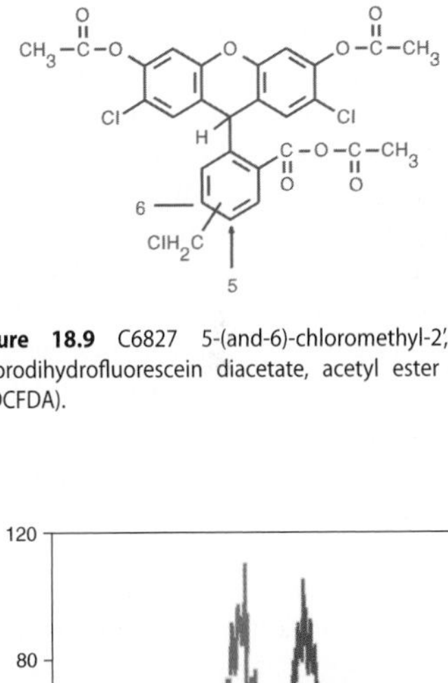

Figure 18.9 C6827 5-(and-6)-chloromethyl-2′,7′-dichlorodihydrofluorescein diacetate, acetyl ester (CM-H_2DCFDA).

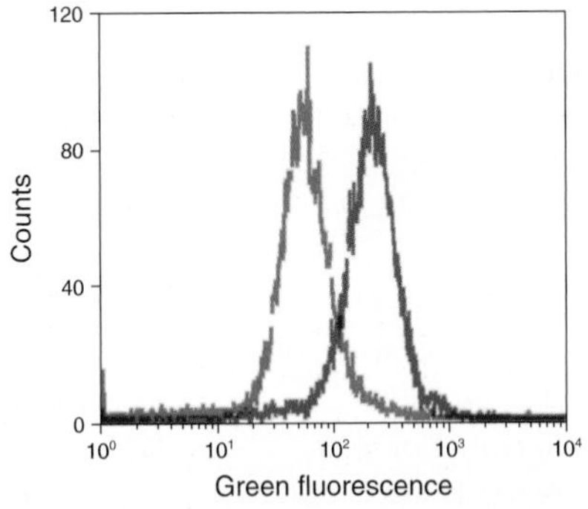

Figure 18.10 An oxidative burst was detected by flow cytometry of cells labeled with 5-(and 6-)chloromethyl-2′,7′-dichlorodihydrofluorescein diacetate, acetyl ester (CM-H_2DCFDA, C6827). Jurkat cells were incubated with 100 nM CM-H_2DCFDA. The cells were washed and resuspended in either phosphate-buffered saline (PBS, red) or PBS with 0.03% H_2O_2 (blue). The samples were analyzed on a flow cytometer equipped with a 488 nm argon-ion laser and a 525 ± 10 nm bandpass emission filter.

greater resistance to light-induced oxidation (Table 18.3). Both of these fluorescein derivatives are essentially nonfluorescent until they react with the hydroxyl radical or peroxynitrite anion (Figure 18.11). APF will also react with the hypochlorite anion ($^-$OCl), making it possible to use APF and HPF together to selectively detect hypochlorite anion (Section 21.2). In the presence of these specific ROS, both APF and HPF yield a bright green-fluorescent product (excitation/emission maxima ~490/515 nm) and are compatible with all fluorescence instrumentation capable of visualizing fluorescein. Using APF, researchers have been able to detect the hypochlorite anion generated by activated neutrophils, a feat that has not been possible with traditional ROS indicators.[213]

Dihydrocalcein AM

Calcein AM (C1430, C3099, C3100MP; Section 15.2, Figure 15.2) is extremely useful as a probe for the study of cell viability, adhesion, multidrug resistance, chemotaxis and other processes. We have combined the superior retention of calcein — the hydrolytic product of calcein AM in viable cells — and the oxidation sensitivity of dihydrofluoresceins to yield the probe dihydrocalcein AM (D23805, Figure 15.4). Dihydrocalcein AM is freely permeant to cell membranes and is oxidized to green-fluorescent calcein, which has superior retention properties in cells that have intact membranes (Figure 15.3). Dihydrocalcein AM is provided specially packaged as a set of 20 vials, each containing 50 µg of the probe.

OxyBURST® Green Reagents

Molecular Probes' Fc OxyBURST® Green assay reagent (F2902) was developed in collaboration with Elizabeth Simons of Boston University to monitor the oxidative burst in phagocytic cells using fluorescence instrumentation. The Fc OxyBURST® Green assay reagent comprises bovine serum albumin (BSA) that has been covalently linked to dichlorodihydrofluorescein (H_2DCF) and then complexed with purified rabbit polyclonal anti-BSA antibodies. When these immune complexes bind to Fc receptors, the nonfluorescent H_2DCF molecules are internalized within the phagovacuole and subsequently oxidized to green-fluorescent dichlorofluorescein (DCF, Figure 16.1; Figure 16.2). Unlike dichlorodihydrofluorescein diacetate (H_2DCFDA), the Fc OxyBURST® Green assay reagent does not require intracellular esterases for activation, making this reagent particularly suitable for detecting the oxidative burst in cells with low esterase activity such as monocytes.[214] The Fc OxyBURST® Green assay reagent reportedly produces >8 times more fluorescence than does H_2DCFDA at 60 seconds and >20 times more at 15 minutes following internalization of the immune complex.[215]

OxyBURST® Green H_2HFF BSA (O13291) is a sensitive fluorogenic reagent for detecting extracellular release of oxidative products in a spectrofluorometer or a fluorescence microscope (Figure 16.4). This reagent comprises BSA that has been covalently linked to dihydro-2′,4,5,6,7,7′-hexafluorofluorescein (H_2HFF), a reduced dye with improved stability. Unlike our Fc OxyBURST® Green assay reagent, OxyBURST® Green H_2HFF BSA is not complexed with IgG. OxyBURST® Green H_2HFF BSA provides up to 1000-fold greater sensitivity than conventional methods based on spectrophotometric detection of superoxide dismutase–inhibitable reduction of cytochrome *c*[216,217] and allows researchers to take advantage of the sample stirring and temperature control capabilities available in many spectrofluorometers. Because OxyBURST® Green H_2HFF BSA is a protein conjugate, it is superior to low molecular weight probes such as dihydrotetramethylrosamine and dihydrorhodamine 123, which are cell permeant and therefore do not exclusively detect extracellular oxidants.

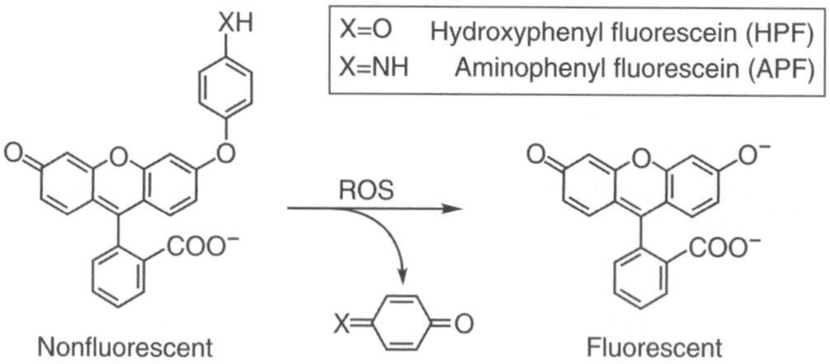

Figure 18.11 Detection of reactive oxygen species (ROS) with 3′-(*p*-hydroxyphenyl) fluorescein (HPF, H36004) and 3′-(*p*-aminophenyl) fluorescein (APF, A36003). Nonfluorescent HPF and APF become fluorescent in the presence of a ROS.

Table 18.3 — Fluorescence response of 3′-(*p*-aminophenyl) fluorescein (APF), 3′-(*p*-hydroxyphenyl) fluorescein (HPF) and dichlorodihydrofluorescein diacetate (H_2DCFDA) to various reactive oxygen species (ROS)

Reactive Oxygen Species (ROS)	ROS Generation Method	APF *	HPF *	H_2DCFDA *
Hydrogen peroxide (H_2O_2)	100 µM of H_2O_2	<1	2	190
Hydroxyl radical (HO·)	100 µM of ferrous perchlorate (II) and 1 mM of H_2O_2	1200	730	7400
Hypochlorite anion ($^-$OCl)	3 µM (final) of $^-$OCl	3600	6	86
Nitric oxide (NO)	100 µM of 1-hydroxy-2-oxo-3-(3-aminopropyl)-3-methyl-1-triazene	<1	6	150
Peroxyl radical (ROO·)	100 µM of 2,2′-azobis(2-amidinopropane), dihydrochloride (AAPH)	2	17	710
Peroxynitrite anion ($ONOO^-$)	3 µM (final) of $ONOO^-$	560	120	6600
Singlet oxygen ($^1O_2$)	100 µM of 3-(1,4-dihydro-1,4-epidioxy-1-naphthyl)propionic acid	9	5	26
Superoxide anion ($\cdot O_2^-$)	100 µM KO_2	6	8	67
Autooxidation	2.5 hours exposure to fluorescent light source	<1	<1	2000

* 10 µm of APF, HPF or H_2DCFDA were added to sodium phosphate buffer (0.1 M, pH 7.4), ROS were generated as indicated, and fluorescence was measured using excitation/emission wavelengths of 490/515 nm (for APF and HPF) or 500/520 nm (for H_2DCFDA).

Amine-Reactive OxyBURST® Green Reagent

As an alternative to our Fc OxyBURST® Green assay reagent and OxyBURST® Green H_2HFF BSA, Molecular Probes offers amine-reactive OxyBURST® Green H_2DCFDA succinimidyl ester (2′,7′-dichlorodihydrofluorescein diacetate, SE; D2935; Figure 16.6), which can be used to prepare oxidation-sensitive conjugates of a wide variety of biomolecules and particles, including antibodies, antigens, peptides, proteins, dextrans, bacteria, yeast and polystyrene microspheres.[215,218] Following conjugation to amines, the two acetates of OxyBURST® Green H_2DCFDA can be removed by treatment with hydroxylamine at neutral pH to yield the dihydrofluorescein conjugate. The OxyBURST® Green H_2DCFDA conjugates are nonfluorescent until they are oxidized to the corresponding fluorescein derivatives. Thus, like our Fc OxyBURST® Green assay reagent, they provide a means of detecting the oxidative burst in phagocytic cells. In one application, OxyBURST® Green H_2DCFDA succinimidyl ester was conjugated to an antibody that binds specifically to YAC tumor cells. YAC cells opsonized with this customized OxyBURST® reagent were then used in a fluorescence microscopy study to show that Fc receptor–activated neutrophils appear to deliver reactive oxygen species to the surface of their target cells.[218]

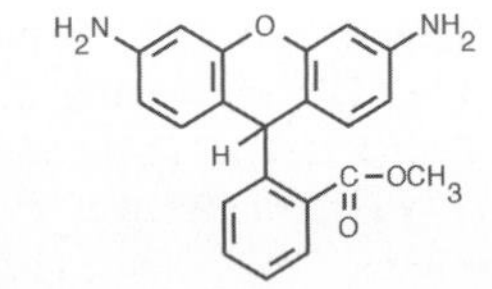

Figure 18.12 D632 dihydrorhodamine 123.

Dihydrorhodamine 123

Dihydrorhodamine 123 (D632, D23806; Figure 18.12, Figure 18.13) is the uncharged and nonfluorescent reduction product of the mitochondrion-selective dye rhodamine 123 (R302; FluoroPure™ Grade, R22420; Section 12.2). This leuco dye passively diffuses across most cell membranes where it is oxidized to cationic rhodamine 123 (Figure 12.21), which localizes in the mitochondria. Like H_2DCF, dihydrorhodamine 123 does not directly detect superoxide,[181] but rather reacts with hydrogen peroxide in the presence of peroxidase,[181] cytochrome *c* or Fe^{2+}.[182] However, dihydrorhodamine 123 also reacts with peroxynitrite,[219,220] the anion formed when nitric oxide reacts with superoxide.[221,222] Peroxynitrite, which may play a role in many pathological conditions,[61,220] has been shown to react with sulfhydryl groups,[223] DNA[224] and membrane phospholipids,[225] as well as with tyrosine[226] and other phenolic compounds.[227]

Dihydrorhodamine 123 has been used to investigate reactive oxygen intermediates produced by human and murine phagocytes,[228] activated rat mast cells[229] and cultured endothelial cells.[182] It has also been employed to study the role of the CD14 cell-surface marker in H_2O_2 production by human monocytes.[230] In addition, dihydrorhodamine 123 has been used with the Fura Red™ calcium indicator (F3020, F3021; Section 19.3) to simultaneously measure oxidative bursts and Ca^{2+} fluxes in monocytes and granulocytes.[231] Dihydrorhodamine 123 is reportedly a more sensitive probe than H_2DCFDA for detecting granulocyte respiratory bursts.[232–234]

Dihydrorhodamine 123 is available as a 10 mg vial (D632) or as a stabilized 5 mM solution in DMSO (D23806). Because of the susceptibility of dihydrorhodamine 123 to air oxidation, the DMSO solution is recommended when only small quantities are to be used at a time.

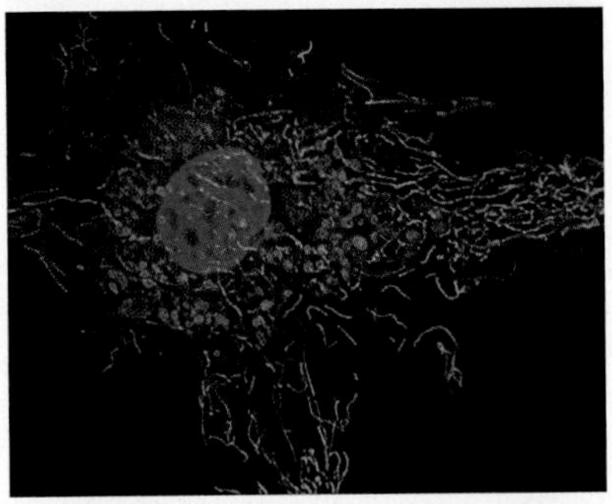

Figure 18.13 Live bovine pulmonary artery endothelial cells were first stained with LysoTracker® Red DND-99 (L7528). Then, a solution of dihydrorhodamine 123 (D632, D23806) and Hoechst 33258 (H1398, H3569, H21491) was added and allowed to incubate with the cells for an additional 10 minutes before the cells were subsequently washed and visualized. The green-fluorescent oxidation product (rhodamine 123, R302) localized primarily to the mitochondria. The red-fluorescent LysoTracker® Red DND-99 stain accumulated in the lysosomes, and the blue-fluorescent Hoechst 33258 dye stained the nuclei. The image was acquired with filters appropriate for DAPI, fluorescein and the Texas Red® dye. The image was deconvolved using Huygens software (Scientific Volume Imaging, www.svi.nl). 3-D reconstruction was performed using Imaris software (Bitplane AG, www.bitplane.com).

A Longer-Wavelength Reduced Rhodamine

Intracellular oxidation of dihydrorhodamine 6G (D633) yields rhodamine 6G (R634), which localizes in the mitochondria of live cells (Section 12.2). This cationic oxidation product has longer-wavelength spectra than those of dihydrorhodamine 123, making it especially useful for multicolor applications and in some autofluorescent cells and tissues. Dihydrorhodamine 6G has been used in the study of chloride conductance and mutations of the cystic fibrosis transmembrane conductance regulator.[235]

Reduced MitoTracker® Probes

Two of our MitoTracker® probes — MitoTracker® Orange CM-H_2TMRos (M7511, Figure 12.10) and MitoTracker® Red CM-H_2XRos (M7513, Figure 12.11) — are chemically reactive reduced rosamines. Unlike MitoTracker® Orange CMTMRos and MitoTracker® Red CMXRos (M7510, M7512; Section 12.2), the reduced versions of these probes do not fluoresce until they enter an actively respiring cell, where they are oxidized by reactive oxygen species to the fluorescent mitochondrion-selective probe and then sequestered in the mitochondria. Both MitoTracker® Orange CMTMRos and the reduced MitoTracker® Orange CM-H_2TMRos have been used to investigate the metabolic state of *Pneumocystis carinii* mitochondria.[236]

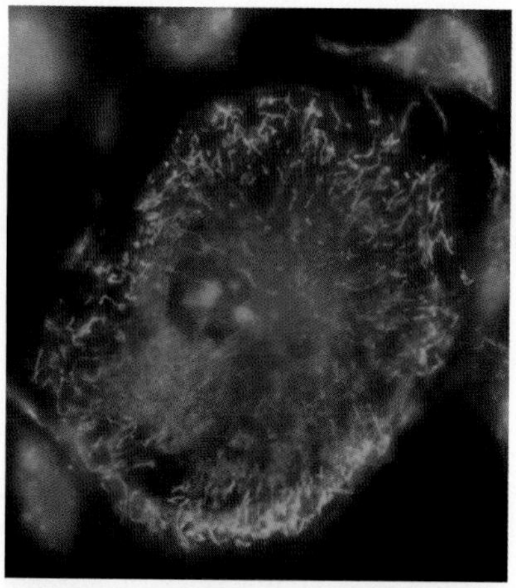

Figure 18.14 Live bovine pulmonary artery endothelial cells were incubated with the cell-permeant, weakly blue-fluorescent dihydroethidium (D1168, D11347, D23107) and the green-fluorescent mitochondrial stain, MitoTracker® Green FM (M7514). Upon oxidation, red-fluorescent ethidium accumulated in the nucleus.

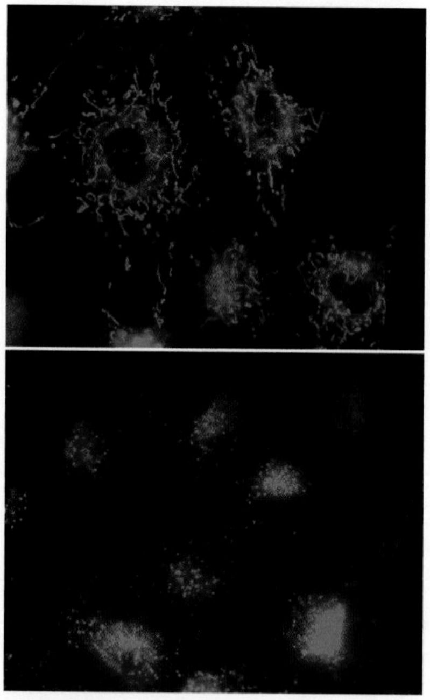

Figure 18.15 Cellular proliferation state determines the distribution of the oxidized product of RedoxSensor™ Red CC-1 (R14060). Normal rat kidney (NRK) cells in different growth states were stained with RedoxSensor™ Red CC-1. In proliferating cells (upper panel), the oxidized dye accumulates in mitochondria. In quiescent cells (lower panel), the oxidized product localizes in the lysosomes.

Dihydroethidium (Hydroethidine)

Although dihydroethidium (Figure 15.23), which is also called hydroethidine, is commonly used to analyze respiratory burst in phagocytes,[237–239] it has been reported that this probe undergoes significant oxidation in resting leukocytes, possibly through the uncoupling of mitochondrial oxidative phosphorylation.[180] Cytosolic dihydroethidium exhibits blue fluorescence; however, once this probe is oxidized to ethidium (E1305, Section 8.1, Figure 8.13), it intercalates within the cell's DNA, staining its nucleus a bright fluorescent red[240–242] (Figure 18.14). The mechanism of dihydroethidium's interaction with lysosomes and DNA has been described.[243] A recent report suggests that oxidation of dihydroethidium by superoxide produces a fluorescent product that is distinctly different from ethidium and that exhibits shorter-wavelength fluorescence upon binding to DNA.[244] Dihydroethidium has been used for many purposes, including:

- Detecting multidrug-resistant cancer cells[245] (Section 15.6)
- Following phagocytosis and oxidative bursts by phagocytic blood cells[237,238,246,247]
- Investigating spermatozoal viability[248,249]
- Quantitating killer cell–target cell conjugates by flow cytometry methods[250–252]

Dihydroethidium (hydroethidine) is available in a 25 mg vial (D1168), as a stabilized 5 mM solution in DMSO (D23107) or specially packaged in 10 vials of 1 mg each (D11347); the stabilized DMSO solution or special packaging is recommended when small quantities of the dye will be used over a long period of time.

RedoxSensor™ Red CC-1 Stain

The fluorescence localization of our RedoxSensor™ Red CC-1 stain (2,3,4,5,6-pentafluorotetramethyldihydrorosamine, R14060; Figure 12.18) appears to be based on a cell's cytosolic redox potential. Once it passively enters live cells, the RedoxSensor™ Red CC-1 stain may be oxidized in the cytosol to a red-fluorescent product (excitation/emission maxima ~540/600 nm), which then accumulates in the mitochondria. Alternatively, this nonfluorescent probe may be transported to the lysosomes where it is oxidized. The differential distribution of the oxidized product between mitochondria and lysosomes appears to depend on the redox potential of the cytosol.[253] In proliferating cells, mitochondrial staining predominates; whereas in contact-inhibited cells, the staining is primarily lysosomal (Figure 18.15). The best method we have found to quantitate the distribution of the oxidized product is to use the mitochondrion-selective MitoTracker® Green FM stain (M7514) in conjunction with the RedoxSensor™ Red CC-1 stain.[253]

Glutathiolation Detection with BioGEE

Biotinylated glutathione ethyl ester (BioGEE, G36000) is a cell-permeant, biotinylated glutathione analog for the detection of glutathiolation. Under conditions of oxidative stress, cells may transiently incorporate glutathione into proteins. Stressed cells incubated with BioGEE will also incorporate this biotinylated glutathione derivative into proteins, facilitating the identification of oxidation-sensitive proteins.[254] Once these cells are fixed and permeabilized, glutathiolation levels can be detected with a fluorescent streptavidin conjugate (Section 7.6, Table 7.22) using either flow cytometry or fluorescence microscopy. Proteins glutathiolated with BioGEE can also be extracted and analyzed by mass spectrometry or by Western blotting methods in conjunction with fluorophore- or enzyme-labeled streptavidin conjugates.

Tetrazolium Salts: Chromogenic Redox Indicators

Tetrazolium salts — especially MTT (M6494) — are widely used for detecting the redox potential of cells for viability, proliferation and cytotoxicity assays. Upon reduction, these water-soluble colorless compounds form uncharged, brightly colored formazans. Several of the formazans precipitate out of solution and are useful for histochemical localization of the site of reduction or, after solubilization in organic solvent, for quantitation by standard spectrophotometric techniques. The extremely water-soluble formazan product of XTT (X6493) does not require solubilization prior to quantitation. Many of these salts are reduced by specific components of the electron transport chain and may be useful for determining the site of action of specific toxins.[255] Selected applications of the tetrazolium salts are listed in Table 18.2. Our Vybrant® MTT Cell Proliferation Assay Kit (V13154, Section 15.4) provides a means of counting metabolically active cells; the Vybrant® MTT assay can detect from 2000 to 250,000 cells, depending on the cell type and conditions. See also Section 15.2 for applications of tetrazolium salts in cells.

References

1. J Photochem Photobiol B 11, 241 (1991); **2.** J Am Chem Soc 104, 5541 (1982); **3.** J Chem Soc Faraday Trans I 82, 1627 (1986); **4.** Methods Enzymol 186, 635 (1990); **5.** Photochem Photobiol 55, 81 (1992); **6.** Proc Natl Acad Sci USA 76, 6047 (1979); **7.** J Am Chem Soc 111, 2909 (1989); **8.** Photochem Photobiol 65, 352 (1997); **9.** Photochem Photobiol 61, 632 (1995); **10.** Photochem Photobiol 61, 529 (1995); **11.** Pharmacol Ther 63, 1 (1994); **12.** J Photochem Photobiol A 64, 273 (1992); **13.** Photochem Photobiol 54, 95 (1991); **14.** Photochem Photobiol 53, 169 (1991); **15.** Biochem Pharmacol 47, 373 (1994); **16.** Biochem Biophys Res Commun 165, 1207 (1989); **17.** Biochem Pharmacol 46, 1929 (1993); **18.** Antiviral Res 17, 63 (1992); **19.** Photochem Photobiol 52, 609 (1990); **20.** Photochem Photobiol 43, 677 (1986); **21.** Adv Photochem 18, 315 (1993); **22.** Photochem Photobiol 66, 374 (1997); **23.** Biochim Biophys Acta 1105, 333 (1992); **24.** Arch Biochem Biophys 291, 43 (1991); **25.** J Photochem Photobiol A 58, 339 (1991); **26.** J Photochem Photobiol B 1, 437 (1988); **27.** J Immunol Methods 168, 245 (1994); **28.** Arch Biochem Biophys 300, 714 (1993); **29.** Bone Marrow Transplant 12, 191 (1993); **30.** Cancer Res 53, 806 (1993); **31.** Free Radic Biol Med 12, 389 (1992); **32.** Biochim Biophys Acta 1075, 28 (1991); **33.** J Infect Dis 163, 1312 (1991); **34.** Photochem Photobiol 53, 1 (1991); **35.** Cancer Res 49, 3637 (1989); **36.** Biochim Biophys Acta 882, 210 (1986); **37.** Methods Enzymol 133, 569 (1986); **38.** Biochem Biophys Res Commun 123, 869 (1984); **39.** Arch Biochem Biophys 314, 284 (1994); **40.** J Reprod Fertil 97, 441 (1993); **41.** Methods Enzymol 12, 5 (1967); **42.** Anal Biochem 290, 138 (2001); **43.** J Biol Chem 273, 32030 (1998); **44.** Curr Biol 6, 1497 (1996); **45.** Methods Cell Biol 44, 715 (1994); **46.** Proc Natl Acad Sci U S A 91, 2659 (1994); **47.** Nucleic Acids Res 22, 4789 (1994); **48.** Bioconjug Chem 4, 69 (1993); **49.** Methods Enzymol 208, 414 (1991); **50.** Annu Rev Biochem 59, 207 (1990); **51.** J Am Chem Soc 111, 4941 (1989); **52.** Proc Natl Acad Sci U S A 86, 9702 (1989); **53.** Biochemistry 29, 8447 (1990); **54.** J Am Chem Soc 109, 1990 (1987); **55.** Anal Biochem 212, 85 (1993); **56.** Anal Chem 68, 867 (1996); **57.** FASEB J 9, 1085 (1995); **58.** Anal Chem 69, 4295 (1997); **59.** J Biol Chem 279, 23453 (2004); **60.** J Biol Chem 276, 35253 (2001); **61.** Proc Natl Acad Sci U S A 87, 1620 (1990); **62.** Eur J Biochem 221, 695 (1994); **63.** Anal Biochem 206, 273 (1992); **64.** Arch Biochem Biophys 373, 447 (2000); **65.** Circ Res 84, 1203 (1999); **66.** Biochem Biophys Res Commun 248, 382 (1998); **67.** J Biol Chem 273, 33972 (1998); **68.** Inflammation 20, 151 (1996); **69.** J Biolumin Chemilumin 12, 277 (1997); **70.** J Immunol Methods 97, 209 (1987); **71.** Blood 83, 3324 (1994); **72.** Free Radic Biol Med 15, 447 (1993); **73.** Cytometry 18, 147 (1994); **74.** Free Radic Biol Med 17, 117 (1994); **75.** J Cell Physiol 151, 466 (1992); **76.** Biochem J 289, 587 (1993); **77.** Free Radic Biol Med 15, 143 (1993); **78.** Am J Physiol 266, G799 (1994); **79.** Life Sci 55, 1427 (1994); **80.** Chem Soc Rev 6, 195 (1977); **81.** Can J Biochem 51, 158 (1973); **82.** Biochim Biophys Acta 385, 232 (1975); **83.** Biochem Biophys Res Commun 163, 836 (1989); **84.** Biochim Biophys Acta 981, 235 (1989); **85.** FEBS Lett 169, 169 (1984); **86.** J Cell Biol 273, 26900 (1998); **87.** Neurochem Res 22, 333 (1997); **88.** Am J Physiol 271, F209 (1996); **89.** Biochim Biophys Acta 1487, 61 (2000); **90.** Circ Res 84, 229 (1999); **91.** J Biol Chem 276, 15575 (2001); **92.** Plant Physiol 125, 1591 (2001); **93.** Atherosclerosis 152, 307 (2000); **94.** J Biol Chem 269, 798 (1994); **95.** J Biol Chem 274, 2234 (1999); **96.** Free Radic Biol Med 11, 81 (1991); **97.** J Exp Med 139, 208 (1974); **98.** DNA Cell Biol 21, 251 (2002); **99.** Free Radic Biol Med 22, 93 (1997); **100.** Anal Biochem 253, 162 (1997); **101.** Proc Soc Exp Biol Med 206, 53 (1994); **102.** Biochem Int 10, 205 (1985); **103.** J Immunol Methods 202, 133 (1997); **104.** Anal Biochem 253, 169 (1997); **105.** J Invest Dermatol 112, 751 (1999); **106.** Free Radic Biol Med 27, 1197 (1999); **107.** J Invest Dermatol 110, 966 (1998); **108.** Anal Chim Acta 402, 47 (1999); **109.** Proc Natl Acad Sci U S A 97, 10930 (2000); **110.** Science 293, 1806 (2001); **111.** Theriogenology 57, 1025 (2002); **112.** J Neurochem 79, 266 (2001); **113.** Am J Physiol Lung Cell Mol Physiol 281, L993 (2001); **114.** Anal Biochem 300, 245 (2002); **115.** Mol Hum Reprod 7, 237 (2001); **116.** J Biol Chem 275, 15749 (2000); **117.** Am J Physiol Endocrinol Metab 282, E474 (2002); **118.** Anal Biochem 320, 292 (2003); **119.** Biochemistry 37, 13781 (1998); **120.** Biochim Biophys Acta 1330, 127 (1997); **121.** J Biochem Biophys Methods 35, 23 (1997); **122.** J Biol Chem 272, 12328 (1997); **123.** Biochemistry 34, 12755 (1995); **124.** Proc Natl Acad Sci U S A 91, 1183 (1994); **125.** Arch Biochem Biophys 297, 147 (1992); **126.** Cytometry 13, 686 (1992); **127.** Anal Biochem 196, 443 (1991); **128.** Chem Phys Lipids 53, 309 (1990); **129.** Biochim Biophys Acta 944, 29 (1988); **130.** Cell 75, 241 (1993); **131.** Biochemistry 16, 819 (1977); **132.** Proc Natl Acad Sci USA 77, 26 (1980); **133.** Biosci Biotechnol Biochem 56, 605 (1992); **134.** Anal Lett 21, 965 (1988); **135.** Proc Natl Acad Sci U S A 99, 11599 (2002); **136.** J Chromatogr A 881, 159 (2000); **137.** Lipids 31, 1091 (1996); **138.** J Chromatogr 617, 205 (1993); **139.** J Chromatogr 622, 153 (1993); **140.** Free Radic Biol Med 31, 164 (2001); **141.** FEBS Lett 474, 137 (2000); **142.** Free Radic Res 29, 43 (1998); **143.** J Agric Food Chem 48, 1150 (2000); **144.** Anal Biochem 265, 290 (1998); **145.** Clin Exp Med 2, 105 (2002); **146.** Methods Enzymol 319, 603 (2000); **147.** FEBS Lett 453, 278 (1999); **148.** J Androl 23, 259 (2002); **149.** Biochim Biophys Acta 1298, 119 (1996); **150.** Free Radic Biol Med 21, 241 (1996); **151.** Biochem Pharmacol 49, 1649 (1995); **152.** Clin Chem 41, 1738 (1995); **153.** Biochemistry 31, 8090 (1992); **154.** Anal Biochem 177, 300 (1989); **155.** Life Sci 60, PL 301 (1997); **156.** Free Radic Biol Med 18, 29 (1995); **157.** J Biol Chem 273, 33279 (1998); **158.** FASEB J 2, 2487 (1988); **159.** Biochem Mol Biol Int 33, 1179 (1994); **160.** Free Radic Biol Med 6, 623 (1989); **161.** J Immunol 129, 1589 (1982); **162.** J Appl Physiol 76, 539 (1994); **163.** J Leukoc Biol 54, 300 (1993); **164.** J Biochem (Tokyo) 106, 355 (1989); **165.** Biochem Biophys Res Commun 155, 106 (1988); **166.** Am J Physiol 262, G1015 (1992); **167.** Arch Biochem Biophys 310, 352 (1994); **168.** Anal Chem 65, 1794 (1993); **169.** Biochem J 290, 51 (1993); **170.** Free Radic Biol Med 18, 1 (1995); **171.** J Lipid Res 33, 1051 (1992); **172.** Methods Enzymol 233, 324 (1994); **173.** Lipids 33, 1235 (1998); **174.** Biochim Biophys Acta 1097, 145 (1991); **175.** Biomed Biochim Acta 49, 991 (1990); **176.** Proc Natl Acad Sci U S A 89, 11426 (1992); **177.** Arch Toxicol 68, 582 (1994); **178.** Brain Res 635, 113 (1994); **179.** Chem Res Toxicol 5, 227 (1992); **180.** J Leukoc Biol 47, 440 (1990); **181.** Eur J Biochem 217, 973 (1993); **182.** Arch Biochem Biophys 302, 348 (1993); **183.** J Immunol Methods 159, 173 (1993); **184.** J Immunol Methods 159, 131 (1993); **185.** Exp Cell Res 209, 375 (1993); **186.** Cytometry 13, 615 (1992); **187.** Cytometry 13, 525 (1992); **188.** Free Radic Biol Med 33, 938 (2002); **189.** Biochem Pharmacol 65, 1575 (2003); **190.** Methods Enzymol 233, 128 (1994); **191.** Lab Invest 64, 167 (1991); **192.** Am J Physiol 264, H881 (1993); **193.** Lab Invest 70, 579 (1994); **194.** Free Radic Res Commun 16, 217 (1992); **195.** Cytometry 14, 287 (1993); **196.** Cell 77, 817 (1994); **197.** Brain Res 610, 172 (1993); **198.** J Neurosci 14, 2260 (1994); **199.** Eur J Cell Biol 65, 200 (1994); **200.** J Biol Chem 269, 14546 (1994); **201.** Toxicol Appl Pharmacol 120, 29 (1993); **202.** J Cell Biol 126, 1079 (1994); **203.** J Leukoc Biol 51, 496 (1992); **204.** J Biol Chem 274, 28161 (1999); **205.** Biochem Biophys Res Commun 304, 619 (2003); **206.** Free Radic Biol Med 16, 509 (1994); **207.** Biochemistry 34, 7194 (1995); **208.** J Biol Chem 274, 19323 (1999); **209.** J Pharmacol Exp Ther 300, 9 (2002); **210.** J Biol Chem 276, 21938 (2001); **211.** Proc Natl Acad Sci U S A 98, 1643 (2001); **212.** J Biol Chem 275, 27838 (2000); **213.** J Biol Chem 278, 3170 (2003); **214.** J Leukoc Biol 43, 304 (1988); **215.** J Immunol Methods 130, 223 (1990); **216.** J Biol Chem 255, 1874 (1980); **217.** J Clin Invest 61, 1081 (1978); **218.** J Cell Physiol 156, 428 (1993); **219.** Biochemistry 34, 3544 (1995); **220.** Free Radic Biol Med 16, 149 (1994); **221.** Free Radic Res Commun 18, 195 (1993); **222.** Free Radic Res Commun 10, 221 (1990); **223.** J Biol Chem 266, 4244 (1991); **224.** J Am Chem Soc 114, 5430 (1992); **225.** Arch Biochem Biophys 288, 481 (1991); **226.** Arch Biochem Biophys 298, 431 (1992); **227.** Arch Biochem Biophys 298, 438 (1992); **228.** J Immunol Methods 131, 269 (1990); **229.** APMIS 102, 474 (1994); **230.** FEBS Lett 273, 55 (1990); **231.** Cytometry 13, 693 (1992); **232.** J Immunol Methods 178, 89 (1995); **233.** J Immunol Methods 162, 261 (1993); **234.** Naturwissenschaften 75, 354 (1988); **235.** Proc Natl Acad Sci U S A 93, 1167 (1996); **236.** J Eukaryot Microbiol 41, 79S (1994); **237.** FEMS Microbiol Lett 122, 187 (1994); **238.** J Immunol Methods 170, 117 (1994); **239.** Cytometry 12, 687 (1991); **240.** J Leukoc Biol 55, 253 (1994); **241.** J Histochem Cytochem 34, 1109 (1986); **242.** Biotechniques 3, 270 (1985); **243.** Histochemistry 94, 205 (1990); **244.** Free Radic Biol Med 34, 1359 (2003); **245.** Exp Cell Res 190, 69 (1990); **246.** Cytometry 17, 294 (1994); **247.** J Immunol 151, 1463 (1993); **248.** J Histochem Cytochem 39, 485 (1991); **249.** Gamete Res 22, 355 (1989); **250.** Cytometry 12, 666 (1991); **251.** J Immunol Methods 139, 281 (1991); **252.** J Immunol Methods 130, 251 (1990); **253.** Free Radic Biol Med 28, 1266 (2000); **254.** Biochemistry 39, 11121 (2000); **255.** Toxicity Testing Using Microorganisms, Vol. I, Bitton G, Dutka BJ, Eds. pp. 27–55 (1986).

Data Table — 18.2 Generating and Detecting Reactive Oxygen Species

Cat #	MW	Storage	Soluble	Abs	EC	Em	Solvent	Notes
A6551	425.57	FF,D,AA	DMSO	286	8,000	none	MeOH	1
A7896	366.32	D,L	H_2O	400	8,500	429	pH 7	
A7923	376.48	F,D,L	DMSO	358	11,000	424	MeOH	2
A12222	257.25	FF,D,A	DMSO	280	6,000	none	pH 8	3
A22177	257.25	FF,D,A	DMSO	280	6,000	none	pH 8	
A36003	423.42	RO,L	DMF	454	24,000	515	pH 9	4, 5
A36006	~300	FF,D,A	DMSO	293	11,000	none	pH 8	6
B3932	448.32	F,L	DMSO, $CHCl_3$	665	161,000	676	MeOH	
C400	531.30	F,D	DMSO, EtOH	290	5,600	none	MeCN	7
C2938	675.43	F,D,AA	DMSO	291	5,700	none	MeOH	7
C2944	423.47	FF,D,LL,AA	MeOH	429	7,500	see Notes	pH 7	8, 9, 10
C6827	577.80	F,D,AA	DMSO	287	9,100	none	MeOH	7
C7924	487.62	F,D,L	DMSO, H_2O	385	5,800	485	pH 7	2
C7933	287.23	F,D,L	DMSO	299	16,000	431	MeOH	11
C13293	498.39	F,D	DMSO, EtOH	290	5,500	none	MeCN	12
D399	487.29	F,D	DMSO, EtOH	258	11,000	none	MeOH	7
D632	346.38	F,D,L,AA	DMF, DMSO	289	7,100	none	MeOH	13, 14
D633	444.57	F,D,L,AA	DMF, DMSO	296	11,000	none	MeOH	13, 14
D1168	315.42	FF,L,AA	DMF, DMSO	355	14,000	see Notes	MeCN	13, 15
D2935	584.37	F,D,AA	DMF	258	11,000	none	MeOH	7
D3861	504.43	F,L	DMSO	582	140,000	591	MeOH	16
D7894	386.43	F,D,LL	MeCN	358	29,000	none	MeOH	17
D11347	315.42	FF,L,AA	DMF, DMSO	355	14,000	see Notes	MeCN	13, 15
D23107	315.42	FF,D,L,AA	DMSO	355	14,000	see Notes	MeCN	15, 18
D23805	1068.95	F,D	DMSO	285	5,800	none	MeCN	19
D23806	346.38	F,D,L,AA	DMSO	289	7,100	none	MeOH	14, 18
F2902	see Notes	RR,L,AA	H_2O	<300		none		4, 20, 21
G36000	561.67	F,D	DMSO	<300		none		
H7476	504.45	F,D,L	DMSO, DMF	591	37,000	594	EtOH	
H7515	546.53	F,D,L	DMSO	463	24,000	600	MeOH	22
H7516	528.51	F,D,L	DMSO	459	23,000	616	MeOH	22
H36004	424.41	RO,L	DMF	454	28,000	515	pH 9	4, 5
I6496	505.70	D	H_2O, DMSO	249	38,000	none	MeOH	
L6868	510.50	L	H_2O	455	7,400	505	H_2O	23, 24
L8455	177.16	D,L	DMF	355	7,500	411	MeOH	24
M689	485.98	F,DD,L	DMF, DMSO	629	75,000	none	MeCN	25
M6494	414.32	D,L	H_2O, DMSO	375	8,300	none	MeOH	26, 27
M7511	392.93	F,D,L,AA	DMSO	235	57,000	none	MeOH	13, 14
M7513	497.08	F,D,L,AA	DMSO	245	45,000	none	MeOH	13, 14
M7913	258.32	F,L	DMF, DMSO	352	30,000	401	MeOH	28
M23800	291.74	FF,D,LL,AA	DMSO	430	8,400	546	MeOH	29
M24571	569.67	D,L	DMSO, EtOH	555	143,000	578	MeOH	
N6495	817.65	D,L	H_2O, DMSO	256	64,000	none	MeOH	26
N7897	316.26	D,L	H_2O	289	8,100	337	MeOH	
P244	274.36	L	DMF, $CHCl_3$	341	41,000	376	MeOH	31
P394	344.50	L	DMF, $CHCl_3$	341	42,000	377	MeOH	31
P800	~240000	RR,L	see Notes	546	2,410,000	575	pH 7	32
P801	~240000	RR,L	see Notes	565	1,960,000	578	pH 7	32
P6878	316.16	F,D,L	DMSO	270	29,000	none	$CHCl_3$	
P6879	363.16	F,D,L	DMSO	270	28,000	none	$CHCl_3$	33
P7071	1089.97	D,L	pH 7	396	4,900	none	pH 7.4	34, 35, 36
P13290	627.48	F,D,AA	DMSO	259	22,000	none	MeOH	37
P36005	276.42	FF,LL,AA	EtOH	304	77,000	416	MeOH	4, 38
R14000	1057.75	F,D	DMSO	313	9,700	none	MeOH	39
R14060	434.41	F,D,L,AA	DMSO	239	52,000	none	MeOH	13, 40
S36002	~600	F,D,L	DMSO	508	105,000	528	pH 7	41, 42
X6493	674.53	F,D	H_2O, DMSO	286	15,000	none	MeOH	43

For definitions of the contents of this data table, see "Navigating *The Handbook*" in the introductory pages.

Notes

1. Peroxidase-catalyzed reaction of A6551 with H_2O_2 produces fluorescent 2-dodecylresorufin (Abs = 578 nm (EC = 69,000 $cm^{-1}M^{-1}$), Em = 597 nm in MeOH).
2. Fluorescence of A7923 and C7924 is weak. Reaction of the nitroxide moiety with superoxide or hydroxyl radicals results in increased fluorescence without a spectral shift (Anal Biochem 212, 85 (1993)).
3. Peroxidase-catalyzed reaction of the Amplex® Red reagent (A12222, A22177) with H_2O_2 produces fluorescent resorufin (R363).
4. This product is supplied as a ready-made solution in the solvent indicated under "Soluble."
5. Fluorescence of A36003 and H36004 is extremely weak. Highly fluorescent fluorescein F1300 is generated upon oxidation (J Biol Chem 278, 3170 (2003)).
6. Peroxidase-catalyzed reaction of the Amplex® UltraRed reagent (A36006) with H_2O_2 yields a fluorescent product with Abs = 568 nm (EC = 57,000 $cm^{-1}M^{-1}$), Em = 581 nm in pH 7.5 buffer.

7. Dihydrofluorescein diacetates are colorless and nonfluorescent until both of the acetate groups are hydrolyzed and the products are subsequently oxidized to fluorescein derivatives. The materials contain less than 0.1% of oxidized derivative when initially prepared. The oxidation products of C400, C2938, C6827, D399 and D2935 are 2′,7′-dichlorofluorescein derivatives with spectra similar to C368.
8. C2944 emits chemiluminescence (Em = 466 nm) on oxidation by superoxide (Anal Biochem 206, 273 (1992)).
9. Do NOT dissolve in DMSO.
10. Aqueous solutions of coelenterazine (>1 mM) can be prepared in pH 7 buffer containing 50 mM 2-hydroxypropyl-β-cyclodextrin (Biosci Biotechnol Biochem 61, 1219 (1997)).
11. Enzymatic hydroxylation yields a 7-hydroxycoumarin derivative with spectroscopic properties similar to H185.
12. Difluorodihydrofluorescein diacetates are colorless and nonfluorescent. Acetate hydrolysis and subsequent oxidation generate a fluorescent 2′,7′-difluorofluorescein derivative with spectra similar to O6146.
13. This compound is susceptible to oxidation, especially in solution. Store solutions under argon or nitrogen. Oxidation may be induced by illumination.
14. These compounds are essentially colorless and nonfluorescent until oxidized. Oxidation products (in parentheses) are as follows: D632 and D23806 (R302); D633 (R634); M7511 (M7510); M7513 (M7512).
15. Dihydroethidium has blue fluorescence (Em ~420 nm) until oxidized to ethidium (E1305). The reduced dye does not bind to nucleic acids (FEBS Lett 26, 169 (1972)).
16. Oxidation of the polyunsaturated butadienyl portion of the BODIPY® 581/591 dye results in a shift of the fluorescence emission peak from ~590 nm to ~510 nm (Methods Enzymol 319, 603 (2000); FEBS Lett 453, 278 (1999)).
17. Oxidation of D7894 occurs rapidly in solution when illuminated. The oxidation product is strongly fluorescent. Em = 379 nm.
18. This product is supplied as a ready-made solution in DMSO with sodium borohydride added to inhibit oxidation.
19. D23805 is colorless and nonfluorescent until the AM ester groups are hydrolyzed and the resulting leuco dye is subsequently oxidized. The final product is calcein (C481).
20. F2902 is essentially colorless and nonfluorescent until oxidized. A small amount (~5%) of oxidized material is normal and acceptable for the product as supplied. The oxidation product is fluorescent (Abs = 495 nm, Em = 524 nm) (J Immunol Methods 130, 223 (1990)).
21. This product consists of a dye–bovine serum albumin conjugate (MW ~66,000) complexed with IgG in a ratio of approximately 1:4 mol:mol (BSA:IgG)
22. H7515 and H7516 have weaker absorption peaks at longer wavelengths: Abs = 581 nm (EC = 12,000 $cm^{-1}M^{-1}$) for H7515, Abs = 580 nm (EC = 9000 $cm^{-1}M^{-1}$) for H7516. Their quantum yields for singlet oxygen production (0.83 for H7515, 0.76 for H7516) are essentially independent of the irradiation wavelength between 430 and 580 nm (J Photochem Photobiol A 64, 273 (1992)).
23. L6868 has much stronger absorption at shorter wavelengths (Abs = 368 nm (EC = 36,000 $cm^{-1}M^{-1}$)).
24. This compound emits chemiluminescence upon oxidation in basic aqueous solutions. Emission peaks are at 425 nm (L8455) and 470 nm (L6868).
25. Isothiocyanates are unstable in water and should not be stored in aqueous solution.
26. Enzymatic reduction products are water-insoluble formazans with Abs = 505 nm (M6494) and 605 nm (N6495) after solubilization in DMSO or DMF. See literature sources for further information (Histochemistry 76, 381 (1982); Prog Histochem Cytochem 9, 1 (1976)).
27. M6494 also has Abs = 242 nm (EC = 21,000 $cm^{-1}M^{-1}$) in MeOH.
28. Generates chemiluminescence (Em = 465 nm in 0.1 M SDS) upon reaction with $^1O_2$ (J Am Chem Soc 108, 4498 (1986)).
29. Generates chemiluminescence (Em = 455 nm) upon reaction with superoxide.
30. The product generated by reaction of M36008 with superoxide has similar spectroscopic properties to E1305.
31. Pyrene derivatives exhibit structured spectra. The absorption maximum is usually about 340 nm with a subsidiary peak at about 325 nm. There are also strong absorption peaks below 300 nm. The emission maximum is usually about 376 nm with a subsidiary peak at 396 nm. Excimer emission at about 470 nm may be observed at high concentrations.
32. Phycobiliproteins are packaged as suspensions in 60% ammonium sulfate, pH 7.0. Store refrigerated at 4°C but DO NOT FREEZE.
33. Iodoacetamides in solution undergo rapid photodecomposition to unreactive products. Minimize exposure to light prior to reaction.
34. Unstable in water. Use immediately.
35. All photoactivatable probes are sensitive to light. They should be protected from illumination except when photolysis is intended.
36. Releases O_2 upon photolysis at 355 nm. Recommended solution pH for optimal stability is 7.4 (Proc Natl Acad Sci U S A 92, 8105 (1995)).
37. Acetate hydrolysis and subsequent oxidation of P13290 generate P12925.
38. *Cis*-parinaric acid is readily oxidized to nonfluorescent products. Use under N_2 or Ar except when oxidation is intended. Stock solutions should be prepared in deoxygenated solvents. *Cis*-parinaric acid is appreciably fluorescent in lipid environments and organic solvents but is nonfluorescent in water.
39. Acetate hydrolysis of R14000 yields rose bengal (Abs = 556 nm (EC = 104,000 $cm^{-1}M^{-1}$) Em = 572 nm in MeOH) (Photochem Photobiol 66, 374 (1997)).
40. R14060 is colorless and nonfluorescent until oxidized. The spectral characteristics of the oxidation product (2,3,4,5,6-pentafluorotetramethylrosamine) are similar to those of T639.
41. MW: The preceding ~ symbol indicates an approximate value, not including counterions.
42. The fluorescence of S36002 is relatively weak. Reaction of the dye with singlet oxygen ($^1O_2$) results in fluorescence enhancement with essentially no change in absorption or emission wavelengths.
43. Enzymatic reduction product is a water-soluble formazan, Abs = 475 nm.

Product List — 18.2 Generating and Detecting Reactive Oxygen Species

Cat #	Product Name	Unit Size
A6551	10-acetyl-3,7-dihydroxy-2-dodecylphenoxazine *special packaging*	10 x 100 µg
A7923	4-((9-acridinecarbonyl)amino)-2,2,6,6-tetramethylpiperidin-1-oxyl, free radical (TEMPO-9-AC)	5 mg
A36003	3′-(*p*-aminophenyl) fluorescein (APF) *5 mM solution in DMF*	470 µL
A22188	Amplex® Red Hydrogen Peroxide/Peroxidase Assay Kit *500 assays*	1 kit
A12222	Amplex® Red reagent (10-acetyl-3,7-dihydroxyphenoxazine)	5 mg
A22177	Amplex® Red reagent *packaged for high-throughput screening*	10 x 10 mg
A22182	Amplex® Red Xanthine/Xanthine Oxidase Assay Kit *400 assays*	1 kit
A36006	Amplex® UltraRed reagent	5 x 1 mg
A7896	anthracene-9,10-dipropionic acid, disodium salt	25 mg
B3932	(*E,E*)-3,5-bis-(4-phenyl-1,3-butadienyl)-4,4-difluoro-4-bora-3a,4a-diaza-*s*-indacene (BODIPY® 665/676)	5 mg
C400	5-(and-6)-carboxy-2′,7′-dichlorodihydrofluorescein diacetate (carboxy-H_2DCFDA) *mixed isomers*	25 mg
C2938	6-carboxy-2′,7′-dichlorodihydrofluorescein diacetate, di(acetoxymethyl ester)	5 mg
C13293	5-(and-6)-carboxy-2′,7′-difluorodihydrofluorescein diacetate (carboxy-H_2DFFDA) *mixed isomers*	5 mg
C7924	5-(2-carboxyphenyl)-5-hydroxy-1-((2,2,5,5-tetramethyl-1-oxypyrrolidin-3-yl)methyl)-3-phenyl-2-pyrrolin-4-one, potassium salt (proxyl fluorescamine)	5 mg
C6827	5-(and-6)-chloromethyl-2′,7′-dichlorodihydrofluorescein diacetate, acetyl ester (CM-H_2DCFDA) *mixed isomers* *special packaging*	20 x 50 µg
C2944	coelenterazine	250 µg
C7933	coumarin-3-carboxylic acid, succinimidyl ester (SECCA)	25 mg
D399	2′,7′-dichlorodihydrofluorescein diacetate (2′,7′-dichlorofluorescin diacetate; H_2DCFDA)	100 mg
D2935	2′,7′-dichlorodihydrofluorewscein diacetate, succinimidyl ester (OxyBURST® Green H_2DCFDA, SE)	5 mg
D3861	4,4-difluoro-5-(4-phenyl-1,3-butadienyl)-4-bora-3a,4a-diaza-*s*-indacene-3-undecanoic acid (BODIPY® 581/591 C_{11})	1 mg
D23805	dihydrocalcein, AM *special packaging*	20 x 50 µg
D1168	dihydroethidium (hydroethidine)	25 mg
D11347	dihydroethidium (hydroethidine) *special packaging*	10 x 1 mg
D23107	dihydroethidium (hydroethidine) *5 mM stabilized solution in DMSO*	1 mL
D632	dihydrorhodamine 123	10 mg
D23806	dihydrorhodamine 123 *5 mM stabilized solution in DMSO*	1 mL
D633	dihydrorhodamine 6G	25 mg
D7894	diphenyl-1-pyrenylphosphine (DPPP)	5 mg
F2902	Fc OxyBURST® Green assay reagent *25 assays* *3 mg/mL*	500 µL
G36000	glutathione ethyl ester, biotin amide (BioGEE) *glutathiolation detection reagent* *special packaging*	10 x 100 µg
H36004	3′-(*p*-hydroxyphenyl) fluorescein (HPF) *5 mM solution in DMF*	470 µL
H7476	hypericin	1 mg
H7515	hypocrellin A	1 mg
H7516	hypocrellin B	1 mg
I6496	4-iodonitrotetrazolium violet (INT; 2-(4-iodophenyl)-3-(4-nitrophenyl)-5-phenyltetrazolium chloride)	1 g
L6868	lucigenin (bis-*N*-methylacridinium nitrate) *high purity*	10 mg
L8455	luminol (3-aminophthalhydrazide)	25 g
M689	malachite green isothiocyanate	10 mg
M24571	merocyanine 540	25 mg
M7913	*trans*-1-(2′-methoxyvinyl)pyrene	1 mg
M23800	2-methyl-6-(4-methoxyphenyl)-3,7-dihydroimidazo[1,2-a]pyrazin-3-one, hydrochloride (MCLA)	5 mg
M7511	MitoTracker® Orange CM-H_2TMRos *special packaging*	20 x 50 µg
M7513	MitoTracker® Red CM-H_2XRos *special packaging*	20 x 50 µg
M6494	MTT (3-(4,5-dimethylthiazol-2-yl)-2,5-diphenyltetrazolium bromide)	1 g
N7897	naphthalene-1,4-dipropionic acid, disodium salt	25 mg
N6495	nitro blue tetrazolium chloride (NBT)	1 g
O13291	OxyBURST® Green H_2HFF BSA *special packaging*	5 x 1 mg
P36005	*cis*-parinaric acid *3 mM in ethanol*	10 mL
P13290	5-(pentafluorobenzoylamino)dihydrofluorescein diacetate (PFB-H_2FDA)	5 mg
P7071	(µ-peroxo) (µ-hydroxo)bis(bis(bipyridyl)cobalt(III)) perchlorate (caged oxygen)	25 mg
P6878	*N*-(1,10-phenanthrolin-5-yl)bromoacetamide	5 mg
P6879	*N*-(1,10-phenanthrolin-5-yl)iodoacetamide	5 mg
P800	B-phycoerythrin *4 mg/mL*	0.5 mL
P801	R-phycoerythrin *4 mg/mL*	0.5 mL
P244	1-pyrenebutanol	100 mg
P394	1-pyrenenonanol	25 mg
R14060	RedoxSensor™ Red CC-1 *special packaging*	10 x 50 µg
R14000	rose bengal diacetate	5 mg
S36002	Singlet Oxygen Sensor Green *special packaging*	10 x 100 µg
X6493	XTT (2,3-bis-(2-methoxy-4-nitro-5-sulfophenyl)-2*H*-tetrazolium-5-carboxanilide)	100 mg

For current prices or to order online, visit probes.invitrogen.com

18.3 Probes for Nitric Oxide Research

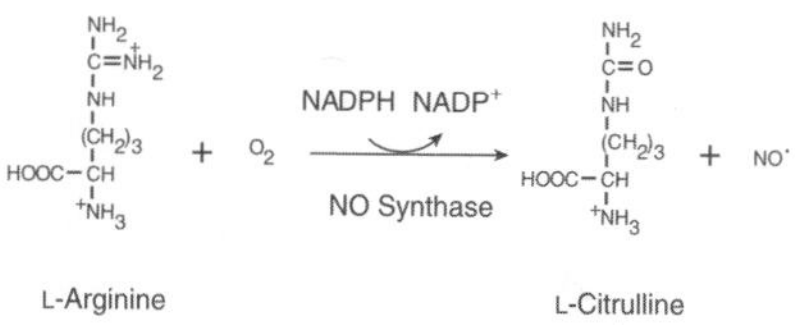

Figure 18.16 Nitric oxide synthase production of nitric oxide (NO) and L-citrulline from L-arginine and dioxygen (O_2).

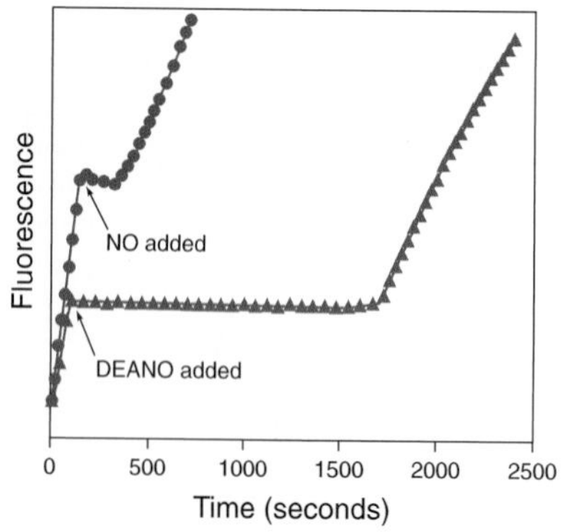

Figure 18.18 Inhibition of phenobarbital-induced rat hepatic microsomal dealkylase activity by 100 µM NO (●, added from a saturated aqueous stock solution) or 50 µM DEANO (▲, D7915). Enzymatic activity was monitored using the fluorogenic substrate, resorufin benzyl ether (R441). Reprinted with permission from (Arch Biochem Biophys 300, 115 (1993)).

Nitric oxide (NO), the molecule that makes the firefly glow,[1,2] plays a critical role as a molecular mediator of a variety of physiological processes, including blood-pressure regulation and neurotransmission.[3–8] In endothelial cells, as well as neurons and astrocytes, NO is synthesized from L-arginine in a reaction catalyzed by nitric oxide synthase[9–12] (NOS) (Figure 18.16). NO that diffuses into smooth muscle cells binds to the heme group of guanylate cyclase. Because free NO is a transient species with a half-life of about 5 seconds, many investigations of this gaseous molecule have relied largely on studies of NOS. Preparing NO solutions and detecting NO in experimental systems require special precautions to achieve reproducibility.[13] NO can also complex with superoxide to form the strong oxidant, peroxynitrite anion[14] ($ONOO^-$, Table 18.1), which may be a major cytotoxic agent produced during inflammation, sepsis and ischemia/reperfusion.[15] Activated macrophage and neutrophils produce nitric oxide and superoxide, and thus peroxynitrite anion, at similar rates.[16] NO generators are also reported to produce an accumulation of chelatable Zn^{2+} in hippocampal neuronal perikarya, as determined with some of our Zn^{2+} indicators[17] (Section 19.7, Table 19.6).

Spontaneous Nitric Oxide Donors and Antagonist

DEANO and Spermine NONOate

The DEANO (diethylamine nitric oxide, D7915) and spermine NONOate (S7916) solids provide a means of preparing aqueous NO solutions.[18] When these solids are dissolved in buffer, cell culture medium or blood, they dissociate to form two molecules of NO and one molecule of the corresponding amine[19] (Figure 18.17). The delivery of NO can be easily controlled by preparing moderately basic solutions of these NONOates and then lowering the pH to initiate NO generation.

DEANO has a half-life of about two minutes in pH 7.4 phosphate buffer at 37°C, releasing two molecules of NO and one molecule of diethylamine.[18–21] DEANO therefore allows more sustained delivery of NO than is possible using NO-saturated aqueous solutions (Figure 18.18). The data in Figure 18.18 are from a study of cytochrome P450 inhibition by NO in which DEANO was used in conjunction with fluorogenic microsomal dealkylase substrates[22] (R441, R352; Section 10.6). DEANO has also been used as a NO donor to stimulate ADP-ribosylation of various proteins.[23]

With a half-life of 39 minutes at 37°C in pH 7.4 buffer, spermine NONOate releases NO much more slowly than does DEANO, making it suitable for whole animal infusions and experiments with long incubations.[19] Also, spermine, the by-product of spermine NONOate dissociation, is less likely to be deleterious in living systems and may also demonstrate biological activity of its own.[24] Both DEANO and spermine NONOate are reported to inhibit *in vitro* proliferation of A375 melanoma cells.[25]

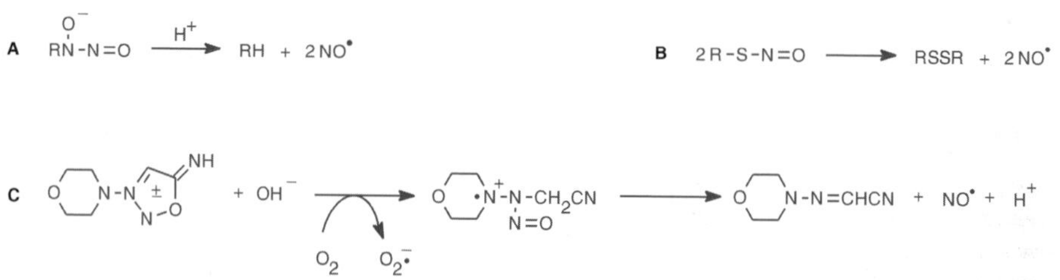

Figure 18.17 Mechanisms of spontaneous NO release by: **A)** DEANO (D7915) or spermine NONOate (S7916); **B)** SNAP (N7892, N7927); and **C)** SIN-1 (M7891, M7926).

SNAP and SIN-1

Molecular Probes also offers the NO donors SNAP (*S*-nitroso-*N*-acetylpenicillamine, N7892, N7927) and SIN-1 (3-morpholinosydnonimine, hydrochloride; M7891, M7926), which spontaneously release NO (and superoxide in the case of SIN-1) under physiological conditions (Figure 18.17), thereby stimulating cyclic GMP production.[26–30] SNAP and SIN-1 have been shown to be potent vasodilators *in vivo* and *in vitro* and to inhibit smooth muscle cell mitogenesis and proliferation.[31–34] The relationship between NO generated from SNAP and SIN-1 and intracellular Ca^{2+} has been studied using fluorescent Ca^{2+} indicators[35–37] (Chapter 19). It has also been reported that NO released from SNAP stimulates Ca^{2+}-independent synaptic vesicle release,[37] which can be detected with FM® 1-43 (T3163, T35356; Section 14.4, Section 16.1). We offer SNAP and SIN-1 in 25 mg vials (N7892, M7891) and, because of their potential instability in solution, as specially packaged sets of 20 vials, each containing 1 mg (N7927, M7926).

Carboxy-PTIO: A Nitric Oxide Antagonist

Molecular Probes offers carboxy-PTIO (C7912), a water-soluble and stable free radical molecule that reacts stoichiometrically with NO.[38–40] Carboxy-PTIO can be used *in vivo* to inhibit the physiological effects mediated by NO,[38,40,41] or *in vitro* to quantitate NO levels by ESR spectrometry.[42,43]

SNAP: A Photoactivatable Nitric Oxide Donor

The potential spatial and temporal control of nitric oxide release made possible by photolysis of NO precursors makes this an attractive approach for generating NO in experimental systems. SNAP (*S*-nitroso-*N*-acetylpenicillamine, N7892, N7927) has been shown to release NO in response to light stimulation in both aqueous and isopropyl alcohol solutions.[44]

L-NMMA: A Nitric Oxide Synthase Inhibitor

Nitric oxide synthase catalyzes the NADPH- and O_2-dependent oxidation of L-arginine to NO and L-citrulline[9–12] (Figure 18.16). L-NMMA (N^G-methyl-L-arginine, M7898) competitively inhibits NOS in a wide variety of cells, including neurons, endothelial cells and macrophages.[45,46]

Detecting Nitric Oxide, Nitrite and Nitrate

The nitric oxide (NO) radical is very unstable, and no equilibrium indicators for NO are known. However, NO is readily oxidized to the nitrosonium cation (NO^+), which is moderately stable in aqueous solutions but highly reactive with nucleophiles, or other nitrogen oxides. Under aerobic conditions, these reactive nitrogen oxides (Table 18.1) can be trapped by various amines, in particular by aromatic amines to form diazonium salts or aromatic 1,2-diamines to form benzotriazoles (Figure 18.19).

DAF-FM and DAF-FM Diacetate: The Preferred Indicators for Intracellular Nitric Oxide

Probably the most successful indicator for nitric oxide has been 4,5-diaminofluorescein diacetate (DAF-2 diacetate),[47,48] which was developed by Kojima and collaborators. As with other fluorescein diacetates (Section 15.2), DAF-2 diacetate is membrane permeant and is deacetylated by intracellular esterases to 4,5-diaminofluorescein (DAF-2). DAF-2, however, remains essentially nonfluorescent until it reacts with the nitrosonium cation (produced by spontaneous oxidation of nitric oxide) to form a fluorescent heterocycle, which becomes trapped in the cell's cytoplasm. DAF-2 has been used to identify individual nitric oxide–producing neurons in brain slices,[49,50] in mitochondria[51] and in living plant cells.[52] Simultaneous measurements of intracellular Ca^{2+} with fura-2 and nitric oxide production with DAF-2 have been reported.[53]

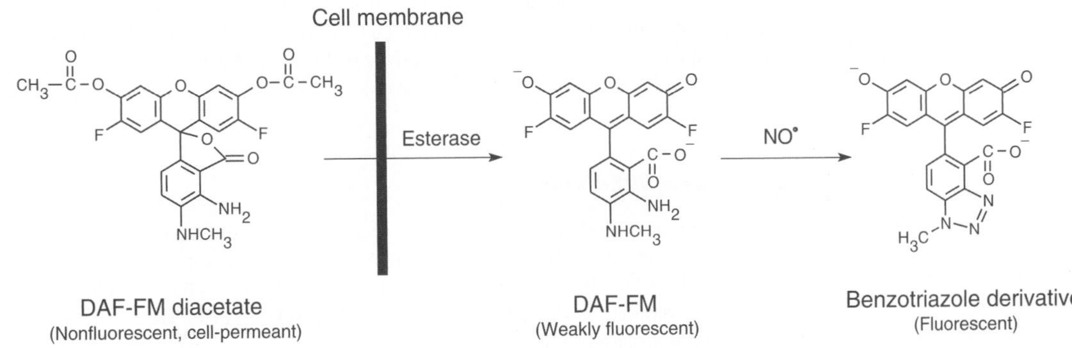

Figure 18.19 Reaction scheme for the detection of nitric oxide (NO) by DAF-FM (D23841) and DAF-FM diacetate (D23842, D23844).

DAF-FM[53] (4-amino-5-methylamino-2′,7′-difluorofluorescein, D23841) and its diacetate derivative (DAF-FM diacetate, D23842; D23844) have significant utility for measuring nitric oxide production in living cells or solutions[54–57] (Figure 18.19, Figure 18.20). The fluorescence quantum yield of DAF-FM is reported to be 0.005 but increases about 160-fold to 0.81 after reacting with NO.[53] DAF-FM reagent has some important advantages over DAF-2:

- Spectra of the NO (NO_2^-) adduct of DAF-FM are independent of pH above pH 5.5.[53]
- The NO_2^- adduct of DAF-FM is significantly more photostable than that of DAF-2.[53]
- DAF-FM is a more sensitive reagent for NO_2^- than is DAF-2; the NO and NO_2^- detection limit for DAF-FM is ~3 nM[53] versus ~5 nM for DAF-2.[47]
- The higher absorptivity and greater water solubility of the NO_2^- adduct of DAF-FM should make this assay much more sensitive than detection with 2,3-diaminonaphthalene (see below) or other aromatic diamines.

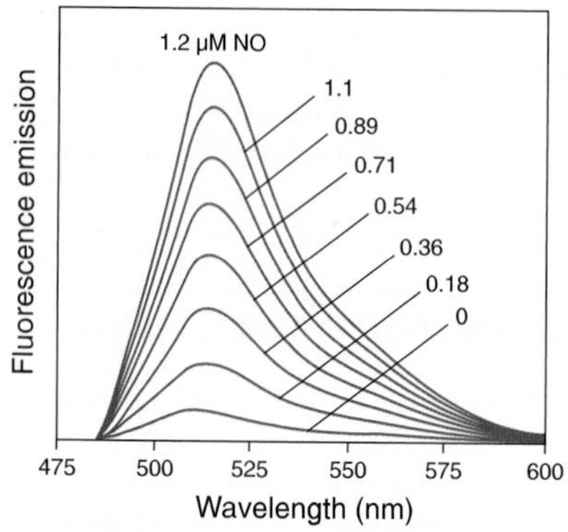

Figure 18.20 Fluorescence emission spectra of DAF-FM (D23841, D23842) in solutions containing zero to 1.2 µM nitric oxide (NO).

DAF-2 reportedly also reacts with dehydroascorbic acid and ascorbic acid, generating products with fluorescence spectra similar to those of the NO_2^- adduct of DAF-2.[58] Therefore, when using DAF-2 and potentially DAF-FM for measuring nitric oxide levels in cells, it is important to also perform control experiments with nitric oxide synthase inhibitors to distinguish the source of the fluorescent species. Although DAF-2 and its diacetate are not available from Molecular Probes, we maintain a bibliography (D23843) for these reagents. We anticipate that DAF-FM should give equal or superior performance to DAF-2 in most applications.

Griess Reagent Kit

Under physiological conditions, NO is readily oxidized to nitrite and nitrate or it is trapped by thiols as an *S*-nitroso adduct. The Griess reagent provides a simple and well characterized colorimetric assay for nitrites, and nitrates that have been reduced to nitrites, with a detection limit of about 100 nM.[59–61] Nitrites react with sulfanilic acid in acidic solution to form an intermediate diazonium salt that couples to *N*-(1-naphthyl)ethylenediamine to yield a purple azo derivative that can be monitored by absorbance at 548 nm (Figure 18.21). Our Griess Reagent Kit (G7921) contains all of the reagents required for nitrite quantitation, including:

- *N*-(1-Naphthyl)ethylenediamine dihydrochloride
- Sulfanilic acid in 5% H_3PO_4
- Concentrated nitrite standard for generating calibration curves
- Detailed protocols for spectrophotometer and microplate reader assays

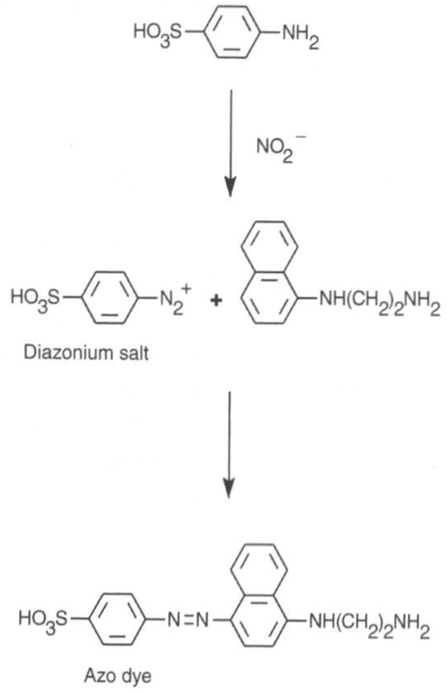

Figure 18.21 Principle of nitrite quantitation using the Griess Reagent Kit (G7921). Formation of the azo dye is detected via its absorbance at 548 nm.

Both the *N*-(1-naphthyl)ethylenediamine dihydrochloride and the sulfanilic acid in 5% H_3PO_4 are provided in convenient dropper bottles for easy preparation of the Griess reagent. Sample pretreatment with nitrate reductase and glucose 6-phosphate dehydrogenase is reported to reduce nitrate without producing excess NADPH, which can interfere with the Griess reaction.[62] The Griess Reagent Kit can also be used to analyze NO that has been trapped as an *S*-nitroso derivative by a modification that uses mercuric chloride or copper (II) acetate to release the NO from its complex.[63,64]

2,3-Diaminonaphthalene

In a reaction similar to that of DAF-FM (Figure 18.19), 2,3-diaminonaphthalene (D7918) reacts with the nitrosonium cation that forms spontaneously from NO to form the fluorescent product 1*H*-naphthotriazole.[59,65] Using 2,3-diaminonaphthalene, researchers have developed a rapid, quantitative fluorometric assay that can detect from 10 nM to 10 µM nitrite and is compatible with a 96-well microplate format.[66]

1,2-Diaminoanthraquinone

For directly detecting NO levels *in vivo*, we offer 1,2-diaminoanthraquinone (DAA, D23840). This nitric oxide probe is reported to be nonfluorescent until it reacts with NO to produce a red-fluorescent precipitate. 1,2-Diaminoanthraquinone has been used to detect changes in NO levels in rat retinas after injury to the optic nerve.[67] This methodology may make it possible to test the actions of NO in neurodegeneration, inflammation and other biological processes. The role of NO production in hippocampal long-term potentiation has also been investigated using 1,2-diaminoanthraquinone for spatial imaging of NO in rat brain slices.[68,69]

NBD Methylhydrazine

NBD methylhydrazine (*N*-methyl-4-hydrazino-7-nitrobenzofurazan, M20490) is a unique reagent for the detection of nitrite. Reaction of NBD methylhydrazine with NO_2^- in the presence of mineral acids leads to formation of fluorescent products with excitation/emission maxima of ~468/537 nm. This reaction serves as the principle behind a selective fluorogenic method for the determination of NO_2^- (Figure 18.22). Although NBD methylhydrazine has been used to quantitate nitrite in water using a fluorescence microplate reader,[70] it does not seem to have been used yet to detect nitrite formed by spontaneous oxidation of NO.

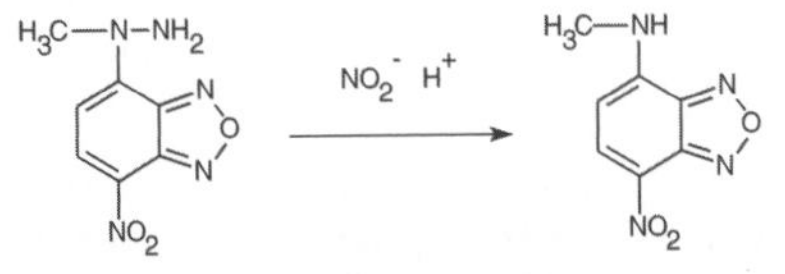

Figure 18.22 Reaction scheme illustrating the principle of nitrite detection by NBD methylhydrazine (M20490).

Dichlorodihydrofluorescein Diacetate and Dihydrorhodamine 123

In addition to their extensive use for detecting other reactive oxygen species such as superoxide (Section 18.2), dichlorodihydrofluorescein diacetate (H_2DCFDA, D399; Section 18.2) and dihydrorhodamine 123 (D632, Section 18.2) have been reported to be useful for detecting peroxynitrite formation in both solution and in certain living cells.[14,71–75]

Anti-Nitrotyrosine Antibody

High levels of nitrotyrosine are associated with a large number of diseases, including multiple sclerosis, Alzheimer's and Parkinson's.[76,77] Increased levels of nitrotyrosine are also indicative of vascular and tissue injury from ischemia–reperfusion and inflammation.[78] At the protein level, tyrosine nitration can lead to loss or alteration of protein function, as demonstrated for the oncogenic protein p53[79] and the mitochondrial protein manganese superoxide dismutase.[80]

Several pathways for the nitration of tyrosine have been suggested. Nitric oxide (NO) can interact rapidly with superoxide ($\cdot O_2^-$) to form peroxynitrite ($OONO^-$), a potent oxidant of aromatic, aliphatic and sulfhydryl residues.[14,80] Heme peroxidases, such as myeloperoxidase and eosinophil peroxidase, have been shown to utilize hydrogen peroxide (H_2O_2) to oxidize nitrite (NO_2^-) and catalyze tyrosine nitration.[81] In addition, other heme proteins such as hemoglobin and catalase may contribute to tyrosine nitration using NO as a substrate.[82] Tryptophan residues can also be oxidized by peroxynitrite.[83]

Molecular Probes offers a high-activity rabbit polyclonal anti-nitrotyrosine antibody (A21285) for detecting nitrotyrosine-containing proteins and peptides. This antibody is suitable for both immunohistochemical (Figure 7.77) and Western blotting applications (Figure 18.23) and should be useful for identifying nitrated proteins and determining the level of protein nitrosylation in tissues. This rabbit IgG antibody can be used in combination with any of our Zenon® Rabbit IgG Antibody Labeling Kits (Section 7.3, Table 7.13) to localize nitrotyrosine-containing targets in cells and on blots.

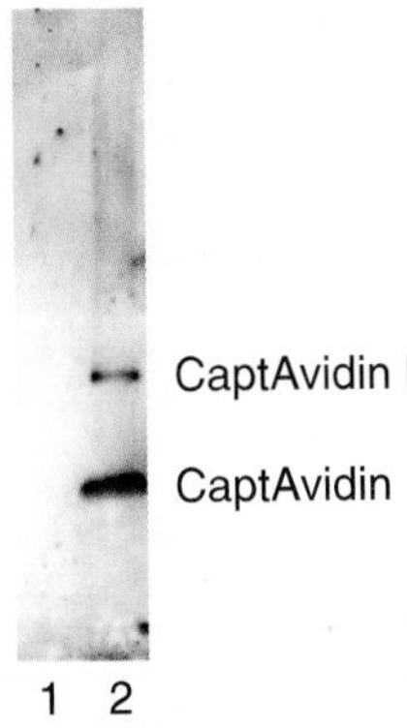

Figure 18.23 Specificity of our rabbit anti-nitrotyrosine antibody (A21285) to nitrated proteins. Equal amounts of avidin (A887, lane 1) and CaptAvidin™ biotin-binding protein (C21385, lane 2) were run on an SDS-polyacrylamide gel (4–20%) and blotted onto a PVDF membrane. CaptAvidin™ biotin-binding protein, a derivative of avidin, has nitrated tyrosine residues in the biotin-binding site. Using the Pro-Q® Western Blot Stain Kit #3 (P21864), nitrated proteins were identified with the anti-nitrotyrosine antibody, in combination with an alkaline phosphatase conjugate of goat anti-rabbit IgG antibody (G21079) and the red-fluorescent substrate, DDAO phosphate (D6487).

References

1. Science 292, 2413 (2001); **2.** Science 292, 2486 (2001); **3.** Curr Biol 7, R376 (1997); **4.** J Med Chem 38, 4343 (1995); **5.** Annu Rev Biochem 63, 175 (1994); **6.** Cell 78, 919 (1994); **7.** Am J Physiol 262, G379 (1992); **8.** Science 257, 494 (1992); **9.** Biochem J 357, 593 (2001); **10.** Biochem J 298, 249 (1994); **11.** Cell 78, 915 (1994); **12.** J Med Chem 37, 1899 (1994); **13.** Methods Mol Biol 100, 215 (1998); **14.** Free Radic Biol Med 30, 463 (2001); **15.** Arch Biochem Biophys 298, 431 (1992); **16.** Methods Enzymol 233, 229 (1994); **17.** Brain Res 799, 118 (1998); **18.** Methods Enzymol 268, 281 (1996); **19.** J Med Chem 34, 3242 (1991); **20.** J Biol Chem 270, 17355 (1995); **21.** J Biol Chem 270, 655 (1995); **22.** Arch Biochem Biophys 300, 115 (1993); **23.** J Leukoc Biol 57, 152 (1995); **24.** (1989); **25.** Cancer Res 53, 564 (1993); **26.** Nature 364, 626 (1993); **27.** Nature 375, 68 (1995); **28.** Brain Res 619, 344 (1993); **29.** FEBS Lett 315, 139 (1993); **30.** Thromb Res 70, 405 (1993); **31.** J Pharmacol Exp Ther 260, 286 (1992); **32.** Eur J Pharmacol 144, 379 (1987); **33.** J Pharmacol Exp Ther 248, 762 (1989); **34.** J Clin Invest 83, 1774 (1989); **35.** Am J Physiol 266, L9 (1994); **36.** Life Sci 54, 1449 (1994); **37.** Neuron 12, 1235 (1994); **38.** Biochemistry 34, 7177 (1995); **39.** Biochem Biophys Res Commun 202, 923 (1994); **40.** Biochemistry 32, 827 (1993); **41.** Infect Immun 61, 3552 (1993); **42.** Photochem Photobiol 61, 325 (1995); **43.** Life Sci 54, 185 (1994); **44.** Photochem Photobiol 67, 282 (1998); **45.** FEBS Lett 294, 221 (1991); **46.** J Biol Chem 269, 32318 (1994); **47.** Anal Chem 70, 2446 (1998); **48.** Chem Pharm Bull (Tokyo) 46, 373 (1998); **49.** J Neurosci Methods 92, 101 (1999); **50.** Brain Res 852, 239 (2000); **51.** Biochem Biophys Res Commun 272, 129 (2000); **52.** Plant J 23, 817 (2000); **53.** Angew Chem Int Ed Engl 38, 3209 (1999); **54.** FASEB J 18, 531 (2004); **55.** Free Radic Biol Med 35, 1217 (2003); **56.** J Neurosci 23, 10302 (2003); **57.** Anal Biochem 287, 203 (2000); **58.** J Biol Chem 277, 48472 (2002); **59.** Luminescence 14, 283 (1999); **60.** FASEB J 7, 349 (1993); **61.** Anal Biochem 126, 131 (1982); **62.** Anal Biochem 224, 502 (1995); **63.** Anal Biochem 238, 150 (1996); **64.** Chem Biol 3, 655 (1996); **65.** Methods Enzymol 268, 105 (1996); **66.** Anal Biochem 214, 11 (1993); **67.** Neuroreport 9, 4051 (1998); **68.** Neurobiol Dis 11, 96 (2002); **69.** Neuroimage 15, 633 (2002); **70.** Anal Chem 71, 3003 (1999); **71.** J Biol Chem 273, 12716 (1998); **72.** FEBS Lett 416, 175 (1997); **73.** Free Radic Res 27, 245 (1997); **74.** Clin Hemorheol 16, 685 (1996); **75.** Free Radic Biol Med 20, 373 (1996); **76.** J Biol Chem 278, 8380 (2003); **77.** Methods Enzymol 301, 373 (1999); **78.** Free Radic Res 33, 771 (2000); **79.** Biochem Biophys Res Commun 267, 609 (2000); **80.** Proc Natl Acad Sci U S A 93, 11853 (1996); **81.** Biochem Biophys Res Commun 285, 273 (2001); **82.** Biochim Biophys Acta 1528, 97 (2001); **83.** Biochem Biophys Res Commun 234, 82 (1997).

Data Table — 18.3 Probes for Nitric Oxide Research

Cat #	MW	Storage	Soluble	Abs	EC	Em	Solvent	Notes
C7912	315.39	FF,D	H_2O	367	9,300	none	MeOH	
D7909	314.55	F,D,L	DMSO, DMF	263	17,000	none	MeOH	
D7915	155.13	FF,DD,A	H_2O, DMSO	248	8,000	none	pH 12	1
D7918	158.20	L	DMSO, MeOH	340	5,100	377	MeOH	2
D23840	336.32	F,D,L	DMSO	521	6,000	none	MeOH	3
D23841	412.35	F,D,L	DMSO	487	84,000	see Notes	pH 8	4
D23842	496.42	F,D,L	DMSO	<300		none		5
D23844	496.42	F,D,L	DMSO	<300		none		5
M7891	206.63	FF,D,LL	DMSO, H_2O	291	11,000	none	pH 7	6
M7898	248.28	D	H_2O	<300		none		
M7906	248.28	D	H_2O	<300		none		
M7926	206.63	FF,D,LL	DMSO, H_2O	291	11,000	none	pH 7	6
M20490	209.16	F,L	MeCN	487	24,000	none	MeOH	7
N7892	220.24	FF,D,LL	DMSO, H_2O	342	700	none	MeOH	6
N7927	220.24	FF,D,LL	DMSO, H_2O	342	700	none	MeOH	6
S7916	262.35	FF,DD,A	H_2O, DMSO	248	8,200	none	pH 12	1

For definitions of the contents of this data table, see "Navigating *The Handbook*" in the introductory pages.

Notes

1. Releases nitric oxide upon acid-catalyzed dissociation in solution. Stable in alkaline solutions (Methods Enzymol 268, 281 (1996)).
2. Fluorescence of D7918 is weak. Reaction with nitrite yields highly fluorescent 1*H*-naphthotriazole (Abs = 365 nm, Em = 415 nm in H_2O (pH 12)) (Methods Enzymol 268, 105 (1996)).
3. 1,2-Diaminoanthraquinone reacts with nitrite or nitric oxide to produce 1*H*-anthratriazole-6,11-dione which forms a red-fluorescent (Em >580 nm) precipitate in water (Neuroreport 9, 4051 (1998)).
4. DAF-FM fluorescence is very weak. Reaction with nitrite or nitric oxide generates a highly fluorescent benzotriazole derivative with Abs = 495 nm (EC = 73,000 $cm^{-1}M^{-1}$), Em = 515 nm in pH 7.4 buffer (Angew Chem Int Ed Engl 38, 3209 (1999)).
5. Acetate hydrolysis and subsequent reaction with nitrite or nitric oxide generate a highly fluorescent benzotriazole derivative with Abs = 495 nm (EC = 73,000 $cm^{-1}M^{-1}$), Em = 515 nm in pH 7.4 buffer (Angew Chem Int Ed Engl 38, 3209 (1999)).
6. Spontaneously decomposes in solution.
7. NBD methylhydrazine reacts with nitrite in the presence of strong acid to form fluorescent *N*-methyl-4-amino-7-nitrobenzofurazan (Abs = 459 nm, Em = 537 nm in MeCN) (Anal Chem 71, 3003 (1999)).

Product List — 18.3 Probes for Nitric Oxide Research

Cat #	Product Name	Unit Size
A21285	anti-nitrotyrosine, rabbit IgG fraction *1 mg/mL*	0.5 mL
C7912	2-(4-carboxyphenyl)-4,4,5,5-tetramethylimidazoline-1-oxyl-3-oxide, potassium salt (carboxy-PTIO)	25 mg
D23841	DAF-FM (4-amino-5-methylamino-2′,7′-difluorofluorescein)	1 mg
D23842	DAF-FM diacetate (4-amino-5-methylamino-2′,7′-difluorofluorescein diacetate)	1 mg
D23844	DAF-FM diacetate (4-amino-5-methylamino-2′,7′-difluorofluorescein diacetate) *special packaging*	10 x 50 µg
D23840	1,2-diaminoanthraquinone sulfate (DAA) *high purity*	5 mg
D7918	2,3-diaminonaphthalene	100 mg
D7915	diethylamine nitric oxide, sodium salt (DEANO)	25 mg
D7909	diphenyleneiodonium chloride	25 mg
G7921	Griess Reagent Kit *for nitrite quantitation*	1 kit
M7906	N^G-methyl-D-arginine, acetate salt (D-NMMA)	25 mg
M7898	N^G-methyl-L-arginine, acetate salt (L-NMMA)	25 mg
M20490	*N*-methyl-4-hydrazino-7-nitrobenzofurazan (NBD methylhydrazine)	25 mg
M7891	3-morpholinosydnonimine, hydrochloride (SIN-1)	25 mg
M7926	3-morpholinosydnonimine, hydrochloride (SIN-1) *special packaging*	20 x 1 mg
N7892	*S*-nitroso-*N*-acetylpenicillamine (SNAP)	25 mg
N7927	*S*-nitroso-*N*-acetylpenicillamine (SNAP) *special packaging*	20 x 1 mg
S7916	spermine NONOate	10 mg

For current prices or to order online, visit probes.invitrogen.com

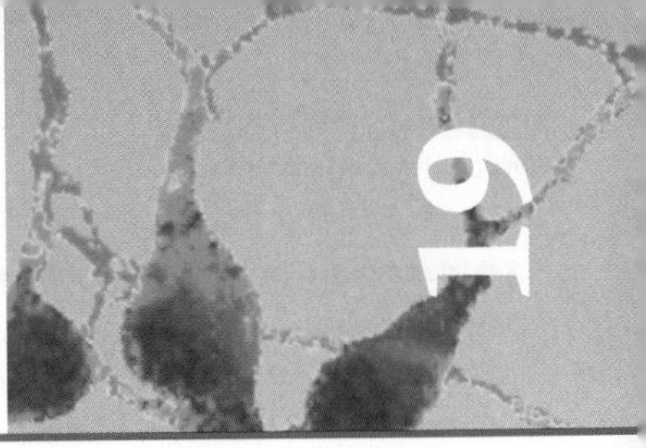

Chapter 19

Indicators for Ca^{2+}, Mg^{2+}, Zn^{2+} and Other Metal Ions

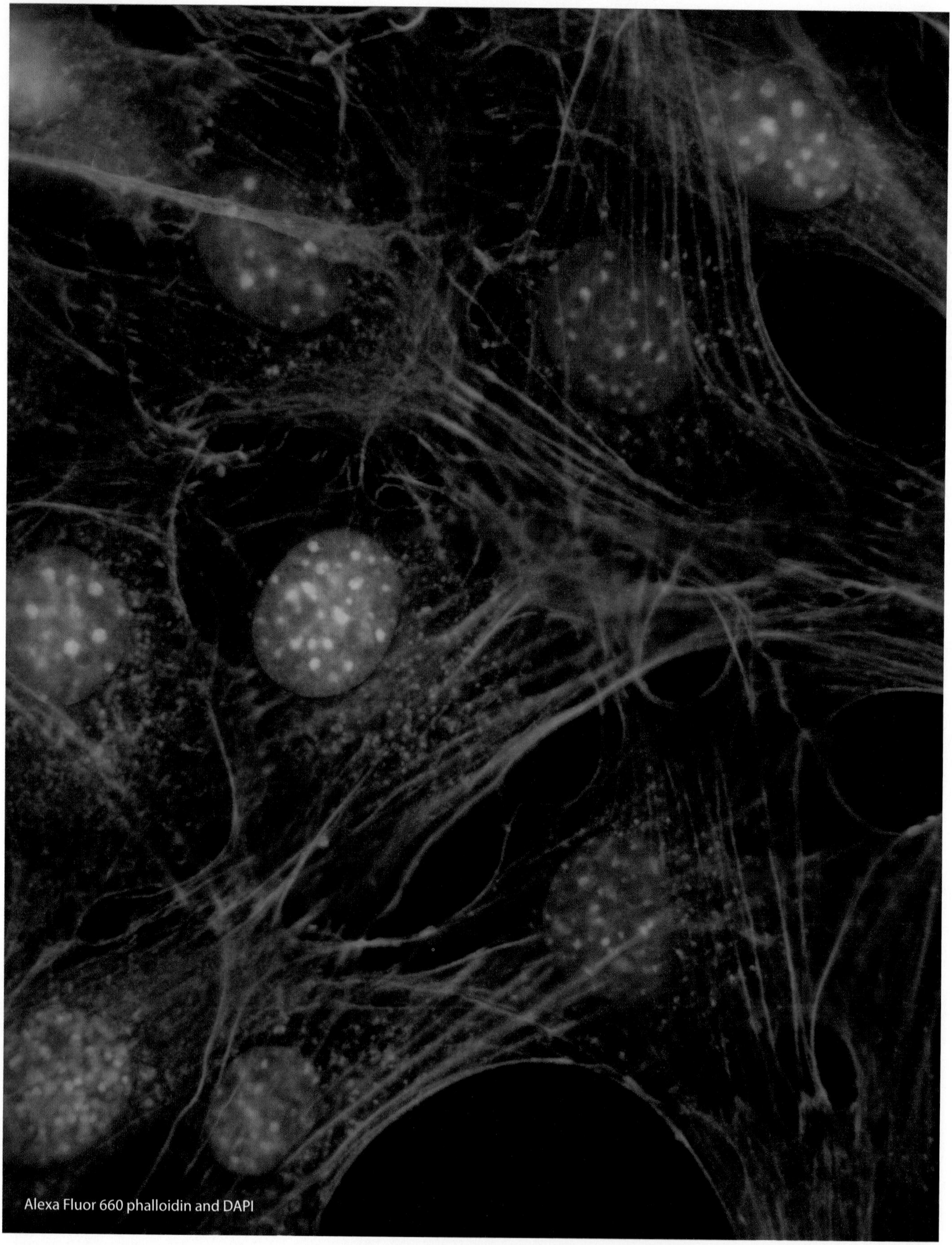

Alexa Fluor 660 phalloidin and DAPI

19.1 Introduction to Ca^{2+} Measurements with Fluorescent Indicators

Fluorescent probes that show a spectral response upon binding Ca^{2+} have enabled researchers to investigate changes in intracellular free Ca^{2+} concentrations using fluorescence microscopy, flow cytometry and fluorescence spectroscopy.[1–6] These fluorescent indicators, most of which are derivatives of the Ca^{2+} chelators EGTA, APTRA and BAPTA,[7] have evolved largely through the efforts of Roger Tsien and his colleagues and, more recently, through those of scientists at Molecular Probes. Recent reviews of these indicators include those by Katerinopoulos and Foukaraki,[8] O'Malley, Burbach and Adams,[9] Williams, Bowser and Petrou,[10] Haugland and Johnson,[6] Scheenen, Hofer and Pozzan,[11], Takahashi and co-workers,[3] Silver,[5] and Kao.[4] Several earlier reviews of ion indicators also contain useful technical information.[12–15]

Selection Criteria for Fluorescent Ca^{2+} Indicators

Molecular Probes offers the widest available selection of fluorescent Ca^{2+} indicators for detecting changes in intracellular Ca^{2+} over the range of <50 nM to >50 µM (Table 19.1). We and our distributors are the primary suppliers of fura-2, indo-1, fluo-3 (Figure 19.1), fluo-4 and rhod-2, and we exclusively offer a number of other indicators for intracellular Ca^{2+}. Our fura-4F, fura-5F, fura-6F and fura-FF indicators provide increased response sensitivity to intracellular Ca^{2+} concentration in the 0.5–5 µM range, as compared with fura-2. The fluo-3, fluo-4, Oregon Green® 488 BAPTA, Calcium Green™, X-rhod-1 and Fura Red™ indicators and their variants allow Ca^{2+} detection over a wide concentration range and offer increased brightness and reduced phototoxicity. We also offer indicators that are conjugated to high– or low–molecular weight dextrans for improved cellular retention and less compartmentalization, as well as lipophilic Ca^{2+} indicators for possible use in studying near-membrane Ca^{2+} (Section 19.4). Molecular Probes strives to

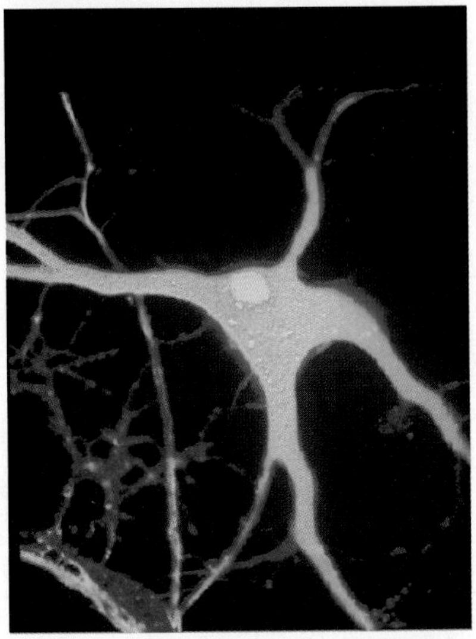

Figure 19.1 A pyramidal neuron from rat hippocampus was first exposed to Alzheimer's β-amyloid peptide and then to the excitatory amino acid glutamate. Confocal laser-scanning microscopy imaging using the intracellular Ca^{2+} indicator fluo-3 (F1241, F1242, F14218, F14242, F23915) shows that β-amyloid peptide destabilizes the neuron's calcium homeostasis and increases its vulnerability to excitotoxicity. The image was contributed by Mark P. Mattson, Sanders-Brown Center on Aging, University of Kentucky.

Table 19.1 — Summary of fluorescent Ca^{2+} indicators available from Molecular Probes

Ca^{2+} Indicator	Salt *	AM Ester †	Dextran ‡	Mode §	K_d (nM) **	Notes
Bis-fura	B6810			Ex 340/380	370	1
BTC	B6790	B6791		Ex 400/480	7000	2
Calcium Green™-1	C3010MP	C3011MP, C3012	C6765, C3713, C3714	Em 530	190	3, 4
Calcium Green™-2	C3730	C3732		Em 535	550	3, 5
Calcium Green™-5N	C3737	C3739		Em 530	14,000	3
Calcium Orange™	C3013	C3015		Em 575	185	2
Calcium Crimson™		C3018		Em 615	185	2
Fluo-3	F1240, F3715	F1241, F1242, F14218, F14242, F23915		Em 525	390	3, 4
Fluo-4	F14200	F14201, F14202, F14217, F23917	F14240 ††, F36250 ‡‡	Em 520	345	3, 6
Fluo-5F	F14221	F14222		Em 520	2300	3
Fluo-4FF	F23980	F23981		Em 520	9700	3
Fluo-5N	F14203	F14204		Em 520	90,000	3
Fura-2	F1200, F6799	F1201, F1221, F1225, F14185	F3029	Ex 340/380	145	2
Fura-4F	F14174	F14175		Ex 340/380	770	2
Fura-5F	F14176	F14177		Ex 340/380	400	2
Fura-6F	F14178	F14179		Ex 340/380	5300	2
Fura-FF	F14180	F14181		Ex 340/380	5500	2
Fura Red™	F14219	F3020, F3021		Ex 420/480	140	2, 7
Indo-1	I1202	I1203, I1223, I1226	I3032	Em 405/485	230	2
Indo-5F	I23912	I23913		Em 405/485	470	2
Mag-fluo-4	M14205	M14206		Em 520	22,000	3
Mag-fura-2	M1290	M1291, M1292		Ex 340/380	25,000	2
Mag-fura-5	M3103	M3105		Ex 340/380	28,000	2
Mag-indo-1	M1293	M1295		Em 405/485	35,000	2, 8

Table 19.1 — Summary of fluorescent Ca^{2+} indicators available from Molecular Probes — continued

Ca^{2+} Indicator	Salt *	AM Ester †	Dextran ‡	Mode §	K_d (nM) **	Notes
Magnesium Green™	M3733	M3735		Em 530	6000	3
Oregon Green® 488 BAPTA-1	O6806	O6807	O6798, O6797	Em 520	170	3
Oregon Green® 488 BAPTA-2	O6808	O6809		Em 520	580	3, 9
Oregon Green® 488 BAPTA-6F	O23990	O23991		Em 520	3000	3
Oregon Green® 488 BAPTA-5N	O6812	O6813		Em 520	20,000	3
Quin-2	Q23918	Q1289		Em 495	60	2, 10
Rhod-2	R14220	R1244, R1245MP	R34677 ††, R34676 ‡‡	Em 580	570	3, 11
Rhod-FF	R23982	R23983		Em 580	19,000	3
Rhod-5N	R14207	R14208		Em 580	320,000	3
X-rhod-1	X14209	X14210	X34675	Em 600	700	3, 12
X-rhod-5F	X23984	X23985		Em 600	1600	3
X-rhod-FF		X23987		Em 600	17,000	3

* Catalog number(s) for the cell-impermeant salt. † Catalog number(s) for the cell-permeant AM ester. ‡ Catalog number(s) for the dextran conjugates. § Measurement wavelengths, in nm, where Ex = fluorescence excitation and Em = fluorescence emission. Indicators for which a pair of wavelengths are listed have dual-wavelength, ratio-measurement capability. ** Ca^{2+} dissociation constant, measured at Molecular Probes *in vitro* at 22°C in 100 mM KCl, 10 mM MOPS, pH 7.2, unless otherwise noted. K_d values depend on temperature, ionic strength, pH and other factors, and are usually higher *in vivo*. Because indicator dextrans are intrinsically polydisperse and have variable degrees of substitution, these values may vary; lot-specific K_d values are printed on the vial in most cases. †† Low-affinity dextran conjugate. ‡‡ High-affinity dextran conjugate. **1.** Ca^{2+}-dependent fluorescence response similar to fura-2 but ~75% greater molar absorptivity. **2.** The AM ester form is fluorescent (a major potential source of error in Ca^{2+} measurements). **3.** The AM ester form is nonfluorescent. **4.** Calcium Green™-1 is more fluorescent than fluo-3 in both Ca^{2+}-bound and Ca^{2+}-free forms. The magnitude of the Ca^{2+}-dependent fluorescence increase is greater for fluo-3; see Figure 19.24. **5.** Larger Ca^{2+}-dependent fluorescence increase than Calcium Green™-1. **6.** The K_d value for the low-affinity fluo-4 dextran (F14240) is ~3 µM, which is much higher than that of the free dye. The K_d value for the high-affinity fluo-4 dextran (F36250) is ~600 nM. **7.** Can also be used in combination with fluo-3 for dual-wavelength ratio measurements, Ex = 488 nm, Em = 530/670 nm (Cell Calcium 18, 377 (1995); Cytometry 17, 135 (1994); Cell Calcium 14, 359 (1993)). **8.** K_d determined in 100 mM KCl, 40 mM HEPES, pH 7.0 at 22°C (Biochem Biophys Res Commun 177, 184 (1991)). **9.** Larger Ca^{2+}-dependent fluorescence increase than Oregon Green® 488 BAPTA-1. **10.** K_d determined in 120 mM KCl, 20 mM NaCl, pH 7.05 at 37°C (Methods Enzymol 172, 230 (1989)). **11.** The K_d value for the low-affinity rhod dextran (R34677) is ~5.2 µM, which is much higher than that of the free dye. The K_d value for the high-affinity rhod dextran (R34676) is ~750 nM. **12.** The K_d value for the X-rhod dextran (R34677) is ~1.8 µM.

provide the highest-purity indicators available anywhere. The AM ester forms of most of our indicators are typically at least 95% pure by HPLC analysis, although purity often exceeds 98%. Furthermore, the AM esters of many of the Ca^{2+} and Mg^{2+} indicators are available in special packaging for more convenient handling and for reduced risk of deterioration during storage. Fluo-3 AM and fluo-4 AM, both of which are extensively used for high-throughput screening for new drug candidates, are available specially packaged at a discounted price (F14242, F14202; Section 19.3).

A number of factors should be considered when selecting a fluorescent Ca^{2+} indicator, some of which are summarized in Table 19.1 and include the following:

- **Indicator form** (salt, AM ester or dextran conjugate), which influences the cell-loading method and affects the indicator's intracellular distribution and retention (see Note 19.1 "Technical Focus: Loading and Calibration of Intracellular Ion Indicators"). The salt and dextran forms are typically loaded by microinjection, microprojectile bombardment or electroporation or by using our Influx™ pinocytic cell-loading reagent (I14402, Section 19.8) (Table 14.1). In contrast, the cell-permeant acetoxymethyl (AM) esters can be passively loaded into cells, where they are cleaved to cell-impermeant products by intracellular esterases.
- **Measurement mode**, which is dictated by whether qualitative or quantitative ion concentration data are required. Ion indicators that exhibit spectral shifts upon ion binding can be used for ratiometric measurements of Ca^{2+} concentration, which are essentially independent of uneven dye loading, cell thickness, photobleaching effects and dye leakage (see Note 19.1 "Technical Focus: Loading and Calibration of Intracellular Ion Indicators"). Excitation and emission wavelength preferences depend on the type of instrumentation being used, as well as on sample autofluorescence and on the presence of other fluorescent or photoactivatable probes in the experiment.
- **Dissociation constant** (K_d), which must be compatible with the Ca^{2+} concentration range of interest. Indicators have a detectable response in the concentration range from approximately $0.1 \times K_d$ to $10 \times K_d$. For ratiometric indicators, the Ca^{2+} response range is also somewhat dependent on the measurement wavelengths used.[16,17] The K_d of Ca^{2+} indicators is dependent on many factors, including pH, temperature,[18–21] ionic strength, viscosity, protein binding and the presence of Mg^{2+} and other ions. Consequently, K_d values for intracellular indicators are usually significantly higher than corresponding values measured in cell-free solutions (Table 19.2).

Intracellular calibration of Ca^{2+} indicators may be achieved either by manipulating Ca^{2+} levels inside cells using an ionophore or by releasing the indicator into the surrounding medium of known Ca^{2+} concentration via detergent lysis of the cells. We also offer several compounds and buffers for measuring and manipulating intracellular and extracellular Ca^{2+}. These products, which are discussed in Section 19.8, include caged Ca^{2+} reagents and caged chelators (NP-EGTA, DMNP-EDTA and diazo-2), as well as Calcium Calibration Buffer Kits, BAPTA-derived buffers, ion-selective chelating polymers (Calcium Sponge™) and the important Ca^{2+} ionophores ionomycin, A-23187 and its nonfluorescent analog, 4-bromo A-23187. Reagents for probing Ca^{2+} regulation and second messenger activity are described in more detail in Chapter 17. Our reagents for the study of Ca^{2+} channels are described in Section 16.3.

Note 19.1 — Technical Focus

Loading and Calibration of Intracellular Ion Indicators

There are two major prerequisites for measuring intracellular ion concentrations using fluorescent indicators:

- **Loading:** The indicator must be localized in the region (most commonly the cytosol but sometimes the mitochondria) where the ion concentration is to be measured.
- **Calibration:** The fluorescence of the indicator must be quantitatively related to the concentration of the free ion.

This technical note focuses on these prerequisites. Further information on the practical aspects of ion measurements using fluorescent indicators can be found in several reviews.[1–8]

Loading

Cell loading methods can be divided into two groups. Bulk loading procedures are applicable to large populations of cells and include:

- Acetoxymethyl (AM) ester loading [5,9]
- Acid loading [10,11] (particularly applicable to plant cells)
- ATP-induced permeabilization [12]
- Electroporation [13]
- Hypoosmotic shock [14]
- Influx™ pinocytic cell-loading reagent [15] (I14402, Section 19.8)
- Ballistic microprojectile delivery [16]

Procedures such as microinjection [17] and infusion from whole-cell patch pipettes [18,19] must be carried out one cell at a time. Reviews of some of these techniques have been published;[20] see also Table 14.1.

The AM Ester Loading Technique

The noninvasive and technically straightforward AM ester technique is by far the most popular method for loading fluorescent ion indicators (Figure 1). The carboxylate groups of indicators for Ca^{2+} and other cations and the phenolic hydroxyl groups of pH indicators are derivatized as acetoxymethyl or acetate esters, respectively, rendering the indicator permeant to membranes and insensitive to ions. Once inside the cell, these derivatized indicators are hydrolyzed by ubiquitous intracellular esterases, releasing the ion-sensitive polyanionic indicator.

In practice, a 1–10 mM stock solution of the ester probe in *anhydrous* dimethylsulfoxide (DMSO) is prepared and divided into appropriately sized aliquots that can be stored desiccated at –20°C. This procedure will curtail the spontaneous ester hydrolysis that can occur in moist environments. Before loading, the DMSO stock solution should be diluted at least 1:200 in *serum-free* culture medium to a final concentration of about 1–10 µM. The nonionic and nondenaturing detergent Pluronic F-127 (P3000MP, P6866, P6867; Section 19.8) is frequently added to help disperse the indicator in the loading medium.[5] After incubation at 20–37°C for 15–60 minutes, the cells should be washed two to three times with fresh *serum-free* culture medium (serum may contain esterase activity). The loading medium should also be free of amino acids or buffers containing primary or secondary amines because aliphatic amines may cleave the AM esters and prevent loading. The overall loading efficiency is typically 10–40%, depending on the molecular structure of the indicator, the type of cells and the incubation conditions.

Problems with AM Ester Loading

Compartmentalization: For calibration purposes (see below), it is usually assumed that fluorescent indicators are homogeneously distributed in the cytosol and equally responsive to variations of intracellular ion concentration. However, AM esters and their hydrolysis products are capable of accumulating in any membrane-enclosed structure within the cell. In addition, indicators in polyanionic form may be sequestered within organelles via active transport processes.[21] Compartmentalization is usually more pronounced at higher loading temperatures and is particularly acute in plant and fungal cells.[22,23] The extent of compartmentalization can be assessed by image analysis, as well as fluorometrically using membrane permeabilization reagents, such as Triton X-100.[5]

Incomplete AM ester hydrolysis: Residual unhydrolyzed AM esters may be present extracellularly due to incomplete removal by washing. Inside the cell, low levels of intracellular esterase activity, which can vary considerably from one cell type to another, may produce only partial AM ester hydrolysis.[24–26] Because even partially hydrolyzed AM esters are Ca^{2+}-insensitive, detection of their fluorescence as part of the total signal leads to an underestimation of the Ca^{2+} concentration.[27,28] Fluorescence quenching by Mn^{2+}, which only binds with high affinity to completely de-esterified indicators, can be used to quantitate these effects. Note that although some indicators are fluorescent in the AM ester form, others are not (Table 19.1).

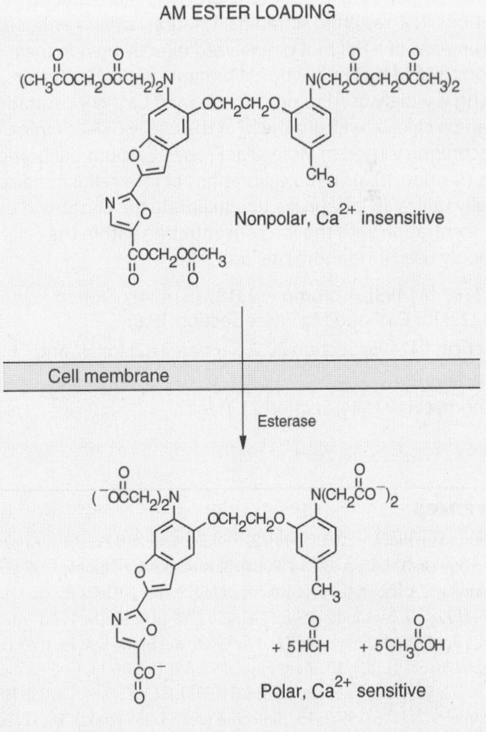

Figure 1. Schematic diagram of the processes involved in loading cells using membrane-permeant acetoxymethyl (AM) ester derivatives of fluorescent indicators, in this case fura-2. Note the generation of potentially toxic by-products (formaldehyde and acetic acid).

continued on next page

continued from previous page

Leakage: Extrusion of anionic indicators from cells by organic ion transporters can be reduced by cooling the sample or by applying inhibitors such as probenecid and sulfinpyrazone.[21] AM esters are extruded by the P-glycoprotein multidrug transporter[29] (Section 15.6). Ratiometric measurements (see below) help to minimize the impact of indicator leakage on experimental data.

Calibration

Ion Dissociation Constants

The dissociation constant (K_d) is the key conversion parameter linking fluorescence signals to ion concentrations, assuming that the indicator is operating as an equilibrium sensor.[30] For pH indicators, K_d is conventionally expressed as its negative log (pK_a). The concentration range over which an indicator produces an observable response is approximately $0.1 \times K_d$ to $10 \times K_d$. For ratiometric measurements, the response range also depends on wavelength-dependent parameters.[31,32] For BAPTA-based Ca^{2+} indicators in particular, the K_d is very sensitive to a number of environmental factors, including temperature, pH, ionic strength and interactions of the indicator with proteins.[33–36] Examination of published data shows that values of K_d determined *in situ* within cells can be up to fivefold higher than values determined *in vitro*[33,37–40] (Table 19.2), underscoring the importance of performing calibrations to determine the K_d directly in the system under study.

Calibration Methodology

Calibration procedures basically consist of recording fluorescence signals corresponding to a series of precisely manipulated ion concentrations. The resulting sigmoidal titration curve is either linearized by means of a Hill plot or analyzed directly by nonlinear regression to yield K_d. For *in vitro* calibrations of Ca^{2+} indicators, EGTA buffering is widely used to produce defined Ca^{2+} concentrations that can be calculated from the K_d of the Ca^{2+}-EGTA complex.[5,7,41] This technique is used in Molecular Probes' Calcium Calibration Buffer Kits (Section 19.8). *In situ* calibrations of intracellular indicators generally utilize an ionophore to equilibrate the controlled external ion concentration with the ion concentration within the cell.[4,42] Commonly used ionophores include:

- A-23187 (A1493), 4-bromo A-23187 (B1494) or ionomycin (I24222) for Ca^{2+} and Mg^{2+} (see Section 19.8)
- Nigericin (N1495; Section 20.2, Section 21.2) for H^+ and Cl^-
- Gramicidin (G6888, Section 21.1) for Na^+
- Valinomycin (V1644, Section 21.1) for K^+

Ratiometric Calibration

Indicators that show an excitation or emission spectral shift upon ion binding can be calibrated using a ratio of the fluorescence intensities measured at two different wavelengths, resulting in the cancellation of artifactual variations in the fluorescence signal that might otherwise be misinterpreted as changes in ion concentration (Figure 2). Note that background levels must be subtracted from the component fluorescence intensities *before* calculation of the ratio. Examples of indicators exhibiting ion-dependent spectral shifts can be found in Figure 19.3, Figure 19.4, Figure 20.3 and Figure 20.11. The ratio of two intensities with opposite ion-sensitive responses (for example, 340 nm/380 nm in Figure 19.11) gives the largest possible dynamic range of ratio signals for a particular indicator. Alternatively, the ratio of an ion-sensitive intensity to an ion-insensitive intensity (measured at a spectral isosbestic point, e.g., 360 nm in Figure 19.3) can be used (Figure 2). Ratiometric measurements reduce or eliminate variations of several determining factors in the measured fluorescence intensity, including indicator concentration, excitation path length, excitation intensity and detection efficiency.[43,44] Artifacts that are eliminated include photobleaching and leakage of the indicator, variable cell thickness, and nonuniform indicator distribution within cells (due to compartmentalization) or among populations of cells (due to loading efficacy variations).

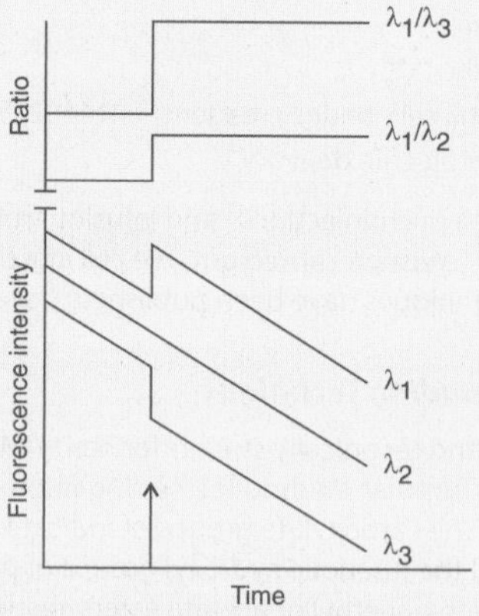

Figure 2. Simulated data demonstrating the practical importance of ratiometric fluorescence techniques. The figure represents an ion indicator that exhibits a fluorescence intensity increase in response to ion binding at wavelength λ_1 and a corresponding decrease at λ_3. Fluorescence measured at an isosbestic point (λ_2) is independent of ion concentration. The intracellular indicator concentration diminishes rapidly due to photobleaching, leakage (assuming the extracellular indicator is not detectable) or some other process. The change of intracellular ion concentration due to a stimulus applied at the time indicated by the arrow is unambiguously identified by recording the fluorescence intensity ratios λ_1/λ_3 or λ_1/λ_2.

References

1. Methods Mol Biol 122, 261 (1999); **2.** Cellular Calcium Practical Approach, 2nd Ed., Tepikin A, Ed. pp. 17–44 (2001); **3.** Methods Cell Biol 56, 237 (1998); **4.** Cell Biology: A Laboratory Handbook, 2nd Ed., Vol. 3, Celis JE, Ed. pp. 363–374 (1998); **5.** Methods Cell Biol 40, 155 (1994); **6.** Methods Enzymol 192, 38 (1990); **7.** Methods Enzymol 172, 230 (1989); **8.** Physiol Rev 79, 1089 (1999); **9.** Nature 290, 527 (1981); **10.** Plant Physiol 93, 841 (1990); **11.** Cell Calcium 8, 455 (1987); **12.** J Biol Chem 262, 8884 (1987); **13.** Cytometry 24, 226 (1996); **14.** Cytometry 28, 316 (1997); **15.** Biotechniques 33, 358 (2002); **16.** J Neurosci Methods 119, 37 (2002); **17.** Biochem J 302, 5 (1994); **18.** Imaging Neurons, Yuste R, Lanni F, Konnerth A, Eds. pp. 35.1–35.10 (2000); **19.** Meth Neurosci 19, 340 (1994); **20.** Proc Natl Acad Sci U S A 98, 4295 (2001); **21.** Cell Calcium 11, 57 (1990); **22.** J Exp Biol 196, 419 (1994); **23.** J Microsc 166, 57 (1992); **24.** Cell Calcium 11, 63 (1990); **25.** Am J Physiol 255, C304 (1988); **26.** Anal Biochem 169, 159 (1988); **27.** Biophys J 67, 476 (1994); **28.** Biophys J 65, 561 (1993); **29.** J Biol Chem 268, 21493 (1993); **30.** This conventional assumption requires that the concentration of the indicator is close to the K_d value. Because intracellular indicator concentrations can easily reach 10–100 µM, even if the externally applied concentration is only 1–10 µM, this assumption is not always valid (Mol Pharmacol 62, 618–627 (2002)); **31.** Cell Calcium 12, 29 (1991); **32.** Cell Calcium 24, 17 (1998); **33.** Biophys J 67, 1646 (1994); **34.** Biophys J 63, 89 (1992); **35.** Biochem Biophys Res Commun 180, 209 (1991); **36.** Biochem Biophys Res Commun 177, 184 (1991); **37.** Cell Calcium 34, 1 (2003); **38.** Cell Calcium 28, 213 (2000); **39.** Biophys J 68, 1453 (1995); **40.** Biophys J 65, 865 (1993); **41.** Cell Calcium 12, 279 (1991); **42.** Cell Calcium 21, 233 (1997); **43.** Methods Cell Biol 30, 157 (1989); **44.** J Biol Chem 260, 3440 (1985).

Table 19.2 — Comparison of *in vitro* and *in situ* K_d values for various Ca^{2+} indicators

Indicator	K_d *in vitro* (nM) *	K_d *in situ* (nM) †	Cell/Tissue Type
Calcium Green™-1	190	930	HeLa cells [1]
Fluo-3	390	2570	Frog skeletal muscle [2]
Fluo-4	345	1000	HeLa cells [1]
Fura-2	145	371	U373-MG astrocytoma cell [3]
Fura-2	145	350	Rabbit gastric gland [4]
Indo-1	230	844	Rabbit cardiac myocyte [5]
Oregon Green® 488 BAPTA-1	170	430	HeLa cells [1]
Rhod-2	570	720	Mouse heart [6]

* Values determined at 22°C in 100 mM KCl, 10 mM MOPS, pH 7.2, 0–10 mM CaEGTA.
† Values determined in the cellular environments listed in the adjacent column. **1.** Cell Calcium 28, 213 (2000); **2.** Biophys J 65, 865 (1993); **3.** Cell Calcium 21, 233 (1997); **4.** Methods Enzymol 192, 38 (1990); **5.** Biophys J 68, 1453 (1995); **6.** Cell Calcium 29, 217 (2001).

References

1. Cellular Calcium Practical Approach, 2nd Ed., Tepikin A, Ed. pp. 17–44 (2001); **2.** Methods 21, 221 (2000); **3.** Physiol Rev 79, 1089 (1999); **4.** Methods Cell Biol 40, 155 (1994); **5.** Methods Cell Biol 56, 237 (1998); **6.** Fluorescent and Luminescent Probes for Biological Activity, 2nd Ed., Mason WT, Ed., pp. 40-50 (1999); **7.** Biochemistry 19, 2396 (1980); **8.** Curr Med Chem 9, 275 (2002); **9.** Methods Mol Biol 122, 261 (1999); **10.** Methods Enzymol 307, 441 (1999); **11.** Cell Biology: A Laboratory Handbook, 2nd Ed., Vol. 3, Celis JE, Ed. pp. 363–374 (1998); **12.** Biochem J 248, 313 (1987); **13.** Methods Enzymol 192, 38 (1990); **14.** Methods Enzymol 172, 230 (1989); **15.** Cellular Calcium: A Practical Approach, McCormack JG, Cobbold PH, Eds. pp. 1–54 (1991); **16.** Cell Calcium 12, 29 (1991); **17.** Cell Calcium 24, 17 (1998); **18.** J Physiol 542, 843 (2002); **19.** Biophys J 78, 2116 (2000); **20.** Anal Biochem 273, 60 (1999); **21.** Biochem Biophys Res Commun 171, 102 (1990).

19.2 Fluorescent Ca^{2+} Indicators Excited with UV Light

Fura-2, Indo-1 and Related Derivatives

Fura-2 and Indo-1

Fura-2 and indo-1 are UV light–excitable, ratiometric Ca^{2+} indicators that are generally considered to be interchangeable in most experiments. Fura-2 has become the dye of choice for ratio-imaging microscopy (Figure 19.2), in which it is more practical to change excitation wavelengths than emission wavelengths.[1] Upon binding Ca^{2+}, fura-2 exhibits an absorption shift that can be observed by scanning the excitation spectrum between 300 and 400 nm, while monitoring the emission at ~510 nm (Figure 19.3). In contrast, indo-1 is a preferred dye for flow cytometry, where it is more practical to use a single laser for excitation — usually the 351–364 nm spectral lines of the argon-ion laser — and monitor two emissions.[2,3] The emission maximum of indo-1 shifts from ~475 nm in Ca^{2+}-free medium to ~400 nm when the dye is saturated with Ca^{2+} (Figure 19.4). Modern two-photon excitation imaging techniques used with fura-2 and indo-1 [4–8] avoid the deleterious effects of conventional ultraviolet illumination on living specimens. Indo-1 may be less subject to compartmentalization than fura-2,[9] whereas fura-2 is more resistant to photobleaching than indo-1.[10,11] Both fura-2 and indo-1 exhibit K_d values that are close to typical basal Ca^{2+} levels in mammalian cells (~100 nM), and display high selectivity for Ca^{2+} binding relative to Mg^{2+}.[12] Nevertheless, Ca^{2+} binding is discernibly perturbed by physiological levels of Mg^{2+}; the K_d for Ca^{2+} of fura-2 is ~135 nM in Mg^{2+}-free Ca^{2+} buffers and ~224 nM in the presence of 1 mM Mg^{2+}.[12,13] Fura-2 and indo-1 also exhibit high affinities for other divalent cations such as Zn^{2+} and Mn^{2+}, a property that is discussed further in Section 19.7.

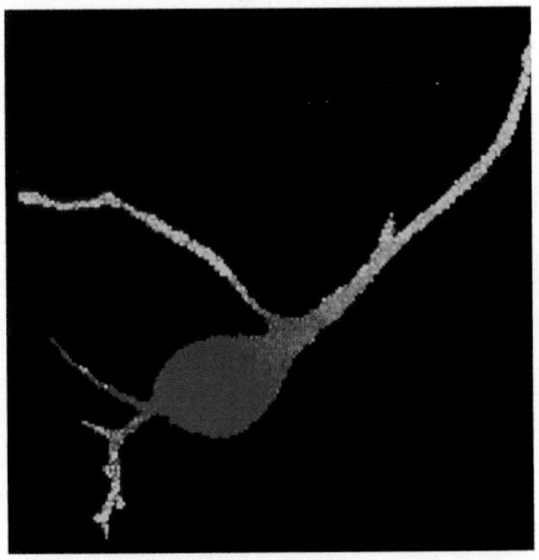

Figure 19.2 False-color image of free Ca^{2+} concentration in a Purkinje neuron from embryonic mouse cerebellum. Neurons were grown in dispersed tissue culture for 12 days, loaded with the pentapotassium salt of fura-2 (F1200) using a microelectrode and then challenged with *trans*-ACPD, an agonist of metabotropic glutamate receptors, in the absence of extracellular Ca^{2+}. The composite image, which represents the ratio of images obtained with excitation at 340 nm and 380 nm, reveals the mobilization of internal Ca^{2+} stores without contribution from Ca^{2+} influx. The image was contributed by D.J. Linden, Johns Hopkins University, and M. Smeyne and J.A. Connor, Roche Institute of Molecular Biology.

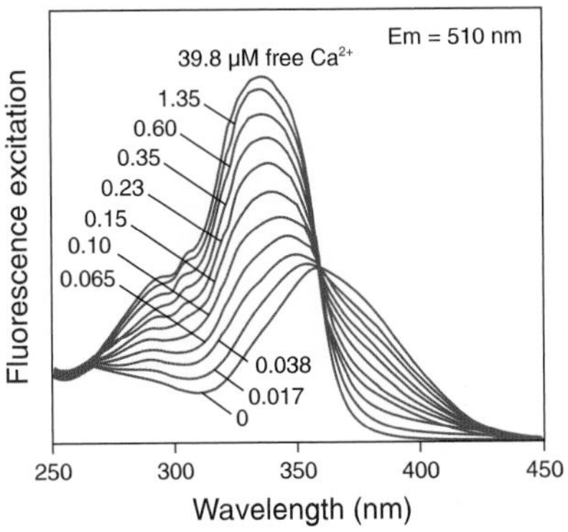

Figure 19.3 Fluorescence excitation spectra of fura-2 (F1200, F6799) in solutions containing 0–39.8 µM free Ca^{2+}.

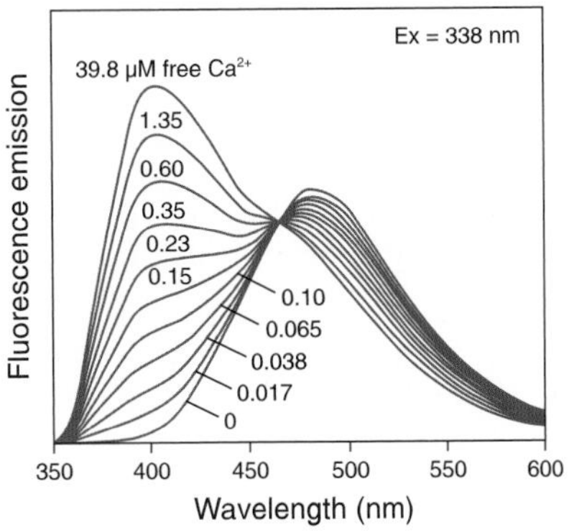

Figure 19.4 Fluorescence emission spectra of indo-1 (I1202) in solutions containing 0–39.8 µM free Ca^{2+}.

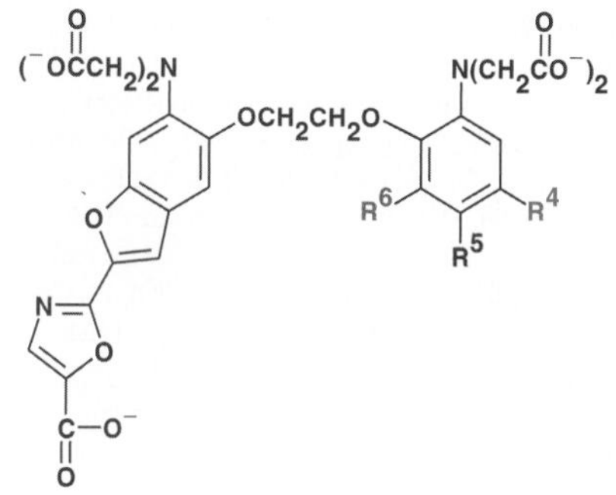

Indicator	$K_d(Ca^{2+})$	R^4	R^5	R^6
Fura-2	0.14 µM	H	CH_3	H
Fura-5F	0.40 µM	H	F	H
Fura-4F	0.77 µM	F	H	H
Fura-6F	5.30 µM	H	H	F
Fura-FF	5.50 µM	H	F	F

Figure 19.5 Fura indicators with varying Ca^{2+} affinities.

The sodium and potassium salts of fura-2 (F6799, F1200; Figure 19.5, Figure 19.6) and potassium salt of indo-1 (I1202, Figure 19.7) are cell-impermeant probes that can be delivered into cells by microinjection or using our Influx™ pinocytic cell-loading reagent (I14402, Section 19.8). Free acids of fura-2 and indo-1 can also be loaded into some plant cells at pH 4–5.[14–18] In addition, these salts are useful as standards for calibrating Ca^{2+} measurements.

Unlike the salt forms, the acetoxymethyl (AM) esters of fura-2 (Figure 19.8) and indo-1 (Figure 19.9) can passively diffuse across cell membranes, enabling researchers to avoid the use of invasive loading techniques. Once inside the cell, these esters are cleaved by intracellular esterases to yield cell-impermeant fluorescent indicators (see Note 19.1 "Technical Focus: Loading and Calibration of Intracellular Ion Indicators" in Section 19.1). Molecular Probes offers fura-2 AM and indo-1 AM in 1 mg vials (F1201, I1203) or specially packaged in 20 vials of 50 µg each (F1221, I1223); the special packaging is recommended when small quantities of the dyes are to be used over a long period of time. We also provide stock solutions of fura-2 AM and indo-1 AM in anhydrous DMSO at 1 mg/mL (~1 mM; F1225, I1226). Our standard analytical specifications for fura-2 AM require ≥95% purity by HPLC. We also offer a special packaged high-purity grade of fura-2 AM that is specified to have ≥98% purity by HPLC (as a set of 20 vials, each containing 50 µg; FluoroPure™ Grade, F14185). Dextran conjugates of fura and indo, as well as lipid analogs of fura for measuring near-membrane Ca^{2+}, are described in Section 19.4.

Fura-2 Calcium Imaging Calibration Kit

The Fura-2 Calcium Imaging Calibration Kit (F6774), which is designed to facilitate rapid calibration and standardization of digital imaging microscopes,[19,20] contains the same 11 prediluted buffers as our Calcium Calibration Buffer Kit #2 (C3009, Section 19.8). However, in this kit the buffers also include 50 µM fura-2, as well as 15 µm unstained polystyrene microspheres to act both as spacers that ensure uniform separation between the slide and the coverslip and as focus-

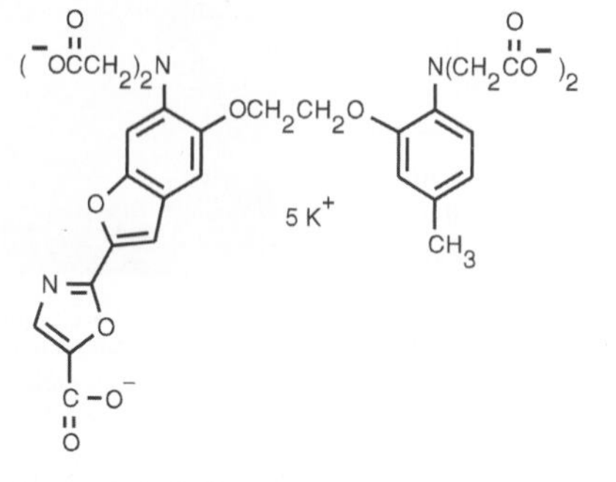

Figure 19.6 F1200 fura-2, pentapotassium salt.

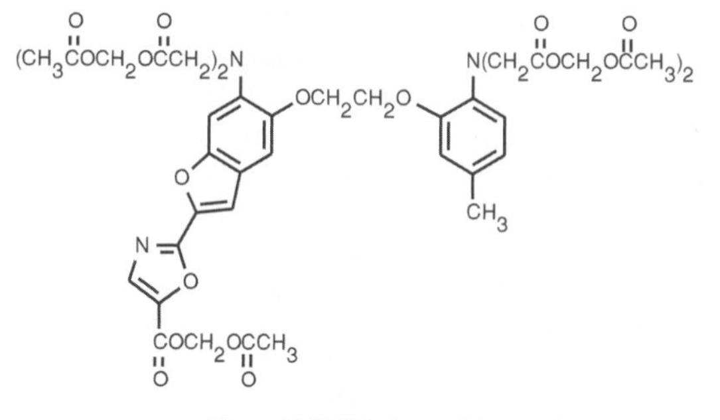

Figure 19.8 F1201 fura-2, AM.

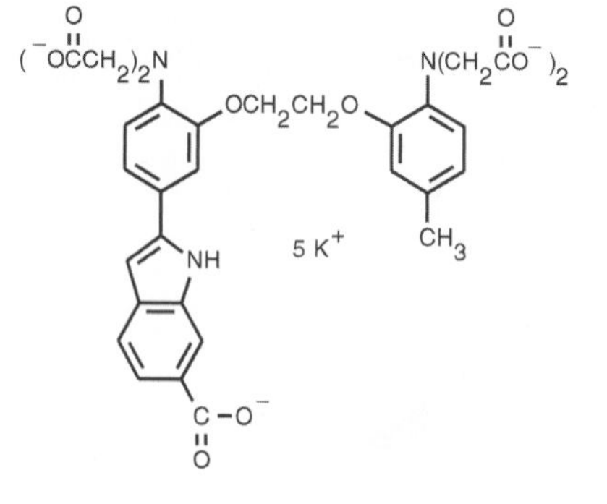

Figure 19.7 I1202 indo-1, pentapotassium salt.

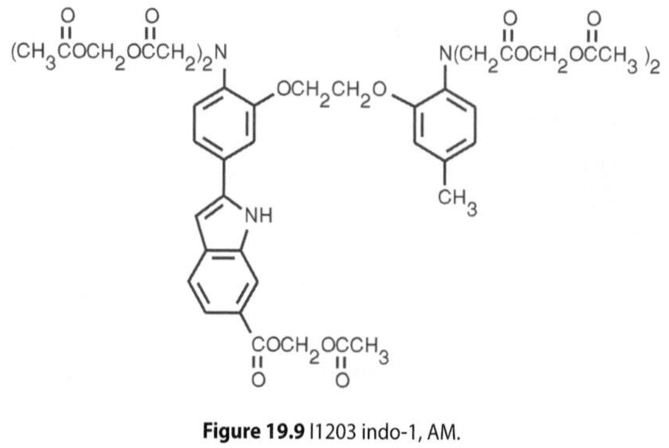

Figure 19.9 I1203 indo-1, AM.

ing aids. We also provide a twelfth buffer — identical to the 10 mM CaEGTA standard but lacking fura-2 — that serves as a control for background fluorescence. All of our Calcium Calibration Kits are described further in Section 19.8.

A product information sheet and extensive bibliographies are available for fura-2 and indo-1. Our bibliographic database currently contains over 4000 publications that cite the use of fura-2 AM for measuring intracellular free Ca^{2+} and over 1000 publications for indo-1 AM. For more information, contact our Technical Assistance Department.

Bis-Fura-2: Brighter Signal with Lower Affinity for Ca^{2+}

By linking two fura fluorophores with one BAPTA chelator (Figure 19.10), we have produced bis-fura-2, a Ca^{2+} indicator that exhibits approximately twice the absorptivity of fura-2. Bis-fura-2 has a K_d for Ca^{2+} of ~370 nM and ~525 nM in the absence and presence of 1 mM Mg^{2+}, respectively.[21] In other aspects, the quantum yield of bis-fura-2 and its spectral response to Ca^{2+} (Figure 19.11) are virtually identical to those of fura-2. Although the difference between the K_d of fura-2 and bis-fura-2 for Ca^{2+} is small, the change in excitation ratio for bis-fura-2 in response to Ca^{2+} concentrations >500 nM is larger than that of fura-2 (Figure 19.3); this difference can improve the dynamic range for Ca^{2+} measurements in cells.[22] Other potential advantages of bis-fura-2 include:

- Higher fluorescence output per indicator, which may allow the use of lower dye concentrations[22]
- Lower affinity for Ca^{2+}, which should decrease the buffering of intracellular Ca^{2+} and produce a faster response to Ca^{2+} spikes[23]
- An additional negative charge, which may facilitate dye retention

The hexapotassium salt of bis-fura-2[24–26] (B6810) is available for loading by microinjection,[27] by diffusion from a patch-pipette[28] or using our Influx™ pinocytic cell-loading reagent (I14402, Section 19.8); we do not currently offer a membrane-permeant AM ester of bis-fura-2.

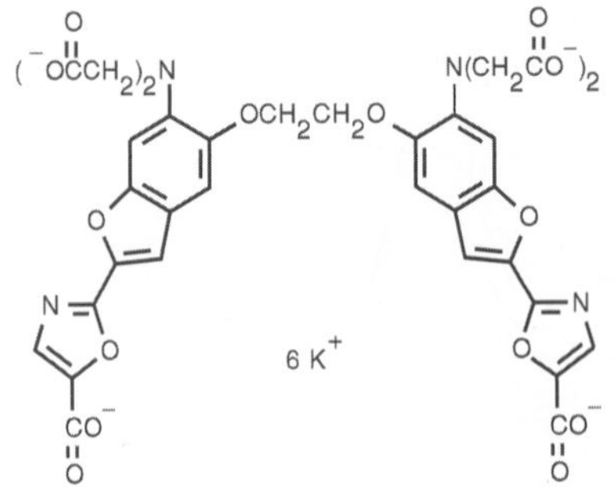

Figure 19.10 B6810 bis-fura-2, hexapotassium salt.

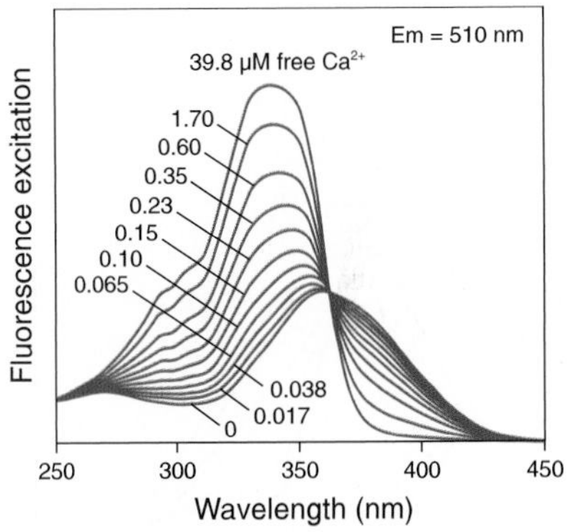

Figure 19.11 Fluorescence excitation spectra of bis-fura-2 (B6810) in solutions containing 0–39.8 µM free Ca^{2+}.

Quin-2 and Quin-2 AM

Quin-2 belongs to the first generation of Ca^{2+} indicators developed by Tsien[29] (Figure 19.12). Quin-2 has lower absorptivity and quantum yield values than the fura-2, indo-1, fluo-3, fluo-4 and Calcium Green™ indicators and thus requires higher loading concentrations. The resulting high intracellular concentration of the indicator may buffer intracellular Ca^{2+} transients.[30] Quin-2 AM has been used to intentionally deplete cytosolic free Ca^{2+}[31,32] and to ensure unidirectional Ca^{2+} influx.[33] Measurement of cytosolic free Ca^{2+} with quin-2 has been thoroughly reviewed by Tsien and Pozzan.[34] Molecular Probes offers quin-2 as a high-purity, cell-impermeant free acid (Q23918) and as its cell-permeant AM ester (Q1289).

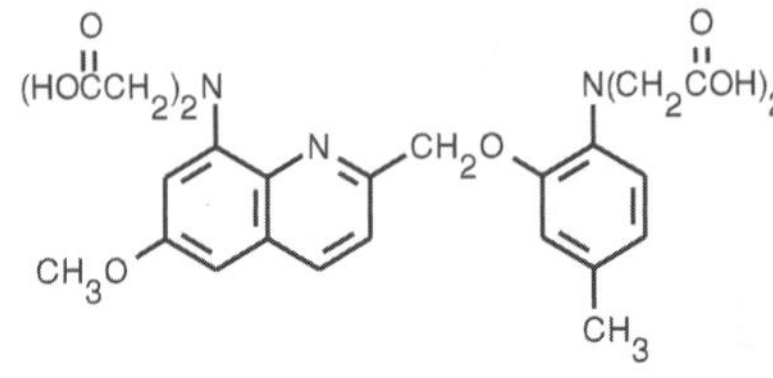

Figure 19.12 Q23918 quin-2, free acid.

Indicators with Intermediate Calcium-Binding Affinity

Fura-4F, Fura-5F and Fura-6F

Calcium concentrations above 1 µM produce almost complete binding saturation of fura-2 but very low fractional saturation of the low-affinity fura analog mag-fura-2 (M1290, see below). To bridge this gap in the Ca^{2+} measurement range of fura-type indicators, we offer three additional ratiometric Ca^{2+} indicators — fura-4F (F14174), fura-5F (F14176) and fura-6F (F14178) — and their corresponding membrane-permeant AM ester derivatives[35] (F14175, F14177, F14179). Attachment of a single electron-withdrawing fluorine substituent at different positions on the BAPTA chelator moiety of fura-2 results in an increase of the K_d value[36] to ~770 nM, ~400 nM and 5.3 µM for fura-4F, fura-5F and fura-6F, respectively (Figure 19.5). Except for the change in the Ca^{2+} concentration response range (Figure 19.13), the Ca^{2+}-de-

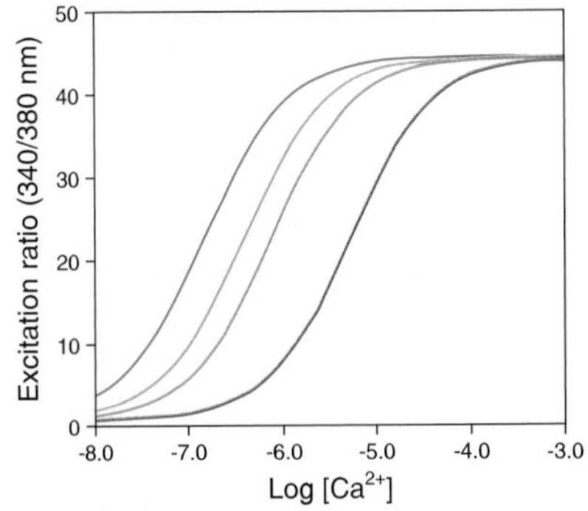

Figure 19.13 Fluorescence excitation ratio versus Ca^{2+} concentration curves for fura-2 (red), fura-5F (orange), fura-4F (green) and fura-6F (blue).

pendent spectral shifts produced by fura-4F, fura-5F and fura-6F are essentially identical to those of fura-2 (Figure 19.14) and the probes use the same optical filter sets (Table 23.9).

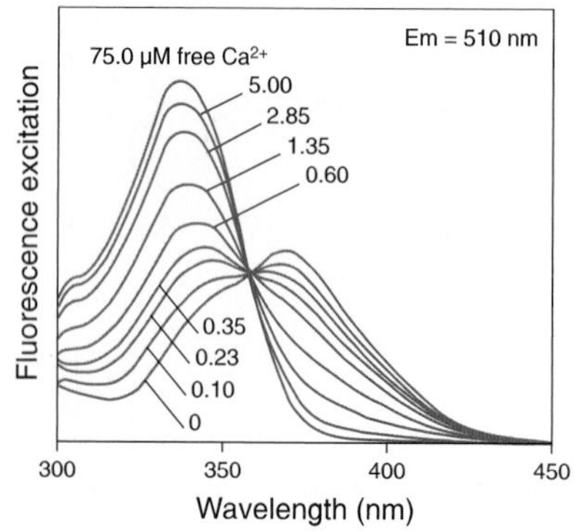

Figure 19.14 Ca^{2+}-dependent fluorescence excitation spectra of fura-4F (F14174).

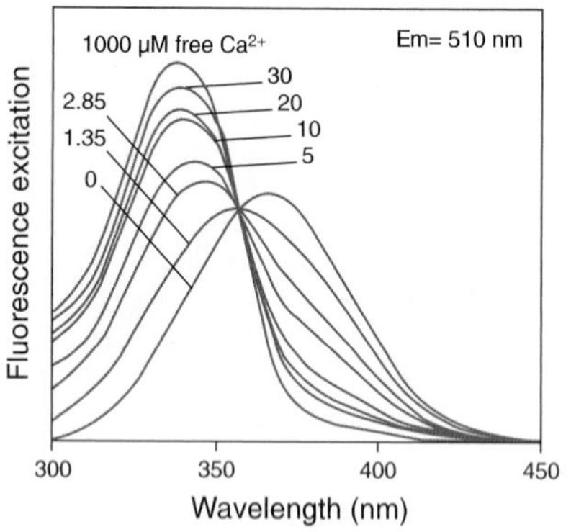

Figure 19.15 Ca^{2+}-dependent fluorescence excitation spectra of fura-FF (F14180).

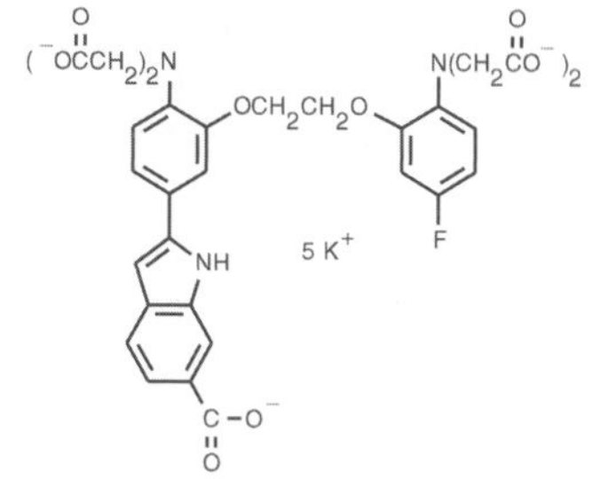

Figure 19.16 I23912 indo-5F, pentapotassium salt.

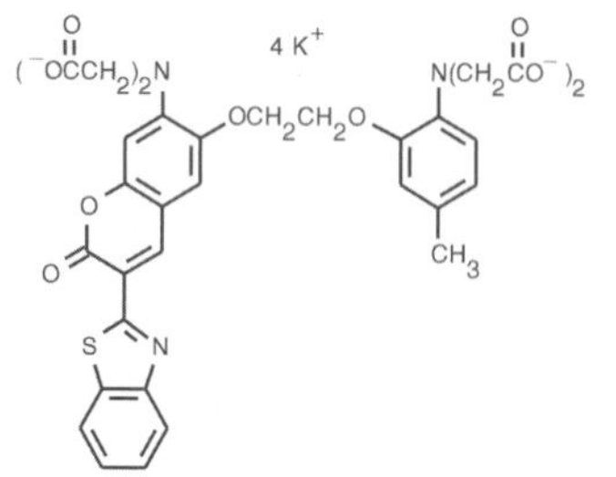

Figure 19.17 B6790 BTC, tetrapotassium salt.

Fura-FF

Fura-FF is a difluorinated derivative of fura-2 (Figure 19.5, Figure 19.15) with a K_d value [36] of ~5.5 µM.[37–39] Fura-FF has high selectivity for Ca^{2+}, a wide dynamic range and low pH sensitivity, making it an optimal low-affinity Ca^{2+} indicator for most imaging applications.[37] Although its spectroscopic characteristics are very similar to those of mag-fura-2, fura-FF has negligible Mg^{2+} sensitivity, making Ca^{2+} detection less susceptible to interference.[38,39] These properties have made fura-FF particularly useful for spatial and functional characterization of intracellular Ca^{2+} stores [40–42] and for tracking Ca^{2+} oscillations driven by the inositol 1,4,5-triphosphate receptor.[43,44] The low-affinity indicator fura-FF detected NMDA- and kainate-induced neuronal Ca^{2+} fluxes that were not detectable with the higher-affinity indicator fura-2.[45] Fura-FF has also been used in combination with fura-2 and mag-fura-5 to compare the actions of Sr^{2+} and Ca^{2+} as mediators of synaptic transmission.[38] Fura-FF is available in water-soluble potassium salt form (F14180) and as a membrane-permeant AM ester derivative (F14181).

Indo-5F

Indo-5F (Figure 19.16) is an analog of indo-1 designed for measuring Ca^{2+} concentrations above 1 µM. Like indo-1,[38] indo-5F exhibits Ca^{2+}-dependent dual-emission, making it suitable for ratiometric detection by flow cytometry. Molecular Probes prepares indo-5F as a high-purity cell-impermeant potassium salt (I23912) and as its cell-permeant AM ester (I23913).

Low-Affinity Calcium Indicators

BTC

The coumarin benzothiazole–based Ca^{2+} indicator BTC (B6790, Figure 19.17) and its cell-permeant derivative BTC AM (B6791) were developed by Molecular Probes in collaboration with Haralambos Katerinopoulos of the University of Crete.[46] This Ca^{2+} indicator exhibits a shift in excitation maximum from about 480 nm to 400 nm upon binding Ca^{2+} (Figure 19.18), permitting ratiometric measurements that are essentially independent of uneven dye loading, cell thickness, photobleaching and dye leakage. Its high selectivity and moderate affinity for Ca^{2+} (K_d ~7 µM) allows accurate quantitation of high intracellular Ca^{2+} levels that are underestimated by fura-2 measurements.[47,48] Furthermore, because BTC is excited at longer wavelengths than the ratioable fura-2 and indo-1 indicators, cellular photodamage and autofluorescence may be less of a problem. When loaded into neurons as its AM ester, BTC exhibits little compartmentalization. However, prolonged excitation appears to cause conversion of the indicator to a calcium-insensitive form.[48]

BTC has been employed in investigations of Ca^{2+}-dependent exocytosis in pancreatic β-cells,[49] CHO fibroblasts [50] and phaeochromocytoma cells.[51,52] Neuronal Ca^{2+} transients detected by the low-affinity Ca^{2+} indicators BTC and mag-fura-2 are significantly more rapid than those reported by the higher-affinity indicators fura-2 and Calcium Green™-2.[48,53] BTC may also be useful as an indicator for Zn^{2+}.[37] A report by Papazoglou and co-workers describes the unusual use of the tetrapotassium salt of BTC to localize atherosclerotic plaque.[54]

Mag-Fura-2, Mag-Fura-5 and Mag-Indo-1

Mag-fura-2 (also called furaptra, Figure 19.67), mag-fura-5 and mag-indo-1 were originally designed to report intracellular Mg^{2+} levels (Section 19.6); however, these indicators actually have much higher affinity for Ca^{2+} than for Mg^{2+}. Although Ca^{2+} binding by these indicators may complicate analysis when they are employed to measure intracellular Mg^{2+},[55,56] their increased effective range and improved linearity for Ca^{2+} measurements has been exploited for measuring intracellular Ca^{2+} levels between 1 µM and 100 µM.[37,57–59]

The spectral shifts of mag-fura-2, mag-fura-5 and mag-indo-1 are very similar to those of fura-2 and indo-1 but occur at higher Ca^{2+} concentrations. Because the off-rates for Ca^{2+} binding of these indicators are much faster than those of fura-2 and indo-1, these dyes have been used to monitor action potentials in skeletal muscle and nerve terminals with little or no kinetic delay[60–63] (Figure 19.19). The spectral properties, kinetics and selectivity of several of our low-Ca^{2+} indicators have been reviewed by Zhao,[64] Hyrc[37] and their co-workers.

The moderate Ca^{2+} affinity of mag-fura-2 and the tendency of its AM ester to accumulate in subcellular compartments have proven useful for *in situ* monitoring of inositol 1,4,5-triphosphate–sensitive Ca^{2+} stores.[65–69] Mag-fura-2 has also been employed to follow Ca^{2+} transients in presynaptic nerve terminals,[53,70–72] gastric epithelial cells[73] and cultured myocytes.[74] Imaging of mag-fura-2 using a single excitation wavelength (420 nm) is reported to improve the detection of high-level Ca^{2+} transients in various cells, including Purkinje neurons and frog muscle.[57,63] Mag-indo-1 has been used to detect gonadotropin-releasing hormone–induced Ca^{2+} oscillations in gonadotropes[75] and to investigate the role of Ca^{2+}/K^+ exchange in intracellular Ca^{2+} storage and release processes.[76] Measurements of Ca^{2+} currents in presynaptic boutons and granule cell parallel fibers with our mag-fura-5 and Magnesium Green™ indicators were shown to be superior to those made using fura-2.[77,78] Mag-fura-2, mag-fura-5 and mag-indo-1 are available as cell-impermeant potassium salts (M1290, M3103, M1293) or as cell-permeant AM esters (M1291, M1292, M3105, M1295) and are accompanied by a detailed protocol.

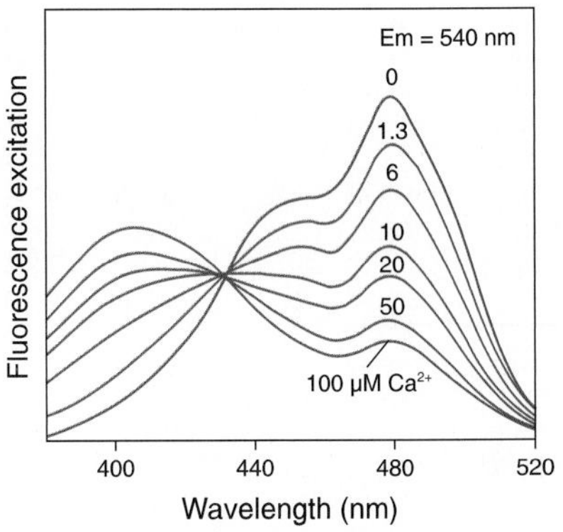

Figure 19.18 Fluorescence excitation spectra of BTC (B6790) in solutions containing 0–100 µM free Ca^{2+}.

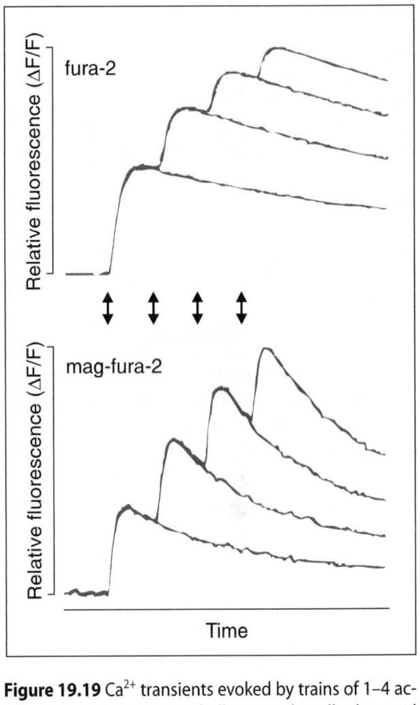

Figure 19.19 Ca^{2+} transients evoked by trains of 1–4 action potentials in rat cerebellar granule cells detected by fura-2 (upper panel; F1200) and mag-fura-2 (lower panel; M1290). The stimulus pulses are 50 milliseconds apart (20 Hz); timing is indicated by the double-headed arrows. The amplitude of the transients detected by fura-2 decreases with each successive stimulus due to Ca^{2+} saturation. Mag-fura-2 avoids saturation due to its lower Ca^{2+} binding affinity (K_d for Ca^{2+} = 25 µM), recording transients of approximately equal amplitude from successive action potentials. Adapted with permission from Biophys J 68, 2165 (1995).

References

1. Methods Cell Biol 56, 237 (1998); **2.** Methods 21, 221 (2000); **3.** Methods Cell Biol 41, 149 (1994); **4.** Biophys J 86, 1726 (2004); **5.** Biophys J 75, 1669 (1998); **6.** Nat Neurosci 3, 452 (2000); **7.** J Biol Chem 273, 34961 (1998); **8.** J Microsc 185, 9 (1997); **9.** Cell Calcium 11, 487 (1990); **10.** Chem Biol 3, 765 (1996); **11.** Am J Physiol 253, C613 (1987); **12.** J Biol Chem 260, 3440 (1985); **13.** Measured at 37°C in 100 mM KCl, 10 mM MOPS, pH 7.0; **14.** Proc Natl Acad Sci U S A 89, 3591 (1992); **15.** Plant Physiol 93, 841 (1990); **16.** Plant Sci 67, 125 (1990); **17.** Cell Calcium 8, 455 (1987); **18.** Eur J Cell Biol 46, 466 (1988); **19.** J Neurochem 62, 890 (1994); **20.** Cell Calcium 11, 75 (1990); **21.** K_d values for Ca^{2+} are determined at Molecular Probes at ~22°C using our Calcium Calibration Buffer Kits; **22.** Biophys J 75, 1635 (1998); **23.** Cell Calcium 22, 255 (1997); **24.** Neuron 25, 229 (2000); **25.** J Neurosci Res 57, 906 (1999); **26.** Neuron 24, 727 (1999); **27.** J Neurophysiol 81, 2508 (1999); **28.** Brain Res 831, 113 (1999); **29.** Biochemistry 19, 2396 (1980); **30.** J Biol Chem 258, 4876 (1983); **31.** J Biol Chem 273, 8203 (1998); **32.** Brain Res 528, 48 (1990); **33.** Biochemistry 26, 6995 (1987); **34.** Methods Enzymol 172, 230 (1989); **35.** Bioorg Med Chem Lett 10, 1515 (2000); **36.** Measured at 22°C in 100 mM KCl, 10 mM MOPS, pH 7.2; **37.** Cell Calcium 27, 75 (2000); **38.** Biophys J 76, 2029 (1999); **39.** Am J Physiol 266, C1313 (1994); **40.** J Biol Chem 276, 22461 (2001); **41.** J Physiol 529, 553 (2000); **42.** Science 275, 1643 (1997); **43.** J Biol Chem 274, 14157 (1999); **44.** EMBO J 16, 3533 (1997); **45.** J Neurosci 18, 7727 (1998); **46.** Cell Calcium 15, 190 (1994); **47.** J Neurosci 17, 6669 (1997); **48.** Cell Calcium 24, 165 (1998); **49.** J Cell Biol 138, 55 (1997); **50.** J Biol Chem 271, 17751 (1996); **51.** J Physiol 533, 627 (2001); **52.** J Physiol 494, 53 (1996); **53.** Biophys J 68, 2156 (1995); **54.** J Photochem Photobiol B 27, 81 (1995); **55.** Anal Biochem 290, 221 (2001); **56.** Am J Physiol 263, C300 (1992); **57.** Pflugers Arch 429, 587 (1995); **58.** Proc Natl Acad Sci U S A 90, 2598 (1993); **59.** Neuron 10, 21 (1993); **60.** Proc Natl Acad Sci U S A 93, 8095 (1996); **61.** J Physiol 475, 319 (1994); **62.** Biochem Biophys Res Commun 177, 184 (1991); **63.** J Gen Physiol 97, 271 (1991); **64.** Biophys J 70, 896 (1996); **65.** J Physiol 530, 533 (2001); **66.** J Cell Biol 140, 325 (1998); **67.** Cell Calcium 20, 235 (1996); **68.** EMBO J 17, 1986 (1998); **69.** Am J Physiol 276, C426 (1999); **70.** J Physiol 527 Pt 1, 33 (2000); **71.** Biophys J 72, 1458 (1997); **72.** Biophys J 72, 637 (1997); **73.** Am J Physiol 267, G442 (1994); **74.** Am J Physiol 264, C1259 (1993); **75.** Proc Natl Acad Sci U S A 91, 9750 (1994); **76.** Nature 395, 908 (1998); **77.** Biophys J 74, 1549 (1998); **78.** Biophys J 73, 2476 (1997).

Data Table — 19.2 Fluorescent Ca^{2+} Indicators Excited with UV Light

				Low Ca^{2+}				High Ca^{2+}						
Cat #	**MW**	**Storage**	**Soluble**	**Abs**	**EC**	**Em**	**Solvent**	**Abs**	**EC**	**Em**	**Solvent**	**Product**	**K_d**	**Notes**
B6790	844.03	L	pH >6	464	29,000	533	H_2O	401	20,000	529	H_2O/Ca^{2+}		7.0 µM	1, 2, 3
B6791	979.92	F,D,L	DMSO	433	39,000	504	MeOH					B6790		
B6810	1007.14	D,L	pH >6	366	56,000	511	H_2O	338	68,000	504	H_2O/Ca^{2+}		370 nM	1, 2, 4, 5
F1200	832.00	D,L	pH >6	363	28,000	512	H_2O	335	34,000	505	H_2O/Ca^{2+}		145 nM	1, 2, 4, 5
F1201	1001.86	F,D,L	DMSO	370	31,000	476	EtOAc					F1200		
F1221	1001.86	F,D,L	DMSO	370	31,000	476	EtOAc					F1200		
F1225	1001.86	F,D,L	DMSO	370	31,000	476	EtOAc					F1200		6
F6799	751.45	D,L	pH >6	363	28,000	512	H_2O	335	34,000	505	H_2O/Ca^{2+}		145 nM	1, 2, 4, 5
F14174	835.96	D,L	pH >6	366	21,000	511	H_2O	336	23,000	505	H_2O/Ca^{2+}		770 nM	1, 2, 4
F14175	1005.82	F,D,L	DMSO	370	29,000	475	EtOAc					F14174		
F14176	835.96	D,L	pH >6	363	26,000	512	H_2O	336	29,000	506	H_2O/Ca^{2+}		400 nM	1, 2, 4
F14177	1005.82	F,D,L	DMSO	369	31,000	476	EtOAc					F14176		
F14178	835.96	D,L	pH >6	364	25,000	512	H_2O	336	28,000	505	H_2O/Ca^{2+}		5.3 µM	1, 2, 3
F14179	1005.82	F,D,L	DMSO	369	30,000	477	EtOAc					F14178		
F14180	853.95	D,L	pH >6	364	25,000	510	H_2O	335	28,000	506	H_2O/Ca^{2+}		5.5 µM	1, 2, 3
F14181	1023.82	F,D,L	DMSO	370	30,000	476	EtOAc					F14180		
F14185	1001.86	F,D,L	DMSO	370	31,000	476	EtOAc					F1200		7
I1202	840.06	D,L	pH >6	346	33,000	475	H_2O	330	33,000	401	H_2O/Ca^{2+}		230 nM	1, 2, 4, 5
I1203	1009.93	F,D,L	DMSO	356	39,000	478	MeOH					I1202		
I1223	1009.93	F,D,L	DMSO	356	39,000	478	MeOH					I1202		
I1226	1009.93	F,D,L	DMSO	356	39,000	478	MeOH					I1202		6
I23912	844.03	D,L	pH >6	347	20,000	475	H_2O	331	20,000	412	H_2O/Ca^{2+}		470 nM	1, 2, 4
I23913	1013.89	F,D,L	DMSO	355	39,000	480	MeOH					I23912		
M1290	586.68	L	pH >6	369	22,000	511	H_2O	329	26,000	508	H_2O/Ca^{2+}		25 µM	1, 2, 3
M1291	722.57	F,D,L	DMSO	366	31,000	475	EtOAc					M1290		
M1292	722.57	F,D,L	DMSO	366	31,000	475	EtOAc					M1290		
M1293	594.74	L	pH >6	349	38,000	480	H_2O	328	35,000	390	H_2O/Ca^{2+}		35 µM	1, 2, 8, 9
M1295	730.63	F,D,L	DMSO	354	37,000	472	MeOH					M1293		
M3103	600.70	L	pH >6	369	23,000	505	H_2O	330	25,000	500	H_2O/Ca^{2+}		28 µM	1, 2, 3
M3105	736.60	F,D,L	DMSO	365	31,000	461	EtOAc					M3103		
Q1289	829.77	F,D,L	DMSO	348	4,000	446	MeOH					Q23918		
Q23918	541.51	D,L	pH >6	353	4,000	495	H_2O	333	3,900	495	H_2O/Ca^{2+}		60 nM	1, 2, 10

For definitions of the contents of this data table, see "Navigating *The Handbook*" in the introductory pages.

Notes

1. Dissociation constants are known to vary considerably depending on the temperature, pH, ionic strength, viscosity, protein binding, presence of other ions (especially polyvalent ions), instrument setup and other factors. It is strongly recommended that these values be verified under user-specific experimental conditions.
2. Spectra measured in aqueous buffers containing 10 mM EGTA (H_2O) or a >10-fold excess of free Ca^{2+} relative to the K_d (H_2O/Ca^{2+}).
3. Dissociation constant determined at Molecular Probes by fluorescence measurements in 100 mM KCl, 10 mM MOPS pH 7.2, 0 to 1 mM free Ca^{2+} at 22°C.
4. Dissociation constant determined at Molecular Probes by fluorescence measurements in 100 mM KCl, 10 mM MOPS, pH 7.2, 0 to 39 µM free Ca^{2+} at 22°C.
5. $K_d(Ca^{2+})$ for fura-2 and indo-1 from the original reference by Grynkiewicz, Poenie and Tsien (J Biol Chem 260, 3440 (1985)) are 224 nM and 250 nM, respectively, measured in 1 mM EGTA, 100 mM KCl, 1 mM free Mg^{2+}, 10 mM MOPS, pH 7.0 at 37°C. For bis-fura-2, $K_d(Ca^{2+})$ in presence of Mg^{2+} is 525 nM (determined at Molecular Probes in 100 mM KCl, 10 mM MOPS, pH 7.2, 1 mM Mg^{2+} at 22°C).
6. This product is supplied as a ready-made solution in the solvent indicated under "Soluble."
7. This product is specified to equal or exceed 98% analytical purity by HPLC.
8. The emission spectrum of Ca^{2+}-bound M1293 excited at 340 nm has approximately equal peak intensities at ~390 nm and ~480 nm (Biochemistry 30, 702 (1991)).
9. Dissociation constant determined in 100 mM KCl, 40 mM HEPES, pH 7.0 at 22°C (Biochem Biophys Res Commun 177, 184 (1991)).
10. $K_d(Ca^{2+})$ for quin-2 was measured in 120 mM KCl, 20 mM NaCl, pH 7.05 at 37°C. Under the same conditions with addition of 1 mM Mg^{2+}, K_d = 115 nM (Methods Enzymol 172, 230 (1989)).

Product List — 19.2 Fluorescent Ca^{2+} Indicators Excited with UV Light

Cat #	Product Name	Unit Size
B6810	bis-fura-2, hexapotassium salt *cell impermeant*	1 mg
B6791	BTC, AM *cell permeant* *special packaging*	20 x 50 µg
B6790	BTC, tetrapotassium salt *cell impermeant*	1 mg
F1201	fura-2, AM *cell permeant*	1 mg
F1221	fura-2, AM *cell permeant* *special packaging*	20 x 50 µg
F1225	fura-2, AM *1 mM solution in dry DMSO* *cell permeant*	1 mL
F14185	fura-2, AM *FluoroPure™ grade* *special packaging*	20 x 50 µg
F6774	Fura-2 Calcium Imaging Calibration Kit *zero to 10 mM CaEGTA, 50 µM fura-2 (11 x 1 mL)*	1 kit
F1200	fura-2, pentapotassium salt *cell impermeant*	1 mg
F6799	fura-2, pentasodium salt *cell impermeant*	1 mg
F14175	fura-4F, AM *cell permeant* *special packaging*	10 x 50 µg

For current prices or to order online, visit probes.invitrogen.com

Cat #	Product Name	Unit Size
F14174	fura-4F, pentapotassium salt *cell impermeant*	500 µg
F14177	fura-5F, AM *cell permeant* *special packaging*	10 x 50 µg
F14176	fura-5F, pentapotassium salt *cell impermeant*	500 µg
F14179	fura-6F, AM *cell permeant* *special packaging*	10 x 50 µg
F14178	fura-6F, pentapotassium salt *cell impermeant*	500 µg
F14181	fura-FF, AM *cell permeant* *special packaging*	10 x 50 µg
F14180	fura-FF, pentapotassium salt *cell impermeant*	500 µg
I1203	indo-1, AM *cell permeant*	1 mg
I1223	indo-1, AM *cell permeant* *special packaging*	20 x 50 µg
I1226	indo-1, AM *1 mM solution in dry DMSO* *cell permeant*	1 mL
I1202	indo-1, pentapotassium salt *cell impermeant*	1 mg
I23913	indo-5F, AM *cell permeant* *special packaging*	10 x 50 µg
I23912	indo-5F, pentapotassium salt *cell impermeant*	500 µg
M1291	mag-fura-2, AM *cell permeant*	1 mg
M1292	mag-fura-2, AM *cell permeant* *special packaging*	20 x 50 µg
M1290	mag-fura-2, tetrapotassium salt *cell impermeant*	1 mg
M3105	mag-fura-5, AM *cell permeant* *special packaging*	20 x 50 µg
M3103	mag-fura-5, tetrapotassium salt *cell impermeant*	1 mg
M1295	mag-indo-1, AM *cell permeant* *special packaging*	20 x 50 µg
M1293	mag-indo-1, tetrapotassium salt *cell impermeant*	1 mg
Q1289	quin-2, AM *cell permeant* *special packaging*	10 x 1 mg
Q23918	quin-2, free acid *cell impermeant*	5 mg

For current prices or to order online, visit probes.invitrogen.com

19.3 Fluorescent Ca^{2+} Indicators Excited with Visible Light

Visible light–excitable Ca^{2+} indicators offer several advantages over UV light–excitable indicators:

- Efficient excitation with most laser-based instrumentation, including confocal laser-scanning microscopes and flow cytometers
- Reduced interference from sample autofluorescence
- Less cellular photodamage and light scatter
- Stronger absorption by the dyes, which may permit the use of lower dye concentrations and therefore lower phototoxicity to live cells
- Compatibility with photoactivatable ("caged") probes and other UV light–absorbing reagents, increasing options for multiparameter measurements
- Large Ca^{2+}-dependent fluorescence intensity increases, resulting in sensitive detection of Ca^{2+} transients

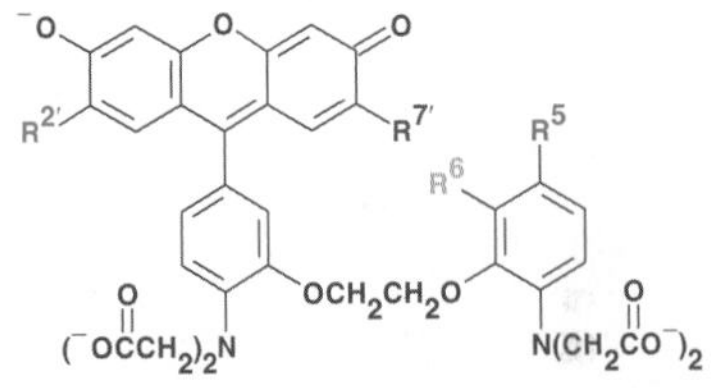

Indicator	$K_d(Ca^{2+})$	R2′	R7′	R5	R6
Fluo-3	0.39 µM	Cl	Cl	CH_3	H
Fluo-4	0.35 µM	F	F	CH_3	H
Fluo-5F	2.3 µM	F	F	F	H
Fluo-5N	90 µM	F	F	NO_2	H
Fluo-4FF	9.7 µM	F	F	F	F

Figure 19.20 Fluo indicators.

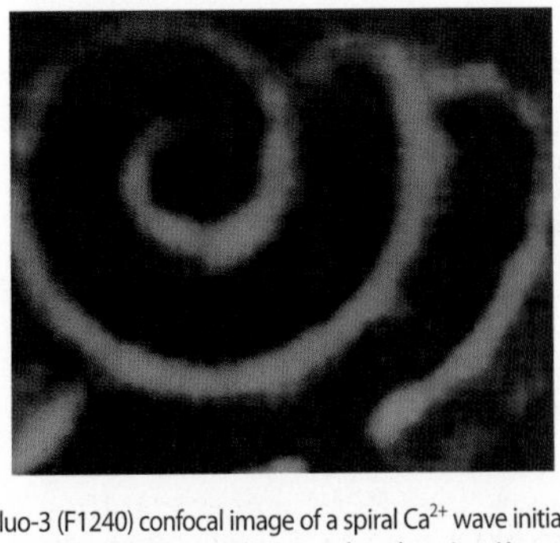

Figure 19.21 Fluo-3 (F1240) confocal image of a spiral Ca^{2+} wave initiated by injection of a nonhydrolyzable analog of inositol 1,4,5-triphosphate in a *Xenopus laevis* oocyte. The image was contributed by David Clapham, Harvard University, and reproduced with permission from Cell 69, 283 (1992).

Fluo-3, Fluo-4, Rhod-2 and Related Derivatives

Fluo-3

The Ca^{2+} indicator fluo-3 (Figure 19.20) was developed by Tsien and colleagues for use with visible-light excitation sources in flow cytometry and confocal laser-scanning microscopy [1] (Figure 19.21, Figure 19.22). More

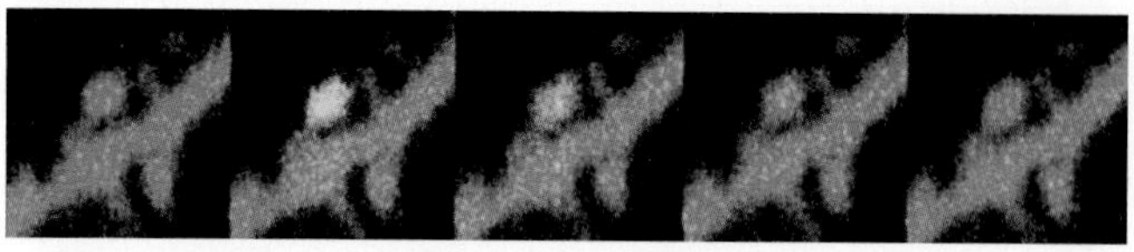

Figure 19.22 Two-photon excitation imaging of Ca^{2+} influx in a CA1 pyramidal cell spine. The images are overlays of anatomical images generated by Alexa Fluor® 594 hydrazide (A10438, A10442) and Ca^{2+} signals generated by fluo-5F (F14221). The imaging system uses two-photon excitation at 810 nm and two-channel emission detection (fluo-5F in the green channel, Alexa Fluor® 594 hydrazide in the red channel). The observed Ca^{2+} influx is through NMDA receptors that are activated by glutamate released from the presynaptic terminal following electrode stimulation of a collateral CA3 pyramidal cell axon. The brief (0.2 ms) depolarizing stimulus was applied after the first frame in the image sequence. The frame rate is four frames/second, and each frame represents an area of 5 µm x 5 µm. The image was contributed by Thomas Oertner and Karel Svoboda, Cold Spring Harbor Laboratory.

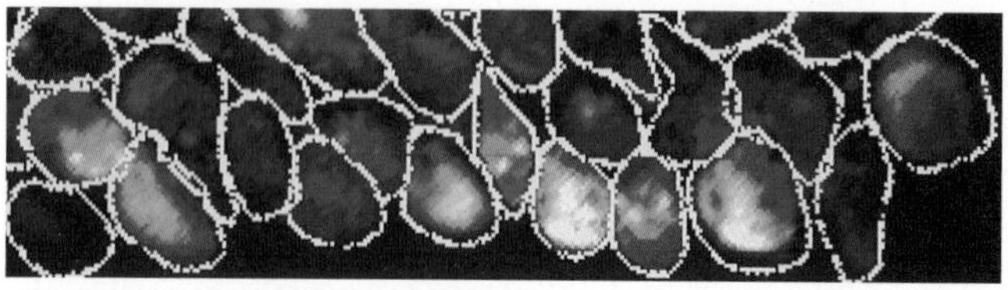

Figure 19.23 Spontaneous intracellular Ca^{2+} fluctuations of neurons developing *in vivo*. The spinal cord was dissected from a neurula-stage *Xenopus* embryo and loaded with fluo-3 AM (F1241, F1242, F14218, F14242, F23915). Regions of fluo-3 fluorescence on the ventral side of the spinal cord are presented pseudocolored in gold and indicate areas of highest intracellular Ca^{2+} (Nature 375, 784 (1995)). The image was obtained with a Bio-Rad MRC600 confocal laser-scanning microscope. The image was contributed by Nicholas C. Spitzer, University of California, San Diego.

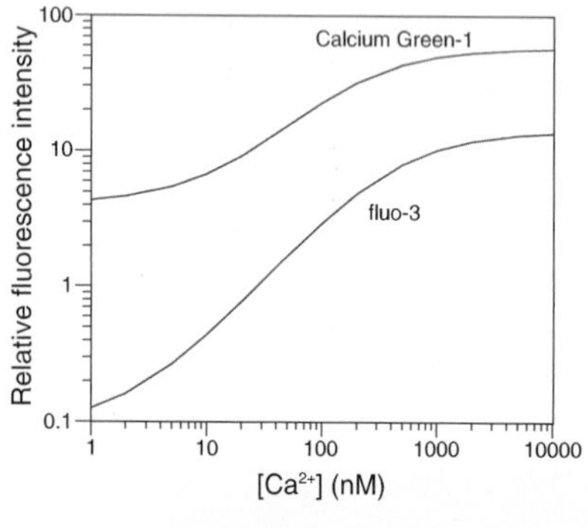

Figure 19.24 Comparison of fluorescence intensity responses to Ca^{2+} for the fluo-3 (F1240, F3715) and Calcium Green™-1 (C3010MP) indicators. Responses were calculated from the Ca^{2+} dissociation constants for the two indicators and the extinction coefficients and fluorescence quantum yields of their ion-free and ion-bound forms. They, therefore, represent the relative fluorescence intensities that would be obtained from equal concentrations of the two indicators excited and detected at their peak wavelengths.

recently, fluo-3 imaging has been extended to include two-photon excitation techniques[2,3] (Figure 19.22). Fluo-3 imaging has revealed the spatial dynamics of many elementary processes in Ca^{2+} signaling[4–10] (Figure 19.21, Figure 19.23). Since about 1996, fluo-3 has also been extensively used in cell-based high-throughput screening assays for drug discovery.[11,12] Fluo-3 is essentially nonfluorescent unless bound to Ca^{2+} and exhibits a quantum yield at saturating Ca^{2+} of ~0.14 (Figure 19.24) and a K_d for Ca^{2+} of 390 nM.[13] The intact acetoxymethyl (AM) ester derivative of fluo-3 is also nonfluorescent, unlike the AM esters of fura-2 and indo-1. The green-fluorescent emission (~525 nm) of Ca^{2+}-bound fluo-3 is conventionally detected using optical filter sets (Table 23.9) designed for fluorescein (FITC). As prepared by Minta, Kao and Tsien,[1] fluo-3 was originally reported to undergo an ~40-fold increase in fluorescence upon binding Ca^{2+}. Fluo-3 produced by Molecular Probes exhibits an at least 100-fold Ca^{2+}-dependent fluorescence enhancement[14] (Figure 19.25).

In a careful study of the spectral properties of highly purified fluo-3, Harkins, Kurebayashi and Baylor characterized the effects of pH and viscosity on Ca^{2+} measurements with fluo-3 and demonstrated that binding of the indicator to proteins has a significant effect on its K_d for Ca^{2+}[14] (Table 19.2). The temperature dependence of the K_d for fluo-3 has also been reported.[15] In addition, the fluorescence output of fluo-3 — the product of the molar absorptivity and the fluorescence quantum yield — may also vary significantly in different cellular environments.[16,17]

Fluo-3 lacks a significant shift in emission or excitation wavelength upon binding to Ca^{2+}, which precludes the use of ratiometric measurements (see Note 19.1 "Technical Focus: Loading and Calibration of Intracellular Ion Indicators" in Section 19.1). Simultaneous loading of cells with fluo-3 and our Fura Red™ indicator (see below), which exhibit reciprocal shifts in fluorescence intensity upon binding Ca^{2+}, has enabled researchers to make ratiometric measurements of intracellular Ca^{2+} (Figure 19.26) using confocal laser-scanning microscopy[18–22] (Figure 19.27) or flow cytometry.[23,24] For ratiometric measurements, fluo-3 can also be co-loaded into cells with a Ca^{2+}-insensitive dye. For instance, carboxy SNARF®-1 AM, acetate (C1271, C1272; Section 20.2) — a dye that can be excited at the same wavelengths as fluo-3 but detected at much longer wavelengths (Figure 20.11) — can serve as the Ca^{2+}-insensitive dye, provided that the pH within the cells remains constant during the experi-

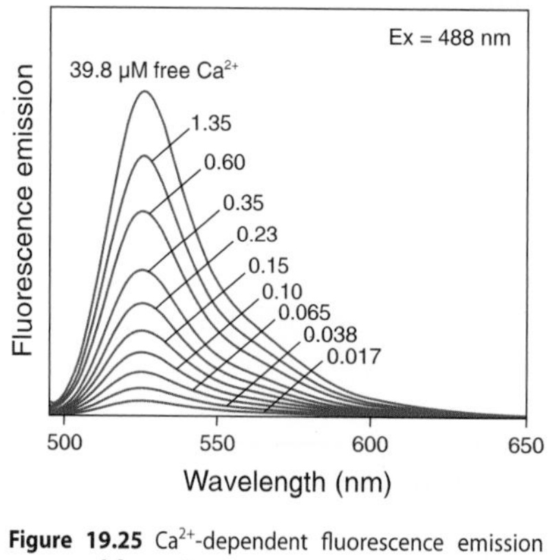

Figure 19.25 Ca^{2+}-dependent fluorescence emission spectra of fluo-3 (F1240, F3715). The spectrum for the Ca^{2+}-free solution is indistinguishable from the baseline.

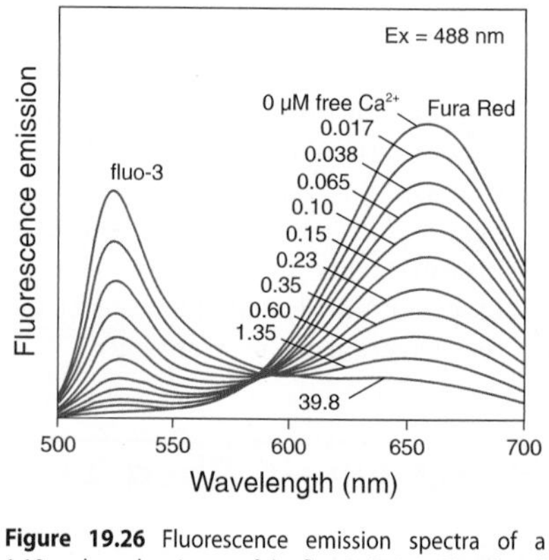

Figure 19.26 Fluorescence emission spectra of a 1:10 mole:mole mixture of the fluo-3 (F1240, F3715) and Fura Red™ (F14219) indicators, simultaneously excited at 488 nm, in solutions containing 0–39.8 µM free Ca^{2+}.

ment.[25–28] SNARF®-4F carboxylic acid, which can be loaded into cells as its AM ester (S23921, Section 20.2), has a lower pK_a of ~6.4 (Figure 20.19), likely making it the preferred probe for this application. Co-loading of fluo-3 and carboxy SNARF®-1 also permits the simultaneous imaging of Ca^{2+} transients and intracellular pH in experiments in which the concentrations of both ions are changing.[29,30]

Fluo-3 is available as a cell-impermeant potassium salt (F3715) or ammonium salt (F1240). The cell-permeant fluo-3 AM is available as a 1 mg vial (F1241), as a set of 20 vials each containing 50 µg (F1242), as a set of 10 vials each containing 50 µg of our high-purity grade fluo-3 AM (FluoroPure™ Grade, F23915) and as a 1 mM solution in DMSO (F14218). A set of 40 vials, each containing 1 mg of fluo-3 AM, is available at a discounted price to provide a larger quantity for high-throughput screening applications (F14242).

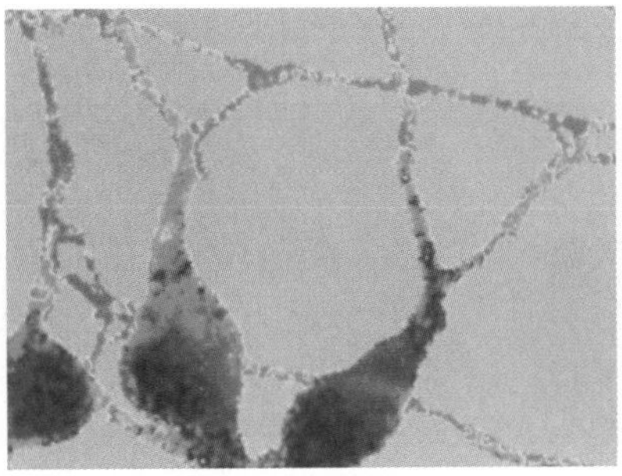

Figure 19.27 Frog olfactory bulb neurons labeled with fluo-3 (F1240, F3715) and Fura Red™ (F14219) Ca^{2+} indicators, demonstrating a Ca^{2+} response to treatment with KCl and nifedipine (J Physiol 487, 305 (1995)). The image is a ratio of fluo-3 and Fura Red™ fluorescence images acquired with a Leica confocal laser-scanning microscope. The image was contributed by J. Bischofberger and D. Schild, Physiology Institute, University of Göttingen.

Note 19.2

FluoroPure™ Grade

More than 90% of Molecular Probes' products are manufactured in our ISO-certified facilities in Eugene, Oregon. Compared with most other suppliers of research biochemicals, relatively few of our products are purchased from outside companies for resale. Having close control over manufacturing processes enables us to continually seek out and implement improvements in our chemical synthesis and purification methods. Consequently, we can now offer more of our most popular dyes and probes in FluoroPure™ grade with standard specifications of ≥98% purity by HPLC (see table). Lack of the FluoroPure™ label does not indicate that a product is <98% pure by HPLC, however.

FluoroPure™ grade dyes and probes

Dye or Probe	Application	Catalog and Section Number	Unit Size
Cell-Permeant Calcium Indicators			
Fluo-3 AM	Intracellular Ca^{2+} indicator	F23915, Section 19.3	10 × 50 µg
Fluo-4 AM (see Figure)	Intracellular Ca^{2+} indicator	F23917, Section 19.3	10 × 50 µg
Fura-2 AM	Intracellular Ca^{2+} indicator	F14185, Section 19.2	20 × 50 µg
Nucleic Acid Stains			
Propidium iodide	Nucleic acid stain, necrotic cell indicator	P21493, Section 8.1	100 mg
DAPI	Nucleic acid stain	D21490, Section 8.1	10 mg
Hoechst 33258	Nucleic acid stain	H21491, Section 8.1	100 mg
Hoechst 33342	Nucleic acid stain, apoptosis marker	H21492, Section 8.1	100 mg
Cell Function and Viability Probes			
D-Luciferin, sodium salt	Luciferase substrate, ATP detection	L22172, Section 10.6	10 mg
Monobromobimane	Intracellular glutathione probe	M20381, Section 2.3	25 mg
Rhodamine 123	Potential-dependent staining of mitochondria	R22420, Section 12.2	25 mg
$DiBAC_4(3)$	High-throughput screening for activators and blockers of K_{ATP} channels	B24570, Section 22.3	5 mg
Reactive Dyes and Tracers			
Fluorescamine	Fluorogenic detection reagent for aliphatic amines	F20261, Section 1.8	100 mg
NBD chloride	Reactive dye for amine and thiol modification	C20260, Section 1.8	100 mg
5-(and 6-)Carboxy-fluorescein	Fluid-phase tracer	C1904, Section 14.3	100 mg

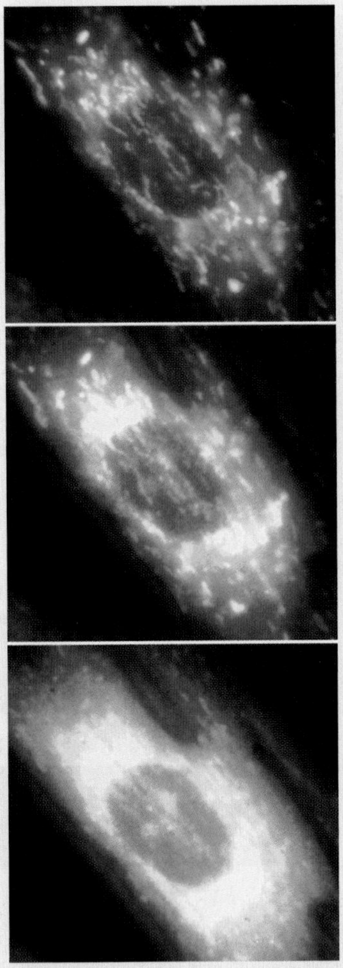

Figure. Staining of rat cortical astrocytes by rhodamine 123. Potential-dependent accumulation of the cationic dye in mitochondria results in a relatively weak fluorescence signal due to self-quenching (top panel). Dissipation of the mitochondrial membrane potential by the uncoupler FCCP is marked by increasing fluorescence (middle panel) and subsequent redistribution of the dye throughout the cell (bottom panel). Images courtesy of Michael Duchen, University College London.

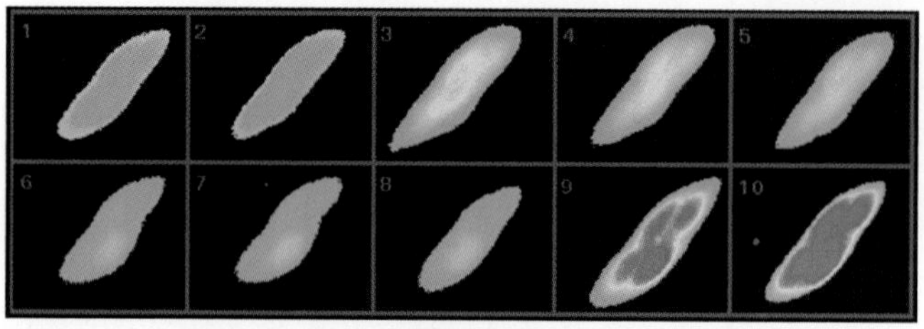

Figure 19.28 Pseudocolored images of changes in intracellular free Ca^{2+} in AtT-20/D16v-F2 cells, monitored at 9-second intervals with fluo-4, AM (F14201, F14202, F14217, F23917). In order to induce an influx of Ca^{2+}, the cells were depolarized with 50 mM KCl in frame 2 and exposed to 5 µM ionomycin (I24222, a Ca^{2+} ionophore) in frame 8. The images are pseudocolored according to fluorescence intensity, with red representing high Ca^{2+} concentrations and blue representing low Ca^{2+} concentrations. The images were acquired using a fluorescence microscope equipped with a longpass filter set appropriate for fluorescein and a Photometrics Quantix cooled CCD camera.

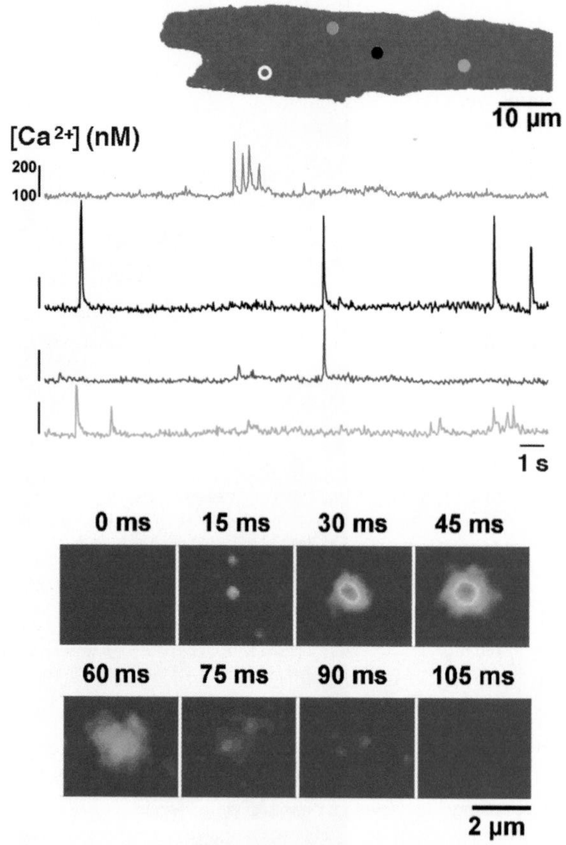

Figure 19.29 Fast confocal recording of spontaneous Ca^{2+} sparks in a rat ventricular myocyte. Single myocytes were isolated from rat hearts and loaded with fluo-4 AM (F14201, F14202, F14217, F23917). Images of loaded cells were obtained with a PerkinElmer UltraVIEW LCI confocal imaging system at a constant frame rate of 66 frames/second. Panel A illustrates the outline of a single cell and the position of the four regions of interest that were averaged to produce the kinetic traces shown in panel B. The traces are color coded in accordance with the regions marked in panel A and show numerous spontaneous Ca^{2+} sparks. Panel C illustrates a sequence of confocal images taken around the black region in panel A, indicating the spatiotemporal properties of an individual Ca^{2+} spark. The image was contributed by Peter Lipp, The Babraham Institute, Cambridge, UK, and reproduced with permission from Biomedical Products 9, 52 (2001).

Fluo-4

Fluo-4 (Figure 19.28), our patented analog of fluo-3 with the two chlorine substituents replaced by fluorine atoms (Figure 19.20), exhibits a K_d for Ca^{2+} of 345 nM;[13,31–33] the temperature dependence of the K_d for fluo-4 has been reported.[15] The fluorescence quantum yields of Ca^{2+}-bound fluo-3 and fluo-4 are essentially identical. Significantly, however, the absorption maximum of fluo-4 is blue-shifted about 12 nm, as compared with fluo-3, resulting in increased fluorescence excitation at 488 nm and consequently higher signal levels for confocal laser-scanning microscopy (Figure 19.29), flow cytometry and microplate screening applications (Figure 19.30, Figure 19.31). Intracellular Ca^{2+} measurements using fluo-3 have become essential for certain types of high-throughput pharmacological screening.[11,12,34] Applications of this technology include screening for compounds that affect G-protein–coupled receptors and identifying receptors for ligands known to be pharmacologically active. Molecular Devices' FLIPR (Fluorometric Imaging Plate Reader) system has been the leading instrument platform for these measurements[12,34] (Figure 19.31). Parallel comparisons of fluo-4 with fluo-3, carried out in collaboration with researchers at Molecular Devices, show that the advantages of fluo-4 in microscopy and solution fluorometry measurements are replicated in the FLIPR system. For example, fluo-4 generates the same fluorescence response as fluo-3 to carbachol-stimulated Ca^{2+} activation in Chinese hamster ovary (CHO) cells using half the AM ester–loading concentration and half the incubation time (Table 19.3). When fluo-4 is substituted for fluo-3 (i.e., using identical loading protocols), fluorescence signals are at least doubled (Table 19.3). The stronger fluorescence signals provided by fluo-4 are particularly advantageous in cell types such as human embryonic kidney (HEK 293) cells, which are seeded at low densities for pharmacological screening assays.

Fluo-4 is available as a cell-impermeant potassium salt (F14200) or as its cell-permeant AM ester. The AM ester is available specially packaged as a 1 mM solution in DMSO (F14217), as a set of 10 vials, each containing 50 µg (F14201; FluoroPure™ Grade, F23917) or — for high-throughput screening applications — as a set of five vials, each containing 1 mg (F14202). We also offer both low-affinity and high-affinity 10,000 MW dextran conjugates of the fluo-4 indicator[35] (F14240, F36250; Section 19.4). To create unique fluorescent Ca^{2+}-sensitive probes, we offer the thiol-reactive fluo-4 iodoacetamide (F36200), which can react with sulfhydryl groups on proteins, peptides and thiol-modified surfaces, as well as the amine-containing fluo-4 cadaverine (F36201), which can react with aldehydes, ketones and activated esters.

Table 19.3 — Parallel performance comparison of fluo-3 and fluo-4 on Molecular Devices' FLIPR system

Indicator	µM *	Time *(min)	Fluorescence †		Increase §
			Basal	Stimulated ‡	
Fluo-3	4	60	1700	5700	3.4-fold
Fluo-4	4	60	4900	21300	4.3-fold
Fluo-4	2	30	1200	5400	4.5-fold

* CHO cells stably transfected with rat muscarinic M_1 receptors were loaded with fluo-3 AM or fluo-4 AM according to standard protocols (Molecular Devices Corp.), with variations in indicator concentration (µM) and incubation time, as shown. † Relative fluorescence intensities after subtraction of background fluorescence. ‡ Cells were stimulated by addition of the muscarinic agonist carbachol (50 µM). § Ratio of stimulated to basal fluorescence intensities.

Rhod-2 and X-Rhod-1

The long-wavelength Ca^{2+} indicators rhod-2 (Figure 19.32, Figure 19.33) and X-rhod-1 are valuable for measuring Ca^{2+} in cells and tissues that have high levels of autofluorescence[36] and also for detecting Ca^{2+} release generated by photoreceptors and photoactivatable chelators.[37,38] Rhod-2 was originally reported to exhibit only a three- to fourfold enhancement of fluorescence upon binding Ca^{2+}.[1] Our chemists have considerably improved the purification of rhod-2, yielding a highly purified preparation that shows greater than 100-fold enhancement in fluorescence upon binding Ca^{2+} (Figure 19.34). Note that, as a consequence of this increased purity, the K_d for Ca^{2+} of rhod-2 in the absence of Mg^{2+} has now been determined to be 570 nM,[13] which is considerably lower than that cited in the original paper on rhod-2.[1] X-rhod-1 is a Ca^{2+} indicator with excitation/emission maxima of ~580/602 nm and a K_d for Ca^{2+} of 700 nM.[13] It has spectral characteristics that are similar to our Calcium Crimson™ indicator (see below), but the fluorescence response of X-rhod-1 is much more sensitive to Ca^{2+} binding (Figure 19.35). The long-wavelength emission characteristics of X-rhod-1 allow simultaneous detection Ca^{2+} transients and green-fluorescent protein (GFP) with minimal crosstalk[39] (see Note 12.1 "Product Highlight: Fluorescent Probes for Use with GFP" in Section 12.1).

Rhod-2 is available as a cell-impermeant potassium salt (R14220) or as a cell-permeant AM ester in either a 1 mg vial (R1244) or specially packaged as a set of 20 vials, each containing 50 µg (R1245MP). X-rhod-1 is available as its cell-impermeant potassium salt (X14209) or as a cell-permeant AM ester (X14210). This AM ester is specially packaged as a set of 10 vials, each containing 50 µg.

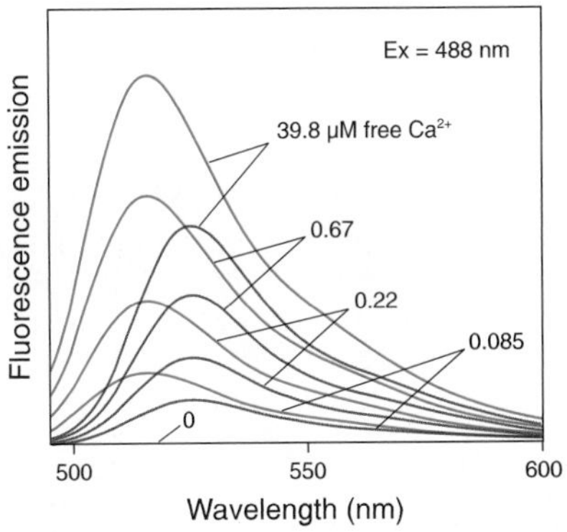

Figure 19.30 Fluorescence emission spectra at equal concentrations of fluo-4 (blue, F14200) and fluo-3 (red; F1240, F3715) in solutions containing 0–39.8 µM free Ca^{2+}.

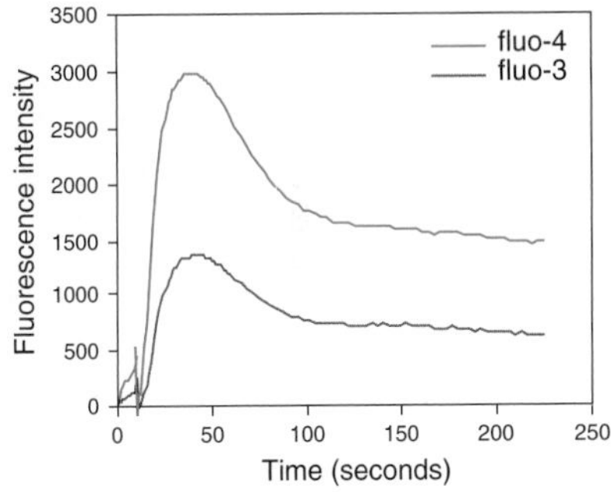

Figure 19.31 High-throughput Ca^{2+} influx assays for G-protein–coupled receptor activation. CHO (DHFR-) cells, co-transfected with the orphanin FQ receptor and $G\alpha_{qi3}$ chimeric G-protein, were loaded with 4 µM fluo-3 AM (F1241, F1242, F14218, F14242; FluoroPure™ Grade, F23915) or fluo-4 AM (F14201, F14202, F14217; FluoroPure™ Grade, F23917) for 60 minutes at 37°C. Ca^{2+}-dependent fluorescence traces (1 data point/second, excitation at 488 nm) from loaded cell samples in a 96-well microplate were measured simultaneously by a Fluorometric Imaging Plate Reader (FLIPR, Molecular Devices Corp.). Ca^{2+} transients were initiated by addition of 25 nM orphanin FQ (nociceptin), as indicated by the baseline discontinuities at approximately 10 seconds. Each trace represents the average of five transient recordings from separate microplate wells. The data were supplied by Sven Merten, Hans-Peter Nothacker and Olivier Civelli, University of California, Irvine.

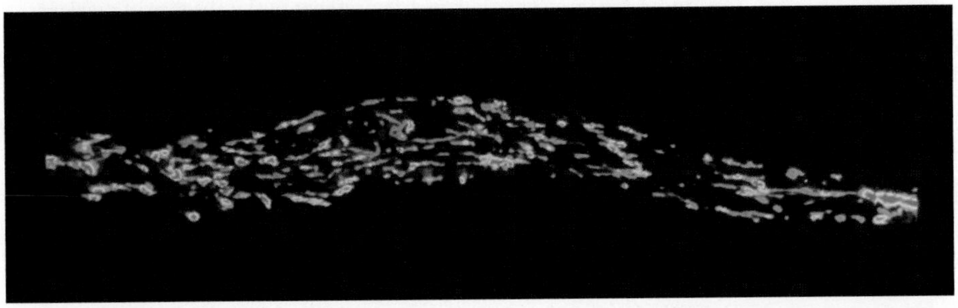

Figure 19.33 Pseudocolored micrograph of a single living smooth muscle cell labeled with a reduced form of rhod-2 AM (R1244, R1245MP), dihydrorhod-2. Images were acquired at focal planes spaced at 0.25 µm intervals and then processed using a constrained iterative deconvolution algorithm. This image shows that the rhod-2 fluorescence primarily arises from the mitochondria. The image was contributed by Fredric S. Fay, Program in Molecular Medicine, University of Massachusetts Medical Center.

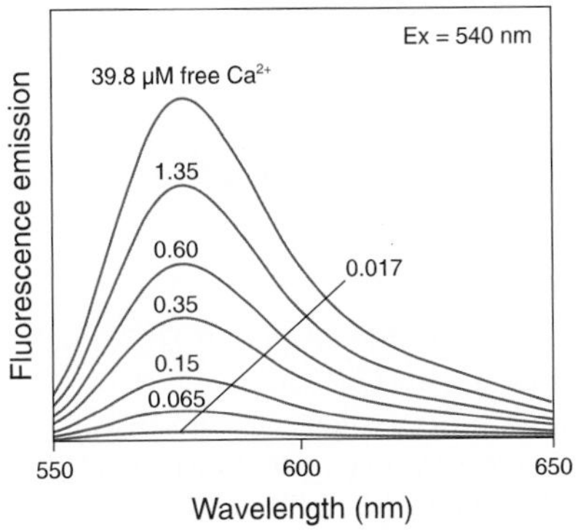

Figure 19.34 Fluorescence emission spectra of rhod-2 (R14220) in solutions containing 0–39.8 µM free Ca^{2+}. The spectrum for the Ca^{2+}-free solution is indistinguishable from the baseline.

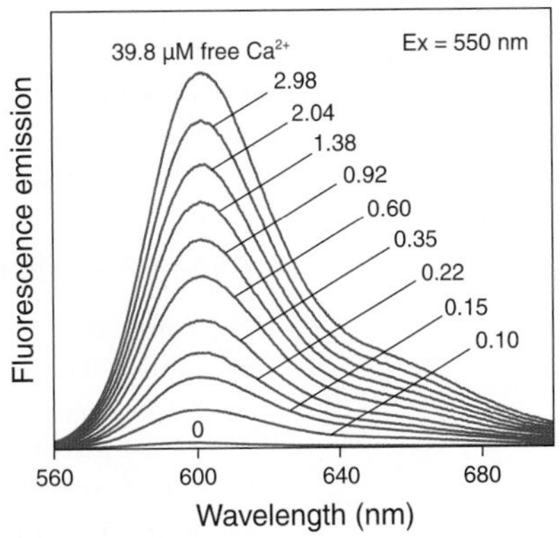

Figure 19.35 Fluorescence emission spectra of X-rhod-1 (X14209) in solutions containing 0—39.8 µM free Ca^{2+}.

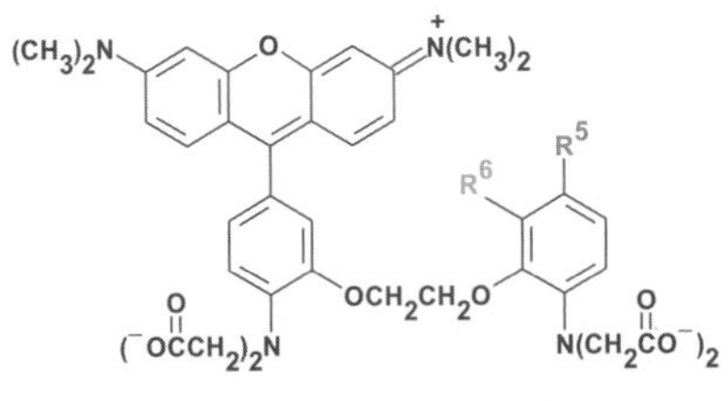

Indicator	$K_d(Ca^{2+})$	R^5	R^6
Rhod-2	0.57 µM	CH_3	H
Rhod-FF	19 µM	F	F
Rhod-5N	320 µM	NO_2	H

Figure 19.32 Rhod indicators with varying Ca^{2+} affinities.

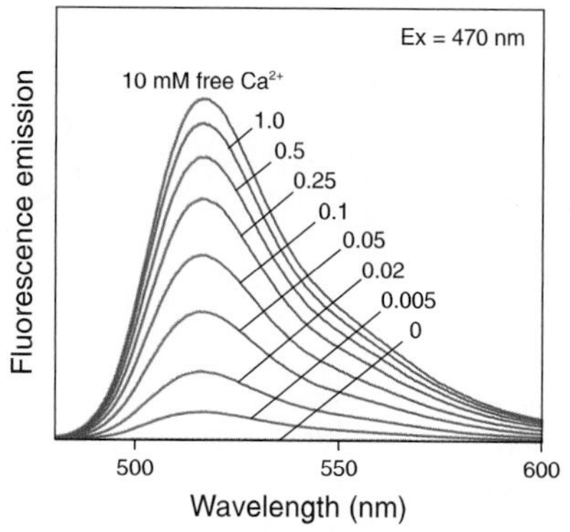

Figure 19.36 Ca^{2+}-dependent fluorescence emission spectra of fluo-5N (F14203).

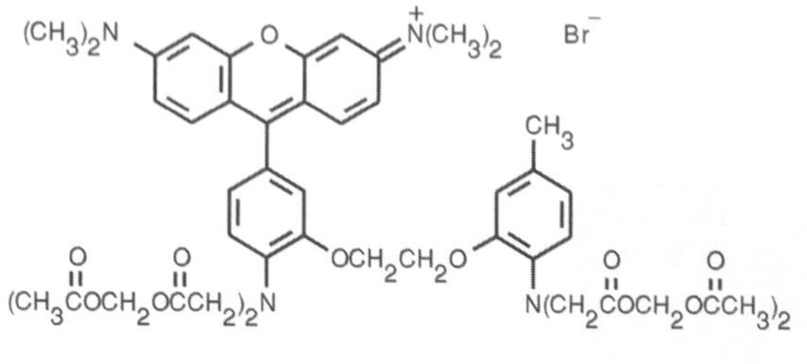

Figure 19.37 R1244 rhod-2, AM.

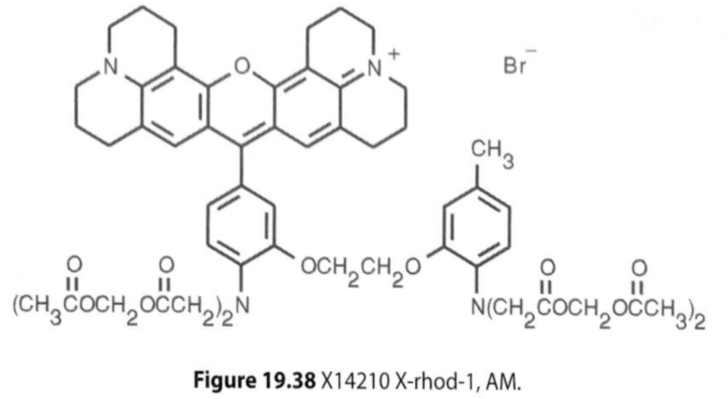

Figure 19.38 X14210 X-rhod-1, AM.

Lower-Affinity Calcium Indicators Based on Fluo-3 and Rhod-2

With Ca^{2+} dissociation constants well above 1 µM, our relatively low-affinity Ca^{2+} indicators can be used to detect intracellular Ca^{2+} levels in the micromolar range — levels that would saturate the response of fluo-3 and rhod-2. Such elevated Ca^{2+} levels are generated by mobilization of intracellular Ca^{2+} stores [40] and by excitatory stimulation of smooth muscle [41,42] and neurons.[43,44] Moreover, low-affinity indicators have faster ion dissociation rates, making them more suitable for tracking the kinetics of rapid Ca^{2+} fluxes than indicators with K_d values of Ca^{2+} <1 µM.[41,42,45–47]

Fluo-5F, Fluo-4FF, Fluo-5N and Mag-Fluo-4

Fluo-5F, fluo-4FF, fluo-5N and mag-fluo-4 [45] are analogs of fluo-4 with much lower Ca^{2+}-binding affinity, making them suitable for detecting intracellular Ca^{2+} levels in the 1 µM to 1 mM range. Fluo-5F, fluo-4FF, fluo-5N and mag-fluo-4 have K_d values for Ca^{2+} of ~2.3 µM, ~9.7 µM, ~90 µM and ~22 µM, respectively,[13] as compared with fluo-4, which has a K_d for Ca^{2+} of ~345 nM (Figure 19.20). The temperature dependence of the K_d for fluo-5F has been reported.[15] These low Ca^{2+}-binding affinities are ideal for detecting high concentrations of Ca^{2+} in the endoplasmic reticulum [48,49] and neurons (Figure 19.22), as well as for tracking Ca^{2+} flux kinetics.[45] Like fluo-4, these indicators are essentially nonfluorescent in the absence of divalent cations and exhibit strong fluorescence enhancement with no spectral shift upon binding Ca^{2+} (Figure 19.36). Because mag-fluo-4 is less Ca^{2+}/Mg^{2+} selective than fluo-5N, it is also useful as an indicator for intracellular Mg^{2+} levels (Section 19.6). Fluo-5F (F14221, F14222), fluo-4FF (F23980, F23981), fluo-5N (F14203, F14204) and mag-fluo-4 (M14205, M14206) are available as cell-impermeant potassium salts or as cell-permeant AM esters. The AM esters are specially packaged as a set of 10 vials, each containing 50 µg.

Rhod-5N

Rhod-5N (Figure 19.32) has a lower binding affinity for Ca^{2+} than any other BAPTA-based indicator (K_d = ~320 µM) [13] and is suitable for Ca^{2+} measurements from 10 µM to 1 mM. Like the parent rhod-2 indicator, rhod-5N is essentially nonfluorescent in the absence of divalent cations and exhibits strong fluorescence enhancement with no spectral shift upon binding Ca^{2+}. Furthermore, rhod-5N has very little detectable response to Mg^{2+} concentrations up to at least 100 mM. Rhod-5N is available as a cell-impermeant potassium salt (R14207) or as a cell-permeant AM ester (R14208). The AM ester is specially packaged as a set of 10 vials, each containing 50 µg.

Rhod-FF, X-Rhod-5F and X-Rhod-FF

The fluorinated analogs of rhod-2 — rhod-FF (Figure 19.32), X-rhod-5F [50] and X-rhod-FF — have intermediate Ca^{2+} sensitivity relative to rhod-2 and mag-rhod-2. Their Ca^{2+} dissociation constants (K_d) are 19 µM, 1.6 µM and 17 µM, respectively, as compared with ~0.57 µM for rhod-2 and ~70 µM for mag-rhod-2.[13] Rhod-FF and X-rhod-5F are available as water-soluble potassium salts (R23982, X23984), and rhod-FF, X-rhod-5F and X-rhod-FF are available as cell-permeant AM esters (R23983, X23985, X23987). The AM esters are specially packaged as a set of 10 vials, each containing 50 µg.

Indicators of Mitochondrial Ca^{2+} Transients

Our AM esters of rhodamine-based indicators, which include:

- Rhod-2 (R1244, R1245MP)
- Rhod-5N (R14208)
- Rhod-FF (R23983)
- X-rhod-1 (X14210)
- X-rhod-5F (X23985)
- X-rhod-FF (X23987)

are a set of cell-permeant Ca^{2+} indicators with a net positive charge (Figure 19.37, Figure 19.38). This property promotes their sequestration into mitochondria in some cells, most likely via membrane potential–driven uptake, and results in a staining pattern that is characteristic of mitochondria (Figure 19.33, Figure 19.39, Figure 19.40). Mitochondria have a high capacity for Ca^{2+} uptake and therefore require low-affinity Ca^{2+} indicators to accurately measure internal Ca^{2+} concentrations. Because the range of Ca^{2+} concentrations that can be detected using rhod-2 AM is limited to within about one order-of-magnitude above and below its Ca^{2+} dissociation constant (K_d = 570 nM), we offer a selection of rhod-2 analogs with Ca^{2+} dissociation constants up to 320 µM (Table 19.1, Figure 19.32).

The extent of mitochondrial versus cytosolic localization is influenced by the temperature and incubation time used for AM ester loading.[51–53] By reducing rhod-2 AM to the colorless, nonfluorescent dihydrorhod-2 AM, the discrimination between cytosolic and mitochondrially localized dye can be further improved.[54–57] The AM ester of dihydrorhod-2 exhibits Ca^{2+}-dependent fluorescence only after it is oxidized and its AM esters are cleaved to yield the rhod-2 indicator, processes that occur rapidly in the mitochondrial environment.[58] A detailed protocol for reducing rhod-2 AM to generate dihydrorhod-2 AM is available. The procedure should also be suitable for reduction of the AM esters of the other rhod indicators. Co-loading of cells with rhod-2 AM and green-fluorescent Ca^{2+} indicators such as fura-2, fluo-3, fluo-4, Calcium Green™-1 and Oregon Green® 488 BAPTA-1 enables simultaneous two-color imaging of mitochondrial and cytoplasmic Ca^{2+} [57,59,60] (Figure 19.41). Mitochondrial Ca^{2+} and mitochondrial NADH can be simultaneously measured using rhod-2 and intrinsic NADH fluorescence, respectively.[61]

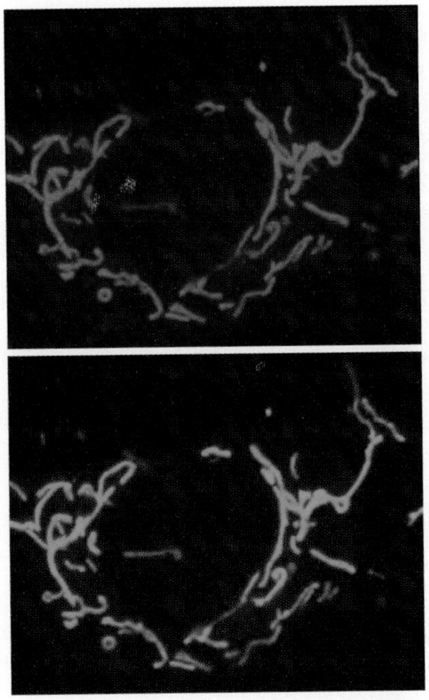

Figure 19.39 Colocalization of fluorescent staining by rhod-2 AM (R1244, R1245MP; upper panel) and mitochondrion-selective MitoFluor™ Green stain (M7502; lower panel) in an adult rat cortical astrocyte. Cells were simultaneously loaded with rhod-2 AM (4.5 µM) and the MitoFluor™ Green stain (20 nM) for 30 minutes at 22°C. Confocal laser-scanning microscopy using 488 nm excitation and spectrally resolved detection, at 505–530 nm for MitoFluor™ Green stain and ≥585 nm for rhod-2, shows almost identical staining distribution. The narrow spectral bandwidth of MitoFluor™ Green emission results in very little signal spillover into the rhod-2 detection channel. The images were contributed by Michael Duchen, University College, London. Reproduced with permission from J Cell Biol 145, 795 (1999).

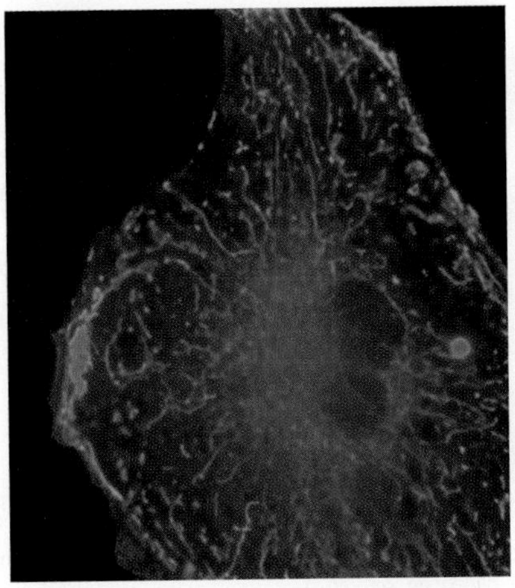

Figure 19.40 A live bovine pulmonary artery endothelial cell stained with 500 nM X-rhod-1 AM (X14210) for 30 minutes at 30°C. The image was deconvolved using Huygens software (Scientific Volume Imaging).

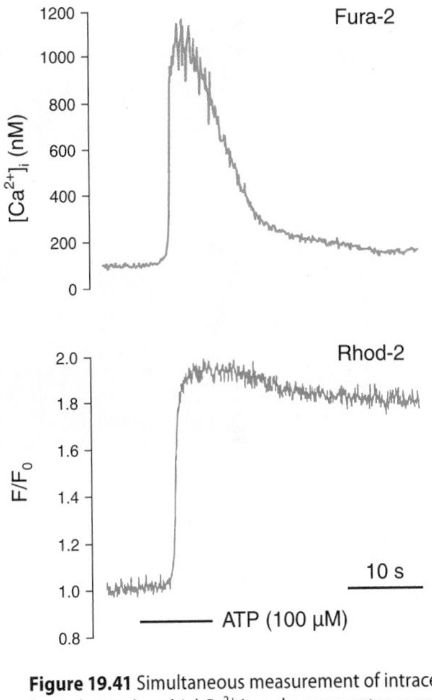

Figure 19.41 Simultaneous measurement of intracellular and mitochondrial Ca^{2+} in pulmonary artery smooth muscle cells. Cells were loaded with 2 µM rhod-2 AM, R1244, R1245MP) for 60 minutes at 22°C and were subsequently patch-clamped for electrophysiological measurements. Fura-2 (50 µM; F1200, F6799) was loaded by infusion from the patch pipette; at the same time, residual cytosolic rhod-2 was dialyzed out. Fluorescence excitation was rapidly alternated between 340 nm and 380 nm (for fura-2) and 500 nm (for rhod-2). The Ca^{2+} transient was detected following application of 100 µM ATP for 10 seconds. The observed increases in mitochondrial Ca^{2+} may provide a feedback mechanism for matching ATP supply and demand by activating Ca^{2+}-dependent dehydrogenases in the ATP synthesis pathway. The figure was reproduced with permission from J Physiol 516, 139 (1999).

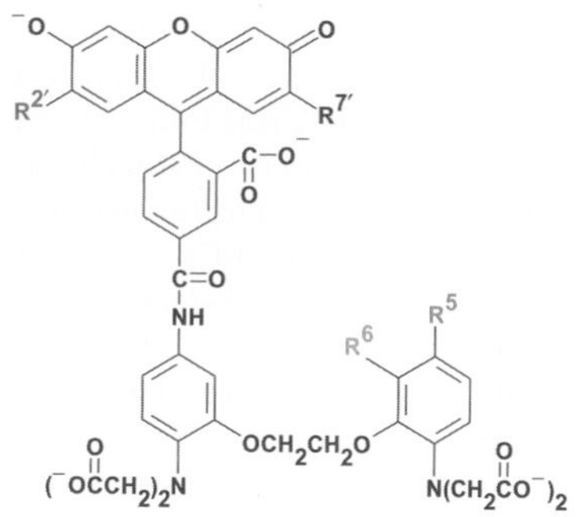

Indicator	$K_d(Ca^{2+})$	R2′	R7′	R5	R6
Calcium Green-1	0.19 µM	Cl	Cl	H	H
Calcium Green-5N	14 µM	Cl	Cl	NO_2	H
Oregon Green 488 BAPTA-1	0.17 µM	F	F	H	H
Oregon Green 488 BAPTA-6F	3 µM	F	F	H	F
Oregon Green 488 BAPTA-5N	20 µM	F	F	NO_2	H

Figure 19.42 Calcium Green™ and Oregon Green® 488 BAPTA indicators with varying Ca^{2+} affinities.

Calcium Green™, Calcium Orange™ and Calcium Crimson™ Indicators

Calcium Green™-1 and Calcium Green™-2 Indicators

The Calcium Green™-1 (Figure 19.42, Figure 19.43) and Calcium Green™-2 (Figure 19.44) indicators, as well as Calcium Orange™ and Calcium Crimson™ indicators (described below), are visible light–excitable indicators developed at Molecular Probes. Like fluo-3 and fluo-4, the Calcium Green™ indicators exhibit an increase in fluorescence emission intensity upon binding Ca^{2+} with little shift in wavelength[62] (Figure 19.45, Figure 19.46); the fluorescence spectra of the Calcium Green™ indicators are almost identical to those of fluo-3. Further comparison of the Calcium Green™ indicators and fluo-3 reveals that, at high Ca^{2+} levels, Calcium Green™-1 and Calcium Green™-2 are several times brighter than fluo-3 (Figure 19.24). Calcium Green™-1 has a quantum yield of 0.75 at saturating Ca^{2+} concentrations,[63] as compared with about 0.14 for fluo-3.[1]

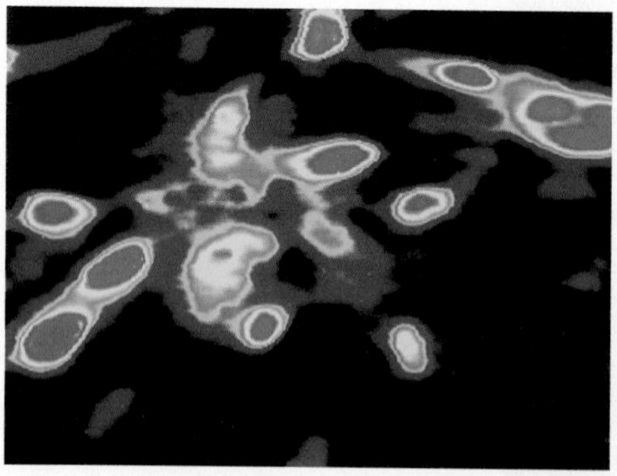

Figure 19.43 Brain cells from mediobasal hypothalamus stained with Calcium Green™-1, AM (C3011MP, C3012). The cells are responding to the neurotransmitter, glutamate, with an increase in cytoplasmic Ca^{2+} concentration as shown by this pseudocolored image. The image was contributed by Anthony N. van den Pol, Yale University School of Medicine.

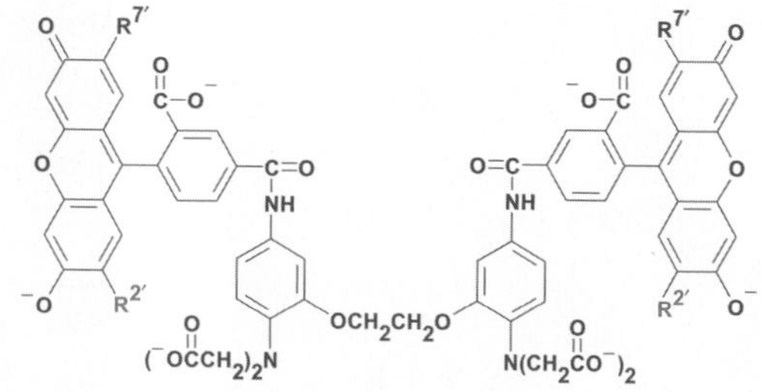

Indicator	$K_d(Ca^{2+})$	R2′	R7′
Calcium Green-2	0.55 µM	Cl	Cl
Oregon Green 488 BAPTA-2	0.58 µM	F	F

Figure 19.44 Calcium Green™-2 and Oregon Green® 488 BAPTA-2 Ca^{2+} indicators.

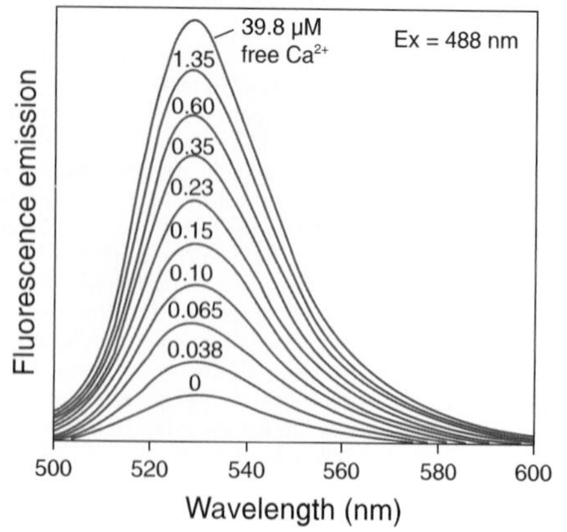

Figure 19.45 Ca^{2+}-dependent fluorescence emission spectra of the Calcium Green™-1 indicator (C3010MP).

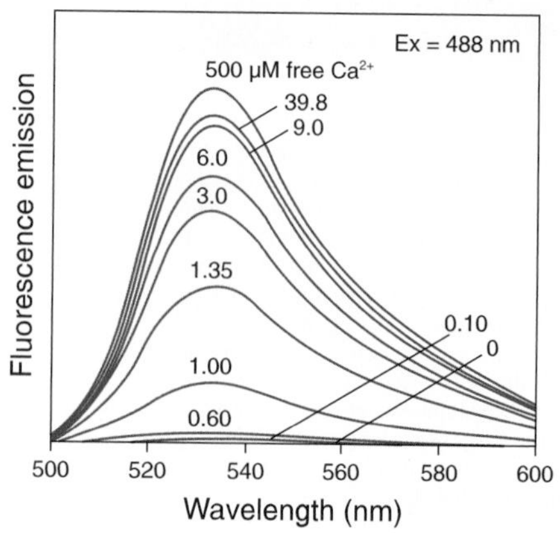

Figure 19.46 Ca^{2+}-dependent fluorescence emission spectra of the Calcium Green™-2 indicator (C3730).

The Calcium Green™ indicators have several other important features:

- Calcium Green™-1 is more fluorescent in resting cells than is fluo-3 (Figure 19.24), which increases the visibility of unstimulated cells, facilitates the determination of baseline fluorescence and makes calculations of intracellular Ca^{2+} concentrations more reliable.
- Calcium Green™-1 has been a preferred indicator for multiphoton excitation imaging of Ca^{2+} in living tissues.[2,64–67]
- Calcium Green™-1 is useful for measuring intracellular Ca^{2+} by fluorescence lifetime imaging.[68,69]
- The Ca^{2+} affinity of Calcium Green™-1 in the absence of Mg^{2+} (K_d for Ca^{2+} = 190 nM) is higher than that of fluo-3 (K_d for Ca^{2+} = 390 nM) or Calcium Green™-2 (K_d for Ca^{2+} = 550 nM).[13]
- Like fluo-3 and fluo-4, Calcium Green™-2 is essentially nonfluorescent in the absence of Ca^{2+} and exhibits an approximately 100-fold increase in emission intensity upon Ca^{2+} binding, which leads to a very large dynamic range.
- Like fluo-3 AM and fluo-4 AM, the AM esters of the Calcium Green™ indicators are nonfluorescent.

Furthermore, the Calcium Green™ indicators are less phototoxic to cells than fluo-3.[70,71] This observation stems at least in part from the fact that the Calcium Green™ indicators are intrinsically more fluorescent than fluo-3, thus requiring lower illumination intensities and lower dye concentrations to achieve the same signal[72] (Figure 19.24). Advantages of using Calcium Green™-1 over other fluorescent Ca^{2+} indicators have been described.[73] Calcium Green™-1 has been used to image spiral Ca^{2+} waves[74–76] (Figure 19.21) and to measure Ca^{2+} release invoked by photolysis of caged inositol 1,4,5-triphosphate[40,77] (I23580, Section 17.2).

Simultaneous loading of Calcium Green™-2 and carboxy SNARF®-1 AM, acetate (C1271, C1272; Section 20.2) enabled researchers to make ratiometric measurements of intracellular Ca^{2+} in cardiac myocytes.[72] A variation on this approach has been reported by Oheim and co-workers in which Calcium Green™-1 and a Ca^{2+}-insensitive reference dye similar to lucifer yellow CH (L453, L12926; Section 14.3) were loaded into bovine adrenal chromaffin cells by whole-cell patch clamping.[78] Ratio images were obtained using 420/488 nm dual excitation (emission >515 nm) and exhibited superior signal-to-noise characteristics, as compared with conventional UV-excited fura-2 images. This technique should be equally applicable to other 488 nm–excited Ca^{2+} indicators such as fluo-3, fluo-4, fluo-5N and the Oregon Green® 488 BAPTA series. Calcium Green™-1 and Calcium Green™-2 are available as cell-impermeant potassium salts (C3010MP, C3730) or as cell-permeant AM esters (C3011MP, C3012, C3732).

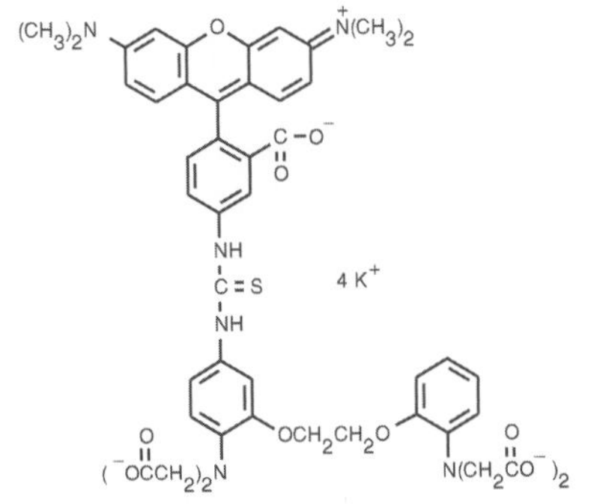

Figure 19.47 C3013 Calcium Orange™, tetrapotassium salt.

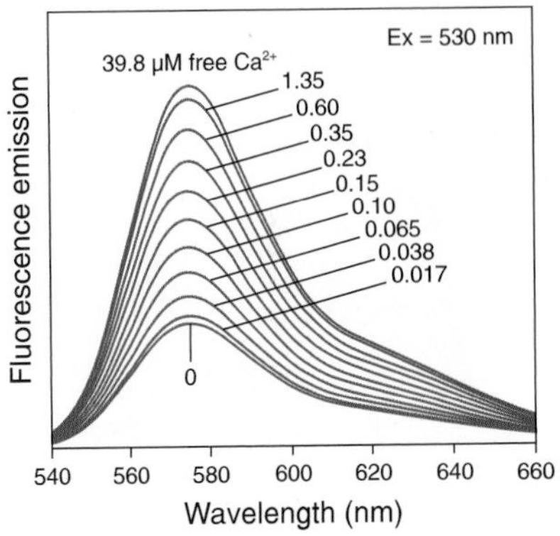

Figure 19.48 Ca^{2+}-dependent fluorescence emission spectra of the Calcium Orange™ indicator (C3013).

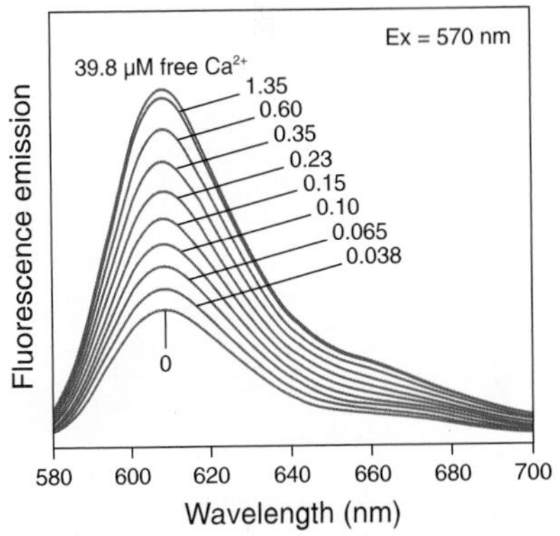

Figure 19.49 Ca^{2+}-dependent fluorescence emission spectra of the Calcium Crimson™ indicator (available as the cell-permeant acetoxymethyl (AM) ester, C3018).

Calcium Orange™ and Calcium Crimson™ Indicators

Like the Calcium Green™ indicators, Calcium Orange™ (C3013, Figure 19.47) and Calcium Crimson™ exhibit an increase in fluorescence emission intensity upon binding to Ca^{2+} with little shift in wavelength (Figure 19.48, Figure 19.49) and can be loaded into cells as their AM esters (C3015, C3018). Both indicators are more photostable than either fluo-3 or the Calcium Green™ indicators.[16]

Calcium Orange™ has an excitation maximum near 550 nm and is compatible with standard tetramethylrhodamine optical filters (Table 23.9). Calcium Orange™ has been used to monitor Ca^{2+} in intact photoreceptors containing a genetically altered rhodopsin pigment,[38] as well as to follow Ca^{2+} influx and release in hippocampal astrocytes.[79]

The excitation maximum (~590 nm) of Calcium Crimson™ makes it useful in situations where interference by cellular autofluorescence is problematic.[80] Selective uptake of Calcium Crimson™ AM (C3018) at *Drosophila* motor nerve terminals has been used to obtain images of stimulus-dependent Ca^{2+} influx.[81]

Calcium Green™-5N and Magnesium Green™: Low-Affinity Ca^{2+} Indicators

The Ca^{2+} indicators Calcium Green™-5N (Figure 19.42) and Magnesium Green™ (Figure 19.50) have dissociation constants for Ca^{2+} in the absence of Mg^{2+} of ~14 µM and ~6 µM, respectively[13] (Figure 19.51). These low-affinity Ca^{2+} indicators exhibit relatively little fluorescence, except in cells in which high-amplitude Ca^{2+} influx or release is occurring.[82,83] Calcium Green™-5N and Magnesium Green™ buffer intracellular Ca^{2+} to a lesser extent than do the higher-affinity Ca^{2+} indicators. Furthermore, the high Ca^{2+} dissociation rates of these indicators are advantageous for tracking rapid Ca^{2+}-release kinetics.[84–87] Use of the low-affinity Ca^{2+} indicator

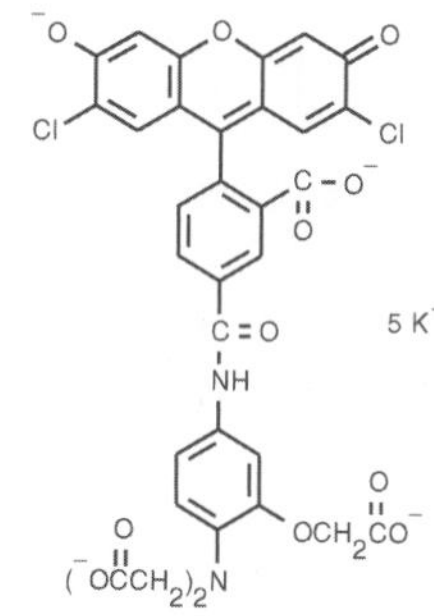

Figure 19.50 M3733 Magnesium Green™, pentapotassium salt.

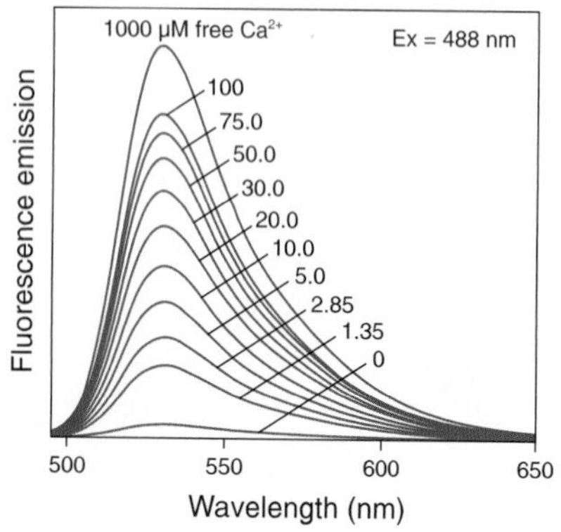

Figure 19.51 Ca^{2+}-dependent fluorescence emission spectra of the Calcium Green™-5N indicator (C3737).

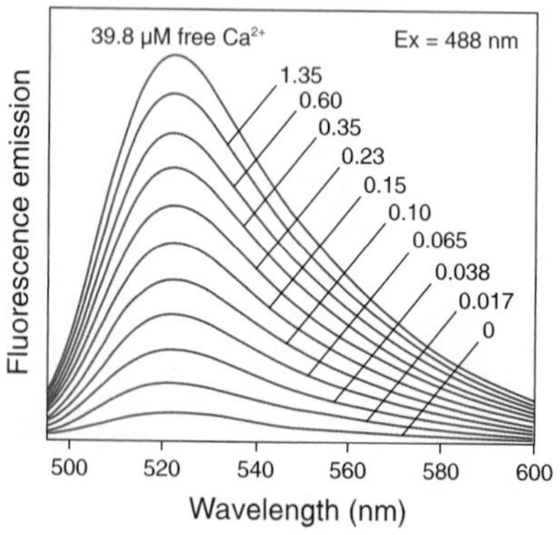

Figure 19.52 Ca^{2+}-dependent fluorescence emission spectra of the Oregon Green® 488 BAPTA-1 indicator (O6806).

Calcium Green™-5N in combination with the higher-affinity indicator Calcium Green™-2 in the same experimental protocol can give an indication of the absolute magnitude of Ca^{2+} spikes.[88] Furthermore, coinjection of Ca^{2+}-sensitive Calcium Green™-5N and Ca^{2+}-insensitive 8-aminonaphthalene-1,3,6-trisulfonic acid (ANTS, A350; Section 14.3) into *Limulus* ventral nerve photoreceptors permitted ratiometric measurement of Ca^{2+} flux.[89] Calcium Green™-5N is also effective for:

- Detecting permeability transition pore–associated Ca^{2+} fluxes in skeletal muscle mitochondria [90]
- Following changes in inositol 1,4,5-triphosphate–mediated Ca^{2+} distribution in *Xenopus* oocytes [40,86,91]
- Measuring rapid transient Ca^{2+} transients in neuronal axons and dendrites [92–94]
- Monitoring increases in neuronal free Ca^{2+} associated with glutamate excitotoxicity [44,95]
- Studying light-stimulated Ca^{2+} flux in *Drosophila* photoreceptors [96]
- Visualizing Ca^{2+} transients in a single sarcomere with pulsed-laser excitation and confocal spot detection [97]

Calcium Green™-5N is available as a cell-impermeant potassium salt (C3737) or as a cell-permeant AM ester (C3739). Magnesium Green™, which is also discussed in Section 19.6 with the other Mg^{2+} indicators, is available as a cell-impermeant potassium salt (M3733) or as a cell-permeant AM ester (M3735).

Oregon Green® 488 BAPTA Indicators

Our Oregon Green® 488 BAPTA indicators are based on our outstanding Oregon Green® 488 dyes (Section 1.5). These indicators have spectra that are virtually identical to those of fluorescein (excitation/emission maxima ~492/517 nm). The Oregon Green® 488 BAPTA indicators are more efficiently excited by the 488 nm spectral line of the argon-ion laser than are the fluo-3 and Calcium Green™ indicators, both of which are based on the 2′,7′-dichlorofluorescein chromophore (excitation/emission maxima ~504/529 nm).

Oregon Green® 488 BAPTA-1 and Oregon Green® 488 BAPTA-2

The spectral properties of the Oregon Green® 488 BAPTA indicators should permit the use of lower dye concentrations when using argon-ion laser excitation sources, making the Oregon Green® 488 BAPTA indicators well suited for intracellular Ca^{2+} measurements by confocal laser-scanning microscopy.[98–102] Oregon Green® 488 BAPTA-1 is also recommended for high-throughput measurements of intracellular Ca^{2+} using fluorescence microplate readers [103,104] and applications involving photoactivatable ("caged") probes [105,106] (Figure 5.2).

The absorptivity of Oregon Green® 488 BAPTA-1 (Figure 19.42) at 488 nm is ~93% of its peak value, whereas the absorptivity of fluo-3 and the Calcium Green™ indicators at 488 nm is only ~45% of their maxima. Furthermore, the quantum yields of the Ca^{2+} complexes of Oregon Green® 488 BAPTA-1 and Calcium Green™-1 are ~0.7, as compared with only ~0.14 for fluo-3. As with Calcium Green™-1 (Figure 19.24), Oregon Green® 488 BAPTA-1 is moderately fluorescent in Ca^{2+}-free solution, and its fluorescence is enhanced about 14-fold at saturating Ca^{2+} (Figure 19.52). Oregon Green® 488 BAPTA-1 has a K_d for Ca^{2+} in the absence of Mg^{2+} of about 170 nM.[13] Oregon Green® 488 BAPTA-2 is similar to Calcium Green™-2 in that it contains two dye molecules per BAPTA chelator (Figure 19.44) and exhibits very low fluorescence in the absence of Ca^{2+}. The fluorescence of Oregon Green® 488 BAPTA-2 is enhanced at least 37-fold at saturating Ca^{2+}, and it has a K_d for Ca^{2+} in the absence of Mg^{2+} of ~580 nM [13] (Figure 19.53).

Several research groups are exploiting the power of two-photon laser-scanning microscopy and fluorescent Ca^{2+} indicators for functional imaging of neurons in brain slice preparations [107] and intact live brains.[65] Oregon Green® 488 BAPTA-1 and Calcium Green™-1 (see above), excited in the wavelength range 800–850 nm are the indicators of choice in many of these investigations.[64,108–113] The Oregon Green® 488 BAPTA-2 Ca^{2+} indicator and red-fluorescent, Ca^{2+}-insensitive sulforhodamine 101 reference dye (S359, Section 14.3) have been loaded together into optic nerves to image Ca^{2+} distribution in axons.[98]

Oregon Green® 488 BAPTA-1 and Oregon Green® 488 BAPTA-2 are available as cell-impermeant potassium salts (O6806, O6808) or as cell-permeant AM esters (O6807, O6809), which are specially packaged as a set of 10 vials, each containing 50 µg. Dextran conjugates of the Oregon Green® BAPTA-1 indicator (O6798, O6797) are described in Section 19.4.

Oregon Green® 488 BAPTA-6F and Oregon Green® 488 BAPTA-5N

Oregon Green® 488 BAPTA-6F (Figure 19.42) and Oregon Green® 488 BAPTA-5N (Figure 19.42) are low-affinity Ca^{2+} indicators (K_d for Ca^{2+} ~3 µM and ~20 µM, respectively) [13] designed for measuring intracellular Ca^{2+} levels above 1 µM.[114–117] By simultaneously imaging Oregon Green® 488 BAPTA-5N and rhod-2, researchers have been able to compare cytosolic and mitochondrial Ca^{2+} responses to action potentials in amphibian motor nerve terminals.[57,118] Oregon Green® 488 BAPTA-6F and Oregon Green® BAPTA-5N are available as cell-impermeant potassium salts (O23990, O6812) or as cell-permeant AM esters (O23991, O6813), which are specially packaged as a set of 10 vials, each containing 50 µg.

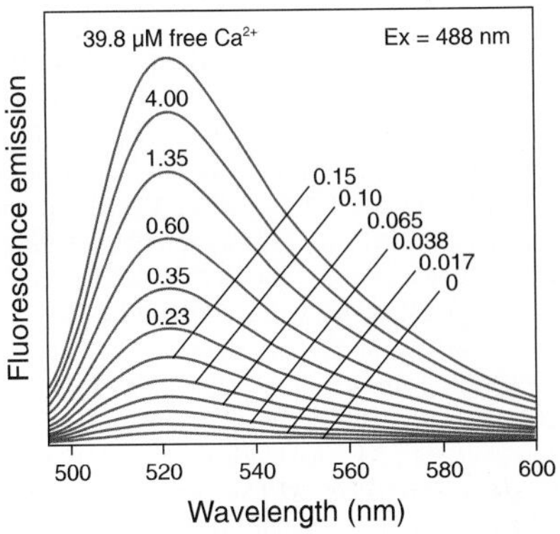

Figure 19.53 Ca^{2+}-dependent fluorescence emission spectra of the Oregon Green® 488 BAPTA-2 indicator (O6808).

Fura Red™ Indicator

Our visible light–excitable fura-2 analog, the Fura Red™ indicator (Figure 19.54) offers unique possibilities for ratiometric measurement of Ca^{2+} in single cells by microphotometry, imaging or flow cytometry. The visible-wavelength excitation (450–500 nm) and very long-wavelength emission maximum (~660 nm) of the Fura Red™ indicator (Figure 19.55) minimize interference from autofluorescence and pigmentation in tissues and biological fluids.[119] Fluorescence of the Fura Red™ indicator excited at 488 nm *decreases* once the indicator binds Ca^{2+} (Figure 19.26). Even in the absence of Ca^{2+}, fluorescence of the Fura Red™ indicator is much weaker than that of the other visible light–excitable Ca^{2+} indicators, necessitating use of higher concentrations of the indicator in cells to produce equivalent fluorescence.

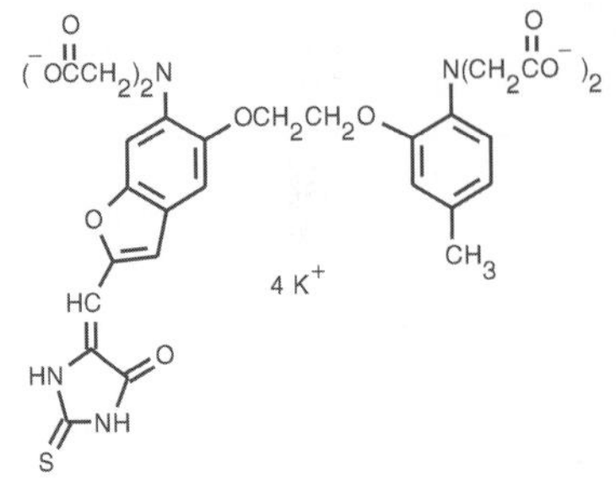

Figure 19.54 F14219 Fura Red™, tetrapotassium salt.

Ratiometric measurements of Ca^{2+} levels in frog skeletal muscle fibers with Fura Red™ have been made using excitation wavelengths of 420 nm and 480 nm.[120] A simultaneous assay for Ca^{2+} uptake and ATP hydrolysis by sarcoplasmic reticulum has been developed that uses the large *absorbance* change of Fura Red™ upon Ca^{2+} binding.[121] This assay can measure Ca^{2+} uptake — and probably uptake of heavy metal ions through channels — from the medium in real time without the use of radioactive Ca^{2+}, making it generally useful for measuring Ca^{2+} uptake by cells. In several cell types, simultaneous labeling with Fura Red™ and fluo-3 has enabled researchers to use ratiometric measurements for estimating intracellular Ca^{2+} levels using confocal laser-scanning microscopy [18–22] (Figure 19.27) or flow cytometry.[23,24]

Furthermore, the huge Stokes shift of Fura Red™ permits multicolor analysis of Fura Red™ fluorescence in combination with fluorescein or fluorescein-like dyes using only a single excitation wavelength (Figure 19.26). For example, researchers have been able to simultaneously measure Ca^{2+} fluxes and oxidative bursts in monocytes and granulocytes by simultaneously measuring the fluorescence of Fura Red™ and rhodamine 123 — the oxidation product of the probe dihydrorhodamine 123 [122] (D632, D23806; Section 16.1). Fura Red™ has also been used in combination with blue-fluorescent protein in transfected cells.[39]

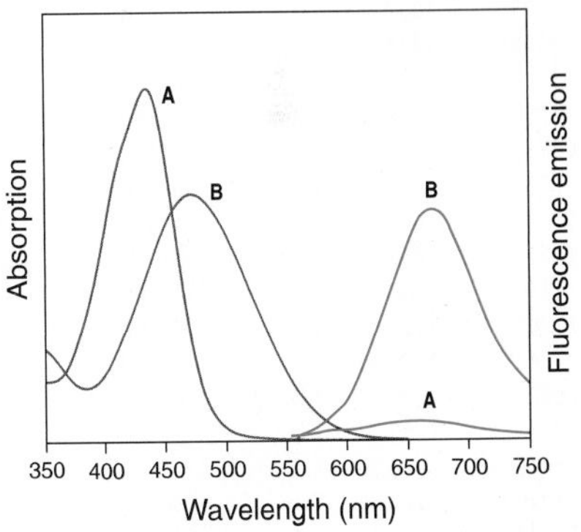

Figure 19.55 Absorption and fluorescence emission (excited at 488 nm) spectra of Ca^{2+}-saturated (A) and Ca^{2+}-free (B) Fura Red™ in pH 7.2 buffer.

Fura Red™ is available as either a cell-impermeant tetrapotassium salt (F14219) or as a cell-permeant AM ester (F3020, F3021).

Calcein

Calcein (C481, Section 19.7) is a relatively low-affinity Ca^{2+} chelator. The dissociation constants for both the Ca^{2+} and Mg^{2+} complexes of calcein at physiological pH are about 10^{-3} to 10^{-4} M.[123] As a derivative of iminodiacetic acid (Figure 14.32), this dye exhibits an ion affinity that increases considerably at higher pH, and thus it is not particularly useful for measuring Ca^{2+} or Mg^{2+} in cells. Calcein is essentially nonfluorescent above pH 12 but forms fluorescent complexes with Ca^{2+}, Mg^{2+} and several other metals [124–127] (Section 19.7). Calcein has been used to assay for Ca^{2+} in serum [128,129] and to measure Ca^{2+} binding to sarcoplasmic reticulum.[123] However, it is much more widely used for fluorescence quenching–based detection of Ni^{2+}, Co^{2+}, Cu^{2+} and Fe^{3+} (Section 19.7).

References

1. J Biol Chem 264, 8171 (1989); **2.** Biophys J 78, 2655 (2000); **3.** J Physiol 526 Pt 3, 551 (2000); **4.** Neuron 22, 125 (1999); **5.** Am J Physiol 274, C1755 (1998); **6.** Am J Physiol 274, C1346 (1998); **7.** Biophys J 74, 153 (1998); **8.** J Physiol 508, 801 (1998); **9.** J Physiol 512, 669 (1998); **10.** J Physiol 508, 145 (1998); **11.** Methods Enzymol 294, 20 (1999); **12.** Genet Eng News 19, 44 (1999); **13.** K_d values for Ca^{2+} are determined at Molecular Probes at ~22°C using our Calcium Calibration Buffer Kits; **14.** Biophys J 65, 865 (1993); **15.** J Physiol 542, 843 (2002); **16.** Cell Calcium 28, 213 (2000); **17.** Cell Calcium 21, 275 (1997); **18.** Cell Calcium 19, 255 (1996); **19.** Cell Calcium 18, 377 (1995); **20.** Cell Calcium 16, 279 (1994); **21.** Cell Calcium 15, 341 (1994); **22.** Cell Calcium 14, 359 (1993); **23.** Methods 21, 221 (2000); **24.** Cytometry 17, 135 (1994); **25.** Exp Cell Res 217, 410 (1995); **26.** J Biol Chem 270, 29781 (1995); **27.** J Biol Chem 269, 30636 (1994); **28.** Cytometry 11, 923 (1990); **29.** Cytometry 24, 99 (1996); **30.** Cytometry 14, 257 (1993); **31.** Cell Calcium 27, 97 (2000); **32.** J Physiol 518, 815 (1999); **33.** Nature 400, 261 (1999); **34.** Anal Biochem 270, 242 (1999); **35.** Neuron 27, 25 (2000); **36.** J Physiol 507, 405 (1998); **37.** J Neurosci 17, 1701 (1997); **38.** Neuron 13, 837 (1994); **39.** Biochem J 356, 345 (2001); **40.** Cell Calcium 20, 105 (1996); **41.** Biophys J 70, 896 (1996); **42.** J Gen Physiol 97, 271 (1991); **43.** Proc Natl Acad Sci U S A 92, 10272 (1995); **44.** Neurosci Lett 162, 149 (1993); **45.** J Neurosci 20, 6773 (2000); **46.** Pflugers Arch 434, 615 (1997); **47.** Biophys J 68, 2156 (1995); **48.** J Physiol 534, 87 (2001); **49.** EMBO J 19, 5729 (2000); **50.** J Biol Chem 279, 16903 (2004); **51.** Methods Enzymol 302, 341 (1999); **52.** Mol Pharmacol 53, 974 (1998); **53.** Biochem Biophys Res Commun 236, 738 (1997); **54.** Methods Enzymol 307, 441 (1999); **55.** Biophys J 75, 2004 (1998); **56.** Cell 82, 415 (1995); **57.** J Physiol 509, 59 (1998); **58.** Am J Physiol 255, C304 (1988); **59.** J Physiol 508, 413 (1998); **60.** J Physiol 516, 139 (1999); **61.** Biophys J 83, 587 (2002); **62.** Biochem Biophys Res Commun 180, 209 (1991); **63.** Proc Natl Acad Sci U S A 89, 3591 (1992); **64.** J Neurosci 19, 1976 (1999); **65.** Nature 385, 161 (1997); **66.** Proc Natl Acad Sci U S A 93, 10763 (1996); **67.** J Neurosci Methods 54, 151 (1994); **68.** J Fluorescence 4, 291 (1994); **69.** Proc SPIE-Int Soc Opt Eng 1640, 390 (1992); **70.** Three-Dimensional Confocal Microscopy, Stevens JK, Mills LR, Trogadis JE, Eds. pp. 281–300 (1994); **71.** Dev Biol 149, 370 (1992); **72.** Pflugers Arch 430, 579 (1995); **73.** Anal Biochem 273, 186 (1999); **74.** Adv Second Messenger Phosphoprotein Res 30, 1 (1995); **75.** Science 260, 229 (1993); **76.** Biophys J 61, 509 (1992); **77.** J Biol Chem 267, 17722 (1992); **78.** Cell Calcium 24, 71 (1998); **79.** J Neurosci 16, 71 (1996); **80.** J Neurosci 15, 5535 (1995); **81.** J Neurosci 18, 3233 (1998); **82.** Proc Natl Acad Sci U S A 87, 1461 (1990); **83.** J Theor Biol 93, 1009 (1981); **84.** Biophys J 74, 1549 (1998); **85.** J Neurosci 16, 5661 (1996); **86.** Biophys J 70, 1006 (1996); **87.** FEBS Lett 364, 335 (1995); **88.** J Neurosci 15, 4209 (1995); **89.** J Gen Physiol 105, 95 (1995); **90.** J Biol Chem 273, 12662 (1998); **91.** J Biol Chem 273, 4052 (1998); **92.** Nature 396, 24 (1998); **93.** J Physiol 502, 509 (1997); **94.** J Physiol 495, 641 (1996); **95.** Neuron 11, 751 (1993); **96.** Neuron 12, 1257 (1994); **97.** Nature 367, 739 (1994); **98.** J Neurosci Methods 102, 165 (2000); **99.** Cell Calcium 21, 441 (1997); **100.** J Physiol 502, 521 (1997); **101.** J Physiol 509, 67 (1998); **102.** Neuron 22, 115 (1999); **103.** J Biomol Screen 7, 233 (2002); **104.** Biotechniques 26, 318 (1999); **105.** EMBO J 19, 3608 (2000); **106.** Proc Natl Acad Sci U S A 97, 8635 (2000); **107.** Methods 18, 231 (1999); **108.** J Neurosci 20, 2523 (2000); **109.** Proc Natl Acad Sci U S A 96, 7035 (1999); **110.** J Physiol 520 Pt 1, 65 (1999); **111.** Nature 399, 151 (1999); **112.** Nat Neurosci 2, 65 (1999); **113.** Nat Neurosci 2, 989 (1999); **114.** Biophys J 79, 202 (2000); **115.** J Biol Chem 276, 10655 (2001); **116.** J Neurosci 20, 7290 (2000); **117.** Nat Neurosci 4, 275 (2001); **118.** J Neurosci 19, 7495 (1999); **119.** Am J Physiol 273, H2161 (1997); **120.** Biophys J 64, 1934 (1993); **121.** Anal Biochem 227, 328 (1995); **122.** Cytometry 13, 693 (1992); **123.** Biophys J 18, 3 (1977); **124.** Anal Chem 46, 2036 (1974); **125.** Anal Chem 35, 1035 (1963); **126.** Anal Chem 31, 456 (1959); **127.** Analyst 82, 284 (1957); **128.** Analyst 113, 251 (1988); **129.** Anal Chem 35, 1238 (1963).

Data Table — 19.3 Fluorescent Ca^{2+} Indicators Excited with Visible Light

				Low Ca^{2+}				High Ca^{2+}						
Cat #	MW	Storage	Soluble	Abs	EC	Em	Solvent	Abs	EC	Em	Solvent	Product	K_d	Notes
C3010MP	1147.19	F,D,L	pH >6	506	81,000	531	H_2O	506	82,000	531	H_2O/Ca^{2+}		190 nM	1, 2, 3, 4
C3011MP	1290.98	F,D,L	DMSO	302	17,000	none	MeOH					C3010MP		
C3012	1290.98	F,D,L	DMSO	302	17,000	none	MeOH					C3010MP		
C3013	1087.33	D,L	pH >6	549	80,000	575	H_2O	549	80,000	576	H_2O/Ca^{2+}		185 nM	1, 2, 3, 4
C3015	1223.23	F,D,L	DMSO	540	94,000	566	MeOH	-				C3013		
C3018	1368.40	F,D,L	DMSO	583	113,000=	602	MeOH					see Notes		5
C3730	1665.58	D,L	pH >6	506	95,000	536	H_2O	503	147,000	536	H_2O/Ca^{2+}		550 nM	1, 2, 3, 4
C3732	1817.26	F,D	DMSO	302	29,000	none	MeOH					C3730		
C3737	1192.19	D,L	pH >6	506	83,000	532	H_2O	506	82,000	532	H_2O/Ca^{2+}		14 µM	1, 2, 4, 6
C3739	1335.98	F,D	DMSO	361	15,000	none	EtOAc					C3737		
C6771	1268.22	F,D,L	DMSO	540	85,000	566	MeOH					C6770		
F1240	854.70	D,L	pH >6	503	92,000	see Notes	H_2O	505	102,000	526	H_2O/Ca^{2+}		390 nM	1, 2, 3, 7
F1241	1129.86	F,D,L	DMSO	464	26,000	see Notes	MeOH					F1240		8
F1242	1129.86	F,D,L	DMSO	464	26,000	see Notes	MeOH					F1240		8
F3020	1089.00	F,D,L	DMSO	458	43,000	597	MeOH					F14219		
F3021	1089.00	F,D,L	DMSO	458	43,000	597	MeOH					F14219		
F3715	960.00	D,L	pH >6	506	90,000	see Notes	H_2O	506	100,000	526	H_2O/Ca^{2+}		390 nM	1, 2, 3, 7
F14200	927.09	D,L	pH >6	491	82,000	see Notes	H_2O	494	88,000	516	H_2O/Ca^{2+}		345 nM	1, 2, 3, 7
F14201	1096.95	F,D,L	DMSO	456	26,000	see Notes	MeOH					F14200		8
F14202	1096.95	F,D,L	DMSO	456	26,000	see Notes	MeOH					F14200		8
F14203	958.06	D,L	pH >6	491	72,000	see Notes	H_2O	493	74,000	518	H_2O/Ca^{2+}		90 µM	1, 2, 6, 7
F14204	1127.92	F,D,L	DMSO	456	26,000	see Notes	MeOH					F14203		8
F14217	1096.95	F,D,L	DMSO	456	26,000	see Notes	MeOH					F14200		8, 9
F14218	1129.86	F,D,L	DMSO	464	26,000	see Notes	MeOH					F1240		8, 9
F14219	808.98	F,D,L	pH >6, MeOH	473	29,000	670	H_2O	436	41,000	655	H_2O/Ca^{2+}		140 nM	1, 2, 3, 10
F14221	931.05	D,L	pH >6	491	71,000	see Notes	H_2O	494	74,000	518	H_2O/Ca^{2+}		2.3 µM	1, 2, 6, 7
F14222	1100.92	F,D,L	DMSO	456	24,000	see Notes	MeOH					F14221		8
F14242	1129.86	F,D,L	DMSO	464	26,000	see Notes	MeOH					F1240		8
F23915	1129.86	F,D,L	DMSO	464	26,000	see Notes	MeOH					F1240		8, 11
F23917	1096.95	F,D,L	DMSO	456	26,000	see Notes	MeOH					F14200		8, 11
F23980	949.04	D,L	pH >6	491	72,000	see Notes	H_2O	494	75,000	516	H_2O/Ca^{2+}		9.7 µM	1, 2, 6, 7
F23981	1118.91	F,D,L	DMSO	456	25,000	see Notes	MeOH					F23980		8
F36200	1223.19	F,D,L	pH >6	492	72,000	see Notes	H_2O	494	76,000	518	H_2O/Ca^{2+}		950 nM	1, 2, 3, 7, 12, 13
F36201	1055.26	F,D,L	pH >6	491	74,000	see Notes	H_2O	494	78,000	518	H_2O/Ca^{2+}		950 nM	1, 2, 3, 7
M3733	915.90	L	pH >6	506	77,000	531	H_2O	506	77,000	531	H_2O/Ca^{2+}		6 µM	1, 2, 4, 6

				Low Ca^{2+}				High Ca^{2+}						
Cat #	**MW**	**Storage**	**Soluble**	**Abs**	**EC**	**Em**	**Solvent**	**Abs**	**EC**	**Em**	**Solvent**	**Product**	**K_d**	**Notes**
M3735	1025.71	F,D	DMSO	302	16,000	none	MeOH					M3733		
M14205	681.77	D,L	pH >6	490	74,000	see Notes	H_2O	493	75,000	517	H_2O/Ca^{2+}		22 μM	1, 2, 6, 7
M14206	817.66	F,D,L	DMSO	457	25,000	see Notes	MeOH					M14205		8
M14213	623.74	D,L	pH >6	547	68,000	see Notes	H_2O	549	69,000	578	H_2O/Ca^{2+}		70 μM	1, 2, 6, 7
M14214	844.67	F,D,L	DMSO	553	98,000	570	$CHCl_3$					M14213		8
M14215	727.90	D,L	pH >6	575	82,000	see Notes	H_2O	578	82,000	602	H_2O/Ca^{2+}		45 μM	1, 2, 6, 7
M14216	948.82	F,D,L	DMSO	576	122,000	597	MeOH					M14215		8
O6806	1114.28	D,L	pH >6	494	76,000	523	H_2O	494	78,000	523	H_2O/Ca^{2+}		170 nM	1, 2, 3, 4
O6807	1258.07	F,D	DMSO	299	19,000	none	EtOAc					O6806		
O6808	1599.77	F,D,L	pH >6	494	105,000	523	H_2O	494	140,000	523	H_2O/Ca^{2+}		580 nM	1, 2, 3, 4
O6809	1751.45	F,D,L	DMSO	299	31,000	none	MeOH					O6808		
O6812	1159.28	F,D,L	pH >6	494	72,000	521	H_2O	494	76,000	521	H_2O/Ca^{2+}		20 μM	1, 2, 4, 6
O6813	1303.07	F,D,L	DMSO	300	17,000	none	MeOH					O6812		
O23990	1132.27	D,L	pH >6	494	75,000	523	H_2O	494	77,000	523	H_2O/Ca^{2+}		3 μM	1, 2, 4, 6
O23991	1276.06	F,D,L	DMSO	300	18,000	none	EtOAc					O23990		
R1244	1123.96	F,D,L	DMSO	550	125,000	571	see Notes					R14220		14
R1245MP	1123.96	F,D,L	DMSO	550	125,000	571	see Notes					R14220		14
R14207	900.03	D,L	pH >6	549	64,000	see Notes	H_2O	551	63,000	577	H_2O/Ca^{2+}		320 μM	1, 2, 7, 15
R14208	1154.93	F,D,L	DMSO	552	103,000	570	$CHCl_3$					R14207		
R14220	869.06	D,L	pH >6	548	91,000	see Notes		552	96,000	578	H_2O/Ca^{2+}		570 nM	1, 2, 3, 7
R23982	891.02	D,L	pH >6	548	73,000	see Notes	H_2O	552	78,000	577	H_2O/Ca^{2+}		19 μM	1, 2, 6, 7
R23983	1145.91	F,D,L	DMSO	551	104,000	566	$CHCl_3$					R23982		
X14209	973.21	D,L	pH >6	576	88,000	see Notes	H_2O	580	92,000	602	H_2O/Ca^{2+}		700 nM	1, 2, 3, 7
X14210	1228.11	F,D,L	DMSO	578	133,000	596	$CHCl_3$					X14209		
X14211	1004.19	D,L	pH >6	580	76,000	see Notes	H_2O	581	78,000	602	H_2O/Ca^{2+}		350 μM	1, 2, 7, 15
X14212	1259.08	F,D,L	DMSO	579	114,000	594	see Notes					X14211		14
X23984	977.18	D,L	pH >6	576	73,000	see Notes	H_2O	580	73,000	602	H_2O/Ca^{2+}		1.6 μM	1, 2, 6, 7
X23985	1232.07	F,D,L	DMSO	578	92,000	590	$CHCl_3$					X23984		
X23987	1250.06	F,D,L	DMSO	577	97,000	590	$CHCl_3$					X23986		

For definitions of the contents of this data table, see "Navigating *The Handbook*" in the introductory pages.

Notes

1. Dissociation constants are known to vary considerably depending on the temperature, pH, ionic strength, viscosity, protein binding, presence of other ions (especially polyvalent ions), instrument setup and other factors. It is strongly recommended that these values be verified under user-specific experimental conditions.
2. Spectra measured in aqueous buffers containing 10 mM EGTA (H_2O) or a >10-fold excess of free Ca^{2+} relative to the K_d (H_2O/Ca^{2+}).
3. Dissociation constant determined at Molecular Probes by fluorescence measurements in 100 mM KCl, 10 mM MOPS, pH 7.2, 0 to 39 μM free Ca^{2+} at 22°C.
4. This indicator exhibits fluorescence enhancement in response to ion binding, with essentially no change in absorption or emission wavelengths.
5. Acetoxymethyl ester hydrolysis yields Calcium Crimson™ indicator, Abs = 589 nm (EC = 92,000 $cm^{-1}M^{-1}$), Em = 615 nm in 100 mM KCl, 10 mM MOPS, pH 7.2 containing 39.8 μM free Ca^{2+}. $K_d(Ca^{2+})$ for the free indicator is 185 nM.
6. Dissociation constant determined at Molecular Probes by fluorescence measurements in 100 mM KCl, 10 mM MOPS pH 7.2, 0 to 1 mM free Ca^{2+} at 22°C.
7. Fluorescence of the free indicator is very weak and is enhanced >100-fold on binding Ca^{2+}.
8. Fluorescence of this AM ester derivative is very weak and is enhanced only after hydrolytic cleavage followed by binding of divalent cations to the anionic indicator.
9. This product is supplied as a ready-made solution in the solvent indicated under "Soluble."
10. The fluorescence quantum yield of Fura Red™ is low (~0.013 in Ca^{2+}-free solution) (Methods Cell Biol 40, 155 (1994)).
11. This product is specified to equal or exceed 98% analytical purity by HPLC.
12. Aqueous stock solutions should be used within 24 hours; long-term storage is NOT recommended.
13. Iodoacetamides in solution undergo rapid photodecomposition to unreactive products. Minimize exposure to light prior to reaction.
14. Spectra measured in 90:10 (v/v) $CHCl_3$:MeOH.
15. Dissociation constant determined at Molecular Probes by fluorescence measurements in 100 mM KCl, 10 mM MOPS pH 7.2, 0 to 10 mM free Ca^{2+} at 22°C.

Product List — 19.3 Fluorescent Ca^{2+} Indicators Excited with Visible Light

Cat #	Product Name	Unit Size
C3018	Calcium Crimson™, AM *cell permeant* *special packaging*	10 x 50 µg
C3011MP	Calcium Green™-1, AM *cell permeant*	500 µg
C3012	Calcium Green™-1, AM *cell permeant* *special packaging*	10 x 50 µg
C3010MP	Calcium Green™-1, hexapotassium salt *cell impermeant*	500 µg
C3732	Calcium Green™-2, AM *cell permeant* *special packaging*	10 x 50 µg
C3730	Calcium Green™-2, octapotassium salt *cell impermeant*	500 µg
C3739	Calcium Green™-5N, AM *cell permeant* *special packaging*	10 x 50 µg
C3737	Calcium Green™-5N, hexapotassium salt *cell impermeant*	500 µg
C3015	Calcium Orange™, AM *cell permeant* *special packaging*	10 x 50 µg
C3013	Calcium Orange™, tetrapotassium salt *cell impermeant*	500 µg
C6771	Calcium Orange™-5N, AM *cell permeant* *special packaging*	10 x 50 µg
F1241	fluo-3, AM *cell permeant*	1 mg
F1242	fluo-3, AM *cell permeant* *special packaging*	20 x 50 µg
F23915	fluo-3, AM *FluoroPure™ grade* *special packaging*	10 x 50 µg
F14218	fluo-3, AM *1 mM solution in DMSO* *cell permeant*	1 mL
F14242	fluo-3, AM *packaged for high-throughput screening*	40 x 1 mg
F1240	fluo-3, pentaammonium salt *cell impermeant*	1 mg
F3715	fluo-3, pentapotassium salt *cell impermeant*	1 mg
F14201	fluo-4, AM *cell permeant* *special packaging*	10 x 50 µg
F23917	fluo-4, AM *FluoroPure™ grade* *special packaging*	10 x 50 µg
F14217	fluo-4, AM *1 mM solution in DMSO* *cell permeant*	500 µL
F14202	fluo-4, AM *packaged for high-throughput screening*	5 x 1 mg
F14200	fluo-4, pentapotassium salt *cell impermeant*	500 µg
F23981	fluo-4FF, AM *cell permeant* *special packaging*	10 x 50 µg
F23980	fluo-4FF, pentapotassium salt *cell impermeant*	500 µg
F14222	fluo-5F, AM *cell permeant* *special packaging*	10 x 50 µg
F14221	fluo-5F, pentapotassium salt *cell impermeant*	500 µg
F14204	fluo-5N, AM *cell permeant* *special packaging*	10 x 50 µg
F14203	fluo-5N, pentapotassium salt *cell impermeant*	500 µg
F36201	fluo-4 cadaverine, pentapotassium salt	500 µg
F36200	fluo-4 iodoacetamide, pentapotassium salt	500 µg
F3020	Fura Red™, AM *cell permeant*	500 µg
F3021	Fura Red™, AM *cell permeant* *special packaging*	10 x 50 µg
F14219	Fura Red™, tetrapotassium salt *cell impermeant*	500 µg
M14206	mag-fluo-4, AM *cell permeant* *special packaging*	10 x 50 µg
M14205	mag-fluo-4, tetrapotassium salt *cell impermeant*	500 µg
M3735	Magnesium Green™, AM *cell permeant* *special packaging*	20 x 50 µg
M3733	Magnesium Green™, pentapotassium salt *cell impermeant*	1 mg
M14214	mag-rhod-2, AM *cell permeant* *special packaging*	10 x 50 µg
M14213	mag-rhod-2, dipotassium salt *cell impermeant*	500 µg
M14216	mag-X-rhod-1, AM *cell permeant* *special packaging*	10 x 50 µg
M14215	mag-X-rhod-1, dipotassium salt *cell impermeant*	500 µg
O6807	Oregon Green® 488 BAPTA-1, AM *cell permeant* *special packaging*	10 x 50 µg
O6806	Oregon Green® 488 BAPTA-1, hexapotassium salt *cell impermeant*	500 µg
O6809	Oregon Green® 488 BAPTA-2, AM *cell permeant* *special packaging*	10 x 50 µg
O6808	Oregon Green® 488 BAPTA-2, octapotassium salt *cell impermeant*	500 µg
O6813	Oregon Green® 488 BAPTA-5N, AM *cell permeant* *special packaging*	10 x 50 µg
O6812	Oregon Green® 488 BAPTA-5N, hexapotassium salt *cell impermeant*	500 µg
O23991	Oregon Green® 488 BAPTA-6F, AM *cell permeant* *special packaging*	10 x 50 µg
O23990	Oregon Green® 488 BAPTA-6F, hexapotassium salt *cell impermeant*	500 µg
R1244	rhod-2, AM *cell permeant*	1 mg
R1245MP	rhod-2, AM *cell permeant* *special packaging*	20 x 50 µg
R14220	rhod-2, tripotassium salt *cell impermeant*	1 mg
R23983	rhod-FF, AM *cell permeant* *special packaging*	10 x 50 µg
R23982	rhod-FF, tripotassium salt *cell impermeant*	500 µg
R14208	rhod-5N, AM *cell permeant* *special packaging*	10 x 50 µg
R14207	rhod-5N, tripotassium salt *cell impermeant*	500 µg
X14210	X-rhod-1, AM *cell permeant* *special packaging*	10 x 50 µg
X14209	X-rhod-1, tripotassium salt *cell impermeant*	500 µg
X23985	X-rhod-5F, AM *cell permeant* *special packaging*	10 x 50 µg
X23984	X-rhod-5F, tripotassium salt *cell impermeant*	500 µg
X14212	X-rhod-5N, AM *cell permeant* *special packaging*	10 x 50 µg
X14211	X-rhod-5N, tripotassium salt *cell impermeant*	500 µg
X23987	X-rhod-FF, AM *cell permeant* *special packaging*	10 x 50 µg

For current prices or to order online, visit probes.invitrogen.com

19.4 Fluorescent Ca^{2+} Indicator Conjugates

Dextran Conjugates

When ion indicators are loaded into cells as their acetoxymethyl (AM) esters, they may translocate to intracellular compartments, where they are still fluorescent but no longer respond to changes in cytosolic ion levels.[1,2] This problem frequently limits the experiment's duration because sequestration of the indicator into organelles will cause errors in the estimated cytosolic ion levels. Furthermore, Ca^{2+} indicators such as fura-2 and indo-1 may bind to cellular proteins,[1–5] which can markedly alter the indicator's response to Ca^{2+} (Table 19.2).

To overcome these limitations, Molecular Probes has prepared dextran conjugates of some of its ion indicators[6] (Table 19.1). Dextrans are hydrophilic polysaccharides characterized by their moderate to high molecular weight, good water solubility and low toxicity. They are also biologically inert due to their uncommon poly-(α-D-1,6-glucose) linkages, which render them resistant to cleavage by most endogenous cellular glycosidases. Indicator dextrans must be loaded into cells by microinjection, whole-cell patch clamping, microprojectile bombardment[7,8] or electroporation,[9] or by using our Influx™ pinocytic cell-loading reagent (I14402, Section 19.8, Figure 19.100). Dextran conjugates above ~2000 MW are well retained in viable cells, will not pass through gap junctions and are less likely to become compartmentalized.[10,11] Also, fluorescence photobleaching measurements have shown that, as compared with low molecular weight dyes, dextran conjugates are much less likely to bind to proteins.[12] Because dextran conjugates are intrinsically polydisperse and their degree of substitution may vary with the production lot, the Ca^{2+} dissociation constant of each lot of these indicators should be calibrated independently using one of our Calcium Calibration Buffer Kits (Section 19.8).

Fura and Indo Dextrans

Molecular Probes' patented dextran conjugates of fura and indo tend to remain in the cytosol without compartmentalization or leakage and are less likely to bind to cellular proteins, making them useful for long-term Ca^{2+} measurements.[13] Although the spectral response curves of the conjugates are very similar to those of the free dyes, their affinity for Ca^{2+} is somewhat weaker. The dissociation constants for Ca^{2+} of the fura and indo dextrans in the absence of Mg^{2+} vary between 200 nM and 400 nM,[14] depending on the molecular weight of the dextran and individual batch characteristics.

Dye compartmentalization has been especially problematic for measurements of ions in plant cells, where the dye is frequently transported out of the cytosol in minutes. Unlike microinjected fura-2 salt, fura dextran is retained for hours in the cytosol of stamen hair cells and *Lilium* pollen tubes[15] (Figure 19.56). A comparison of the dextran conjugates of fura and Calcium Green™ with conventional indicators for imaging Ca^{2+} levels in plant and fungal cells has been published.[16] Fura dextran has been used to monitor Ca^{2+} levels in a wide variety of cells, including:

- *Dictyostelium discoideum*, where it was used for long-term Ca^{2+} measurements[13,17]
- Fertilized bovine eggs,[18] rabbit eggs,[19] chicken eggs[20] and *Fucus* eggs[21]
- Frog skeletal muscle fibers[22]
- Growing unicells of green algae[23–25]
- Isolated liver nuclei, where fura dextran is uniformly distributed in the nucleoplasm[26,27]
- Mouse neuroblastoma cells, where fura dextran has been used to determine the effect of Ca^{2+} buffers on the propagation of Ca^{2+} waves[28]
- Plant and fungal cells[16,29]
- Retrograde-labeled chick embryo neurons[20,30]

Indo dextran has been used to measure the Ca^{2+}-feedback signal in the phototransduction cascade of vertebrate rods,[31,32] to visualize Ca^{2+} oscillations in plant cells[33] and to detect Ca^{2+} passage between fused sperm and egg cells.[34,35] Fura and indo are each available conjugated to a 10,000 MW dextran (F3029, I3032).

Calcium Green™, Oregon Green® 488 BAPTA, Fluo-4, Rhod and X-Rhod Dextrans

Molecular Probes offers 3000 MW; 10,000 MW; and 70,000 MW dextran conjugates of the Calcium Green™-1 indicator (C6765, C3713, C3714), as well as 10,000 and 70,000 MW dextran conjugates of the Oregon Green® 488 BAPTA-1 indicator (O6798, O6797) and a 10,000 MW dextran conjugate of the X-rhod-1 indicator[6] (X34675). We have also developed both low-affinity and high-affinity 10,000 MW dextran conjugates of our fluo-4 indicator (F14240, F36250) and low-affinity and high-affinity 10,000 MW dextran conjugates of our rhod

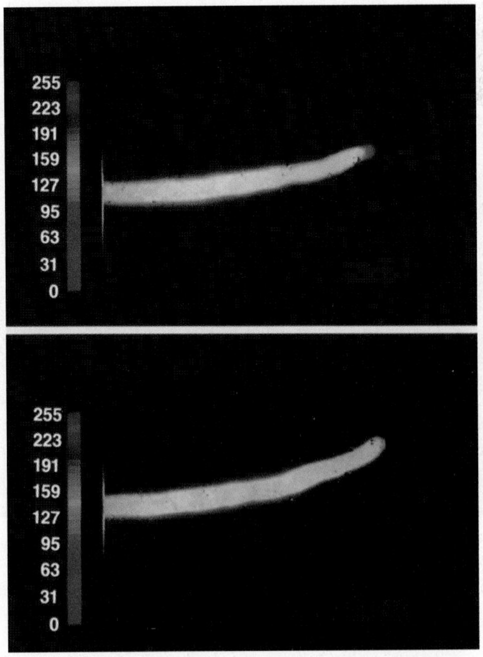

Figure 19.56 Top panel: Pseudocolored image of a pollen tube of *Lillium longiflorum* injected with fura dextran (F3029). The cell continues elongating and clearly shows a Ca^{2+} gradient. Bottom panel: The same pollen tube after injection with dibromo BAPTA (D1211) remains healthy but is no longer elongating. The images were contributed by Debra Miller, Dale Callaham, David Gross and Peter Hepler, University of Massachusetts.

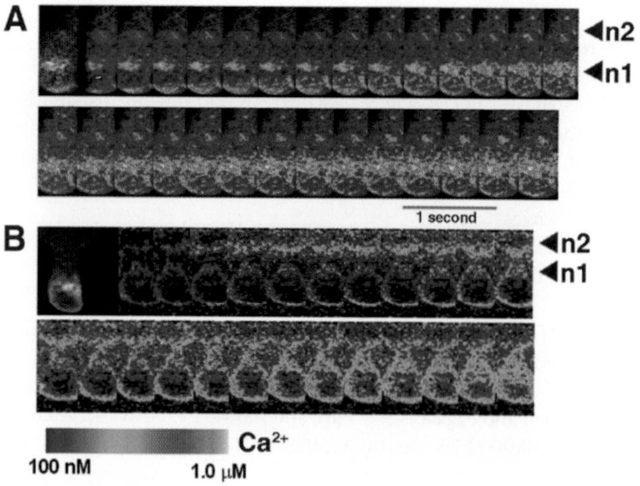

Figure 19.57 Rhizoid cells from the marine alga *Fucus serratus* were pressure-microinjected with Ca^{2+}-sensitive 10,000 MW Calcium Green™-1 dextran (C3713) and Ca^{2+}-insensitive 10,000 MW Texas Red® dextran (D1828). Patterns of Ca^{2+} elevation following hypoosmotic treatment in dividing cells were visualized by confocal ratio imaging of Calcium Green™-1 (excited at 488 nm) and Texas Red® (excited at 568 nm). Emission ratio values were pseudocolored to represent calcium concentrations according to the scale bar in the lower left-hand corner. A) Sequential ratio images during the onset of a hypoosmotically induced (100% seawater to 50% seawater) Ca^{2+} wave shows an initial elevation of Ca^{2+} in the rhizoid apex, which declines before the onset of Ca^{2+} elevation arising in the apical nucleus (n1) region. B) A variation in this pattern was evident in a minority of cells where Ca^{2+} elevations were observed to arise in the subapical nucleus (n2) simultaneously with the apical Ca^{2+} elevation. The image was contributed by Colin Brownlee, Marine Biological Association of the United Kingdom, Plymouth, UK, and reproduced with permission from Proc Natl Acad Sci U S A 97, 1932 (2000).

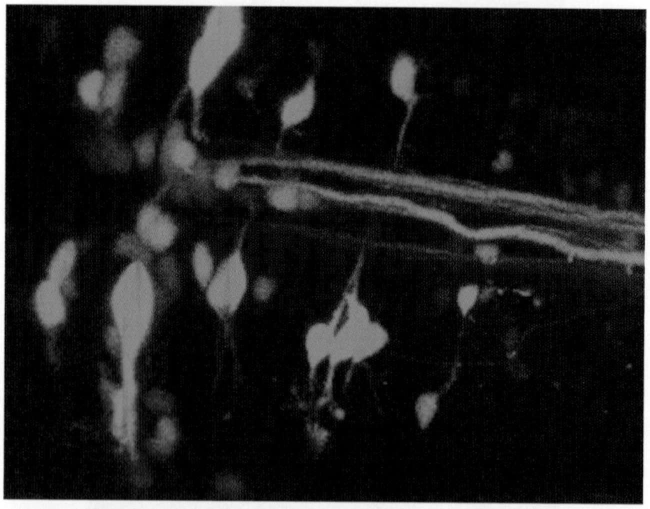

Figure 19.58 Reticulospinal neurons in the hindbrain of a live zebrafish labeled with 10,000 MW Calcium Green™-1 dextran (C3713) and optically sectioned in a Bio-Rad MRC 600 confocal laser-scanning microscope. Image contributed by D.M. O'Malley and J.R. Fetcho, SUNY at Stony Brook.

indicator[6] (R34677, R34676). Table 19.1 provides a complete list of our Ca^{2+} indicator dextran conjugates.

The 3000 MW Calcium Green™ dextran conjugate (C6765) is actively transported in adult nerve fibers over a significant distance and is retained in presynaptic terminals in a form that allows monitoring of presynaptic Ca^{2+} levels.[36] A review by Read and co-workers compares the Calcium Green™-1 and fura dextrans with conventional indicators for imaging Ca^{2+} levels in plant and fungal cells.[16] The Calcium Green™ dextran conjugates (and the other green-fluorescent Ca^{2+}-indicating dextrans) can be coinjected with red-fluorescent Texas Red® dextrans (Section 14.5, Table 14.4) to permit ratiometric measurements of Ca^{2+} flux in cells that can be microinjected, including oocytes[37,38] (Figure 19.57). Spectra of the Oregon Green® 488 BAPTA-1 dextrans and fluo-4 dextrans match the 488 nm spectral line of the argon-ion laser and standard fluorescein optical filters (Table 23.9) better than do dextran conjugates of the Calcium Green™-1 indicator, which should permit the use of lower probe concentrations to achieve the same signal. The red-orange–fluorescent rhod dextrans, which exhibit a 50-fold fluorescence enhancement upon Ca^{2+} binding, are valuable for multicolor applications and for experiments in cells and tissues that have high levels of autofluorescence.

The visible light–excitable Calcium Green™-1 and Oregon Green® 488 BAPTA-1 indicator dextrans have been used to:

- Monitor presynaptic Ca^{2+} dynamics in projection fibers[39]
- Label neurons via retrograde or anterograde transport, allowing real-time imaging of neuronal activity[30,40–42] (Figure 19.58)
- Visualize fertilization-induced Ca^{2+} waves in starfish eggs[43] (Figure 19.59)
- Detect changes in Ca^{2+} levels during cell cleavage in mouse[44] and zebrafish[45] embryos
- Monitor Ca^{2+}-regulated exocytosis[46] and caffeine-induced Ca^{2+} release[47] in sea urchin eggs and embryos
- Assay Ca^{2+} influx in taste receptors responding to bitter stimuli[48]
- Detect changes in intraciliary Ca^{2+}-controlling ciliary motility in the ctenophore *Mnemiopsis leidyi*[49]

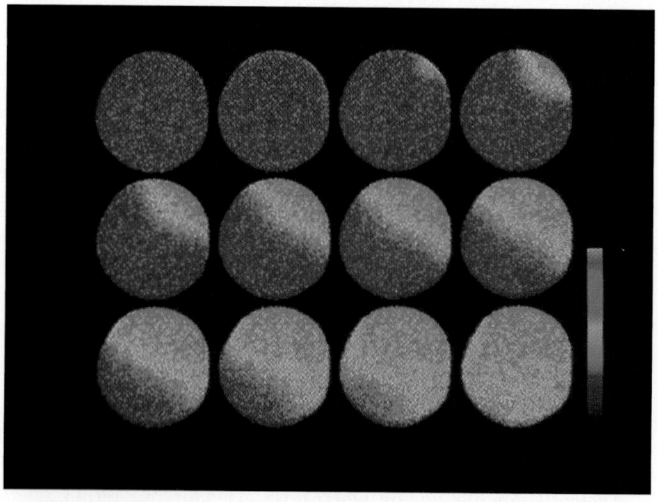

Figure 19.59 Confocal images taken at five-second intervals of a fertilization-induced calcium wave in a *Pisaster ochraceus* starfish oocyte that was microinjected with 10,000 MW Calcium Green™-1 dextran (C3713). The image was contributed by Stephen A. Stricker, University of New Mexico.

- Investigate NMDA receptor–mediated control of presynaptic Ca^{2+} [50]
- Detect depletion of Ca^{2+} stores in organelles of yeast and mammalian cells [51]
- Examine the regulation of size-specific entry of molecules into the *Xenopus* oocyte nucleus by the nuclear Ca^{2+} store [52]
- Investigate the role of gibberellic and abscisic acids on Ca^{2+}-modulated secretion in barley aleurone protoplasts [53]
- Detect transmission of changes in cytosolic Ca^{2+} levels to the nucleus by the nuclear membrane [54]
- Simultaneously detect Ca^{2+} and catecholamine exocytosis when immobilized on a fiber optic sensor [55]
- Monitor changes in intracellular free Ca^{2+} accompanying photolysis of diazo-2, caged EGTA, caged EDTA or other caged Ca^{2+} probes [56–58] (Section 19.8)

In mammalian presynaptic terminals, the response of Calcium Green™-1 dextran to successive electrical stimuli progressively weakens due to Ca^{2+}-binding saturation (Figure 19.60). To solve this problem, we have synthesized fluo-4 dextran (F14240) with a lower Ca^{2+} binding affinity (a batch-dependent K_d for Ca^{2+} ~3 µM). Developed in collaboration with Wade Regehr's laboratory at Harvard University, the low-affinity fluo-4 dextran is a potentially valuable tool for recording Ca^{2+} transients in presynaptic terminals of long axonal projections in heterogeneous fiber tracts.[39] We also offer a high-affinity fluo-4 dextran (K_d for Ca^{2+} ~600 nM, F36250). Coinjection of fluo-4 dextran together with a reference marker (e.g., 10,000 MW Texas Red® dextran, D1828; Section 14.5) may be necessary for initial identification of labeled cells due to the intrinsically weak fluorescence of the fluo-4 indicator in the absence of Ca^{2+}.[39]

The lack of a ratiometric Ca^{2+} response (see Note 19.1 "Technical Focus: Loading and Calibration of Intracellular Ion Indicators" in Section 19.1) among the visible light–excitable indicator dextrans can be partially circumvented by co-loading Ca^{2+}-insensitive reference markers. Mixtures of Calcium Green™ dextran and Ca^{2+}-insensitive dextrans (such as the tetramethylrhodamine or Texas Red® dextrans in Section 14.5) have been co-loaded into cells for use in ratio-imaging microscopy[45,53,59–61] (Figure 19.100).

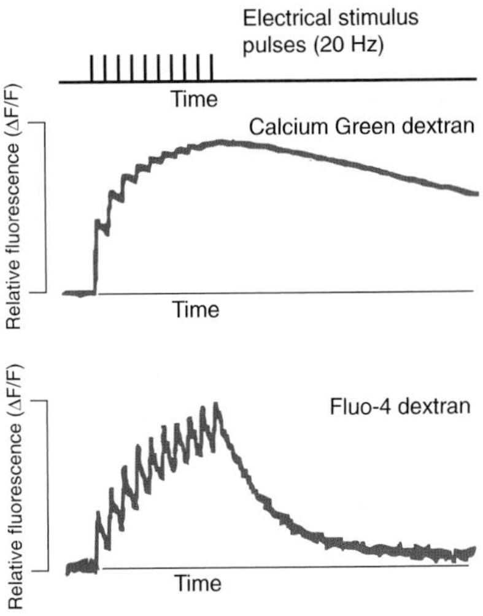

Figure 19.60 Ca^{2+} transients in rat climbing fiber presynaptic terminals evoked by sequences of 10 applied electrical stimulus pulses (20 Hz) monitored by 10,000 MW Calcium Green™-1 dextran (C3713) (upper panel) and the low-affinity version of fluo-4 dextran (F14240) (lower panel). Each trace represents an average of five recordings. Adapted with permission from Neuron 27, 25 (2000).

Lipophilic Derivatives for Detecting Near-Membrane Calcium

Changes in intracellular Ca^{2+} levels often involve Ca^{2+} ions moving through channels and transporters in the plasma membrane.[62,63] Consequently, Ca^{2+} concentrations at the inner-membrane surface may, at least transiently, reach levels markedly different from those in the cytosol. One approach to detecting these localized concentration changes is to use fluorescent indicators that bind to membrane surfaces and selectively respond to Ca^{2+} changes only in the immediate vicinity. Two such lipophilic Ca^{2+} indicators — fura-C_{18} (F6792) and fura-FF-C_{18} (F24051) — are available.

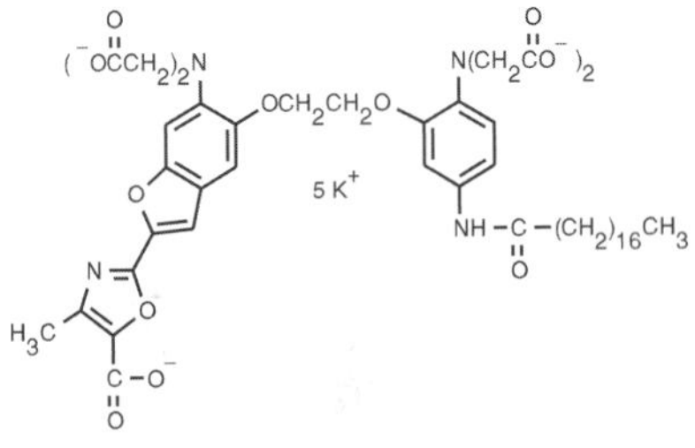

Figure 19.61 F6792 fura-C_{18}, pentapotassium salt.

Fura-C_{18} and Fura-FF-C_{18}

Fura-C_{18} (F6792, Figure 19.61) and fura-FF-C_{18} (F24051, Figure 19.62) are lipophilic Ca^{2+} indicators that preferentially associate with cell membranes. Etter and colleagues have described the use of our fura-C_{18} to investigate changes in near-membrane Ca^{2+} levels in isolated smooth muscle cells upon membrane depolarization.[64] Their results suggest that this lipophilic Ca^{2+} indicator can be used to resolve localized changes in Ca^{2+} concentration that cannot be detected with indicators distributed throughout the cytosol. Fura-C_{18} has also been used to measure Ca^{2+} changes associated with uncoupling of gap-junctional communication in microinjected *Xenopus* oocytes.[65] Fura-C_{18} and fura-FF-C_{18} have spectral properties similar to fura-2, except that fura-FF-C_{18} is sensitive to much higher Ca^{2+} concentrations than fura-C_{18}. Ion-binding dissociation constants for these indicators are dependent on membrane-surface electrostatic potentials.

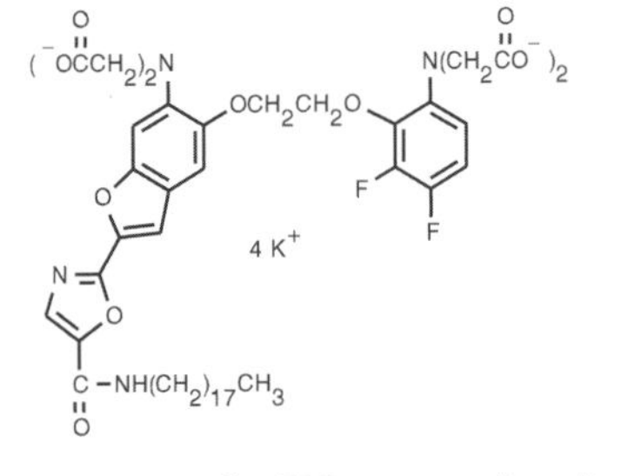

Figure 19.62 F24051 fura-FF-C_{18}, tetrapotassium salt.

Reactive Fluo-4 Derivatives for Creating Ca^{2+} Indicator Conjugates

To create unique fluorescent Ca^{2+}-sensitive probes, we offer the thiol-reactive fluo-4 iodoacetamide (F36200, Section 19.3), which can react with sulfhydryl groups on proteins, peptides and thiol-modified surfaces, as well as the amine-containing fluo-4 cadaverine (F36201, Section 19.3), which can react with aldehydes, ketones and activated esters.

References

1. Biophys J 58, 1491 (1990); **2.** Cell Calcium 11, 63 (1990); **3.** Biophys J 67, 1646 (1994); **4.** Biophys J 65, 865 (1993); **5.** Cell Calcium 13, 59 (1992); **6.** J Neurophysiol 92, 591 (2004); **7.** J Neurosci Methods 119, 37 (2002); **8.** Nature 418, 177 (2002); **9.** Biophys J 73, 1785 (1997); **10.** J Exp Biol 196, 419 (1994); **11.** Methods Cell Biol 29, 59 (1989); **12.** J Cell Physiol 141, 410 (1989); **13.** Eur J Cell Biol 58, 172 (1992); **14.** K_d values for Ca^{2+} are determined at Molecular Probes at ~22°C using our Calcium Calibration Buffer Kits; **15.** J Cell Sci 101, 7 (1992); **16.** J Microsc 166, 57 (1992); **17.** Cell Calcium 22, 65 (1997); **18.** Biol Reprod 47, 960 (1992); **19.** Dev Biol 166, 634 (1994); **20.** J Neurosci 14, 6354 (1994); **21.** Development 120, 155 (1994); **22.** J Gen Physiol 111, 505 (1998); **23.** J Exp Biol 49, 1761 (1998); **24.** Plant Physiol 117, 545 (1998); **25.** Eur J Cell Biol 67, 363 (1995); **26.** J Lipid Mediat Cell Signal 17, 167 (1997); **27.** Cell 80, 439 (1995); **28.** Biophys J 69, 1683 (1995); **29.** Cell 85, 673 (1996); **30.** J Neurosci Methods 46, 91 (1993); **31.** Neuron 17, 323 (1996); **32.** Neuron 13, 849 (1994); **33.** Biochem Biophys Res Commun 234, 690 (1997); **34.** Development 125, 4627 (1998); **35.** Biophys J 75, 2079 (1998); **36.** Neurosci Lett 258, 124 (1998); **37.** Development 125, 4099 (1998); **38.** Proc Natl Acad Sci U S A 97, 1932 (2000); **39.** Neuron 27, 25 (2000); **40.** Brain Res 663, 61 (1994); **41.** J Neurophysiol 73, 399 (1995); **42.** J Neurosci Methods 72, 97 (1997); **43.** J Cell Biol 138, 1303 (1997); **44.** J Cell Biol 132, 915 (1996); **45.** J Cell Biol 131, 1539 (1995); **46.** J Cell Biol 131, 1747 (1995); **47.** Dev Biol 161, 370 (1994); **48.** Science 291, 1557 (2001); **49.** J Cell Biol 125, 1127 (1994); **50.** J Neurosci 19, 193 (1999); **51.** Proc Natl Acad Sci U S A 96, 121 (1999); **52.** Science 270, 1835 (1995); **53.** Proc Natl Acad Sci U S A 89, 3591 (1992); **54.** Nature 367, 745 (1994); **55.** Anal Chem 70, 1677 (1998); **56.** Cell 92, 193 (1998); **57.** Cell Calcium 22, 5 (1997); **58.** Biotechniques 23, 268 (1997); **59.** Biotechniques 29, 492 (2000); **60.** Biol Bull 187, 234 (1994); **61.** Dev Biol 170, 496 (1995); **62.** Endocrinology 132, 2176 (1993); **63.** J Immunol 150, 2620 (1993); **64.** J Biol Chem 269, 10141 (1994); **65.** Pflugers Arch 431, 379 (1996).

Data Table — 19.4 Fluorescent Ca^{2+} Indicator Conjugates

				Low Ca^{2+}				High Ca^{2+}					
Cat #	MW	Storage	Soluble	Abs	EC	Em	Solvent	Abs	EC	Em	Solvent	K_d	Notes
C3713	see Notes	F,D,L	H_2O	508	ND	533	H_2O	508	ND	533	H_2O/Ca^{2+}	260 nM	1, 2, 3, 4, 5, 6, 7
C3714	see Notes	F,D,L	H_2O	510	ND	535	H_2O	510	ND	535	H_2O/Ca^{2+}	240 nM	1, 2, 3, 4, 5, 6, 7
C6765	see Notes	F,D,L	H_2O	510	ND	535	H_2O	510	ND	535	H_2O/Ca^{2+}	540 nM	1, 2, 3, 4, 5, 6, 7
C6766	see Notes	F,D,L	H_2O	509	ND	534	H_2O	509	ND	534	H_2O/Ca^{2+}	310 nM	1, 2, 3, 4, 5, 6, 7
F3029	see Notes	F,D,L	H_2O	364	ND	501	H_2O	338	ND	494	H_2O/Ca^{2+}	240 nM	1, 2, 3, 4, 5, 7
F6792	1113.48	D,L	pH >6	365	25,000	501	H_2O	338	30,000	494	H_2O/Ca^{2+}	150 nM	1, 2, 8
F14240	see Notes	F,D,L	H_2O	493	ND	see Notes	H_2O	495	ND	518	H_2O/Ca^{2+}	3.0 µM	1, 2, 3, 5, 7, 9, 10
F24051	1067.36	D,L	DMSO	366	24,000	504	H_2O	337	29,000	495	H_2O/Ca^{2+}	ND	2, 7
F36250	see Notes	F,D,L	H_2O	493	ND	see Notes	H_2O	496	ND	518	H_2O/Ca^{2+}	600 nM	1, 2, 3, 4, 5, 7, 10
I3032	see Notes	F,D,L	H_2O	356	ND	466	H_2O	341	ND	408	H_2O/Ca^{2+}	320 nM	1, 2, 3, 4, 5, 7
I3033	see Notes	F,D,L	H_2O	352	ND	464	H_2O	340	ND	408	H_2O/Ca^{2+}	360 nM	1, 2, 3, 4, 5, 7
M24050	800.08	D,L	DMSO	365	24,000	505	H_2O	336	30,000	497	H_2O/Ca^{2+}	ND	2, 7
O6797	see Notes	F,D,L	H_2O	496	ND	524	H_2O	498	ND	524	H_2O/Ca^{2+}	225 nM	1, 2, 3, 4, 5, 6, 7
O6798	see Notes	F,D,L	H_2O	496	ND	524	H_2O	497	ND	524	H_2O/Ca^{2+}	265 nM	1, 2, 3, 4, 5, 6, 7
R34676	see Notes	F,D,L	H_2O	549	ND	see Notes	H_2O	556	ND	578	H_2O/Ca^{2+}	780 nM	1, 2, 3, 4, 5, 7, 10
R34677	see Notes	F,D,L	H_2O	548	ND	see Notes	H_2O	555	ND	579	H_2O/Ca^{2+}	5.2 µM	1, 2, 3, 5, 7, 9, 10
X34675	see Notes	F,D,L	H_2O	578	ND	see Notes	H_2O	583	ND	605	H_2O/Ca^{2+}	1.8 µM	1, 2, 3, 4, 5, 7, 10

For definitions of the contents of this data table, see "Navigating *The Handbook*" in the introductory pages.

Notes

1. Dissociation constants are known to vary considerably depending on the temperature, pH, ionic strength, viscosity, protein binding, presence of other ions (especially polyvalent ions), instrument setup and other factors. It is strongly recommended that these values be verified under user-specific experimental conditions.
2. Spectra measured in aqueous buffers containing 10 mM EGTA (H_2O) or a >10-fold excess of free Ca^{2+} relative to the K_d (H_2O/Ca^{2+}).
3. Because indicator dextran conjugates are polydisperse both in molecular weight and degree of substitution, dissociation constants and spectra may vary between batches.
4. Dissociation constant determined at Molecular Probes by fluorescence measurements in 100 mM KCl, 10 mM MOPS, pH 7.2, 0 to 39 µM free Ca^{2+} at 22°C.
5. The molecular weight is nominally as specified in the product name but may have a broad distribution.
6. This indicator exhibits fluorescence enhancement in response to ion binding, with essentially no change in absorption or emission wavelengths.
7. ND = not determined.
8. K_d value for F6792 bound to smooth muscle cell membranes (J Biol Chem 269, 10141 (1994)).
9. Dissociation constant determined at Molecular Probes by fluorescence measurements in 100 mM KCl, 10 mM MOPS pH 7.2, 0 to 1 mM free Ca^{2+} at 22°C.
10. Fluorescence of the free indicator is very weak and is enhanced >100-fold on binding Ca^{2+}.

Product List — 19.4 Fluorescent Ca^{2+} Indicator Conjugates

Cat #	Product Name	Unit Size
C6765	Calcium Green™-1 dextran, potassium salt, 3000 MW, anionic	5 mg
C3713	Calcium Green™-1 dextran, potassium salt, 10,000 MW, anionic	5 mg
C3714	Calcium Green™-1 dextran, potassium salt, 70,000 MW, anionic	5 mg
C6766	Calcium Green™-1 dextran, potassium salt, 500,000 MW, anionic	5 mg
F36250	fluo-4 dextran, potassium salt, 10,000 MW, anionic (high-affinity version)	5 mg
F14240	fluo-4 dextran, potassium salt, 10,000 MW, anionic (low-affinity version)	5 mg
F6792	fura-C_{18}, pentapotassium salt	1 mg
F3029	fura dextran, potassium salt, 10,000 MW, anionic	5 mg
F24051	fura-FF-C_{18}, tetrapotassium salt	1 mg
I3032	indo dextran, potassium salt, 10,000 MW, anionic	5 mg
I3033	indo dextran, potassium salt, 70,000 MW, anionic	5 mg
M24050	mag-fura-C_{18}, tripotassium salt	1 mg
O6798	Oregon Green® 488 BAPTA-1 dextran, potassium salt, 10,000 MW, anionic	5 mg
O6797	Oregon Green® 488 BAPTA-1 dextran, potassium salt, 70,000 MW, anionic	5 mg
R34676	rhod dextran, potassium salt, 10,000 MW, anionic (high-affinity version)	5 mg
R34677	rhod dextran, potassium salt, 10,000 MW, anionic (low-affinity version)	5 mg
X34675	X-rhod dextran, potassium salt, 10,000 MW, anionic	5 mg

For current prices or to order online, visit probes.invitrogen.com

19.5 Aequorin: A Bioluminescent Ca^{2+} Indicator

Bioluminescence is defined as the production of light by biological organisms. Because light is produced by a chemical reaction of specific photoproteins within the organism and does not require illumination, bioluminescence-based assays can be extremely sensitive and free of background. However, the intensity of light produced by bioluminescent cells is often very low, necessitating the use of image enhancement to obtain sufficient signals. A useful practical overview of bioluminescence methods for monitoring intracellular Ca^{2+} has been published.[1]

Properties and Applications of Aequorin

Molecular Probes offers a full line of reagents for quantitative Ca^{2+} measurements with aequorin, a photoprotein originally isolated from luminescent jellyfish and other marine organisms. The aequorin complex comprises a 22,000-dalton apoaequorin protein,[2] molecular oxygen and the luminophore coelenterazine[3–7] (Figure 19.63). When three Ca^{2+} ions bind to this complex, coelenterazine is oxidized to coelenteramide, with a concomitant release of carbon dioxide and blue light[8–10] (Figure 19.64, Figure 19.65). The approximately third-power dependence of aequorin's bioluminescence on Ca^{2+} concentration gives it a broad detection range, allowing the measurement of Ca^{2+} concentrations from ~0.1 µM to >100 µM.[1,11]

Unlike fluorescent Ca^{2+} indicators, Ca^{2+}-bound aequorin[12] can be detected without illuminating the sample, thereby eliminating interference from autofluorescence and allowing simultaneous labeling with caged probes[13] (Section 5.3). Moreover, aequorin that has been microinjected into eggs usually reports higher wave amplitudes (3–30 µM) than do fluorescent ion indicators.[14–17] Aequorin is not exported or secreted, nor is it compartmentalized or sequestered within cells; thus, aequorin measurements can be used to detect Ca^{2+} changes that occur over relatively long periods. In several experimental systems, aequorin's luminescence was detectable many hours to days after cell loading.[1,18,19] Aequorin also does not disrupt cell functions or embryo development[1] (Figure 19.66).

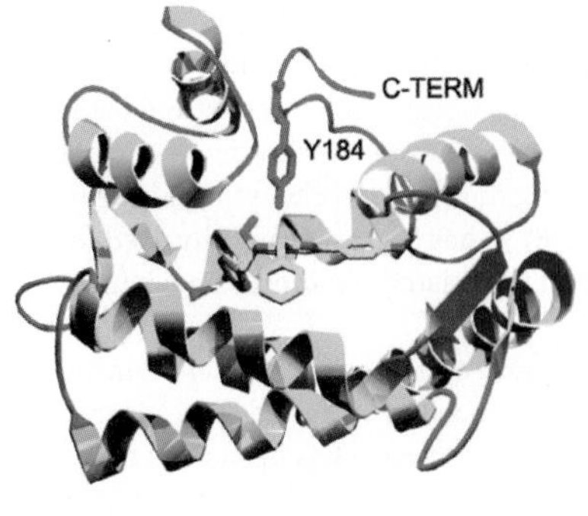

Figure 19.63 Ribbon representation of the aequorin/coelenterazine complex showing the secondary structural elements in the protein. Coelenterazine and the side chain of Tyr 184 are shown as stick representations. Reproduced with permission from Nature 405, 372 (2000).

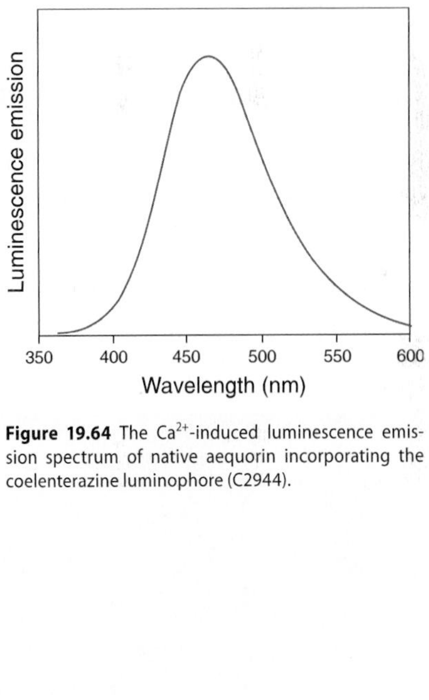

Figure 19.64 The Ca^{2+}-induced luminescence emission spectrum of native aequorin incorporating the coelenterazine luminophore (C2944).

Recombinant Aequorin

Conventional purification of aequorin from the jellyfish *Aequorea victoria* requires laborious extraction procedures and sometimes yields preparations that are substantially heterogeneous or that are toxic to the organisms under study.[20,21] Two tons of jellyfish typically yield ~125 mg of the purified photoprotein.[22] In contrast, recombinant AquaLite aequorin (A6785) is produced by purifying apoaequorin from genetically engineered *Escherichia coli*, followed by reconstitution of the aequorin complex *in vitro* with pure coelenterazine.[23] This method of preparation yields a pure, nontoxic, fully charged aequorin complex that is suitable for measuring intracellular Ca^{2+} by microinjection or other loading techniques, as well as for calibrating aequorin-based assays. Pressure injection is a commonly cited loading method, despite the fact that only large cells can

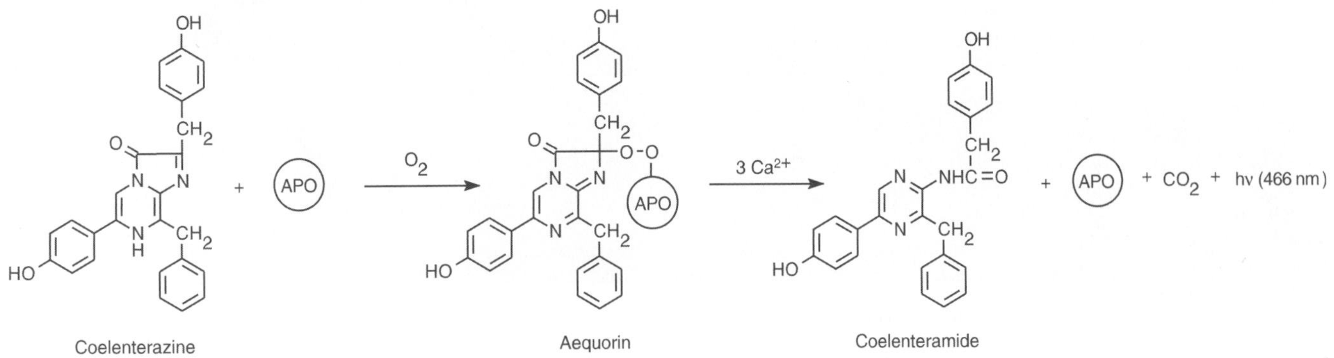

Figure 19.65 Ca^{2+}-dependent generation of luminescence by the aequorin complex, which contains apoaequorin (APO) and coelenterazine (C2944).

be loaded in this way. Pressure injection has been employed to study the effects of caffeine on mouse diaphragm muscle fibers[24] and the role of Ca^{2+} in the fertilization of sea urchin eggs.[25] Alternatively, human platelets have been transiently permeabilized to the aequorin complex with DMSO,[26] and monkey kidney cells have been loaded by hypoosmotic shock.[27] A method based on the osmotic lysis of pinocytic vesicles — a technique that can be conveniently implemented using our Influx™ pinocytic cell-loading reagent (I14402, Section 19.8) — has been successfully used for cellular loading of aequorin and the related photoprotein obelin.[28]

Because of its Ca^{2+}-dependent luminescence, the aequorin complex has been extensively used as an intracellular Ca^{2+} indicator. *Aequorea victoria* aequorin has been used to:

- Analyze the secretion response of single adrenal chromaffin cells to nicotinic cholinergic agonists[29]
- Clarify the role of Ca^{2+} release in heart muscle damage[30]
- Demonstrate the massive release of Ca^{2+} during fertilization[31]
- Study the regulation of the sarcoplasmic reticulum Ca^{2+} pump expression in developing chick myoblasts[32]
- Calibrate micropipets with injection volumes of as little as 3 picoliters[33]

Coelenterazine and Its Synthetic Analogs

Molecular Probes offers coelenterazine and several synthetic coelenterazine analogs for reconstituting aequorin in cells that have been transfected with apoaequorin cDNA. Cell permeation of coelenterazine, which has been demonstrated in organisms as diverse as *Escherichia coli*,[34] yeast,[35,36] *Dictyostelium* cells,[37] fish eggs,[38] mammalian cells[39–41] and plants,[13,42,43] is the rate-limiting step in the reconstitution process.[44] Coelenterazine is also required for generating the bioluminescent aequorin complex when using chimeric aequorin constructs.[45] Furthermore, coelenterazine and its analogs are substrates for the bioluminescent *Renilla* luciferase.[46,47]

In addition to native coelenterazine (C2944), we have synthesized five derivatives of coelenterazine that confer different Ca^{2+} affinities and spectral properties on the aequorin complex[48–50] (Table 19.4). Like native coelenterazine, these five novel derivatives can be used to reconstitute the aequorin complex both *in vivo* and *in vitro*. Recombinant apoaequorin reconstituted with coelenterazine *hcp* (C14261) is reported to have the best luminescence overall, with both a high quantum yield and a fast response time[51,52] (Table 19.4). However, intracellular re-

Table 19.4 — Coelenterazines and their properties

Cat #	Coelenterazine Analog	Em * (nm)	RLC †	Relative Intensity ‡	Half-Rise Time (msec) §
C2944	native	466	1.00	1	6–30
C14260	*cp*	442	0.63	28	2–5
C6779	*f*	472	0.80	20	6–30
C6780	*h*	466	0.75	16	6–30
C14261	*hcp*	445	0.65	500	2–5
C6776	*n*	468	0.25	0.15	6–30

* Emission maxima. † Relative luminescence capacity = total time-integrated emission of aequorin in saturating Ca^{2+} relative to native aequorin = 1.0. ‡ Relative intensity at 100 nM Ca^{2+}. § Half-rise time = time for the luminescence signal to reach 50% of the maximum after addition of 1 mM Ca^{2+} to a standard of aequorin reconstituted with the coelenterazine analog of interest. All data are from Cell Calcium 14, 373 (1993).

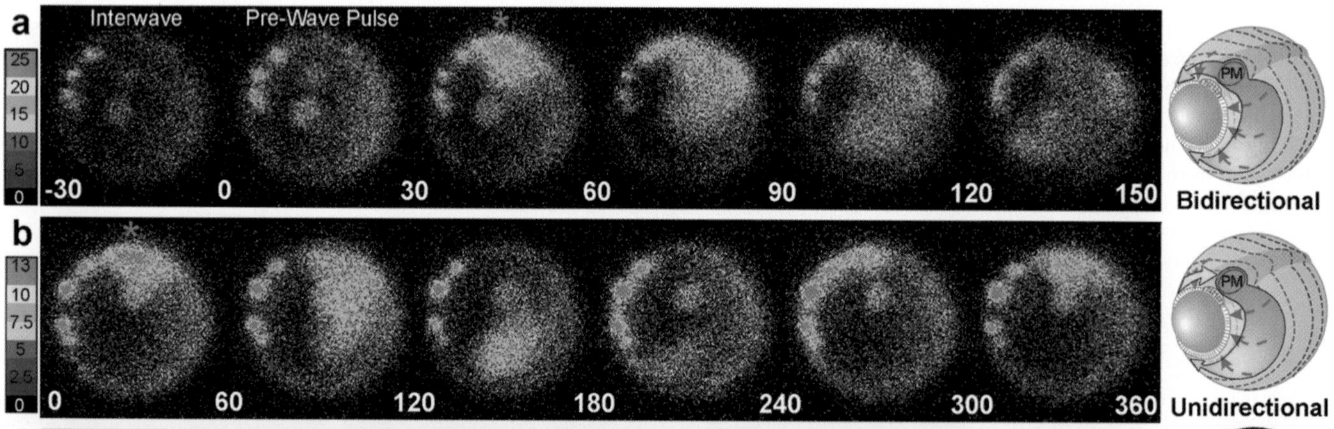

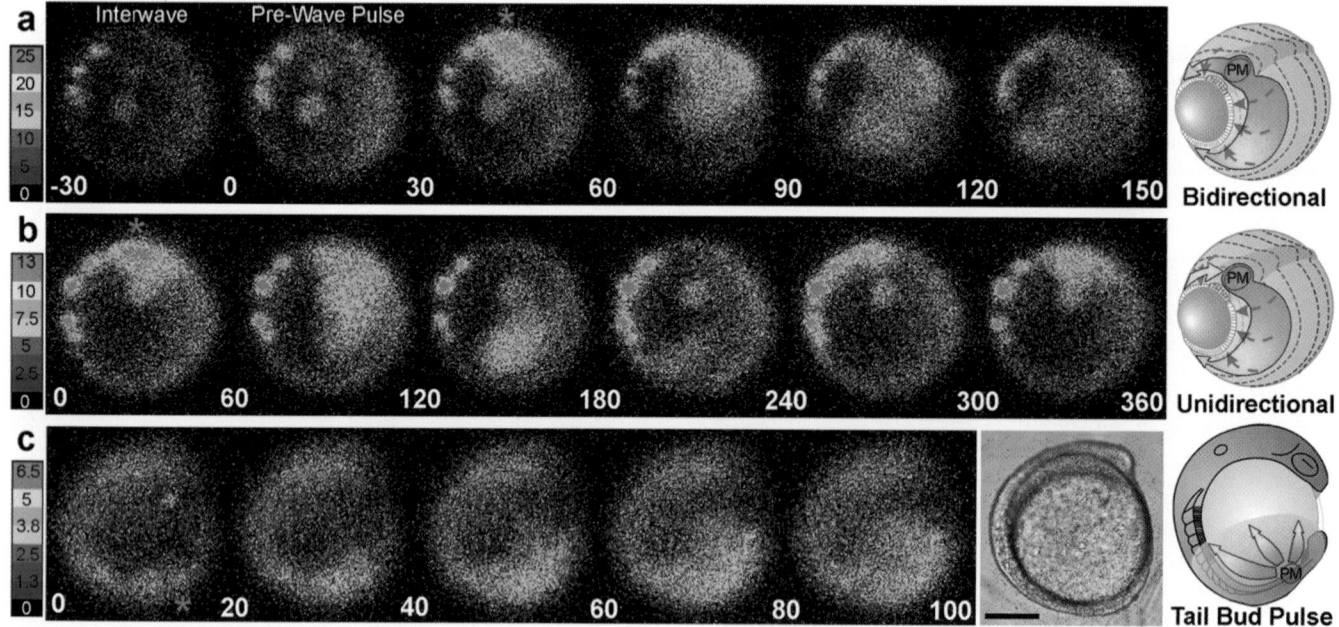

Figure 19.66 Images of Ca^{2+} waves in gastrulating zebrafish embryos detected by microinjected *f*-aequorin (recombinant aequorin reconstituted with the coelenterazine *f* luminophore (C6779)). The images are pseudocolored to represent Ca^{2+}-dependent luminescent flux in (photons/pixel/second × 10^{-2}) according to the color scales shown at the left of each of the three time-lapse image sequences (a,b,c). Time in seconds is indicated in the lower left-hand corner of each frame. The sequences depict three different spatial wave types that are represented schematically at the end of each sequence. PM indicates the dorsal midline pacemaker; its position in the luminescence images is marked by a red asterisk. The image was contributed by Edwin Gilland, Marine Biological Laboratory, Woods Hole, MA, and reproduced with permission from Proc Natl Acad Sci U S A 96, 157 (1999).

constitution of aequorin from coelenterazine analogs can be relatively slow.[49] Aequorins containing the *cp, f* or *h* form of coelenterazine (C14260, C6779, C6780) exhibit relative intensities that are reported to be 10–20 times that of apoaequorin reconstituted with native coelenterazine.[13,50,53] Coelenterazine *cp* has been used in an automated high-throughput screening assay for G-protein–coupled receptors.[54] Coelenterazine *n* (C6776) is reportedly the most useful low-sensitivity coelenterazine, producing an apoaequorin/coelenterazine *n* complex that exhibits 3000-fold lower luminescent intensity than the apoaequorin/coelenterazine *hcp* complex.[51,55] To facilitate the evaluation of the various coelenterazines, we offer a Coelenterazine Sampler Kit (C6777), which contains 25 µg samples of coelenterazine *f, h, hcp, cp* and *n,* as well as 25 µg of native coelenterazine. Coelenterazine is readily solubilized in aqueous solutions containing 50 mM hydroxypropyl-β-cyclodextrin.[56]

References

1. Methods Cell Biol 40, 305 (1994); **2.** Nature 405, 372 (2000); **3.** Trends Biotechnol 17, 477 (1999); **4.** J Biochem (Tokyo) 105, 473 (1989); **5.** J Chem Soc Chem Comm 21, 1566 (1986); **6.** Methods Enzymol 57, 271 (1978); **7.** Symp Soc Exp Biol 30, 41 (1976); **8.** J Cell Comp Physiol 62, 1 (1962); **9.** J Cell Comp Physiol 59, 223 (1962); **10.** Chem Biol 3, 337 (1996); **11.** Methods Enzymol 172, 164 (1989); **12.** Trends Biotechnol 16, 216 (1998); **13.** Cell Biol Int 17, 111 (1993); **14.** Cell Calcium 14, 736 (1993); **15.** Ann N Y Acad Sci 639, 112 (1991); **16.** Dev Biol 135, 182 (1989); **17.** Dev Biol 118, 259 (1986); **18.** Cellular Calcium: A Practical Approach, McCormack JG, Cobbold PH, Eds. pp. 1–54 (1991); **19.** J Cell Biol 115, 1259 (1991); **20.** Biochem J 270, 309 (1990); **21.** J Gen Physiol 85, 189 (1985); **22.** Biochemistry 11, 1602 (1972); **23.** Biochem Biophys Res Commun 126, 1259 (1985); **24.** Neurosci Lett 127, 28 (1991); **25.** J Cell Biol 100, 1522 (1985); **26.** Biochem Biophys Res Commun 177, 888 (1991); **27.** Am J Physiol 247, C396 (1984); **28.** Cell Calcium 6, 69 (1985); **29.** FEBS Lett 211, 44 (1987); **30.** Nature 312, 444 (1984); **31.** Proc Natl Acad Sci U S A 74, 623 (1977); **32.** Am J Physiol 251, C512 (1986); **33.** Anal Chem 69, 3115 (1997); **34.** FEBS Lett 282, 405 (1991); **35.** Biochem Biophys Res Commun 174, 115 (1991); **36.** Proc Natl Acad Sci U S A 88, 6878 (1991); **37.** FEBS Lett 337, 43 (1994); **38.** J Neurochem 71, 1298 (1998); **39.** Nature 358, 325 (1992); **40.** Anal Biochem 209, 343 (1993); **41.** Cell Calcium 14, 663 (1993); **42.** Nature 352, 524 (1991); **43.** J Cell Biol 121, 83 (1993); **44.** Cell Calcium 22, 439 (1997); **45.** J Biolumin Chemilumin 4, 346 (1989); **46.** Biotechniques 24, 185 (1998); **47.** Biochem Biophys Res Commun 233, 349 (1997); **48.** Biochem J 306, 537 (1995); **49.** Biochem J 296, 549 (1993); **50.** Biochem J 261, 913 (1989); **51.** Cell Calcium 14, 373 (1993); **52.** Optics Comm 64, 457 (1987); **53.** Cell Calcium 12, 635 (1991); **54.** Anal Biochem 272, 34 (1999); **55.** J Biol Chem 272, 27694 (1997); **56.** Biosci Biotechnol Biochem 61, 1219 (1997).

Data Table — 19.5 Aequorin: A Bioluminescent Ca^{2+} Indicator

Cat #	MW	Storage	Soluble	Abs	EC	Em	Solvent	Notes
C2944	423.47	FF,D,LL,AA	MeOH	429	7,500	see Notes	pH 7	1, 2, 3
C6776	457.53	FF,D,LL,AA	MeOH	431	9,000	see Notes	MeOH	1, 2
C6779	425.46	FF,D,LL,AA	MeOH	437	8,700	see Notes	MeOH	1, 2
C6780	407.47	FF,D,LL,AA	MeOH	437	9,500	see Notes	MeOH	1, 2
C14260	415.49	FF,D,LL,AA	MeOH	430	7,000	see Notes	MeOH	1, 2
C14261	399.49	FF,D,LL,AA	MeOH	433	10,000	see Notes	MeOH	1, 2

For definitions of the contents of this data table, see "Navigating *The Handbook*" in the introductory pages.

Notes

1. Coelenterazine complexes with apoaequorin emit calcium-dependent bioluminescence. Bioluminescence emission maxima (relative intensity at 100 nM Ca^{2+}) are as follows: C2944, 466 nm (1); C6776, 468 nm (0.15); C6779, 472 nm (20); C6780, 466 nm (16); C14260, 442 nm (28); C14261, 445 nm (500) (Cell Calcium 14, 373 (1993)).
2. Do NOT dissolve in DMSO.
3. Aqueous solutions of coelenterazine (>1 mM) can be prepared in pH 7 buffer containing 50 mM 2-hydroxypropyl-β-cyclodextrin (Biosci Biotechnol Biochem 61, 1219 (1997)).

Product List — 19.5 Aequorin: A Bioluminescent Ca^{2+} Indicator

Cat #	Product Name	Unit Size
A6785	AquaLite® aequorin (aequorin) *recombinant*	25 µg
C2944	coelenterazine	250 µg
C14260	coelenterazine cp	250 µg
C6779	coelenterazine f	250 µg
C6780	coelenterazine h	250 µg
C14261	coelenterazine hcp	250 µg
C6776	coelenterazine n	250 µg
C6777	Coelenterazine Sampler Kit *coelenterazine and five analogs, 25 µg each*	1 kit

For current prices or to order online, visit probes.invitrogen.com

19.6 Fluorescent Mg^{2+} Indicators

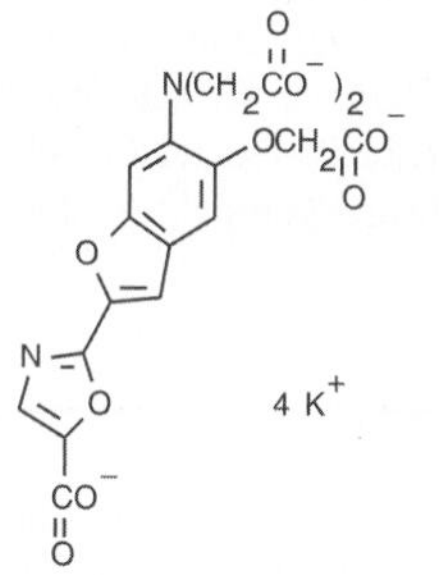

Figure 19.67 M1290 mag-fura-2, tetrapotassium salt.

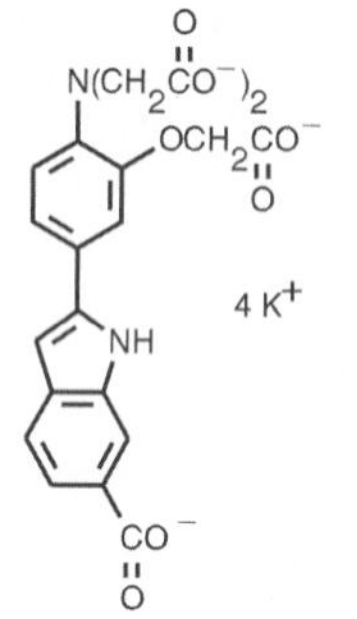

Figure 19.68 M1293 mag-indo-1, tetrapotassium salt.

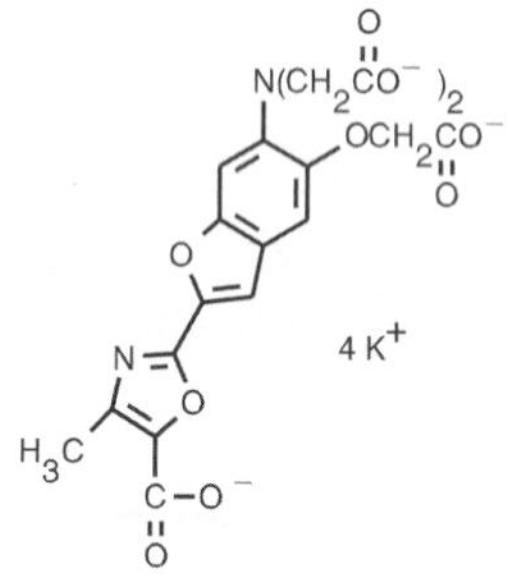

Figure 19.69 M3103 mag-fura-5, tetrapotassium salt.

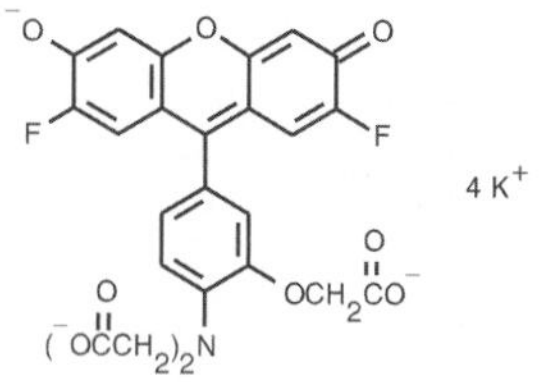

Figure 19.73 M14205 mag-fluo-4, tetrapotassium salt.

Intracellular Mg^{2+} is important for mediating enzymatic reactions, DNA synthesis, hormonal secretion and muscular contraction. To facilitate the investigation of magnesium's role in these and other cellular functions, Molecular Probes offers several different fluorescent indicators for measuring intracellular Mg^{2+} concentration.[1] They include furaptra,[2,3] which we refer to as mag-fura-2 to denote the similarity of its structure (Figure 19.67) and spectral response with the Ca^{2+} indicator fura-2; mag-indo-1, with a structure (Figure 19.68) and spectral response similar to that of indo-1; and mag-fura-5 (Figure 19.69). For applications such as confocal laser-scanning microscopy and flow cytometry, we offer the Magnesium Green™ and mag-fluo-4 indicators. The various methods for measuring intracellular Mg^{2+} have been reviewed.[2,4,5]

Mg^{2+} indicators are generally designed to maximally respond to the Mg^{2+} concentrations commonly found in cells, typically ranging from about 0.1 mM to 6 mM.[6,7] Intracellular free Mg^{2+} levels have been reported to be ~0.3 mM in synaptosomes,[7] 0.37 mM in hepatocytes[8] and 0.5–1.2 mM in cardiac cells,[5] whereas the concentration of Mg^{2+} in normal serum is ~0.44–1.5 mM.[9] Mg^{2+} indicator salts have frequently been microinjected in skeletal muscle.[10–13] Measurements using fluorescent Mg^{2+} indicators are somewhat more demanding than intracellular Ca^{2+} determinations because physiological changes in Mg^{2+} concentration are relatively small.[14] Compartmentalization and binding to proteins can also be a problem in use of these indicators in cells.[15] Mg^{2+} indicators also bind Ca^{2+}; however, typical physiological Ca^{2+} concentrations (10 nM–1 µM) usually do not interfere with Mg^{2+} measurements because the affinity of these indicators for Ca^{2+} is low. Although Ca^{2+} binding by Mg^{2+} indicators can be a complicating factor in Mg^{2+} measurements,[16,17] this property can also be exploited for measuring high Ca^{2+} concentrations (1–100 µM);[18–20] see Section 19.2 and Section 19.3 for further examples.

For intracellular calibration of Mg^{2+} indicators, Molecular Probes offers the ionophores A-23187 and the nonfluorescent 4-bromo A-23187 (A1493, B1494; Section 19.8), which are preferred over ionomycin (I24222, Section 19.8) because they transport Mg^{2+} more effectively.[3,12] Solutions used to calibrate Mg^{2+} indicators should be initially free of heavy metals such as Mn^{2+} that can interact with the indicators. These metals can be removed by treating the solution with the divalent cation chelator TPEN (T1210, Section 19.8).

Magnesium Indicators Excited by UV Light

Mag-Fura-2, Mag-Fura-5 and Mag-Indo-1

The dissociation constants for Mg^{2+} of mag-fura-5 and mag-indo-1 are 2.3 mM and 2.7 mM, respectively, slightly higher than that of mag-fura-2, which is 1.9 mM. Mag-fura-2 was first used to detect Mg^{2+} fluctuations in embryonic chicken heart cells[21] and rat liver cells.[3] The lower-affinity mag-fura-5 and mag-indo-1 indicators are sensitive to somewhat higher spikes in intracellular Mg^{2+}.[11,14,22] The affinities of mag-fura-2 and mag-indo-1 for Mg^{2+} are reported to be essentially invariant at pH values between 5.5 and 7.4 and at temperatures between 22°C and 37°C.[23] A detailed study of the photophysics of mag-fura-2 has been published.[24] Comparisons of intracellular and solution dissociation constants for mag-fura-2 have been published by Hurley and co-workers[16] and by Tashiro and Konishi.[12]

As with their Ca^{2+}-indicating analogs, mag-fura-2 undergoes an appreciable shift in excitation wavelength upon Mg^{2+} binding (Figure 19.70), and mag-indo-1 exhibits a shift in both its excitation and emission wavelengths (Figure 19.71). Equipment, optical filters (Table 23.9) and calibration methods are very similar to those required for the Ca^{2+} indicators. The excitation-ratioable mag-fura-2 and mag-fura-5 indicators are most useful for fluorescence microscopy, whereas the emission-ratioable mag-indo-1 indicator is preferred for flow cytometry. Simultaneous flow cytometric measurements of Ca^{2+} and Mg^{2+} have been made using fluo-3 and mag-indo-1.[25] Researchers have used mag-fura-2 to measure intracellular Mg^{2+} in a wide variety of cells, organelles and tissues, including:

- Mouse distal convoluted tubule cells[26–28]
- Jurkat cells[29]
- Rat hepatocytes[30]
- Smooth muscle[12,31]
- Cortical neurons[32]
- Platelets[33,34]
- Isolated mitochondria[35,36]

Mag-fura-2 and mag-fura-5 have also been used to measure levels of intracellular free Zn^{2+} [37,38] (Section 19.7).

In addition to the cell-impermeant potassium salts (M1290, M3103, M1293), we offer the cell-permeant AM esters of mag-fura-2, mag-fura-5 and mag-indo-1 as a set of 20 vials, each containing 50 µg (M1292, M3105, M1295). The special packaging is recommended when small quantities of the dyes are to be used over a long period of time. Mag-fura-2 AM is also available in a single vial containing 1 mg (M1291).

Magnesium Indicators Excited by Visible Light

Molecular Probes offers several visible light–excitable Mg^{2+} indicators, including the Magnesium Green™ and mag-fluo-4 indicators. As with mag-fura-2, mag-fura-5 and mag-indo-1, these visible light–excitable Mg^{2+} indicators can also be used as low-affinity Ca^{2+} indicators (Section 19.3) and may be useful as indicators for Zn^{2+} and other metals (Section 19.7).

Magnesium Green™ Indicator

Our Magnesium Green™ indicator (Figure 19.50) exhibits a higher affinity for Mg^{2+} (K_d ~1.0 mM) than does mag-fura-2 (K_d ~1.9 mM) or mag-indo-1 (K_d ~2.7 mM); this indicator also binds Ca^{2+} with moderate affinity (K_d for Ca^{2+} in the absence of Mg^{2+} ~6 µM).[39] The spectral properties of the Magnesium Green™ indicator are similar to those of the Calcium Green™ indicators. Upon binding Mg^{2+}, Magnesium Green™ exhibits an increase in fluorescence emission intensity without a shift in wavelength (Figure 19.72). The Magnesium Green™ indicator has been used to investigate the binding of free Mg^{2+} by the bacterial SecA protein[40] and by protein tyrosine kinases.[41] By exploiting the fact that ATP has greater Mg^{2+}-binding affinity than ADP, researchers have used Magnesium Green™ to detect ATP hydrolysis in spontaneously contracting cardiomyocytes.[42,43] Magnesium Green™ is available as a cell-impermeant potassium salt (M3733) or as a cell-permeant AM ester (M3735).

Mag-Fluo-4

Mag-fluo-4 (Figure 19.73) is an analog of fluo-4 with a K_d for Mg^{2+} of 4.7 mM and a K_d for Ca^{2+} of 22 µM,[39] making it useful as an intracellular Mg^{2+} indicator as well as a low-affinity Ca^{2+} indicator (Section 19.3). Mag-fluo-4 has a much more sensitive fluorescence response to Mg^{2+} binding than does our Magnesium Green™ indicator. Because physiological fluctuations of intracellular Mg^{2+} concentration are typically small, this increased sensitivity is a considerable advantage. Like fluo-4, mag-fluo-4 is essentially nonfluorescent in the absence of divalent cations and exhibits strong fluorescence enhancement with no spectral shift upon binding Mg^{2+} (Figure 19.74). Mag-fluo-4 is available as a cell-impermeant potassium salt (M14205) or as a cell-permeant AM ester (M14206).

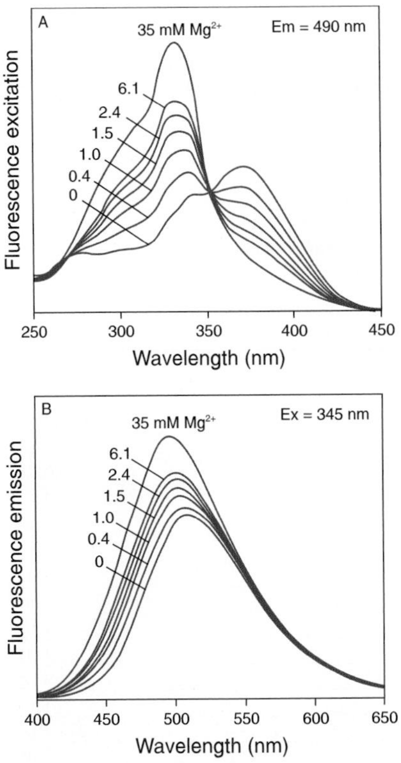

Figure 19.70 A) Fluorescence excitation and B) fluorescence emission spectra of mag-fura-2 (M1290) in solutions containing 0–35 mM Mg^{2+}.

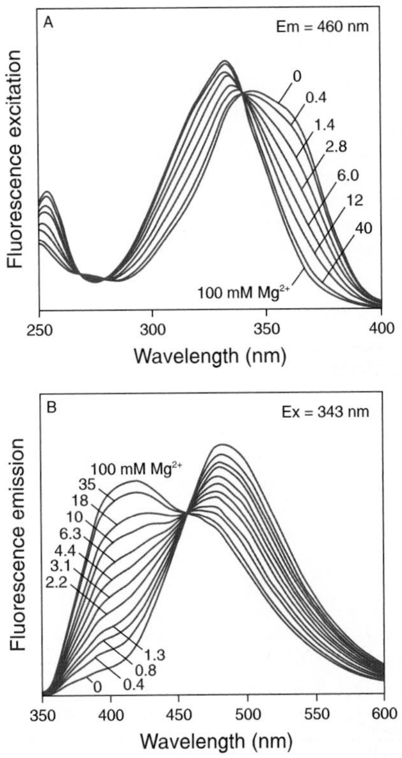

Figure 19.71 A) Fluorescence excitation and B) fluorescence emission spectra of mag-indo-1 (M1293) in solutions containing 0–100 mM Mg^{2+}.

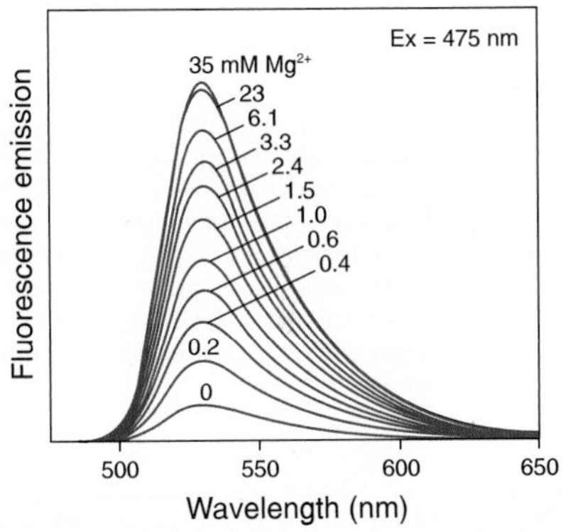

Figure 19.72 Mg^{2+}-dependent fluorescence emission spectra of Magnesium Green™ (M3733).

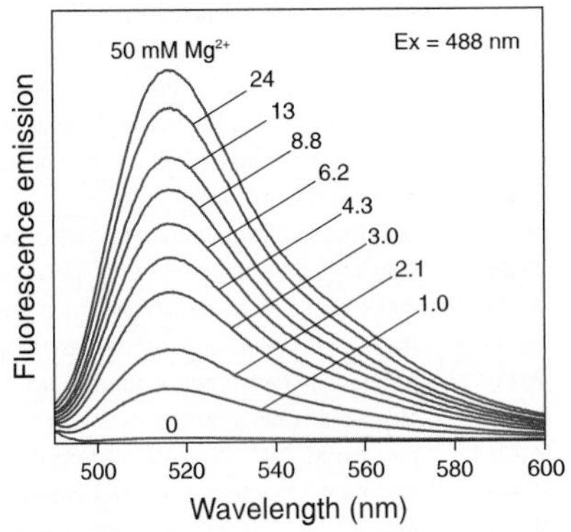

Figure 19.74 Fluorescence emission spectra of mag-fluo-4 (M14205) in solutions containing 0–50 mM Mg^{2+}.

References

1. Curr Med Chem 9, 275 (2002); **2.** Annu Rev Physiol 53, 241 (1991); **3.** Am J Physiol 256, C540 (1989); **4.** Physiol Rev 81, 51 (2001); **5.** Annu Rev Physiol 53, 273 (1991); **6.** Pflugers Arch 420, 347 (1992); **7.** Biochim Biophys Acta 898, 331 (1987); **8.** J Biol Chem 261, 2567 (1986); **9.** Clin Chem 35, 1492 (1989); **10.** Hypertension 34, 442 (1999); **11.** Biophys J 75, 957 (1998); **12.** Biophys J 73, 3358 (1997); **13.** Biophys J 70, 896 (1996); **14.** Pflugers Arch 422, 179 (1992); **15.** Anal Biochem 290, 221 (2001); **16.** Am J Physiol 263, C300 (1992); **17.** Mol Cell Biochem 136, 11 (1994); **18.** J Cell Biol 140, 325 (1998); **19.** Biophys J 74, 1549 (1998); **20.** J Gen Physiol 97, 271 (1991); **21.** Proc Natl Acad Sci U S A 86, 2981 (1989); **22.** J Physiol 475, 319 (1994); **23.** Biochem Biophys Res Commun 177, 184 (1991); **24.** Chem Phys Lett 287, 412 (1998); **25.** Biochem J 289, 373 (1993); **26.** Am J Physiol 274, F336 (1998); **27.** Am J Physiol 274, F328 (1998); **28.** Am J Physiol 272, F759 (1997); **29.** Shock 1, 213 (1994); **30.** Biochem J 326, 823 (1997); **31.** Biophys J 73, 3371 (1997); **32.** Neuron 11, 751 (1993); **33.** Clin Chem 42, 744 (1996); **34.** Am J Physiol 274, R548 (1998); **35.** Biochim Biophys Acta 1320, 310 (1997); **36.** J Biol Chem 273, 7850 (1998); **37.** Neurobiol Dis 4, 275 (1997); **38.** J Biochem Biophys Methods 27, 25 (1993); **39.** K_d values for Ca^{2+} are determined at Molecular Probes at ~22°C using our Calcium Calibration Buffer Kits; **40.** J Biol Chem 270, 18975 (1995); **41.** Biochemistry 36, 2139 (1997); **42.** J Physiol 496, 111 (1996); **43.** J Biol Chem 273, 3320 (1998).

Data Table — 19.6 Fluorescent Mg^{2+} Indicators

				Low Mg^{2+}				High Mg^{2+}						
Cat #	**MW**	**Storage**	**Soluble**	**Abs**	**EC**	**Em**	**Solvent**	**Abs**	**EC**	**Em**	**Solvent**	**Product**	**K_d**	**Notes**
M1290	586.68	L	pH >6	369	22,000	511	H_2O	330	24,000	491	H_2O/Mg^{2+}		1.9 mM	1, 2, 3, 4
M1291	722.57	F,D,L	DMSO	366	31,000	475	EtOAc					M1290		
M1292	722.57	F,D,L	DMSO	366	31,000	475	EtOAc					M1290		
M1293	594.74	L	pH >6	349	38,000	480	H_2O	330	33,000	417	H_2O/Mg^{2+}		2.7 mM	1, 2, 3, 4
M1295	730.63	F,D,L	DMSO	354	37,000	472	MeOH					M1293		
M3103	600.70	L	pH >6	369	23,000	505	H_2O	332	25,000	482	H_2O/Mg^{2+}		2.3 mM	1, 2, 3, 4
M3105	736.60	F,D,L	DMSO	365	31,000	461	EtOAc					M3103		
M3733	915.90	L	pH >6	506	77,000	531	H_2O	506	75,000	531	H_2O/Mg^{2+}		1.0 mM	1, 2, 3, 4, 5
M3735	1025.71	F,D	DMSO	302	16,000	none	MeOH					M3733		
M6890	856.04	L	pH >6	550	76,000	575	H_2O	550	74,000	575	H_2O/Mg^{2+}		3.9 mM	1, 2, 3, 4, 5
M6892	563.66	L	pH >6	483	23,000	659	H_2O	427	29,000	631	H_2O/Mg^{2+}		2.5 mM	1, 2, 3, 4
M14205	681.77	D,L	pH >6	490	74,000	see Notes	H_2O	493	75,000	517	H_2O/Mg^{2+}		4.7 mM	1, 2, 3, 4, 6
M14206	817.66	F,D,L	DMSO	457	25,000	see Notes	MeOH					M14205		7
M14213	623.74	D,L	pH >6	547	68,000	see Notes	H_2O	549	69,000	578	H_2O/Mg^{2+}		ND	2, 4, 6, 8
M14214	844.67	F,D,L	DMSO	553	98,000	570	$CHCl_3$					M14213		7
M14215	727.90	D,L	pH >6	575	82,000	see Notes	H_2O	578	82,000	602	H_2O/Mg^{2+}		10.7 mM	1, 2, 3, 4, 6
M14216	948.82	F,D,L	DMSO	576	122,000	597	MeOH					M14215		7
M24050	800.08	D,L	DMSO	365	24,000	505	H_2O	337	31,000	497	H_2O/Mg^{2+}		ND	4, 8

For definitions of the contents of this data table, see "Navigating *The Handbook*" in the introductory pages.

Notes

1. Dissociation constants are known to vary considerably depending on the temperature, pH, ionic strength, viscosity, protein binding, presence of other ions (especially polyvalent ions), instrument setup and other factors. It is strongly recommended that these values be verified under user-specific experimental conditions.
2. This indicator binds Ca^{2+} with higher affinity than Mg^{2+}, producing a similar spectral response.
3. $K_d(Mg^{2+})$ values have been determined at Molecular Probes in 115 mM KCl, 20 mM NaCl, 10 mM Tris, pH 7.05, 0 to 35 mM Mg^{2+} at 22°C.
4. Spectra measured in aqueous buffers containing zero or 35 mM Mg^{2+}, indicated as H_2O and H_2O/Mg^{2+} respectively.
5. This indicator exhibits fluorescence enhancement in response to ion binding, with essentially no change in absorption or emission wavelengths.
6. Fluorescence of the free indicator is very weak and is enhanced >100-fold on binding Mg^{2+}.
7. Fluorescence of this AM ester derivative is very weak and is enhanced only after hydrolytic cleavage followed by binding of divalent cations to the anionic indicator.
8. ND = not determined.

Product List — 19.6 Fluorescent Mg^{2+} Indicators

Cat #	Product Name	Unit Size
M14206	mag-fluo-4, AM *cell permeant* *special packaging*	10 x 50 µg
M14205	mag-fluo-4, tetrapotassium salt *cell impermeant*	500 µg
M1291	mag-fura-2, AM *cell permeant*	1 mg
M1292	mag-fura-2, AM *cell permeant* *special packaging*	20 x 50 µg
M1290	mag-fura-2, tetrapotassium salt *cell impermeant*	1 mg
M3105	mag-fura-5, AM *cell permeant* *special packaging*	20 x 50 µg
M3103	mag-fura-5, tetrapotassium salt *cell impermeant*	1 mg
M24050	mag-fura-C_{18}, tripotassium salt	1 mg
M6892	Mag-Fura Red™, tripotassium salt *cell impermeant*	1 mg
M1295	mag-indo-1, AM *cell permeant* *special packaging*	20 x 50 µg
M1293	mag-indo-1, tetrapotassium salt *cell impermeant*	1 mg
M3735	Magnesium Green™, AM *cell permeant* *special packaging*	20 x 50 µg
M3733	Magnesium Green™, pentapotassium salt *cell impermeant*	1 mg
M6890	Magnesium Orange™, tripotassium salt *cell impermeant*	1 mg
M14214	mag-rhod-2, AM *cell permeant* *special packaging*	10 x 50 µg
M14213	mag-rhod-2, dipotassium salt *cell impermeant*	500 µg
M14216	mag-X-rhod-1, AM *cell permeant* *special packaging*	10 x 50 µg
M14215	mag-X-rhod-1, dipotassium salt *cell impermeant*	500 µg

For current prices or to order online, visit probes.invitrogen.com

19.7 Fluorescent Indicators for Zn^{2+} and Other Metal Ions

Not only do certain metal ions play an important role in biological structure and activity, but they can also serve as useful probes of biological processes, including ion transport through Ca^{2+} channels.[1,2] Metal contamination, however, can cause ecological problems and present significant risks to health. For example, Hg^{2+} at submicromolar concentrations can cause a rapid and sustained increase in intracellular Ca^{2+} levels in rat T-lymphocytes[3] and modify the depolarization- and agonist-stimulated Ca^{2+} signals in neuroadrenergic PC12 cells.[4] Furthermore, Pb^{2+} can mimic Ca^{2+} in important cellular processes; rat astrocytes exposed to Pb^{2+} show significant increases in the levels of intracellular inositol 1,4,5-triphosphate.[5]

Existing spectrophotometric methods for detecting metal ions in environmental samples have usually required sample pretreatment, separation or concentration.[6] With fluorescent indicators, a solution of the indicating dye is simply added to an aqueous sample, and the resulting fluorescence intensity is compared with that of a target-ion–free control. Measuring heavy metal ion concentrations in cells and environmental samples with indicators originally designed for detection of Ca^{2+} and Mg^{2+} has been hampered by competitive binding of other, more abundant, cations.[7] However, new detection methods rely both on novel fluorescent ion sensors specifically designed for metal detection, as well as on new applications for indicators originally designed for detection of Ca^{2+} and Mg^{2+}[8] (Table 19.5, Figure 19.75, Figure 19.76).

Several of our fluorescent indicators can be used to selectively determine polyvalent cation concentrations inside cells or to follow metal ion transport through ion channels. Other indicators are primarily useful for measurements in solutions or in extracts of environmental samples.[9] In most cases, the high affinity of the indicators for metal ions allows interference from other compounds to be minimized by diluting the sample with deionized water. As with Ca^{2+} and Mg^{2+} detection, spectroscopic responses to metal ion binding and dissociation constant (K_d) values are dependent on many factors, including pH, temperature, viscosity, protein binding and the presence of other ions. These responses may vary significantly in complex environments such as seawater and the cytosol.[10]

Applications of Ca^{2+} and Mg^{2+} Indicators for Detection of Zn^{2+} and Other Metals

We have tested the responses of many of the Ca^{2+} and Mg^{2+} indicators (described in Section 19.2 through Section 19.6) to a series of polyvalent metal ions (Figure 19.75, Figure 19.76). The BAPTA-based indicators, including the Calcium Green™ dyes, fluo-3 and fluo-4, exhibit the highest emission intensities upon binding La^{3+}, Hg^{2+} and Cd^{2+}. The response of the Calcium Green™-1 and Magnesium Green™ indicators shows relatively little variability amongst the ions tested. Indicators nominally designed for detecting low Ca^{2+} concentrations, such as Calcium Green™-5N, fluo-5N and rhod-5N, show little response to transition metal ions such as Fe^{2+}, Co^{2+}, Ni^{2+} and Co^{2+} and much stronger responses to heavier ions such as Cd^{2+}, Hg^{2+} and Pb^{2+}. Note that the responses shown in Figure 19.76 are not necessarily saturated or even uniform in some cases. Some indication of the overall response pattern can be obtained by comparing the effects of the 1 µM and 100 µM ion concentrations sampled in these experiments. Also, note that our selection of excitation and emission wavelengths for the measurements may significantly affect the absolute and relative magnitudes of the changes observed.

Table 19.5 — Response of fura-2 and indo-1 to some divalent cations other than Ca^{2+} and Mg^{2+}

Ion	Indicator	K_d*	Spectroscopic Effect	Reference
Ba^{2+}	fura-2	1.4×10^{-6} M	Spectra similar to Ca^{2+} complex; no quenching	1
Cd^{2+}	fura-2	1.0×10^{-12} M	Spectra similar to Ca^{2+} complex; higher intensity	2
Co^{2+}	fura-2	8.6×10^{-9} M	>99% Quenched relative to Ca^{2+} complex	1
Mn^{2+}	fura-2	2.8×10^{-9} M	>99% Quenched relative to Ca^{2+} complex	1
Pb^{2+}	fura-2	4.2×10^{-12} M	Spectra shifted relative to Ca^{2+} complex; no quenching	3
Pb^{2+}	indo-1	3.5×10^{-11} M	Fluorescence quenched	4
Sr^{2+}	fura-2	7.6×10^{-6} M	Spectra similar to Ca^{2+} complex; no quenching	1
Zn^{2+}	fura-2	3.0×10^{-9} M	Spectra similar to Ca^{2+} complex; no quenching	5
Zn^{2+}	indo-1	1.6×10^{-10} M	Spectra similar to Ca^{2+} complex; no quenching	6

* Dissociation constant reported in cited literature reference. **1.** J Biol Chem 265, 678 (1990); **2.** J Biol Chem 267, 25553 (1992); **3.** Am J Physiol 259, C762 (1990); **4.** J Biol Chem 272, 8346 (1997); **5.** J Biol Chem 270, 2473 (1995); **6.** Anal Biochem 187, 328 (1990).

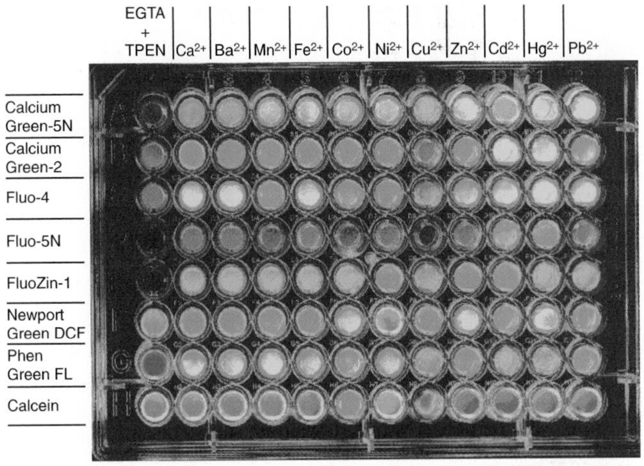

Figure 19.75 Visual screening of fluorescent indicator responses to metal ions. The image shows a 96-well microplate containing various combinations of ions and indicators in 50 mM MOPS pH 7.0. Each row of wells represents a different indicator; each column of wells represents a different ion. The indicators (top to bottom) are: Calcium Green™-5N (0.5 µM), Calcium Green™-2 (0.2 µM), fluo-4 (2 µM), fluo-5N (2 µM), FluoZin™-1 (2 µM), Newport Green™ DCF (2 µM), Phen Green™ FL (2 µM; this indicator salt is no longer routinely available, please inquire) and calcein (0.5 µM). The left-hand column of wells contains 10 mM EGTA + 10 µM TPEN (ion-free reference solution). Subsequent columns (left to right) represent 1 µM concentrations of Ca^{2+}, Ba^{2+}, Mn^{2+}, Fe^{2+}, Co^{2+}, Ni^{2+}, Cu^{2+}, Zn^{2+}, Cd^{2+}, Hg^{2+}, and Pb^{2+}, respectively. The microplate was scanned using a FLA3000G laser scanner (Fuji Photo Film Co.) with excitation at 473 nm and fluorescence emission detected at 520 nm. The image is pseudocolored according to fluorescence intensity (high = red > orange > yellow > green > blue = low).

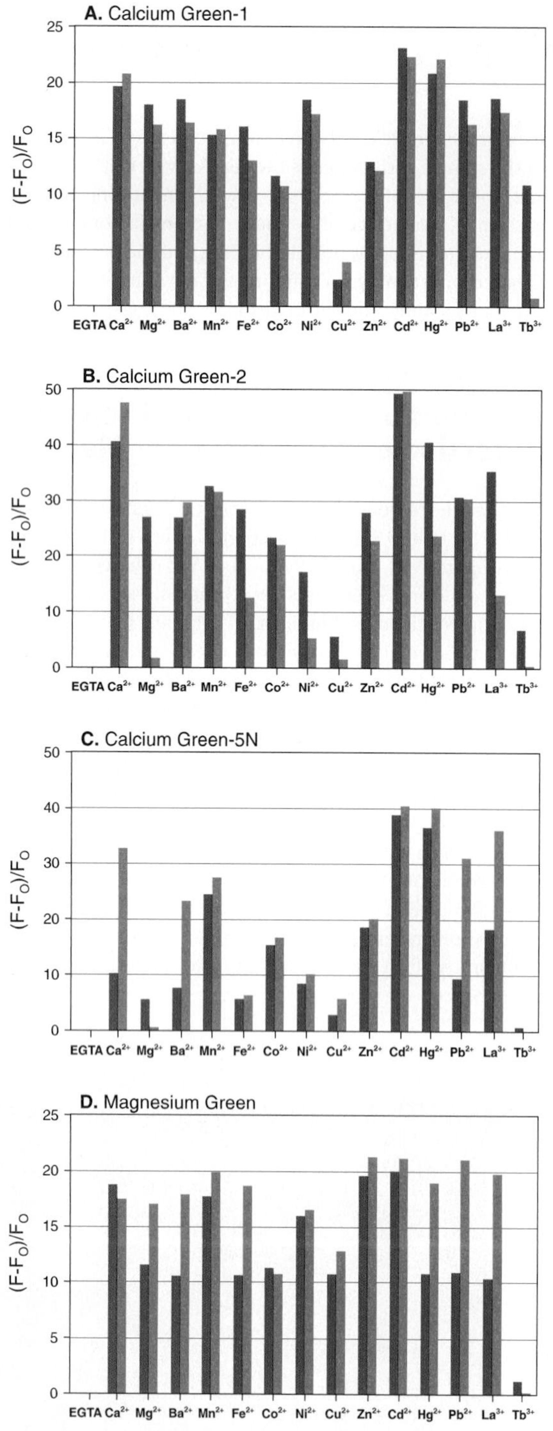

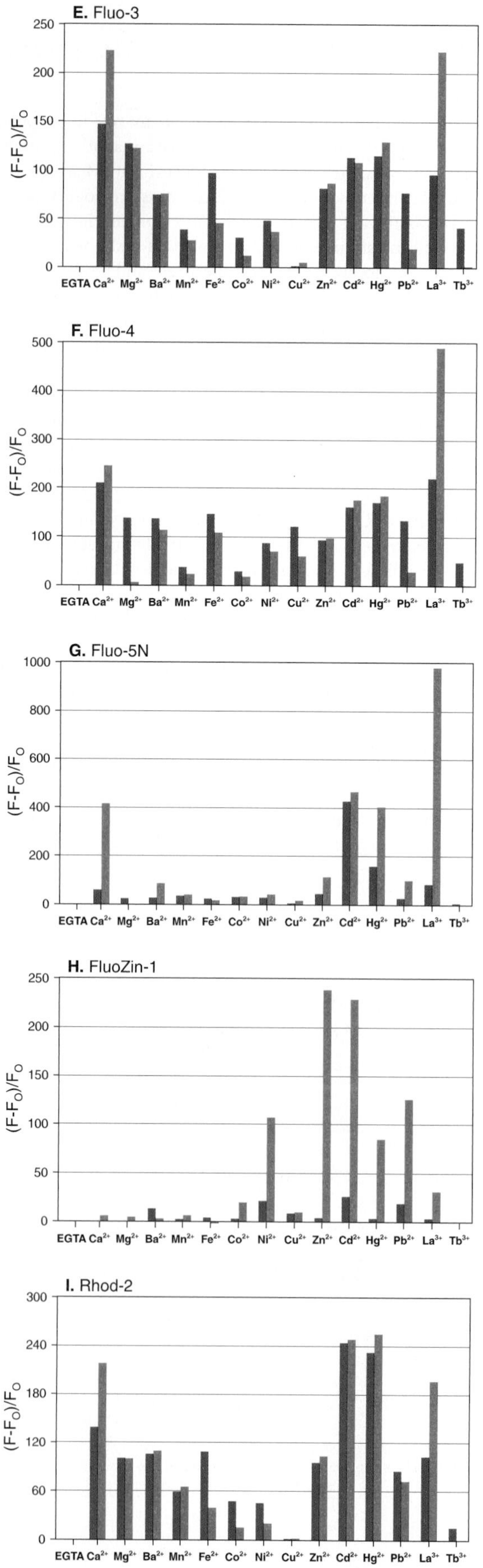

Figure 19.76 Metal-ion response screening for various fluorescent indicators. The maximum relative fluorescence intensity was measured for identical indicator concentrations in solutions containing 10 mM EGTA + 10 µM TPEN, 1 µM ion (100 µM for Mg^{2+}) and 100 µM ion (10 mM for Mg^{2+}). Results are plotted as fluorescence changes relative to the ion-free (10 mM EGTA + 10 µM TPEN) reference solution expressed as $(F-F_0)/F_0$, where F is the fluorescence intensity of ion-containing solutions and F_0 is the fluorescence intensity of the reference solution. Blue bars indicate the response to 1 µM ion (100 µM for Mg^{2+}), and red bars indicate the response to 100 µM ion (10 mM for Mg^{2+}). The indicators represented are: A) Calcium Green™-1, B) Calcium Green™-2, C) Calcium Green™-5N, D) Magnesium Green™, E) fluo-3, F) fluo-4, G) fluo-5N, H) FluoZin™-1, I) rhod-2, J) rhod-5N, K) X-rhod-1, L) fura-2, M) mag-fura-2, N) FuraZin™-1, O) Fura Red™, P) fura-FF, Q) indo-1, R) FluoZin™-3 and S) BTC.

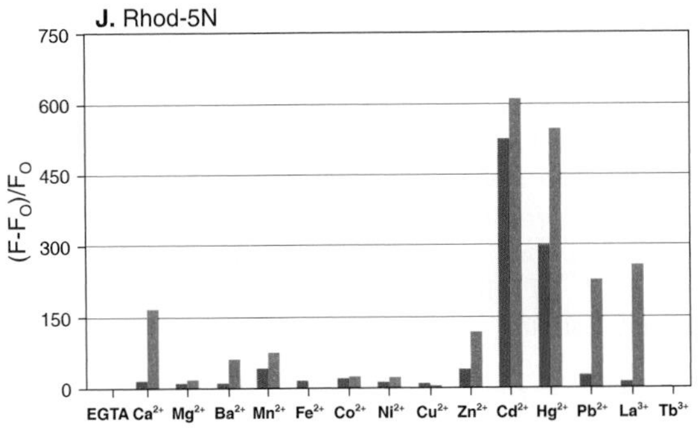
J. Rhod-5N
750
600
450
300
150
0
(F-F$_O$)/F$_O$
EGTA Ca²⁺ Mg²⁺ Ba²⁺ Mn²⁺ Fe²⁺ Co²⁺ Ni²⁺ Cu²⁺ Zn²⁺ Cd²⁺ Hg²⁺ Pb²⁺ La³⁺ Tb³⁺

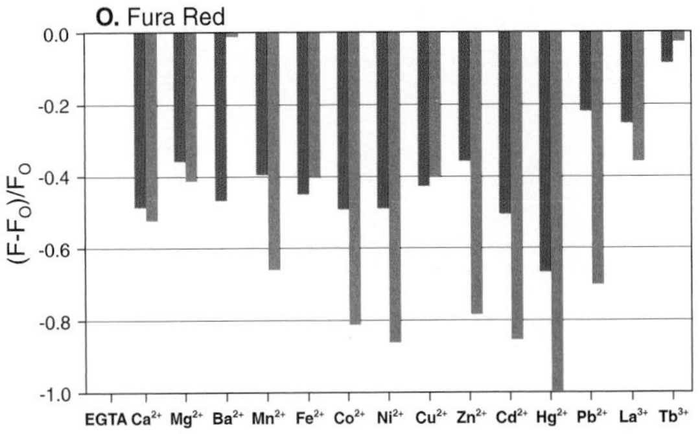
O. Fura Red
0.0
-0.2
-0.4
-0.6
-0.8
-1.0
(F-F$_O$)/F$_O$
EGTA Ca²⁺ Mg²⁺ Ba²⁺ Mn²⁺ Fe²⁺ Co²⁺ Ni²⁺ Cu²⁺ Zn²⁺ Cd²⁺ Hg²⁺ Pb²⁺ La³⁺ Tb³⁺

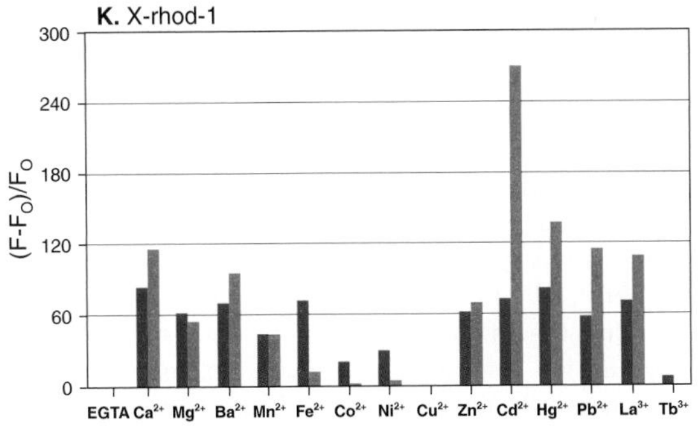
K. X-rhod-1
300
240
180
120
60
0
(F-F$_O$)/F$_O$
EGTA Ca²⁺ Mg²⁺ Ba²⁺ Mn²⁺ Fe²⁺ Co²⁺ Ni²⁺ Cu²⁺ Zn²⁺ Cd²⁺ Hg²⁺ Pb²⁺ La³⁺ Tb³⁺

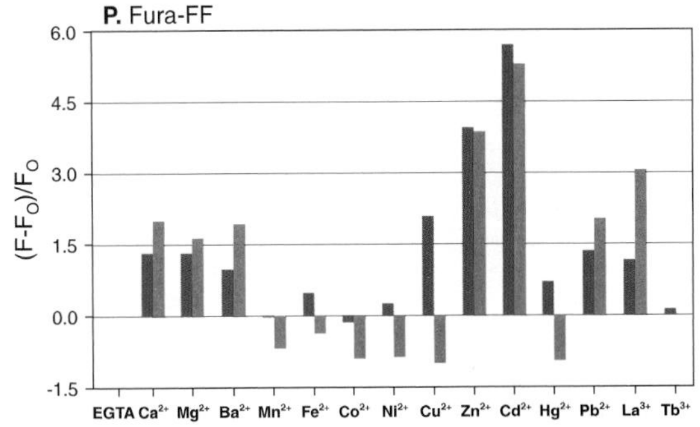
P. Fura-FF
6.0
4.5
3.0
1.5
0.0
-1.5
(F-F$_O$)/F$_O$
EGTA Ca²⁺ Mg²⁺ Ba²⁺ Mn²⁺ Fe²⁺ Co²⁺ Ni²⁺ Cu²⁺ Zn²⁺ Cd²⁺ Hg²⁺ Pb²⁺ La³⁺ Tb³⁺

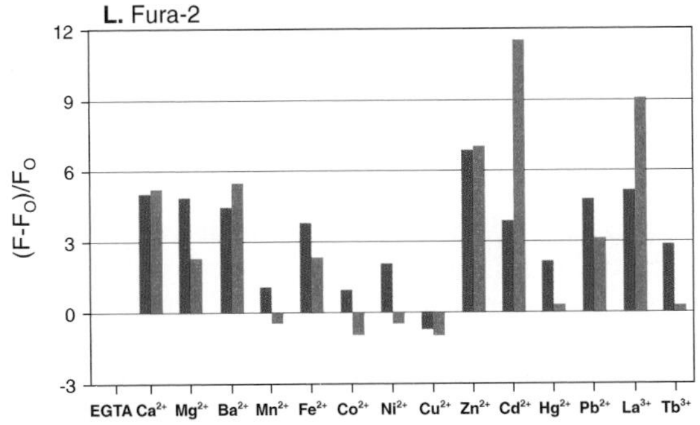
L. Fura-2
12
9
6
3
0
-3
(F-F$_O$)/F$_O$
EGTA Ca²⁺ Mg²⁺ Ba²⁺ Mn²⁺ Fe²⁺ Co²⁺ Ni²⁺ Cu²⁺ Zn²⁺ Cd²⁺ Hg²⁺ Pb²⁺ La³⁺ Tb³⁺

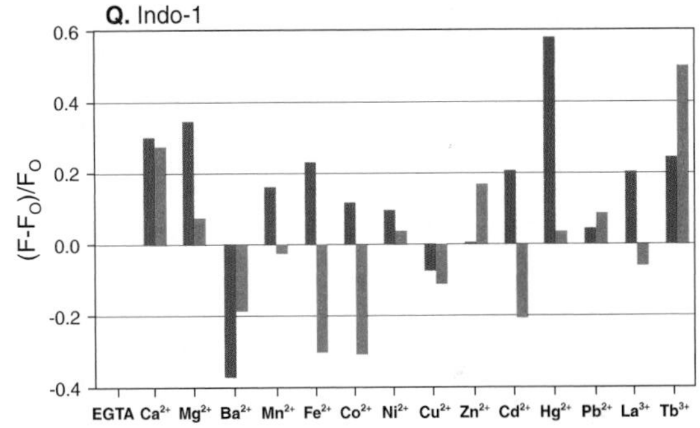
Q. Indo-1
0.6
0.4
0.2
0.0
-0.2
-0.4
(F-F$_O$)/F$_O$
EGTA Ca²⁺ Mg²⁺ Ba²⁺ Mn²⁺ Fe²⁺ Co²⁺ Ni²⁺ Cu²⁺ Zn²⁺ Cd²⁺ Hg²⁺ Pb²⁺ La³⁺ Tb³⁺

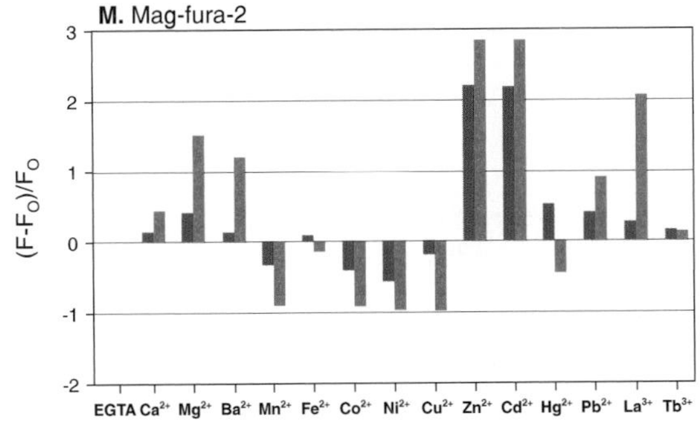
M. Mag-fura-2
3
2
1
0
-1
-2
(F-F$_O$)/F$_O$
EGTA Ca²⁺ Mg²⁺ Ba²⁺ Mn²⁺ Fe²⁺ Co²⁺ Ni²⁺ Cu²⁺ Zn²⁺ Cd²⁺ Hg²⁺ Pb²⁺ La³⁺ Tb³⁺

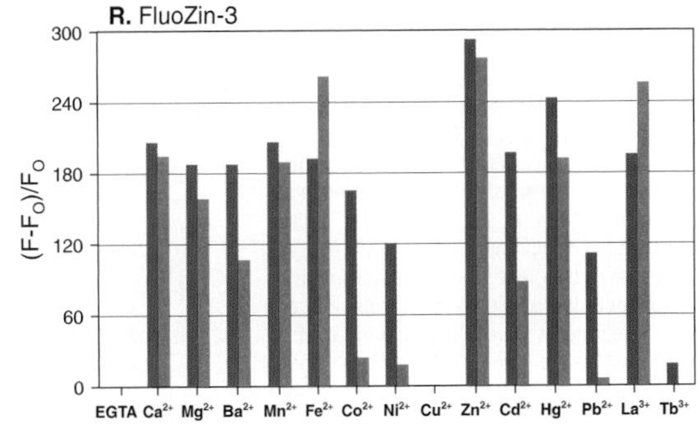
R. FluoZin-3
300
240
180
120
60
0
(F-F$_O$)/F$_O$
EGTA Ca²⁺ Mg²⁺ Ba²⁺ Mn²⁺ Fe²⁺ Co²⁺ Ni²⁺ Cu²⁺ Zn²⁺ Cd²⁺ Hg²⁺ Pb²⁺ La³⁺ Tb³⁺

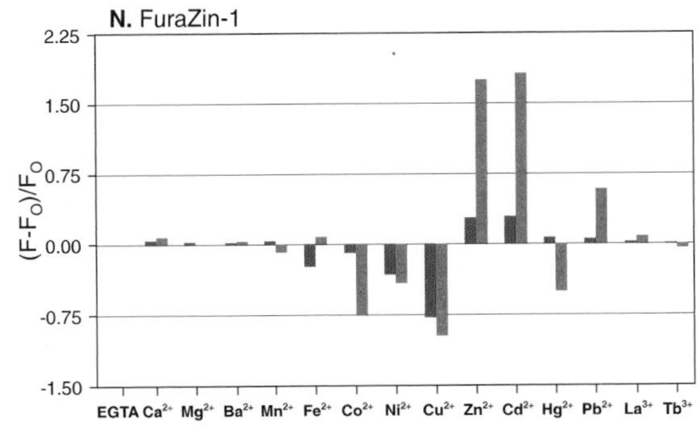
N. FuraZin-1
2.25
1.50
0.75
0.00
-0.75
-1.50
(F-F$_O$)/F$_O$
EGTA Ca²⁺ Mg²⁺ Ba²⁺ Mn²⁺ Fe²⁺ Co²⁺ Ni²⁺ Cu²⁺ Zn²⁺ Cd²⁺ Hg²⁺ Pb²⁺ La³⁺ Tb³⁺

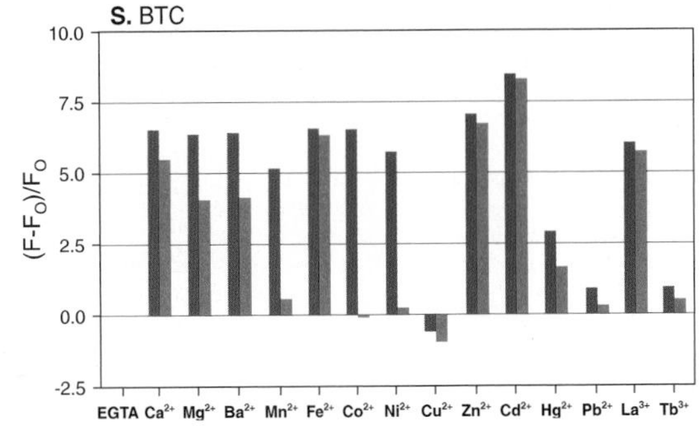
S. BTC
10.0
7.5
5.0
2.5
0.0
-2.5
(F-F$_O$)/F$_O$
EGTA Ca²⁺ Mg²⁺ Ba²⁺ Mn²⁺ Fe²⁺ Co²⁺ Ni²⁺ Cu²⁺ Zn²⁺ Cd²⁺ Hg²⁺ Pb²⁺ La³⁺ Tb³⁺

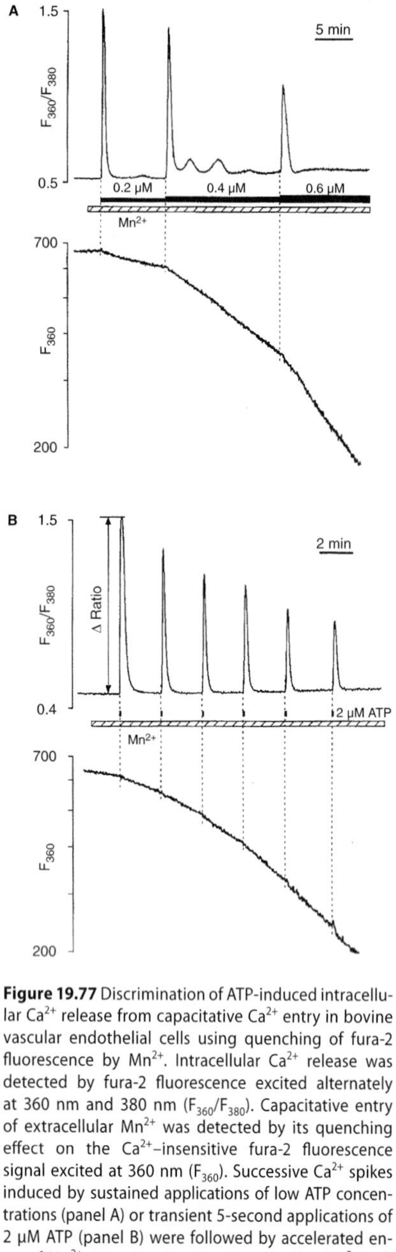

Figure 19.77 Discrimination of ATP-induced intracellular Ca^{2+} release from capacitative Ca^{2+} entry in bovine vascular endothelial cells using quenching of fura-2 fluorescence by Mn^{2+}. Intracellular Ca^{2+} release was detected by fura-2 fluorescence excited alternately at 360 nm and 380 nm (F_{360}/F_{380}). Capacitative entry of extracellular Mn^{2+} was detected by its quenching effect on the Ca^{2+}–insensitive fura-2 fluorescence signal excited at 360 nm (F_{360}). Successive Ca^{2+} spikes induced by sustained applications of low ATP concentrations (panel A) or transient 5-second applications of 2 µM ATP (panel B) were followed by accelerated entry of Mn^{2+}. Experiments were conducted in Ca^{2+}-free extracellular medium containing 100 µM Mn^{2+}. Under these conditions, Mn^{2+} functions as an ionic surrogate for Ca^{2+} with respect to transmembrane conductance, and Ca^{2+} signals can be unambiguously attributed to release from intracellular stores. Figure reproduced with permission from J Physiol 523 Pt 3, 549 (2000).

Fura-2 and indo-1, like other BAPTA-based Ca^{2+} indicators, are highly selective for Ca^{2+} over Mg^{2+}; however, they bind other divalent and trivalent cations with significantly higher affinity. In terms of spectroscopic detection, some of these ions (e.g., Ba^{2+}, Cd^{2+} and Sr^{2+}) mimic the effects of Ca^{2+};[11–13] others (e.g., Mn^{2+}, Co^{2+} and Ni^{2+}) exert strong fluorescence quenching effects (Table 19.5). Although heavy metal cations are a potentially serious source of interference in Ca^{2+} measurements using fluorescent indicators, intracellular concentrations are fortunately very low in most cases. When interference occurs, it can be identified and controlled using the selective heavy metal ion chelator TPEN[14,15] (T1210, Section 19.8). Quenching of indicator fluorescence by Mn^{2+} has several useful applications:

- Calibrating the intracellular Ca^{2+} response of fluo-3, fluo-4, rhod-2 and related indicators[16–18]
- Discriminating fluorescence signals from mitochondrial and cytosolic indicator populations[19,20]
- Estimating the fraction of residual Ca^{2+}-insensitive indicators after AM ester loading[21]
- Estimating indicator leakage in measurements on cell suspensions in cuvettes[22]

Mn^{2+} is also extensively used as an ionic surrogate for measuring Ca^{2+} influx through ion channels[23–28] (Figure 19.77). Because the effect of Mn^{2+} on fura-2 fluorescence is quite different than that of Ca^{2+} (Table 19.5), influx can be clearly distinguished from Ca^{2+} elevation due to mobilization of intracellular stores,[28] although such clarity may be impaired by the existence of alternative Mn^{2+}-influx pathways.[29] A similar analysis applies when using fura-2 and indo-1 to study the antagonistic effects of ions such as Ni^{2+}, La^{3+} and Co^{2+} on voltage-activated and Ca^{2+} release–activated Ca^{2+} channels. In this case, the Ca^{2+}-dependent fluorescence signal is of primary interest and permeability of the antagonist ion, resulting in direct interactions with the indicator, will usually invalidate the measurement.[2,30,31] For the Calcium Green™, Oregon Green® 488 BAPTA and Magnesium Green™ indicator series, the response to Mn^{2+} is not markedly different from the Ca^{2+} response (Figure 19.76), making these indicators generally unsuitable for the applications based on Ca^{2+}/Mn^{2+} discrimination described above. A variety of fluorescent indicators, including fura-2, fura-FF, mag-fura-5, and our Calcium Orange™ and Magnesium Green™ indicators, have been utilized to detect Sr^{2+}, an ion that can replace Ca^{2+} in triggering neurotransmitter release.[32–35]

Calcein (C481) is now rarely used as a Ca^{2+} or Mg^{2+} indicator because its fluorescence is directly sensitive to these ions only at strongly alkaline pH (Section 19.3). Fluorescence of calcein is quenched strongly by Co^{2+}, Ni^{2+} and Cu^{2+} and appreciably by Fe^{3+} and Mn^{2+} at physiological pH[36] (panel A, Figure 19.78). This fluorescence quenching response can be exploited for detecting the opening of the mitochondrial permeability transition pore,[37] for assaying membrane fusion (see Note 14.3 "Technical Focus: Assays of Volume Change, Membrane Fusion and Membrane Permeability" in Section 14.3) and for monitoring cellular iron transport and the cellular labile iron pool.[36,38–41]

Table 19.6 — Fluorescent indicators for Zn^{2+}

Indicator	Water-Soluble Form	Permeant Ester Form	Ex/Em *	K_d for Zn^{2+} †
FuraZin™-1	F24182	F24183	325, 375/510 ‡	3 µM
IndoZin™-1	I24184	I24185	345/405, 475 §	3 µM
FluoZin™-1	F24180	F24181	495/515	8 µM
FluoZin™-2	F24188	F24189	495/525	2 µM
FluoZin™-3	F24194	F24195	494/516	15 nM **
RhodZin™-1	R24186	R24187	555/575	23 µM
RhodZin™-3	R36350	R36351	550/575	65 nM
Newport Green™ DCF	N7990	N7991	505/535	1 µM
Newport Green™ PDX	N24190	N24191	495/520	30 µM

* Excitation (Ex) and Emission (Em) maxima, in nm. † Dissociation constant of the indicator Zn^{2+} complex measured in MOPS, pH 7.0, at 22°C. ‡ Excitation peak shifts upon binding Zn^{2+}. § Emission peak shifts upon binding Zn^{2+}. ** K_d determined in 135 mM NaCl, 1.1 mM EGTA, 20 mM HEPES, pH 7.4, 0–10 µM free Zn^{2+} at 22°C.

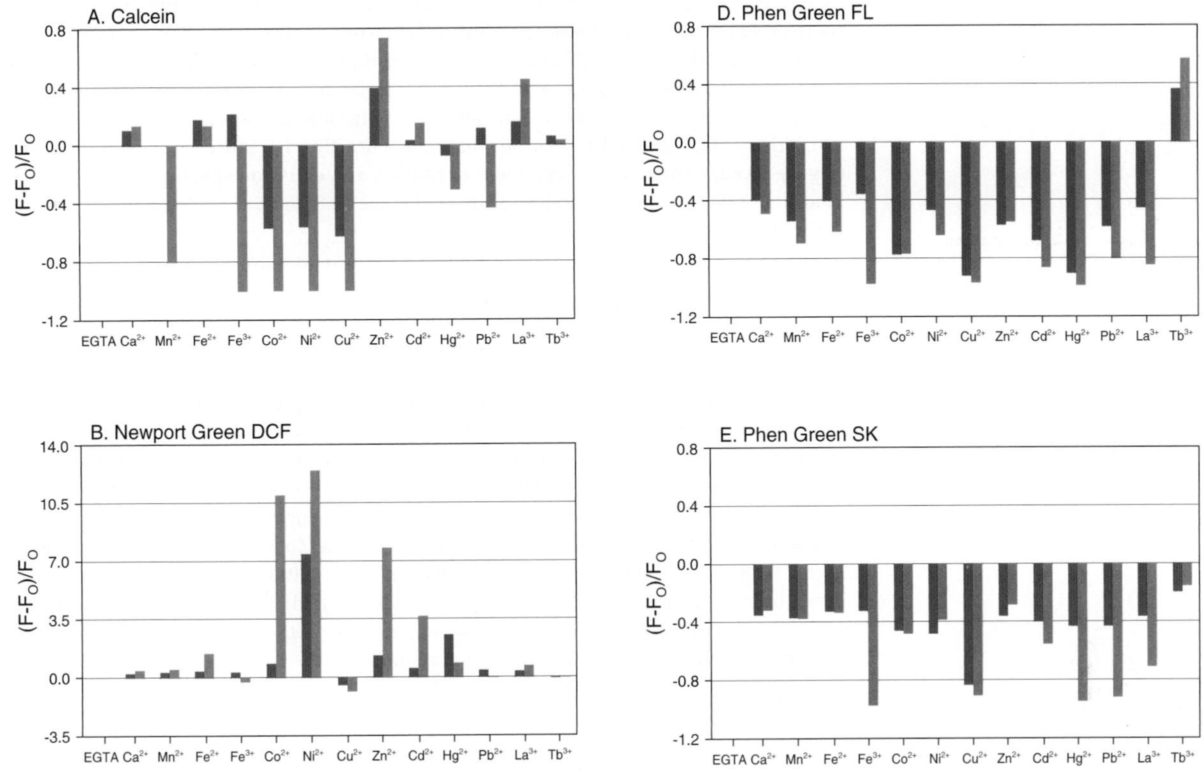

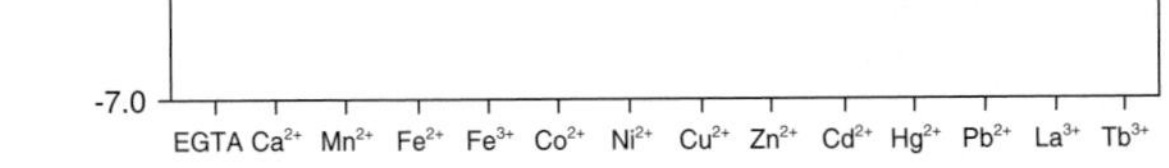

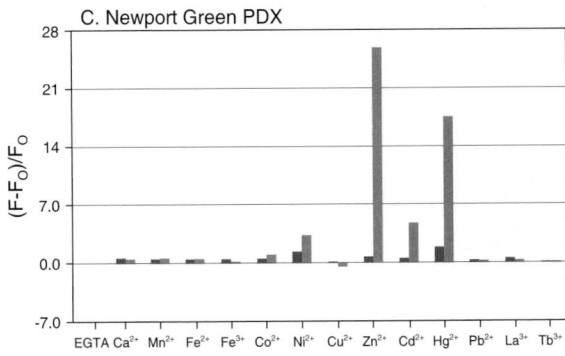

Figure 19.78 Metal-ion response screening for calcein, Newport Green™ and Phen Green™ indicators. The maximum relative fluorescence intensity was measured for identical indicator concentrations in solutions containing 10 mM EGTA + 10 µM TPEN, 1 µM ion and 100 µM ion. Results are plotted as fluorescence changes relative to the ion-free (10 mM EGTA + 10 µM TPEN) reference solution expressed as $(F-F_o)/F_o$, where F is the fluorescence intensity of ion-containing solutions and F_o is the fluorescence intensity of the reference solution. Blue bars indicate the response to 1 µM ion, and red bars indicate the response to 100 µM ion. The indicators represented are: A) calcein, B) Newport Green™ DCF, C) Newport Green™ PDX, D) Phen Green™ FL (this indicator salt is no longer routinely available, please inquire) and E) Phen Green™ SK.

Indicators for Zinc

Zinc is an important divalent cation in biological systems, influencing DNA synthesis, microtubule polymerization, gene expression, apoptosis, immune system function and the activity of enzymes such as carbonic anhydrase and matrix metalloproteinases[42,43] (MMP). Zn^{2+} is also functionally active in synaptic transmission and is a contributory factor in neurological disorders including epilepsy and Alzheimer's disease.[44,45] Free Zn^{2+} is released from metalloprotein complexes during oxidative stress or on release of nitric oxide in neurons.[46] The intracellular concentration of free Zn^{2+} is extremely low in most cells (<1 nM), with the remainder being bound to proteins or nucleic acids.[47] One calculation[48] yields an intracellular free Zn^{2+} concentration of six orders of magnitude less than one atom per cell. Molecular Probes prepares a variety of Zn^{2+} indicators,[49] including several that are exclusively available from the company and its distributors (Table 19.6), to help elucidate the role of Zn^{2+} release and the localization of free or chelatable Zn^{2+} in cells.

FuraZin™-1, IndoZin™-1, FluoZin™-1, RhodZin™-1 and Related Indicators

Zinc concentrations in the 1–100 nM range can be measured using fluorescent indicators nominally designed for Ca^{2+} detection such as fura-2 (see below), or more recently developed indicators with greater Zn^{2+} selectivity.[50–52] We have focused our development efforts on probes for detection of higher Zn^{2+} concentrations that are present in synaptic vesicles and released in response to electrical

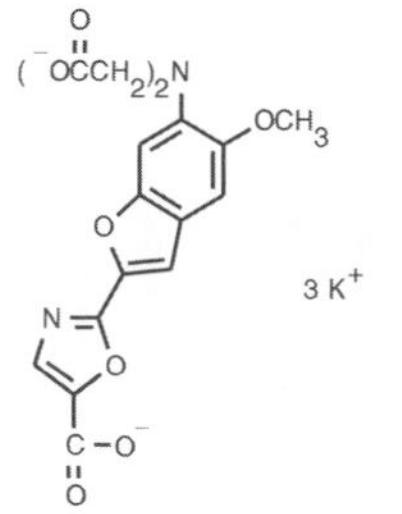

Figure 19.79 F24182 FuraZin™-1, tripotassium salt.

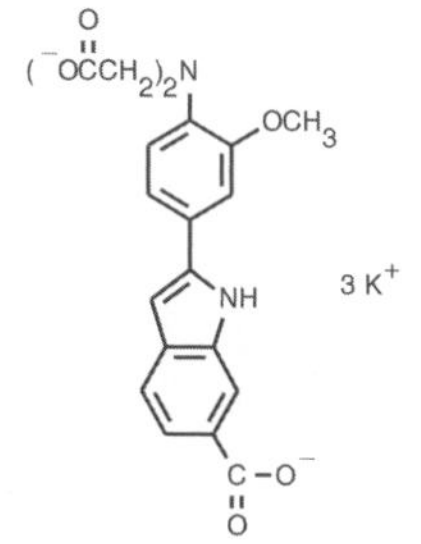

Figure 19.80 I24184 IndoZin™-1, tripotassium salt.

stimulation or excitotoxic agonists.[44] Peak concentrations of synaptically released Zn^{2+} may exceed 100 µM. We have developed FuraZin™-1 (F24182, F24183, Figure 19.79), IndoZin™-1 (I24184, I24185, Figure 19.80), FluoZin™-1 [53] (F24180, F24181), FluoZin™-2 (F24188, F24189) and RhodZin™-1 (R24186, R24187), a series of unique indicators designed for detection of Zn^{2+} in the 0.1–100 µM range with minimal interfering Ca^{2+} sensitivity [49] (panels H and N, Figure 19.76). The spectral responses of these indicators closely mimic those of the similarly named Ca^{2+} indicators. For instance, FuraZin™-1 (Figure 19.81) and IndoZin™-1 (Figure 19.82) exhibit Zn^{2+}-dependent excitation and emission spectral shifts, respectively; FluoZin™-2 (Figure 19.83) and RhodZin™-1 (Figure 19.84) show Zn^{2+}-dependent fluorescence without accompanying spectral shifts.

FluoZin™-3 Indicator

The FluoZin™-3 indicator [49,54] (F24194, Figure 19.85) is a Zn^{2+}-selective indicator with a structure that resembles fluo-4. FluoZin™-3 exhibits high Zn^{2+}-binding affinity (K_d for Zn^{2+} ~15 nM, Figure 19.86) that is unperturbed by Ca^{2+} concentrations up to at least 1 µM. The Zn^{2+}-specificity of FluoZin™-3 evident from measurements in calibration solutions is reproduced in cell-based experiments. Molecular Probes' researchers have found that in HeLa cells loaded with the cell-permeant AM ester form of FluoZin™-3 (F24195), the addition of 1 µM Ca^{2+} in the presence of the Ca^{2+} ionophore ionomycin (I24222, Section 19.8) produces no detectable response, whereas subsequent addition of 10 nM Zn^{2+} in the presence of the Zn^{2+} ionophore pyrithione results in a large fluorescence increase. In addition, FluoZin™-3 exhibits a large increase in fluorescence in response to saturating levels of Zn^{2+} (greater than 50 fold). FluoZin™-3 has been found to be a brighter alternative to Zinquin for measuring the exocytotic release of Zn^{2+} from pancreatic β-cells after stimulation with glucose or potassium.[55]

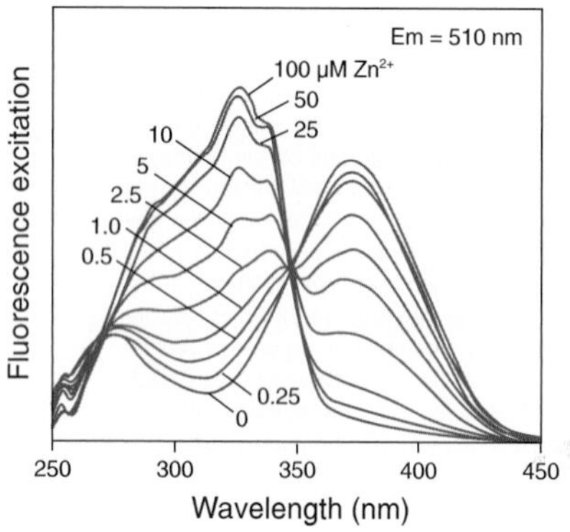

Figure 19.81 Zn^{2+} dependence of the fluorescence excitation spectra of FuraZin™-1 (F24182).

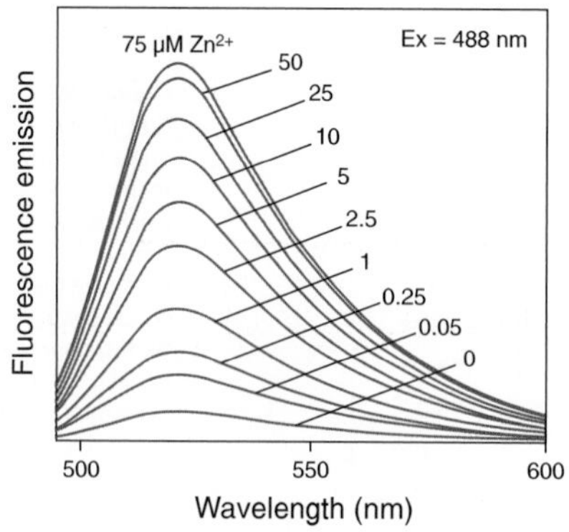

Figure 19.83 Zn^{2+} dependence of the fluorescence emission spectra of FluoZin™-2 (F24188).

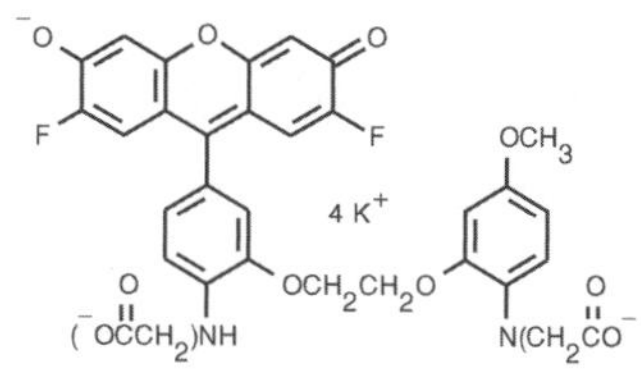

Figure 19.85 F24194 FluoZin™-3, tetrapotassium salt.

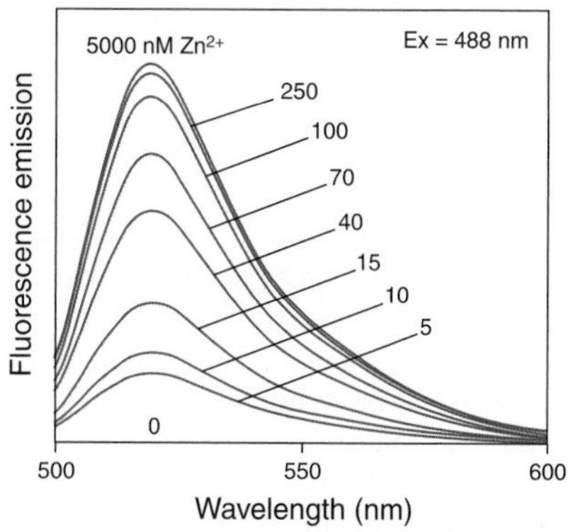

Figure 19.86 Zn^{2+} dependence of the fluorescence emission spectra of FluoZin™-3 (F24194).

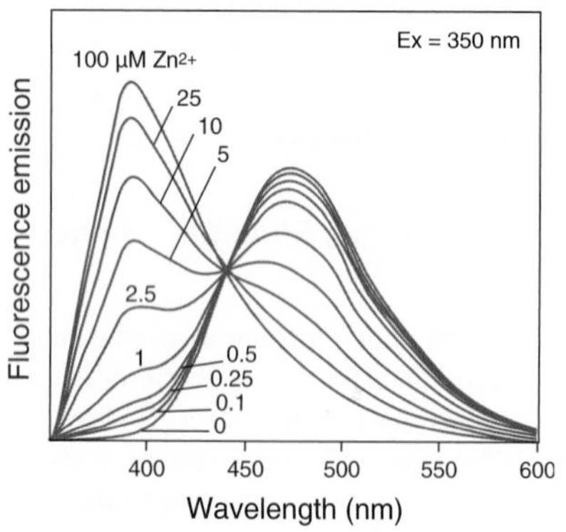

Figure 19.82 Zn^{2+} dependence of the fluorescence emission spectra of IndoZin™-1 (I24184).

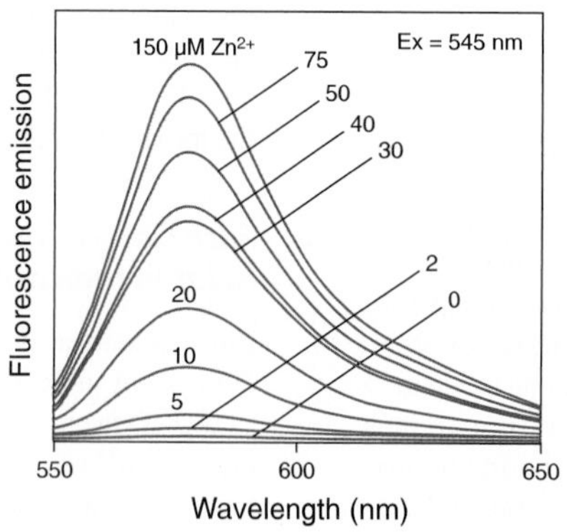

Figure 19.84 Zn^{2+} dependence of the fluorescence emission spectra of RhodZin™-1 (R24186).

RhodZin™-3 Indicator

The orange-fluorescent RhodZin™-3 zinc indicator exhibits a dramatic 75-fold increase in fluorescence at saturating levels of Zn^{2+} and also possesses a K_d for Zn^{2+} of ~65 nM.[56] The cell-permeant AM ester form of RhodZin™-3 (R36351) effectively localizes into mitochondria and is expected to be a valuable tool for investigating the complex role of intracellular Zn^{2+}; it may also be useful for monitoring changes in Zn^{2+} levels associated with pro-apoptosis. The cell-impermeant RhodZin™-3 salt (R36350) can be used to measure extracellular Zn^{2+} concentrations.

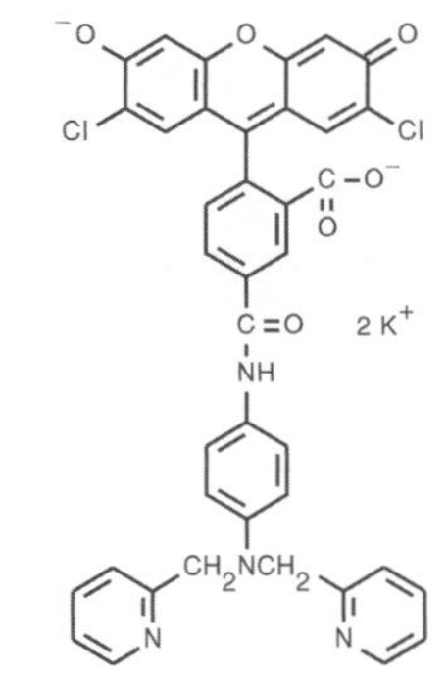

Figure 19.87 N7990 Newport Green™ DCF, dipotassium salt.

Newport Green™ DCF and Newport Green™ PDX Indicators

The Newport Green™ DCF indicator (N7990, N7991) has moderate zinc-binding affinity (K_d for Zn^{2+} ~1 µM) but is essentially insensitive to Ca^{2+} (K_d for Ca^{2+} >100 µM), making this a valuable probe for detecting Zn^{2+} influx into neurons through voltage- or glutamate-gated channels.[57–62] When used alongside dyes with dual Ca^{2+}/Zn^{2+} sensitivity such as fura-2 and mag-fura-2, Newport Green™ DCF provides confirmation that changes in Zn^{2+} levels, and not Ca^{2+} or Mg^{2+}, are being detected.[59,63] Newport Green™ DCF has also been used in conjunction with Texas Red® 10,000 MW dextran to create a ratiometric fluorescent PEBBLE (Probe Encapsulated By Biologically Localized Embedding) nanosensor for real-time measurements of intra- and intercellular free zinc.[64]

Newport Green™ PDX[49] (N24190, N24191) incorporates the same di-(2-picolyl)amine chelator as Newport Green™ DCF (Figure 19.87, Figure 19.88) but has a higher Zn^{2+} dissociation constant (K_d for Zn^{2+} ~30 µM) and a larger Zn^{2+}-free to Zn^{2+}-saturated fluorescence intensity increase. Newport Green™ DCF has been used to identify insulin-producing β-cells from human pancreatic islets based on their high intracellular Zn^{2+} content[65] (Figure 19.89).

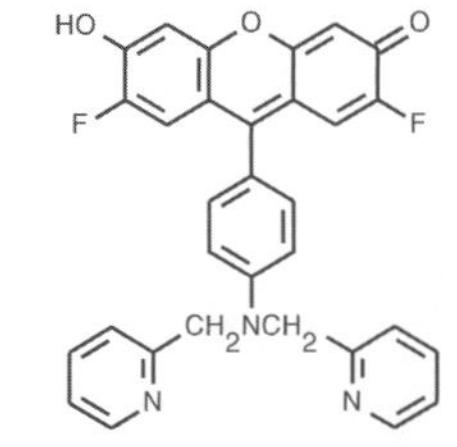

Figure 19.88 N24190 Newport Green™ PDX.

TSQ

Use of the membrane-permeant probe *N*-(6-methoxy-8-quinolyl)-*p*-toluenesulfonamide (TSQ, M688; Figure 19.90) in cells was first described by Fredrickson.[66] TSQ is selective for Zn^{2+} in the presence of physiological concentrations of Ca^{2+} and Mg^{2+} ions. The complex of TSQ with free Zn^{2+} apparently has a stoichiometry of two dye molecules per metal atom,[67] but a 1:1 complex may be formed with metalloproteins. The intracellular Zn^{2+} chelator dithizone blocks TSQ binding of Zn^{2+}.[68]

Several reports suggest that TSQ can be used to localize Zn^{2+} pools in the central nervous system.[69–71] Zn^{2+} moves from presynaptic nerve terminals into postsynaptic nerve terminals when blood flow is constricted in the brain. This translocation is reported to correlate with ischemia-caused neurodegeneration, as determined by the fluorescence of TSQ.[68] TSQ has also been used to detect nitric oxide–induced accumulation of free Zn^{2+} in neuronal perikarya[46] and changes in Zn^{2+} distribution in the rat hippocampus and amygdala[72] during and after kainic acid–induced seizures. TSQ (like Newport Green™ DCF, see below) is a selective nontoxic stain for pancreatic islet cells, which have a high content of Zn^{2+}, and may be useful for their flow cytometric isolation.[73–75]

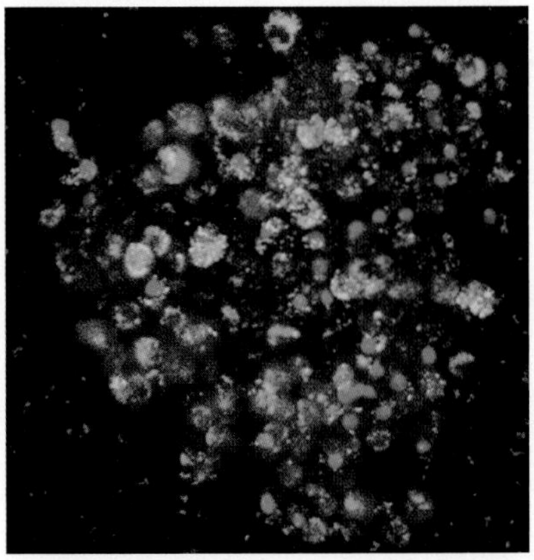

Figure 19.89 A human pancreatic islet stained with Newport Green™ DCF diacetate (N7991) and propidium iodide (P1304MP, P3566, P21493). The image represents a projection of 60 optical sections acquired at 2 µm intervals by confocal laser-scanning microscopy. The green-fluorescent Newport Green™ DCF indicator identifies viable insulin-producing β-cells via binding to intracellular zinc. Dead cells are identified by red-fluorescent propidium iodide staining. Image contributed by Brigitte Vandewalle, University of Lille, and reproduced with permission from J Histochem Cytochem 49, 519 (2001).

TSQ-based assays for Zn^{2+} in seawater and other biological systems exhibit a detection limit of ~0.1 nM.[76,77] The simultaneous determination of Zn^{2+} and Cd^{2+} by spectrofluorometry using TSQ in an SDS micelle has also been reported.[67] TSQ has been used to measure Zn^{2+} levels in artificial lipid vesicles and live sperm cells by flow cytometry.[78] In this latter study, the fluorescence yield of the TSQ–Zn^{2+} complex was shown to be much higher when bound to lipids than in aqueous solution, indicating that quantitative cell assays for Zn^{2+} based on the fluorescence intensity of TSQ may not be accurate because of uncertainty in the quantum yield of the dye when bound to membranes.

Traditional Ca^{2+} and Mg^{2+} Indicators as Zn^{2+} Indicators

Zn^{2+} binds to most BAPTA-based Ca^{2+} indicators with substantially higher affinity than Ca^{2+}.[79] For example, fura-2 (F1200, F6799; Section 19.2) exhibits a K_d for Zn^{2+} in the absence of Ca^{2+} of 3 nM (Table 19.5). The lack of saturation of fura-2 fluorescence in resting cells is indicative of the low intracellular concentration of free Zn^{2+}. Fura-2 remains sensitive to nanomolar Zn^{2+} levels in the presence of 25–100 nM free Ca^{2+}, allowing detection of intracellular Zn^{2+} influx via voltage-gated Ca^{2+} channels,[80] and examining Zn^{2+} levels in living neurons[62,81,82] and myocytes.[83] Fura-2 has also been used as an indicator for nanomolar levels of free Zn^{2+} and other ions in solution.[11]

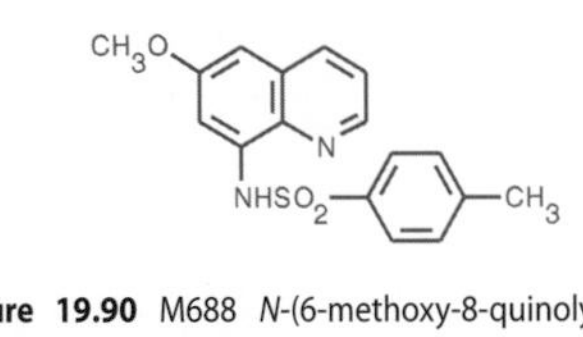

Figure 19.90 M688 *N*-(6-methoxy-8-quinolyl)-*p*-toluenesulfonamide (TSQ).

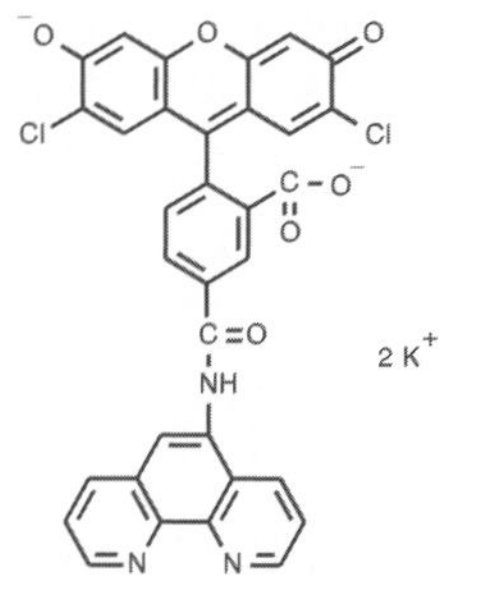

Figure 19.91 P14312 Phen Green™ SK, dipotassium salt.

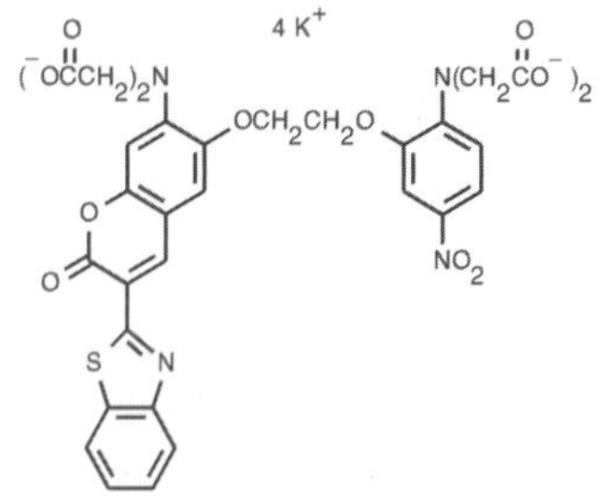

Figure 19.92 B6845 BTC-5N, tetrapotassium salt.

Mag-fura-2 (M1290, Section 19.6) exhibits slightly altered spectral characteristics upon binding Zn^{2+} (K_d ~20 nM at pH 7.0–7.8 and 37°C), allowing Zn^{2+} to be measured in the presence of Ca^{2+}.[84] A review by Canzoniero and co-workers[62] evaluates the performance of currently available fluorescent indicators for neuronal Zn^{2+}. As usual, the key to indicator selection is matching the ion binding affinity (K_d) to the prevailing range of ion concentrations. In the case of neuronal free Zn^{2+}, physiological concentrations apparently are about 1–50 nM. Under these conditions, indicators nominally designed for detection of intracellular magnesium, such as mag-fura-2 and mag-fura-5, with K_d for Zn^{2+} around 20 nM, appear to be the most suitable.[82] Based on their similar ion-binding properties, the Magnesium Green™ indicator (K_d for Zn^{2+} = 20 nM[85]) (M3733, Section 19.6) and our mag-fluo-4 indicator (M14205, Section 19.6) are suitable for confocal imaging of Zn^{2+} influx.[86]

Indicators for Copper

Copper is third in abundance (after Fe^{3+} and Zn^{2+}) among the essential heavy metals in the human body. Dietary copper is required for normal hemoglobin synthesis, for prevention of anemia and for some enzyme activity. It may also play a role in dexamethasone- and etoposide-induced apoptosis.[87] Recent results suggest that free intracellular copper ions are absent in cells.[88,89] Reduction of Cu^{2+} to Cu^{+} is catalyzed by the β-amyloid precursor protein, which is converted to plaques that are characteristic of Alzheimer's disease.[90]

Phen Green™ FL for Cu^{2+}

The phenanthroline-based Phen Green™ FL indicator, available only as the cell-permant diacetate (P6763), is an excellent general-purpose heavy metal sensor capable of detecting a broad range of metal ions, including both Cu^{2+} and Cu^{+}.[85,91] The use of Phen Green™ FL for detecting Fe^{2+}, Hg^{2+}, Pb^{2+}, Cd^{2+} and Ni^{2+} at submicromolar concentrations is described below. Uncomplexed Phen Green™ FL is brightly fluorescent, with a fluorescence quantum yield of ~0.8. Binding of certain heavy metal ions is registered by strong fluorescence quenching (Figure 19.78). The emission intensity of Phen Green™ FL depends both on metal ion concentration and on the indicator's concentration. Phen Green™ FL diacetate has allowed researchers to discern significant differences in intracellular Cu^{2+} levels for four types of lobster hepatopancreatic epithelial cells.[85]

Traditional Ca^{2+} and Mg^{2+} Indicators as Cu^{2+} Indicators

Fluorescence of calcein (C481) is strongly quenched by Cu^{2+} at neutral pH[36] (Figure 19.78), although this spectroscopic response does not appear to have been exploited for Cu^{2+} detection. Cu^{2+} has also been measured in solution using fura-2.[11] Indicators designed for detection of Ca^{2+}, Mg^{2+} and Zn^{2+} generally exhibit relatively weak responses to Cu^{2+}. Fluo-4 and FuraZin™-1 appear to be the best choices for detection of Cu^{2+} from among this group of indicators (Figure 19.76).

Indicators for Iron

Phen Green™ FL and Phen Green™ SK

The intracellular pool of chelatable iron is considered to be a decisive pathogenic factor for various kinds of cell injury.[92,93] Our general-purpose heavy metal sensors, Phen Green™ FL (available only as the cell-permant diacetate, (P6763)) and Phen Green™ SK (P14312, Figure 19.91; cell-permeant diacetate, P14313), are capable of detecting Fe^{2+}, as well as Cu^{2+}, Cu^{+}, Hg^{2+}, Pb^{2+}, Cd^{2+} and Ni^{2+}.[85] Fluorescence of the Phen Green™ indicators is quenched upon binding Fe^{2+} (Figure 19.75) and Fe^{3+} (Figure 19.78). The emission intensity of the Phen Green™ FL indicator depends on both the metal ion's concentration and the indicator's concentration.[93] Phen Green™ SK diacetate has been successfully used to quantitate the intracellular pool of chelatable iron in rat hepatocytes,[92–94] to directly measure Fe^{2+} transport into membrane vesicles[95] and to follow the accelerated rate of intracellular iron reduction in L929 cells in the presence of D-glucose.[96]

Calcein

Cabantchik and co-workers have exploited the fluorescence quenching of calcein at neutral pH to follow intracellular release of Fe^{2+} from transferrin.[36,97,98] Using passively loaded calcein AM

(C1430, C3099, C3100MP), they were able to measure cytosolic Fe^{2+} concentrations from about 0.1 µM to 1.0 µM. However, more recent studies on the mechanism of iron chelation indicate that quenching of calcein fluorescence is primarily due to Fe^{3+} and is relatively insensitive to Fe^{2+} [99] (Figure 19.78). Nontransferrin-bound iron (NTBI) occurs in the serum of individuals with iron overload and in a variety of other pathological conditions, including thalassemia. A microplate assay based on the fluorescence quenching of calcein by iron has been developed to measure NTBI.[100] Calcein and calcein AM have also been utilized to measure the sequestering of iron by ferritin.[101]

Indicators for Mercury, Lead, Barium and Cadmium

Phen Green™ FL and Phen Green™ SK

Our phenanthroline-based Phen Green™ FL and Phen Green™ SK indicators (P14312, Figure 19.91), which can be passively loaded into cells as their membrane-permeant diacetates (P6763, P14313), are excellent general-purpose heavy metal sensors that are capable of detecting a broad range of metal ions — including Cu^{2+}, Cu^{+} and Fe^{2+} (see above) — as well as micromolar concentrations of Hg^{2+}, Pb^{2+}, Cd^{2+}, Zn^{2+} and Ni^{2+}.[85,93] The fluorescence of 1 µM Phen Green™ FL is ~90% quenched by 1 µM Hg^{2+}, as compared with ~43% quenching for Phen Green™ SK (Figure 19.78). Like phenanthroline itself, the stoichiometry of metal binding to Phen Green™ indicator is not always 1:1, permitting the detection range to be tuned by varying the indicator's concentration. For Hg^{2+}, the metal concentration that yields the half-maximal fluorescence response is 0.02 µM when the Phen Green™ FL concentration is 0.12 µM and increases to 1.2 µM when the Phen Green™ FL concentration is 5 µM. Concentrations of soluble Pb^{2+} as low as ~2 µM can be determined using ~1 µM Phen Green™ FL. Reducing the Phen Green™ FL concentration to <1 µM further improves the sensitivity for detection of Pb^{2+}.

We have used these versatile sensors to detect metal ions in a variety of matrices, including seawater and various contaminated solids such as paint sludge and soil. In such samples, Phen Green™ FL and Phen Green™ SK detect only the readily soluble (bioavailable) fraction of the total metal ions. Phen Green™ FL and Phen Green™ SK are well suited for initial field testing of metal ion contamination in aqueous samples; the large fluorescence changes produced by micromolar ion concentrations of these heavy metals are easily visible upon illuminating the sample with a hand-held light source (Figure 19.75).

BTC-5N

The fluorescence of BTC-5N (B6845, B6846; Figure 19.92) excited at 405–415 nm increases upon binding Cd^{2+} [102] and Zn^{2+} [103] but is not significantly affected by millimolar levels of Ca^{2+}, Mg^{2+}, Na^{+} or K^{+}, or by 25 µM levels of Al^{3+}, Bi^{3+}, Cu^{+}, Cu^{2+}, Ni^{2+} or Pb^{2+}. We have determined the K_d of BTC-5N for Cd^{2+}, Zn^{2+}, Hg^{2+}, Pb^{2+} and Ba^{2+} to be 0.1, 0.2, 0.4, 6.3 and 68 µM, respectively.[104] However, as with most fluorescent indicators, complex ionic environments result in somewhat lower detection sensitivity; for example, the K_d of BTC-5N for Cd^{2+} in seawater is ~1.4 µM.[104] BTC-5N has been used to detect large concentrations of intracellularly released Co^{2+} in a study of cation-induced exocytosis.[105]

Traditional Ca^{2+} and Mg^{2+} Indicators as Ba^{2+}, Cd^{2+} and Pb^{2+} Indicators

The fluorescence of several of our traditional Ca^{2+} and Mg^{2+} indicators is strongly affected by binding of Cd^{2+}, Hg^{2+} and Pb^{2+} (Figure 19.76). Fura-2 and quin-2 bind Cd^{2+} with extremely high affinity (Table 19.5). The excitation response of fura-2 to Cd^{2+} — almost identical to its Ca^{2+} response — has been used to monitor Cd^{2+} uptake by cells and to image intracellular free Cd^{2+}.[106] The response is reversed by TPEN (T1210, Section 19.8), which complexes many heavy metals but not Ca^{2+} or Mg^{2+}.[14] Mag-fura-2 (M1290, Section 19.6) is also a useful intracellular Cd^{2+} indicator,[107] and indo-1 can be used to simultaneously determine the intracellular concentrations of Ca^{2+} and Cd^{2+} or Ca^{2+} and Ba^{2+}. Use of fura-2 AM to measure the concentration of cytosolic Ba^{2+} has also been reported,[12] as has fluorometric detection of Cd^{2+} at pH 13.3 using calcein [108] (C481). Pb^{2+} entry into cells has been monitored using fura-2 or indo-1 as intracellular indicators.[109–113] Pb^{2+} is efficiently transported into cells with high selectivity by ionomycin [114] (I24222, Section 19.8). ^{19}F NMR can also be used to detect Pb^{2+} uptake by platelets using fluorinated BAPTA derivatives [115] (Section 19.8).

Indicators for Nickel and Cobalt

Newport Green™ Indicators

Much of the recent interest in Ni^{2+} comes from its use in the detection (Section 9.4) and isolation of oligohistidine fusion proteins by metal-chelate affinity chromatography.[116,117] We have developed the Newport Green™ DCF indicator (N7990, Figure 19.87), which we find to be an exceptionally sensitive probe for Ni^{2+} and Zn^{2+} in solution (K_d = 1.0 µM for Zn^{2+} and 1.5 µM for Ni^{2+}).[104] 100 µM Ni^{2+} enhances the fluorescence of the Newport Green™ DCF reagent approximately 13-fold without a spectral shift; Zn^{2+} and Co^{2+} enhance this indicator's fluorescence to a lesser extent (Figure 19.78). Newport Green™ DCF diacetate (N7991) has been used to measure the cellular uptake of Ni^{2+} in hydrogen peroxide–stimulated L929 cells.[118] Newport Green™ PDX (N24190, N24191) incorporates the same di-(2-picolyl)amine chelator as Newport Green™ DCF (Figure 19.87, Figure 19.88) and should prove to have similar utility for detection of Ni^{2+}.

Luminol: An Ultrasensitive Indicator for Co^{2+}

In an unusual method for assaying a metal, the catalytic effect of Co^{2+} on the oxidation of luminol (L8455, Section 10.5) by hydrogen peroxide in an alkaline solution has been utilized to measure subnanomolar concentrations of Co^{2+} in seawater.[119] Interference by Fe^{2+}, which also catalyzes the oxidation of luminol, is readily removed; no other tested ions interfered with this chemiluminescent assay.

Traditional Ca^{2+} and Mg^{2+} Indicators as Ni^{2+} and Co^{2+} Indicators

Co^{2+} enhances the fluorescence of the Calcium Green™-2 indicator at least 20-fold and strongly quenches fluorescence of the Fura Red™ indicator (Figure 19.76). Co^{2+} and Ni^{2+}, as well as Cu^{2+} and Fe^{3+} (Figure 19.78), strongly quench the fluorescence of calcein, even at pH 7.[120–122] Consequently, it should be possible to follow the kinetics of uptake of these ions into cells loaded with calcein AM (C1430, C3099, C3100MP). Note that the 1:1 stoichiometry of calcein–metal binding will require the use of low loading levels of this probe to achieve significant quenching by limited amounts of metal transport.

The efficient quenching of calcein fluorescence by Co^{2+} or Ni^{2+} [36] has been used to detect liposome fusion [121] (see Note 14.3 "Technical Focus: Assays of Volume Change, Membrane Fusion and Membrane Permeability" in Section 14.3). Fura-2 has been used to measure low levels of Ni^{2+} and Co^{2+} in solution.[11]

Indicators for Aluminum

Al^{3+} binding has little effect on the fluorescence of most of the traditional Ca^{2+} and Mg^{2+} indicators. However, Al^{3+} is reported to selectively form a fluorescent complex with calcein (C481) at acidic pH that can be detected with micromolar sensitivity.[123] Quenching of the Al^{3+}-calcein complex fluorescence has been used as the basis of a method for fluoride determination, with a detection limit of 0.2 ng/mL.[124]

Indicators for Lanthanides

Naphthoyltrifluoroacetone

Europium ions form highly fluorescent complexes with naphthoyltrifluoroacetone (T411). The resulting chelates have extremely long lifetimes and are widely used in highly sensitive time-resolved fluoroimmunoassays [125] (TR-FIA).

Traditional Ca^{2+} and Mg^{2+} Indicators as Lanthanide Indicators

La^{3+} has a strong effect on the fluorescence of indicators designed for detection of Ca^{2+}, Mg^{2+} and Zn^{2+} (Figure 19.76). For example, fluo-4 fluorescence increases more than 400-fold in the presence of 100 µM La^{3+}, a response that is about twice as large as that generated by Ca^{2+} saturation. Detection of La^{3+} by the prototypical BAPTA-based Ca^{2+} indicator quin-2 has been used to investigate the ion transport selectivity of 4-bromo A-23187 (B1494, Section 19.8) and other ionophores.[126] These indicators generally exhibit relatively weak responses to Tb^{3+}; fluo-3 and fluo-4 are apparently the most sensitive (~40-fold fluorescence enhancement with 1 µM Tb^{3+}) (Figure 19.76). Long-lived luminescence of Tb^{3+} (from $TbCl_3$, T1247) is also used to probe Ca^{2+} and other metal binding sites of alkaline phosphatase,[127] glutamine synthetase,[128] integrins,[129] protein kinase C [130] and other proteins.

References

1. Mol Cell Biochem 151, 91 (1995); **2.** Endocrinology 131, 1936 (1992); **3.** J Toxicol Environ Health 38, 159 (1993); **4.** FASEB J 7, 1507 (1993); **5.** Brain Res 618, 9 (1993); **6.** Photometric Determination of Trace Metals, 4th Ed., Vol. 3, Part IIA, Onishi H (Complete Volume), (1986); **7.** Anal Biochem 267, 185 (1999); **8.** Curr Med Chem 9, 275 (2002); **9.** Fresenius J Anal Chem 368, 182 (2000); **10.** Cell Calcium 28, 225 (2000); **11.** Anal Biochem 284, 307 (2000); **12.** J Biol Chem 275, 20274 (2000); **13.** J Biol Chem 275, 6980 (2000); **14.** J Biol Chem 260, 2719 (1985); **15.** Biophys J 71, 1048 (1996); **16.** Cell Calcium 29, 217 (2001); **17.** Methods Cell Biol 40, 155 (1994); **18.** J Cell Biol 136, 833 (1997); **19.** J Physiol 507, 379 (1998); **20.** Cell Calcium 16, 87 (1994); **21.** Cell Calcium 18, 420 (1995); **22.** Cell Calcium 10, 171 (1989); **23.** J Physiol 523 Pt 3, 549 (2000); **24.** Neurosci Lett 229, 109 (1997); **25.** Cell Calcium 22, 157 (1997); **26.** Methods Enzymol 288, 301 (1997); **27.** Biochem J 302, 5 (1994); **28.** J Biol Chem 264, 1522 (1989); **29.** Pflugers Arch 423, 225 (1993); **30.** Cell Calcium 22, 385 (1997); **31.** J Biol Chem 264, 197 (1989); **32.** Biochem J 320, 505 (1996); **33.** Biophys J 76, 2029 (1999); **34.** Cell Calcium 13, 19 (1992); **35.** Eur J Biochem 192, 239 (1990); **36.** Am J Physiol 268, C1354 (1995); **37.** Biophys J 76, 725 (1999); **38.** J Biol Chem 275, 35738 (2000); **39.** Mol Biochem Parasitol 101, 43 (1999); **40.** Blood 94, 2128 (1999); **41.** J Biol Chem 275, 1651 (2000); **42.** Sci STKE 2003, pe18 (2003); **43.** J Nutr 130, 1341S (2000); **44.** Trends Pharmacol Sci 21, 395 (2000); **45.** Science 265, 1464 (1994); **46.** Brain Res 799, 118 (1998); **47.** J Membr Biol 123, 63 (1991); **48.** Science 292, 2488 (2001); **49.** Cell Calcium 31, 245 (2002); **50.** J Am Chem Soc 122, 5644 (2000); **51.** J Am Chem Soc 119, 3443 (2000); **52.** J Am Chem Soc 118, 6514 (1996); **53.** J Biol Chem 279, 12043 (2004); **54.** J Am Chem Soc 124, 776 (2002); **55.** Anal Chem 75, 3136 (2003); **56.** Cell Calcium 34, 281 (2003); **57.** J Neurosci 22, 1273 (2002); **58.** J Physiol 528 Pt 1, 39 (2000); **59.** Proc Natl Acad Sci U S A 96, 2414 (1999); **60.** J Neurosci 19, RC31 (1999); **61.** Eur J Neurosci 12, 3813 (2000); **62.** Neurobiol Dis 4, 275 (1997); **63.** J Neurochem 75, 1878 (2000); **64.** Analyst 127, 11 (2002); **65.** J Histochem Cytochem 49, 519 (2001); **66.** J Neurosci Methods 20, 91 (1987); **67.** J Fluorescence 1, 267 (1991); **68.** Science 272, 1013 (1996); **69.** Pain 86, 177 (2000); **70.** J Neurosci 19, 2288 (1999); **71.** Eur J Neurosci 12, 8 (2000); **72.** Brain Res 480, 317 (1989); **73.** Biotech Histochem 68, 196 (1993); **74.** Transplantation 56, 1282 (1993); **75.** Diabetes 41, 1056 (1992); **76.** Anal Chem 66, 2732 (1994); **77.** Biol Res 27, 49 (1994); **78.** Cytometry 21, 153 (1995); **79.** Cell Calcium 27, 75 (2000); **80.** J Biol Chem 270, 2473 (1995); **81.** J Neurochem 71, 2401 (1998); **82.** J Neurosci 17, 9554 (1997); **83.** Am J Physiol 272, H2095 (1997); **84.** J Biochem Biophys Methods 27, 25 (1993); **85.** Proc SPIE-Int Soc Opt Eng 2388, 238 (1995); **86.** J Physiol 529 Pt 1, 83 (2000); **87.** FEBS Lett 352, 58 (1994); **88.** Science 284, 748 (1999); **89.** Science 284, 805 (1999); **90.** Science 271, 1406 (1996); **91.** J Exp Biol 204, 1433 (2001); **92.** Biochem J 356, 61 (2001); **93.** Hepatology 29, 1171 (1999); **94.** Arch Biochem Biophys 376, 74 (2000); **95.** Anal Biochem 296, 106 (2001); **96.** Biochem J 368, 517 (2002); **97.** J Biol Chem 270, 24209 (1995); **98.** FEBS Lett 382, 304 (1996); **99.** J Biol Chem 274, 13375 (1999); **100.** Blood 95, 2975 (2000); **101.** J Biol Chem 273, 15382 (1998); **102.** Toxicol Lett 81, 151 (1995); **103.** Neuron 26, 187 (2000); **104.** These K_d values are from approximate (estimated precision ±50%) determinations in 5 mM MOPS, pH 7, at 22°C; **105.** J Physiol 533, 627 (2001); **106.** J Biol Chem 267, 25553 (1992); **107.** Kidney Int 41, 1237 (1992); **108.** Anal Chem 46, 2036 (1974); **109.** Toxicol Sci 46, 90 (1998); **110.** Neurotoxicology 21, 365 (2000); **111.** J Biol Chem 272, 8346 (1997); **112.** Toxicol Appl Pharmacol 146, 127 (1997); **113.** Am J Physiol 259, C762 (1990); **114.** J Biol Chem 275, 7071 (2000); **115.** Biochim Biophys Acta 1092, 341 (1991); **116.** Bio/Technology 6, 1321 (1988); **117.** J Biol Chem 258, 5994 (1983); **118.** Free Radic Biol Med 25, 712 (1998); **119.** Anal Chem 71, 1975 (1999); **120.** Chem Pharm Bull (Tokyo) 39, 227 (1991); **121.** Biochim Biophys Acta 691, 332 (1982); **122.** Anal Chem 56, 810 (1984); **123.** Anal Chem 35, 1035 (1963); **124.** Fresenius J Anal Chem 368, 501 (2000); **125.** Analyst 117, 1879 (1992); **126.** Biophys J 75, 1244 (1998); **127.** J Photochem Photobiol B 13, 289 (1992); **128.** Biochemistry 30, 3417 (1991); **129.** Biochemistry 33, 12238 (1994); **130.** J Biol Chem 265, 4223 (1990).

Data Table — 19.7 Fluorescent Indicators for Zn^{2+} and Other Metal Ions

				Low Zn^{2+}				High Zn^{2+}						
Cat #	**MW**	**Storage**	**Soluble**	**Abs**	**EC**	**Em**	**Solvent**	**Abs**	**EC**	**Em**	**Solvent**	**Product**	**K_d**	**Notes**
A6895	598.71	L	pH >6	466	31,000	520	H_2O	380	16,000	530	H_2O/Zn^{2+}		1.4 µM	1, 2, 3
A6896	700.63	F,D,L	DMSO	429	41,000	496	MeOH					A6895		
B6845	875.00	L	pH >6	459	40,000	517	H_2O	417	25,000	532	H_2O/Zn^{2+}		210 nM	1, 2, 4
B6846	1010.89	F,D,L	DMSO	428	42,000	482	EtOAc					B6845		
B6847	946.96	L	pH >6	455	53,000	529	H_2O	405	42,000	505	H_2O/Cd^{2+}		140 nM	1, 2
C481	622.54	L	pH >5	494	77,000	517	pH 9			see Notes			see Notes	5, 6
C1430	994.87	F,D	DMSO	<300		none						C481		
C3099	994.87	F,D	DMSO	<300		none						C481		7
C3100MP	994.87	F,D	DMSO	<300		none						C481		
E6960	366.41	D	H_2O	337	17,000	613	H_2O							8, 9
F6864	677.77	F,D,L	H_2O	493	80,000	517	pH 9			see Notes				10
F6865	734.82	F,D,L	H_2O	493	84,000	517	pH 9			see Notes				10
F24180	599.67	D,L	pH >6	490	68,000	see Notes	H_2O	495	58,000	517	H_2O/Zn^{2+}		8.2 µM	1, 2, 11, 12
F24181	701.59	F,D,L	DMSO	456	26,000	see Notes	MeOH					F24180		13
F24182	504.58	D,L	pH >6	373	25,000	512	H_2O	325	27,000	505	H_2O/Zn^{2+}		3.0 µM	1, 2
F24183	606.50	F,D,L	DMSO	372	36,000	479	EtOAc					F24182		
F24188	800.89	D,L	pH >6	494	74,000	522	H_2O	494	75,000	521	H_2O/Zn^{2+}		2.0 µM	1, 2, 11
F24189	876.73	F,D,L	DMSO	299	16,000	none	MeOH					F24188		
F24194	846.96	D,L	pH >6	491	82,000	see Notes	H_2O	494	88,000	516	H_2O/Zn^{2+}		15 nM	1, 2, 11, 12, 14
F24195	982.85	F,D,L	DMSO	455	26,000	see Notes	MeOH					F24194		13
I24184	512.64	D,L	pH >6	350	32,000	481	H_2O	326	28,000	398	H_2O/Zn^{2+}		3.3 µM	1, 2
I24185	614.56	F,D,L	DMSO	356	36,000	482	MeOH					I24184		
M688	328.38	L	EtOH	334	4,200	385	MeOH			see Notes				15
N7990	793.74	D,L	pH >6	506	82,000	535	H_2O	506	82,000	535	H_2O/Zn^{2+}		1.0 µM	1, 2, 11
N7991	801.64	F,D	DMSO	302	15,000	none	MeOH					N7990		
N24190	521.52	D,L	pH >6	490	76,000	518	H_2O	491	77,000	518	H_2O/Zn^{2+}		30 µM	1, 2, 11
N24191	593.59	F,D	DMSO	457	21,000	538	MeOH					N24190		
P6763	668.68	F,D	DMSO	<300		none						P6801		
P14312	698.60	D,L	pH >6	507	86,000	532	pH 9			see Notes				16
P14313	706.49	F,D	DMSO	<300		none						P14312		
R24186	541.64	D,L	pH >6	547	76,000	see Notes	H_2O	553	75,000	582	H_2O/Zn^{2+}		23 µM	1, 2, 11, 12
R24187	728.59	F,D,L	DMSO	549	100,000	568	see Notes					R24186		17
R36350	788.94	D,L	pH >6	549	80,000	see Notes	H_2O	552	82,000	576	H_2O/Zn^{2+}		65 nM	1, 2, 11, 12, 14
R36351	1009.86	F,D,L	DMSO	546	110,000	570	see Notes					R36350		17
T411	266.22	D,L	DMF, EtOH	337	17,000	483	MeOH							
T1247	373.38	D	H_2O	270	4,700	545	H_2O							9, 18
T6931	790.79	D,L	pH >6, DMSO	414	416,000	645	pH 9			see Notes				19

For definitions of the contents of this data table, see "Navigating *The Handbook*" in the introductory pages.

Notes

1. Dissociation constants are known to vary considerably depending on the temperature, pH, ionic strength, viscosity, protein binding, presence of other ions (especially polyvalent ions), instrument setup and other factors. It is strongly recommended that these values be verified under user-specific experimental conditions.
2. Spectra measured in aqueous buffers containing zero (H_2O) or a >10-fold excess of free cation X (H_2O/X) relative to the listed dissociation constant (K_d) for cation X.
3. A6895 also binds Cd^{2+} with similar affinity (K_d ~1 µM) and spectral response.
4. Fluorescence excited at 415 nm increases 20-fold on binding Zn^{2+}. Fluorescence enhancements, emission maxima and K_d values for other ions (Cd^{2+}, Hg^{2+}, Pb^{2+}, Ba^{2+}) are variable.
5. C481 fluorescence is strongly quenched by micromolar concentrations of Fe^{3+}, Co^{2+}, Ni^{2+} and Cu^{2+} at pH 7 (Am J Physiol 268, C1354 (1995); J Biol Chem 274, 13375 (1999)).
6. $K_d(Co^{2+})$ for calcein is 120 nM, determined in 10 mM HEPES, 1 µM Ca^{2+}, 1 mM Mg^{2+}, 100 mM KCl (Anal Biochem 248, 31 (1997)).
7. This product is supplied as a ready-made solution in the solvent indicated under "Soluble."
8. Absorption and luminescence of E6960 are extremely weak unless it is chelated. Data are for the detergent-solubilized NTA (T411) chelate.
9. MW is for the hydrated form of this product.
10. Fluorescence of F6864 and F6865 is quenched by micromolar concentrations of Cu^{+} and Hg^{2+} with no change in emission wavelength.
11. This indicator exhibits fluorescence enhancement in response to ion binding, with essentially no change in absorption or emission wavelengths.
12. Fluorescence of the free indicator is very weak and is enhanced >100-fold on binding Zn^{2+}.
13. Fluorescence of this AM ester derivative is very weak and is enhanced only after hydrolytic cleavage followed by binding of divalent cations to the anionic indicator.
14. $K_d(Zn^{2+})$ determined in 135 mM NaCl, 1.1 mM EGTA, 20 mM HEPES pH 7.4, 0 to 10 µM free Zn^{2+} at 22°C. $K_d(Zn^{2+})$ is unchanged in the presence of 1 µM free Ca^{2+} (J Am Chem Soc 124, 776 (2002); Cell Calcium 34, 281 (2003)).
15. Fluorescence of M688 is very sensitive to solvent polarity. Em = 495 nm in aqueous buffer (pH 7.4). Fluorescence is enhanced on binding Zn^{2+} (0.01–10 µM) with no change in emission wavelength (Cytometry 21, 153 (1995)).
16. Fluorescence of Phen Green™ indicators is quenched by Fe^{2+}, Fe^{3+}, Cu^{2+}, Cd^{2+}, Hg^{2+} and Pb^{2+} with no change in emission wavelength. The extent of quenching is dependent on the concentration of indicator as well as the ion concentration.
17. Spectra measured in 90:10 (v/v) $CHCl_3$:MeOH.
18. Absorption and luminescence of T1247 are extremely weak unless it is chelated. Data are for dipicolinic acid (DPA) chelate. The luminescence spectrum has secondary peak at 490 nm.
19. Binding of Cu^{+} (K_d ~500 nM) results in fluorescence quenching with no change in emission wavelength.

Product List — 19.7 Fluorescent Indicators for Zn^{2+} and Other Metal Ions

Cat #	Product Name	Unit Size
A6896	APTRA-BTC, AM *cell permeant*	20 x 50 µg
A6895	APTRA-BTC, tripotassium salt *cell impermeant*	1 mg
B6847	bis-BTC, tetraammonium salt *cell impermeant*	1 mg
B6846	BTC-5N, AM *cell permeant* *special packaging*	20 x 50 µg
B6845	BTC-5N, tetrapotassium salt *cell impermeant*	1 mg
C481	calcein *high purity*	100 mg
C1430	calcein, AM	1 mg
C3099	calcein, AM *1 mg/mL solution in dry DMSO*	1 mL
C3100MP	calcein, AM *special packaging*	20 x 50 µg
E6960	europium(III) chloride, hexahydrate *99.99%*	1 g
F6865	(fluorescein-5-thioureidyl)glycylglycyl-L-histidine, dipotassium salt (FITC-Gly-Gly-His)	1 mg
F6864	(fluorescein-5-thioureidyl)glycyl-L-histidine, dipotassium salt (FITC-Gly-His)	1 mg
F24181	FluoZin™-1, AM *cell permeant* *special packaging*	10 x 50 µg
F24180	FluoZin™-1, tripotassium salt *cell impermeant*	500 µg
F24189	FluoZin™-2, AM *cell permeant* *special packaging*	10 x 50 µg
F24188	FluoZin™-2, tetrapotassium salt *cell impermeant*	500 µg
F24195	FluoZin™-3, AM *cell permeant* *special packaging*	10 x 50 µg
F24194	FluoZin™-3, tetrapotassium salt *cell impermeant*	500 µg
F24183	FuraZin™-1, AM *cell permeant* *special packaging*	10 x 50 µg
F24182	FuraZin™-1, tripotassium salt *cell impermeant*	500 µg
I24185	IndoZin™-1, AM *cell permeant* *special packaging*	10 x 50 µg
I24184	IndoZin™-1, tripotassium salt *cell impermeant*	500 µg
M688	*N*-(6-methoxy-8-quinolyl)-*p*-toluenesulfonamide (TSQ)	25 mg
N7991	Newport Green™ DCF diacetate *cell permeant*	1 mg
N7990	Newport Green™ DCF, dipotassium salt *cell impermeant*	1 mg
N24190	Newport Green™ PDX	1 mg
N24191	Newport Green™ PDX acetoxymethyl ether	1 mg
P6763	Phen Green™ FL, diacetate *cell permeant*	1 mg
P14313	Phen Green™ SK, diacetate	1 mg
P14312	Phen Green™ SK, dipotassium salt	1 mg
R24187	RhodZin™-1, AM *cell permeant* *special packaging*	10 x 50 µg
R24186	RhodZin™-1, potassium salt *cell impermeant*	500 µg
R36351	RhodZin™-3, AM *cell permeant* *special packaging*	10 x 50 µg
R36350	RhodZin™-3, dipotassium salt *cell impermeant*	500 µg
T1247	terbium(III) chloride, hexahydrate	1 g
T6931	tetrakis-(4-carboxyphenyl)porphine (TCPP)	5 mg
T411	2-((trifluoroacetyl)acetyl)naphthalene (naphthoyltrifluoroacetone)	100 mg

For current prices or to order online, visit probes.invitrogen.com

19.8 Chelators, Calibration Buffers, Ionophores and Cell-Loading Reagents

Caged Calcium and Caged Calcium Chelators

Nitrophenyl EGTA: A Superior Caged Calcium Reagent

As an alternative to solely monitoring Ca^{2+} changes using fluorescent indicators, scientists may want to rapidly raise or lower the intracellular Ca^{2+} concentration and study the physiological response that results. Ellis-Davies and Kaplan have developed a photolabile chelator, *o*-nitrophenyl EGTA (NP-EGTA, N6802; Figure 19.93), that exhibits a high selectivity for Ca^{2+}, a dramatic 12,500-fold decrease in affinity for Ca^{2+} upon UV illumination (its K_d increases from 80 nM to >1 mM) and a high photochemical quantum yield [1–3] (~0.2). Photolysis of NP-EGTA is slightly faster than that of DMNP-EDTA,[4] another "caged Ca^{2+}" reagent that is frequently called DM-Nitrophen (see below). Furthermore, with a K_d for Mg^{2+} of 9 mM, NP-caged EGTA does not bind physiological levels of Mg^{2+} and thus reduces interference from this abundant cation.[5] Skinned muscle fibers equilibrated with NP-EGTA were shown to contract maximally upon irradiation with a single flash from a frequency-doubled ruby laser [3] (347 nm illumination). Some applications of NP-EGTA include:

- Measuring the Ca^{2+} buffering capacity of the neuronal cytosol [6]
- Assessing Ca^{2+} binding to troponin C in skeletal muscle fibers [7]
- Studying the mechanism of Ca^{2+}-induced exocytosis in pancreatic beta-cells [8–10]
- Generating Ca^{2+} pulses in astrocytes that are transmitted to hippocampal neurons via NMDA receptor transduction [11]
- Investigating the coupling of rapid Ca^{2+} release to depolarization in *Limulus* photoreceptors [12]

We exclusively offer the tetrapotassium salt (N6802) and the acetoxymethyl (AM) ester (NP-EGTA AM, N6803) of NP-EGTA. The NP-EGTA salt can be complexed with Ca^{2+} to generate a caged Ca^{2+} reagent that will rapidly deliver Ca^{2+} upon photolysis (Figure 17.4). The cell-permeant AM ester of NP-EGTA does not bind Ca^{2+} unless its AM ester groups are removed. NP-EGTA AM can serve as a photolabile buffer in cells because, once converted to NP-EGTA by intracellular esterases, it will bind Ca^{2+} with high affinity until photolyzed with UV light.[13]

DMNP-EDTA

The first caged Ca^{2+} reagent to be described by Kaplan and Ellis-Davies was 1-(4,5-dimethoxy-2-nitrophenyl)-EDTA (DMNP-EDTA, D6814), which they named DM-Nitrophen [14,15] (now a trademark of Calbiochem-Novabiochem Corp.). Because its structure more closely resembles that of EDTA than EGTA, we named it as a caged EDTA derivative (Figure 17.5). Upon illumination, DMNP-EDTA's dissociation constant for Ca^{2+} increases from 5 nM to 3 mM. Thus, photolysis of DMNP-EDTA complexed with Ca^{2+} results in a pulse of free Ca^{2+}. Furthermore, DMNP-EDTA has significantly higher affinity for Mg^{2+} (K_d = 2.5 µM) than does NP-EGTA [14] (K_d = 9 mM). Because the photolysis product's K_d for Mg^{2+} is ~3 mM, DMNP-EDTA is an effective caged Mg^{2+} source, in addition to its applications for photolytic Ca^{2+} release.[16,17] Photorelease of Ca^{2+} has been shown to occur in <180 µsec, with even faster photorelease of Mg^{2+}.[18] Moreover, DMNP-EDTA is also useful for photolytic release of other divalent cations such as Sr^{2+}, Ba^{2+}, Mn^{2+}, Co^{2+} and Cd^{2+}.[19] A paper by Neher and Zucker reviews the uses and limitations of DMNP-EDTA.[17] Photolysis of DMNP-EDTA has been used extensively to release Ca^{2+} in a variety of systems. This caged Ca^{2+} reagent has been employed to:

- Evoke secretion in bovine chromaffin cells [17]
- Investigate temperature modulation of Ca^{2+}-activated neurotransmitter release from squid neurons [20]
- Measure Ca^{2+} pump kinetics in erythrocyte ghosts using the Calcium Green™-2 and Calcium Green™-5N indicators [21]
- Generate rapid (~low milliseconds) Ca^{2+} transients, as detected by Calcium Orange™-5N fluorescence [22]
- Stimulate neurotransmitter release in nerve terminals [23]
- Induce Ca^{2+} transients approximating the size and amplitude of ryanodine receptor–generated Ca^{2+} sparks in cardiac muscle by two-photon photolysis [24,25] (Figure 19.94)

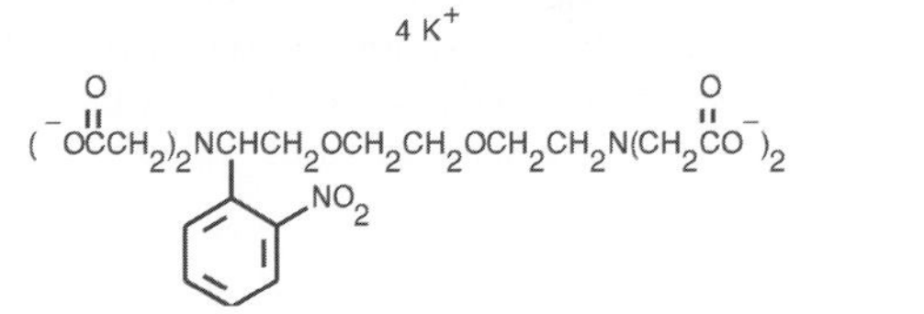

Figure 19.93 N6802 *o*-nitrophenyl EGTA, tetrapotassium salt (NP-EGTA).

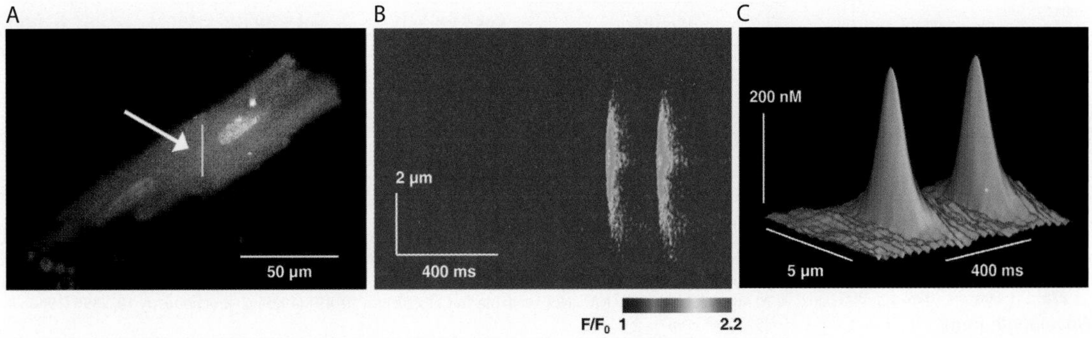

Figure 19.94 A) Confocal image of a guinea pig ventricular myocyte filled with fluo-3, potassium salt (F3715). The vertical yellow line (arrow) indicates the region scanned repetitively to generate the line-scan image shown in panel B. B) Two precisely localized Ca^{2+} transients were elicited by two-photon photolysis of DMNP-EDTA (D6814) using ultrafast high-repetition (120 fs, 80 MHz) laser pulses at 700 nm. The color scale bar represents fluo-3 fluorescence intensities corresponding to resting (blue) to high (red) Ca^{2+} concentrations. C) Surface plot of Ca^{2+} concentration plotted against space and time. The spatial spread of the Ca^{2+} transients was about 2 µm at half-maximum amplitude. Images contributed by Ernst Niggli, University of Bern, and reproduced with permission from Nat Cell Biol 1, 323 (1999).

In addition to high-purity DMNP-EDTA (D6814), we have prepared the AM ester of this probe[26] (D6815).

Photoactivatable Calcium Scavenger

In contrast to NP-EGTA and DMNP-EDTA, diazo-2 is a photoactivatable Ca^{2+} scavenger. Diazo-2 (Figure 5.20), which was introduced by Adams, Kao and Tsien,[27,28] is a relatively weak chelator (K_d for Ca^{2+} = 2.2 µM). However, following flash photolysis at ~360 nm, cytosolic free Ca^{2+} rapidly binds to the high-affinity photolysis product of diazo-2 (K_d = 73 nM). Photolysis of diazo-2 has been used to decrease cytosolic Ca^{2+} in less than three milliseconds in tensed frog muscle cells,[29] rat fibroblasts[28] and rabbit arterial smooth muscle.[30] Trapping of Ca^{2+} following photolysis of diazo-2 results in relaxation of skinned cardiac or skeletal muscle[31] and rapid depletion of Ca^{2+} in ventricular myocytes.[32] Microinjecting a relatively low concentration of a visible light–excitable Ca^{2+} indicator — such as fluo-3, fluo-4 or one of our Calcium Green™ or Oregon Green® 488 BAPTA indicators — along with a known quantity of diazo-2 permits measurement of the extent of depletion of cytosolic Ca^{2+} following photolysis.[28,33,34]

Diazo-2 can be microinjected into larger cells[5] or electroporated into smaller cells[35] as its potassium salt (D3034). Diazo-2 also has been loaded into cells permeabilized by *Staphylococcus aureus* α-toxin.[30] Alternatively, diazo-2 can be passively loaded into cells as its AM ester (D3036) and most likely with our Influx™ pinocytic cell-loading reagent (I14402, see below).

Nonfluorescent Chelators

BAPTA and BAPTA AM

The BAPTA buffers developed by Tsien[36] are highly selective for Ca^{2+} over Mg^{2+} and can be used to control the level of both intracellular and extracellular Ca^{2+} (Table 19.7, Figure 19.95). The BAPTA buffers are more selective for Ca^{2+} than EDTA and EGTA, and their metal binding is also much less pH sensitive. Furthermore, BAPTA buffers bind and release Ca^{2+} ions about 50–400 times faster than EGTA. Both BAPTA and its membrane-permeant AM ester are extensively used to clamp intracellular Ca^{2+} concentrations, providing insights on the role of free cytosolic Ca^{2+} in a number of important cell systems.

BAPTA is available as a cell-impermeant potassium, cesium[37] or sodium salt (B1204, B1212, B1214); the Cs^+ salt of BAPTA has frequently been used for patch-clamp experiments.[37] In addition, we offer the cell-permeant BAPTA AM ester (B1205). We also make BAPTA AM available in a special packaged set of 20 vials, each containing 1 mg (B6769). In addition to these products, we offer a polystyrene conjugate of BAPTA for selective removal of Ca^{2+} from solutions, which we call Calcium Sponge™ S (C3047); a complete description of this product occurs later in this section.

Other BAPTA Derivatives

Other BAPTA derivatives available from Molecular Probes are listed in Table 19.7, along with their dissociation constants for Ca^{2+}. The most powerful Ca^{2+} chelator among these is 5,5′-dimethyl BAPTA[38–41] (D1206), which is also available as its cell-permeant AM ester (D1207).

BAPTA derivatives with intermediate affinity for Ca^{2+}, such as 5,5′-dibromo BAPTA (D1211), have been extensively used to study Ca^{2+} mobilization, spatial Ca^{2+} buffering and Ca^{2+} shuttling in a variety of cells, including *Xenopus* eggs,[42–45] fucoid eggs,[46] plants[47–49] and hair cells.[50] 5,5′-Dibromo BAPTA has also been used to block nuclear vesicle fusion in *Xenopus* egg extracts,[51] to determine the affinity of a Ca^{2+}-binding protein[52] and to load Ca^{2+} into stamenal hairs of *Setcreasea purpurea* in a study of cytoplasmic streaming.[53] 5,5′-Dibromo BAPTA and other lower-affinity chelators protect neurons against excitotoxic and ischemic injury, without markedly attenuating intracellular Ca^{2+} levels.[54]

Fluorinated BAPTA derivatives, such as 5,5′-difluoro BAPTA and its AM ester (D1208, D1209), have been employed for optical imaging studies[55,56] but are most widely used for NMR analysis of Ca^{2+} in live cells and tissues,[57] including kidney,[58–60] heart,[61–64] brain,[65] erythrocytes[66] and platelets.[67] The ^{19}F NMR shifts of the 5,5′-difluoro BAPTA have been reported to correlate with intracellular Ca^{2+} in BALB/c thymocytes,[57] normal[68] and sickle[69] erythrocytes and ferret hearts.[64,70] In addition, ^{19}F NMR has been used with 5,5′-difluoro

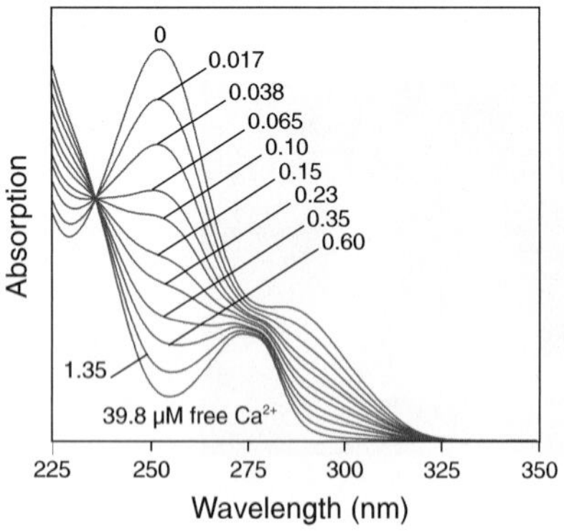

Figure 19.95 Absorption spectra of BAPTA (B1204) in solutions containing 0–39.8 µM free Ca^{2+}.

Table 19.7 — Ca^{2+} affinities of BAPTA chelators

Chelator	Cat # for Salt	Cat # for AM Ester	K_d for Ca^{2+}
BAPTA	B1204, B1212, B1214	B1205, B6769	No Mg^{2+}: 160 nM * 1 mM Mg^{2+}: 700 nM †
5,5′-Dibromo BAPTA	D1211	NA	No Mg^{2+}: 1.6 µM ‡
5,5′-Difluoro BAPTA	D1208	D1209	No Mg^{2+}: 635 nM § 1 mM Mg^{2+}: 705 nM §
5,5′-Dimethyl BAPTA	D1206	D1207	No Mg^{2+}: 40 nM ‡
4-Trifluoromethyl BAPTA	T24220	NA	No Mg^{2+}: 570 nM *

* Measured at Molecular Probes in 10 mM MOPS, 100 mM KCl, pH 7.2 at 22°C. † Measured in 10 mM HEPES, 300 mM KCl, pH 7.0 at 22°C.[1] ‡ Measured in 10 mM MOPS, 100 mM KCl, pH 7.3 at 22°C.[2] § Measured in 10 mM HEPES, 115 mM KCl, 20 mM NaCl, pH 7.05.[3] NA = Not available. **1.** Cell Calcium 10, 491 (1989); **2.** Biochemistry 19, 2396 (1980); **3.** Am J Physiol 252, C441 (1987).

BAPTA to detect Pb^{2+} uptake by platelets.[67] 4-Trifluoromethyl BAPTA (T24220) may also be a useful probe for ^{19}F NMR analysis of intracellular Ca^{2+}.

BAPTA Acetoxymethyl Esters

Molecular Probes offers three different cell-permeant acetoxymethyl esters of BAPTA:

- BAPTA AM (B1205, B6769)
- 5,5′-Dimethyl BAPTA AM (D1207)
- 5,5′-Difluoro BAPTA AM (D1209)

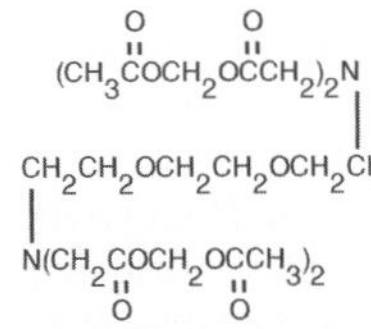

Figure 19.96 E1219 EGTA, tetra(acetoxymethyl ester) (EGTA, AM).

EGTA AM

Molecular Probes' AM ester derivative of EGTA (E1219, Figure 19.96) can be passively loaded into cells to generate intracellular EGTA. The slower on-rate of EGTA relative to the BAPTA-based buffers reduces its ability to inhibit Ca^{2+} diffusion in cells.[71,72] Because Ca^{2+} binding by intracellular EGTA is relatively slow it is possible to distinguish between buffering of rapid Ca^{2+} transients, which can occur with BAPTA-derived buffers, and the slower effects of general Ca^{2+} buffering.[38,54,73] EGTA AM has been reported to:

- Block oxidative stress caused by hydroperoxide formation in kidney proximal tubular cells[74]
- Selectively remove Ca^{2+} from presynaptic terminals, allowing unambiguous detection of strontium fluxes[75]
- Confer neuroprotective activity[54]
- Inhibit the substance K^+–induced Ca^{2+} rise in glioma cells[76]

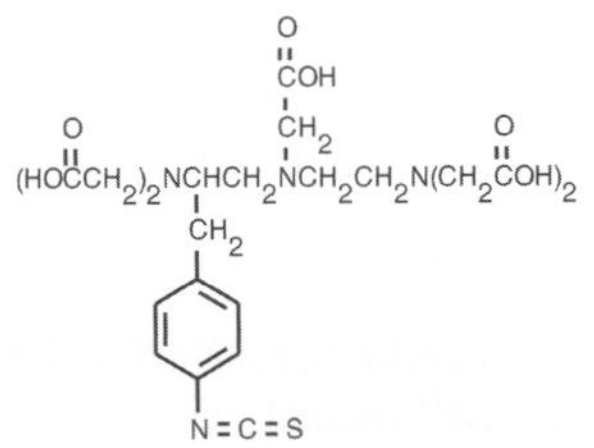

Figure 19.97 I24221 (*S*)-1-*p*-isothiocyanatobenzyldiethylenetriaminepentaacetic acid (DTPA isothiocyanate).

DTPA Isothiocyanate

DTPA isothiocyanate (I24221) can be coupled to antibodies and other biomolecules by conventional amine-reactive chemistry, thereby introducing a high-affinity binding site for a variety of metal ions. Unlike reactive anhydride forms of DTPA, the isothiocyanate derivative yields conjugates that retain all five carboxylate groups (Figure 19.97), resulting in more stable metal complexation.[77] Antibodies labeled with the fluorescent lanthanides europium and terbium (T1247, Section 19.7) are widely utilized in time-resolved fluorescence–based immunoassays.[78] DTPA-gadolinium (Gd^{3+}) complexes are extensively used as contrast agents for magnetic resonance imaging.[79] DTPA isothiocyanate–labeled antibodies also have potentially important therapeutic applications for targeted delivery of radionuclides such as indium-111 and yttrium-90.[80]

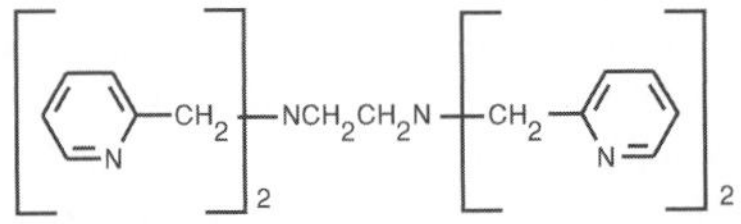

Figure 19.98 T1210 tetrakis-(2-pyridylmethyl)ethylenediamine (TPEN).

Calcium Sponge™ Polymer

Molecular Probes offers a biologically compatible conjugate of the BAPTA chelator to selectively remove specific polyvalent ions from solution, as well as from the binding sites of indicators, proteins and polynucleotides. Our BAPTA polystyrene conjugate — Calcium Sponge™ S — is selective for Ca^{2+} and certain other ions, including Zn^{2+} and some heavy metals, in the presence of relatively high levels of Mg^{2+}. Many contaminating polycations can be selectively removed from aqueous solutions simply by stirring a solution with the water-insoluble Calcium Sponge™ S polymer[81] (BAPTA polystyrene, C3047). For example, free Ca^{2+} can be reduced to less than 40 nM (measured with fura-2) by passing 3 mL of a 100 µM $CaCl_2$ solution through one gram of Calcium Sponge™ S. The polymer can be regenerated several times by washing it with pH 4 buffer, then readjusting to neutral pH with base.

TPEN

TPEN (T1210, Figure 19.98) selectively chelates intracellular heavy metal ions such as Zn^{2+}, Cu^{2+} and Fe^{2+} without disturbing Ca^{2+} and Mg^{2+} concentrations, revealing distortions in intracellular Ca^{2+} measurements caused by high-affinity binding of these ions to fluorescent indicators.[82] TPEN has been used to show that the effects of BAPTA on mitotic progression and nuclear assembly are specifically Ca^{2+}-mediated and are not attributable to binding of essential heavy metal ions.[83,84] TPEN has also been used to modulate the effects of Zn^{2+} on enzymatic activity[85] and protein conformation.[86]

Calcium Calibration Buffer Kits

Calibration of fluorescent Ca^{2+} indicators is a prerequisite for accurate Ca^{2+} measurements. Molecular Probes offers a number of kits designed to facilitate this calibration using a laboratory fluorometer or quantitative imaging system. All of these kits contain buffers and detailed protocols — including methods for calculating K_d, a sample response curve and tables to help determine the exact concentration of free Ca^{2+} under conditions of varying pH, temperature and ionic strength. A discussion of methods to correct the fura-2 dissociation constants for differences in temperature and ionic strength has been published.[87] A computer program is now available on the Web for calculating the free Ca^{2+} concentrations in solutions that contain several chelating species, or that contain ions such as Zn^{2+} that compete with Ca^{2+} for binding to BAPTA or EGTA (see Note 19.3 "Technical Focus: MAXC Computer Program for Calculating Free Ca^{2+} Concentrations").

Calcium Calibration Buffer Kits for High- to Moderate-Affinity Ca^{2+} Indicators

Because cells contain very low levels of *free* Ca^{2+}, it is essential to use calibrated Ca^{2+} buffers such as EGTA to precisely calibrate the Ca^{2+} indicators in a researcher's own equipment under their own experimental conditions. When the concentrations of Ca^{2+} and EGTA are very close to each other, the only free Ca^{2+} available is the Ca^{2+} that is in equilibrium with EGTA. Thus, the concentration of free Ca^{2+} is determined by the K_d of CaEGTA at a controlled pH, temperature and ionic strength. In order to attain Ca^{2+} and EGTA concentrations sufficiently close to each other, our Calcium Calibration Buffer Kits (C3008MP, C3009, C3721, C3722) contain CaEGTA solutions that have been accurately prepared using Roger Tsien's "pH-metric" method, which makes use of the fact that ion binding by EGTA causes an acidification of the solution.[88] These kits can be used to obtain calibration curves and Ca^{2+} dissociation constants for all of our high- to moderate-affinity Ca^{2+} indicators, including fura-2, fura-4F, fura-5F, indo-1, fluo-3, fluo-4 and the Calcium Green™-1, Calcium Green™-2, Calcium Orange™, Calcium Crimson™, Oregon Green® 488 BAPTA-1, Oregon Green® 488 BAPTA-2 and Fura Red™ indicators.

Calcium Calibration Buffer Kit #1 (C3008MP) contains:

- 10 mM K_2EGTA buffered solution ("zero" free Ca^{2+})
- 10 mM CaEGTA buffered solution (40 µM free Ca^{2+})
- A detailed protocol for calibrating Ca^{2+} indicators

When used according to the protocol provided, each kit provides sufficient reagents for five complete calibrations using 2 mL samples and a standard fluorometer cuvette. Many more calibrations can be done by digital imaging microscopy.[89,90] This kit employs a reciprocal dilution method — an equal amount of dye is added to a portion of the zero and 40 µM free Ca^{2+} solutions, and the two are then crossdiluted to give a series of solutions — which minimizes indicator concentration errors but requires more effort in making the dilutions than does Kit #2 (see below). With ratiometric indicators, this method yields a series of curves that exhibit an accurate isosbestic point (see, for example, (Figure 19.3); it is the method regularly used at Molecular Probes to determine Ca^{2+} affinities. Our Calcium Calibration Buffer Kit #1 was used as a source of known free Ca^{2+} concentrations in an experiment that examined the effect of Ca^{2+} binding on the fluorescence of calretinin.[91]

A concentrated form of Calcium Calibration Buffer Kit #1 (Calcium Calibration Buffer Concentrate Kit, C3723) is also offered. This kit allows the researcher to dilute the Ca^{2+} concentrates into buffered solutions of any composition and thus to more closely mimic the pH, ionic strength or viscosity of the cytoplasmic environment or of solutions with unusual ion levels, such as seawater.

In Calcium Calibration Buffer Kit #2 (C3009), 11 prediluted K_2EGTA/CaEGTA solutions containing from 0 to 10 mM CaEGTA (0 to 40 µM free Ca^{2+}) are bottled separately, making the calibrations faster, especially for cases in which all the dilutions are not required. This kit is intrinsically less accurate than Kit #1 because it requires precise addition of the same amount of fluorescent indicator to each solution. Calcium Calibration Buffer Kit #2 is preferred for calibrating the response of Ca^{2+} imaging systems, in which single drops of the fura-2–containing buffer are placed on a microscope slide.[89,90] Calcium Calibration Buffer Kit #2 was used to calibrate a fiber-optic Ca^{2+} sensor constructed by covalent immobilization of a Calcium Green™ derivative.[92]

Calcium Calibration Buffer Kits with Magnesium

The two Calcium Calibration Buffer Kits with Magnesium (C3721, C3722) are analogous to the Calcium Calibration Buffer Kits #1 and #2 except that the buffers additionally contain 1 mM Mg^{2+}. This approximately physiological Mg^{2+} level may strongly affect the K_d for Ca^{2+} of the BAPTA-derived indicators. Thus, these kits are suitable for simulating the intracellular Mg^{2+} environment during the calibration procedure and for determining the effect of this ion on the K_d of the Ca^{2+} indicator. Such effects can be significant; for example, Tsien

Note 19.3 — Technical Focus

MAXC Computer Program for Calculating Free Ca^{2+} Concentrations

In solutions that contain several chelating species, or that contain ions such as Zn^{2+} that compete with Ca^{2+} for binding to BAPTA or EGTA, calculating the free Ca^{2+} concentration requires simultaneously solving multiple equilibrium expressions. Except for the simplest cases where analytical solutions are feasible, researchers must use an iterative computer program to complete these calculations. MAXC, a program developed for this purpose,[1] is freely accessible on the Web at www.stanford.edu/~cpatton/maxc.html.

Reference

1. Methods Cell Biol 40, 3 (1994).

reports that the K_d of fura-2 increases from 135 nM in the absence of Mg^{2+} to 224 nM in the presence of 1 mM Mg^{2+}.[93]

Calcium Calibration Buffer Kit for Low-Affinity Ca^{2+} Indicators

The Calcium Calibration Buffer Kit #3 (C6775) provides 11 ready-to-use Ca^{2+} solutions containing from 1 µM to 1 mM free Ca^{2+}. The K_2EGTA/CaEGTA buffering system is employed to generate the two lowest Ca^{2+} concentrations; solutions with higher Ca^{2+} concentrations do not have a buffered Ca^{2+} level and are verified using an ion-selective electrode. This kit is ideal for calibrating our low-affinity Ca^{2+} indicators, including fluo-5N, Calcium Green™-5N, Oregon Green® BAPTA-5N, fura-6F, fura-FF, mag-fura-2, mag-fura-5 and our ratioable Ca^{2+} indicator, BTC.

Fura-2 Calcium Imaging Calibration Kit

The Fura-2 Calcium Imaging Calibration Kit (F6774), which is designed to facilitate rapid calibration and standardization of digital imaging microscopes,[89,90] contains the same 11 prediluted buffers as in our Calcium Calibration Buffer Kit #2. However, in this kit the buffers also include 50 µM fura-2, as well as 15 µm unstained polystyrene microspheres to act both as spacers that ensure uniform separation between the slide and the coverslip and as focusing aids. We also provide a twelfth buffer, identical to the 10 mM CaEGTA standard but lacking fura-2, that serves as a control for background fluorescence.

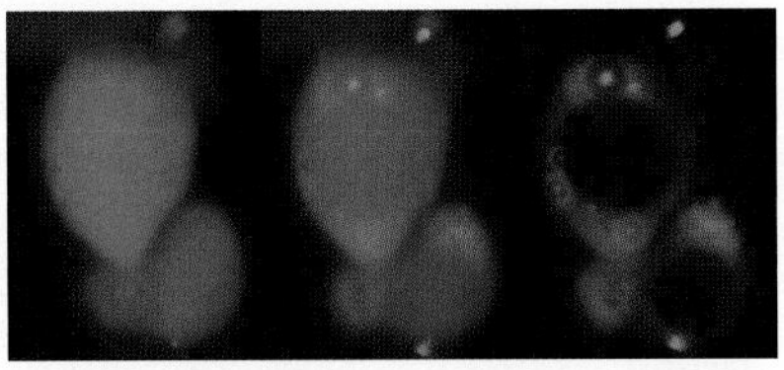

Figure 19.100 Adherent 3T3 fibroblasts labeled with 3000 MW Texas Red® dextran (D3329) and 70,000 MW Calcium Green™-1 dextran (C3714). Both dextrans were loaded into the fibroblasts using the Influx™ pinocytic cell-loading reagent (I14402). The images were acquired using a fluorescence microscope equipped with a cooled CCD camera and bandpass filter sets appropriate for either the Texas Red® dye (left image) or fluorescein (right image). The center image represents a composite of the cells labeled with both dextrans. The 3000 MW Texas Red® dextran is distributed throughout the cell, but the 70,000 MW Calcium Green™-1 dextran is excluded from the nucleus by the nuclear membrane.

Influx™ Pinocytic Cell-Loading Reagent

Our Influx™ pinocytic cell-loading reagent (I14402) facilitates the loading of water-soluble materials into live cells via a rapid and simple technique based on the osmotic lysis of pinocytic vesicles.[94] Simply mix the water-soluble probe at high concentration with the Influx™ reagent blended into growth medium, then incubate the cells in the medium to allow pinocytic uptake of the surrounding solution. When the cells are subsequently transferred to a slightly hypotonic medium, pinocytic vesicles within the cells release the trapped material and fill the cytosol with the probe (Figure 19.99, Figure 14.44). A detailed description of the Influx™ pinocytic cell-loading reagent together with general guidelines and detailed suggestions for optimizing cell loading is provided in the reagent's product information sheet.

The Influx™ pinocytic cell-loading reagent is highly effective for loading a diverse array of probes — including calcein (Figure 14.46, Figure 14.43), Alexa Fluor® hydrazides (Figure 14.44), dextran conjugates of fluorophores[95] and ion indicators (Figure 19.100), fura-2 salts, Oregon Green® 514 dye–labeled tubulin, Alexa Fluor® 488 dye–labeled actin, heparin,[96] hydroxyurea,[97] DNA, siRNAs,[98] antisense oligonucleotides,[99,100] SYTOX® Green nucleic acid stain and propidium iodide — into a variety of cell lines. We (or other researchers) have successfully tested the reagent and loading method with:

- Bovine pulmonary artery endothelial cells (BPAEC)
- Human epidermoid carcinoma cells (A431)
- Human T cell leukemia cells (Jurkat)
- Murine fibroblasts (NIH 3T3 and CRE BAG 2)
- Murine monocyte-macrophages (RAW264.7 and J774A.1)
- Murine myeloma cells (P3x63AG8)
- Rat basophilic leukemia cells (RBL)
- Dorsal root ganglion cells

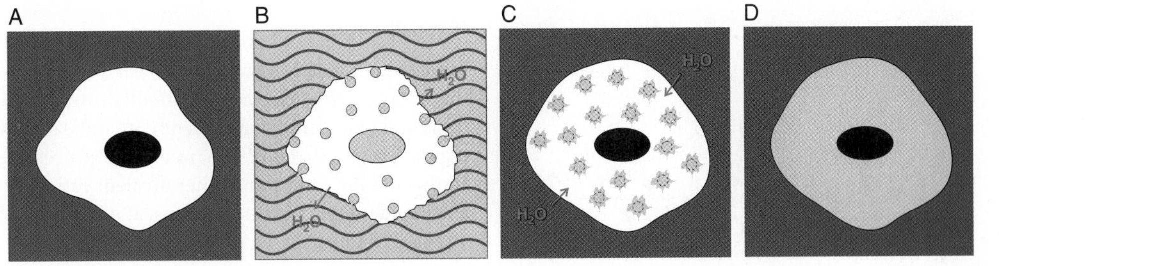

Figure 19.99 Principle of the Influx™ reagent pinocytic cell-loading method (I14402). Cultured cells (panel A) are placed in hypertonic Influx™ loading reagent, along with the material to be loaded into the cells (yellow fluid, panel B), allowing the material to be carried into the cells via pinocytic vesicles. When the cells are placed in hypotonic medium, the pinocytic vesicles burst (panel C), releasing their contents into the cytosol (panel D).

More than 80% of the cells remained viable, as determined by subsequent exclusion of propidium iodide.

In addition to the Influx™ pinocytic cell-loading reagent and cell growth medium, all that is required to perform the loading procedure is sterile deionized water and the fluorescent probe or other polar molecule of interest. Cell labeling can be accomplished in a single 30-minute loading cycle and may be enhanced by repetitive loading. Although most types of cells load quickly and easily, optimal conditions for loading must be determined for each cell type. It is also important to note that cell-to-cell variability in the degree of loading is typical (Figure 14.44) and that higher variability is generally observed when using large compounds, such as >10,000 MW dextrans and proteins.

The Influx™ pinocytic cell-loading reagent is packaged as a set of 10 tubes (I14402), each containing sufficient material to load 50 samples of cells grown on coverslips following the standard protocol supplied. Cells in suspension or in culture flasks may also be easily loaded; however, the number of possible cell loadings will depend on the cell suspension volume or size of culture flask used. The information provided with the Influx™ reagent includes general guidelines and detailed suggestions for optimizing cell loading. Use of the custom coverslip mini-rack (C14784, Section 23.3, Figure 23.54) or coverslip maxi-rack (C24784, Section 23.3, Figure 23.55) facilitates cell loading and slide handling when using the Influx™ reagent.

Loading $P2X_7$ Receptor–Expressing Cells

$P2X_7$ receptor–expressing cells such as macrophages and thymocytes exhibit reversible pore opening that can be exploited to provide an entry pathway for intracellular loading of both cationic and anionic fluorescent dyes with molecular weights of up to 900 daltons.[101–103] Pore opening is induced by treatment with 5 mM ATP for five minutes and subsequently reversed by addition of divalent cations (Ca^{2+} or Mg^{2+}). Dyes that have been successfully loaded into macrophage cells by this method include:

- Ca^{2+} indicator: fura-2 [103] (F1200, F6799; Section 19.2)
- pH indicator: HPTS [102] (H348, Section 20.2)
- Aqueous tracers: lucifer yellow CH [104,105] (L453, L682, L1177, L12926; Section 14.3) and 6-carboxyfluorescein (C1360, Section 1.5)
- Nucleic acid stain: YO-PRO®-1 [106] (Y3603, Section 8.1)

One of the most potent and widely used P2X receptor agonists, BzBzATP (2′-(or 3′-)O-(4-benzoylbenzoyl)adenosine 5′-triphosphate, B22358, Section 17.3), is available from Molecular Probes,[107,108] along with the corresponding GTP derivative (B22357, Section 17.3). Both BzBzATP and BzBzGTP have more general applications for site-directed irreversible modification of nucleotide-binding proteins via photoaffinity labeling;[109,110] see Section 17.3 for more information on nucleotide analogs.

Ionophores

A-23187 and 4-Bromo A-23187

The Ca^{2+} ionophore A-23187 (A1493, Figure 19.101) is commonly used for *in situ* calibrations of fluorescent Ca^{2+} indicators, to equilibrate intracellular and extracellular Ca^{2+} concentrations and to permit Mn^{2+} to enter the cell to quench intracellular dye fluorescence. Although the intrinsic fluorescence of A-23187 is too high for use with fura-2, indo-1 and quin-2, it is suitable for use with the visible light–excitable indicators, including Calcium Green™, Magnesium Green™, Calcium Orange™, Calcium Crimson™, Oregon Green® 488 BAPTA, fluo-3, fluo-4, rhod-2, X-rhod-1 and Fura Red™. Brominated A-23187 (4-bromo A-23187, B1494; Figure 19.101), which is essentially nonfluorescent, is the best ionophore for use with fura-2, indo-1 and other UV light–excited Ca^{2+} indicators. Like A-23187, 4-bromo A-23187 rapidly transports both Ca^{2+} and Mn^{2+} into cells.[111] Both A-23187 and 4-bromo A-23187 can also be used to equilibrate intracellular and extracellular Mg^{2+} concentrations, making them useful for calibrating Mg^{2+} indicators (Section 19.7). Furthermore, 4-bromo A-23187 (B1494) has occasionally been used to equilibrate intracellular Zn^{2+} with controlled extracellular levels for *in situ* calibration of fluorescent indicators.[112] The zero reference level for intracellular Zn^{2+} calibrations is usually set by addition of TPEN [113] (K_d for Zn^{2+} = 2.6×10^{-16} M) (T1210).

Caged 4-Bromo A-23187

We have introduced a unique tool for the study of ion transport and Ca^{2+} regulation. Our patented caged ionophore derived from 4-bromo A-23187 (B7108) enters cells passively, where it subsequently may be photoactivated with a UV flashlamp or laser pulse to stimulate ion movement across the plasma membrane or to liberate Ca^{2+} from intracellular stores.[114–116] The product is inactive until uncaged with UV light. See Section 5.3 for further discussion of caged probes.

Ionomycin

Ionomycin (I24222, Figure 19.102) is an effective Ca^{2+} ionophore that is commonly used both to modify intracellular Ca^{2+} concentrations and to calibrate fluorescent Ca^{2+} indicators when studying the regulatory properties of Ca^{2+} in cellular processes. Ionomycin also transports Pb^{2+} and some other divalent cations, as well as several lanthanide series trivalent cations, at efficiencies that are greater than or equal to those for Ca^{2+}.[117,118]

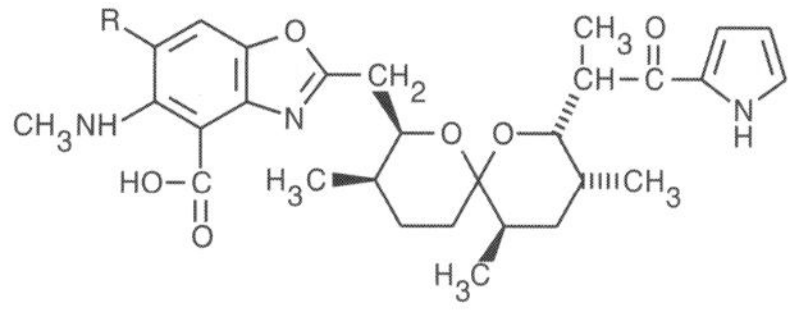

Figure 19.101 Chemical structures of the ionophores A-23187 (R = H, A1493) and 4-bromo A-23187 (R = Br, B1494).

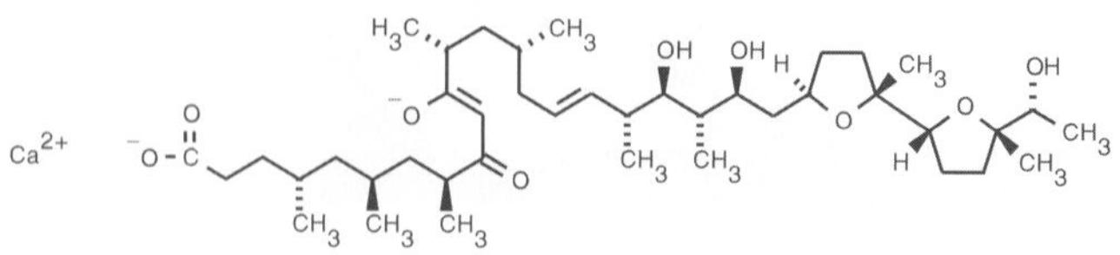

Figure 19.102 I24222 ionomycin, calcium salt.

Pluronic F-127: A Useful Dispersing Reagent

Because acetoxymethyl (AM) esters have low aqueous solubility,[119] dispersing agents — typically fetal calf serum, bovine serum albumin or Pluronic F-127 — are often used to facilitate cell loading.[120,121] Molecular Probes provides Pluronic F-127 in three forms, all of which have low UV absorbance ($OD_{280\ nm}$ <0.02 at 10 mg/mL):

- Powder (P6867)
- 10% Solution in water (P6866), filtered through a 0.2 µm–pore size membrane filter for use in tissue culture and other applications
- 20% Solution in DMSO (P3000MP)

Reagents for Investigating Calcium Modulation and Second Messenger Activity

Molecular Probes prepares several important reagents to investigate signal transduction, second messenger activity, ion channels and endogenous modulators of intracellular Ca^{2+} concentrations that are described further in Section 16.3 or Chapter 17.

- cADP ribose (C7619), caged cADP ribose (C7074) and 8-amino cADP ribose (A7621)
- Caged D-*myo*-inositol 1,4,5-triphosphate (NPE-caged Ins 1,4,5-P_3, I23580, Figure 17.2)
- Thapsigargin (T7458, T7459)
- BODIPY® FL thapsigargin (B7487) and BODIPY® TR-X thapsigargin (B13800)
- Fluorescent bisindolylmaleimide analogs, FIM-1 (F7462) and FIM-1 diacetate (F7453)
- BODIPY® FL forskolin (B7469)
- Fluorescent phosphatidylinositol polyphosphates (Table 17.3) and Shuttle PIP carriers to transport these probes into live cells (Section 17.4, Figure 17.34)
- Fluorescent dihydropyridines (D7443, S7445) for L-type Ca^{2+} channels
- High-purity ryanodine (R7478) and BODIPY® FL-X ryanodine[122–128] for Ins 1,4,5-P_3–insensitive intracellular Ca^{2+} channels

References

1. J Biol Chem 270, 23966 (1995); **2.** Science 267, 1997 (1995); **3.** Proc Natl Acad Sci U S A 91, 187 (1994); **4.** Biophys J 70, 1006 (1996); **5.** Cell Calcium 19, 185 (1996); **6.** Biochem Biophys Res Commun 250, 786 (1998); **7.** J Biol Chem 272, 6018 (1997); **8.** J Physiol 503, 399 (1997); **9.** J Cell Biol 138, 55 (1997); **10.** J Physiol 502, 105 (1997); **11.** J Neurosci 18, 6822 (1998); **12.** J Neurosci 17, 1701 (1997); **13.** Am J Physiol 277, L893 (1999); **14.** Proc Natl Acad Sci U S A 85, 6571 (1988); **15.** Science 241, 842 (1988); **16.** Methods Cell Biol 40, 31 (1994); **17.** Neuron 10, 21 (1993); **18.** Biochemistry 31, 8856 (1992); **19.** J Physiol 533, 627 (2001); **20.** J Physiol 426, 473 (1990); **21.** Biophys J 69, 30 (1995); **22.** Pflugers Arch 434, 615 (1997); **23.** J Physiol 462, 243 (1993); **24.** J Physiol 508, 801 (1998); **25.** Nat Cell Biol 1, 323 (1999); **26.** Adv Exp Med Biol 332, 97 (1993); **27.** Biochim Biophys Acta 1035, 378 (1990); **28.** J Am Chem Soc 111, 7957 (1989); **29.** FEBS Lett 255, 196 (1989); **30.** Biophys J 69, 2611 (1995); **31.** Pflugers Arch 425, 175 (1993); **32.** Cell Calcium 19, 255 (1996); **33.** Nature 371, 603 (1994); **34.** Biophys J 65, 2537 (1993); **35.** Proc Natl Acad Sci U S A 89, 11804 (1992); **36.** Biochemistry 19, 2396 (1980); **37.** J Neurosci 15, 903 (1995); **38.** J Neurosci 15, 2867 (1995); **39.** Exp Physiol 79, 269 (1994); **40.** J Biol Chem 268, 6511 (1993); **41.** Mol Biol Cell 4, 293 (1993); **42.** Biol Bull 183, 368 (1993); **43.** Dev Biol 158, 200 (1993); **44.** J Cell Biol 122, 387 (1993); **45.** J Cell Sci 106, 523 (1993); **46.** Proc Natl Acad Sci U S A 86, 6607 (1989); **47.** Cell Calcium 16, 322 (1994); **48.** Plant Cell 6, 1815 (1994); **49.** J Cell Sci 101, 7 (1992); **50.** Nature 363, 74 (1993); **51.** Cell 73, 1411 (1993); **52.** J Biol Chem 265, 9838 (1990); **53.** Planta 182, 34 (1990); **54.** J Neurophysiol 72, 1973 (1994); **55.** Neuron 11, 221 (1993); **56.** Proc Natl Acad Sci U S A 83, 6179 (1986); **57.** Proc Natl Acad Sci U S A 80, 7178 (1983); **58.** Biochim Biophys Acta 1226, 83 (1994); **59.** J Biol Chem 268, 991 (1993); **60.** J Biol Chem 267, 3637 (1992); **61.** Am J Physiol 266, C1323 (1994); **62.** Biophys J 65, 2547 (1993); **63.** J Biol Chem 265, 1394 (1990); **64.** Proc Natl Acad Sci U S A 84, 6005 (1987); **65.** J Neurochem 55, 878 (1990); **66.** Biochim Biophys Acta 1136, 155 (1992); **67.** Biochim Biophys Acta 1092, 341 (1991); **68.** Am J Physiol 252, C441 (1987); **69.** Blood 69, 1469 (1987); **70.** Am J Physiol 258, H9 (1990); **71.** Biophys J 69, 1683 (1995); **72.** J Physiol Paris 86, 129 (1992); **73.** J Neurosci 14, 523 (1994); **74.** J Biol Chem 269, 14546 (1994); **75.** Biophys J 76, 2029 (1999); **76.** Proc Natl Acad Sci U S A 88, 6878 (1991); **77.** Bioconjug Chem 2, 180 (1991); **78.** J Photochem Photobiol B 27, 3 (1995); **79.** Chem Rev 87, 901 (1987); **80.** J Med Chem 32, 236 (1989); **81.** J Biol Chem 275, 20572 (2000); **82.** Biophys J 71, 1048 (1996); **83.** J Cell Biol 111, 183 (1990); **84.** Cell Calcium 23, 151 (1998); **85.** Exp Cell Res 239, 393 (1998); **86.** Mol Carcinog 21, 205 (1998); **87.** Cell Calcium 12, 279 (1991); **88.** Methods Enzymol 172, 230 (1989); **89.** J Neurochem 62, 890 (1994); **90.** Cell Calcium 11, 75 (1990); **91.** Biochemistry 34, 15389 (1995); **92.** Anal Chem 68, 1414 (1996); **93.** J Biol Chem 260, 3440 (1985); **94.** Cell 29, 33 (1982); **95.** J Virol 76, 11505 (2002); **96.** FEBS Lett 508, 484 (2001); **97.** J Virol 76, 5167 (2002); **98.** Biotechniques 37, 96 (2004); **99.** Antisense Nucleic Acid Drug Dev 10, 263 (2000); **100.** EMBO J 21, 1743 (2002); **101.** J Physiol 519 Pt 2, 335 (1999); **102.** Am J Physiol 275, C1158 (1998); **103.** J Biol Chem 262, 8884 (1987); **104.** FASEB J 14, 2466 (2000); **105.** Am J Physiol 276, C1139 (1999); **106.** Br J Pharmacol 130, 513 (2000); **107.** J Physiol 519 Pt 3, 723 (1999); **108.** Mol Pharmacol 56, 1171 (1999); **109.** J Neurochem 61, 1657 (1993); **110.** Biochemistry 28, 3989 (1989); **111.** Anal Biochem 146, 349 (1985); **112.** J Neurochem 71, 2401 (1998); **113.** J Biol Chem 260, 2719 (1985); **114.** Planta 203, 495 (1997); **115.** J Biol Chem 262, 12801 (1987); **116.** Biotechniques 23, 268 (1997); **117.** J Biol Chem 275, 7071 (2000); **118.** Biophys J 75, 1244 (1998); **119.** Methods Cell Biol 40, 155 (1994); **120.** Proc Natl Acad Sci U S A 84, 7793 (1987); **121.** Science 233, 886 (1986); **122.** J Neurosci 20, 9059 (2000); **123.** J Gen Physiol 116, 697 (2000); **124.** Cell Calcium 28, 127 (2000); **125.** J Biol Chem 275, 9596 (2000); **126.** Biochem J 340, 519 (1999); **127.** J Biol Chem 274, 14147 (1999); **128.** J Physiol 506, 109 (1998).

Data Table — 19.8 Chelators, Calibration Buffers, Ionophores and Cell-Loading Reagents

Cat #	MW	Storage	Soluble	Abs	EC	Em	Solvent	Product	K_d	Notes
A1493	523.63	F,L	DMSO, EtOH	378	8,900	438	MeOH			
A7109	732.83	FF,D,LL	DMSO, EtOH	370	10,000	none	MeOH			1
B1204	628.80	D	pH >6	284	5,100	see Notes	pH 7.2		160 nM	2, 3, 4, 5, 6
B1205	764.69	F,D	DMSO	287	5,900	ND	$CHCl_3$	B1204		7
B1212	1004.03	D	pH >6	285	5,200	see Notes	pH 7.2		160 nM	2, 3, 4, 5, 6
B1214	564.37	D	pH >6	285	5,100	see Notes	pH 7.2		160 nM	2, 3, 4, 5, 6
B1494	602.52	F,D	DMSO, EtOH	289	20,000	none	MeOH			8
B6769	764.69	F,D	DMSO	287	5,900	ND	$CHCl_3$	B1204		7
B7108	811.73	FF,D,LL	DMSO, EtOH	337	11,000	none	MeOH			1
D1206	656.85	D	pH >6	290	5,100	ND	pH 7.2		40 nM	2, 5, 6, 7, 9
D1207	792.75	F,D	DMSO	291	5,900	ND	$CHCl_3$	D1206		7
D1208	664.78	D	pH >6	289	5,100	ND	pH 7.2		635 nM	2, 5, 6, 7, 10
D1209	800.67	F,D	DMSO	290	5,700	ND	EtOAc	D1208		7
D1211	786.59	D	pH >6	263	18,000	ND	pH 7.2		1.6 µM	2, 5, 6, 7, 9
D1213	922.48	F,D	DMSO	296	6,900	ND	EtOAc	D1211		7
D3001	566.43	D,L	pH >6	431	30,000	ND	pH 7.2		7.4 mM	2, 3, 5, 6, 7
D3034	710.86	F,D,LL	pH >6	369	18,000	none	pH 7.2		2.2 µM	1, 2, 6, 11
D3036	846.75	F,D,LL	DMSO	342	22,000	none	MeOH	D3034		
D6814	473.39	D,LL	DMSO	348	4,200	none	pH 7.2		5 nM	1, 2, 6, 12
D6815	761.65	F,D,LL	DMSO	333	4,600	none	MeOH	D6814		13
E1218	580.50	F,D	DMSO	<300		none				
E1219	668.60	F,D	DMSO	<300		none				13
I24221	540.54	F,DD	DMSO	<300		none				14
I24222	747.08	F,D	DMSO, EtOH	300	22,000	none	MeOH			
N6802	653.81	FF,D,LL	pH >6	260	3,500	none	pH 7.2		80 nM	1, 2, 6, 8, 15
N6803	789.70	FF,D,LL	DMSO	250	4,200	none	MeCN	N6802		13, 16
T1210	424.55	D	EtOH	261	14,000	ND	MeOH		see Notes	17
T24220	696.80	D	pH >6	288	5,100	ND	pH 7.2		570 nM	2, 3, 5, 6, 7

For definitions of the contents of this data table, see "Navigating *The Handbook*" in the introductory pages.

Notes

1. All photoactivatable probes are sensitive to light. They should be protected from illumination except when photolysis is intended.
2. Dissociation constants are known to vary considerably depending on the temperature, pH, ionic strength, viscosity, protein binding, presence of other ions (especially polyvalent ions), instrument setup and other factors. It is strongly recommended that these values be verified under user-specific experimental conditions.
3. Dissociation constant determined at Molecular Probes from absorption measurements in 100 mM KCl, 10 mM MOPS, pH 7.2 at 22°C. Ca^{2+} concentrations below 5 µM were controlled using CaEGTA buffering (Calcium Calibration Buffer Kit #1, C3008MP).
4. BAPTA is weakly fluorescent in aqueous solutions (Em = 363 nm, QY = 0.03) (Biochemistry 19, 2396 (1980)).
5. Absorption spectra of BAPTA and its derivatives are Ca^{2+}-dependent.
6. Abs and EC values determined in Ca^{2+}-free solution (100 mM KCl, 10 mM EGTA, 10 mM MOPS, pH 7.2).
7. ND = not determined.
8. This compound has weaker visible absorption at >300 nm but no discernible absorption peaks in this region.
9. Dissociation constant determined in CaEGTA buffers in 100 mM KCl, 10 mM MOPS, pH 7.3 (Biochemistry 19, 2396 (1980)).
10. D1208 dissociation constant determined in 115 mM KCl, 20 mM NaCl, 10 mM HEPES, pH 7.05 (Am J Physiol 252, C441 (1987); Am J Physiol 266, C1313 (1994)).
11. The Ca^{2+} dissociation constant of diazo-2 is 2200 nM before photolysis and 73 nM after ultraviolet photolysis. The absorption spectrum of the photolysis product is similar to that of B1204 (J Am Chem Soc 111, 7957 (1989)).
12. $K_d(Ca^{2+})$ increases from 5 nM to 3 mM after ultraviolet photolysis. K_d values determined in 130 mM KCl, 10 mM HEPES, pH 7.1 (Proc Natl Acad Sci U S A 85, 6571 (1988)).
13. This product is intrinsically a liquid or an oil at room temperature.
14. Isothiocyanates are unstable in water and should not be stored in aqueous solution.
15. $K_d (Ca^{2+})$ increases from 80 nM to 1 mM after ultraviolet photolysis. K_d values determined in 100 mM KCl, 40 mM HEPES, pH 7.2 (Proc Natl Acad Sci U S A 91, 187 (1994)).
16. N6803 is converted to N6802 via hydrolysis of its acetoxymethyl ester (AM) groups.
17. TPEN has very high affinity for Zn^{2+} ($K_d = 2.6 \times 10^{-16}$ M), Fe^{2+} ($K_d = 2.4 \times 10^{-15}$ M) and Mn^{2+} ($K_d = 5.4 \times 10^{-11}$ M) but relatively low affinity for Ca^{2+} ($K_d = 4.0 \times 10^{-5}$ M) and Mg^{2+} ($K_d = 2.0 \times 10^{-2}$ M) (J Biol Chem 260, 2719 (1985)).

Product List — 19.8 Chelators, Calibration Buffers, Ionophores and Cell-Loading Reagents

Cat #	Product Name	Unit Size
A7109	A-23187, 1-(4,5-dimethoxy-2-nitrophenyl)ethyl ester (DMNPE-caged A-23187)	1 mg
A1493	A-23187 free acid (calcimycin)	10 mg
B1205	BAPTA, AM *cell permeant*	25 mg
B6769	BAPTA, AM *cell permeant* *special packaging*	20 x 1 mg
B1212	BAPTA, tetracesium salt *cell impermeant*	1 g
B1204	BAPTA, tetrapotassium salt *cell impermeant*	1 g
B1214	BAPTA, tetrasodium salt *cell impermeant*	1 g
B7108	4-bromo A-23187, 1-(4,5-dimethoxy-2-nitrophenyl)ethyl ester (DMNPE-caged Br A-23187)	1 mg
B1494	4-bromo A-23187, free acid	1 mg
C3723	Calcium Calibration Buffer Concentrate Kit *zero and 100 mM CaEGTA (2 x 5 mL)*	1 kit
C3008MP	Calcium Calibration Buffer Kit #1 *zero and 10 mM CaEGTA (2 x 50 mL)*	1 kit
C3009	Calcium Calibration Buffer Kit #2 *zero to 10 mM CaEGTA (11 x 10 mL)*	1 kit
C6775	Calcium Calibration Buffer Kit #3 *1 µM to 1 mM range (11 x 10 mL)*	1 kit
C3721	Calcium Calibration Buffer Kit with Magnesium #1 *zero and 10 mM CaEGTA with 1 mM Mg^{2+} (2 x 50 mL)*	1 kit
C3722	Calcium Calibration Buffer Kit with Magnesium #2 *zero to 10 mM CaEGTA with 1 mM Mg^{2+} (11 x 10 mL)*	1 kit
C3047	Calcium Sponge™ S (BAPTA polystyrene)	1 g
D3036	diazo-2, AM *cell permeant* *special packaging*	20 x 50 µg
D3034	diazo-2, tetrapotassium salt *cell impermeant*	1 mg
D1213	5,5′-dibromo BAPTA, AM *cell permeant*	25 mg
D1211	5,5′-dibromo BAPTA, tetrapotassium salt *cell impermeant*	100 mg
D1209	5,5′-difluoro BAPTA, AM *cell permeant*	25 mg
D1208	5,5′-difluoro BAPTA, tetrapotassium salt *cell impermeant*	100 mg
D6814	1-(4,5-dimethoxy-2-nitrophenyl)-1,2-diaminoethane-*N,N,N′,N′*-tetraacetic acid (DMNP-EDTA) *cell impermeant*	5 mg
D6815	1-(4,5-dimethoxy-2-nitrophenyl)-1,2-diaminoethane-*N,N,N′,N′*-tetraacetic acid, tetra(acetoxymethyl ester) (DMNP-EDTA, AM) *cell permeant* *special packaging*	20 x 50 µg
D1207	5,5′-dimethyl BAPTA, AM *cell permeant*	25 mg
D1206	5,5′-dimethyl BAPTA, tetrapotassium salt *cell impermeant*	100 mg
D3001	5,5′-dinitro BAPTA, free acid *cell impermeant*	25 mg
E1218	EDTA, tetra(acetoxymethyl ester) (EDTA, AM)	25 mg
E1219	EGTA, tetra(acetoxymethyl ester) (EGTA, AM)	10 mg
F6774	Fura-2 Calcium Imaging Calibration Kit *zero to 10 mM CaEGTA, 50 µM fura-2 (11 x 1 mL)*	1 kit
I14402	Influx™ pinocytic cell-loading reagent *makes 10 x 5 mL*	1 set
I24222	ionomycin, calcium salt	1 mg
I24221	(*S*)-1-*p*-isothiocyanatobenzyldiethylenetriaminepentaacetic acid (DTPA isothiocyanate)	1 mg
N6803	*o*-nitrophenyl EGTA, AM (NP-EGTA, AM) *cell permeant* *special packaging*	20 x 50 µg
N6802	*o*-nitrophenyl EGTA, tetrapotassium salt (NP-EGTA) *cell impermeant*	1 mg
P6867	Pluronic® F-127 *low UV absorbance*	2 g
P3000MP	Pluronic® F-127 *20% solution in DMSO*	1 mL
P6866	Pluronic® F-127 *10% solution in water* *0.2 µm filtered*	30 mL
T1210	tetrakis-(2-pyridylmethyl)ethylenediamine (TPEN)	100 mg
T24220	4-trifluoromethyl BAPTA, tetrapotassium salt	5 mg

For current prices or to order online, visit probes.invitrogen.com

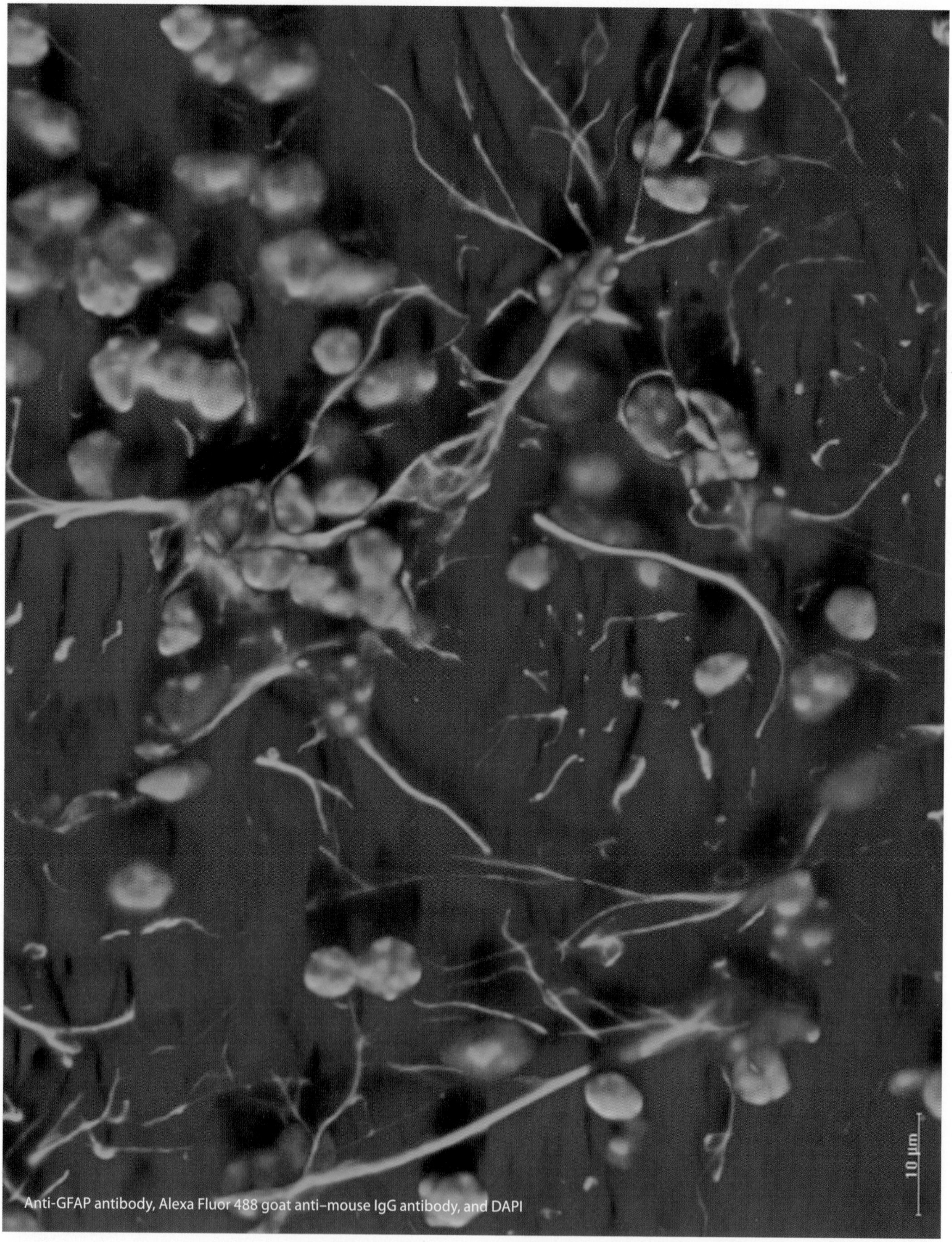

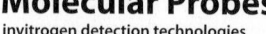

Anti-GFAP antibody, Alexa Fluor 488 goat anti–mouse IgG antibody, and DAPI

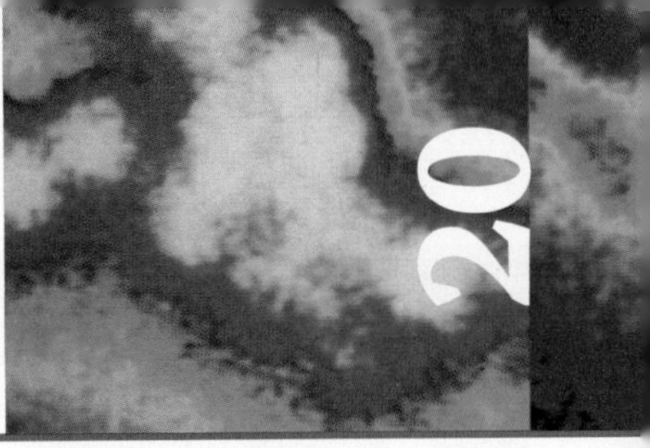

Chapter 20

pH Indicators

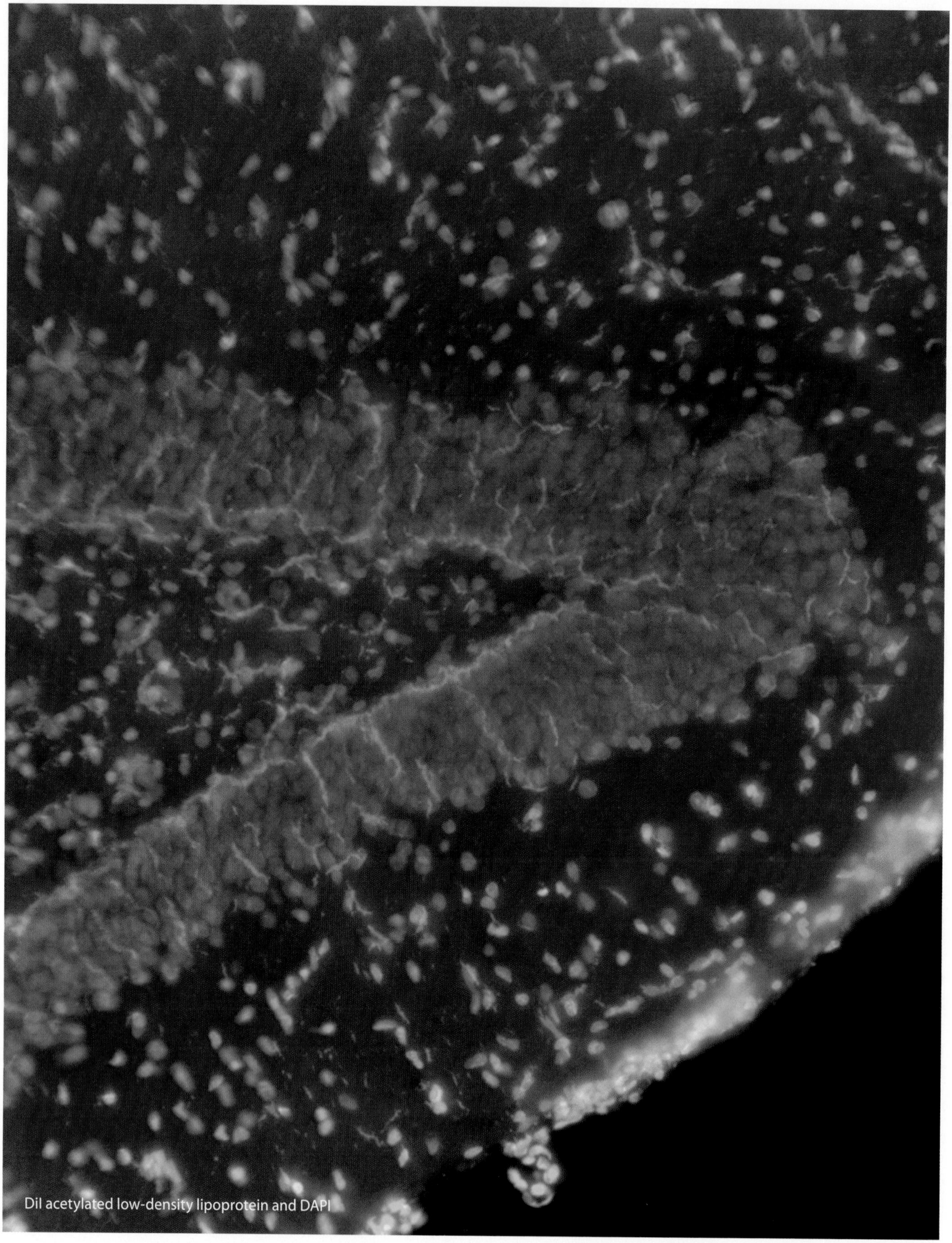

DiI acetylated low-density lipoprotein and DAPI

20.1 Overview of pH Indicators

The ability of dyes — notably litmus, phenolphthalein and phenol red — to change their color in response to a pH change has found widespread application in research and industry. However, fluorescent dyes provide the increased sensitivity required for optical pH measurements *inside* live cells. They also offer much greater spatial sampling capability when compared with microelectrode techniques. These advantages have spurred the development of improved fluorescent dyes that can sense pH changes within physiological ranges. Of course, many of the same fluorescent pH indicators can also be used as pH sensors in cell-free media.

To quantitatively measure pH, it is essential to match the indicator's pK_a to the pH of the experimental system. Consequently, the following two sections of this chapter are divided into pH indicators for use in environments with near-neutral pH (Section 20.2) and pH indicators for use in relatively acidic environments (Section 20.3). Intracellular pH is generally between ~6.8 and 7.4 in the cytosol and ~4.5 and 6.0 in the cell's acidic organelles. Unlike intracellular free Ca^{2+} concentrations, which can rapidly change by perhaps 100-fold, the pH inside a cell varies by only fractions of a pH unit, and such changes may be quite slow. Although the optical change of even the best fluorescent pH probes is usually relatively small, they have proven to be effective tools for investigating the role of intracellular pH in diverse physiological and pathological processes, including cell proliferation,[1] apoptosis,[2–5] muscle contraction,[6–8] malignancy,[9,10] multidrug resistance,[11–13] ion transport and homeostasis,[14–16] endocytosis[17] and Alzheimer's disease.[18,19]

Molecular Probes offers a variety of fluorescent pH indicators, their conjugates and other reagents for pH measurements in biological systems. Among these are several probes with unique optical response and specialized localization characteristics:

- Our visible light–excitable SNARF® pH indicators enable researchers to determine intracellular pH in the physiological range using dual-emission or dual-excitation ratiometric techniques (Section 20.2), thus providing important tools for confocal laser-scanning microscopy and flow cytometry.
- Our LysoSensor™ probes, as well as indicators based on the Oregon Green® fluorophore, can be used to estimate the pH in a cell's acidic organelles (Section 20.3).
- We also offer a number of fluorescent pH indicators coupled to dextrans (Section 20.4). Following loading into cells, indicator dextrans are extremely well retained, do not bind to cellular proteins and have a reduced tendency to compartmentalize.[20]

Families of pH indicators available from Molecular Probes are listed in Table 20.1 in approximate order of decreasing pK_a value.

Table 20.1 — Molecular Probes' pH indicator families, in order of decreasing pK_a

Parent Fluorophore	pH Range	Typical Measurement
SNARF® indicators	6.0–8.0	Emission ratio 580/640 nm
HPTS (pyranine)	7.0–8.0	Excitation ratio 450/405 nm
BCECF	6.5–7.5	Excitation ratio 490/440 nm
Fluoresceins and carboxyfluoresceins	6.0–7.2	Excitation ratio 490/450 nm
LysoSensor™ Green DND-189	4.5–6.0	Single emission 520 nm
Oregon Green® dyes	4.2–5.7	Excitation ratio 510/450 nm or excitation ratio 490/440 nm
LysoSensor™ Yellow/Blue DND-160	3.5–6.0	Emission ratio 450/510 nm

References

1. J Cell Physiol 177, 109 (1998); **2.** J Biol Chem 271, 16260 (1996); **3.** J Biol Chem 270, 6235 (1995); **4.** Proc Natl Acad Sci U S A 93, 654 (1996); **5.** J Immunol Methods 221, 43 (1998); **6.** Pflugers Arch 435, 575 (1998); **7.** Am J Physiol 275, H1788 (1998); **8.** J Physiol 512, 831 (1998); **9.** Cancer Res 54, 5670 (1994); **10.** Nat Med 3, 177 (1997); **11.** Biochemistry 35, 2811 (1996); **12.** Biophys J 69, 883 (1995); **13.** Proc Natl Acad Sci U S A 91, 1128 (1994); **14.** J Neurochem 71, 1051 (1998); **15.** Biochemistry 35, 13419 (1996); **16.** J Physiol 506, 415 (1998); **17.** Proc Natl Acad Sci U S A 92, 3156 (1995); **18.** Biochem Biophys Res Commun 194, 537 (1993); **19.** Neuroreport 9, 1553 (1998); **20.** Methods Cell Biol 29, 59 (1989).

20.2 Probes Useful at Near-Neutral pH

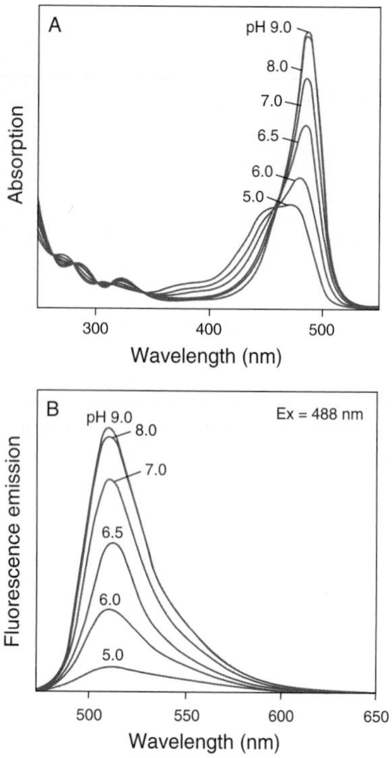

Figure 20.2 The pH-dependent spectra of fluorescein (F1300): **A)** absorption spectra, **B)** emission spectra.

Fluorescein and Fluorescein Derivatives

Fluorescein and many of its derivatives exhibit multiple, pH-dependent ionic equilibria.[1–5] Both the phenol and carboxylic acid functional groups of fluorescein are almost totally ionized in aqueous solutions above pH 9 (Figure 20.1). Acidification of the fluorescein dianion first protonates the phenol (pK_a ~6.4) to yield the fluorescein monoanion, then the carboxylic acid (pK_a <5) to produce the neutral species of fluorescein. Further acidification generates a fluorescein cation (pK_a ~2.1). Only the monoanion and dianion of fluorescein are fluorescent, with quantum yields of 0.37 and 0.93, respectively. However, excitation of either the neutral or cationic species is reported to produce emission from the anion with effective quantum yields of 0.31 and 0.18, respectively.[2] A further equilibrium involves formation of a colorless, nonfluorescent lactone (Figure 20.1). The lactone is not formed in aqueous solution above pH 5 but may be the dominant form of neutral fluorescein in solvents such as acetone. The pH-dependent absorption spectra of fluorescein (Figure 20.2) clearly show the blue shift and decreased absorptivity indicative of the formation of protonated species. However, the fluorescence emission spectrum of most fluorescein derivatives, even in acidic solution, is dominated by the dianion, with only small contributions from the monoanion. Consequently, the wavelength and shape of the emission spectra resulting from excitation close to the dianion absorption peak at 490 nm are relatively independent of pH, but the fluorescence intensity is dramatically reduced at acidic pH (Figure 20.2).

Molecular Probes offers a broad variety of fluorescein-derived reagents and fluoresceinated probes that can serve as sensitive fluorescent pH indicators in a wide range of applications. Chemical substitutions of fluorescein may shift absorption and fluorescence maxima and change the pK_a of the dye; however, the effects of acidification on the spectral characteristics illustrated in Figure 20.2 are generally maintained in all fluorescein derivatives.

Fluorescein and Its Diacetate

The cell-permeant fluorescein diacetate (FDA, F1303) is still occasionally used to measure intracellular pH,[6] as well as to study cell adhesion[7] or, in combination with propidium iodide (P1304MP, P3566, P21493; Section 8.1), to determine cell viability.[8,9] However, fluorescein (F1300), which is formed by intracellular hydrolysis of FDA, rapidly leaks from cells (Figure 15.3). Thus, other cell-permeant dyes such as the acetoxymethyl (AM) esters of BCECF and calcein are now preferred for intracellular pH measurements and cell viability assays (Section 15.2).

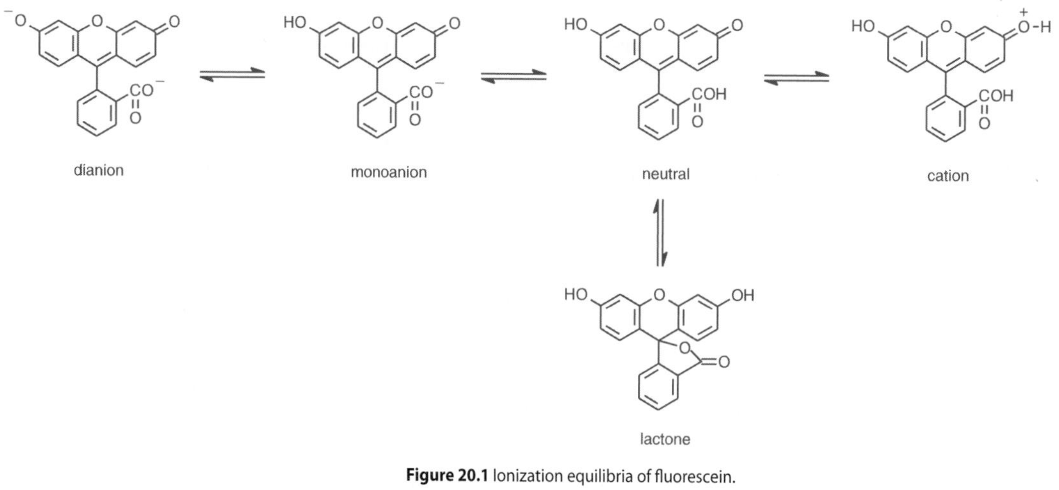

Figure 20.1 Ionization equilibria of fluorescein.

Carboxyfluorescein and Its Cell-Permeant Esters

The high leakage rate of fluorescein from cells makes it very difficult to quantitate intracellular pH because the decrease in the cell's fluorescence due to dye leakage cannot be easily distinguished from that due to acidification. The use of carboxyfluorescein diacetate (CFDA, C195) for intracellular pH measurements partially addresses this problem.[10] CFDA is moderately permeant to most cell membranes and, upon hydrolysis by intracellular nonspecific esterases, forms carboxyfluorescein (5(6)-FAM, C194; FluoroPure™ Grade, C1904), which has a pH-dependent spectral response very similar to that of fluorescein. As compared with fluorescein, carboxyfluorescein contains an extra negative charge and is therefore better retained in cells[11] (Figure 15.3). The mixed-isomer preparation of CFDA (C195) is usually adequate for intracellular pH measurements because the single isomers of carboxyfluorescein exhibit essentially identical pH-dependent spectra with a pK_a ~6.5. For experiments requiring a pure isomer, the single-isomer preparations of carboxyfluorescein (C1359, C1360; Section 1.5) and CFDA (C1361, C1362; Section 15.2) are available. In addition, we offer the AM ester of CFDA (5-CFDA, AM, C1354; Figure 15.7), which is electrically neutral and facilitates cell loading. Upon hydrolysis by intracellular esterases, this AM ester also yields carboxyfluorescein.[12–14]

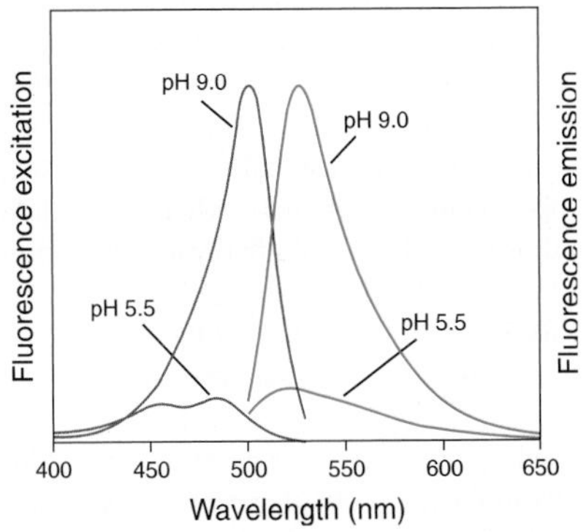

Figure 20.4 Fluorescence excitation (detected at 535 nm) and emission (excited at 490 nm) spectra of BCECF in pH 9.0 and 5.5 buffers.

Intracellular pH measurements have been made using carboxyfluorescein,[15–17] although the SNARF® and BCECF indicators (see below) exhibit superior spectral and pK_a properties for most pH studies. Carboxyfluorescein is also commonly employed as a polar tracer (Section 14.3), and CFDA and its AM ester are used for monitoring cell viability,[14,18] apoptosis[19–22] and cell adhesion[11,23,24] (Section 15.2, Section 15.5, Section 15.6).

BCECF and Its AM Ester

Although carboxyfluorescein is better retained in cells than is fluorescein, its pK_a of ~6.5 is lower than the cytosolic pH of most cells (pH ~6.8–7.4). Consequently, its fluorescence change is less than optimal for detecting small pH changes above pH 7. Since its introduction by Roger Tsien in 1982,[25,26] the polar fluorescein derivative BCECF (B1151) and its membrane-permeant AM ester (B1150, B1170, B3051) have become the most widely used fluorescent indicators for estimating intracellular pH. Also, a flow cytometric assay has been developed that uses BCECF to estimate the concentration of intracellular K^+.[27] BCECF's four to five negative charges at pH 7–8 improve its retention in cells (Figure 15.3), and its pK_a of 6.98 is ideal for typical intracellular pH measurements.

As with fluorescein and carboxyfluorescein, absorption of the phenolate anion (basic) form of BCECF is red-shifted and has increased molar absorptivity relative to the protonated (acidic) form (Figure 20.3); there is little, if any, pH-dependent shift in the fluorescence emission spectrum of BCECF upon excitation at 505 nm (Figure 20.3, Figure 20.4). BCECF is typically used as a dual-excitation ratiometric pH indicator. Signal errors caused by variations in concentration, path length, leakage and photobleaching are greatly reduced with ratiometric methods (see Note 19.1 "Technical Focus: Loading and Calibration of Intracellular Ion Indicators" in

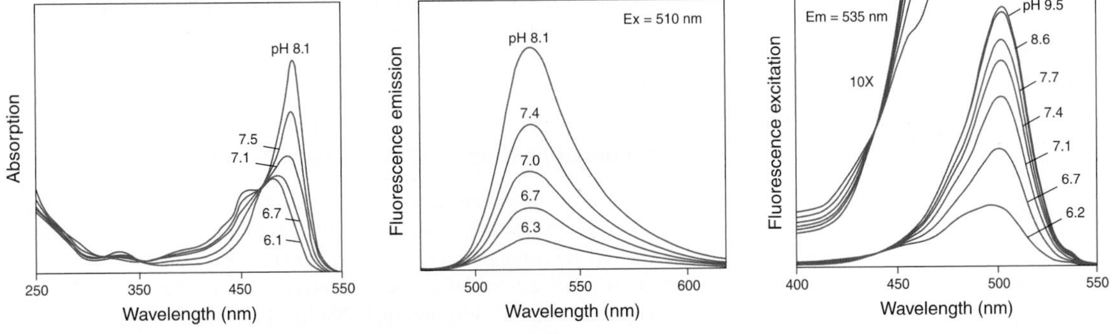

Figure 20.3 The pH-dependent spectra of BCECF (B1151): **A)** absorption spectra, **B)** emission spectra and **C)** excitation spectra. The fluorescence excitation spectra have been enlarged on the left to reveal BCECF's 439 nm isosbestic point. Note that the isosbestic point of the excitation spectra of BCECF is different from that of the absorption spectra (compare panels A and C).

Section 19.1). Intracellular pH measurements with BCECF are made by determining the pH-dependent ratio of emission intensity (detected at 535 nm) when the dye is excited at ~490 nm versus the emission intensity when excited at its isosbestic point of ~440 nm (Figure 20.3, Figure 20.4). Because BCECF's absorption at 440 nm is quite weak, increasing the denominator wavelength to ~450 nm provides improved signal-to-noise characteristics for ratio imaging applications.[28–30] As with other intracellular pH indicators, *in situ* calibration of BCECF's fluorescence response is usually accomplished using 10–50 µM nigericin (N1495, see below) in the presence of 100–150 mM K^+ to equilibrate internal and external pH.[10,31] Alternative calibration methods have also been reported.[32–34]

Loading of live cells for measurement of intracellular pH is readily accomplished by incubating cell suspensions or adherent cells in a 1–10 µM solution of the AM ester of BCECF. At least three different molecular species can be obtained in synthetic preparations of the AM ester of BCECF; however, all three forms shown in Figure 20.5 appear to be converted to the same product — BCECF acid (B1151, Figure 20.6) — by intracellular esterase hydrolysis. Although we can readily prepare the pure tri(acetoxymethyl) ester form (Form I in Figure 20.5), some researchers have found that cell loading with a mixture of the lactone Forms II and III is more efficient. Consequently, we produce BCECF AM predominantly as a mixture of Forms II and III with a typical percentage composition ratio of 45:55, as determined by HPLC, NMR and mass spectrometry. Because the

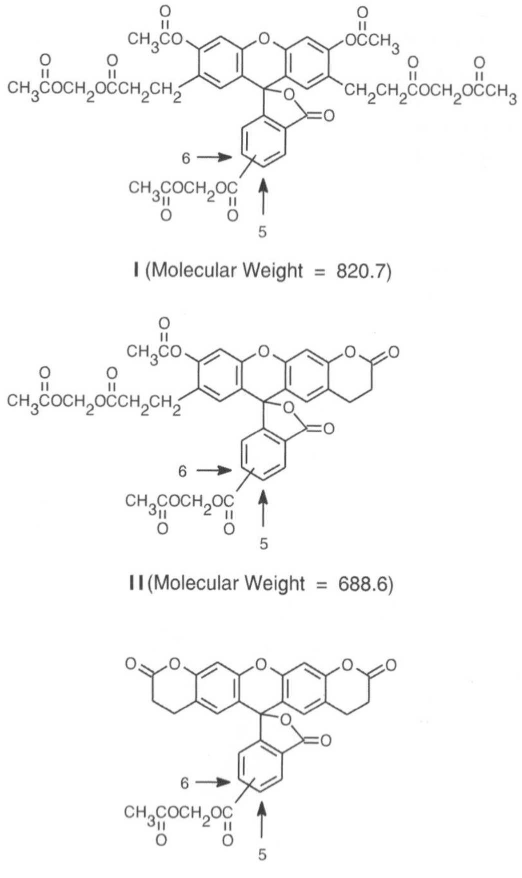

I (Molecular Weight = 820.7)

II (Molecular Weight = 688.6)

III (Molecular Weight = 556.5)

Figure 20.5 Structures of the AM esters of BCECF (B1150, B1170, B3051).

molecular weights of the different species are not equal, the effective molecular weight for each production lot is reported on the product's label. The AM ester of BCECF is available in a single 1 mg vial (B1150), specially packaged as a set of 20 vials that each contains 50 µg (B1170) and as a 1 mg/mL solution (~1.6 mM) in anhydrous dimethylsulfoxide (DMSO) (B3051). We highly recommend purchasing the set of 20 vials in order to reduce the potential for product deterioration caused by exposure to moisture.

Our bibliography for BCECF AM lists more than 1200 journal citations, including references for the use of BCECF AM to investigate:

- Cl^-/HCO_3^- exchange[35–37]
- K^+/H^+ exchange[38,39]
- Lactate transport and metabolism[40–42]
- Na^+/H^+ exchange[43–46]
- Na^+/Ca^{2+} exchange[47,48]
- NH_4^+ transport[49,50]
- Apoptosis[51–55] (Section 15.5)
- Cytotoxicity[56–59]
- Multidrug resistance[60–63] (Section 15.6)
- Cell volume changes[64–66]
- Cytosolic pH regulation in osteoblasts[67] and osteoclasts[68,69]
- Phagocytosis[70–72] (Section 16.1)

The cell-impermeant BCECF acid (B1151, Figure 20.6) is useful for pH measurements in intercellular spaces of epithelial cell monolayers,[73] interstitial spaces of normal and neoplastic tissue[74] and isolated cell fractions.[75] BCECF has also been employed for two-photon fluorescence lifetime imaging of the skin stratum corneum to detect aqueous acid pockets within the lipid-rich extracellular matrix.[76] The free acid of BCECF can be loaded into cells by microinjection[34] or electroporation or by using our Influx™ pinocytic cell-loading reagent (I14402, Section 19.8). It has also been loaded into bacterial cells by brief incubation at pH ~2.[77–79] In addition to the cell-permeant BCECF AM and cell-impermeant BCECF acid, Molecular Probes offers dextran conjugates of BCECF (D1878, D1880; Section 20.4).

Fluorescein Sulfonic Acid and Its Diacetate

The fluorescein-5-(and 6-)sulfonic acid (F1130) is much more polar than carboxyfluorescein. Consequently, once inside cells or liposomes, it is relatively well retained. Some cells can be loaded directly with 5-sulfofluorescein diacetate[80–83] (SFDA, S1129). Direct ratiometric measurement of the pH in the trans-Golgi of live human fibroblasts was achieved by simultaneously microinjecting liposomes loaded with both fluorescein sulfonic acid and sulforhodamine 101[84] (S359, Section 14.3). Fluorescein-5-(and 6-)sulfonic acid is more commonly used to measure barrier permeability of membranes[85,86] (Section 14.3).

Chemically Reactive Fluorescein Diacetates

One means for overcoming the cell leakage problem common to the above pH indicators, including BCECF, is to trap the indicator inside the cell via conjugation to intracellular constituents. The chloromethyl derivatives CellTracker™ Green CMFDA (C2925, C7025; Figure 14.10) and chloromethyl SNARF®-1 (C6826, see below) probably have the greatest potential for relatively long-term cell tracing and pH studies. In many cell types, the weakly thiol-reactive chloromethyl moiety of CMFDA reacts with intracellular thiols, including glutathione and proteins, to yield well-retained products (Figure 15.3). Cleavage of the acetate groups of the CMFDA conjugate by intracellular esterases yields a conjugate that retains the pH-dependent spectral properties of fluorescein.

Similarly, the amine-reactive succinimidyl ester of CFDA (5(6)-CFDA SE, also called CFSE, C1157) can potentially be used for long-term pH studies of live cells, producing a conjugate with the pH-sensitive properties of carboxyfluorescein. Because it is intrinsically more reactive, the succinimidyl ester of CFDA is more likely to react at sites on the extracellular surface than is CMFDA.

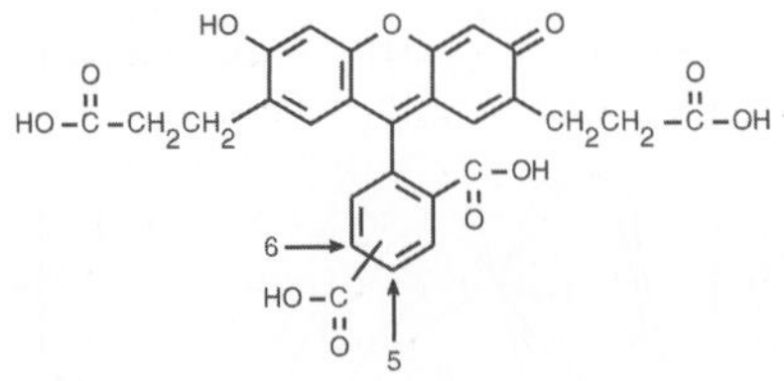

Figure 20.6 B1151 2′,7′-bis-(2-carboxyethyl)-5-(and-6)-carboxyfluorescein (BCECF acid).

Carboxynaphthofluorescein

Carboxynaphthofluorescein (C652, Figure 20.7) has pH-dependent red fluorescence (excitation/emission maxima ~598/668 nm at pH >9) with a relatively high pK_a of ~7.6. The long wavelength–fluorescent pH-dependent spectra of carboxynaphthofluorescein have been exploited in the construction of fiber-optic pH sensors.[87,88] This long-wavelength pH indicator is also available in membrane-permeant diacetate form (C13196) for passive intracellular loading and as an amine-reactive succinimidyl ester (C653, Section 20.4) for preparing pH-sensitive conjugates.

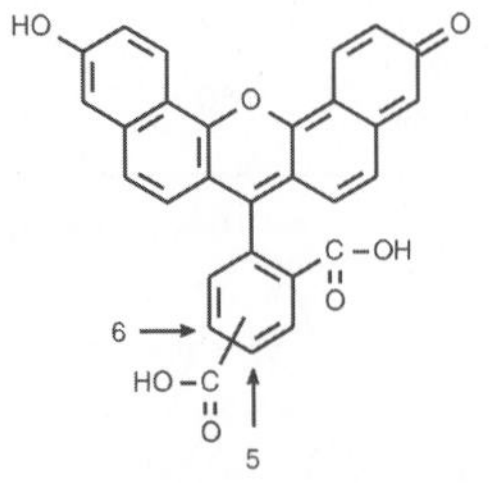

Figure 20.7 C652 5-(and-6)-carboxynaphthofluorescein.

SNARF® and SNAFL® pH Indicators

Our patented seminaphthorhodafluors (SNARF® dyes) and seminaphthofluoresceins (SNAFL® dyes) are visible light–excitable fluorescent pH indicators developed at Molecular Probes.[89] The SNARF® and SNAFL® indicators have both dual-emission and dual-excitation properties, making them particularly useful for confocal laser-scanning microscopy[90–93] (Figure 20.8), flow cytometry[30,94–96] and microplate reader–based measurements.[97] The dual-emission properties of the SNARF® indicators may make them the preferred probes for use in fiber-optic pH sensors.[98–100] These pH indicators can be excited by the 488 or 514 nm spectral lines of the argon-ion laser and are sensitive to pH values within the physiological range. Dextran conjugates of the SNARF® dyes are described in Section 20.4.

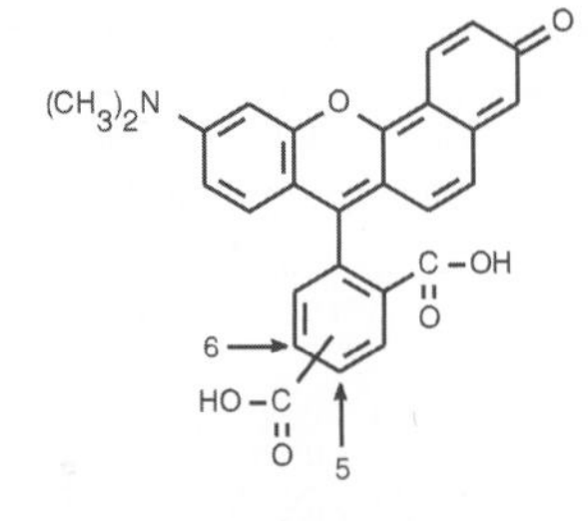

Figure 20.9 C1270 5-(and-6)-carboxy SNARF®-1.

Carboxy SNARF®-1 Dye and Its Cell-Permeant Ester

The carboxy SNARF®-1 dye (C1270, Figure 20.9), which is easily loaded into cells as its cell-permeant AM ester acetate (C1271, C1272), has a pK_a of about 7.5 at room temperature and 7.3–7.4 at 37°C. Thus, carboxy SNARF®-1 is useful for measuring pH changes between pH 7 and 8. Like fluorescein and BCECF, the absorption spectrum of the carboxy SNARF®-1 pH indicator undergoes a shift to longer wavelengths upon deprotonation of its phenolic substituent (Figure 20.10). In contrast to the fluorescein-based indicators, however, carboxy SNARF®-1 also exhibits a sig-

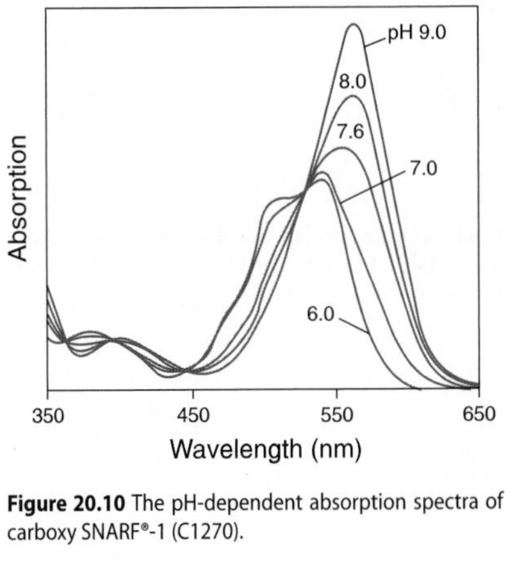

Figure 20.10 The pH-dependent absorption spectra of carboxy SNARF®-1 (C1270).

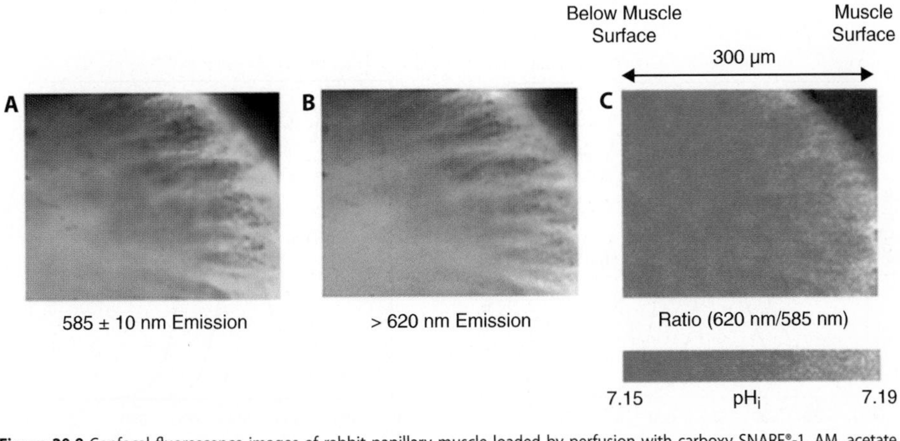

Figure 20.8 Confocal fluorescence images of rabbit papillary muscle loaded by perfusion with carboxy SNARF®-1, AM, acetate (C1271, C1272). Images A and B were acquired through 585 ± 10 nm bandpass and >620 nm longpass emission filters, respectively. The 620 nm/585 nm fluorescence ratio image (panel C) is more uniform than the component images A and B due to cancellation of intensity variations resulting from heterogeneous uptake of the fluorescent indicator. Images contributed by Barbara Muller-Borer and John Lemasters, University of North Carolina and reprinted with permission from Am J Physiol 275, H1937 (1998).

nificant pH-dependent emission shift from yellow-orange to deep red fluorescence under acidic and basic conditions, respectively (Figure 20.11, Figure 20.12). This pH dependence allows the ratio of the fluorescence intensities from the dye at two emission wavelengths (Figure 20.8) — typically 580 nm and 640 nm — to be used for quantitative determinations of pH (see Note 19.1 "Technical Focus: Loading and Calibration of Intracellular Ion Indicators" in Section 19.1). For practical purposes, it is often desirable to bias the detection of carboxy SNARF®-1 fluorescence towards the less fluorescent acidic form by using an excitation wavelength between 488 nm and the excitation isosbestic point at ~530 nm, yielding balanced signals for the two emission-ratio components (Figure 20.11, Figure 20.13). When excited at 488 nm, carboxy SNARF®-1 exhibits an emission isosbestic point of ~610 nm and a lower fluorescent signal than obtained with 514 nm excitation.[93] Alternatively, when excited by the 568 nm spectral line of the Ar–Kr laser found in some confocal laser-scanning microscopes, carboxy SNARF®-1 exhibits a fluorescence increase at 640 nm as the pH increases and an emission isosbestic point at 585 nm.[93] As with other ion indicators, intracellular environments may cause significant changes to both the spectral properties and pK_a of carboxy SNARF®-1,[101–104] and the indicator should always be calibrated in the system under study.

The spectra of carboxy SNARF®-1 are well resolved from those of fura-2,[105,106] and indo-1[107] (Section 19.2), as well as those of the fluo-3,[106,108,109] fluo-4, Calcium Green™ and Oregon Green® 488 BAPTA Ca^{2+} indicators (Section 19.3), permitting simultaneous measurements of intracellular pH and Ca^{2+} (Figure 20.14). Carboxy SNARF®-1 has also been used in combination with the Na^+ indicator SBFI (S1262, S1263, S1264; Section 21.1) to simultaneously detect pH and Na^+ changes in heart mitochondria.[110] The relatively long-wavelength excitation and emission characteristics of carboxy SNARF®-1 facilitate studies in autofluorescent cells[111] and permit experiments that employ the anion-transport inhibitor DIDS[112,113] (D337, Section 16.3), amiloride derivatives[112,114] (Section 16.3), caged probes (Section 5.3) and other modifiers of cell function that require UV light excitation. In addition, the ability to excite carboxy SNARF®-1 near 490 nm and to observe red fluorescence beyond 600 nm permits its use as a Ca^{2+}-*insensitive* reference dye in order to make ratiometric measurements of intracellular Ca^{2+} with the nonratiometric Ca^{2+} indicators fluo-3,[115–118] fluo-4 and Calcium Green™-2.[119] Incubation of cells for several hours after loading with carboxy SNARF®-1 AM ester acetate results in compartmentally selective retention of the dye, allowing *in situ* measurements of mitochondrial pH[120] (Figure 20.15).

SNARF®-4F and SNARF®-5F Dyes

Although the carboxy SNARF®-1 indicator possesses excellent spectral properties, its pK_a of ~7.5 may be too high for measurements of intracellular pH in some cells. For quantitative measurements of pH changes in the typical cytosolic range (pH ~6.8–7.4), we now recommend SNARF®-5F carboxylic acid (Figure 20.16), which has a pK_a value of ~7.2, as the indicator with the best spectral properties for estimating cytosolic pH (Figure 20.17). SNARF®-4F carboxylic acid (Figure 20.18) has a somewhat more acidic pH sensitivity maximum (pK_a ~6.4) but retains its dual-emission spectral properties (Figure 20.19). Both SNARF®-4F and SNARF®-5F[121] allow

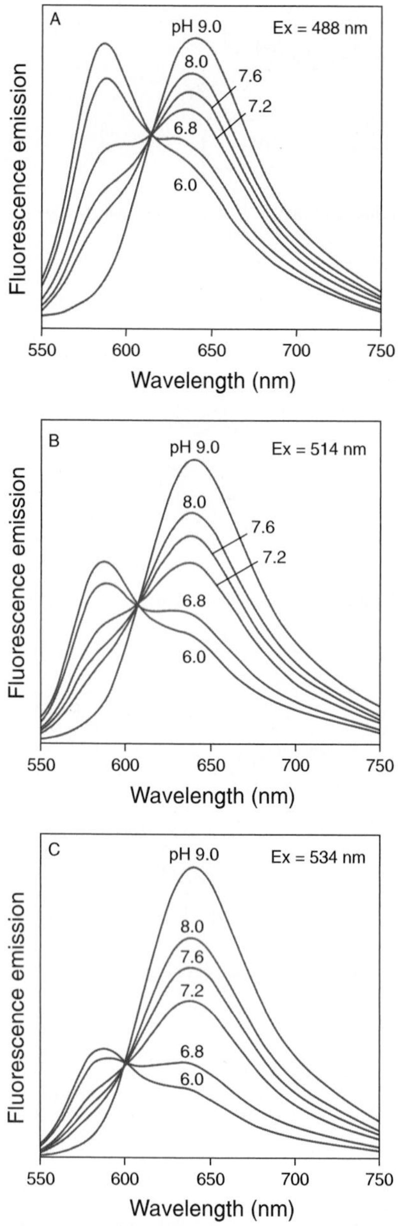

Figure 20.11 The pH-dependent emission spectra of carboxy SNARF®-1 (C1270) when it is excited at **A)** 488 nm, **B)** 514 nm and **C)** 534 nm.

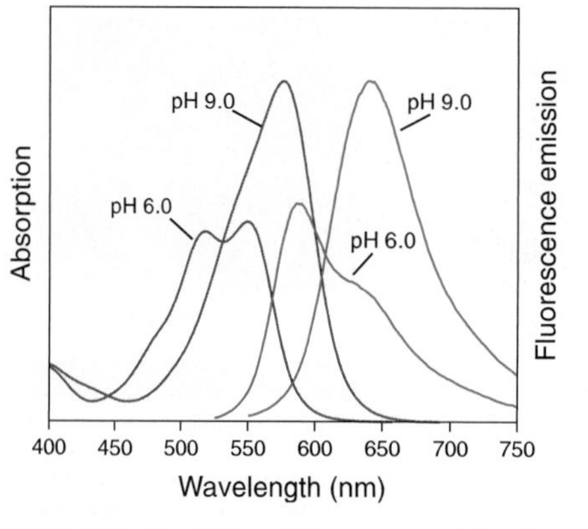

Figure 20.12 Absorption and fluorescence emission (excited at 514 nm) spectra of carboxy SNARF®-1 in pH 9.0 and 6.0 buffers.

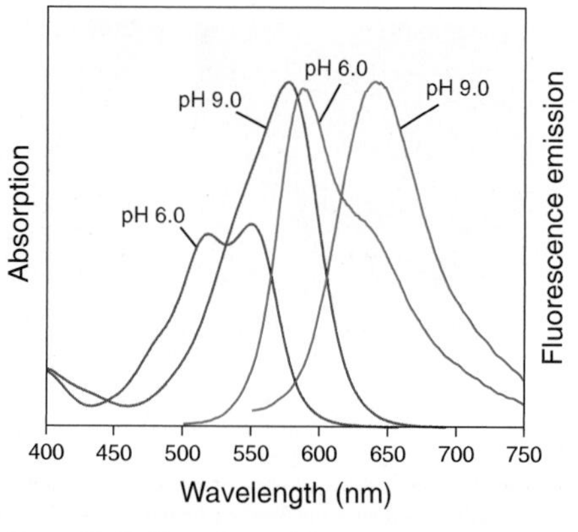

Figure 20.13 Absorption and fluorescence emission (excited at 488 nm) spectra of carboxy SNARF®-1 in pH 9.0 and pH 6.0 buffers.

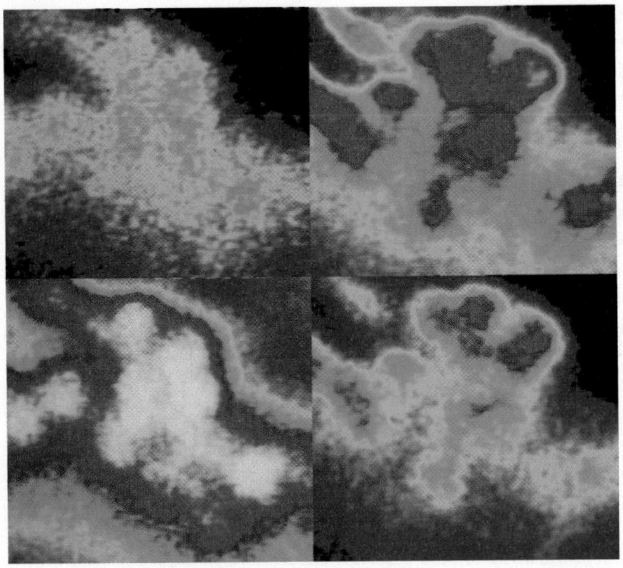

Figure 20.14 Rat pituitary intermediate lobe melanotropes labeled with the indo-1 AM (I1203, I1223, I1226) and carboxy SNARF®-1, AM, acetate (C1271, C1272) indicators. Pseudocolored fluorescence from the dual-emission Ca^{2+} indicator indo-1 is shown at 405 and 475 nm (left panels). Pseudocolored fluorescence from the dual-emission pH indicator carboxy SNARF®-1 is shown at 575 and 640 nm (right panels). Image contributed by Stephen J. Morris, University of Missouri-Kansas City, and Diane M. Beatty, Molecular Probes, Inc.

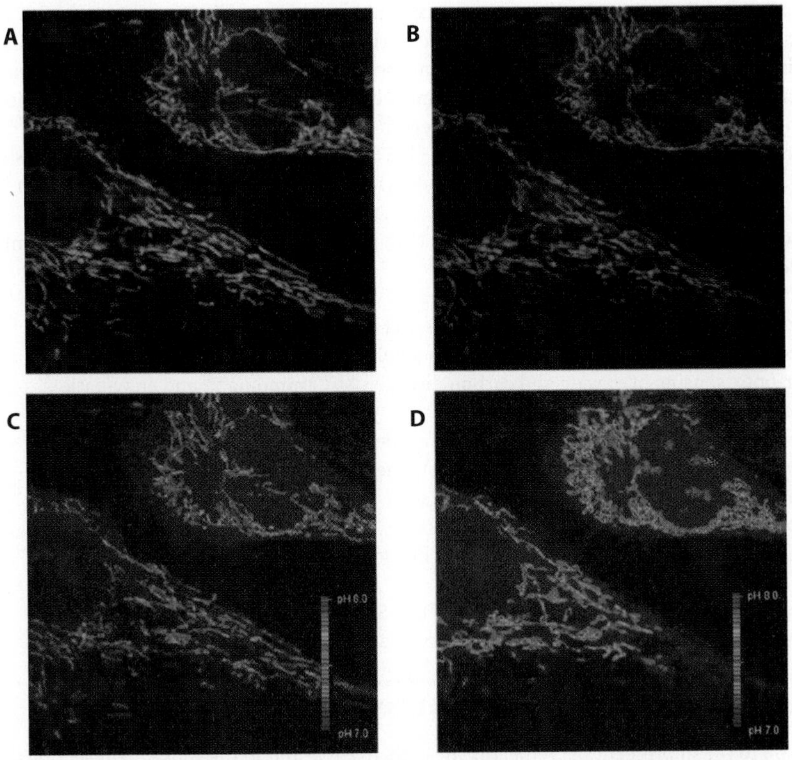

Figure 20.15 Selective loading of carboxy SNARF®-1 into mitochondria. BHK cells were loaded with 10 µM carboxy SNARF®-1, AM, acetate (C1271, C1272) for 10 minutes, followed by incubation for 4 hours at room temperature. **A)** Confocal image (488 nm excitation) of mitochondrial-selective loading of carboxy SNARF®-1 visualized through a 560–600 nm bandpass filter. **B)** Confocal image of the same cells as in **A**, but using a 605 nm dichroic mirror and a 610 nm longpass filter. **C)** Ratio image (**A** and **B**) of mitochondria in cells pseudocolored to represent different pH levels. **D)** Change in mitochondrial pH following the addition of 10 µM carbonyl cyanide *m*-chlorophenylhydrazone (CCCP), resulting in a decrease (acidification) of mitochondrial pH. Image contributed by Brian Herman, University of Texas Health Science Center, San Antonio, and reprinted with permission from Biotechniques 30, 804 (2001).

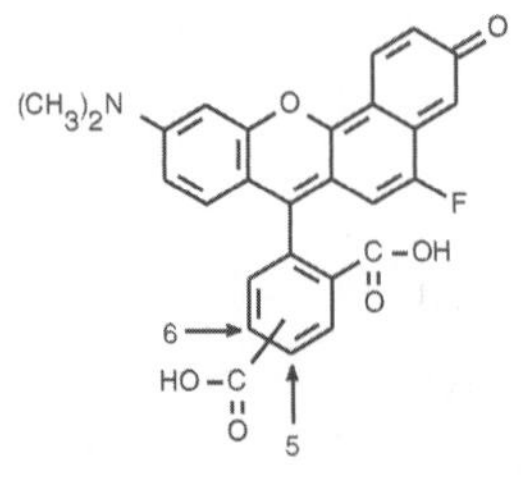

Figure 20.16 S23922 SNARF®-5F 5-(and-6)-carboxylic acid.

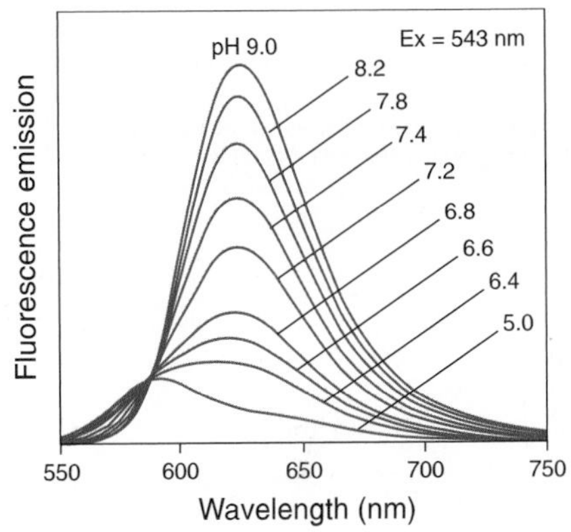

Figure 20.17 Fluorescence emission spectra of SNARF®-5F 5-(and 6-)carboxylic acid (S23922) as a function of pH.

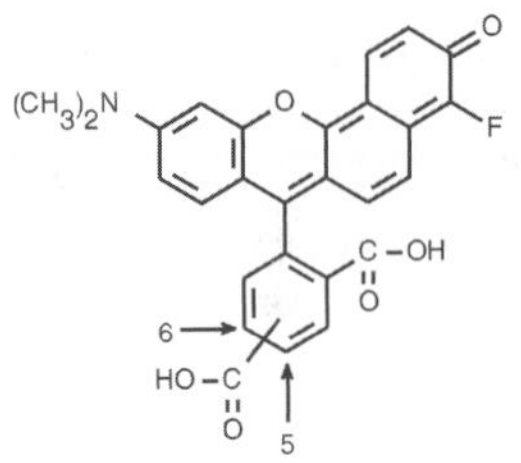

Figure 20.18 S23920 SNARF®-4F 5-(and-6)-carboxylic acid.

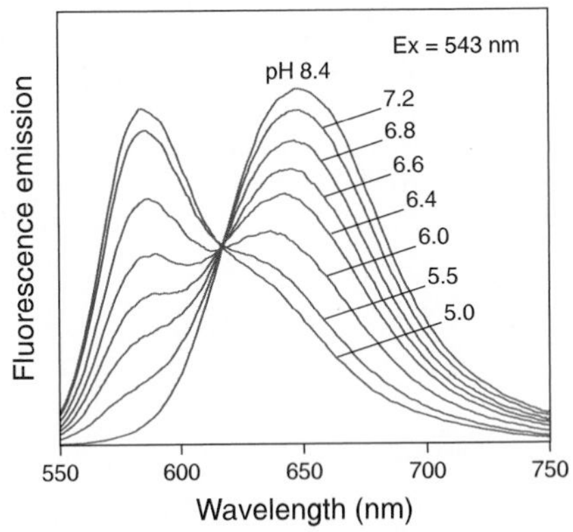

Figure 20.19 Fluorescence emission spectra of SNARF®-4F 5-(and 6-)carboxylic acid (S23920) showing the pH-dependent spectral shift that is characteristic of this and other SNARF® pH indicators.

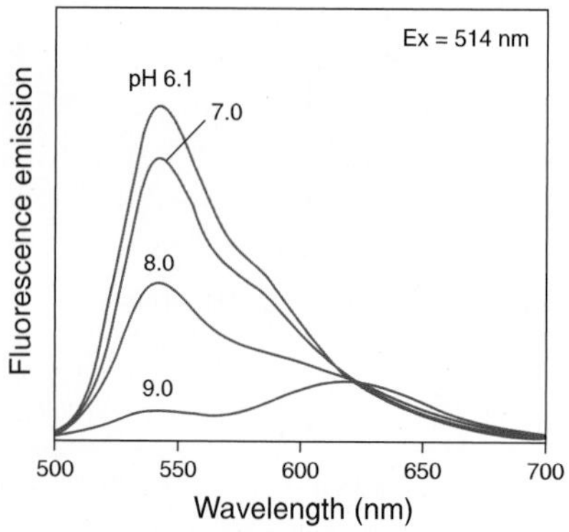

Figure 20.20 The pH-dependent emission spectra of 5-(and 6-)carboxy SNAFL®-1 (C1255).

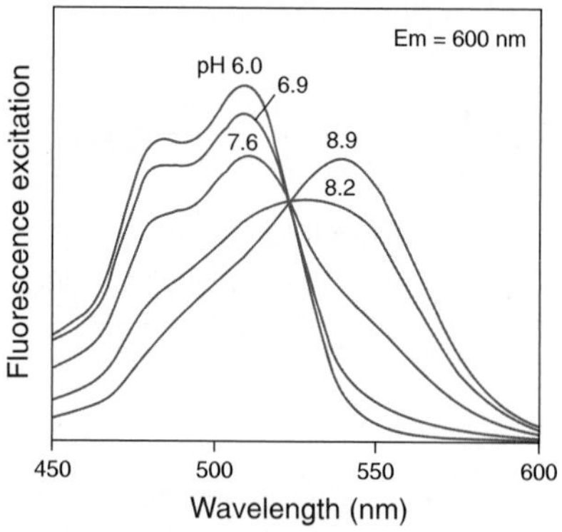

Figure 20.21 The pH-dependent excitation spectra of 5-(and 6-)carboxy SNAFL®-1 (C1255).

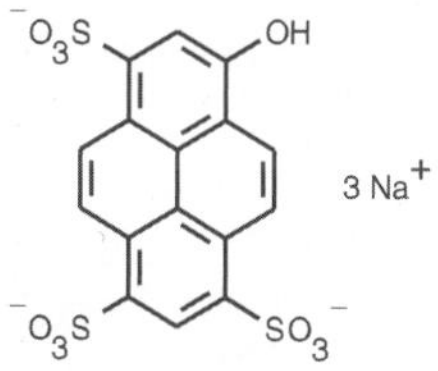

Figure 20.22 H348 8-hydroxypyrene-1,3,6-trisulfonic acid, trisodium salt (HPTS, pyranine).

dual-excitation and dual-emission ratiometric pH measurements, making them compatible with the same instrument configurations used for carboxy SNARF®-1 in ratio imaging and flow cytometry applications. SNARF®-4F and SNARF®-5F are available as free carboxylic acids (S23920, S23922) and as cell-permeant diacetate derivatives (S23921, S23923).

Chloromethyl SNARF®-1 Acetate

Our 5-(and 6-)chloromethyl SNARF®-1 acetate (C6826) contains a chloromethyl group that is mildly reactive with intracellular thiols (Figure 14.19), forming adducts that should improve cellular retention of the SNARF® fluorophore (Figure 14.21). As with CellTracker™ Green CMFDA (see above), improved retention of this conjugate in cells may permit monitoring of intracellular pH over longer time periods than is possible with other intracellular pH indicators. Like our CellTracker™ dyes (Section 14.2), chloromethyl SNARF®-1 acetate is also useful simply as a long-term cell tracer.

Carboxy SNAFL®-1

In contrast to fluorescein and its derivatives, the acidic form of the SNAFL®-1 pH indicator has a higher fluorescence quantum yield than its basic form.[122,123] SNAFL® indicators can be used for either dual-emission[122] (Figure 20.20) or dual-excitation (Figure 20.21) ratiometric pH measurements. SNAFL® indicators have also been incorporated in fluorescence lifetime–based pH and CO_2 sensors and in fiber-optic pH sensors.[77] Carboxy SNAFL®-1 is available as a free acid (C1255) and as a cell-permeant diacetate derivative (C1256).

8-Hydroxypyrene-1,3,6-Trisulfonic Acid (HPTS)

8-Hydroxypyrene-1,3,6-trisulfonic acid (HPTS, also known as pyranine; H348; Figure 20.22) is an inexpensive, highly water-soluble, membrane-impermeant pH indicator with a pK_a of ~7.3 in aqueous buffers.[124] The pK_a of HPTS is reported to rise to 7.5–7.8 in the cytosol of some cells.[125] Unlike indicators based on the SNARF® and fluorescein dyes, there is no membrane-permeant form of HPTS available. Consequently, HPTS must be introduced into cells by microinjection, electroporation[126] or liposome-mediated delivery,[127–129] through ATP-gated ion channels[130] or by other relatively invasive means (Table 14.1). HPTS exhibits a pH-dependent absorption shift (Figure 20.23), allowing ratiometric measurements using an excitation ratio of 450/405 nm.[131]

The unique pH-dependent spectral properties, high water solubility and low cost of HPTS make its applications numerous. They include:

- Detecting proton permeability in liposomes and cells[132–134]
- Investigating pH-mediated changes of intracellular Ca^{2+}[135]
- Fiber-optic sensing of oxygen and carbon dioxide,[136,137] ammonia[138] and enzymatic activity[139]
- Detecting bioenergetically linked proton-transfer processes[140–144]
- Measuring acidity of lysosomes and other organelles (Section 20.3)
- Detecting membrane fusion and lysis[145,146]
- Following endocytosis[147–149] (Section 16.1)
- Detecting targeted intracellular delivery of liposome-encapsulated molecules[127,128,150,151]

We also offer a dextran conjugate of HPTS (D7179, Section 20.4).

Auxiliary Probes for pH Measurements

In addition to the fluorescent pH indicators described above and in the subsequent sections, Molecular Probes provides nigericin, which is widely used for calibrating intracellular pH indicators, as well as a unique caged compound that can be used for localized generation of protons by UV photolysis.

Nigericin

Intracellular calibration of the fluorescence response of cytosolic pH indicators is typically performed using the K^+/H^+ ionophore nigericin (N1495), which causes equilibration of intracellular and extracellular pH in the presence of a depolarizing concentration of extracellular K^+[10,31] (see Note 19.1 "Technical Focus: Loading and Calibration of Intracellular Ion Indicators" in Section 19.1). Nett and Deitmer have compared this technique with calibrations performed by direct insertion of pH-sensitive microelectrodes in leech giant glial cells.[34]

Caged Proton

Photolysis of NPE-caged phosphate[152–155] (N7065) liberates inorganic phosphate, which rapidly ionizes to release a proton. This caged phosphate can be used to produce a pulse of phosphate and to generate a photolysis-dependent proton release that results in a rapid drop in pH. See Section 5.3 for a more complete discussion of the properties and applications of caged probes.

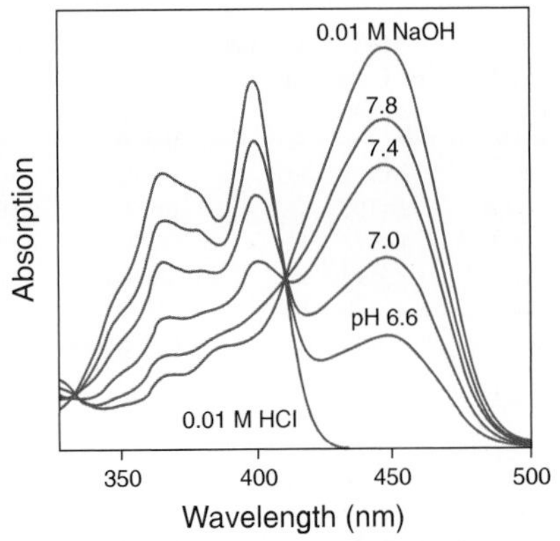

Figure 20.23 The pH-dependent absorption spectra of 8-hydroxypyrene-1,3,6-trisulfonic acid (HPTS, H348).

References

1. J Fluorescence 6, 147 (1996); **2.** Spectrochim Acta A 51, 7 (1995); **3.** Photochem Photobiol 60, 435 (1994); **4.** J Luminescence 10, 381 (1975); **5.** J Phys Chem 75, 245 (1971); **6.** FEBS Lett 341, 125 (1994); **7.** J Immunol Methods 157, 117 (1993); **8.** Methods Mol Biol 43, 211 (1995); **9.** J Histochem Cytochem 33, 77 (1985); **10.** Biochemistry 18, 2210 (1979); **11.** J Immunol Methods 172, 115 (1994); **12.** Biochemistry 34, 1606 (1995); **13.** Cytometry 13, 739 (1992); **14.** J Immunol Methods 130, 251 (1990); **15.** Appl Environ Microbiol 63, 178 (1997); **16.** Cytometry 19, 235 (1995); **17.** Photochem Photobiol 60, 274 (1994); **18.** Anticancer Res 14, 927 (1994); **19.** J Immunol Methods 243, 191 (2000); **20.** J Immunol Methods 243, 155 (2000); **21.** J Cell Biol 134, 757 (1996); **22.** Exp Cell Res 211, 322 (1994); **23.** Micron 31, 41 (2000); **24.** J Cell Biol 124, 609 (1994); **25.** Proc Natl Acad Sci U S A 81, 7436 (1984); **26.** J Cell Biol 95, 189 (1982); **27.** Cytometry 28, 42 (1997); **28.** Methods Cell Biol 30, 157 (1989); **29.** Cell Biology: A Laboratory Handbook, 2nd Ed., Vol. 3, Celis JE, Ed. pp. 380–386 (1998); **30.** Methods Cell Biol 41, 135 (1994); **31.** Methods Enzymol 192, 38 (1990); **32.** J Cell Physiol 151, 596 (1992); **33.** J Fluorescence 2, 191 (1992); **34.** Biophys J 71, 394 (1996); **35.** Kidney Int 53, 432 (1998); **36.** Am J Physiol 274, F358 (1998); **37.** J Membr Biol 159, 253 (1997); **38.** Biochemistry 34, 15157 (1995); **39.** J Biol Chem 272, 25668 (1997); **40.** J Biol Chem 273, 15920 (1998); **41.** J Biol Chem 273, 27162 (1998); **42.** J Biol Chem 271, 861 (1996); **43.** J Biol Chem 273, 20828 (1998); **44.** J Cell Biol 140, 335 (1998); **45.** J Biol Chem 273, 2035 (1998); **46.** J Biol Chem 273, 8790 (1998); **47.** J Neurochem 71, 1051 (1998); **48.** J Biol Chem 270, 9137 (1995); **49.** Am J Physiol 273, F817 (1997); **50.** Plant Physiol 113, 451 (1997); **51.** J Biol Chem 276, 514 (2001); **52.** J Mol Cell Cardiol 30, 519 (1998); **53.** J Biol Chem 273, 12662 (1998); **54.** J Biol Chem 270, 6235 (1995); **55.** J Biol Chem 271, 16260 (1996); **56.** Proc Natl Acad Sci U S A 98, 3434 (2001); **57.** Biotechniques 23, 139 (1997); **58.** J Microbiol Methods 28, 35 (1997); **59.** J Immunol Methods 172, 255 (1994); **60.** Eur J Biochem 243, 219 (1997); **61.** Am J Physiol 274, C182 (1998); **62.** Br J Cancer 75, 810 (1997); **63.** Biochemistry 36, 11169 (1997); **64.** Meth Neurosci 27, 361 (1995); **65.** Pflugers Arch 435, 74 (1997); **66.** Neuroscience 69, 283 (1995); **67.** Miner Electrolyte Metab 20, 16 (1994); **68.** Am J Physiol Cell Physiol 279, C751 (2000); **69.** J Biol Chem 272, 6354 (1997); **70.** J Biol Chem 272, 29810 (1997); **71.** J Leukoc Biol 62, 329 (1997); **72.** J Biol Chem 271, 2005 (1996); **73.** J Membr Biol 140, 89 (1994); **74.** Cancer Res 54, 5670 (1994); **75.** Biochemistry 35, 13419 (1996); **76.** Biophys J 83, 1682 (2002); **77.** Anal Chem 71, 154 (1999); **78.** Mol Membr Biol 13, 173 (1996); **79.** Biochim Biophys Acta 1115, 75 (1991); **80.** J Cell Biol 111, 3129 (1990); **81.** J Immunol Methods 133, 87 (1990); **82.** FEBS Lett 200, 203 (1986); **83.** Biotechniques 3, 270 (1985); **84.** J Biol Chem 270, 4967 (1995); **85.** Am J Physiol Gastrointest Liver Physiol 268, 361 (1995); **86.** Am J Physiol Gastrointest Liver Physiol 281, G833 (2001); **87.** Mikrochim Acta 108, 133 (1992); **88.** Anal Chem 69, 863 (1997); **89.** Anal Biochem 194, 330 (1991); **90.** Methods Enzymol 302, 341 (1999); **91.** Micron 24, 573 (1993); **92.** Am J Physiol 275, H1937 (1998); **93.** Biophys J 66, 942 (1994); **94.** Cytometry 14, 916 (1993); **95.** J Immunol Methods 221, 43 (1998); **96.** J Cell Physiol 177, 109 (1998); **97.** Am J Physiol 273, C1783 (1997); **98.** J Biomed Mater Res 39, 9 (1998); **99.** J Immunol Methods 159, 145 (1993); **100.** Anal Chem 65, 2329 (1993); **101.** J Photochem Photobiol B 37, 18 (1997); **102.** Pflugers Arch 427, 332 (1994); **103.** Anal Biochem 204, 65 (1992); **104.** J Fluorescence 2, 75 (1992); **105.** J Cell Physiol 161, 129 (1994); **106.** Cell Calcium 19, 337 (1996); **107.** Endocrinology 133, 972 (1993); **108.** J Physiol 528 Pt 1, 25 (2000); **109.** Cytometry 24, 99 (1996); **110.** J Biol Chem 270, 672 (1995); **111.** Am J Physiol 267, L211 (1994); **112.** J Biol Chem 270, 1315 (1995); **113.** Pflugers Arch 417, 234 (1990); **114.** Arch Biochem Biophys 356, 25 (1998); **115.** J Biol Chem 270, 29781 (1995); **116.** J Biol Chem 269, 30636 (1994); **117.** Biochem J 289, 373 (1993); **118.** Cytometry 11, 923 (1990); **119.** Pflugers Arch 430, 579 (1995); **120.** Biotechniques 30, 804 (2001); **121.** Bioorg Med Chem Lett 11, 2903 (2001); **122.** J Photochem Photobiol B 28, 19 (1995); **123.** Anal Chim Acta 274, 47 (1993); **124.** Fresenius Z Anal Chem 314, 119 (1983); **125.** Anal Biochem 167, 362 (1987); **126.** J Bacteriol 177, 1017 (1995); **127.** Pharm Res 14, 1203 (1997); **128.** Proc Natl Acad Sci U S A 94, 8795 (1997); **129.** Curr Eye Res 16, 1073 (1997); **130.** Am J Physiol 275, C1158 (1998); **131.** Proc Natl Acad Sci U S A 92, 3156 (1995); **132.** Biophys J 70, 339 (1996); **133.** Biophys J 71, 3091 (1996); **134.** Biophys J 68, 1518 (1995); **135.** J Physiol 530, 405 (2001); **136.** Anal Chem 67, 2264 (1995); **137.** Analyst 121, 339 (1996); **138.** Anal Chim Acta 185, 321 (1986); **139.** Anal Biochem 252, 190 (1997); **140.** J Biol Chem 276, 25480 (2001); **141.** Biochemistry 37, 2496 (1998); **142.** Biochemistry 34, 8820 (1995); **143.** Biophys J 71, 1011 (1996); **144.** Biophys J 73, 2638 (1997); **145.** Biochemistry 36, 6251 (1997); **146.** J Cell Biol 131, 679 (1995); **147.** J Cell Biol 121, 305 (1993); **148.** Biochemistry 37, 12875 (1998); **149.** J Biochem (Tokyo) 117, 34 (1995); **150.** Biochemistry 36, 66 (1997); **151.** J Biol Chem 271, 7249 (1996); **152.** FEBS Lett 405, 81 (1997); **153.** J Physiol 451, 247 (1992); **154.** Biophys J 72, 1780 (1997); **155.** J Mol Biol 184, 645 (1985).

Data Table — 20.2 Probes Useful at Near-Neutral pH

				Acidic/Neutral Solution				Basic Solution						
Cat #	MW	Storage	Soluble	Abs	EC	Em	Solvent	Abs	EC	Em	Solvent	pK_a	Product	Notes
B1150	~615	F,D	DMSO	<300		none							B1151	1
B1151	520.45	L	pH >6	482	35,000	520	pH 5	503	90,000	528	pH 9	7.0		2, 3
B1170	~615	F,D	DMSO	<300		none							B1151	1
B3051	~615	F,D	DMSO	<300		none							B1151	1, 4
B14440	548.50	L	pH >6	483	36,000	520	pH 5	504	92,000	529	pH 9	7.0		2, 3
B14441	848.77	F,D	DMSO	<300		none							B14440	
C194	376.32	L	pH >6, DMF	475	28,000	517	pH 5	492	75,000	517	pH 9	6.4		2, 3
C195	460.40	F,D	DMSO	<300		none							C194	
C652	476.44	L	pH >6, DMF	512	11,000	563	pH 6	598	49,000	668	pH 10	7.6		2, 3, 5
C1157	557.47	F,D	DMF, DMSO	<300		none							C1311	
C1255	426.38	L	pH >6	508	29,000	543	pH 6	540	52,000	623	pH 10	7.8		2, 3, 6
C1256	510.46	F,D	DMSO	<350		none							C1255	
C1260	460.83	L	pH >6	514	31,000	546	pH 6	543	50,000	630	pH 10	7.7		2, 3, 6
C1261	544.90	F,D	DMSO	<350		none							C1260	
C1270	453.45	L	pH >6	548	27,000	587	pH 6	576	48,000	635	pH 10	7.5		2, 3, 6
C1271	567.55	F,D	DMSO	<350		none							C1270	
C1272	567.55	F,D	DMSO	<350		none							C1270	
C1354	532.46	F,D	DMSO	<300		none							C1359	
C1904	376.32	L	pH >6, DMF	475	29,000	517	pH 5	492	78,000	517	pH 9	6.4		2, 3, 7
C2925	464.86	F,D	DMSO	<300		none							see Notes	8
C6826	499.95	F,D	DMSO	<350		none							see Notes	9
C7025	464.86	F,D	DMSO	<300		none							see Notes	8
C13196	560.52	F,D	DMSO	<300		none							C652	
F1130	478.32	D,L	H_2O, DMF	476	31,000	519	pH 5	495	76,000	519	pH 9	6.4		2, 3
F1300	332.31	L	pH >6, DMF	473	34,000	514	pH 5	490	93,000	514	pH 9	6.4		2, 3
F1303	416.39	F,D	DMSO	<300		none							F1300	
H348	524.37	D,L	H_2O	403	20,000	511	pH 4	454	24,000	511	pH 9	7.3		2, 3, 10
N1495	724.97	F,D	MeOH	<300		none								
N7065	281.20	F,D,LL	H_2O	259	5,700	none	MeOH							11, 12
S1129	518.43	F,D	DMSO	<300		none							F1130	
S23920	471.44	L	pH >6	552	27,000	589	pH 5	581	48,000	652	pH 9	6.4		2, 3
S23921	585.54	F,D	DMSO	<350		none							S23920	
S23922	471.44	L	pH >6	555	27,000	590	pH 5	579	49,000	630	pH 9	7.2		2, 3
S23923	585.54	F,D	DMSO	<350		none							S23922	

For definitions of the contents of this data table, see "Navigating *The Handbook*" in the introductory pages.

Notes

1. MW value is approximate. BCECF, AM is a mixture of molecular species. Lot-specific average MW values are printed on product labels.
2. pK_a values may vary considerably depending on the temperature, ionic strength, viscosity, protein binding and other factors. Unless otherwise noted, values listed have been determined from pH-dependent fluorescence measurements at 22°C.
3. Spectra are in aqueous buffers adjusted to >1 pH unit above and >1 pH unit below the pK_a.
4. This product is supplied as a ready-made solution in the solvent indicated under "Soluble."
5. Data on pH-dependence of C652 spectra obtained at Molecular Probes. Additional relevant data are reported elsewhere (Mikrochim Acta 108, 133 (1992)).
6. Values of pK_a for these SNAFL® and SNARF® indicators are as reported in published references (Anal Biochem 194, 330 (1991)).
7. This product is specified to equal or exceed 98% analytical purity by HPLC.
8. Acetate hydrolysis of this compound yields a fluorescent product with similar pH-dependent spectral characteristics to C1904.
9. C6826 is converted to a fluorescent product with spectra similar to C1270 after acetate hydrolysis.
10. The pK_a for H348 was determined in 0.066 M phosphate buffers at 22°C (Fresenius Z Anal Chem 314, 119 (1983)).
11. All photoactivatable probes are sensitive to light. They should be protected from illumination except when photolysis is intended.
12. This compound has weaker visible absorption at >300 nm but no discernible absorption peaks in this region.

Product List — 20.2 Probes Useful at Near-Neutral pH

Cat #	Product Name	Unit Size
B1151	2',7'-bis-(2-carboxyethyl)-5-(and-6)-carboxyfluorescein (BCECF acid) *mixed isomers*	1 mg
B1150	2',7'-bis-(2-carboxyethyl)-5-(and-6)-carboxyfluorescein, acetoxymethyl ester (BCECF, AM)	1 mg
B1170	2',7'-bis-(2-carboxyethyl)-5-(and-6)-carboxyfluorescein, acetoxymethyl ester (BCECF, AM) *special packaging*	20 x 50 µg
B3051	2',7'-bis-(2-carboxyethyl)-5-(and-6)-carboxyfluorescein, acetoxymethyl ester (BCECF, AM) *1 mg/mL solution in dry DMSO*	1 mL
B14440	2',7'-bis-(3-carboxypropyl)-5-(and-6)-carboxyfluorescein (BCPCF acid) *mixed isomers*	1 mg
B14441	2',7'-bis-(3-carboxypropyl)-5-(and-6)-carboxyfluorescein, acetoxymethyl ester (BCPCF, AM)	1 mg
C1904	5-(and-6)-carboxyfluorescein (5(6)-FAM) *FluoroPure™ grade* *mixed isomers*	100 mg
C194	5-(and-6)-carboxyfluorescein *mixed isomers*	5 g
C195	5-(and-6)-carboxyfluorescein diacetate (5(6)-CFDA) *mixed isomers*	100 mg

For current prices or to order online, visit probes.invitrogen.com

Cat #	Product Name	Unit Size
C1354	5-carboxyfluorescein diacetate, acetoxymethyl ester (5-CFDA, AM)	5 mg
C1157	5-(and-6)-carboxyfluorescein diacetate, succinimidyl ester (5(6)-CFDA, SE; CFSE) *mixed isomers*	25 mg
C652	5-(and-6)-carboxynaphthofluorescein *mixed isomers*	100 mg
C13196	5-(and-6)-carboxynaphthofluorescein diacetate	10 mg
C1255	5-(and-6)-carboxy SNAFL®-1	1 mg
C1256	5-(and-6)-carboxy SNAFL®-1, diacetate	1 mg
C1260	5-(and-6)-carboxy SNAFL®-2	1 mg
C1261	5-(and-6)-carboxy SNAFL®-2, diacetate	1 mg
C1270	5-(and-6)-carboxy SNARF®-1	1 mg
C1271	5-(and-6)-carboxy SNARF®-1, acetoxymethyl ester, acetate	1 mg
C1272	5-(and-6)-carboxy SNARF®-1, acetoxymethyl ester, acetate *special packaging*	20 x 50 µg
C2925	CellTracker™ Green CMFDA (5-chloromethylfluorescein diacetate)	1 mg
C7025	CellTracker™ Green CMFDA (5-chloromethylfluorescein diacetate) *special packaging*	20 x 50 µg
C6826	5-(and-6)-chloromethyl SNARF®-1, acetate *mixed isomers* *special packaging*	20 x 50 µg
F1300	fluorescein *reference standard*	1 g
F1303	fluorescein diacetate (FDA)	1 g
F1130	fluorescein-5-(and-6)-sulfonic acid, trisodium salt	100 mg
H348	8-hydroxypyrene-1,3,6-trisulfonic acid, trisodium salt (HPTS; pyranine)	1 g
N1495	nigericin, free acid	10 mg
N7065	1-(2-nitrophenyl)ethyl phosphate, diammonium salt (NPE-caged phosphate)	5 mg
S23920	SNARF®-4F 5-(and-6)-carboxylic acid	1 mg
S23921	SNARF®-4F 5-(and-6)-carboxylic acid, acetoxymethyl ester, acetate *special packaging*	20 x 50 µg
S23922	SNARF®-5F 5-(and-6)-carboxylic acid	1 mg
S23923	SNARF®-5F 5-(and-6)-carboxylic acid, acetoxymethyl ester, acetate *special packaging*	20 x 50 µg
S1129	5-sulfofluorescein diacetate, sodium salt (SFDA)	25 mg

For current prices or to order online, visit probes.invitrogen.com

20.3 Probes Useful at Acidic pH

Eukaryotic cells contain compartments with different degrees of acidity. For example, biomolecules brought into cells by receptor-mediated endocytosis or phagocytosis (Section 16.1) are initially processed through organelles of decreasing pH, and specialized organelles such as plant vacuoles and the acrosome of spermatozoa are intrinsically acidic. A low intracompartmental pH activates enzymes and other protein functions — for instance iron release from transferrin — that would be too slow at neutral pH, thereby facilitating cellular metabolism. Abnormal lysosomal or endosomal acidification is associated with various pathological conditions. For example, lysosomes in some tumor cells have been reported to have a lower pH than normal lysosomes,[1] whereas other tumor cells contain lysosomes with higher pH.[2]

The fluorescent pH indicators used to detect acidic organelles and to follow trafficking through acidic organelles must have a different fluorescence response — including a lower pK_a — than those described in Section 20.2. Also, unlike most pH indicators for cytosolic measurements, pH indicators for acidic organelles need not be intrinsically permeant to membranes. More often they are covalently attached to large biomolecules that are actively taken up and processed through acidic organelles by the cell's own mechanisms (Chapter 16).

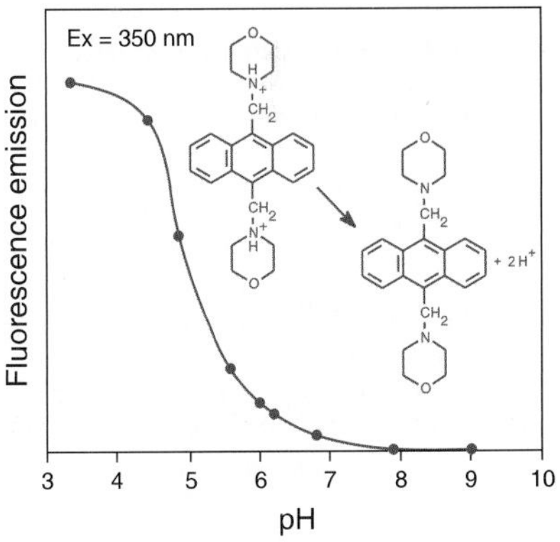

Figure 20.24 The pH titration curve of LysoSensor™ Blue DND-167 probe (L7533), which exhibits a pK_a ~5.1.

LysoSensor™ Probes

Our LysoSensor™ probes are weak bases that are selectively concentrated in acidic organelles as a result of protonation. This protonation also relieves the fluorescence quenching of the dye that results from photoinduced electron transfer (PET) by its weak-base side chain. Thus, unlike most other pH indicators in this chapter, the LysoSensor™ dyes become *more* fluorescent in acidic environments (Figure 20.24). Because accumulation of LysoSensor™ probes also appears to cause lysosomal alkalinization, pH measurements should be made rapidly after cells are incubated briefly (1–5 minutes at 37°C) with the dye.

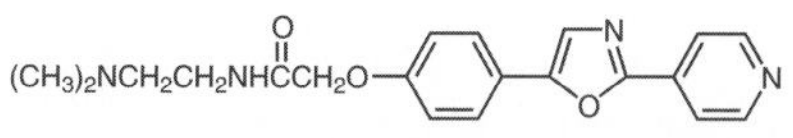

Figure 20.25 L7545 LysoSensor™ Yellow/Blue DND-160.

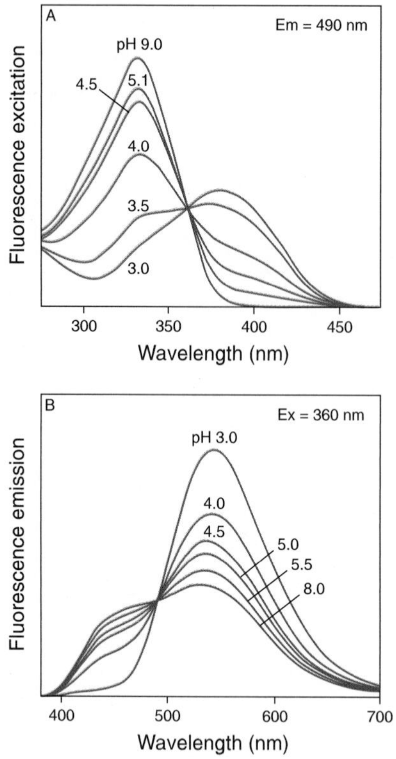

Figure 20.26 The pH-dependent spectral response of LysoSensor™ Yellow/Blue DND-160 (L7545): **A)** fluorescence excitation spectra and **B)** fluorescence emission spectra.

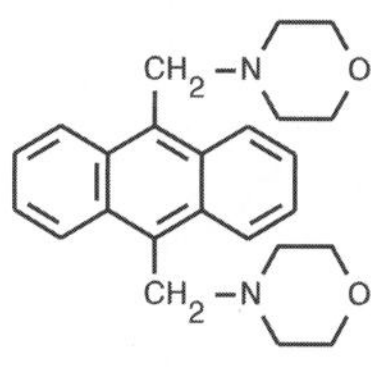

Figure 20.27 L7533 LysoSensor™ Blue DND-167.

LysoSensor™ Yellow/Blue DND-160 (L7545, Figure 20.25) undergoes a pH-dependent emission shift to longer wavelengths in acidic environments when illuminated near its excitation isosbestic point (~360 nm) (Figure 20.26). It also undergoes a pH-dependent excitation shift when detected near its emission isosbestic point (~490 nm) (Figure 20.26). These properties can be exploited for dual-emission ratio imaging of lysosomal pH [3] (Figure 12.35) (emission 450/510 nm, excitation at 365 nm). Yellow-fluorescent staining by LysoSensor™ Yellow/Blue DND-160 has been used to identify lysosomes as the accumulation site for anthracyclines in a drug-resistant cell line.[4] We also offer a 10,000 MW dextran conjugate of the LysoSensor™ Yellow/Blue dye (L22460, Section 20.4).

The green-fluorescent LysoSensor™ Green probes are available with optimal pH sensitivity in either the acidic or neutral range (pK_a ~5.2 or ~7.5), and the blue-fluorescent LysoSensor™ Blue DND-167 has a pK_a of ~5.1 (Table 20.2). With their low pK_a values, LysoSensor™ Blue DND-167 (L7533, Figure 20.27) and LysoSensor™ Green DND-189 (L7535, Figure 20.28) are almost nonfluorescent except when inside acidic compartments, whereas LysoSensor™ Green DND-153 (L7534, Figure 20.29) is brightly fluorescent, even at neutral pH. LysoSensor™ Green DND-189 has been used to monitor the dissipation of neurite vesicle transmembrane pH gradients by bafilomycin A1.[5]

Oregon Green® and Dichlorofluorescein Derivatives

Introduction of electron-withdrawing groups into fluorescein dyes lowers the pK_a of the phenolic group to 5 or below, as exemplified by our Oregon Green® dyes and their insensitivity to pH changes in the near-neutral pH range.[6] However, these fluorinated fluorescein dyes are still pH sensitive in moderately acidic solutions, with pK_a values of ~4.7 (Figure 20.30). With the exception of their lower pK_a values, the pH-dependent spectral characteristics of the Oregon Green® dyes closely parallel those of other fluorescein-based dyes (Figure 20.2, Figure 20.3), allowing dual-excitation ratiometric measurements with the same general configuration used for BCECF (Section 20.2).

Oregon Green® 514 carboxylic acid (O6138, Figure 1.63), Oregon Green® 488 carboxylic acid (O6146, Figure 1.62) and 5-(and 6-)carboxy-2′,7′-dichlorofluorescein (C368) do not readily enter cells but may be useful as fluid phase markers for endocytosis. These fluorinated and chlorinated fluorescein derivatives will probably be most useful in the form of conjugates that are endocytosed and processed through acidic organelles (Section 20.4); dextran conjugates of the Oregon Green® 488 and Oregon Green® 514 dyes are described in Section 20.4. Cell-permeant diacetate derivatives of carboxydichlorofluorescein (carboxy-DCFDA, C369) and carboxydifluorofluorescein (carboxy-DFFDA, O6151) are also available. Carboxy-DCFDA has been used to measure the pH in acidic organelles,[7] as well as in the cytosol and vacuoles of plants and yeast.[8,9] The mechanism of vacuolar pH rectification following exposure to ammonia has been investigated in rice and maize root hair cells loaded with carboxy-DFFDA.[10]

Other pH Indicators for Use in Acidic Environments

9-Amino-6-Chloro-2-Methoxyacridine

The nucleic acid stain 9-amino-6-chloro-2-methoxyacridine (ACMA, A1324; Figure 20.31) apparently binds to membranes in the energized state, and its fluorescence becomes quenched if a pH gradient forms.[11] Mechanistically, this probe resembles the membrane potential–sensitive carbocyanines (Section 22.3) more than the other probes in this chapter. ACMA is primarily employed to detect the proton-translocating activity of *Escherichia coli* ATP synthase [12–15] and yeast vacuolar H^+-ATPase.[16–18]

HPTS

Although HPTS (H348, Section 20.2) has a pK_a ~7.3 and is primarily used as a pH indicator in the near-neutral range (Section 20.2), it offers several advantages for monitoring intraorganelle pH in endosomal/lysosomal pathways:[19]

- The highly polar character that results from its three sulfonic acid groups prevents leakage across intracellular membranes.
- Uptake by fluid-phase endocytosis is efficient and easily accomplished.
- Determination of excitation ratios allows pH measurements that are independent of vesicular size and indicator concentration.
- Precise calibration permits pH values as low as 4.4 to be accurately measured.
- HPTS is nontoxic and does not perturb normal physiological function.

HPTS can be introduced into cells by microinjection, electroporation or liposome-mediated delivery or through ATP-gated ion channels.[20] HPTS has also been loaded into cells using a patch pipette.[21] HPTS has been reported to be less phototoxic than BCECF.[20] Laser excitation of HPTS results in a submicrosecond pulse of photons and localized acidification.[22,23]

References

1. J Cell Sci 107, 2381 (1994); **2.** Biochemistry 35, 2811 (1996); **3.** Chem Biol 6, 411 (1999); **4.** Blood 89, 3745 (1997); **5.** J Neurochem 69, 1927 (1997); **6.** J Org Chem 62, 6469 (1997); **7.** Anal Biochem 187, 109 (1990); **8.** Plant Physiol 98, 680 (1992); **9.** Methods Enzymol 194, 644 (1991); **10.** Planta 206, 154 (1998); **11.** Biochim Biophys Acta 722, 107 (1983); **12.** J Biol Chem 273, 16229 (1998); **13.** Biochemistry 37, 10846 (1998); **14.** J Biol Chem 273, 16241 (1998); **15.** Biochim Biophys Acta 1183, 161 (1993); **16.** J Biol Chem 271, 22487 (1996); **17.** J Biol Chem 271, 2018 (1996); **18.** J Biol Chem 269, 13224 (1994); **19.** Proc Natl Acad Sci U S A 92, 3156 (1995); **20.** Am J Physiol 275, C1158 (1998); **21.** J Physiol 530, 405 (2001); **22.** Biochemistry 36, 13919 (1997); **23.** Proc Natl Acad Sci U S A 93, 10747 (1996).

Table 20.2 — Summary of the pH response of our LysoSensor™ probes

Cat #	LysoSensor™ Probe	Abs/Em * (nm)	pK_a †	Useful pH Range †
L7533	LysoSensor™ Blue DND-167	373/425	5.1	4.5–6.0
L7534	LysoSensor™ Green DND-153	442/505	7.5	6.5–8.0
L7535	LysoSensor™ Green DND-189	443/505	5.2	4.5–6.0
L7545	LysoSensor™ Yellow/Blue DND-160	384/540 ‡ 329/440 §	4.2	3.5–6.0

* Absorption (Abs) and fluorescence emission (Em) maxima, at pH 5; values may vary somewhat in cellular environments. † All pK_a values were determined *in vitro*; values are likely to be different in cells. ‡ At pH 3. § At pH 7.

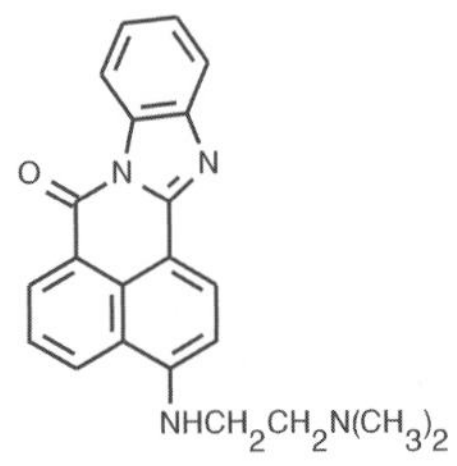

Figure 20.29 L7534 LysoSensor™ Green DND-153.

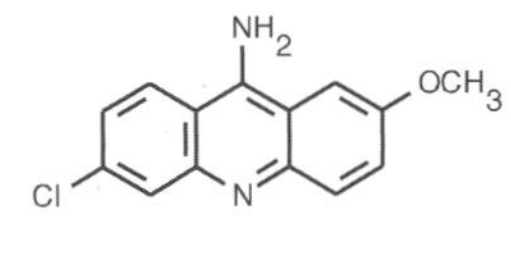

Figure 20.31 A1324 9-amino-6-chloro-2-methoxyacridine (ACMA).

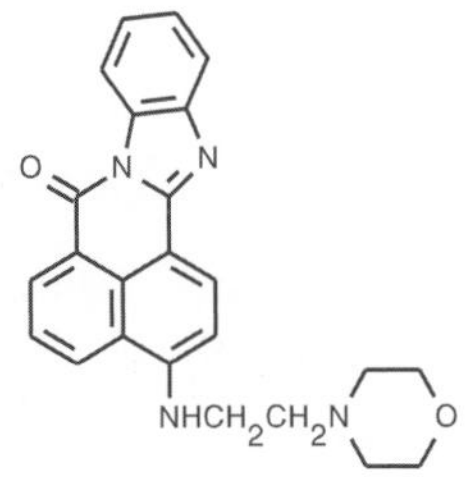

Figure 20.28 L7535 LysoSensor™ Green DND-189.

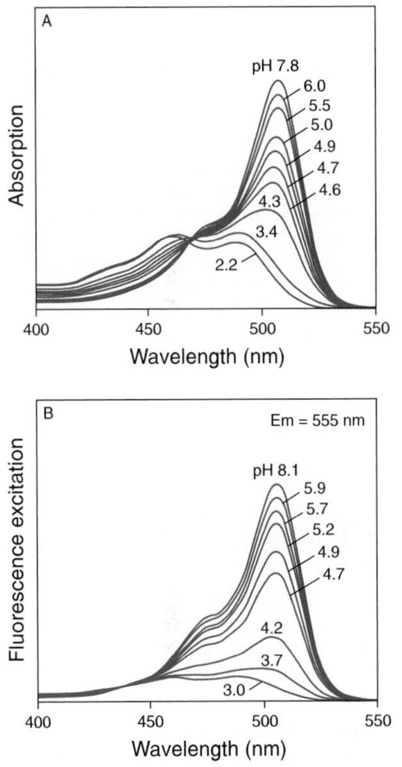

Figure 20.30 The pH-dependent spectra of Oregon Green® 514 carboxylic acid (O6138): **A)** absorption spectra and **B)** excitation spectra.

Data Table — 20.3 Probes Useful at Acidic pH

				Acidic/Neutral Solution				Neutral/Basic Solution					
Cat #	MW	Storage	Soluble	Abs	EC	Em	Solvent	Abs	EC	Em	Solvent	pK_a	Notes
A1324	258.71	L	DMF, DMSO	412	8,200	471	MeOH	see Notes		see Notes		8.6	1, 2
C368	445.21	L	pH >6, DMF	495	38,000	529	pH 4	504	107,000	529	pH 8	4.8	3, 4
C369	529.29	F,D	DMSO	<300		none							5
L7532	292.42	F,D,L	DMSO	374	11,000	424	pH 5	374	11,000	424	pH 9	7.5	3, 4, 6, 7
L7533	376.50	F,D,L	DMSO	373	11,000	425	pH 3	373	11,000	425	pH 7	5.1	3, 4, 6, 7
L7534	356.43	F,D,L	DMSO	442	17,000	505	pH 5	442	17,000	505	pH 9	7.5	3, 4, 6, 7
L7535	398.46	F,D,L	DMSO	443	16,000	505	pH 3	443	16,000	505	pH 7	5.2	3, 4, 6, 7
L7545	366.42	F,D,L	DMSO	384	21,000	540	pH 3	329	23,000	440	pH 7	4.2	3, 4, 6, 8
O6135	448.35	L	pH >6, DMF	481	29,000	517	pH 3	497	84,000	517	pH 9	4.7	3, 4, 9
O6138	512.36	L	pH >6, DMF	489	26,000	526	pH 3	506	86,000	526	pH 9	4.7	3, 4, 9
O6146	412.30	L	pH >6, DMF	478	27,000	518	pH 3	492	85,000	518	pH 9	4.7	3, 4, 10
O6151	496.38	F,D	DMSO	<300		none							11
R6152	411.80	DD,L	pH >6, DMF	480	42,000	521	pH 3	494	73,000	521	pH 9	5.6	3, 4

For definitions of the contents of this data table, see "Navigating *The Handbook*" in the introductory pages.

Notes

1. Absorption and fluorescence spectra of the protonated and deprotonated forms of A1324 are quite similar. This observation, and the listed pK_a value, are reported in published references (Eur Biophys J 13, 251 (1986)). Accumulation of the probe in the presence of transmembrane pH gradients results in fluorescence quenching (Biochim Biophys Acta 722, 107 (1983)).
2. Spectra of this compound are in methanol acidified with a trace of HCl.
3. pK_a values may vary considerably depending on the temperature, ionic strength, viscosity, protein binding and other factors. Unless otherwise noted, values listed have been determined from pH-dependent fluorescence measurements at 22°C.
4. Spectra are in aqueous buffers adjusted to >1 pH unit above and >1 pH unit below the pK_a.
5. C369 is converted to a fluorescent product (C368) after acetate hydrolysis.
6. This product is supplied as a ready-made solution in the solvent indicated under "Soluble."
7. This LysoSensor™ dye exhibits increasing fluorescence as pH decreases with no spectral shift. L7533 has additional absorption and fluorescence emission peaks at Abs = 394 nm and Em = 401 nm.
8. The pK_a value for this product is determined from the pH-dependent variation of the absorption spectrum.
9. The fluorescence lifetime (τ) of the Oregon Green® 514 dye in pH 9.0 buffer at 20°C is 4.2 nanoseconds. Data provided by the SPEX Fluorescence Group, Jobin Yvon Inc.
10. The fluorescence lifetime (τ) of the Oregon Green® 488 dye (O6146) in pH 9.0 buffer at 20°C is 4.1 nanoseconds. Data provided by the SPEX Fluorescence Group, Jobin Yvon Inc.
11. Acetate hydrolysis of this compound yields a fluorescent product with similar spectral characteristics to O6146.

Product List — 20.3 Probes Useful at Acidic pH

Cat #	Product Name	Unit Size
A1324	9-amino-6-chloro-2-methoxyacridine (ACMA)	100 mg
C368	5-(and-6)-carboxy-2′,7′-dichlorofluorescein *mixed isomers*	100 mg
C369	5-(and-6)-carboxy-2′,7′-dichlorofluorescein diacetate (carboxy-DCFDA) *mixed isomers*	100 mg
L7533	LysoSensor™ Blue DND-167 *1 mM solution in DMSO* *special packaging*	20 x 50 µL
L7532	LysoSensor™ Blue DND-192 *1 mM solution in DMSO* *special packaging*	20 x 50 µL
L7534	LysoSensor™ Green DND-153 *1 mM solution in DMSO* *special packaging*	20 x 50 µL
L7535	LysoSensor™ Green DND-189 *1 mM solution in DMSO* *special packaging*	20 x 50 µL
L7545	LysoSensor™ Yellow/Blue DND-160 *1 mM solution in DMSO* *special packaging*	20 x 50 µL
O6146	Oregon Green® 488 carboxylic acid *5-isomer*	5 mg
O6151	Oregon Green® 488 carboxylic acid diacetate (carboxy-DFFDA) *6-isomer*	5 mg
O6135	Oregon Green® 500 carboxylic acid *5-isomer*	5 mg
O6138	Oregon Green® 514 carboxylic acid	5 mg
R6152	Rhodol Green™ carboxylic acid, hydrochloride (5(6)-CRF 492) *mixed isomers*	5 mg

For current prices or to order online, visit probes.invitrogen.com

20.4 pH Indicator Conjugates

This section includes our selection of pH indicators conjugated to dextrans and lipids, as well as our chemically reactive pH indicators for preparing new pH-sensitive conjugates.

pH Indicator Dextrans

The pH-sensitive properties of the pH indicators described in Section 20.2 and Section 20.3 are usually not significantly affected upon conjugation to dextrans. However, coupling of pH indicators to these relatively inert polysaccharides changes several other properties of the dyes:

- The conjugates have high water solubility and therefore must be loaded into cells by microinjection, whole-cell patch-clamping, endocytosis or liposome fusion or by using our Influx™ pinocytic cell loading reagent (I14402, Section 19.8).
- Once loaded, the dextrans are retained in viable cells for long periods and (at least those dextrans with average molecular weights above 3000) will not pass through gap junctions.
- Attachment to a dextran significantly decreases the likelihood that the indicator will become compartmentalized, thereby avoiding a substantial problem associated with cell-permeant acetoxymethyl (AM) ester derivatives.[1]

The properties of some of the most useful pH indicator dextrans available from Molecular Probes are listed in Table 20.3 in approximate order of decreasing pK_a value. Our numerous labeled dextrans are discussed in Section 14.5 (Table 14.4).

Indicator Dextrans for Measuring Near-Neutral pH

Our 10,000 MW and 70,000 MW BCECF dextrans (D1878, D1880) are important dual-excitation pH indicator conjugates for pH measurements near pH 7.0. BCECF dextran–labeled Swiss 3T3 cells have been shown to produce much more stable fluorescent signals, reduced probe compartmentalization and 10-fold greater resistance to light-induced damage when compared with BCECF AM–labeled cells.[2] The 10,000 MW BCECF dextran (D1878) has been used to monitor intracellular pH increases during developmental processes [3–5] and to measure pH in submucosal gland secretions from human lung tissues.[6] Cytoplasmic Ca^{2+}/H^+ buffering in green algae has been investigated using BCECF dextran in combination with fura dextran [7] (F3029, Section 19.4).

A dextran conjugate of the carboxy SNARF®-1 pH indicator (D3303, D3304) has been microinjected into rhizoid cells of the alga *Pelvetia fastigata* and used with ratiometric imaging to measure pH gradients associated with polar tip growth.[8] SNARF®-1 dextran has also been used to detect cytosolic alkalinization associated with multidrug transporter activity [9] and to investigate pH regulation of connexin 43 channels.[10] SNARF® dextran conjugates have been scrape-loaded into the cytosol of MDF-7/ADR cells. It was found that the 70,000 MW SNARF® dextran conjugate remained exclusively cytosolic, whereas the 10,000 MW conjugate reported the pH of both cytosolic and nuclear compartments.[11]

The absorption and emission spectra of HPTS dextran (D7179) are shifted to longer wavelengths by about 20 nm relative to those of free HPTS (Figure 20.23). Also, due to a change in the shape of the spectrum, the absorption maximum of the acid form in aqueous solution (~375 nm) is actually shorter than that of the free dye (~403 nm). HPTS dextran retains the ratiometric capabilities of the parent fluorophore discussed in Section 20.2 and exhibits a pK_a of almost exactly 7.0.

Table 20.3 — Molecular Probes' pH indicator dextrans, in order of decreasing pK_a

Dye	Cat #	pK_a *	Measurement Wavelengths	Application Notes
SNARF®	D3303, D3304	~7.5	Emission ratio 580/640 nm excited at 514 or 488 nm	• Best conjugate for ratiometric emission measurements, with spectra similar to carboxy SNARF®-1 (Figure 20.11)
HPTS	D7179	~7.0	Excitation ratio 470/380 nm detected at 530 nm	• Spectra of dextran conjugate are significantly shifted (~20 nm) relative to free dye
BCECF	D1878, D1880	~7.0	Excitation ratio 490/440 nm detected at 530 nm	• Best conjugate for ratiometric excitation measurements, with spectra similar to BCECF (Figure 20.3)
Fluorescein	D1821, D1823, D1844, D3305	~6.4	Excitation ratio 490/450 nm detected at 520 nm	• Fluorescence is strongly quenched upon uptake into acidic organelles (Figure 20.2)
Fluorescein and tetramethylrhodamine	D1950, D1951	~6.4	Excitation ratio 495/555 nm detected at 580 nm †	• Conjugate incorporating both pH-sensitive and pH-insensitive fluorescent dyes (Figure 20.32)
Oregon Green® 488	D7170, D7172	~4.7	Excitation ratio 490/440 nm detected at 520 nm	• Good photostability • Optimum pH sensitivity for measurements in lysosomes and late endosomes
Oregon Green® 514	D7176	~4.7	Excitation ratio 510/450 nm detected at 530 nm	• Excellent photostability • Optimum pH sensitivity for measurements in lysosomes and late endosomes (Figure 20.30)
LysoSensor™ Yellow/Blue	L22460	~4.2	Excitation ratio 340/400 nm detected at 520 nm; emission ratio 450/510 nm excited at 365 nm	• Options for dual excitation or dual emission ratio measurements • Optimum pH sensitivity for measurements in lysosomes and late endosomes

* pK_a values are those determined for the free dyes. Actual values for dextran conjugates may differ by up to +/– 0.3 pH units and may vary with production lots. † Ratiometric emission measurements at 520/580 nm (with excitation at 495 nm) are also possible in principle; however, the response may be complicated by fluorescence resonance energy transfer.

Indicator Dextrans for Measuring Acidic pH

Although the fluorescein, BCECF, HPTS and SNARF® dextrans are intended for pH measurements between pH ~6 and 8, these dextrans are also useful for detecting uptake into acidic organelles, such as occurs during endocytosis. In particular, when these indicator dextrans enter moderately acidic compartments (pH <5.5):

- Fluorescence of the fluorescein, BCECF and HPTS dextrans is strongly quenched[12–14] (Figure 20.2, Figure 20.3).
- The 520/570 nm emission intensity ratio of the double-labeled fluorescein–tetramethylrhodamine dextrans (D1950, D1951) decreases[15] (Figure 20.32).
- The 580/640 nm emission ratio of the SNARF®-1 dextrans increases (Figure 20.11).

The indicator dextrans discussed above are useful for detecting translocation into compartments that have an acidic pH; however, the relative insensitivity of their fluorescence below pH ~6 limits quantitative pH estimation. The lower pK_a values of our Oregon Green® 488 and Oregon Green® 514 dextran conjugates (Table 20.3) make them more suitable indicators for estimating the pH of relatively acidic lysosomal environments. Moreover, the shift in their excitation spectra in acidic media permits ratiometric pH measurements.

We have also developed a 10,000 MW dextran conjugate of the LysoSensor™ Yellow/Blue dye (L22460), which can be used to quickly and accurately measure the pH of lysosomes. As this labeled dextran is taken up by the cells and moves through the endocytic pathway, the fluorescence of the LysoSensor™ dye changes from blue fluorescent in the near-neutral endosomes to longer-wavelength yellow fluorescent in the acidic lysosomes.[16] The greatest change in fluorescence emission occurs near the pK_a of the dye at pH ~4.2. The pH in lysosomes can be measured with LysoSensor™ Yellow/Blue dextran using fluorescence microscopy (Figure 12.37) or flow cytometry.

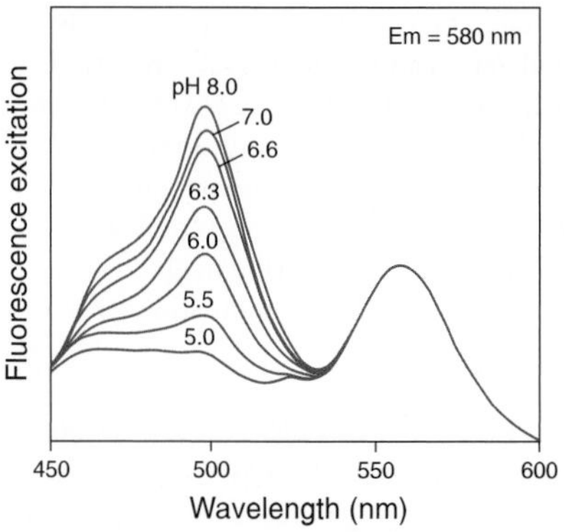

Figure 20.32 The excitation spectra of double-labeled fluorescein–tetramethylrhodamine dextran (D1950, D1951), which contains pH-dependent (fluorescein) and pH-independent (tetramethylrhodamine) dyes.

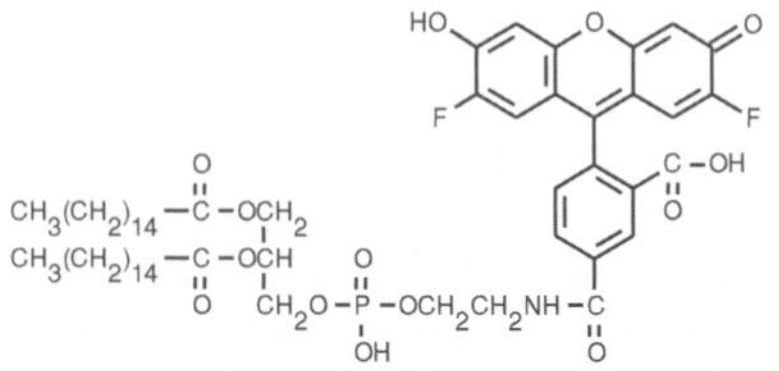

Figure 20.33 O12650 Oregon Green® 488 1,2-dihexadecanoyl-*sn*-glycero-3-phosphoethanolamine (Oregon Green® 488 DHPE).

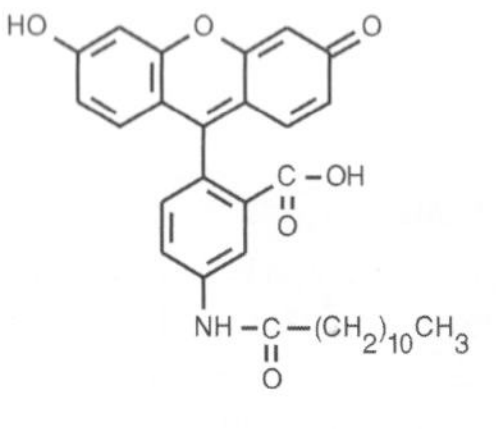

Figure 20.34 D109 5-dodecanoylaminofluorescein.

Lipophilic pH Indicators

Lipophilic Fluoresceins

Measurement of the pH adjacent to membrane surfaces is often complicated by electrostatic charge and solvation effects on the pK_a of surface-bound indicators.[17,18] The pK_a of membrane-intercalated fluorescein DHPE (F362) is ~6.2, quite close to that of free fluorescein.[17] Researchers have used the pH-dependent fluorescence of fluorescein DHPE to measure lateral proton conduction along lipid monolayers.[19–22] This fluorescein-labeled phospholipid has also been used to follow proton translocation from internal compartments in phospholipid vesicles.[23] For more acidic environments, Oregon Green® 488 DHPE (O12650, Figure 20.33) has potentially similar applications. Other related lipophilic fluorescein derivatives, including 5-dodecanoylaminofluorescein (D109, Figure 20.34), 5-hexadecanoylaminofluorescein (H110) and 5-octadecanoylaminofluorescein (O322), are described in Section 13.5.

Lipophilic Coumarin

4-Heptadecyl-7-hydroxycoumarin (H22730) is an alkyl derivative of the pH-sensitive blue-fluorescent 7-hydroxycoumarin (umbelliferone) fluorophore (Figure 13.48). As with other lipophilic coumarins,[24] 4-heptadecyl-7-hydroxycoumarin is primarily used as a probe of membrane surfaces. Deprotonation of the 7-hydroxyl group is expected to be strongly dependent on membrane-surface electrostatic potential. The pK_a of 4-heptadecyl-7-hydroxycoumarin varies from 6.35 in the cationic detergent CTAB to 11.15 in the anionic detergent sodium dodecyl sulfate (SDS), as measured by its fluorescence response.[18] The pK_a values of lipophilic pH indicators are strongly dependent on the ionic composition of the membrane surface,[18,25] making them sensitive probes of membrane-surface electrostatic potential.[26–28] 4-Heptadecyl-7-hydroxycoumarin has been used to measure pH differences at membrane interfaces in isolated plasma membranes of normal and multidrug-resistant murine leukemia cells[29,30] and to characterize interactions of cationic lipids with DNA.[26,27,31]

Reactive Dyes for Preparing pH-Sensitive Conjugates

Many of the pH indicators described in Section 20.2 and Section 20.3 can be conjugated to biological molecules in order to generate pH-sensitive tracers. The resulting conjugates can be used to follow endocytosis, phagocytosis, organelle trafficking and other processes, as described in Section 16.1. For example, the pH sensitivity of fluorescein-labeled transferrin (T2871, Section 16.1) has frequently been exploited to detect pH changes associated with the endocytic processing of this important iron-transporting glycoprotein.[32–35] For these types of applications, fluorescein conjugates are less than optimal because they have little sensitivity in the pH range below pH 5.5. The response range can be extended using conjugates of our Oregon Green® 488 dye, including Oregon Green® 488 transferrin (T13341, Section 16.1), which has a much lower pK_a than fluorescein (4.7 compared with 6.4, Figure 1.12) but essentially identical spectra. Our collaborators, Dr. Elizabeth Simons and her co-workers, have labeled fungi (*Cryptococcus neoformans*) with FITC (F143, F1906, F1907; Section 1.5) or Oregon Green® 488 isothiocyanate (O6080, Section 1.5) and used them to study the influence of phagosomal pH on the fungicidal and fungistatic activity of human monocyte–derived macrophages.[36] At pH levels evoked by phagocytosis of live and heat-killed fungi (pH 4.7–5.7), standard curves of the 498/450 nm fluorescence excitation ratio as a function pH (Figure 20.35) illustrate the greater sensitivity of the Oregon Green® 488 conjugates. Vergne and co-workers have used zymosan (heat-killed yeast) double-labeled with the succinimidyl esters of Oregon Green® 488 carboxylic acid (O6147) and carboxytetramethylrhodamine (C1171, Section 1.6) to measure phagosomal pH in J774 macrophages. Using dual-emission (530/585 nm) flow cytometry, they were able to estimate pH values as low as 4.0.[37]

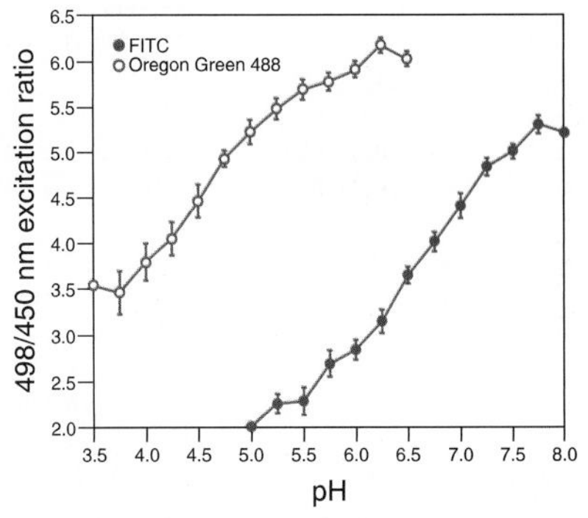

Figure 20.35 Calibration curves for intraphagosomal pH measurements using fungi (*Cryptococcus neoformans*) labeled with Oregon Green® 488 isothiocyanate (O6080) or fluorescein isothiocyanate (FITC, F143, F1906, F1907). Human monocyte-derived macrophages laden with phagocytosed *C. neoformans* were exposed to pH-controlled buffers in the presence of the K^+/H^+ ionophore nigericin (N1495). The 498/450 nm fluorescence excitation ratios corresponding to different pH levels were measured in a spectrofluorometer. The data were provided by Dr. Elizabeth Simons, Boston University.

Many of the reagents or methods required to prepare conjugates have been described in Chapter 1. The most common method of producing a useful conjugate is the reaction of amines with succinimidyl esters or isothiocyanates of the pH indicator. Examples of amine-reactive pH indicators include the succinimidyl esters of the carboxy SNARF®-1, carboxy SNAFL®-1 and carboxynaphthofluorescein dyes (S22801, C3061, C653). A heptapeptide containing a peroxisomal targeting signal was conjugated to the carboxy SNAFL®-2 succinimidyl ester to produce a pH-sensitive peptide that was also cell permeant and localized in peroxisomes; a pH-insensitive peptide was also synthesized using the BODIPY® 581/591 succinimidyl ester.[38] The succinimidyl esters of the chlorinated fluorescein derivatives 6-JOE (pK_a ~11.5, C6171MP; Section 1.5), 6-TET (pK_a ~4.5, C20092; Section 1.5) and 6-HEX (pK_a ~3, C20091; Section 1.5) can be used to prepare conjugates that are responsive to strongly acidic (6-HEX) or alkaline (6-JOE) pH levels. When the amine-reactive pH indicator is not available, sulfosuccinimidyl esters can generally be prepared *in situ* simply by dissolving the carboxylic acid dye in a buffer that contains *N*-hydroxysulfosuccinimide and 1-ethyl-3-(3-dimethylaminopropyl)carbodiimide (NHSS, H2249; EDAC, E2247; Section 3.3). Addition of NHSS to the buffer has been shown to enhance the yield of carbodiimide-mediated conjugations.[39] Suitable amine-reactive pH indicators or dyes that can be made reactive using EDAC/NHSS are listed in Table 20.4.

Table 20.4 — Reactive pH indicator dyes

pH Indicator	Preferred Reactive Form
BCECF	BCECF (B1151, Section 20.2) *
Carboxyfluorescein	5-(and 6-)carboxyfluorescein, succinimidyl ester (C1311, Section 1.5)
6-HEX	6-carboxy-2′,4,4′,5′,7,7′-hexachlorofluorescein, succinimidyl ester (C20091, Section 1.5)
6-JOE	6-carboxy-4′,5′-dichloro-2′,7′-dimethoxyfluorescein, succinimidyl ester (C6171MP, Section 1.5)
Naphthofluorescein	5-(and 6-)carboxynaphthofluorescein, succinimidyl ester (C653)
Oregon Green® 488	Oregon Green® 488 carboxylic acid, succinimidyl ester (O6147, O6149)
Oregon Green® 514	Oregon Green® 514 carboxylic acid, succinimidyl ester (O6139)
SNAFL®-1	5-(and 6-)carboxy SNAFL®-1, succinimidyl ester (C3061)
SNARF®-1	SNARF®-1 carboxylic acid, acetate, succinimidyl ester (S22801); 5-(and 6-)carboxy SNARF®-1 (C1270, Section 20.2) *
6-TET	6-carboxy-2′,4,7,7′-tetrachlorofluorescein, succinimidyl ester (C20092, Section 1.5)

* Carboxylic acids require activation with EDAC/NHSS before reaction with amines (Section 1.1).

References

1. J Exp Biol 196, 419 (1994); 2. J Cell Physiol 141, 410 (1989); 3. Dev Biol 191, 53 (1997); 4. Development 120, 433 (1994); 5. Dev Biol 156, 176 (1993); 6. Proc Natl Acad Sci U S A 98, 8119 (2001); 7. Protoplasma 198, 107 (1997); 8. Science 263, 1419 (1994); 9. J Histochem Cytochem 38, 685 (1990); 10. Biophys J 70, 1294 (1996); 11. Proc Natl Acad Sci U S A 96, 4432 (1999); 12. Proc Natl Acad Sci U S A 91, 4811 (1994); 13. J Biol Chem 268, 25320 (1993); 14. J Cell Sci 105, 861 (1993); 15. J Cell Biol 130, 821 (1995); 16. Nucleic Acids Res 30, 1338 (2002); 17. Biochim Biophys Acta 939, 289 (1988); 18. J Phys Chem 81, 1755 (1977); 19. Biochemistry 29, 59 (1990); 20. J Am Chem Soc 113, 8818 (1991); 21. Eur J Biochem 162, 379 (1987); 22. Nature 322, 756 (1986); 23. Biochim Biophys Acta 766, 161 (1984); 24. Biochim Biophys Acta 1284, 191 (1996); 25. Biochim Biophys Acta 323, 326 (1973); 26. Biochim Biophys Acta 1464, 251 (2000); 27. Biochim Biophys Acta 1368, 115 (1998); 28. Methods Enzymol 171, 376 (1989); 29. Biochemistry 29, 7275 (1990); 30. Biochim Biophys Acta 729, 185 (1983); 31. Biochim Biophys Acta 1419, 207 (1999); 32. Biochemistry 31, 5820 (1992); 33. Cell 37, 789 (1984); 34. J Biol Chem 266, 3469 (1991); 35. J Biol Chem 265, 6688 (1990); 36. Infect Immun 67, 885 (1999); 37. Anal Biochem 255, 127 (1998); 38. Histochem J 33, 65 (2001); 39. Anal Biochem 156, 220 (1986).

Data Table — 20.4 pH Indicator Conjugates

				Acidic Solution				Neutral/Basic Solution					
Cat #	**MW**	**Storage**	**Soluble**	**Abs**	**EC**	**Em**	**Solvent**	**Abs**	**EC**	**Em**	**Solvent**	**pK_a**	**Notes**
C653	573.51	F,D,L	DMF, DMSO	515	10,000	565	pH 6	602	42,000	672	pH 10	7.6	1, 2
C3061	523.45	F,D,L	DMSO	510	26,000	545	pH 6	542	47,000	625	pH 10	7.8	1, 2
C3062	557.90	F,D,L	DMSO	520	29,000	545	pH 6	550	47,000	632	pH 10	7.7	1, 2, 3
D1821	see Notes	F,L	H_2O	473	ND	514	pH 5	490	ND	513	pH 9	6.4	1, 4, 5, 6
D1823	see Notes	F,L	H_2O	473	ND	514	pH 5	490	ND	514	pH 9	6.4	1, 4, 5, 6
D1844	see Notes	F,L	H_2O	473	ND	514	pH 5	490	ND	514	pH 9	6.4	1, 4, 5, 6
D1878	see Notes	F,L	H_2O	482	ND	520	pH 5	503	ND	528	pH 9	7.0	1, 4, 5, 6
D1879	see Notes	F,L	H_2O	482	ND	520	pH 5	503	ND	528	pH 9	7.0	1, 4, 5, 6
D1880	see Notes	F,L	H_2O	482	ND	520	pH 5	503	ND	528	pH 9	7.0	1, 4, 5, 6
D1950	see Notes	F,L	H_2O	see Notes		see Notes						ND	1, 4, 5, 7
D1951	see Notes	F,L	H_2O	see Notes		see Notes						ND	1, 4, 5, 7
D3303	see Notes	F,L	H_2O	548	ND	587	pH 6	576	ND	635	pH 10	7.5	1, 4, 5, 6
D3304	see Notes	F,L	H_2O	548	ND	587	pH 6	576	ND	635	pH 10	7.5	1, 4, 5, 6
D3305	see Notes	F,L	H_2O	473	ND	514	pH 5	490	ND	514	pH 9	6.4	1, 4, 5, 6
D7170	see Notes	F,L	H_2O	478	ND	518	pH 3	492	ND	518	pH 9	4.7	1, 4, 5, 6
D7172	see Notes	F,L	H_2O	478	ND	518	pH 3	492	ND	518	pH 9	4.7	1, 4, 5, 6
D7174	see Notes	F,L	H_2O	489	ND	526	pH 3	506	ND	526	pH 9	4.7	1, 4, 5, 6
D7176	see Notes	F,L	H_2O	489	ND	526	pH 3	506	ND	526	pH 9	4.7	1, 4, 5, 6
D7179	see Notes	F,L	H_2O	375	ND	536	pH 5	469	ND	532	pH 9	7.0	1, 4, 5, 8
D12760	436.58	L	DMSO, EtOH	326	13,000	387	$MeOH/H^+$	366	15,000	454	$MeOH/OH^-$	see Notes	9, 10
D12980	see Notes	FF,L	H_2O	510	ND	556	pH 3	525	ND	556	pH 9	~11.5	4, 5
D12981	see Notes	FF,L	H_2O	511	ND	556	pH 3	525	ND	556	pH 9	~11.5	4, 5
F362	1182.54	FF,D,L	see Notes	476	32,000	519	$MeOH/H^+$	496	88,000	519	$MeOH/OH^-$	6.2	9, 11
H22730	400.60	L	DMSO, EtOH	325	15,000	385	$MeOH/H^+$	366	20,000	453	$MeOH/OH^-$	8.9	9
L22460	see Notes	F,D,L	H_2O	384	ND	540	pH 3	329	ND	440	pH 7	4.2	1, 4, 5, 6
O6139	609.43	F,D,L	DMF, DMSO	489	26,000	526	pH 3	506	85,000	526	pH 9	4.7	2
O6147	509.38	F,D,L	DMF, DMSO	480	24,000	521	pH 3	495	76,000	521	pH 9	4.7	2
O6149	509.38	F,D,L	DMF, DMSO	480	26,000	516	pH 3	496	82,000	516	pH 9	4.7	2
O12650	1086.25	FF,D,L	see Notes	485	26,000	526	$MeOH/H^+$	501	85,000	526	$MeOH/OH^-$	ND	5, 9, 11
S22801	592.56	F,D	DMSO	<350		none		<350		none			12

For definitions of the contents of this data table, see "Navigating *The Handbook*" in the introductory pages.

Notes

1. Spectra are in aqueous buffers adjusted to >1 pH unit above and >1 pH unit below the pK_a.
2. Spectral data for this product represent the unreacted succinimidyl ester. The pK_a value and the spectral data for acidic solutions have been estimated based on the spectra of the parent carboxylic acid.
3. Examples of pH-dependent spectra for C3062 conjugated to peptides have been published elsewhere (Cytometry 15, 148 (1994)).
4. The molecular weight is nominally as specified in the product name but may have a broad distribution.
5. ND = not determined.
6. Abs, Em and pK_a values listed for this dextran conjugate are those obtained for the free dye. Values for actual conjugates are typically very similar, with slight variations between different production lots.
7. These conjugates contain both pH-sensitive fluorescein (Abs = 495, Em = 520 nm) and pH-insensitive tetramethylrhodamine (Abs = 555 nm, Em = 575 nm) fluorophores.
8. The pK_a value and spectral parameters may vary between different lots of this product.
9. The pK_a values of lipophilic pH indicators may vary considerably depending on the electrostatic properties of membrane surfaces (Biochemistry 32, 10057 (1993); J Phys Chem 81, 1755 (1977); Biochim Biophys Acta 939, 289 (1988)). The pK_a values listed are for electrostatically neutral liposomes or micelles. Spectra are in MeOH containing a trace of HCl ($MeOH/H^+$) or a trace of KOH ($MeOH/OH^-$).
10. The pK_a of D12760 bound to phospholipid bilayer membranes is ~6.1.
11. Chloroform is the most generally useful solvent for preparing stock solutions of phospholipids (including sphingomyelins). Glycerophosphocholines are usually freely soluble in ethanol. Most other glycerophospholipids (phosphoethanolamines, phosphatidic acids and phosphoglycerols) are less soluble in ethanol, but solutions up to 1–2 mg/mL should be obtainable, using sonication to aid dispersion if necessary. Labeling of cells with fluorescent phospholipids can be enhanced by addition of cyclodextrins during incubation (J Biol Chem 274, 35359 (1999)).
12. S22801 is converted to a fluorescent product with spectra similar to C1270 after acetate hydrolysis.

Product List — 20.4 pH Indicator Conjugates

Cat #	Product Name	Unit Size
C653	5-(and-6)-carboxynaphthofluorescein, succinimidyl ester *mixed isomers*	25 mg
C3061	5-(and-6)-carboxy SNAFL®-1, succinimidyl ester *mixed isomers*	1 mg
C3062	5-(and-6)-carboxy SNAFL®-2, succinimidyl ester *mixed isomers*	1 mg
D1878	dextran, BCECF, 10,000 MW, anionic	10 mg
D1879	dextran, BCECF, 40,000 MW, anionic	10 mg
D1880	dextran, BCECF, 70,000 MW, anionic	10 mg
D12980	dextran, 4',5'-dichloro-2',7'-dimethoxyfluorescein, 10,000 MW, anionic	5 mg
D12981	dextran, 4',5'-dichloro-2',7'-dimethoxyfluorescein, 70,000 MW, anionic	5 mg
D3305	dextran, fluorescein, 3000 MW, anionic	10 mg
D1821	dextran, fluorescein, 10,000 MW, anionic	25 mg
D1844	dextran, fluorescein, 40,000 MW, anionic	25 mg
D1823	dextran, fluorescein, 70,000 MW, anionic	25 mg
D1950	dextran, fluorescein and tetramethylrhodamine, 10,000 MW, anionic	10 mg
D1951	dextran, fluorescein and tetramethylrhodamine, 70,000 MW, anionic	10 mg
D7179	dextran, 8-hydroxypyrene-1,3,6-trisulfonic acid, 10,000 MW, anionic (HPTS dextran)	5 mg
D7170	dextran, Oregon Green® 488; 10,000 MW, anionic	5 mg
D7172	dextran, Oregon Green® 488; 70,000 MW, anionic	5 mg
D7174	dextran, Oregon Green® 514; 10,000 MW, anionic	5 mg
D7176	dextran, Oregon Green® 514; 70,000 MW, anionic	5 mg
D3303	dextran, SNARF®-1, 10,000 MW, anionic	5 mg
D3304	dextran, SNARF®-1, 70,000 MW, anionic	5 mg
D12760	6,8-difluoro-4-heptadecyl-7-hydroxycoumarin (C_{17}DiFU)	10 mg
F362	*N*-(fluorescein-5-thiocarbamoyl)-1,2-dihexadecanoyl-*sn*-glycero-3-phosphoethanolamine, triethylammonium salt (fluorescein DHPE)	5 mg
H22730	4-heptadecyl-7-hydroxycoumarin	10 mg
L22460	LysoSensor™ Yellow/Blue dextran, 10,000 MW, anionic, fixable	5 mg
O6147	Oregon Green® 488 carboxylic acid, succinimidyl ester *5-isomer*	5 mg
O6149	Oregon Green® 488 carboxylic acid, succinimidyl ester *6-isomer*	5 mg
O12650	Oregon Green® 488 1,2-dihexadecanoyl-*sn*-glycero-3-phosphoethanolamine (Oregon Green® 488 DHPE)	1 mg
O6139	Oregon Green® 514 carboxylic acid, succinimidyl ester	5 mg
S22801	SNARF®-1 carboxylic acid, acetate, succinimidyl ester *special packaging*	10 x 50 µg

For current prices or to order online, visit probes.invitrogen.com

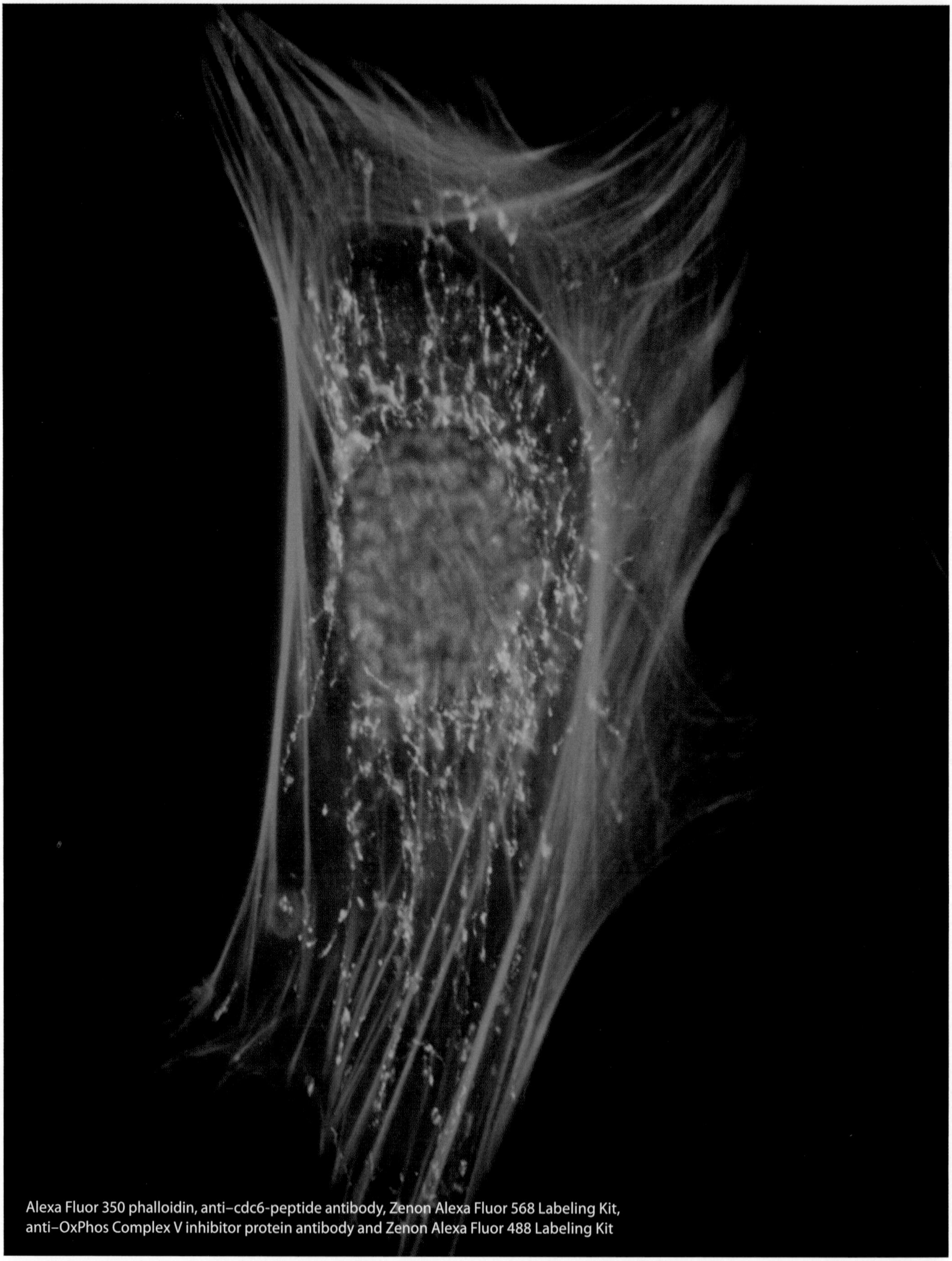

Alexa Fluor 350 phalloidin, anti–cdc6-peptide antibody, Zenon Alexa Fluor 568 Labeling Kit, anti–OxPhos Complex V inhibitor protein antibody and Zenon Alexa Fluor 488 Labeling Kit

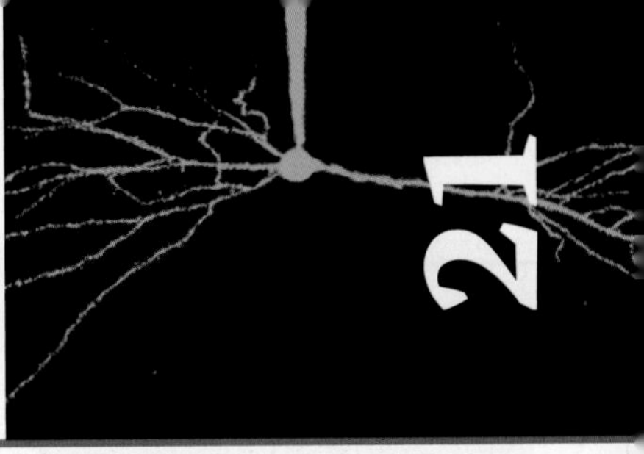

Chapter 21

Indicators for Na^+, K^+, Cl^- and Miscellaneous Ions

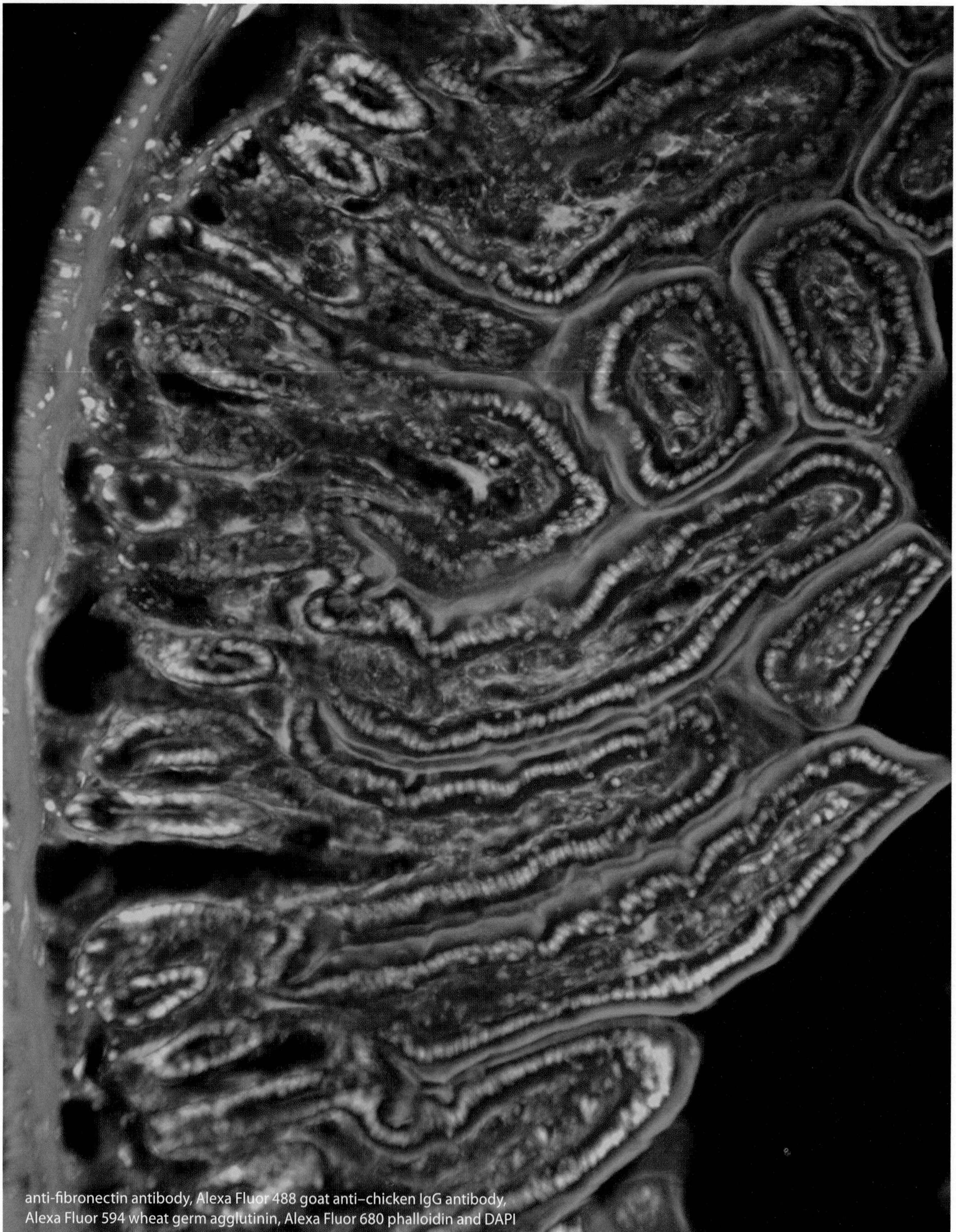

anti-fibronectin antibody, Alexa Fluor 488 goat anti–chicken IgG antibody, Alexa Fluor 594 wheat germ agglutinin, Alexa Fluor 680 phalloidin and DAPI

21.1 Fluorescent Na+ and K+ Indicators

SBFI and PBFI

Properties of SBFI and PBFI

SBFI[1] and PBFI[1,2] are fluorescent indicators for sodium and potassium, respectively. Although the selectivity of SBFI and PBFI for their target ions is less than that of calcium indicators such as fura-2, it is sufficient for the detection of physiological concentrations of Na^+ and K^+ in the presence of other monovalent cations.[1] Furthermore, the spectral responses of SBFI and PBFI upon ion binding permit excitation ratio measurements (see Note 19.1 "Technical Focus: Loading and Calibration of Intracellular Ion Indicators" in Section 19.1), and these indicators can be used with the same optical filters and equipment used for fura-2[3,4] (Table 23.9).

SBFI (Figure 21.1) and PBFI (Figure 21.2) comprise benzofuranyl fluorophores linked to a crown ether chelator. The cavity size of the crown ether confers selectivity for Na^+ versus K^+ (or *vice versa* in the case of PBFI). When an ion binds to SBFI or PBFI, the indicator's fluorescence quantum yield increases, its excitation peak narrows and its excitation maximum shifts to shorter wavelengths (Figure 21.3), causing a significant change in the ratio of fluorescence intensities excited at 340/380 nm (Figure 21.4, Figure 21.5). This fluorescence signal is slightly sensitive to changes in pH between 6.5 and 7.5,[5,6] but it is strongly affected by ionic strength[7] and viscosity.[8] Researchers have described the use of SBFI for emission ratio detection[9] (410/590 nm, excited at 340 nm). More recently, the implementation of two-photon excitation of SBFI with infrared light has been reported for Na^+ imaging in spines and fine dendrites of central neurons[10,11] (Figure 21.6).

Although SBFI is quite selective for the Na^+ ion, K^+ has some effect on the native affinity of SBFI for Na^+ (Figure 21.4). The dissociation constant (K_d) of SBFI for Na^+ is 3.8 mM in the absence of K^+, and 11.3 mM in solutions with a combined Na^+ and K^+ concentration of 135 mM, which approximates physiological ionic strength. SBFI is ~18-fold more selective for Na^+ than for K^+. Likewise, the K_d of PBFI for K^+ is strongly dependent on whether Na^+ is present (Figure 21.5), with a value of 5.1 mM in the absence of Na^+ and 44 mM in solutions with a combined Na^+ and K^+ concentration of 135 mM. In buffers in which the Na^+ is replaced by tetramethylammonium

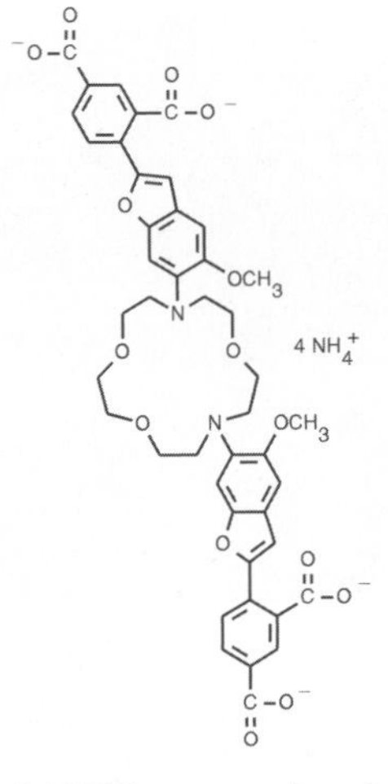

Figure 21.1 S1262 SBFI, tetraammonium salt.

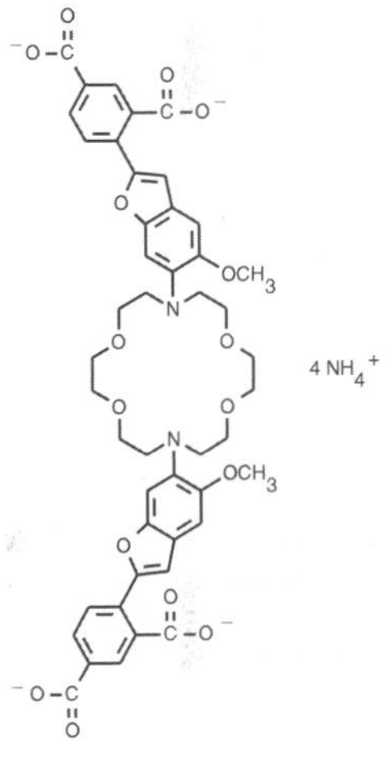

Figure 21.2 P1265MP PBFI, tetraammonium salt.

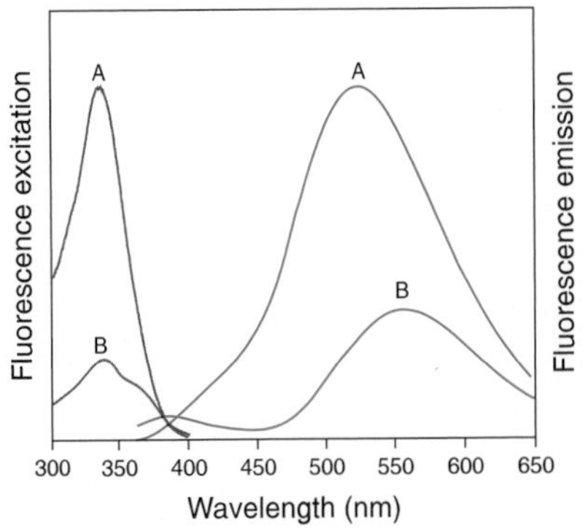

Figure 21.3 Fluorescence excitation (detected at 505 nm) and emission (excited at 340 nm) spectra of SBFI in pH 7.0 buffer containing 135 mM (A) or zero (B) Na^+.

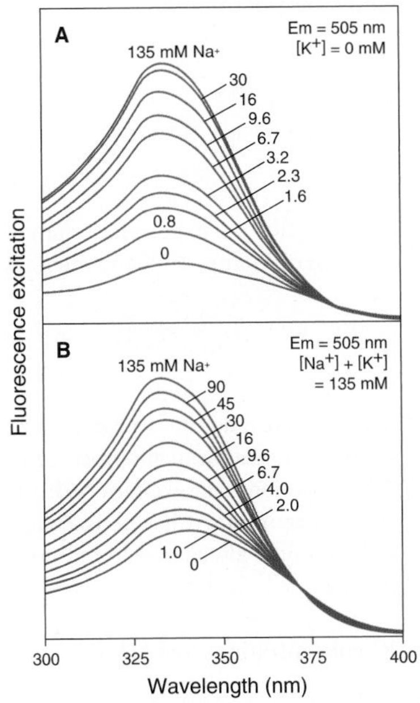

Figure 21.4 The excitation spectral response of SBFI (S1262) to Na^+: A) in K^+-free solution and B) in solutions containing K^+ with the combined Na^+ and K^+ concentration equal to 135 mM. The scale on the vertical axis is the same for both panels.

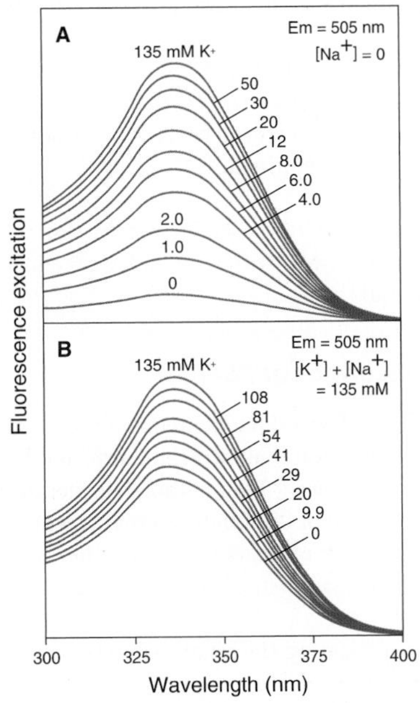

Figure 21.5 The excitation spectral response of PBFI (P1265MP) to K^+: A) in Na^+-free solution and B) in solutions containing Na^+ with the combined K^+ and Na^+ concentration equal to 135 mM. The scale on the vertical axis is the same for both panels.

chloride, the K_d of PBFI for K^+ is 11 mM; choline chloride and *N*-methylglucamine are two other possible replacements for Na^+ in the medium. Although PBFI is only 1.5-fold more selective for K^+ than for Na^+, this selectivity is often sufficient because intracellular K^+ concentrations are normally about 10 times higher than Na^+ concentrations.

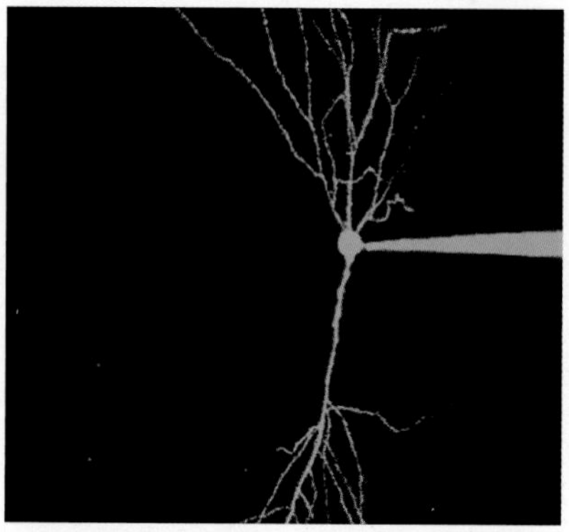

Figure 21.6 CA1 pyramidal neuron in a hippocampal slice filled with SBFI (S1262) delivered from a patch pipette (visible on the right). The image was obtained using two-photon excitation of SBFI at 790 nm. Image contributed by Christine R. Rose, Physiological Institute, University of Munich.

The K_d of all ion indicators depends on factors such as pH, temperature, ionic strength, concentrations of other ions and dye–protein interactions. Due to these environmental factors, the K_d determined *in situ* for intracellular SBFI is substantially higher than that determined in cell-free buffer solutions. K_d (Na^+) values of 29 mM, 26.6 mM and 18.0 mM have been determined for SBFI in lizard peripheral axons, porcine adrenal chromaffin cells and rat hippocampal neurons, respectively.[5,6,12] Consequently, intracellular SBFI should be calibrated using the pore-forming antibiotic gramicidin[3] (G6888). Palytoxin, an ionophoric toxin isolated from marine coelenterates, is much more effective than gramicidin for equilibrating intracellular and extracellular Na^+.[12] Intracellular PBFI should be calibrated using the K^+ ionophore valinomycin[13] (V1644).

Cell Loading with SBFI and PBFI

SBFI and PBFI are available both as cell-impermeant acid salts (S1262, P1265MP) and as cell-permeant acetoxymethyl (AM) esters (S1263, S1264, P1267MP). The anionic acid forms can be loaded into cells using our Influx™ pinocytic cell-loading reagent (I14402, Section 19.8), or by microinjection, patch-pipette infusion or electroporation. For AM ester loading (see Note 19.1 "Technical Focus: Loading and Calibration of Intracellular Ion Indicators" in Section 19.1), addition of the dispersing agent Pluronic F-127 and relatively long incubation times — up to four hours — are typically necessary.[3] Pluronic F-127 is available as a 20% solution in dimethylsulfoxide (DMSO, P3000MP), as a 0.2 µm–filtered 10% solution in water (P6866) and as a solid (P6867). ATP-induced permeabilization reportedly produces increased uptake of SBFI AM by bovine pulmonary arterial endothelial cells[14] (BPAEC). Somewhat higher working concentrations of PBFI and SBFI than those used for fura-2 may be required because of the lower fluorescence quantum yields of these indicators. AM ester loading sometimes produces intracellular compartmentalization of SBFI.[8,15] As with other AM esters, reducing the incubation temperature below 37°C may inhibit compartmentalization. Other practical aspects of loading and calibrating SBFI have been reviewed by Negulescu and Machen.[3]

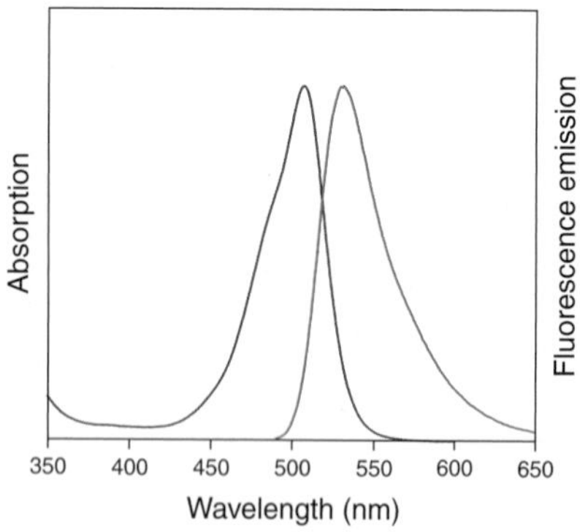

Figure 21.7 Absorption and fluorescence emission spectra of Sodium Green™ in pH 7.0 buffer containing 135 mM Na^+.

Applications of SBFI

SBFI has been employed to estimate Na^+ gradients in isolated mitochondria,[15–17] as well as to measure intracellular Na^+ levels or Na^+ efflux in cells from a variety of tissues:

- Blood — platelets,[18,19] monocytes[20] and lymphocytes[21]
- Brain — astrocytes,[22,23] neurons,[5,6,24–28] and presynaptic terminals[29,30]
- Muscle — perfused heart,[31,32] cardiomyocytes[33–36] and smooth muscle[37,38]
- Secretory epithelia[39–43]

SBFI has also been used in combination with other fluorescent indicators to correlate changes in intracellular Na^+ with Ca^{2+} and Mg^{2+} concentrations,[29,44–48] intracellular pH[49,50] and membrane potential.[51]

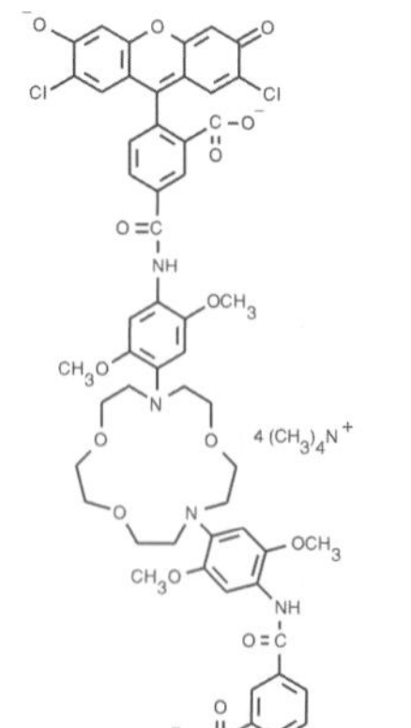

Figure 21.8 S6900 Sodium Green™, tetra(tetramethylammonium) salt.

Applications of PBFI

PBFI[2] has fewer documented applications than SBFI. Renewed interest has been prompted by the observation that intracellular K^+ levels appear to be a controlling factor in apoptotic cell death pathways.[52] Flow cytometric measurements using UV argon-ion laser excitation (351 nm and 364 nm) of PBFI indicate that K^+ efflux induces shrinkage of apoptotic cells and is a trigger for activation of caspases.[53–56] Furthermore, PBFI provides a potential alternative to radiometric K^+ efflux assays using ^{86}Rb.[13] Other applications of PBFI include:

- Investigating the relationship between cytoplasmic K^+ concentrations and NMDA excitotoxicity[57]
- Evaluating the mediating effects of K^+ depletion on monocytic cell necrosis[58]
- Detecting adrenoceptor-stimulated decreases of intracellular K^+ concentration in astrocytes and neurons[59]
- Monitoring mitochondrial K_{ATP} channel activation[60,61]

- Assessing the effects of mitochondrial K^+ on Ca^{2+}-dependent cytotoxicity in rat hepatocytes [62]
- Measuring K^+ levels in plant cells and vacuoles [63–65]
- Detecting elevated intracellular K^+ levels associated with HIV-induced cytopathology [66]
- Following ionophore-induced K^+ transport and associated volume changes in PBFI-loaded liposomes [67,68]
- Quantitating light-induced K^+ and H^+ fluxes in liposomes [69,70]
- Measuring K^+ in isolated cochlear outer hair cells [71] and in mammalian ventricles using patch-clamp techniques [72]

Sodium Green™ Na⁺ Indicator

Molecular Probes' patented Sodium Green™ indicator can be excited at 488 nm (Figure 21.7), providing a valuable alternative to the UV light–excitable SBFI for use with confocal laser-scanning microscopes [73] and flow cytometers.[74] We offer the cell-impermeant tetra(tetramethylammonium) salt of the Sodium Green™ indicator (S6900), as well as its cell-permeant tetraacetate (S6901). The Sodium Green™ indicator comprises two 2′,7′-dichlorofluorescein dyes linked to the nitrogen atoms of a crown ether (Figure 21.8) with a cavity size that confers selectivity for the Na^+ ion. Upon binding Na^+, the Sodium Green™ indicator exhibits an increase in fluorescence emission intensity with little shift in wavelength (Figure 21.9). Although the Sodium Green™ indicator lacks the direct ratiometric readout capability of SBFI, fluorescence intensity fluctuations due to cell size variability can be compensated to some extent by using forward light scatter as a reference signal in flow cytometry.[74] Ratiometric detection using a co-loaded Na^+-insensitive reference should be feasible based on analogous Ca^{2+} detection techniques [75–77] (Section 19.3) but apparently has yet to be demonstrated in practice.

As compared with SBFI, the Sodium Green™ indicator shows greater selectivity for Na^+ than K^+ (~41-fold versus ~18-fold) and displays a much higher fluorescence quantum yield (0.2 versus 0.08) in Na^+-containing solutions. The longer-wavelength absorption of the Sodium Green™ indicator results in reduction of the potential for photodamage to the cell because the energy of the excitation light is lower than that of the UV light required for excitation of SBFI. The K_d of the Sodium Green™ indicator for Na^+ is about 6 mM in K^+-free solution and about 21 mM in solutions with combined Na^+ and K^+ concentration of 135 mM, approximating physiological ionic strength. Because its K_d may be shifted due to intracellular interactions, the Sodium Green™ indicator should be calibrated *in situ* using the pore-forming antibiotic gramicidin [74] (G6888). In some cases, dye–protein interactions may cause severe dampening or even complete elimination of the Na^+-dependent fluorescence response of intracellular Sodium Green™ indicator. Nevertheless, flow cytometric measurements in Chinese hamster ovary (CHO) are well correlated with spectrofluorometric measurements using SBFI.[74] Other applications include:

- Assessing the regulation of Na^+, K^+-ATPase by persistent Na^+ accumulation in rat thalamic neurons [78]
- Detecting anoxia-induced Na^+ influx in neurons [79]
- Determining the intracellular Na^+ concentration in crayfish presynaptic terminals using an area-ratio method [80]
- Fluorescence lifetime imaging of intracellular Na^+ [81–83]
- Investigating the effects of amiloride on transport of Na^+ in submandibular salivary ducts without interference from UV light–excited amiloride fluorescence [84]
- Measuring the effect of hyperthermia on Na^+ concentration in Chinese hamster ovary and HeLa cells [85,86]
- Confocal imaging of Na^+ transport in rat colonic mucosa [87] and cochlear hair cells by flow cytometry [88]
- Measuring Na^+ flux in colonic crypts [87]

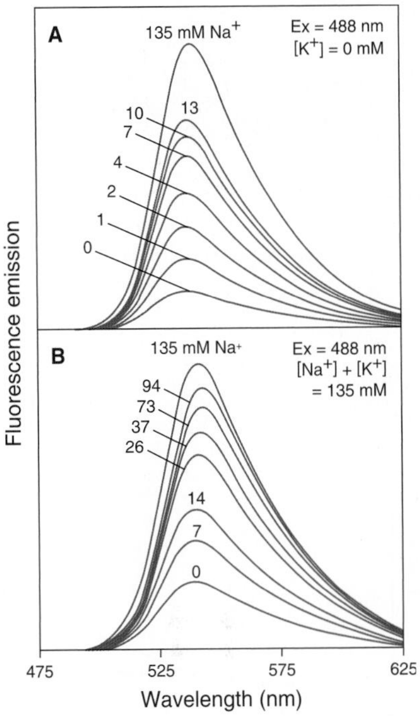

Figure 21.9 Emission spectral response of the Sodium Green™ indicator (S6900) to Na^+: A) in K^+-free solution and B) in solutions containing K^+ with the combined Na^+ and K^+ concentration equal to 135 mM. The scale on the vertical axis is the same for both panels.

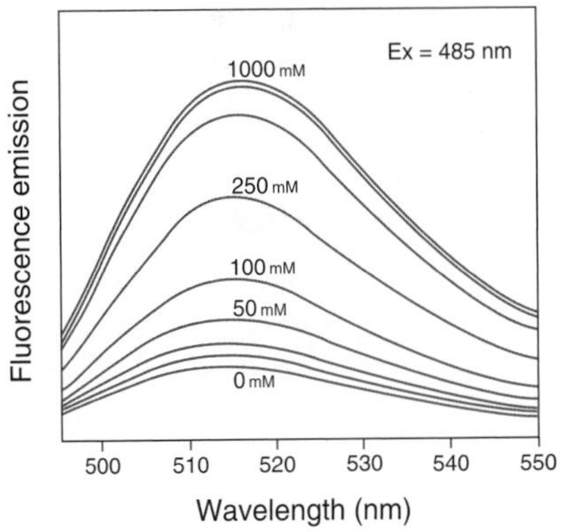

Figure 21.10 Fluorescence emission spectra of the CoroNa™ Green indicator (C36675, C36676) in 50 mM MOPS, pH 7.0 (adjusted with tetramethylammonium hydroxide), containing 100 mm K^+ and variable concentrations of Na^+ as indicated.

CoroNa™ Green Na⁺ Indicator

The CoroNa™ Green dye is another green-fluorescent Na^+ indicator that exhibits an increase in fluorescence emission intensity upon binding Na^+, with little shift in wavelength (Figure 21.10). Similar to our SBFI and Sodium Green™ Na^+ indicators, the CoroNa™ Green indicator allows spatial and temporal resolution of Na^+ concentrations selectively in the presence of physiological concentrations of other monovalent cations. Comprising a fluorescein molecule linked to

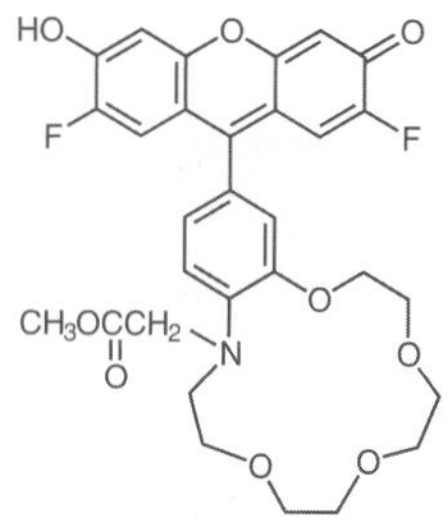

Figure 21.11 C36675 CoroNa™ Green.

a crown ether with a cavity size that confers selectivity for the Na^+ ion (Figure 21.11), the CoroNa™ Green indicator is less than half the size of the Sodium Green™ indicator (molecular weight 586 and 1668, respectively). This smaller size appears to help the cell-permeant CoroNa™ Green AM load cells better than the Sodium Green™ tetraacetate. Researchers at Molecular Probes found that, under similar conditions, ~20% of a cell population was successfully loaded with the CoroNa™ Green dye, as compared with <3% with the Sodium Green™ dye (Figure 21.12). Furthermore, the CoroNa™ Green indicator responds to a broader range of Na^+ concentration, with a K_d of ~80 mM. With absorption and fluorescence emission maxima of 492 and 516 nm, respectively, for the Na^+-bound form, the CoroNa™ Green dye can be detected by any instrument that can detect fluorescein, including flow cytometers, fluorescence microscopes, fluorescence microplate readers and fluorometers. The cell-impermeant CoroNa™ Green indicator (C36675) is supplied in a unit size of 1 mg. The cell-permeant AM ester of the CoroNa™ Green indicator (C36676) is supplied as a set of 20 vials, each containing 50 µg.

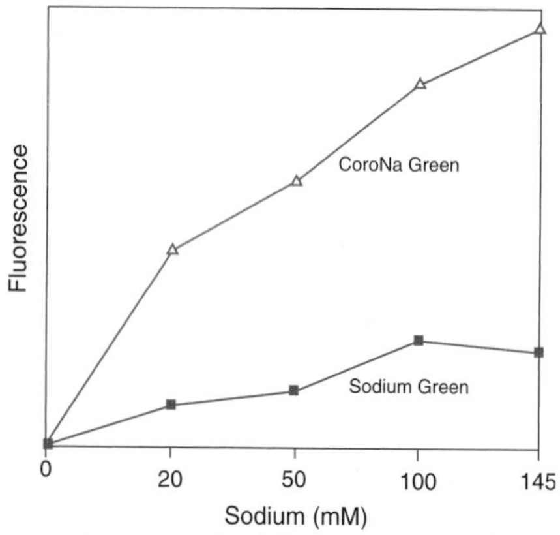

Figure 21.12 Fluorescence intensity of live cells loaded with the cell-permeant CoroNa™ Green AM (C36676) or Sodium Green™ tetraacetate (S6901). Jurkat cells were loaded with 10 µM dye for one hour at 37°C. Cells were then washed and resuspended in sodium gluconate in the presence of 20 µM monensin for 30 minutes at 37°C. Fluorescence was measured by flow cytometry.

CoroNa™ Red Na^+ Indicator

CoroNa™ Red chloride (C24430, C24431) is based on a crown ether that has structural similarity to the Ca^{2+} chelator BAPTA (Figure 21.13). Unlike SBFI and the Sodium Green™ indicator, the net positive charge of CoroNa™ Red chloride targets the indicator to mitochondria (Figure 21.14) and loading of cells does not require use of a permeant ester derivative of the dye. Cells are typically loaded by adding 0.5–1.0 µM CoroNa™ Red chloride from a 1 mM stock solution in DMSO, incubating for 10–30 minutes at 37°C and finally washing with dye-free medium before commencing fluorescence analysis. The CoroNa™ Red indicator is only weakly fluorescent in the absence of Na^+ and its fluorescence increases ~15-fold upon binding Na^+ (Figure 21.15). Despite its relatively high K_d for Na^+ of ~200 mM, the CoroNa™ Red indicator exhibits sensitive responses to cellular Na^+ influxes through voltage-gated channels and ATP-gated cation pores. Verkman and co-workers have immobilized the CoroNa™ Red indicator on polystyrene microspheres and used this complex to measure Na^+ concentrations around 100 mM in the tracheal airway–surface liquid (ASL) of cultured epithelial cells and human lung tissues.[89,90] The CoroNa™ Red indicator has also been employed to investigate the Na^+ channel permeation pathway using polyhistidine-tagged and pore-only constructs of a voltage-dependent Na^+ channel.[91] The CoroNa™ Red indicator is available as a single 1 mg vial (C24430) or as a set of 20 vials, each containing 50 µg of the indicator (C24431).

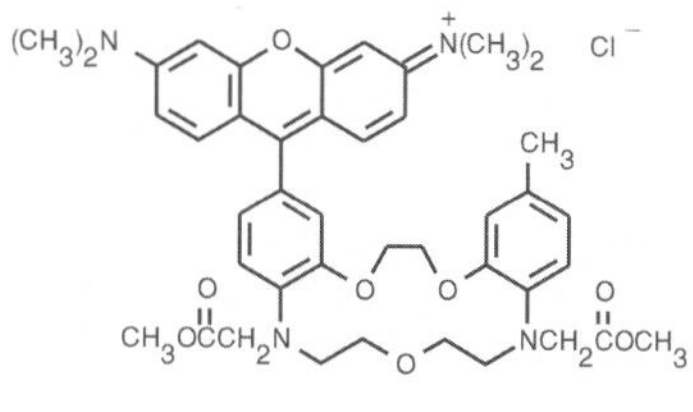

Figure 21.13 C24430 CoroNa™ Red chloride.

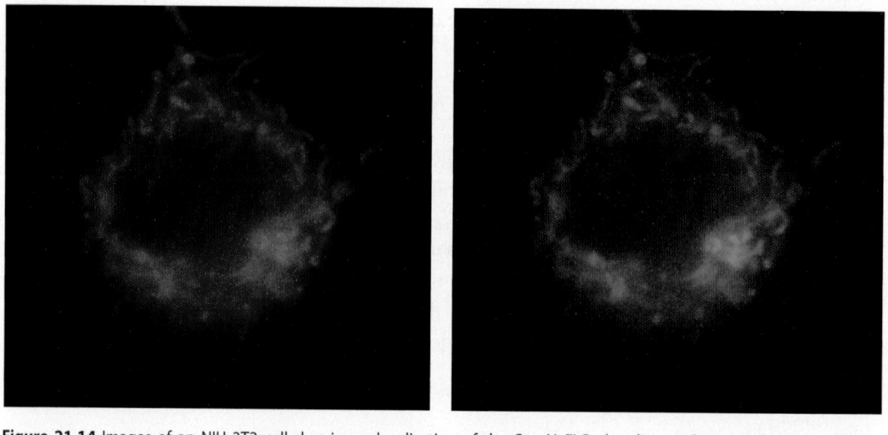

Figure 21.14 Images of an NIH 3T3 cell showing colocalization of the CoroNa™ Red sodium indicator (left panel; C24430, C24431) with the MitoTracker® Green FM mitochondrial marker (right panel, M7514). A cell loaded with both dyes was imaged consecutively using Omega Optical bandpass filter set XF41 for CoroNa™ Red sodium indicator and set XF23 for MitoTracker® Green FM.

Alternative Fluorescence Techniques for Measuring Na^+ and K^+

Researchers have discovered a variety of other less direct fluorescence techniques for measuring Na^+ and K^+:

- Ion channel–mediated K^+ fluxes are frequently detected via the accompanying membrane potential changes registered by voltage-sensitive dyes such as $DiBAC_4(3)$ [92–94] (B438; FluoroPure™ Grade, B24570; Section 22.3).
- Quenching of polyanionic fluorophores such as ANTS (A350, Section 14.3) by the K^+ analogs thallium (Tl^+) or cesium (Cs^+) is often exploited for monitoring K^+ fluxes in reconstituted-vesicle preparations.[95–97]
- The fluorescent pH indicator BCECF AM (B1150, B1170, B3051; Section 20.2) is useful for flow cytometric measurements of intracellular K^+ by exploiting the K^+/H^+ clamping action of the ionophore nigericin [98] (N1495, Section 21.2).
- Various amphiphilic fluorophores have been used in combination with ion-selective carriers to construct membrane- or polymer-based sensors for Na^+ or K^+.[99–103]
- A unique fiber-optical sensor for K^+ that is sensitive over the range of 1 µM to 1 mM employs our red-fluorescent FluoSpheres® microspheres (Section 6.5) in combination with a pH-sensitive dye.[104]

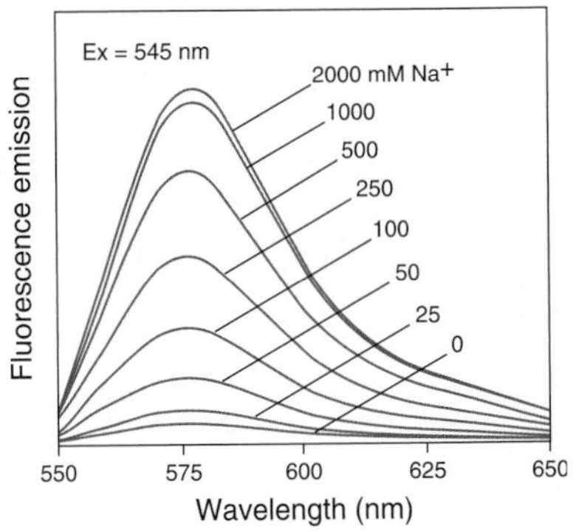

Figure 21.15 Fluorescence emission spectra of the CoroNa™ Red indicator (C24430, C24431) in 50 mM MOPS (pH 7.0, adjusted with tetramethylammonium hydroxide) containing 100 mM K^+ and variable concentrations of Na^+ as indicated.

References

1. J Biol Chem 264, 19449 (1989); **2.** Biophys J 68, 2469 (1995); **3.** Methods Enzymol 192, 38 (1990); **4.** Proc Natl Acad Sci U S A 94, 7053 (1997); **5.** Am J Physiol Cell Physiol 280, C1623 (2001); **6.** J Physiol 498, 295 (1997); **7.** Cell Regul 1, 259 (1990); **8.** J Biol Chem 264, 19458 (1989); **9.** J Mol Cell Cardiol 29, 3375 (1997); **10.** J Neurosci 21, 4207 (2001); **11.** Pflugers Arch 439, 201 (1999); **12.** J Neurosci Methods 75, 21 (1997); **13.** J Biol Chem 265, 10522 (1990); **14.** J Appl Physiol 81, 509 (1996); **15.** J Physiol 448, 493 (1992); **16.** J Biol Chem 270, 672 (1995); **17.** Am J Physiol 262, C1047 (1992); **18.** Biochim Biophys Acta 1220, 248 (1994); **19.** J Endocrinol 138, 565 (1993); **20.** J Biol Chem 272, 4753 (1997); **21.** Biochim Biophys Acta 1137, 143 (1992); **22.** J Neurochem 68, 1451 (1997); **23.** J Neurosci 14, 2464 (1994); **24.** Eur J Neurosci 12, 2199 (2000); **25.** J Physiol 517, 135 (1999); **26.** Eur J Neurosci 10, 3572 (1998); **27.** J Neurochem 71, 112 (1998); **28.** J Neurophysiol 78, 1188 (1997); **29.** Biophys J 73, 2476 (1997); **30.** J Neurochem 70, 1513 (1998); **31.** Am J Physiol Heart Circ Physiol 280, H280 (2001); **32.** Am J Physiol 273, H1246 (1997); **33.** Am J Physiol Heart Circ Physiol 279, H1661 (2000); **34.** Am J Physiol Heart Circ Physiol 279, H2143 (2000); **35.** J Mol Cell Cardiol 29, 2653 (1997); **36.** Am J Physiol 270, H2149 (1996); **37.** Biophys J 73, 3371 (1997); **38.** Proc Natl Acad Sci U S A 90, 8058 (1993); **39.** Am J Physiol Cell Physiol 279, C1648 (2000); **40.** Am J Physiol Gastrointest Liver Physiol 278, G400 (2000); **41.** J Biol Chem 273, 32602 (1998); **42.** J Biol Chem 272, 287 (1997); **43.** Am J Physiol 267, G601 (1994); **44.** J Pharmacol Exp Ther 300, 9 (2002); **45.** J Biol Chem 276, 13657 (2001); **46.** J Physiol 509, 103 (1998); **47.** Neuron 17, 969 (1996); **48.** Am J Physiol 266, H568 (1994); **49.** J Biol Chem 272, 20179 (1997); **50.** Am J Physiol 262, C348 (1992); **51.** Neuroscience 68, 1051 (1995); **52.** Curr Opin Cell Biol 13, 405 (2001); **53.** J Biol Chem 275, 19609 (2000); **54.** J Biol Chem 274, 21953 (1999); **55.** J Biol Chem 272, 32436 (1997); **56.** J Biol Chem 272, 30567 (1997); **57.** Mol Pharmacol 56, 619 (1999); **58.** Am J Physiol 276, C717 (1999); **59.** Neurosci Lett 238, 33 (1997); **60.** J Biol Chem 273, 13578 (1998); **61.** J Biol Chem 271, 8796 (1996); **62.** Biochem J 299, 539 (1994); **63.** J Exp Botany 48, 1609 (1997); **64.** J Biol Chem 270, 4368 (1995); **65.** Planta 195, 525 (1995); **66.** J Virol 70, 5447 (1996); **67.** Biochim Biophys Acta 1146, 87 (1993); **68.** Biophys J 71, 3242 (1996); **69.** J Biol Chem 271, 6199 (1996); **70.** J Biol Chem 271, 2615 (1996); **71.** Brain Res 636, 153 (1994); **72.** Circ Res 74, 829 (1994); **73.** Methods Enzymol 307, 119 (1999); **74.** Cytometry 21, 248 (1995); **75.** Cytometry 11, 923 (1990); **76.** Cell Calcium 24, 71 (1998); **77.** J Gen Physiol 105, 95 (1995); **78.** J Physiol 525 Pt 2, 343 (2000); **79.** Brain Res 663, 329 (1994); **80.** J Neurosci Methods 118, 163 (2002); **81.** Anal Biochem 281, 159 (2000); **82.** Anal Biochem 250, 131 (1997); **83.** Methods Enzymol 240, 723 (1994); **84.** J Biol Chem 270, 19606 (1995); **85.** Radiat Res 146, 283 (1996); **86.** J Membr Biol 152, 217 (1996); **87.** J Physiol 514, 211 (1999); **88.** Hear Res 119, 1 (1998); **89.** Proc Natl Acad Sci U S A 98, 8119 (2001); **90.** J Clin Invest 107, 317 (2001); **91.** J Biol Chem 277, 24653 (2002); **92.** J Exp Med 191, 1167 (2000); **93.** Br J Pharmacol 129, 1323 (2000); **94.** J Physiol 517, 781 (1999); **95.** Proc Natl Acad Sci U S A 77, 4509 (1980); **96.** Methods Enzymol 207, 501 (1992); **97.** J Biol Chem 273, 27620 (1998); **98.** Cytometry 28, 42 (1997); **99.** Anal Chim Acta 334, 125 (1996); **100.** Biophys Chem 33, 295 (1989); **101.** Analyst 113, 693 (1988); **102.** Anal Chim Acta 251, 184 (1986); **103.** Analyst 115, 353 (1990); **104.** Anal Chem 65, 123 (1993).

Data Table — 21.1 Fluorescent Na^+ and K^+ Indicators

				Low Ion*				High Ion*						
Cat #	**MW**	**Storage**	**Soluble**	**Abs**	**EC**	**Em**	**Solvent**	**Abs**	**EC**	**Em**	**Solvent**	**Product**	**K_d**	**Notes**
C24430	773.32	L	DMSO	547	92,000	570	H_2O	551	92,000	576	H_2O/Na^+		200 mM	1, 2, 3, 4
C24431	773.32	L	DMSO	547	92,000	570	H_2O	551	92,000	576	H_2O/Na^+		200 mM	1, 2, 3, 4
C36675	585.56	F,D,L	pH >6	492	68,000	516	H_2O	492	68,000	516	H_2O/Na^+		80 mM	1, 2, 5, 6
C36676	657.62	F,D,L	DMSO	454	23,000	516	pH 7					C36675		
G6888	~1880	D	MeOH	<300		none								
P1265MP	950.99	L	pH >6	336	33,000	557	H_2O	338	41,000	507	H_2O/K^+		5.1 mM	1, 5, 7
P1267MP	1171.13	F,D,L	DMSO	369	37,000	see Notes	MeOH					P1265MP		8
S1262	906.94	L	pH >8	339	45,000	565	H_2O	333	52,000	539	H_2O/Na^+		3.8 mM	1, 5, 9
S1263	1127.07	F,D,L	DMSO	379	32,000	see Notes	MeOH					S1262		8
S1264	1127.07	F,D,L	DMSO	379	32,000	see Notes	MeOH					S1262		8
S6900	1667.57	L	pH >6	506	117,000	532	H_2O	507	133,000	532	H_2O/Na^+		6.0 mM	1, 2, 5, 9
S6901	1543.17	F,D,L	DMSO	302	21,000	none	MeOH					S6900		
V1644	1111.33	F,L	EtOH	<300		none	MeCN							

For definitions of the contents of this data table, see "Navigating *The Handbook*" in the introductory pages.

* For "Low Ion" spectra, the concentration of Na^+ or K^+ is zero. For "High Ion" spectra, the concentration of Na^+ or K^+ is in excess of that required to saturate the response of the indicator.

Notes

1. Dissociation constant values vary considerably depending on presence of other ions, temperature, pH, ionic strength, viscosity, protein binding and other factors. It is essential that the spectral response of the probe be calibrated in your system.
2. This indicator exhibits fluorescence enhancement in response to ion binding, with essentially no change in absorption or emission wavelengths.
3. K_d determined at Molecular Probes in 50 mM MOPS, pH 7.0 (adjusted with tetramethylammonium hydroxide) containing 40% DMSO at 22°C.
4. Spectra measured in aqueous buffers containing 40% DMSO and zero (H_2O) or 1 M Na^+ (H_2O/Na^+).
5. Spectra measured in aqueous buffers containing zero (H_2O) or a >10-fold excess of free cation X (H_2O/X) relative to the listed dissociation constant (K_d) for cation X.
6. $K_d(Na^+)$ determined at Molecular Probes in 50 mM MOPS, pH 7.0 (adjusted with tetramethylammonium hydroxide) at 22°C.
7. $K_d(K^+)$ has been determined at Molecular Probes in 10 mM MOPS, pH 7.0 (adjusted with tetramethylammonium hydroxide) at 22°C. $K_d(K^+)$ is strongly dependent on the concentration of Na^+. In solutions with $[Na^+] + [K^+] = 135$ mM, $K_d(K^+) = 44$ mM.
8. Fluorescence of SBFI, AM and PBFI, AM is very weak.
9. $K_d(Na^+)$ has been determined at Molecular Probes in 10 mM MOPS, pH 7.0 (adjusted with tetramethylammonium hydroxide) at 22°C. Na^+ dissociation constants for these indicators are dependent on K^+ concentration. In solutions with total $[Na^+] + [K^+] = 135$ mM, $K_d(Na^+) = 11.3$ mM (S1262) and 21 mM (S6900).

Product List — 21.1 Fluorescent Na^+ and K^+ Indicators

Cat #	Product Name	Unit Size
C36675	CoroNa™ Green *cell impermeant*	1 mg
C36676	CoroNa™ Green, AM *cell permeant* *special packaging*	20 x 50 µg
C24430	CoroNa™ Red chloride	1 mg
C24431	CoroNa™ Red chloride *special packaging*	20 x 50 µg
G6888	gramicidin	100 mg
P1267MP	PBFI, AM *cell permeant* *special packaging*	20 x 50 µg
P1265MP	PBFI, tetraammonium salt *cell impermeant*	1 mg
P6867	Pluronic® F-127 *low UV absorbance*	2 g
P3000MP	Pluronic® F-127 *20% solution in DMSO*	1 mL
P6866	Pluronic® F-127 *10% solution in water* *0.2 µm filtered*	30 mL
S1263	SBFI, AM *cell permeant*	1 mg
S1264	SBFI, AM *cell permeant* *special packaging*	20 x 50 µg
S1262	SBFI, tetraammonium salt *cell impermeant*	1 mg
S6901	Sodium Green™ tetraacetate *cell permeant* *special packaging*	20 x 50 µg
S6900	Sodium Green™, tetra(tetramethylammonium) salt *cell impermeant*	1 mg
V1644	valinomycin	25 mg

For current prices or to order online, visit probes.invitrogen.com

21.2 Detecting Chloride, Phosphate, Nitrite and Other Anions

This section describes fluorescent indicators for intracellular and extracellular chloride together with an assortment of analytical reagents and methods for direct or indirect quantitation of other inorganic anions, including bromide, iodide, hypochlorite, cyanide, sulfide, sulfite, nitrite, nitrate, phosphate, pyrophosphate and selenide.[1]

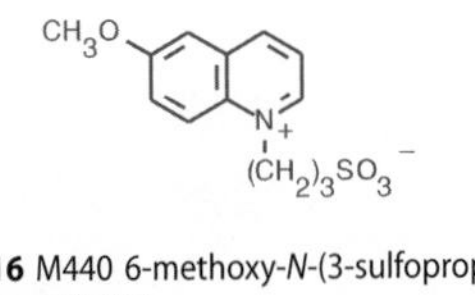

Figure 21.16 M440 6-methoxy-*N*-(3-sulfopropyl)quinolinium, inner salt (SPQ).

Fluorescent Cl^- Indicators

Most of Molecular Probes' fluorescent chloride indicators are 6-methoxyquinolinium derivatives, the prototype of which is 6-methoxy-*N*-(3-sulfopropyl)quinolinium[2,3] (SPQ, Figure 21.16). Cl^- detection sensitivity has been improved by modifications of the quinolinium *N* substituent.[4,5] Our current range of Cl^- indicators consists of:

- 6-Methoxy-*N*-(3-sulfopropyl)quinolinium (SPQ, M440)
- *N*-(Ethoxycarbonylmethyl)-6-methoxyquinolinium bromide (MQAE, E3101)
- 6-Methoxy-*N*-ethylquinolinium iodide (MEQ, M6886)
- Lucigenin (L6868)

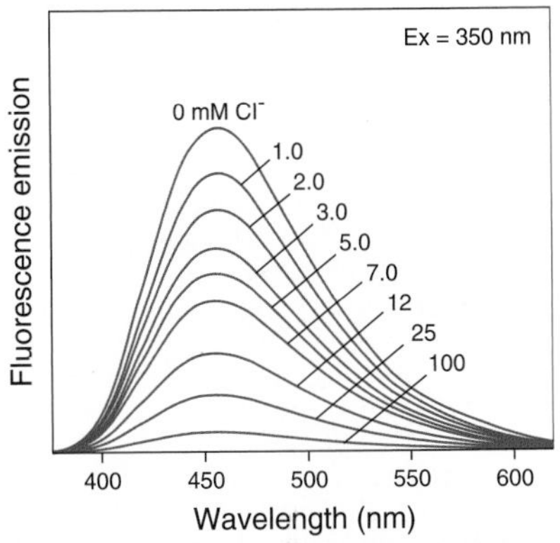

Figure 21.17 Fluorescence emission spectra of MQAE (E3101) in increasing concentrations of Cl^-.

All of these indicators detect Cl^- via diffusion-limited collisional quenching.[6] This detection mechanism is different from that of fluorescent indicators for Ca^{2+}, Mg^{2+}, Zn^{2+}, Na^+ and K^+. It involves a transient interaction between the excited state of the fluorophore and a halide ion — no ground-state complex is formed. Quenching is not accompanied by spectral shifts (Figure 21.17) and, consequently, ratio measurements are not directly feasible. Quenching by other halides, such as Br^- and I^-, and other anions, such as thiocyanate, is more efficient than Cl^- quenching.[6] Fortunately, physiological concentrations of noncholoride ions do not significantly affect the fluorescence of SPQ and other methoxyquinolinium-based Cl^- indicators. With some exceptions,[7] fluorescence of these indicators is not pH sensitive in the physiological range.[4] Because Cl^--dependent fluorescence quenching is a diffusional process, it is quite sensitive to solution viscosity and volume. Exploiting this property, SPQ has been used to measure intracellular volume changes.[8]

The efficiency of collisional quenching is characterized by the Stern–Volmer constant (K_{SV}) — the reciprocal of the ion concentration that produces 50% of maximum quenching. For SPQ, K_{SV} is reported to be 118 M^{-1} in aqueous solution and 12 M^{-1} inside cells.[9] For MQAE, *in situ* K_{SV} values of 25–28 M^{-1} have been determined in various cell types,[10,11] compared with the solution value of 200 M^{-1}. Intracellular Cl^- indicators are generally calibrated using high-K^+ buffers and the K^+/H^+ ionophore nigericin (N1495) in conjunction with tributyltin chloride, an organometallic compound that acts as a Cl^-/OH^- antiporter.[4,5,12] With the exception of diH-MEQ (see below), Cl^- indicators must be loaded into cells by long-term incubation (up to eight hours) in the presence of a large excess of dye or by brief hypotonic permeabilization. Because membranes are slightly permeable to the indicator, rapid leakage may occur. Experimentally determined estimates of leakage vary quite widely.[10–12]

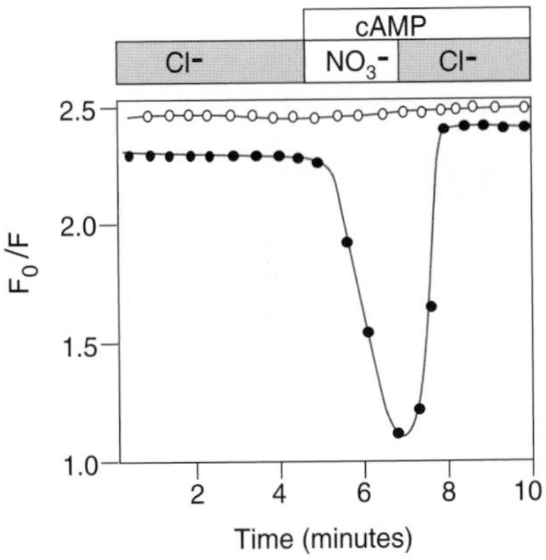

Figure 21.18 Detection of cystic fibrosis transmembrane conductance regulator (CFTR) activity using 6-methoxy-*N*-(3-sulfopropyl)quinolinium, inner salt (SPQ, M440). Fluorescence of intracellular SPQ is quenched by collision with chloride ions, indicated by $F_0/F > 1$ (F_0 = fluorescence intensity in absence of chloride, F = fluorescence intensity at time points indicated on the x-axis). Upon addition of cyclic AMP to initiate channel opening, and exchange of extracellular Cl^- (135 mM) for nitrate (NO_3^-), SPQ quenching decreases in CFTR-expressing cells (filled circles) as CFTR-mediated anion transport results in replacement of intracellular Cl^- with nonquenching NO_3^-. Control cells with no CFTR expression (open circles) show no response.

Measurement of intracellular Cl^- concentrations and the study of Cl^- channels have been stimulated by the discovery that cystic fibrosis is caused by mutations in a gene encoding a Cl^- transport channel, which is known as the cystic fibrosis transmembrane conductance regulator[13] (CFTR). Cl^- permeability assays are used to detect activity of the CFTR and other anion transporters.[14–17] In these assays, SPQ- or MQAE-loaded cells are successively perfused with chloride-containing extracellular medium followed by medium in which the Cl^- content is replaced by nitrate (NO_3^-). NO_3^- is used in this assay protocol because it produces no fluorescence quenching of the indicator, yet its channel permeability is essentially the same as that of Cl^-[14,15] (Figure 21.18).

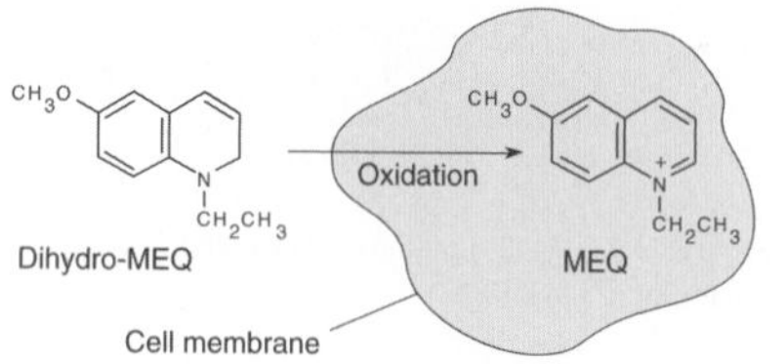

Figure 21.19 Intracellular delivery of the fluorescent chloride indicator 6-methoxy-*N*-ethylquinolinium iodide (MEQ, M6886), via oxidation of the membrane-permeant precursor dihydro-MEQ.

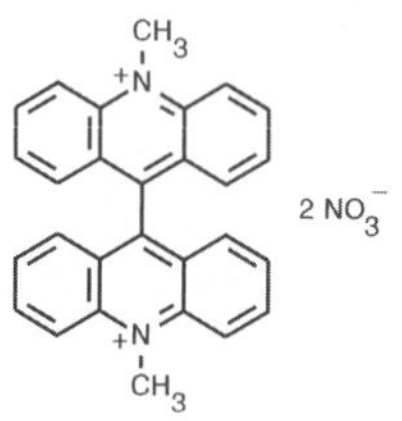

Figure 21.20 L6868 lucigenin (bis-*N*-methylacridinium nitrate).

SPQ

SPQ is currently in widespread use for detecting CFTR activity using the Cl^-/NO_3^- exchange technique described above.[16,18–24] SPQ has also has been employed to investigate Cl^- fluxes through several other transporters such as the $GABA_A$ receptor,[25,26] erythrocyte Cl^-/HCO_3^- exchangers[27,28] and the mitochondrial uncoupling protein.[29–31] Although SPQ requires UV excitation (as do MQAE and MEQ), techniques for flow cytometric detection and calibration of the indicator using argon-ion laser excitation at 351 nm and 364 nm have been successfully demonstrated.[12]

MQAE

MQAE has greater sensitivity to Cl^-[4,5] and a higher fluorescence quantum yield than SPQ; consequently, it is currently the more widely used of the two indicators. However, the ester group of MQAE may slowly hydrolyze inside cells, resulting in a change in its fluorescence response.[32] MQAE has been used in a fluorescence-based microplate assay that has potential for screening compounds that modify Cl^- ion-channel activity.[10] Other applications have included Cl^- measurements in cytomegalovirus-infected fibroblasts,[33] smooth muscle cells[32] and salivary glands,[17] as well as in reconstituted membranes containing the $GABA_A$ receptor[26] or the mitochondrial-uncoupling protein[34,35] (UCP-1).

MEQ and Cell-Permeant Dihydro-MEQ

The Cl^- indicator 6-methoxy-*N*-ethylquinolinium iodide (MEQ) can be rendered cell-permeant by masking its positively charged nitrogen to create a lipophilic, Cl^--insensitive compound, 6-methoxy-*N*-ethyl-1,2-dihydroquinoline[36] (dihydro-MEQ). This reduced quinoline derivative can then be loaded noninvasively into cells, where it is rapidly reoxidized in most cells to the cell-impermeant, Cl^--sensitive MEQ (Figure 21.19). Using this technique, researchers have loaded live brain slices and hippocampal neurons with MEQ for confocal imaging of Cl^- responses to $GABA_A$ receptor activation and glutamatergic excitotoxicity.[37–41] Quenching of intracellular MEQ fluorescence by Cl^- has a K_{SV} of 19 M^{-1}, a value that is slightly higher than that reported for SPQ in fibroblasts. MEQ is available in solid form (M6886) and is supplied with a simple protocol for reducing it to dihydro-MEQ with sodium borohydride (not supplied) just prior to cell loading.

Lucigenin

The fluorescence of lucigenin (L6868, Figure 21.20) is quantitatively quenched by high levels of Cl^- with a reported K_{SV} = 390 M^{-1}.[42] Lucigenin absorbs maximally at both 368 nm (ε = 36,000 $cm^{-1}M^{-1}$) and 455 nm (ε = 7400 $cm^{-1}M^{-1}$), with an emission maximum at 505 nm. Its fluorescence emission has a quantum yield of ~0.6 and is insensitive to nitrate, phosphate and sulfate. Lucigenin is a useful Cl^- indicator in liposomes and reconstituted membrane vesicles; however, because its fluorescence is reported to be unstable in the cytoplasm, it may not always be suitable for determining intracellular Cl^-.[42] Lucigenin has been used to detect chloride uptake in tonoplast vesicles.[43] Lucigenin is also a potentially valuable tool for measuring Cl^- efflux from cells in which the extracellular medium is suddenly made Cl^--free by superfusion. Lucigenin from Molecular Probes has been highly purified to remove a blue-fluorescent contaminant that is found in some commercial samples and can interfere with these measurements.

Alternative Detection Techniques for Halides

As mentioned above, the fluorescence of SPQ and related Cl^- indicators is quenched by collision with a variety of anions, including (in order of increasing quenching efficiency) Cl^-, Br^-, I^- and thiocyanate[44] (SCN^-). For example, fluorescence of SPQ is partially quenched by the anionic pH buffer TES (*N-tris*(hydroxymethyl)methyl-2-aminoethanesulfonic acid) but not by the protonated TES zwitterion, a property that has been exploited to measure proton efflux from proteoliposomes.[31] Anion detectability using diffusional fluorescence quenching of these fluorophores is typically limited to the millimolar range. I^- quenches many other fluorophores and is commonly used to determine the accessibility of fluorophores to quenching in proteins and membranes.[45,46]

In addition, halides can be oxidized to hypohalites (^-OCl, ^-OBr, ^-OI), which react with rhodamine 6G (R634, Section 12.2) to yield chemiluminescent products.[47,48] A cell produces ^-OCl by oxidizing Cl^- within the phagovacuole.[49,50] The reaction of ^-OCl with fluorescein conjugates is the basis of a sensitive chemiluminescent immunoassay.[51] ^-OCl also reacts with fluorescein (F1300, Section 1.5) to yield fluorescent products,[52] permitting analysis of ^-OCl levels in water.

Alternatively, 3′-(*p*-aminophenyl) fluorescein (APF) and 3′-(*p*-hydroxyphenyl) fluorescein (HPF), (A36003, H36004; Section 18.2), two new ROS indicators developed by Nagano,[53] can be used for the selective detection of ^-OCl. Both of these fluorescein derivatives are essentially nonfluorescent until they react with the hydroxyl radical (HO·) or peroxynitrite anion ($ONOO^-$) (Figure 18.11). APF will also react with the hypochlorite anion (^-OCl), making it possible to use APF and HPF together to selectively detect hypochlorite anion. In the presence of these specific ROS, both APF and HPF yield a bright green-fluorescent product (excitation/emission maxima ~490/515 nm) and are compatible with all fluorescence instrumentation capable of visualizing fluorescein. Using APF, researchers have been able to detect the ^-OCl generated by activated neutrophils, a feat that has not been possible with traditional ROS indicators.[53]

Cyanide

The homologous aromatic dialdehydes, *o*-phthaldialdehyde[54] (OPA, P2331MP) and naphthalene-2,3-dicarboxaldehyde[55] (NDA, N1138), are essentially nonfluorescent until reacted with a primary amine in the presence of excess cyanide or a thiol, such as 2-mercaptoethanol, 3-mercaptopropionic acid or the less obnoxious sulfite,[56] to yield a fluorescent isoindole (Figure 1.117, Figure 1.118). Modified protocols that use an excess of an amine and limiting amounts of other nucleophiles permit the determination of cyanide in blood, urine and other samples.[57–60]

Molecular Probes also offers the ATTO-TAG™ CBQCA (A6222) and ATTO-TAG™ FQ (A10192) reagents, which are similar to OPA and NDA in that they react with primary amines in the presence of cyanide or thiols to form highly fluorescent isoindoles[61–69] (Figure 1.119). The ATTO-TAG™ CBQCA and ATTO-TAG™ FQ reagents should also be useful for detecting cyanide in a variety of biological samples.

We have found that our Thiol and Sulfide Quantitation Kit (T6060, see below) also provides an ultrasensitive enzymatic assay for cyanide, with a detection limit of ~5 nanomoles. In this case, interference would be expected from thiols, sulfides, sulfites and other reducing agents. See below for a complete description of the kit contents.

Sulfide, Sulfite, Sulfate and Thiosulfate

Thiol and Sulfide Quantitation Kit

Colorimetric and fluorometric detection and quantitation of thiols, sulfites and related environmental pollutants are now possible using a variety of reagents available from Molecular Probes. In particular, our Thiol and Sulfide Quantitation Kit (T6060) provides an ultrasensitive colorimetric assay for thiols (also called mercaptans or sulfhydryls) and inorganic sulfides (or hydrogen sulfide). In this assay, which is based on a method reported by Singh,[70,71] thiols or sulfides reduce a disulfide-inhibited derivative of papain, stoichiometrically releasing the active enzyme. Activity of the enzyme is then measured using the chromogenic papain substrate L-BAPNA (Figure 5.7).

Although thiols and sulfides can also be quantitated using 5,5′-dithiobis-(2-nitrobenzoic acid) (DTNB or Ellman's reagent, D8451), the enzymatic amplification step in the Thiol and Sulfide Quantitation Kit enables researchers to detect as little as 0.2 nanomoles of thiols or sulfides — a sensitivity that is about 100-fold better than that achieved with DTNB. Furthermore, incorporation of the disulfide cystamine into the solution permits quantitation of accessible thiols on proteins and potentially other high molecular weight molecules. The Thiol and Sulfide Quantitation Kit contains:

- Papain–$SSCH_3$, the disulfide-inhibited papain derivative
- L-BAPNA, a chromogenic papain substrate
- DTNB (Ellman's reagent), for calibrating the assay
- Cystamine
- L-Cysteine, a thiol standard
- Buffer
- Detailed protocols for measuring thiols, inorganic sulfides and maleimides

Sufficient reagents are provided for approximately 50 assays using 1 mL assay volumes and standard cuvettes or 250 assays using a microplate format. This kit can also be used to detect phosphines, sulfites and cyanides, with detection limits of about 0.5, 1 and 5 nanomoles, respectively. We expect that this kit can be adapted to directly detect other disulfide-reducing reagents and to indirectly detect certain heavy metals that are quantitatively precipitated by low levels of sulfide such as Hg^{2+}, Pb^{2+} and Cd^{2+}.

Other Related Reagents

A number of reagents that react with thiols are described in Chapter 2. 5,5′-Dithiobis-(2-nitrobenzoic acid) (DTNB or Ellman's reagent, D8451) is, by far, the most common reagent for colorimetric thiol quantitation (Section 2.1). Among the reagents for fluorometric analysis, the nonfluorescent reagent monobromobimane (M1378; FluoroPure™ Grade, M20381) can detect inorganic sulfide, sulfite and thiosulfate, including levels dissolved in plasma, by conversion to fluorescent products followed by chromatographic separation.[72] Sulfite, and indirectly sulfur dioxide, can be quantitated by making it the limiting reagent in combination with excess amine and *o*-phthaldialdehyde (P2331MP) or naphthalene-2,3-dicarboxaldehyde[56,73–75] (N1138). Fluorescence-based assays for sulfate have not yet been reported. However, we propose that a combination of an indicator whose fluorescence is altered by binding Ba^{2+} such as Calcium Green™-1 (C3010MP, Section 19.3), Calcium Green™-2 (C3730, Section 19.3) or BTC (B6790, Section 19.2) can be used to indirectly detect sulfate, which will quantitatively precipitate Ba^{2+} from the solution.

Nitrite, Nitrate and Nitric Oxide

Until recently, the primary application for nitrite (NO_2^-) detection was in the testing of processed meats. However, with the discovery of the role of nitric oxide in signal transduction (Section 18.3), assays for NO_2^- have assumed new importance. Because inorganic nitrite is spontaneously produced by air oxidation of nitric oxide, the same reagents that have been utilized to detect nitric oxide production in cells should be useful for detecting nitrite in aqueous samples. Furthermore, inorganic nitrate (NO_3^-) can be reduced to NO_2^- by both chemical and enzymatic means, permitting the quantitative analysis of NO_3^- in samples.

Griess Reagent Kit

Under physiological conditions, NO is readily oxidized to NO_2^- and NO_3^- or it is trapped by thiols as an *S*-nitroso adduct. The Griess reagent provides a simple and well-characterized colorimetric assay for nitrites — and nitrates that have been reduced to nitrites — with a detection limit of about 100 nM.[76–78] The Griess assay is suitable for measuring the activity of nitrate reductase in a microplate.[79] Nitrite reacts with the Griess reagent to form a purple azo derivative that can be monitored by absorbance at 548 nm (Figure 18.21). Our Griess Reagent Kit (G7921) contains all of the reagents required for NO_2^- quantitation, including:

- *N*-(1-Naphthyl)ethylenediamine dihydrochloride
- Sulfanilic acid in 5% H_3PO_4
- A concentrated nitrite standard for generating calibration curves
- Detailed protocols for spectrophotometer- and microplate reader–based assays

Both the *N*-(1-naphthyl)ethylenediamine dihydrochloride and the sulfanilic acid in 5% H_3PO_4 are provided in convenient dropper bottles for easy preparation of the Griess reagent. Sample pretreatment with nitrate reductase and glucose 6-phosphate dehydrogenase is reported to reduce NO_3^- without producing excess NADPH, which can interfere with the Griess reaction.[80] NO that has been trapped as an *S*-nitroso derivative can also be analyzed with the Griess Reagent Kit after first releasing the NO from its complex using mercuric chloride or copper (II) acetate.[81,82]

DAF-FM

DAF-FM[83] (4-amino-5-methylamino-2′,7′-difluorofluorescein; D23841; Figure 21.21) and its diacetate derivative (DAF-FM diacetate, D23842; D23844; Section 18.3) have significant utility for measuring nitric oxide and nitrite production in live cells and solutions. The fluorescence quantum yield of DAF-FM is reported to be 0.005 but increases about 160 fold to 0.81 after reacting with nitrite[83] (Figure 18.20). DAF-FM has some important advantages over the similar nitric oxide sensor, DAF-2, and other aromatic diamines:

- Spectra of the NO (NO_2^-) adduct of DAF-FM are independent of pH above pH 5.5.[83]
- The NO_2^- adduct of DAF-FM is significantly more photostable than that of DAF-2.[83]
- DAF-FM is a more sensitive reagent for NO_2^- than is DAF-2; the NO and NO_2^- detection limit for DAF-FM is ~3 nM[83] versus ~5 nM for DAF-2.[84])

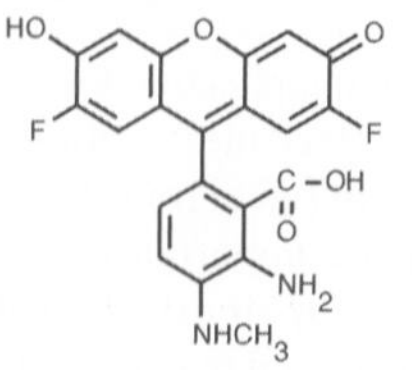

Figure 21.21 D23841 DAF-FM (4-amino-5-methylamino-2′,7′-difluorofluorescein).

- The higher absorptivity and greater water solubility of the NO_2^- adduct of DAF-FM should make this assay much more sensitive than detection with 2,3-diaminonaphthalene (see below) or other aromatic diamines.

DAF-2 reportedly also reacts with dehydroascorbic acid and ascorbic acid, generating products with fluorescence spectra similar to those of the NO_2^- adduct of DAF-2.[85] Therefore, when using DAF-2 and potentially DAF-FM for measuring nitric oxide levels in cells, it is important to also perform control experiments with nitric oxide synthase inhibitors to distinguish the source of the fluorescent species. Although DAF-2 and its diacetate are not available from Molecular Probes, we maintain a bibliography (D23843) for these reagents. We anticipate that DAF-FM should give equal or superior performance to DAF-2 in most applications.

2,3-Diaminonaphthalene

We also offer 2,3-diaminonaphthalene (D7918), which reacts with NO_2^- to form the fluorescent product 1*H*-naphthotriazole. A rapid, quantitative fluorometric assay that employs 2,3-diaminonaphthalene can reportedly detect from 10 nM to 10 µM NO_2^-, and is compatible with a 96-well microplate format.[86] Nitrate (NO_3^-) does not interfere with this assay; however, NO_3^- can be reduced to NO_2^- by hydrazine and then detected using the same reagent.[87]

NBD Methylhydrazine

NBD methylhydrazine (*N*-methyl-4-hydrazino-7-nitrobenzofurazan, M20490) has been used to measure NO_2^- in water[88] and also to monitor aldehydes and ketones in automobile exhaust.[89] Reaction of NBD methylhydrazine with NO_2^- in the presence of mineral acids leads to formation of fluorescent products with excitation/emission maxima of ~468/537 nm. This reaction serves as the principle behind a selective fluorogenic method for the determination of NO_2^-. The assay is suitable for measurements by absorption or fluorescence spectroscopy or by fluorescence-detected HPLC.[88]

Rhodamine 110

Rhodamine 110 (R6479) has proven useful in a fluorescence quenching method for determining trace nitrite.[90] This sensitive assay takes advantage of the reaction of the highly green-fluorescent rhodamine 110 with nitrite at acidic pH to form a product that exhibits much less fluorescence. With a linear range of 1×10^{-8} to 3×10^{-7} moles/L and a detection limit of 7×10^{-10} moles/L, this assay has been used to measure nitrite in tap water and lake water without any prior extraction procedures.

Other Related Reagents

Efficient quenching of SPQ fluorescence (M440, see above) by nitrite (but not nitrate) has been used for direct measurement of NO_2^- transport across erythrocyte membranes.[91] Membrane-based fluorescent sensors incorporating octadecyl rhodamine B (O246, Section 13.5) have been designed for detection of both NO_2^- and NO_3^-.

We have shown that 6-chloro-9-nitro-5-oxo-5*H*-benzo[a]phenoxazine (CNOB, C22220; Section 10.6) is a useful fluorogenic substrate for continuous measurement of bacterial nitrate reductase from *E. coli*. This enzyme reduces the nonfluorescent CNOB to a highly fluorescent aminophenoxazine, with fluorescence excitation/emission maxima at 617 nm/625 nm. Nitrate would likely interfere with this reaction, and therefore it may be possible to use CNOB in conjunction with the bacterial nitrate reductase for nitrate detection.

Phosphate and Pyrophosphate

P_iPer™ Phosphate Assay Kit

Molecular Probes' patented P_iPer™ Phosphate Assay Kit (P22061) provides an ultrasensitive assay that detects free phosphate in solution through formation of the fluorescent product resorufin. Because resorufin also has strong absorption, the assay can be performed either fluorometrically or spectrophotometrically. This kit can be used to detect inorganic phosphate (P_i) in a variety of samples or to monitor the kinetics of phosphate release by a variety of enzymes, including ATPases, GTPases, 5′-nucleotidase, protein phosphatases, acid and alkaline phosphatases and phosphorylase kinase. Furthermore, the assay can be modified to detect virtually any naturally occurring organic phosphate molecule by including an enzyme that can specifically digest the organic phosphate to liberate inorganic phosphate.

In the P_iPer™ phosphate assay (Figure 10.39), maltose phosphorylase converts maltose (in the presence of P_i) to glucose 1-phosphate and glucose. Then glucose oxidase converts the glucose to gluconolactone and H_2O_2. Finally, with horseradish peroxidase as a catalyst, the H_2O_2 reacts with the Amplex® Red reagent (10-acetyl-3,7-dihydroxyphenoxazine) to generate resorufin, which has absorption/emission maxima of ~571/585 nm.[92,93] The resulting increase in fluorescence or absorption is proportional to the amount of P_i in the sample. This kit can be used to detect as little as 0.2 µM P_i by fluorescence (Figure 10.40) or 0.4 µM P_i by absorption.

Each P_iPer™ Phosphate Assay Kit contains:

- Amplex® Red reagent
- Dimethylsulfoxide (DMSO)
- Concentrated reaction buffer
- Recombinant maltose phosphorylase from *Escherichia coli*
- Maltose
- Glucose oxidase from *Aspergillus niger*
- Horseradish peroxidase
- Phosphate standard
- Hydrogen peroxide
- A detailed protocol for detecting phosphatase activity

Each kit provides sufficient reagents for approximately 1000 assays using a reaction volume of 100 µL per assay and either a fluorescence or absorbance microplate reader.

P_iPer™ Pyrophosphate Assay Kit

Our patented P_iPer™ Pyrophosphate Assay Kit (P22062) provides a sensitive fluorometric or colorimetric method for measuring the inorganic pyrophosphate (PP_i) in experimental samples or for monitoring the kinetics of PP_i release by a variety of enzymes, including DNA and RNA polymerases, adenylate cyclase and *S*-acetyl coenzyme A synthetase. In the P_iPer™ pyrophosphate assay, inorganic pyrophosphatase hydrolyzes PP_i to two molecules of inorganic phosphate (P_i). The P_i then enters into the same cascade of reactions as it does in the P_iPer™ Phosphate Assay Kit (Figure 10.39). In this case, the resulting increase in fluorescence or absorption is proportional to the amount of PP_i in the sample. This kit can be used to detect as little as 0.1 µM PP_i by fluorescence or 0.2 µM PP_i by absorption (Figure 10.41).

Each P_iPer™ Pyrophosphate Assay Kit contains:

- Amplex® Red reagent
- Dimethylsulfoxide (DMSO)
- Concentrated reaction buffer
- Recombinant maltose phosphorylase from *Escherichia coli*
- Maltose
- Glucose oxidase from *Aspergillus niger*
- Horseradish peroxidase
- Inorganic pyrophosphatase from baker's yeast
- Pyrophosphate standard
- A detailed protocol for detecting phosphatase activity

Each kit provides sufficient reagents for approximately 1000 assays using a reaction volume of 100 µL per assay and either a fluorescence or absorbance microplate reader.

EnzChek® Phosphate Assay Kit

Our EnzChek® Phosphate Assay Kit (E6646), which is based on a method originally described by Webb,[94,95] provides an easy enzymatic assay for detecting P_i from multiple sources through formation of a chromophoric product (Figure 10.42). Although this kit is usually used to determine the P_i produced by a wide variety of enzymes such as ATPases, kinases and phosphatases (Section 10.3), it can also be used to specifically quantitate P_i with a sensitivity of ~2 µM P_i (~0.2 µg/mL) (w). Moreover, this colorimetric assay has proven useful for determining

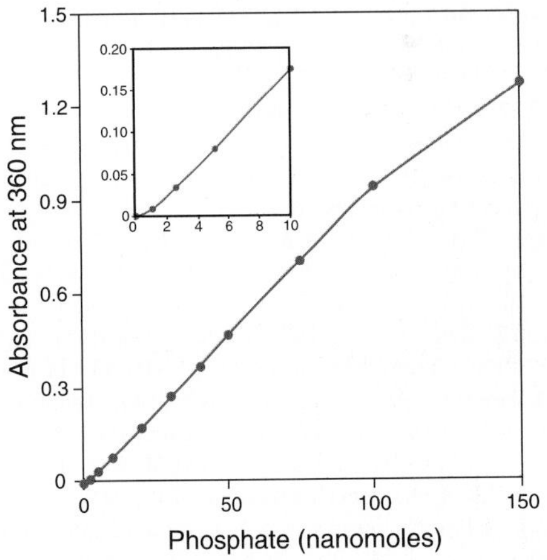

Figure 21.22 Quantitative analysis of inorganic phosphate using the EnzChek® Phosphate Assay Kit (E6646). KH_2PO_4 was used as the source for the inorganic phosphate, and the absorbance at 360 nm was corrected for background absorbance. The inset shows an enlargement of the standard curve, demonstrating the lower range of the assay; the units are the same.

the level of P_i contamination in the presence of high concentrations of acid-labile phosphates using a microplate reader.[96] Each EnzChek® Phosphate Assay Kit contains:

- 2-Amino-6-mercapto-7-methylpurine riboside (MESG)
- Purine nucleoside phosphorylase (PNP)
- Concentrated reaction buffer
- KH_2PO_4 standard
- A detailed protocol for detecting and quantitating P_i

In the presence of P_i, MESG is enzymatically converted by PNP to ribose 1-phosphate and the chromophoric product 2-amino-6-mercapto-7-methylpurine (Figure 10.42). This kit contains sufficient reagents for about 100 phosphate assays using 1 mL assay volumes and standard cuvettes.

EnzChek® Pyrophosphate Assay Kit

We have adapted the method provided in our EnzChek® Phosphate Assay Kit to permit the sensitive spectrophotometric detection of PP_i, which is converted by the enzyme pyrophosphatase to P_i.[97] Because two moles of P_i are released per mole of PP_i consumed, the sensitivity limit of the EnzChek® Pyrophosphatase Assay Kit is 1 µM PP_i (~0.2 µg/mL). This assay has been modified to continuously detect several enzymes that liberate PP_i [98–101] such as aminoacyl-tRNA synthetase,[102] luciferase, cytidylyl transferase [103] and *S*-acetyl coenzyme A synthetase [97] and potentially DNA and RNA polymerases, adenylate cyclase and guanylyl cyclase.[104] Each EnzChek® Pyrophosphate Assay Kit contains:

- Inorganic pyrophosphatase
- 2-Amino-6-mercapto-7-methylpurine riboside (MESG)
- Purine nucleoside phosphorylase (PNP)
- Concentrated reaction buffer
- $Na_2P_2O_7$ standard
- A detailed protocol for detecting and quantitating PP_i

This kit contains sufficient reagents for about 100 PP_i assays using standard 1 mL assay volumes and standard cuvettes.

Selenium

Selenium, hydrogen selenide and selenium-containing compounds such as selenomethionine are readily assayed by their specific formation of a fluorescent compound (excitation/emission maxima ~375–380 nm /520–580 nm) with 2,3-diaminonaphthalene [105–110] (D7918). Detection limits of less than 100 picograms of selenium are attainable.[111] This technique has been adapted for detection of selenium-containing compounds on TLC sheets.[112]

References

1. Analyst 107, 465 (1982); **2.** J Heterocyclic Chem 19, 841 (1982); **3.** Biochemistry 26, 1215 (1987); **4.** Anal Biochem 178, 355 (1989); **5.** Am J Physiol 259, C375 (1990); **6.** Biophys Chem 85, 49 (2000); **7.** Am J Physiol 264, C27 (1993); **8.** Am J Physiol 272, C1405 (1997); **9.** Biophys J 53, 955 (1988); **10.** Anal Biochem 241, 51 (1996); **11.** Neuroscience 28, 725 (1989); **12.** Cytometry 28, 316 (1997); **13.** Annu Rev Physiol 60, 689 (1998); **14.** Proc Natl Acad Sci U S A 88, 7500 (1991); **15.** Biochim Biophys Acta 1152, 83 (1993); **16.** Am J Physiol 274, C310 (1998); **17.** Pflugers Arch 427, 24 (1994); **18.** Hum Gene Ther 10, 861 (1999); **19.** Biophys J 78, 1293 (2000); **20.** Am J Physiol Cell Physiol 279, C1088 (2000); **21.** Biochemistry 37, 15222 (1998); **22.** J Biol Chem 272, 27830 (1997); **23.** J Biol Chem 270, 17033 (1995); **24.** Biochemistry 36, 1287 (1997); **25.** Pflugers Arch 437, 289 (1999); **26.** Biochemistry 33, 755 (1994); **27.** J Membr Biol 159, 197 (1997); **28.** Anal Biochem 230, 1 (1995); **29.** J Biol Chem 274, 26003 (1999); **30.** FEBS Lett 408, 166 (1997); **31.** J Biol Chem 269, 7435 (1994); **32.** Am J Physiol 267, H2114 (1994); **33.** Am J Physiol 275, C1330 (1998); **34.** Biochemistry 40, 5243 (2001); **35.** J Biol Chem 273, 24368 (1998); **36.** Biochemistry 30, 7879 (1991); **37.** Methods Enzymol 307, 469 (1999); **38.** Methods 18, 197 (1999); **39.** J Neurochem 71, 1396 (1998); **40.** J Neurochem 70, 2500 (1998); **41.** J Neurosci Methods 75, 127 (1997); **42.** Anal Biochem 219, 139 (1994); **43.** J Membr Biol 177, 199 (2000); **44.** Fresenius Z Anal Chem 314, 577 (1983); **45.** Chem Phys Lipids 60, 127 (1991); **46.** Anal Biochem 114, 199 (1981); **47.** Analyst 114, 1275 (1989); **48.** Anal Lett 21, 1887 (1988); **49.** J Biol Chem 259, 4812 (1984); **50.** Chem Res Toxicol 10, 1080 (1997); **51.** US 4,491,634; **52.** Chem Pharm Bull 32, 3702 (1984); **53.** J Biol Chem 278, 3170 (2003); **54.** Proc Natl Acad Sci U S A 72, 619 (1975); **55.** Anal Chem 59, 1096 (1987); **56.** J Chromatogr A 668, 323 (1994); **57.** J Chromatogr 582, 131 (1992); **58.** Anal Chim Acta 225, 351 (1989); **59.** Biomed Chromatogr 3, 209 (1989); **60.** Anal Sci 2, 491 (1986); **61.** Anal Chem 66, 3512 (1994); **62.** Anal Chem 66, 3477 (1994); **63.** Electrophoresis 14, 373 (1993); **64.** Anal Chem 64, 973 (1992); **65.** Anal Chem 63, 413 (1991); **66.** Anal Chem 63, 408 (1991); **67.** J Chromatogr 559, 223 (1991); **68.** Proc Natl Acad Sci U S A 88, 2302 (1991); **69.** J Chromatogr 499, 579 (1990); **70.** Bioconjug Chem 5, 348 (1994); **71.** Anal Biochem 213, 49 (1993); **72.** Chem Pharm Bull (Tokyo) 40, 3000 (1992); **73.** Anal Chem 73, 3187 (2001); **74.** J Chromatogr 564, 258 (1991); **75.** Anal Chem 61, 408 (1989); **76.** Luminescence 14, 283 (1999); **77.** FASEB J 7, 349 (1993); **78.** Anal Biochem 126, 131 (1982); **79.** Anal Biochem 282, 1 (2000); **80.** Anal Biochem 224, 502 (1995); **81.** Chem Biol 3, 655 (1996); **82.** Anal Biochem 238, 150 (1996); **83.** Angew Chem Int Ed Engl 38, 3209 (1999); **84.** Anal Chem 70, 2446 (1998); **85.** J Biol Chem 277, 48472 (2002); **86.** Anal Biochem 214, 11 (1993); **87.** Anal Lett 4, 761 (1971); **88.** Anal Chem 71, 3003 (1999); **89.** Anal Chem 71, 1893 (1999); **90.** Spectrochim Acta A 59, 1667 (2003); **91.** J Bioenerg Biomembr 29, 611 (1997); **92.** Anal Biochem 253, 162 (1997); **93.** J Immunol Methods 202, 133 (1997); **94.** Anal Biochem 218, 449 (1994); **95.** Proc Natl Acad Sci U S A 89, 4884 (1992); **96.** Anal Biochem 230, 173 (1995); **97.** Anal Biochem 243, 41 (1996); **98.** J Biol Chem 275, 17962 (2000); **99.** Biochemistry 39, 2297 (2000); **100.** J Biol Chem 273, 16555 (1998); **101.** J Biol Chem 273, 22151 (1998); **102.** Nucleic Acids Res 23, 2886 (1995); **103.** Biochemistry 40, 5041 (2001); **104.** Biochemistry 35, 11013 (1996); **105.** Anal Chem 73, 4711 (2001); **106.** Analyst 108, 505 (1983); **107.** Talanta 29, 1117 (1982); **108.** Analyst 104, 778 (1979); **109.** Anal Chim Acta 89, 29 (1977); **110.** Analyst 87, 558 (1962); **111.** Anal Biochem 241, 206 (1996); **112.** J Chromatogr 537, 397 (1991).

Data Table — 21.2 Detecting Chloride, Phosphate, Nitrite and Other Anions

Cat #	MW	Storage	Soluble	Abs	EC	Em	Solvent	K_{SV}	Notes
A1139	234.25	L	EtOH	546	ND	570	MeOH		1, 2
A6222	305.29	F,D,L	MeOH	465	ND	560	MeOH		2, 3, 4
A6871	410.38	F,D,L	DMSO, MeCN	386	8,200	448	MeCN		
A10192	251.24	F,L	EtOH	486	ND	591	MeOH		2, 5
D7918	158.20	L	DMSO, MeOH	340	5,100	377	MeOH		6
D8451	396.35	D	pH >6	324	18,000	none	pH 8		7
D23841	412.35	F,D,L	DMSO	487	84,000	see Notes	pH 8		8
E3101	326.19	F,D,L	H_2O	350	2,800	460	H_2O	200 M^{-1}	9, 10, 11, 12
E6645	313.33	FF,D	H_2O	332	16,000	none	pH 7		13, 14
E6646	313.33	F,D	H_2O	332	16,000	none	pH 7		13, 14
L6868	510.50	L	H_2O	455	7,400	505	H_2O	390 M^{-1}	9, 10, 12, 15, 16
M440	281.33	L	H_2O	344	3,700	443	H_2O	118 M^{-1}	9, 10, 11, 12
M1378	271.11	F,L	DMF, MeCN	398	5,000	see Notes	pH 7		17
M6886	315.15	L	H_2O	344	3,900	442	H_2O	145 M^{-1}	9, 10, 11, 12, 18
M20381	271.11	F,L	DMF, MeCN	398	5,000	see Notes	pH 7		17, 19
M20490	209.16	F,L	MeCN	487	24,000	none	MeOH		20
N1138	184.19	L	DMF, MeCN	419	9,400	493	see Notes		21
N1495	724.97	F,D	MeOH	<300		none			
P2331MP	134.13	L	EtOH	334	5,700	455	pH 9		22
S460	301.36	L	H_2O	417	4,200	489	H_2O	5 M^{-1}	9, 10, 12

For definitions of the contents of this data table, see "Navigating *The Handbook*" in the introductory pages.

Notes

1. Spectra of A1139 with butylamine + cyanide. Absorption spectrum has multiple peaks. Unreacted reagent Abs = 361 nm (EC = 5400 $cm^{-1}M^{-1}$), Em = 410 nm in MeOH.
2. ND = not determined.
3. Spectral data are for the reaction product with glycine in the presence of cyanide. Unreacted reagent in MeOH: Abs = 254 nm (EC = 46,000 $cm^{-1}M^{-1}$), nonfluorescent.
4. Solubility in methanol is improved by addition of base (e.g., 1–5% (v/v) 0.2 M KOH).
5. Spectral data are for the reaction product with glycine in the presence of cyanide. Unreacted reagent in MeOH: Abs = 282 nm (EC = 21,000 $cm^{-1}M^{-1}$), nonfluorescent.
6. Fluorescence of D7918 is weak. Reaction with nitrite yields highly fluorescent 1*H*-naphthotriazole (Abs = 365 nm, Em = 415 nm in H_2O (pH 12)) (Methods Enzymol 268, 105 (1996)).
7. D8451 reaction product with thiols has Abs = 410 nm (EC = 14,000 $cm^{-1}M^{-1}$) (Methods Enzymol 233, 380 (1994)).
8. DAF-FM fluorescence is very weak. Reaction with nitrite or nitric oxide generates a highly fluorescent benzotriazole derivative with Abs = 495 nm (EC = 73,000 $cm^{-1}M^{-1}$), Em = 515 nm in pH 7.4 buffer (Angew Chem Int Ed Engl 38, 3209 (1999)).
9. Values of K_{SV} are taken from published references (Anal Biochem 219, 139 (1994); Am J Physiol 262, C242 (1992); Biochemistry 30, 7879 (1991); Anal Biochem 178, 355 (1989)).
10. K_{SV} is the Stern-Volmer quenching constant for Cl^- ions (units are M^{-1}), representing the reciprocal of the ion concentration that produces 50% fluorescence quenching. The quenching constant is very dependent on viscosity and is usually significantly lower in cells. These indicators are quenched more effectively by bromide, iodide and certain other anions.
11. This quinolinium dye also has a slightly stronger (~50%) absorption peak 25–30 nm shorter than the listed Abs wavelength.
12. This product undergoes Cl^--dependent fluorescence quenching with essentially no change in absorption or emission wavelengths.
13. Data represent the substrate component of this kit.
14. Enzymatic phosphorylation of this substrate yields 2-amino-6-mercapto-7-methylpurine (Abs = 355 nm) (Proc Natl Acad Sci U S A 89, 4884 (1992)).
15. L6868 has much stronger absorption at shorter wavelengths (Abs = 368 nm (EC = 36,000 $cm^{-1}M^{-1}$)).
16. This compound emits chemiluminescence upon oxidation in basic aqueous solutions. Emission peaks are at 425 nm (L8455) and 470 nm (L6868).
17. Bimanes are almost nonfluorescent until reacted with thiols. For monobromobimane conjugated to glutathione, Abs = 394 nm, Em = 490 nm (QY ~0.1–0.3) in pH 8 buffer (Methods Enzymol 143, 76 (1987); Methods Enzymol 251, 133 (1995)).
18. M6886 may be chemically reduced to cell-permeant diH-MEQ (Biochemistry 30, 7879 (1991)).
19. This product is specified to equal or exceed 98% analytical purity by HPLC.
20. NBD methylhydrazine reacts with nitrite in the presence of strong acid to form fluorescent *N*-methyl-4-amino-7-nitrobenzofurazan (Abs = 459 nm, Em = 537 nm in MeCN) (Anal Chem 71, 3003 (1999)).
21. Spectral data are for the reaction product with glycine in the presence of cyanide, measured in pH 7.0 buffer/MeCN (40:60) (Anal Chem 59, 1102 (1987)). Unreacted reagent in MeOH: Abs = 279 nm (EC = 5500 $cm^{-1}M^{-1}$), Em = 330 nm.
22. Spectral data are for the reaction product of P2331MP with alanine and 2-mercaptoethanol. The spectra and stability of the adduct depend on the amine and thiol reactants (Biochim Biophys Acta 576, 440 (1979)). Unreacted reagent in H_2O: Abs = 257 nm (EC = 1000 $cm^{-1}M^{-1}$).

Product List — 21.2 Detecting Chloride, Phosphate, Nitrite and Other Anions

Cat #	Product Name	Unit Size
A1139	anthracene-2,3-dicarboxaldehyde (ADA)	25 mg
A6871	anthracene-1,5-dicarboxylic acid, di(acetoxymethyl ester) (ADC, AM)	5 mg
A6222	ATTO-TAG™ CBQCA derivatization reagent (CBQCA; 3-(4-carboxybenzoyl)quinoline-2-carboxaldehyde)	10 mg
A10192	ATTO-TAG™ FQ derivatization reagent (FQ; 3-(2-furoyl)quinoline-2-carboxaldehyde)	10 mg
D23841	DAF-FM (4-amino-5-methylamino-2′,7′-difluorofluorescein)	1 mg
D7918	2,3-diaminonaphthalene	100 mg
D8451	5,5′-dithiobis-(2-nitrobenzoic acid) (DTNB; Ellman's reagent)	10 g
E6646	EnzChek® Phosphate Assay Kit *100 assays*	1 kit
E6645	EnzChek® Pyrophosphate Assay Kit *100 assays*	1 kit
E3101	*N*-(ethoxycarbonylmethyl)-6-methoxyquinolinium bromide (MQAE)	100 mg
G7921	Griess Reagent Kit *for nitrite quantitation*	1 kit
L6868	lucigenin (bis-*N*-methylacridinium nitrate) *high purity*	10 mg
M6886	6-methoxy-*N*-ethylquinolinium iodide (MEQ)	100 mg
M440	6-methoxy-*N*-(3-sulfopropyl)quinolinium, inner salt (SPQ)	100 mg
M20490	*N*-methyl-4-hydrazino-7-nitrobenzofurazan (NBD methylhydrazine)	25 mg
M1378	monobromobimane (mBBr)	25 mg
M20381	monobromobimane (mBBr) *FluoroPure™ grade*	25 mg
N1138	naphthalene-2,3-dicarboxaldehyde (NDA)	100 mg
N1495	nigericin, free acid	10 mg
P2331MP	*o*-phthaldialdehyde (OPA) *high purity*	1 g
P22061	P_iPer™ Phosphate Assay Kit *1000 assays*	1 kit
P22062	P_iPer™ Pyrophosphate Assay Kit *1000 assays*	1 kit
S460	*N*-(3-sulfopropyl)acridinium, inner salt (SPA)	100 mg
T6060	Thiol and Sulfide Quantitation Kit *50-250 assays*	1 kit

For current prices or to order online, visit probes.invitrogen.com

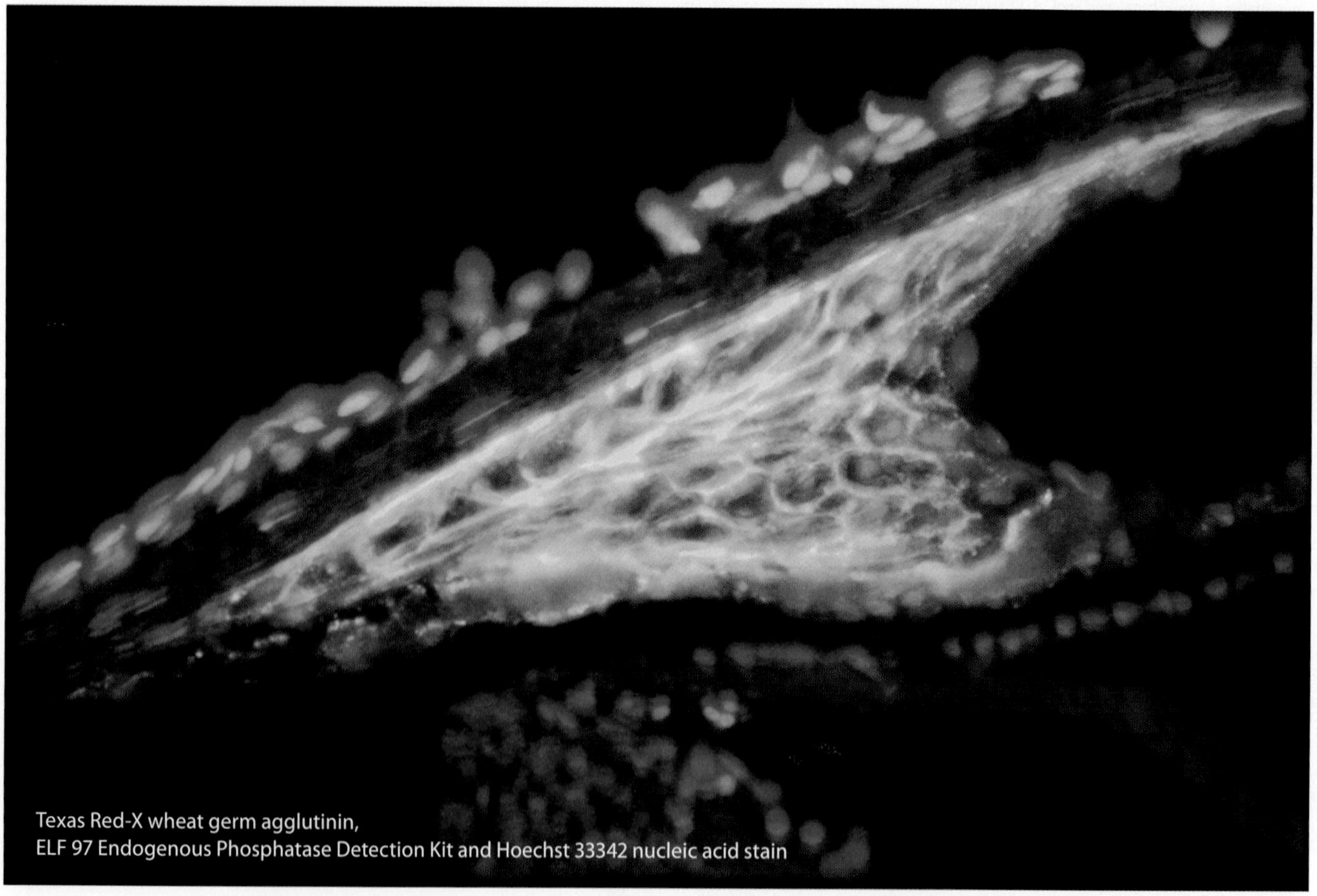

Texas Red-X wheat germ agglutinin,
ELF 97 Endogenous Phosphatase Detection Kit and Hoechst 33342 nucleic acid stain

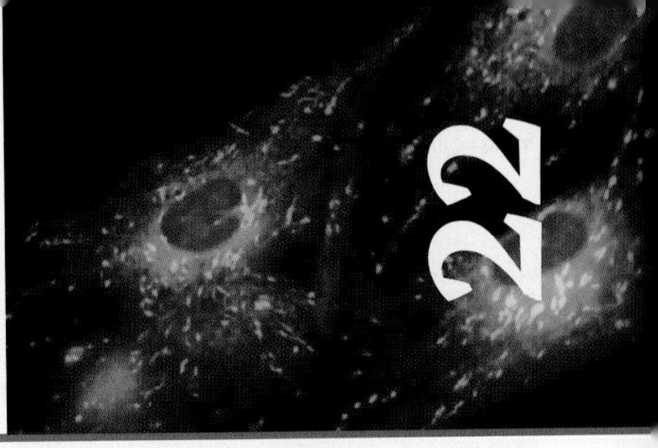

Chapter 22

Probes for Membrane Potential

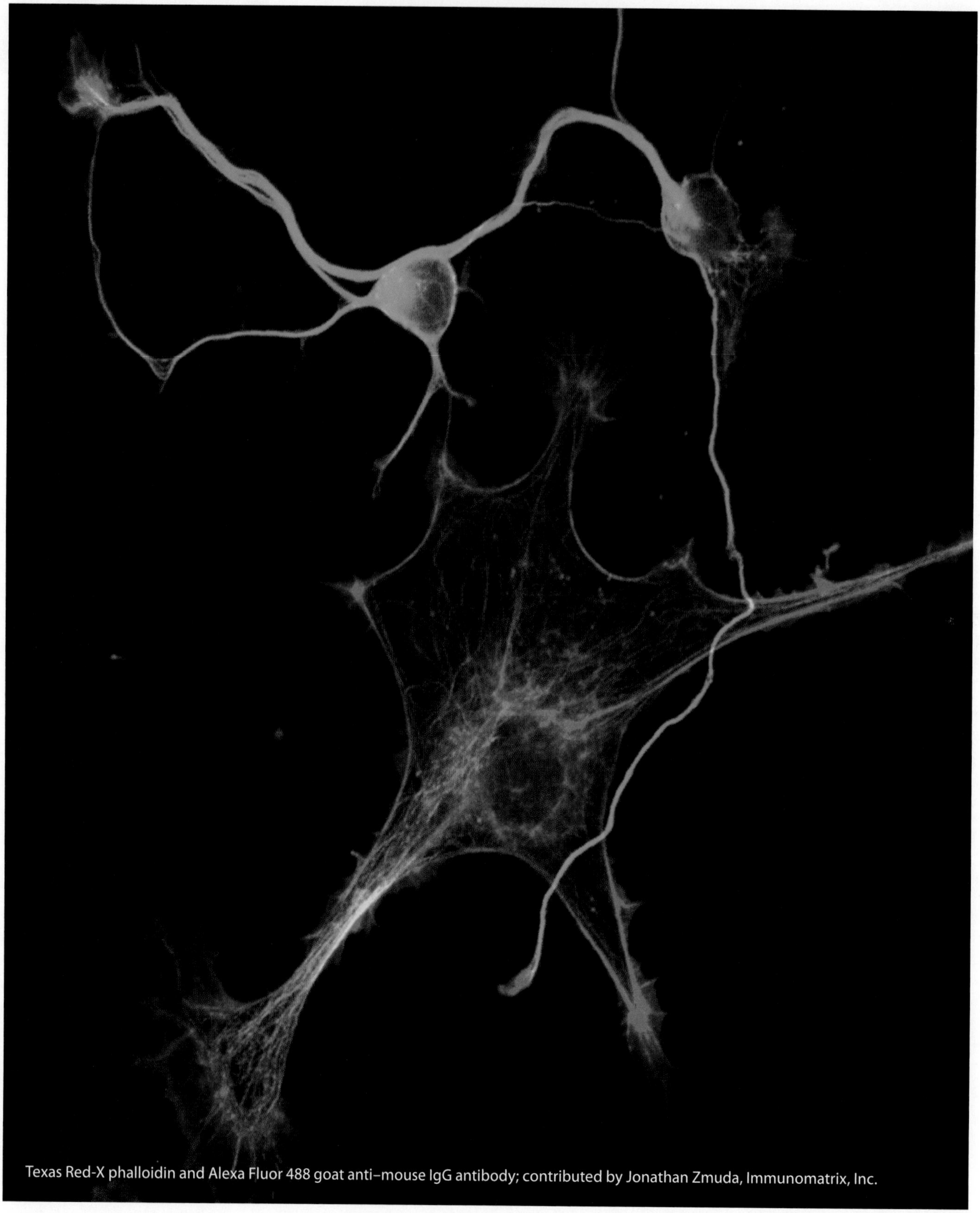

Texas Red-X phalloidin and Alexa Fluor 488 goat anti–mouse IgG antibody; contributed by Jonathan Zmuda, Immunomatrix, Inc.

22.1 Introduction to Potentiometric Probes

Potentiometric optical probes enable researchers to perform membrane potential measurements in organelles and in cells that are too small for microelectrodes. Moreover, in conjunction with imaging techniques, these probes can be employed to map variations in membrane potential across excitable cells and perfused organs,[1] with spatial resolution and sampling frequency that are difficult to achieve using microelectrodes.

Applications for Potentiometric Probes

The plasma membrane of a cell typically has a transmembrane potential of approximately –70 mV (negative inside) as a consequence of K^+, Na^+ and Cl^- concentration gradients that are maintained by active transport processes. Potentiometric probes offer an indirect method of detecting the translocation of these ions, whereas the fluorescent ion indicators discussed in Chapter 21 can be used to directly measure changes in specific ion concentrations. Increases and decreases in membrane potential — referred to as membrane hyperpolarization and depolarization, respectively — play a central role in many physiological processes, including nerve-impulse propagation, muscle contraction, cell signaling and ion-channel gating. Potentiometric probes are important tools for studying these processes, as well as for visualizing mitochondria (which exhibit transmembrane potentials of approximately –150 mV, negative inside matrix) (Section 12.2), for assessing cell viability (Section 15.2) and for high-throughput screening of new drug candidates. Potentiometric probes include the cationic or zwitterionic styryl dyes, the cationic carbocyanines and rhodamines, the anionic oxonols and hybrid oxonols and merocyanine 540. The class of dye determines factors such as accumulation in cells, response mechanism and toxicity. Surveys of techniques and applications using membrane potential probes can be found in several reviews.[2–9]

Selecting a Potentiometric Probe

Selecting the best potentiometric probe for a particular application can be complicated by the substantial variations in their optical responses, phototoxicity and interactions with other molecules. Probes can be divided into two categories based on their response mechanism:

- Fast-response probes (usually styrylpyridinium dyes; Section 22.2) operate by means of a change in their electronic structure, and consequently their fluorescence properties, in response to a change in the surrounding electric field (Figure 22.1). Their optical response is sufficiently fast to detect transient (millisecond) potential changes in excitable cells, including single neurons, cardiac cells and intact brains. However, the magnitude of their potential-dependent fluorescence change is often small; fast-response probes typically show a 2–10% fluorescence change per 100 mV.
- Slow-response probes (Section 22.3) exhibit potential-dependent changes in their transmembrane distribution that are accompanied by a fluorescence change (Figure 22.1). The magnitude of their optical responses is much larger than that of fast-response probes (typically a 1% fluorescence change per mV). Slow-response probes, which include cationic carbocyanines and rhodamines and anionic oxonols, are suitable for detecting changes in average membrane potentials of nonexcitable cells caused by respiratory activity, ion-channel permeability, drug binding and other factors.

Calibration of potentiometric probes can be accomplished by imposing a transmembrane potential using valinomycin (V1644, Section 21.1) in conjunction with externally applied K^+ solutions.[10,11] The descriptions in this chapter focus on the response characteristics of the various types of potential-sensitive dyes offered by Molecular Probes.

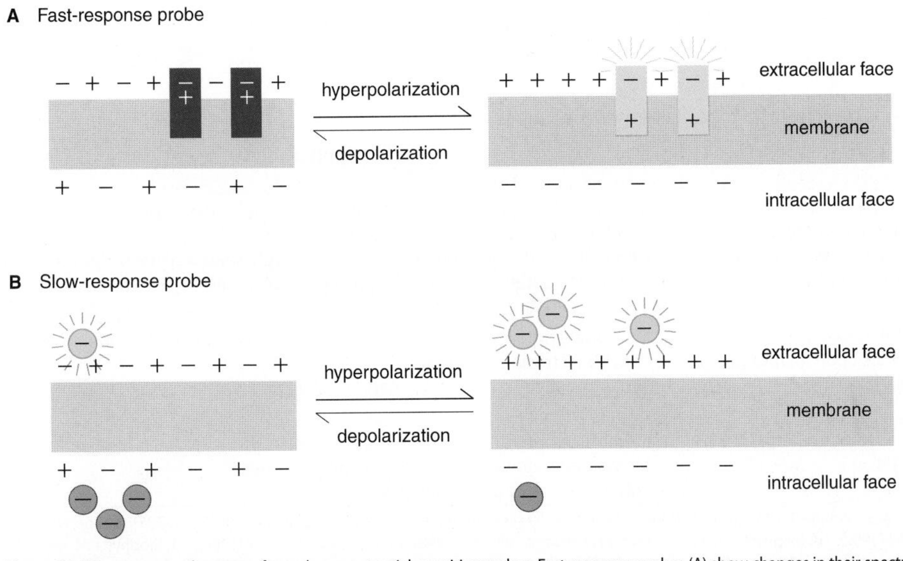

Figure 22.1 Response mechanisms of membrane potential–sensitive probes. Fast-response probes (A) show changes in their spectral profile when subjected to electric field–driven changes of intramolecular charge distribution. Slow-response probes (B) are lipophilic anions (in this illustration) or cations translocated across membranes by an electrophoretic mechanism. Fluorescence changes associated with transmembrane redistribution (of electrons or of whole molecules) result from sensitivity of the probe to intracellular and extracellular environments. Thus, potentiometric response speeds directly reflect the time constants of the underlying processes.

References

1. Nature 392, 78 (1998); **2.** Biol Bull 198, 1 (2000); **3.** J Photochem Photobiol B 33, 101 (1996); **4.** Adv Chem Ser 235, 151 (1994); **5.** Methods 21, 271 (2000); **6.** Cell Biology: A Laboratory Handbook, 2nd Ed., Vol. 3, Celis JE, Ed. pp. 375–379 (1998); **7.** Biochim Biophys Acta 1016, 1 (1990); **8.** Pure Appl Chem 68, 1405 (1996); **9.** Trends Neurosci 23, 166 (2000); **10.** Biochemistry 28, 4536 (1989); **11.** Annu Rev Biophys Bioeng 8, 47 (1979).

22.2 Fast-Response Probes

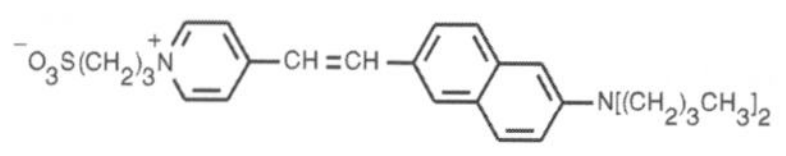

Figure 22.2 D1199 di-4-ANEPPS.

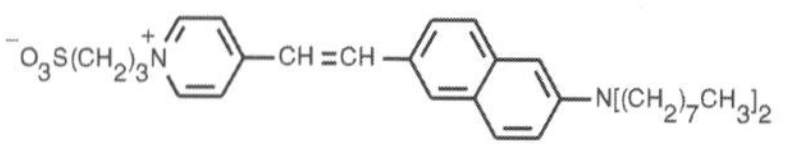

Figure 22.3 D3167 di-8-ANEPPS.

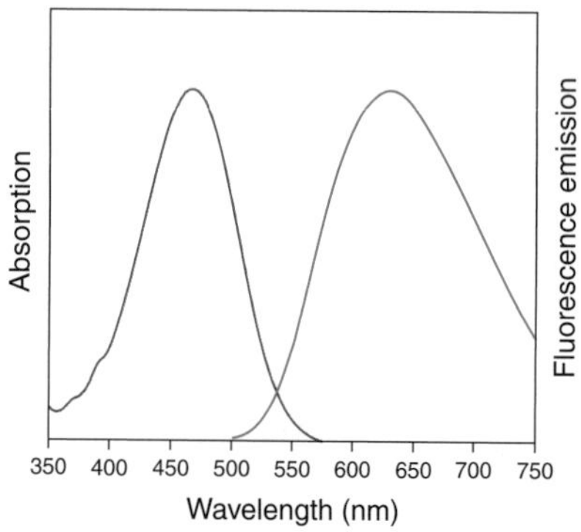

Figure 22.4 Absorption and fluorescence emission spectra of di-8-ANEPPS bound to phospholipid bilayer membranes.

Our fast-response potential-sensitive probes (Figure 22.1) are listed in Table 22.1, along with their charge, optical response and selected applications.

Styryl Dyes

Di-4-ANEPPS and Di-8-ANEPPS

The ANEP (AminoNaphthylEthenylPyridinium) dyes (Figure 22.2, Figure 22.3) developed by Leslie Loew and colleagues [1] are among the most sensitive of the fast-response probes. Di-4-ANEPPS (D1199) and di-8-ANEPPS (D3167, Figure 22.4) exhibit fairly uniform 10% per 100 mV changes in fluorescence intensity in a variety of tissue, cell and model membrane systems.[2,3] The millisecond-range temporal characteristics of the ANEP dyes compensate for this modest response amplitude (Figure 22.5). Di-4-ANEPPS is internalized in the cell rather rapidly, precluding its use in all but very short-term experiments, whereas di-8-ANEPPS (D3167) is better retained in the outer leaflet of the plasma membrane. In addition, although both ANEP dyes exhibit good photostability and low toxicity, di-8-ANEPPS is reported to be slightly more photostable and significantly less phototoxic than di-4-ANEPPS.[4–6]

Like other styryl dyes, the ANEP dyes are essentially nonfluorescent in aqueous solutions and exhibit spectral properties that are strongly dependent on their environment.[7] When bound to phospholipid vesicles, di-8-ANEPPS has absorption/emission maxima of ~467/631 nm (Figure 22.4), as compared with ~498/713 nm in methanol. The fluorescence excitation/emission maxima of di-4-ANEPPS bound to neuronal membranes are ~475/617 nm.[8] Both di-4-ANEPPS and di-8-ANEPPS respond to increases in membrane potential (hyperpolarization) with a decrease in fluorescence excited at approximately 440 nm and an increase in fluorescence excited at 530 nm.[7,9] These spectral shifts permit the use of ratiometric methods (see Note 19.1 "Technical Focus: Loading and Calibration of Intracellular Ion Indicators" in Section 19.1) to correlate the change in fluorescence signal with membrane potential.[2] Using di-8-ANEPPS, Loew and colleagues were able to follow changes in membrane potential along the surface of a single mouse neuroblastoma cell in their study of the mechanisms underlying cathode-directed neurite elongation [10] and to define differences between transmembrane potentials of neurites and somata.[11] Potential-dependent fluorescence emission ratio measurements (ratio of emission intensities at 560 nm and 620 nm following excitation at 475 nm) have also been reported using both di-4-ANEPPS and di-8-ANEPPS [12–15] (Figure 22.5). Some other applications are listed in Table 22.1.

Table 22.1 — Characteristics and selected applications of Molecular Probes' fast-response probes

Dyes (Cat #)	Structure (Charge)	Optical Response	Selected Applications
Di-4-ANEPPS (D1199) Di-8-ANEPPS (D3167) Di-2-ANEPEQ (D6923) Di-8-ANEPPQ (D6925) Di-12-ANEPPQ (D6927)	Styryl (cationic or zwitterionic)	FAST; fluorescence excitation ratio 440/505 nm decreases upon membrane hyperpolarization	• Mapping of membrane potentials along neurons [1–6] and muscle fibers [7–10] • Combined potentiometric and Ca^{2+} measurements [7,11,12] • Combined optical potentiometric and electrophysiological measurements [13] • Membrane potential changes in response to pharmacological stimuli [14,15] • Imaging electrical activity from intact heart tissues [16–18]
RH 237 (S1109) RH 414 (T1111) RH 421 (S1108) RH 795 (R649)	Styryl (cationic or zwitterionic)	FAST; fluorescence decreases upon membrane depolarization	• Membrane potentials evoked by visual [19,20] and olfactory [21–23] stimuli • Functional tracing of neurons [24–27] • Synaptic activity [28–31] and ion channel activity [32,33]
RH 155 (R1114)	Hybrid oxonol (anionic)	FAST; absorbance (at ~720 nm) changes	• Membrane potentials in invertebrate neurons [34,35] • Membrane potentials in muscle and nerve tissues [36–38] • Voltage-sensitive Ca^{2+} channel activity [39,40]

1. J Neurosci 18, 9977 (1998); **2.** J Neurosci 15, 1392 (1995); **3.** Neuroimage 5, 154 (1997); **4.** Neuron 13, 1187 (1994); **5.** Neuron 9, 393 (1992); **6.** Brain Res 700, 235 (1995); **7.** Biophys J 78, 1777 (2000); **8.** Biophys J 66, 719 (1994); **9.** Nature 355, 349 (1992); **10.** Biophys J 67, 1301 (1994); **11.** J Physiol 508, 145 (1998); **12.** Biophys J 71, 1057 (1996); **13.** Biophys J 74, 48 (1998); **14.** Am J Physiol 274, H60 (1998); **15.** Pharmacol Res 34, 125 (1996); **16.** Am J Physiol Heart Circ Physiol 280, H2053 (2001); **17.** Biophys J 80, 516 (2001); **18.** Am J Physiol Heart Circ Physiol 279, H1421 (2000); **19.** J Neurosci 14, 2545 (1994); **20.** Proc Natl Acad Sci U S A 94, 7621 (1997); **21.** J Neurosci 20, 749 (2000); **22.** Annu Rev Neurosci 15, 321 (1992); **23.** J Neurosci 12, 976 (1992); **24.** J Neurosci Methods 54, 151 (1994); **25.** Proc Natl Acad Sci U S A 91, 4604 (1994); **26.** Exp Brain Res 94, 371 (1993); **27.** J Neurosci 12, 3054 (1992); **28.** J Physiol 519 Pt 2, 427 (1999); **29.** J Neurosci 14, 3319 (1994); **30.** Nature 364, 635 (1993); **31.** J Exp Biol 200, 161 (1997); **32.** J Biol Chem 269, 21620 (1994); **33.** Nature 367, 739 (1994); **34.** J Neurosci 14, 1366 (1994); **35.** Biophys J 56, 213 (1989); **36.** Circulation 85, 1865 (1992); **37.** Circ Res 69, 842 (1991); **38.** J Neurosci 16, 313 (1996); **39.** Proc Natl Acad Sci U S A 85, 4075 (1988); **40.** J Neurosci 7, 3877 (1987).

Other ANEP Dyes

In collaboration with Leslie Loew and Joe Wuskell of the University of Connecticut, Molecular Probes offers a series of four potential-sensitive ANEP dyes.[16–18] The water-soluble di-2-ANEPEQ[19] (JPW 1114, D6923; Figure 22.6) can be either microinjected into cells, a mode of delivery that intensifies the staining of remote neuronal processes, or applied topically to deeply stain brain tissue.[20] Microinjection of di-2-ANEPEQ into neurons in ganglia of the snail *Helix aspersa* produced an approximately 50-fold improvement in voltage-sensitive signals from distal processes over that obtained with conventional absorption- and fluorescence-based staining methods.[21] Di-8-ANEPPQ (D6925) and di-12-ANEPPQ (D6927) are useful for potential-sensitive retrograde labeling of neurons[17,22] using techniques similar to those employed for lipophilic carbocyanine and aminostyryl tracers (Section 14.4). Di-1-ANEPIA (D36800) has been coupled to the cysteines in a voltage-gated potassium channel and then used to monitor localized electric field changes during the gating process with submillisecond resolution.[16]

RH Dyes

Originally synthesized by Rina Hildesheim, the RH dyes include an extensive series of dialkylaminophenylpolyenylpyridinium dyes that are principally used for functional imaging of neurons (Table 22.1). The existence of numerous RH dye analogs reflects the observation that no single dye provides the optimal response under all experimental conditions.[5,23,24] Currently, the most widely used RH dyes are RH 414 (T1111, Figure 22.7), RH 795 (R649, Figure 22.8) and RH 237 (S1109). The RH 421 probe (S1108) has yielded the most sensitive response recorded for a fast potentiometric probe, exhibiting a >20% fluorescence change per 100 mV on neuroblastoma cells.[25] Physiological effects of staining with different analogs are not equivalent. For example, staining of the cortex with RH 414 causes arterial constriction, whereas staining with RH 795 does not.[26] RH 795 produced negligible side effects when tested *in vitro* using hippocampal slices and *in vivo* using single-unit recordings in cat and monkey visual cortices.[27] Electrophysiological measurements indicate a broadening of action potentials that is attributable to the staining of cultured neurons with RH 237.[28]

Like the ANEP dyes, the RH dyes exhibit varying degrees of fluorescence excitation and emission spectral shifts in response to membrane potential changes.[8] Their absorption and fluorescence spectra are also strongly dependent on the environment.[29] Spectra of RH 414 bound to phospholipid vesicles are similar to those obtained on neuronal plasma membranes.[8] The RH dyes belong to the same structural class as our FM® dyes (Section 16.1), and can likewise be used to detect activity-dependent synaptosomal recycling at live nerve terminals.[30,31]

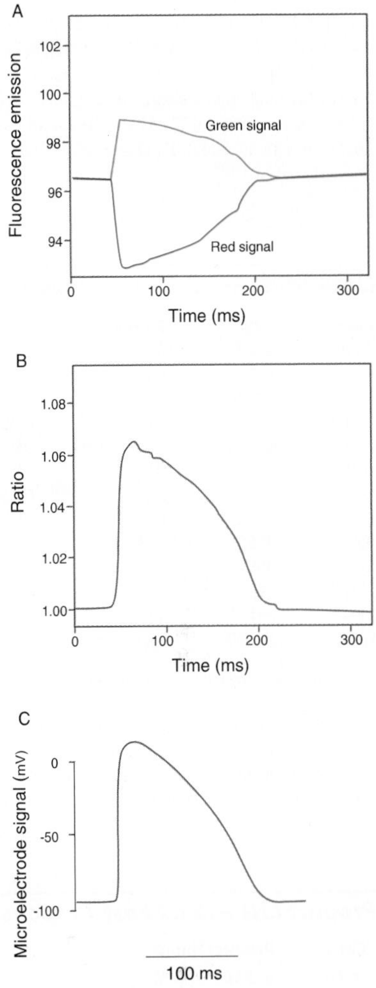

Figure 22.5 Detection of action potentials in intact rabbit hearts using the fast potentiometric probe di-4-ANEPPS (D1199). Excised rabbit hearts were loaded with di-4-ANEPPS by perfusion with dye-containing medium. Fluorescence was excited at 488 nm by an argon-ion laser. Emission components at 540 ± 6 nm (green) and >610 nm (red) were detected simultaneously by two photomultipliers (panel A). The ratio of the green to red signals (panel B) displayed a larger fractional change during action potential cycles than either of the component signals; it also followed transmembrane voltage contours recorded simultaneously by an intracellular microelectrode (panel C). In addition, fluorescence ratio measurements reduce the motion artifacts that typically distort optical signals detected from contracting hearts. Figure reproduced with permission from Am J Physiol Heart Circ Physiol 279, H1421 (2000).

Impermeant Oxonol: RH 155

RH 155 (R1114, Figure 22.9) is an oxonol dye with phenylsulfonate substituents that tend to make it impermeant to cell membranes. Consequently, its potentiometric response is faster but of smaller magnitude than those of other oxonol dyes[32] (Section 22.3). Because it is anionic, adsorption of this dye to the membrane increases upon depolarization. RH 155 is nonfluorescent; its potentiometric response is detected using absorption changes at approximately 720 nm.[33,34]

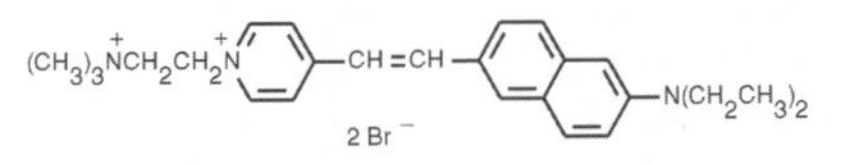

Figure 22.6 D6923 di-2-ANEPEQ (JPW 1114).

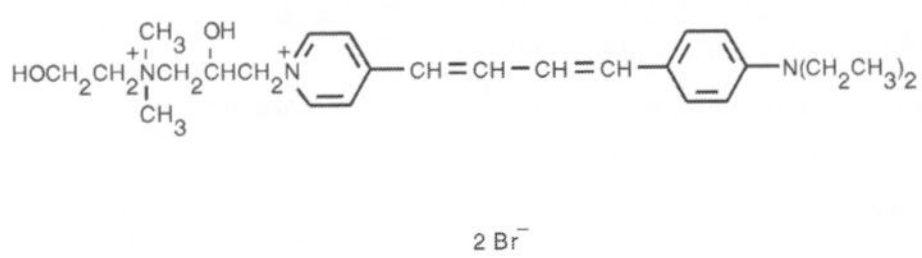

Figure 22.8 R649 RH 795.

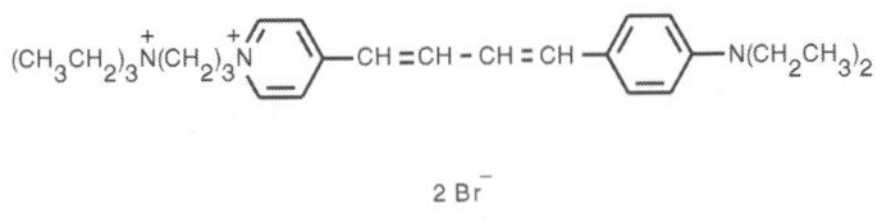

Figure 22.7 T1111 *N*-(3-triethylammoniumpropyl)-4-(4-(4-(diethylamino)phenyl)butadienyl)pyridinium dibromide (RH 414).

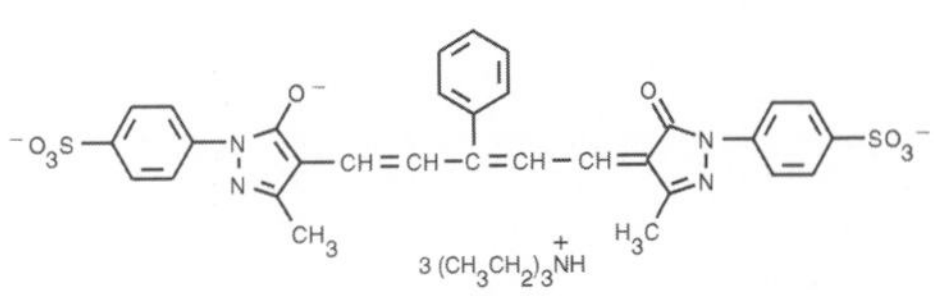

Figure 22.9 R1114 RH 155.

Important Licensing Information
These products may be covered by one or more Limited Use Label Licenses (See the Invitrogen Web site, www.invitrogen.com, or the Molecular Probes Web site, probes.invitrogen.com). By the use of these products you accept the terms and conditions of all applicable Limited Use Label Licenses. All products are for research use only. CAUTION: Not intended for human or animal diagnostic or therapeutic uses.

References

1. Biochemistry 24, 5749 (1985); **2.** Biophys J 74, 48 (1998); **3.** J Membr Biol 130, 1 (1992); **4.** Biophys J 76, 2272 (1999); **5.** Biophys J 67, 1301 (1994); **6.** Pflugers Arch 426, 548 (1994); **7.** Biochemistry 28, 4536 (1989); **8.** Biochim Biophys Acta 1150, 111 (1993); **9.** Biophys J 67, 208 (1994); **10.** Neuron 9, 393 (1992); **11.** Neuron 13, 1187 (1994); **12.** Am J Physiol Heart Circ Physiol 279, H1421 (2000); **13.** Biophys J 81, 1163 (2001); **14.** Am J Physiol 270, H2216 (1996); **15.** Am J Physiol 274, H60 (1998); **16.** Neuron 37, 85 (2003); **17.** J Neurosci Methods 70, 121 (1996); **18.** Pure Appl Chem 68, 1405 (1996); **19.** Biol Bull 198, 1 (2000); **20.** Proc Natl Acad Sci U S A 94, 7621 (1997); **21.** J Neurosci 15, 1392 (1995); **22.** J Neurosci Methods 70, 111 (1996); **23.** Physiol Rev 68, 1285 (1988); **24.** Annu Rev Neurosci 8, 263 (1985); **25.** Biophys J 42, 195 (1983); **26.** Nature 324, 361 (1986); **27.** J Neurosci 14, 2545 (1994); **28.** Biophys J 69, 299 (1995); **29.** Biophys J 68, 1406 (1995); **30.** J Exp Biol 200, 161 (1997); **31.** Science 255, 200 (1992); **32.** Chem Phys Lett 129, 225 (1986); **33.** Annu Rev Physiol 51, 507 (1989); **34.** J Neurosci 7, 649 (1987).

Data Table — 22.2 Fast-Response Probes

Cat #	MW	Storage	Soluble	Abs	EC	Em	Solvent	Notes
D1199	480.66	D,L	DMSO, EtOH	497	42,000	705	MeOH	1
D3167	592.88	D,L	DMSO, EtOH	498	37,000	713	MeOH	1
D6923	549.39	D,L	DMSO, EtOH	517	36,000	721	EtOH	
D6925	731.74	D,L	DMSO, EtOH	516	36,000	721	EtOH	1
D6927	843.95	D,L	DMSO, EtOH	519	36,000	719	EtOH	1
D6928	865.35	D,L	DMSO, EtOH	501	36,000	705	EtOH	1
R649	585.42	D,L	DMSO, EtOH	530	33,000	712	MeOH	1
R1114	950.26	D,L	DMSO, EtOH	650	120,000	none	MeOH	
R6922	775.08	F,D,L	DMSO, EtOH	629	83,000	659	MeOH	
S1108	498.72	D,L	DMSO, EtOH	515	50,000	704	MeOH	1, 2
S1109	496.71	D,L	DMSO, EtOH	528	53,000	782	MeOH	1, 2
T1111	581.48	D,L	DMSO, EtOH	532	55,000	716	MeOH	1
W435	757.00	D,L	DMSO, EtOH	605	120,000	639	MeOH	3

For definitions of the contents of this data table, see "Navigating *The Handbook*" in the introductory pages.

Notes

1. Abs and Em of styryl dyes are at shorter wavelengths in membrane environments than in reference solvents such as methanol. The difference is typically 20 nm for absorption and 80 nm for emission, but varies considerably from one dye to another. Styryl dyes are generally nonfluorescent in water.
2. Abs/Em for these dyes adsorbed on neuronal plasma membranes are 493/638 nm (S1108) and 506/687 nm (S1109) (Biochim Biophys Acta 1150, 111 (1993)).
3. Fluorescence excitation/emission maxima of W435 are 615/650 nm in cell suspensions (Biophys J 57, 835 (1990)).

Product List — 22.2 Fast-Response Probes

Cat #	Product Name	Unit Size
D6923	di-2-ANEPEQ (JPW 1114)	5 mg
D36800	di-1-ANEPIA	1 mg
D6925	di-8-ANEPPQ	5 mg
D6927	di-12-ANEPPQ	5 mg
D1199	di-4-ANEPPS	5 mg
D3167	di-8-ANEPPS	5 mg
D6928	di-18:2-ANEPPS	5 mg
R6922	RGA-30	5 mg
R1114	RH 155	25 mg
R649	RH 795	1 mg
S1109	*N*-(4-sulfobutyl)-4-(6-(4-(dibutylamino)phenyl)hexatrienyl)pyridinium, inner salt (RH 237)	5 mg
S1108	*N*-(4-sulfobutyl)-4-(4-(4-(dipentylamino)phenyl)butadienyl)pyridinium, inner salt (RH 421)	25 mg
T1111	*N*-(3-triethylammoniumpropyl)-4-(4-(4-(diethylamino)phenyl)butadienyl)pyridinium dibromide (RH 414)	5 mg
W435	WW 781, triethylammonium salt	25 mg

For current prices or to order online, visit probes.invitrogen.com

22.3 Slow-Response Probes

Our slow-response potential-sensitive probes[1] (Figure 22.1) are listed in Table 22.2, along with their charges, optical responses and selected applications.

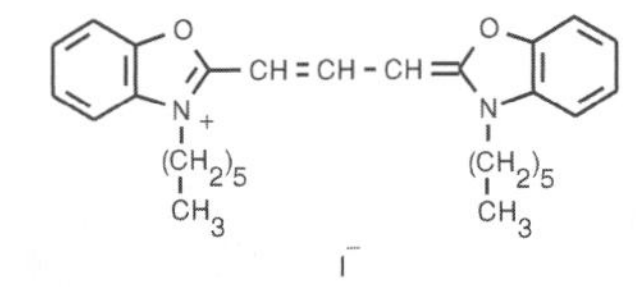

Figure 22.10 D273 3,3′-dihexyloxacarbocyanine iodide ($DiOC_6(3)$).

Carbocyanines

DiI, DiS and DiO Derivatives

Indo- (DiI), thia- (DiS) and oxa- (DiO) carbocyanines with short alkyl tails (<7 carbon atoms) were among the first potentiometric fluorescent probes developed.[2] These cationic dyes accumulate on hyperpolarized membranes and are translocated into the lipid bilayer.[3] Aggregation within the confined membrane interior usually results in decreased fluorescence and absorption shifts,[4] although the magnitude and even the direction of the fluorescence response is strongly dependent on the concentration of the dye and its structural characteristics.[2,5]

$DiOC_6(3)$ (D273, Figure 22.10) has been the most widely used carbocyanine dye for membrane potential measurements,[6] followed closely by $DiOC_5(3)$ (D272), see Table 22.2 for selected refer-

Table 22.2 — Characteristics and selected applications of Molecular Probes' slow-response probes

Dyes (Cat #)	Structure (Charge)	Optical Response	Selected Applications
$DiOC_2(3)$ (D14730) $DiOC_5(3)$ (D272) $DiOC_6(3)$ (D273) $DiSC_3(5)$ (D306) $DiIC_1(5)$ (H14700)	Carbocyanine (cationic)	SLOW; fluorescence response to depolarization depends on the staining concentration and detection method	• Ca^{2+} channels[1,2] and other ion transport systems[3–5] • Mitochondrial activity[6–9] • Neurons and brain tissue[10–12] • Flow cytometry assays of membrane potential[13,14] • Membrane potential in intact yeast cells[15]
JC-1 (T3168) JC-9 (D22421)	Carbocyanine (cationic)	SLOW; fluorescence emission ratio 585/520 nm increases upon membrane hyperpolarization	• Apoptotic mitochondrial depolarization[16–18] • Ca^{2+} regulation by mitochondria[19–21] • Mitochondrial response to glutamate excitotoxicity[22,23] • Mitochondrial function in brain slices[24]
Tetramethylrhodamine methyl and ethyl esters (T668, T669) Rhodamine 123 (R302, R22420)	Rhodamine (cationic)	SLOW; used to obtain unbiased images of potential-dependent dye distribution	• Ratiometric fluorescence measurements of mitochondrial membrane potential[25] • Ca^{2+} regulation by mitochondria[26–28] • Mitochondrial permeability transition[29–31] • Confocal imaging of membrane potential[32–35]
Oxonol V (O266) Oxonol VI (O267)	Oxonol (anionic)	SLOW; fluorescence decreases upon membrane hyperpolarization	• Plant physiology[36–38] • Ion channels and electrogenic pumps[39–43] • Liposomes[44–46]
$DiBAC_4(3)$ (B438, B24570) $DiBAC_4(5)$ (B436) $DiSBAC_2(3)$ (B413)	Oxonol (anionic)	SLOW; fluorescence decreases upon membrane hyperpolarization	• Combined potentiometric and Ca^{2+} measurements[47–54] • Stimulus–secretion coupling[55,56] • Flow cytometry assays of cell viability[57–62] • ATP-sensitive K^+ channel activation[63–66] • Confocal imaging of membrane potential[67]
Merocyanine 540 (M24571)	Merocyanine	FAST/SLOW (biphasic response)	• Membrane potentials in mitochondria[68,69] and skeletal muscle[70] • Structure of membrane surfaces[71–73] • Membrane lipid asymmetry[74,75] • Photodynamic therapy

1. Am J Physiol 266, C67 (1994); **2.** J Biol Chem 272, 26471 (1997); **3.** J Biol Chem 269, 29509 (1994); **4.** J Biol Chem 269, 21962 (1994); **5.** J Biol Chem 268, 206 (1993); **6.** J Biol Chem 270, 3788 (1995); **7.** Biophys J 56, 979 (1989); **8.** Cytometry 33, 333 (1998); **9.** J Biol Chem 273, 33942 (1998); **10.** Brain Res 595, 79 (1992); **11.** Glia 4, 611 (1991); **12.** J Neurosci Methods 13, 199 (1985); **13.** Methods Cell Biol 41, 121 (1994); **14.** J Immunol Methods 107, 129 (1988); **15.** Yeast 14, 1189 (1998); **16.** Methods Cell Biol 63, 467 (2001); **17.** J Cell Biol 138, 449 (1997); **18.** FEBS Lett 411, 77 (1997); **19.** J Biol Chem 275, 38680 (2000); **20.** J Physiol 509, 81 (1998); **21.** Biophys J 75, 2004 (1998); **22.** J Neurosci 16, 5688 (1996); **23.** Neuron 15, 961 (1995); **24.** Methods 18, 104 (1999); **25.** Biophys J 76, 469 (1999); **26.** J Physiol 522 Pt 3, 375 (2000); **27.** J Biol Chem 276, 23329 (2001); **28.** J Neurosci 20, 7290 (2000); **29.** Biochem J 343 Pt 2, 311 (1999); **30.** Am J Physiol 272, C1286 (1997); **31.** Biophys J 74, 2129 (1998); **32.** Methods Enzymol 302, 341 (1999); **33.** Cell Biology: A Laboratory Handbook, 2nd Ed., Vol. 3, Celis JE, Ed. pp. 375–379 (1998); **34.** Methods Cell Biol 38, 195 (1993); **35.** Biophys J 56, 1053 (1989); **36.** J Biol Chem 267, 21850 (1992); **37.** Plant J 2, 97 (1992); **38.** Biophys J 76, 360 (1999); **39.** J Biol Chem 268, 23122 (1993); **40.** Biochemistry 29, 3859 (1990); **41.** Biochim Biophys Acta 1023, 81 (1990); **42.** Biochim Biophys Acta 1017, 221 (1990); **43.** Biochim Biophys Acta 980, 139 (1989); **44.** Biochim Biophys Acta 1146, 87 (1993); **45.** Biochem Biophys Res Commun 173, 1008 (1990); **46.** Biophys Chem 34, 225 (1989); **47.** Methods 21, 335 (2000); **48.** Am J Physiol 266, H1416 (1994); **49.** J Biol Chem 269, 29451 (1994); **50.** J Biol Chem 269, 23597 (1994); **51.** J Cell Biol 120, 1003 (1993); **52.** Am J Physiol 263, C1302 (1992); **53.** Proc Natl Acad Sci U S A 89, 1690 (1992); **54.** Am J Physiol 273, C909 (1997); **55.** J Cell Physiol 158, 309 (1994); **56.** Biochem J 287, 59 (1992); **57.** Methods Cell Biol 64, 553 (2001); **58.** J Appl Microbiol 84, 988 (1998); **59.** J Microsc 176, 8 (1994); **60.** J Immunol Methods 161, 119 (1993); **61.** Yeast 14, 147 (1998); **62.** J Microbiol Methods 32, 45 (1998); **63.** Br J Pharmacol 129, 1323 (2000); **64.** J Physiol 517, 781 (1999); **65.** J Physiol 502, 397 (1997); **66.** Pflugers Arch 434, 712 (1997); **67.** Exp Cell Res 231, 260 (1997); **68.** J Biol Chem 266, 803 (1991); **69.** J Membr Biol 123, 23 (1991); **70.** J Gen Physiol 95, 147 (1990); **71.** Biochim Biophys Acta 1146, 169 (1993); **72.** Biochim Biophys Acta 1107, 245 (1992); **73.** J Cell Physiol 138, 61 (1989); **74.** Biochim Biophys Acta 1062, 24 (1991); **75.** Proc Natl Acad Sci U S A 83, 3311 (1986).

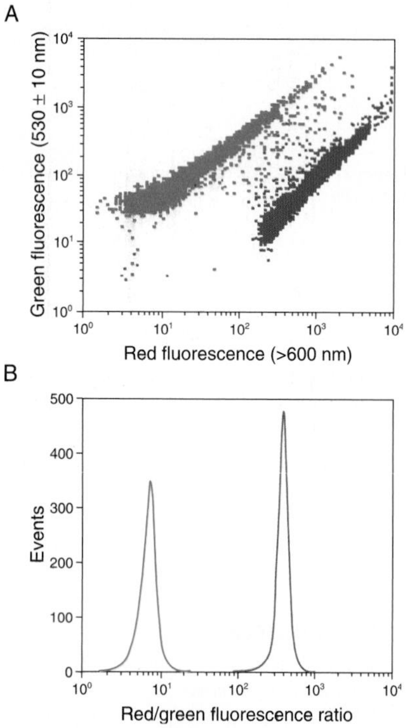

Figure 22.11 A) Two-color flow cytometric analysis of *Staphylococcus aureus* populations stained with 30 µM $DiOC_2(3)$ (D14730) in the presence (red) or absence (blue) of the metabolic uncoupler carbonyl cyanide *m*-chlorophenylhydrazone (CCCP). Note the variability (~100-fold range) of the green and red fluorescence intensities. B) The same data expressed as red/green fluorescence intensity ratios. Ratio values are calculated by subtracting the logarithmic green fluorescence channel value from the corresponding logarithmic red fluorescence channel value (Cytometry 35, 55 (1999)). Figure supplied by Dr. Howard M. Shapiro, Harvard Medical School, Boston, MA.

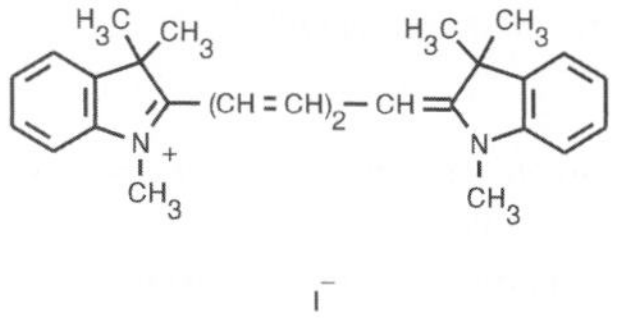

Figure 22.12 H14700 1,1′,3,3,3′,3′-hexamethylindodicarbocyanine iodide ($DiIC_1(5)$).

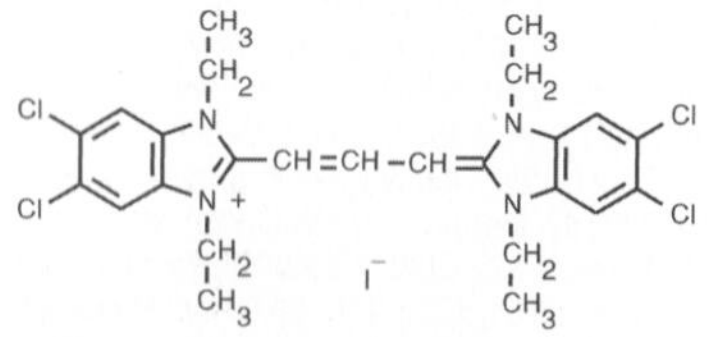

Figure 22.13 T3168 5,5′,6,6′-tetrachloro-1,1′,3,3′-tetraethylbenzimidazolylcarbocyanine iodide (JC-1; $CBIC_2(3)$).

ences. In flow cytometric measurements, the detected intensity of carbocyanine fluorescence is dependent not only on the membrane potential, but also on cell size. In some cases, measurements of forward light scatter have been used to normalize the optical changes for cell size variability. A fluorescence ratio method (Figure 22.11) that exploits a potential-dependent red shift in the emission spectrum of $DiOC_2(3)$ (D14730) has been developed for membrane potential measurements in bacteria [7,8] (B34950, see below). The 633 nm light–excitable indocarbocyanine $DiIC_1(5)$ [9] (H14700, Figure 22.12) was used to measure mitochondrial potential in apoptotic cells that were also stained with propidium iodide (P1304MP; P3566; FluoroPure™ Grade, P21493; Section 8.1) and fluoresceinated annexin V [10] (A13199, Section 15.5), a method we have utilized in two of our MitoProbe™ Assay Kits for flow cytometry (M34151, M34150; see below). Cells undergoing apoptosis were analyzed by flow cytometry, and loss of membrane potential was detected as a reduced $DiIC_1(5)$ signal in the near-infrared channel. Carbocyanine dyes, particularly thiacyanines such as $DiSC_3(5)$ (D306), can inhibit respiration [5,11] and may therefore be relatively cytotoxic.[12]

JC-1 and JC-9

JC-1 (5,5′,6,6′-tetrachloro-1,1′,3,3′-tetraethylbenzimidazolylcarbocyanine iodide, T3168; Figure 22.13) exists as a green-fluorescent monomer at low concentrations or at low membrane potential. However, at higher concentrations (aqueous solutions above 0.1 µM) or higher potentials, JC-1 forms red-fluorescent "J-aggregates," which exhibit a broad excitation spectrum and a very narrow emission spectrum (Figure 22.14). Because J-aggregate formation increases linearly with applied membrane potential over the range of 30–180 mV, this phenomenon can be exploited for potentiometric measurements [13,14] (Table 22.2). Various types of ratio measurements are possible by combining signals from the green-fluorescent JC-1 monomer (absorption/emission maxima ~514/529 nm) and the red-fluorescent J-aggregate (Figure 22.15) (absorption/emission maxima ~585/590 nm), which can be effectively excited anywhere between 485 nm and its absorption maximum. Optical filters designed for fluorescein and tetramethylrhodamine (Table 23.9) can be used to separately visualize the monomer and J-aggregate forms, respectively. Alternatively, both forms can be observed simultaneously using a fluorescein longpass optical filter set. A review by Chen and Smiley describes the properties of JC-1 and its use for investigating mitochondrial potentials in live cells.[15] For flow cytometry, JC-1 can be excited at 488 nm and detected in bivariate mode using the green channel for the monomer and the red channel for the J-aggregate form [16] (Figure 22.16). JC-1 is widely used for detecting mitochondrial depolarization in apoptotic cells [17–20] (MitoProbe™ JC-1 Assay Kit, M34152, described below) and for assaying multidrug-resistant cells [21] (Section 15.6). We have discovered another mitochondrial marker, JC-9 (3,3′-dimethyl-α-naphthoxacarbocyanine iodide, D22421; Figure 22.17), with similar potential-dependent spectroscopic properties (Figure 22.18). However, the green fluorescence of JC-9 is essentially invariant with membrane potential, whereas the red fluorescence is significantly increased at hyperpolarized membrane potentials.

MitoProbe™ JC-1 Assay Kit for Flow Cytometry

The MitoProbe™ JC-1 Assay Kit (M34152) provides the cationic dye JC-1 and a mitochondrial membrane potential disrupter, CCCP (carbonyl cyanide 3-chlorophenylhydrazone), for the study of mitochondrial membrane potential. JC-1 (Figure 22.13) exhibits potential-dependent accumulation in mitochondria, indicated by a fluorescence emission shift from green (~529 nm) to red (~590 nm), due to concentration-dependent formation of red-fluorescent J-aggregates.[13,14,22] Consequently, mitochondrial depolarization is indicated by a decrease in the red/green fluorescence intensity ratio, which is dependent only on the membrane potential and not on other factors such as mitochondrial size, shape and density, which may influence single-component fluorescence measurements. Use of fluorescence ratio detection therefore allows researchers to make comparative measurements of membrane potential and to determine the percentage of mitochondria within a population that respond to an applied stimulus. Subtle heterogeneity in cellular responses can be discerned in this way.[14,23] For example, four distinct patterns of mitochondrial membrane potential change in response to glutamate receptor activation in neurons have been identified using confocal ratio imaging of JC-1 fluorescence.[24]

Each MitoProbe™ JC-1 Assay Kit provides:

- JC-1
- Dimethylsulfoxide (DMSO)

- CCCP
- Concentrated phosphate-buffered saline (PBS)
- A detailed protocol

Sufficient reagents are provided for 100 assays, based on a labeling volume of 1 mL. JC-1 can be used as an indicator of mitochondrial potential in a variety of cell types, including myocytes [22] and neurons,[24] as well as in intact tissues [25] and isolated mitochondria.[23] JC-1 is more specific for mitochondrial versus plasma membrane potential and more consistent in its response to depolarization than some other cationic dyes such as $DiOC_6(3)$ and rhodamine 123.[19] The most widely implemented application for JC-1 is the detection of mitochondrial depolarization occurring in apoptosis [19,20,26,27] (Section 15.5, Figure 15.98).

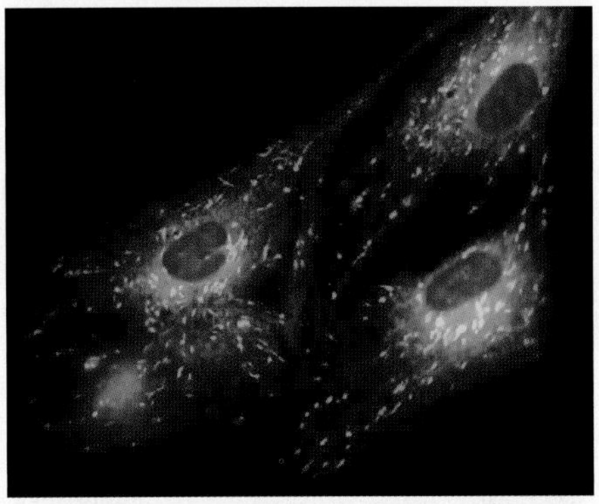

Figure 22.14 Cultured human pre-adipocytes loaded with the ratiometric mitochondrial potential indicator JC-1 (T3168) at 5 µM for 30 minutes at 37°C. In live cells, JC-1 exists either as a green-fluorescent monomer at depolarized membrane potentials or as an orange-fluorescent J-aggregate at hyperpolarized membrane potentials. Cells were then treated with 50 nM FCCP, a protonophore, to depolarize the mitochondrial membrane. Approximately 10 minutes after the addition of the uncoupler, the cells were illuminated at 488 nm and the emission was collected between 515–545 nm and 575–625 nm. Image contributed by Bob Terry, BioImage A/S, Denmark.

MitoProbe™ $DiIC_1(5)$ and MitoProbe™ $DiOC_2(3)$ Assay Kits for Flow Cytometry

Cationic carbocyanine dyes have been shown to accumulate in cells in response to membrane potential,[28] and membrane potential changes have been studied in association with apoptosis.[17,29] The MitoProbe™ $DiIC_1(5)$ and MitoProbe™ $DiOC_2(3)$ Assay Kits (M34151, M34150) provide solutions of the far-red–fluorescent $DiIC_1(5)$ (1,1′,3,3,3′,3′-hexamethylindodicarbocyanine iodide) and green-fluorescent $DiOC_2(3)$ (3,3′-diethyloxacarbocyanine iodide) carbocyanine dyes, respectively, along with a mitochondrial membrane potential disrupter, CCCP, for the study of mitochondrial membrane potential. These $DiIC_1(5)$ and $DiOC_2(3)$ carbocyanine dyes penetrate the cytosol of eukaryotic cells and, at concentrations below 100 nM, accumulate primarily in mitochondria with active membrane potentials. In the case of $DiOC_2(3)$, this accumulation is accompanied by a shift from green to red emission due to dye stacking (Figure 22.11), allowing the use of a ratiometric parameter (red/green fluorescence ratio) that corrects for size differences when measuring membrane potential in bacteria.[7,8] $DiIC_1(5)$ and $DiOC_2(3)$ stain intensities decrease

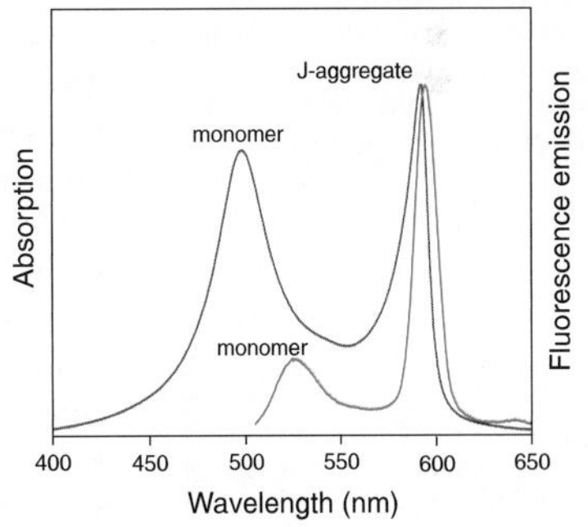

Figure 22.15 Absorption and fluorescence emission (excited at 488 nm) spectra of JC-1 in pH 8.2 buffer containing 1% (v/v) DMSO.

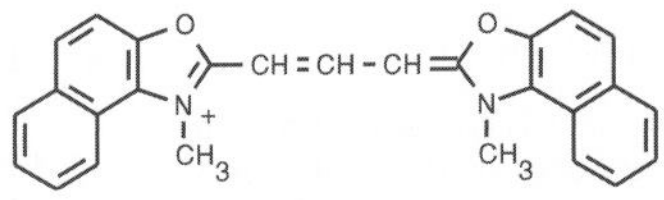

Figure 22.17 D22421 3,3′-dimethyl-α-naphthoxacarbocyanine iodide (JC-9; $DiNOC_1(3)$).

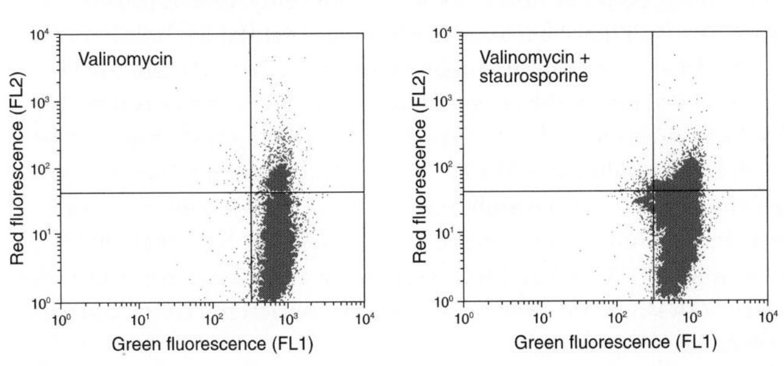

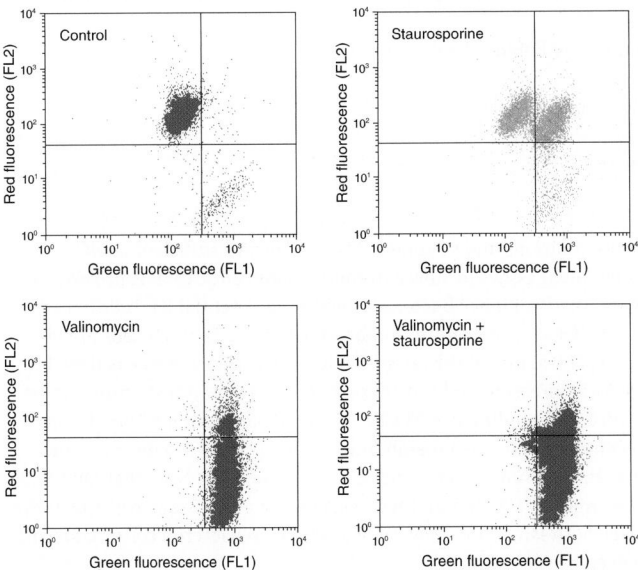

Figure 22.16 Bivariate JC-1 (T3168) analysis of mitochondrial membrane potential in HL60 cells by flow cytometry. The sensitivity of this technique is demonstrated by the response to K^+/valinomycin (V1644, Section 21.1)–induced depolarization (panels B and D). Distinct populations of cells with different extents of mitochondrial depolarization are detectable following apoptosis-inducing treatment with 5 µM staurosporine for two hours (panel C). Figure courtesy of Andrea Cossarizza, University of Modena and Reggio Emilia, Italy.

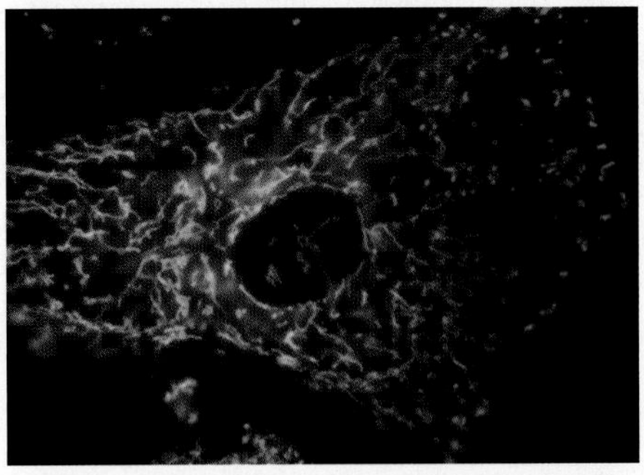

Figure 22.18 A viable bovine pulmonary artery endothelial cell incubated with the ratiometric mitochondrial potential indicator, JC-9 (D22421). In live cells, JC-9 exists either as a green-fluorescent monomer at depolarized membrane potentials, or as a red-fluorescent J-aggregate at hyperpolarized membrane potentials.

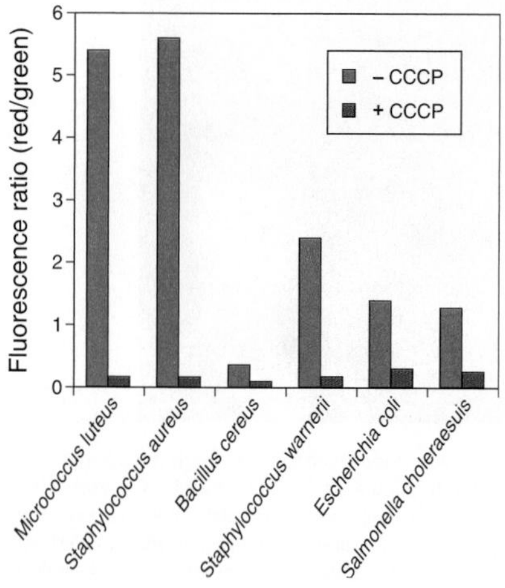

Figure 22.19 Detection of membrane potential in various bacteria with the *Bac*Light™ Bacterial Membrane Potential Kit (B34950). Red/green fluorescence ratios were calculated using population mean fluorescence intensities for gram-positive (*Micrococcus luteus, Staphylococcus aureus, Bacillus cereus* and *Staphylococcus warnerii*) and gram-negative (*Escherichia coli* and *Salmonella choleraesuis*) bacteria incubated with 30 µM $DiOC_2(3)$ for 30 minutes in either the presence or absence of 5 µM CCCP, according to the kit protocol.

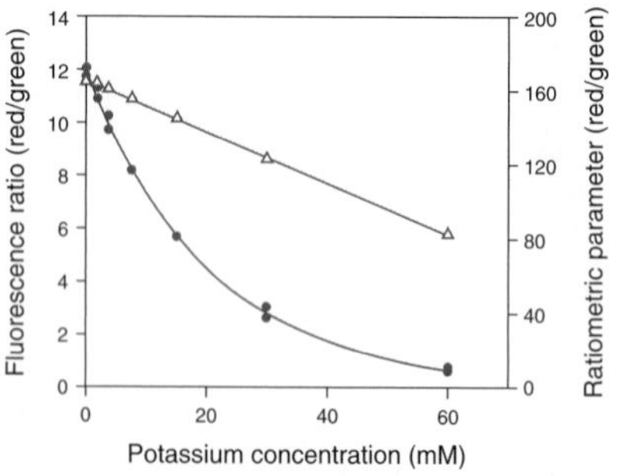

Figure 22.20 Response of *Staphylococcus aureus* to valinomycin and external potassium ions, as measured with the *Bac*Light™ Bacterial Membrane Potential Kit (B34950). Samples containing *S. aureus* were treated with 5 µM valinomycin in different concentrations of potassium buffer, and then stained using 30 µM $DiOC_2(3)$ for 30 minutes, according to kit protocol. Data are expressed either using a ratiometric parameter based on the formula provided in the kit protocol (triangles, right axis) or as the ratio of population mean red-fluorescence intensity/mean green-fluorescence intensity (circles, left axis).

when cells are treated with reagents that disrupt mitochondrial membrane potential, such as CCCP. Each MitoProbe™ $DiIC_1(5)$ and MitoProbe™ $DiOC_2(3)$ Assay Kit provides:

- $DiIC_1(5)$ (in Kit M34151) or $DiOC_2(3)$ (in Kit M34150)
- CCCP
- Detailed protocols for labeling cells with the short-chain carbocyanine dye, as well as with annexin V conjugates (not included)

Cells stained with $DiIC_1(5)$ can be visualized by flow cytometry with red excitation and far-red emission filters; cells stained with $DiOC_2(3)$ can be visualized by flow cytometry with blue excitation and green and red emission filters. $DiIC_1(5)$ can be paired with other reagents, such as propidium iodide and the green-fluorescent Alexa Fluor® 488 annexin V (both provided in the Vybrant® Apoptosis Assay Kit #2, V13241), for multiparameter study of vitality and apoptosis. $DiOC_2(3)$ can be paired with other reagents, such as the far-red–fluorescent allophycocyanin annexin V (A35110), for multiparameter study of vitality and apoptosis (Figure 15.99). Combining these short-chain carbocyanine dyes with annexin V conjugates results in superior resolution of subpopulations when compared with results obtained with other commonly used dyes.

*Bac*Light™ Bacterial Membrane Potential Kit

The *Bac*Light™ Bacterial Membrane Potential Kit (B34950) provides a fluorescent membrane-potential indicator dye, $DiOC_2(3)$, along with a proton ionophore (CCCP) and premixed buffer. At low concentrations, $DiOC_2(3)$ exhibits green fluorescence in all bacterial cells, but it becomes more concentrated in healthy cells that are maintaining a membrane potential, causing the dye to self-associate and the fluorescence emission to shift to red. The red- and green-fluorescent bacterial populations are easily distinguished using a flow cytometer. CCCP is included in the kit for use as a control because it eradicates the proton gradient, eliminating bacterial membrane potential.[8,30]

Using the *Bac*Light™ Bacterial Membrane Potential Kit, we have detected membrane potentials in all bacteria tested (including logarithmically growing cultures of *Micrococcus luteus, Staphylococcus aureus, Bacillus cereus, Staphylococcus warnerii, Escherichia coli* and *Salmonella choleraesuis*), although the magnitude varies with species (Figure 22.19). For many gram-positive species, such as *M. luteus* and *S. aureus*, the $DiOC_2(3)$ red:green ratio has been shown to vary with the intensity of the proton gradient (Figure 22.20). In gram-negative bacteria, such as *E. coli* and *S. choleraesuis*, a $DiOC_2(3)$ response is observed in the presence of a membrane potential but the response does not appear to be proportional to proton gradient intensity.

Each *Bac*Light™ Bacterial Membrane Potential Kit contains:

- $DiOC_2(3)$ in dimethylsulfoxide (DMSO)
- CCCP in DMSO
- Phosphate-buffered saline (PBS)
- A detailed protocol

Using the recommended reagent dilutions and volumes, this kit provides sufficient $DiOC_2(3)$ to perform approximately 100 individual assays by flow cytometry; sufficient CCCP is provided for 30 depolarized control samples. The *Bac*Light™ Bacterial Membrane Potential Kit is designed to assay bacterial concentrations between 10^5 and 10^7 organisms per mL. Stained cells are efficiently excited by the 488 nm spectral line of the argon-ion laser, and fluorescence is detected using emission filters suitable for fluorescein and the Texas Red® dye. $DiOC_2(3)$ staining can be combined with the impermeant DNA-binding dye TO-PRO®-3 (T3605, Section 8.1) to distinguish depolarized cells from cells with damaged membranes.[30] The TO-PRO®-3 dye must be excited with a red laser such as the 633 nm spectral line of the He–Ne laser. Note that $DiOC_2(3)$ and CCCP are inhibitors of respiration.[31] Although these dyes do not alter assay results over the recommended staining periods, both $DiOC_2(3)$ and CCCP are toxic to bacterial cells, rendering the cells nonculturable after even brief exposure.

Rhodamine Probes

Rhodamine 123 (R302; FluoroPure™ Grade, R22420) is widely used as a structural marker for mitochondria (Section 12.2) and as an indicator of mitochondrial activity (Section 15.6, Figure 22.21). Highly selective, potential-dependent staining of mitochondria is obtained by setting the extracellular K^+ concentration close to intracellular values (~137 mM), thereby depolarizing the plasma membrane.[32]

TMRM (T668) and TMRE (T669), the methyl and ethyl esters of tetramethylrhodamine (Figure 22.22, Figure 22.23), are closely related to rhodamine 123. They are primarily mitochondrial membrane potential sensors.[33,34] As with rhodamine 123, accumulation of these cationic dyes in mitochondria results in diminished fluorescence due to self-quenching.[34] TMRM and TMRE cross the plasma membrane more rapidly than rhodamine 123, and their strong fluorescence means that they can be used at low concentrations, thus avoiding aggregation. Because their fluorescence is relatively insensitive to the environment, spatially resolved fluorescence of TMRM and TMRE presents an unbiased profile of their transmembrane distribution that can be directly related to the plasma membrane potential via the Nernst equation.[34–38] TMRE has been successfully used in a high-throughput screening assay for drugs that affect mitochondrial membrane potential in live cells.[39]

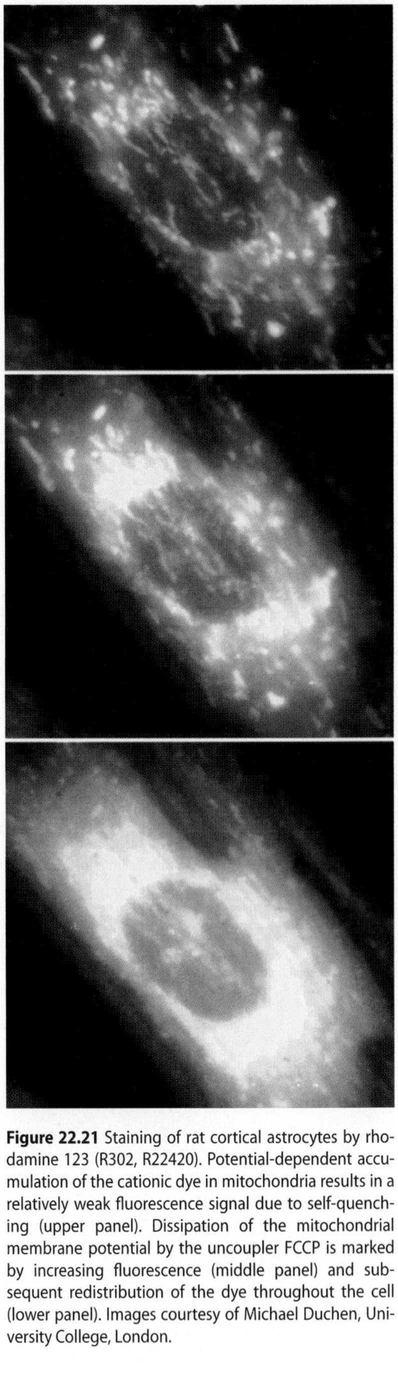

Figure 22.21 Staining of rat cortical astrocytes by rhodamine 123 (R302, R22420). Potential-dependent accumulation of the cationic dye in mitochondria results in a relatively weak fluorescence signal due to self-quenching (upper panel). Dissipation of the mitochondrial membrane potential by the uncoupler FCCP is marked by increasing fluorescence (middle panel) and subsequent redistribution of the dye throughout the cell (lower panel). Images courtesy of Michael Duchen, University College, London.

Oxonols

Oxonol V and Oxonol VI

The anionic bis-isoxazolone oxonols (O266, O267; Figure 22.24) accumulate in the cytoplasm of depolarized cells by a Nernst equilibrium–dependent uptake from the extracellular solution.[40] Their voltage-dependent partitioning between water and membranes is often measured by absorption rather than fluorescence. Of the oxonols studied by Smith and Chance,[41] oxonol VI (O267) gave the largest spectral shifts, with an isosbestic point at 603 nm. In addition, oxonol VI responds to changes in potential more rapidly than oxonol V and is therefore considered to be the better probe for measuring fast potential changes.[42]

DiBAC (Bis-oxonol) Dyes

The three bis-barbituric acid oxonols, often referred to as DiBAC dyes, form a family of spectrally distinct potentiometric probes with excitation maxima at approximately 490 nm ($DiBAC_4(3)$; B438; FluoroPure™ Grade, B24570), 530 nm ($DiSBAC_2(3)$, B413) and 590 nm ($DiBAC_4(5)$, B436). Several papers have referred to these dyes simply as "bis-oxonol" and it is not always possible to determine which of the dyes was used; however, $DiBAC_4(3)$ (Figure 22.25) has been used in the majority of publications that cite a "bis-oxonol." The dyes enter depolarized cells where they bind to intracellular proteins or membranes and exhibit enhanced fluorescence and red spectral shifts.[43] Increased depolarization results in more influx of the anionic dye and thus an increase in fluorescence (Figure 22.26). Conversely, hyperpolarization is indicated by a decrease in fluorescence (Figure 22.27). Potential-dependent fluorescence changes generated by $DiBAC_4(3)$ are typically ~1% per mV.[44,45] The long-wavelength $DiSBAC_2(3)$ probe has frequently been used in combination with the UV light–excitable Ca^{2+} indicators indo-1 or fura-2 for simultaneous measurements of membrane potential and Ca^{2+} concentrations (Table 22.2). Interactions between anionic oxonols and the cationic K^+-valinomycin complex complicate the use of this

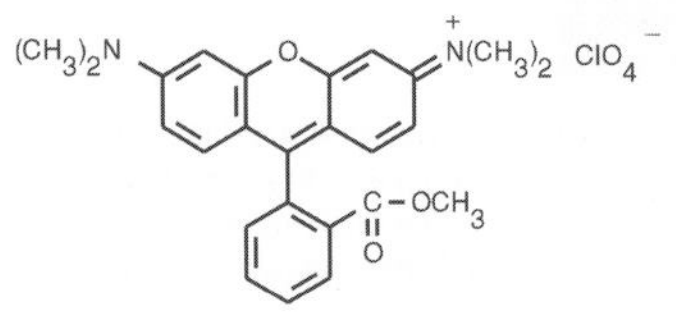

Figure 22.22 T668 tetramethylrhodamine, methyl ester, perchlorate (TMRM).

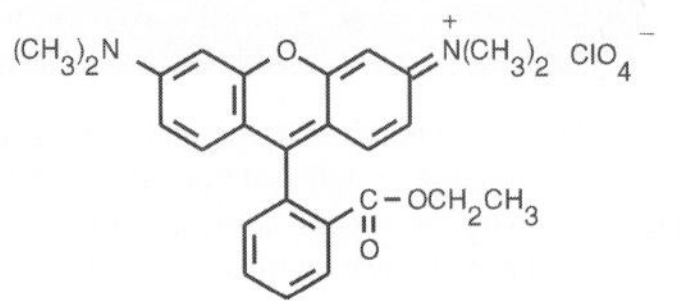

Figure 22.23 T669 tetramethylrhodamine, ethyl ester, perchlorate (TMRE).

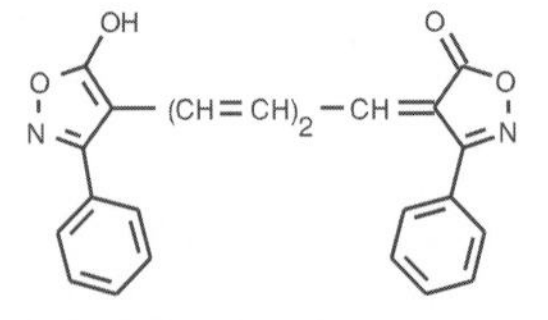

Figure 22.24 O266 oxonol V (bis-(3-phenyl-5-oxoisoxazol-4-yl)pentamethine oxonol).

ionophore when calibrating potentiometric responses.[46,47] Like the bis-isoxazolone oxonols, the DiBAC dyes are excluded from mitochondria because of their overall negative charge, making them superior to carbocyanines for measuring plasma membrane potentials by flow cytometry (Table 22.2).

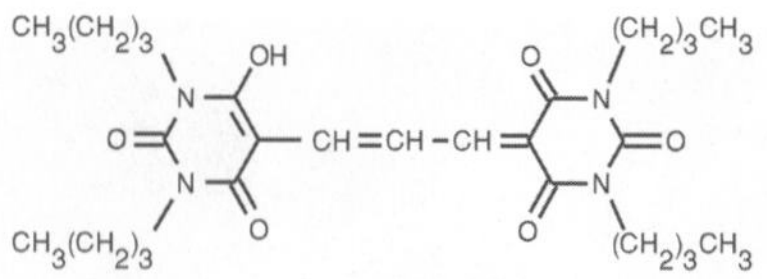

Figure 22.25 B438 bis-(1,3-dibutylbarbituric acid)trimethine oxonol ($DiBAC_4(3)$).

Merocyanine 540

Although merocyanine 540 (M24571) was among the first fluorescent dyes to be used as a potentiometric probe,[48] its use for this application has declined with the advent of superior probes. A significant disadvantage of merocyanine 540 is its extreme phototoxicity; consequently, it is now more commonly used as a photosensitizer.[49–58] Merocyanine 540 exhibits a biphasic kinetic response to membrane polarization changes. It binds to the surface of polarized membranes in a perpendicular orientation, reorienting as the membrane depolarizes to form nonfluorescent dimers with altered absorption spectra.[59,60] This fast (microseconds) reorientation is followed by a slower response caused by an increased dye uptake. Merocyanine 540 is also a useful probe of lipid packing because it binds preferentially to membranes with highly disordered lipids.[61,62] Fluorescence of merocyanine 540 is sensitive to heat-induced changes in the organization of membrane lipids.[63]

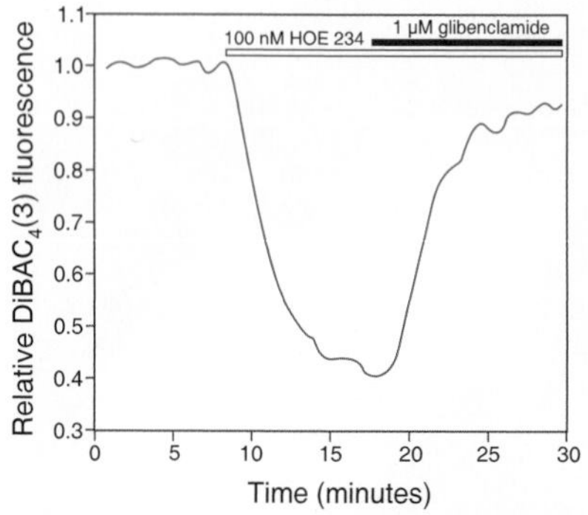

Figure 22.27 Detection of ATP-sensitive potassium (K_{ATP}) activation in isolated capillaries from guinea pig hearts using $DiBAC_4(3)$ (B438; FluoroPure™ Grade, B24570), a slow potentiometric probe. Application of a K^+ channel opener (HOE 234) induced membrane hyperpolarization, resulting in a net efflux of intracellular $DiBAC_4(3)$, which is registered as a decrease of fluorescence intensity. These effects were reversed by subsequent treatment with the channel blocker glibenclamide. Figure reproduced with permission from (J Physiol 502, 397 (1997)).

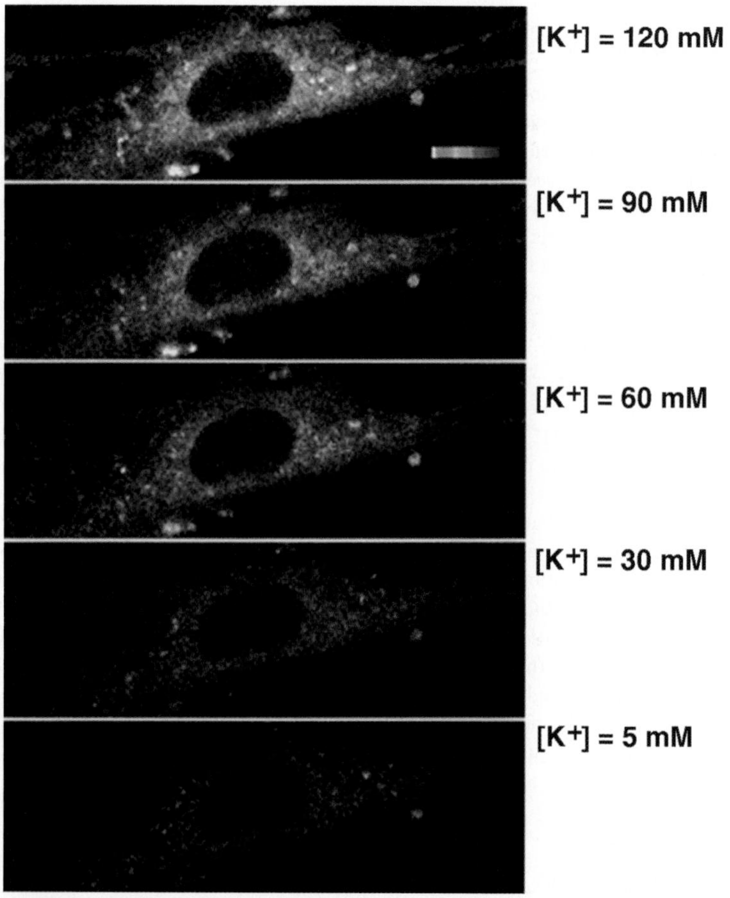

Figure 22.26 NIH 3T3 fibroblast undergoing progressive depolarization induced by the stepwise increase of KCl concentration from 5 mM (bottom panel) to 120 mM (top panel). The cell culture was loaded with $DiSBAC_2(3)$ (B413) and examined under a confocal laser-scanning microscope after each appropriate medium change, keeping a constant plane of section (Exp Cell Res 231, 260 (1997)). The image was contributed by Rita Gatti, Institute of Histology and General Embryology, University of Parma, Parma, Italy.

References

1. J Photochem Photobiol B 33, 101 (1996); **2.** Biochemistry 13, 3315 (1974); **3.** J Membr Biol 92, 171 (1986); **4.** J Membr Biol 59, 1 (1981); **5.** Biophys J 56, 979 (1989); **6.** Biochim Biophys Acta 1404, 393 (1998); **7.** Methods 21, 271 (2000); **8.** Cytometry 35, 55 (1999); **9.** Cytometry 41, 245 (2000); **10.** Cell 94, 339 (1998); **11.** J Biol Chem 256, 1108 (1981); **12.** Biochem Pharmacol 45, 691 (1993); **13.** Biochemistry 30, 4480 (1991); **14.** Proc Natl Acad Sci U S A 88, 3671 (1991); **15.** Fluorescent and Luminescent Probes for Biological Activity, Mason WT, Ed. pp. 124–132 (1993); **16.** Biochem Biophys Res Commun 197, 40 (1993); **17.** Methods Cell Biol 63, 467 (2001); **18.** Cytometry 29, 97 (1997); **19.** FEBS Lett 411, 77 (1997); **20.** J Cell Biol 138, 449 (1997); **21.** Leukemia 11, 1147 (1997); **22.** J Physiol 486, 1 (1995); **23.** Exp Cell Res 222, 84 (1996); **24.** J Neurosci 16, 5688 (1996); **25.** Methods 18, 104 (1999); **26.** Exp Cell Res 245, 170 (1998); **27.** J Neurosci 18, 932 (1998); **28.** Proc Natl Acad Sci U S A 76, 5728 (1979); **29.** Exp Cell Res 214, 323 (1994); **30.** Antimicrob Agents Chemother 44, 827 (2000); **31.** Glia 4, 611 (1991); **32.** Methods Cell Biol 29, 103 (1989); **33.** Trends Neurosci 23, 166 (2000); **34.** Biophys J 76, 469 (1999); **35.** Methods Enzymol 302, 341 (1999); **36.** Neuron 15, 961 (1995); **37.** Biophys J 74, 2129 (1998); **38.** Am J Physiol 272, C1286 (1997); **39.** J Biomol Screen 7, 383 (2002); **40.** Biochim Biophys Acta 903, 480 (1987); **41.** J Membr Biol 46, 255 (1979); **42.** Biophys Chem 34, 225 (1989); **43.** Chem Phys Lipids 69, 137 (1994); **44.** J Physiol 502, 397 (1997); **45.** Biochim Biophys Acta 771, 208 (1984); **46.** Biophys J 57, 835 (1990); **47.** Biochim Biophys Acta 809, 228 (1985); **48.** Annu Rev Biophys Bioeng 8, 47 (1979); **49.** J Immunol Methods 168, 245 (1994); **50.** Pharmacol Ther 63, 1 (1994); **51.** Arch Biochem Biophys 300, 714 (1993); **52.** Bone Marrow Transplant 12, 191 (1993); **53.** Cancer Res 53, 806 (1993); **54.** Free Radic Biol Med 12, 389 (1992); **55.** Biochim Biophys Acta 1075, 28 (1991); **56.** J Infect Dis 163, 1312 (1991); **57.** Photochem Photobiol 53, 1 (1991); **58.** Cancer Res 49, 3637 (1989); **59.** Biochemistry 24, 7117 (1985); **60.** Biochemistry 17, 5228 (1978); **61.** Biochim Biophys Acta 1146, 136 (1993); **62.** Biochim Biophys Acta 732, 387 (1983); **63.** Biochim Biophys Acta 1030, 269 (1990).

Data Table — 22.3 Slow-Response Probes

Cat #	MW	Storage	Soluble	Abs	EC	Em	Solvent	Notes
B413	436.54	L	DMSO, EtOH	535	170,000	560	MeOH	1
B436	542.67	L	DMSO, EtOH	590	160,000	616	MeOH	1
B438	516.64	L	DMSO, EtOH	493	140,000	516	MeOH	1, 2
B24570	516.64	L	DMSO, EtOH	493	140,000	516	MeOH	1, 2, 3
D272	544.47	D,L	DMSO	484	155,000	500	MeOH	
D273	572.53	D,L	DMSO	484	154,000	501	MeOH	
D306	546.53	D,L	DMSO	651	258,000	675	MeOH	
D14730	460.31	D,L	DMSO	482	165,000	497	MeOH	4
D22421	532.38	D,L	DMSO, DMF	522	143,000	535	$CHCl_3$	5
H14700	510.46	L	DMSO	638	230,000	658	MeOH	6
M24571	569.67	D,L	DMSO, EtOH	555	143,000	578	MeOH	
O266	384.39	L	DMSO, EtOH	610	135,000	639	MeOH	1
O267	316.36	L	DMSO, EtOH	599	136,000	634	MeOH	1
R302	380.83	F,D,L	MeOH, DMF	507	101,000	529	MeOH	
R22420	380.83	F,D,L	MeOH, DMF	507	101,000	529	MeOH	3
T668	500.93	F,D,L	DMSO, MeOH	549	115,000	573	MeOH	
T669	514.96	F,D,L	DMSO, EtOH	549	109,000	574	MeOH	
T3168	652.23	D,L	DMSO, DMF	514	195,000	529	MeOH	7

For definitions of the contents of this data table, see "Navigating *The Handbook*" in the introductory pages.

Notes

1. Oxonols may require addition of a base to be soluble.
2. Fluorescence of $DiBAC_4(3)$ increases about 3-fold relative to H_2O on binding to proteins (Abs = 499 nm, Em = 519 nm) (Chem Phys Lipids 69, 137 (1994)).
3. This product is specified to equal or exceed 98% analytical purity by HPLC.
4. QY for $DiOC_2(3)$ in MeOH = 0.04. Abs = 478 nm, Em = 496 nm in H_2O (Biochemistry 13, 3315 (1974)).
5. JC-9 exhibits long-wavelength J-aggregate emission at ~635 nm in aqueous solutions and polarized mitochondria.
6. $DiIC_1(5)$ in H_2O; Abs = 636 nm, Em = 658 nm.
7. JC-1 forms J-aggregates with Abs/Em = 585/590 nm at concentrations above 0.1 µM in aqueous solutions (pH 8.0) (Biochemistry 30, 4480 (1991)).

Product List — 22.3 Slow-Response Probes

Cat #	Product Name	Unit Size
B34950	*Bac*Light™ Bacterial Membrane Potential Kit *for flow cytometry* *100 assays*	1 kit
B436	bis-(1,3-dibutylbarbituric acid)pentamethine oxonol ($DiBAC_4(5)$)	25 mg
B438	bis-(1,3-dibutylbarbituric acid)trimethine oxonol ($DiBAC_4(3)$)	25 mg
B24570	bis-(1,3-dibutylbarbituric acid)trimethine oxonol ($DiBAC_4(3)$) *FluoroPure™ grade*	5 mg
B413	bis-(1,3-diethylthiobarbituric acid)trimethine oxonol ($DiSBAC_2(3)$)	100 mg
D14730	3,3′-diethyloxacarbocyanine iodide ($DiOC_2(3)$)	100 mg
D273	3,3′-dihexyloxacarbocyanine iodide ($DiOC_6(3)$)	100 mg
D22421	3,3′-dimethyl-α-naphthoxacarbocyanine iodide (JC-9; $DiNOC_1(3)$)	5 mg
D272	3,3′-dipentyloxacarbocyanine iodide ($DiOC_5(3)$)	100 mg
D306	3,3′-dipropylthiadicarbocyanine iodide ($DiSC_3(5)$)	100 mg
H14700	1,1′,3,3,3′,3′-hexamethylindodicarbocyanine iodide ($DiIC_1(5)$)	100 mg
M24571	merocyanine 540	25 mg
M34151	MitoProbe™ $DiIC_1(5)$ Assay Kit *for flow cytometry* *100 assays*	1 kit
M34150	MitoProbe™ $DiOC_2(3)$ Assay Kit *for flow cytometry* *100 assays*	1 kit
M34152	MitoProbe™ JC-1 Assay Kit *for flow cytometry* *100 assays*	1 kit
O266	oxonol V (bis-(3-phenyl-5-oxoisoxazol-4-yl)pentamethine oxonol)	100 mg
O267	oxonol VI (bis-(3-propyl-5-oxoisoxazol-4-yl)pentamethine oxonol)	100 mg
R302	rhodamine 123	25 mg
R22420	rhodamine 123 *FluoroPure™ grade*	25 mg
T3168	5,5′,6,6′-tetrachloro-1,1′,3,3′-tetraethylbenzimidazolylcarbocyanine iodide (JC-1; $CBIC_2(3)$)	5 mg
T669	tetramethylrhodamine, ethyl ester, perchlorate (TMRE)	25 mg
T668	tetramethylrhodamine, methyl ester, perchlorate (TMRM)	25 mg

For current prices or to order online, visit probes.invitrogen.com

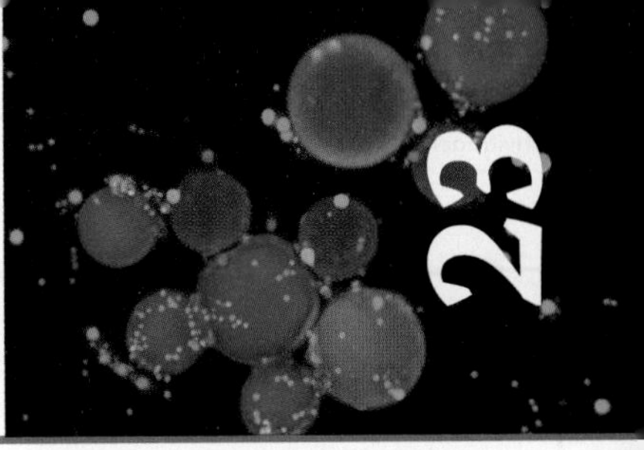

Chapter 23

Tools for Fluorescence Applications

23.1 Reference Standards and Antifade Reagents

To obtain accurate and reproducible results from fluorescence imaging applications, it is essential to maximize the performance of the optical system. Careful calibration and instrumentation adjustment are required for high-precision imaging of fluorescent probes, particularly in multicolor applications that involve multiple exposures, repetitive scans or three-dimensional sectioning.

Molecular Probes offers a variety of microsphere reference standards designed to facilitate adjustment and calibration of both conventional fluorescence microscopes and confocal laser-scanning microscopes. Our Reference Dye Sampler Kit (R14782) provides ready-made stock solutions of five extensively characterized fluorescence standards for use in spectrofluorometers and fluorescence microplate readers. Molecular Probes is also the source of the NIST-traceable fluorescein standard (F36915), which is directly traceable to the fluorescein standard chosen by the National Institute of Standards and Technology. Because imaging sensitivity depends not only on a well-adjusted instrument, but also on the intensity and stability of the fluorescence signal, Molecular Probes has developed several effective antifade reagents to minimize photobleaching of fluorescently labeled specimens (Figure 23.26, Figure 23.27, Figure 23.29). In addition, the Image-iT™ FX signal enhancer (I36933) can dramatically improve the signal-to-noise ratio of immunolabeled cells and tissues, allowing clear visualization of targets that would normally be indistinguishable due to background fluorescence (Figure 7.47, Figure 7.48, Figure 23.32). Lastly, our popular FluoCells® prepared microscope slides (Figure 23.18, Figure 23.19, Figure 23.20, Figure 23.21, Figure 23.22, Figure 23.23, Figure 23.24) are extremely useful products for educational and commercial demonstrations.

FocalCheck™ Fluorescent Microspheres

FocalCheck™ Ring-Stained Fluorescent Microspheres

Our patented FocalCheck™ fluorescent microspheres are specifically designed for examining the alignment, sensitivity and stability of confocal laser-scanning microscopes.[1] They are particularly useful for confirming the optical sectioning thickness (Z-resolution) in three-dimensional imaging applications. These polystyrene beads — available in 6 µm and 15 µm diameters — have been treated using a proprietary method in which a fluorescent dye is allowed to penetrate to only a limited depth within the microsphere. The resulting beads have a well-defined dye layer that, when viewed in cross section in the confocal laser-scanning microscope, appears as a fluorescent ring of varying dimensions depending on the focal plane (Figure 23.1,

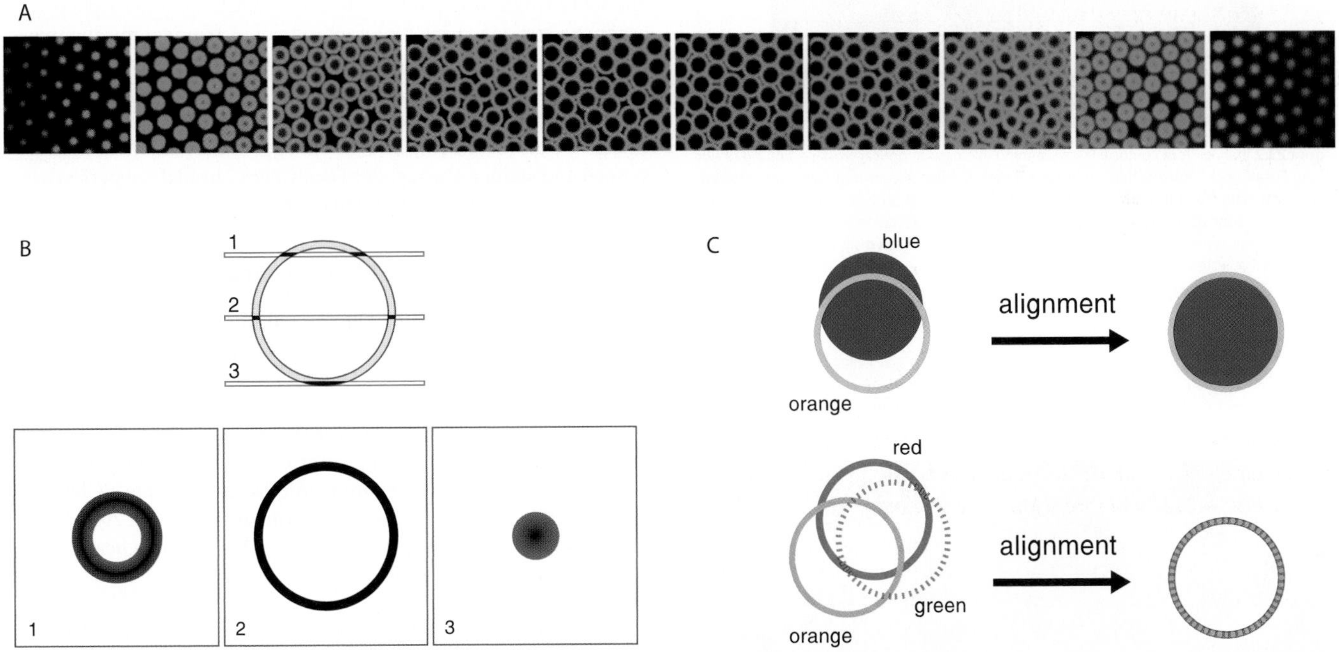

Figure 23.1 Confocal laser-scanning microscope optical cross-sectioning and alignment with FocalCheck™ microspheres. A) Serial optical sectioning from top to bottom along the z-axis of ring-stained microspheres reveals a continuous pattern of disc-to-ring-to-disc images. B) The diameter of the fluorescent ring (or disc) seen is dependent on the depth of the optical focal plane. C) In the confocal laser-scanning microscope, separate light paths exist for UV and visible wavelengths. Also, emitted fluorescence is detected by different photomultipliers. Proper optical alignment may be obtained with either of two types of FocalCheck™ microspheres. For example, the microspheres with an orange ring stain that are blue-fluorescent throughout the bead allow UV/visible wavelength alignment in three dimensions upon aligning the orange ring with the blue disc. Focal alignment is also possible simultaneously in three colors by aligning the green, orange and dark red rings of the FocalCheck™ microspheres containing fluorescent green/orange/dark red ring stains.

Figure 23.2). We refer to this proprietary staining procedure as ring staining to differentiate it from routine staining throughout the bead.

FocalCheck™ microspheres are available in a variety of color configurations provided by five different fluorescent stains:

- Blue (365/430 nm)
- Green (505/515 nm)
- Orange (560/580 nm)
- Red (575/600 nm)
- Dark red (660/680 nm)

The excitation/emission maxima of the different stains are well matched to the laser sources and optical filters commonly used in confocal laser-scanning microscopy and are especially useful in testing and aligning confocal laser-scanning microscopes with multiple laser lines and detection channels (Figure 23.3). Moreover, because the dyes are localized *within* the bead and therefore protected from environmental factors, the FocalCheck™ microspheres are brighter and much more photostable than conventional surface-stained beads.

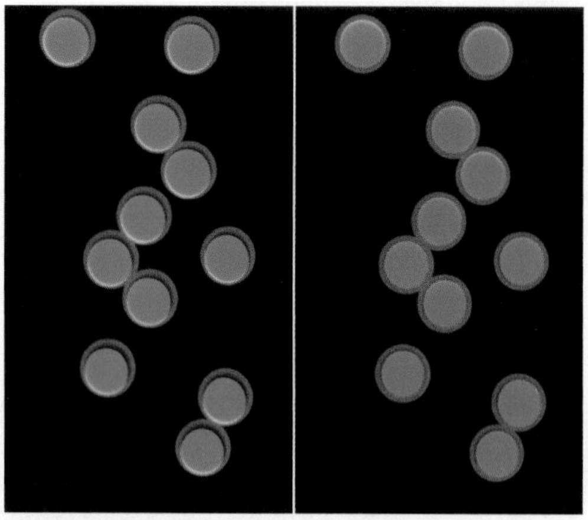

Figure 23.2 Images from confocal laser-scanning microscope optical cross-sectioning of our 15 µm FocalCheck™ microspheres that have a dark red-fluorescent ring stain with a green-fluorescent stain throughout the bead (F7239). The left panel provides a clear visual representation of poor instrument alignment. Correct image registration has been achieved in the right panel, where the dark red ring is aligned with the green disk. The image was contributed by Paulette Brunner, Keck Imaging Center, University of Washington, and Yu-Zhong Zhang, Molecular Probes, Inc.

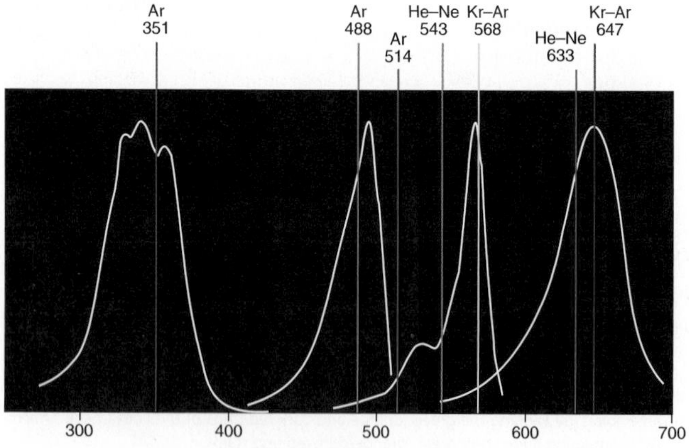

Figure 23.3 Normalized excitation spectra of the dyes contained in the FocalCheck™ microspheres. Emission lines of several commonly used laser excitation sources are superimposed on the dyes' excitation spectra to illustrate the wide range of usage of these beads as calibration references. Ar = Argon-ion laser. Kr–Ar = Krypton–argon laser. He–Ne = Helium–neon laser.

FocalCheck™ products are available in seven different color configurations, including three suspensions that contain microspheres exhibiting ring stains of two or three different fluorescent colors:

- Blue-fluorescent and orange-fluorescent ring stains (15 µm, F7234)
- Green-fluorescent and dark red–fluorescent ring stains (15 µm, F7240)
- Green-fluorescent, orange-fluorescent and dark red–fluorescent ring stains (6 µm, F14806; 15 µm, F7235)

We also supply four suspensions that contain microspheres exhibiting a ring stain of one fluorescent color combined with a stain of a second fluorescent color throughout the bead:

- Green-fluorescent ring stain with blue-fluorescent stain throughout (6 µm, F14808; 15 µm, F7237)
- Green-fluorescent ring stain with dark red–fluorescent stain throughout (15 µm, F7238)
- Orange-fluorescent ring stain with blue-fluorescent stain throughout (15 µm, F7236)
- Dark red–fluorescent ring stain with green-fluorescent stain throughout (6 µm, F14807; 15 µm, F7239, Figure 23.2)

The sharp ring stains exhibited by the FocalCheck™ microspheres produce a striking visual representation of instrument misalignment or other aberrations, making them ideal as reference standards for confocal laser-scanning microscopy. Correct image registration is indicated when the multiple ring images of the ring-stained FocalCheck™ beads (or the ring and disk images of the combination ring-stained and stained-throughout FocalCheck™ beads) are perfectly coincident in all dimensions (Figure 23.1).

FocalCheck™ Thin-Ring Fluorescent Microspheres

Our FocalCheck™ Thin-Ring Fluorescent Microspheres Kit (F14791) contains smaller-diameter microspheres that have spectral and imaging features similar to those of our 6 µm and 15 µm FocalCheck™ microspheres. Because we prepare these 1.0 µm beads using fluorescent stains that are restricted to the surface only, they exhibit sharper and thinner fluorescent ring patterns when viewed in cross section with a confocal laser-scanning microscope. The FocalCheck™ Thin-Ring Fluorescent Microspheres Kit contains three 200 µL suspensions of 1.0 µm beads. Each suspension contains beads with a different color configuration:

- Green-fluorescent (495/515 nm) and red-fluorescent (575/600 nm) ring stains
- Green-fluorescent (495/515 nm) ring stain with dark red–fluorescent (660/680 nm) stain throughout the bead
- Red-fluorescent (575/600 nm) ring stain with blue-fluorescent (365/430 nm) stain throughout the bead

FocalCheck™ Microspheres Pre-Mounted on Microscope Slides

In addition to the bead suspensions described above, we offer FocalCheck™ microspheres pre-mounted on microscope slides. The FocalCheck™ Fluorescent Microsphere Kits feature mounted samples of three different color configurations, in either the 6 µm (F24633) or the 15 µm (F24634) bead size:

- FocalCheck™ beads with green-fluorescent, orange-fluorescent and dark red–fluorescent ring stains
- FocalCheck™ beads with green-fluorescent ring stain and blue-fluorescent stain throughout the bead
- FocalCheck™ beads with dark red–fluorescent ring stain and green-fluorescent stain throughout the bead

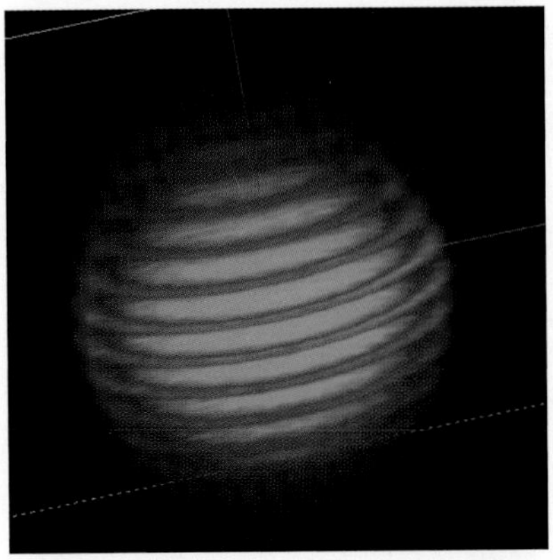

Figure 23.4 A double-labeled microsphere from the FocalCheck™ DoubleGreen Fluorescent Microsphere Kit (F36905). The bead was imaged as a z-series using a Carl Zeiss LSM 510 META system. The two green-fluorescent dyes were separated by spectral unmixing, and one of the dyes was pseudocolored red. In this composite image, the complete z-series is shown prior to software rendering. Rendering fills in the missing information between the slices by interpolation to create a solid object.

FocalCheck™ Fluorescent Microspheres for Testing Spectral Separation

Molecular Probes has prepared four FocalCheck™ Fluorescent Microspheres Kits for testing spectral separation on the Zeiss META system and other spectral imaging systems. These microspheres are stained with two different fluorescent dyes that appear similar in color by eye but are sufficiently different to be resolved by linear-unmixing techniques. When linear-unmixing data-processing algorithms are applied, the dyes are shown to be spectrally distinct and spatially separated — one appears only within the outer ring and the other appears throughout the microsphere (Figure 23.4). These 6 µm, dual-stained microspheres are provided mounted on a microscope slide in each of the following four kits:

- FocalCheck™ DoubleGreen Fluorescent Microspheres Kit (F36905), with a green-fluorescent (500/512 nm) ring dye and a slightly longer-wavelength green-fluorescent (512/525 nm) core dye
- FocalCheck™ DoubleOrange Fluorescent Microspheres Kit (F36906), with an orange-fluorescent (532/552 nm) ring dye and a slightly longer-wavelength orange-fluorescent (545/565 nm) core dye
- FocalCheck™ DoubleRed Fluorescent Microspheres Kit (F36907), with a red-fluorescent (580/610 nm) ring dye and a slightly shorter-wavelength red-fluorescent (569/574 nm) core dye
- FocalCheck™ DoubleFarRed Fluorescent Microspheres Kit (F36908), with a far-red–fluorescent (665/695 nm) ring dye and a slightly shorter-wavelength far-red–fluorescent (640/674 nm) core dye

For generating reference spectra, these kits also contain two additional slides containing microspheres stained uniformly with each of the individual dyes.

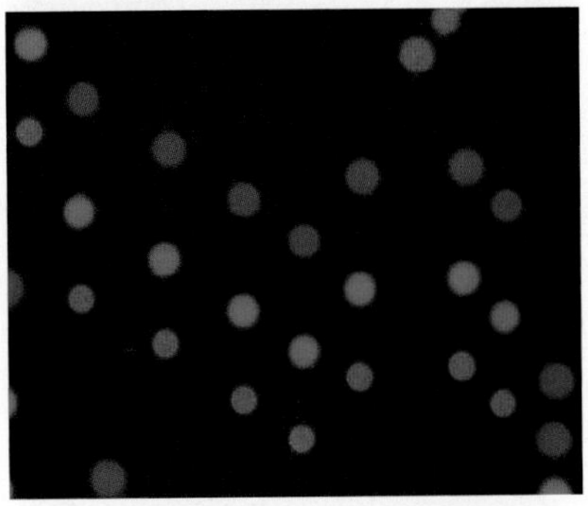

Figure 23.5 Multiple exposures of a prepared slide from our MultiSpeck™ Multispectral Fluorescence Microscopy Standards Kit (M7901). This kit provides fluorescent MultiSpeck™ microspheres that exhibit three relatively distinct excitation/emission bands — blue, green and red — all in the same particle. Thus, the same microsphere can appear a different color depending on the optical filter set used. This photograph was taken through bandpass optical filter sets appropriate for DAPI, fluorescein and Texas Red® dyes, with the field of view shifted slightly between exposures.

MultiSpeck™, TetraSpeck™ and Constellation™ Fluorescent Microspheres

Our unique MultiSpeck™ and TetraSpeck™ fluorescent microspheres greatly facilitate the adjustment and calibration of conventional fluorescence microscopes, confocal laser-scanning microscopes and associated image-processing equipment for multicolor applications. These uniform, multiply stained microspheres are useful for colocalizing and focusing different wavelengths of light in the same optical plane, as well as for checking multicolor image resolution, magnification and sensitivity.

MultiSpeck™ Multispectral Fluorescence Microscopy Standards Kit

The 4 µm MultiSpeck™ microspheres in our MultiSpeck™ Multispectral Fluorescence Microscopy Standards Kit (M7901) exhibit three relatively distinct emission bands — blue, green and red — throughout every particle (Figure 23.5). The spectral characteristics (excitation/emission peaks at 365/405 nm, 520/525 nm and 580/600 nm) are compatible with optical filter sets designed for commonly used blue, green and red fluorophores (e.g., DAPI, fluorescein and rhodamine or Texas Red® dyes or their Alexa Fluor® dye counterparts). The MultiSpeck™ beads can be used as external references for comparing images collected with different optics, on different instruments and in different laboratories, as well as for monitoring routine day-to-day variations in instrument performance. Furthermore, because a single multispectral microsphere will appear as different colors depending on the optical filters used for observation, these beads can be used to assess image registration in two and three dimensions, allowing the researcher to accurately determine the spatial relationships of different labels in a multiparameter experiment. The MultiSpeck™ Multispectral Fluorescence Microscopy Standards Kit contains:

- Suspension of MultiSpeck™ multispectral microspheres
- Mixed suspension of separately stained blue-, green- and red-fluorescent microspheres, which exhibit the same three excitation/emission bands as the multispectral microspheres but in separate beads
- Mounting medium
- A slide-mounting protocol

Both suspensions are provided at a ready-to-use density and can be mounted on slides or incorporated into an experimental sample. Each kit supplies a sufficient amount of material for ~50 slide preparations using either of the two bead suspensions provided.

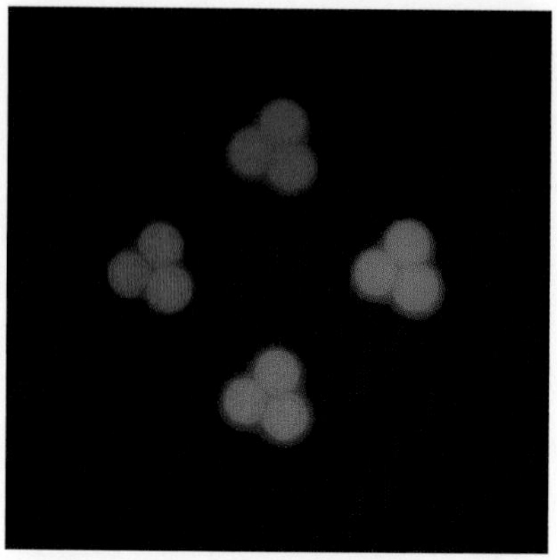

Figure 23.6 Four separate exposures of three TetraSpeck™ beads (T7283) photographed using optical filter sets appropriate for DAPI, fluorescein, tetramethylrhodamine and the Texas Red® dye. The stage was shifted after each exposure. Note that the same beads appear blue, green, orange or red, depending on the filters used.

TetraSpeck™ Fluorescent Microspheres and Sampler Kits

Our TetraSpeck™ fluorescent microspheres [1,2] expand the multispectral strategy introduced with the MultiSpeck™ beads in two important ways. First, the TetraSpeck™ beads have been stained throughout with a mixture of four different fluorescent dyes, yielding four well-separated excitation and emission peaks (Figure 23.6). The excitation/emission maxima of the dyes are 365/430 nm (blue), 505/515 nm (green), 560/580 nm (orange) and 660/680 nm (dark red). Second, these microspheres are available in five nominal sizes (actual bead diameters are indicated on the product labels), spanning the range from subresolution to nearly cell-size particles:

- 0.1 µm (T7279)
- 0.2 µm (T7280)
- 0.5 µm (T7281)
- 1.0 µm (T7282)
- 4.0 µm (T7283)

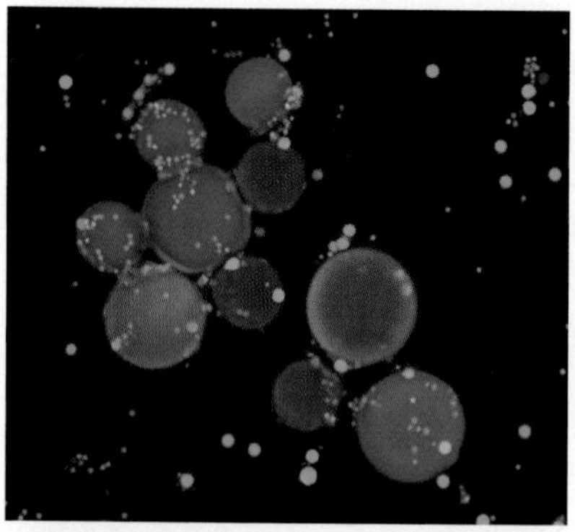

Figure 23.7 Constellation™ microspheres (C14837) provide an assortment of sizes and colors for use in fluorescence microscopy demonstrations.

Each of these products provides a 0.5 mL suspension sample of TetraSpeck™ microspheres that is sufficient for about 100 slides. We offer the TetraSpeck™ Fluorescent Microspheres Sampler Kit (T7284) and the TetraSpeck™ Fluorescent Microspheres Size Kit (T14792). The TetraSpeck™ Fluorescent Microspheres Sampler Kit consists of separate suspension samples of our 0.1 µm, 0.5 µm and 4.0 µm TetraSpeck™ beads, each sufficient for preparing about 20 slides. The TetraSpeck™ Fluorescent Microspheres Size Kit contains six microscope slides; five slides with a mounted sample of the 0.1 µm–, 0.2 µm–, 0.5 µm–, 1.0 µm– or 4.0 µm–diameter TetraSpeck™ microspheres, and a sixth slide with a mixture of all five sizes.

Constellation™ Microspheres for Imaging

Constellation™ microspheres for imaging (C14837, Figure 6.3, Figure 23.7) are 3 mL suspensions of assorted fluorescent microspheres with a variety of sizes and colors. Designed for use in laboratory tutorials and customer training sessions, they provide inexpensive and robust test samples for demonstrating filter switching, focus adjustment and other functional capabilities of fluorescence microscopes. The Constellation™ microspheres can be stored at room temperature, protected from light.

PS-Speck™ Microscope Point Source Kit

The fluorescent microspheres in Molecular Probes' PS-Speck™ Microscope Point Source Kit (P7220) have a diameter of 0.175 ± 0.005 µm, making them ideal subresolution fluorescent sources for calibrating instrument optics. They are particularly useful for measuring the point-spread function required for computational image deconvolution procedures [3] (Figure 23.8, Figure 23.9). This kit's four ready-to-use suspensions contain bright monodisperse particles in the following fluorescent colors (and excitation/emission peaks):

- Blue (360/440 nm)
- Green (505/515 nm)
- Orange (540/560 nm)
- Deep red (633/660 nm)

The kit also includes mounting medium and a mounting protocol for the user's convenience. Each suspension provides sufficient material to mount about 100 slides.

InSpeck™ Microscopy Image Intensity Calibration Kits

InSpeck™ Microscope Image Intensity Calibration Kits provide microsphere standards that generate a series of well-defined fluorescence intensity levels (Figure 23.10) for constructing calibration curves and evaluating sample brightness. Most of the kits are offered in a choice of two different microsphere sizes (2.5 µm or 6 µm) and five different fluorescent colors:

- InSpeck™ Blue (350/440 nm) Kit, (2.5 µm, I7221)
- InSpeck™ Green (505/515 nm) Kits (2.5 µm, I7219; 6 µm, I14785)
- InSpeck™ Orange (540/560 nm) Kits (2.5 µm, I7223; 6 µm, I14786)
- InSpeck™ Red (580/605 nm) Kits (2.5 µm, I7224; 6 µm, I14787)
- InSpeck™ Deep Red (633/660 nm) Kit (2.5 µm, I7225)

Each kit includes six separate suspensions of InSpeck™ fluorescent microspheres with relative fluorescence intensities of 100%, 30%, 10%, 3%, 1% and 0.3% (Figure 23.10), covering the range of intensities commonly encountered in microscopy applications. Unstained control beads and mounting medium are also supplied. The aqueous suspensions of microspheres may be applied directly to the sample for calibrating fluorescence intensities or mounted separately in an adjacent well or on another slide. Each suspension provides sufficient material to prepare about 100 slides.

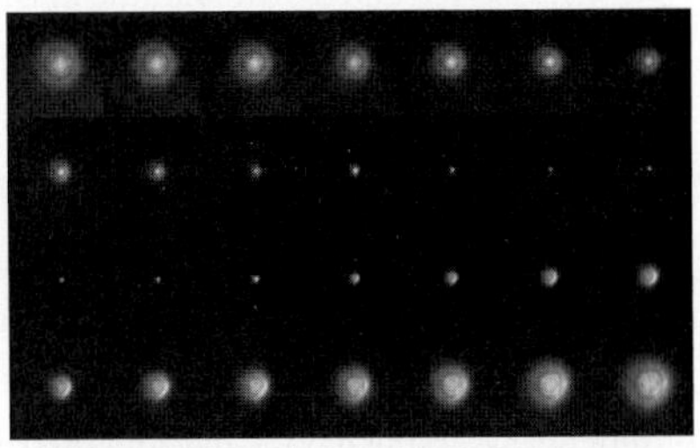

Figure 23.8 One PS-Speck™ green-fluorescent microsphere (P7220) used for point-spread function analysis. Shown are individual images taken in x-y planes with incremental variation in the z-axis.

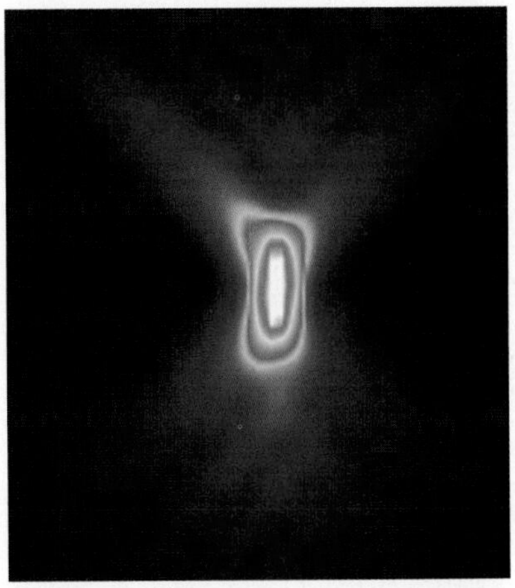

Figure 23.9 An orthogonal (x-z) pseudocolored display representing a point-spread function of a particular microscope's optics, using a microsphere from the PS-Speck™ Microscope Point Source Kit (P7220).

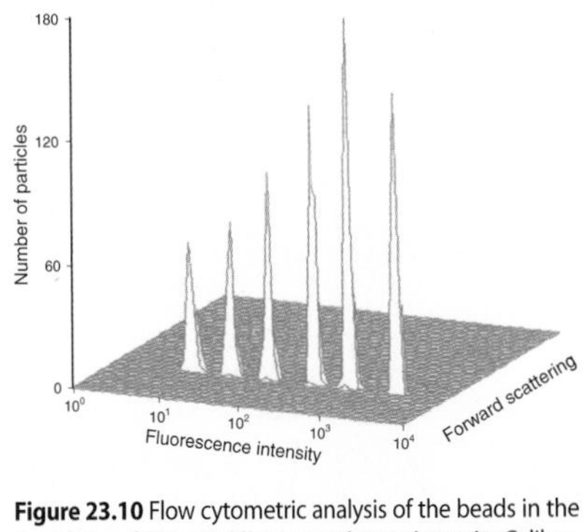

Figure 23.10 Flow cytometric analysis of the beads in the 6 µm InSpeck™ Green Microscope Image Intensity Calibration Kit (I14785). The microspheres have nominal relative fluorescence intensities of 100%, 30%, 10%, 3%, 1%, 0.3%. For each lot, actual relative intensities are determined by flow cytometry and printed on the product labels.

Fluorescence Reference Standards

Fluorescein NIST-Traceable Standard

The National Institute of Standards and Technology (NIST) chose a high-grade fluorescein synthesized by Molecular Probes to create Standard Reference Material 1932 (SRM 1932), a certified fluorescein solution. Molecular Probes now offers a NIST-traceable fluorescein standard (F36915) that not only meets the stringent criteria established by NIST, but is also directly traceable to SRM 1932. We supply our NIST-traceable fluorescein standard as a calibrated 50 µM solution of fluorescein in 100 mM sodium borate buffer, pH 9.5; under these conditions, fluorescein is completely ionized[4] and is therefore in its most fluorescent form (Figure 20.1, Figure 20.2), exhibiting an extremely high quantum yield of 0.93 (Section 20.2).

Academic researchers and industry scientists alike can use our NIST-traceable fluorescein standard to assess day-to-day or experiment-to-experiment variation in fluorescence-based instrumentation, as well as to determine the Molecules of Equivalent Soluble Fluorophore (MESF) value for an experimental solution. The MESF value is defined not as the actual number of dye molecules present, but rather as the number of fluorophores that would yield a fluorescence intensity equivalent to that of the experimental solution when analyzed on the same instrument under the same conditions.[5–7] Consequently, the MESF value is an important tool for characterizing the fluorescence intensity of a solution containing spectrally similar dye molecules attached to antibodies, nucleic acids, microspheres or other substrates that might enhance or diminish the fluorescence. When its pH is carefully matched with that of the experimental solution, our NIST-traceable fluorescein standard can be used for accurate MESF determinations of a wide range of green-fluorescent dye solutions and on an assortment of fluorescence-based instruments.

Reference Dye Sampler Kit

Our Reference Dye Sampler Kit (R14782) provides samples of five extensively characterized fluorescence standards with emission spectra covering the entire visible wavelength range. All five fluorescent standards are supplied as 1 mM stock solutions in 1 mL units, sufficient to prepare approximately 500 diluted working samples for spectrofluorometry. The compositions of the stock solutions are as follows:

- Quinine sulfate in 0.1 M sulfuric acid (H_2SO_4) (Figure 23.11)
- Fluorescein in dimethylsulfoxide (DMSO) (Figure 23.12)
- 5-Carboxytetramethylrhodamine in DMSO (Figure 23.13)
- Sulforhodamine 101 in DMSO (Figure 23.14)
- Nile blue perchlorate in DMSO (Figure 23.15)

Spectroscopic data for the five standards are summarized in Table 23.1.

RediPlate™ Microplate Intensity Standards

Our RediPlate™ 96 microplate intensity standards provide a means of reliably assessing day-to-day and instrument-to-instrument variability, as well as instrument performance. Fluorescence intensities are influenced by a variety of sample-related and instrument-related parameters. Consequently, comparisons of data acquired on different instruments or with long intervals (several days or more) between measurements must be made with reference to standard fluorescent materials.

The RediPlate™ 96 microplate intensity standards provide stable and consistent reference materials for standardizing fluorescence measurements in 96-well microplates. Each microplate intensity standard consists of a conventional 96-well microplate containing a fluorescent dye that is present at 11 different intensity levels and that is suspended in a proprietary matrix to protect the fluorophore during transport and storage. The RediPlate™ 96 microplate intensity standards can be used to generate a linear series of fluorescence intensities covering three orders of magnitude in twofold increments (Table 23.2) and are suitable for use with both top- and bottom-reading fluorescence microplate readers. The highly reproducible analytical curves generated from the fluorescence output of these standards offer:

Table 23.1 — Spectroscopic data for components of Molecular Probes' Reference Dye Sampler Kit

Component	Solvent	Abs (nm) *	Em (nm) *	QY †
Quinine sulfate	Water	347 ‡	455 ‡	0.55 ‡
Fluorescein	Water	490 §	514 §	0.92 §
5-CTMR **	Methanol	542	568	0.68
Sulforhodamine 101	Ethanol	578	605	0.90
Nile blue	Ethanol	636	665	0.27

* Approximate absorbance (Abs) and fluorescence emission (Em) maxima.
† Fluorescence quantum yield at 22°C. ‡ Standard values in 0.5 M H_2SO_4. § Standard values in 0.1 M NaOH. ** CTMR = Carboxytetramethylrhodamine.

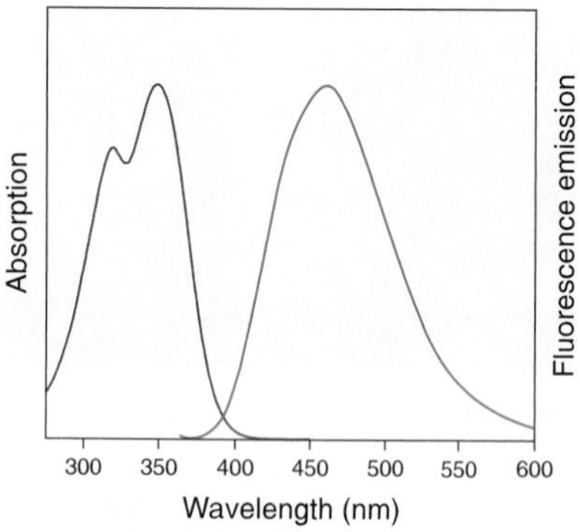

Figure 23.11 Absorption and fluorescence emission spectra of quinine sulfate, dihydrate in 0.5 M sulfuric acid.

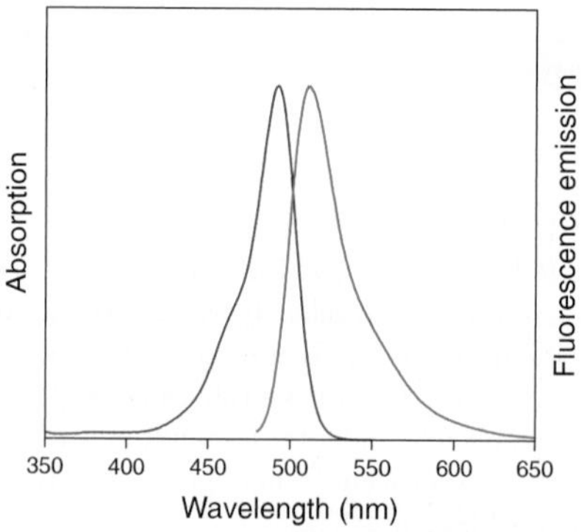

Figure 23.12 Absorption and fluorescence emission spectra of fluorescein in 0.1 M sodium hydroxide.

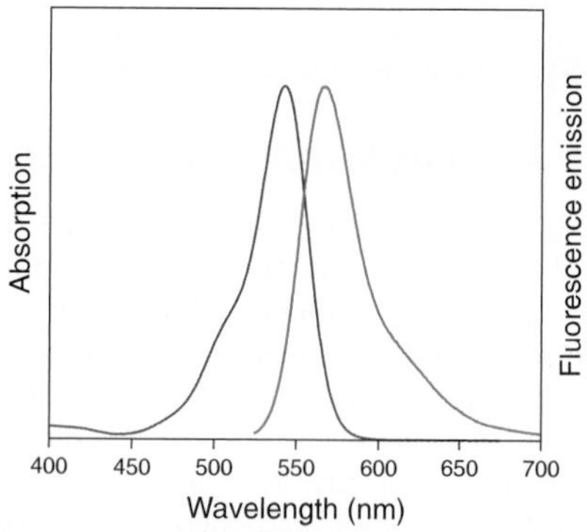

Figure 23.13 Absorption and fluorescence emission spectra of 5-carboxytetramethylrhodamine (5-TAMRA) in methanol.

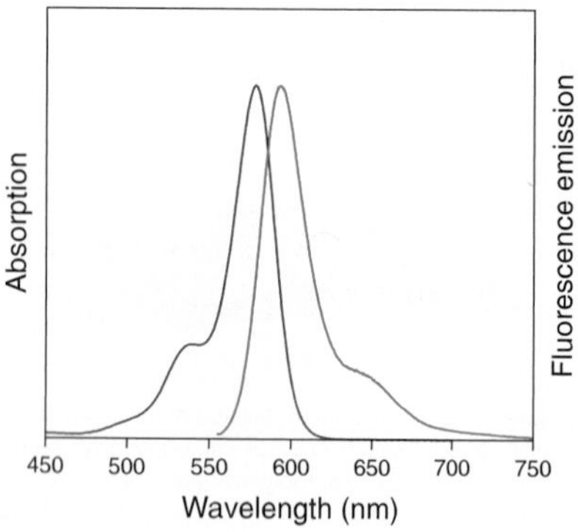

Figure 23.14 Absorption and fluorescence emission spectra of sulforhodamine 101 in ethanol.

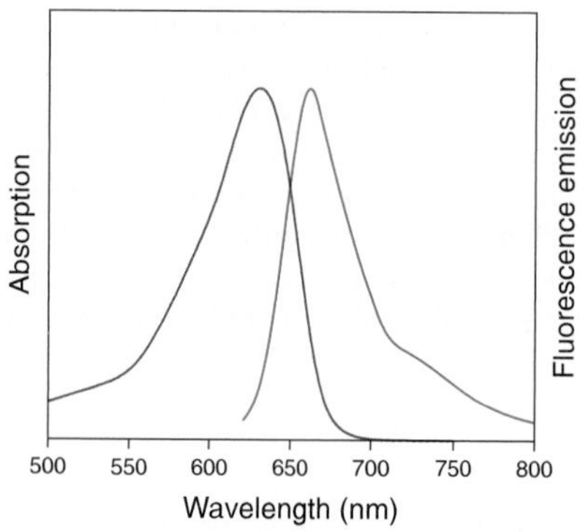

Figure 23.15 Absorption and fluorescence emission spectra of nile blue in ethanol.

Table 23.2 — Layout of RediPlate™ 96 microplate intensity standards

Column	Relative Dye Amount *
1	1024
2	512
3	256
4	128
5	64
6	32
7	16
8	8
9	4
19	2
11	1
12	0 (background)

* Fluorescence intensity is directly proportional to the amount of dye.

- **Linearity.** $R^2 \geq 0.99$ for each RediPlate™ 96 microplate intensity standard over several weeks (Figure 23.16).
- **Broad measurement range.** The fluorophore concentration spans three orders of magnitude.
- **Reliability.** The standards are optically and physically stable for several months and after multiple measurements.

The RediPlate™ 96 microplate intensity standards are available in four different excitation and emission wavelengths, spanning the spectrum from the visible to near infrared (Figure 23.17):

- **RediPlate™ 96 microplate intensity standards for green fluorescence (490/510 nm)** (R36901) such as Alexa Fluor® 488, fluorescein (FITC), Oregon Green® 488, BODIPY® FL, enhanced green-fluorescent protein (EGFP), PicoGreen®, RiboGreen® and OliGreen® dyes.
- **RediPlate™ 96 microplate intensity standards for orange fluorescence (565/580 nm)** (R36902) such as Alexa Fluor® 555, Alexa Fluor® 546, Alexa Fluor® 568, BODIPY® TMR, Cy3 and tetramethylrhodamine (TRITC) dyes.
- **RediPlate™ 96 microplate intensity standards for red fluorescence (590/605 nm)** (R36903) such as Alexa Fluor® 594, Texas Red® and BODIPY® TR dyes.
- **RediPlate™ 96 microplate intensity standards for far-red fluorescence (660/675 nm)** (R36904) such as Alexa Fluor® 647 and Cy5 dyes.

We also offer a RediPlate™ 96 microplate intensity standards set (R36910) that contains one 96-well microplate each of the green-fluorescent, orange-fluorescent, red-fluorescent and far-red–fluorescent microplate standards. In addition to these RediPlate™ microplate intensity standards, the Reference Dye Sampler Kit (R14782), described above, can be used to calibrate fluorescence microplate readers using five extensively characterized fluorescence standards spanning the entire visible spectrum.

FluoCells® Prepared Microscope Slides

Ideal for educators and instrument manufacturers, our popular FluoCells® prepared microscope slides contain multilabeled cell preparations for observation by epifluorescence or confocal laser-scanning microscopy. The multicolor staining in these cell preparations results in stunning, publication-quality images and lasts through repeated viewings. These slides are especially useful for setting up microscopes and camera systems and for assessing the capabilities of optical filter sets. When stored properly, these permanently mounted specimens will retain their bright and specific staining patterns for at least six months from the date of purchase. We currently offer five different FluoCells® prepared microscope slides:

- FluoCells® prepared slide #1 [2] (F14780, Figure 23.18) shows bovine pulmonary artery endothelial cells (BPAEC) stained with Mito-

Day	R^2
One	1
Two	1
Three	1
Four	1
Five	1
Six	1
Seven	1
Eight	0.9999
Nine	0.9999
Ten	1
Eleven	1
Twelve	1
Thirteen	1
Fourteen	1
Average	0.9999
Standard Deviation	0.00004
% CV	0.004

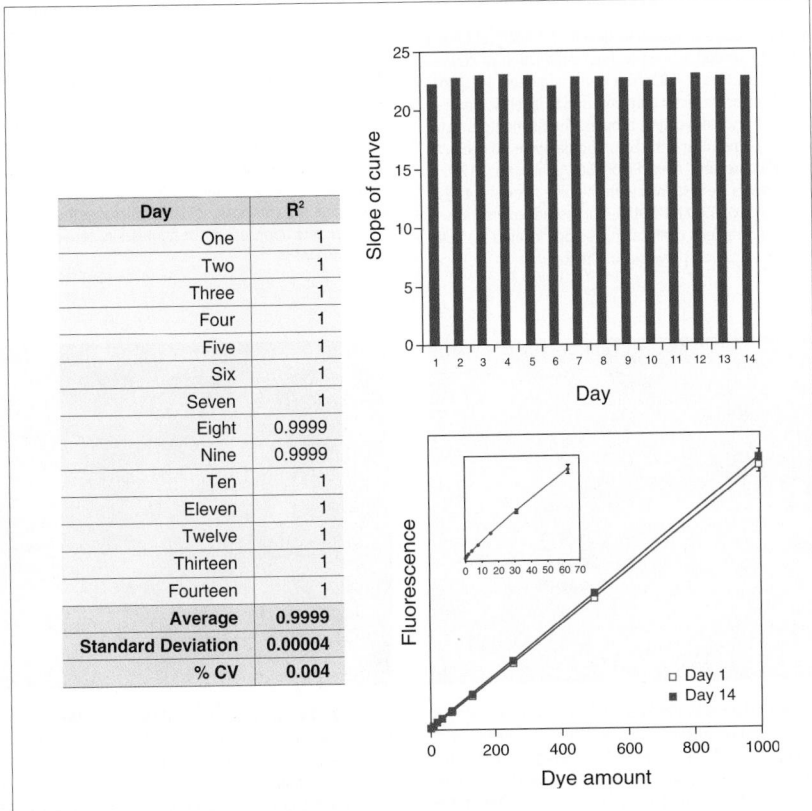

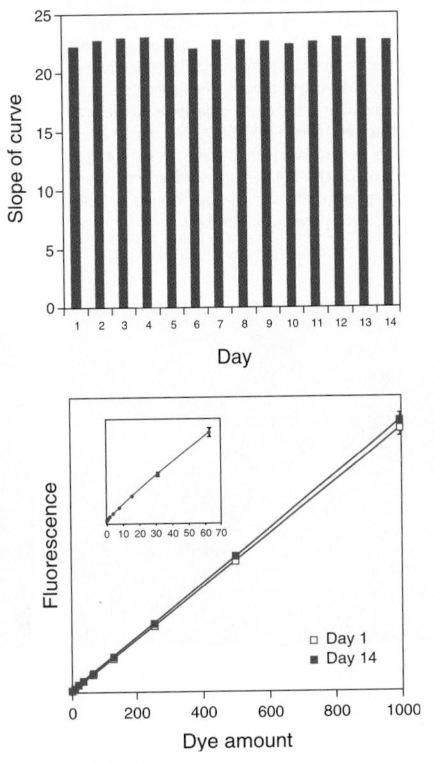

Figure 23.16 Day-to-day variation of the RediPlate™ 96 microplate intensity standards. Ten times a day, for a period of 14 days, an entire green-fluorescent RediPlate™ 96 microplate intensity standard (R36901) was read and the average intensity for each well was plotted against the relative dye concentration (bottom line graph). Over this time period, the slope and R^2 value changed minimally as demonstrated by the low CV (top bar graph).

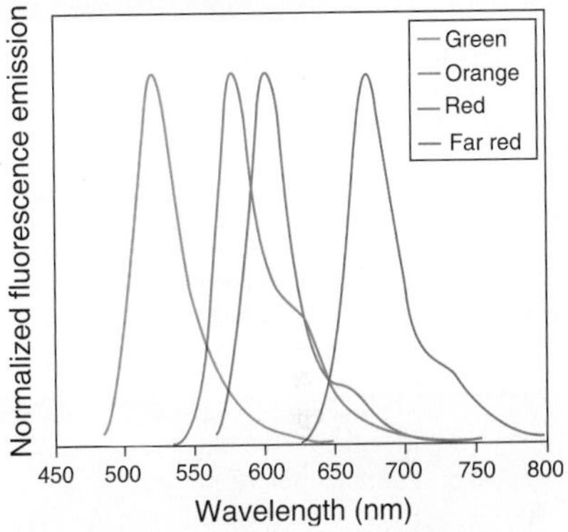

Figure 23.17 Normalized emission spectra for the RediPlate™ 96 microplate intensity standards (R36901, R36902, R36903, R36904).

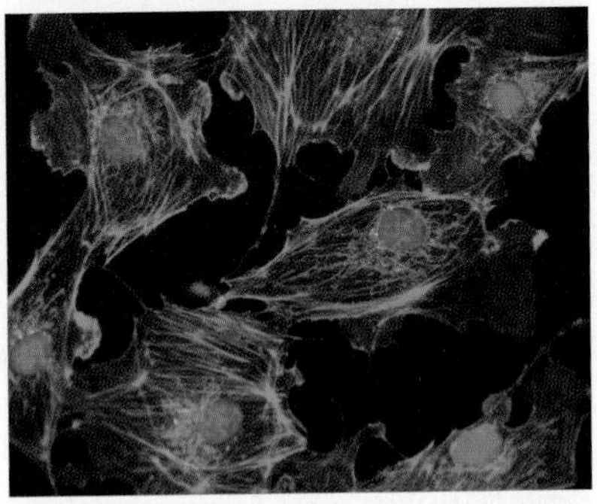

Figure 23.18 FluoCells® prepared slide #1 (F14780) showing bovine pulmonary artery endothelial cells (BPAEC) that have been labeled with MitoTracker® Red CMXRos (M7512) for mitochondria, and then fixed, permeabilized and stained with BODIPY® FL phallacidin (B607) for F-actin and DAPI (D1306, D3571, D21490) for nuclei. This multiple-exposure image was acquired using DAPI, fluorescein and Texas Red® bandpass optical filter sets.

Tracker® Red CMXRos for labeling mitochondria, BODIPY® FL phallacidin for labeling F-actin and DAPI for labeling the nucleus.

- FluoCells® prepared slide #2 [2] (F14781, Figure 23.19) again contains BPAEC, but this time stained with Texas Red®-X phalloidin for labeling F-actin, mouse monoclonal anti–α-tubulin antibody in conjunction with BODIPY® FL goat anti–mouse IgG antibody for labeling microtubules and DAPI for labeling the nucleus.
- FluoCells® prepared slide #3 (F24630; Figure 23.20, Figure 23.21, Figure 23.22) contains a 16 µm cryostat section of a mouse kidney. Green-fluorescent Alexa Fluor® 488 wheat germ agglutinin stains the glomeruli and convoluted tubules; red-fluorescent Alexa Fluor® 568 phalloidin labels actin, which is especially prevalent in glomeruli and the brush border of proximal convoluted tubules; finally, DAPI stains the nuclei with blue fluorescence.
- FluoCells® prepared slide #4 (F24631, Figure 23.23) contains a 16 µm cryostat section of a mouse intestine. Alexa Fluor® 350 wheat germ agglutinin labels the mucus of goblet cells with blue fluorescence; the red-fluorescent Alexa Fluor® 568 phalloidin labels actin filaments, which are especially prevalent in the brush border of the intestinal mucosa; and SYTOX® Green nucleic acid stain labels nuclei with green fluorescence.
- FluoCells® prepared slide #6 (F36925, Figure 23.24) contains muntjac skin fibroblast cells stained with a combination of fluorescent stains. Green-fluorescent Alexa Fluor® 488 phalloidin labels the

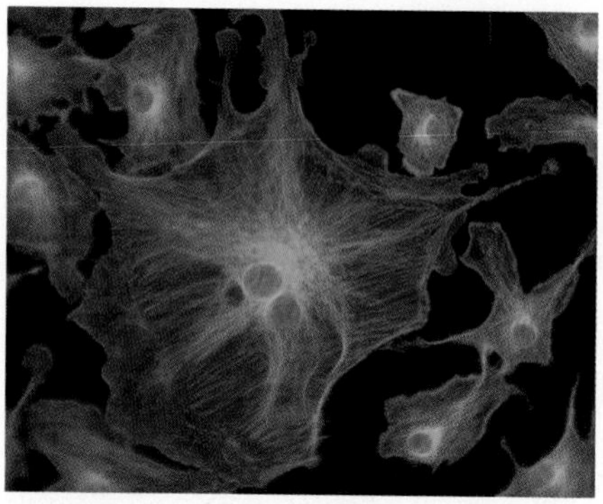

Figure 23.19 FluoCells® prepared slide #2 (F14781), which shows bovine pulmonary artery endothelial cells (BPAEC) that have been stained with an anti–β-tubulin mouse monoclonal antibody in conjunction with BODIPY® FL goat anti–mouse IgG (B2752) for labeling microtubules, Texas Red®-X phalloidin (T7471) for labeling F-actin and DAPI (D1306, D3571, D21490) for labeling nuclei. This multiple-exposure image was acquired using bandpass optical filter sets appropriate for DAPI, fluorescein and Texas Red® dye.

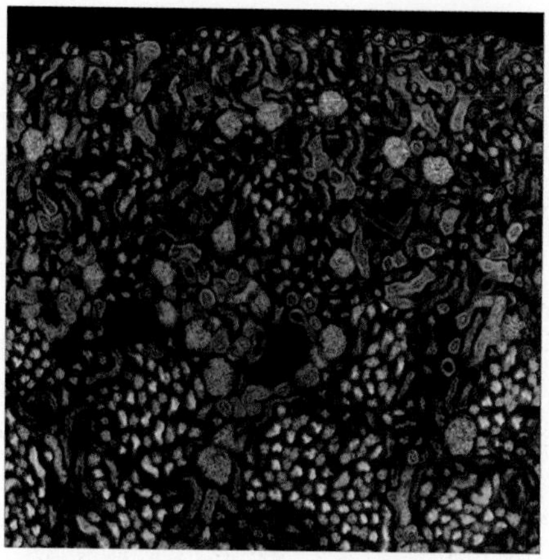

Figure 23.20 FluoCells® prepared slide #3 (F24630) contains a mouse kidney section stained with a combination of fluorescent dyes. Alexa Fluor® 488 wheat germ agglutinin (W11261) is a green-fluorescent lectin that was used to label elements of the glomeruli and convoluted tubules. The filamentous actin prevalent in glomeruli and the brush border were stained with red-orange–fluorescent Alexa Fluor® 568 phalloidin (A12380). Finally, the nuclei were stained with the blue-fluorescent DNA stain DAPI (D1306, D3571, D21490). This pseudocolored image was acquired on a Zeiss confocal microscope located at the Institute of Neuroscience, University of Oregon.

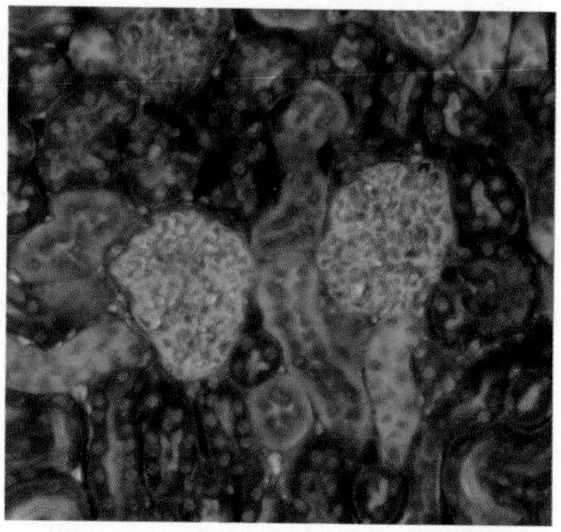

Figure 23.21 FluoCells® prepared slide #3 (F24630) contains a section of mouse kidney stained with a combination of fluorescent dyes. Alexa Fluor® 488 wheat germ agglutinin (W11261), a green-fluorescent lectin, was used to label elements of the glomeruli and convoluted tubules. The filamentous actin prevalent in glomeruli and the brush border were stained with red-fluorescent Alexa Fluor® 568 phalloidin (A12380). Finally, the nuclei were counterstained with the blue-fluorescent DNA stain DAPI (D1306, D3571, D21490). This image is a composite of three micrographs acquired using filter sets appropriate for fluorescein, tetramethylrhodamine and DAPI.

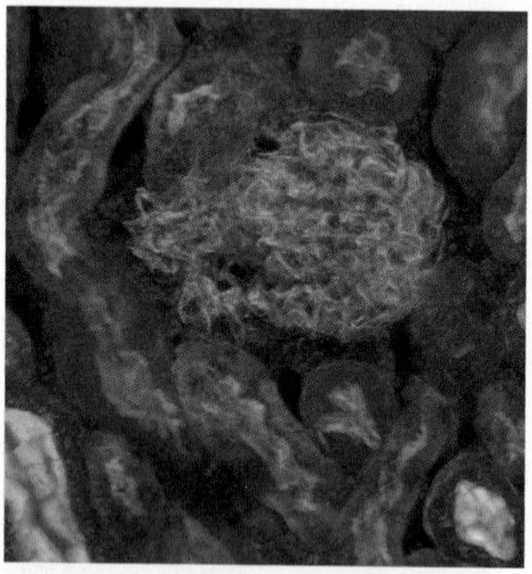

Figure 23.22 FluoCells® prepared slide #3 (F24630) containing a 16 µm cryostat section of mouse kidney stained with green-fluorescent Alexa Fluor® 488 wheat germ agglutinin (W11261), red-orange–fluorescent Alexa Fluor® 568 phalloidin (A12380) and blue-fluorescent DAPI (D1306, D3571, D21490). The image represents an optical section obtained by simultaneous two-photon excitation of all three dyes at 797 nm using a Bio-Rad Radiance 2100 multiphoton microscope system. The image was acquired at the 2001 3-D Microscopy of Living Cells Course, University of British Columbia, Vancouver, Canada, by John Jordan, Bio-Rad Laboratories; and Iain Johnson, Molecular Probes, Inc.

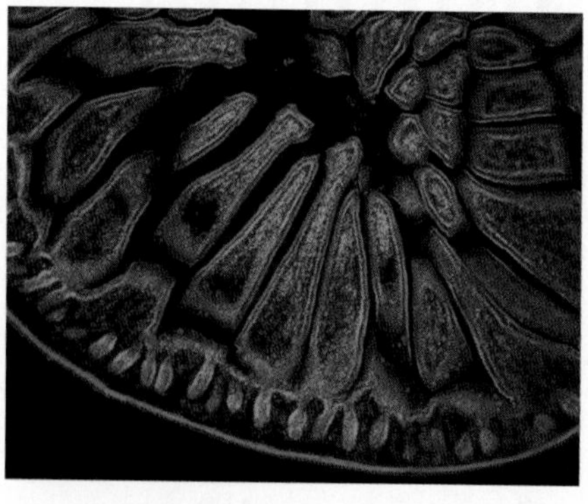

Figure 23.23 FluoCells® prepared slide #4 (F24631) contains a section of mouse intestine stained with a combination of fluorescent stains. Alexa Fluor® 350 wheat germ agglutinin (W11263) is a blue-fluorescent lectin that was used to stain the mucus of goblet cells. The filamentous actin prevalent in the brush border was stained with red-orange–fluorescent Alexa Fluor® 568 phalloidin (A12380). Finally, the nuclei were stained with SYTOX® Green nucleic acid stain (S7020). This image is a composite of three digitized images obtained with filter sets appropriate for fluorescein, DAPI and tetramethylrhodamine.

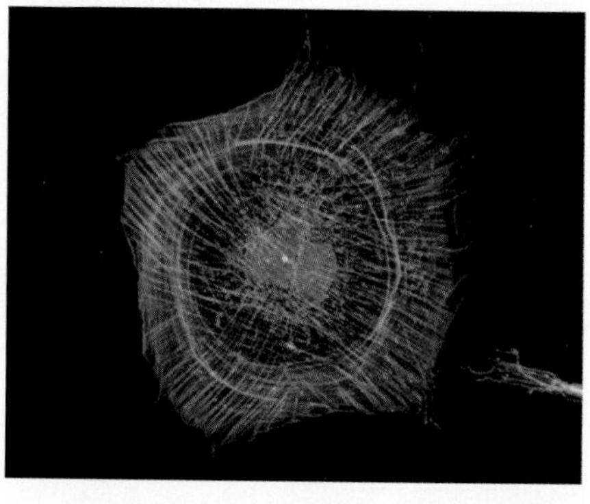

Figure 23.24 FluoCells prepared slide #6 (F36925) showing a fixed, permeabilized, and labeled muntjac skin fibroblast. Mitochondria were labeled with anti–OxPhos Complex V inhibitor protein mouse IgG_1 and visualized using orange-fluorescent Alexa Fluor® 555 goat anti–mouse IgG (A21422). F-actin was labeled with green-fluorescent Alexa Fluor® 488 phalloidin (A12379), and the nucleus was stained with TO-PRO®-3 iodide (T3605, pseudocolored magenta).

prominent filamentous actin in these cells; a mouse monoclonal anti–OxPhos Complex V inhibitor protein antibody in conjunction with the orange-fluorescent Alexa Fluor® 555 goat anti–mouse IgG antibody labels mitochondria; far-red–fluorescent TO-PRO®-3 nucleic acid stain labels nuclei. Because it contains no blue-fluorescent dyes, this slide is ideal for use with confocal laser-scanning microscopes that rely on non–UV laser light sources.

ProLong® and *SlowFade*® Antifade Reagents

Loss of fluorescence through irreversible photobleaching processes can lead to a significant reduction in sensitivity, particularly when target molecules are of low abundance or when excitation light is of high intensity or long duration. To minimize photobleaching of experimental samples, we have developed the ProLong®, ProLong® Gold, *SlowFade*® and *SlowFade*® *Light* Antifade Kits and reagents, which have been shown to increase the photostability of many of our fluorophores in fixed cells, fixed tissues and cell-free preparations. The primary function of any antifade reagent is to sustain dye fluorescence, usually by inhibiting the generation and diffusion of reactive oxygen species. Strategies for further maximizing the fluorescence signal in both living and nonliving specimens include reducing the excitation light intensity by using neutral density filters, high–numerical aperture objectives, relatively low magnification, high-quality optical filters and high-speed film or high-efficiency detectors.

ProLong® Gold Antifade Reagent

ProLong® Gold antifade reagent is a new and even more effective version of the ProLong® antifade reagent, a component of the ProLong® Antifade Kit described below (see below). The ProLong® Gold antifade reagent outperforms all other commercially available antifade reagents and causes little or no quenching of the fluorescent signal (Figure 23.25, Figure 23.26, Figure 23.27). Furthermore, unlike the reagents in the ProLong® Antifade Kit, the ProLong® Gold antifade reagent is premixed and ready to use — just add a drop to the preparation and mount. As with our original ProLong® antifade reagent, ProLong® Gold reagent cures within 24 hours and the sample can be saved for months after mounting. ProLong® Gold reagent offers excellent compatibility with a multitude of dyes and dye complexes, making it an especially valuable tool for multicolor applications. The ProLong® Gold antifade reagent is available in a single 10 mL bottle (P36930), as well as in a set of five 2 mL bottles (P36934).

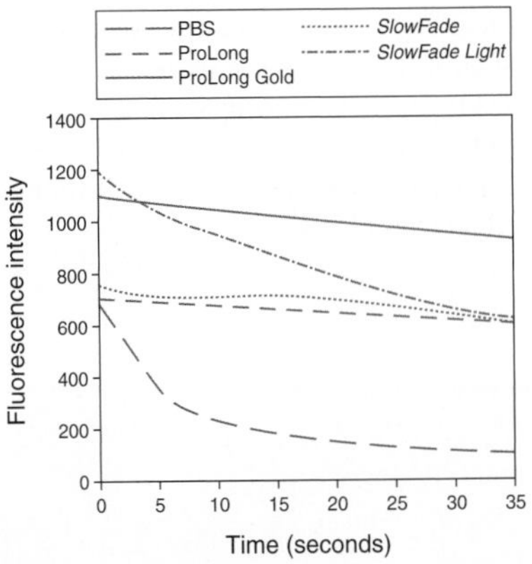

Figure 23.25 The superior performance of ProLong® Gold antifade reagent (P36930), as compared with other antifade reagents offered by Molecular Probes. Bovine pulmonary arterial endothelial cells were labeled with fluorescein phalloidin and mounted in various antifade reagents. Samples were imaged using a 1.3 NA 40× oil immersion lens, Omega XF100-2 filter set and frame-capture rate of 1 image/second. Images were acquired with a Hamamatsu Orca ER camera using the same exposure time for all samples. Y-axis values represent averages of the top 10% of the intensity-binned pixel values.

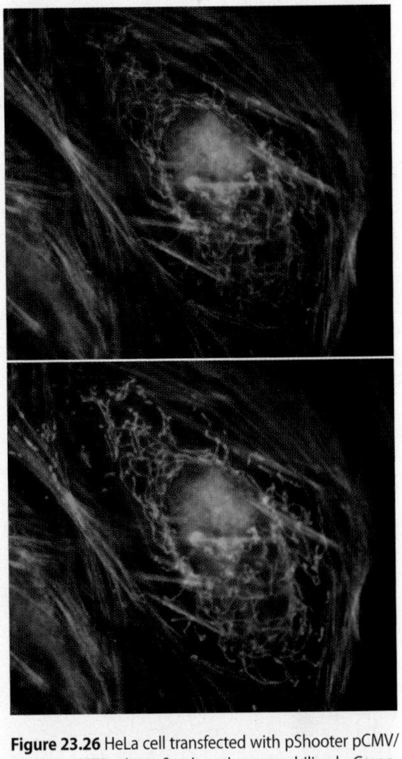

Figure 23.26 HeLa cell transfected with pShooter pCMV/myc/mito/GFP, then fixed and permeabilized. Green-fluorescent protein (GFP) localized in the mitochondria was labeled with anti-GFP mouse IgG_{2a} (A11120) and detected with orange-fluorescent Alexa Fluor® 555 goat anti–mouse IgG (A21422), which colocalized with the dim GFP fluorescence. F-actin was labeled with green-fluorescent Alexa Fluor® 488 phalloidin (A12379), and the nucleus was stained with blue-fluorescent DAPI (D1306, D3571, D21490). The sample was mounted using ProLong® Gold antifade reagent (P36930). Some GFP fluorescence is retained in the mitochondria after fixation (top), but immunolabeling and detection greatly improve visualization (bottom).

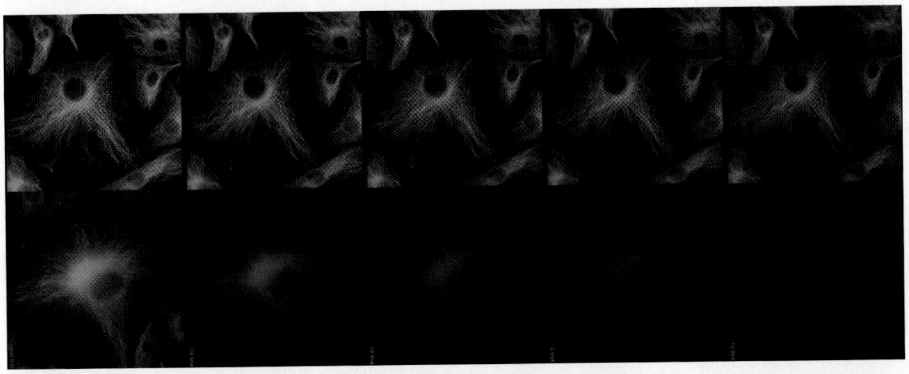

Figure 23.27 A 20-second time series showing enhanced resistance to photobleaching afforded by ProLong® Gold antifade reagent. Fixed bovine pulmonary artery endothelial cells were labeled with anti–α-tubulin (A11126) and visualized with fluorescein goat anti-mouse IgG (F2761). The samples were mounted in ProLong® Gold antifade reagent (P36930; top) or phosphate-buffered saline (bottom). Images were acquired at 5 second intervals using a 40x/1.3 NA oil immersion objective with continuous illumination from a standard 100 watt Hg-arc lamp.

As an added convenience, we also offer ProLong® Gold antifade reagent containing DAPI, the popular nuclear and chromosome stain that emits blue fluorescence upon binding to DNA. The addition of DAPI in the mounting media eliminates the need for a separate counterstaining step. The ProLong® Gold antifade reagent with DAPI is available in a single 10 mL bottle (P36931), as well as in a set of five 2 mL bottles (P36935).

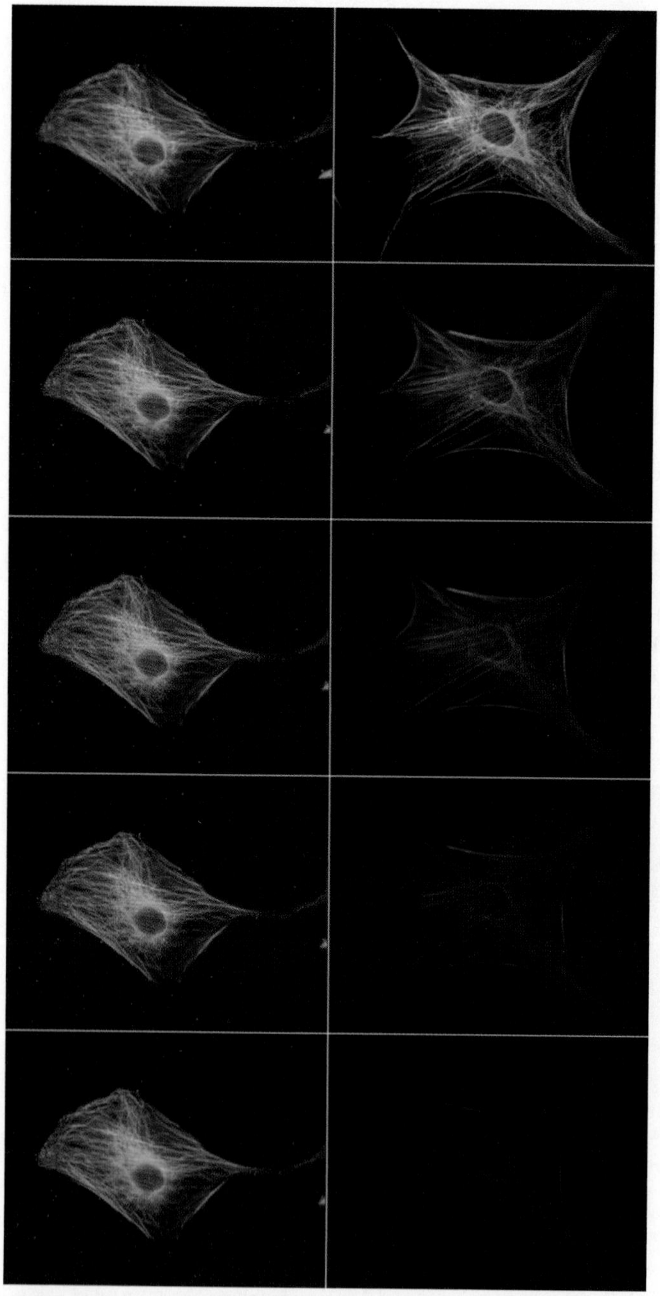

Figure 23.28 The relative photobleaching rates of fluorescein and Texas Red® fluorophores with buffer alone (right series) or after treatment with the ProLong® antifade reagent (left series). Bovine pulmonary artery endothelial cells were fixed, permeabilized and labeled with Texas Red®-X phalloidin (T7471), which labels F-actin, and with a mouse monoclonal anti–β-tubulin antibody and fluorescein goat anti-mouse IgG antibody (F2761), which label microtubules. Images were acquired at appropriate wavelengths using a cooled CCD camera.

ProLong® Antifade Kit

The ProLong® Antifade Kit (P7481, Figure 23.28) contains our original ProLong® antifade reagent, which has proven to effectively enhance the resistance of many different fluorophores to photobleaching. Furthermore, specimens mounted using the ProLong® Antifade Kit exhibit little or no quenching of the fluorescent signal of most dyes. Each ProLong® Antifade Kit contains:

- ProLong® antifade reagent powder
- ProLong® mounting medium
- A protocol for mounting samples

Bovine pulmonary artery endothelial cells labeled with fluorescein phalloidin (F432) photobleached to about 12% of the initial value in 30 seconds in PBS, while staying at the initial value under the same illumination conditions when mounted using the ProLong® Antifade Kit (Figure 23.29). As shown in Figure 23.30, the ProLong® Antifade Kit provides more fluorescence output than a popular *p*-phenylenediamine–containing antifade reagent [8] when used to mount fluorescein-stained HEp-2 cells. Furthermore, fluorescence of the Texas Red® dye when viewed through the appropriate Texas Red® optical filter (Table 23.9) becomes noticeably brighter upon addition of the ProLong® antifade reagent. The ProLong® antifade reagent also inhibits the fading of tetramethylrhodamine, as well as the fading of DNA-bound nucleic acid stains such as DAPI, propidium iodide and YOYO®-1 (Section 8.1), again without significantly quenching the fluorescence of these dyes. The compatibility of the ProLong® antifade reagent with a multitude of dyes and dye complexes makes it an especially valuable tool for multicolor analysis procedures such as multiplexed fluorescence *in situ* hybridization [9] (FISH, Section 8.5).

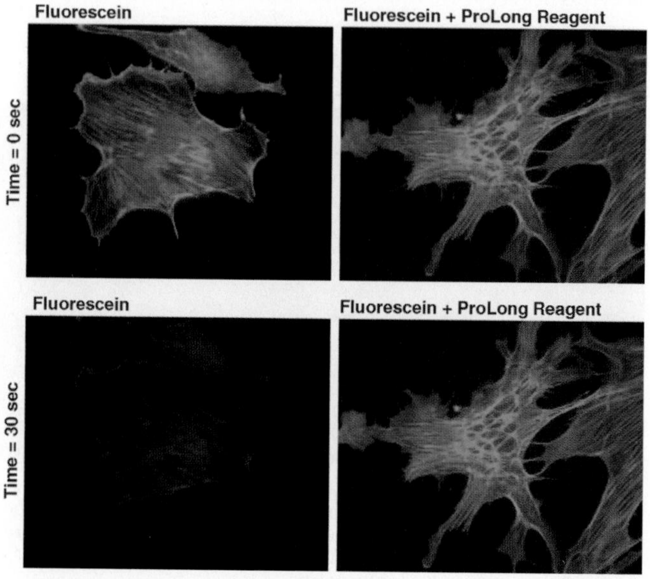

Figure 23.29 Bovine pulmonary artery endothelial cells were labeled with fluorescein phalloidin (F432), which labels filamentous actin, and placed under constant illumination on the microscope with a FITC filter set using a 60× objective. Images were acquired at one-second intervals for 30 seconds. Under these illumination conditions, fluorescein photobleached to about 12% of its initial value in 30 seconds in PBS (left), but stayed at the initial value under the same illumination conditions when mounted using the reagents in the ProLong® Antifade Kit (right, P7481).

SlowFade® *and* SlowFade® Light *Antifade Kits*

Our original *SlowFade*® formulation (S2828) was designed to reduce the fading rate of fluorescein to almost zero. Because it provides nearly constant emission intensity from fluorescein, the *SlowFade*® reagent is especially useful for quantitative measurements and applications that employ a confocal laser-scanning microscope, in which the excitation intensities can be extreme and prolonged. The *SlowFade*® reagent can extend the useful fluorescence emission of fluorescein more than 50-fold and can preserve the signal in cell and tissue mounts for up to two years. However, the original *SlowFade*® formulation substantially quenches the fluorescence of fluorescein and almost completely quenches that of the Alexa Fluor® 350, Alexa Fluor® 405 and Cascade Blue® fluorophores.

To overcome this limitation, Molecular Probes' researchers have developed the *SlowFade® Light* Antifade Kit (S7461). The antifade formulation in our *SlowFade® Light* Antifade Kit slows fluorescein's fading rate by about fivefold without significantly reducing fluorescein's initial fluorescence intensity (Figure 23.31), thereby dramatically increasing the signal-to-noise ratio in photomicroscopy. Moreover, quenching of the Alexa Fluor® 350, Alexa Fluor® 405, Cascade Blue®, tetramethylrhodamine and Texas Red® dyes is minimal. In fact, the *SlowFade® Light* antifade reagent reduces the fading rate of the Cascade Blue® fluorophore to almost zero, while decreasing its emission intensity by only about 30%.

Each *SlowFade*® or *SlowFade® Light* Antifade Kit contains:

- *SlowFade*® (in Kit S2828) or *SlowFade® Light* (in Kit S7461) antifade reagent in 50% (v/v) glycerol, ready to use and sufficient for at least 200 coverslip-size experiments
- 2X Concentrated *SlowFade*® or *SlowFade® Light* antifade reagent solution, provided for those applications in which glycerol may not be compatible
- Equilibration buffer, which raises the pH of the sample, increasing the protection afforded by both *SlowFade*® formulations
- A detailed protocol for mounting samples

We have also formulated the *SlowFade*® and *SlowFade® Light* Antifade Kits (S24635, S24636) to include the blue-fluorescent nuclear counterstain DAPI (Section 8.6). These kits permit simultaneous staining and protection of the stained sample from photobleaching.

The *SlowFade*® Antifade Kits are especially designed for those who want a quick and easy solution to photobleaching. Unlike the ProLong® Antifade Kit, the *SlowFade*® Kits require no reagent mixing. Simply pre-wash fluorescently labeled specimens in the equilibration buffer provided and then apply the mounting medium directly from the convenient applicator bottle.

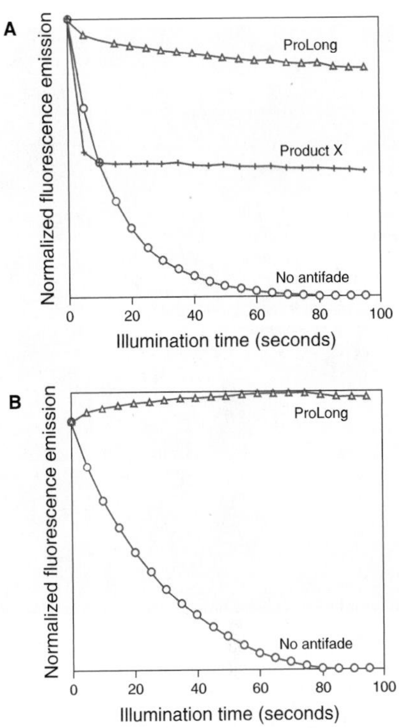

Figure 23.30 Bleaching profiles of A) fluorescein and B) Texas Red® dye conjugates in cell samples. In these photobleaching experiments, human epithelial cells (HEp-2) were probed with human anti-nuclear antibodies and then developed for visualization with fluorophore-labeled secondary reagents. Identical samples were mounted in ProLong® antifade reagent (△: in Kit P7481), Product X (+) or medium containing no antifade reagent (○). Although these data were normalized, we observed little or no quenching of samples mounted with the ProLong® mounting medium.

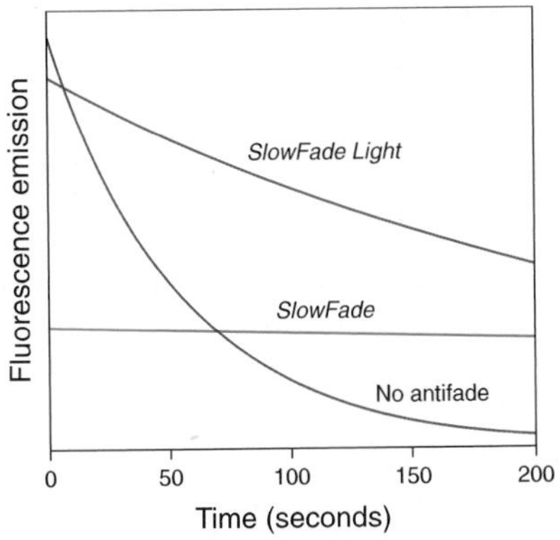

Figure 23.31 The fluorescence intensity of fluorescein as a function of illumination time, under the following conditions: in the presence of the *SlowFade® Light* antifade reagent (in Kit S7461; green), in the presence of the *SlowFade*® antifade reagent (in Kit S2828; red) and in the absence of an antifade reagent (blue). In these experiments, we added free fluorescein directly to a solution and then examined the mixture in a capillary tube using a 20× lens. In real samples such as cells and tissues, we find that the local environment influences the bleaching rate, yielding results that are sometimes different from those shown here.

Image-iT™ FX Kits: All-in-One Kits for Fluorescence Imaging of Fixed Cells

Image-iT™ FX Kits

The Image-iT™ FX Kits (Table 7.6) provide the best secondary detection reagents and supporting materials needed for optimal imaging of fixed cells and tissue sections:

- Alexa Fluor® conjugates of goat anti–mouse IgG antibody, goat anti–rabbit IgG antibody or streptavidin deliver superior photostability and brightness (Table 7.7, see Section 7.2 for more specific information)
- ProLong® Gold antifade reagent reduces photobleaching (Figure 23.25, Figure 23.26, Figure 23.27)

- Image-iT™ FX signal enhancer improves the signal-to-noise ratio (Figure 7.47, Figure 7.48, Figure 23.32)
- A sample pack of two CultureWell chambered coverglasses makes sample processing more convenient (Figure 23.42, see Section 23.3 for more details)

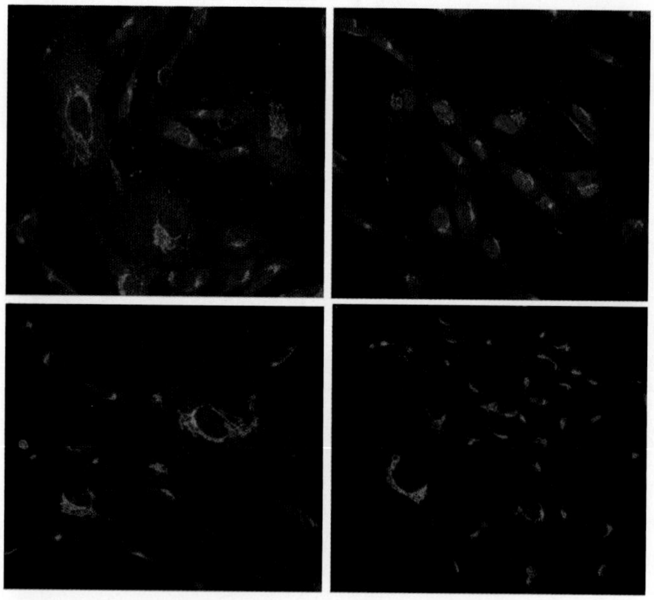

Figure 23.32 Increased label specificity and resolution afforded by Image-iT™ FX signal enhancer. Fixed and permeabilized MRC-5 human lung fibroblast cells were labeled with mouse anti–human Golgin-97 primary antibody (A21270), then visualized with either fluorescein goat anti–mouse IgG (F2761, top row) or Alexa Fluor® 488 goat anti–mouse IgG (A11001, bottom row). Cells on the right were treated with Image-iT™ FX signal enhancer (I36933) prior to antibody incubation.

Each Image-iT™ FX Kit provides sufficient materials to perform 50–100 assays. Furthermore, the components of each kit are available separately (Alexa Fluor® secondary antibodies, Section 7.2, Table 7.1; Alexa Fluor® streptavidin, Section 7.6, Table 7.22; ProLong® Gold antifade reagent, P36930; Image-iT™ FX signal enhancer, I36933; CultureWell chambered coverglasses, C37000, C37005, Section 23.3) for flexibility in experimental design.

Image-iT™ FX Signal Enhancer

By efficiently blocking nonspecific interactions of a wide variety of fluorescent dyes with cell and tissue constituents, the Image-iT™ FX signal enhancer (I36933) dramatically improves the signal-to-noise ratio of immunolabeled cells and tissues, allowing clear visualization of targets that would normally be indistinguishable due to background fluorescence (Figure 7.47, Figure 7.48, Figure 23.32). Background staining seen with fluorescent conjugates of streptavidin, goat anti–mouse IgG antibody or goat anti–rabbit IgG antibody is largely eliminated when Image-iT™ FX signal enhancer is applied to fixed and permeabilized cells prior to staining. Image-iT™ FX signal enhancer may also effectively prevent nonspecific staining that is typically blocked with 1–2% BSA or 10% serum treatment, in some cases eliminating the need for another step in the staining protocol.

References

1. Appl Immunohistochem Mol Morphol 7, 156 (1999); **2.** Methods 18, 447 (1999); **3.** Biophys J 80, 2455 (2001); **4.** J Fluorescence 6, 147 (1996); **5.** J Res Natl Inst Stand Technol 107, 83 (2002); **6.** J Res Natl Inst Stand Technol 106, 381 (2001); **7.** J Res Natl Inst Stand Technol 107, 83 (2002); **8.** J Histochem Cytochem 41, 1833 (1993); **9.** Cytometry 32, 163 (1998).

Product List — 23.1 Reference Standards and Antifade Reagents

Cat #	Product Name	Unit Size
C14837	Constellation™ microspheres for imaging *mixture of assorted sizes and colors*	3 mL
F14780	FluoCells® prepared slide #1 *BPAE cells with MitoTracker® Red CMXRos, BODIPY® FL phallacidin, DAPI*	each
F14781	FluoCells® prepared slide #2 *BPAE cells with mouse anti-α-tubulin, BODIPY® FL goat anti-mouse IgG, Texas Red®-X phalloidin, DAPI*	each
F24630	FluoCells® prepared slide #3 *mouse kidney section with Alexa Fluor® 488 WGA, Alexa Fluor® 568 phalloidin, DAPI*	each
F24631	FluoCells® prepared slide #4 *mouse intestine section with Alexa Fluor® 350 WGA, Alexa Fluor® 568 phalloidin, SYTOX® Green*	each
F36925	FluoCells® prepared slide #6 *muntjac cells with mouse anti-OxPhos Complex V inhibitor protein, Alexa Fluor® 555 goat anti-mouse IgG, Alexa Fluor® 488 phalloidin, TO-PRO®-3*	each
F36915	fluorescein *NIST-traceable standard* *nominal concentration 50 µM* *special packaging*	5 x 1 mL
F36908	FocalCheck™ DoubleFarRed Fluorescent Microspheres Kit, 6 µm *mounted on slides*	1 kit
F36905	FocalCheck™ DoubleGreen Fluorescent Microspheres Kit, 6 µm *mounted on slides*	1 kit
F36906	FocalCheck™ DoubleOrange Fluorescent Microspheres Kit, 6 µm *mounted on slides*	1 kit
F36907	FocalCheck™ DoubleRed Fluorescent Microspheres Kit, 6 µm *mounted on slides*	1 kit
F24633	FocalCheck™ Fluorescent Microspheres Kit, 6 µm *mounted on slides*	1 kit
F24634	FocalCheck™ Fluorescent Microspheres Kit, 15 µm *mounted on slides*	1 kit
F14807	FocalCheck™ microspheres, 6 µm, fluorescent dark-red ring stain/green throughout	0.5 mL
F14806	FocalCheck™ microspheres, 6 µm, fluorescent green/orange/dark-red ring stains	0.5 mL
F14808	FocalCheck™ microspheres, 6 µm, fluorescent green ring stain/blue throughout	0.5 mL
F7234	FocalCheck™ microspheres, 15 µm, fluorescent blue/orange ring stains	0.5 mL
F7239	FocalCheck™ microspheres, 15 µm, fluorescent dark-red ring stain/green throughout	0.5 mL

For current prices or to order online, visit probes.invitrogen.com

Cat #	Product Name	Unit Size
F7240	FocalCheck™ microspheres, 15 µm, fluorescent green/dark-red ring stains	0.5 mL
F7235	FocalCheck™ microspheres, 15 µm, fluorescent green/orange/dark-red ring stains	0.5 mL
F7237	FocalCheck™ microspheres, 15 µm, fluorescent green ring stain/blue throughout	0.5 mL
F7238	FocalCheck™ microspheres, 15 µm, fluorescent green ring stain/dark red throughout	0.5 mL
F7236	FocalCheck™ microspheres, 15 µm, fluorescent orange ring stain/blue throughout	0.5 mL
F14791	FocalCheck™ Thin-Ring Fluorescent Microspheres Kit, 1.0 µm *three suspensions*	1 kit
I37150	Image-iT™ FX Kit #1 *with Alexa Fluor® 350 goat anti-mouse IgG (A21049), ProLong® Gold antifade (P36930) and Image-iT™ FX signal enhancer (I36933)*	1 kit
I37151	Image-iT™ FX Kit #2 *with Alexa Fluor® 488 goat anti-mouse IgG (A11029), ProLong® Gold antifade (P36930) and Image-iT™ FX signal enhancer (I36933)*	1 kit
I37152	Image-iT™ FX Kit #3 *with Alexa Fluor® 555 goat anti-mouse IgG (A21424), ProLong® Gold antifade (P36930) and Image-iT™ FX signal enhancer (I36933)*	1 kit
I37153	Image-iT™ FX Kit #4 *with Alexa Fluor® 594 goat anti-mouse IgG (A11032), ProLong® Gold antifade (P36930) and Image-iT™ FX signal enhancer (I36933)*	1 kit
I37154	Image-iT™ FX Kit #5 *with Alexa Fluor® 647 goat anti-mouse IgG (A21236), ProLong® Gold antifade (P36930) and Image-iT™ FX signal enhancer (I36933)*	1 kit
I37155	Image-iT™ FX Kit #6 *with Alexa Fluor® 350 goat anti-rabbit IgG (A21068), ProLong® Gold antifade (P36930) and Image-iT™ FX signal enhancer (I36933)*	1 kit
I37156	Image-iT™ FX Kit #7 *with Alexa Fluor® 488 goat anti-rabbit IgG (A11034), ProLong® Gold antifade (P36930) and Image-iT™ FX signal enhancer (I36933)*	1 kit
I37157	Image-iT™ FX Kit #8 *with Alexa Fluor® 555 goat anti-rabbit IgG (A21429), ProLong® Gold antifade (P36930) and Image-iT™ FX signal enhancer (I36933)*	1 kit
I37158	Image-iT™ FX Kit #9 *with Alexa Fluor® 594 goat anti-rabbit IgG (A11037), ProLong® Gold antifade (P36930) and Image-iT™ FX signal enhancer (I36933)*	1 kit
I37159	Image-iT™ FX Kit #10 *with Alexa Fluor® 647 goat anti-rabbit IgG (A21245), ProLong® Gold antifade (P36930) and Image-iT™ FX signal enhancer (I36933)*	1 kit
I37160	Image-iT™ FX Kit #11 *with Alexa Fluor® 350 streptavidin (S11249), ProLong® Gold antifade (P36930) and Image-iT™ FX signal enhancer (I36933)*	1 kit
I37161	Image-iT™ FX Kit #12 *with Alexa Fluor® 488 streptavidin (S11223), ProLong® Gold antifade (P36930) and Image-iT™ FX signal enhancer (I36933)*	1 kit
I37162	Image-iT™ FX Kit #13 *with Alexa Fluor® 555 streptavidin (S21381), ProLong® Gold antifade (P36930) and Image-iT™ FX signal enhancer (I36933)*	1 kit
I37163	Image-iT™ FX Kit #14 *with Alexa Fluor® 594 streptavidin (S11227), ProLong® Gold antifade (P36930) and Image-iT™ FX signal enhancer (I36933)*	1 kit
I37164	Image-iT™ FX Kit #15 *with Alexa Fluor® 647 streptavidin (S21374), ProLong® Gold antifade (P36930) and Image-iT™ FX signal enhancer (I36933)*	1 kit
I36933	Image-iT™ FX signal enhancer	10 mL
I7221	InSpeck™ Blue (350/440) Microscope Image Intensity Calibration Kit, 2.5 µm	1 kit
I7225	InSpeck™ Deep Red (633/660) Microscope Image Intensity Calibration Kit, 2.5 µm	1 kit
I7219	InSpeck™ Green (505/515) Microscope Image Intensity Calibration Kit, 2.5 µm	1 kit
I14785	InSpeck™ Green (505/515) Microscope Image Intensity Calibration Kit, 6 µm	1 kit
I7223	InSpeck™ Orange (540/560) Microscope Image Intensity Calibration Kit, 2.5 µm	1 kit
I14786	InSpeck™ Orange (540/560) Microscope Image Intensity Calibration Kit, 6 µm	1 kit
I7224	InSpeck™ Red (580/605) Microscope Image Intensity Calibration Kit, 2.5 µm	1 kit
I14787	InSpeck™ Red (580/605) Microscope Image Intensity Calibration Kit, 6 µm	1 kit
M7901	MultiSpeck™ Multispectral Fluorescence Microscopy Standards Kit *in suspension*	1 kit
P7481	ProLong® Antifade Kit	1 kit
P36930	ProLong® Gold antifade reagent	10 mL
P36934	ProLong® Gold antifade reagent *special packaging*	5 x 2 mL
P36931	ProLong® Gold antifade reagent with DAPI	10 mL
P36935	ProLong® Gold antifade reagent with DAPI *special packaging*	5 x 2 mL
P7220	PS-Speck™ Microscope Point Source Kit *blue, green, orange and deep red fluorescent beads*	1 kit
R36904	RediPlate™ 96 microplate intensity standards, far red fluorescent (660/675) *one 96-well microplate*	each
R36901	RediPlate™ 96 microplate intensity standards, green fluorescent (490/510) *one 96-well microplate*	each
R36902	RediPlate™ 96 microplate intensity standards, orange fluorescent (565/580) *one 96-well microplate*	each
R36903	RediPlate™ 96 microplate intensity standards, red fluorescent (590/605) *one 96-well microplate*	each
R36910	RediPlate™ 96 microplate intensity standards set *includes one each of R36901, R36902, R36903 and R36904*	1 set
R14782	Reference Dye Sampler Kit *five 1 mM solutions, 1 mL each*	1 kit
S2828	*SlowFade®* Antifade Kit	1 kit
S24635	*SlowFade®* Antifade Kit with DAPI	1 kit
S7461	*SlowFade® Light* Antifade Kit	1 kit
S24636	*SlowFade® Light* Antifade Kit with DAPI	1 kit
T7284	TetraSpeck™ Fluorescent Microspheres Sampler Kit	1 kit
T14792	TetraSpeck™ Fluorescent Microspheres Size Kit *mounted on slides*	1 kit
T7279	TetraSpeck™ microspheres, 0.1 µm, fluorescent blue/green/orange/dark red	0.5 mL
T7280	TetraSpeck™ microspheres, 0.2 µm, fluorescent blue/green/orange/dark red	0.5 mL
T7281	TetraSpeck™ microspheres, 0.5 µm, fluorescent blue/green/orange/dark red	0.5 mL
T7282	TetraSpeck™ microspheres, 1.0 µm, fluorescent blue/green/orange/dark red	0.5 mL
T7283	TetraSpeck™ microspheres, 4.0 µm, fluorescent blue/green/orange/dark red	0.5 mL

For current prices or to order online, visit probes.invitrogen.com

23.2 Flow Cytometry Reference Standards

Flow cytometers are designed to perform quantitative measurements on individual cells and other particles with high precision, speed and accuracy. As with all high-performance instrumentation, flow cytometers must be calibrated frequently to ensure accuracy and reliability. The stability, uniformity and reproducibility of our fluorescent microsphere products make them ideal reference standards for flow cytometry. Our flow cytometry reference standards exhibit superior stability and greater uniformity than other commercially available microparticles, and they are accompanied by a full one-year warranty (see Note 23.1 "Product Highlight: Warranty for Flow Cytometry Standards"). Known numbers of fluorescent microspheres can also be added to samples to facilitate the estimation of cell numbers,[1] as in our Bacteria Counting Kit[2–4] (B7277, see below). Unfortunately, because of high variability in quantum yields of dyes bound to an antibody, heterogeneity of antibody labeling, problems with stoichiometry and accessibility in binding to targets, improper calibration procedures and several other factors, bead standards containing a known number of fluorophores per bead do not necessarily provide accurate information about the number of ligands bound to a cell.[5]

AlignFlow™ and AlignFlow™ Plus Flow Cytometry Alignment Beads

Due to advances in flow cytometric instrumentation and the development of fluorescent probes, a scientist can now perform multiparameter analyses on biological samples. In order to ensure accurate and reproducible results, flow cytometers should be checked at least daily for proper performance. Molecular Probes' AlignFlow™ and AlignFlow™ Plus flow cytometry alignment beads permit the calibration of a flow cytometer's laser(s), optics and stream flow without wasting valuable and sensitive experimental material. These fluorescently stained polystyrene microspheres are highly uniform with respect to both size and fluorescence intensity, and are designed to approximately replicate the size, emission wavelength and intensity of biological samples. Because the dyes are contained inside the microsphere's matrix, instead of on the bead's surface, AlignFlow™ beads have excellent photochemical and physical stability, providing reliable reference signals for aligning, focusing and calibrating flow cytometers. The fluorescent dyes have been carefully selected for optimal excitation by laser sources commonly used in flow cytometry.

The 2.5 µm AlignFlow™ beads are each available in four versions: for UV (350–370 nm) excitation (A7304), for 488 nm excitation (A7302), for 633 nm excitation (A7312) and for 630–660 nm excitation (A14835). The 6 µm AlignFlow™ Plus beads are available for the same four excitation-wavelength ranges: for UV (350–370 nm) excitation (A7305), for 488 nm excitation (A7303), for 633 nm excitation (A7313) and for 630–660 nm excitation (A14836). The UV light–excitable beads emit from 400 nm to 470 nm, the 488 nm light–excitable beads emit broadly from 515 nm to 660 nm (Figure 23.33), the 633 nm light–excitable beads emit from 645 nm to 680 nm, and the 630–660 nm light–excitable beads emit from 670 nm to 720 nm. The AlignFlow™ and AlignFlow™ Plus flow cytometry alignment beads are supplied as suspensions packaged in dropper vials for convenient dispensation.

CompenFlow™ Flow Cytometry Compensation Kit

Subsets of cells that are differentially labeled with fluorescent probes can be readily identified and sorted with a modern flow cytometer using multicolor analysis. However, the emission spectra of the dyes typically used for cell labeling are broader than the light collection windows delineated by a flow cytometer's optical filters. Thus, the fluorescence signal of a dye may be registered in more than one detection channel. The emission spillover can be corrected using electronic processing called "color compensation." Molecular Probes' CompenFlow™ Flow Cytometry Compensation Kits (2.5 µm beads, C14820; 6 µm beads, C7301) are designed to help flow cytometer operators set up compensation circuits that properly remove unwanted signals from secondary channels (Figure 23.34). The CompenFlow™ beads have

Note 23.1 — Product Highlight

Warranty for Flow Cytometry Standards

Guaranteed Stability

We warrant that our flow cytometry standards will remain suitable for calibration of flow cytometers for one year from the date of purchase, if stored properly. We will replace or refund the purchase price of any product returned to us that we find to be out of compliance with our specifications — just contact our Technical Service Department.

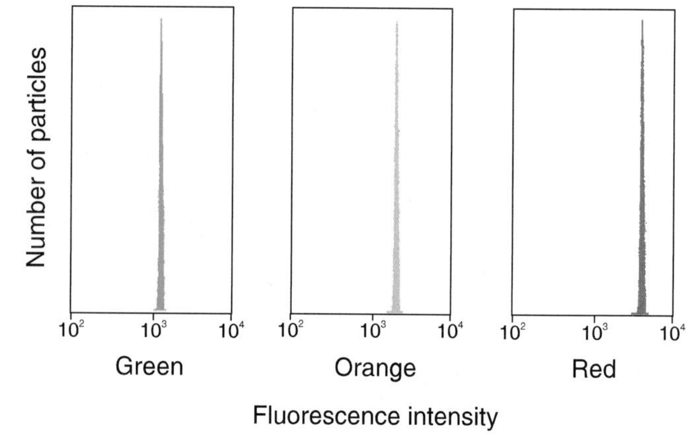

Figure 23.33 AlignFlow™ Plus (A7303) beads excited at 488 nm by an argon-ion laser and monitored in three emission channels. The broad fluorescence emission is detected in all three channels. Note the exceptionally small variation of fluorescence intensity of the beads. Contributed by Carleton Stewart, Roswell Park Cancer Institute.

several unique properties and show a nearly perfect spectral match to labeled cells.[6] Each CompenFlow™ Kit contains three suspensions of either 2.5 µm or 6 µm polystyrene microspheres packaged in dropper vials for convenient dispensation:

- Fluorescein-like beads
- R-phycoerythrin–like beads
- Control beads

When excited at 488 nm by an argon-ion laser, the fluorescein-like polystyrene beads emit yellow–green light that virtually matches the spectrum of fluorescein-labeled cells (Figure 23.35). The R-phycoerythrin–like polystyrene beads emit red–orange light that virtually matches the spectrum of R-phycoerythrin–labeled cells (Figure 23.36). Control beads have been lightly stained with a mixture of dyes to mimic the autofluorescence of typical unstained lymphocytes. Because CompenFlow™ microspheres are stained internally, rather than on the surface, their fluorescence is not susceptible to environment-dependent quenching.[6] Furthermore, because our fluorescein-like beads are stained with a dye that is pH insensitive, their fluorescence intensity will not vary with changes in pH, as with conventional fluorescein-labeled beads. Consequently, the CompenFlow™ beads demonstrate a constant intensity for much longer than other commercially available beads that are surface-labeled. Our stability tests indicate that after dilution into sheath fluid, CompenFlow™ bead suspensions are stable for at least a week; beads from other sources fade after only one day. When stored as supplied, CompenFlow™ beads are stable for at least one year.

LinearFlow™ Flow Cytometry Intensity Calibration Kits

LinearFlow™ Flow Cytometry Intensity Calibration Kits provide flow cytometer operators with intensity references for generating calibration curves, establishing photomultiplier settings and evaluating sample brightness. Each kit contains fluorescent microspheres in which the degree of staining has been carefully controlled to provide precisely determined intensity levels when excited in a flow cytometer (Figure 23.37). The microspheres are supplied as suspensions packaged in dropper vials for convenient dispensation. The LinearFlow™ Flow Cytometry Intensity Calibration Kits are available in two different bead sizes (2.5 µm or 6 µm) and five different fluorescent colors covering the spectral ranges commonly encountered in flow cytometry:

- **Blue** (for UV excitation/430 nm emission). Available in 2.5 µm (L14812) and 6 µm (L14813) sizes; both kits contain microspheres stained at 100%, 20%, 4.0% and 0.8% relative fluorescence intensity levels.
- **Green** (for 488 nm excitation/515 emission). Available in 2.5 µm (L14821) and 6 µm (L14822) sizes; both kits contain microspheres stained at 100%, 10%, 2.0%, 0.4%, 0.1% and 0.02% relative fluorescence intensity levels. The LinearFlow™ Green Flow Cytometry Low-Intensity Calibration Kits contain 2.5 µm (L14823) or 6 µm (L14824) diameter beads stained at 0.1%, 0.02%, 0.004% and 0.001% relative fluorescence intensity levels. The fluorescence from the beads with the lowest intensity level is approximately half that of the autofluorescence typically observed from unstained cells.
- **Orange** (for 488 nm excitation/575 nm emission). Available in 2.5 µm (L14814) and 6 µm (L14815) sizes; both kits contain micro-

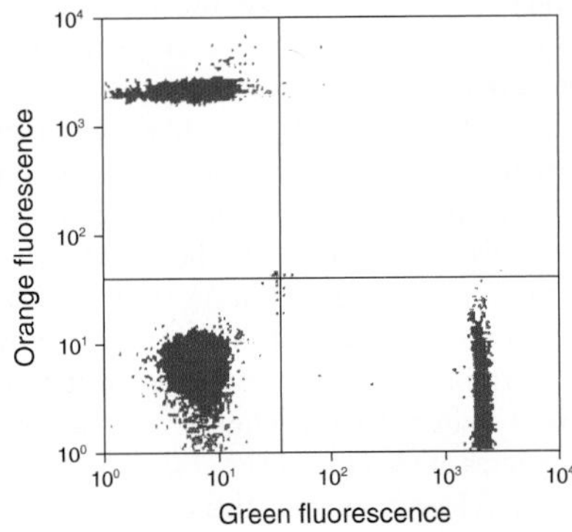

Figure 23.34 Flow cytometric analysis of the polystyrene beads supplied in our CompenFlow™ Flow Cytometry Compensation Kits (C7301, C14820) demonstrates the clear separation of fluorescein-like (lower right), R-phycoerythrin–like (upper left) and control (lower left) populations.

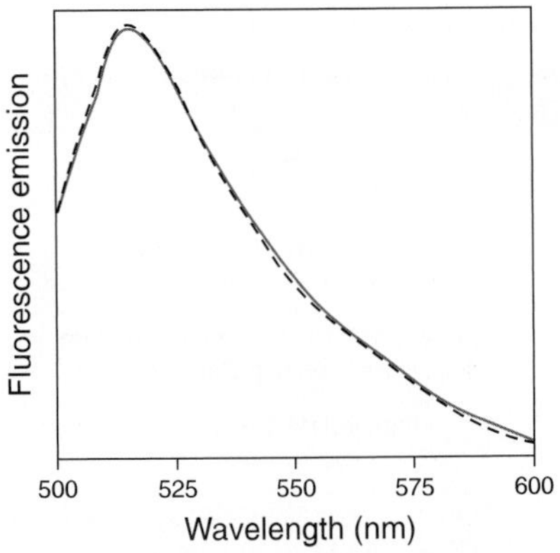

Figure 23.35 Normalized emission spectra of CompenFlow™ fluorescein-like beads (green, C7301) and beads surface-labeled with fluorescein (black dashes). Multiple dyes are used in the CompenFlow™ beads to ensure an almost total spectral match with fluorescein, but with much greater fluorescence signal stability than is possible using fluorescein.

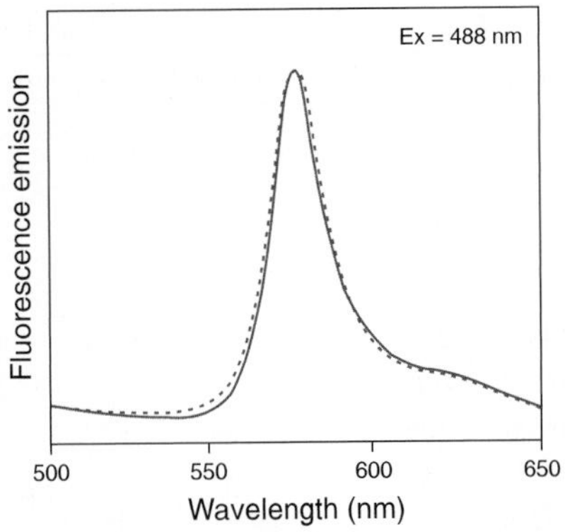

Figure 23.36 Spectral comparison of R-phycoerythrin–like beads and the R-phycoerythrin–labeled cells. The R-phycoerythrin–like beads included in our CompenFlow™ Flow Cytometry Compensation Kits (C7301, C14820; dashed line) almost perfectly match the emission spectra of blood cells stained with an R-phycoerythrin conjugate of mouse monoclonal anti-CD4 antibody (A21337; solid line) when excited at 488 nm.

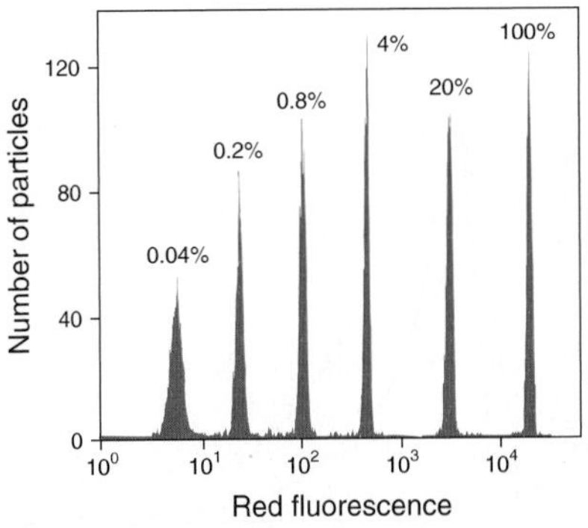

Figure 23.37 Fluorescence intensity histogram of the six, 6 µm polystyrene bead samples supplied in our LinearFlow™ Deep Red Flow Cytometry Intensity Calibration Kit (L14819). Fluorescence measurements were performed with a flow cytometer using excitation at 633 nm. This figure is a composite of two graphs; the same mixture of microspheres was sampled and analyzed using two distinct PMT voltage settings in order to cover the full intensity range.

spheres stained at 100%, 10%, 2.0%, 0.4%, 0.1% and 0.02% relative fluorescence intensity levels.
- **Carmine** (for 488 nm excitation/620 nm emission). Available in 2.5 µm (L14816) and 6 µm (L14817) sizes; both kits contain microspheres stained at 100%, 10%, 2.0%, 0.4%, 0.1% and 0.02% relative fluorescence intensity levels.
- **Deep Red** (for 633 nm excitation/660 nm emission). Available in 2.5 µm (L14818) and 6 µm (L14819, Figure 23.37) sizes; both kits contain microspheres stained at 100%, 20%, 4.0%, 0.8%, 0.2% and 0.04% relative fluorescence intensity levels.

The 365/430 nm fluorescence excitation/emission maxima of the microspheres in the LinearFlow™ Blue Kits provide a close spectral match to samples stained with DAPI and the Hoechst 33258 and Hoechst 33342 nucleic acid stains. These kits are ideal for intensity calibration of flow cytometers equipped with UV laser excitation. The microspheres in the LinearFlow™ Green Kits are designed for calibrating the green detection channel. Although the microspheres actually have an excitation maximum of ~505 nm, they are effectively excited by the 488 nm spectral line of the argon-ion laser. Their emission maximum of ~515 nm closely matches that of samples labeled with the fluorescein, Oregon Green® 488 or Alexa Fluor® 488 dyes or with the SYTOX® Green nucleic acid stain. Microspheres in the LinearFlow™ Orange Kit are spectrally similar to phycoerythrin and tetramethylrhodamine conjugates, making this kit useful for calibrating the orange channel. Although these microspheres actually have an excitation maximum of ~570 nm, they are effectively excited by the 488 nm spectral line of the argon-ion laser. Microspheres in the LinearFlow™ Carmine Kit exhibit excitation and emission spectra similar to those of the propidium iodide complex with DNA or with Texas Red® or Alexa Fluor® 594 conjugates and are suitable for calibrating the red channel. The microspheres in the LinearFlow™ Carmine Kit have an excitation maximum of ~580 nm but they can also be excited by the 488 nm spectral line of the argon-ion laser. The microspheres in the LinearFlow™ Deep Red Kit have maximal emission at ~660 nm, closely matching that of the Alexa Fluor® 647 dye, Cy5 dye and allophycocyanin conjugates and are useful for calibrating flow cytometers equipped with 633 nm He–Ne laser excitation. Although primarily intended for 633 nm excitation, the Deep Red LinearFlow™ microspheres can still be adequately excited at 488 nm, where they will still provide accurate relative intensity readings.

PeakFlow™ Flow Cytometry Reference Beads

Molecular Probes' PeakFlow™ beads are stained with fluorescent dyes that have been carefully selected to produce emission peaks coincident with labeled cells used in typical flow cytometry applications (Table 23.3). The emission profiles for these standards are intentionally narrow in comparison to fluorescein-labeled cells (Figure 23.38). Consequently, PeakFlow™ beads serve as reference sources with emissions centered upon the expected fluorescence of the experimental sample. Furthermore, in setting up for multicolor experiments, there is minimal spectral overlap between PeakFlow™ beads of two different fluorescent colors, and little or no color compensation is needed. These fluorescent polystyrene microspheres are supplied as suspensions packaged in dropper vials for convenient dispensation, with a choice of seven fluorescent colors and, for most products, two different sizes (Table 23.3).

Because PeakFlow™ beads are highly uniform with respect to both size and fluorescence intensity, and because they approximate the size, emission wavelength and intensity of many biological samples, they can be used to calibrate a flow cytometer's laser source, optics, stream flow and cell sorting system without wasting valuable and sensitive experimental material. As with all of our flow cytometry standard microspheres, PeakFlow™ beads are stained internally rather than on the surface. The dyes are therefore insulated from environmental interactions that could cause variable fluorescence output, resulting in excellent signal stability.

Flow Cytometry Size Calibration Kit

Our Flow Cytometry Size Calibration Kit (F13838) provides nonfluorescent particle-size calibration standards for use in forward light scattering measurements of cell size by flow cytometry. The kit contains suspensions of six different nonfluorescent microspheres packaged in convenient dropper vials. The individual standards contain highly uniform polystyrene microspheres with nominal diameters of 1.0 µm, 2.0 µm, 4.0 µm, 6 µm, 10 µm and 15 µm. Our nominally 0.1 µm FluoSpheres® yellow-green–fluorescent microspheres (F8803, Section 6.5) have been used to measure side scatter in a flow-stream waveguide flow cytometer.[7]

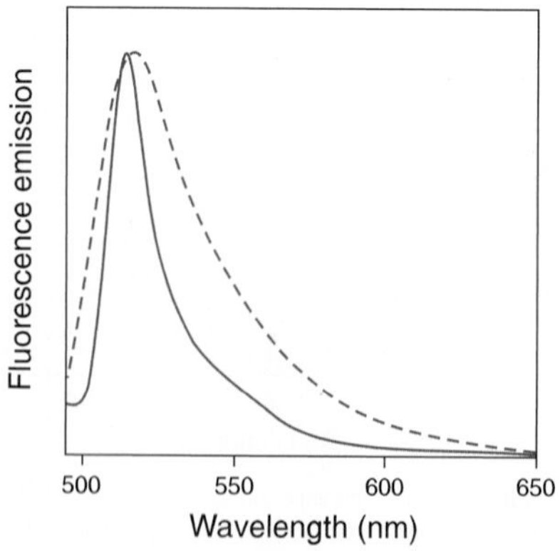

Figure 23.38 Normalized emission spectra of PeakFlow™ flow cytometry reference beads (P14827, solid line) and fluorescein-labeled cells (dashed line). The narrow emission spectrum of PeakFlow™ beads is approximately centered on the broader emission spectrum of fluorescein.

Table 23.3 — Spectral characteristics of PeakFlow™ flow cytometry reference beads

Cat #	Size (µm)	Nominal Color	Abs * (nm)	Em * (nm)	Emission Matches Cells Stained With:
P14825	2.5	Blue	400 †	460	DAPI, Hoechst dyes
P14826	6.0				
P14827	2.5	Green	505 ‡	515	Fluorescein, Alexa Fluor® 488 dye, Oregon Green® 488 dye, DiOC$_{18}$(3) ('DiO')
P14828	6.0				
P14829	2.5	Orange	570 ‡	575	R-phycoerythrin, tetramethylrhodamine, Alexa Fluor® 568 dye, DiIC$_{18}$(3) ('DiI')
P14830	6.0				
P14831	2.5	Carmine	580 ‡	620	Propidium iodide, Texas Red® dye, Alexa Fluor® 594 dye
P14832	6.0				
P24670	6.0	Claret	645 §	680	TOTO®-3, Alexa Fluor® 647 dye, Cy5 dye, DiIC$_{18}$(5) ('DiD')
P24671	6.0	Ultra Red	665 §	695	Alexa Fluor® 660 dye, Cy5.5 dye
P24672	6.0	Infrared	735	770	Alexa Fluor® 750 dye, Cy7 dye, DiIC$_{18}$(7) ('DiR')

* Approximate absorption and emission maxima for beads in suspension. † Suitable for excitation by the UV (351–364 nm) spectral line of argon-ion lasers. ‡ Suitable for excitation by the 488 nm spectral line of argon-ion lasers. § Suitable for excitation by the 633 nm spectral line of He–Ne lasers.

Bacteria Counting Kit

Accurate enumeration of low numbers of bacteria in samples must be performed daily in many quality-control laboratories. To facilitate this determination by flow cytometry, Molecular Probes has developed the Bacteria Counting Kit (B7277), which provides:

- The cell-permeant, green-fluorescent SYTO® BC nucleic acid stain to label bacteria
- Fluorescent polystyrene microspheres to calibrate the volume of bacterial suspension analyzed
- A detailed protocol

The patented SYTO® BC dye, which is also available separately (S34855, Section 8.1), is a high-affinity nucleic acid stain that easily penetrates both gram-negative and gram-positive bacteria, producing an exceptionally bright green-fluorescent signal. The calibrated suspension of polystyrene microspheres contains beads that exhibit a uniform density, low-level fluorescence and optimal size to clearly separate the light scattering of the microspheres from that of most bacteria. The fluorescent microspheres in our Bacteria Counting Kit have also been recommended for the enumeration of yeast.[3]

The Bacteria Counting Kit is particularly valuable for monitoring antibiotic sensitivity because it provides a convenient and accurate means for assessing changes in a bacterial population over time. A sample of the population is simply diluted, stained briefly with the SYTO® BC dye, mixed with a fixed number of microspheres and analyzed on a flow cytometer. Signals from both the stained bacteria and the beads are easily detected in the green (fluorescein) channel of most flow cytometers and can be distinguished on a plot of forward scatter versus fluorescence (Figure 15.73). The density of the bacteria in the sample can be determined from the ratio of bacteria signals to microsphere signals in the cytogram. The Bacteria Counting Kit can be used with a variety of gram-negative and gram-positive species of bacteria and provides sufficient reagents for approximately 100 flow cytometry assays. In addition to the Bacteria Counting Kit, we offer the LIVE/DEAD® *Bac*Light™ Bacterial Counting and Viability Kit (L34856, Section 15.3), which allows researchers to reliably distinguish and quantitate live and dead bacteria with the aid of a flow cytometer, even in a mixed population containing a range of bacterial types.

References

1. Cytometry 40, 26 (2000); **2.** Appl Environ Microbiol 64, 1725 (1998); **3.** Yeast 14, 147 (1998); **4.** Microbiol Rev 60, 641 (1996); **5.** Cytometry 8, 632 (1987); **6.** Cytometry 33, 244 (1998); **7.** Cytometry 37, 160 (1999).

Product List — 23.2 Flow Cytometry Reference Standards

Cat #	Product Name	Unit Size
A7304	AlignFlow™ flow cytometry alignment beads, 2.5 µm *for UV excitation*	3 mL
A7302	AlignFlow™ flow cytometry alignment beads, 2.5 µm *for 488 nm excitation*	3 mL
A14835	AlignFlow™ flow cytometry alignment beads, 2.5 µm *for 630-660 nm excitation*	3 mL
A7312	AlignFlow™ flow cytometry alignment beads, 2.5 µm *for 633 nm excitation*	3 mL
A7305	AlignFlow™ Plus flow cytometry alignment beads, 6 µm *for UV excitation*	3 mL
A7303	AlignFlow™ Plus flow cytometry alignment beads, 6 µm *for 488 nm excitation*	3 mL
A14836	AlignFlow™ Plus flow cytometry alignment beads, 6 µm *for 630-660 nm excitation*	3 mL
A7313	AlignFlow™ Plus flow cytometry alignment beads, 6 µm *for 633 nm excitation*	3 mL
B7277	Bacteria Counting Kit *for flow cytometry*	1 kit
C14820	CompenFlow™ Flow Cytometry Compensation Kit, 2.5 µm	1 kit
C7301	CompenFlow™ Flow Cytometry Compensation Kit, 6 µm	1 kit
F13838	Flow Cytometry Size Calibration Kit *nonfluorescent microspheres*	1 kit
L14812	LinearFlow™ Blue Flow Cytometry Intensity Calibration Kit, 2.5 µm *for UV excitation/430 nm emission*	1 kit
L14813	LinearFlow™ Blue Flow Cytometry Intensity Calibration Kit, 6 µm *for UV excitation/430 nm emission*	1 kit
L14816	LinearFlow™ Carmine Flow Cytometry Intensity Calibration Kit, 2.5 µm *for 488 nm excitation/620 nm emission*	1 kit
L14817	LinearFlow™ Carmine Flow Cytometry Intensity Calibration Kit, 6 µm *for 488 nm excitation/620 nm emission*	1 kit
L14818	LinearFlow™ Deep Red Flow Cytometry Intensity Calibration Kit, 2.5 µm *for 633 nm excitation/660 nm emission*	1 kit
L14819	LinearFlow™ Deep Red Flow Cytometry Intensity Calibration Kit, 6 µm *for 633 nm excitation/660 nm emission*	1 kit
L14821	LinearFlow™ Green Flow Cytometry Intensity Calibration Kit, 2.5 µm *for 488 nm excitation/515 nm emission*	1 kit
L14822	LinearFlow™ Green Flow Cytometry Intensity Calibration Kit, 6 µm *for 488 nm excitation/515 nm emission*	1 kit
L14823	LinearFlow™ Green Flow Cytometry Low Intensity Calibration Kit, 2.5 µm *for 488 nm excitation/515 nm emission*	1 kit
L14824	LinearFlow™ Green Flow Cytometry Low Intensity Calibration Kit, 6 µm *for 488 nm excitation/515 nm emission*	1 kit
L14814	LinearFlow™ Orange Flow Cytometry Intensity Calibration Kit, 2.5 µm *for 488 nm excitation/575 nm emission*	1 kit
L14815	LinearFlow™ Orange Flow Cytometry Intensity Calibration Kit, 6 µm *for 488 nm excitation/575 nm emission*	1 kit
P14825	PeakFlow™ Blue flow cytometry reference beads, 2.5 µm *460 nm emission*	3 mL
P14826	PeakFlow™ Blue flow cytometry reference beads, 6 µm *460 nm emission*	3 mL
P14831	PeakFlow™ Carmine flow cytometry reference beads, 2.5 µm *620 nm emission*	3 mL
P14832	PeakFlow™ Carmine flow cytometry reference beads, 6 µm *620 nm emission*	3 mL
P24670	PeakFlow™ Claret flow cytometry reference beads, 6 µm *680 nm emission*	3 mL
P14827	PeakFlow™ Green flow cytometry reference beads, 2.5 µm *515 nm emission*	3 mL
P14828	PeakFlow™ Green flow cytometry reference beads, 6 µm *515 nm emission*	3 mL
P24672	PeakFlow™ Infrared flow cytometry reference beads, 6 µm *770 nm emission*	3 mL
P14829	PeakFlow™ Orange flow cytometry reference beads, 2.5 µm *575 nm emission*	3 mL
P14830	PeakFlow™ Orange flow cytometry reference beads, 6 µm *575 nm emission*	3 mL
P24671	PeakFlow™ Ultra Red flow cytometry reference beads, 6 µm *695 nm emission*	3 mL

For current prices or to order online, visit probes.invitrogen.com

23.3 Accessories for Fluorescence Microscopy and Magnetic Separation

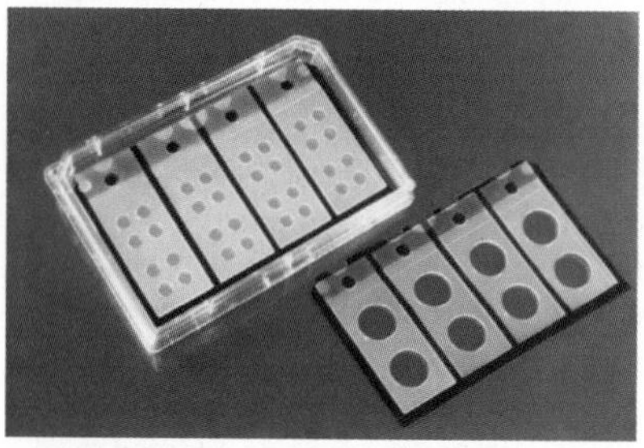

Figure 23.39 CultureWell cell culture system.

Sample Chambers, Slides and Coverslips

In collaboration with Grace Bio-Labs, we offer a collection of accessories for imaging and microscopy. These accessories make slide preparation easy, facilitate sample perfusion and simplify sample manipulation during *in situ* hybridization and other procedures that involve multiple wash steps.

CultureWell Cell Culture Systems

The CultureWell cell culture systems provide an integrated set of tools for preparing cultured cells for staining and imaging. Each system uses medical-grade silicone gaskets preassembled with standard optical-quality coverslips into convenient inserts that fit into matching cell culture plates (Figure 23.39). The entire system is provided sterile and ready to use. Cell culture, treatment and staining are performed on the coverslip, which adheres securely to the culture plate via a silicone backing. The samples can then be imaged with or without the silicone gaskets. Two types of systems are available in several configurations to suit a variety of needs (Table 23.4).

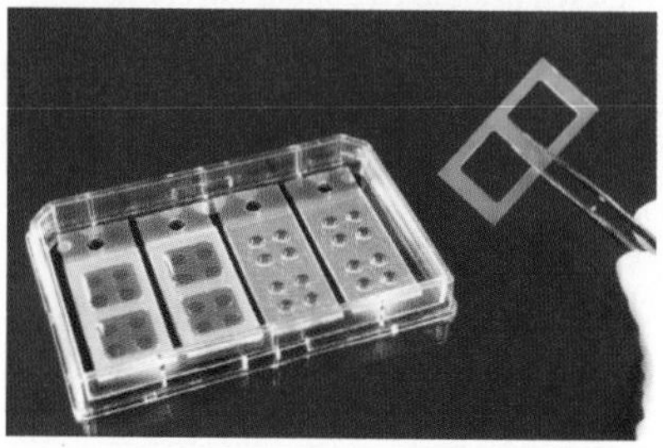

Figure 23.40 CultureWell silicone dividers (C24770).

The CultureWell multiwell cell culture systems use precut silicone gaskets to form convenient no-leak wells on 24 × 50 mm coverslips. The wells are spaced for compatibility with microfluidic handling robots. Low numbers of wells are ideal for titering antibody dilutions or other staining conditions, whereas the higher numbers of wells facilitate high-throughput screening. Each insert includes four coverslips with gaskets, preassembled into a culture plate. Silicone dividers (C24770, Figure 23.40) are also available for separating portions of the coverslip into leak-proof wells, for different treatment and washing conditions.

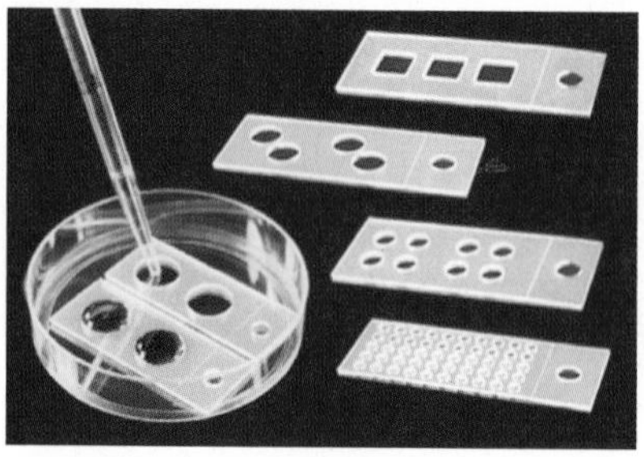

Figure 23.41 CultureWell chambered coverslips.

The CultureWell multislip cell culture systems comprise multiple coverslips arrayed on a sheet of silicone and assembled into a convenient insert. The silicone backing adheres the coverslips to the tissue culture plate, preventing movement during plating, cell culture and washing steps.

Table 23.4 — CultureWell cell culture systems and chambered coverslips

Cat #	Size of Coverslip (mm)	Number of Wells per Coverslip	Well Dimensions	Depth	Number of Coverslips per Insert
CultureWell multiwell cell culture systems * †					
C24762	24 × 50	2	15 mm diameter	1 mm	4
C24763	24 × 50	2	15 mm diameter	2 mm	4
C24764	24 × 50	3	9.5 mm square	1 mm	4
C24765	24 × 50	4	9 mm diameter	1 mm	4
C24766	24 × 50	8	6 mm diameter	1 mm	4
C24768	24 × 50	50	3 mm diameter	1 mm	4
CultureWell chambered coverslips ‡					
C24775	24 × 50	2	15 mm diameter	1 mm	NA
C24776	24 × 50	2	15 mm diameter	2 mm	NA
C24777	24 × 50	3	9.5 mm diameter	1 mm	NA
C24778	24 × 50	4	9 mm diameter	1 mm	NA
C24779	24 × 50	8	6 mm diameter	1 mm	NA
C24780	24 × 50	50	3 mm diameter	1 mm	NA
CultureWell multislip cell culture systems *					
C24761	18 × 18	NA	NA	NA	8
C24760	12 × 12	NA	NA	NA	15

* Each system is supplied in packages of 10 inserts, each preassembled in an 86 cm × 128 cm plate. † A trial size is also available (C24767) that includes two inserts — four coverslips with eight 6 mm wells each — in two plates. ‡ Chambered coverslips are supplied in sets of coverslips, in five pouches of four coverslips each. Packs of 10 sterile plates are also available separately (C24769).

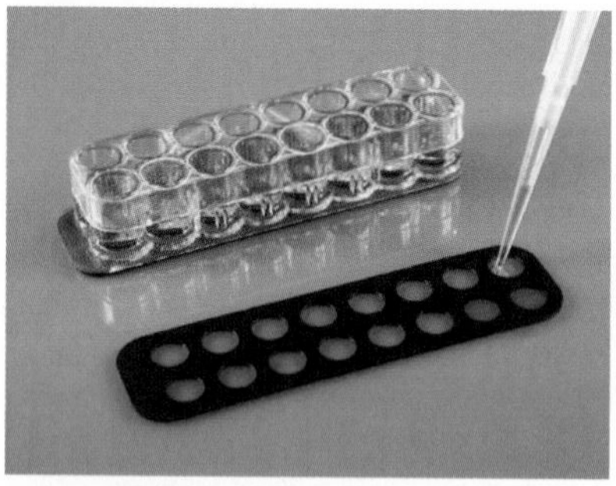

Figure 23.42 The CultureWell removable chambered coverglass for cell culture (C37000).

Each coverslip can be removed separately for individual staining experiments. The CultureWell cell culture systems are provided in a set of 10 preassembled inserts in plates.

CultureWell Chambered Coverslips

The CultureWell chambered coverslips (Table 23.4, Figure 23.41) are the same gasketed coverslips provided in our CultureWell cell culture systems (see above), but they are not preassembled into inserts. The chambered coverslip can be placed in CultureWell plates (C24769) or other cell culture dishes for cell culture and staining. The silicone gasket can be easily removed and the coverslip placed on a slide for microscopy. The CultureWell chambered coverslips provide maximum versatility for designing smaller scale cell culture applications. They are provided in sets of five sterile pouches, with four chambered coverslips per pouch.

CultureWell Chambered Coverglasses

The CultureWell chambered coverglass for cell culture is ideal for cell culture and fluorescence imaging applications. The chambered coverglass — provided sterile and ready to use — contains 16 wells that can each hold up to 250 µL, allowing cells to be cultured in a number of different conditions on a single slide (Figure 23.42). A noncytotoxic silicone gasket forms a leakproof seal between the polystyrene upper structure and the coverglass. When the cells are ready to be imaged, coverglass removal is made easy by the use of a simple tool (included with C37000) that separates the parts without the need for excessive force, eliminating the risk of coverglass breakage (Figure 23.43). Removal of the silicone gasket leaves no residue. The components of the chambered coverglass are manufactured and assembled with special orientation features to allow easy location of a specific specimen after the coverglass is mounted. Frosted microscope slides are also provided for mounting. The CultureWell removable chambered coverglass has several important features:

- Black silicone gasket reduces light scatter, enhancing fluorescence applications.
- Inert, noncytotoxic silicone permits edge-to-edge growth of cells in the wells.
- Wells are spaced to allow the use of multichannel pipettes for fast and easy cell culturing.
- Silicone gasket remains attached to the coverglass after separation, allowing the wells to be used as reagent reservoirs.
- Gasket design is ideally suited for small-volume incubations, *in situ* hybridization and immunostaining.
- Chambered coverglass is provided sterile and ready to use.

We offer the CultureWell chambered coverglass in a package containing eight chambered coverglasses and the removal tool (C37000), as well as in a sample size containing a pair of chambered coverglasses (C37005).

CoverWell Imaging Chamber Gaskets

CoverWell imaging chamber gaskets (Table 23.5, Figure 23.44) incorporate a thin, optically clear plastic cover, making them ideal for

Table 23.5 — CoverWell chamber gaskets

Cat #	Number of Wells	Well Dimensions	Depth	Approximate Volume Per Chamber	Quantity per Package
CoverWell incubation chamber gaskets					
C18150	1	40 mm × 22 mm	0.2 mm	200 µL	25
C18151	1	40 mm × 22 mm	0.5 mm	500 µL	50
C18155	1	13 mm diameter	0.2 mm	20 µL	25
C18156	1	13 mm diameter	0.5 mm	20 µL	50
CoverWell imaging chamber gaskets					
C18160	1	20 mm diameter	0.5 mm	180 µL	40
C18161	1	20 mm diameter	1.0 mm	300 µL	40
C24726 *	1	20 mm diameter	0.5 mm	180 µL	40
C24727 *	1	20 mm diameter	1.0 mm	300 µL	40
CoverWell perfusion chamber gaskets					
C18120	1	32 mm × 19 mm	0.5 mm	350 µL	40
C18121	1	32 mm × 19 mm	1.0 mm	550 µL	40
C18128	4	19 mm × 6 mm	0.5 mm	70 µL	40
C18136	1	20 mm diameter	1.0 mm	300 µL	40
C18139	8	9 mm diameter	0.5 mm	35 µL	20
C18140	8	9 mm diameter	1.0 mm	60 µL	20
C18141	8	9 mm diameter	2.0 mm	100 µL	20
C18142	8	9 mm diameter	2.5 mm	150 µL	20

* With adhesive on one side.

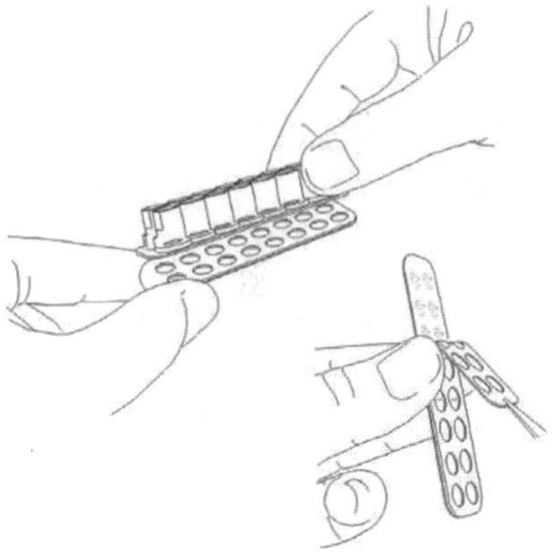

Figure 23.43 Using the CultureWell removable chambered coverglass for cell culture (C37000). When the cells are ready to be imaged, coverglass removal is made easy by the use of a simple tool (included with the coverglass) that separates the parts without the need for excessive force, eliminating the risk of coverglass breakage.

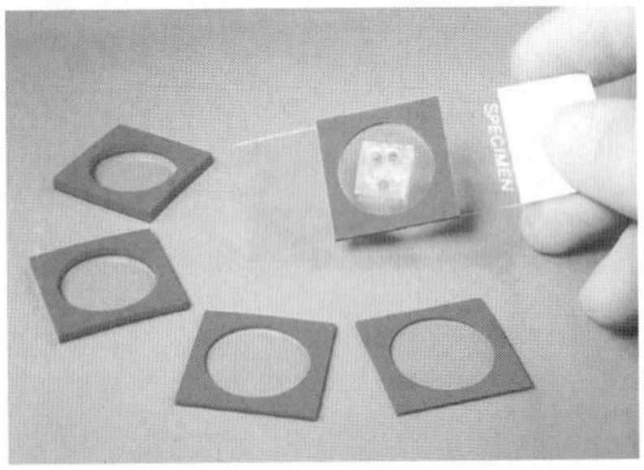

Figure 23.44 CoverWell imaging chamber gaskets.

light, epifluorescence and confocal laser-scanning microscopy. By simply pressing an imaging chamber gasket to a microscope slide or coverslip, a sealed chamber is formed to contain mounting medium. The watertight chamber supports and stabilizes thick and free-floating specimens, permitting resolution of fine internal structures and analysis of markers without the compression or movement artifacts that affect observations made using an ordinary coverslip.

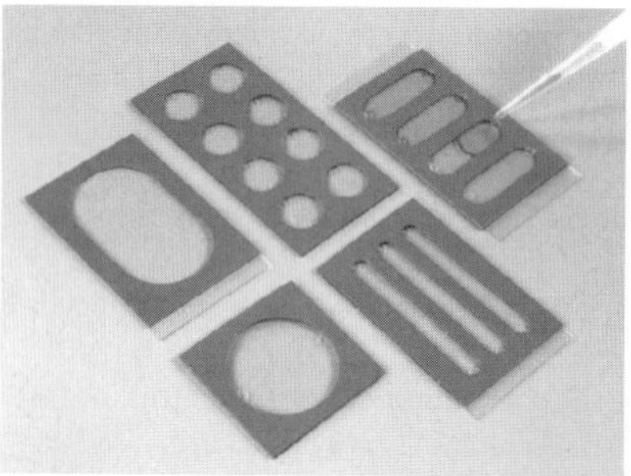

Figure 23.45 CoverWell perfusion chamber gaskets.

CoverWell Perfusion Chamber Gaskets

CoverWell perfusion chamber gaskets (Table 23.5, Figure 23.45) are designed for live-cell imaging and manipulation. With the same silicone gasket technology as the CoverWell imaging chamber gaskets, these gaskets form watertight "press-to-seal" chambers with dual-access ports for addition and removal of perfusing media. The access ports can be covered using adhesive seal tabs (A18211), which are available separately. The heat-resistant gaskets can be sterilized and used for direct culturing of cells and tissues. CoverWell perfusion chamber gaskets are available in single- or multiwell configurations, allowing multiple experiments to be performed on a single microscope slide or coverslip.

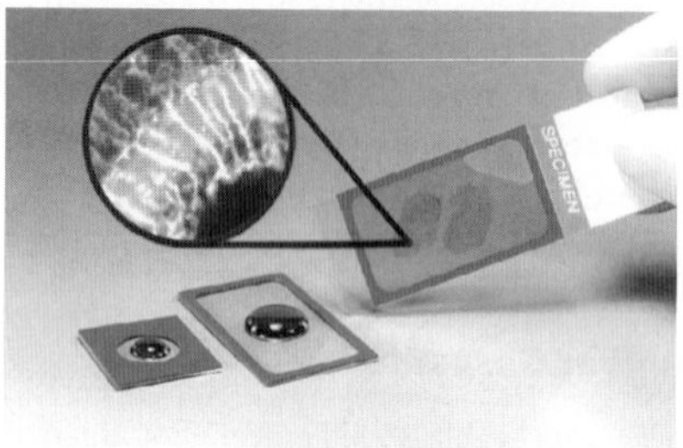

Figure 23.46 CoverWell incubation chamber gaskets.

CoverWell Incubation Chamber Gaskets

CoverWell incubation chamber gaskets (Table 23.5, Figure 23.46) are silicone gaskets with a clear plastic cover that are expressly designed for immunocytochemistry and *in situ* hybridization.[1–3] The gasket is simply pressed onto a wet or dry microscope slide to form a watertight chamber that holds reactants in place and prevents evaporation. The chambers improve the uniformity and sensitivity of staining by enclosing a large sample area while minimizing the reagent volume required. The incubation chamber gaskets are easily removed and reapplied for multiple-step procedures. These chamber gaskets are heat resistant, autoclavable and nuclease free.

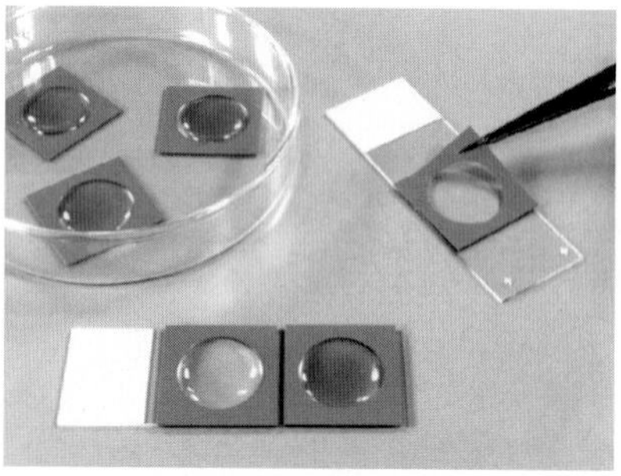

Figure 23.47 Press-to-Seal silicone isolators.

Press-to-Seal Silicone Isolators and Secure-Seal Adhesive Spacers

For the ultimate in utility and flexibility, Press-to-Seal silicone isolators (Table 23.6, Figure 23.47) are removable hydrophobic barriers that can be customized to meet specific experimental requirements. They may be used to isolate cells grown in culture dishes or to separate specimens on microscopy slides during staining procedures. The silicone material can be autoclaved and adheres to any smooth surface. Isolators without adhesive can be easily removed and reapplied for multiple incubation steps. Isolators are also available with adhesive on one side for added security or permanent mounting. In addition, we offer uncut silicone sheets that can easily be trimmed to prepare customized enclosures.

Table 23.6 — Press-to-Seal gaskets and Secure-Seal spacers

Cat #	Number of Wells	Well Dimensions	Depth	Quantity per Package
Press-to-Seal silicone isolators				
P18174	1	20 mm diameter	0.5 mm	50
P18175	1	20 mm diameter	1.0 mm	50
P24740 *	1	20 mm diameter	0.5 mm	50
P24741 *	1	20 mm diameter	1.0 mm	50
P24742 *	24	4.5 mm diameter	2.0 mm	25
P24743 *	8	9 mm diameter	0.5 mm	25
P24744 *	8	9 mm diameter	1.0 mm	25
Secure-Seal adhesive spacers				
S24735 *	1	13 mm diameter	0.12 mm	100
S24736 *	1	20 mm diameter	0.12 mm	100
S24737 *	8	9 mm diameter	0.12 mm	100
Press-to-Seal silicone sheets (13 cm × 18 cm)				
P18178	NA	NA	0.5 mm	5
P18179	NA	NA	1.0 mm	5
P24745 *	NA	NA	0.5 mm	5

* With adhesive on one side. NA = Not applicable.

Similar to the Press-to-Seal silicone isolators, Secure-Seal adhesive spacers are ultra-thin gaskets with adhesive that can be stacked to any depth desired. For high-resolution microscopy, the spacer and specimen can be sandwiched between two No. 0 glass coverslips. The spacers are available in several configurations (Table 23.6).

HybriSlip Hybridization Covers

HybriSlip hybridization covers (Table 23.7, Figure 23.48) are nuclease free, ready-to-use and designed specifically for *in situ* hybridization. These hydrophobic coverslips do not require lengthy preparation or blocking procedures to prevent probe trapping or binding. They are heat resistant and do not curl, even at high temperatures, making them ideal for denaturation steps or *in situ* PCR incubations. HybriSlip covers are available in three sizes.

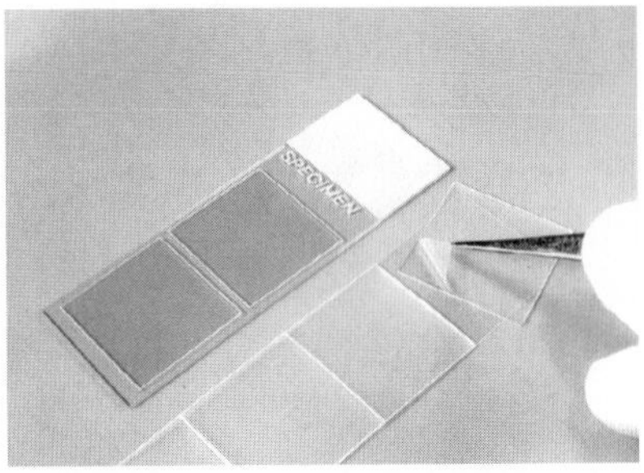

Figure 23.48 HybriSlip hybridization covers.

HybriWell Hybridization Sealing Systems

HybriWell hybridization sealing systems (Table 23.7, Figure 23.49) are coverslip–seal combinations that attach to microscope slides to form microwells optimized for carrying out *in situ* hybridization procedures. These ready-to-use hybridization gaskets have a special adhesive that bonds to glass slides in seconds, creating a water-tight seal that is temperature resistant but can also be removed cleanly and easily after hybridization. Solutions are easily added or removed through dual-access ports without disrupting the specimen. The hydrophobic coverslips are nuclease free and will not trap or bind probes, allowing uniform distribution of the reagent over the specimen. The HybriWell sealing systems also include a quick-seal tool to secure the hydrophobic cover to the microscope slide, as well as nuclease-free adhesive seal tabs to cover the access ports. Adhesive seal tabs (A18211) are also available separately in sets of 400.

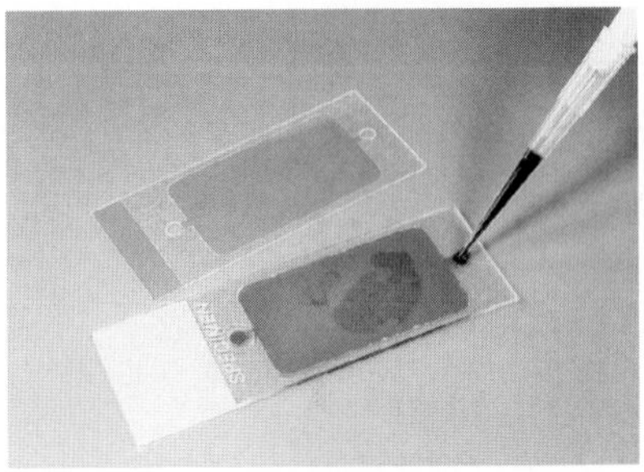

Figure 23.49 HybriWell hybridization sealing systems.

Secure-Seal Hybridization Chambers

Like the HybriWell hybridization sealing systems, Secure-Seal hybridization chambers (Table 23.7, Figure 23.50) are designed to isolate single or multiple specimens on a slide during *in situ* hybridization procedures. Access ports in the chamber surface allow for the addition or removal of solutions and are easily sealed using adhesive seal tabs (A18211), available separately. Because they are deeper than the HybriWell chambers, the Secure-Seal chambers provide optimum surface-to-volume fluid dynamics, which facilitate more uniform hybridization. However, the shallower chambers created by the HybriWell sealing systems hold a smaller reagent volume, minimizing the amount of valuable probe required.

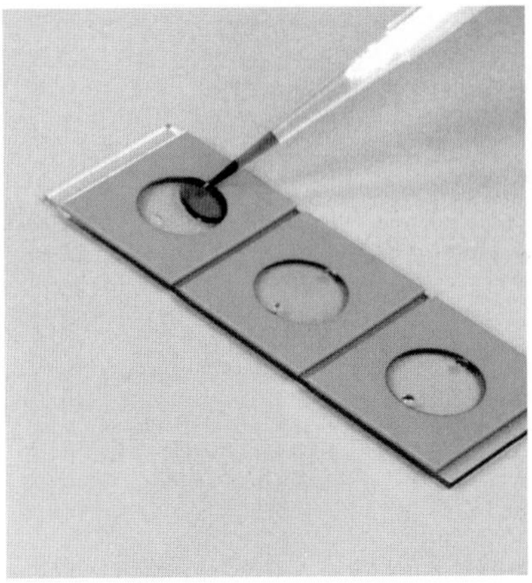

Figure 23.50 Secure-Seal hybridization chambers.

Table 23.7 — Tools for hybridization experiments

Cat #	Chamber Dimensions	Depth	Usable Volume	Quantity per Package
HybriWell hybridization sealing system				
H24720	13 mm diameter	0.25 mm	30 µL	100
H24721	20 mm diameter	0.15 mm	30 µL	100
H24723	22 mm × 22 mm	0.15 mm	30–50 µL	100
H18210	40 mm × 21 mm	0.15 mm	50–100 µL	100
H24722	40 mm × 22 mm	0.25 mm	180–200 µL	100
Secure-Seal hybridization chambers				
S24734	22 mm × 22 mm	0.8 mm	250 µL	50
S24730	20 mm diameter	0.8 mm	200 µL	40
S24731	20 mm diameter	1.3 mm	280 µL	40
S24732	9 mm diameter	0.8 mm	20 µL	20
S24733	9 mm diameter	1.3 mm	40 µL	20
HybriSlip hybridization covers				
H18200	22 mm × 22 mm	NA	NA	500
H18201	40 mm × 22 mm	NA	NA	500
H18202	60 mm × 22 mm	NA	NA	500
Seal tabs				
A18211	Adhesive seal tab	NA	NA	400

NA = Not applicable.

ONCYTE MultiWells with Slide and Matching Gasket

The versatile ONCYTE MultiWells (Figure 23.51) consist of a two-piece set that includes a slide printed with nitrocellulose circles and a matching removable gasket to enclose and isolate each sample. The nitrocellulose coating on the slide is specially formulated for fluorescence imaging. This ultra-thin microporous coating ensures uniform binding of tissue prints, cells or macromolecules and becomes transparent in a variety of mounting media. The matching press-to-seal silicone gaskets adhere easily to the surface of the slide to isolate specimens and reagents and prevent cross contamination. A coverslip can be added to create enclosed chambers for long incubations. Gaskets can be removed and cleaned simply by peeling them off. ONCYTE MultiWells are available in two configurations: a set of 20 slides and gaskets, each with 12 wells, 5 mm in diameter (O24750), or a set of 20 slides and gaskets, each with a single well, 13 mm in diameter (O24751).

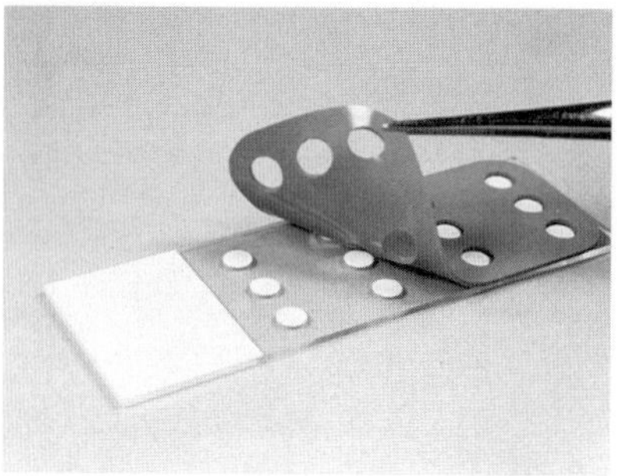

Figure 23.51 ONCYTE MultiWells.

ProPlate Multi-Array System

The ProPlate multi-array system (P37004) from Grace Bio-Labs allows integration of microscope array technology with automated microplate processing (Figure 23.52). Individual modules (P37001), covered with seal strips (P37002), fit into a tray (P37003), producing a modular plate with a standard microplate footprint and well spacing. The modular design allows loading of 1–4 slides per tray for plate washing and reading. Individual ProPlate modules may also be processed by hand without the use of the tray. The large well volumes and isolation of 16 individual arrays (2 × 8) on a single microscope slide is particularly well suited for proteomics applications, including protein expression analysis, protein-protein interactions, antibody profiling and high-throughput automated analysis of multiple proteins. The ProPlate multi-array system can also be used to process cDNA or oligonucleotide arrays.

Figure 23.52 ProPlate multi-array system (P37004). Individual modules (P37001), covered with seal strips (P37002), fit into a tray (P37003), producing a modular plate with a standard microplate footprint and well spacing.

Attofluor Cell Chamber

The Attofluor cell chamber (A7816, Figure 23.53) is a durable and practical coverslip holder designed for viewing live-cell specimens on upright or inverted microscopes. Features include:

- Surgical stainless steel construction
- Autoclavable, allowing cells to be grown directly in the chamber
- O-ring seal design that prevents sample contamination by oil and leakage of media from the coverslip
- Accepts 25 mm–diameter round coverslips and mounts in a standard 35 mm–diameter stage holder
- Thin 0.5 mm base, allowing clearance for the objective when focusing

For detailed specifications, please contact our Technical Assistance Department. Spare O-rings for the Attofluor cell chamber are available in sets of 10 (O14804).

Figure 23.53 Attofluor cell chamber (A7816).

Coverslip Mini-Rack and Coverslip Maxi-Rack

Our unique coverslip mini-rack (C14784, Figure 23.54) is a miniature support designed to vertically hold eight standard round or square coverslips. The mini-rack fits easily into a standard 50 milliliter beaker and can accommodate a small stir bar beneath the rack. Use of the mini-rack eliminates the necessity for repeatedly moving coverslips between solutions with forceps. Because it is constructed of Teflon, the mini-rack does not adsorb biopolymers, withstands strong acids and bases, is not damaged by heat and may be sterilized by a variety of methods such as autoclaving, organic solvent treatment or ethylene oxide exposure. The mini-rack is easily disassembled for cleaning and storage. The mini-rack is particularly useful in procedures involving sequential wash steps where thorough dilution and removal of material from the coverslips is critical such as:

- The hypotonic treatment and recovery steps of our Influx™ pinocytic cell-loading reagent (I14402, Section 19.8)
- Cell permeabilization using organic solvents or detergent solutions
- *In situ* hybridization procedures
- Immunocytochemical staining procedures
- Cleaning of coverslips for intracellular calcium calibrations
- Surface preparation of coverslips for cell or tissue culture

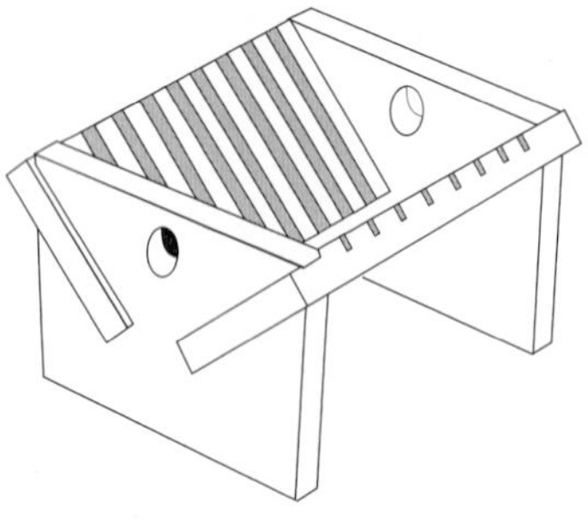

Figure 23.54 Coverslip mini-rack (C14784).

The coverslip maxi-rack (C24784, Figure 23.55) provides efficient support for the simultaneous staining of up to 50 samples in a self-contained covered container. The maxi-rack includes a convenient handle to remove the rack from the staining solution.

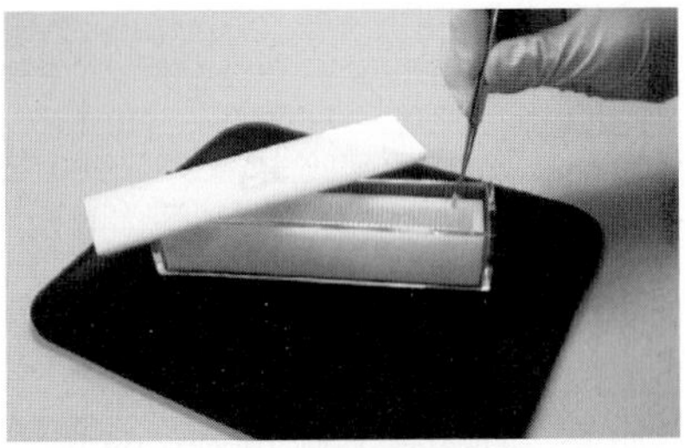

Figure 23.55 Coverslip maxi-rack (C24784).

Accessories for Magnetic Separation

Captivate™ Microscope-Mounted Magnetic Yoke Assembly

The Captivate™ microscope-mounted magnetic yoke assembly (C24700, Figure 23.56) houses permanent magnets suitable for performing cell separations using the Captivate™ ferrofluid conjugates (Section 7.2, Section 7.6; Figure 7.58). The Captivate™ microscope-mounted magnetic yoke assembly includes one free set of 10 disposable sample chambers (C24701, see below). Samples are placed in the accompanying sample chamber, which is then inserted into the yoke. The entire assembly is then placed on a microscope stage. Cells labeled with the Captivate™ ferrofluid conjugate move quickly into position at the upper surface of the sample chamber, under the influence of the strong magnetic gradient provided by the yoke (Figure 7.108).

Figure 23.56 Captivate™ microscope-mounted magnetic yoke assembly (C24700).

Captivate™ Disposable Sample Chamber

Used in conjunction with the Captivate™ magnetic yoke assembly (see above), the Captivate™ disposable sample chamber (C24701, Figure 23.57) can accommodate up to 400 µL of a cell suspension or blood sample. Cells labeled with the Captivate™ ferrofluid conjugates move to the upper surface of the sample chamber, where they can be imaged and analyzed, or recovered as an enriched population (Figure 7.58).

Magnetic Separators

Molecular Probes has available Captivate™ magnetic separators[4] for both microplates (C24702, Figure 23.58) and microtubes (C24703, Figure 23.59) that we find to be particularly useful with the Captivate™ ferrofluid products (Section 7.2, Section 7.6). The microplate separator is compatible with most 96-well microplates, whereas the microtube separator can accommodate six 1.5 mL microcentrifuge tubes. Both separators provide excellent separation efficiency and pull magnetic particles to one side, allowing easier removal of supernatants.

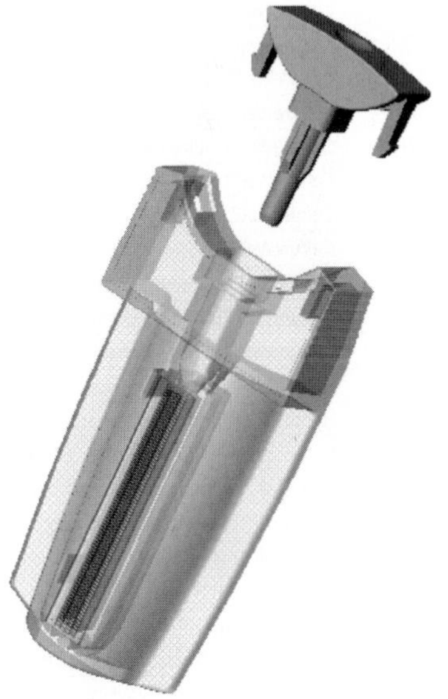

Figure 23.57 Captivate™ disposable sample chamber (C24701).

References

1. Biotechniques 20, 641 (1996); **2.** Cell Vision 2, 165 (1995); **3.** J Histotechnol 18, 115 (1995); **4.** These products are not manufactured by Immunicon.

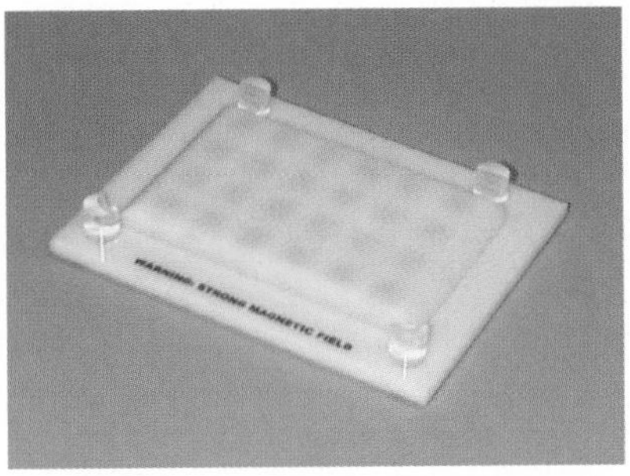

Figure 23.58 Captivate™ magnetic separator for 96-well microplates (C24702).

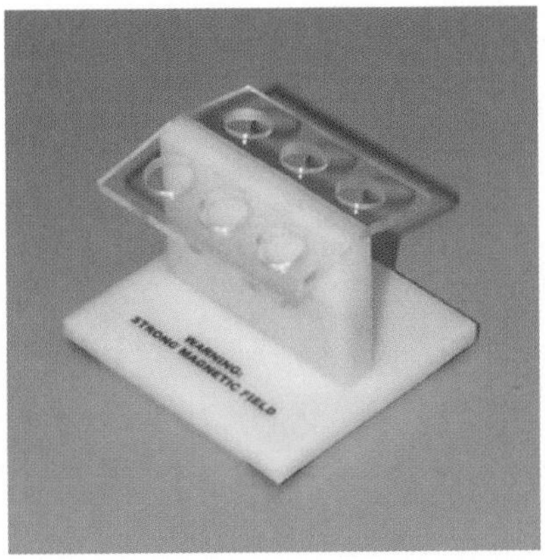

Figure 23.59 Captivate™ magnetic separator for six microtubes (C24703).

Product List — 23.3 Accessories for Fluorescence Microscopy and Magnetic Separation

Cat #	Product Name	Unit Size
A18211	Adhesive seal-tab, for HybriWell™ hybridization sealing system *set of 400*	1 set
A7816	Attofluor® cell chamber *for microscopy*	each
C24701	Captivate™ disposable sample chamber *for Captivate™ magnetic yoke* *set of 10*	1 set
C24702	Captivate™ magnetic separator for 96-well microplates	each
C24703	Captivate™ magnetic separator for six microtubes	each
C24700	Captivate™ microscope-mounted magnetic yoke assembly *includes 10 sample chambers*	each
C24784	coverslip maxi-rack *for 50 coverslips*	each
C14784	coverslip mini-rack *for 8 coverslips*	each
C18160	CoverWell™ imaging chamber gasket, one chamber, 20 mm diameter, 0.5 mm deep *set of 40*	1 set
C18161	CoverWell™ imaging chamber gasket, one chamber, 20 mm diameter, 1.0 mm deep *set of 40*	1 set
C24726	CoverWell™ imaging chamber gasket with adhesive, one chamber, 20 mm diameter, 0.5 mm deep *set of 40*	1 set
C24727	CoverWell™ imaging chamber gasket with adhesive, one chamber, 20 mm diameter, 1.0 mm deep *set of 40*	1 set
C18155	CoverWell™ incubation chamber gasket, one chamber, 13 mm diameter, 0.2 mm deep *set of 25*	1 set
C18156	CoverWell™ incubation chamber gasket, one chamber, 13 mm diameter, 0.5 mm deep *set of 50*	1 set
C18150	CoverWell™ incubation chamber gasket, one chamber, 40 mm x 22 mm, 0.2 mm deep *set of 25*	1 set
C18151	CoverWell™ incubation chamber gasket, one chamber, 40 mm x 22 mm, 0.5 mm deep *set of 50*	1 set
C18139	CoverWell™ perfusion chamber gasket, eight chambers, 9 mm diameter, 0.5 mm deep *set of 20*	1 set
C18140	CoverWell™ perfusion chamber gasket, eight chambers, 9 mm diameter, 1.0 mm deep *set of 20*	1 set
C18141	CoverWell™ perfusion chamber gasket, eight chambers, 9 mm diameter, 2.0 mm deep *set of 20*	1 set
C18142	CoverWell™ perfusion chamber gasket, eight chambers, 9 mm diameter, 2.5 mm deep *set of 20*	1 set
C18128	CoverWell™ perfusion chamber gasket, four chambers, 19 mm x 6 mm, 0.5 mm deep *set of 40*	1 set
C18136	CoverWell™ perfusion chamber gasket, one chamber, 20 mm diameter, 1.0 mm deep *set of 40*	1 set
C18120	CoverWell™ perfusion chamber gasket, one chamber, 32 mm x 19 mm, 0.5 mm deep *set of 40*	1 set
C18121	CoverWell™ perfusion chamber gasket, one chamber, 32 mm x 19 mm, 1.0 mm deep *set of 40*	1 set
C24769	CultureWell™ cell culture plate *set of 10*	1 set
C37000	CultureWell™ chambered coverglass for cell culture *sixteen wells per coverglass* *set of 8*	1 set
C37005	CultureWell™ chambered coverglass for cell culture *sixteen wells per coverglass* *set of 2*	1 pack
C24770	CultureWell™ coverslip divider *set of 4*	1 set
C24760	CultureWell™ multislip cell culture system MSI-12 *plate and insert, fifteen 12 mm coverslips per insert* *set of 10*	1 set
C24761	CultureWell™ multislip cell culture system MSI-18 *plate and insert, eight 18 mm coverslips per insert* *set of 10*	1 set
C24762	CultureWell™ multiwell cell culture system CWI 2R-1.0 *plate and insert, four 24 mm x 50 mm coverslips per insert, two 1 mm-deep wells per coverslip* *set of 10*	1 set
C24763	CultureWell™ multiwell cell culture system CWI 2R-2.0 *plate and insert, four 24 mm x 50 mm coverslips per insert, two 2 mm-deep wells per coverslip* *set of 10*	1 set
C24764	CultureWell™ multiwell cell culture system CWI 3S-1.0 *plate and insert, four 24 mm x 50 mm coverslips per insert, three 1 mm-deep wells per coverslip* *set of 10*	1 set
C24765	CultureWell™ multiwell cell culture system CWI 4R-1.0 *plate and insert, four 24 mm x 50 mm coverslips per insert, four 1 mm-deep wells per coverslip* *set of 10*	1 set
C24766	CultureWell™ multiwell cell culture system CWI 8R-1.0 *plate and insert, four 24 mm x 50 mm coverslips per insert, eight 1 mm-deep wells per coverslip* *set of 10*	1 set
C24767	CultureWell™ multiwell cell culture system CWI 8R-1.0 TS *plate and insert, four 24 mm x 50 mm coverslips per insert, eight 1 mm-deep wells per coverslip* *set of 2*	1 set
C24768	CultureWell™ multiwell cell culture system CWI 50R-1.0 *plate and insert, four 24 mm x 50 mm coverslips per insert, fifty 1 mm-deep wells per coverslip* *set of 10*	1 set
C24775	CultureWell™ multiwell chambered coverslip CWCS 2R-1.0 *24 mm x 50 mm coverslips, two 1 mm-deep wells per coverslip* *set of 20*	1 set
C24776	CultureWell™ multiwell chambered coverslip CWCS 2R-2.0 *24 mm x 50 mm coverslips, two 2 mm-deep wells per coverslip* *set of 20*	1 set
C24777	CultureWell™ multiwell chambered coverslip CWCS 3S-1.0 *24 mm x 50 mm coverslips, three 1 mm-deep wells per coverslip* *set of 20*	1 set
C24778	CultureWell™ multiwell chambered coverslip CWCS 4R-1.0 *24 mm x 50 mm coverslips, four 1 mm-deep wells per coverslip* *set of 20*	1 set
C24779	CultureWell™ multiwell chambered coverslip CWCS 8R-1.0 *24 mm x 50 mm coverslips, eight 1 mm-deep wells per coverslip* *set of 20*	1 set
C24780	CultureWell™ multiwell chambered coverslip CWCS 50R-1.0 *24 mm x 50 mm coverslips, fifty 1 mm-deep wells per coverslip* *set of 20*	1 set
H18200	HybriSlip™ hybridization cover, 22 mm x 22 mm *RNase free* *set of 500*	1 set
H18201	HybriSlip™ hybridization cover, 40 mm x 22 mm *RNase free* *set of 500*	1 set
H18202	HybriSlip™ hybridization cover, 60 mm x 22 mm *RNase free* *set of 500*	1 set
H24720	HybriWell™ hybridization sealing system, 13 mm diameter chamber, 0.25 mm deep *set of 100*	1 set
H24721	HybriWell™ hybridization sealing system, 20 mm diameter chamber, 0.15 mm deep *set of 100*	1 set
H24723	HybriWell™ hybridization sealing system, 22 mm x 22 mm chamber, 0.15 mm deep *set of 100*	1 set
H18210	HybriWell™ hybridization sealing system, 40 mm x 21 mm chamber, 0.15 mm deep *set of 100*	1 set
H24722	HybriWell™ hybridization sealing system, 40 mm x 22 mm chamber, 0.25 mm deep *set of 100*	1 set
O24751	ONCYTE® MultiWells, one well, 13 mm diameter, with slide and matching gasket *set of 20*	1 set
O24750	ONCYTE® MultiWells, 12 wells, 5 mm diameter, with slide and matching gasket *set of 20*	1 set
O14804	O-rings for Attofluor® cell chamber, set of 10	each
P18174	Press-to-Seal™ silicone isolator, one well, 20 mm diameter, 0.5 mm deep *set of 50*	1 set
P18175	Press-to-Seal™ silicone isolator, one well, 20 mm diameter, 1.0 mm deep *set of 50*	1 set
P24743	Press-to-Seal™ silicone isolator with adhesive, eight wells, 9 mm diameter, 0.5 mm deep *set of 25*	1 set

For current prices or to order online, visit probes.invitrogen.com

Cat #	Product Name	Unit Size
P24744	Press-to-Seal™ silicone isolator with adhesive, eight wells, 9 mm diameter, 1.0 mm deep *set of 25*	1 set
P24740	Press-to-Seal™ silicone isolator with adhesive, one well, 20 mm diameter, 0.5 mm deep *set of 50*	1 set
P24741	Press-to-Seal™ silicone isolator with adhesive, one well, 20 mm diameter, 1.0 mm deep *set of 50*	1 set
P24742	Press-to-Seal™ silicone isolator with adhesive, 24 wells, 2.5 mm diameter, 2.0 mm deep *set of 25*	1 set
P18178	Press-to-Seal™ silicone sheet, 13 cm x 18 cm, 0.5 mm thick *set of 5*	1 set
P18179	Press-to-Seal™ silicone sheet, 13 cm x 18 cm, 1.0 mm thick *set of 5*	1 set
P24745	Press-to-Seal™ silicone sheet with adhesive, 13 cm x 18 cm, 0.5 mm thick *set of 5*	1 set
P37001	ProPlate™ multi-array slide module *set of 2*	1 set
P37004	ProPlate™ multi-array system *includes four 16-well slide modules, one tray and cover, ten seal-strips and one applicator*	1 set
P37002	ProPlate™ adhesive seal-strips *set of 50 seal-strips and one applicator*	1 set
P37003	ProPlate™ tray and cover *includes one tray and cover*	1 set
S24732	Secure-Seal™ hybridization chamber gasket, eight chambers, 9 mm diameter, 0.8 mm deep *set of 20*	1 set
S24733	Secure-Seal™ hybridization chamber gasket, eight chambers, 9 mm diameter, 1.3 mm deep *set of 20*	1 set
S24730	Secure-Seal™ hybridization chamber gasket, one chamber, 20 mm diameter, 0.8 mm deep *set of 40*	1 set
S24731	Secure-Seal™ hybridization chamber gasket, one chamber, 20 mm diameter, 1.3 mm deep *set of 40*	1 set
S24734	Secure-Seal™ hybridization chamber gasket, one chamber, 22 mm x 22 mm, 0.8 mm deep *set of 50*	1 set
S24737	Secure-Seal™ spacer, eight wells, 9 mm diameter, 0.12 mm deep *set of 100*	1 set
S24735	Secure-Seal™ spacer, one well, 13 mm diameter, 0.12 mm deep *set of 100*	1 set
S24736	Secure-Seal™ spacer, one well, 20 mm diameter, 0.12 mm deep *set of 100*	1 set

For current prices or to order online, visit probes.invitrogen.com

23.4 Photographic Filters for Electrophoretic Gels and Blots

Molecular Probes offers a number of fluorescent reagents for staining nucleic acids and proteins in gels and on blots. Preeminent among these stains are our SYBR® Green and SYBR® Gold nucleic acid gel stains (Section 8.4) and our SYPRO® protein stains for gels and blots (Section 9.3, Section 9.4) as well as our DyeChrome™, Amplex® Gold and Pro-Q® Western Blot Stain Kits, Pro-Q® Oligohistidine Stain Kits and reagents and our Pro-Q® Glycoprotein Stain Kits (Section 9.4). To achieve optimal sensitivity with these exceptional fluorescent dyes, it is *essential* to photograph the gel or blot because the camera's integrating capability can make bands visible that are not detected by eye. Photographs should be taken using a photographic filter with spectral properties closely matched to those of the fluorescent dye used. Molecular Probes provides 75 mm × 75 mm gelatin filters (Figure 23.60) optimized for photographing stained gels or blots with a Polaroid camera and Polaroid 667 black-and-white print film. Note that these gelatin filters are generally not suitable for use with portable or stationary gel-documentation systems or with CCD cameras (Table 9.5).

Figure 23.60 Molecular Probes' 75 mm × 75 mm gelatin photographic filters for use with Polaroid black-and-white print film photography.

SYBR® Photographic Filter

To achieve optimal sensitivity using Polaroid 667 black-and-white print film and UV illumination, DNA or RNA gels stained with our proprietary SYBR® Green I, SYBR® Green II or SYBR® Gold nucleic acid gel stains (Section 8.4) should be photographed through the SYBR® photographic filter (S7569, Figure 23.61). The SYBR® photographic filter is also recommended for photographing Southern blots or dot blots stained with our SYBR® DX DNA blot stain (S7550, Section 8.5).

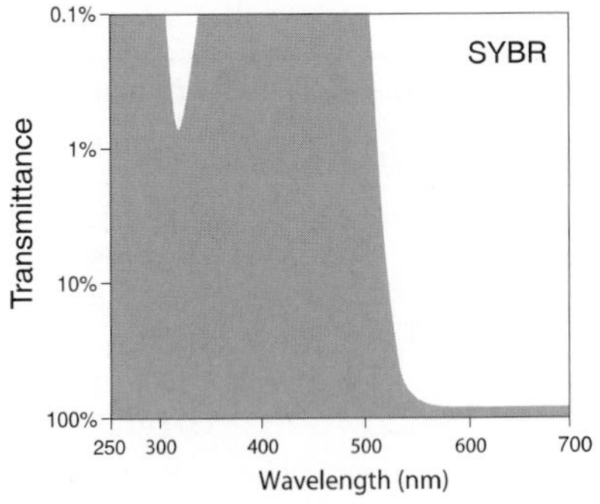

Figure 23.61 Transmittance profile of the SYBR® photographic filter (S7569).

SYBR Safe™ Photographic Filter

The SYBR Safe™ photographic filter (S37100) is ideal for black-and-white photography of gels stained with the SYBR Safe™ DNA gel stain (Section 8.4), the safer ethidium bromide alternative. Note that the SYBR Safe™ photographic filter is identical to the SYPRO® photographic filter, which is described below (Figure 23.62).

SYPRO® Photographic Filter

To achieve optimal sensitivity using Polaroid 667 black-and-white print film and UV illumination, protein gels or blots stained with any of our proprietary SYPRO® protein stains (including the SYPRO® Orange, SYPRO® Red, SYPRO® Tangerine and SYPRO® Ruby protein gel stains and the SYPRO® Ruby and SYPRO® Rose Plus protein blot stains) should be photographed through our SYPRO® photographic filter (S6656, Figure 23.62). The SYPRO® photographic filter is also ideal for photographing DDAO, used in some of our Western Blot Stain Kits, Glycoprotein Stain Kits and Oligohistidine Blot Stain Kits, which are described in Section 9.4. This filter can also be used with our Pro-Q® Sapphire oligohistidine gel stains, which are described in Section 9.4.

DyeChrome™ Red/Green Photographic Filter Set

The use of photographic filters to document fluorescent staining patterns not only maximizes sensitivity, but also provides an opportunity to separate multiple fluorescent signals on the same blot. Our DyeChrome™ Red/Green Photographic Filter Set (D24771) is optimized for nearly flawless separation of the red- and green-fluorescent signals produced by the reagents in the DyeChrome™ Western Blot Stain Kits (Section 9.4, Figure 23.63, Figure 23.64), while maintaining excellent sensitivity. Use of this filter set makes it possible to perform sophisticated multicolor experiments without the need to invest in expensive digital imaging devices or laser-scanning instruments. The filter set works equally well for separating DDAO and BODIPY® FL-X signals (products of the reagents used in the DyeChrome™ Western Blot Stain Kits #1, #2 and #3) or ELF® 39 alcohol and BODIPY® TR-X signals (products of the reagents used in the DyeChrome™ Western Blot Stain Kits #4, #5 and #6).

Amplex® Gold Photographic Filter

The Amplex® Gold photographic filter (A24772), which has the same transmittance profile as the "green" filter used in the DyeChrome™ Red/Green Photographic Filter Set (Figure 23.63) is optimal for detecting the fluorescence of the oxidized Amplex® Gold horseradish peroxidase substrate, which is used in our Amplex® Gold Western Blot Stain Kits #1, #2 and #3 (Section 9.4) and the DyeChrome™ Double Western Blot Stain Kit (D21887, Section 9.4).

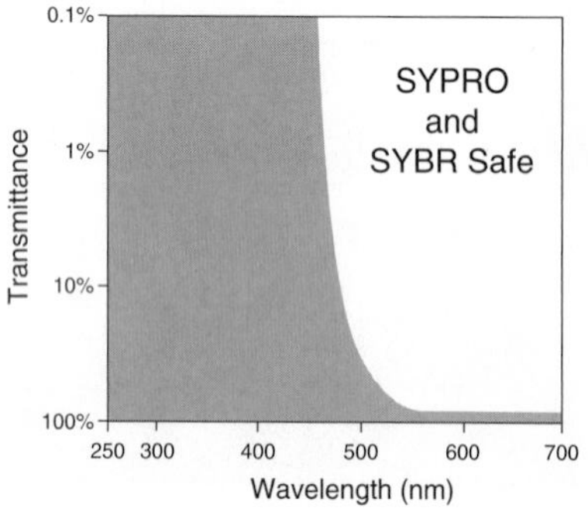

Figure 23.62 Transmittance profile of the SYBR Safe™ photographic filter (S37100) and the SYPRO® photographic filter (S6656), which are identical.

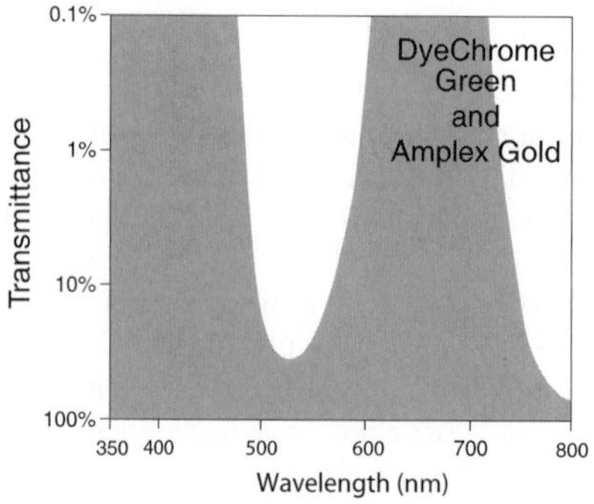

Figure 23.63 Transmittance profile of the DyeChrome™ Green photographic filter (part of D24771) and Amplex® Gold photographic filter (A24772).

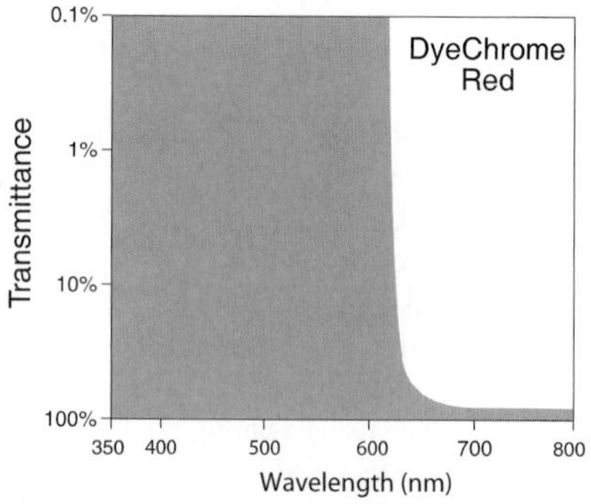

Figure 23.64 Transmittance profile of the DyeChrome™ Red photographic filter (part of D24771).

Product List — 23.4 Photographic Filters for Electrophoretic Gels and Blots

Cat #	Product Name	Unit Size
A24772	Amplex® Gold photographic filter	each
D24771	DyeChrome™ Red/Green Photographic Filter Set *two filters*	1 set
S7569	SYBR® photographic filter	each
S37100	SYBR Safe™ photographic filter	each
S6656	SYPRO® photographic filter	each

For current prices or to order online, visit probes.invitrogen.com

23.5 Optical Filters for Fluorescence Microscopy

Sensitive and versatile fluorescence detection techniques are of ever-increasing importance and popularity in biological research microscopy. In the now-standard epi-illuminated microscope configuration, the optical filter set performs a critical function in separating the fluorescence emission photons that will form the final image from the more-intense excitation light field. For practical purposes, it is necessary to reduce the excitation light intensity in the detection path by a factor of 10^6–10^7. This design objective has to be achieved in parallel with capturing as many of the available fluorescence photons as possible. High capture efficiency allows compensating reductions in overall excitation light levels, with accompanying reductions in dye photobleaching and cellular phototoxicity.

Although Molecular Probes does not sell optical filters for microscopy, this section of the Handbook provides basic information on optical filters and tabulated spectral data that are useful in selecting the optimal filters for many of our dyes (Table 23.8, Table 23.9).

The Optical Filter Set

A set of optical filters for selective excitation and detection of fluorescence typically consists of a minimum of three components: an excitation filter, a dichroic beamsplitter ("dichroic mirror") and an emission filter ("barrier filter") (Figure 23.65). The excitation filter selectively transmits a portion of the spectral output from the light source (Table 23.8). The dichroic beamsplitter then reflects the selected light, directing it to the sample. Fluorescence emission photons traveling from the sample towards the detector are transmitted by the dichroic beamsplitter, while excitation light reflected back from the sample is diverted out of the detection light path. The emission filter blocks unwanted spectral components of the emitted fluorescence (e.g., sample autofluorescence) as well as any residual excitation light. An interactive Java tutorial demonstrating these functions is available online at the Molecular Expressions web site of Florida State University (http://micro.magnet.fsu.edu/primer/java/fluorescence/filtersetprofiles/index.html).

The Trade-Off in Optical Filter Set Design

For optimal fluorescence detection when using a single dye, the excitation and emission filters should be centered on the dye's absorption and emission peaks. To maximize the signal, one can choose excitation and emission filters with wide bandwidths. However, this strategy may result in unacceptable overlap of the emission signal with the excitation signal, resulting in poor resolution. To minimize spectral overlap, one can instead choose excitation and emission filters that are narrow in bandwidth and are spectrally well separated to increase signal isolation. This approach will reduce optical noise but may also reduce the signal strength to unacceptable levels. When overlapping signals from multiple fluorophores in the same sample are being differentiated, both the spectra of the dyes and their expected intensities must be considered before choosing an optical filter. The absorption and emission maxima for a wide variety of our dyes and some appropriate optical filters are given in Table 23.9. An interactive Java tutorial illustrating the trade-off among these parameters is available online at the Molecular Expressions web site of Florida State University (http://micro.magnet.fsu.edu/primer/java/fluorescence/fluorocubes/index.html).

Table 23.8 — Fluorescence excitation sources

Source	Principal Lines (nm)
Mercury-arc lamp	366, 405, 436, 546, 578 *
Xenon-arc lamp	250–1000 *
Tungsten–halogen lamp	350–1000 *
Blue diode laser	405
Helium–cadmium laser	325, 442
Argon-ion laser	457, 488, 514
Nd:YAG laser	532 †
Helium–neon laser	543, 594, 633
Yellow diode laser	561
Krypton-ion laser	568, 647

* Continuous white-light source. † Frequency-doubled principal line output.

Selecting an Optical Filter Set

Filter set selection may involve a straightforward recommendation or a complex analysis of the spectral relationships of dyes and optical filters.[1] Emission filters are available with either longpass or bandpass wavelength transmission profiles. A typical longpass emission filter might transmit all wavelengths ≥530 nm, whereas a typical bandpass filter might transmit only wavelengths between 515 and 545 nm. Longpass filters should be used when the application requires maximum emission collection and when spectral discrimination is not desirable or necessary, which is generally the case for probes that generate a single emit-

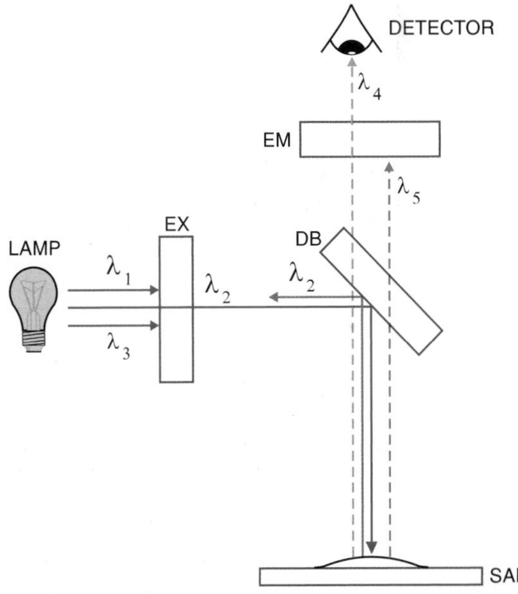

Figure 23.65 Functions of fluorescence microscope filter set components. The desired excitation wavelength (λ_2) is selected from the spectral output of the lamp by the excitation filter (EX) and directed to the sample via the dichroic beamsplitter (DB). The beamsplitter separates emitted fluorescence (---) from scattered excitation light (—). The emission filter (EM) selectively transmits a portion of the sample's fluorescence emission (λ_4) for detection and blocks other emission components (λ_5).

ting species in specimens with relatively low levels of background autofluorescence. Longpass filters are also useful for simultaneous detection of spectrally distinct dual emissions such as the monomer and J-aggregate forms of JC-1 (T3168, Section 12.2, Figure 12.19) and the monomer and excimer forms of BODIPY® FL C_5-ceramide (D3521, B22650; Section 12.4; Figure 12.51).

Bandpass filters are designed to maximize the signal-to-noise ratio for applications where discrimination of signal components is more important than overall image brightness. The spectral sensitivity of the detection system should also be considered in order to achieve optimum detector signal-to-noise or accurate color rendition. Some applications, such as confocal laser-scanning microscopy, may require the use of sensitive photomultiplier (PMT) detectors. Alternatively, a linear photometric charge-coupled device (CCD), diode array or intensified video camera may be employed for quantitative imaging or microspectrofluorometry. Dual-, triple- and quadruple-band filter sets enable microscopists to excite and detect two, three or four fluorophores simultaneously instead of performing sequential image acquisitions with intervening filter changes (Figure 23.66).

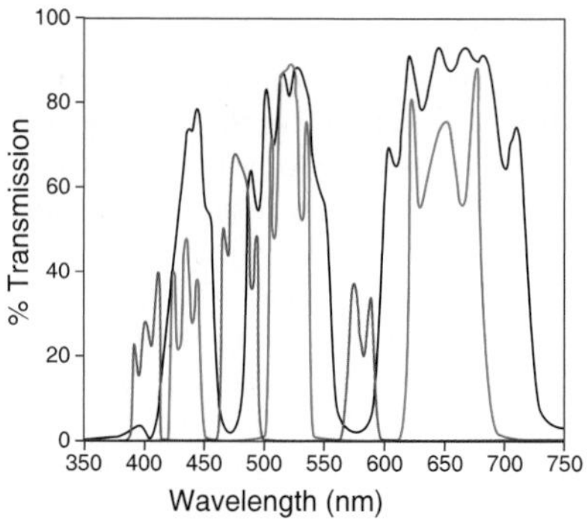

Figure 23.66 Optical transmission characteristics of a triple-band filter set (XF63, Omega Optical Inc.) designed for simultaneous imaging of DAPI, fluorescein, and Texas Red® dyes. Transmission curves for the individual filter set components are shown in blue (excitation filter), black (dichroic beamsplitter) and red (emission filter). Graphic supplied by and used with permission of Omega Optical Inc., Brattleboro, VT.

Selecting optimal filter sets for fluorescence microscopy applications requires matching optical filter specifications to the spectral characteristics of dyes. Comparisons should be made with care because some dyes have significantly different spectral properties in a particular application than those reported for the dye in solution. For example, the spectral characteristics of many nucleic acid stains depend on whether the dyes are in aqueous solution or bound to DNA or RNA. Similarly, styryl dyes such as FM® 1-43 (T3163, T35356; Section 14.4, Section 16.1) and di-4-ANEPPS (D1199, Section 22.2) have emission maxima that depend on whether they are dissolved in solvent or associated with membranes. To provide selection guidelines, we have compiled filter set recommendations for some of our most widely used dyes and probes for fluorescence microscopy applications (Table 23.9). This table includes fluorescence excitation and emission maxima for the most common environment in which the dye would be found in typical experimental specimens, as well as links to plots of the full spectra.

Reference

1. Biophotonics Int 6, 54 (1999).

Technical Service

We invite customers to call our technical service scientists for help in selecting the correct optical filter for a specific application. When calling, please be prepared to describe the dye(s), instrumentation and method of detection being used. A technical service scientist will offer advice on the most effective filter configuration for the specified purposes. Please refer to the inside back cover of *The Handbook* to find contact information for the distributor or branch office nearest you. Alternatively, we recommend contacting Omega Optical, Inc., Chroma Technology Corp. or the microscope manufacturer for this information. Omega Optical and Chroma Technology provide complete transmittance curves and information on their specialty filters at their respective web sites (www.omegafilters.com, www.chroma.com).

Table 23.9 — Spectral characteristics and recommended bandpass filter sets for Molecular Probes' dyes

Dye	Excitation Maximum (nm)	Emission Maximum (nm)	Omega Filter Set*	Chroma Filter Set*
Acridine orange	500 (+DNA) 460 (+RNA)	526 (+DNA) 650 (+RNA)	XF104 (DNA) XF21 (RNA)	41001 (DNA) 31001 (RNA)
Alexa Fluor® 350 dye, AMC †	346	442	XF136 XF06	31000 31013
Alexa Fluor® 405 dye	402	421	XF113 XF10	31021 31009
Alexa Fluor® 430 dye	434	539	XF14	31010
Alexa Fluor® 488 dye	495	519	XF100 XF23	41001 31001
Alexa Fluor® 500 dye	503	525	XF100 XF23	41001 31001
Alexa Fluor® 514 dye	518	540	XF104	41026
Alexa Fluor® 532 dye	531	554	XF104 XF99	41011
Alexa Fluor® 546 dye	556	573	XF108 XF32	41002 31002
Alexa Fluor® 555 dye	555	565	XF108 XF32	41002 31002

Table 23.9 — Spectral characteristics and recommended bandpass filter sets for Molecular Probes' dyes — continued

Dye	Excitation Maximum (nm)	Emission Maximum (nm)	Omega Filter Set*	Chroma Filter Set*
Alexa Fluor® 568 dye	578	603	XF102 XF41	41034 31004
Alexa Fluor® 594 dye	590	617	XF102 XF43	41004 31004
Alexa Fluor® 610 dye	612	628	XF102 XF43	41004 31004
Alexa Fluor® 633 dye	632	647	XF110 XF70	41008 31023
Alexa Fluor® 635 dye	633	647	XF110 XF70	41008 31023
Alexa Fluor® 647 dye	650	668	XF110 XF47	41008 31023 41019 ‡
Alexa Fluor® 660 dye	663	690	XF110 XF140	41022 31027
Alexa Fluor® 680 dye	679	702	XF110	41022 31029
Alexa Fluor® 700 dye	702	723	XF110	41022 31029
Alexa Fluor® 750 dye	749	775	XF112	41009
Allophycocyanin	650	660	XF44 XF110	41013 31006
7-Aminoactinomycin D (7-AAD) §	546	647	XF103 XF35	41005
BCECF indicator	482 (low pH) 503 (high pH)	520 (low pH) 528 (high pH)	XF16 **	71001 **
Bimane	380	458	XF136 XF06	31000 31013
BOBO™-1, BO-PRO™-1	462	481	XF114	31044
BODIPY® 630/650 dye	630	650	XF110 XF70	41008 31023
BODIPY® 650/665 dye	650	665	XF110 XF47	41008 31023
BODIPY® FL dye	505	513	XF100 XF23	41001 31001
BODIPY® TMR-X dye	542	574	XF108 XF32	41002 31002
BODIPY® TR-X dye	589	617	XF102 XF43	41004 31004
Calcein	494	517	XF100 XF23	41001 31001
Calcium Crimson™ indicator	590	615	XF102 XF43	41004 31004
Calcium Green™ indicators	506	533	XF104 XF23	41028 31001
Calcium Orange™ indicator	549	576	XF108 XF32	41002 31002
Carboxy SNARF® indicators	548 (low pH) 576 (high pH)	587 (low pH) 635 (high pH)	XF72 ††	71005 ††
6-Carboxyrhodamine 6G	525	555	XF104 XF99	41011
Cascade Blue® dye	400	420	XF113 XF10	31021 31009
Cascade Yellow™ dye	402	545	XF14	31038
DAPI §	358	461	XF136 XF06	31000 31013
Di-8-ANEPPS, Di-4-ANEPPS ‡‡	468	635	XF17 **	71006 **
DiA ‡‡	456	590	XF21	31024
DiD (DiIC$_{18}$(5))	644	665	XF110 XF47	41008 31023
DiI (DiIC$_{18}$(3))	549	565	XF108 XF32	41002 31002
DiO (DiOC$_{18}$(3))	484	501	XF100 XF23	41001 31001

Table 23.9 — Spectral characteristics and recommended bandpass filter sets for Molecular Probes' dyes — continued

Dye	Excitation Maximum (nm)	Emission Maximum (nm)	Omega Filter Set*	Chroma Filter Set*
DiR (DiIC$_{18}$(7))	750	779	XF112	41009
ELF® 97 alcohol	345	530	XF09	
Eosin	524	544	XF104	41011
ER-Tracker™ Blue-White DPX ‡‡	372	556	XF09	31034
EthD-1 §	528	617	XF103 XF35	41005 31005
Ethidium bromide §	518	605	XF103 XF33	41006 31008
Fluo-3 indicator	506	526	XF104 XF23	41028 31001
Fluo-4 indicator	494	516	XF100 XF23	41001 31001
Fluorescein, FITC	494	518	XF100 XF23	41001 31001
FM® 1-43, FM® 1-43FX ‡‡	479	598	XF21	31024
FM® 4-64 ‡‡	506	750	XF103 XF27	41005 31012
Fura-2 indicator	363 (low [Ca^{2+}]) 335 (high [Ca^{2+}])	512 (low [Ca^{2+}]) 505 (high [Ca^{2+}])	XF04 **	71000 **
Fura Red™ indicator	472 (low [Ca^{2+}]) 436 (high [Ca^{2+}])	657 (low [Ca^{2+}]) 637 (high [Ca^{2+}])	XF17 **	71003 **
Hoechst 33258, Hoechst 33342 §	352	461	XF136 XF06	31000 31013
7-Hydroxy-4-methylcoumarin	360	455	XF136 XF06	31000 31013
Indo-1	346 (low [Ca^{2+}]) 330 (high [Ca^{2+}])	475 (low [Ca^{2+}]) 401 (high [Ca^{2+}])	XF07 ††	71002 ††
JC-1	498 (monomer) 593 (aggregate)	525 (monomer) 595 (aggregate)	XF26 ††	71010 ††
JC-9	506	525 (monomer) 635 (aggregate)	XF26 ††	71010 ††
JOE dye	525	555	XF104 XF99	41011
Lissamine rhodamine B	570	590	XF102 XF41	41034 31004
Lucifer yellow CH	428	536	XF96 XF14	32000 31010
LysoSensor™ Blue DND-167	374	425	XF06	31013
LysoSensor™ Green DND-153, DND-189	442	505	XF71	32000
LysoSensor™ Yellow/Blue	384 (low pH) 329 (high pH)	540 (low pH) 440 (high pH)	XF04 ** XF07 ††	71000 ** 71002 ††
LysoTracker® Green	504	511	XF100 XF23	41001 31001
LysoTracker® Red	577	592	XF102 XF41	41034 31004
Magnesium Green™ indicator	506	531	XF104 XF23	41028 31001
Marina Blue® dye	365	460	XF136 XF06	31000 31013
MitoTracker® Green FM	490	516	XF100 XF23	41001 31001
MitoTracker® Orange CMTMRos	551	576	XF108 XF32	41002 31002
MitoTracker® Red CMXRos	578	599	XF102 XF41	41034 31004
Monobromobimane §§	394	490	XF76	32000
NBD amines	465	535	XF100 XF23	41001 31018
NeuroTrace® 500/525 green-fluorescent Nissl stain §	500	525	XF100 XF23	41001 31001
Nile red ††	549	628	XF103 XF35	41005 31014

Table 23.9 — Spectral characteristics and recommended bandpass filter sets for Molecular Probes' dyes — continued

Dye	Excitation Maximum (nm)	Emission Maximum (nm)	Omega Filter Set*	Chroma Filter Set*
Oregon Green® 488 dye and Oregon Green® 488 BAPTA indicators	496	524	XF100 XF23	41001 31001
Oregon Green® 514 dye	511	530	XF104	41026
Pacific Blue™ dye	410	455	XF119 XF11	31037
POPO™-1, PO-PRO™-1 §	434	456	XF114	31044
Propidium iodide §	536	617	XF103 XF35	41005 31005
Rhodamine 110	496	520	XF100 XF23	41001 31001
Rhodamine Red™ dye	570	590	XF102 XF41	41034 31004
R-phycoerythrin	565	575	XF108 XF32	41002 31014
Resorufin	571	585	XF39	41010
RH 414 ‡‡	500	635	XF21	31011
Rhod-2 indicator	552	578	XF108 XF32	41002 31002
Rhodamine Green™ dye	502	527	XF100 XF23	41001 31001
Rhodamine 123	507	529	XF104 XF23	41028 31001
ROX dye	580	605	XF102 XF41	41034 31004
Sodium Green™ indicator	507	535	XF104 XF23	41028 31001
SYTO® blue-fluorescent nucleic acid stains 40, 41, 42, 43 §	428 ± 6	454 ± 13	XF119	31037
SYTO® blue-fluorescent nucleic acid stains 44, 45 §	450 ± 5	478 ± 7	XF114	31036 31044
SYTO® green-fluorescent nucleic acid stains 12, 13, 16, 21, 23, 24 §	494 ± 6	515 ± 7	XF100 XF23	41001 31001
SYTO® green-fluorescent nucleic acid stains 11, 14, 15, 20, 22, 25 §	515 ± 7	543 ± 13	XF104 XF99	41026 41028
SYTO® orange-fluorescent nucleic acid stains 80, 81, 82, 83 §	537 ± 7	552 ± 8	XF99 XF104	41011
SYTO® orange-fluorescent nucleic acid stains 84, 85 §	567	583	XF39	41010 31002
SYTO® red-fluorescent nucleic acid stains 17, 59, 61, 64 §	615 ± 15	632 ± 13	XF43 XF44	31006
SYTO® red-fluorescent nucleic acid stains 60, 62, 63 §	655 ± 3	675 ± 3	XF110 XF47	41008 31023
SYTOX® Blue nucleic acid stain §	445	470	XF114	31036 31044
SYTOX® Green nucleic acid stain §	504	523	XF104 XF23	41028 31001
SYTOX® Orange nucleic acid stain §	547	570	XF108 XF32	41002 31002
Tetramethylrhodamine, Rhodamine B	555	580	XF108 XF32	41002 31002
Texas Red® and Texas Red®-X dye	595	615	XF102 XF43	41004 31004
TOTO®-1, TO-PRO®-1 §	514	533	XF104 XF99	41028 41026
TOTO®-3, TO-PRO®-3 §	642	660	XF110 XF47	41008 31023
X-rhod-1 indicator	580	602	XF102 XF41	41034 31004
YOYO®-1, YO-PRO®-1 §	491	509	XF100 XF23	41001 31001
YOYO®-3, YO-PRO®-3 §	612	631	XF43 XF44	31006

*Omega filters are supplied by Omega Optical, Inc. (www.omegafilters.com); Chroma filters are supplied by Chroma Technology Corp. (www.chroma.com). † AMC = 7-amino-4-methylcoumarin. ‡ Filter set designed for direct detection of fluorescence by the human eye. § Excitation and emission peaks listed for dye/nucleic acid complex. ** Dual-wavelength excitation filter set. †† Dual-wavelength emission filter set. ‡‡ Excitation and emission peaks listed for lipid-bound dye. §§ Excitation and emission peaks listed for glutathione-conjugated dye.

23.6 Books from Molecular Probes

To augment our selection of fluorescent probes and research products, we offer several valuable reference books for scientists who utilize fluorescence techniques for their research applications. We recommend these editions to anyone interested in up-to-date guides on fluorescence methods.

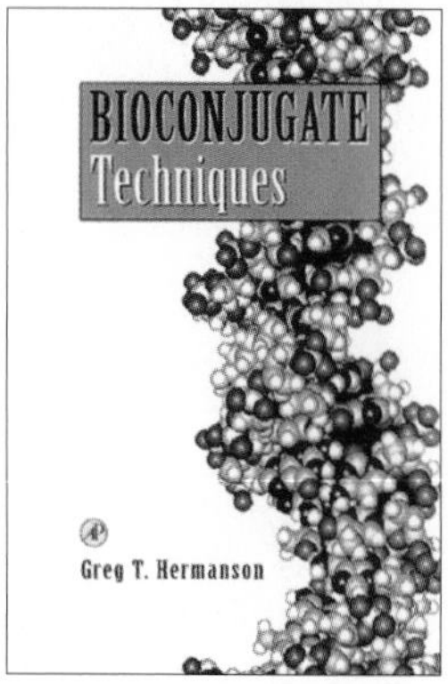

Bioconjugate Techniques

Bioconjugate Techniques (B7884), written by G.T. Hermanson and published in 1996, is an essential guide that captures the entire field of bioconjugate chemistry in a single volume. The chemistry, reagents and applications for generating conjugated molecules are described in detail. In addition, this well-illustrated and highly referenced book provides easy-to-follow protocols for creating modified and crosslinked reagents that can be used for detecting, quantitating and analyzing biomolecules in research, diagnostic and clinical applications.

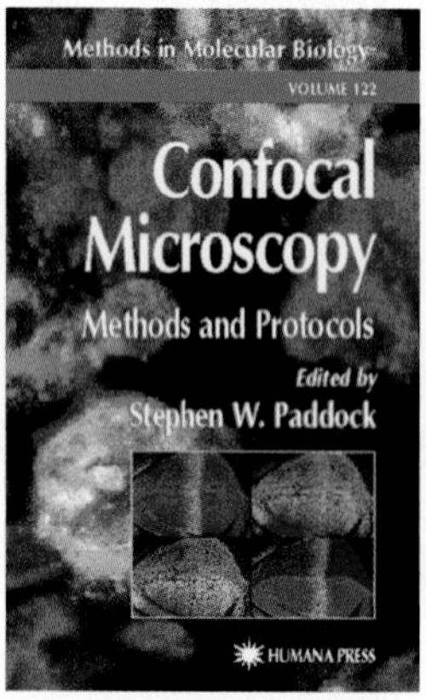

Confocal Microscopy (Methods in Molecular Biology, Volume 122)

Confocal Microscopy (C14946), edited by S.W. Paddock and published in 1998, provides researchers who want to use confocal microscopy techniques with all of the information they need to produce high-quality images; tissue-sampling methods and the staining process, as well as manipulation, presentation and publication of the realized image, are all discussed in detail. Written in a user-friendly, nontechnical style, the methods specifically cover most of the commonly used model organisms: worms, sea urchins, flies, plants, yeast, frogs and zebrafish.

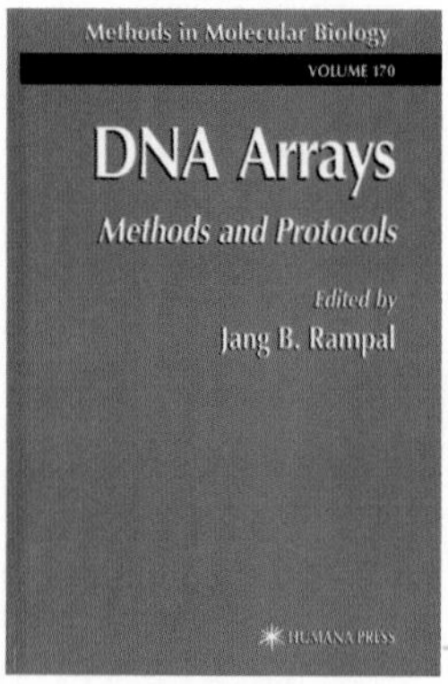

DNA Arrays: Methods and Protocols (Methods in Molecular Biology, Volume 170)

The development and application of microarray technologies has proceeded rapidly, driven by the need to analyze the copious amount of genetic information generated by the Human Genome Project. *DNA Arrays: Methods and Protocols* (D24835), edited by J.B. Rampal and published in 2001, provides biomedical researchers with a forward-looking and state-of-the-art overview of these techniques. In 312 information-packed pages, this benchtop manual provides step-by-step instructions for array printing, DNA and RNA sample preparation, hybridization conditions, signal detection, probe optimization, data collection and bioinformatics. Additional topics include genotyping, sequencing by hybridization, antisense reagents and gene expression analysis.

Fluorescent and Luminescent Probes for Biological Activity, Second Edition

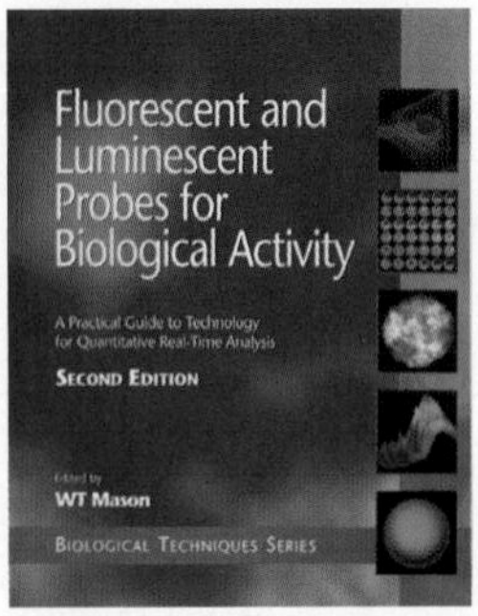

The development of optical probes for biological activity has contributed greatly to important technical and experimental advances in the biomedical sciences. Fluorescent and luminescent probes have, in many instances, displaced radioisotopes as standard research tools, providing significant improvements in speed and ease of detection. *Fluorescent and Luminescent Probes for Biological Activity, Second Edition* (F14944), a comb-bound guide edited by W.T. Mason and published in 1999, provides a comprehensive survey of the current scope of optical probe techniques. Also presented are detailed discussions of practical biological questions, underlying principles of optical and microelectronic instrumentation and future developments of optical probe technology.

Fundamentals of Light Microscopy and Electronic Imaging

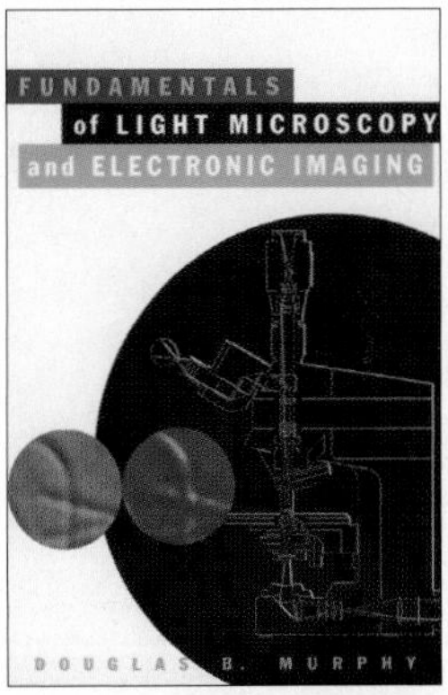

Modern research microscopes are advanced electronic imaging systems designed for resolving the structural and functional intricacies of complex biological specimens. Covering optical infrastructure, cameras and image processing techniques from the standpoints of both fundamental principles and practical implementation, this comprehensive 384-page reference provides researchers with the technical background essential for obtaining peak performance from these technically sophisticated instruments. Written in a practical, accessible style by D.B. Murphy and published in 2001, *Fundamentals of Light Microscopy and Electronic Imaging* (F24840) provides comprehensive coverage of essential topics, including:

- Illuminators, filters and isolation of specific wavelengths
- Phase contrast and differential interference contrast
- Properties of polarized light and polarization microscopy
- Fluorescence and confocal laser-scanning microscopy
- Digital CCD microscopy and image processing

Each chapter includes practical demonstrations and exercises, along with a discussion of the relevant material. In addition, a thorough glossary assists with complex terminology and an appendix contains lists of materials, procedures for specimen preparation and answers to questions.

Product List — 23.6 Books from Molecular Probes

Cat #	Product Name	Unit Size
B7884	Bioconjugate Techniques. G.T. Hermanson, Academic Press (1996); 785 pages, soft cover	each
C14946	Confocal Microscopy (Methods in Molecular Biology Volume 122). Stephen Paddock, ed. Humana Press (1998); 464 pages, hard cover	each
D24835	DNA Arrays: Methods and Protocols (Methods in Molecular Biology Volume 170). J.B. Rampal, ed. Humana Press (2001); 312 pages, hard cover	each
F14944	Fluorescent and Luminescent Probes for Biological Activity. A Practical Guide to Technology for Quantitative Real-Time Analysis, Second Ed. W.T. Mason, ed. Academic Press (1999); 647 pp, comb bound	each
F24840	Fundamentals of Light Microscopy and Electronic Imaging. D.B. Murphy. John Wiley & Sons, Inc. (2001); 384 pages, hard cover	each
M14943	Methods in Enzymology, Volume 291: Caged Compounds. Gerard Marriott, ed. Academic Press (1998); 529 pages, hard cover	each

For current prices or to order online, visit probes.invitrogen.com

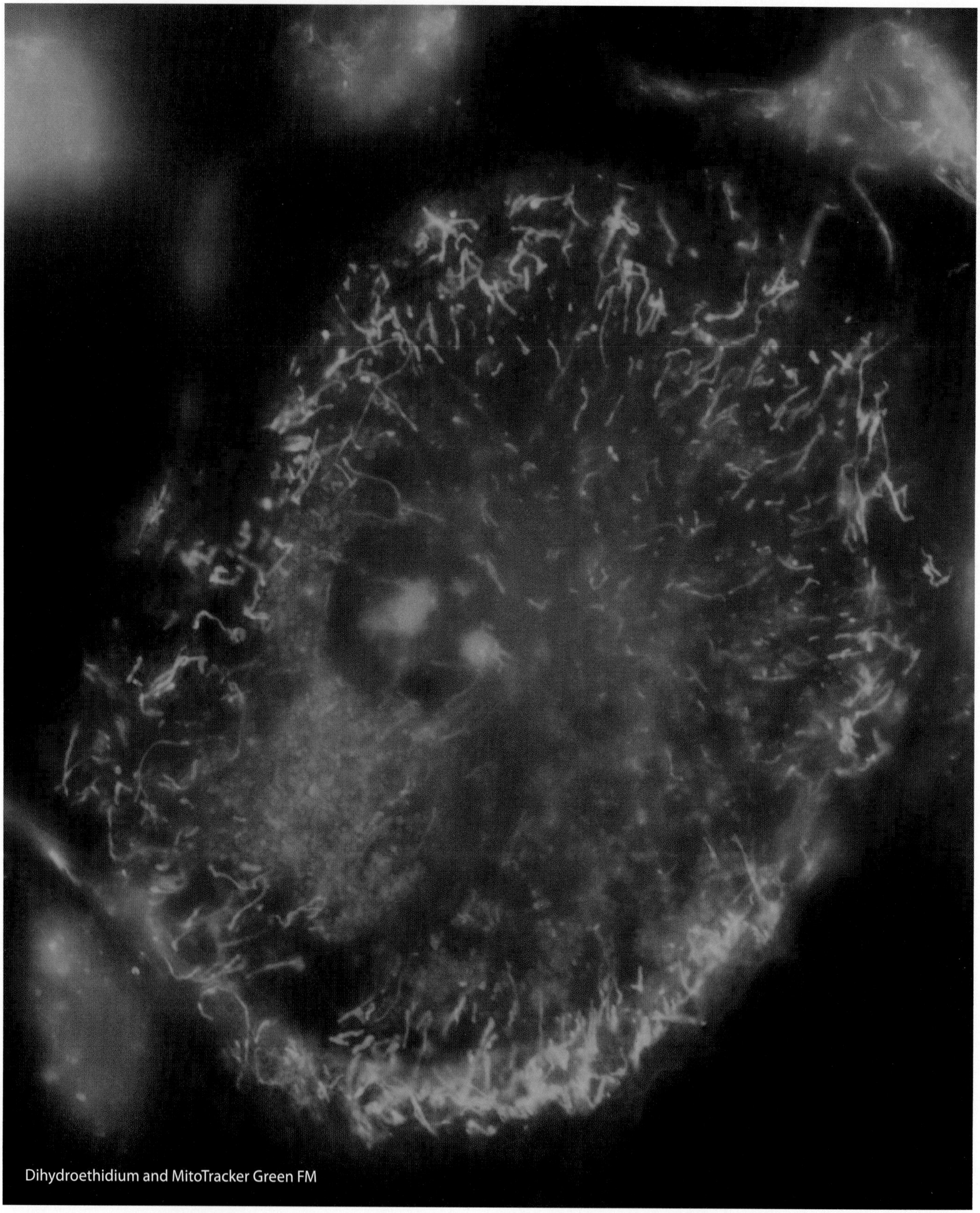

Dihydroethidium and MitoTracker Green FM

Trademark Information

Molecular Probes has achieved recognition of its trademarks worldwide. Please respect our trademarks; we will vigorously protect their proper usage. All names containing the designation ® are registered with the U.S. Patent and Trademark Office.

The Following are Trademarks of Molecular Probes™:

Alexa Fluor®
AlignFlow™
Amplex®
Antibody Beacon™
ARES™
ATTO-TAG™
*Bac*Light™
BENZOBODIPY™
BioParticles®
BioProbes®
Biotective™
BlockAid™
BO-PRO™
BOBO™
BOCILLIN™
BODIPY®
BrainStain™
Calcium Crimson™
Calcium Green™
Calcium Orange™
Calcium Sponge™
CandyCane™
CaptAvidin™
Captivate™
Cascade Blue®
Cascade Yellow™
CellTrace™
CellTracker™
ChromaTide®
CompenFlow™
Constellation™
Coomassie Fluor™
CoroNa™
CyQUANT®
Dapoxyl®
DEAD Red™
DetectaGene™
DQ™
DSB-X™
DyeChrome™
DyeMer™
ELF®
EnzChek®
ER-Tracker™
EZQ®
FAST CAT®
FAST DiA™
FAST DiI™
FAST DiO™
FluoCells®
FluoReporter®
FluoroMyelin™
FluoroPure™
FluoroTide™
FluoSpheres®
FluoZin™
FM®
FocalCheck™
FUN®
Fura Red™
FuraZin™
Hg-Link™
Image-iT™
ImaGene Green™
ImaGene Red™
IndoZin™
Influx™
InSpeck™
JO-PRO™
JOJO™
LaserPro™
Leadmium™
LinearFlow™
LIVE/DEAD®
LO-PRO™
LOLO™
LysoSensor™
LysoTracker®
Mag-Fura Red™
Magnesium Green™
Magnesium Orange™
Marina Blue®
MitoFluor™
MitoFOX™
MitoProbe™
MitoSOX™
MitoTracker®
Molecular Probes logo®
Multiplexed Proteomics®
MultiSpeck™
MycoFluor™
NanoOrange®
NeuroTrace®
Newport Green™
OliGreen®
Oregon Green®
OxyBURST®
P$_i$Per™
Pacific Blue™
Panomer™
PARAGON™
PeakFlow™
PeppermintStick™
Phen Green™
PicoGreen®
PO-PRO™
POPO™
Pro-Q®
ProLong®
PS-Speck™
QSY®
Quant-iT™
RediPlate™
RedoxSensor™
Rhinohide™
Rhodamine Green™
Rhodamine Red™
Rhodol Green™
RhodZin™
RiboGreen®
RNASelect™
SelectFX™
SlowFade®
SNAFL®
SNARF®
Sodium Green™
SYBR Safe™
SYBR®
SYPRO®
SYTO®
SYTOX®
TetraSpeck™
Texas Red®
TO-PRO®
TOTO®
TransFluoSpheres®
TS-Link™
ViaGram™
Vybrant®
YO-PRO®
YOYO®
Zenon®

Trademarks of Other Companies Referred to in our Product Literature Include:

ABSOLUTE-S™ (Phoenix Flow Systems, Inc.)
ABTS™ (Boehringer Mannheim GmbH)
Acrobat Reader® (Adobe Systems, Inc.)
Acrobat® (Adobe Systems, Inc.)
ADIFAB™ (FFA Sciences LLC.)
Adobe® (Adobe Systems, Inc.)
alamarBlue™ (Accumed International, Inc.)
ALPHA VIVID™ (Omega Optical, Inc.)
Ambion® (Ambion, Inc.)
Ampholine™ (Amersham Biosciences)
Angiostatin® (Entremed, Inc.)
APO-BrdU™ (Phoenix Flow Systems, Inc.)
Apple® (Apple Computer, Inc.)
AquaLite® (Chemicon International)
Aroclor® (Monsanto Chemical Company)
ArrayIt™ (TeleChem International, Inc.)
Atlas™ PowerScript™ (BD Biosciences Clontech)
Attofluor® (Atto BioScience, Inc.)
AuroDye® (Amersham Biosciences)
AVANCE™ (Bruker BioSpin Corp.)
Bio-Gel® (Bio-Rad Laboratories, Inc.)
Bio-Lyte™ (Bio-Rad Laboratories, Inc.)
Bio-Rad® (Bio-Rad Laboratories)
BioImager® (Genomic Solutions)
Biomek® (Beckman Instruments, Inc.)
BOLD™ (Serologicals Corporation)
Calcofluor™ (American Cyanamid)
Celite® (Celite Corp.)
Cellomics™ (Cellomics, Inc.)
Cellosolve® (Union Carbide Corp.)
Chelex® (Bio-Rad Laboratories)
ChemWindow® (SoftShell International, Ltd.)
Chroma® (Chroma Technology)
Colcemid® (Ciba Ltd.)
CometAssay™ (Trevigen, Inc.)
CometSlide™ (Trevigen, Inc.)
Coolscan™ (Nikon, Inc.)
Coomassie® (BASF Aktiengesellschaft)
COPAS (Union Biometrica, a Harvard Bioscience Company)
Corrositex® (In Vitro International, Inc.)
Coulter (Beckman Coulter, Inc.)

continued on next page

Trademarks of Other Companies, *continued*

CoverWell™ (Grace Bio-Labs, Inc.)
CultureWell™ (Grace Bio-Labs, Inc.)
Cy® (Amersham Biosciences)
CytoFluor® (Applera Corp.)
Cytoseal™ (Stephens Scientific)
DarkReader™ (Clare Chemical Research)
Delta2D™ (DECODON GmbH)
Diaphot TMD™ (Nikon, Inc.)
DIG (Roche Diagnostics, Inc.)
DM-Nitrophen™ (Calbiochem-Novabiochem Corp.)
Drierite® (W.A. Hammond Drierite Co.)
Duracryl™ (ESA, Inc.)
Eagle Eye® (Stratagene)
ECL™ (Amersham Biosciences)
Eclipse E800™ (Nikon, Inc.)
Ektachrome® (Eastman Kodak Co.)
ElutaTube™ (Fermentas, Inc.)
Endostatin™ (Entremed, Inc.)
Exhaustive Photon Reassignment™ (Scanalytics, Inc.)
Explorer™ (Microsoft Corporation)
FACS® (Becton Dickinson and Co.)
FACScan™ (Becton Dickinson and Co.)
FairPlay™ (Stratagene)
Ficoll® (Amersham Biosciences)
FLA-3000 (Fuji Photo Film, Inc.)
FLICA™ (Immunochemistry Technologies, LLC)
FLIPR™ (Molecular Devices Corp.)
Fluor-S® (Bio-Rad Laboratories)
FluorImager™ (Amersham Biosciences)
Fluoro-Gold™ (Fluorochrome, Inc.)
FluoroNanogold™ (Nanoprobes, Inc.)
Fluorosensor® (Atto BioScience, Inc.)
FMBIO® (Hitachi Software Engineering Co., Ltd.)
FOTO/UV® (Fotodyne, Inc.)
Fotodyne® (Fotodyne, Inc.)
Fuji® (Fuji Photo Film, Inc.)
GelBond® (FMC Corp.)
GelCode® (Pierce Biotechnology, Inc.)
GenePix Pro® (Axon Instruments, Inc.)
GenePix® (Axon Instruments, Inc.)
GlykoTrack™ (ProZyme)
Haema-Line® (Serono Diagnostics, Inc.)
Hybond® (Amersham Biosciences)
HybriSlip™ (Grace Bio-Labs, Inc.)
HybriWell™ (Grace Bio-Labs, Inc.)
HydroGel™ (PerkinElmer, Inc.)
Image-1® (Universal Imaging Corp.)
Imaris® (Bitplane AG Corp.)
Immobiline™ (Amersham Biosciences)
Immobilon™ (Millipore Corp.)
Java® JavaScript® (Sun Microsystems)
Jaz® (Iomega Corporation)
Kodachrome® (Eastman Kodak Co.)
Kodak® (Eastman Kodak Co.)
LabMap™ (Luminex Corporation)
Labophot® (Nikon, Inc.)
LifterSlip™ (Erie Scientific Company)
Lissamine™ (Imperial Chemical Industries)
LSC® (CompuCyte)
Lumi-Imager™ (Roche/Boehringer-Mannheim)
Mac® (Apple Computer, Inc.)
Mac®OS (Apple Computer, Inc.)
MetaMorph® (Universal Imaging Corp.)
Microsoft® (Microsoft Corporation)
Molecular Dynamics® (Amersham Biosciences)
Molecular Imager® (Bio-Rad Laboratories)
MultiPROBE® (Packard Instrument Co.)
NanoDrop® (NanoDrop Technologies)
NANOGOLD® (Nanoprobes, Inc.)
Nanosep® (Pall Corporation)
Netscape Communicator® (Netscape Communications Corporation)
Netscape Navigator® (Netscape Communications Corporation)
Netscape® (Netscape Communications Corporation)
Neurobiotin™ (Vector Laboratories)
NeutrAvidin™ (Pierce Chemical Co.)
Nikon® (Nikon, Inc.)
Nonidet™ (Shell International Petroleum Co., Ltd.)
Omega® (Omega Optical, Inc.)
OmniGrid® (GeneMachines)
ONCYTE® (Grace Bio-Labs, Inc.)
Parafilm® (American National Can Co.)
Penta·His™ (QIAGEN)
PermaFluor® (Thermo Shandon, Pittsburgh PA)
PerSeptive Biosystems® (The PE Corporation)
Pharmacia® (Amersham Biosciences)
Pharmalyte™ (Amersham Biosciences)
PhastGel® (Amersham Biosciences)
PhastTransfer® (Amersham Biosciences)
Photometrics® (Roper Scientific, Inc.)
Photoshop® (Adobe Systems, Inc.)
PIP Array™ (Echelon Biosciences)
PIP Beads™ (Echelon Biosciences)
PIP MicroStrips™ (Echelon Biosciences)
PIP Strips™ (Echelon Biosciences)
Plan Apo™ (Nikon, Inc.)
Plan Fluor™ (Nikon, Inc.)
Pluronic® (BASF Corp.)
Polaroid® (Polaroid-Land Corp.)
Precision Protein™ (Bio-Rad Laboratories, Inc.)
Press-to-Seal™ (Grace Bio-Labs, Inc.)
ProPlate™ (Grace Bio-Labs, Inc.)
Quadfluor™ (Nikon, Inc.)
Quantix™ (Roper Scientific, Inc.)
QuickTime® (Apple Computer, Inc.)
RatioVision® (Atto BioScience, Inc.)
Rubbermaid® (Rubbermaid, Inc.)
Safire™ (Tecan)
Saran Wrap® (Dow Chemical Co.)
ScanArray™ (PerkinElmer Life and Analytical Services, Inc.)
Seal-A-Meal® (Dazey Corp.)
Secure-Seal™ (Grace Bio-Labs, Inc.)
Sephadex® (Amersham Biosciences)
Servalyt® (Serva Feinbiochemica Gmbh and Co.)
Servin' Saver™ (Rubbermaid, Inc.)
Shuttle PIP™ (Echelon Biosciences)
SoftShell® (SoftShell International, Ltd.)
SPECTRAmax® (Molecular Devices Corp.)
SPECTRAmax® GEMINI (Molecular Devices Corp.)
SpectrumAqua™ (Vysis, Inc.)
SPF-500™ (SLM-Aminco)
SphingoStrips™ (Echelon Biosciences)
SRM® (National Institute of Standards and Technology)
Star 1™ (Photometrics)
Star® (Star Micronics America, Inc.)
Storm™ (Amersham Biosciences)
Stratagene® (Stratagene)
Superfrost Plus® (Erie Scientific Co.)
TaqMan® (Roche Molecular Systems)
Taxol® (Bristol-Myers Squibb Co.)
Teflon® (E.I. DuPont de Nemours & Co., Inc.)
The Acrobat logo (Adobe Systems, Inc.)
Threshold® (Molecular Devices Corp.)
Titertek® (ICN Biomedicals, Inc.)
TRITON® (Union Carbide Chemicals & Plastics Technology Corp)
TSA™ (PerkinElmer Life Sciences, Inc.)
Tween® (ICI Americas, Inc.)
ULS™ (KREATECH Biotechnology B.V.)
Ultraview™ (PerkinElmer Life Sciences, Inc.)
ULYSIS® (KREATECH Biotechnology B.V.)
Vantage™ (Becton Dickinson and Co.)
VECTASHIELD® (Vector Laboratories, Inc.)
Visi-Blue™ (UVP Laboratory Products)
Windows® (Microsoft Corporation)
Wratten® (Eastman Kodak Co.)
Z3 (Compugen)
Zeiss® (Carl Zeiss, Inc.)
Zip® (Iomega Corporation)

Limited Use Label Licenses

Limited Use Label License No. 154: SYBR® Technology

The manufacture, use, sale or import of this product may be subject to one or more of US patent Nos. 5,436,134, 5,534,416, 5,545,535, 5,658,751, 5,863,753; 6,664,047; pending applications and corresponding foreign equivalents, owned by Invitrogen Corporation. The purchase of this product conveys to the buyer the non-transferable right to use the purchased amount of the product and components of the product in research conducted by the buyer (whether the buyer is an academic or for-profit entity). The buyer cannot sell or otherwise transfer (a) this product (b) its components or (c) materials made using this product or its components to a third party or otherwise use this product or its components or materials made using this product or its components for Commercial Purposes. The buyer may transfer information or materials made through the use of this product to a scientific collaborator, provided that such transfer is not for any Commercial Purpose, and that such collaborator agrees in writing (a) to not transfer such materials to any third party, and (b) to use such transferred materials and/or information solely for research and not for Commercial Purposes. Commercial Purposes means any activity by a party for consideration and may include, but is not limited to: (1) use of the product or its components in manufacturing; (2) use of the product or its components to provide a service, information, or data; (3) use of the product or its components for therapeutic, diagnostic or prophylactic purposes; or (4) resale of the product or its components, whether or not such product or its components are resold for use in research. Invitrogen Corporation will not assert a claim against the buyer of infringement of the above patents based upon the manufacture, use or sale of a therapeutic, clinical diagnostic, vaccine or prophylactic product developed in research by the buyer in which this product or its components was employed, provided that neither this product nor any of its components was used in the manufacture of such product. If the purchaser is not willing to accept the limitations of this limited use statement, Invitrogen is willing to accept return of the product with a full refund. For information on purchasing a license to this product for purposes other than research, contact Molecular Probes, Inc., Business Development, 29851 Willow Creek Road, Eugene, OR 97402. Tel: (541) 465-8300. Fax: (541) 335-0504.

Limited Use Label License No. 183: Alexa Fluor® Dyes

The manufacture, use, sale or import of this product may be subject to one or more of U.S. Patent Nos. 5,696,157; 6,130,101; 6,716,979; pending applications and corresponding foreign equivalents, owned by Invitrogen Corporation. The purchase of this product conveys to the buyer the non-transferable right to use the purchased amount of the product and components of the product in research conducted by the buyer (whether the buyer is an academic or for-profit entity). The buyer cannot sell or otherwise transfer (a) this product (b) its components or (c) materials made using this product or its components to a third party or otherwise use this product or its components or materials made using this product or its components for Commercial Purposes. The buyer may transfer information or materials made through the use of this product to a scientific collaborator, provided that such transfer is not for any Commercial Purpose, and that such collaborator agrees in writing (a) to not transfer such materials to any third party, and (b) to use such transferred materials and/or information solely for research and not for Commercial Purposes. Commercial Purposes means any activity by a party for consideration and may include, but is not limited to: (1) use of the product or its components in manufacturing; (2) use of the product or its components to provide a service, information, or data; (3) use of the product or its components for therapeutic, diagnostic or prophylactic purposes; or (4) resale of the product or its components, whether or not such product or its components are resold for use in research. Invitrogen Corporation will not assert a claim against the buyer of infringement of the above patents based upon the manufacture, use or sale of a therapeutic, clinical diagnostic, vaccine or prophylactic product developed in research by the buyer in which this product or its components was employed, provided that neither this product nor any of its components was used in the manufacture of such product. If the purchaser is not willing to accept the limitations of this limited use statement, Invitrogen is willing to accept return of the product with a full refund. For information on purchasing a license to this product for purposes other than research, contact Molecular Probes, Inc., Business Development, 29851 Willow Creek Road, Eugene, OR 97402, Tel: (541)465-8300. Fax: (541)335-0504.

Limited Use Label License No. 188: SYBR Safe™ Nucleic Acid Stain

This product is provided under an agreement only for the use in staining nucleic acids in gels.

Limited Use Label License No. 190: Protein Stains

The manufacture, use, sale or import of this product may be subject to one or more US Patent Nos. 6,316,267; 6,329,205; 6,579,718; 5,616,502 and corresponding foreign equivalents, owned by Invitrogen Corporation. The purchase of this product conveys to the buyer the non-transferable right to use the purchased amount of the product and components of the product in research conducted by the buyer (whether the buyer is an academic or for-profit entity). The buyer cannot sell or otherwise transfer (a) this product (b) its components or (c) materials made using this product or its components to a third party or otherwise use this product or its components or materials made using this product or its components for Commercial Purposes. The buyer may transfer information or materials made through the use of this product to a scientific collaborator, provided that such transfer is not for any Commercial Purpose, and that such collaborator agrees in writing (a) to not transfer such materials to any third party, and (b) to use such transferred materials and/or information solely for research and not for Commercial Purposes. Commercial Purposes means any activity by a party for consideration and may include, but is not limited to: (1) use of the product or its components in manufacturing; (2) use of the product or its components to provide a service, information, or data; (3) use of the product or its components for therapeutic, diagnostic or prophylactic purposes; or (4) resale of the product or its components, whether or not such product or its components are resold for use in research. Invitrogen Corporation will not assert a claim against the buyer of infringement of the above patents based upon the manufacture, use or sale of a therapeutic, clinical diagnostic, vaccine or prophylactic product developed in research by the buyer in which this product or its components was employed, provided that neither this product nor any of its components was used in the manufacture of such product. If the purchaser is not willing to accept the limitations of this limited use statement, Invitrogen is willing to accept return of the product with a full refund. For information on purchasing a license to this product for purposes other than research, contact Molecular Probes, Inc., Business Development, 29851 Willow Creek Road, Eugene, OR 97402. Tel: (541)465-8300. Fax: (541)335-0504.

Limited Use Label License No. 191: Oregon Green® Dyes

The manufacture, use, sale or import of this product may be subject to one or more US Patents Nos. 6,162,931, and 6,229,055 and corresponding foreign equivalents, owned by Invitrogen Corporation. The purchase of this product conveys to the buyer the non-transferable right to use the purchased amount of the product and components of the product in research conducted by the buyer (whether the buyer is an academic or for-profit entity). The buyer cannot sell or otherwise transfer (a) this product (b) its components or (c) materials made using this product or its components to a third party or otherwise use this product or its components or materials made using this product or its components for Commercial Purposes. The buyer may transfer information or materials made through the use of this product to a scientific collaborator, provided that such transfer is not for any Commercial Purpose, and that such collaborator agrees in writing (a) to not transfer such materials to any third party, and (b) to use such transferred materials and/or information solely for research and not for Commercial Purposes. Commercial Purposes means any activity by a party for consideration and may include, but is not limited to: (1) use of the product or its components in manufacturing; (2) use of the product or its components to provide a service, information, or data; (3) use of the product or its components for therapeutic, diagnostic or prophylactic purposes; or (4) resale of the product or its components, whether or not such product or its components are resold for use in research. Invitrogen Corporation will not assert a claim against the buyer of infringement of the above patents based upon the manufacture, use or sale of a therapeutic, clinical diagnostic, vaccine or prophylactic product developed in research by the buyer in which this product or its components was employed, provided that neither this product nor any of its components was used in the manufacture of such product. If the purchaser is not willing to accept the limitations of this limited use statement, Invitrogen is willing to accept return of the product with a full refund. For information on purchasing a license to this product for purposes other than research, contact Molecular Probes, Inc., Business Development, 29851 Willow Creek Road, Eugene, OR 97402. Tel: (541)465-8300. Fax: (541)335-0504.

Limited Use Label License No. 192: Pacific Blue™ Dyes

The manufacture, use, sale or import of this product may be subject to US Patent No. 5,830,912, and foreign equivalents, owned by Invitrogen Corporation. The purchase of this product conveys to the buyer the non-transferable right to use the purchased amount of the product and components of the product in research conducted by the buyer (whether the buyer is an academic or for-profit entity). The buyer cannot sell or otherwise transfer (a) this product (b) its components or (c) materials made using this product or its components to a third party or otherwise use this product or its components or materials made using this product or its components for Commercial Purposes. The buyer may transfer information or materials made through the use of this product to a scientific collaborator, provided that such transfer is not for any Commercial Purpose, and that such collaborator agrees in writing (a) to not transfer such materials to any third party, and (b) to use such transferred materials and/or information solely for research and not for Commercial Purposes. Commercial Purposes means any activity by a party for consideration and may include, but is not limited to: (1) use of the product or its components in manufacturing; (2) use of the product or its components to provide a service, information, or data; (3) use of the product or its components for therapeutic, diagnostic or prophylactic purposes; or (4) resale of the product or its components, whether or not such product or its components are resold for use in research. Invitrogen Corporation will not assert a claim against the buyer of infringement of the above patents based upon the manufacture, use or sale of a therapeutic, clinical diagnostic, vaccine or prophylactic product developed in research by the buyer in which this product or its components was employed, provided that neither this product nor any of its components was used in the manufacture of such product. If the purchaser is not willing to accept the limitations of this limited use statement, Invitrogen is willing to accept return of the product with a full refund. For information on purchasing a license to this product for purposes other than research, contact Molecular Probes, Inc., Business Development, 29851 Willow Creek Road, Eugene, OR 97402. Tel: (541)465-8300. Fax: (541)335-0504.

Limited Use Label License No. 193: BODIPY® Dyes

The manufacture, use, sale or import of this product may be subject to one or more of US Patent Nos. 4,774,339, 5,187,288, 5,248,782, 5,274,113, 5,338,854, 5,433,896, 5,451,663, 6,005,113 and corresponding foreign equivalents, owned by Invitrogen Corporation. The purchase of this product conveys to the buyer the non-transferable right to use the purchased amount of the product and components of the product in research conducted by the buyer (whether the buyer is an academic or for-profit entity). The buyer cannot sell or otherwise transfer (a) this product (b) its components or (c) materials made using this product or its components to a third party or otherwise use this product or its components or materials made using this product or its components for Commercial Purposes. The buyer may transfer information or materials made through the use of this product to a scientific collaborator, provided that such transfer is not for any Commercial Purpose, and that such collaborator agrees in writing (a) to not transfer such materials to any third party, and (b) to use such transferred materials and/or information solely for research and not for Commercial Purposes. Commercial Purposes means any activity by a party for consideration and may include, but is not limited to: (1) use of the product or its components in manufacturing; (2) use of the product or its components to provide a service, information, or data; (3) use of the product or its components for therapeutic, diagnostic or prophylactic purposes; or (4) resale of the product or its components, whether or not such product or its components are resold for use in research. Invitrogen Corporation will not assert a claim against the buyer of infringement of the above patents based upon the manufacture, use or sale of a therapeutic, clinical diagnostic, vaccine or prophylactic product developed in research by the buyer in which this product or its components was employed, provided that neither this product nor any of its components was used in the manufacture of such product. If the purchaser is not willing to accept the limitations of this limited use statement, Invitrogen is willing to accept return of the product with a full refund. For information on purchasing a license to this product for purposes other than research, contact Molecular Probes, Inc., Business Development, 29851 Willow Creek Road, Eugene, OR 97402. Tel: (541)465-8300. Fax: (541)335-0504.

Limited Use Label License No. 203: EnzChek® Technology

The manufacture, use, sale or import of this product may be subject to U.S. Patent No. 5,719,031, owned by Invitrogen Corporation. The purchase of this product conveys to the buyer the non-transferable right to use the purchased amount of the product and components of the product in research conducted by the buyer (whether the buyer is an academic or for-profit entity). The buyer cannot sell or otherwise transfer (a) this product, (b) its components, or (c) materials made by the employment of this product or its components to a third party or otherwise use this product or its components or materials made by the employment of this product or its components for Commercial Purposes. The buyer may transfer information or materials made through the employment of this product to a scientific collaborator, provided that such transfer is not for any Commercial Purpose, and that such collaborator agrees in writing (a) not to transfer such materials to any third party, and (b) to use such transferred materials and/or information solely for research and not for Commercial Purposes. Commercial Purposes means any activity by a party for consideration and may include, but is not limited to: (1) use of the product or its components in manufacturing; (2) use of the product or its components to provide a service, information, or data; (3) use of the product or its components for therapeutic, diagnostic or prophylactic purposes; or (4) resale of the product or its components, whether or not such product or its components are resold for use in research. Invitrogen Corporation will not assert a claim against the buyer of infringement of the above patents based upon the manufacture, use or sale of a therapeutic, clinical diagnostic, vaccine or prophylactic product developed in research by the buyer in which this product or its components was employed, provided that none of this product or any of its components was used in the manufacture of such product. If the purchaser is not willing to accept the limitations of this limited use statement, Invitrogen is willing to accept return of the product with a full refund. For information on purchasing a license to this product for purposes other than research, contact Molecular Probes, Inc., Business Development, 29851 Willow Creek Road, Eugene, OR 97402. Tel: (541)465-8300. Fax: (541)335-0504.

Limited Use Label License No. 204: Metal Ion Indicator Dyes

This product is licensed to Molecular Probes, Inc. and is subject to one or more of US Patent Nos. 5,049,673; 5,516,911 and corresponding foreign equivalents. For research use only.

Limited Use Label License No. 205: FHIT Reagents

The manufacture, use, sale or import of this product may be subject to U.S. Patent No. 6,323,186, owned by Invitrogen Corporation. The purchase of this product conveys to the buyer the non-transferable right to use the purchased amount of the product and components of the product in research conducted by the buyer (whether the buyer is an academic or for-profit entity). The buyer cannot sell or otherwise transfer (a) this product, (b) its components, or (c) materials made by the employment of this product or its components to a third party or otherwise use this product or its components or materials made by the employment of this product or its components for Commercial Purposes. The buyer may transfer information or materials made through the employment of this product to a scientific collaborator, provided that such transfer is not for any Commercial Purpose, and that such collaborator agrees in writing (a) not to transfer such materials to any third party, and (b) to use such transferred materials and/or information solely for research and not for Commercial Purposes. Commercial Purposes means any activity by a party for consideration and may include, but is not limited to: (1) use of the product or its components in manufacturing; (2) use of the product or its components to provide a service, information, or data; (3) use of the product or its components for therapeutic, diagnostic or prophylactic purposes; or (4) resale of the product or its components, whether or not such product or its components are resold for use in research. Invitrogen Corporation will not assert a claim against the buyer of infringement of the above patents based upon the manufacture, use or sale of a therapeutic, clinical diagnostic, vaccine or prophylactic product developed in research by the buyer in which this product or its components was employed, provided that none of this product or any of its components was used in the manufacture of such product. If the purchaser is not willing to accept the limitations of this limited use statement, Invitrogen is willing to accept return of the product with a full refund. For information on purchasing a license to this product for purposes other than research, contact Molecular Probes, Inc., Business Development, 29851 Willow Creek Road, Eugene, OR 97402. Tel: (541)465-8300. Fax: (541)335-0504.

Limited Use Label License No. 206: Metal Ion Indicators

The manufacture, use, sale or import of this product may be subject to U.S. Patent No. 5,453,517 and 5,405,975 owned by Invitrogen Corporation. The purchase of this product conveys to the buyer the non-transferable right to use the purchased amount of the product and components of the product in research conducted by the buyer (whether the buyer is an academic or for-profit entity). The buyer cannot sell or otherwise transfer (a) this product, (b) its components, or (c) materials made by the employment of this product or its components to a third party or otherwise use this product or its components or materials made by the employment of this product or its components for Commercial Purposes. The buyer may transfer information or materials made through the employment of this product to a scientific collaborator, provided that such transfer is not for any Commercial Purpose, and that such collaborator agrees in writing (a) not to transfer such materials to any third party, and (b) to use such transferred materials and/or information solely for research and not for Commercial Purposes. Commercial Purposes means any activity by a party for consideration and may include, but is not limited to: (1) use of the product or its components in manufacturing; (2) use of the product or its components to provide a service, information, or data; (3) use of the product or its components for therapeutic, diagnostic or prophylactic purposes; or (4) resale of the product or its components, whether or not such product or its components are resold for use in research. Invitrogen Corporation will not assert a claim against the buyer of infringement of the above patents based upon the manufacture, use or sale of a therapeutic, clinical diagnostic, vaccine or prophylactic product developed in research by the buyer in which this product or its components was employed, provided that none of this product or any of its components was used in the manufacture of such product. If the purchaser is not willing to accept the limitations of this limited use statement, Invitrogen is willing to accept return of the product with a full refund. For information on purchasing a license to this product for purposes other than research, contact Molecular Probes, Inc., Business Development, 29851 Willow Creek Road, Eugene, OR 97402. Tel: (541)465-8300. Fax: (541)335-0504.

Limited Use Label License No. 208: SNARF® Technology

The manufacture, use, sale or import of this product may be subject to U.S. Patent No. 4,945,171, owned by Invitrogen Corporation. The purchase of this product conveys to the buyer the non-transferable right to use the purchased amount of the product and components of the product in research conducted by the buyer (whether the buyer is an academic or for-profit entity). The buyer cannot sell or otherwise transfer (a) this product, (b) its components, or (c) materials made by the employment of this product or its components to a third party or otherwise use this product or its components or materials made by the employment of this product or its components for Commercial Purposes. The buyer may transfer information or materials made through the employment of this product to a scientific collaborator, provided that such transfer is not for any Commercial Purpose, and that such collaborator agrees in writing (a) not to transfer such materials to any third party, and (b) to use such transferred materials and/or information solely for research and not for Commercial Purposes. Commercial Purposes means any activity by a party for consideration and may include, but is not limited to: (1) use of the product or its components in manufacturing; (2) use of the product or its components to provide a service, information, or data; (3) use of the product or its components for therapeutic, diagnostic or prophylactic purposes; or (4) resale of the product or its components, whether or not such product or its components are resold for use in research. Invitrogen Corporation will not assert a claim against the buyer of infringement of the above patents based upon the manufacture, use or sale of a therapeutic, clinical diagnostic, vaccine or prophylactic product developed in research by the buyer in which this product or its components was employed, provided that none of this product or any of its components was used in the manufacture of such product. If the purchaser is not willing to accept the limitations of this limited use statement, Invitrogen is willing to accept return of the product with a full refund. For information on purchasing a license to this product for purposes other than research, contact Molecular Probes, Inc., Business Development, 29851 Willow Creek Road, Eugene, OR 97402. Tel: (541)465-8300. Fax: (541)335-0504.

Limited Use Label License No. 209: TO-PRO® Technology

The manufacture, use, sale or import of this product may be subject to U.S. Patent No. 5,321,130, owned by Invitrogen Corporation. The purchase of this product conveys to the buyer the non-transferable right to use the purchased amount of the product and components of the product in research conducted by the buyer (whether the buyer is an academic or for-profit entity). The buyer cannot sell or otherwise transfer (a) this product, (b) its components, or (c) materials made by the employment of this product or its components to a third party or otherwise use this product or its components or materials made by the employment of this product or its components for Commercial Purposes. The buyer may transfer information or materials made through the employment of this product to a scientific collaborator, provided that such transfer is not for any Commercial Purpose, and that such collaborator agrees in writing (a) not to transfer such materials to any third party, and (b) to use such transferred materials and/or information solely for research and not for Commercial Purposes. Commercial Purposes means any activity by a party for consideration and may include, but is not limited to: (1) use of the product or its components in manufacturing; (2) use of the product or its components to provide a service, information, or data; (3) use of the product or its components for therapeutic, diagnostic or prophylactic purposes; or (4) resale of the product or its components, whether or not such product or its components are resold for use in research. Invitrogen Corporation will not assert a claim against the buyer of infringement of the above patents based upon the manufacture, use or sale of a therapeutic, clinical diagnostic, vaccine or prophylactic product developed in research by the buyer in which this product or its components was employed, provided that none of this product or any of its components was used in the manufacture of such product. If the purchaser is not willing to accept the limitations of this limited use statement, Invitrogen is willing to accept return of the product with a full refund. For information on purchasing a license to this product for purposes other than research, contact Molecular Probes, Inc., Business Development, 29851 Willow Creek Road, Eugene, OR 97402. Tel: (541)465-8300. Fax: (541)335-0504.

Limited Use Label License No. 210: LIVE/DEAD® Technology

The manufacture, use, sale or import of this product may be subject to U.S. Patent No. 5,314,805, owned by Invitrogen Corporation. The purchase of this product conveys to the buyer the non-transferable right to use the purchased amount of the product and components of the product in research conducted by the buyer (whether the buyer is an academic or for-profit entity). The buyer cannot sell or otherwise transfer (a) this product, (b) its components, or (c) materials made by the employment of this product or its components to a third party or otherwise use this product or its components or materials made by the employment of this product or its components for Commercial Purposes. The buyer may transfer information or materials made through the employment of this product to a scientific collaborator, provided that such transfer is not for any Commercial Purpose, and that such collaborator agrees in writing (a) not to transfer such materials to any third party, and (b) to use such transferred materials and/or information solely for research and not for Commercial Purposes. Commercial Purposes means any activity by a party for consideration and may include, but is not limited to: (1) use of the product or its components in manufacturing; (2) use of the product or its components to provide a service, information, or data; (3) use of the product or its components for therapeutic, diagnostic or prophylactic purposes; or (4) resale of the product or its components, whether or not such product or its components are resold for use in research. Invitrogen Corporation will not assert a claim against the buyer of infringement of the above patents based upon the manufacture, use or sale of a therapeutic, clinical diagnostic, vaccine or prophylactic product developed in research by the buyer in which this product or its components was employed, provided that none of this product or any of its components was used in the manufacture of such product. If the purchaser is not willing to accept the limitations of this limited use statement, Invitrogen is willing to accept return of the product with a full refund For information on purchasing a license to this product for purposes other than research, contact Molecular Probes, Inc., Business Development, 29851 Willow Creek Road, Eugene, OR 97402. Tel: (541)465-8300. Fax: (541)335-0504.

Limited Use Label License No. 211: Texas Red®-X Dyes

The manufacture, use, sale or import of this product may be subject to one or more of U.S. Patent Nos. 5,798,276, 5,955,612, and 6,562,632 owned by Invitrogen Corporation. The purchase of this product conveys to the buyer the non-transferable right to use the purchased amount of the product and components of the product in research conducted by the buyer (whether the buyer is an academic or for-profit entity). The buyer cannot sell or otherwise transfer (a) this product, (b) its components, or (c) materials made by the employment of this product or its components to a third party or otherwise use this product or its components or materials made by the employment of this product or its components for Commercial Purposes. The buyer may transfer information or materials made through the employment of this product to a scientific collaborator, provided that such transfer is not for any Commercial Purpose, and that such collaborator agrees in writing (a) not to transfer such materials to any third party, and (b) to use such transferred materials and/or information solely for research and not for Commercial Purposes. Commercial Purposes means any activity by a party for consideration and may include, but is not limited to: (1) use of the product or its components in manufacturing; (2) use of the product or its components to provide a service, information, or data; (3) use of the product or its components for therapeutic, diagnostic or prophylactic purposes; or (4) resale of the product or its components, whether or not such product or its components are resold for use in research. Invitrogen Corporation will not assert a claim against the buyer of infringement of the above patents based upon the manufacture, use or sale of a therapeutic, clinical diagnostic, vaccine or prophylactic product developed in research by the buyer in which this product or its components was employed, provided that none of this product or any of its components was used in the manufacture of such product. If the purchaser is not willing to accept the limitations of this limited use statement, Invitrogen is willing to accept return of the product with a full refund. For information on purchasing a license to this product for purposes other than research, contact Molecular Probes, Inc., Business Development, 29851 Willow Creek Road, Eugene, OR 97402. Tel: (541)465-8300. Fax: (541)335-0504.

Limited Use Label License No. 212: Haloalkyl Technology

The manufacture, use, sale or import of this product may be subject to one or more of U.S. Patent Nos. 5,362,628; 5,773,236 and 5,576,424; pending applications and foreign equivalents, owned by Invitrogen Corporation. The purchase of this product conveys to the buyer the non-transferable right to use the purchased amount of the product and components of the product in research conducted by the buyer (whether the buyer is an academic or for-profit entity). The buyer cannot sell or otherwise transfer (a) this product, (b) its components, or (c) materials made by the employment of this product or its components to a third party or otherwise use this product or its components or materials made by the employment of this product or its components for Commercial Purposes. The buyer may transfer information or materials made through the employment of this product to a scientific collaborator, provided that such transfer is not for any Commercial Purpose, and that such collaborator agrees in writing (a) not to transfer such materials to any third party, and (b) to use such transferred materials and/or information solely for research and not for Commercial Purposes. Commercial Purposes means any activity by a party for consideration and may include, but is not limited to: (1) use of the product or its components in manufacturing; (2) use of the product or its components to provide a service, information, or data; (3) use of the product or its components for therapeutic, diagnostic or prophylactic purposes; or (4) resale of the product or its components, whether or not such product or its components are resold for use in research. Invitrogen Corporation will not assert a claim against the buyer of infringement of the above patents based upon the manufacture, use or sale of a therapeutic, clinical diagnostic, vaccine or prophylactic product developed in research by the buyer in which this product or its components was employed, provided that none of this product or any of its components was used in the manufacture of such product. If the purchaser is not willing to accept the limitations of this limited use statement, Invitrogen is willing to accept return of the product with a full refund. For information on purchasing a license to this product for purposes other than research, contact Molecular Probes, Inc., Business Development, 29851 Willow Creek Road, Eugene, OR 97402. Tel: (541)465-8300. Fax: (541)335-0504.

Limited Use Label License No. 213: Detection of Apoptotic Cells

This product is provided under an agreement between Nexins Research and Molecular Probes, Inc, and is subject to US Patent No. 5,834,196 and corresponding foreign patents. Purchase of labeled annexins from Molecular Probes, Inc. includes a nontransferable authorization for research use by the purchaser; commercial use, including modification of the purchased product for resale, requires a separate license.

Limited Use Label License No. 214: Anti-BrdU Antibodies

This product is provided under an agreement between Phoenix Flow Systems, Inc. and Molecular Probes, Inc. and the use of this product is subject to one or more of US Patent Nos. 5,747,258 and 5,912,126. For research use only.

Limited Use Label License No. 215: Multi Drug Resistance

This product is provided under an agreement between Solvo Biotechnology, Inc and Molecular Probes, Inc, and the use of this product is subject to one or more of US Patent Nos. 5,872,014 and US 6,277,655. For research use only.

Limited Use Label License No. 216: LysoTracker® Technology

The manufacture, use, sale or import of this product may be subject to U.S. Patent 5,869,689, owned by Invitrogen Corporation. The purchase of this product conveys to the buyer the non-transferable right to use the purchased amount of the product and components of the product in research conducted by the buyer (whether the buyer is an academic or for-profit entity). The buyer cannot sell or otherwise transfer (a) this product, (b) its components, or (c) materials made by the employment of this product or its components to a third party or otherwise use this product or its components or materials made by the employment of this product or its components for Commercial Purposes. The buyer may transfer information or materials made through the employment of this product to a scientific collaborator, provided that such transfer is not for any Commercial Purpose, and that such collaborator agrees in writing (a) not to transfer such materials to any third party, and (b) to use such transferred materials and/or information solely for research and not for Commercial Purposes. Commercial Purposes means any activity by a party for consideration and may include, but is not limited to: (1) use of the product or its components in manufacturing; (2) use of the product or its components to provide a service, information, or data; (3) use of the product or its components for therapeutic, diagnostic or prophylactic purposes; or (4) resale of the product or its components, whether or not such product or its components are resold for use in research. Invitrogen Corporation will not assert a claim against the buyer of infringement of the above patents based upon the manufacture, use or sale of a therapeutic, clinical diagnostic, vaccine or prophylactic product developed in research by the buyer in which this product or its components was employed, provided that none of this product or any of its components was used in the manufacture of such product. If the purchaser is not willing to accept the limitations of this limited use statement, Invitrogen is willing to accept return of the product with a full refund. For information on purchasing a license to this product for purposes other than research, contact Molecular Probes, Inc., Business Development, 29851 Willow Creek Road, Eugene, OR 97402. Tel: (541)465-8300. Fax: (541)335-0504.

Limited Use Label License No. 217: MitoTracker® Technology

The manufacture, use, sale or import of this product may be subject to one or more of U.S. Patent Nos. 5,459,268, 5,686,261, 6,291,203 and corresponding foreign equivalents, owned by Invitrogen Corporation. The purchase of this product conveys to the buyer the non-transferable right to use the purchased amount of the product and components of the product in research conducted by the buyer (whether the buyer is an academic or for-profit entity). The buyer cannot sell or otherwise transfer (a) this product, (b) its components, or (c) materials made by the employment of this product or its components to a third party or otherwise use this product or its components or materials made by the employment of this product or its components for Commercial Purposes. The buyer may transfer information or materials made through the employment of this product to a scientific collaborator, provided that such transfer is not for any Commercial Purpose, and that such collaborator agrees in writing (a) not to transfer such materials to any third party, and (b) to use such transferred materials and/or information solely for research and not for Commercial Purposes. Commercial Purposes means any activity by a party for consideration and may include, but is not limited to: (1) use of the product or its components in manufacturing; (2) use of the product or its components to provide a service, information, or data; (3) use of the product or its components for therapeutic, diagnostic or prophylactic purposes; or (4) resale of the product or its components, whether or not such product or its components are resold for use in research. Invitrogen Corporation will not assert a claim against the buyer of infringement of the above patents based upon the manufacture, use or sale of a therapeutic, clinical diagnostic, vaccine or prophylactic product developed in research by the buyer in which this product or its components was employed, provided that none of this product or any of its components was used in the manufacture of such product. If the purchaser is not willing to accept the limitations of this limited use statement, Invitrogen is willing to accept return of the product with a full refund. For information on purchasing a license to this product for purposes other than research, contact Molecular Probes, Inc., Business Development, 29851 Willow Creek Road, Eugene, OR 97402. Tel: (541)465-8300. Fax: (541)335-0504.

Limited Use Label License No. 218: Cascade Blue® Dyes

The manufacture, use, sale or import of this product may be subject to U.S. Patent No. 5,132,432, owned by Invitrogen Corporation. The purchase of this product conveys to the buyer the non-transferable right to use the purchased amount of the product and components of the product in research conducted by the buyer (whether the buyer is an academic or for-profit entity). The buyer cannot sell or otherwise transfer (a) this product (b) its components or (c) materials made using this product or its components to a third party or otherwise use this product or its components or materials made using this product or its components for Commercial Purposes. The buyer may transfer information or materials made through the use of this product to a scientific collaborator, provided that such transfer is not for any Commercial Purpose, and that such collaborator agrees in writing (a) to not transfer such materials to any third party, and (b) to use such transferred materials and/or information solely for research and not for Commercial Purposes. Commercial Purposes means any activity by a party for consideration and may include, but is not limited to: (1) use of the product or its components in manufacturing; (2) use of the product or its components to provide a service, information, or data; (3) use of the product or its components for therapeutic, diagnostic or prophylactic purposes; or (4) resale of the product or its components, whether or not such product or its components are resold for use in research. Invitrogen Corporation will not assert a claim against the buyer of infringement of the above patents based upon the manufacture, use, or sale of a therapeutic, clinical diagnostic, vaccine or prophylactic product developed in research by the buyer in which this product or its components was employed, provided that neither this product nor any of its components was used in the manufacture of such product. If the purchaser is not willing to accept the limitations of this limited use statement, Invitrogen is willing to accept return of the product with a full refund For information on purchasing a license to this product for purposes other than research, contact Molecular Probes, Inc., Business Development, 29851 Willow Creek Road, Eugene, OR 97402. Tel: (541)465-8300. Fax: (541)335-0504.

Limited Use Label License No. 223: Labeling and Detection Technology

The manufacture, use, sale or import of this product may be subject to one or more pending US patent applications and corresponding foreign equivalents owned by Invitrogen Corporation. The purchase of this product conveys to the buyer the non-transferable right to use the purchased amount of the product and components of the product in research conducted by the buyer (whether the buyer is an academic or for-profit entity). The buyer cannot sell or otherwise transfer (a) this product (b) its components or (c) materials made using this product or its components to a third party or otherwise use this product or its components or materials made using this product or its components for Commercial Purposes. The buyer may transfer information or materials made through the use of this product to a scientific collaborator, provided that such transfer is not for any Commercial Purpose, and that such collaborator agrees in writing (a) to not transfer such materials to any third party, and (b) to use such transferred materials and/or information solely for research and not for Commercial Purposes. Commercial Purposes means any activity by a party for consideration and may include, but is not limited to: (1) use of the product or its components in manufacturing; (2) use of the product or its components to provide a service, information, or data; (3) use of the product or its components for therapeutic, diagnostic or prophylactic purposes; or (4) resale of the product or its components, whether or not such product or its components are resold for use in research. Invitrogen Corporation will not assert a claim against the buyer of infringement of the above patents based upon the manufacture, use, or sale of a therapeutic, clinical diagnostic, vaccine or prophylactic product developed in research by the buyer in which this product or its components was employed, provided that neither this product nor any of its components was used in the manufacture of such product. If the purchaser is not willing to accept the limitations of this limited use statement, Invitrogen is willing to accept return of the product with a full refund For information on purchasing a license to this product for purposes other than research, contact Molecular Probes, Inc., Business Development, 29851 Willow Creek Road, Eugene, OR 97402. Tel: (541)465-8300. Fax: (541)335-0504.

Limited Use Label License No. 224: Dye Extraction Blood Flow Technology

This product is licensed from Triton Technology, Inc. and the manufacture, use, sale and US import of dye extraction blood flow technology is subject to US Patent No. 5,230,343 and 5,253,649. For research use only.

Limited Use Label License No. 225: ChromaTide® Nucleotides

The dUTP and UTP nucleotides are NEN-brand products that are distributed and sold under an agreement between ENZO DIAGNOSTICS, INC. and PERKINELMER LIFE SCIENCES, INC. (previously NEN LIFE SCIENCES, INC.) for research purposes only by the end-user in the research market and are not intended for diagnostic or therapeutic use. Purchase does not include or carry any right or license to use, develop or otherwise exploit this product commercially. Any commercial use, development or exploitation of these products without the express prior written authorization of ENZO DIAGNOSTICS, INC. and PERKINELMER LIFE SCIENCES, INC. is strictly prohibited. These products or the use of these products may be covered by one or more Enzo patents, including the following: U.S. Patent Nos. 5,328,824; 5,449,767; 4,707,440; 4,952,685;5,002,885 and 5,013,831; and DK 164 407 8; and by one or more PERKINELMER patents, including U.S. Patent Nos. 5,047,519; 5,151,507 and 5,608,063.

Limited Use Label License No. 226: Antibodies

This product is provided under an agreement with Molecular Probes, Inc. for research use only.

Limited Use Label License No. 227: Fluorescent Microparticles

The manufacture, use, sale or import of this product may be subject to one or more of U.S. Patent Nos. 5,326,692; 5,573,909; 5,723,218 and 5,786,219 and corresponding foreign equivalents, owned by Invitrogen Corporation. The purchase of this product conveys to the buyer the non-transferable right to use the purchased amount of the product and components of the product in research conducted by the buyer (whether the buyer is an academic or for-profit entity). The buyer cannot sell or otherwise transfer (a) this product (b) its components or (c) materials made using this product or its components to a third party or otherwise use this product or its components or materials made using this product or its components for Commercial Purposes. The buyer may transfer information or materials made through the use of this product to a scientific collaborator, provided that such transfer is not for any Commercial Purpose, and that such collaborator agrees in writing (a) to not transfer such materials to any third party, and (b) to use such transferred materials and/or information solely for research and not for Commercial Purposes. Commercial Purposes means any activity by a party for consideration and may include, but is not limited to: (1) use of the product or its components in manufacturing; (2) use of the product or its components to provide a service, information, or data; (3) use of the product or its components for therapeutic, diagnostic or prophylactic purposes; or (4) resale of the product or its components, whether or not such product or its components are resold for use in research. Invitrogen Corporation will not assert a claim against the buyer of infringement of the above patents based upon the manufacture, use, or sale of a therapeutic, clinical diagnostic, vaccine or prophylactic product developed in research by the buyer in which this product or its components was employed, provided that neither this product nor any of its components was used in the manufacture of such product. If the purchaser is not willing to accept the limitations of this limited use statement, Invitrogen is willing to accept return of the product with a full refund For information on purchasing a license to this product for purposes other than research, contact Molecular Probes, Inc., Business Development, 29851 Willow Creek Road, Eugene, OR 97402. Tel: (541)465-8300. Fax: (541)335-0504.

Limited Use Label License No. 228: Nucleic Acid Detection Dyes

The manufacture, use, sale or import of this product may be subject to one or more of U.S. Patent Nos. 5,582,977; 5,437,980; 5,656,449 and 5,410,030 and corresponding foreign equivalents, owned by Invitrogen Corporation. The purchase of this product conveys to the buyer the non-transferable right to use the purchased amount of the product and components of the product in research conducted by the buyer (whether the buyer is an academic or for-profit entity). The buyer cannot sell or otherwise transfer (a) this product (b) its components or (c) materials made using this product or its components to a third party or otherwise use this product or its components or materials made using this product or its components for Commercial Purposes. The buyer may transfer information or materials made through the use of this product to a scientific collaborator, provided that such transfer is not for any Commercial Purpose, and that such collaborator agrees in writing (a) to not transfer such materials to any third party, and (b) to use such transferred materials and/or information solely for research and not for Commercial Purposes. Commercial Purposes means any activity by a party for consideration and may include, but is not limited to: (1) use of the product or its components in manufacturing; (2) use of the product or its components to provide a service, information, or data; (3) use of the product or its components for therapeutic, diagnostic or prophylactic purposes; or (4) resale of the product or its components, whether or not such product or its components are resold for use in research. Invitrogen Corporation will not assert a claim against the buyer of infringement of the above patents based upon the manufacture, use, or sale of a therapeutic, clinical diagnostic, vaccine or prophylactic product developed in research by the buyer in which this product or its components was employed, provided that neither this product nor any of its components was used in the manufacture of such product. If the purchaser is not willing to accept the limitations of this limited use statement, Invitrogen is willing to accept return of the product with a full refund For information on purchasing a license to this product for purposes other than research, contact Molecular Probes, Inc., Business Development, 29851 Willow Creek Road, Eugene, OR 97402. Tel: (541)465-8300. Fax: (541)335-0504.

Limited Use Label License No. 229: Lipophilic Stains

The manufacture, use, sale or import of this product may be subject to U.S. Patent No. 6,004,536, owned by Invitrogen Corporation. The purchase of this product conveys to the buyer the non-transferable right to use the purchased amount of the product and components of the product in research conducted by the buyer (whether the buyer is an academic or for-profit entity). The buyer cannot sell or otherwise transfer (a) this product (b) its components or (c) materials made using this product or its components to a third party or otherwise use this product or its components or materials made using this product or its components for Commercial Purposes. The buyer may transfer information or materials made through the use of this product to a scientific collaborator, provided that such transfer is not for any Commercial Purpose, and that such collaborator agrees in writing (a) to not transfer such materials to any third party, and (b) to use such transferred materials and/or information solely for research and not for Commercial Purposes. Commercial Purposes means any activity by a party for consideration and may include, but is not limited to: (1) use of the product or its components in manufacturing; (2) use of the product or its components to provide a service, information, or data; (3) use of the product or its components for therapeutic, diagnostic or prophylactic purposes; or (4) resale of the product or its components, whether or not such product or its components are resold for use in research. Invitrogen Corporation will not assert a claim against the buyer of infringement of the above patents based upon the manufacture, use, or sale of a therapeutic, clinical diagnostic, vaccine or prophylactic product developed in research by the buyer in which this product or its components was employed, provided that neither this product nor any of its components was used in the manufacture of such product. If the purchaser is not willing to accept the limitations of this limited use statement, Invitrogen is willing to accept return of the product with a full refund For information on purchasing a license to this product for purposes other than research, contact Molecular Probes, Inc., Business Development, 29851 Willow Creek Road, Eugene, OR 97402. Tel: (541)465-8300. Fax: (541)335-0504.

Limited Use Label License No. 231: Nanogold® Technology

This product is prepared for Molecular Probes, Inc. by Nanoprobes Inc. For research use only.

Limited Use Label License No. 232: Attofluor® Cell Chamber

This product is manufactured by Atto Instruments, Inc. under an agreement between Molecular Probes, Inc. and Atto Instruments, Inc and may be subject to US Patent No. 5,439,797. For research use only.

Limited Use Label License No. 233: Magnetic Separation Technology

This product is provided under an agreement between Immunicon and Molecular Probes, Inc. and the manufacture, use, sale or import of this product is subject to one or more of US Patent Nos. 4,551,435; 4,795,698; 4,925,788; 5,108,933; 5,186,827; 5,200,084; 5,597,531; 5,646,001; 5,698,271; 5,795,470; and 6,120,856. The purchase of this product conveys to the buyer the non-transferable right to use the purchased amount of the product and components of the product in research conducted by the buyer (whether the buyer is an academic or for-profit entity). The buyer cannot sell or otherwise transfer (a) this product (b) its components or (c) materials made using this product or its components to a third party or otherwise use this product or its components or materials made using this product or its components for Commercial Purposes. The buyer may transfer information or materials made through the use of this product to a scientific collaborator, provided that such transfer is not for any Commercial Purpose, and that such collaborator agrees in writing (a) to not transfer such materials to any third party, and (b) to use such transferred materials and/or information solely for research and not for Commercial Purposes. Commercial Purposes means any activity by a party for consideration and may include, but is not limited to: (1) use of the product or its components in manufacturing; (2) use of the product or its components to provide a service, information, or data; (3) use of the product or its components for therapeutic, diagnostic or prophylactic purposes; or (4) resale of the product or its components, whether or not such product or its components are resold for use in research.

Limited Use Label License No. 234: DDAO Dyes

The manufacture, use, sale and import of this product is subject to US Patent No. 4,810,636 and any corresponding foreign equivalents. For research use only.

Limited Use Label License No. 235: Tyramide Signal Amplification Technology

This product is distributed and sold to the End-User pursuant to a license from PerkinElmer Life Sciences Inc., for use of its tyramide technology by the End-User for life science research applications in the fields of cytochemistry, flow cytometry, histochemistry and *in situ* hybridization, but not for diagnostic applications. Purchase does not include or carry any right to resell or transfer this product either as a stand-alone product or as a component of another product. Any use of this product other than the licensed use without the express written authorization of PerkinElmer Life Sciences, Inc. and Molecular Probes, Inc, is strictly prohibited. The manufacture, use, sale or import of this product is subject to one or more of US Patent Nos. 5,196,306; 5,227,487; 5,583,001 and 5,731,158.

Limited Use Label License No. 242: Glycosidase Substrates

The manufacture, use, sale or import of this product may be subject to one or more of U.S. Patent Nos. 5,208,148 and 5,242,805, owned by Invitrogen Corporation. The purchase of this product conveys to the buyer the non-transferable right to use the purchased amount of the product and components of the product in research conducted by the buyer (whether the buyer is an academic or for-profit entity). The buyer cannot sell or otherwise transfer (a) this product (b) its components or (c) materials made using this product or its components to a third party or otherwise use this product or its components or materials made using this product or its components for Commercial Purposes. The buyer may transfer information or materials made through the use of this product to a scientific collaborator, provided that such transfer is not for any Commercial Purpose, and that such collaborator agrees in writing (a) to not transfer such materials to any third party, and (b) to use such transferred materials and/or information solely for research and not for Commercial Purposes. Commercial Purposes means any activity by a party for consideration and may include, but is not limited to: (1) use of the product or its components in manufacturing; (2) use of the product or its components to provide a service, information, or data; (3) use of the product or its components for therapeutic, diagnostic or prophylactic purposes; or (4) resale of the product or its components, whether or not such product or its components are resold for use in research. Invitrogen Corporation will not assert a claim against the buyer of infringement of the above patents based upon the manufacture, use, or sale of a therapeutic, clinical diagnostic, vaccine or prophylactic product developed in research by the buyer in which this product or its components was employed, provided that neither this product nor any of its components was used in the manufacture of such product. If the purchaser is not willing to accept the limitations of this limited use statement, Invitrogen is willing to accept return of the product with a full refund For information on purchasing a license to this product for purposes other than research, contact Molecular Probes, Inc., Business Development, 29851 Willow Creek Road, Eugene, OR 97402. Tel: (541)465-8300. Fax: (541)335-0504.

Limited Use Label License No. 243: Fatty Acid Indicators

This product is provided under an agreement between FFA Sciences, Inc. and Molecular Probes, Inc. and the manufacture, use, sale or import of this product is subject to US Patent No. 5,470,714. For research use only.

Limited Use Label License No. 244: ATTO-TAG™ Reagents and CBQCA Reagents

This product is provided under an agreement with Molecular Probes, Inc. The manufacture, use, sale or import of this product is subject to one or more US Patent Nos. 5,631,374; 5,459,272 and international equivalents. The purchase of this product conveys to the buyer the non-transferable right to use the purchased amount of the product and components of the product in research conducted by the buyer (whether the buyer is an academic or for-profit entity). The buyer cannot sell or otherwise transfer (a) this product (b) its components or (c) materials made using this product or its components to a third party or otherwise use this product or its components or materials made using this product or its components for Commercial Purposes. Not for use in human diagnostic products.

Limited Use Label License No. 245: Heavy Metal Indicator Dyes

The manufacture, use, sale or import of this product may be subject to one or more of U.S. Patent Nos. 5,459,276; 5,501,980; 5,648,270 and 6,013,802, owned by Invitrogen Corporation. The purchase of this product conveys to the buyer the non-transferable right to use the purchased amount of the product and components of the product in research conducted by the buyer (whether the buyer is an academic or for-profit entity). The buyer cannot sell or otherwise transfer (a) this product (b) its components or (c) materials made using this product or its components to a third party or otherwise use this product or its components or materials made using this product or its components for Commercial Purposes. The buyer may transfer information or materials made through the use of this product to a scientific collaborator, provided that such transfer is not for any Commercial Purpose, and that such collaborator agrees in writing (a) to not transfer such materials to any third party, and (b) to use such transferred materials and/or information solely for research and not for Commercial Purposes. Commercial Purposes means any activity by a party for consideration and may include, but is not limited to: (1) use of the product or its components in manufacturing; (2) use of the product or its components to provide a service, information, or data; (3) use of the product or its components for therapeutic, diagnostic or prophylactic purposes; or (4) resale of the product or its components, whether or not such product or its components are resold for use in research. Invitrogen Corporation will not assert a claim against the buyer of infringement of the above patents based upon the manufacture, use, or sale of a therapeutic, clinical diagnostic, vaccine or prophylactic product developed in research by the buyer in which this product or its components was employed, provided that neither this product nor any of its components was used in the manufacture of such product. If the purchaser is not willing to accept the limitations of this limited use statement, Invitrogen is willing to accept return of the product with a full refund For information on purchasing a license to this product for purposes other than research, contact Molecular Probes, Inc., Business Development, 29851 Willow Creek Road, Eugene, OR 97402. Tel: (541)465-8300. Fax: (541)335-0504.

Limited Use Label License No. 246: α-Carboxy Caged Compounds

The manufacture, use, sale or import of this product may be subject to one U.S. Patent No. 5,635,608, owned by Invitrogen Corporation. The purchase of this product conveys to the buyer the non-transferable right to use the purchased amount of the product and components of the product in research conducted by the buyer (whether the buyer is an academic or for-profit entity). The buyer cannot sell or otherwise transfer (a) this product (b) its components or (c) materials made using this product or its components to a third party or otherwise use this product or its components or materials made using this product or its components for Commercial Purposes. The buyer may transfer information or materials made through the use of this product to a scientific collaborator, provided that such transfer is not for any Commercial Purpose, and that such collaborator agrees in writing (a) to not transfer such materials to any third party, and (b) to use such transferred materials and/or information solely for research and not for Commercial Purposes. Commercial Purposes means any activity by a party for consideration and may include, but is not limited to: (1) use of the product or its components in manufacturing; (2) use of the product or its components to provide a service, information, or data; (3) use of the product or its components for therapeutic, diagnostic or prophylactic purposes; or (4) resale of the product or its components, whether or not such product or its components are resold for use in research. Invitrogen Corporation will not assert a claim against the buyer of infringement of the above patents based upon the manufacture, use, or sale of a therapeutic, clinical diagnostic, vaccine or prophylactic product developed in research by the buyer in which this product or its components was employed, provided that neither this product nor any of its components was used in the manufacture of such product. If the purchaser is not willing to accept the limitations of this limited use statement, Invitrogen is willing to accept return of the product with a full refund For information on purchasing a license to this product for purposes other than research, contact Molecular Probes, Inc., Business Development, 29851 Willow Creek Road, Eugene, OR 97402. Tel: (541)465-8300. Fax: (541)335-0504.

Limited Use Label License No. 247: Caged Nucleotides

This product is provided under an agreement with Molecular Probes, Inc. The manufacture, use, sale or import of this product is subject to one or more US Patent Nos. 5,486,604; 6,593,307 and international equivalents. The purchase of this product conveys to the buyer the non-transferable right to use the purchased amount of the product and components of the product in research conducted by the buyer (whether the buyer is an academic or for-profit entity). The buyer cannot sell or otherwise transfer (a) this product (b) its components or (c) materials made using this product or its components to a third party or otherwise use this product or its components or materials made using this product or its components for Commercial Purposes.

Limited Use Label License No. 248: Amine-Reactive Biotin

This product is provided under an agreement between Molecular Probes, Inc. and Molecular Devices Corp. The manufacture, use, sale or import of this product is subject to US Patent No. 5,180,828. The purchase of this product conveys to the buyer the non-transferable right to use the purchased amount of the product and components of the product in research conducted by the buyer (whether the buyer is an academic or for-profit entity). The buyer cannot sell or otherwise transfer (a) this product (b) its components or (c) materials made using this product or its components to a third party or otherwise use this product or its components or materials made using this product or its components for Commercial Purposes.

Limited Use Label License No. 249: Photolabile Caged Ionophores

The manufacture, use, sale or import of this product may be subject to one or more of U.S. Patent No. 5,888,829 and foreign equivalents, owned by Invitrogen Corporation. The purchase of this product conveys to the buyer the non-transferable right to use the purchased amount of the product and components of the product in research conducted by the buyer (whether the buyer is an academic or for-profit entity). The buyer cannot sell or otherwise transfer (a) this product (b) its components or (c) materials made using this product or its components to a third party or otherwise use this product or its components or materials made using this product or its components for Commercial Purposes. The buyer may transfer information or materials made through the use of this product to a scientific collaborator, provided that such transfer is not for any Commercial Purpose, and that such collaborator agrees in writing (a) to not transfer such materials to any third party, and (b) to use such transferred materials and/or information solely for research and not for Commercial Purposes. Commercial Purposes means any activity by a party for consideration and may include, but is not limited to: (1) use of the product or its components in manufacturing; (2) use of the product or its components to provide a service, information, or data; (3) use of the product or its components for therapeutic, diagnostic or prophylactic purposes; or (4) resale of the product or its components, whether or not such product or its components are resold for use in research. Invitrogen Corporation will not assert a claim against the buyer of infringement of the above patents based upon the manufacture, use, or sale of a therapeutic, clinical diagnostic, vaccine or prophylactic product developed in research by the buyer in which this product or its components was employed, provided that neither this product nor any of its components was used in the manufacture of such product. If the purchaser is not willing to accept the limitations of this limited use statement, Invitrogen is willing to accept return of the product with a full refund For information on purchasing a license to this product for purposes other than research, contact Molecular Probes, Inc., Business Development, 29851 Willow Creek Road, Eugene, OR 97402. Tel: (541)465-8300. Fax: (541)335-0504.

Limited Use Label License No. 250: CaptAvidin™ Technology

This product is provided under a license agreement between Molecular Probes, Inc. and Baxter Healthcare Corp. The manufacture, use, sale or import of this product is subject to US Patent No. 5,973,124. The purchase of this product conveys to the buyer the non-transferable right to use the purchased amount of the product and components of the product in research conducted by the buyer (whether the buyer is an academic or for-profit entity). The buyer cannot sell or otherwise transfer (a) this product (b) its components or (c) materials made using this product or its components to a third party or otherwise use this product or its components or materials made using this product or its components for Commercial Purposes.

Limited Use Label License No. 251: Gram Stain Technology

This product is provided under a license agreement between Molecular Probes, Inc. and UNCW. The manufacture, use, sale or import of this product is subject to US Patent No. 5,137,810. The purchase of this product conveys to the buyer the non-transferable right to use the purchased amount of the product and components of the product in research conducted by the buyer (whether the buyer is an academic or for-profit entity). The buyer cannot sell or otherwise transfer (a) this product (b) its components or (c) materials made using this product or its components to a third party or otherwise use this product or its components or materials made using this product or its components for Commercial Purposes.

Limited Use Label License No. 252: OBEA Nucleotides

This product is manufactured by Serologicals Corp. under an agreement between Molecular Probes, Inc. and Serologicals Corp. This product is subject to US Patent No. 5,684,142. The purchase of this product conveys to the buyer the non-transferable right to use the purchased amount of the product and components of the product in research conducted by the buyer (whether the buyer is an academic or for-profit entity). The buyer cannot sell or otherwise transfer (a) this product (b) its components or (c) materials made using this product or its components to a third party or otherwise use this product or its components or materials made using this product or its components for Commercial Purposes.

Limited Use Label License No. 253: Precipitating Substrates

The manufacture, use, sale or import of this product may be subject to one or more of U.S. Patent No. 5,316,906; 5,443,986 and foreign equivalents, owned by Invitrogen Corporation. The purchase of this product conveys to the buyer the non-transferable right to use the purchased amount of the product and components of the product in research conducted by the buyer (whether the buyer is an academic or for-profit entity). The buyer cannot sell or otherwise transfer (a) this product (b) its components or (c) materials made using this product or its components to a third party or otherwise use this product or its components or materials made using this product or its components for Commercial Purposes. The buyer may transfer information or materials made through the use of this product to a scientific collaborator, provided that such transfer is not for any Commercial Purpose, and that such collaborator agrees in writing (a) to not transfer such materials to any third party, and (b) to use such transferred materials and/or information solely for research and not for Commercial Purposes. Commercial Purposes means any activity by a party for consideration and may include, but is not limited to: (1) use of the product or its components in manufacturing; (2) use of the product or its components to provide a service, information, or data; (3) use of the product or its components for therapeutic, diagnostic or prophylactic purposes; or (4) resale of the product or its components, whether or not such product or its components are resold for use in research. Invitrogen Corporation will not assert a claim against the buyer of infringement of the above patents based upon the manufacture, use, or sale of a therapeutic, clinical diagnostic, vaccine or prophylactic product developed in research by the buyer in which this product or its components was employed, provided that neither this product nor any of its components was used in the manufacture of such product. If the purchaser is not willing to accept the limitations of this limited use statement, Invitrogen is willing to accept return of the product with a full refund For information on purchasing a license to this product for purposes other than research, contact Molecular Probes, Inc., Business Development, 29851 Willow Creek Road, Eugene, OR 97402. Tel: (541)465-8300. Fax: (541)335-0504.

Limited Use Label License No. 254: Caged HPTS

The manufacture, use, sale or import of this product may be subject to U.S. Patent No. 5,514,710, owned by Invitrogen Corporation. The purchase of this product conveys to the buyer the non-transferable right to use the purchased amount of the product and components of the product in research conducted by the buyer (whether the buyer is an academic or for-profit entity). The buyer cannot sell or otherwise transfer (a) this product (b) its components or (c) materials made using this product or its components to a third party or otherwise use this product or its components or materials made using this product or its components for Commercial Purposes. The buyer may transfer information or materials made through the use of this product to a scientific collaborator, provided that such transfer is not for any Commercial Purpose, and that such collaborator agrees in writing (a) to not transfer such materials to any third party, and (b) to use such transferred materials and/or information solely for research and not for Commercial Purposes. Commercial Purposes means any activity by a party for consideration and may include, but is not limited to: (1) use of the product or its components in manufacturing; (2) use of the product or its components to provide a service, information, or data; (3) use of the product or its components for therapeutic, diagnostic or prophylactic purposes; or (4) resale of the product or its components, whether or not such product or its components are resold for use in research. Invitrogen Corporation will not assert a claim against the buyer of infringement of the above patents based upon the manufacture, use, or sale of a therapeutic, clinical diagnostic, vaccine or prophylactic product developed in research by the buyer in which this product or its components was employed, provided that neither this product nor any of its components was used in the manufacture of such product. If the purchaser is not willing to accept the limitations of this limited use statement, Invitrogen is willing to accept return of the product with a full refund For information on purchasing a license to this product for purposes other than research, contact Molecular Probes, Inc., Business Development, 29851 Willow Creek Road, Eugene, OR 97402. Tel: (541)465-8300. Fax: (541)335-0504.

Limited Use Label License No. 255: DAF-FM Indicator Compounds

This product is subject to US Patent Nos. 5,874,590 and 6,441,197 B1 and related foreign patents and patent applications owned by Daiichi Pure Chemicals Co., Ltd. and to US Patent Nos. 6,162,931 and 6,229,055 and related foreign patents and patent applications owned by Molecular Probes, Inc., and is sold for internal research and development use only, where internal research and development use expressly excludes (i) the use of this product for providing medical, diagnostic, forensic, or any other testing, analysis, or screening services in return for compensation by an unrelated party, and (ii) incorporation of this product into another product for commercialization, even if such other product would be commercialized for research and/or development use.

Limited Use Label License No. 256: Fura-Red™ Reagents

This product is provided under an agreement with Molecular Probes, Inc. The manufacture, use, sale or import of this product is subject to one or more of US Patent No. 4,849,362 and international equivalents. The purchase of this product conveys to the buyer the non-transferable right to use the purchased amount of the product and components of the product in research conducted by the buyer (whether the buyer is an academic or for-profit entity). The buyer cannot sell or otherwise transfer (a) this product (b) its components or (c) materials made using this product or its components to a third party or otherwise use this product or its components or materials made using this product or its components for Commercial Purposes.

Limited Use Label License No. 257: CAT Substrates

The manufacture, use, sale or import of this product may be subject to one or more of U.S. Patent No. 5,262,545 and 5,364,764, owned by Invitrogen Corporation. The purchase of this product conveys to the buyer the non-transferable right to use the purchased amount of the product and components of the product in research conducted by the buyer (whether the buyer is an academic or for-profit entity). The buyer cannot sell or otherwise transfer (a) this product (b) its components or (c) materials made using this product or its components to a third party or otherwise use this product or its components or materials made using this product or its components for Commercial Purposes. The buyer may transfer information or materials made through the use of this product to a scientific collaborator, provided that such transfer is not for any Commercial Purpose, and that such collaborator agrees in writing (a) to not transfer such materials to any third party, and (b) to use such transferred materials and/or information solely for research and not for Commercial Purposes. Commercial Purposes means any activity by a party for consideration and may include, but is not limited to: (1) use of the product or its components in manufacturing; (2) use of the product or its components to provide a service, information, or data; (3) use of the product or its components for therapeutic, diagnostic or prophylactic purposes; or (4) resale of the product or its components, whether or not such product or its components are resold for use in research. Invitrogen Corporation will not assert a claim against the buyer of infringement of the above patents based upon the manufacture, use, or sale of a therapeutic, clinical diagnostic, vaccine or prophylactic product developed in research by the buyer in which this product or its components was employed, provided that neither this product nor any of its components was used in the manufacture of such product. If the purchaser is not willing to accept the limitations of this limited use statement, Invitrogen is willing to accept return of the product with a full refund For information on purchasing a license to this product for purposes other than research, contact Molecular Probes, Inc., Business Development, 29851 Willow Creek Road, Eugene, OR 97402. Tel: (541)465-8300. Fax: (541)335-0504.

Limited Use Label License No. 258: Rhodamine Red™-X Compounds

The manufacture, use, sale or import of this product may be subject to U.S. Patent No. 5,846,737, owned by Invitrogen Corporation. The purchase of this product conveys to the buyer the non-transferable right to use the purchased amount of the product and components of the product in research conducted by the buyer (whether the buyer is an academic or for-profit entity). The buyer cannot sell or otherwise transfer (a) this product (b) its components or (c) materials made using this product or its components to a third party or otherwise use this product or its components or materials made using this product or its components for Commercial Purposes. The buyer may transfer information or materials made through the use of this product to a scientific collaborator, provided that such transfer is not for any Commercial Purpose, and that such collaborator agrees in writing (a) to not transfer such materials to any third party, and (b) to use such transferred materials and/or information solely for research and not for Commercial Purposes. Commercial Purposes means any activity by a party for consideration and may include, but is not limited to: (1) use of the product or its components in manufacturing; (2) use of the product or its components to provide a service, information, or data; (3) use of the product or its components for therapeutic, diagnostic or prophylactic purposes; or (4) resale of the product or its components, whether or not such product or its components are resold for use in research. Invitrogen Corporation will not assert a claim against the buyer of infringement of the above patents based upon the manufacture, use, or sale of a therapeutic, clinical diagnostic, vaccine or prophylactic product developed in research by the buyer in which this product or its components was employed, provided that neither this product nor any of its components was used in the manufacture of such product. If the purchaser is not willing to accept the limitations of this limited use statement, Invitrogen is willing to accept return of the product with a full refund For information on purchasing a license to this product for purposes other than research, contact Molecular Probes, Inc., Business Development, 29851 Willow Creek Road, Eugene, OR 97402. Tel: (541)465-8300. Fax: (541)335-0504.

Limited Use Label License No. 259: QSY® Compounds

The manufacture, use, sale or import of this product may be subject to one or more of U.S. Patent No. 6,399,392, pending applications and international equivalents, owned by Invitrogen Corporation. The purchase of this product conveys to the buyer the non-transferable right to use the purchased amount of the product and components of the product in research conducted by the buyer (whether the buyer is an academic or for-profit entity). The buyer cannot sell or otherwise transfer (a) this product (b) its components or (c) materials made using this product or its components to a third party or otherwise use this product or its components or materials made using this product or its components for Commercial Purposes. The buyer may transfer information or materials made through the use of this product to a scientific collaborator, provided that such transfer is not for any Commercial Purpose, and that such collaborator agrees in writing (a) to not transfer such materials to any third party, and (b) to use such transferred materials and/or information solely for research and not for Commercial Purposes. Commercial Purposes means any activity by a party for consideration and may include, but is not limited to: (1) use of the product or its components in manufacturing; (2) use of the product or its components to provide a service, information, or data; (3) use of the product or its components for therapeutic, diagnostic or prophylactic purposes; or (4) resale of the product or its components, whether or not such product or its components are resold for use in research. Invitrogen Corporation will not assert a claim against the buyer of infringement of the above patents based upon the manufacture, use, or sale of a therapeutic, clinical diagnostic, vaccine or prophylactic product developed in research by the buyer in which this product or its components was employed, provided that neither this product nor any of its components was used in the manufacture of such product. If the purchaser is not willing to accept the limitations of this limited use statement, Invitrogen is willing to accept return of the product with a full refund For information on purchasing a license to this product for purposes other than research, contact Molecular Probes, Inc., Business Development, 29851 Willow Creek Road, Eugene, OR 97402. Tel: (541)465-8300. Fax: (541)335-0504.

Limited Use Label License No. 260: Phosphate Detection

The manufacture, use, sale or import of this product may be subject to U.S. Patent No. 6,265,179 owned by Invitrogen Corporation. The purchase of this product conveys to the buyer the non-transferable right to use the purchased amount of the product and components of the product in research conducted by the buyer (whether the buyer is an academic or for-profit entity). The buyer cannot sell or otherwise transfer (a) this product (b) its components or (c) materials made using this product or its components to a third party or otherwise use this product or its components or materials made using this product or its components for Commercial Purposes. The buyer may transfer information or materials made through the use of this product to a scientific collaborator, provided that such transfer is not for any Commercial Purpose, and that such collaborator agrees in writing (a) to not transfer such materials to any third party, and (b) to use such transferred materials and/or information solely for research and not for Commercial Purposes. Commercial Purposes means any activity by a party for consideration and may include, but is not limited to: (1) use of the product or its components in manufacturing; (2) use of the product or its components to provide a service, information, or data; (3) use of the product or its components for therapeutic, diagnostic or prophylactic purposes; or (4) resale of the product or its components, whether or not such product or its components are resold for use in research. Invitrogen Corporation will not assert a claim against the buyer of infringement of the above patents based upon the manufacture, use, or sale of a therapeutic, clinical diagnostic, vaccine or prophylactic product developed in research by the buyer in which this product or its components was employed, provided that neither this product nor any of its components was used in the manufacture of such product. If the purchaser is not willing to accept the limitations of this limited use statement, Invitrogen is willing to accept return of the product with a full refund For information on purchasing a license to this product for purposes other than research, contact Molecular Probes, Inc., Business Development, 29851 Willow Creek Road, Eugene, OR 97402. Tel: (541)465-8300. Fax: (541)335-0504.

Limited Use Label License No. 261: Rhodol Dyes

The manufacture, use, sale or import of this product may be subject to one or more of U.S. Patent Nos. 5,227,487 and 5,442,045 owned by Invitrogen Corporation. The purchase of this product conveys to the buyer the non-transferable right to use the purchased amount of the product and components of the product in research conducted by the buyer (whether the buyer is an academic or for-profit entity). The buyer cannot sell or otherwise transfer (a) this product (b) its components or (c) materials made using this product or its components to a third party or otherwise use this product or its components or materials made using this product or its components for Commercial Purposes. The buyer may transfer information or materials made through the use of this product to a scientific collaborator, provided that such transfer is not for any Commercial Purpose, and that such collaborator agrees in writing (a) to not transfer such materials to any third party, and (b) to use such transferred materials and/or information solely for research and not for Commercial Purposes. Commercial Purposes means any activity by a party for consideration and may include, but is not limited to: (1) use of the product or its components in manufacturing; (2) use of the product or its components to provide a service, information, or data; (3) use of the product or its components for therapeutic, diagnostic or prophylactic purposes; or (4) resale of the product or its components, whether or not such product or its components are resold for use in research. Invitrogen Corporation will not assert a claim against the buyer of infringement of the above patents based upon the manufacture, use, or sale of a therapeutic, clinical diagnostic, vaccine or prophylactic product developed in research by the buyer in which this product or its components was employed, provided that neither this product nor any of its components was used in the manufacture of such product. If the purchaser is not willing to accept the limitations of this limited use statement, Invitrogen is willing to accept return of the product with a full refund For information on purchasing a license to this product for purposes other than research, contact Molecular Probes, Inc., Business Development, 29851 Willow Creek Road, Eugene, OR 97402. Tel: (541)465-8300. Fax: (541)335-0504.

Limited Use Label License No. 262: FDG Technology

This product is provided under an agreement between Molecular Probes, Inc. and The Board of Trustees of Leland Stanford Junior University. The manufacture, use, sale or import of this product may be subject to US Patent No. 5,070,012. The purchase of this product conveys to the buyer the non-transferable right to use the purchased amount of the product and components of the product in research conducted by the buyer (whether the buyer is an academic or for-profit entity) using flow cytometry. For information on purchasing a license to this product for purposes other than as set forth above, contact The Board of Trustees of Leland Stanford Junior University.

Master Product List

Cat #	Product Name	Unit Size	Sections	Limited Use Label License #
A7109	A-23187, 1-(4,5-dimethoxy-2-nitrophenyl)ethyl ester (DMNPE-caged A-23187)	1 mg	5.3, 19.8	None
A1493	A-23187 free acid (calcimycin)	10 mg	19.8	None
A1310	7-AAD (7-aminoactinomycin D)	1 mg	8.1, 8.6, 15.4, 15.5	None
F6053	ABD-F (7-fluorobenz-2-oxa-1,3-diazole-4-sulfonamide)	10 mg	2.2	None
A23150	ABSOLUTE-S™ SBIP Cell Proliferation Assay Kit *with Alexa Fluor® 488 anti-BrdU* *50 assays*	1 kit	7.5, 15.4	214, 183
A484	4-acetamido-4′-((iodoacetyl)amino)stilbene-2,2′-disulfonic acid, disodium salt	25 mg	2.3	None
A339	4-acetamido-4′-isothiocyanatostilbene-2,2′-disulfonic acid, disodium salt (SITS)	100 mg	16.3	None
A485	4-acetamido-4′-maleimidylstilbene-2,2′-disulfonic acid, disodium salt	25 mg	2.3	None
A1642	2-acetamido-4-mercaptobutanoic acid hydrazide (AMBH)	100 mg	3.2, 5.2	None
A22010	5-acetylaminofluorescein di-β-D-galactopyranoside (C_2FDG)	5 mg	10.2	242
A7509	acetyl ceramide; C_2-ceramide (*N*-acetyl-D-erythro-sphingosine)	5 mg	13.3, 17.4	None
A6551	10-acetyl-3,7-dihydroxy-2-dodecylphenoxazine *special packaging*	10 x 100 µg	10.5, 15.5, 18.2	None
A12222	10-acetyl-3,7-dihydroxyphenoxazine (Amplex® Red reagent)	5 mg	10.2, 10.5, 18.2	None
A7509	*N*-acetyl-D-erythro-sphingosine (acetyl ceramide; C_2-ceramide)	5 mg	13.3, 17.4	None
A685	5-((2-(and-3)-*S*-(acetylmercapto)succinoyl)amino)fluorescein (SAMSA fluorescein) *mixed isomers*	25 mg	5.2	None
L35354	AcLDL (low-density lipoprotein from human plasma, acetylated) *2.5 mg/mL*	200 µL	16.1	None
A1324	ACMA (9-amino-6-chloro-2-methoxyacridine)	100 mg	8.1, 8.6, 20.3	None
A7923	4-((9-acridinecarbonyl)amino)-2,2,6,6-tetramethylpiperidin-1-oxyl, free radical (TEMPO-9-AC)	5 mg	18.2	None
A666	acridine homodimer (bis-(6-chloro-2-methoxy-9-acridinyl)spermine)	10 mg	8.1	None
A3568	acridine orange *10 mg/mL solution in water*	10 mL	8.1, 12.3, 15.2, 15.4, 15.5	None
A1301	acridine orange	1 g	8.1, 12.3, 15.2, 15.4, 15.5	None
A1372	acridine orange 10-nonyl bromide (nonyl acridine orange)	100 mg	12.2, 15.5	None
A33405	acrylamide/bis-acrylamide mixture (37.5:1 ratio) *electrophoresis grade*	300 g	9.3, 9.4	None
A433	acrylodan (6-acryloyl-2-dimethylaminonaphthalene)	25 mg	2.3	None
A20770	6-((acryloyl)amino)hexanoic acid, succinimidyl ester (acryloyl-X, SE)	5 mg	5.2, 9.2	None
A433	6-acryloyl-2-dimethylaminonaphthalene (acrylodan)	25 mg	2.3	None
A12375	actin from rabbit muscle	1 mg	11.1	None
A12373	actin from rabbit muscle, Alexa Fluor® 488 conjugate *in solution*	200 µg	11.1	183
A12374	actin from rabbit muscle, Alexa Fluor® 568 conjugate *in solution*	200 µg	11.1	183
A34050	actin from rabbit muscle, Alexa Fluor® 594 conjugate *in solution*	200 µg	11.1	183
A34051	actin from rabbit muscle, Alexa Fluor® 647 conjugate *in solution*	200 µg	11.1	183
A7592	actinomycin D	10 mg	8.1	None
A1139	ADA (anthracene-2,3-dicarboxaldehyde)	25 mg	1.8, 21.2	None
A1400	ADAM (9-anthryldiazomethane)	25 mg	3.3	None
A6871	ADC, AM (anthracene-1,5-dicarboxylic acid, di(acetoxymethyl ester))	5 mg	21.2	None
A22359	adenosine 5′-diphosphate, BODIPY® TR 2′-(or-3′)-*O*-(*N*-(2-aminoethyl)urethane), disodium salt (BODIPY® TR ADP) *5 mM in buffer*	100 µL	17.3	193
A7056	adenosine 5′-diphosphate, P^2-(1-(2-nitrophenyl)ethyl) ester, monopotassium salt (NPE-caged ADP)	5 mg	5.3, 17.3	None
A22184	adenosine 5′-*O*-(3-thiotriphosphate), BODIPY® FL thioester, sodium salt (BODIPY® FL ATP-γ-S, thioester) *5 mM in buffer*	50 µL	10.3, 17.3	193
A22362	adenosine 5′-triphosphate, Alexa Fluor® 647 2′-(or-3′)-*O*-(*N*-(2-aminoethyl)urethane), hexa(triethylammonium) salt (Alexa Fluor® 647 ATP) *5 mM in buffer*	100 µL	17.3	183
A12410	adenosine 5′-triphosphate, BODIPY® FL 2′-(or-3′)-*O*-(*N*-(2-aminoethyl)urethane), trisodium salt (BODIPY® FL ATP) *5 mM in buffer*	100 µL	17.3	193
A22352	adenosine 5′-triphosphate, BODIPY® TR 2′-(or-3′)-*O*-(*N*-(2-aminoethyl)urethane), trisodium salt (BODIPY® TR ATP) *5 mM in buffer*	100 µL	17.3	193
A1049	adenosine 5′-triphosphate, P^3-(1-(4,5-dimethoxy-2-nitrophenyl)ethyl) ester, disodium salt (DMNPE-caged ATP)	5 mg	5.3, 17.3	None
A1048	adenosine 5′-triphosphate, P^3-(1-(2-nitrophenyl)ethyl) ester, disodium salt (NPE-caged ATP)	5 mg	5.3, 17.3	None
A12412	adenosine 5′-triphosphate, P^3-(5-sulfo-1-naphthylamide), tetra(triethylammonium) salt (ATP γ-AmNS) *5 mM in buffer*	400 µL	17.3	None
A18211	Adhesive seal-tab, for HybriWell™ hybridization sealing system *set of 400*	1 set	8.5, 23.3	None
A3880	ADIFAB fatty acid indicator	200 µg	13.2, 17.4	243
A6785	aequorin (AquaLite® aequorin) *recombinant*	25 µg	19.5	None
A32760	aha-dUTP (5-aminohexylacrylamido-dUTP) *2 mM in TE buffer*	500 µL	8.2, 8.5	None
A32761	aha-dUTP (5-aminohexylacrylamido-dUTP) *50 mM in TE buffer*	50 µL	8.2, 8.5	None
A13100	albumin from bovine serum (BSA), Alexa Fluor® 488 conjugate	5 mg	14.7	183
A13101	albumin from bovine serum (BSA), Alexa Fluor® 594 conjugate	5 mg	14.7	183
A34785	albumin from bovine serum (BSA), Alexa Fluor® 647 conjugate	5 mg	14.7	183

For current prices or to order online, visit probes.invitrogen.com

Cat #	Product Name	Unit Size	Sections	Limited Use Label License #
A2750	albumin from bovine serum (BSA), BODIPY® FL conjugate	5 mg	14.7	193
A23018	albumin from bovine serum (BSA), 2,4-dinitrophenylated (DNP-BSA)	5 mg	14.7	None
A23015	albumin from bovine serum (BSA), fluorescein conjugate	5 mg	14.7	None
A23016	albumin from bovine serum (BSA), tetramethylrhodamine conjugate	5 mg	14.7	None
A23017	albumin from bovine serum (BSA), Texas Red® conjugate	5 mg	14.7	None
L23380	Alexa Fluor® 488 AcLDL (low-density lipoprotein from human plasma, acetylated, Alexa Fluor® 488 conjugate) *1 mg/mL*	200 µL	16.1	183
L35353	Alexa Fluor® 594 AcLDL (low-density lipoprotein from human plasma, acetylated, Alexa Fluor® 594 conjugate) *1 mg/mL*	200 µL	16.1	183
A32762	Alexa Fluor® 555-aha-dUTP *1 mM in TE buffer*	50 µL	8.2, 8.5	183
A32763	Alexa Fluor® 647-aha-dUTP *1 mM in TE buffer*	50 µL	8.2, 8.5	183
A21000	Alexa Fluor® 680–allophycocyanin goat anti-mouse IgG (H+L) *1 mg/mL*	100 µL	6.4, 7.2	183
A21006	Alexa Fluor® 750–allophycocyanin goat anti-mouse IgG (H+L) *1 mg/mL*	100 µL	6.4, 7.2	183
A21001MP	Alexa Fluor® 680–allophycocyanin goat anti-rabbit IgG (H+L) *1 mg/mL*	100 µL	6.4, 7.2	183
S21002	Alexa Fluor® 680–allophycocyanin streptavidin (streptavidin, Alexa Fluor® 680–allophycocyanin conjugate) *1 mg/mL*	100 µL	6.4, 7.6	183
S21005	Alexa Fluor® 700–allophycocyanin streptavidin (streptavidin, Alexa Fluor® 700–allophycocyanin conjugate) *1 mg/mL*	100 µL	6.4, 7.6	183
S21008	Alexa Fluor® 750–allophycocyanin streptavidin (streptavidin, Alexa Fluor® 750–allophycocyanin conjugate) *1 mg/mL*	100 µL	6.4, 7.6	223, 183
A35775	Alexa Fluor® 488 8-(6-aminohexyl)aminoadenosine 3',5'-cyclicmonophosphate, bis(triethylammonium) salt (Alexa Fluor® 488 cAMP) *5 mM in buffer*	100 µL	17.3	183
A35776	Alexa Fluor® 555 8-(6-aminohexyl)aminoadenosine 3',5'-cyclicmonophosphate, tetra(triethylammonium) salt (Alexa Fluor® 555 cAMP) *5 mM in buffer*	100 µL	17.3	183
A35777	Alexa Fluor® 647 8-(6-aminohexyl)aminoadenosine 3',5'-cyclicmonophosphate, tetra(triethylammonium) salt (Alexa Fluor® 647 cAMP) *5 mM in buffer*	100 µL	17.3	183
A22362	Alexa Fluor® 647 ATP (adenosine 5'-triphosphate, Alexa Fluor® 647 2'-(or-3')-*O*-(*N*-(2-aminoethyl)urethane), hexa(triethylammonium) salt) *5 mM in buffer*	100 µL	17.3	183
A12924	Alexa Fluor® 488 biocytin, disodium salt (biocytin Alexa Fluor® 488)	250 µg	4.3, 14.3	183
A12923	Alexa Fluor® 546 biocytin, sodium salt (biocytin Alexa Fluor® 546)	250 µg	4.3, 14.3	183
A12922	Alexa Fluor® 594 biocytin, sodium salt (biocytin Alexa Fluor® 594)	250 µg	4.3, 14.3	183
A30505	Alexa Fluor® 350 C_5-maleimide	1 mg	2.3	183
A30458	Alexa Fluor® 405 C_5-maleimide	1 mg	2.3	183
A10254	Alexa Fluor® 488 C_5-maleimide	1 mg	2.2	183
A10255	Alexa Fluor® 532 C_5-maleimide	1 mg	2.2	183
A10258	Alexa Fluor® 546 C_5-maleimide	1 mg	2.2	183
A20346	Alexa Fluor® 555 C_2-maleimide	1 mg	2.2	183
A20341	Alexa Fluor® 568 C_5-maleimide	1 mg	2.2	183
A10256	Alexa Fluor® 594 C_5-maleimide	1 mg	2.2	183
A20342	Alexa Fluor® 633 C_5-maleimide	1 mg	2.2	183
A20347	Alexa Fluor® 647 C_2-maleimide	1 mg	2.2	183
A20343	Alexa Fluor® 660 C_2-maleimide	1 mg	2.2	183
A20344	Alexa Fluor® 680 C_2-maleimide	1 mg	2.2	183
A30674	Alexa Fluor® 350 cadaverine	1 mg	3.3	183
A30675	Alexa Fluor® 405 cadaverine, trisodium salt	1 mg	3.3, 14.3	218
A30676	Alexa Fluor® 488 cadaverine, sodium salt	1 mg	3.3	183
A30677	Alexa Fluor® 555 cadaverine, disodium salt	1 mg	3.3	183
A30680	Alexa Fluor® 568 cadaverine, diammonium salt	1 mg	3.3	183
A30678	Alexa Fluor® 594 cadaverine	1 mg	3.3	183
A30679	Alexa Fluor® 647 cadaverine, disodium salt	1 mg	3.3	183
A30627	Alexa Fluor® 350 C_5-aminooxyacetamide, trifluoroacetate salt (Alexa Fluor® 350 hydroxylamine)	1 mg	3.2, 14.3	183
A30629	Alexa Fluor® 488 C_5-aminooxyacetamide, bis(triethylammonium) salt (Alexa Fluor® 488 hydroxylamine)	1 mg	3.2, 14.3	183
A30632	Alexa Fluor® 647 C_5-aminooxyacetamide, bis(triethylammonium) salt (Alexa Fluor® 647 hydroxylamine)	1 mg	3.2, 14.3	183
A35775	Alexa Fluor® 488 cAMP (Alexa Fluor® 488 8-(6-aminohexyl)aminoadenosine 3',5'-cyclicmonophosphate, bis(triethylammonium) salt) *5 mM in buffer*	100 µL	17.3	183
A35776	Alexa Fluor® 555 cAMP (Alexa Fluor® 555 8-(6-aminohexyl)aminoadenosine 3',5'-cyclicmonophosphate, tetra(triethylammonium) salt) *5 mM in buffer*	100 µL	17.3	183
A35777	Alexa Fluor® 647 cAMP (Alexa Fluor® 647 8-(6-aminohexyl)aminoadenosine 3',5'-cyclicmonophosphate, tetra(triethylammonium) salt) *5 mM in buffer*	100 µL	17.3	183
A10168	Alexa Fluor® 350 carboxylic acid, succinimidyl ester	5 mg	1.3, 1.7	183
A30000	Alexa Fluor® 405 carboxylic acid, succinimidyl ester	1 mg	1.3, 1.7, 4.2, 14.3	183
A30100	Alexa Fluor® 405 carboxylic acid, succinimidyl ester	5 mg	1.3, 1.7, 4.2, 14.3	183
A10169	Alexa Fluor® 430 carboxylic acid, succinimidyl ester	5 mg	1.3, 1.7	None
A20000	Alexa Fluor® 488 carboxylic acid, succinimidyl ester *mixed isomers*	1 mg	1.3, 4.2	183
A20100	Alexa Fluor® 488 carboxylic acid, succinimidyl ester *mixed isomers*	5 mg	1.3, 4.2	183

For current prices or to order online, visit probes.invitrogen.com

Cat #	Product Name	Unit Size	Sections	Limited Use Label License #
A21435	Alexa Fluor® 555 goat anti-guinea pig IgG (H+L) *highly cross-adsorbed* *2 mg/mL*	0.5 mL	7.2	183
A11075	Alexa Fluor® 568 goat anti-guinea pig IgG (H+L) *highly cross-adsorbed* *2 mg/mL*	0.5 mL	7.2	183
A11076	Alexa Fluor® 594 goat anti-guinea pig IgG (H+L) *highly cross-adsorbed* *2 mg/mL*	0.5 mL	7.2	183
A21105	Alexa Fluor® 633 goat anti-guinea pig IgG (H+L) *highly cross-adsorbed* *2 mg/mL*	0.5 mL	7.2	183
A21450	Alexa Fluor® 647 goat anti-guinea pig IgG (H+L) *highly cross-adsorbed* *2 mg/mL*	0.5 mL	7.2	183
A21106	Alexa Fluor® 660 goat anti-guinea pig IgG (H+L) *highly cross-adsorbed* *2 mg/mL*	0.5 mL	7.2	183
A21110	Alexa Fluor® 488 goat anti-hamster IgG (H+L) *2 mg/mL*	0.5 mL	7.2	183
A21111	Alexa Fluor® 546 goat anti-hamster IgG (H+L) *2 mg/mL*	0.5 mL	7.2	183
A21112	Alexa Fluor® 568 goat anti-hamster IgG (H+L) *2 mg/mL*	0.5 mL	7.2	183
A21113	Alexa Fluor® 594 goat anti-hamster IgG (H+L) *2 mg/mL*	0.5 mL	7.2	183
A21114	Alexa Fluor® 633 goat anti-hamster IgG (H+L) *2 mg/mL*	0.5 mL	7.2	183
A21451	Alexa Fluor® 647 goat anti-hamster IgG (H+L) *2 mg/mL*	0.5 mL	7.2	183
A11013	Alexa Fluor® 488 goat anti-human IgG (H+L) *2 mg/mL*	0.5 mL	7.2	183
A21089	Alexa Fluor® 546 goat anti-human IgG (H+L) *2 mg/mL*	0.5 mL	7.2	183
A21433	Alexa Fluor® 555 goat anti-human IgG (H+L) *2 mg/mL*	0.5 mL	7.2	183
A21090	Alexa Fluor® 568 goat anti-human IgG (H+L) *2 mg/mL*	0.5 mL	7.2	183
A11014	Alexa Fluor® 594 goat anti-human IgG (H+L) *2 mg/mL*	0.5 mL	7.2	183
A21091	Alexa Fluor® 633 goat anti-human IgG (H+L) *2 mg/mL*	0.5 mL	7.2	183
A21445	Alexa Fluor® 647 goat anti-human IgG (H+L) *2 mg/mL*	0.5 mL	7.2	183
A21215	Alexa Fluor® 488 goat anti-human IgM (μ chain) *2 mg/mL*	250 μL	7.2	183
A21216	Alexa Fluor® 594 goat anti-human IgM (μ chain) *2 mg/mL*	250 μL	7.2	183
A21249	Alexa Fluor® 647 goat anti-human IgM (μ chain) *2 mg/mL*	250 μL	7.2	183
A31560	Alexa Fluor® 488 goat anti-mouse IgG, 5 nm colloidal gold conjugate *30 μg protein/mL*	0.5 mL	7.2	183
A31561	Alexa Fluor® 488 goat anti-mouse IgG, 10 nm colloidal gold conjugate *30 μg protein/mL*	0.5 mL	7.2	183
A21120	Alexa Fluor® 350 goat anti-mouse IgG_1 (γ1) *2 mg/mL*	250 μL	7.2	183
A21121	Alexa Fluor® 488 goat anti-mouse IgG_1 (γ1) *2 mg/mL*	250 μL	7.2	183
A21123	Alexa Fluor® 546 goat anti-mouse IgG_1 (γ1) *2 mg/mL*	250 μL	7.2	183
A21127	Alexa Fluor® 555 goat anti-mouse IgG_1 (γ1) *2 mg/mL*	250 μL	7.2	183
A21124	Alexa Fluor® 568 goat anti-mouse IgG_1 (γ1) *2 mg/mL*	250 μL	7.2	183
A21125	Alexa Fluor® 594 goat anti-mouse IgG_1 (γ1) *2 mg/mL*	250 μL	7.2	183
A21126	Alexa Fluor® 633 goat anti-mouse IgG_1 (γ1) *2 mg/mL*	250 μL	7.2	183
A21240	Alexa Fluor® 647 goat anti-mouse IgG_1 (γ1) *2 mg/mL*	250 μL	7.2	183
A21130	Alexa Fluor® 350 goat anti-mouse IgG_{2a} (γ2a) *2 mg/mL*	250 μL	7.2	183
A21131	Alexa Fluor® 488 goat anti-mouse IgG_{2a} (γ2a) *2 mg/mL*	250 μL	7.2	183
A21133	Alexa Fluor® 546 goat anti-mouse IgG_{2a} (γ2a) *2 mg/mL*	250 μL	7.2	183
A21137	Alexa Fluor® 555 goat anti-mouse IgG_{2a} (γ2a) *2 mg/mL*	250 μL	7.2	183
A21134	Alexa Fluor® 568 goat anti-mouse IgG_{2a} (γ2a) *2 mg/mL*	250 μL	7.2	183
A21135	Alexa Fluor® 594 goat anti-mouse IgG_{2a} (γ2a) *2 mg/mL*	250 μL	7.2	183
A21136	Alexa Fluor® 633 goat anti-mouse IgG_{2a} (γ2a) *2 mg/mL*	250 μL	7.2	183
A21241	Alexa Fluor® 647 goat anti-mouse IgG_{2a} (γ2a) *2 mg/mL*	250 μL	7.2	183
A21140	Alexa Fluor® 350 goat anti-mouse IgG_{2b} (γ2b) *2 mg/mL*	250 μL	7.2	183
A21141	Alexa Fluor® 488 goat anti-mouse IgG_{2b} (γ2b) *2 mg/mL*	250 μL	7.2	183
A21143	Alexa Fluor® 546 goat anti-mouse IgG_{2b} (γ2b) *2 mg/mL*	250 μL	7.2	183
A21147	Alexa Fluor® 555 goat anti-mouse IgG_{2b} (γ2b) *2 mg/mL*	250 μL	7.2	183
A21144	Alexa Fluor® 568 goat anti-mouse IgG_{2b} (γ2b) *2 mg/mL*	250 μL	7.2	183
A21145	Alexa Fluor® 594 goat anti-mouse IgG_{2b} (γ2b) *2 mg/mL*	250 μL	7.2	183
A21146	Alexa Fluor® 633 goat anti-mouse IgG_{2b} (γ2b) *2 mg/mL*	250 μL	7.2	183
A21242	Alexa Fluor® 647 goat anti-mouse IgG_{2b} (γ2b) *2 mg/mL*	250 μL	7.2	183
A21151	Alexa Fluor® 488 goat anti-mouse IgG_3 (γ3) *2 mg/mL*	250 μL	7.2	183
A21157	Alexa Fluor® 555 goat anti-mouse IgG_3 (γ3) *2 mg/mL*	250 μL	7.2	183
A21155	Alexa Fluor® 594 goat anti-mouse IgG_3 (γ3) *2 mg/mL*	250 μL	7.2	183
A11045	Alexa Fluor® 350 goat anti-mouse IgG (H+L) *2 mg/mL*	0.5 mL	7.2	183
A31553	Alexa Fluor® 405 goat anti-mouse IgG (H+L) *2 mg/mL*	0.5 mL	7.2	183
A11063	Alexa Fluor® 430 goat anti-mouse IgG (H+L) *2 mg/mL*	0.5 mL	7.2	183
A11001	Alexa Fluor® 488 goat anti-mouse IgG (H+L) *2 mg/mL*	0.5 mL	7.2	183
A31554	Alexa Fluor® 500 goat anti-mouse IgG (H+L) *2 mg/mL*	0.5 mL	7.2	183
A31555	Alexa Fluor® 514 goat anti-mouse IgG (H+L) *2 mg/mL*	0.5 mL	7.2	183
A11002	Alexa Fluor® 532 goat anti-mouse IgG (H+L) *2 mg/mL*	0.5 mL	7.2	183

For current prices or to order online, visit probes.invitrogen.com

Cat #	Product Name	Unit Size	Sections	Limited Use Label License #
A11003	Alexa Fluor® 546 goat anti-mouse IgG (H+L) *2 mg/mL*	0.5 mL	7.2	183
A21422	Alexa Fluor® 555 goat anti-mouse IgG (H+L) *2 mg/mL*	0.5 mL	7.2	183
A11004	Alexa Fluor® 568 goat anti-mouse IgG (H+L) *2 mg/mL*	0.5 mL	7.2	183
A11005	Alexa Fluor® 594 goat anti-mouse IgG (H+L) *2 mg/mL*	0.5 mL	7.2	183
A31550	Alexa Fluor® 610 goat anti-mouse IgG (H+L) *2 mg/mL*	0.5 mL	7.2	183
A21050	Alexa Fluor® 633 goat anti-mouse IgG (H+L) *2 mg/mL*	0.5 mL	7.2	183
A31574	Alexa Fluor® 635 goat anti-mouse IgG (H+L) *2 mg/mL*	0.5 mL	7.2	183
A21235	Alexa Fluor® 647 goat anti-mouse IgG (H+L) *2 mg/mL*	0.5 mL	7.2	183
A21054	Alexa Fluor® 660 goat anti-mouse IgG (H+L) *2 mg/mL*	0.5 mL	7.2	183
A21057	Alexa Fluor® 680 goat anti-mouse IgG (H+L) *2 mg/mL*	0.5 mL	7.2	183
A21036	Alexa Fluor® 700 goat anti-mouse IgG (H+L) *2 mg/mL*	0.5 mL	7.2	183
A21037	Alexa Fluor® 750 goat anti-mouse IgG (H+L) *2 mg/mL*	0.5 mL	7.2	183
A21049	Alexa Fluor® 350 goat anti-mouse IgG (H+L) *highly cross-adsorbed* *2 mg/mL*	0.5 mL	7.2	183
A11029	Alexa Fluor® 488 goat anti-mouse IgG (H+L) *highly cross-adsorbed* *2 mg/mL*	0.5 mL	7.2	183
A11030	Alexa Fluor® 546 goat anti-mouse IgG (H+L) *highly cross-adsorbed* *2 mg/mL*	0.5 mL	7.2	183
A21424	Alexa Fluor® 555 goat anti-mouse IgG (H+L) *highly cross-adsorbed* *2 mg/mL*	0.5 mL	7.2	183
A11031	Alexa Fluor® 568 goat anti-mouse IgG (H+L) *highly cross-adsorbed* *2 mg/mL*	0.5 mL	7.2	183
A11032	Alexa Fluor® 594 goat anti-mouse IgG (H+L) *highly cross-adsorbed* *2 mg/mL*	0.5 mL	7.2	183
A21052	Alexa Fluor® 633 goat anti-mouse IgG (H+L) *highly cross-adsorbed* *2 mg/mL*	0.5 mL	7.2	183
A31575	Alexa Fluor® 635 goat anti-mouse IgG (H+L) *highly cross-adsorbed* *2 mg/mL*	0.5 mL	7.2	183
A21236	Alexa Fluor® 647 goat anti-mouse IgG (H+L) *highly cross-adsorbed* *2 mg/mL*	0.5 mL	7.2	183
A21055	Alexa Fluor® 660 goat anti-mouse IgG (H+L) *highly cross-adsorbed* *2 mg/mL*	0.5 mL	7.2	183
A21058	Alexa Fluor® 680 goat anti-mouse IgG (H+L) *highly cross-adsorbed* *2 mg/mL*	0.5 mL	7.2	183
A31552	Alexa Fluor® 350 goat anti-mouse IgM (μ chain) *2 mg/mL*	250 μL	7.2	183
A21042	Alexa Fluor® 488 goat anti-mouse IgM (μ chain) *2 mg/mL*	250 μL	7.2	183
A21045	Alexa Fluor® 546 goat anti-mouse IgM (μ chain) *2 mg/mL*	250 μL	7.2	183
A21426	Alexa Fluor® 555 goat anti-mouse IgM (μ chain) *2 mg/mL*	250 μL	7.2	183
A21043	Alexa Fluor® 568 goat anti-mouse IgM (μ chain) *2 mg/mL*	250 μL	7.2	183
A21044	Alexa Fluor® 594 goat anti-mouse IgM (μ chain) *2 mg/mL*	250 μL	7.2	183
A21046	Alexa Fluor® 633 goat anti-mouse IgM (μ chain) *2 mg/mL*	250 μL	7.2	183
A21238	Alexa Fluor® 647 goat anti-mouse IgM (μ chain) *2 mg/mL*	250 μL	7.2	183
A21047	Alexa Fluor® 660 goat anti-mouse IgM (μ chain) *2 mg/mL*	250 μL	7.2	183
A21048	Alexa Fluor® 680 goat anti-mouse IgM (μ chain) *2 mg/mL*	250 μL	7.2	183
A31565	Alexa Fluor® 488 goat anti-rabbit IgG, 5 nm colloidal gold conjugate *30 μg protein/mL*	0.5 mL	7.2	183
A31566	Alexa Fluor® 488 goat anti-rabbit IgG, 10 nm colloidal gold conjugate *30 μg protein/mL*	0.5 mL	7.2	183
A11046	Alexa Fluor® 350 goat anti-rabbit IgG (H+L) *2 mg/mL*	0.5 mL	7.2	183
A31556	Alexa Fluor® 405 goat anti-rabbit IgG (H+L) *2 mg/mL*	0.5 mL	7.2	183
A11064	Alexa Fluor® 430 goat anti-rabbit IgG (H+L) *2 mg/mL*	0.5 mL	7.2	183
A11008	Alexa Fluor® 488 goat anti-rabbit IgG (H+L) *2 mg/mL*	0.5 mL	7.2	183
A31557	Alexa Fluor® 500 goat anti-rabbit IgG (H+L) *2 mg/mL*	0.5 mL	7.2	183
A31558	Alexa Fluor® 514 goat anti-rabbit IgG (H+L) *2 mg/mL*	0.5 mL	7.2	183
A11009	Alexa Fluor® 532 goat anti-rabbit IgG (H+L) *2 mg/mL*	0.5 mL	7.2	183
A11010	Alexa Fluor® 546 goat anti-rabbit IgG (H+L) *2 mg/mL*	0.5 mL	7.2	183
A21428	Alexa Fluor® 555 goat anti-rabbit IgG (H+L) *2 mg/mL*	0.5 mL	7.2	183
A11011	Alexa Fluor® 568 goat anti-rabbit IgG (H+L) *2 mg/mL*	0.5 mL	7.2	183
A11012	Alexa Fluor® 594 goat anti-rabbit IgG (H+L) *2 mg/mL*	0.5 mL	7.2	183
A31551	Alexa Fluor® 610 goat anti-rabbit IgG (H+L) *2 mg/mL*	0.5 mL	7.2	183
A21070	Alexa Fluor® 633 goat anti-rabbit IgG (H+L) *2 mg/mL*	0.5 mL	7.2	183
A31576	Alexa Fluor® 635 goat anti-rabbit IgG (H+L) *2 mg/mL*	0.5 mL	7.2	183
A21244	Alexa Fluor® 647 goat anti-rabbit IgG (H+L) *2 mg/mL*	0.5 mL	7.2	183
A21073	Alexa Fluor® 660 goat anti-rabbit IgG (H+L) *2 mg/mL*	0.5 mL	7.2	183
A21076	Alexa Fluor® 680 goat anti-rabbit IgG (H+L) *2 mg/mL*	0.5 mL	7.2	183
A21038	Alexa Fluor® 700 goat anti-rabbit IgG (H+L) *2 mg/mL*	0.5 mL	7.2	183
A21039	Alexa Fluor® 750 goat anti-rabbit IgG (H+L) *2 mg/mL*	0.5 mL	7.2	183
A21068	Alexa Fluor® 350 goat anti-rabbit IgG (H+L) *highly cross-adsorbed* *2 mg/mL*	0.5 mL	7.2	183
A11034	Alexa Fluor® 488 goat anti-rabbit IgG (H+L) *highly cross-adsorbed* *2 mg/mL*	0.5 mL	7.2	183
A11035	Alexa Fluor® 546 goat anti-rabbit IgG (H+L) *highly cross-adsorbed* *2 mg/mL*	0.5 mL	7.2	183
A21429	Alexa Fluor® 555 goat anti-rabbit IgG (H+L) *highly cross-adsorbed* *2 mg/mL*	0.5 mL	7.2	183

For current prices or to order online, visit probes.invitrogen.com

Cat #	Product Name	Unit Size	Sections	Limited Use Label License #
A11036	Alexa Fluor® 568 goat anti-rabbit IgG (H+L) *highly cross-adsorbed* *2 mg/mL*	0.5 mL	7.2	183
A11037	Alexa Fluor® 594 goat anti-rabbit IgG (H+L) *highly cross-adsorbed* *2 mg/mL*	0.5 mL	7.2	183
A21071	Alexa Fluor® 633 goat anti-rabbit IgG (H+L) *highly cross-adsorbed* *2 mg/mL*	0.5 mL	7.2	183
A31577	Alexa Fluor® 635 goat anti-rabbit IgG (H+L) *highly cross-adsorbed* *2 mg/mL*	0.5 mL	7.2	183
A21245	Alexa Fluor® 647 goat anti-rabbit IgG (H+L) *highly cross-adsorbed* *2 mg/mL*	0.5 mL	7.2	183
A21074	Alexa Fluor® 660 goat anti-rabbit IgG (H+L) *highly cross-adsorbed* *2 mg/mL*	0.5 mL	7.2	183
A21109	Alexa Fluor® 680 goat anti-rabbit IgG (H+L) *highly cross-adsorbed* *2 mg/mL*	0.5 mL	7.2	183
A21093	Alexa Fluor® 350 goat anti-rat IgG (H+L) *2 mg/mL*	0.5 mL	7.2	183
A11006	Alexa Fluor® 488 goat anti-rat IgG (H+L) *2 mg/mL*	0.5 mL	7.2	183
A11081	Alexa Fluor® 546 goat anti-rat IgG (H+L) *2 mg/mL*	0.5 mL	7.2	183
A21434	Alexa Fluor® 555 goat anti-rat IgG (H+L) *2 mg/mL*	0.5 mL	7.2	183
A11077	Alexa Fluor® 568 goat anti-rat IgG (H+L) *2 mg/mL*	0.5 mL	7.2	183
A11007	Alexa Fluor® 594 goat anti-rat IgG (H+L) *2 mg/mL*	0.5 mL	7.2	183
A21094	Alexa Fluor® 633 goat anti-rat IgG (H+L) *2 mg/mL*	0.5 mL	7.2	183
A21247	Alexa Fluor® 647 goat anti-rat IgG (H+L) *2 mg/mL*	0.5 mL	7.2	183
A21095	Alexa Fluor® 660 goat anti-rat IgG (H+L) *2 mg/mL*	0.5 mL	7.2	183
A21096	Alexa Fluor® 680 goat anti-rat IgG (H+L) *2 mg/mL*	0.5 mL	7.2	183
A21212	Alexa Fluor® 488 goat anti-rat IgM (μ chain) *2 mg/mL*	250 μL	7.2	183
A21213	Alexa Fluor® 594 goat anti-rat IgM (μ chain) *2 mg/mL*	250 μL	7.2	183
A21248	Alexa Fluor® 647 goat anti-rat IgM (μ chain) *2 mg/mL*	250 μL	7.2	183
A10439	Alexa Fluor® 350 hydrazide, sodium salt	5 mg	3.2, 14.3	183
A10436	Alexa Fluor® 488 hydrazide, sodium salt	1 mg	3.2, 14.3	183
A20501MP	Alexa Fluor® 555 hydrazide, tris(triethylammonium) salt	1 mg	3.2, 14.3	183
A10437	Alexa Fluor® 568 hydrazide, sodium salt	1 mg	3.2, 14.3	183
A10438	Alexa Fluor® 594 hydrazide, sodium salt	1 mg	3.2, 14.3	183
A30634	Alexa Fluor® 633 hydrazide, bis(triethylammonium) salt	1 mg	3.2, 14.3	183
A20502	Alexa Fluor® 647 hydrazide, tris(triethylammonium) salt	1 mg	3.2, 14.3	183
A10440	Alexa Fluor® 488 hydrazide, sodium salt *for microinjection* *10 mM in 200 mM KCl*	125 μL	14.3	183
A10441	Alexa Fluor® 568 hydrazide, sodium salt *for microinjection* *10 mM in 200 mM KCl*	125 μL	14.3	183
A10442	Alexa Fluor® 594 hydrazide, sodium salt *for microinjection* *10 mM in 200 mM KCl*	125 μL	14.3	183
A30627	Alexa Fluor® 350 hydroxylamine (Alexa Fluor® 350 C_5-aminooxyacetamide, trifluoroacetate salt)	1 mg	3.2, 14.3	183
A30629	Alexa Fluor® 488 hydroxylamine (Alexa Fluor® 488 C_5-aminooxyacetamide, bis(triethylammonium) salt)	1 mg	3.2, 14.3	183
A30632	Alexa Fluor® 647 hydroxylamine (Alexa Fluor® 647 C_5-aminooxyacetamide, bis(triethylammonium) salt)	1 mg	3.2, 14.3	183
M23271	Alexa Fluor® 488 methotrexate (methotrexate, Alexa Fluor® 488, inner salt) *mixed isomers*	500 μg	15.6	183
A20180	Alexa Fluor® 350 Monoclonal Antibody Labeling Kit *5 labelings*	1 kit	1.2, 1.7	183
A20181	Alexa Fluor® 488 Monoclonal Antibody Labeling Kit *5 labelings*	1 kit	1.2, 1.3	183
A20182	Alexa Fluor® 532 Monoclonal Antibody Labeling Kit *5 labelings*	1 kit	1.2, 1.3	183
A20183	Alexa Fluor® 546 Monoclonal Antibody Labeling Kit *5 labelings*	1 kit	1.2, 1.3	183
A20187	Alexa Fluor® 555 Monoclonal Antibody Labeling Kit *5 labelings*	1 kit	1.2, 1.3	183
A20184	Alexa Fluor® 568 Monoclonal Antibody Labeling Kit *5 labelings*	1 kit	1.2, 1.3	183
A20185	Alexa Fluor® 594 Monoclonal Antibody Labeling Kit *5 labelings*	1 kit	1.2, 1.3	183
A20186	Alexa Fluor® 647 Monoclonal Antibody Labeling Kit *5 labelings*	1 kit	1.2, 1.3	183
A20190	Alexa Fluor® 350 Oligonucleotide Amine Labeling Kit *3 labelings*	1 kit	1.2, 1.7, 8.2	183
A20191	Alexa Fluor® 488 Oligonucleotide Amine Labeling Kit *3 labelings*	1 kit	1.2, 1.3, 8.2	183
A20192	Alexa Fluor® 532 Oligonucleotide Amine Labeling Kit *3 labelings*	1 kit	1.2, 1.3, 8.2	183
A20193	Alexa Fluor® 546 Oligonucleotide Amine Labeling Kit *3 labelings*	1 kit	1.2, 1.3, 8.2	183
A20197	Alexa Fluor® 555 Oligonucleotide Amine Labeling Kit *3 labelings*	1 kit	1.2, 1.3, 8.2	183
A20194	Alexa Fluor® 568 Oligonucleotide Amine Labeling Kit *3 labelings*	1 kit	1.2, 1.3, 8.2	183
A20195	Alexa Fluor® 594 Oligonucleotide Amine Labeling Kit *3 labelings*	1 kit	1.2, 1.3, 8.2	183
A20196	Alexa Fluor® 647 Oligonucleotide Amine Labeling Kit *3 labelings*	1 kit	1.2, 1.3, 8.2	183
A34054	Alexa Fluor® 635 phalloidin	300 U	11.1	183
A22281	Alexa Fluor® 350 phalloidin	300 U	11.1	183
A12379	Alexa Fluor® 488 phalloidin	300 U	11.1	183
A22282	Alexa Fluor® 532 phalloidin	300 U	11.1	183
A22283	Alexa Fluor® 546 phalloidin	300 U	11.1	183
A12380	Alexa Fluor® 568 phalloidin	300 U	11.1	183
A12381	Alexa Fluor® 594 phalloidin	300 U	11.1	183
A22284	Alexa Fluor® 633 phalloidin	300 U	11.1	183

For current prices or to order online, visit probes.invitrogen.com

Cat #	Product Name	Unit Size	Sections	Limited Use Label License #
A22287	Alexa Fluor® 647 phalloidin	300 U	11.1	183
A22285	Alexa Fluor® 660 phalloidin	300 U	11.1	183
A22286	Alexa Fluor® 680 phalloidin	300 U	11.1	183
A10170	Alexa Fluor® 350 Protein Labeling Kit *3 labelings*	1 kit	1.2, 1.3, 1.7	183
A10171	Alexa Fluor® 430 Protein Labeling Kit *3 labelings*	1 kit	1.2, 1.3, 1.7	None
A10235	Alexa Fluor® 488 Protein Labeling Kit *3 labelings*	1 kit	1.2, 1.3	183
A10236	Alexa Fluor® 532 Protein Labeling Kit *3 labelings*	1 kit	1.2, 1.3	183
A10237	Alexa Fluor® 546 Protein Labeling Kit *3 labelings*	1 kit	1.2, 1.3	183
A20174	Alexa Fluor® 555 Protein Labeling Kit *3 labelings*	1 kit	1.2, 1.3	183
A10238	Alexa Fluor® 568 Protein Labeling Kit *3 labelings*	1 kit	1.2, 1.3	183
A10239	Alexa Fluor® 594 Protein Labeling Kit *3 labelings*	1 kit	1.2, 1.3	183
A20170	Alexa Fluor® 633 Protein Labeling Kit *3 labelings*	1 kit	1.2, 1.3	183
A20173	Alexa Fluor® 647 Protein Labeling Kit *3 labelings*	1 kit	1.2, 1.3	183
A20171	Alexa Fluor® 660 Protein Labeling Kit *3 labelings*	1 kit	1.2, 1.3	183
A20172	Alexa Fluor® 680 Protein Labeling Kit *3 labelings*	1 kit	1.2, 1.3	183
A11078	Alexa Fluor® 488 rabbit anti-goat IgG (H+L) *2 mg/mL*	0.5 mL	7.2	183
A21085	Alexa Fluor® 546 rabbit anti-goat IgG (H+L) *2 mg/mL*	0.5 mL	7.2	183
A21431	Alexa Fluor® 555 rabbit anti-goat IgG (H+L) *2 mg/mL*	0.5 mL	7.2	183
A11079	Alexa Fluor® 568 rabbit anti-goat IgG (H+L) *2 mg/mL*	0.5 mL	7.2	183
A11080	Alexa Fluor® 594 rabbit anti-goat IgG (H+L) *2 mg/mL*	0.5 mL	7.2	183
A21086	Alexa Fluor® 633 rabbit anti-goat IgG (H+L) *2 mg/mL*	0.5 mL	7.2	183
A21446	Alexa Fluor® 647 rabbit anti-goat IgG (H+L) *2 mg/mL*	0.5 mL	7.2	183
A21087	Alexa Fluor® 660 rabbit anti-goat IgG (H+L) *2 mg/mL*	0.5 mL	7.2	183
A21088	Alexa Fluor® 680 rabbit anti-goat IgG (H+L) *2 mg/mL*	0.5 mL	7.2	183
A21218	Alexa Fluor® 488 rabbit anti-human IgG (H+L) *2 mg/mL*	0.5 mL	7.2	183
A21062	Alexa Fluor® 350 rabbit anti-mouse IgG (H+L) *2 mg/mL*	0.5 mL	7.2	183
A11059	Alexa Fluor® 488 rabbit anti-mouse IgG (H+L) *2 mg/mL*	0.5 mL	7.2	183
A11060	Alexa Fluor® 546 rabbit anti-mouse IgG (H+L) *2 mg/mL*	0.5 mL	7.2	183
A21427	Alexa Fluor® 555 rabbit anti-mouse IgG (H+L) *2 mg/mL*	0.5 mL	7.2	183
A11061	Alexa Fluor® 568 rabbit anti-mouse IgG (H+L) *2 mg/mL*	0.5 mL	7.2	183
A11062	Alexa Fluor® 594 rabbit anti-mouse IgG (H+L) *2 mg/mL*	0.5 mL	7.2	183
A21063	Alexa Fluor® 633 rabbit anti-mouse IgG (H+L) *2 mg/mL*	0.5 mL	7.2	183
A21239	Alexa Fluor® 647 rabbit anti-mouse IgG (H+L) *2 mg/mL*	0.5 mL	7.2	183
A21064	Alexa Fluor® 660 rabbit anti-mouse IgG (H+L) *2 mg/mL*	0.5 mL	7.2	183
A21065	Alexa Fluor® 680 rabbit anti-mouse IgG (H+L) *2 mg/mL*	0.5 mL	7.2	183
A21210	Alexa Fluor® 488 rabbit anti-rat IgG (H+L) *2 mg/mL*	0.5 mL	7.2	183
A21211	Alexa Fluor® 594 rabbit anti-rat IgG (H+L) *2 mg/mL*	0.5 mL	7.2	183
A32751	Alexa Fluor® 594 reactive dye decapack *for microarrays* *set of 10 vials*	1 set	1.3, 8.2, 8.5	183
A32755	Alexa Fluor® 555 and Alexa Fluor® 647 reactive dye decapacks *for microarrays* *set of 2 x 10 vials* *includes A32756 and A32757 decapacks*	1 set	1.3, 8.2, 8.5	183
A32756	Alexa Fluor® 555 reactive dye decapack *for microarrays* *set of 10 vials*	1 set	1.3, 8.2, 8.5	183
A32757	Alexa Fluor® 647 reactive dye decapack *for microarrays* *set of 10 vials*	1 set	1.3, 8.2, 8.5	183
A20980	Alexa Fluor® 610–R-phycoerythrin goat anti-mouse IgG (H+L) *1 mg/mL*	100 µL	6.4, 7.2	183
A20990	Alexa Fluor® 647–R-phycoerythrin goat anti-mouse IgG (H+L) *1 mg/mL*	100 µL	6.4, 7.2	183
A20983	Alexa Fluor® 680–R-phycoerythrin goat anti-mouse IgG (H+L) *1 mg/mL*	100 µL	6.4, 7.2	183
A20981	Alexa Fluor® 610–R-phycoerythrin goat anti-rabbit IgG (H+L) *1 mg/mL*	100 µL	6.4, 7.2	183
A20991	Alexa Fluor® 647–R-phycoerythrin goat anti-rabbit IgG (H+L) *1 mg/mL*	100 µL	6.4, 7.2	183
A20984	Alexa Fluor® 680–R-phycoerythrin goat anti-rabbit IgG (H+L) *1 mg/mL*	100 µL	6.4, 7.2	183
S20982	Alexa Fluor® 610–R-phycoerythrin streptavidin (streptavidin, Alexa Fluor® 610–R-phycoerythrin conjugate) *1 mg/mL*	100 µL	6.4, 7.6	183
S20992	Alexa Fluor® 647–R-phycoerythrin streptavidin (streptavidin, Alexa Fluor® 647–R-phycoerythrin conjugate) *1 mg/mL*	100 µL	6.4, 7.6	183
S20985	Alexa Fluor® 680–R-phycoerythrin streptavidin (streptavidin, Alexa Fluor® 680–R-phycoerythrin conjugate) *1 mg/mL*	100 µL	6.4, 7.6	183
S32363	Alexa Fluor® 750–R-phycoerythrin streptavidin (streptavidin, Alexa Fluor® 750–R-phycoerythrin conjugate) *1 mg/mL*	100 µL	6.4, 7.6	183
A11053	Alexa Fluor® 488 Signal-Amplification Kit for Fluorescein- and Oregon Green® Dye–Conjugated Probes *60-120 assays*	1 kit	7.2, 7.4	183
A11054	Alexa Fluor® 488 Signal-Amplification Kit for Mouse Antibodies *60-300 assays*	1 kit	7.2	183
A11066	Alexa Fluor® 568 Signal-Amplification Kit for Mouse Antibodies *60-300 assays*	1 kit	7.2	183
A11067	Alexa Fluor® 594 Signal-Amplification Kit for Mouse Antibodies *60-300 assays*	1 kit	7.2	183
A32360	Alexa Fluor® 488 streptavidin, 5 nm colloidal gold conjugate *30 µg protein/mL*	0.5 mL	7.6	183
A32361	Alexa Fluor® 488 streptavidin, 10 nm colloidal gold conjugate *30 µg protein/mL*	0.5 mL	7.6	183

For current prices or to order online, visit probes.invitrogen.com

Cat #	Product Name	Unit Size	Sections	Limited Use Label License #
A30005	Alexa Fluor® 488 5-TFP (Alexa Fluor® 488 carboxylic acid, 2,3,5,6-tetrafluorophenyl ester) *5-isomer*	1 mg	1.3	183
A7304	AlignFlow™ flow cytometry alignment beads, 2.5 µm *for UV excitation*	3 mL	23.2	None
A7302	AlignFlow™ flow cytometry alignment beads, 2.5 µm *for 488 nm excitation*	3 mL	23.2	None
A14835	AlignFlow™ flow cytometry alignment beads, 2.5 µm *for 630-660 nm excitation*	3 mL	23.2	227
A7312	AlignFlow™ flow cytometry alignment beads, 2.5 µm *for 633 nm excitation*	3 mL	23.2	227, 193
A7305	AlignFlow™ Plus flow cytometry alignment beads, 6 µm *for UV excitation*	3 mL	23.2	None
A7303	AlignFlow™ Plus flow cytometry alignment beads, 6 µm *for 488 nm excitation*	3 mL	23.2	None
A14836	AlignFlow™ Plus flow cytometry alignment beads, 6 µm *for 630-660 nm excitation*	3 mL	23.2	227
A7313	AlignFlow™ Plus flow cytometry alignment beads, 6 µm *for 633 nm excitation*	3 mL	23.2	228, 193
A803	allophycocyanin *4 mg/mL*	0.5 mL	6.4, 14.7	None
A819	allophycocyanin, crosslinked (APC-XL) *4 mg/mL*	250 µL	6.4, 14.7	None
A865	allophycocyanin, crosslinked, goat anti-mouse IgG (H+L) *1 mg/mL*	0.5 mL	6.4, 7.2	None
A10931	allophycocyanin, crosslinked, goat anti-rabbit IgG (H+L) *1 mg/mL*	0.5 mL	6.4, 7.2	None
A1642	AMBH (2-acetamido-4-mercaptobutanoic acid hydrazide)	100 mg	3.2, 5.2	None
A6118	AMCA-X, SE (6-((7-amino-4-methylcoumarin-3-acetyl)amino)hexanoic acid, succinimidyl ester)	10 mg	1.7	None
A1363	5-(aminoacetamido)fluorescein (fluoresceinyl glycine amide)	10 mg	3.3	None
A1364	4′-((aminoacetamido)methyl)fluorescein	10 mg	3.3	None
A6289	2-aminoacridone, hydrochloride	25 mg	3.2	None
A1310	7-aminoactinomycin D (7-AAD)	1 mg	8.1, 8.6, 15.4, 15.5	None
A21664	5-(3-aminoallyl)-2′-deoxyuridine 5′-triphosphate, trisodium salt (aminoallyl dUTP) *2 mM in TE buffer*	500 µL	8.2, 8.5	None
A32764	5-(3-aminoallyl)-2′-deoxyuridine 5′-triphosphate, trisodium salt (aminoallyl dUTP) *50 mM in TE buffer*	50 µL	8.2, 8.5	None
A21664	aminoallyl dUTP (5-(3-aminoallyl)-2′-deoxyuridine 5′-triphosphate, trisodium salt) *2 mM in TE buffer*	500 µL	8.2, 8.5	None
A32764	aminoallyl dUTP (5-(3-aminoallyl)-2′-deoxyuridine 5′-triphosphate, trisodium salt) *50 mM in TE buffer*	50 µL	8.2, 8.5	None
A21663	5-(3-aminoallyl)uridine 5′-triphosphate, trisodium salt (aminoallyl UTP) *2 mM in TE buffer*	500 µL	8.2, 8.5	None
A32765	5-(3-aminoallyl)uridine 5′-triphosphate, trisodium salt (aminoallyl UTP) *50 mM in TE buffer*	50 µL	8.2, 8.5	None
A21663	aminoallyl UTP (5-(3-aminoallyl)uridine 5′-triphosphate, trisodium salt) *2 mM in TE buffer*	500 µL	8.2, 8.5	None
A32765	aminoallyl UTP (5-(3-aminoallyl)uridine 5′-triphosphate, trisodium salt) *50 mM in TE buffer*	50 µL	8.2, 8.5	None
A11760	4-amino-4′-benzamidostilbene-2,2′-disulfonic acid, disodium salt (MBDS)	100 mg	9.2, 13.5	None
A7110	γ-aminobutyric acid, α-carboxy-2-nitrobenzyl ester, trifluoroacetic acid salt (*O*-(CNB-caged) GABA)	5 mg	5.3, 16.2	246
A7621	8-amino-cADP-ribose (8-amino-cyclic adenosine 5′-diphosphate ribose)	10 µg	17.2	247
A1324	9-amino-6-chloro-2-methoxyacridine (ACMA)	100 mg	8.1, 8.6, 20.3	None
C2110	7-amino-4-chloromethylcoumarin (CellTracker™ Blue CMAC)	5 mg	10.1, 14.2	212
A6520	7-amino-4-chloromethylcoumarin, *t*-BOC-L-leucyl-L-methionine amide (CMAC, *t*-BOC-Leu-Met)	5 mg	10.4, 15.5	212
A6575	7-amino-4-chloromethylcoumarin, CBZ-L-arginine amide, hydrochloride (CMAC, CBZ-Arg)	5 mg	10.4	212
A7621	8-amino-cyclic adenosine 5′-diphosphate ribose (8-amino-cADP-ribose)	10 µg	17.2	247
A2952	3-amino-3-deoxydigoxigenin hemisuccinamide, succinimidyl ester	5 mg	4.2	None
A117	5-aminoeosin	100 mg	3.3	None
A1339	*N*-(2-aminoethyl)-4-amino-3,6-disulfo-1,8-naphthalimide, dipotassium salt (lucifer yellow ethylenediamine)	25 mg	3.3, 14.3	None
A91	5-((2-aminoethyl)amino)naphthalene-1-sulfonic acid, sodium salt (EDANS)	1 g	3.3, 9.5	None
A1593	*N*-(2-aminoethyl)biotinamide, hydrobromide (biotin ethylenediamine)	25 mg	4.2, 14.3	None
A32760	5-aminohexylacrylamido-dUTP (aha-dUTP) *2 mM in TE buffer*	500 µL	8.2, 8.5	None
A32761	5-aminohexylacrylamido-dUTP (aha-dUTP) *50 mM in TE buffer*	50 µL	8.2, 8.5	None
D23841	4-amino-5-methylamino-2′,7′-difluorofluorescein (DAF-FM)	1 mg	18.3, 21.2	255, 191
D23842	4-amino-5-methylamino-2′,7′-difluorofluorescein diacetate (DAF-FM diacetate)	1 mg	18.3	255, 191
D23844	4-amino-5-methylamino-2′,7′-difluorofluorescein diacetate (DAF-FM diacetate) *special packaging*	10 x 50 µg	18.3	255, 191
A191	7-amino-4-methylcoumarin *reference standard*	100 mg	3.2, 3.3, 10.1	None
A6118	6-((7-amino-4-methylcoumarin-3-acetyl)amino)hexanoic acid, succinimidyl ester (AMCA-X, SE)	10 mg	1.7	None
A22127	7-amino-4-methylcoumarin, *N*-CBZ-L-isoleucyl-L-glutamyl-L-threonyl-L-aspartic acid amide (Z-IETD-AMC)	5 mg	10.4, 15.5	None
A6521	7-amino-4-methylcoumarin, CBZ-L-phenylalanyl-L-arginine amide, hydrochloride	25 mg	10.4	None
A1351	4′-(aminomethyl)fluorescein, hydrochloride	25 mg	3.3	None
A1353	5-(aminomethyl)fluorescein, hydrochloride	10 mg	3.3	None
P2421	1-aminomethylpyrene, hydrochloride (1-pyrenemethylamine, hydrochloride)	100 mg	3.3	None
A22840	7-aminonaphthalene-1,3-disulfonic acid, potassium salt (ANDS) *FluoroPure™ grade*	1 g	3.2, 14.3	None
A350	8-aminonaphthalene-1,3,6-trisulfonic acid, disodium salt (ANTS)	1 g	3.2, 14.3	None
A10550	*N*-(aminooxyacetyl)-*N*′-(D-biotinoyl) hydrazine, trifluoroacetic acid salt (ARP)	10 mg	4.2, 8.2, 8.7	None
A1318	5-(and-6)-((*N*-(5-aminopentyl)amino)carbonyl)tetramethylrhodamine (tetramethylrhodamine cadaverine) *mixed isomers*	10 mg	3.3	None
A1340	*N*-(5-aminopentyl)-4-amino-3,6-disulfo-1,8-naphthalimide, dipotassium salt (lucifer yellow cadaverine)	25 mg	3.3, 14.3	None
A1594	*N*-(5-aminopentyl)biotinamide, trifluoroacetic acid salt (biotin cadaverine)	25 mg	4.2, 14.3	None

For current prices or to order online, visit probes.invitrogen.com

Cat #	Product Name	Unit Size	Sections	Limited Use Label License #
A434	5-((5-aminopentyl)thioureidyl)eosin, hydrochloride (eosin cadaverine)	25 mg	3.3	None
A10466	5-((5-aminopentyl)thioureidyl)fluorescein, dihydrobromide salt (fluorescein cadaverine)	25 mg	3.3	None
A36003	3′-(*p*-aminophenyl) fluorescein (APF) *5 mM solution in DMF*	470 µL	18.2	None
L8455	3-aminophthalhydrazide (luminol)	25 g	8.5, 10.5, 15.2, 18.2	None
A6257	8-aminopyrene-1,3,6-trisulfonic acid, trisodium salt (APTS)	10 mg	3.2, 14.3	None
A10461	3*S*-(4-(3-aminopyrrolidin-1-yl))-7-nitrobenz-2-oxa-1,3-diazole ((*S*)-NBD-APy)	10 mg	3.3	None
A22850	aminostilbamidine, methanesulfonate	10 mg	14.3	None
A22121	7-amino-4-trifluoromethylcoumarin, *N*-CBZ-L-aspartyl-L-glutamyl-L-valyl-L-aspartic acid amide (Z-DEVD-AFC)	5 mg	10.4, 15.5	None
A22128	7-amino-4-trifluoromethylcoumarin, *N*-CBZ-L-isoleucyl-L-glutamyl-L-threonyl-L-aspartic acid amide (Z-IETD-AFC)	5 mg	10.4, 15.5	None
A24772	Amplex® Gold photographic filter	each	9.4, 23.4	None
A21890	Amplex® Gold Western Blot Stain Kit #1 *with goat anti-mouse IgG* *20 minigel blots*	1 kit	9.4	191
A21891	Amplex® Gold Western Blot Stain Kit #2 *with goat anti-rabbit IgG* *20 minigel blots*	1 kit	9.4	191
A21892	Amplex® Gold Western Blot Stain Kit #3 *with streptavidin* *20 minigel blots*	1 kit	9.4	191
A12217	Amplex® Red Acetylcholine/Acetylcholinesterase Assay Kit *500 assays*	1 kit	10.5, 16.2	None
A22180	Amplex® Red Catalase Assay Kit *400 assays*	1 kit	10.5	None
A12216	Amplex® Red Cholesterol Assay Kit *500 assays*	1 kit	10.5, 13.3	None
A22170	Amplex® Red ELISA Kit #1 *with goat anti-mouse IgG, horseradish peroxidase conjugate* *1000 assays*	1 kit	7.2, 10.5	None
A22171	Amplex® Red ELISA Kit #2 *with protein G, horseradish peroxidase conjugate* *1000 assays*	1 kit	7.2, 10.5	None
A22179	Amplex® Red Galactose/Galactose Oxidase Assay Kit *400 assays*	1 kit	10.2, 10.5	None
A22189	Amplex® Red Glucose/Glucose Oxidase Assay Kit *500 assays*	1 kit	10.2, 10.5	None
A12221	Amplex® Red Glutamic Acid/Glutamate Oxidase Assay Kit *200 assays*	1 kit	10.5, 16.2	None
A22188	Amplex® Red Hydrogen Peroxide/Peroxidase Assay Kit *500 assays*	1 kit	10.5, 18.2	None
A12214	Amplex® Red Monoamine Oxidase Assay Kit *500 assays*	1 kit	10.5	None
A22178	Amplex® Red Neuraminidase (Sialidase) Assay Kit *400 assays*	1 kit	10.2, 10.5	None
A12218	Amplex® Red Phosphatidylcholine-Specific Phospholipase C Assay Kit *500 assays*	1 kit	10.5, 17.4	None
A12219	Amplex® Red Phospholipase D Assay Kit *500 assays*	1 kit	10.5, 17.4	None
A12222	Amplex® Red reagent (10-acetyl-3,7-dihydroxyphenoxazine)	5 mg	10.2, 10.5, 18.2	None
A22177	Amplex® Red reagent *packaged for high-throughput screening*	10 x 10 mg	10.5, 18.2	None
A12220	Amplex® Red Sphingomyelinase Assay Kit *500 assays*	1 kit	10.5, 13.3, 17.4	None
A22181	Amplex® Red Uric Acid/Uricase Assay Kit *400 assays*	1 kit	10.5	None
A22182	Amplex® Red Xanthine/Xanthine Oxidase Assay Kit *400 assays*	1 kit	10.5, 18.2	None
A36006	Amplex® UltraRed reagent	5 x 1 mg	10.5, 18.2	223
A22840	ANDS (7-aminonaphthalene-1,3-disulfonic acid, potassium salt) *FluoroPure™ grade*	1 g	3.2, 14.3	None
A23375	Angiostatin® protein (human, recombinant) *1 mg/mL*	250 µL	15.4	None
A13439	angiotensin II, Alexa Fluor® 488 conjugate	25 µg	16.2	183
A13438	angiotensin II, fluorescein conjugate	25 µg	16.2	None
A50	2-anilinonaphthalene-6-sulfonic acid (2,6-ANS)	100 mg	13.5	None
A47	1-anilinonaphthalene-8-sulfonic acid (1,8-ANS) *high purity*	100 mg	13.5	None
A23202	annexin V, Alexa Fluor® 350 conjugate *100 assays*	500 µL	15.5	213, 183
A13201	annexin V, Alexa Fluor® 488 conjugate *100 assays*	500 µL	15.5	213, 183
A13202	annexin V, Alexa Fluor® 568 conjugate *100 assays*	500 µL	15.5	213, 183
A13203	annexin V, Alexa Fluor® 594 conjugate *100 assays*	500 µL	15.5	213, 183
A23204	annexin V, Alexa Fluor® 647 conjugate *100 assays*	500 µL	15.5	213, 223
A35110	annexin V, allophycocyanin conjugate (APC annexin V) *50 assays*	250 µL	6.4, 15.5	213
A13204	annexin V, biotin-X conjugate *100 assays*	500 µL	4.3, 15.5	213
A13199	annexin V, fluorescein conjugate (FITC annexin V) *100 assays*	500 µL	15.5	213
A13200	annexin V, Oregon Green® 488 conjugate *100 assays*	500 µL	15.5	213, 191
A35111	annexin V, R-phycoerythrin conjugate (R-PE annexin V) *50 assays*	250 µL	6.4, 15.5	213
A50	2,6-ANS (2-anilinonaphthalene-6-sulfonic acid)	100 mg	13.5	None
A47	1,8-ANS (1-anilinonaphthalene-8-sulfonic acid) *high purity*	100 mg	13.5	None
A1139	anthracene-2,3-dicarboxaldehyde (ADA)	25 mg	1.8, 21.2	None
A6871	anthracene-1,5-dicarboxylic acid, di(acetoxymethyl ester) (ADC, AM)	5 mg	21.2	None
A7896	anthracene-9,10-dipropionic acid, disodium salt	25 mg	18.2	None
A176	9-anthracenepropionic acid	100 mg	1.8, 13.2	None
A448	2-anthracenesulfonyl chloride	100 mg	1.8	None
A1440	9-anthroylnitrile	25 mg	3.1	None
A1322	9-anthroyl ouabain	5 mg	16.3	None
A1122	4-(9-anthroyloxy)phenacyl bromide (panacyl bromide)	100 mg	3.3	None

For current prices or to order online, visit probes.invitrogen.com

Cat #	Product Name	Unit Size	Sections	Limited Use Label License #
A37	2-(9-anthroyloxy)stearic acid (2-AS)	100 mg	13.2	None
A242	6-(9-anthroyloxy)stearic acid (6-AS)	25 mg	13.2	None
A1400	9-anthryldiazomethane (ADAM)	25 mg	3.3	None
A11133	anti-albumin (bovine serum), rabbit IgG fraction (anti-BSA) *2 mg/mL*	0.5 mL	7.5, 14.7	183
A5760	anti-Alexa Fluor® 405/Cascade Blue®, rabbit IgG fraction *3 mg/mL*	0.5 mL	7.4	218, 183
A11094	anti-Alexa Fluor® 488, rabbit IgG fraction *1 mg/mL*	0.5 mL	7.4	None
A6458	anti-alkaline phosphatase (yeast vacuolar), mouse IgG_1, monoclonal 1D3 *in conditioned culture medium*	2.5 mL	7.5, 12.3	226
A21355	anti-ATP synthase IP; anti-F_1F_0-ATPase IP (anti-OxPhos Complex V inhibitor protein, mouse IgG_1, monoclonal 5E2) *human mitochondrial reactivity*	100 µg	7.5, 12.2	226
A21351	anti-ATP synthase subunit β; anti-F_1F_0-ATPase subunit β (anti-OxPhos Complex V subunit β, mouse IgG_1, monoclonal 3D5) *human mitochondrial reactivity*	100 µg	7.5, 12.2	226
A21350	anti-ATP synthase subunit α; anti-F_1F_0-ATPase subunit α (anti-OxPhos Complex V subunit α, mouse IgG_{2b}, monoclonal 7H10) *human mitochondrial reactivity*	100 µg	7.5, 12.2	226
A21353	anti-ATP synthase subunit d; anti-F_1F_0-ATPase subunit d (anti-OxPhos Complex V subunit d, mouse IgG_{2b}, monoclonal 7F9) *human mitochondrial reactivity*	100 µg	7.5, 12.2	226
A21354	anti-ATP synthase subunit OSCP; anti-F_1F_0-ATPase subunit OSCP (anti-OxPhos Complex V subunit OSCP, mouse IgG_1, monoclonal 4C11) *human mitochondrial reactivity*	100 µg	7.5, 12.2	226
A11242	anti-biotin, mouse IgG_1, monoclonal 2F5	100 µg	7.4, 7.6	226
A31801	anti-biotin, mouse IgG_1, monoclonal 2F5, Alexa Fluor® 488 conjugate *1 mg/mL*	100 µL	7.4, 7.6	183
A31800	anti-biotin, mouse IgG_1, monoclonal 2F5, Alexa Fluor® 594 conjugate *1 mg/mL*	100 µL	7.4, 7.6	183
A5770	anti-BODIPY® FL, rabbit IgG fraction *3 mg/mL*	0.5 mL	7.4	None
A35725	Antibody Beacon™ Tyrosine Kinase Assay Kit *400 assays*	1 kit	10.3, 17.3	223, 191
A21300	anti-BrdU (anti-bromodeoxyuridine, mouse IgG_1, monoclonal PRB-1)	350 µL	7.5, 15.4	214
A21303	anti-BrdU, Alexa Fluor® 488 conjugate (anti-bromodeoxyuridine, mouse IgG_1, monoclonal PRB-1, Alexa Fluor® 488 conjugate)	350 µL	7.5, 15.4	214, 183
A21307	anti-BrdU, Alexa Fluor® 532 conjugate (anti-bromodeoxyuridine, mouse IgG_1, monoclonal PRB-1, Alexa Fluor® 532 conjugate)	350 µL	7.5, 15.4	214, 183
A21308	anti-BrdU, Alexa Fluor® 546 conjugate (anti-bromodeoxyuridine, mouse IgG_1, monoclonal PRB-1, Alexa Fluor® 546 conjugate)	350 µL	7.5, 15.4	214, 183
A21304	anti-BrdU, Alexa Fluor® 594 conjugate (anti-bromodeoxyuridine, mouse IgG_1, monoclonal PRB-1, Alexa Fluor® 594 conjugate)	350 µL	7.5, 15.4	214, 183
A21305	anti-BrdU, Alexa Fluor® 647 conjugate (anti-bromodeoxyuridine, mouse IgG_1, monoclonal PRB-1, Alexa Fluor® 647 conjugate)	350 µL	7.5, 15.4	214, 183
A21306	anti-BrdU, Alexa Fluor® 660 conjugate (anti-bromodeoxyuridine, mouse IgG_1, monoclonal PRB-1, Alexa Fluor® 660 conjugate)	350 µL	7.5, 15.4	214, 183
A21301MP	anti-BrdU, biotin conjugate (anti-bromodeoxyuridine, mouse IgG_1, monoclonal PRB-1, biotin-XX conjugate)	350 µL	4.3, 7.5, 15.4	214
A21300	anti-bromodeoxyuridine, mouse IgG_1, monoclonal PRB-1 (anti-BrdU)	350 µL	7.5, 15.4	214
A21303	anti-bromodeoxyuridine, mouse IgG_1, monoclonal PRB-1, Alexa Fluor® 488 conjugate (anti-BrdU, Alexa Fluor® 488 conjugate)	350 µL	7.5, 15.4	214, 183
A21307	anti-bromodeoxyuridine, mouse IgG_1, monoclonal PRB-1, Alexa Fluor® 532 conjugate (anti-BrdU, Alexa Fluor® 532 conjugate)	350 µL	7.5, 15.4	214, 183
A21308	anti-bromodeoxyuridine, mouse IgG_1, monoclonal PRB-1, Alexa Fluor® 546 conjugate (anti-BrdU, Alexa Fluor® 546 conjugate)	350 µL	7.5, 15.4	214, 183
A21304	anti-bromodeoxyuridine, mouse IgG_1, monoclonal PRB-1, Alexa Fluor® 594 conjugate (anti-BrdU, Alexa Fluor® 594 conjugate)	350 µL	7.5, 15.4	214, 183
A21305	anti-bromodeoxyuridine, mouse IgG_1, monoclonal PRB-1, Alexa Fluor® 647 conjugate (anti-BrdU, Alexa Fluor® 647 conjugate)	350 µL	7.5, 15.4	214, 183
A21306	anti-bromodeoxyuridine, mouse IgG_1, monoclonal PRB-1, Alexa Fluor® 660 conjugate (anti-BrdU, Alexa Fluor® 660 conjugate)	350 µL	7.5, 15.4	214, 183
A21301MP	anti-bromodeoxyuridine, mouse IgG_1, monoclonal PRB-1, biotin-XX conjugate (anti-BrdU, biotin conjugate)	350 µL	4.3, 7.5, 15.4	214
A11133	anti-BSA (anti-albumin (bovine serum), rabbit IgG fraction) *2 mg/mL*	0.5 mL	7.5, 14.7	None
A6428	anti-carboxypeptidase Y (yeast vacuolar), mouse IgG_1, monoclonal 10A5 (anti-CPY)	250 µg	7.5, 12.3	226
A21330	anti-CD3, mouse IgG_1, monoclonal 289-13801 *0.2 mg/mL*	0.5 mL	7.5	None
A21331	anti-CD3, mouse IgG_1, monoclonal 289-13801, Alexa Fluor® 488 conjugate *0.2 mg/mL*	0.5 mL	7.5	183
A21332	anti-CD3, mouse IgG_1, monoclonal 289-13801, Alexa Fluor® 647 conjugate *0.2 mg/mL*	0.5 mL	7.5	183
A21333	anti-CD3, mouse IgG_1, monoclonal 289-13801, R-phycoerythrin conjugate *0.2 mg/mL*	0.5 mL	6.4, 7.5	None
A21334	anti-CD4, mouse IgG_1, monoclonal 289-14120 *0.2 mg/mL*	0.5 mL	7.5	None
A21335	anti-CD4, mouse IgG_1, monoclonal 289-14120, Alexa Fluor® 488 conjugate *0.2 mg/mL*	0.5 mL	7.5	183
A21336	anti-CD4, mouse IgG_1, monoclonal 289-14120, Alexa Fluor® 647 conjugate *0.2 mg/mL*	0.5 mL	7.5	183
A21337	anti-CD4, mouse IgG_1, monoclonal 289-14120, R-phycoerythrin conjugate *0.2 mg/mL*	0.5 mL	6.4, 7.5	None
A21338	anti-CD8, mouse IgG_{2a}, monoclonal 289-13804 *0.2 mg/mL*	0.5 mL	7.5	None
A21339	anti-CD8, mouse IgG_{2a}, monoclonal 289-13804, Alexa Fluor® 488 conjugate *0.2 mg/mL*	0.5 mL	7.5	183
A21340	anti-CD8, mouse IgG_{2a}, monoclonal 289-13804, Alexa Fluor® 647 conjugate *0.2 mg/mL*	0.5 mL	7.5	183
A21286	anti–cdc6 peptide (human), mouse IgG_{2a}, monoclonal 37F4 *for immunohistochemistry*	100 µg	7.5, 15.4	226
A21281	anti-c-myc, chicken IgY fraction *1 mg/mL*	100 µL	7.5	None
A21280	anti-c-myc, mouse IgG_1, monoclonal 289-19510 *1 mg/mL*	100 µL	7.5	None
A6428	anti-CPY (anti-carboxypeptidase Y (yeast vacuolar), mouse IgG_1, monoclonal 10A5)	250 µg	7.5, 12.3	226
A21320	anti-cyclin D1, mouse IgG_{2a}, monoclonal DCS-6	100 µg	7.5, 15.4	226
A21321	anti-cyclin D2, mouse IgG_{2b}, monoclonal DCS-5.2	100 µg	7.5, 15.4	226
A21322	anti-cyclin D3, mouse IgG_1, monoclonal DCS-22	100 µg	7.5, 15.4	226
A6403	anti-cytochrome oxidase subunit I (anti-OxPhos Complex IV subunit I, mouse IgG_{2a}, monoclonal 1D6) *human mitochondrial reactivity*	100 µg	7.5, 12.2	226

For current prices or to order online, visit probes.invitrogen.com

Cat #	Product Name	Unit Size	Sections	Limited Use Label License #
A21297	anti-cytochrome oxidase subunit I, Alexa Fluor® 594 conjugate (anti-OxPhos Complex IV subunit I, mouse IgG$_{2a}$, monoclonal 1D6, Alexa Fluor® 594 conjugate) *1 mg/mL* *human mitochondrial reactivity*	100 µL	7.5, 12.2	226, 183
A21296	anti-cytochrome oxidase subunit I, Alexa Fluor® 488 conjugate (anti-OxPhos Complex IV subunit I, mouse IgG$_{2a}$, monoclonal 1D6, Alexa Fluor® 488 conjugate) *1 mg/mL* *human mitochondrial reactivity*	100 µL	7.5, 12.2	226, 183
A6404	anti-cytochrome oxidase subunit II (anti-OxPhos Complex IV subunit II, mouse IgG$_{2a}$, monoclonal 12C4) *human mitochondrial reactivity*	100 µg	7.5, 12.2	226
A21347	anti-cytochrome oxidase subunit IV (anti-OxPhos Complex IV subunit IV, mouse IgG$_{2a}$, monoclonal 10G8) *human mitochondrial reactivity*	100 µg	7.5, 12.2	226
A21363	anti-cytochrome oxidase subunit Va (anti-OxPhos Complex IV subunit Va, mouse IgG$_{2a}$, monoclonal 6E9) *human mitochondrial reactivity*	100 µg	7.5, 12.2	226
A21349	anti-cytochrome oxidase subunit Vb (anti-OxPhos Complex IV subunit Vb, mouse IgG$_{2b}$, monoclonal 16H12) *human mitochondrial reactivity*	100 µg	7.5, 12.2	226
A21365	anti-cytochrome oxidase subunit VIa-L (anti-OxPhos Complex IV subunit VIa-L, mouse IgG$_1$, monoclonal 14A3) *human mitochondrial reactivity*	100 µg	7.5, 12.2	226
A21366	anti-cytochrome oxidase subunit VIb (anti-OxPhos Complex IV subunit VIb, mouse IgG$_1$, monoclonal 3F9) *human mitochondrial reactivity*	100 µg	7.5, 12.2	226
A6401	anti-cytochrome oxidase subunit VIc (anti-OxPhos Complex IV subunit VIc, mouse IgG$_{2b}$, monoclonal 3G5) *human mitochondrial reactivity*	100 µg	7.5, 12.2	226
A21367	anti-cytochrome oxidase subunit VIIa-H/L (anti-OxPhos Complex IV subunit VIIa-H/L, mouse IgG$_{2a}$, monoclonal 6D7) *human mitochondrial reactivity*	100 µg	7.5, 12.2	226
A21368	anti-cytochrome oxidase subunit VIIb (anti-OxPhos Complex IV subunit VIIb, mouse IgG$_1$, monoclonal 2G7) *human mitochondrial reactivity*	100 µg	7.5, 12.2	226
A21348	anti-cytochrome oxidase subunit IV (anti-OxPhos Complex IV subunit IV, mouse IgG$_{2a}$, monoclonal 20E8) *human mitochondrial reactivity*	100 µg	7.5, 12.2	226
A6405	anti-cytochrome oxidase subunit I (yeast) (anti-OxPhos Complex IV subunit I (yeast), mouse IgG$_{2b}$, monoclonal 11D8)	100 µg	7.5, 12.2	226
A6407	anti-cytochrome oxidase subunit II (yeast) (anti-OxPhos Complex IV subunit II (yeast), mouse IgG$_{2a}$, monoclonal 4B12)	250 µg	7.5, 12.2	226
A6408	anti-cytochrome oxidase subunit III (yeast) (anti-OxPhos Complex IV subunit III (yeast), mouse IgG$_{2a}$, monoclonal DA5)	250 µg	7.5, 12.2	226
A6432	anti-cytochrome oxidase subunit IV (yeast) (anti-OxPhos Complex IV subunit IV (yeast), mouse IgG$_1$, monoclonal 1A12)	250 µg	7.5, 12.2	226
A6398	anti-dansyl, rabbit IgG fraction *1 mg/mL*	0.5 mL	7.4	None
A21283	anti-desmin, mouse IgG$_1$, monoclonal 131-15014 *1 mg/mL*	100 µL	7.5, 11.2	None
A6430	anti-dinitrophenyl-KLH, rabbit IgG fraction *2 mg/mL*	0.5 mL	7.4	None
A11097	anti-dinitrophenyl-KLH, rabbit IgG fraction, Alexa Fluor® 488 conjugate *2 mg/mL*	0.5 mL	7.4	183
A6435	anti-dinitrophenyl-KLH, rabbit IgG fraction, biotin-XX conjugate *2 mg/mL*	0.5 mL	4.3, 7.4	None
A6423	anti-dinitrophenyl-KLH, rabbit IgG fraction, fluorescein conjugate *2 mg/mL*	0.5 mL	7.4	None
A6429	anti-dolichol phosphate mannose synthase (yeast), mouse IgG$_1$, monoclonal 5C5	250 µg	7.5, 12.4	226
A21316	anti-fibronectin (human), chicken IgY fraction *1 mg/mL*	0.5 mL	7.5, 15.6	None
A11095	anti-fluorescein/Oregon Green®, goat IgG fraction *1 mg/mL*	0.5 mL	7.4	None
A11096	anti-fluorescein/Oregon Green®, goat IgG fraction, Alexa Fluor® 488 conjugate *1 mg/mL*	0.5 mL	7.4	183
A6421	anti-fluorescein/Oregon Green®, mouse IgG$_{2a}$, monoclonal 4-4-20	0.5 mg	7.4	226
A6413	anti-fluorescein/Oregon Green®, rabbit IgG Fab fragment *0.5 mg/mL*	0.5 mL	7.4	None
A21254	anti-fluorescein/Oregon Green®, rabbit IgG F(ab')$_2$ fragment, horseradish peroxidase conjugate	250 µg	7.4	None
A889	anti-fluorescein/Oregon Green®, rabbit IgG fraction *1 mg/mL*	0.5 mL	7.4	226
A11090	anti-fluorescein/Oregon Green®, rabbit IgG fraction, Alexa Fluor® 488 conjugate *1 mg/mL*	0.5 mL	7.4	226, 183
A11091	anti-fluorescein/Oregon Green®, rabbit IgG fraction, Alexa Fluor® 594 conjugate *1 mg/mL*	0.5 mL	7.4	226, 183
A982	anti-fluorescein/Oregon Green®, rabbit IgG fraction, biotin-XX conjugate *1 mg/mL*	0.5 mL	4.3, 7.4	226
A21253	anti-fluorescein/Oregon Green®, rabbit IgG fraction, horseradish peroxidase conjugate	0.5 mg	7.4	None
A21250	anti-fluorescein/Oregon Green®, rabbit IgG fraction, R-phycoerythrin conjugate *2 mg/mL*	250 µL	6.4, 7.4	226
A11132	anti-β-galactosidase, rabbit IgG fraction *2 mg/mL*	0.5 mL	7.5, 10.2	None
A21282	anti-GFAP (anti-glial fibrillary acidic protein, mouse IgG$_1$, monoclonal 131-17719) *1 mg/mL*	100 µL	7.5, 11.2	None
A21294	anti-GFAP, Alexa Fluor® 488 conjugate (anti-glial fibrillary acidic protein, mouse IgG$_1$, monoclonal 131-17719, Alexa Fluor® 488 conjugate) *1 mg/mL*	50 µL	7.5, 11.2	183
A21295	anti-GFAP, Alexa Fluor® 594 conjugate (anti-glial fibrillary acidic protein, mouse IgG$_1$, monoclonal 131-17719, Alexa Fluor® 594 conjugate) *1 mg/mL*	50 µL	7.5, 11.2	183
A11122	anti-GFP, IgG (anti-green fluorescent protein, rabbit IgG fraction) *2 mg/mL*	100 µL	7.5	None
A21311	anti-GFP, IgG, Alexa Fluor® 488 conjugate (anti-green fluorescent protein, rabbit IgG fraction, Alexa Fluor® 488 conjugate) *2 mg/mL*	100 µL	7.5	183
A31851	anti-GFP, IgG, Alexa Fluor® 555 conjugate (anti-green fluorescent protein, rabbit IgG fraction, Alexa Fluor® 555 conjugate) *2 mg/mL*	100 µL	7.5	183
A21312	anti-GFP, IgG, Alexa Fluor® 594 conjugate (anti-green fluorescent protein, rabbit IgG fraction, Alexa Fluor® 594 conjugate) *2 mg/mL*	100 µL	7.5	183
A31852	anti-GFP, IgG, Alexa Fluor® 647 conjugate (anti-green fluorescent protein, rabbit IgG fraction, Alexa Fluor® 647 conjugate) *2 mg/mL*	100 µL	7.5	223
A11120	anti-GFP, mAb 3E6 (anti-green fluorescent protein, mouse IgG$_{2a}$, monoclonal 3E6)	100 µg	7.5	None

For current prices or to order online, visit probes.invitrogen.com

Cat #	Product Name	Unit Size	Sections	Limited Use Label License #
A11121	anti-GFP, mAb 11E5 (anti-green fluorescent protein, mouse IgG_1, monoclonal 11E5)	100 µg	7.5	None
A6455	anti-GFP, serum (anti-green fluorescent protein, rabbit serum)	100 µL	7.5	226
A21282	anti-glial fibrillary acidic protein, mouse IgG_1, monoclonal 131-17719 (anti-GFAP) *1 mg/mL*	100 µL	7.5, 11.2	None
A21294	anti-glial fibrillary acidic protein, mouse IgG_1, monoclonal 131-17719, Alexa Fluor® 488 conjugate (anti-GFAP, Alexa Fluor® 488 conjugate) *1 mg/mL*	50 µL	7.5, 11.2	183
A21295	anti-glial fibrillary acidic protein, mouse IgG_1, monoclonal 131-17719, Alexa Fluor® 594 conjugate (anti-GFAP, Alexa Fluor® 594 conjugate) *1 mg/mL*	50 µL	7.5, 11.2	183
A5790	anti-β-glucuronidase, rabbit IgG fraction *2 mg/mL*	0.5 mL	7.5, 10.2	None
A5800	anti-glutathione *S*-transferase, rabbit IgG fraction *3 mg/mL*	0.5 mL	7.5, 9.2	None
A11131	anti-glutathione *S*-transferase, rabbit IgG fraction, Alexa Fluor® 488 conjugate *2 mg/mL*	0.5 mL	7.5, 9.2	183
A21270	anti-Golgi (anti-golgin-97 (human), mouse IgG_1, monoclonal CDF4)	100 µg	7.5, 12.4	226
A21270	anti-golgin-97 (human), mouse IgG_1, monoclonal CDF4 (anti-Golgi)	100 µg	7.5, 12.4	226
A11120	anti-green fluorescent protein, mouse IgG_{2a}, monoclonal 3E6 (anti-GFP, mAb 3E6)	100 µg	7.5	None
A11121	anti-green fluorescent protein, mouse IgG_1, monoclonal 11E5 (anti-GFP, mAb 11E5)	100 µg	7.5	None
A11122	anti-green fluorescent protein, rabbit IgG fraction (anti-GFP, IgG) *2 mg/mL*	100 µL	7.5	None
A21311	anti-green fluorescent protein, rabbit IgG fraction, Alexa Fluor® 488 conjugate (anti-GFP, IgG, Alexa Fluor® 488 conjugate) *2 mg/mL*	100 µL	7.5	183
A31851	anti-green fluorescent protein, rabbit IgG fraction, Alexa Fluor® 555 conjugate (anti-GFP, IgG, Alexa Fluor® 555 conjugate) *2 mg/mL*	100 µL	7.5	183
A21312	anti-green fluorescent protein, rabbit IgG fraction, Alexa Fluor® 594 conjugate (anti-GFP, IgG, Alexa Fluor® 594 conjugate) *2 mg/mL*	100 µL	7.5	183
A31852	anti-green fluorescent protein, rabbit IgG fraction, Alexa Fluor® 647 conjugate (anti-GFP, IgG, Alexa Fluor® 647 conjugate) *2 mg/mL*	100 µL	7.5	223
A6455	anti-green fluorescent protein, rabbit serum (anti-GFP, serum)	100 µL	7.5	226
A21287	anti-HA, Alexa Fluor® 488 conjugate (anti-hemagglutinin, mouse IgG_1, monoclonal 16B12, Alexa Fluor® 488 conjugate) *1 mg/mL*	100 µL	7.5	226, 183
A21288	anti-HA, Alexa Fluor® 594 conjugate (anti-hemagglutinin, mouse IgG_1, monoclonal 16B12, Alexa Fluor® 594 conjugate) *1 mg/mL*	100 µL	7.5	226, 183
A6422	anti-H^+-ATPase 69 kDa subunit (yeast vacuolar), mouse IgG_{2a}, monoclonal 8B1	250 µg	7.5, 12.3	226
A6426	anti-H^+-ATPase 100 kDa subunit (yeast vacuolar), mouse IgG_{2a}, monoclonal 10D7	250 µg	7.5, 12.3	226
A6427	anti-H^+-ATPase 60 kDa subunit (yeast vacuolar), mouse IgG_1, monoclonal 13D11	250 µg	7.5, 12.3	226
A21287	anti-hemagglutinin, mouse IgG_1, monoclonal 16B12, Alexa Fluor® 488 conjugate (anti-HA, Alexa Fluor® 488 conjugate) *1 mg/mL*	100 µL	7.5	226, 183
A21288	anti-hemagglutinin, mouse IgG_1, monoclonal 16B12, Alexa Fluor® 594 conjugate (anti-HA, Alexa Fluor® 594 conjugate) *1 mg/mL*	100 µL	7.5	226, 183
A21271	anti-HuC/HuD neuronal protein (human), mouse IgG_{2b}, monoclonal 16A11	100 µg	7.5	226
A21272	anti-HuC/HuD neuronal protein (human), mouse IgG_{2b}, monoclonal 16A11, biotin-XX conjugate	100 µg	4.3, 7.5	226
A21277	anti-HuR mRNA-binding protein (human), mouse IgG_1, monoclonal 19F12	100 µg	7.5	226
A5750	anti-lucifer yellow, rabbit IgG fraction *3 mg/mL*	0.5 mL	7.4	None
A5751	anti-lucifer yellow, rabbit IgG fraction, biotin-XX conjugate *3 mg/mL*	0.5 mL	4.3, 7.4	None
A21290	anti-matrix metalloproteinase-1 (hinge region), affinity-purified rabbit antibody (anti-MMP-1) *1 mg/mL*	100 µL	7.5, 10.4	None
A21291	anti-matrix metalloproteinase-2 (hinge region), affinity-purified rabbit antibody (anti-MMP-2) *1 mg/mL*	100 µL	7.5, 10.4	None
A21292	anti-matrix metalloproteinase-3 (hinge region), affinity-purified rabbit antibody (anti-MMP-3) *1 mg/mL*	100 µL	7.5, 10.4	None
A21293	anti-matrix metalloproteinase-9 (hinge region), affinity-purified rabbit antibody (anti-MMP-9) *1 mg/mL*	100 µL	7.5, 10.4	None
A21290	anti-MMP-1 (anti-matrix metalloproteinase-1 (hinge region), affinity-purified rabbit antibody) *1 mg/mL*	100 µL	7.5, 10.4	None
A21291	anti-MMP-2 (anti-matrix metalloproteinase-2 (hinge region), affinity-purified rabbit antibody) *1 mg/mL*	100 µL	7.5, 10.4	None
A21292	anti-MMP-3 (anti-matrix metalloproteinase-3 (hinge region), affinity-purified rabbit antibody) *1 mg/mL*	100 µL	7.5, 10.4	None
A21293	anti-MMP-9 (anti-matrix metalloproteinase-9 (hinge region), affinity-purified rabbit antibody) *1 mg/mL*	100 µL	7.5, 10.4	None
A21285	anti-nitrotyrosine, rabbit IgG fraction *1 mg/mL*	0.5 mL	7.4, 18.3	None
A6473	anti-NMDA receptor, subunit 2A (rat), rabbit IgG fraction *affinity purified*	10 µg	7.5, 16.2	None
A6474	anti-NMDA receptor, subunit 2B (rat), rabbit IgG fraction *affinity purified*	10 µg	7.5, 16.2	None
A6475	anti-NMDA receptor, subunit 2C (rat), rabbit IgG fraction *affinity purified*	10 µg	7.5, 16.2	None
A21359	anti-OxPhos Complex I 17 kDa subunit, mouse IgG_{2b}, monoclonal 21C11 *human mitochondrial reactivity*	100 µg	7.5, 12.2	226
A21343	anti-OxPhos Complex I 30 kDa subunit, mouse IgG_1, monoclonal 3F9 *human mitochondrial reactivity*	100 µg	7.5, 12.2	226
A21344	anti-OxPhos Complex I 39 kDa subunit, mouse IgG_1, monoclonal 20C11 *human mitochondrial reactivity*	100 µg	7.5, 12.2	226
A11142	anti-OxPhos Complex II 70 kDa subunit, mouse IgG_1, monoclonal 2E3 *human mitochondrial reactivity*	50 µg	7.5, 12.2	226
A21345	anti-OxPhos Complex II 30 kDa subunit, mouse IgG_{2a}, monoclonal 21A11 *human mitochondrial reactivity*	100 µg	7.5, 12.2	226
A21361	anti-OxPhos Complex III 10 kDa subunit, mouse IgG_{2a}, monoclonal 1H9 *human mitochondrial reactivity*	100 µg	7.5, 12.2	226
A21362	anti-OxPhos Complex III core 1 subunit, mouse IgG_1, monoclonal 16D10 *human mitochondrial reactivity*	100 µg	7.5, 12.2	226
A11143	anti-OxPhos Complex III core 2 subunit, mouse IgG_1, monoclonal 13G12 *human mitochondrial reactivity*	100 µg	7.5, 12.2	226
A21346	anti-OxPhos Complex III subunit FeS, mouse IgG_{2b}, monoclonal 5A5 *human mitochondrial reactivity*	100 µg	7.5, 12.2	226

For current prices or to order online, visit probes.invitrogen.com

Cat #	Product Name	Unit Size	Sections	Limited Use Label License #
A6403	anti-OxPhos Complex IV subunit I, mouse IgG_{2a}, monoclonal 1D6 (anti-cytochrome oxidase subunit I) *human mitochondrial reactivity*	100 µg	7.5, 12.2	226
A21296	anti-OxPhos Complex IV subunit I, mouse IgG_{2a}, monoclonal 1D6, Alexa Fluor® 488 conjugate (anti-cytochrome oxidase subunit I, Alexa Fluor® 488 conjugate) *1 mg/mL* *human mitochondrial reactivity*	100 µL	7.5, 12.2	226, 183
A21297	anti-OxPhos Complex IV subunit I, mouse IgG_{2a}, monoclonal 1D6, Alexa Fluor® 594 conjugate (anti-cytochrome oxidase subunit I, Alexa Fluor® 594 conjugate) *1 mg/mL* *human mitochondrial reactivity*	100 µL	7.5, 12.2	226, 183
A6404	anti-OxPhos Complex IV subunit II, mouse IgG_{2a}, monoclonal 12C4 (anti-cytochrome oxidase subunit II) *human mitochondrial reactivity*	100 µg	7.5, 12.2	226
A21347	anti-OxPhos Complex IV subunit IV, mouse IgG_{2a}, monoclonal 10G8 (anti-cytochrome oxidase subunit IV) *human mitochondrial reactivity*	100 µg	7.5, 12.2	226
A21348	anti-OxPhos Complex IV subunit IV, mouse IgG_{2a}, monoclonal 20E8 (anti-cytochrome oxidase subunit IV) *human mitochondrial reactivity*	100 µg	7.5, 12.2	226
A21363	anti-OxPhos Complex IV subunit Va, mouse IgG_{2a}, monoclonal 6E9 (anti-cytochrome oxidase subunit Va) *human mitochondrial reactivity*	100 µg	7.5, 12.2	226
A21349	anti-OxPhos Complex IV subunit Vb, mouse IgG_{2b}, monoclonal 16H12 (anti-cytochrome oxidase subunit Vb) *human mitochondrial reactivity*	100 µg	7.5, 12.2	226
A21365	anti-OxPhos Complex IV subunit VIa-L, mouse IgG_1, monoclonal 14A3 (anti-cytochrome oxidase subunit VIa-L) *human mitochondrial reactivity*	100 µg	7.5, 12.2	226
A21366	anti-OxPhos Complex IV subunit VIb, mouse IgG_1, monoclonal 3F9 (anti-cytochrome oxidase subunit VIb) *human mitochondrial reactivity*	100 µg	7.5, 12.2	226
A6401	anti-OxPhos Complex IV subunit VIc, mouse IgG_{2b}, monoclonal 3G5 (anti-cytochrome oxidase subunit VIc) *human mitochondrial reactivity*	100 µg	7.5, 12.2	226
A21367	anti-OxPhos Complex IV subunit VIIa-H/L, mouse IgG_{2a}, monoclonal 6D7 (anti-cytochrome oxidase subunit VIIa-H/L) *human mitochondrial reactivity*	100 µg	7.5, 12.2	226
A21368	anti-OxPhos Complex IV subunit VIIb, mouse IgG_1, monoclonal 2G7 (anti-cytochrome oxidase subunit VIIb) *human mitochondrial reactivity*	100 µg	7.5, 12.2	226
A6405	anti-OxPhos Complex IV subunit I (yeast), mouse IgG_{2b}, monoclonal 11D8 (anti-cytochrome oxidase subunit I (yeast))	100 µg	7.5, 12.2	226
A6407	anti-OxPhos Complex IV subunit II (yeast), mouse IgG_{2a}, monoclonal 4B12 (anti-cytochrome oxidase subunit II (yeast))	250 µg	7.5, 12.2	226
A6408	anti-OxPhos Complex IV subunit III (yeast), mouse IgG_{2a}, monoclonal DA5 (anti-cytochrome oxidase subunit III (yeast))	250 µg	7.5, 12.2	226
A6432	anti-OxPhos Complex IV subunit IV (yeast), mouse IgG_1, monoclonal 1A12 (anti-cytochrome oxidase subunit IV (yeast))	250 µg	7.5, 12.2	226
A21355	anti-OxPhos Complex V inhibitor protein, mouse IgG_1, monoclonal 5E2 (anti-ATP synthase IP; anti-F_1F_0-ATPase IP) *human mitochondrial reactivity*	100 µg	7.5, 12.2	226
A21350	anti-OxPhos Complex V subunit α, mouse IgG_{2b}, monoclonal 7H10 (anti-ATP synthase subunit α; anti-F_1F_0-ATPase subunit α) *human mitochondrial reactivity*	100 µg	7.5, 12.2	226
A21351	anti-OxPhos Complex V subunit β, mouse IgG_1, monoclonal 3D5 (anti-ATP synthase subunit β; anti-F_1F_0-ATPase subunit β) *human mitochondrial reactivity*	100 µg	7.5, 12.2	226
A21353	anti-OxPhos Complex V subunit d, mouse IgG_{2b}, monoclonal 7F9 (anti-ATP synthase subunit d; anti-F_1F_0-ATPase subunit d) *human mitochondrial reactivity*	100 µg	7.5, 12.2	226
A21354	anti-OxPhos Complex V subunit OSCP, mouse IgG_1, monoclonal 4C11 (anti-ATP synthase subunit OSCP; anti-F_1F_0-ATPase subunit OSCP) *human mitochondrial reactivity*	100 µg	7.5, 12.2	226
A31856	anti-OxPhos Complex I 15 kDa subunit, mouse IgG_1, monoclonal 17G3 *human mitochondrial reactivity*	100 µg	7.5, 12.2	226
A31857	anti-OxPhos Complex I 20 kDa subunit, mouse IgG_1, monoclonal 20E9 *human mitochondrial reactivity*	100 µg	7.5, 12.2	226
A21319	anti-p21WAF1/CIP1, mouse IgG_{2a}, monoclonal DCS-60	100 µg	7.5, 15.4	226
A21323	anti-PDH E1α subunit (anti-pyruvate dehydrogenase E1α subunit (human mitochondrial), mouse IgG_1, monoclonal 9H9)	100 µg	7.5, 12.2	226
A31853	anti-PDH E1α subunit, Alexa Fluor® 594 conjugate (anti-pyruvate dehydrogenase E1α subunit (human mitochondrial), mouse IgG_1, monoclonal 9H9, Alexa Fluor® 594 conjugate) *1 mg/mL*	100 µL	7.5, 12.2	226, 183
A21324	anti-PDH E1β subunit (anti-pyruvate dehydrogenase E1β subunit (human mitochondrial), mouse IgG_1, monoclonal 17A5)	100 µg	7.5, 12.2	226
A21326	anti-PDH E2/E3bp subunit (anti-pyruvate dehydrogenase E2/E3bp subunit (human mitochondrial), mouse IgG_{2a}, monoclonal 13G2)	100 µg	7.5, 12.2	226
A21325	anti-PDH E2 subunit (anti-pyruvate dehydrogenase E2 subunit (human mitochondrial), mouse IgG_1, monoclonal 15D3)	100 µg	7.5, 12.2	226
A31854	anti-PDH E2 subunit, Alexa Fluor® 488 conjugate (anti-pyruvate dehydrogenase E2 subunit (human mitochondrial), mouse IgG_1, monoclonal 15D3, Alexa Fluor® 488 conjugate) *1 mg/mL*	100 µL	7.5, 12.2	226, 183
P21315	anti-pentahistidine (Penta·His™ mouse IgG_1, monoclonal antibody) *BSA free*	100 µg	7.5, 9.4	None
A21273	anti-Pep12p (yeast), mouse IgG_1, monoclonal 2C3 *0.5 mg/mL*	100 µL	7.5, 12.3, 12.4	None
A6457	anti-PGK (anti-3-phosphoglycerate kinase (yeast), mouse IgG_1, monoclonal 22C5)	250 µg	7.5, 12.3	226
A21327	anti-phosphatidylinositol 4,5-diphosphate, mouse IgM, monoclonal 2C11 (anti-PtdIns(4,5)P_2) *1 mg/mL*	100 µL	7.5, 17.4	226
A21328	anti-phosphatidylinositol 3,4,5-triphosphate, mouse IgM, monoclonal RC6F8 (anti-PtdIns(3,4,5)P_3) *1 mg/mL*	100 µL	7.5, 17.4	226
A6457	anti-3-phosphoglycerate kinase (yeast), mouse IgG_1, monoclonal 22C5 (anti-PGK)	250 µg	7.5, 12.3	226
A21317	anti-porin (human mitochondrial), mouse IgG_{2b}, monoclonal 20B12	100 µg	7.5, 12.2	226
A31855	anti-porin (human mitochondrial), mouse IgG_{2b}, monoclonal 31HL *1 mg/mL*	100 µL	7.5, 12.2	226
A6449	anti-porin (yeast mitochondrial), mouse IgG_1, monoclonal 16G9	250 µg	7.5, 12.2	226
A21327	anti-PtdIns(4,5)P_2 (anti-phosphatidylinositol 4,5-diphosphate, mouse IgM, monoclonal 2C11) *1 mg/mL*	100 µL	7.5, 17.4	226
A21328	anti-PtdIns(3,4,5)P_3 (anti-phosphatidylinositol 3,4,5-triphosphate, mouse IgM, monoclonal RC6F8) *1 mg/mL*	100 µL	7.5, 17.4	226
A21323	anti-pyruvate dehydrogenase E1α subunit (human mitochondrial), mouse IgG_1, monoclonal 9H9 (anti-PDH E1α subunit)	100 µg	7.5, 12.2	226

For current prices or to order online, visit probes.invitrogen.com

Cat #	Product Name	Unit Size	Sections	Limited Use Label License #
A31853	anti-pyruvate dehydrogenase E1α subunit (human mitochondrial), mouse IgG_1, monoclonal 9H9, Alexa Fluor® 594 conjugate (anti-PDH E1α subunit, Alexa Fluor® 594 conjugate) *1 mg/mL*	100 µL	7.5, 12.2	226, 183
A21324	anti-pyruvate dehydrogenase E1β subunit (human mitochondrial), mouse IgG_1, monoclonal 17A5 (anti-PDH E1β subunit)	100 µg	7.5, 12.2	226
A21325	anti-pyruvate dehydrogenase E2 subunit (human mitochondrial), mouse IgG_1, monoclonal 15D3 (anti-PDH E2 subunit)	100 µg	7.5, 12.2	226
A21326	anti-pyruvate dehydrogenase E2/E3bp subunit (human mitochondrial), mouse IgG_{2a}, monoclonal 13G2 (anti-PDH E2/E3bp subunit)	100 µg	7.5, 12.2	226
A31854	anti-pyruvate dehydrogenase E2 subunit (human mitochondrial), mouse IgG_1, monoclonal 15D3, Alexa Fluor® 488 conjugate (anti-PDH E2 subunit, Alexa Fluor® 488 conjugate) *1 mg/mL*	100 µL	7.5, 12.2	226, 183
A6442	anti-synapsin I (bovine), rabbit IgG fraction *affinity purified*	10 µg	7.5, 16.1, 17.3	None
A6397	anti-tetramethylrhodamine, rabbit IgG fraction *1 mg/mL*	0.5 mL	7.4	None
A6399	anti-Texas Red®, rabbit IgG fraction *1 mg/mL*	0.5 mL	7.4	None
A11130	anti-transferrin receptor (human), mouse IgG_1, monoclonal 236-15375	50 µg	7.5, 16.1	None
A11126	anti-α-tubulin (bovine), mouse IgG_1, monoclonal 236-10501	50 µg	7.5, 11.2	None
A21371	anti-α-tubulin (bovine), mouse IgG_1, monoclonal 236-10501, biotin-XX conjugate	50 µg	4.3, 7.5, 11.2	None
A21274	anti-Vps10p (yeast), mouse IgG_{2a}, monoclonal 18C8 *0.5 mg/mL*	500 µL	12.4	None
A350	ANTS (8-aminonaphthalene-1,3,6-trisulfonic acid, disodium salt)	1 g	3.2, 14.3	None
A13541	apamin, Alexa Fluor® 488 conjugate	25 µg	16.3	183
A13542	apamin, BODIPY® FL conjugate	25 µg	16.3	193
A35110	APC annexin V (annexin V, allophycocyanin conjugate) *50 assays*	250 µL	6.4, 15.5	213
A819	APC-XL (allophycocyanin, crosslinked) *4 mg/mL*	250 µL	6.4, 14.7	None
A36003	APF (3′-(*p*-aminophenyl) fluorescein) *5 mM solution in DMF*	470 µL	18.2	None
A23210	APO-BrdU™ TUNEL Assay Kit *with Alexa Fluor® 488 anti-BrdU* *60 assays*	1 kit	7.5, 15.5	214, 183
A6896	APTRA-BTC, AM *cell permeant*	20 x 50 µg	19.7	245
A6895	APTRA-BTC, tripotassium salt *cell impermeant*	1 mg	19.7	245
A6257	APTS (8-aminopyrene-1,3,6-trisulfonic acid, trisodium salt)	10 mg	3.2, 14.3	None
A6785	AquaLite® aequorin (aequorin) *recombinant*	25 µg	19.5	None
A21665	ARES™ Alexa Fluor® 488 DNA Labeling Kit *10 labelings*	1 kit	1.2, 1.3, 8.2	183
A21666	ARES™ Alexa Fluor® 532 DNA Labeling Kit *10 labelings*	1 kit	1.2, 1.3, 8.2	183
A21667	ARES™ Alexa Fluor® 546 DNA Labeling Kit *10 labelings*	1 kit	1.2, 1.3, 8.2	183
A21677	ARES™ Alexa Fluor® 555 DNA Labeling Kit *10 labelings*	1 kit	1.2, 1.3, 8.2	183
A21668	ARES™ Alexa Fluor® 568 DNA Labeling Kit *10 labelings*	1 kit	1.2, 1.3, 8.2	183
A21669	ARES™ Alexa Fluor® 594 DNA Labeling Kit *10 labelings*	1 kit	1.2, 1.3, 8.2	183
A21676	ARES™ Alexa Fluor® 647 DNA Labeling Kit *10 labelings*	1 kit	1.2, 1.3, 8.2	183
A21671	ARES™ Alexa Fluor® 660 DNA Labeling Kit *5-10 labelings*	1 kit	1.2, 1.3, 8.2	183
A21672	ARES™ Alexa Fluor® 680 DNA Labeling Kit *5-10 labelings*	1 kit	1.2, 1.3, 8.2	183
R2931	Arg-Glu(EDANS)-Ile-His-Pro-Phe-His-Leu-Val-Ile-His-Thr-Lys(dabcyl)-Arg (Renin Substrate 1)	1 mg	10.4	None
H2930	Arg-Glu(EDANS)-Ser-Gln-Asn-Tyr-Pro-Ile-Val-Gln-Lys(dabcyl)-Arg (HIV Protease Substrate 1)	1 mg	10.4	None
A10550	ARP (*N*-(aminooxyacetyl)-*N*′-(D-biotinoyl) hydrazine, trifluoroacetic acid salt)	10 mg	4.2, 8.2, 8.7	None
A37	2-AS (2-(9-anthroyloxy)stearic acid)	100 mg	13.2	None
A242	6-AS (6-(9-anthroyloxy)stearic acid)	25 mg	13.2	None
A2521	ATFB (4-azido-2,3,5,6-tetrafluorobenzoic acid)	100 mg	5.3	None
A2522	ATFB, SE (4-azido-2,3,5,6-tetrafluorobenzoic acid, succinimidyl ester)	25 mg	5.3	None
A10661	ATFB, STP ester (4-azido-2,3,5,6-tetrafluorobenzoic acid, STP ester, sodium salt)	10 mg	5.3	None
E23691	ε-ATP (1,N^6-ethenoadenosine 5′-triphosphate) *5 mM in buffer*	2 mL	17.3	None
A12412	ATP γ-AmNS (adenosine 5′-triphosphate, P^3-(5-sulfo-1-naphthylamide), tetra(triethylammonium) salt) *5 mM in buffer*	400 µL	17.3	None
A22066	ATP Determination Kit *special packaging* *200-1000 assays*	1 kit	10.3, 15.3	None
A7816	Attofluor® cell chamber *for microscopy*	each	23.3	232
A2333	ATTO-TAG™ CBQCA Amine-Derivatization Kit	1 kit	1.8, 9.3	244
A6222	ATTO-TAG™ CBQCA derivatization reagent (CBQCA; 3-(4-carboxybenzoyl)quinoline-2-carboxaldehyde)	10 mg	1.8, 9.2, 9.3, 21.2	244
A2334	ATTO-TAG™ FQ Amine-Derivatization Kit	1 kit	1.8, 9.3	244
A10192	ATTO-TAG™ FQ derivatization reagent (FQ; 3-(2-furoyl)quinoline-2-carboxaldehyde)	10 mg	1.8, 9.3, 21.2	244
A21370	avidin, Alexa Fluor® 488 conjugate	1 mg	7.6	183
A887	avidin, egg white	100 mg	7.6	None
A2667	avidin, egg white	5 mg	7.6	None
A821	avidin, fluorescein conjugate	5 mg	7.6	None
A11236	avidin, NeutrAvidin™, Alexa Fluor® 350 conjugate	1 mg	7.6	183
A2666	avidin, NeutrAvidin™ biotin-binding protein	5 mg	7.6	None
A2661	avidin, NeutrAvidin™, BODIPY® FL conjugate	1 mg	7.6	193
A2663	avidin, NeutrAvidin™, Cascade Blue® conjugate	1 mg	7.6	218

For current prices or to order online, visit probes.invitrogen.com

Cat #	Product Name	Unit Size	Sections	Limited Use Label License #
A2662	avidin, NeutrAvidin™, fluorescein conjugate	1 mg	7.6	None
A2664	avidin, NeutrAvidin™, horseradish peroxidase conjugate	1 mg	7.6	None
A11230	avidin, NeutrAvidin™, Marina Blue® conjugate	1 mg	7.6	192
A6374	avidin, NeutrAvidin™, Oregon Green® 488 conjugate	1 mg	7.6	191
A6378	avidin, NeutrAvidin™, Rhodamine Red™-X conjugate	1 mg	7.6	None
A2660	avidin, NeutrAvidin™, R-phycoerythrin conjugate *1 mg/mL*	1 mL	6.4, 7.6	None
A6373	avidin, NeutrAvidin™, tetramethylrhodamine conjugate	1 mg	7.6	None
A2665	avidin, NeutrAvidin™, Texas Red® conjugate	1 mg	7.6	None
A820	avidin, Texas Red® conjugate	5 mg	7.6	None
A6310	5-azidonaphthalene-1-sulfonyl chloride	10 mg	5.3	None
A1506	4-azidophenyl disulfide (4,4'-dithiobis-(phenylazide))	100 mg	5.3	None
A2521	4-azido-2,3,5,6-tetrafluorobenzoic acid (ATFB)	100 mg	5.3	None
A10661	4-azido-2,3,5,6-tetrafluorobenzoic acid, STP ester, sodium salt (ATFB, STP ester)	10 mg	5.3	None
A2522	4-azido-2,3,5,6-tetrafluorobenzoic acid, succinimidyl ester (ATFB, SE)	25 mg	5.3	None
A6311	*N*-(2-((2-(((4-azido-2,3,5,6-tetrafluoro)benzoyl)amino)ethyl)dithio)ethyl)maleimide (TFPAM-SS1)	5 mg	5.3	None
A10662	4-azido-2,3,5,6-tetrafluorobenzyl amine, hydrochloride	25 mg	5.3	None
B35000	*Bac*Light™ Green bacterial stain *special packaging*	20 x 50 µg	15.4	217
B34950	*Bac*Light™ Bacterial Membrane Potential Kit *for flow cytometry* *100 assays*	1 kit	15.3, 22.3	None
B35001	*Bac*Light™ Red bacterial stain *special packaging*	20 x 50 µg	15.4	217
B7277	Bacteria Counting Kit *for flow cytometry*	1 kit	15.4, 23.2	154
B6057	badan (6-bromoacetyl-2-dimethylaminonaphthalene)	10 mg	2.3, 3.3	None
B1205	BAPTA, AM *cell permeant*	25 mg	19.8	None
B6769	BAPTA, AM *cell permeant* *special packaging*	20 x 1 mg	19.8	None
C3047	BAPTA polystyrene (Calcium Sponge™ S)	1 g	19.8	206
B1212	BAPTA, tetracesium salt *cell impermeant*	1 g	19.8	None
B1204	BAPTA, tetrapotassium salt *cell impermeant*	1 g	19.8	None
B1214	BAPTA, tetrasodium salt *cell impermeant*	1 g	19.8	None
D1379	bBBr (dibromobimane)	25 mg	2.3, 5.2	None
B1151	BCECF acid (2',7'-bis-(2-carboxyethyl)-5-(and-6)-carboxyfluorescein) *mixed isomers*	1 mg	14.3, 20.2	None
B1150	BCECF, AM (2',7'-bis-(2-carboxyethyl)-5-(and-6)-carboxyfluorescein, acetoxymethyl ester)	1 mg	15.2, 15.6, 20.2	None
B1170	BCECF, AM (2',7'-bis-(2-carboxyethyl)-5-(and-6)-carboxyfluorescein, acetoxymethyl ester) *special packaging*	20 x 50 µg	15.2, 15.6, 20.2	None
B3051	BCECF, AM (2',7'-bis-(2-carboxyethyl)-5-(and-6)-carboxyfluorescein, acetoxymethyl ester) *1 mg/mL solution in dry DMSO*	1 mL	15.2, 15.6, 20.2	None
B6492	BCIP, Na (5-bromo-4-chloro-3-indolyl phosphate, disodium salt)	1 g	10.3	None
B14440	BCPCF acid (2',7'-bis-(3-carboxypropyl)-5-(and-6)-carboxyfluorescein) *mixed isomers*	1 mg	20.2	None
B14441	BCPCF, AM (2',7'-bis-(3-carboxypropyl)-5-(and-6)-carboxyfluorescein, acetoxymethyl ester)	1 mg	20.2	None
D7135	BDA-3000 (dextran, biotin, 3000 MW, lysine fixable)	10 mg	4.3, 14.5	None
D1956	BDA-10,000 (dextran, biotin, 10,000 MW, lysine fixable)	25 mg	4.3, 14.5	None
D1957	BDA-70,000 (dextran, biotin, 70,000 MW, lysine fixable)	25 mg	4.3, 14.5	None
D7142	BDA-500,000 (dextran, biotin, 500,000 MW, lysine fixable)	10 mg	4.3, 14.5	None
H3569	bis-benzimide (Hoechst 33258, pentahydrate) *10 mg/mL solution in water*	10 mL	8.1, 8.3, 8.6, 15.4	None
H1398	bis-benzimide (Hoechst 33258, pentahydrate)	100 mg	8.1, 8.3, 8.6, 15.4	None
H21491	bis-benzimide (Hoechst 33258, pentahydrate) *FluoroPure™ grade*	100 mg	8.1, 8.3, 8.6, 15.4	None
B1526	benzophenone-4-isothiocyanate	100 mg	5.3	None
B1508	benzophenone-4-maleimide	100 mg	5.3	None
B1577	4-benzoylbenzoic acid, succinimidyl ester	100 mg	5.3	None
B22358	2'-(or-3')-*O*-(4-benzoylbenzoyl)adenosine 5'-triphosphate, tris(triethylammonium) salt (BzBzATP) *5 mM in buffer*	2 mL	5.3, 17.3	None
B22357	2'-(or-3')-*O*-(4-benzoylbenzoyl)guanosine 5'-triphosphate, tris(triethylammonium) salt (BzBzGTP) *5 mM in buffer*	2 mL	5.3, 17.3	None
R441	benzyloxyresorufin (resorufin benzyl ether)	10 mg	10.6	None
B30633	bimane amine	5 mg	3.3	None
B30600	bimane azide	5 mg	5.3, 13.5	None
B30501	bimane C_3-maleimide	5 mg	2.3	None
B30500	bimane iodoacetamide	5 mg	2.3	None
B30250	bimane mercaptoacetic acid (carboxymethylthiobimane)	5 mg	1.7	None
B30251	bimane mercaptoacetic acid, succinimidyl ester	5 mg	1.7	None
B7884	Bioconjugate Techniques. G.T. Hermanson, Academic Press (1996); 785 pages, soft cover	each	23.6	None
B1592	biocytin (ε-biotinoyl-L-lysine)	100 mg	4.2, 14.3	None
A12924	biocytin Alexa Fluor® 488 (Alexa Fluor® 488 biocytin, disodium salt)	250 µg	4.3, 14.3	183
A12923	biocytin Alexa Fluor® 546 (Alexa Fluor® 546 biocytin, sodium salt)	250 µg	4.3, 14.3	183

For current prices or to order online, visit probes.invitrogen.com

Cat #	Product Name	Unit Size	Sections	Limited Use Label License #
A12922	biocytin Alexa Fluor® 594 (Alexa Fluor® 594 biocytin, sodium salt)	250 µg	4.3, 14.3	183
B1603	biocytin hydrazide	25 mg	4.2, 14.3	None
L6950	biocytin lucifer yellow (lucifer yellow biocytin, potassium salt)	5 mg	4.3, 14.3	None
O12920	biocytin Oregon Green® 488 (Oregon Green® 488 biocytin)	5 mg	4.3, 14.3	191
T12921	biocytin TMR (5-(and-6)-tetramethylrhodamine biocytin)	5 mg	4.3, 14.3	None
B6350	biocytin-X hydrazide (ε-(6-(biotinoyl)amino)hexanoyl-L-lysine, hydrazide)	25 mg	4.2, 14.3	None
G36000	BioGEE (glutathione ethyl ester, biotin amide) *glutathiolation detection reagent* *special packaging*	10 x 100 µg	4.3, 9.4, 15.6, 18.2	None
B20656	D-biotin *50 mM aqueous solution*	10 mL	4.2, 7.6	None
B1595	D-biotin	1 g	4.2, 7.6	None
B32766	biotin-aha-dUTP *1 mM in TE buffer*	25 µL	4.3, 8.2, 8.5	None
A1594	biotin cadaverine (*N*-(5-aminopentyl)biotinamide, trifluoroacetic acid salt)	25 mg	4.2, 14.3	None
B1550	biotin DHPE (*N*-(biotinoyl)-1,2-dihexadecanoyl-*sn*-glycero-3-phosphoethanolamine, triethylammonium salt)	10 mg	4.3, 5.2, 13.2	None
E3477	biotin EGF (epidermal growth factor, biotin-XX conjugate)	20 µg	4.3, 16.1	None
A1593	biotin ethylenediamine (*N*-(2-aminoethyl)biotinamide, hydrobromide)	25 mg	4.2, 14.3	None
B10570	biotin-4-fluorescein	5 mg	4.3, 14.3	None
B1582	6-((biotinoyl)amino)hexanoic acid, succinimidyl ester (biotin-X, SE; biotinamidocaproate, *N*-hydroxysuccinimidyl ester)	100 mg	4.2, 14.3	None
B6353	6-((biotinoyl)amino)hexanoic acid, sulfosuccinimidyl ester, sodium salt (Sulfo-NHS-LC-Biotin; biotin-X, SSE)	25 mg	4.2, 14.3	None
B1597	2-(((*N*-(biotinoyl)amino)hexanoyl)amino)ethylamine (biotin-X ethylenediamine)	10 mg	4.2, 14.3	None
B2600	6-((6-((biotinoyl)amino)hexanoyl)amino)hexanoic acid, hydrazide (biotin-XX hydrazide)	25 mg	4.2	None
B1606	6-((6-((biotinoyl)amino)hexanoyl)amino)hexanoic acid, succinimidyl ester (biotin-XX, SE)	100 mg	4.2	None
B6352	6-((6-((biotinoyl)amino)hexanoyl)amino)hexanoic acid, sulfosuccinimidyl ester, sodium salt (biotin-XX, SSE)	25 mg	4.2, 14.3	None
B1596	5-(((*N*-(biotinoyl)amino)hexanoyl)amino)pentylamine, trifluoroacetic acid salt (biotin-X cadaverine)	10 mg	4.2, 14.3	None
B1370	5-((*N*-(5-(*N*-(6-(biotinoyl)amino)hexanoyl)amino)pentyl)thioureidyl)fluorescein (fluorescein biotin)	5 mg	4.3, 14.3	None
B1616	*N*-((6-(biotinoyl)amino)hexanoyl)-1,2-dihexadecanoyl-*sn*-glycero-3-phosphoethanolamine, triethylammonium salt (biotin-X DHPE)	5 mg	4.3, 5.2, 13.2	None
B6350	ε-(6-(biotinoyl)amino)hexanoyl-L-lysine, hydrazide (biocytin-X hydrazide)	25 mg	4.2, 14.3	None
B1550	*N*-(biotinoyl)-1,2-dihexadecanoyl-*sn*-glycero-3-phosphoethanolamine, triethylammonium salt (biotin DHPE)	10 mg	4.3, 5.2, 13.2	None
B20651	ε-biotinoyl-α-(9-fluorenylmethoxycarbonyl)-L-lysine (FMOC biocytin)	25 mg	4.2, 9.5	None
B1591	*N*-(biotinoyl)-*N'*-(iodoacetyl)ethylenediamine	25 mg	4.2	None
B1592	ε-biotinoyl-L-lysine (biocytin)	100 mg	4.2, 14.3	None
B1513	D-biotin, succinimidyl ester (succinimidyl D-biotin)	100 mg	4.2, 14.3	None
B1596	biotin-X cadaverine (5-(((*N*-(biotinoyl)amino)hexanoyl)amino)pentylamine, trifluoroacetic acid salt)	10 mg	4.2, 14.3	None
B1616	biotin-X DHPE (*N*-((6-(biotinoyl)amino)hexanoyl)-1,2-dihexadecanoyl-*sn*-glycero-3-phosphoethanolamine, triethylammonium salt)	5 mg	4.3, 5.2, 13.2	None
B2604	biotin-X 2,4-dinitrophenyl-X-L-lysine, succinimidyl ester (DNP-X-biocytin-X, SE)	5 mg	4.2	248
B1597	biotin-X ethylenediamine (2-(((*N*-(biotinoyl)amino)hexanoyl)amino)ethylamine)	10 mg	4.2, 14.3	None
B11790	biotin-X nitrilotriacetic acid, tripotassium salt (biotin-X NTA)	5 mg	4.2, 9.4	None
B11790	biotin-X NTA (biotin-X nitrilotriacetic acid, tripotassium salt)	5 mg	4.2, 9.4	None
B1582	biotin-X, SE; biotinamidocaproate, *N*-hydroxysuccinimidyl ester (6-((biotinoyl)amino)hexanoic acid, succinimidyl ester)	100 mg	4.2, 14.3	None
B11027	biotin-XX F(ab')$_2$ fragment of goat anti-mouse IgG (H+L) *2 mg/mL*	250 µL	4.3, 7.2	None
B21078	biotin-XX F(ab')$_2$ fragment of goat anti-rabbit IgG (H+L) *2 mg/mL*	250 µL	4.3, 7.2	None
B2763	biotin-XX goat anti-mouse IgG (H+L) *2 mg/mL*	0.5 mL	4.3, 7.2	None
B2770	biotin-XX goat anti-rabbit IgG (H+L) *2 mg/mL*	0.5 mL	4.3, 7.2	None
B2600	biotin-XX hydrazide (6-((6-((biotinoyl)amino)hexanoyl)amino)hexanoic acid, hydrazide)	25 mg	4.2	None
B7474	biotin-XX phalloidin	50 U	4.3, 11.1	None
B1606	biotin-XX, SE (6-((6-((biotinoyl)amino)hexanoyl)amino)hexanoic acid, succinimidyl ester)	100 mg	4.2	None
B6352	biotin-XX, SSE (6-((6-((biotinoyl)amino)hexanoyl)amino)hexanoic acid, sulfosuccinimidyl ester, sodium salt)	25 mg	4.2, 14.3	None
B6357	*S*-biotinylhomocysteine	5 mg	4.3, 14.3	None
B153	bis-ANS (4,4'-dianilino-1,1'-binaphthyl-5,5'-disulfonic acid, dipotassium salt)	10 mg	11.2, 13.5	None
B7701	bis-BODIPY® FL C_{11}-PC (1,2-bis-(4,4-difluoro-5,7-dimethyl-4-bora-3a,4a-diaza-*s*-indacene-3-undecanoyl)-*sn*-glycero-3-phosphocholine)	100 µg	13.2, 17.4	193
B6847	bis-BTC, tetraammonium salt *cell impermeant*	1 mg	19.7	245
B1151	2',7'-bis-(2-carboxyethyl)-5-(and-6)-carboxyfluorescein (BCECF acid) *mixed isomers*	1 mg	14.3, 20.2	None
B1150	2',7'-bis-(2-carboxyethyl)-5-(and-6)-carboxyfluorescein, acetoxymethyl ester (BCECF, AM)	1 mg	15.2, 15.6, 20.2	None
B1170	2',7'-bis-(2-carboxyethyl)-5-(and-6)-carboxyfluorescein, acetoxymethyl ester (BCECF, AM) *special packaging*	20 x 50 µg	15.2, 15.6, 20.2	None
B3051	2',7'-bis-(2-carboxyethyl)-5-(and-6)-carboxyfluorescein, acetoxymethyl ester (BCECF, AM) *1 mg/mL solution in dry DMSO*	1 mL	15.2, 15.6, 20.2	None
B13650	α,γ-bis-(α-carboxy-2-nitrobenzyl)-L-glutamic acid, trifluoroacetic acid salt (α,γ-bis-(CNB-caged) L-glutamic acid)	5 mg	5.3, 16.2	None
B14440	2',7'-bis-(3-carboxypropyl)-5-(and-6)-carboxyfluorescein (BCPCF acid) *mixed isomers*	1 mg	20.2	None
B14441	2',7'-bis-(3-carboxypropyl)-5-(and-6)-carboxyfluorescein, acetoxymethyl ester (BCPCF, AM)	1 mg	20.2	None

For current prices or to order online, visit probes.invitrogen.com

Cat #	Product Name	Unit Size	Sections	Limited Use Label License #
A666	bis-(6-chloro-2-methoxy-9-acridinyl)spermine (acridine homodimer)	10 mg	8.1	None
B13650	α,γ-bis-(CNB-caged) L-glutamic acid (α,γ-bis-(α-carboxy-2-nitrobenzyl)-L-glutamic acid, trifluoroacetic acid salt)	5 mg	5.3, 16.2	None
B436	bis-(1,3-dibutylbarbituric acid)pentamethine oxonol ($DiBAC_4(5)$)	25 mg	16.3, 22.3	None
B438	bis-(1,3-dibutylbarbituric acid)trimethine oxonol ($DiBAC_4(3)$)	25 mg	22.3	None
B24570	bis-(1,3-dibutylbarbituric acid)trimethine oxonol ($DiBAC_4(3)$) *FluoroPure™ grade*	5 mg	22.3	None
B413	bis-(1,3-diethylthiobarbituric acid)trimethine oxonol ($DiSBAC_2(3)$)	100 mg	22.3	None
B7701	1,2-bis-(4,4-difluoro-5,7-dimethyl-4-bora-3a,4a-diaza-*s*-indacene-3-undecanoyl)-*sn*-glycero-3-phosphocholine (bis-BODIPY® FL C_{11}-PC)	100 µg	13.2, 17.4	193
B6810	bis-fura-2, hexapotassium salt *cell impermeant*	1 mg	19.2	None
D7475	bisindolylmaleimide; GF 109203X (2-(1-(3-dimethylaminopropyl)-indol-3-yl)-3-(indol-3-yl)maleimide)	~1 mg	17.3	None
B10621	bis-((*N*-iodoacetyl)piperazinyl)sulfonerhodamine	5 mg	2.2, 5.2	None
L6868	bis-*N*-methylacridinium nitrate (lucigenin) *high purity*	10 mg	12.2, 18.2, 21.2	None
B3932	(*E,E*)-3,5-bis-(4-phenyl-1,3-butadienyl)-4,4-difluoro-4-bora-3a,4a-diaza-*s*-indacene (BODIPY® 665/676)	5 mg	13.5, 18.2	193
O266	bis-(3-phenyl-5-oxoisoxazol-4-yl)pentamethine oxonol (oxonol V)	100 mg	22.3	None
B3781	1,2-bis-(1-pyrenebutanoyl)-*sn*-glycero-3-phosphocholine	1 mg	13.2, 17.4	None
B162	1,10-bis-(1-pyrene)decane	25 mg	13.5	None
B3782	1,2-bis-(1-pyrenedecanoyl)-*sn*-glycero-3-phosphocholine	1 mg	13.2, 17.4	None
B311	1,3-bis-(1-pyrenyl)propane	25 mg	13.5	None
B10710	BlockAid™ blocking solution *for use with microspheres*	50 mL	6.5, 7.6	None
B3586	BOBO™-3 iodide (570/602) *1 mM solution in DMSO*	200 µL	8.1	228
B3582	BOBO™-1 iodide (462/481) *1 mM solution in DMSO*	200 µL	8.1, 8.6	228
B30300	*N*-(*t*-BOC)-aminooxyacetic acid, tetrafluorophenyl ester	25 mg	1.8, 3.2	None
B6217	α-(*t*-BOC)-ε-dabcyl-L-lysine (α-(*t*-BOC)-ε-(4-dimethylaminophenylazobenzoyl)-L-lysine)	100 mg	9.5	None
B6217	α-(*t*-BOC)-ε-(4-dimethylaminophenylazobenzoyl)-L-lysine (α-(*t*-BOC)-ε-dabcyl-L-lysine)	100 mg	9.5	None
B6215	5-((2-(*t*-BOC)-γ-L-glutamylaminoethyl)amino)naphthalene-1-sulfonic acid (γ-EDANS-α-(*t*-BOC)-L-glutamic acid)	100 mg	9.5	None
B13233	BOCILLIN™ FL penicillin, sodium salt	1 mg	9.4, 15.2	193
B13234	BOCILLIN™ 650/665 penicillin, sodium salt	1 mg	9.4, 15.2	193
D3922	BODIPY® 493/503 (4,4-difluoro-1,3,5,7,8-pentamethyl-4-bora-3a,4a-diaza-*s*-indacene)	10 mg	13.5	193
D6103	BODIPY® 500/510 (4,4-difluoro-4-bora-3a,4a-diaza-*s*-indacene-3,5-dipropionic acid)	5 mg	1.4	193
D3921	BODIPY® 505/515 (4,4-difluoro-1,3,5,7-tetramethyl-4-bora-3a,4a-diaza-*s*-indacene)	10 mg	13.5	193
G35779	BODIPY® 515/530 GTP-γ-S, thioester (guanosine 5′-*O*-(3-thiotriphosphate), BODIPY® 515/530 thioester, sodium salt) *1 mM in buffer*	100 µL	17.3	205, 193
B3932	BODIPY® 665/676 ((*E,E*)-3,5-bis-(4-phenyl-1,3-butadienyl)-4,4-difluoro-4-bora-3a,4a-diaza-*s*-indacene)	5 mg	13.5, 18.2	193
D3825	BODIPY® 500/510 C_8, C_5 (4,4-difluoro-5-octyl-4-bora-3a,4a-diaza-*s*-indacene-3-pentanoic acid)	1 mg	13.2	193
B3824	BODIPY® 500/510 C_4, C_9 (5-butyl-4,4-difluoro-4-bora-3a,4a-diaza-*s*-indacene-3-nonanoic acid)	1 mg	13.2	193
D3823	BODIPY® 500/510 C_1, C_{12} (4,4-difluoro-5-methyl-4-bora-3a,4a-diaza-*s*-indacene-3-dodecanoic acid)	1 mg	13.2	193
D3832	BODIPY® 530/550 C_{12} (4,4-difluoro-5,7-diphenyl-4-bora-3a,4a-diaza-*s*-indacene-3-dodecanoic acid)	1 mg	13.2	193
D3835	BODIPY® 558/568 C_{12} (4,4-difluoro-5-(2-thienyl)-4-bora-3a,4a-diaza-*s*-indacene-3-dodecanoic acid)	1 mg	13.2	193
D3838	BODIPY® 564/570 C_5 (4,4-difluoro-5-styryl-4-bora-3a,4a-diaza-*s*-indacene-3-pentanoic acid)	1 mg	13.2	193
D3839	BODIPY® 564/570 C_{11} (4,4-difluoro-5-styryl-4-bora-3a,4a-diaza-*s*-indacene-3-undecanoic acid)	1 mg	13.2	193
D3859	BODIPY® 576/589 C_{11} (4,4-difluoro-5-(2-pyrrolyl)-4-bora-3a,4a-diaza-*s*-indacene-3-undecanoic acid)	1 mg	13.2	193
D3860	BODIPY® 581/591 C_5 (4,4-difluoro-5-(4-phenyl-1,3-butadienyl)-4-bora-3a,4a-diaza-*s*-indacene-3-pentanoic acid)	1 mg	13.2	193
D3861	BODIPY® 581/591 C_{11} (4,4-difluoro-5-(4-phenyl-1,3-butadienyl)-4-bora-3a,4a-diaza-*s*-indacene-3-undecanoic acid)	1 mg	13.2, 18.2	193
D3795	β-C_8-BODIPY® 500/510 C_5-HPC (2-(4,4-difluoro-5-octyl-4-bora-3a,4a-diaza-*s*-indacene-3-pentanoyl)-1-hexadecanoyl-*sn*-glycero-3-phosphocholine)	100 µg	13.2	193
B3794	β-C_4-BODIPY® 500/510 C_9-HPC (2-(5-butyl-4,4-difluoro-4-bora-3a,4a-diaza-*s*-indacene-3-nonanoyl)-1-hexadecanoyl-*sn*-glycero-3-phosphocholine)	100 µg	13.2	193
D3793	β-BODIPY® 500/510 C_{12}-HPC (2-(4,4-difluoro-5-methyl-4-bora-3a,4a-diaza-*s*-indacene-3-dodecanoyl)-1-hexadecanoyl-*sn*-glycero-3-phosphocholine)	100 µg	13.2	193
D3815	β-BODIPY® 530/550 C_5-HPC (2-(4,4-difluoro-5,7-diphenyl-4-bora-3a,4a-diaza-*s*-indacene-3-pentanoyl)-1-hexadecanoyl-*sn*-glycero-3-phosphocholine)	100 µg	13.2	193
D3806	β-BODIPY® 581/591 C_5-HPC (2-(4,4-difluoro-5-(4-phenyl-1,3-butadienyl)-4-bora-3a,4a-diaza-*s*-indacene-3-pentanoyl)-1-hexadecanoyl-*sn*-glycero-3-phosphocholine)	100 µg	13.2	193
D3799	BODIPY® 530/550 DHPE (*N*-(4,4-difluoro-5,7-diphenyl-4-bora-3a,4a-diaza-*s*-indacene-3-propionyl)-1,2-dihexadecanoyl-*sn*-glycero-3-phosphoethanolamine, triethylammonium salt)	100 µg	13.2	193
D3238	BODIPY® 492/515 disulfonate (4,4-difluoro-1,3,5,7,8-pentamethyl-4-bora-3a,4a-diaza-*s*-indacene-2,6-disulfonic acid, disodium salt)	10 mg	14.3	None
D2391	BODIPY® 530/550 EDA (4,4-difluoro-5,7-diphenyl-4-bora-3a,4a-diaza-*s*-indacene-3-propionyl ethylenediamine, hydrochloride)	5 mg	3.3	193
D2183	BODIPY® FL (4,4-difluoro-5,7-dimethyl-4-bora-3a,4a-diaza-*s*-indacene-3-propionic acid)	5 mg	1.4	193
L3485	BODIPY® FL AcLDL (low-density lipoprotein from human plasma, acetylated, BODIPY® FL conjugate) *1 mg/mL*	200 µL	16.1	193

For current prices or to order online, visit probes.invitrogen.com

Cat #	Product Name	Unit Size	Sections	Limited Use Label License #
B6905	BODIPY® FL amiloride	25 µg	16.3	193
B10250	BODIPY® FL *N*-(2-aminoethyl)maleimide	5 mg	2.2	193
B22356	BODIPY® FL AMPPNP (2′-(or-3′)-*O*-(BODIPY® FL)-β:γ-imidoadenosine 5′-triphosphate, trisodium salt) *5 mM in buffer*	50 µL	17.3	193
A12410	BODIPY® FL ATP (adenosine 5′-triphosphate, BODIPY® FL 2′-(or-3′)-*O*-(*N*-(2-aminoethyl)urethane), trisodium salt) *5 mM in buffer*	100 µL	17.3	193
A22184	BODIPY® FL ATP-γ-S, thioester (adenosine 5′-*O*-(3-thiotriphosphate), BODIPY® FL thioester, sodium salt) *5 mM in buffer*	50 µL	10.3, 17.3	193
D10620	BODIPY® FL bis-(methyleneiodoacetamide) (4,4-difluoro-3,5-di(iodoacetamidomethyl)-4-bora-3a,4a-diaza-*s*-indacene)	5 mg	2.2, 5.2	193
D7546	BODIPY® FL Br_2C_5-ceramide (*N*-(2,6-dibromo-4,4-difluoro-5,7-dimethyl-4-bora-3a,4a-diaza-*s*-indacene-3-pentanoyl)sphingosine)	250 µg	12.4, 13.3, 17.4	193
D6144	BODIPY® FL Br_2, SE (2,6-dibromo-4,4-difluoro-5,7-dimethyl-4-bora-3a,4a-diaza-*s*-indacene-3-propionic acid, succinimidyl ester)	5 mg	1.4	193
D3834	BODIPY® FL C_5 (4,4-difluoro-5,7-dimethyl-4-bora-3a,4a-diaza-*s*-indacene-3-pentanoic acid)	1 mg	1.4, 13.2	193
D3862	BODIPY® FL C_{11} (4,4-difluoro-5,7-dimethyl-4-bora-3a,4a-diaza-*s*-indacene-3-undecanoic acid)	1 mg	13.2	193
D3822	BODIPY® FL C_{12} (4,4-difluoro-5,7-dimethyl-4-bora-3a,4a-diaza-*s*-indacene-3-dodecanoic acid)	1 mg	13.2	193
D3821	BODIPY® FL C_{16} (4,4-difluoro-5,7-dimethyl-4-bora-3a,4a-diaza-*s*-indacene-3-hexadecanoic acid)	1 mg	13.2	193
D3521	BODIPY® FL C_5-ceramide (*N*-(4,4-difluoro-5,7-dimethyl-4-bora-3a,4a-diaza-*s*-indacene-3-pentanoyl)sphingosine)	250 µg	12.4, 13.3, 17.4	193
B22650	BODIPY® FL C_5-ceramide complexed to BSA	5 mg	12.4, 13.3, 17.4	193
B22621	BODIPY® FL C_5, C_6-phosphatidylinositol (BODIPY® FL C_5, C_6-PtdIns)	50 µg	13.2, 17.4	193
B22622	BODIPY® FL C_5, C_6-phosphatidylinositol 3-phosphate (BODIPY® FL C_5, C_6-PtdIns(3)P)	50 µg	13.2, 17.4	193
B22618	BODIPY® FL C_5, C_{16}-phosphatidylinositol 3-phosphate (BODIPY® FL C_5, C_{16}-PtdIns(3)P)	50 µg	13.2, 17.4	193
B22623	BODIPY® FL C_5, C_6-phosphatidylinositol 4-phosphate (BODIPY® FL C_5, C_6-PtdIns(4)P)	50 µg	13.2, 17.4	193
B22619	BODIPY® FL C_5, C_{16}-phosphatidylinositol 4-phosphate (BODIPY® FL C_5, C_{16}-PtdIns(4)P)	50 µg	13.2, 17.4	193
B22620	BODIPY® FL C_5, C_{16}-phosphatidylinositol 5-phosphate (BODIPY® FL C_5, C_{16}-PtdIns(5)P)	50 µg	13.2, 17.4	193
B22624	BODIPY® FL C_5, C_6-phosphatidylinositol 5-phosphate (BODIPY® FL C_5, C_6-PtdIns(5)P)	50 µg	13.2, 17.4	193
B22625	BODIPY® FL C_5, C_6-phosphatidylinositol 3,4-diphosphate (BODIPY® FL C_5, C_6-PtdIns(3,4)P_2)	50 µg	13.2, 17.4	193
B22615	BODIPY® FL C_5, C_6-Phosphatidylinositol 3,4-Diphosphate Cell-Labeling Kit	1 kit	13.2, 17.4	193
B22626	BODIPY® FL C_5, C_6-phosphatidylinositol 3,5-diphosphate (BODIPY® FL C_5, C_6-PtdIns(3,5)P_2)	50 µg	13.2, 17.4	193
B22627	BODIPY® FL C_5, C_6-phosphatidylinositol 4,5-diphosphate (BODIPY® FL C_5, C_6-PtdIns(4,5)P_2)	50 µg	13.2, 17.4	193
B22616	BODIPY® FL C_5, C_6-Phosphatidylinositol 4,5-Diphosphate Cell-Labeling Kit	1 kit	13.2, 17.4	193
B22628	BODIPY® FL C_5, C_6-phosphatidylinositol 3,4,5-triphosphate (BODIPY® FL C_5, C_6-PtdIns(3,4,5)P_3)	50 µg	13.2, 17.4	193
B22617	BODIPY® FL C_5, C_6-Phosphatidylinositol 3,4,5-Triphosphate Cell-Labeling Kit	1 kit	13.2, 17.4	193
B22621	BODIPY® FL C_5, C_6-PtdIns (BODIPY® FL C_5, C_6-phosphatidylinositol)	50 µg	13.2, 17.4	193
B22618	BODIPY® FL C_5, C_{16}-PtdIns(3)P (BODIPY® FL C_5, C_{16}-phosphatidylinositol 3-phosphate)	50 µg	13.2, 17.4	193
B22619	BODIPY® FL C_5, C_{16}-PtdIns(4)P (BODIPY® FL C_5, C_{16}-phosphatidylinositol 4-phosphate)	50 µg	13.2, 17.4	193
B22620	BODIPY® FL C_5, C_{16}-PtdIns(5)P (BODIPY® FL C_5, C_{16}-phosphatidylinositol 5-phosphate)	50 µg	13.2, 17.4	193
B22622	BODIPY® FL C_5, C_6-PtdIns(3)P (BODIPY® FL C_5, C_6-phosphatidylinositol 3-phosphate)	50 µg	13.2, 17.4	193
B22623	BODIPY® FL C_5, C_6-PtdIns(4)P (BODIPY® FL C_5, C_6-phosphatidylinositol 4-phosphate)	50 µg	13.2, 17.4	193
B22624	BODIPY® FL C_5, C_6-PtdIns(5)P (BODIPY® FL C_5, C_6-phosphatidylinositol 5-phosphate)	50 µg	13.2, 17.4	193
B22625	BODIPY® FL C_5, C_6-PtdIns(3,4)P_2 (BODIPY® FL C_5, C_6-phosphatidylinositol 3,4-diphosphate)	50 µg	13.2, 17.4	193
B22626	BODIPY® FL C_5, C_6-PtdIns(3,5)P_2 (BODIPY® FL C_5, C_6-phosphatidylinositol 3,5-diphosphate)	50 µg	13.2, 17.4	193
B22627	BODIPY® FL C_5, C_6-PtdIns(4,5)P_2 (BODIPY® FL C_5, C_6-phosphatidylinositol 4,5-diphosphate)	50 µg	13.2, 17.4	193
B22628	BODIPY® FL C_5, C_6-PtdIns(3,4,5)P_3 (BODIPY® FL C_5, C_6-phosphatidylinositol 3,4,5-triphosphate)	50 µg	13.2, 17.4	193
D7519	BODIPY® FL C_{12}-galactocerebroside (*N*-(4,4-difluoro-5,7-dimethyl-4-bora-3a,4a-diaza-*s*-indacene-3-dodecanoyl)sphingosyl 1-β-D-galactopyranoside)	25 µg	10.2, 13.3, 17.4	193
B13950	BODIPY® FL C_5-ganglioside G_{M1}	25 µg	13.3, 17.4	193
B34401	BODIPY® FL C_5-ganglioside G_{M1} complexed to BSA	1 mg	13.3, 17.4	193
D7548	BODIPY® FL C_5-glucocerebroside (*N*-(4,4-difluoro-5,7-dimethyl-4-bora-3a,4a-diaza-*s*-indacene-3-pentanoyl)sphingosyl 1-β-D-glucopyranoside)	250 µg	10.2, 13.3, 17.4	193
D7547	BODIPY® FL C_{12}-glucocerebroside (*N*-(4,4-difluoro-5,7-dimethyl-4-bora-3a,4a-diaza-*s*-indacene-3-dodecanoyl)sphingosyl 1-β-D-glucopyranoside)	250 µg	10.2, 13.3, 17.4	193
D3805	β-BODIPY® FL C_5-HPA (2-(4,4-difluoro-5,7-dimethyl-4-bora-3a,4a-diaza-*s*-indacene-3-pentanoyl)-1-hexadecanoyl-*sn*-glycero-3-phosphate, diammonium salt)	100 µg	13.2	193
D3803	β-BODIPY® FL C_5-HPC (2-(4,4-difluoro-5,7-dimethyl-4-bora-3a,4a-diaza-*s*-indacene-3-pentanoyl)-1-hexadecanoyl-*sn*-glycero-3-phosphocholine)	100 µg	13.2, 17.4	193
D3792	β-BODIPY® FL C_{12}-HPC (2-(4,4-difluoro-5,7-dimethyl-4-bora-3a,4a-diaza-*s*-indacene-3-dodecanoyl)-1-hexadecanoyl-*sn*-glycero-3-phosphocholine)	100 µg	13.2	193
D6003	BODIPY® FL C_1-IA (*N*-(4,4-difluoro-5,7-dimethyl-4-bora-3a,4a-diaza-*s*-indacene-3-yl)methyl)iodoacetamide)	5 mg	2.2	193
D13951	BODIPY® FL C_5-lactosylceramide (*N*-(4,4-difluoro-5,7-dimethyl-4-bora-3a,4a-diaza-*s*-indacene-3-pentanoyl)sphingosyl 1-β-D-lactoside)	25 µg	10.2, 12.4, 13.3, 17.4	193
B34402	BODIPY® FL C_5-lactosylceramide complexed to BSA	1 mg	10.2, 12.4, 13.3, 17.4	193
D6184	BODIPY® FL C_5, SE (4,4-difluoro-5,7-dimethyl-4-bora-3a,4a-diaza-*s*-indacene-3-pentanoic acid, succinimidyl ester)	5 mg	1.4	193

For current prices or to order online, visit probes.invitrogen.com

Cat #	Product Name	Unit Size	Sections	Limited Use Label License #
D3522	BODIPY® FL C_5-sphingomyelin (*N*-(4,4-difluoro-5,7-dimethyl-4-bora-3a,4a-diaza-*s*-indacene-3-pentanoyl)sphingosyl phosphocholine)	250 µg	12.4, 13.3, 17.4	193
D7711	BODIPY® FL C_{12}-sphingomyelin (*N*-(4,4-difluoro-5,7-dimethyl-4-bora-3a,4a-diaza-*s*-indacene-3-dodecanoyl)sphingosyl phosphocholine) *1 mg/mL in DMSO*	250 µL	12.4, 13.3, 17.4	193
B20340	BODIPY® FL L-cystine	1 mg	2.2	193
D3800	BODIPY® FL DHPE (*N*-(4,4-difluoro-5,7-dimethyl-4-bora-3a,4a-diaza-*s*-indacene-3-propionyl)-1,2-dihexadecanoyl-*sn*-glycero-3-phosphoethanolamine, triethylammonium salt)	100 µg	13.2	193
D12656	BODIPY® FL dicaproyl PE (*N*-(4,4-difluoro-5,7-dimethyl-4-bora-3a,4a-diaza-*s*-indacene-3-propionyl)-1,2-dihexanoyl-*sn*-glycero-3-phosphoethanolamine, triethylammonium salt)	100 µg	13.2	193
B23460	BODIPY® FL digoxigenin	100 µg	16.3	193
D2390	BODIPY® FL EDA (4,4-difluoro-5,7-dimethyl-4-bora-3a,4a-diaza-*s*-indacene-3-propionyl ethylenediamine, hydrochloride)	5 mg	3.3	193
B7469	BODIPY® FL forskolin	100 µg	15.6, 17.3	193
G22360	BODIPY® FL GDP (guanosine 5′-diphosphate, BODIPY® FL 2′-(or-3′)-*O*-(*N*-(2-aminoethyl)urethane), bis(triethylammonium) salt) *5 mM in water*	100 µL	17.3	193
B7439	BODIPY® FL glibenclamide (BODIPY® FL glyburide)	100 µg	16.3	193
B7439	BODIPY® FL glyburide (BODIPY® FL glibenclamide)	100 µg	16.3	193
B22355	BODIPY® FL GMPPNP (2′-(or-3′)-*O*-(BODIPY® FL)-β:γ-imidoguanosine 5′-triphosphate, trisodium salt) *5 mM in buffer*	50 µL	17.3	193
B2752	BODIPY® FL goat anti-mouse IgG (H+L)	1 mg	7.2	193
B2766	BODIPY® FL goat anti-rabbit IgG (H+L)	1 mg	7.2	193
G12411	BODIPY® FL GTP (guanosine 5′-triphosphate, BODIPY® FL 2′-(or-3′)-*O*-(*N*-(2-aminoethyl)urethane), trisodium salt) *5 mM in water*	100 µL	17.3	193
G35778	BODIPY® FL GTP-γ-NH, amide (guanosine 5′-*O*-(3-iminotriphosphate), BODIPY® FL ethylamide, sodium salt) *1 mM in buffer*	100 µL	17.3	205, 193
G22183	BODIPY® FL GTP-γ-S, thioester (guanosine 5′-*O*-(3-thiotriphosphate), BODIPY® FL thioester, sodium salt) *5 mM in buffer*	50 µL	10.3, 17.3	205, 193
B22461	BODIPY® FL histamine	1 mg	12.3	193
H23379	BODIPY® FL hyaluronic acid (hyaluronic acid, BODIPY® FL conjugate)	500 µg	16.1	193
D2371	BODIPY® FL hydrazide (4,4-difluoro-5,7-dimethyl-4-bora-3a,4a-diaza-*s*-indacene-3-propionic acid, hydrazide)	5 mg	3.2	193
B22356	2′-(or-3′)-*O*-(BODIPY® FL)-β:γ-imidoadenosine 5′-triphosphate, trisodium salt (BODIPY® FL AMPPNP) *5 mM in buffer*	50 µL	17.3	193
B22355	2′-(or-3′)-*O*-(BODIPY® FL)-β:γ-imidoguanosine 5′-triphosphate, trisodium salt (BODIPY® FL GMPPNP) *5 mM in buffer*	50 µL	17.3	193
B13510	BODIPY® FL ivermectin *mixed isomers*	100 µg	16.3	193
L3483	BODIPY® FL LDL (low-density lipoprotein from human plasma, BODIPY® FL complex) *1 mg/mL*	200 µL	16.1	193
M23272	BODIPY® FL methotrexate (methotrexate, BODIPY® FL)	500 µg	15.6	193
B23461	BODIPY® FL ouabain	100 µg	16.3	193
B607	BODIPY® FL phallacidin	300 U	11.1	193
D7441	BODIPY® FL phenylalkylamine (DM-BODIPY® PAA)	25 µg	16.3	193
B7436	BODIPY® FL pirenzepine, hydrochloride	100 µg	16.2	193
B3460	BODIPY® FL PPHT	200 µg	16.2	193
B7433	BODIPY® FL prazosin	100 µg	15.6, 16.2	193
B3420	BODIPY® FL SCH 23390	1 mg	16.2	193
D2184	BODIPY® FL, SE (4,4-difluoro-5,7-dimethyl-4-bora-3a,4a-diaza-*s*-indacene-3-propionic acid, succinimidyl ester)	5 mg	1.4	193
D6140	BODIPY® FL, SSE (4,4-difluoro-5,7-dimethyl-4-bora-3a,4a-diaza-*s*-indacene-3-propionic acid, sulfosuccinimidyl ester, sodium salt)	5 mg	1.4	193
B10006	BODIPY® FL, STP ester, sodium salt	5 mg	1.4	193
P7500	BODIPY® FL Taxol (paclitaxel, BODIPY® FL conjugate)	10 µg	11.2	193
B7487	BODIPY® FL thapsigargin	100 µg	17.2	193
V34850	BODIPY® FL vancomycin (vancomycin, BODIPY® FL conjugate)	100 µg	15.2	193
B7431	BODIPY® FL verapamil, hydrochloride	1 mg	15.6, 16.3	193
V12390	BODIPY® FL vinblastine (vinblastine, BODIPY® FL conjugate)	100 µg	11.2, 15.6	193
D6101	BODIPY® FL-X (6-((4,4-difluoro-5,7-dimethyl-4-bora-3a,4a-diaza-*s*-indacene-3-propionyl)amino)hexanoic acid)	5 mg	1.4	193
B7505	BODIPY® FL-X ryanodine	25 µg	16.3, 17.2	193
D6102	BODIPY® FL-X, SE (6-((4,4-difluoro-5,7-dimethyl-4-bora-3a,4a-diaza-*s*-indacene-3-propionyl)amino)hexanoic acid, succinimidyl ester)	5 mg	1.4, 4.2, 9.3	193
D6004	BODIPY® 507/545 IA (*N*-(4,4-difluoro-1,3,5,7-tetramethyl-4-bora-3a,4a-diaza-*s*-indacene-2-yl)iodoacetamide)	5 mg	2.2	193
D2006	BODIPY® 530/550 IA (*N*-(4,4-difluoro-5,7-diphenyl-4-bora-3a,4a-diaza-*s*-indacene-3-propionyl)-*N*′-iodoacetylethylenediamine)	5 mg	2.2	193
D20350	BODIPY® 499/508 maleimide (4,4-difluoro-1,3,5,7-tetramethyl-8-(4-maleimidylphenyl)-4-bora-3a,4a-diaza-*s*-indacene)	5 mg	2.2	None
D20351	BODIPY® 577/618 maleimide (4,4-difluoro-3,5-bis(4-methoxyphenyl)-8-(4-maleimidylphenyl)-4-bora-3a,4a-diaza-*s*-indacene)	5 mg	2.2	None
B2103	BODIPY® 493/503 methyl bromide (8-bromomethyl-4,4-difluoro-1,3,5,7-tetramethyl-4-bora-3a,4a-diaza-*s*-indacene)	5 mg	2.2, 3.3, 14.2	212
B22802	BODIPY® 630/650 methyl bromide (8-bromomethyl-4,4-difluoro-3,5-bis-(2-thienyl)-4-bora-3a,4a-diaza-*s*-indacene)	1 mg	2.2, 3.3, 14.2	193
B3475	BODIPY® 558/568 phalloidin	300 U	11.1	193
B3416	BODIPY® 581/591 phalloidin	300 U	11.1	193
B12382	BODIPY® 650/665 phalloidin	300 U	11.1	193

For current prices or to order online, visit probes.invitrogen.com

Cat #	Product Name	Unit Size	Sections	Limited Use Label License #
B7437	BODIPY® 558/568 pirenzepine, hydrochloride	100 µg	16.2	193
B7434	BODIPY® 558/568 prazosin	100 µg	15.6, 16.2	193
G22350	BODIPY® R6G GTP (guanosine 5′-triphosphate, BODIPY® R6G 2′-(or-3′)-*O*-(*N*-(2-aminoethyl)urethane), trisodium salt) *5 mM in water*	100 µL	17.3	193
D6180	BODIPY® R6G, SE (4,4-difluoro-5-phenyl-4-bora-3a,4a-diaza-*s*-indacene-3-propionic acid, succinimidyl ester)	5 mg	1.4	193
D6186	BODIPY® R6G-X, SE (6-((4,4-difluoro-5-phenyl-4-bora-3a,4a-diaza-*s*-indacene-3-propionyl)amino)hexanoic acid, succinimidyl ester)	5 mg	1.4	193
D2191	BODIPY® 493/503, SE (4,4-difluoro-1,3,5,7-tetramethyl-4-bora-3a,4a-diaza-*s*-indacene-8-propionic acid, succinimidyl ester)	5 mg	1.4	None
D2187	BODIPY® 530/550, SE (4,4-difluoro-5,7-diphenyl-4-bora-3a,4a-diaza-*s*-indacene-3-propionic acid, succinimidyl ester)	5 mg	1.4	193
D2219	BODIPY® 558/568, SE (4,4-difluoro-5-(2-thienyl)-4-bora-3a,4a-diaza-*s*-indacene-3-propionic acid, succinimidyl ester)	5 mg	1.4	193
D2222	BODIPY® 564/570, SE (4,4-difluoro-5-styryl-4-bora-3a,4a-diaza-*s*-indacene-3-propionic acid, succinimidyl ester)	5 mg	1.4	193
D2225	BODIPY® 576/589, SE (4,4-difluoro-5-(2-pyrrolyl)-4-bora-3a,4a-diaza-*s*-indacene-3-propionic acid, succinimidyl ester)	5 mg	1.4	193
D2228	BODIPY® 581/591, SE (4,4-difluoro-5-(4-phenyl-1,3-butadienyl)-4-bora-3a,4a-diaza-*s*-indacene-3-propionic acid, succinimidyl ester)	5 mg	1.4	193
P7501	BODIPY® 564/570 Taxol (paclitaxel, BODIPY® 564/570 conjugate)	10 µg	11.2	193
D6012	BODIPY® TMR cadaverine IA (*N*-(5-((4,4-difluoro-1,3-dimethyl-5-(4-methoxyphenyl)-4-bora-3a,4a-diaza-*s*-indacene-2-propionyl)amino)pentyl)iodoacetamide)	5 mg	2.2	193
B10002	BODIPY® TMR, STP ester, sodium salt	5 mg	1.4	193
B22637	BODIPY® TMR-X C_6-PtdIns(4,5)P_2 (BODIPY® TMR-X C_6-phosphatidylinositol 4,5-diphosphate)	50 µg	13.2, 17.4	193
B22631	BODIPY® TMR-X C_6-phosphatidylinositol (BODIPY® TMR-X C_6-PtdIns)	50 µg	13.2, 17.4	193
B22632	BODIPY® TMR-X C_6-phosphatidylinositol 3-phosphate (BODIPY® TMR-X C_6-PtdIns(3)P)	50 µg	13.2, 17.4	193
B22633	BODIPY® TMR-X C_6-phosphatidylinositol 4-phosphate (BODIPY® TMR-X C_6-PtdIns(4)P)	50 µg	13.2, 17.4	193
B22634	BODIPY® TMR-X C_6-phosphatidylinositol 5-phosphate (BODIPY® TMR-X C_6-PtdIns(5)P)	50 µg	13.2, 17.4	193
B22635	BODIPY® TMR-X C_6-phosphatidylinositol 3,4-diphosphate (BODIPY® TMR-X C_6-PtdIns(3,4)P_2)	50 µg	13.2, 17.4	193
B22636	BODIPY® TMR-X C_6-phosphatidylinositol 3,5-diphosphate (BODIPY® TMR-X C_6-PtdIns(3,5)P_2)	50 µg	13.2, 17.4	193
B22637	BODIPY® TMR-X C_6-phosphatidylinositol 4,5-diphosphate (BODIPY® TMR-X C_6-PtdIns(4,5)P_2)	50 µg	13.2, 17.4	193
B22638	BODIPY® TMR-X C_6-phosphatidylinositol 3,4,5-triphosphate (BODIPY® TMR-X C_6-PtdIns(3,4,5)P_3)	50 µg	13.2, 17.4	193
B22631	BODIPY® TMR-X C_6-PtdIns (BODIPY® TMR-X C_6-phosphatidylinositol)	50 µg	13.2, 17.4	193
B22632	BODIPY® TMR-X C_6-PtdIns(3)P (BODIPY® TMR-X C_6-phosphatidylinositol 3-phosphate)	50 µg	13.2, 17.4	193
B22633	BODIPY® TMR-X C_6-PtdIns(4)P (BODIPY® TMR-X C_6-phosphatidylinositol 4-phosphate)	50 µg	13.2, 17.4	193
B22634	BODIPY® TMR-X C_6-PtdIns(5)P (BODIPY® TMR-X C_6-phosphatidylinositol 5-phosphate)	50 µg	13.2, 17.4	193
B22635	BODIPY® TMR-X C_6-PtdIns(3,4)P_2 (BODIPY® TMR-X C_6-phosphatidylinositol 3,4-diphosphate)	50 µg	13.2, 17.4	193
B22636	BODIPY® TMR-X C_6-PtdIns(3,5)P_2 (BODIPY® TMR-X C_6-phosphatidylinositol 3,5-diphosphate)	50 µg	13.2, 17.4	193
B22638	BODIPY® TMR-X C_6-PtdIns(3,4,5)P_3 (BODIPY® TMR-X C_6-phosphatidylinositol 3,4,5-triphosphate)	50 µg	13.2, 17.4	193
D6117	BODIPY® TMR-X, SE (6-((4,4-difluoro-1,3-dimethyl-5-(4-methoxyphenyl)-4-bora-3a,4a-diaza-*s*-indacene-2-propionyl)amino)hexanoic acid, succinimidyl ester)	5 mg	1.4	193
A22359	BODIPY® TR ADP (adenosine 5′-diphosphate, BODIPY® TR 2′-(or-3′)-*O*-(*N*-(2-aminoethyl)urethane), disodium salt) *5 mM in buffer*	100 µL	17.3	193
A22352	BODIPY® TR ATP (adenosine 5′-triphosphate, BODIPY® TR 2′-(or-3′)-*O*-(*N*-(2-aminoethyl)urethane), trisodium salt) *5 mM in buffer*	100 µL	17.3	193
D6251	BODIPY® TR cadaverine (5-(((4-(4,4-difluoro-5-(2-thienyl)-4-bora-3a,4a-diaza-*s*-indacene-3-yl)phenoxy)acetyl)amino) pentylamine, hydrochloride)	5 mg	3.3	193
B34400	BODIPY® TR C_5-ceramide complexed to BSA	5 mg	12.4, 13.3, 17.4	193
D7540	BODIPY® TR ceramide (*N*-((4-(4,4-difluoro-5-(2-thienyl)-4-bora-3a,4a-diaza-*s*-indacene-3-yl)phenoxy)acetyl)sphingosine)	250 µg	12.4, 13.3, 17.4	193
B13540	BODIPY® TR glibenclamide (BODIPY® TR glyburide)	100 µg	16.3	193
B13540	BODIPY® TR glyburide (BODIPY® TR glibenclamide)	100 µg	16.3	193
G22351	BODIPY® TR GTP (guanosine 5′-triphosphate, BODIPY® TR 2′-(or-3′)-*O*-(*N*-(2-aminoethyl)urethane), trisodium salt) *5 mM in water*	100 µL	17.3	193
G35780	BODIPY® TR GTP-γ-S, thioester (guanosine 5′-*O*-(3-thiotriphosphate), BODIPY® TR thioester, sodium salt) *1 mM in buffer*	100 µL	17.3	205, 193
B22641	BODIPY® TR-X C_6-phosphatidylinositol (BODIPY® TR-X C_6-PtdIns)	50 µg	13.2, 17.4	193
B22642	BODIPY® TR-X C_6-phosphatidylinositol 3-phosphate (BODIPY® TR-X C_6-PtdIns(3)P)	50 µg	13.2, 17.4	193
B22643	BODIPY® TR-X C_6-phosphatidylinositol 4-phosphate (BODIPY® TR-X C_6-PtdIns(4)P)	50 µg	13.2, 17.4	193
B22644	BODIPY® TR-X C_6-phosphatidylinositol 5-phosphate (BODIPY® TR-X C_6-PtdIns(5)P)	50 µg	13.2, 17.4	193
B22645	BODIPY® TR-X C_6-phosphatidylinositol 3,4-diphosphate (BODIPY® TR-X C_6-PtdIns(3,4)P_2)	50 µg	13.2, 17.4	193
B22646	BODIPY® TR-X C_6-phosphatidylinositol 3,5-diphosphate (BODIPY® TR-X C_6-PtdIns(3,5)P_2)	50 µg	13.2, 17.4	193
B22647	BODIPY® TR-X C_6-phosphatidylinositol 4,5-diphosphate (BODIPY® TR-X C_6-PtdIns(4,5)P_2)	50 µg	13.2, 17.4	193
B22648	BODIPY® TR-X C_6-phosphatidylinositol 3,4,5-triphosphate (BODIPY® TR-X C_6-PtdIns(3,4,5)P_3)	50 µg	13.2, 17.4	193
B22641	BODIPY® TR-X C_6-PtdIns (BODIPY® TR-X C_6-phosphatidylinositol)	50 µg	13.2, 17.4	193
B22642	BODIPY® TR-X C_6-PtdIns(3)P (BODIPY® TR-X C_6-phosphatidylinositol 3-phosphate)	50 µg	13.2, 17.4	193
B22643	BODIPY® TR-X C_6-PtdIns(4)P (BODIPY® TR-X C_6-phosphatidylinositol 4-phosphate)	50 µg	13.2, 17.4	193

For current prices or to order online, visit probes.invitrogen.com

Cat #	Product Name	Unit Size	Sections	Limited Use Label License #
B22644	BODIPY® TR-X C_6-PtdIns(5)P (BODIPY® TR-X C_6-phosphatidylinositol 5-phosphate)	50 µg	13.2, 17.4	193
B22645	BODIPY® TR-X C_6-PtdIns(3,4)P_2 (BODIPY® TR-X C_6-phosphatidylinositol 3,4-diphosphate)	50 µg	13.2, 17.4	193
B22646	BODIPY® TR-X C_6-PtdIns(3,5)P_2 (BODIPY® TR-X C_6-phosphatidylinositol 3,5-diphosphate)	50 µg	13.2, 17.4	193
B22647	BODIPY® TR-X C_6-PtdIns(4,5)P_2 (BODIPY® TR-X C_6-phosphatidylinositol 4,5-diphosphate)	50 µg	13.2, 17.4	193
B22648	BODIPY® TR-X C_6-PtdIns(3,4,5)P_3 (BODIPY® TR-X C_6-phosphatidylinositol 3,4,5-triphosphate)	50 µg	13.2, 17.4	193
B13511	BODIPY® TR-X ivermectin *mixed isomers*	100 µg	16.3	193
B7464	BODIPY® TR-X phallacidin	300 U	11.1	193
D6116	BODIPY® TR-X, SE (6-(((4-(4,4-difluoro-5-(2-thienyl)-4-bora-3a,4a-diaza-*s*-indacene-3-yl)phenoxy)acetyl)amino)hexanoic acid, succinimidyl ester)	5 mg	1.4, 9.3	193
B10003	BODIPY® TR-X, STP ester, sodium salt	5 mg	1.4	193
B13800	BODIPY® TR-X thapsigargin	25 µg	17.2	193
D10001	BODIPY® 650/665-X, SE (6-(((4,4-difluoro-5-(2-pyrrolyl)-4-bora-3a,4a-diaza-*s*-indacene-3-yl)styryloxy)acetyl)aminohexanoic acid, succinimidyl ester)	5 mg	1.4	193
B10005	BODIPY® 650/665-X, STP ester, sodium salt	5 mg	1.4	193
B21901	BOLD™ APB chemiluminescent substrate *for membrane-based alkaline phosphatase detection* *25 minigel blots*	25 mL	8.5, 9.4, 10.3	None
B3583	BO-PRO™-1 iodide (462/481) *1 mM solution in DMSO*	1 mL	8.1	209
B3587	BO-PRO™-3 iodide (575/599) *1 mM solution in DMSO*	1 mL	8.1	209
D7766	Br_2-DiIC_{18}(3) (5,5′-dibromo-1,1′-dioctadecyl-3,3,3′,3′-tetramethylindocarbocyanine perchlorate)	5 mg	13.4, 14.4	None
B23151	BrdU (5-bromo-2′-deoxyuridine)	100 mg	8.2, 15.4	None
B21550	BrdUTP (5-bromo-2′-deoxyuridine 5′-triphosphate) *10 mM in TE buffer*	25 µL	8.2, 15.4	None
B7450	brefeldin A *from *Penicillium brefeldianum**	5 mg	12.4	None
B7449	brefeldin A, BODIPY® 558/568 conjugate *isomer 1*	25 µg	12.4	193
B7447	brefeldin A, BODIPY® FL conjugate *isomer 1*	25 µg	12.4	193
B1690	5-bromo-4-chloro-3-indolyl β-D-galactopyranoside (X-Gal)	1 g	10.2	None
B22015	5-bromo-4-chloro-3-indolyl β-D-galactopyranoside (X-Gal) *bulk packaging*	25 g	10.2	None
B1689	5-bromo-4-chloro-3-indolyl β-D-glucopyranoside (X-Glu)	100 mg	10.2	None
B1691	5-bromo-4-chloro-3-indolyl β-D-glucuronide, cyclohexylammonium salt (X-GlcU, CHA)	100 mg	10.2	None
B6492	5-bromo-4-chloro-3-indolyl phosphate, disodium salt (BCIP, Na)	1 g	10.3	None
B8408	5-bromo-6-chloro-3-indolyl β-D-glucuronide, cyclohexylammonium salt	25 mg	10.2	None
B6057	6-bromoacetyl-2-dimethylaminonaphthalene (badan)	10 mg	2.3, 3.3	None
B7108	4-bromo A-23187, 1-(4,5-dimethoxy-2-nitrophenyl)ethyl ester (DMNPE-caged Br A-23187)	1 mg	5.3, 19.8	249
B1494	4-bromo A-23187, free acid	1 mg	19.8	None
B23151	5-bromo-2′-deoxyuridine (BrdU)	100 mg	8.2, 15.4	None
B21550	5-bromo-2′-deoxyuridine 5′-triphosphate (BrdUTP) *10 mM in TE buffer*	25 µL	8.2, 15.4	None
B22802	8-bromomethyl-4,4-difluoro-3,5-bis-(2-thienyl)-4-bora-3a,4a-diaza-*s*-indacene (BODIPY® 630/650 methyl bromide)	1 mg	2.2, 3.3, 14.2	193
B2103	8-bromomethyl-4,4-difluoro-1,3,5,7-tetramethyl-4-bora-3a,4a-diaza-*s*-indacene (BODIPY® 493/503 methyl bromide)	5 mg	2.2, 3.3, 14.2	212
B1355	5-(bromomethyl)fluorescein	10 mg	2.2, 3.3	None
B21551	5-bromouridine 5′-triphosphate (BrUTP) *10 mM in TE buffer*	25 µL	8.2, 15.4	None
T7017	Br_4TFFDA (2′,4′,5′,7′-tetrabromo-4,5,6,7-tetrafluorofluorescein diacetate)	5 mg	14.2	None
B21551	BrUTP (5-bromouridine 5′-triphosphate) *10 mM in TE buffer*	25 µL	8.2, 15.4	None
B6791	BTC, AM *cell permeant* *special packaging*	20 x 50 µg	19.2	245
B6790	BTC, tetrapotassium salt *cell impermeant*	1 mg	19.2	245
B6846	BTC-5N, AM *cell permeant* *special packaging*	20 x 50 µg	19.7	245
B6845	BTC-5N, tetrapotassium salt *cell impermeant*	1 mg	19.7	245
B1601	α-bungarotoxin *from *Bungarus multicinctus**	1 mg	16.2	None
B13422	α-bungarotoxin, Alexa Fluor® 488 conjugate	500 µg	16.2	183
B13423	α-bungarotoxin, Alexa Fluor® 594 conjugate	500 µg	16.2	183
B35450	α-bungarotoxin, Alexa Fluor® 647 conjugate	500 µg	16.2	None
B1196	α-bungarotoxin, biotin-XX conjugate	500 µg	4.3, 16.2	None
F1176	α-bungarotoxin, fluorescein conjugate (fluorescein α-bungarotoxin)	500 µg	16.2	None
B7488	α-bungarotoxin, Oregon Green® 514 conjugate	500 µg	16.2	191
T1175	α-bungarotoxin, tetramethylrhodamine conjugate (tetramethylrhodamine α-bungarotoxin)	500 µg	16.2	None
B3824	5-butyl-4,4-difluoro-4-bora-3a,4a-diaza-*s*-indacene-3-nonanoic acid (BODIPY® 500/510 C_4, C_9)	1 mg	13.2	193
B3794	2-(5-butyl-4,4-difluoro-4-bora-3a,4a-diaza-*s*-indacene-3-nonanoyl)-1-hexadecanoyl-*sn*-glycero-3-phosphocholine (β-C_4-BODIPY® 500/510 C_9-HPC)	100 µg	13.2	193
R6501	BZAR (rhodamine 110, bis-(CBZ-L-arginine amide), dihydrochloride)	5 mg	10.4	None
B22358	BzBzATP (2′-(or-3′)-*O*-(4-benzoylbenzoyl)adenosine 5′-triphosphate, tris(triethylammonium) salt) *5 mM in buffer*	2 mL	5.3, 17.3	None
B22357	BzBzGTP (2′-(or-3′)-*O*-(4-benzoylbenzoyl)guanosine 5′-triphosphate, tris(triethylammonium) salt) *5 mM in buffer*	2 mL	5.3, 17.3	None
R6505	BZiPAR (rhodamine 110, bis-(CBZ-L-isoleucyl-L-prolyl-L-arginine amide), dihydrochloride)	5 mg	10.4	None

For current prices or to order online, visit probes.invitrogen.com

Cat #	Product Name	Unit Size	Sections	Limited Use Label License #
C7619	cADP-ribose (cyclic adenosine 5′-diphosphate ribose)	100 µg	17.2	None
P7071	caged oxygen ((µ-peroxo) (µ-hydroxo)bis(bis(bipyridyl)cobalt(III)) perchlorate)	25 mg	5.3, 18.2	None
C481	calcein *high purity*	100 mg	14.3, 16.1, 19.7	None
C1430	calcein, AM	1 mg	14.3, 15.2, 15.6, 19.7	None
C3099	calcein, AM *1 mg/mL solution in dry DMSO*	1 mL	14.3, 15.2, 15.6, 19.7	None
C3100MP	calcein, AM *special packaging*	20 x 50 µg	14.3, 15.2, 15.6, 19.7	None
C1429	calcein blue, AM	1 mg	15.2	None
A1493	calcimycin (A-23187 free acid)	10 mg	19.8	None
C3723	Calcium Calibration Buffer Concentrate Kit *zero and 100 mM CaEGTA (2 x 5 mL)*	1 kit	19.8	None
C3008MP	Calcium Calibration Buffer Kit #1 *zero and 10 mM CaEGTA (2 x 50 mL)*	1 kit	19.8	None
C3009	Calcium Calibration Buffer Kit #2 *zero to 10 mM CaEGTA (11 x 10 mL)*	1 kit	19.8	None
C6775	Calcium Calibration Buffer Kit #3 *1 µM to 1 mM range (11 x 10 mL)*	1 kit	19.8	None
C3721	Calcium Calibration Buffer Kit with Magnesium #1 *zero and 10 mM CaEGTA with 1 mM Mg^{2+} (2 x 50 mL)*	1 kit	19.8	None
C3722	Calcium Calibration Buffer Kit with Magnesium #2 *zero to 10 mM CaEGTA with 1 mM Mg^{2+} (11 x 10 mL)*	1 kit	19.8	None
C3018	Calcium Crimson™, AM *cell permeant* *special packaging*	10 x 50 µg	19.3	206
C3011MP	Calcium Green™-1, AM *cell permeant*	500 µg	19.3	206
C3012	Calcium Green™-1, AM *cell permeant* *special packaging*	10 x 50 µg	19.3	206
C6765	Calcium Green™-1 dextran, potassium salt, 3000 MW, anionic	5 mg	19.4	206
C3713	Calcium Green™-1 dextran, potassium salt, 10,000 MW, anionic	5 mg	19.4	206
C3714	Calcium Green™-1 dextran, potassium salt, 70,000 MW, anionic	5 mg	19.4	206
C6766	Calcium Green™-1 dextran, potassium salt, 500,000 MW, anionic	5 mg	19.4	206
C3010MP	Calcium Green™-1, hexapotassium salt *cell impermeant*	500 µg	19.3	206
C3732	Calcium Green™-2, AM *cell permeant* *special packaging*	10 x 50 µg	19.3	206
C3730	Calcium Green™-2, octapotassium salt *cell impermeant*	500 µg	19.3	206
C3739	Calcium Green™-5N, AM *cell permeant* *special packaging*	10 x 50 µg	19.3	206
C3737	Calcium Green™-5N, hexapotassium salt *cell impermeant*	500 µg	19.3	206
C3015	Calcium Orange™, AM *cell permeant* *special packaging*	10 x 50 µg	19.3	206
C3013	Calcium Orange™, tetrapotassium salt *cell impermeant*	500 µg	19.3	206
C6771	Calcium Orange™-5N, AM *cell permeant* *special packaging*	10 x 50 µg	19.3	206
C3047	Calcium Sponge™ S (BAPTA polystyrene)	1 g	19.8	206
C13844	calmodulin from bovine brain, Alexa Fluor® 488 conjugate	200 µg	17.3	183
C13845	calmodulin from bovine brain, Alexa Fluor® 594 conjugate	200 µg	17.3	183
C21852	CandyCane™ glycoprotein molecular weight standards *200 gel lanes*	400 µL	9.4	None
C21387	CaptAvidin™ acrylamide	1 mg	7.6, 9.2	250
C21386	CaptAvidin™ agarose *sedimented bead suspension*	5 mL	7.6, 9.2	250
C21385	CaptAvidin™ biotin-binding protein	1 mg	7.6, 9.2	250
C24701	Captivate™ disposable sample chamber *for Captivate™ magnetic yoke* *set of 10*	1 set	7.2, 7.6, 23.3	233
C21473	Captivate™ ferrofluid goat anti-mouse IgG (H+L) *0.5 mg Fe/mL*	1 mL	7.2, 9.2	233
C21474	Captivate™ ferrofluid goat anti-rabbit IgG (H+L) *0.5 mg Fe/mL*	1 mL	7.2, 9.2	233
C21476	Captivate™ ferrofluid streptavidin (streptavidin, Captivate™ ferrofluid conjugate) *0.5 mg Fe/mL*	1 mL	7.6, 9.2	233
C24702	Captivate™ magnetic separator for 96-well microplates	each	7.2, 7.6, 23.3	233
C24703	Captivate™ magnetic separator for six microtubes	each	7.2, 7.6, 23.3	233
C33355	Captivate™ Microscale Phosphopeptide Isolation Kit *for magnetic separation* *50 isolations of 10 µmol each*	1 kit	9.2	233, 223, 206
C24700	Captivate™ microscope-mounted magnetic yoke assembly *includes 10 sample chambers*	each	7.2, 7.6, 23.3	233
C356	5-(((2-(carbohydrazino)methyl)thio)acetyl)aminofluorescein	25 mg	3.2	None
C369	carboxy-DCFDA (5-(and-6)-carboxy-2′,7′-dichlorofluorescein diacetate) *mixed isomers*	100 mg	15.2, 20.3	None
O6151	carboxy-DFFDA (Oregon Green® 488 carboxylic acid diacetate) *6-isomer*	5 mg	15.2, 20.3	191
O34550	carboxy-DFFDA, SE (Oregon Green® 488 carboxylic acid diacetate, succinimidyl ester) *mixed isomers*	1 mg	14.2, 15.4	191
C34555	carboxy-DFFDA, SE (CellTrace™ Oregon Green® 488 carboxylic acid diacetate, succinimidyl ester) *cell permeant* *mixed isomers*	20 x 50 µg	14.2, 15.4	191
C400	5-(and-6)-carboxy-2′,7′-dichlorodihydrofluorescein diacetate (carboxy-H_2DCFDA) *mixed isomers*	25 mg	10.5, 15.2, 18.2	None
C2938	6-carboxy-2′,7′-dichlorodihydrofluorescein diacetate, di(acetoxymethyl ester)	5 mg	15.2, 15.5, 18.2	None
C6171MP	6-carboxy-4′,5′-dichloro-2′,7′-dimethoxyfluorescein, succinimidyl ester (6-JOE, SE)	5 mg	1.5	None
C368	5-(and-6)-carboxy-2′,7′-dichlorofluorescein *mixed isomers*	100 mg	14.3, 20.3	None
C369	5-(and-6)-carboxy-2′,7′-dichlorofluorescein diacetate (carboxy-DCFDA) *mixed isomers*	100 mg	15.2, 20.3	None
C1165	5-(and-6)-carboxy-2′,7′-dichlorofluorescein diacetate, succinimidyl ester *mixed isomers*	25 mg	14.2	None
C13293	5-(and-6)-carboxy-2′,7′-difluorodihydrofluorescein diacetate (carboxy-H_2DFFDA) *mixed isomers*	5 mg	10.5, 18.2	191
C301	5-(and-6)-carboxyeosin *mixed isomers*	100 mg	1.5	None

For current prices or to order online, visit probes.invitrogen.com

Cat #	Product Name	Unit Size	Sections	Limited Use Label License #
C22803	5-(and-6)-carboxyeosin diacetate, succinimidyl ester *mixed isomers*	5 mg	14.2, 15.4, 16.3	None
C1359	5-carboxyfluorescein (5-FAM) *single isomer*	100 mg	1.5	None
C1360	6-carboxyfluorescein (6-FAM) *single isomer*	100 mg	1.5	None
C1904	5-(and-6)-carboxyfluorescein (5(6)-FAM) *FluoroPure™ grade* *mixed isomers*	100 mg	1.5, 14.3, 20.2	None
C194	5-(and-6)-carboxyfluorescein *mixed isomers*	5 g	14.3, 20.2	None
C20050	5-carboxyfluorescein-bis-(5-carboxymethoxy-2-nitrobenzyl) ether, β-alanine-carboxamide, succinimidyl ester (CMNB-caged carboxyfluorescein, SE)	1 mg	1.5, 5.3	None
C1361	5-carboxyfluorescein diacetate (5-CFDA) *single isomer*	100 mg	15.2	None
C1362	6-carboxyfluorescein diacetate (6-CFDA) *single isomer*	100 mg	15.2	None
C195	5-(and-6)-carboxyfluorescein diacetate (5(6)-CFDA) *mixed isomers*	100 mg	15.2, 20.2	None
C1354	5-carboxyfluorescein diacetate, acetoxymethyl ester (5-CFDA, AM)	5 mg	15.2, 20.2	None
C1157	5-(and-6)-carboxyfluorescein diacetate, succinimidyl ester (5(6)-CFDA, SE; CFSE) *mixed isomers*	25 mg	14.2, 15.4, 20.2	None
C2210	5-carboxyfluorescein, succinimidyl ester (5-FAM, SE) *single isomer*	10 mg	1.5	None
C6164	6-carboxyfluorescein, succinimidyl ester (6-FAM, SE) *single isomer*	10 mg	1.5	None
C1311	5-(and-6)-carboxyfluorescein, succinimidyl ester (5(6)-FAM, SE) *mixed isomers*	100 mg	1.5	None
C400	carboxy-H_2DCFDA (5-(and-6)-carboxy-2′,7′-dichlorodihydrofluorescein diacetate) *mixed isomers*	25 mg	10.5, 15.2, 18.2	None
C13293	carboxy-H_2DFFDA (5-(and-6)-carboxy-2′,7′-difluorodihydrofluorescein diacetate) *mixed isomers*	5 mg	10.5, 18.2	191
C20091	6-carboxy-2′,4,4′,5′,7,7′-hexachlorofluorescein, succinimidyl ester (6-HEX, SE) *single isomer*	5 mg	1.5	None
C6541MP	6′-(*O*-(carboxymethyl))-2′,7′-dichlorofluorescein 3′-(*O*-(*N*-acetyl-β-D-glucosaminide)) (CM-DCF-NAG)	5 mg	10.2	None
B30250	carboxymethylthiobimane (bimane mercaptoacetic acid)	5 mg	1.7	None
C652	5-(and-6)-carboxynaphthofluorescein *mixed isomers*	100 mg	1.6, 20.2	None
C13196	5-(and-6)-carboxynaphthofluorescein diacetate	10 mg	15.2, 20.2	None
C653	5-(and-6)-carboxynaphthofluorescein, succinimidyl ester *mixed isomers*	25 mg	1.6, 20.4	None
C13654	*N*-(α-carboxy-2-nitrobenzyl)carbamylcholine, trifluoroacetic acid salt (*N*-(CNB-caged) carbachol)	5 mg	5.3, 16.2	246
C7122	*N*-(α-carboxy-2-nitrobenzyl)-L-glutamic acid (*N*-(CNB-caged) L-glutamic acid)	5 mg	5.3, 16.2	246
C7924	5-(2-carboxyphenyl)-5-hydroxy-1-((2,2,5,5-tetramethyl-1-oxypyrrolidin-3-yl)methyl)-3-phenyl-2-pyrrolin-4-one, potassium salt (proxyl fluorescamine)	5 mg	18.2	None
C7912	2-(4-carboxyphenyl)-4,4,5,5-tetramethylimidazoline-1-oxyl-3-oxide, potassium salt (carboxy-PTIO)	25 mg	18.3	None
C7912	carboxy-PTIO (2-(4-carboxyphenyl)-4,4,5,5-tetramethylimidazoline-1-oxyl-3-oxide, potassium salt)	25 mg	18.3	None
C6109	5-carboxyrhodamine 6G, hydrochloride (5-CR 6G) *single isomer*	5 mg	1.6	None
C2213	6-carboxyrhodamine 6G, hydrochloride (6-CR 6G) *single isomer*	5 mg	1.6	None
C6128	6-carboxyrhodamine 6G, succinimidyl ester (6-CR 6G, SE) *single isomer*	5 mg	1.6	None
C6157	5-(and-6)-carboxyrhodamine 6G, succinimidyl ester (5(6)-CR 6G, SE) *mixed isomers*	5 mg	1.6	None
C6127	5-carboxyrhodamine 6G, succinimidyl ester (5-CR 6G, SE) *single isomer*	5 mg	1.6	None
C1255	5-(and-6)-carboxy SNAFL®-1	1 mg	20.2	208
C1256	5-(and-6)-carboxy SNAFL®-1, diacetate	1 mg	20.2	208
C3061	5-(and-6)-carboxy SNAFL®-1, succinimidyl ester *mixed isomers*	1 mg	20.4	208
C1260	5-(and-6)-carboxy SNAFL®-2	1 mg	20.2	208
C1261	5-(and-6)-carboxy SNAFL®-2, diacetate	1 mg	20.2	208
C3062	5-(and-6)-carboxy SNAFL®-2, succinimidyl ester *mixed isomers*	1 mg	20.4	208
C1270	5-(and-6)-carboxy SNARF®-1	1 mg	20.2	208
C1271	5-(and-6)-carboxy SNARF®-1, acetoxymethyl ester, acetate	1 mg	20.2	208
C1272	5-(and-6)-carboxy SNARF®-1, acetoxymethyl ester, acetate *special packaging*	20 x 50 µg	20.2	208
C6166	5-carboxy-2′,4′,5′,7′-tetrabromosulfonefluorescein, succinimidyl ester, bis-(diisopropylethylammonium) salt	5 mg	1.5	None
C20092	6-carboxy-2′,4,7,7′-tetrachlorofluorescein, succinimidyl ester (6-TET, SE) *single isomer*	5 mg	1.5	None
C6121	5-carboxytetramethylrhodamine (5-TAMRA) *single isomer*	10 mg	1.6	None
C6122	6-carboxytetramethylrhodamine (6-TAMRA) *single isomer*	10 mg	1.6	None
C300	5-(and-6)-carboxytetramethylrhodamine (5(6)-TAMRA) *mixed isomers*	100 mg	1.6	None
C2211	5-carboxytetramethylrhodamine, succinimidyl ester (5-TAMRA, SE) *single isomer*	5 mg	1.6	None
C6123	6-carboxytetramethylrhodamine, succinimidyl ester (6-TAMRA, SE) *single isomer*	5 mg	1.6	None
C1171	5-(and-6)-carboxytetramethylrhodamine, succinimidyl ester (5(6)-TAMRA, SE) *mixed isomers*	25 mg	1.6	None
C1488	3-carboxyumbelliferyl β-D-galactopyranoside (CUG)	10 mg	10.2	None
C1492	3-carboxyumbelliferyl β-D-glucuronide (CUGlcU)	10 mg	10.2	None
C6124	5-carboxy-X-rhodamine, triethylammonium salt (5-ROX) *single isomer*	10 mg	1.6	None
C6156	6-carboxy-X-rhodamine (6-ROX) *single isomer*	10 mg	1.6	None
C6125	5-carboxy-X-rhodamine, succinimidyl ester (5-ROX, SE) *single isomer*	5 mg	1.6	None
C6126	6-carboxy-X-rhodamine, succinimidyl ester (6-ROX, SE) *single isomer*	5 mg	1.6	None
C1309	5-(and-6)-carboxy-X-rhodamine, succinimidyl ester (5(6)-ROX, SE) *mixed isomers*	25 mg	1.6	None
C2284	Cascade Blue® acetyl azide, trisodium salt	5 mg	1.7, 4.2, 14.3	218

For current prices or to order online, visit probes.invitrogen.com

Cat #	Product Name	Unit Size	Sections	Limited Use Label License #
C621	Cascade Blue® ethylenediamine, trisodium salt	10 mg	3.3, 14.3	218
C962	Cascade Blue® goat anti-mouse IgG (H+L) *2 mg/mL*	0.5 mL	7.2	218
C2764	Cascade Blue® goat anti-rabbit IgG (H+L) *2 mg/mL*	0.5 mL	7.2	218
C3239	Cascade Blue® hydrazide, trilithium salt	10 mg	14.3	218
C3221	Cascade Blue® hydrazide, tripotassium salt	10 mg	14.3	218
C687	Cascade Blue® hydrazide, trisodium salt	10 mg	3.2, 14.3, 16.1	218
C10164	Cascade Yellow™ succinimidyl ester	5 mg	1.7	None
C2990	casein, fluorescein conjugate	25 mg	10.4, 15.6, 16.1	None
T506	CAT 1 (4-trimethylammonium-2,2,6,6-tetramethylpiperidine-1-oxyl iodide)	100 mg	14.3	None
A6222	CBQCA; 3-(4-carboxybenzoyl)quinoline-2-carboxaldehyde (ATTO-TAG™ CBQCA derivatization reagent)	10 mg	1.8, 9.2, 9.3, 21.2	244
C6667	CBQCA Protein Quantitation Kit *300-800 assays*	1 kit	9.2	244
C7028	Cell Culture Contamination Detection Kit *200 assays*	1 kit	15.4	251, 211, 154
C34853	CellTrace™ calcein blue, AM *special packaging*	20 x 50 µg	15.2	None
C34852	CellTrace™ calcein green, AM *special packaging*	20 x 50 µg	15.2	None
C34851	CellTrace™ calcein red-orange, AM *special packaging*	20 x 50 µg	15.2	223, 193
C34554	CellTrace™ CFSE Cell Proliferation Kit *for flow cytometry*	1 kit	14.2, 15.4	None
C34553	CellTrace™ Far Red DDAO-SE *special packaging*	20 x 50 µg	14.2	234, 223
C34555	CellTrace™ Oregon Green® 488 carboxylic acid diacetate, succinimidyl ester (carboxy-DFFDA, SE) *cell permeant* *mixed isomers*	20 x 50 µg	14.2, 15.4	191
C2110	CellTracker™ Blue CMAC (7-amino-4-chloromethylcoumarin)	5 mg	10.1, 14.2	212
C12881	CellTracker™ Blue CMF$_2$HC (4-chloromethyl-6,8-difluoro-7-hydroxycoumarin)	5 mg	10.1, 14.2	192
C2111	CellTracker™ Blue CMHC (4-chloromethyl-7-hydroxycoumarin)	5 mg	14.2	212
C7001	CellTracker™ CM-DiI	1 mg	13.4, 14.4	229
C7000	CellTracker™ CM-DiI *special packaging*	20 x 50 µg	13.4, 14.4	229
C2102	CellTracker™ Green BODIPY® (8-chloromethyl-4,4-difluoro-1,3,5,7-tetramethyl-4-bora-3a,4a-diaza-*s*-indacene)	5 mg	14.2	212
C2925	CellTracker™ Green CMFDA (5-chloromethylfluorescein diacetate)	1 mg	14.2, 15.2, 15.6, 20.2	212
C7025	CellTracker™ Green CMFDA (5-chloromethylfluorescein diacetate) *special packaging*	20 x 50 µg	14.2, 15.2, 15.6, 20.2	212
C34551	CellTracker™ Orange CMRA *special packaging*	20 x 50 µg	14.2	212
C2927	CellTracker™ Orange CMTMR (5-(and-6)-(((4-chloromethyl)benzoyl)amino)tetramethylrhodamine) *mixed isomers*	1 mg	14.2	212
C34552	CellTracker™ Red CMTPX *special packaging*	20 x 50 µg	14.2	223
C1361	5-CFDA (5-carboxyfluorescein diacetate) *single isomer*	100 mg	15.2	None
C1362	6-CFDA (6-carboxyfluorescein diacetate) *single isomer*	100 mg	15.2	None
C195	5(6)-CFDA (5-(and-6)-carboxyfluorescein diacetate) *mixed isomers*	100 mg	15.2, 20.2	None
C1354	5-CFDA, AM (5-carboxyfluorescein diacetate, acetoxymethyl ester)	5 mg	15.2, 20.2	None
C1157	5(6)-CFDA, SE; CFSE (5-(and-6)-carboxyfluorescein diacetate, succinimidyl ester) *mixed isomers*	25 mg	14.2, 15.4, 20.2	None
C2927	5-(and-6)-(((4-chloromethyl)benzoyl)amino)tetramethylrhodamine (CellTracker™ Orange CMTMR) *mixed isomers*	1 mg	14.2	212
C6827	5-(and-6)-chloromethyl-2′,7′-dichlorodihydrofluorescein diacetate, acetyl ester (CM-H$_2$DCFDA) *mixed isomers* *special packaging*	20 x 50 µg	14.2, 15.2, 15.5, 18.2	None
C12202	4-chloromethyl-6,8-difluoro-7-ethoxycoumarin (CMDiFUEt)	5 mg	10.6	212, 192
C12881	4-chloromethyl-6,8-difluoro-7-hydroxycoumarin (CellTracker™ Blue CMF$_2$HC)	5 mg	10.1, 14.2	192
C2102	8-chloromethyl-4,4-difluoro-1,3,5,7-tetramethyl-4-bora-3a,4a-diaza-*s*-indacene (CellTracker™ Green BODIPY®)	5 mg	14.2	212
C11946	4-chloromethyl-6,8-difluoroumbelliferyl β-D-galactopyranoside (CMDiFUG)	5 mg	10.2	None
C2925	5-chloromethylfluorescein diacetate (CellTracker™ Green CMFDA)	1 mg	14.2, 15.2, 15.6, 20.2	212
C7025	5-chloromethylfluorescein diacetate (CellTracker™ Green CMFDA) *special packaging*	20 x 50 µg	14.2, 15.2, 15.6, 20.2	212
C6533	5-(and-6)-chloromethylfluorescein diethyl ether *mixed isomers*	5 mg	10.6	None
C2111	4-chloromethyl-7-hydroxycoumarin (CellTracker™ Blue CMHC)	5 mg	14.2	212
C6826	5-(and-6)-chloromethyl SNARF®-1, acetate *mixed isomers* *special packaging*	20 x 50 µg	14.2, 15.2, 15.6, 20.2	208, 212
C20260	4-chloro-7-nitrobenz-2-oxa-1,3-diazole (NBD chloride; 4-chloro-7-nitrobenzofurazan) *FluoroPure™ grade*	100 mg	1.8, 2.2	None
C22220	6-chloro-9-nitro-5-oxo-5*H*-benzo[a]phenoxazine (CNOB)	1 mg	10.6	None
C22841	cholera toxin subunit B (recombinant), Alexa Fluor® 488 conjugate	500 µg	7.7, 14.7, 16.1	183
C34775	cholera toxin subunit B (recombinant), Alexa Fluor® 488 conjugate	100 µg	7.7, 14.7, 16.1	183
C22843	cholera toxin subunit B (recombinant), Alexa Fluor® 555 conjugate	500 µg	7.7, 14.7, 16.1	183
C34776	cholera toxin subunit B (recombinant), Alexa Fluor® 555 conjugate	100 µg	7.7, 14.7, 16.1	183
C22842	cholera toxin subunit B (recombinant), Alexa Fluor® 594 conjugate	500 µg	7.7, 14.7, 16.1	183
C34777	cholera toxin subunit B (recombinant), Alexa Fluor® 594 conjugate	100 µg	7.7, 14.7, 16.1	183
C34778	cholera toxin subunit B (recombinant), Alexa Fluor® 647 conjugate	100 µg	7.7, 14.7, 16.1	183
C34779	cholera toxin subunit B (recombinant), biotin-XX conjugate	100 µg	4.3, 7.7, 14.7, 16.1	223
C34780	cholera toxin subunit B (recombinant), horseradish peroxidase conjugate	100 µg	7.7, 14.7, 16.1	223
C12681	cholesteryl BODIPY® 576/589 C$_{11}$ (cholesteryl 4,4-difluoro-5-(2-pyrrolyl)-4-bora-3a,4a-diaza-*s*-indacene-3-undecanoate)	1 mg	13.3	193

For current prices or to order online, visit probes.invitrogen.com

Cat #	Product Name	Unit Size	Sections	Limited Use Label License #
C12680	cholesteryl BODIPY® 542/563 C_{11} (cholesteryl 4,4-difluoro-5-(4-methoxyphenyl)-4-bora-3a,4a-diaza-*s*-indacene-3-undecanoate)	1 mg	13.3	193
C3927MP	cholesteryl BODIPY® FL C_{12} (cholesteryl 4,4-difluoro-5,7-dimethyl-4-bora-3a,4a-diaza-*s*-indacene-3-dodecanoate)	1 mg	13.3	193
C3927MP	cholesteryl 4,4-difluoro-5,7-dimethyl-4-bora-3a,4a-diaza-*s*-indacene-3-dodecanoate (cholesteryl BODIPY® FL C_{12})	1 mg	13.3	193
C12680	cholesteryl 4,4-difluoro-5-(4-methoxyphenyl)-4-bora-3a,4a-diaza-*s*-indacene-3-undecanoate (cholesteryl BODIPY® 542/563 C_{11})	1 mg	13.3	193
C12681	cholesteryl 4,4-difluoro-5-(2-pyrrolyl)-4-bora-3a,4a-diaza-*s*-indacene-3-undecanoate (cholesteryl BODIPY® 576/589 C_{11})	1 mg	13.3	193
C7794	cholesteryl DPH propionate (cholesteryl 3-((6-phenyl)-1,3,5-hexatrienyl)phenylpropionate)	5 mg	13.3	None
C7794	cholesteryl 3-((6-phenyl)-1,3,5-hexatrienyl)phenylpropionate (cholesteryl DPH propionate)	5 mg	13.3	None
C212	cholesteryl 1-pyrenebutyrate	25 mg	13.3	None
C11397	ChromaTide® Alexa Fluor® 488-5-dUTP *1 mM in TE buffer*	25 µL	8.2	225, 183
C11403	ChromaTide® Alexa Fluor® 488-5-UTP *1 mM in TE buffer*	25 µL	8.2	225, 183
C11398	ChromaTide® Alexa Fluor® 532-5-dUTP *1 mM in TE buffer*	25 µL	8.2	225, 183
C11401	ChromaTide® Alexa Fluor® 546-14-dUTP *1 mM in TE buffer*	25 µL	8.2	225, 183
C11404	ChromaTide® Alexa Fluor® 546-14-UTP *1 mM in TE buffer*	25 µL	8.2	225, 183
C11399	ChromaTide® Alexa Fluor® 568-5-dUTP *1 mM in TE buffer*	25 µL	8.2	225, 183
C11400	ChromaTide® Alexa Fluor® 594-5-dUTP *1 mM in TE buffer*	25 µL	8.2	225, 183
C21555	ChromaTide® Alexa Fluor® 488-7-OBEA-dCTP *1 mM in TE buffer*	50 µL	8.2	252, 183
C21556	ChromaTide® Alexa Fluor® 546-16-OBEA-dCTP *1 mM in TE buffer*	50 µL	8.2	252, 183
C21558	ChromaTide® Alexa Fluor® 594-7-OBEA-dCTP *1 mM in TE buffer*	50 µL	8.2	252, 183
C21559	ChromaTide® Alexa Fluor® 647-12-OBEA-dCTP *1 mM in TE buffer*	50 µL	8.2	252, 183
C11395	ChromaTide® BODIPY® 630/650-14-dUTP *1 mM in TE buffer*	25 µL	8.2	225, 193
C11396	ChromaTide® BODIPY® 650/665-14-dUTP *1 mM in TE buffer*	25 µL	8.2	225, 193
C7614	ChromaTide® BODIPY® FL-14-dUTP *1 mM in TE buffer*	25 µL	8.2, 8.7, 15.4, 15.5	225, 193
C7613	ChromaTide® BODIPY® FL-14-UTP *1 mM in TE buffer*	25 µL	8.2	225, 193
C7616	ChromaTide® BODIPY® TMR-14-dUTP *1 mM in TE buffer*	25 µL	8.2	225, 193
C7615	ChromaTide® BODIPY® TMR-14-UTP *1 mM in TE buffer*	25 µL	8.2	225, 193
C7618	ChromaTide® BODIPY® TR-14-dUTP *1 mM in TE buffer*	25 µL	8.2	225, 193
C7617	ChromaTide® BODIPY® TR-14-UTP *1 mM in TE buffer*	25 µL	8.2	225, 193
C7612	ChromaTide® Cascade Blue®-7-dUTP *1 mM in TE buffer*	25 µL	8.2	225, 218
C7610MP	ChromaTide® dinitrophenyl-11-dUTP (DNP-11-dUTP) *1 mM in TE buffer*	25 µL	8.2	225
C7604	ChromaTide® fluorescein-12-dUTP *1 mM in TE buffer*	25 µL	8.2, 15.5	225
C7603	ChromaTide® fluorescein-12-UTP *1 mM in TE buffer*	25 µL	8.2	225
C7630	ChromaTide® Oregon Green® 488-5-dUTP *1 mM in TE buffer*	25 µL	8.2	225, 191
C7629	ChromaTide® Rhodamine Green™-5-dUTP *1 mM in TE buffer*	25 µL	8.2	225
C7628	ChromaTide® Rhodamine Green™-5-UTP *1 mM in TE buffer*	25 µL	8.2	225
C7606MP	ChromaTide® tetramethylrhodamine-6-dUTP *1 mM in TE buffer*	25 µL	8.2	225
C7605MP	ChromaTide® tetramethylrhodamine-6-UTP *1 mM in TE buffer*	25 µL	8.2	225
C7608	ChromaTide® Texas Red®-5-dUTP *1 mM in TE buffer*	25 µL	8.2	225
C7607MP	ChromaTide® Texas Red®-5-UTP *1 mM in TE buffer*	25 µL	8.2	225
C7631	ChromaTide® Texas Red®-12-dUTP *1 mM in TE buffer*	25 µL	8.2	None
C7587	Chromosome Banding Kit #2 *SYTOX® Green/Methyl Green* *200 slides*	1 kit	8.6	154
A6520	CMAC, *t*-BOC-Leu-Met (7-amino-4-chloromethylcoumarin, *t*-BOC-L-leucyl-L-methionine amide)	5 mg	10.4, 15.5	212
A6575	CMAC, CBZ-Arg (7-amino-4-chloromethylcoumarin, CBZ-L-arginine amide, hydrochloride)	5 mg	10.4	212
R6560	CMB-R110, CBZ-Arg (rhodamine 110, 4-(chloromethyl)benzoyl amide, CBZ-L-arginine amide, hydrochloride)	1 mg	10.4	None
C6541MP	CM-DCF-NAG (6′-(*O*-(carboxymethyl))-2′,7′-dichlorofluorescein 3′-(*O*-(*N*-acetyl-β-D-glucosaminide)))	5 mg	10.2	None
C12202	CMDiFUEt (4-chloromethyl-6,8-difluoro-7-ethoxycoumarin)	5 mg	10.6	212, 192
C11946	CMDiFUG (4-chloromethyl-6,8-difluoroumbelliferyl β-D-galactopyranoside)	5 mg	10.2	None
C6827	CM-H_2DCFDA (5-(and-6)-chloromethyl-2′,7′-dichlorodihydrofluorescein diacetate, acetyl ester) *mixed isomers* *special packaging*	20 x 50 µg	14.2, 15.2, 15.5, 18.2	212
C20050	CMNB-caged carboxyfluorescein, SE (5-carboxyfluorescein-bis-(5-carboxymethoxy-2-nitrobenzyl) ether, β-alanine-carboxamide, succinimidyl ester)	1 mg	1.5, 5.3	None
F7103	CMNB-caged fluorescein (fluorescein bis-(5-carboxymethoxy-2-nitrobenzyl) ether, dipotassium salt)	5 mg	5.3, 14.3	None
C13654	*N*-(CNB-caged) carbachol (*N*-(α-carboxy-2-nitrobenzyl)carbamylcholine, trifluoroacetic acid salt)	5 mg	5.3, 16.2	246
A7110	*O*-(CNB-caged) GABA (γ-aminobutyric acid, α-carboxy-2-nitrobenzyl ester, trifluoroacetic acid salt)	5 mg	5.3, 16.2	246
G7055	γ-(CNB-caged) L-glutamic acid (L-glutamic acid, γ-(α-carboxy-2-nitrobenzyl) ester, trifluoroacetic acid salt)	5 mg	5.3, 16.2	246
C7122	*N*-(CNB-caged) L-glutamic acid (*N*-(α-carboxy-2-nitrobenzyl)-L-glutamic acid)	5 mg	5.3, 16.2	246
M7114	β-(CNB-caged) NMDA (*N*-methyl-D-aspartic acid, β-(α-carboxy-2-nitrobenzyl) ester, trifluoroacetic acid salt)	1 mg	5.3, 16.2	246
C2944	coelenterazine	250 µg	10.6, 18.2, 19.5	None
C14260	coelenterazine cp	250 µg	10.6, 19.5	None

For current prices or to order online, visit probes.invitrogen.com

Cat #	Product Name	Unit Size	Sections	Limited Use Label License #
C6779	coelenterazine f	250 µg	10.6, 19.5	None
C6780	coelenterazine h	250 µg	10.6, 19.5	None
C14261	coelenterazine hcp	250 µg	10.6, 19.5	None
C6776	coelenterazine n	250 µg	10.6, 19.5	None
C6777	Coelenterazine Sampler Kit *coelenterazine and five analogs, 25 µg each*	1 kit	10.6, 19.5	None
C22280	cofilin, chicken muscle, recombinant from *Escherichia coli*	50 µg	11.1	None
C13185	collagen, type IV from human placenta, Oregon Green® 488 conjugate	1 mg	15.6	191
C14820	CompenFlow™ Flow Cytometry Compensation Kit, 2.5 µm	1 kit	23.2	227, 193
C7301	CompenFlow™ Flow Cytometry Compensation Kit, 6 µm	1 kit	23.2	227
C11254	concanavalin A, Alexa Fluor® 350 conjugate	5 mg	7.7	183
C11252	concanavalin A, Alexa Fluor® 488 conjugate	5 mg	7.7	183
C11253	concanavalin A, Alexa Fluor® 594 conjugate	5 mg	7.7	183
C21402	concanavalin A, Alexa Fluor® 633 conjugate	5 mg	7.7	183
C21421	concanavalin A, Alexa Fluor® 647 conjugate	5 mg	7.7	183
C21403	concanavalin A, Alexa Fluor® 660 conjugate	5 mg	7.7	183
C21420	concanavalin A, biotin-XX conjugate	10 mg	7.7	None
C827	concanavalin A, fluorescein conjugate	10 mg	7.7	None
C6741	concanavalin A, Oregon Green® 488 conjugate	5 mg	7.7	191
C21401	concanavalin A, succinylated, Alexa Fluor® 488 conjugate	5 mg	7.7	183
C860	concanavalin A, tetramethylrhodamine conjugate	10 mg	7.7	None
C825	concanavalin A, Texas Red® conjugate	10 mg	7.7	None
C14946	Confocal Microscopy (Methods in Molecular Biology Volume 122). Stephen Paddock, ed. Humana Press (1998); 464 pages, hard cover	each	23.6	None
C14837	Constellation™ microspheres for imaging *mixture of assorted sizes and colors*	3 mL	6.5, 23.1	227, 193
C33250	Coomassie Fluor™ Orange protein gel stain *ready-to-use solution*	1 L	9.3	190
C33251	Coomassie Fluor™ Orange protein gel stain *ready-to-use solution* *bulk packaging*	5 L	9.3	190
C36675	CoroNa™ Green *cell impermeant*	1 mg	21.1	223, 191
C36676	CoroNa™ Green, AM *cell permeant* *special packaging*	20 x 50 µg	21.1	223, 191
C24430	CoroNa™ Red chloride	1 mg	21.1	223
C24431	CoroNa™ Red chloride *special packaging*	20 x 50 µg	21.1	223
C7933	coumarin-3-carboxylic acid, succinimidyl ester (SECCA)	25 mg	10.6, 18.2	None
C606	coumarin phallacidin	300 U	11.1	None
C24784	coverslip maxi-rack *for 50 coverslips*	each	23.3	None
C14784	coverslip mini-rack *for 8 coverslips*	each	23.3	None
C18160	CoverWell™ imaging chamber gasket, one chamber, 20 mm diameter, 0.5 mm deep *set of 40*	1 set	23.3	None
C18161	CoverWell™ imaging chamber gasket, one chamber, 20 mm diameter, 1.0 mm deep *set of 40*	1 set	23.3	None
C24727	CoverWell™ imaging chamber gasket with adhesive, one chamber, 20 mm diameter, 1.0 mm deep *set of 40*	1 set	23.3	None
C24726	CoverWell™ imaging chamber gasket with adhesive, one chamber, 20 mm diameter, 0.5 mm deep *set of 40*	1 set	23.3	None
C18155	CoverWell™ incubation chamber gasket, one chamber, 13 mm diameter, 0.2 mm deep *set of 25*	1 set	23.3	None
C18156	CoverWell™ incubation chamber gasket, one chamber, 13 mm diameter, 0.5 mm deep *set of 50*	1 set	23.3	None
C18150	CoverWell™ incubation chamber gasket, one chamber, 40 mm x 22 mm, 0.2 mm deep *set of 25*	1 set	23.3	None
C18151	CoverWell™ incubation chamber gasket, one chamber, 40 mm x 22 mm, 0.5 mm deep *set of 50*	1 set	23.3	None
C18140	CoverWell™ perfusion chamber gasket, eight chambers, 9 mm diameter, 1.0 mm deep *set of 20*	1 set	23.3	None
C18141	CoverWell™ perfusion chamber gasket, eight chambers, 9 mm diameter, 2.0 mm deep *set of 20*	1 set	23.3	None
C18142	CoverWell™ perfusion chamber gasket, eight chambers, 9 mm diameter, 2.5 mm deep *set of 20*	1 set	23.3	None
C18139	CoverWell™ perfusion chamber gasket, eight chambers, 9 mm diameter, 0.5 mm deep *set of 20*	1 set	23.3	None
C18128	CoverWell™ perfusion chamber gasket, four chambers, 19 mm x 6 mm, 0.5 mm deep *set of 40*	1 set	23.3	None
C18136	CoverWell™ perfusion chamber gasket, one chamber, 20 mm diameter, 1.0 mm deep *set of 40*	1 set	23.3	None
C18120	CoverWell™ perfusion chamber gasket, one chamber, 32 mm x 19 mm, 0.5 mm deep *set of 40*	1 set	23.3	None
C18121	CoverWell™ perfusion chamber gasket, one chamber, 32 mm x 19 mm, 1.0 mm deep *set of 40*	1 set	23.3	None
D346	CPM (7-diethylamino-3-(4'-maleimidylphenyl)-4-methylcoumarin)	25 mg	2.3	None
R6152	5(6)-CRF 492 (Rhodol Green™ carboxylic acid, hydrochloride) *mixed isomers*	5 mg	20.3	261
C2213	6-CR 6G (6-carboxyrhodamine 6G, hydrochloride) *single isomer*	5 mg	1.6	None
C6109	5-CR 6G (5-carboxyrhodamine 6G, hydrochloride) *single isomer*	5 mg	1.6	None
C6128	6-CR 6G, SE (6-carboxyrhodamine 6G, succinimidyl ester) *single isomer*	5 mg	1.6	None
C6157	5(6)-CR 6G, SE (5-(and-6)-carboxyrhodamine 6G, succinimidyl ester) *mixed isomers*	5 mg	1.6	None
C6127	5-CR 6G, SE (5-carboxyrhodamine 6G, succinimidyl ester) *single isomer*	5 mg	1.6	None
R6107	5(6)-CR 110, SE (Rhodamine Green™ carboxylic acid, succinimidyl ester, hydrochloride) *mixed isomers*	5 mg	1.5	None
R6112	5(6)-CR 110 TFA, SE (Rhodamine Green™ carboxylic acid, trifluoroacetamide, succinimidyl ester) *mixed isomers*	5 mg	1.5	None

For current prices or to order online, visit probes.invitrogen.com

Cat #	Product Name	Unit Size	Sections	Limited Use Label License #
C23010	α-crystallin from bovine eye lens, Alexa Fluor® 488 conjugate	1 mg	16.1	183
C1488	CUG (3-carboxyumbelliferyl β-D-galactopyranoside)	10 mg	10.2	None
C1492	CUGlcU (3-carboxyumbelliferyl β-D-glucuronide)	10 mg	10.2	None
C24769	CultureWell™ cell culture plate *set of 10*	1 set	23.3	None
C37000	CultureWell™ chambered coverglass for cell culture *sixteen wells per coverglass* *set of 8*	1 set	23.3	None
C37005	CultureWell™ chambered coverglass for cell culture *sixteen wells per coverglass* *set of 2*	1 pack	23.3	None
C24770	CultureWell™ coverslip divider *set of 4*	1 set	23.3	None
C24760	CultureWell™ multislip cell culture system MSI-12 *plate and insert, fifteen 12 mm coverslips per insert* *set of 10*	1 set	23.3	None
C24761	CultureWell™ multislip cell culture system MSI-18 *plate and insert, eight 18 mm coverslips per insert* *set of 10*	1 set	23.3	None
C24762	CultureWell™ multiwell cell culture system CWI 2R-1.0 *plate and insert, four 24 mm x 50 mm coverslips per insert, two 1 mm-deep wells per coverslip* *set of 10*	1 set	23.3	None
C24763	CultureWell™ multiwell cell culture system CWI 2R-2.0 *plate and insert, four 24 mm x 50 mm coverslips per insert, two 2 mm-deep wells per coverslip* *set of 10*	1 set	23.3	None
C24764	CultureWell™ multiwell cell culture system CWI 3S-1.0 *plate and insert, four 24 mm x 50 mm coverslips per insert, three 1 mm-deep wells per coverslip* *set of 10*	1 set	23.3	None
C24765	CultureWell™ multiwell cell culture system CWI 4R-1.0 *plate and insert, four 24 mm x 50 mm coverslips per insert, four 1 mm-deep wells per coverslip* *set of 10*	1 set	23.3	None
C24766	CultureWell™ multiwell cell culture system CWI 8R-1.0 *plate and insert, four 24 mm x 50 mm coverslips per insert, eight 1 mm-deep wells per coverslip* *set of 10*	1 set	23.3	None
C24767	CultureWell™ multiwell cell culture system CWI 8R-1.0 TS *plate and insert, four 24 mm x 50 mm coverslips per insert, eight 1 mm-deep wells per coverslip* *set of 2*	1 set	23.3	None
C24768	CultureWell™ multiwell cell culture system CWI 50R-1.0 *plate and insert, four 24 mm x 50 mm coverslips per insert, fifty 1 mm-deep wells per coverslip* *set of 10*	1 set	23.3	None
C24775	CultureWell™ multiwell chambered coverslip CWCS 2R-1.0 *24 mm x 50 mm coverslips, two 1 mm-deep wells per coverslip* *set of 20*	1 set	23.3	None
C24776	CultureWell™ multiwell chambered coverslip CWCS 2R-2.0 *24 mm x 50 mm coverslips, two 2 mm-deep wells per coverslip* *set of 20*	1 set	23.3	None
C24777	CultureWell™ multiwell chambered coverslip CWCS 3S-1.0 *24 mm x 50 mm coverslips, three 1 mm-deep wells per coverslip* *set of 20*	1 set	23.3	None
C24778	CultureWell™ multiwell chambered coverslip CWCS 4R-1.0 *24 mm x 50 mm coverslips, four 1 mm-deep wells per coverslip* *set of 20*	1 set	23.3	None
C24779	CultureWell™ multiwell chambered coverslip CWCS 8R-1.0 *24 mm x 50 mm coverslips, eight 1 mm-deep wells per coverslip* *set of 20*	1 set	23.3	None
C24780	CultureWell™ multiwell chambered coverslip CWCS 50R-1.0 *24 mm x 50 mm coverslips, fifty 1 mm-deep wells per coverslip* *set of 20*	1 set	23.3	None
C684	3-cyano-7-ethoxycoumarin	10 mg	10.6	None
C183	3-cyano-7-hydroxycoumarin	100 mg	10.1	None
C7619	cyclic adenosine 5′-diphosphate ribose (cADP-ribose)	100 µg	17.2	None
C7074	cyclic adenosine 5′-diphosphate ribose, 1-(1-(2-nitrophenyl)ethyl) ester (NPE-caged cADP-ribose) *mixed isomers*	50 µg	5.3, 17.2	None
C428	*N*-cyclohexyl-*N*′-(4-(dimethylamino)naphthyl)carbodiimide (NCD-4)	25 mg	3.3	None
C7027	CyQUANT® cell lysis buffer *20X concentrate*	50 mL	15.4	None
C7026	CyQUANT® Cell Proliferation Assay Kit *for cells in culture* *1000 assays*	1 kit	15.4	154
C12376	cytochalasin B, BODIPY® FL conjugate	100 µg	11.1	193
C12377	cytochalasin D, BODIPY® FL conjugate	100 µg	11.1	193
C12378	cytochalasin D, BODIPY® TMR conjugate	100 µg	11.1	193
C7590	Cytological Nuclear Counterstain Kit *DAPI/SYTOX® Green/PI* *300 slides*	1 kit	8.6	154
D23840	DAA (1,2-diaminoanthraquinone sulfate) *high purity*	5 mg	18.3	None
D6216	ε-dabcyl-α-FMOC-L-lysine (ε-(4-((4-(dimethylamino)phenyl)azo)benzoyl)-α-9-fluorenylmethoxycarbonyl-L-lysine)	100 mg	9.5	None
D2245	dabcyl, SE (4-((4-(dimethylamino)phenyl)azo)benzoic acid, succinimidyl ester)	100 mg	1.8, 9.5	None
D1521	DABMI (4-dimethylaminophenylazophenyl-4′-maleimide)	100 mg	2.2	None
D1537	dabsyl chloride (4-dimethylaminoazobenzene-4′-sulfonyl chloride)	100 mg	1.8, 9.5	None
D10252	DACIA (*N*-(7-dimethylamino-4-methylcoumarin-3-yl)iodoacetamide)	10 mg	2.3	None
D10166	DACITC (7-dimethylamino-4-methylcoumarin-3-isothiocyanate)	10 mg	1.7	None
D10251	DACM (*N*-(7-dimethylamino-4-methylcoumarin-3-yl)maleimide)	10 mg	2.3	None
D23841	DAF-FM (4-amino-5-methylamino-2′,7′-difluorofluorescein)	1 mg	18.3, 21.2	255, 191
D23842	DAF-FM diacetate (4-amino-5-methylamino-2′,7′-difluorofluorescein diacetate)	1 mg	18.3	255, 191
D23844	DAF-FM diacetate (4-amino-5-methylamino-2′,7′-difluorofluorescein diacetate) *special packaging*	10 x 50 µg	18.3	255, 191
D1552	DAMP (*N*-(3-((2,4-dinitrophenyl)amino)propyl)-*N*-(3-aminopropyl)methylamine, dihydrochloride)	100 mg	12.3	None
D2281	*m*-dansylaminophenylboronic acid	100 mg	3.1	None
D151	dansyl aziridine (5-dimethylaminonaphthalene-1-sulfonyl aziridine)	100 mg	2.3	None
D113	dansyl cadaverine (5-dimethylaminonaphthalene-1-(*N*-(5-aminopentyl))sulfonamide)	100 mg	3.3, 12.3	None

For current prices or to order online, visit probes.invitrogen.com

Cat #	Product Name	Unit Size	Sections	Limited Use Label License #
D21	dansyl chloride (5-dimethylaminonaphthalene-1-sulfonyl chloride)	1 g	1.7, 9.5	None
D57	dansyl DHPE (*N*-(5-dimethylaminonaphthalene-1-sulfonyl)-1,2-dihexadecanoyl-*sn*-glycero-3-phosphoethanolamine, triethylammonium salt)	25 mg	13.2	None
D112	dansyl ethylenediamine (5-dimethylaminonaphthalene-1-(*N*-(2-aminoethyl))sulfonamide)	100 mg	3.3	None
D100	dansyl hydrazine (5-dimethylaminonaphthalene-1-sulfonyl hydrazine)	100 mg	3.2, 9.5	None
D6104	dansyl-X, SE (6-((5-dimethylaminonaphthalene-1-sulfonyl)amino)hexanoic acid, succinimidyl ester)	25 mg	1.7, 4.2	None
D1306	DAPI (4',6-diamidino-2-phenylindole, dihydrochloride)	10 mg	8.1, 8.6, 8.7, 11.2, 14.3, 15.4	None
D21490	DAPI (4',6-diamidino-2-phenylindole, dihydrochloride) *FluoroPure™ grade*	10 mg	8.1, 8.6, 8.7, 11.2, 14.3, 15.4	None
D3571	DAPI, dilactate (4',6-diamidino-2-phenylindole, dilactate)	10 mg	8.1, 8.6, 8.7, 11.2, 14.3, 15.4	None
D10460	Dapoxyl® (2-aminoethyl)sulfonamide	10 mg	3.3, 12.3	None
D10300	Dapoxyl® (2-bromoacetamidoethyl)sulfonamide	10 mg	2.3	None
D10161	Dapoxyl® carboxylic acid, succinimidyl ester	5 mg	1.7	None
D10301	Dapoxyl® 2-(3-(2-pyridyldithio)propionamidoethyl)sulfonamide	10 mg	2.3	None
D10402	Dapoxyl® 3-sulfonamidophenylboronic acid	5 mg	3.1	None
D10162	Dapoxyl® 3-sulfonamidopropionic acid, succinimidyl ester	10 mg	1.7	None
D12800	Dapoxyl® sulfonic acid, sodium salt	10 mg	13.5	None
D10160	Dapoxyl® sulfonyl chloride	10 mg	1.7	None
D10430	Dapoxyl® sulfonyl hydrazine	10 mg	3.2	None
D426	DASPEI (2-(4-(dimethylamino)styryl)-*N*-ethylpyridinium iodide)	1 g	12.2	None
D22361	dATP γ-AmNS (2'-deoxyadenosine 5'-triphosphate, P^3-(5-sulfo-1-naphthylamide)) *5 mM in water*	400 µL	17.3	None
D94	DAUDA (11-((5-dimethylaminonaphthalene-1-sulfonyl)amino)undecanoic acid)	100 mg	13.2, 17.4	None
D675	DBDS (4,4'-dibenzamidostilbene-2,2'-disulfonic acid, disodium salt)	100 mg	16.3	None
D355	DCCH (7-diethylaminocoumarin-3-carboxylic acid, hydrazide)	25 mg	3.2	None
D404	DCIA (7-diethylamino-3-((4'-(iodoacetyl)amino)phenyl)-4-methylcoumarin)	25 mg	2.3	None
D3923	DCVJ (4-(dicyanovinyl)julolidine)	25 mg	11.2, 13.5	None
H6482	DDAO (7-hydroxy-9*H*-(1,3-dichloro-9,9-dimethylacridin-2-one)) *reference standard*	10 mg	10.1	None
D6488	DDAO galactoside (9*H*-(1,3-dichloro-9,9-dimethylacridin-2-one-7-yl) β-D-galactopyranoside)	5 mg	10.2	234
D6486	DDAO GlcU (9*H*-(1,3-dichloro-9,9-dimethylacridin-2-one-7-yl) β-D-glucuronide)	5 mg	10.2	234
D6487	DDAO phosphate (9*H*-(1,3-dichloro-9,9-dimethylacridin-2-one-7-yl) phosphate, diammonium salt)	5 mg	10.3	234
D1463	DDB (1,2-diamino-4,5-dimethoxybenzene, dihydrochloride)	100 mg	3.2	None
D7915	DEANO (diethylamine nitric oxide, sodium salt)	25 mg	18.3	None
D3771	2-decanoyl-1-(*O*-(11-(4,4-difluoro-5,7-dimethyl-4-bora-3a,4a-diaza-*s*-indacene-3-propionyl)amino)undecyl)-*sn*-glycero-3-phosphocholine	1 mg	13.2, 17.4	193
D22361	2'-deoxyadenosine 5'-triphosphate, P^3-(5-sulfo-1-naphthylamide) (dATP γ-AmNS) *5 mM in water*	400 µL	17.3	None
D12371	deoxyribonuclease I, Alexa Fluor® 488 conjugate	5 mg	11.1	183
D12372	deoxyribonuclease I, Alexa Fluor® 594 conjugate	5 mg	11.1	183
D970	deoxyribonuclease I, fluorescein conjugate	5 mg	11.1	None
D7497	deoxyribonuclease I, Oregon Green® 488 conjugate	5 mg	11.1	191
D972	deoxyribonuclease I, Texas Red® conjugate	5 mg	11.1	None
D20657	D-desthiobiotin *50 mM aqueous solution*	10 mL	4.2, 7.6, 9.2	None
D30753	desthiobiotin-X C_2-iodoacetamide (DSB-X™ biotin C_2-iodoacetamide)	5 mg	4.2	None
D20652	ε-desthiobiotinoyl-L-lysine (DSB-X™ desthiobiocytin)	5 mg	4.2, 14.3	None
D30752	desthiobiotin-X ethylenediamine, hydrochloride (DSB-X™ biotin ethylenediamine)	1 mg	4.2, 14.3	None
D2920	DetectaGene™ Green CMFDG *lacZ* Gene Expression Kit	1 kit	10.2	212
D1383	dexamethasone fluorescein	5 mg	16.1	None
D22910	dextran, Alexa Fluor® 488; 10,000 MW, anionic, fixable	5 mg	14.5	183
D22911	dextran, Alexa Fluor® 546; 10,000 MW, anionic, fixable	5 mg	14.5	183
D22912	dextran, Alexa Fluor® 568; 10,000 MW, anionic, fixable	5 mg	14.5	183
D22913	dextran, Alexa Fluor® 594; 10,000 MW, anionic, fixable	5 mg	14.5	183
D22914	dextran, Alexa Fluor® 647; 10,000 MW, anionic, fixable	2 mg	14.5	223
D3330	dextran, amino, 3000 MW	100 mg	14.5	None
D1860	dextran, amino, 10,000 MW	1 g	14.5	None
D1861	dextran, amino, 40,000 MW	1 g	14.5	None
D1862	dextran, amino, 70,000 MW	1 g	14.5	None
D7144	dextran, amino, 500,000 MW	100 mg	14.5	None
D34678	dextran, 5-(and-6)-carboxy-Q-rhodamine, CMNCBZ-caged, 10,000 MW, anionic	5 mg	5.3, 14.5	None
D1878	dextran, BCECF, 10,000 MW, anionic	10 mg	20.4	None

For current prices or to order online, visit probes.invitrogen.com

Cat #	Product Name	Unit Size	Sections	Limited Use Label License #
D1879	dextran, BCECF, 40,000 MW, anionic	10 mg	20.4	None
D1880	dextran, BCECF, 70,000 MW, anionic	10 mg	20.4	None
D7135	dextran, biotin, 3000 MW, lysine fixable (BDA-3000)	10 mg	4.3, 14.5	None
D7134	dextran, biotin, 3000 MW, neutral	10 mg	4.3, 14.5	None
D1956	dextran, biotin, 10,000 MW, lysine fixable (BDA-10,000)	25 mg	4.3, 14.5	None
D1957	dextran, biotin, 70,000 MW, lysine fixable (BDA-70,000)	25 mg	4.3, 14.5	None
D7142	dextran, biotin, 500,000 MW, lysine fixable (BDA-500,000)	10 mg	4.3, 14.5	None
D7168	dextran, BODIPY® FL, 10,000 MW, fixable	5 mg	14.5	193
D7132	dextran, Cascade Blue®, 3000 MW, anionic, lysine fixable	10 mg	14.5	218
D1976	dextran, Cascade Blue®, 10,000 MW, anionic, lysine fixable	25 mg	14.5	218
D12980	dextran, 4',5'-dichloro-2',7'-dimethoxyfluorescein, 10,000 MW, anionic	5 mg	14.5, 20.4	None
D12981	dextran, 4',5'-dichloro-2',7'-dimethoxyfluorescein, 70,000 MW, anionic	5 mg	14.5, 20.4	None
D12983	dextran, 2,4-dinitrophenyl-X, 10,000 MW, lysine fixable	25 mg	14.5	None
D3309	dextran, DMNB-caged fluorescein, 3000 MW, anionic	5 mg	5.3, 14.5	None
D3310	dextran, DMNB-caged fluorescein, 10,000 MW, anionic	5 mg	5.3, 14.5	None
D7146	dextran, DMNB-caged fluorescein and biotin, 10,000 MW, lysine fixable	5 mg	4.3, 5.3, 14.5	None
D7147	dextran, DMNB-caged fluorescein and biotin, 70,000 MW, lysine fixable	5 mg	4.3, 5.3, 14.5	None
D7166	dextran, eosin, 10,000 MW, anionic, lysine fixable	25 mg	14.5	None
D3305	dextran, fluorescein, 3000 MW, anionic	10 mg	14.5, 20.4	None
D3306	dextran, fluorescein, 3000 MW, anionic, lysine fixable	10 mg	14.5	None
D1821	dextran, fluorescein, 10,000 MW, anionic	25 mg	14.5, 20.4	None
D1820	dextran, fluorescein, 10,000 MW, anionic, lysine fixable (fluoro-emerald)	25 mg	14.5	None
D1844	dextran, fluorescein, 40,000 MW, anionic	25 mg	14.5, 20.4	None
D1845	dextran, fluorescein, 40,000 MW, anionic, lysine fixable	25 mg	14.5	None
D1823	dextran, fluorescein, 70,000 MW, anionic	25 mg	14.5, 20.4	None
D1822	dextran, fluorescein, 70,000 MW, anionic, lysine fixable	25 mg	14.5	None
D1815	dextran, fluorescein, 70,000 MW, polyanionic	25 mg	14.5	None
D7136	dextran, fluorescein, 500,000 MW, anionic, lysine fixable	10 mg	14.5	None
D7137	dextran, fluorescein, 2,000,000 MW, anionic, lysine fixable	10 mg	14.5	None
D7156	dextran, fluorescein and biotin, 3000 MW, anionic, lysine fixable (micro-emerald)	5 mg	4.3, 14.5	None
D7178	dextran, fluorescein and biotin, 10,000 MW, anionic, lysine fixable (mini-emerald)	10 mg	4.3, 14.5	None
D1950	dextran, fluorescein and tetramethylrhodamine, 10,000 MW, anionic	10 mg	20.4	None
D1951	dextran, fluorescein and tetramethylrhodamine, 70,000 MW, anionic	10 mg	20.4	None
D7179	dextran, 8-hydroxypyrene-1,3,6-trisulfonic acid, 10,000 MW, anionic (HPTS dextran)	5 mg	20.4	None
D1825	dextran, lucifer yellow, 10,000 MW, anionic, lysine fixable	25 mg	14.5	None
D7170	dextran, Oregon Green® 488; 10,000 MW, anionic	5 mg	14.5, 20.4	183
D7171	dextran, Oregon Green® 488; 10,000 MW, anionic, lysine fixable	5 mg	14.5	183
D7172	dextran, Oregon Green® 488; 70,000 MW, anionic	5 mg	14.5, 20.4	183
D7173	dextran, Oregon Green® 488; 70,000 MW, anionic, lysine fixable	5 mg	14.5	183
D7174	dextran, Oregon Green® 514; 10,000 MW, anionic	5 mg	14.5, 20.4	191
D7175	dextran, Oregon Green® 514; 10,000 MW, anionic, lysine fixable	5 mg	14.5	191
D7176	dextran, Oregon Green® 514; 70,000 MW, anionic	5 mg	14.5, 20.4	191
D1824	dextran, rhodamine B, 10,000 MW, neutral	25 mg	14.5	None
D1841	dextran, rhodamine B, 70,000 MW, neutral	25 mg	14.5	None
D7163	dextran, Rhodamine Green™, 3000 MW	5 mg	14.5	None
D7153	dextran, Rhodamine Green™, 10,000 MW, lysine fixable	10 mg	14.5	None
D3303	dextran, SNARF®-1, 10,000 MW, anionic	5 mg	20.4	208
D3304	dextran, SNARF®-1, 70,000 MW, anionic	5 mg	20.4	208
D3307	dextran, tetramethylrhodamine, 3000 MW, anionic	10 mg	14.5	None
D3308	dextran, tetramethylrhodamine, 3000 MW, anionic, lysine fixable	10 mg	14.5	None
D1868	dextran, tetramethylrhodamine, 10,000 MW, anionic, fixable	25 mg	14.5	None
D1817	dextran, tetramethylrhodamine, 10,000 MW, lysine fixable (fluoro-ruby)	25 mg	14.5	None
D1816	dextran, tetramethylrhodamine, 10,000 MW, neutral	25 mg	14.5	None
D1842	dextran, tetramethylrhodamine, 40,000 MW, neutral	25 mg	14.5	None
D1818	dextran, tetramethylrhodamine, 70,000 MW, lysine fixable	25 mg	14.5	None
D1819	dextran, tetramethylrhodamine, 70,000 MW, neutral	25 mg	14.5	None
D7139	dextran, tetramethylrhodamine, 2,000,000 MW, lysine fixable	10 mg	14.5	None
D7162	dextran, tetramethylrhodamine and biotin, 3000 MW, lysine fixable (micro-ruby)	5 mg	4.3, 14.5	None

For current prices or to order online, visit probes.invitrogen.com

Cat #	Product Name	Unit Size	Sections	Limited Use Label License #
D3312	dextran, tetramethylrhodamine and biotin, 10,000 MW, lysine fixable (mini-ruby)	10 mg	4.3, 14.5	None
D3328	dextran, Texas Red®, 3000 MW, lysine fixable	10 mg	14.5	None
D3329	dextran, Texas Red®, 3000 MW, neutral	10 mg	14.5	None
D1863	dextran, Texas Red®, 10,000 MW, lysine fixable	25 mg	14.5	None
D1828	dextran, Texas Red®, 10,000 MW, neutral	25 mg	14.5	None
D1829	dextran, Texas Red®, 40,000 MW, neutral	25 mg	14.5	None
D1864	dextran, Texas Red®, 70,000 MW, lysine fixable	25 mg	14.5	None
D1830	dextran, Texas Red®, 70,000 MW, neutral	25 mg	14.5	None
D3883	DiA; 4-Di-16-ASP (4-(4-(dihexadecylamino)styryl)-*N*-methylpyridinium iodide)	25 mg	13.4, 14.4	None
D1306	4',6-diamidino-2-phenylindole, dihydrochloride (DAPI)	10 mg	8.1, 8.6, 8.7, 11.2, 14.3, 15.4	None
D21490	4',6-diamidino-2-phenylindole, dihydrochloride (DAPI) *FluoroPure™ grade*	10 mg	8.1, 8.6, 8.7, 11.2, 14.3, 15.4	None
D3571	4',6-diamidino-2-phenylindole, dilactate (DAPI, dilactate)	10 mg	8.1, 8.6, 8.7, 11.2, 14.3, 15.4	None
D23840	1,2-diaminoanthraquinone sulfate (DAA) *high purity*	5 mg	18.3	None
D22185	Diaminobenzidine (DAB) Histochemistry Kit #1 *with goat anti-mouse IgG–HRP*	1 kit	7.2, 10.5	None
D22187	Diaminobenzidine (DAB) Histochemistry Kit #3 *with streptavidin–HRP*	1 kit	7.6, 10.5	None
D1463	1,2-diamino-4,5-dimethoxybenzene, dihydrochloride (DDB)	100 mg	3.2	None
D7918	2,3-diaminonaphthalene	100 mg	3.2, 18.3, 21.2	None
D6923	di-2-ANEPEQ (JPW 1114)	5 mg	22.2	None
D36800	di-1-ANEPIA	1 mg	22.2	None
D6925	di-8-ANEPPQ	5 mg	22.2	None
D6927	di-12-ANEPPQ	5 mg	22.2	None
D1199	di-4-ANEPPS	5 mg	22.2	None
D3167	di-8-ANEPPS	5 mg	22.2	None
D6928	di-18:2-ANEPPS	5 mg	22.2	None
B153	4,4'-dianilino-1,1'-binaphthyl-5,5'-disulfonic acid, dipotassium salt (bis-ANS)	10 mg	11.2, 13.5	None
D308	2-Di-1-ASP (2-(4-(dimethylamino)styryl)-*N*-methylpyridinium iodide)	1 g	12.2	None
D288	4-Di-1-ASP (4-(4-(dimethylamino)styryl)-*N*-methylpyridinium iodide)	1 g	12.2, 16.1	None
D289	4-Di-2-ASP (4-(4-(diethylamino)styryl)-*N*-methylpyridinium iodide)	1 g	16.1	None
D291	4-Di-10-ASP (4-(4-(didecylamino)styryl)-*N*-methylpyridinium iodide)	25 mg	13.4, 14.4	None
D3036	diazo-2, AM *cell permeant* *special packaging*	20 x 50 µg	5.3, 17.2, 19.8	None
D3034	diazo-2, tetrapotassium salt *cell impermeant*	1 mg	5.3, 17.2, 19.8	None
B438	DiBAC$_4$(3) (bis-(1,3-dibutylbarbituric acid)trimethine oxonol)	25 mg	22.3	None
B24570	DiBAC$_4$(3) (bis-(1,3-dibutylbarbituric acid)trimethine oxonol) *FluoroPure™ grade*	5 mg	22.3	None
B436	DiBAC$_4$(5) (bis-(1,3-dibutylbarbituric acid)pentamethine oxonol)	25 mg	16.3, 22.3	None
D675	4,4'-dibenzamidostilbene-2,2'-disulfonic acid, disodium salt (DBDS)	100 mg	16.3	None
D1213	5,5'-dibromo BAPTA, AM *cell permeant*	25 mg	19.8	None
D1211	5,5'-dibromo BAPTA, tetrapotassium salt *cell impermeant*	100 mg	19.8	None
D1379	dibromobimane (bBBr)	25 mg	2.3, 5.2	None
D7546	*N*-(2,6-dibromo-4,4-difluoro-5,7-dimethyl-4-bora-3a,4a-diaza-*s*-indacene-3-pentanoyl)sphingosine (BODIPY® FL Br_2C_5-ceramide)	250 µg	12.4, 13.3, 17.4	193
D6144	2,6-dibromo-4,4-difluoro-5,7-dimethyl-4-bora-3a,4a-diaza-*s*-indacene-3-propionic acid, succinimidyl ester (BODIPY® FL Br_2, SE)	5 mg	1.4	193
D7766	5,5'-dibromo-1,1'-dioctadecyl-3,3,3',3'-tetramethylindocarbocyanine perchlorate (Br_2-DiIC$_{18}$(3))	5 mg	13.4, 14.4	None
D399	2',7'-dichlorodihydrofluorescein diacetate (2',7'-dichlorofluorescin diacetate; H_2DCFDA)	100 mg	10.5, 15.2, 15.5, 18.2	None
D2935	2',7'-dichlorodihydrofluorescein diacetate, succinimidyl ester (OxyBURST® Green H_2DCFDA, SE)	5 mg	16.1, 18.2	None
D6488	9*H*-(1,3-dichloro-9,9-dimethylacridin-2-one-7-yl) β-D-galactopyranoside (DDAO galactoside)	5 mg	10.2	234
D6486	9*H*-(1,3-dichloro-9,9-dimethylacridin-2-one-7-yl) β-D-glucuronide (DDAO GlcU)	5 mg	10.2	234
D6487	9*H*-(1,3-dichloro-9,9-dimethylacridin-2-one-7-yl) phosphate, diammonium salt (DDAO phosphate)	5 mg	10.3	234
D399	2',7'-dichlorofluorescin diacetate; H_2DCFDA (2',7'-dichlorodihydrofluorescein diacetate)	100 mg	10.5, 15.2, 15.5, 18.2	None
D16	5-(4,6-dichlorotriazinyl)aminofluorescein (5-DTAF) *single isomer*	100 mg	1.5, 3.1	None
D3923	4-(dicyanovinyl)julolidine (DCVJ)	25 mg	11.2, 13.5	None
D146	*N,N'*-didansyl-L-cystine	100 mg	2.3	None
D291	4-(4-(didecylamino)styryl)-*N*-methylpyridinium iodide (4-Di-10-ASP)	25 mg	13.4, 14.4	None
D383	1,1'-didodecyl-3,3,3',3'-tetramethylindocarbocyanine perchlorate (DiIC$_{12}$(3))	100 mg	13.4, 14.4	None
D307	'DiD' oil; DiIC$_{18}$(5) oil (1,1'-dioctadecyl-3,3,3',3'-tetramethylindodicarbocyanine perchlorate)	25 mg	13.4, 14.4	None
D337	DIDS (4,4'-diisothiocyanatostilbene-2,2'-disulfonic acid, disodium salt)	100 mg	16.3	None

For current prices or to order online, visit probes.invitrogen.com

Cat #	Product Name	Unit Size	Sections	Limited Use Label License #
D7757	'DiD' solid; DiIC_{18}(5) solid (1,1′-dioctadecyl-3,3,3′,3′-tetramethylindodicarbocyanine, 4-chlorobenzenesulfonate salt)	10 mg	13.4, 14.4	None
D7915	diethylamine nitric oxide, sodium salt (DEANO)	25 mg	18.3	None
D1446	7-diethylaminocoumarin-3-carbonyl azide	25 mg	3.1	None
D1421	7-diethylaminocoumarin-3-carboxylic acid	100 mg	1.7	None
D355	7-diethylaminocoumarin-3-carboxylic acid, hydrazide (DCCH)	25 mg	3.2	None
D1412	7-diethylaminocoumarin-3-carboxylic acid, succinimidyl ester	25 mg	1.7	None
D20382	7-diethylamino-3-((((2-iodoacetamido)ethyl)amino)carbonyl)coumarin (IDCC)	5 mg	2.3	None
D404	7-diethylamino-3-((4′-(iodoacetyl)amino)phenyl)-4-methylcoumarin (DCIA)	25 mg	2.3	None
D10253	7-diethylamino-3-((((2-maleimidyl)ethyl)amino)carbonyl)coumarin (MDCC)	5 mg	2.3	None
D346	7-diethylamino-3-(4′-maleimidylphenyl)-4-methylcoumarin (CPM)	25 mg	2.3	None
D289	4-(4-(diethylamino)styryl)-*N*-methylpyridinium iodide (4-Di-2-ASP)	1 g	16.1	None
D14730	3,3′-diethyloxacarbocyanine iodide (DiOC_2(3))	100 mg	22.3	None
D1209	5,5′-difluoro BAPTA, AM *cell permeant*	25 mg	19.8	None
D1208	5,5′-difluoro BAPTA, tetrapotassium salt *cell impermeant*	100 mg	19.8	None
D6103	4,4-difluoro-4-bora-3a,4a-diaza-*s*-indacene-3,5-dipropionic acid (BODIPY® 500/510)	5 mg	1.4	193
D10620	4,4-difluoro-3,5-di(iodoacetamidomethyl)-4-bora-3a,4a-diaza-*s*-indacene (BODIPY® FL bis-(methyleneiodoacetamide))	5 mg	2.2, 5.2	193
D20351	4,4-difluoro-3,5-bis(4-methoxyphenyl)-8-(4-maleimidylphenyl)-4-bora-3a,4a-diaza-*s*-indacene (BODIPY® 577/618 maleimide)	5 mg	2.2	None
D3822	4,4-difluoro-5,7-dimethyl-4-bora-3a,4a-diaza-*s*-indacene-3-dodecanoic acid (BODIPY® FL C_{12})	1 mg	13.2	193
D3792	2-(4,4-difluoro-5,7-dimethyl-4-bora-3a,4a-diaza-*s*-indacene-3-dodecanoyl)-1-hexadecanoyl-*sn*-glycero-3-phosphocholine (β-BODIPY® FL C_{12}-HPC)	100 µg	13.2	193
D7519	*N*-(4,4-difluoro-5,7-dimethyl-4-bora-3a,4a-diaza-*s*-indacene-3-dodecanoyl)sphingosyl 1-β-D-galactopyranoside (BODIPY® FL C_{12}-galactocerebroside)	25 µg	10.2, 13.3, 17.4	193
D7547	*N*-(4,4-difluoro-5,7-dimethyl-4-bora-3a,4a-diaza-*s*-indacene-3-dodecanoyl)sphingosyl 1-β-D-glucopyranoside (BODIPY® FL C_{12}-glucocerebroside)	250 µg	10.2, 13.3, 17.4	193
D7711	*N*-(4,4-difluoro-5,7-dimethyl-4-bora-3a,4a-diaza-*s*-indacene-3-dodecanoyl)sphingosyl phosphocholine (BODIPY® FL C_{12}-sphingomyelin) *1 mg/mL in DMSO*	250 µL	12.4, 13.3, 17.4	193
D3821	4,4-difluoro-5,7-dimethyl-4-bora-3a,4a-diaza-*s*-indacene-3-hexadecanoic acid (BODIPY® FL C_{16})	1 mg	13.2	193
D3834	4,4-difluoro-5,7-dimethyl-4-bora-3a,4a-diaza-*s*-indacene-3-pentanoic acid (BODIPY® FL C_5)	1 mg	1.4, 13.2	193
D6184	4,4-difluoro-5,7-dimethyl-4-bora-3a,4a-diaza-*s*-indacene-3-pentanoic acid, succinimidyl ester (BODIPY® FL C_5, SE)	5 mg	1.4	193
D3805	2-(4,4-difluoro-5,7-dimethyl-4-bora-3a,4a-diaza-*s*-indacene-3-pentanoyl)-1-hexadecanoyl-*sn*-glycero-3-phosphate, diammonium salt (β-BODIPY® FL C_5-HPA)	100 µg	13.2	193
D3803	2-(4,4-difluoro-5,7-dimethyl-4-bora-3a,4a-diaza-*s*-indacene-3-pentanoyl)-1-hexadecanoyl-*sn*-glycero-3-phosphocholine (β-BODIPY® FL C_5-HPC)	100 µg	13.2, 17.4	193
D3521	*N*-(4,4-difluoro-5,7-dimethyl-4-bora-3a,4a-diaza-*s*-indacene-3-pentanoyl)sphingosine (BODIPY® FL C_5-ceramide)	250 µg	12.4, 13.3, 17.4	193
D7548	*N*-(4,4-difluoro-5,7-dimethyl-4-bora-3a,4a-diaza-*s*-indacene-3-pentanoyl)sphingosyl 1-β-D-glucopyranoside (BODIPY® FL C_5-glucocerebroside)	250 µg	10.2, 13.3, 17.4	193
D13951	*N*-(4,4-difluoro-5,7-dimethyl-4-bora-3a,4a-diaza-*s*-indacene-3-pentanoyl)sphingosyl 1-β-D-lactoside (BODIPY® FL C_5-lactosylceramide)	25 µg	10.2, 12.4, 13.3, 17.4	193
D3522	*N*-(4,4-difluoro-5,7-dimethyl-4-bora-3a,4a-diaza-*s*-indacene-3-pentanoyl)sphingosyl phosphocholine (BODIPY® FL C_5-sphingomyelin)	250 µg	12.4, 13.3, 17.4	193
D2183	4,4-difluoro-5,7-dimethyl-4-bora-3a,4a-diaza-*s*-indacene-3-propionic acid (BODIPY® FL)	5 mg	1.4	193
D2371	4,4-difluoro-5,7-dimethyl-4-bora-3a,4a-diaza-*s*-indacene-3-propionic acid, hydrazide (BODIPY® FL hydrazide)	5 mg	3.2	193
D2184	4,4-difluoro-5,7-dimethyl-4-bora-3a,4a-diaza-*s*-indacene-3-propionic acid, succinimidyl ester (BODIPY® FL, SE)	5 mg	1.4	193
D6140	4,4-difluoro-5,7-dimethyl-4-bora-3a,4a-diaza-*s*-indacene-3-propionic acid, sulfosuccinimidyl ester, sodium salt (BODIPY® FL, SSE)	5 mg	1.4	193
D6101	6-((4,4-difluoro-5,7-dimethyl-4-bora-3a,4a-diaza-*s*-indacene-3-propionyl)amino)hexanoic acid (BODIPY® FL-X)	5 mg	1.4	193
D6102	6-((4,4-difluoro-5,7-dimethyl-4-bora-3a,4a-diaza-*s*-indacene-3-propionyl)amino)hexanoic acid, succinimidyl ester (BODIPY® FL-X, SE)	5 mg	1.4, 4.2, 9.3	193
D3800	*N*-(4,4-difluoro-5,7-dimethyl-4-bora-3a,4a-diaza-*s*-indacene-3-propionyl)-1,2-dihexadecanoyl-*sn*-glycero-3-phosphoethanolamine, triethylammonium salt (BODIPY® FL DHPE)	100 µg	13.2	193
D12656	*N*-(4,4-difluoro-5,7-dimethyl-4-bora-3a,4a-diaza-*s*-indacene-3-propionyl)-1,2-dihexanoyl-*sn*-glycero-3-phosphoethanolamine, triethylammonium salt (BODIPY® FL dicaproyl PE)	100 µg	13.2	193
D2390	4,4-difluoro-5,7-dimethyl-4-bora-3a,4a-diaza-*s*-indacene-3-propionyl ethylenediamine, hydrochloride (BODIPY® FL EDA)	5 mg	3.3	193
D3862	4,4-difluoro-5,7-dimethyl-4-bora-3a,4a-diaza-*s*-indacene-3-undecanoic acid (BODIPY® FL C_{11})	1 mg	13.2	193
D6003	*N*-(4,4-difluoro-5,7-dimethyl-4-bora-3a,4a-diaza-*s*-indacene-3-yl)methyl)iodoacetamide (BODIPY® FL C_1-IA)	5 mg	2.2	193
D6117	6-((4,4-difluoro-1,3-dimethyl-5-(4-methoxyphenyl)-4-bora-3a,4a-diaza-*s*-indacene-2-propionyl)amino)hexanoic acid, succinimidyl ester (BODIPY® TMR-X, SE)	5 mg	1.4	193
D6012	*N*-(5-((4,4-difluoro-1,3-dimethyl-5-(4-methoxyphenyl)-4-bora-3a,4a-diaza-*s*-indacene-2-propionyl)amino)pentyl)iodoa cetamide (BODIPY® TMR cadaverine IA)	5 mg	2.2	193
D3832	4,4-difluoro-5,7-diphenyl-4-bora-3a,4a-diaza-*s*-indacene-3-dodecanoic acid (BODIPY® 530/550 C_{12})	1 mg	13.2	193
D3815	2-(4,4-difluoro-5,7-diphenyl-4-bora-3a,4a-diaza-*s*-indacene-3-pentanoyl)-1-hexadecanoyl-*sn*-glycero-3-phosphocholine (β-BODIPY® 530/550 C_5-HPC)	100 µg	13.2	193

For current prices or to order online, visit probes.invitrogen.com

Cat #	Product Name	Unit Size	Sections	Limited Use Label License #
D2187	4,4-difluoro-5,7-diphenyl-4-bora-3a,4a-diaza-*s*-indacene-3-propionic acid, succinimidyl ester (BODIPY® 530/550, SE)	5 mg	1.4	193
D3799	*N*-(4,4-difluoro-5,7-diphenyl-4-bora-3a,4a-diaza-*s*-indacene-3-propionyl)-1,2-dihexadecanoyl-*sn*-glycero-3-phosphoethanolamine, triethylammonium salt (BODIPY® 530/550 DHPE)	100 µg	13.2	193
D2391	4,4-difluoro-5,7-diphenyl-4-bora-3a,4a-diaza-*s*-indacene-3-propionyl ethylenediamine, hydrochloride (BODIPY® 530/550 EDA)	5 mg	3.3	193
D2006	*N*-(4,4-difluoro-5,7-diphenyl-4-bora-3a,4a-diaza-*s*-indacene-3-propionyl)-*N*′-iodoacetylethylenediamine (BODIPY® 530/550 IA)	5 mg	2.2	193
D12203	6,8-difluoro-7-ethoxy-4-methylcoumarin (DiFMUEt)	5 mg	10.6	192
D6145	2′,7′-difluorofluorescein (Oregon Green® 488)	10 mg	1.5	191
D12760	6,8-difluoro-4-heptadecyl-7-hydroxycoumarin (C_{17}DiFU)	10 mg	13.5, 20.4	192
D11950	6,8-difluoro-4-heptadecylumbelliferyl β-D-galactopyranoside (C_{17}DiFUG)	5 mg	10.2	192
D11953	6,8-difluoro-4-heptadecylumbelliferyl β-D-glucopyranoside (C_{17}DiFUGlu)	5 mg	10.2	192
D6566	6,8-difluoro-7-hydroxy-4-methylcoumarin (DiFMU) *reference standard*	10 mg	10.1	192
D3823	4,4-difluoro-5-methyl-4-bora-3a,4a-diaza-*s*-indacene-3-dodecanoic acid (BODIPY® 500/510 C_1, C_{12})	1 mg	13.2	193
D3793	2-(4,4-difluoro-5-methyl-4-bora-3a,4a-diaza-*s*-indacene-3-dodecanoyl)-1-hexadecanoyl-*sn*-glycero-3-phosphocholine (β-BODIPY® 500/510 C_{12}-HPC)	100 µg	13.2	193
D11945	6,8-difluoro-4-methylumbelliferyl β-D-galactopyranoside (DiFMUG)	10 mg	10.2	192
D11951	6,8-difluoro-4-methylumbelliferyl β-D-glucuronide, lithium salt (DiFMUGlcU)	5 mg	10.2	192
D12200	6,8-difluoro-4-methylumbelliferyl octanoate (DiFMU octanoate)	10 mg	10.6	192
D6567	6,8-difluoro-4-methylumbelliferyl phosphate (DiFMUP)	5 mg	10.3	192
D3825	4,4-difluoro-5-octyl-4-bora-3a,4a-diaza-*s*-indacene-3-pentanoic acid (BODIPY® 500/510 C_8, C_5)	1 mg	13.2	193
D3795	2-(4,4-difluoro-5-octyl-4-bora-3a,4a-diaza-*s*-indacene-3-pentanoyl)-1-hexadecanoyl-*sn*-glycero-3-phosphocholine (β-C_8-BODIPY® 500/510 C_5-HPC)	100 µg	13.2	193
D3922	4,4-difluoro-1,3,5,7,8-pentamethyl-4-bora-3a,4a-diaza-*s*-indacene (BODIPY® 493/503)	10 mg	13.5	193
D3238	4,4-difluoro-1,3,5,7,8-pentamethyl-4-bora-3a,4a-diaza-*s*-indacene-2,6-disulfonic acid, disodium salt (BODIPY® 492/515 disulfonate)	10 mg	14.3	None
D6180	4,4-difluoro-5-phenyl-4-bora-3a,4a-diaza-*s*-indacene-3-propionic acid, succinimidyl ester (BODIPY® R6G, SE)	5 mg	1.4	193
D6186	6-((4,4-difluoro-5-phenyl-4-bora-3a,4a-diaza-*s*-indacene-3-propionyl)amino)hexanoic acid, succinimidyl ester (BODIPY® R6G-X, SE)	5 mg	1.4	193
D3860	4,4-difluoro-5-(4-phenyl-1,3-butadienyl)-4-bora-3a,4a-diaza-*s*-indacene-3-pentanoic acid (BODIPY® 581/591 C_5)	1 mg	13.2	193
D3806	2-(4,4-difluoro-5-(4-phenyl-1,3-butadienyl)-4-bora-3a,4a-diaza-*s*-indacene-3-pentanoyl)-1-hexadecanoyl-*sn*-glycero-3-phosphocholine (β-BODIPY® 581/591 C_5-HPC)	100 µg	13.2	193
D2228	4,4-difluoro-5-(4-phenyl-1,3-butadienyl)-4-bora-3a,4a-diaza-*s*-indacene-3-propionic acid, succinimidyl ester (BODIPY® 581/591, SE)	5 mg	1.4	193
D3861	4,4-difluoro-5-(4-phenyl-1,3-butadienyl)-4-bora-3a,4a-diaza-*s*-indacene-3-undecanoic acid (BODIPY® 581/591 C_{11})	1 mg	13.2, 18.2	193
D2225	4,4-difluoro-5-(2-pyrrolyl)-4-bora-3a,4a-diaza-*s*-indacene-3-propionic acid, succinimidyl ester (BODIPY® 576/589, SE)	5 mg	1.4	193
D3859	4,4-difluoro-5-(2-pyrrolyl)-4-bora-3a,4a-diaza-*s*-indacene-3-undecanoic acid (BODIPY® 576/589 C_{11})	1 mg	13.2	193
D10001	6-(((4,4-difluoro-5-(2-pyrrolyl)-4-bora-3a,4a-diaza-*s*-indacene-3-yl)styryloxy)acetyl)aminohexanoic acid, succinimidyl ester (BODIPY® 650/665-X, SE)	5 mg	1.4	193
D3838	4,4-difluoro-5-styryl-4-bora-3a,4a-diaza-*s*-indacene-3-pentanoic acid (BODIPY® 564/570 C_5)	1 mg	13.2	193
D2222	4,4-difluoro-5-styryl-4-bora-3a,4a-diaza-*s*-indacene-3-propionic acid, succinimidyl ester (BODIPY® 564/570, SE)	5 mg	1.4	193
D3839	4,4-difluoro-5-styryl-4-bora-3a,4a-diaza-*s*-indacene-3-undecanoic acid (BODIPY® 564/570 C_{11})	1 mg	13.2	193
D3921	4,4-difluoro-1,3,5,7-tetramethyl-4-bora-3a,4a-diaza-*s*-indacene (BODIPY® 505/515)	10 mg	13.5	193
D2191	4,4-difluoro-1,3,5,7-tetramethyl-4-bora-3a,4a-diaza-*s*-indacene-8-propionic acid, succinimidyl ester (BODIPY® 493/503, SE)	5 mg	1.4	None
D6004	*N*-(4,4-difluoro-1,3,5,7-tetramethyl-4-bora-3a,4a-diaza-*s*-indacene-2-yl)iodoacetamide (BODIPY® 507/545 IA)	5 mg	2.2	193
D20350	4,4-difluoro-1,3,5,7-tetramethyl-8-(4-maleimidylphenyl)-4-bora-3a,4a-diaza-*s*-indacene (BODIPY® 499/508 maleimide)	5 mg	2.2	None
D3835	4,4-difluoro-5-(2-thienyl)-4-bora-3a,4a-diaza-*s*-indacene-3-dodecanoic acid (BODIPY® 558/568 C_{12})	1 mg	13.2	193
D2219	4,4-difluoro-5-(2-thienyl)-4-bora-3a,4a-diaza-*s*-indacene-3-propionic acid, succinimidyl ester (BODIPY® 558/568, SE)	5 mg	1.4	193
D6116	6-(((4-(4,4-difluoro-5-(2-thienyl)-4-bora-3a,4a-diaza-*s*-indacene-3-yl)phenoxy)acetyl)amino)hexanoic acid, succinimidyl ester (BODIPY® TR-X, SE)	5 mg	1.4, 9.3	193
D6251	5-(((4-(4,4-difluoro-5-(2-thienyl)-4-bora-3a,4a-diaza-*s*-indacene-3-yl)phenoxy)acetyl)amino)pentylamine, hydrochloride (BODIPY® TR cadaverine)	5 mg	3.3	193
D7540	*N*-((4-(4,4-difluoro-5-(2-thienyl)-4-bora-3a,4a-diaza-*s*-indacene-3-yl)phenoxy)acetyl)sphingosine (BODIPY® TR ceramide)	250 µg	12.4, 13.3, 17.4	193
D10000	6-(((4,4-difluoro-5-(2-thienyl)-4-bora-3a,4a-diaza-*s*-indacene-3-yl)styryloxy)acetyl)aminohexanoic acid, succinimidyl ester (BODIPY® 630/650-X, SE)	5 mg	1.4	193
D12203	DiFMUEt (6,8-difluoro-7-ethoxy-4-methylcoumarin)	5 mg	10.6	192
D11945	DiFMUG (6,8-difluoro-4-methylumbelliferyl β-D-galactopyranoside)	10 mg	10.2	192
D11951	DiFMUGlcU (6,8-difluoro-4-methylumbelliferyl β-D-glucuronide, lithium salt)	5 mg	10.2	192
D12200	DiFMU octanoate (6,8-difluoro-4-methylumbelliferyl octanoate)	10 mg	10.6	192
D6567	DiFMUP (6,8-difluoro-4-methylumbelliferyl phosphate)	5 mg	10.3	192
D12760	C_{17}DiFU (6,8-difluoro-4-heptadecyl-7-hydroxycoumarin)	10 mg	13.5, 20.4	192

For current prices or to order online, visit probes.invitrogen.com

Cat #	Product Name	Unit Size	Sections	Limited Use Label License #
D11950	C_{17}DiFUG (6,8-difluoro-4-heptadecylumbelliferyl β-D-galactopyranoside)	5 mg	10.2	192
D11953	C_{17}DiFUGlu (6,8-difluoro-4-heptadecylumbelliferyl β-D-glucopyranoside)	5 mg	10.2	192
D378	3,3′-diheptyloxacarbocyanine iodide ($DiOC_7(3)$)	100 mg	12.2	None
D69	4-dihexadecylamino-7-nitrobenz-2-oxa-1,3-diazole (NBD dihexadecylamine)	100 mg	13.5	None
D3883	4-(4-(dihexadecylamino)styryl)-*N*-methylpyridinium iodide (DiA; 4-Di-16-ASP)	25 mg	13.4, 14.4	None
D1125	3,3′-dihexadecyloxacarbocyanine perchlorate ($DiOC_{16}(3)$)	25 mg	13.4, 14.4	None
D384	1,1′-dihexadecyl-3,3,3′,3′-tetramethylindocarbocyanine perchlorate ($DiIC_{16}(3)$)	100 mg	12.4, 13.4, 14.4	None
D273	3,3′-dihexyloxacarbocyanine iodide ($DiOC_6(3)$)	100 mg	12.2, 12.4, 15.5, 22.3	None
D23805	dihydrocalcein, AM *special packaging*	20 x 50 µg	10.5, 15.2, 15.5, 18.2	None
D1168	dihydroethidium (hydroethidine)	25 mg	8.1, 15.2, 15.5, 18.2	None
D11347	dihydroethidium (hydroethidine) *special packaging*	10 x 1 mg	8.1, 15.2, 15.5, 18.2	None
D23107	dihydroethidium (hydroethidine) *5 mM stabilized solution in DMSO*	1 mL	8.1, 15.2, 15.5, 18.2	None
D632	dihydrorhodamine 123	10 mg	12.2, 15.2, 15.5, 18.2	None
D23806	dihydrorhodamine 123 *5 mM stabilized solution in DMSO*	1 mL	12.2, 15.2, 15.5, 18.2	None
D633	dihydrorhodamine 6G	25 mg	12.2, 15.2, 18.2	None
D282	'DiI'; $DiIC_{18}(3)$ (1,1′-dioctadecyl-3,3,3′,3′-tetramethylindocarbocyanine perchlorate)	100 mg	12.4, 13.4, 14.4	None
D3886	Δ^9-DiI (1,1′-dioleyl-3,3,3′,3′-tetramethylindocarbocyanine methanesulfonate)	25 mg	13.4, 14.4	None
D3911	'DiI'; $DiIC_{18}(3)$ (1,1′-dioctadecyl-3,3,3′,3′-tetramethylindocarbocyanine perchlorate) *crystalline*	25 mg	13.4, 14.4	None
L3484	DiI AcLDL (low-density lipoprotein from human plasma, acetylated, DiI complex) *1 mg/mL*	200 µL	16.1	None
H14700	$DiIC_1(5)$ (1,1′,3,3,3′,3′-hexamethylindodicarbocyanine iodide)	100 mg	22.3	None
D383	$DiIC_{12}(3)$ (1,1′-didodecyl-3,3,3′,3′-tetramethylindocarbocyanine perchlorate)	100 mg	13.4, 14.4	None
D384	$DiIC_{16}(3)$ (1,1′-dihexadecyl-3,3,3′,3′-tetramethylindocarbocyanine perchlorate)	100 mg	12.4, 13.4, 14.4	None
D7776	$DiIC_{18}(3)$-DS (1,1′-dioctadecyl-3,3,3′,3′-tetramethylindocarbocyanine-5,5′-disulfonic acid)	5 mg	13.4, 14.4	None
D12730	$DiIC_{18}(5)$-DS (1,1′-dioctadecyl-3,3,3′,3′-tetramethylindodicarbocyanine-5,5′-disulfonic acid)	5 mg	13.4, 14.4	None
L3482	DiI LDL (low-density lipoprotein from human plasma, DiI complex) *1 mg/mL*	200 µL	16.1	None
D338	4,4′-diisothiocyanatodihydrostilbene-2,2′-disulfonic acid, disodium salt (H_2DIDS)	100 mg	16.3	None
D337	4,4′-diisothiocyanatostilbene-2,2′-disulfonic acid, disodium salt (DIDS)	100 mg	16.3	None
D7758	4-(4-(dilinoleylamino)styryl)-*N*-methylpyridinium 4-chlorobenzenesulfonate (*FAST* DiA™ solid; $DiA^{9,12}$-C_{18}ASP, CBS)	5 mg	13.4, 14.4	None
D3897	4-(4-(dilinoleylamino)styryl)-*N*-methylpyridinium iodide (*FAST* DiA™ oil; $DiA^{9,12}$-C_{18}ASP, I)	5 mg	13.4, 14.4	None
D3898	3,3′-dilinoleyloxacarbocyanine perchlorate (*FAST* DiO™ solid; $DiO\Delta^{9,12}$-$C_{18}(3)$, ClO_4)	5 mg	13.4, 14.4	None
D7756	1,1′-dilinoleyl-3,3,3′,3′-tetramethylindocarbocyanine, 4-chlorobenzenesulfonate (*FAST* DiI™ solid; $DiI\Delta^{9,12}$-$C_{18}(3)$, CBS)	5 mg	13.4, 14.4	None
D3899	1,1′-dilinoleyl-3,3,3′,3′-tetramethylindocarbocyanine perchlorate (*FAST* DiI™ oil; $DiI\Delta^{9,12}$-$C_{18}(3)$, ClO_4)	5 mg	13.4, 14.4	None
D1037	4,5-dimethoxy-2-nitrobenzyl adenosine 3′,5′-cyclicmonophosphate (DMNB-caged cAMP)	5 mg	5.3, 17.3	None
D7060	8-((4,5-dimethoxy-2-nitrobenzyl)oxy)pyrene-1,3,6-trisulfonic acid, trisodium salt (DMNB-caged HPTS)	5 mg	5.3, 14.3	254
D6814	1-(4,5-dimethoxy-2-nitrophenyl)-1,2-diaminoethane-*N,N,N′,N′*-tetraacetic acid (DMNP-EDTA) *cell impermeant*	5 mg	5.3, 17.2, 19.8	None
D2516	1-(4,5-Dimethoxy-2-nitrophenyl)diazoethane Generation Kit	1 kit	5.3	None
D1537	4-dimethylaminoazobenzene-4′-sulfonyl chloride (dabsyl chloride)	100 mg	1.8, 9.5	None
D1332	*N*-(4-(6-dimethylamino-2-benzofuranyl)phenylisothiocyanate	25 mg	1.8	None
D126	7-dimethylaminocoumarin-4-acetic acid (DMACA)	100 mg	1.7	None
D374	7-dimethylaminocoumarin-4-acetic acid, succinimidyl ester (DMACA, SE)	25 mg	1.7	None
D10166	7-dimethylamino-4-methylcoumarin-3-isothiocyanate (DACITC)	10 mg	1.7	None
D10252	*N*-(7-dimethylamino-4-methylcoumarin-3-yl)iodoacetamide (DACIA)	10 mg	2.3	None
D10251	*N*-(7-dimethylamino-4-methylcoumarin-3-yl)maleimide (DACM)	10 mg	2.3	None
D112	5-dimethylaminonaphthalene-1-(*N*-(2-aminoethyl))sulfonamide (dansyl ethylenediamine)	100 mg	3.3	None
D113	5-dimethylaminonaphthalene-1-(*N*-(5-aminopentyl))sulfonamide (dansyl cadaverine)	100 mg	3.3, 12.3	None
D6104	6-((5-dimethylaminonaphthalene-1-sulfonyl)amino)hexanoic acid, succinimidyl ester (dansyl-X, SE)	25 mg	1.7, 4.2	None
D94	11-((5-dimethylaminonaphthalene-1-sulfonyl)amino)undecanoic acid (DAUDA)	100 mg	13.2, 17.4	None
D151	5-dimethylaminonaphthalene-1-sulfonyl aziridine (dansyl aziridine)	100 mg	2.3	None
D21	5-dimethylaminonaphthalene-1-sulfonyl chloride (dansyl chloride)	1 g	1.7, 9.5	None
D22	2-dimethylaminonaphthalene-5-sulfonyl chloride	100 mg	1.7	None
D23	2-dimethylaminonaphthalene-6-sulfonyl chloride	100 mg	1.7	None
D57	*N*-(5-dimethylaminonaphthalene-1-sulfonyl)-1,2-dihexadecanoyl-*sn*-glycero-3-phosphoethanolamine, triethylammonium salt (dansyl DHPE)	25 mg	13.2	None
D100	5-dimethylaminonaphthalene-1-sulfonyl hydrazine (dansyl hydrazine)	100 mg	3.2, 9.5	None
D2245	4-((4-(dimethylamino)phenyl)azo)benzoic acid, succinimidyl ester (dabcyl, SE)	100 mg	1.8, 9.5	None
D6216	ε-(4-((4-(dimethylamino)phenyl)azo)benzoyl)-α-9-fluorenylmethoxycarbonyl-L-lysine (ε-dabcyl-α-FMOC-L-lysine)	100 mg	9.5	None
D1521	4-dimethylaminophenylazophenyl-4′-maleimide (DABMI)	100 mg	2.2	None
D7475	2-(1-(3-dimethylaminopropyl)-indol-3-yl)-3-(indol-3-yl)maleimide (bisindolylmaleimide; GF 109203X)	~1 mg	17.3	None

For current prices or to order online, visit probes.invitrogen.com

Cat #	Product Name	Unit Size	Sections	Limited Use Label License #
D426	2-(4-(dimethylamino)styryl)-*N*-ethylpyridinium iodide (DASPEI)	1 g	12.2	None
D308	2-(4-(dimethylamino)styryl)-*N*-methylpyridinium iodide (2-Di-1-ASP)	1 g	12.2	None
D288	4-(4-(dimethylamino)styryl)-*N*-methylpyridinium iodide (4-Di-1-ASP)	1 g	12.2, 16.1	None
D1207	5,5′-dimethyl BAPTA, AM *cell permeant*	25 mg	19.8	None
D1206	5,5′-dimethyl BAPTA, tetrapotassium salt *cell impermeant*	100 mg	19.8	None
D530	4-(*N,N*-dimethyl-*N*-(2-hydroxyethyl))ammonium-2,2,6,6-tetramethylpiperidine-1-oxyl chloride (TEMPO choline)	25 mg	14.3	None
D2004	*N,N*′-dimethyl-*N*-(iodoacetyl)-*N*′-(7-nitrobenz-2-oxa-1,3-diazol-4-yl)ethylenediamine (IANBD amide)	25 mg	2.2	None
D22421	3,3′-dimethyl-α-naphthoxacarbocyanine iodide (JC-9; DiNOC$_1$(3))	5 mg	12.2, 15.2, 15.5, 22.3	None
D7760	4-(*N,N*-dimethyl-*N*-tetradecylammonium)methyl-(7-hydroxycoumarin) chloride (U-6)	10 mg	13.5	None
M6494	3-(4,5-dimethylthiazol-2-yl)-2,5-diphenyltetrazolium bromide (MTT)	1 g	15.2, 18.2	None
D3001	5,5′-dinitro BAPTA, free acid *cell impermeant*	25 mg	19.8	None
D2248	6-(2,4-dinitrophenyl)aminohexanoic acid, succinimidyl ester (DNP-X, SE)	25 mg	4.2	None
D23739	*N*-((6-(2,4-dinitrophenyl)amino)hexanoyl)-2-(4,4-difluoro-5,7-dimethyl-4-bora-3a,4a-diaza-*s*-indacene-3-pentanoyl)-1-hexadecanoyl-*sn*-glycero-3-phosphoethanolamine, triethylammonium salt (PED6)	1 mg	13.2, 17.4	193
D1552	*N*-(3-((2,4-dinitrophenyl)amino)propyl)-*N*-(3-aminopropyl)methylamine, dihydrochloride (DAMP)	100 mg	12.3	None
D673	4,4′-dinitrostilbene-2,2′-disulfonic acid, disodium salt (DNDS)	1 g	16.3	None
D275	'DiO'; DiOC$_{18}$(3) (3,3′-dioctadecyloxacarbocyanine perchlorate)	100 mg	13.4, 14.4	None
D14730	DiOC$_2$(3) (3,3′-diethyloxacarbocyanine iodide)	100 mg	22.3	None
D272	DiOC$_5$(3) (3,3′-dipentyloxacarbocyanine iodide)	100 mg	12.4, 22.3	None
D273	DiOC$_6$(3) (3,3′-dihexyloxacarbocyanine iodide)	100 mg	12.2, 12.4, 15.5, 22.3	None
D378	DiOC$_7$(3) (3,3′-diheptyloxacarbocyanine iodide)	100 mg	12.2	None
D1125	DiOC$_{16}$(3) (3,3′-dihexadecyloxacarbocyanine perchlorate)	25 mg	13.4, 14.4	None
D7779	1,1′-dioctadecyl-5,5′-diphenyl-3,3,3′,3′-tetramethylindocarbocyanine chloride (5,5′-Ph$_2$-DiIC$_{18}$(3))	5 mg	13.4, 14.4	None
D7778	3,3′-dioctadecyl-5,5′-di(4-sulfophenyl)oxacarbocyanine, sodium salt (SP-DiOC$_{18}$(3))	5 mg	13.4, 14.4	None
D7777	1,1′-dioctadecyl-6,6′-di(4-sulfophenyl)-3,3,3′,3′-tetramethylindocarbocyanine (SP-DiIC$_{18}$(3))	5 mg	13.4, 14.4	None
D275	3,3′-dioctadecyloxacarbocyanine perchlorate ('DiO'; DiOC$_{18}$(3))	100 mg	13.4, 14.4	None
D7776	1,1′-dioctadecyl-3,3,3′,3′-tetramethylindocarbocyanine-5,5′-disulfonic acid (DiIC$_{18}$(3)-DS)	5 mg	13.4, 14.4	None
D282	1,1′-dioctadecyl-3,3,3′,3′-tetramethylindocarbocyanine perchlorate ('DiI'; DiIC$_{18}$(3))	100 mg	12.4, 13.4, 14.4	None
D3911	1,1′-dioctadecyl-3,3,3′,3′-tetramethylindocarbocyanine perchlorate ('DiI'; DiIC$_{18}$(3)) *crystalline*	25 mg	13.4, 14.4	None
D7757	1,1′-dioctadecyl-3,3,3′,3′-tetramethylindodicarbocyanine, 4-chlorobenzenesulfonate salt ('DiD' solid; DiIC$_{18}$(5) solid)	10 mg	13.4, 14.4	None
D12730	1,1′-dioctadecyl-3,3,3′,3′-tetramethylindodicarbocyanine-5,5′-disulfonic acid (DiIC$_{18}$(5)-DS)	5 mg	13.4, 14.4	None
D307	1,1′-dioctadecyl-3,3,3′,3′-tetramethylindodicarbocyanine perchlorate ('DiD' oil; DiIC$_{18}$(5) oil)	25 mg	13.4, 14.4	None
D12731	1,1′-dioctadecyl-3,3,3′,3′-tetramethylindotricarbocyanine iodide ('DiR'; DiIC$_{18}$(7))	10 mg	13.4, 14.4	None
D6562	1,2-dioleoyl-3-(1-pyrenedodecanoyl)-*rac*-glycerol	1 mg	13.3	None
D3886	1,1′-dioleyl-3,3,3′,3′-tetramethylindocarbocyanine methanesulfonate (Δ^9-DiI)	25 mg	13.4, 14.4	None
D272	3,3′-dipentyloxacarbocyanine iodide (DiOC$_5$(3))	100 mg	12.4, 22.3	None
D7909	diphenyleneiodonium chloride	25 mg	18.3	None
D202	1,6-diphenyl-1,3,5-hexatriene (DPH)	100 mg	13.5	None
D476	2-(3-(diphenylhexatrienyl)propanoyl)-1-hexadecanoyl-*sn*-glycero-3-phosphocholine (β-DPH HPC)	1 mg	13.2	None
D7894	diphenyl-1-pyrenylphosphine (DPPP)	5 mg	15.5, 18.2	None
D306	3,3′-dipropylthiadicarbocyanine iodide (DiSC$_3$(5))	100 mg	22.3	None
D12731	'DiR'; DiIC$_{18}$(7) (1,1′-dioctadecyl-3,3,3′,3′-tetramethylindotricarbocyanine iodide)	10 mg	13.4, 14.4	None
B413	DiSBAC$_2$(3) (bis-(1,3-diethylthiobarbituric acid)trimethine oxonol)	100 mg	22.3	None
D306	DiSC$_3$(5) (3,3′-dipropylthiadicarbocyanine iodide)	100 mg	22.3	None
D8451	5,5′-dithiobis-(2-nitrobenzoic acid) (DTNB; Ellman's reagent)	10 g	2.1, 5.2, 21.2	None
A1506	4,4′-dithiobis-(phenylazide) (4-azidophenyl disulfide)	100 mg	5.3	None
D1532	dithiothreitol (DTT)	1 g	2.1, 5.2	None
D1389	*N,N*′-di(3-trimethylammoniumpropyl)thiadicarbocyanine tribromide	10 mg	14.3	None
D126	DMACA (7-dimethylaminocoumarin-4-acetic acid)	100 mg	1.7	None
D374	DMACA, SE (7-dimethylaminocoumarin-4-acetic acid, succinimidyl ester)	25 mg	1.7	None
D7443	DM-BODIPY® (-)-dihydropyridine *high affinity enantiomer*	25 µg	16.3	193
D7444	DM-BODIPY® (+)-dihydropyridine *low affinity enantiomer*	25 µg	16.3	None
D7441	DM-BODIPY® PAA (BODIPY® FL phenylalkylamine)	25 µg	16.3	193
D1037	DMNB-caged cAMP (4,5-dimethoxy-2-nitrobenzyl adenosine 3′,5′-cyclicmonophosphate)	5 mg	5.3, 17.3	None
D3811	*N*-(DMNB-caged fluorescein)-1,2-dihexadecanoyl-*sn*-glycero-3-phosphoethanolamine, triethylammonium salt	1 mg	5.3, 13.2	None
G2504	α-(DMNB-caged) L-glutamic acid (L-glutamic acid, α-(4,5-dimethoxy-2-nitrobenzyl) ester, hydrochloride)	5 mg	5.3, 16.2	None
D7060	DMNB-caged HPTS (8-((4,5-dimethoxy-2-nitrobenzyl)oxy)pyrene-1,3,6-trisulfonic acid, trisodium salt)	5 mg	5.3, 14.3	254
A7109	DMNPE-caged A-23187 (A-23187, 1-(4,5-dimethoxy-2-nitrophenyl)ethyl ester)	1 mg	5.3, 19.8	None

For current prices or to order online, visit probes.invitrogen.com

Cat #	Product Name	Unit Size	Sections	Limited Use Label License #
A1049	DMNPE-caged ATP (adenosine 5′-triphosphate, P^3-(1-(4,5-dimethoxy-2-nitrophenyl)ethyl) ester, disodium salt)	5 mg	5.3, 17.3	None
B7108	DMNPE-caged Br A-23187 (4-bromo A-23187, 1-(4,5-dimethoxy-2-nitrophenyl)ethyl ester)	1 mg	5.3, 19.8	249
G1053	*S*-(DMNPE-caged) GTP-γ-S (guanosine 5′-*O*-(3-thiotriphosphate), $P^{3(S)}$-(1-(4,5-dimethoxy-2-nitrophenyl)ethyl) ester, triammonium salt)	1 mg	5.3, 17.3	None
L7085	DMNPE-caged luciferin (D-luciferin, 1-(4,5-dimethoxy-2-nitrophenyl)ethyl ester)	5 mg	5.3, 10.6	None
D6814	DMNP-EDTA (1-(4,5-dimethoxy-2-nitrophenyl)-1,2-diaminoethane-*N,N,N′,N′*-tetraacetic acid) *cell impermeant*	5 mg	5.3, 17.2, 19.8	None
D24835	DNA Arrays: Methods and Protocols (Methods in Molecular Biology Volume 170). J.B. Rampal, ed. Humana Press (2001); 312 pages, hard cover	each	23.6	None
M13652	β-(DNBH-caged) NMDA (*N*-methyl-D-aspartic acid, β-(2,2′-dinitrobenzhydryl) ester, trifluoroacetic acid salt)	1 mg	5.3, 16.2	None
D673	DNDS (4,4′-dinitrostilbene-2,2′-disulfonic acid, disodium salt)	1 g	16.3	None
C7610MP	DNP-11-dUTP (ChromaTide® dinitrophenyl-11-dUTP) *1 mM in TE buffer*	25 µL	8.2	225
B2604	DNP-X-biocytin-X, SE (biotin-X 2,4-dinitrophenyl-X-L-lysine, succinimidyl ester)	5 mg	4.2	248
D2248	DNP-X, SE (6-(2,4-dinitrophenyl)aminohexanoic acid, succinimidyl ester)	25 mg	4.2	None
D109	5-dodecanoylaminofluorescein	100 mg	13.5	None
D2893	5-dodecanoylaminofluorescein di-β-D-galactopyranoside (C_{12}FDG)	5 mg	10.2	242
D250	6-dodecanoyl-2-dimethylaminonaphthalene (laurdan)	100 mg	13.5	None
D202	DPH (1,6-diphenyl-1,3,5-hexatriene)	100 mg	13.5	None
D476	β-DPH HPC (2-(3-(diphenylhexatrienyl)propanoyl)-1-hexadecanoyl-*sn*-glycero-3-phosphocholine)	1 mg	13.2	None
P459	DPH propionic acid (3-(4-(6-phenyl)-1,3,5-hexatrienyl)phenylpropionic acid)	25 mg	13.5	None
D7894	DPPP (diphenyl-1-pyrenylphosphine)	5 mg	15.5, 18.2	None
X1525	DPX (*p*-xylene-bis-pyridinium bromide)	1 g	14.3	None
D12060	DQ™ collagen, type I from bovine skin, fluorescein conjugate	1 mg	10.4, 14.7	None
D12052	DQ™ collagen, type IV from human placenta, fluorescein conjugate	1 mg	10.4, 14.7	None
D12054	DQ™ gelatin from pig skin, fluorescein conjugate *special packaging*	5 x 1 mg	10.4	None
D12050	DQ™ Green BSA *special packaging*	5 x 1 mg	10.4, 14.7, 16.1	203, 192
D12053	DQ™ ovalbumin *special packaging*	5 x 1 mg	10.4, 14.7, 16.1	203, 193
D12051	DQ™ Red BSA *special packaging*	5 x 1 mg	10.4, 14.7, 16.1	203, 192
D20658	DSB-X™ Bioconjugate Isolation Kit #1 *with streptavidin agarose* *5 isolations*	1 kit	7.6, 9.2	None
D20659	DSB-X™ Bioconjugate Isolation Kit #2 *with DSB-X™ biotin agarose* *5 isolations*	1 kit	4.3, 7.6	None
D30753	DSB-X™ biotin C_2-iodoacetamide (desthiobiotin-X C_2-iodoacetamide)	5 mg	4.2	None
D20698	DSB-X™ biotin donkey anti-goat IgG (H+L) *2 mg/mL*	0.5 mL	4.3, 7.2	None
D20699	DSB-X™ biotin donkey anti-sheep IgG (H+L) *2 mg/mL*	0.5 mL	4.3, 7.2	None
D30752	DSB-X™ biotin ethylenediamine (desthiobiotin-X ethylenediamine, hydrochloride)	1 mg	4.2, 14.3	None
D20692	DSB-X™ biotin F(ab′)$_2$ fragment of goat anti-mouse IgG (H+L) *2 mg/mL*	250 µL	4.3, 7.2	None
D20696	DSB-X™ biotin F(ab′)$_2$ fragment of goat anti-rabbit IgG (H+L) *2 mg/mL*	250 µL	4.3, 7.2	None
D20701	DSB-X™ biotin goat anti-chicken IgG (H+L) *2 mg/mL*	0.5 mL	4.3, 7.2	None
D20700	DSB-X™ biotin goat anti-human IgG (H+L) *2 mg/mL*	0.5 mL	4.3, 7.2	None
D20690	DSB-X™ biotin goat anti-mouse IgG (H+L) *2 mg/mL*	0.5 mL	4.3, 7.2	None
D20691	DSB-X™ biotin goat anti-mouse IgG (H+L) *highly cross-adsorbed* *2 mg/mL*	0.5 mL	4.3, 7.2	None
D20693	DSB-X™ biotin goat anti-mouse IgM (µ chain) *2 mg/mL*	250 µL	4.3, 7.2	None
D20694	DSB-X™ biotin goat anti-rabbit IgG (H+L) *2 mg/mL*	0.5 mL	4.3, 7.2	None
D20695	DSB-X™ biotin goat anti-rabbit IgG (H+L) *highly cross-adsorbed* *2 mg/mL*	0.5 mL	4.3, 7.2	None
D20697	DSB-X™ biotin goat anti-rat IgG (H+L) *2 mg/mL*	0.5 mL	4.3, 7.2	None
D20653	DSB-X™ biotin hydrazide	5 mg	4.2, 14.3	None
D20655	DSB-X™ Biotin Protein Labeling Kit *5 labelings*	1 kit	1.2, 4.2	None
D20652	DSB-X™ desthiobiocytin (ε-desthiobiotinoyl-L-lysine)	5 mg	4.2, 14.3	None
D16	5-DTAF (5-(4,6-dichlorotriazinyl)aminofluorescein) *single isomer*	100 mg	1.5, 3.1	None
D8451	DTNB; Ellman's reagent (5,5′-dithiobis-(2-nitrobenzoic acid))	10 g	2.1, 5.2, 21.2	None
I24221	DTPA isothiocyanate ((*S*)-1-*p*-isothiocyanatobenzyldiethylenetriaminepentaacetic acid)	1 mg	19.8	None
D1532	DTT (dithiothreitol)	1 g	2.1, 5.2	None
D21887	DyeChrome™ Double Western Blot Stain Kit *for mouse IgG, rabbit IgG and total protein detection* *20 minigel blots*	1 kit	9.4	253, 234, 191
D24771	DyeChrome™ Red/Green Photographic Filter Set *two filters*	1 set	23.4	None
D21881	DyeChrome™ Western Blot Stain Kit #1 *with goat anti-mouse IgG, DDAO phosphate and BODIPY® FL-X, SE* *20 minigel blots*	1 kit	9.4	234, 223, 193
D21882	DyeChrome™ Western Blot Stain Kit #2 *with goat anti-rabbit IgG, DDAO phosphate and BODIPY® FL-X, SE* *20 minigel blots*	1 kit	9.4	234, 223, 193
D21883	DyeChrome™ Western Blot Stain Kit #3 *with streptavidin, DDAO phosphate and BODIPY® FL-X, SE* *20 minigel blots*	1 kit	9.4	234, 223, 193
D21884	DyeChrome™ Western Blot Stain Kit #4 *with goat anti-mouse IgG, ELF® 39 phosphate and BODIPY® TR-X, SE* *20 minigel blots*	1 kit	9.4	253, 223, 193

For current prices or to order online, visit probes.invitrogen.com

Cat #	Product Name	Unit Size	Sections	Limited Use Label License #
D21885	DyeChrome™ Western Blot Stain Kit #5 *with goat anti-rabbit IgG, ELF® 39 phosphate and BODIPY® TR-X, SE* *20 minigel blots*	1 kit	9.4	253, 223, 193
D21886	DyeChrome™ Western Blot Stain Kit #6 *with streptavidin, ELF® 39 phosphate and BODIPY® TR-X, SE* *20 minigel blots*	1 kit	9.4	253, 223, 193
D31590	DyeMer™ 488/605 goat anti-mouse IgG (H+L) *1 mg/mL*	0.5 mL	7.2	183
D31591	DyeMer™ 488/615 goat anti-mouse IgG (H+L) *1 mg/mL*	0.5 mL	7.2	183
D31592	DyeMer™ 488/630 goat anti-mouse IgG (H+L) *1 mg/mL*	0.5 mL	7.2	183
D31600	DyeMer™ 488/605 goat anti-rabbit IgG (H+L) *1 mg/mL*	0.5 mL	7.2	183
D31601	DyeMer™ 488/615 goat anti-rabbit IgG (H+L) *1 mg/mL*	0.5 mL	7.2	183
D31602	DyeMer™ 488/630 goat anti-rabbit IgG (H+L) *1 mg/mL*	0.5 mL	7.2	183
E2247	EDAC (1-ethyl-3-(3-dimethylaminopropyl)carbodiimide, hydrochloride)	100 mg	3.3, 5.2	None
A91	EDANS (5-((2-aminoethyl)amino)naphthalene-1-sulfonic acid, sodium salt)	1 g	3.3, 9.5	None
B6215	γ-EDANS-α-(*t*-BOC)-L-glutamic acid (5-((2-(*t*-BOC)-γ-L-glutamylaminoethyl)amino)naphthalene-1-sulfonic acid)	100 mg	9.5	None
F11831	γ-EDANS-α-FMOC-L-glutamic acid (5-((2-(FMOC)-γ-L-glutamylaminoethyl)amino)naphthalene-1-sulfonic acid)	100 mg	9.5	None
E1218	EDTA, AM (EDTA, tetra(acetoxymethyl ester))	25 mg	19.8	None
E1218	EDTA, tetra(acetoxymethyl ester) (EDTA, AM)	25 mg	19.8	None
E3476	EGF (epidermal growth factor) *from mouse submaxillary glands*	100 µg	16.1	None
E1219	EGTA, AM (EGTA, tetra(acetoxymethyl ester))	10 mg	19.8	None
E1219	EGTA, tetra(acetoxymethyl ester) (EGTA, AM)	10 mg	19.8	None
E33075	Electrophoretic Mobility-Shift Assay (EMSA) Kit *with SYBR® Green and SYPRO® Ruby EMSA stains* *10 minigel assays*	1 kit	8.4, 8.7, 9.3	190, 154
E6580	ELF® 97 acetate (ELF® 97 esterase substrate)	5 mg	10.6	253
E22011	ELF® 97 *N*-acetylglucosaminide; ELF® 97 NAG (ELF® 97 chitinase/*N*-acetylglucosaminidase substrate)	5 mg	10.2	253
E6578	ELF® 97 alcohol *1 mM solution in DMSO*	1 mL	6.3, 10.1	253
E22011	ELF® 97 chitinase/*N*-acetylglucosaminidase substrate (ELF® 97 *N*-acetylglucosaminide; ELF® 97 NAG)	5 mg	10.2	253
E6603	ELF® 97 Cytological Labeling Kit *with streptavidin, alkaline phosphatase conjugate* *50 assays*	1 kit	6.3, 10.3	253
E6601	ELF® 97 Endogenous Phosphatase Detection Kit	1 kit	6.3, 10.3	253
E6580	ELF® 97 esterase substrate (ELF® 97 acetate)	5 mg	10.6	253
E6587	ELF® 97 β-D-glucuronidase substrate (ELF® 97 β-D-glucuronide)	5 mg	10.2	253
E6587	ELF® 97 β-D-glucuronide (ELF® 97 β-D-glucuronidase substrate)	5 mg	10.2	253
E6600	ELF® 97 Immunohistochemistry Kit	1 kit	6.3, 10.3	253
E6583	ELF® 97 lipase substrate (ELF® 97 palmitate)	5 mg	10.6	253
E6604	ELF® 97 mRNA *In Situ* Hybridization Kit #1 *50 assays*	1 kit	6.3, 8.5, 10.3	253
E6605	ELF® 97 mRNA *In Situ* Hybridization Kit #2 *with streptavidin, alkaline phosphatase conjugate* *50 assays*	1 kit	6.3, 8.5, 10.3	253
E6583	ELF® 97 palmitate (ELF® 97 lipase substrate)	5 mg	10.6	253
E6589	ELF® 97 phosphatase substrate (ELF® 97 phosphate) *5 mM in water* *contains 2 mM azide*	1 mL	6.3, 10.3	253
E6588	ELF® 97 phosphatase substrate (ELF® 97 phosphate) *5 mM in water* *0.2 µm filtered*	1 mL	6.3, 10.3	253
E6588	ELF® 97 phosphate (ELF® 97 phosphatase substrate) *5 mM in water* *0.2 µm filtered*	1 mL	6.3, 10.3	253
E6589	ELF® 97 phosphate (ELF® 97 phosphatase substrate) *5 mM in water* *contains 2 mM azide*	1 mL	6.3, 10.3	253
E6606	ELF® spin filters *20 filters*	1 box	6.3, 10.3	None
E1374	EMA (ethidium monoazide bromide)	5 mg	5.3, 8.1, 15.2	None
E21390	Endogenous Biotin-Blocking Kit *100 assays*	1 kit	6.3, 7.6, 12.2	None
E23377	Endostatin™ protein (human, recombinant) *1 mg/mL*	250 µL	11.2, 15.4, 16.1	None
E11954	EnzChek® Amylase Assay Kit *1000 assays*	1 kit	10.2	203, 193
E13183	EnzChek® Caspase-3 Assay Kit #1 *Z-DEVD-AMC substrate* *500 assays*	1 kit	10.4, 15.5	None
E13184	EnzChek® Caspase-3 Assay Kit #2 *Z-DEVD-R110 substrate* *500 assays*	1 kit	10.4, 15.5	None
E12056	EnzChek® Elastase Assay Kit *600 assays*	1 kit	10.4	203, 193
E12055	EnzChek® Gelatinase/Collagenase Assay Kit *250-2000 assays*	1 kit	10.4	None
E22013	EnzChek® Lysozyme Assay Kit *400 assays*	1 kit	10.2	None
E12020	EnzChek® Phosphatase Assay Kit *1000 assays*	1 kit	10.3	192
E6646	EnzChek® Phosphate Assay Kit *100 assays*	1 kit	10.3, 21.2	None
E6658	EnzChek® Polarization Assay Kit for Proteases *green fluorescence* *100-1000 assays*	1 kit	10.4	203, 193
E6638	EnzChek® Protease Assay Kit *green fluorescence* *100-1000 assays*	1 kit	10.4, 14.7	203, 193
E6639	EnzChek® Protease Assay Kit *red fluorescence* *100-1000 assays*	1 kit	10.4, 14.7	203, 193
E6645	EnzChek® Pyrophosphate Assay Kit *100 assays*	1 kit	10.3, 21.2	None
E22064	EnzChek® Reverse Transcriptase Assay Kit *1000 assays*	1 kit	8.7	154
A434	eosin cadaverine (5-((5-aminopentyl)thioureidyl)eosin, hydrochloride)	25 mg	3.3	None
E30450	eosin-5-iodoacetamide	25 mg	2.2	None
E18	eosin-5-isothiocyanate	100 mg	1.5, 16.3	None
E118	eosin-5-maleimide	25 mg	2.2	None

For current prices or to order online, visit probes.invitrogen.com

Cat #	Product Name	Unit Size	Sections	Limited Use Label License #
E7463	eosin phalloidin	300 U	11.1	None
E3476	epidermal growth factor (EGF) *from mouse submaxillary glands*	100 µg	16.1	None
E3477	epidermal growth factor, biotin-XX conjugate (biotin EGF)	20 µg	4.3, 16.1	None
E13345	epidermal growth factor, biotinylated, complexed to Alexa Fluor® 488 streptavidin (Alexa Fluor® 488 EGF complex)	100 µg	4.3, 16.1	183
E35350	epidermal growth factor, biotinylated, complexed to Alexa Fluor® 555 streptavidin (Alexa Fluor® 555 EGF complex)	100 µg	4.3, 16.1	223
E35351	epidermal growth factor, biotinylated, complexed to Alexa Fluor® 647 streptavidin (Alexa Fluor® 647 EGF complex)	100 µg	4.3, 16.1	223
E3480	epidermal growth factor, biotinylated, complexed to Texas Red® streptavidin (Texas Red® EGF complex)	100 µg	4.3, 16.1	None
E3478	epidermal growth factor, fluorescein conjugate (fluorescein EGF)	20 µg	16.1	None
E7498	epidermal growth factor, Oregon Green® 514 conjugate (Oregon Green® 514 EGF)	20 µg	16.1	191
E3481	epidermal growth factor, tetramethylrhodamine conjugate (rhodamine EGF)	20 µg	16.1	None
E6051	1-(2,3-epoxypropyl)-4-(5-(4-methoxyphenyl)oxazol-2-yl)pyridinium trifluoromethanesulfonate (PyMPO epoxide)	5 mg	2.2	None
E12353	ER-Tracker™ Blue-White DPX *1 mM solution in DMSO* *special packaging*	20 x 50 µL	12.4	None
E30150	erythrosin-5-isothiocyanate	10 mg	1.5	None
E2870	*Escherichia coli* BioParticles® opsonizing reagent	1 U	16.1	None
E13231	*Escherichia coli* (K-12 strain) BioParticles®, Alexa Fluor® 488 conjugate	2 mg	16.1	183
E23370	*Escherichia coli* (K-12 strain) BioParticles®, Alexa Fluor® 594 conjugate	2 mg	16.1	183
E2864	*Escherichia coli* (K-12 strain) BioParticles®, BODIPY® FL conjugate	10 mg	16.1	193
E2861	*Escherichia coli* (K-12 strain) BioParticles®, fluorescein conjugate	10 mg	16.1	None
E2862	*Escherichia coli* (K-12 strain) BioParticles®, tetramethylrhodamine conjugate	10 mg	16.1	None
E2863	*Escherichia coli* (K-12 strain) BioParticles®, Texas Red® conjugate	10 mg	16.1	None
E1169	EthD-1 (ethidium homodimer-1)	1 mg	8.1, 8.4, 15.2	None
E3599	EthD-2 (ethidium homodimer-2) *1 mM solution in DMSO*	200 µL	8.1, 8.4, 15.2	None
E23691	1,N^6-ethenoadenosine 5′-triphosphate (ε-ATP) *5 mM in buffer*	2 mL	17.3	None
E1305	ethidium bromide	1 g	8.1, 8.4, 8.7, 15.2	None
E3565	ethidium bromide *10 mg/mL solution in water*	10 mL	8.1, 8.4, 8.7, 15.2	None
E3561	ethidium diazide chloride	5 mg	5.3, 8.1	None
E1169	ethidium homodimer-1 (EthD-1)	1 mg	8.1, 8.4, 15.2	None
E3599	ethidium homodimer-2 (EthD-2) *1 mM solution in DMSO*	200 µL	8.1, 8.4, 15.2	None
E1374	ethidium monoazide bromide (EMA)	5 mg	5.3, 8.1, 15.2	None
E3101	*N*-(ethoxycarbonylmethyl)-6-methoxyquinolinium bromide (MQAE)	100 mg	21.2	None
R352	ethoxyresorufin (resorufin ethyl ether)	5 mg	10.6	None
E2882	7-ethoxy-4-trifluoromethylcoumarin	25 mg	10.6	None
E2247	1-ethyl-3-(3-dimethylaminopropyl)carbodiimide, hydrochloride (EDAC)	100 mg	3.3, 5.2	None
E3111	5-(*N*-ethyl-*N*-isopropyl)amiloride, hydrochloride	5 mg	16.3	None
E6960	europium(III) chloride, hexahydrate *99.99%*	1 g	14.3, 17.2, 19.7	None
E33202	EZQ® Phosphopeptide Quantitation Kit *1000 assays*	1 kit	9.2, 9.4	223, 204
E33201	EZQ® Phosphoprotein Quantitation Kit *2000 assays*	1 kit	9.2	223, 204
R33200	EZQ® Protein Quantitation Kit *2000 assays*	1 kit	9.2	223, 190
O3852	F18 (*N*-octadecyl-*N*′-(5-(fluoresceinyl))thiourea)	25 mg	13.5	None
F21452	F(ab′)$_2$ fragment of goat anti-mouse IgG (H+L), alkaline phosphatase conjugate	0.5 mg	7.2	None
F21453	F(ab′)$_2$ fragment of goat anti-mouse IgG (H+L), horseradish peroxidase conjugate	0.5 mg	7.2	None
F21456	F(ab′)$_2$ fragment of goat anti-rabbit IgG (H+L), alkaline phosphatase conjugate	0.5 mg	7.2	None
C1359	5-FAM (5-carboxyfluorescein) *single isomer*	100 mg	1.5	None
C1360	6-FAM (6-carboxyfluorescein) *single isomer*	100 mg	1.5	None
C1904	5(6)-FAM (5-(and-6)-carboxyfluorescein) *FluoroPure™ grade* *mixed isomers*	100 mg	1.5, 14.3, 20.2	None
C2210	5-FAM, SE (5-carboxyfluorescein, succinimidyl ester) *single isomer*	10 mg	1.5	None
C6164	6-FAM, SE (6-carboxyfluorescein, succinimidyl ester) *single isomer*	10 mg	1.5	None
C1311	5(6)-FAM, SE (5-(and-6)-carboxyfluorescein, succinimidyl ester) *mixed isomers*	100 mg	1.5	None
F2900	*FAST* CAT® Chloramphenicol Acetyltransferase Assay Kit *100 assays*	1 kit	10.6	257, 193
F6616	*FAST* CAT® Green (deoxy) Chloramphenicol Acetyltransferase Assay Kit *100 assays*	1 kit	10.6	257, 193
F6617	*FAST* CAT® Yellow (deoxy) Chloramphenicol Acetyltransferase Assay Kit *100 assays*	1 kit	10.6	257, 193
D3897	*FAST* DiA™ oil; DiΔ^{9,12}-C$_{18}$ASP, I (4-(4-(dilinoleylamino)styryl)-*N*-methylpyridinium iodide)	5 mg	13.4, 14.4	None
D7758	*FAST* DiA™ solid; DiΔ^{9,12}-C$_{18}$ASP, CBS (4-(4-(dilinoleylamino)styryl)-*N*-methylpyridinium 4-chlorobenzenesulfonate)	5 mg	13.4, 14.4	None
D3899	*FAST* DiI™ oil; DiIΔ^{9,12}-C$_{18}$(3), ClO$_4$ (1,1′-dilinoleyl-3,3,3′,3′-tetramethylindocarbocyanine perchlorate)	5 mg	13.4, 14.4	None
D7756	*FAST* DiI™ solid; DiIΔ^{9,12}-C$_{18}$(3), CBS (1,1′-dilinoleyl-3,3,3′,3′-tetramethylindocarbocyanine, 4-chlorobenzenesulfonate)	5 mg	13.4, 14.4	None
D3898	*FAST* DiO™ solid; DiOΔ^{9,12}-C$_{18}$(3), ClO$_4$ (3,3′-dilinoleyloxacarbocyanine perchlorate)	5 mg	13.4, 14.4	None
F2902	Fc OxyBURST® Green assay reagent *25 assays* *3 mg/mL*	500 µL	16.1, 18.2	None
F1303	FDA (fluorescein diacetate)	1 g	15.2, 20.2	None

For current prices or to order online, visit probes.invitrogen.com

Cat #	Product Name	Unit Size	Sections	Limited Use Label License #
F1179	FDG (fluorescein di-β-D-galactopyranoside)	5 mg	10.2	None
A22010	C_2FDG (5-acetylaminofluorescein di-β-D-galactopyranoside)	5 mg	10.2	242
O2892	C_8FDG (5-octanoylaminofluorescein di-β-D-galactopyranoside)	5 mg	10.2	None
D2893	C_{12}FDG (5-dodecanoylaminofluorescein di-β-D-galactopyranoside)	5 mg	10.2	242
F2915	FDGlcU (fluorescein di-β-D-glucuronide)	5 mg	10.2	None
F2881	FDGlu (fluorescein di-β-D-glucopyranoside)	5 mg	10.2	None
F2999	FDP (fluorescein diphosphate, tetraammonium salt)	5 mg	10.3	None
O6080	F_2FITC (Oregon Green® 488 isothiocyanate) *mixed isomers*	5 mg	1.5	191
F13191	fibrinogen from human plasma, Alexa Fluor® 488 conjugate	5 mg	15.6, 16.1	183
F13192	fibrinogen from human plasma, Alexa Fluor® 546 conjugate	5 mg	15.6, 16.1	183
F13193	fibrinogen from human plasma, Alexa Fluor® 594 conjugate	5 mg	15.6, 16.1	183
F35200	fibrinogen from human plasma, Alexa Fluor® 647 conjugate	5 mg	15.6, 16.1	183
F7496	fibrinogen from human plasma, Oregon Green® 488 conjugate	5 mg	15.6, 16.1	191
F7462	fim-1	1 mg	17.3	None
F7453	fim-1 diacetate	1 mg	17.3	None
A13199	FITC annexin V (annexin V, fluorescein conjugate) *100 assays*	500 µL	15.5	213
F6865	FITC-Gly-Gly-His ((fluorescein-5-thioureidyl)glycylglycyl-L-histidine, dipotassium salt)	1 mg	19.7	None
F6864	FITC-Gly-His ((fluorescein-5-thioureidyl)glycyl-L-histidine, dipotassium salt)	1 mg	19.7	None
I13269	FITC insulin (insulin, human, recombinant from *E. coli*, fluorescein conjugate) *monolabeled* *zinc free*	100 µg	16.1	None
F1907	FITC 'Isomer I' (fluorescein-5-isothiocyanate) *special packaging*	10 x 100 mg	1.5	None
F1906	FITC 'Isomer I' (fluorescein-5-isothiocyanate) *special packaging*	10 x 10 mg	1.5	None
F143	FITC 'Isomer I' (fluorescein-5-isothiocyanate)	1 g	1.5	None
T13361	FITC tuftsin (tuftsin, fluorescein conjugate)	100 µg	16.1	None
F13838	Flow Cytometry Size Calibration Kit *nonfluorescent microspheres*	1 kit	23.2	None
F1241	fluo-3, AM *cell permeant*	1 mg	19.3	204
F1242	fluo-3, AM *cell permeant* *special packaging*	20 x 50 µg	19.3	204
F23915	fluo-3, AM *FluoroPure™ grade* *special packaging*	10 x 50 µg	19.3	204
F14218	fluo-3, AM *1 mM solution in DMSO* *cell permeant*	1 mL	19.3	204
F14242	fluo-3, AM *packaged for high-throughput screening*	40 x 1 mg	19.3	204
F1240	fluo-3, pentaammonium salt *cell impermeant*	1 mg	19.3	204
F3715	fluo-3, pentapotassium salt *cell impermeant*	1 mg	19.3	204
F14201	fluo-4, AM *cell permeant* *special packaging*	10 x 50 µg	19.3	204, 191
F23917	fluo-4, AM *FluoroPure™ grade* *special packaging*	10 x 50 µg	19.3	204, 191
F14217	fluo-4, AM *1 mM solution in DMSO* *cell permeant*	500 µL	19.3	204, 191
F14202	fluo-4, AM *packaged for high-throughput screening*	5 x 1 mg	19.3	204, 191
F36250	fluo-4 dextran, potassium salt, 10,000 MW, anionic (high-affinity version)	5 mg	19.4	223
F14240	fluo-4 dextran, potassium salt, 10,000 MW, anionic (low-affinity version)	5 mg	19.4	223
F14200	fluo-4, pentapotassium salt *cell impermeant*	500 µg	19.3	204, 191
F23981	fluo-4FF, AM *cell permeant* *special packaging*	10 x 50 µg	19.3	204, 191
F23980	fluo-4FF, pentapotassium salt *cell impermeant*	500 µg	19.3	204, 191
F14222	fluo-5F, AM *cell permeant* *special packaging*	10 x 50 µg	19.3	204
F14221	fluo-5F, pentapotassium salt *cell impermeant*	500 µg	19.3	204
F14204	fluo-5N, AM *cell permeant* *special packaging*	10 x 50 µg	19.3	204
F14203	fluo-5N, pentapotassium salt *cell impermeant*	500 µg	19.3	204
F36201	fluo-4 cadaverine, pentapotassium salt	500 µg	3.3, 19.3	223
F36925	FluoCells® prepared slide #6 *muntjac cells with mouse anti-OxPhos Complex V inhibitor protein, Alexa Fluor® 555 goat anti-mouse IgG, Alexa Fluor® 488 phalloidin, TO-PRO®-3*	each	23.1	209, 183
F14780	FluoCells® prepared slide #1 *BPAE cells with MitoTracker® Red CMXRos, BODIPY® FL phallacidin, DAPI*	each	23.1	217, 193
F14781	FluoCells® prepared slide #2 *BPAE cells with mouse anti-α-tubulin, BODIPY® FL goat anti-mouse IgG, Texas Red®-X phalloidin, DAPI*	each	23.1	211, 193
F24630	FluoCells® prepared slide #3 *mouse kidney section with Alexa Fluor® 488 WGA, Alexa Fluor® 568 phalloidin, DAPI*	each	23.1	183
F24631	FluoCells® prepared slide #4 *mouse intestine section with Alexa Fluor® 350 WGA, Alexa Fluor® 568 phalloidin, SYTOX® Green*	each	23.1	183
F36200	fluo-4 iodoacetamide, pentapotassium salt	500 µg	2.2, 19.3	223
F6290	*N*-(9-fluorenylmethoxycarbonyl) hydrazine (FMOC hydrazine)	25 mg	3.2	None
F11830	*N*α-(9-fluorenylmethoxycarbonyl)-*N*ε-tetramethylrhodamine-(5-carbonyl)-L-lysine (α-FMOC-ε-TMR-L-lysine)	25 mg	9.5	None
F6348	FluoReporter® Biotin/DNP Protein Labeling Kit *5-10 labelings*	1 kit	1.2, 4.2	None
F2610	FluoReporter® Biotin-XX Protein Labeling Kit *5 labelings of 5-20 mg protein each*	1 kit	1.2, 4.2	None
F2962	FluoReporter® Blue Fluorometric dsDNA Quantitation Kit *200-2000 assays*	1 kit	8.3, 15.4	None

For current prices or to order online, visit probes.invitrogen.com

Cat #	Product Name	Unit Size	Sections	Limited Use Label License #
F20650	FluoReporter® Cell-Surface Biotinylation Kit	1 kit	4.2, 7.6	None
F6434	FluoReporter® FITC Protein Labeling Kit *5-10 labelings*	1 kit	1.2, 1.5	None
F6433	FluoReporter® Fluorescein-EX Protein Labeling Kit *5-10 labelings*	1 kit	1.2, 1.5	None
F1931	FluoReporter® *lacZ* Flow Cytometry Kit *250 assays*	1 kit	10.2	262
F1930	FluoReporter® *lacZ* Flow Cytometry Kit *50 assays*	1 kit	10.2	262
F2905	FluoReporter® *lacZ*/Galactosidase Quantitation Kit *1000 assays*	1 kit	10.2	262
F6347	FluoReporter® Mini-biotin-XX Protein Labeling Kit *5 labelings of 0.1-3 mg protein each*	1 kit	1.2, 4.2	None
F6153	FluoReporter® Oregon Green® 488 Protein Labeling Kit *5-10 labelings*	1 kit	1.2, 1.5	191
F6155	FluoReporter® Oregon Green® 514 Protein Labeling Kit *5-10 labelings*	1 kit	1.2, 1.5	191
F6161	FluoReporter® Rhodamine Red™-X Protein Labeling Kit *5-10 labelings*	1 kit	1.2, 1.6	258
F6163	FluoReporter® Tetramethylrhodamine Protein Labeling Kit *5-10 labelings*	1 kit	1.2, 1.6	None
F6162	FluoReporter® Texas Red®-X Protein Labeling Kit *5-10 labelings*	1 kit	1.2, 1.6	211
F20261	fluorescamine *FluoroPure™ grade*	100 mg	1.8, 9.2, 9.3	None
F2332	fluorescamine	100 mg	1.8, 9.2, 9.3	None
F1300	fluorescein *reference standard*	1 g	1.5, 10.1, 20.2	None
F32767	fluorescein-aha-dUTP *1 mM in TE buffer*	25 µL	8.2, 8.5	None
B1370	fluorescein biotin (5-((*N*-(5-(*N*-(6-(biotinoyl)amino)hexanoyl)amino)pentyl)thioureidyl)fluorescein)	5 mg	4.3, 14.3	None
F7103	fluorescein bis-(5-carboxymethoxy-2-nitrobenzyl) ether, dipotassium salt (CMNB-caged fluorescein)	5 mg	5.3, 14.3	None
F1176	fluorescein α-bungarotoxin (α-bungarotoxin, fluorescein conjugate)	500 µg	16.2	None
A10466	fluorescein cadaverine (5-((5-aminopentyl)thioureidyl)fluorescein, dihydrobromide salt)	25 mg	3.3	None
F6218	fluorescein-5-carbonyl azide, diacetate	10 mg	3.1	None
F6106	6-(fluorescein-5-carboxamido)hexanoic acid, succinimidyl ester (5-SFX) *single isomer*	5 mg	1.5	None
F2181	6-(fluorescein-5-(and-6)-carboxamido)hexanoic acid, succinimidyl ester (5(6)-SFX) *mixed isomers*	10 mg	1.5, 4.2	None
F6129	6-(fluorescein-5-(and-6)-carboxamido)hexanoic acid, succinimidyl ester (5(6)-SFX) *mixed isomers* *special packaging*	10 x 1 mg	1.5	None
F362	fluorescein DHPE (*N*-(fluorescein-5-thiocarbamoyl)-1,2-dihexadecanoyl-*sn*-glycero-3-phosphoethanolamine, triethylammonium salt)	5 mg	13.2, 20.4	None
F1303	fluorescein diacetate (FDA)	1 g	15.2, 20.2	None
F1179	fluorescein di-β-D-galactopyranoside (FDG)	5 mg	10.2	None
F2881	fluorescein di-β-D-glucopyranoside (FDGlu)	5 mg	10.2	None
F2915	fluorescein di-β-D-glucuronide (FDGlcU)	5 mg	10.2	None
F2999	fluorescein diphosphate, tetraammonium salt (FDP)	5 mg	10.3	None
F2810	fluorescein donkey anti-sheep IgG (H+L) *2 mg/mL*	0.5 mL	7.2	None
E3478	fluorescein EGF (epidermal growth factor, fluorescein conjugate)	20 µg	16.1	None
F10240	Fluorescein-EX Protein Labeling Kit *3 labelings*	1 kit	1.2, 1.5	None
F6130	fluorescein-5-EX, succinimidyl ester	10 mg	1.5, 4.2	None
F11021	fluorescein F(ab')$_2$ fragment of goat anti-mouse IgG (H+L) *2 mg/mL*	250 µL	7.2	None
F2761	fluorescein goat anti-mouse IgG (H+L) *2 mg/mL*	0.5 mL	7.2	None
F2765	fluorescein goat anti-rabbit IgG (H+L) *2 mg/mL*	0.5 mL	7.2	None
F1907	fluorescein-5-isothiocyanate (FITC 'Isomer I') *special packaging*	10 x 100 mg	1.5	None
F1906	fluorescein-5-isothiocyanate (FITC 'Isomer I') *special packaging*	10 x 10 mg	1.5	None
F143	fluorescein-5-isothiocyanate (FITC 'Isomer I')	1 g	1.5	None
F150	fluorescein-5-maleimide	25 mg	2.2	None
M1198MP	fluorescein methotrexate (methotrexate, fluorescein, triammonium salt)	1 mg	15.6	None
F6489	fluorescein mono-(4-guanidinobenzoate), hydrochloride	5 mg	10.6	None
F36915	fluorescein *NIST-traceable standard* *nominal concentration 50 µM* *special packaging*	5 x 1 mL	1.5, 10.1, 23.1	None
F3857	fluorescein octadecyl ester	10 mg	13.5	None
F432	fluorescein phalloidin	300 U	11.1	None
F1130	fluorescein-5-(and-6)-sulfonic acid, trisodium salt	100 mg	14.3, 20.2	None
F362	*N*-(fluorescein-5-thiocarbamoyl)-1,2-dihexadecanoyl-*sn*-glycero-3-phosphoethanolamine, triethylammonium salt (fluorescein DHPE)	5 mg	13.2, 20.4	None
F121	fluorescein-5-thiosemicarbazide	100 mg	3.2	None
F6865	(fluorescein-5-thioureidyl)glycylglycyl-L-histidine, dipotassium salt (FITC-Gly-Gly-His)	1 mg	19.7	None
F6864	(fluorescein-5-thioureidyl)glycyl-L-histidine, dipotassium salt (FITC-Gly-His)	1 mg	19.7	None
A1363	fluoresceinyl glycine amide (5-(aminoacetamido)fluorescein)	10 mg	3.3	None
F6053	7-fluorobenz-2-oxa-1,3-diazole-4-sulfonamide (ABD-F)	10 mg	2.2	None
D1820	fluoro-emerald (dextran, fluorescein, 10,000 MW, anionic, lysine fixable)	25 mg	14.5	None
F486	4-fluoro-7-nitrobenz-2-oxa-1,3-diazole (NBD fluoride; 4-fluoro-7-nitrobenzofurazan)	25 mg	1.8, 2.2	None
F1501	4-fluoro-3-nitrophenyl azide (FNPA)	100 mg	5.3	None
D1817	fluoro-ruby (dextran, tetramethylrhodamine, 10,000 MW, lysine fixable)	25 mg	14.5	None

For current prices or to order online, visit probes.invitrogen.com

Cat #	Product Name	Unit Size	Sections	Limited Use Label License #
F8760	FluoSpheres® aldehyde-sulfate microspheres, 0.02 µm, yellow-green fluorescent (505/515) *2% solids*	10 mL	6.5	227
F8762	FluoSpheres® aldehyde-sulfate microspheres, 1.0 µm, yellow-green fluorescent (505/515) *2% solids*	10 mL	6.5	227
F8763	FluoSpheres® amine-modified microspheres, 0.2 µm, red fluorescent (580/605) *2% solids*	5 mL	6.5	227
F8764	FluoSpheres® amine-modified microspheres, 0.2 µm, yellow-green fluorescent (505/515) *2% solids*	5 mL	6.5	227
F8765	FluoSpheres® amine-modified microspheres, 1.0 µm, yellow-green fluorescent (505/515) *2% solids*	5 mL	6.5	227
F8766	FluoSpheres® biotin-labeled microspheres, 0.04 µm, yellow-green fluorescent (505/515) *1% solids*	0.4 mL	4.3, 6.5, 7.6	227
F8767	FluoSpheres® biotin-labeled microspheres, 0.2 µm, yellow-green fluorescent (505/515) *1% solids*	0.4 mL	4.3, 6.5, 7.6	227
F8769	FluoSpheres® biotin-labeled microspheres, 1.0 µm, nonfluorescent *1% solids*	0.4 mL	4.3, 6.5, 7.6	None
F8768	FluoSpheres® biotin-labeled microspheres, 1.0 µm, yellow-green fluorescent (505/515) *1% solids*	0.4 mL	4.3, 6.5, 7.6	227
F8890	FluoSpheres® Blood Flow Determination Fluorescent Color Kit #1, polystyrene microspheres, 10 µm *seven colors, 10 mL each* *3.6x10^6 beads/mL*	1 kit	6.5, 14.6	227, 223, 193
F8892	FluoSpheres® Blood Flow Determination Fluorescent Color Kit #3, polystyrene microspheres, 15 µm *five colors, 10 mL each* *1.0x10^6 beads/mL*	1 kit	6.5, 14.6	227, 224, 193
F8891	FluoSpheres® Blood Flow Determination Fluorescent Color Kit #2, polystyrene microspheres, 15 µm *seven colors, 10 mL each* *1.0x10^6 beads/mL*	1 kit	6.5, 14.6	227, 224, 193
F21015	FluoSpheres® Blood Flow Determination Fluorescent Color Kit #4, polystyrene microspheres, 15 µm *four colors, 10 mL each* *1.0x10^6 beads/mL*	1 kit	6.5, 14.6	224, 227, 193
F8781	FluoSpheres® carboxylate-modified microspheres, 0.02 µm, blue fluorescent (365/415) *2% solids*	10 mL	6.5	None
F8782	FluoSpheres® carboxylate-modified microspheres, 0.02 µm, crimson fluorescent (625/645) *2% solids*	2 mL	6.5	227, 193
F8783	FluoSpheres® carboxylate-modified microspheres, 0.02 µm, dark red fluorescent (660/680) *2% solids*	2 mL	6.5	227
F8784	FluoSpheres® carboxylate-modified microspheres, 0.02 µm, nile red fluorescent (535/575) *2% solids*	10 mL	6.5	None
F8786	FluoSpheres® carboxylate-modified microspheres, 0.02 µm, red fluorescent (580/605) *2% solids*	10 mL	6.5	227
F8787	FluoSpheres® carboxylate-modified microspheres, 0.02 µm, yellow-green fluorescent (505/515) *2% solids*	10 mL	6.5	227
F8789	FluoSpheres® carboxylate-modified microspheres, 0.04 µm, dark red fluorescent (660/680) *5% solids, azide free*	1 mL	6.5, 14.6	227
F8791	FluoSpheres® carboxylate-modified microspheres, 0.04 µm, infrared fluorescent (715/755) *5% solids, azide free*	0.4 mL	6.5, 14.6	227, 193
F8792	FluoSpheres® carboxylate-modified microspheres, 0.04 µm, orange fluorescent (540/560) *5% solids, azide free*	1 mL	6.5, 14.6	227
F8793	FluoSpheres® carboxylate-modified microspheres, 0.04 µm, red fluorescent (580/605) *5% solids, azide free*	1 mL	6.5, 14.6	227
F8794	FluoSpheres® carboxylate-modified microspheres, 0.04 µm, red-orange fluorescent (565/580) *5% solids, azide free*	1 mL	6.5, 14.6	227, 193
F8795	FluoSpheres® carboxylate-modified microspheres, 0.04 µm, yellow-green fluorescent (505/515) *5% solids, azide free*	1 mL	6.5, 14.6	227
F8797	FluoSpheres® carboxylate-modified microspheres, 0.1 µm, blue fluorescent (350/440) *2% solids*	10 mL	6.5	None
F8798	FluoSpheres® carboxylate-modified microspheres, 0.1 µm, far red fluorescent (690/720) *2% solids*	1 mL	6.5	227
F8799	FluoSpheres® carboxylate-modified microspheres, 0.1 µm, infrared fluorescent (715/755) *2% solids*	1 mL	6.5	227
F8800	FluoSpheres® carboxylate-modified microspheres, 0.1 µm, orange fluorescent (540/560) *2% solids*	10 mL	6.5	227
F8801	FluoSpheres® carboxylate-modified microspheres, 0.1 µm, red fluorescent (580/605) *2% solids*	10 mL	6.5	227
F8803	FluoSpheres® carboxylate-modified microspheres, 0.1 µm, yellow-green fluorescent (505/515) *2% solids*	10 mL	6.5	227
F8805	FluoSpheres® carboxylate-modified microspheres, 0.2 µm, blue fluorescent (365/415) *2% solids*	10 mL	6.5	None
F8806	FluoSpheres® carboxylate-modified microspheres, 0.2 µm, crimson fluorescent (625/645) *2% solids*	2 mL	6.5	227, 193
F8807	FluoSpheres® carboxylate-modified microspheres, 0.2 µm, dark red fluorescent (660/680) *2% solids*	2 mL	6.5	227
F8809	FluoSpheres® carboxylate-modified microspheres, 0.2 µm, orange fluorescent (540/560) *2% solids*	10 mL	6.5	227
F8810	FluoSpheres® carboxylate-modified microspheres, 0.2 µm, red fluorescent (580/605) *2% solids*	10 mL	6.5	227
F8811	FluoSpheres® carboxylate-modified microspheres, 0.2 µm, yellow-green fluorescent (505/515) *2% solids*	10 mL	6.5	227
F8812	FluoSpheres® carboxylate-modified microspheres, 0.5 µm, red fluorescent (580/605) *2% solids*	10 mL	6.5	227
F8813	FluoSpheres® carboxylate-modified microspheres, 0.5 µm, yellow-green fluorescent (505/515) *2% solids*	10 mL	6.5	227
F8814	FluoSpheres® carboxylate-modified microspheres, 1.0 µm, blue fluorescent (365/415) *2% solids*	10 mL	6.5	None
F8815	FluoSpheres® carboxylate-modified microspheres, 1.0 µm, blue fluorescent (350/440) *2% solids*	10 mL	6.5	None
F8816	FluoSpheres® carboxylate-modified microspheres, 1.0 µm, crimson fluorescent (625/645) *2% solids*	2 mL	6.5	227, 193
F8819	FluoSpheres® carboxylate-modified microspheres, 1.0 µm, nile red fluorescent (535/575) *2% solids*	10 mL	6.5	None
F8820	FluoSpheres® carboxylate-modified microspheres, 1.0 µm, orange fluorescent (540/560) *2% solids*	10 mL	6.5	227
F8821	FluoSpheres® carboxylate-modified microspheres, 1.0 µm, red fluorescent (580/605) *2% solids*	10 mL	6.5	227
F8823	FluoSpheres® carboxylate-modified microspheres, 1.0 µm, yellow-green fluorescent (505/515) *2% solids*	10 mL	6.5	227
F8824	FluoSpheres® carboxylate-modified microspheres, 2.0 µm, blue fluorescent (365/415) *2% solids*	2 mL	6.5	None
F8825	FluoSpheres® carboxylate-modified microspheres, 2.0 µm, nile red fluorescent (535/575) *2% solids*	2 mL	6.5	None
F8826	FluoSpheres® carboxylate-modified microspheres, 2.0 µm, red fluorescent (580/605) *2% solids*	2 mL	6.5	227
F8827	FluoSpheres® carboxylate-modified microspheres, 2.0 µm, yellow-green fluorescent (505/515) *2% solids*	2 mL	6.5	227
F20880	FluoSpheres® carboxylate-modified microspheres, 0.04 µm, europium luminescent (365/610) *0.5% solids*	2 mL	6.5, 14.6	None
F20881	FluoSpheres® carboxylate-modified microspheres, 0.2 µm, europium luminescent (365/610) *0.5% solids*	2 mL	6.5, 14.6	None
F20882	FluoSpheres® carboxylate-modified microspheres, 1.0 µm, europium luminescent (365/610) *0.5% solids*	2 mL	6.5, 14.6	None
F20886	FluoSpheres® carboxylate-modified microspheres, 0.04 µm, platinum luminescent (390/650) *0.5% solids*	2 mL	6.5, 14.6	None
F20887	FluoSpheres® carboxylate-modified microspheres, 0.2 µm, platinum luminescent (390/650) *0.5% solids*	2 mL	6.5, 14.6	None

For current prices or to order online, visit probes.invitrogen.com

Cat #	Product Name	Unit Size	Sections	Limited Use Label License #
F20888	FluoSpheres® carboxylate-modified microspheres, 1.0 µm, platinum luminescent (390/650) *0.5% solids*	2 mL	6.5, 14.6	None
F20893	FluoSpheres® collagen I-labeled microspheres, 2.0 µm, yellow-green fluorescent (505/515) *0.5% solids*	0.4 mL	6.5, 16.1	227
F20892	FluoSpheres® collagen I-labeled microspheres, 1.0 µm, yellow-green fluorescent (505/515) *0.5% solids*	0.4 mL	6.5, 16.1	227
F10720	FluoSpheres® Fluorescent Color Kit, carboxylate-modified microspheres, 0.04 µm *four colors, 1 mL each* *5% solids, azide free*	1 kit	6.5, 14.6	227
F20883	FluoSpheres® NeutrAvidin™ labeled microspheres, 0.04 µm, europium luminescent (365/610) *0.5% solids*	0.4 mL	6.5, 7.6	None
F20884	FluoSpheres® NeutrAvidin™ labeled microspheres, 0.2 µm, europium luminescent (365/610) *0.5% solids*	0.4 mL	6.5, 7.6	None
F20885	FluoSpheres® NeutrAvidin™ labeled microspheres, 1.0 µm, europium luminescent (365/610) *0.5% solids*	0.4 mL	6.5, 7.6	None
F20891	FluoSpheres® NeutrAvidin™ labeled microspheres, 1.0 µm, platinum luminescent (390/650) *0.5% solids*	0.4 mL	6.5, 7.6	None
F8772	FluoSpheres® NeutrAvidin™ labeled microspheres, 0.04 µm, nonfluorescent *1% solids*	0.4 mL	6.5, 7.6	None
F8777	FluoSpheres® NeutrAvidin™ labeled microspheres, 1.0 µm, nonfluorescent *1% solids*	0.4 mL	6.5, 7.6	None
F8770	FluoSpheres® NeutrAvidin™ labeled microspheres, 0.04 µm, red fluorescent (580/605) *1% solids*	0.4 mL	6.5, 7.6	227
F8775	FluoSpheres® NeutrAvidin™ labeled microspheres, 1.0 µm, red fluorescent (580/605) *1% solids*	0.4 mL	6.5, 7.6	227
F8776	FluoSpheres® NeutrAvidin™ labeled microspheres, 1.0 µm, yellow-green fluorescent (505/515) *1% solids*	0.4 mL	6.5, 7.6	227
F8771	FluoSpheres® NeutrAvidin™ labeled microspheres, 0.04 µm, yellow-green fluorescent (505/515) *1% solids*	0.4 mL	6.5, 7.6	227
F8774	FluoSpheres® NeutrAvidin™ labeled microspheres, 0.2 µm, yellow-green fluorescent (505/515) *1% solids*	0.4 mL	6.5, 7.6	227
F13080	FluoSpheres® polystyrene microspheres, 1.0 µm, blue-green fluorescent (430/465) *for tracer studies* *1.0x10^{10} beads/mL*	5 mL	6.5, 14.6	None
F13082	FluoSpheres® polystyrene microspheres, 1.0 µm, orange fluorescent (540/560) *for tracer studies* *1.0x10^{10} beads/mL*	5 mL	6.5, 14.6	227, 193
F13083	FluoSpheres® polystyrene microspheres, 1.0 µm, red fluorescent (580/605) *for tracer studies* *1.0x10^{10} beads/mL*	5 mL	6.5, 14.6	227, 193
F13081	FluoSpheres® polystyrene microspheres, 1.0 µm, yellow-green fluorescent (505/515) *for tracer studies* *1.0x10^{10} beads/mL*	5 mL	6.5, 14.6	227
F8829	FluoSpheres® polystyrene microspheres, 10 µm, blue fluorescent (365/415) *for blood flow determination* *3.6x10^6 beads/mL*	10 mL	6.5, 14.6	224
F8830	FluoSpheres® polystyrene microspheres, 10 µm, blue-green fluorescent (430/465) *for blood flow determination* *3.6x10^6 beads/mL*	10 mL	6.5, 14.6	224
F8831	FluoSpheres® polystyrene microspheres, 10 µm, crimson fluorescent (625/645) *for blood flow determination* *3.6x10^6 beads/mL*	10 mL	6.5, 14.6	227, 224, 193
F8833	FluoSpheres® polystyrene microspheres, 10 µm, orange fluorescent (540/560) *for blood flow determination* *3.6x10^6 beads/mL*	10 mL	6.5, 14.6	227, 224
F8834	FluoSpheres® polystyrene microspheres, 10 µm, red fluorescent (580/605) *for blood flow determination* *3.6x10^6 beads/mL*	10 mL	6.5, 14.6	227, 224
F8836	FluoSpheres® polystyrene microspheres, 10 µm, yellow-green fluorescent (505/515) *for blood flow determination* *3.6x10^6 beads/mL*	10 mL	6.5, 14.6	227, 224
F8837	FluoSpheres® polystyrene microspheres, 15 µm, blue fluorescent (365/415) *for blood flow determination* *1.0x10^6 beads/mL*	10 mL	6.5, 14.6	224
F8838	FluoSpheres® polystyrene microspheres, 15 µm, blue-green fluorescent (430/465) *for blood flow determination* *1.0x10^6 beads/mL*	10 mL	6.5, 14.6	224
F8839	FluoSpheres® polystyrene microspheres, 15 µm, crimson fluorescent (625/645) *for blood flow determination* *1.0x10^6 beads/mL*	10 mL	6.5, 14.6	227, 224, 193
F8841	FluoSpheres® polystyrene microspheres, 15 µm, orange fluorescent (540/560) *for blood flow determination* *1.0x10^6 beads/mL*	10 mL	6.5, 14.6	227, 224
F8842	FluoSpheres® polystyrene microspheres, 15 µm, red fluorescent (580/605) *for blood flow determination* *1.0x10^6 beads/mL*	10 mL	6.5, 14.6	227, 224
F8843	FluoSpheres® polystyrene microspheres, 15 µm, scarlet fluorescent (645/680) *for blood flow determination* *1.0x10^6 beads/mL*	10 mL	6.5, 14.6	227, 224, 193
F8844	FluoSpheres® polystyrene microspheres, 15 µm, yellow-green fluorescent (505/515) *for blood flow determination* *1.0x10^6 beads/mL*	10 mL	6.5, 14.6	227, 224
F21013	FluoSpheres® polystyrene microspheres, 15 µm, carmine fluorescent (580/620) *for blood flow determination* *1.0x10^6 beads/mL*	10 mL	6.5, 14.6	224, 227
F21010	FluoSpheres® polystyrene microspheres, 15 µm, green fluorescent (450/480) *for blood flow determination* *1.0x10^6 beads/mL*	10 mL	6.5, 14.6	224
F21012	FluoSpheres® polystyrene microspheres, 15 µm, red-orange fluorescent (565/580) *for blood flow determination* *1.0x10^6 beads/mL*	10 mL	6.5, 14.6	224, 227, 193
F21011	FluoSpheres® polystyrene microspheres, 15 µm, yellow fluorescent (515/534) *for blood flow determination* *1.0x10^6 beads/mL*	10 mL	6.5, 14.6	224, 227
F8887	FluoSpheres® Size Kit #1, carboxylate-modified microspheres, red fluorescent (580/605) *six sizes, 1 mL each* *2% solids*	1 kit	6.5	227
F8888	FluoSpheres® Size Kit #2, carboxylate-modified microspheres, yellow-green fluorescent (505/515) *six sizes, 1 mL each* *2% solids*	1 kit	6.5	227
F8780	FluoSpheres® streptavidin-labeled microspheres, 0.04 µm, yellow-green fluorescent (505/515) *0.5% solids*	0.4 mL	6.5, 7.6	227
F8845	FluoSpheres® sulfate microspheres, 0.02 µm, yellow-green fluorescent (505/515) *2% solids*	10 mL	6.5	227
F8848	FluoSpheres® sulfate microspheres, 0.2 µm, yellow-green fluorescent (505/515) *2% solids*	10 mL	6.5	227
F8849	FluoSpheres® sulfate microspheres, 1.0 µm, blue fluorescent (365/415) *2% solids*	10 mL	6.5	227
F8851	FluoSpheres® sulfate microspheres, 1.0 µm, red fluorescent (580/605) *2% solids*	10 mL	6.5	227
F8852	FluoSpheres® sulfate microspheres, 1.0 µm, yellow-green fluorescent (505/515) *2% solids*	10 mL	6.5	227

For current prices or to order online, visit probes.invitrogen.com

Cat #	Product Name	Unit Size	Sections	Limited Use Label License #
F8853	FluoSpheres® sulfate microspheres, 2.0 µm, yellow-green fluorescent (505/515) *2% solids*	2 mL	6.5	227
F8854	FluoSpheres® sulfate microspheres, 4.0 µm, blue fluorescent (365/415) *2% solids*	2 mL	6.5	None
F8858	FluoSpheres® sulfate microspheres, 4.0 µm, red fluorescent (580/605) *2% solids*	2 mL	6.5	227
F8859	FluoSpheres® sulfate microspheres, 4.0 µm, yellow-green fluorescent (505/515) *2% solids*	2 mL	6.5	227
F24181	FluoZin™-1, AM *cell permeant* *special packaging*	10 x 50 µg	19.7	191
F24180	FluoZin™-1, tripotassium salt *cell impermeant*	500 µg	19.7	191
F24189	FluoZin™-2, AM *cell permeant* *special packaging*	10 x 50 µg	19.7	191
F24188	FluoZin™-2, tetrapotassium salt *cell impermeant*	500 µg	19.7	191
F24195	FluoZin™-3, AM *cell permeant* *special packaging*	10 x 50 µg	19.7	191
F24194	FluoZin™-3, tetrapotassium salt *cell impermeant*	500 µg	19.7	191
F11831	5-((2-(FMOC)-γ-L-glutamylaminoethyl)amino)naphthalene-1-sulfonic acid (γ-EDANS-α-FMOC-L-glutamic acid)	100 mg	9.5	None
F6290	FMOC hydrazine (*N*-(9-fluorenylmethoxycarbonyl) hydrazine)	25 mg	3.2	None
Q21930	α-FMOC-ε-QSY® 7-L-lysine ($N^ε$-(QSY® 7)-*N*α-(9-fluorenylmethoxycarbonyl)-L-lysine)	5 mg	9.5	259
Q21931	α-FMOC-β-QSY® 35-L-alanine ($N^β$-(QSY® 35)-*N*α-(9-fluorenylmethoxycarbonyl)-L-alanine)	5 mg	9.5	259
F11830	α-FMOC-ε-TMR-L-lysine (*N*α-(9-fluorenylmethoxycarbonyl)-$N^ε$-tetramethylrhodamine-(5-carbonyl)-L-lysine)	25 mg	9.5	None
T3163	FM® 1-43 (*N*-(3-triethylammoniumpropyl)-4-(4-(dibutylamino)styryl)pyridinium dibromide)	1 mg	14.4, 16.1	None
T35356	FM® 1-43 (*N*-(3-triethylammoniumpropyl)-4-(4-(dibutylamino)styryl)pyridinium dibromide) *special packaging*	10 x 100 µg	14.4, 16.1	None
F35355	FM® 1-43FX *fixable analog of FM® 1-43 membrane stain*	10 x 100 µg	14.4, 16.1	None
T3164	FM® 1-84 (*N*-(3-triethylammoniumpropyl)-4-(4-(dipentylamino)styryl)pyridinium dibromide)	1 mg	16.1	None
T7508	FM® 2-10 (*N*-(3-triethylammoniumpropyl)-4-(4-(diethylamino)styryl)pyridinium dibromide)	5 mg	16.1	None
T13320	FM® 4-64 (*N*-(3-triethylammoniumpropyl)-4-(6-(4-(diethylamino)phenyl)hexatrienyl)pyridinium dibromide) *special packaging*	10 x 100 µg	12.3, 14.4, 16.1	None
T3166	FM® 4-64 (*N*-(3-triethylammoniumpropyl)-4-(6-(4-(diethylamino)phenyl)hexatrienyl)pyridinium dibromide)	1 mg	12.3, 14.4, 16.1	None
T23360	FM® 5-95 (*N*-(3-trimethylammoniumpropyl)-4-(6-(4-(diethylamino)phenyl)hexatrienyl)pyridinium dibromide)	1 mg	12.3, 14.4, 16.1	None
F6999	FM® DiI *special packaging*	20 x 50 µg	13.4, 14.4	None
F1501	FNPA (4-fluoro-3-nitrophenyl azide)	100 mg	5.3	None
F36908	FocalCheck™ DoubleFarRed Fluorescent Microspheres Kit, 6 µm *mounted on slides*	1 kit	23.1	227, 193
F36905	FocalCheck™ DoubleGreen Fluorescent Microspheres Kit, 6 µm *mounted on slides*	1 kit	23.1	227
F36906	FocalCheck™ DoubleOrange Fluorescent Microspheres Kit, 6 µm *mounted on slides*	1 kit	23.1	227
F36907	FocalCheck™ DoubleRed Fluorescent Microspheres Kit, 6 µm *mounted on slides*	1 kit	23.1	227
F24633	FocalCheck™ Fluorescent Microspheres Kit, 6 µm *mounted on slides*	1 kit	23.1	227, 193
F24634	FocalCheck™ Fluorescent Microspheres Kit, 15 µm *mounted on slides*	1 kit	23.1	227, 193
F14807	FocalCheck™ microspheres, 6 µm, fluorescent dark-red ring stain/green throughout	0.5 mL	23.1	227
F14806	FocalCheck™ microspheres, 6 µm, fluorescent green/orange/dark-red ring stains	0.5 mL	23.1	227
F14808	FocalCheck™ microspheres, 6 µm, fluorescent green ring stain/blue throughout	0.5 mL	23.1	227
F7234	FocalCheck™ microspheres, 15 µm, fluorescent blue/orange ring stains	0.5 mL	23.1	227, 193
F7239	FocalCheck™ microspheres, 15 µm, fluorescent dark-red ring stain/green throughout	0.5 mL	23.1	227
F7240	FocalCheck™ microspheres, 15 µm, fluorescent green/dark-red ring stains	0.5 mL	23.1	227
F7235	FocalCheck™ microspheres, 15 µm, fluorescent green/orange/dark-red ring stains	0.5 mL	23.1	227, 193
F7237	FocalCheck™ microspheres, 15 µm, fluorescent green ring stain/blue throughout	0.5 mL	23.1	227
F7238	FocalCheck™ microspheres, 15 µm, fluorescent green ring stain/dark red throughout	0.5 mL	23.1	227
F7236	FocalCheck™ microspheres, 15 µm, fluorescent orange ring stain/blue throughout	0.5 mL	23.1	227, 193
F14791	FocalCheck™ Thin-Ring Fluorescent Microspheres Kit, 1.0 µm *three suspensions*	1 kit	23.1	227
F1314	formyl-Nle-Leu-Phe-Nle-Tyr-Lys, fluorescein derivative	1 mg	15.6, 16.1	None
F23103	fosmidomycin, sodium salt (FR-31564)	25 mg	15.2	None
A10192	FQ; 3-(2-furoyl)quinoline-2-carboxaldehyde (ATTO-TAG™ FQ derivatization reagent)	10 mg	1.8, 9.3, 21.2	244
F23103	FR-31564 (fosmidomycin, sodium salt)	25 mg	15.2	None
F23104	FR-900098	25 mg	15.2	None
F24840	Fundamentals of Light Microscopy and Electronic Imaging. D.B. Murphy. John Wiley & Sons, Inc. (2001); 384 pages, hard cover	each	23.6	None
F7030	FUN® 1 cell stain *10 mM solution in DMSO*	100 µL	12.3, 15.2	154
F13150	FUN® 2 cell stain *10 mM solution in DMSO*	100 µL	12.3, 15.2	154
F1221	fura-2, AM *cell permeant* *special packaging*	20 x 50 µg	19.2	207
F14185	fura-2, AM *FluoroPure™ grade* *special packaging*	20 x 50 µg	19.2	207
F1225	fura-2, AM *1 mM solution in dry DMSO* *cell permeant*	1 mL	19.2	207
F1201	fura-2, AM *cell permeant*	1 mg	19.2	207
F6774	Fura-2 Calcium Imaging Calibration Kit *zero to 10 mM CaEGTA, 50 µM fura-2 (11 x 1 mL)*	1 kit	19.2, 19.8	207
F1200	fura-2, pentapotassium salt *cell impermeant*	1 mg	19.2	207
F6799	fura-2, pentasodium salt *cell impermeant*	1 mg	19.2	207

For current prices or to order online, visit probes.invitrogen.com

Cat #	Product Name	Unit Size	Sections	Limited Use Label License #
F14175	fura-4F, AM *cell permeant* *special packaging*	10 x 50 µg	19.2	207
F14174	fura-4F, pentapotassium salt *cell impermeant*	500 µg	19.2	207
F14177	fura-5F, AM *cell permeant* *special packaging*	10 x 50 µg	19.2	207
F14176	fura-5F, pentapotassium salt *cell impermeant*	500 µg	19.2	207
F14179	fura-6F, AM *cell permeant* *special packaging*	10 x 50 µg	19.2	207
F14178	fura-6F, pentapotassium salt *cell impermeant*	500 µg	19.2	207
F6792	fura-C_{18}, pentapotassium salt	1 mg	19.4	206
F3029	fura dextran, potassium salt, 10,000 MW, anionic	5 mg	19.4	206
F14181	fura-FF, AM *cell permeant* *special packaging*	10 x 50 µg	19.2	207
F24051	fura-FF-C_{18}, tetrapotassium salt	1 mg	19.4	207
F14180	fura-FF, pentapotassium salt *cell impermeant*	500 µg	19.2	207
F3020	Fura Red™, AM *cell permeant*	500 µg	19.3	256
F3021	Fura Red™, AM *cell permeant* *special packaging*	10 x 50 µg	19.3	256
F14219	Fura Red™, tetrapotassium salt *cell impermeant*	500 µg	19.3	256
F24183	FuraZin™-1, AM *cell permeant* *special packaging*	10 x 50 µg	19.7	None
F24182	FuraZin™-1, tripotassium salt *cell impermeant*	500 µg	19.7	None
G13360	gastrin, Rhodamine Green™ conjugate	25 µg	16.1	None
G13187	gelatin from pig skin, fluorescein conjugate	5 mg	15.6	None
G13186	gelatin from pig skin, Oregon Green® 488 conjugate	5 mg	15.6	191
G7055	L-glutamic acid, γ-(α-carboxy-2-nitrobenzyl) ester, trifluoroacetic acid salt (γ-(CNB-caged) L-glutamic acid)	5 mg	5.3, 16.2	246
G2504	L-glutamic acid, α-(4,5-dimethoxy-2-nitrobenzyl) ester, hydrochloride (α-(DMNB-caged) L-glutamic acid)	5 mg	5.3, 16.2	None
G2879	glutathione agarose, linked through sulfur *sedimented bead suspension*	10 mL	9.2	None
G21800	glutathione agarose, linked through sulfur *sedimented bead suspension* *bulk packaging*	100 mL	9.2	None
G36000	glutathione ethyl ester, biotin amide (BioGEE) *glutathiolation detection reagent* *special packaging*	10 x 100 µg	4.3, 9.4, 15.6, 18.2	None
G21801	Glutathione Transferase Fusion Protein Purification Kit *5 purifications*	1 kit	7.5, 9.2	None
G7702	glycerol tris-(1-pyrenebutyrate)	5 mg	10.6	None
G21060	goat anti-mouse IgG (H+L), alkaline phosphatase conjugate	1 mg	7.2	None
G21061	goat anti-mouse IgG (H+L), CMNB-caged fluorescein conjugate *2 mg/mL*	250 µL	5.3, 7.2	None
G21040	goat anti-mouse IgG (H+L), horseradish peroxidase conjugate	1 mg	7.2, 10.5	None
G21079	goat anti-rabbit IgG (H+L), alkaline phosphatase conjugate	1 mg	7.2	None
G21080	goat anti-rabbit IgG (H+L), CMNB-caged fluorescein conjugate *2 mg/mL*	250 µL	5.3, 7.2	None
G21234	goat anti-rabbit IgG (H+L), horseradish peroxidase conjugate	1 mg	7.2	None
G6888	gramicidin	100 mg	21.1	None
G7921	Griess Reagent Kit *for nitrite quantitation*	1 kit	18.3, 21.2	None
G22360	guanosine 5'-diphosphate, BODIPY® FL 2'-(or-3')-*O*-(*N*-(2-aminoethyl)urethane), bis(triethylammonium) salt (BODIPY® FL GDP) *5 mM in water*	100 µL	17.3	193
G35779	guanosine 5'-*O*-(3-thiotriphosphate), BODIPY® 515/530 thioester, sodium salt (BODIPY® 515/530 GTP-γ-S, thioester) *1 mM in buffer*	100 µL	17.3	205, 193
G22183	guanosine 5'-*O*-(3-thiotriphosphate), BODIPY® FL thioester, sodium salt (BODIPY® FL GTP-γ-S, thioester) *5 mM in buffer*	50 µL	10.3, 17.3	205, 193
G35780	guanosine 5'-*O*-(3-thiotriphosphate), BODIPY® TR thioester, sodium salt (BODIPY® TR GTP-γ-S, thioester) *1 mM in buffer*	100 µL	17.3	205, 193
G1053	guanosine 5'-*O*-(3-thiotriphosphate), $P^{3(S)}$-(1-(4,5-dimethoxy-2-nitrophenyl)ethyl) ester, triammonium salt (*S*-(DMNPE-caged) GTP-γ-S)	1 mg	5.3, 17.3	None
G12411	guanosine 5'-triphosphate, BODIPY® FL 2'-(or-3')-*O*-(*N*-(2-aminoethyl)urethane), trisodium salt (BODIPY® FL GTP) *5 mM in water*	100 µL	17.3	193
G22350	guanosine 5'-triphosphate, BODIPY® R6G 2'-(or-3')-*O*-(*N*-(2-aminoethyl)urethane), trisodium salt (BODIPY® R6G GTP) *5 mM in water*	100 µL	17.3	193
G22351	guanosine 5'-triphosphate, BODIPY® TR 2'-(or-3')-*O*-(*N*-(2-aminoethyl)urethane), trisodium salt (BODIPY® TR GTP) *5 mM in water*	100 µL	17.3	193
G35778	guanosine 5'-*O*-(3-iminotriphosphate), BODIPY® FL ethylamide, sodium salt (BODIPY® FL GTP-γ-NH, amide) *1 mM in buffer*	100 µL	17.3	205, 193
D338	H_2DIDS (4,4'-diisothiocyanatodihydrostilbene-2,2'-disulfonic acid, disodium salt)	100 mg	16.3	None
H7482	heparin, fluorescein conjugate	1 mg	17.2	None
H22730	4-heptadecyl-7-hydroxycoumarin	10 mg	13.5, 20.4	None
H110	5-hexadecanoylaminofluorescein	100 mg	13.5	None
H3790	1-hexadecanoyl-2-(3-perylenedodecanoyl)-*sn*-glycero-3-phosphocholine	1 mg	13.2	None
H361	1-hexadecanoyl-2-(1-pyrenedecanoyl)-*sn*-glycero-3-phosphocholine (β-py-C_{10}-HPC)	1 mg	13.2, 17.4	None
H3809	1-hexadecanoyl-2-(1-pyrenedecanoyl)-*sn*-glycero-3-phosphoglycerol, ammonium salt (β-py-C_{10}-PG)	1 mg	13.2, 17.4	None
H3810	1-hexadecanoyl-2-(1-pyrenedecanoyl)-*sn*-glycero-3-phosphomethanol, sodium salt (β-py-C_{10}-HPM)	1 mg	13.2, 17.4	None
H3818	1-hexadecanoyl-2-(1-pyrenehexanoyl)-*sn*-glycero-3-phosphocholine (β-py-C_6-HPC)	1 mg	13.2, 17.4	None
H1387	6-hexadecanoyl-2-(((2-(trimethylammonium)ethyl)methyl)amino)naphthalene chloride (patman)	5 mg	13.5	None
H14700	1,1',3,3,3',3'-hexamethylindodicarbocyanine iodide (DiIC_1(5))	100 mg	22.3	None

For current prices or to order online, visit probes.invitrogen.com

Cat #	Product Name	Unit Size	Sections	Limited Use Label License #
H7593	hexidium iodide	5 mg	8.1, 15.2	228
C20091	6-HEX, SE (6-carboxy-2',4,4',5',7,7'-hexachlorofluorescein, succinimidyl ester) *single isomer*	5 mg	1.5	None
H30460	Hg-Link™ Alexa Fluor® 350 phenylmercury	1 mg	2.3	183
H30461	Hg-Link™ Alexa Fluor® 405 phenylmercury, disodium salt	1 mg	2.3	183
H30462	Hg-Link™ Alexa Fluor® 488 phenylmercury	1 mg	2.2	183
H30463	Hg-Link™ Alexa Fluor® 555 phenylmercury, disodium salt	1 mg	2.2	183
H30464	Hg-Link™ Alexa Fluor® 594 phenylmercury, sodium salt	1 mg	2.2	183
H30465	Hg-Link™ Alexa Fluor® 647 phenylmercury, disodium salt	1 mg	2.2	183
H13188	histone H1 from calf thymus, Alexa Fluor® 488 conjugate	1 mg	14.7, 16.1	183
H2930	HIV Protease Substrate 1 (Arg-Glu(EDANS)-Ser-Gln-Asn-Tyr-Pro-Ile-Val-Gln-Lys(dabcyl)-Arg)	1 mg	10.4	None
H3569	Hoechst 33258, pentahydrate (bis-benzimide) *10 mg/mL solution in water*	10 mL	8.1, 8.3, 8.6, 15.4	None
H1398	Hoechst 33258, pentahydrate (bis-benzimide)	100 mg	8.1, 8.3, 8.6, 15.4	None
H21491	Hoechst 33258, pentahydrate (bis-benzimide) *FluoroPure™ grade*	100 mg	8.1, 8.3, 8.6, 15.4	None
H1399	Hoechst 33342, trihydrochloride, trihydrate	100 mg	8.1, 8.6, 15.4, 15.5	None
H3570	Hoechst 33342, trihydrochloride, trihydrate *10 mg/mL solution in water*	10 mL	8.1, 8.6, 15.4, 15.5	None
H21492	Hoechst 33342, trihydrochloride, trihydrate *FluoroPure™ grade*	100 mg	8.1, 8.6, 15.4, 15.5	None
H21486	Hoechst 34580	5 mg	8.1	None
N21485	Hoechst S769121, trihydrochloride, trihydrate (nuclear yellow)	10 mg	8.1, 8.6	None
H36004	HPF (3'-(*p*-hydroxyphenyl) fluorescein) *5 mM solution in DMF*	470 µL	18.2	None
H348	HPTS; pyranine (8-hydroxypyrene-1,3,6-trisulfonic acid, trisodium salt)	1 g	14.3, 16.1, 20.2	None
D7179	HPTS dextran (dextran, 8-hydroxypyrene-1,3,6-trisulfonic acid, 10,000 MW, anionic)	5 mg	20.4	None
H23379	hyaluronic acid, BODIPY® FL conjugate (BODIPY® FL hyaluronic acid)	500 µg	16.1	193
H18200	HybriSlip™ hybridization cover, 22 mm x 22 mm *RNase free* *set of 500*	1 set	8.5, 23.3	None
H18201	HybriSlip™ hybridization cover, 40 mm x 22 mm *RNase free* *set of 500*	1 set	8.5, 23.3	None
H18202	HybriSlip™ hybridization cover, 60 mm x 22 mm *RNase free* *set of 500*	1 set	8.5, 23.3	None
H24720	HybriWell™ hybridization sealing system, 13 mm diameter chamber, 0.25 mm deep *set of 100*	1 set	8.5, 23.3	None
H24721	HybriWell™ hybridization sealing system, 20 mm diameter chamber, 0.15 mm deep *set of 100*	1 set	8.5, 23.3	None
H24723	HybriWell™ hybridization sealing system, 22 mm x 22 mm chamber, 0.15 mm deep *set of 100*	1 set	8.5, 23.3	None
H24722	HybriWell™ hybridization sealing system, 40 mm x 22 mm chamber, 0.25 mm deep *set of 100*	1 set	8.5, 23.3	None
H18210	HybriWell™ hybridization sealing system, 40 mm x 21 mm chamber, 0.15 mm deep *set of 100*	1 set	8.5, 23.3	None
D1168	hydroethidine (dihydroethidium)	25 mg	8.1, 15.2, 15.5, 18.2	None
D11347	hydroethidine (dihydroethidium) *special packaging*	10 x 1 mg	8.1, 15.2, 15.5, 18.2	None
D23107	hydroethidine (dihydroethidium) *5 mM stabilized solution in DMSO*	1 mL	8.1, 15.2, 15.5, 18.2	None
H185	7-hydroxycoumarin-3-carboxylic acid *reference standard*	100 mg	1.7, 14.3	None
H1193	7-hydroxycoumarin-3-carboxylic acid, succinimidyl ester	25 mg	1.7	None
H6482	7-hydroxy-9*H*-(1,3-dichloro-9,9-dimethylacridin-2-one) (DDAO) *reference standard*	10 mg	10.1	None
H189	7-hydroxy-4-methylcoumarin *reference standard*	1 g	10.1	None
H1428	7-hydroxy-4-methylcoumarin-3-acetic acid	100 mg	1.7	None
H36004	3'-(*p*-hydroxyphenyl) fluorescein (HPF) *5 mM solution in DMF*	470 µL	18.2	None
H348	8-hydroxypyrene-1,3,6-trisulfonic acid, trisodium salt (HPTS; pyranine)	1 g	14.3, 16.1, 20.2	None
H22845	hydroxystilbamidine, methanesulfonate	10 mg	8.1, 14.3	None
H2249	*N*-hydroxysulfosuccinimide, sodium salt (NHSS)	100 mg	3.3, 5.2	None
T659	7-hydroxy-4-trifluoromethylcoumarin (β-trifluoromethylumbelliferone) *reference standard*	100 mg	10.1	192
H7476	hypericin	1 mg	17.3, 18.2	None
H7515	hypocrellin A	1 mg	17.3, 18.2	None
H7516	hypocrellin B	1 mg	17.3, 18.2	None
I7	IAANS (2-(4'-(iodoacetamido)anilino)naphthalene-6-sulfonic acid, sodium salt)	100 mg	2.3	None
I14	1,5-IAEDANS (5-((((2-iodoacetyl)amino)ethyl)amino)naphthalene-1-sulfonic acid)	100 mg	2.3	None
I30451	5-IAF (5-iodoacetamidofluorescein)	25 mg	2.2	None
I30452	6-IAF (6-iodoacetamidofluorescein)	25 mg	2.2	None
D2004	IANBD amide (*N,N'*-dimethyl-*N*-(iodoacetyl)-*N'*-(7-nitrobenz-2-oxa-1,3-diazol-4-yl)ethylenediamine)	25 mg	2.2	None
I9	IANBD ester (*N*-((2-(iodoacetoxy)ethyl)-*N*-methyl)amino-7-nitrobenz-2-oxa-1,3-diazole)	100 mg	2.2	None
D20382	IDCC (7-diethylamino-3-((((2-iodoacetamido)ethyl)amino)carbonyl)coumarin)	5 mg	2.3	None
I37150	Image-iT™ FX Kit #1 *with Alexa Fluor® 350 goat anti-mouse IgG (A21049), ProLong® Gold antifade (P36930) and Image-iT™ FX signal enhancer (I36933)*	1 kit	7.2, 23.1	223, 183
I37151	Image-iT™ FX Kit #2 *with Alexa Fluor® 488 goat anti-mouse IgG (A11029), ProLong® Gold antifade (P36930) and Image-iT™ FX signal enhancer (I36933)*	1 kit	7.2, 23.1	223, 183
I37152	Image-iT™ FX Kit #3 *with Alexa Fluor® 555 goat anti-mouse IgG (A21424), ProLong® Gold antifade (P36930) and Image-iT™ FX signal enhancer (I36933)*	1 kit	7.2, 23.1	223, 183

For current prices or to order online, visit probes.invitrogen.com

Cat #	Product Name	Unit Size	Sections	Limited Use Label License #
I37153	Image-iT™ FX Kit #4 *with Alexa Fluor® 594 goat anti-mouse IgG (A11032), ProLong® Gold antifade (P36930) and Image-iT™ FX signal enhancer (I36933)*	1 kit	7.2, 23.1	223, 183
I37154	Image-iT™ FX Kit #5 *with Alexa Fluor® 647 goat anti-mouse IgG (A21236), ProLong® Gold antifade (P36930) and Image-iT™ FX signal enhancer (I36933)*	1 kit	7.2, 23.1	223, 183
I37155	Image-iT™ FX Kit #6 *with Alexa Fluor® 350 goat anti-rabbit IgG (A21068), ProLong® Gold antifade (P36930) and Image-iT™ FX signal enhancer (I36933)*	1 kit	7.2, 23.1	223, 183
I37156	Image-iT™ FX Kit #7 *with Alexa Fluor® 488 goat anti-rabbit IgG (A11034), ProLong® Gold antifade (P36930) and Image-iT™ FX signal enhancer (I36933)*	1 kit	7.2, 23.1	223, 183
I37157	Image-iT™ FX Kit #8 *with Alexa Fluor® 555 goat anti-rabbit IgG (A21429), ProLong® Gold antifade (P36930) and Image-iT™ FX signal enhancer (I36933)*	1 kit	7.2, 23.1	223, 183
I37158	Image-iT™ FX Kit #9 *with Alexa Fluor® 594 goat anti-rabbit IgG (A11037), ProLong® Gold antifade (P36930) and Image-iT™ FX signal enhancer (I36933)*	1 kit	7.2, 23.1	223, 183
I37159	Image-iT™ FX Kit #10 *with Alexa Fluor® 647 goat anti-rabbit IgG (A21245), ProLong® Gold antifade (P36930) and Image-iT™ FX signal enhancer (I36933)*	1 kit	7.2, 23.1	223, 183
I37160	Image-iT™ FX Kit #11 *with Alexa Fluor® 350 streptavidin (S11249), ProLong® Gold antifade (P36930) and Image-iT™ FX signal enhancer (I36933)*	1 kit	7.6, 23.1	223, 183
I37161	Image-iT™ FX Kit #12 *with Alexa Fluor® 488 streptavidin (S11223), ProLong® Gold antifade (P36930) and Image-iT™ FX signal enhancer (I36933)*	1 kit	7.6, 23.1	223, 183
I37162	Image-iT™ FX Kit #13 *with Alexa Fluor® 555 streptavidin (S21381), ProLong® Gold antifade (P36930) and Image-iT™ FX signal enhancer (I36933)*	1 kit	7.6, 23.1	223, 183
I37163	Image-iT™ FX Kit #14 *with Alexa Fluor® 594 streptavidin (S11227), ProLong® Gold antifade (P36930) and Image-iT™ FX signal enhancer (I36933)*	1 kit	7.6, 23.1	223, 183
I37164	Image-iT™ FX Kit #15 *with Alexa Fluor® 647 streptavidin (S21374), ProLong® Gold antifade (P36930) and Image-iT™ FX signal enhancer (I36933)*	1 kit	7.6, 23.1	223, 183
I36933	Image-iT™ FX signal enhancer	10 mL	7.2, 23.1	223
I2904	ImaGene Green™ C_{12}FDG *lacZ* Gene Expression Kit	1 kit	10.2	242
I2908	ImaGene Green™ C_{12}FDGlcU GUS Gene Expression Kit	1 kit	10.2	242
I2906	ImaGene Red™ C_{12}RG *lacZ* Gene Expression Kit	1 kit	10.2	242
I1203	indo-1, AM *cell permeant*	1 mg	19.2	207
I1226	indo-1, AM *1 mM solution in dry DMSO* *cell permeant*	1 mL	19.2	207
I1223	indo-1, AM *cell permeant* *special packaging*	20 x 50 µg	19.2	207
I1202	indo-1, pentapotassium salt *cell impermeant*	1 mg	19.2	207
I23913	indo-5F, AM *cell permeant* *special packaging*	10 x 50 µg	19.2	207
I23912	indo-5F, pentapotassium salt *cell impermeant*	500 µg	19.2	207
I3032	indo dextran, potassium salt, 10,000 MW, anionic	5 mg	19.4	206
I3033	indo dextran, potassium salt, 70,000 MW, anionic	5 mg	19.4	206
I24185	IndoZin™-1, AM *cell permeant* *special packaging*	10 x 50 µg	19.7	None
I24184	IndoZin™-1, tripotassium salt *cell impermeant*	500 µg	19.7	None
I14402	Influx™ pinocytic cell-loading reagent *makes 10 x 5 mL*	1 set	10.2, 14.3, 19.8	None
I3716	D-*myo*-inositol 1,4,5-triphosphate, hexapotassium salt (Ins 1,4,5-P_3)	1 mg	17.2	None
I23580	D-*myo*-inositol 1,4,5-triphosphate, $P_{4(5)}$-(1-(2-nitrophenyl)ethyl) ester, tris(triethylammonium) salt (NPE-caged Ins 1,4,5-P_3)	25 µg	5.3, 17.2	None
I3716	Ins 1,4,5-P_3 (D-*myo*-inositol 1,4,5-triphosphate, hexapotassium salt)	1 mg	17.2	None
I7221	InSpeck™ Blue (350/440) Microscope Image Intensity Calibration Kit, 2.5 µm	1 kit	23.1	None
I7225	InSpeck™ Deep Red (633/660) Microscope Image Intensity Calibration Kit, 2.5 µm	1 kit	23.1	227, 193
I7219	InSpeck™ Green (505/515) Microscope Image Intensity Calibration Kit, 2.5 µm	1 kit	23.1	227
I14785	InSpeck™ Green (505/515) Microscope Image Intensity Calibration Kit, 6 µm	1 kit	23.1	227
I7223	InSpeck™ Orange (540/560) Microscope Image Intensity Calibration Kit, 2.5 µm	1 kit	23.1	227
I14786	InSpeck™ Orange (540/560) Microscope Image Intensity Calibration Kit, 6 µm	1 kit	23.1	227
I7224	InSpeck™ Red (580/605) Microscope Image Intensity Calibration Kit, 2.5 µm	1 kit	23.1	227
I14787	InSpeck™ Red (580/605) Microscope Image Intensity Calibration Kit, 6 µm	1 kit	23.1	227
I13269	insulin, human, recombinant from *E. coli*, fluorescein conjugate (FITC insulin) *monolabeled* *zinc free*	100 µg	16.1	None
I6496	INT; 2-(4-iodophenyl)-3-(4-nitrophenyl)-5-phenyltetrazolium chloride (4-iodonitrotetrazolium violet)	1 g	15.2, 18.2	None
I7	2-(4′-(iodoacetamido)anilino)naphthalene-6-sulfonic acid, sodium salt (IAANS)	100 mg	2.3	None
I30451	5-iodoacetamidofluorescein (5-IAF)	25 mg	2.2	None
I30452	6-iodoacetamidofluorescein (6-IAF)	25 mg	2.2	None
I9	*N*-((2-(iodoacetoxy)ethyl)-*N*-methyl)amino-7-nitrobenz-2-oxa-1,3-diazole (IANBD ester)	100 mg	2.2	None
I14	5-((((2-iodoacetyl)amino)ethyl)amino)naphthalene-1-sulfonic acid (1,5-IAEDANS)	100 mg	2.3	None
I6881	6-iodoamiloride, hydrochloride, dihydrate	5 mg	16.3	None
I6496	4-iodonitrotetrazolium violet (INT; 2-(4-iodophenyl)-3-(4-nitrophenyl)-5-phenyltetrazolium chloride)	1 g	15.2, 18.2	None
I24222	ionomycin, calcium salt	1 mg	19.8	None
I6621	IPTG (isopropyl β-D-thiogalactopyranoside) *dioxane free*	1 g	10.2	None

For current prices or to order online, visit probes.invitrogen.com

Cat #	Product Name	Unit Size	Sections	Limited Use Label License #
I21410	isolectin GS-IB_4 from *Griffonia simplicifolia*	1 mg	7.7	None
I21411	isolectin GS-IB_4 from *Griffonia simplicifolia*, Alexa Fluor® 488 conjugate	500 µg	7.7	183
I21412	isolectin GS-IB_4 from *Griffonia simplicifolia*, Alexa Fluor® 568 conjugate	500 µg	7.7	183
I21413	isolectin GS-IB_4 from *Griffonia simplicifolia*, Alexa Fluor® 594 conjugate	500 µg	7.7	183
I32450	isolectin GS-IB_4 from *Griffonia simplicifolia*, Alexa Fluor® 647 conjugate	500 µg	7.7	183
I21414	isolectin GS-IB_4 from *Griffonia simplicifolia*, biotin-XX conjugate	500 µg	4.3, 7.7	None
I6621	isopropyl β-D-thiogalactopyranoside (IPTG) *dioxane free*	1 g	10.2	None
I24221	(*S*)-1-*p*-isothiocyanatobenzyldiethylenetriaminepentaacetic acid (DTPA isothiocyanate)	1 mg	19.8	None
J7473	jasplakinolide	100 µg	11.1	None
T3168	JC-1; $CBIC_2(3)$ (5,5',6,6'-tetrachloro-1,1',3,3'-tetraethylbenzimidazolylcarbocyanine iodide)	5 mg	12.2, 15.2, 15.5, 22.3	None
D22421	JC-9; $DiNOC_1(3)$ (3,3'-dimethyl-α-naphthoxacarbocyanine iodide)	5 mg	12.2, 15.2, 15.5, 22.3	None
C6171MP	6-JOE, SE (6-carboxy-4',5'-dichloro-2',7'-dimethoxyfluorescein, succinimidyl ester)	5 mg	1.5	None
J11372	JOJO™-1 iodide (529/545) *1 mM solution in DMSO*	200 µL	8.1	154
J11373	JO-PRO™-1 iodide (530/546) *1 mM solution in DMSO*	1 mL	8.1	154
D6923	JPW 1114 (di-2-ANEPEQ)	5 mg	22.2	None
L12370	latrunculin A	100 µg	11.1	None
L22290	latrunculin B	100 µg	11.1	None
D250	laurdan (6-dodecanoyl-2-dimethylaminonaphthalene)	100 mg	13.5	None
L3486	LDL (low-density lipoprotein from human plasma) *2.5 mg/mL*	200 µL	16.1	None
L7595	LDS 751	10 mg	8.1, 15.4, 15.5	None
L21415	lectin GS-II from *Griffonia simplicifolia*, Alexa Fluor® 488 conjugate	500 µg	7.7, 12.4	183
L21416	lectin GS-II from *Griffonia simplicifolia*, Alexa Fluor® 594 conjugate	500 µg	7.7, 12.4	183
L32451	lectin GS-II from *Griffonia simplicifolia*, Alexa Fluor® 647 conjugate	500 µg	7.7, 12.4	183
L11271	lectin HPA from *Helix pomatia* (edible snail), Alexa Fluor® 488 conjugate	1 mg	7.7, 12.4	183
L32454	lectin HPA from *Helix pomatia* (edible snail), Alexa Fluor® 647 conjugate	1 mg	7.7, 12.4	183
L11270	lectin PHA-L from *Phaseolus vulgaris* (red kidney bean), Alexa Fluor® 488 conjugate	1 mg	7.7, 14.7	183
L32455	lectin PHA-L from *Phaseolus vulgaris* (red kidney bean), Alexa Fluor® 568 conjugate	1 mg	7.7, 14.7	183
L32456	lectin PHA-L from *Phaseolus vulgaris* (red kidney bean), Alexa Fluor® 594 conjugate	1 mg	7.7, 14.7	183
L32457	lectin PHA-L from *Phaseolus vulgaris* (red kidney bean), Alexa Fluor® 647 conjugate	1 mg	7.7, 14.7	183
L21409	lectin PNA from *Arachis hypogaea* (peanut), Alexa Fluor® 488 conjugate	1 mg	7.7, 16.1	183
L32458	lectin PNA from *Arachis hypogaea* (peanut), Alexa Fluor® 568 conjugate	1 mg	7.7, 16.1	183
L32459	lectin PNA from *Arachis hypogaea* (peanut), Alexa Fluor® 594 conjugate	1 mg	7.7, 16.1	183
L32460	lectin PNA from *Arachis hypogaea* (peanut), Alexa Fluor® 647 conjugate	1 mg	7.7, 16.1	183
L11272	lectin SBA from *Glycine max* (soybean), Alexa Fluor® 488 conjugate	1 mg	7.7	183
L32461	lectin SBA from *Glycine max* (soybean), Alexa Fluor® 568 conjugate	1 mg	7.7	183
L32462	lectin SBA from *Glycine max* (soybean), Alexa Fluor® 594 conjugate	1 mg	7.7	183
L32463	lectin SBA from *Glycine max* (soybean), Alexa Fluor® 647 conjugate	1 mg	7.7	183
L6543	leupeptin hemisulfate	10 mg	10.4	None
L20492	*N*-levulinoyl-D-mannosamine (ManLev)	25 mg	3.2, 16.1	None
L20493	*N*-levulinoyl-D-mannosamine, tetraacetate (ManLev tetraacetate) *5 mM solution in DMSO*	500 µL	3.2, 16.1	None
L14812	LinearFlow™ Blue Flow Cytometry Intensity Calibration Kit, 2.5 µm *for UV excitation/430 nm emission*	1 kit	23.2	None
L14813	LinearFlow™ Blue Flow Cytometry Intensity Calibration Kit, 6 µm *for UV excitation/430 nm emission*	1 kit	23.2	None
L14816	LinearFlow™ Carmine Flow Cytometry Intensity Calibration Kit, 2.5 µm *for 488 nm excitation/620 nm emission*	1 kit	23.2	227
L14817	LinearFlow™ Carmine Flow Cytometry Intensity Calibration Kit, 6 µm *for 488 nm excitation/620 nm emission*	1 kit	23.2	227
L14818	LinearFlow™ Deep Red Flow Cytometry Intensity Calibration Kit, 2.5 µm *for 633 nm excitation/660 nm emission*	1 kit	23.2	227, 193
L14819	LinearFlow™ Deep Red Flow Cytometry Intensity Calibration Kit, 6 µm *for 633 nm excitation/660 nm emission*	1 kit	23.2	227, 193
L14821	LinearFlow™ Green Flow Cytometry Intensity Calibration Kit, 2.5 µm *for 488 nm excitation/515 nm emission*	1 kit	23.2	227
L14822	LinearFlow™ Green Flow Cytometry Intensity Calibration Kit, 6 µm *for 488 nm excitation/515 nm emission*	1 kit	23.2	227
L14823	LinearFlow™ Green Flow Cytometry Low Intensity Calibration Kit, 2.5 µm *for 488 nm excitation/515 nm emission*	1 kit	23.2	227
L14824	LinearFlow™ Green Flow Cytometry Low Intensity Calibration Kit, 6 µm *for 488 nm excitation/515 nm emission*	1 kit	23.2	227
L14814	LinearFlow™ Orange Flow Cytometry Intensity Calibration Kit, 2.5 µm *for 488 nm excitation/575 nm emission*	1 kit	23.2	227, 193
L14815	LinearFlow™ Orange Flow Cytometry Intensity Calibration Kit, 6 µm *for 488 nm excitation/575 nm emission*	1 kit	23.2	227, 193
L7781	Lipophilic Tracer Sampler Kit	1 kit	13.4, 14.4	229
L23351	lipopolysaccharides from *Escherichia coli* serotype 055:B5, Alexa Fluor® 488 conjugate	100 µg	13.3, 16.1	183
L23352	lipopolysaccharides from *Escherichia coli* serotype 055:B5, Alexa Fluor® 568 conjugate	100 µg	13.3, 16.1	183
L23353	lipopolysaccharides from *Escherichia coli* serotype 055:B5, Alexa Fluor® 594 conjugate	100 µg	13.3, 16.1	183
L23350	lipopolysaccharides from *Escherichia coli* serotype 055:B5, BODIPY® FL conjugate	100 µg	13.3, 16.1	193
L23356	lipopolysaccharides from *Salmonella minnesota*, Alexa Fluor® 488 conjugate	100 µg	13.3, 16.1	183

For current prices or to order online, visit probes.invitrogen.com

Cat #	Product Name	Unit Size	Sections	Limited Use Label License #
L23357	lipopolysaccharides from *Salmonella minnesota*, Alexa Fluor® 568 conjugate	100 µg	13.3, 16.1	183
L23358	lipopolysaccharides from *Salmonella minnesota*, Alexa Fluor® 594 conjugate	100 µg	13.3, 16.1	183
L23355	lipopolysaccharides from *Salmonella minnesota*, BODIPY® FL conjugate	100 µg	13.3, 16.1	183
L24919	LI Silver (LIS) Enhancement Kit	1 kit	7.2, 7.6	None
L1392	Lissamine™ rhodamine B 1,2-dihexadecanoyl-*sn*-glycero-3-phosphoethanolamine, triethylammonium salt (rhodamine DHPE)	5 mg	13.2	None
L2424	Lissamine™ rhodamine B ethylenediamine	10 mg	3.3	None
L20	Lissamine™ rhodamine B sulfonyl chloride *mixed isomers*	1 g	1.6	None
L1908	Lissamine™ rhodamine B sulfonyl chloride *mixed isomers* *special packaging*	10 x 10 mg	1.6	None
L7005	LIVE *BacLight*™ Bacterial Gram Stain Kit *for microscopy and quantitative assays* *1000 assays*	1 kit	15.3	228, 154
L34856	LIVE/DEAD® *BacLight*™ Bacterial Viability and Counting Kit *for flow cytometry* *100 assays*	1 kit	15.3	154
L13152	LIVE/DEAD® *BacLight*™ Bacterial Viability Kit *10 applicator sets* *500 assays*	1 kit	15.3	154
L7007	LIVE/DEAD® *BacLight*™ Bacterial Viability Kit *for microscopy* *1000 assays*	1 kit	15.3	154
L7012	LIVE/DEAD® *BacLight*™ Bacterial Viability Kit *for microscopy and quantitative assays* *1000 assays*	1 kit	15.3	154
L7010	LIVE/DEAD® Cell-Mediated Cytotoxicity Kit *for animal cells* *2000 assays*	1 kit	15.3	None
L34951	LIVE/DEAD® Cell Vitality Assay Kit *C_{12}-resazurin/SYTOX® Green* *1000 assays*	1 kit	15.3	154
L7013	LIVE/DEAD® Reduced Biohazard Cell Viability Kit #1 *green and red fluorescence* *100 assays*	1 kit	15.3	154
L23101	LIVE/DEAD® Reduced Biohazard Cell Viability Kit #2 *green fluorescence* *200 assays*	1 kit	15.3	191
L23102	LIVE/DEAD® Reduced Biohazard Cell Viability Kit #3 *red fluorescence* *200 assays*	1 kit	15.3	211
L23105	LIVE/DEAD® Reduced Biohazard Cell Viability Kit #4 *blue fluorescence* *200 assays*	1 kit	15.3	183
L7011	LIVE/DEAD® Sperm Viability Kit *200-1000 assays*	1 kit	15.3	154
L3224	LIVE/DEAD® Viability/Cytotoxicity Kit *for animal cells* *1000 assays*	1 kit	15.3	210
L7009	LIVE/DEAD® Yeast Viability Kit *1000 assays*	1 kit	15.3	154
L11376	LOLO™-1 iodide (565/579) *1 mM solution in DMSO*	200 µL	8.1	154
L11377	LO-PRO™-1 iodide (567/580) *1 mM solution in DMSO*	1 mL	8.1	154
L3486	low-density lipoprotein from human plasma (LDL) *2.5 mg/mL*	200 µL	16.1	None
L35354	low-density lipoprotein from human plasma, acetylated (AcLDL) *2.5 mg/mL*	200 µL	16.1	None
L23380	low-density lipoprotein from human plasma, acetylated, Alexa Fluor® 488 conjugate (Alexa Fluor® 488 AcLDL) *1 mg/mL*	200 µL	16.1	183
L35353	low-density lipoprotein from human plasma, acetylated, Alexa Fluor® 594 conjugate (Alexa Fluor® 594 AcLDL) *1 mg/mL*	200 µL	16.1	183
L3485	low-density lipoprotein from human plasma, acetylated, BODIPY® FL conjugate (BODIPY® FL AcLDL) *1 mg/mL*	200 µL	16.1	193
L3484	low-density lipoprotein from human plasma, acetylated, DiI complex (DiI AcLDL) *1 mg/mL*	200 µL	16.1	None
L3483	low-density lipoprotein from human plasma, BODIPY® FL complex (BODIPY® FL LDL) *1 mg/mL*	200 µL	16.1	193
L3482	low-density lipoprotein from human plasma, DiI complex (DiI LDL) *1 mg/mL*	200 µL	16.1	None
L7085	D-luciferin, 1-(4,5-dimethoxy-2-nitrophenyl)ethyl ester (DMNPE-caged luciferin)	5 mg	5.3, 10.6	None
L2911	D-luciferin, free acid	25 mg	10.6	None
L2916	D-luciferin, potassium salt	25 mg	10.6	None
L2912	D-luciferin, sodium salt	25 mg	10.6	None
L6950	lucifer yellow biocytin, potassium salt (biocytin lucifer yellow)	5 mg	4.3, 14.3	None
A1340	lucifer yellow cadaverine (*N*-(5-aminopentyl)-4-amino-3,6-disulfo-1,8-naphthalimide, dipotassium salt)	25 mg	3.3, 14.3	None
L2601	lucifer yellow cadaverine biotin-X, dipotassium salt	10 mg	4.3, 14.3	None
L682	lucifer yellow CH, ammonium salt	25 mg	14.3	None
L453	lucifer yellow CH, lithium salt	25 mg	3.2, 14.3, 16.1	None
L12926	lucifer yellow CH, lithium salt *for microinjection* *100 mM in water*	100 µL	14.3	None
L1177	lucifer yellow CH, potassium salt	25 mg	14.3	None
A1339	lucifer yellow ethylenediamine (*N*-(2-aminoethyl)-4-amino-3,6-disulfo-1,8-naphthalimide, dipotassium salt)	25 mg	3.3, 14.3	None
L1338	lucifer yellow iodoacetamide, dipotassium salt	25 mg	2.2, 4.2, 14.3	None
L6868	lucigenin (bis-*N*-methylacridinium nitrate) *high purity*	10 mg	12.2, 18.2, 21.2	None
L8455	luminol (3-aminophthalhydrazide)	25 g	8.5, 10.5, 15.2, 18.2	None
L7533	LysoSensor™ Blue DND-167 *1 mM solution in DMSO* *special packaging*	20 x 50 µL	12.3, 20.3	None
L7532	LysoSensor™ Blue DND-192 *1 mM solution in DMSO* *special packaging*	20 x 50 µL	12.3, 20.3	None
L7534	LysoSensor™ Green DND-153 *1 mM solution in DMSO* *special packaging*	20 x 50 µL	12.3, 20.3	None
L7535	LysoSensor™ Green DND-189 *1 mM solution in DMSO* *special packaging*	20 x 50 µL	12.3, 20.3	None
L22460	LysoSensor™ Yellow/Blue dextran, 10,000 MW, anionic, fixable	5 mg	12.3, 20.4	None
L7545	LysoSensor™ Yellow/Blue DND-160 *1 mM solution in DMSO* *special packaging*	20 x 50 µL	12.3, 20.3	None
L7525	LysoTracker® Blue DND-22 *1 mM solution in DMSO* *special packaging*	20 x 50 µL	12.3	None
L12490	LysoTracker® Blue-White DPX *1 mM solution in DMSO* *special packaging*	20 x 50 µL	12.3	None
L7526	LysoTracker® Green DND-26 *1 mM solution in DMSO* *special packaging*	20 x 50 µL	12.3	216, 193
L7528	LysoTracker® Red DND-99 *1 mM solution in DMSO* *special packaging*	20 x 50 µL	12.3	216, 193

For current prices or to order online, visit probes.invitrogen.com

Cat #	Product Name	Unit Size	Sections	Limited Use Label License #
L12491	LysoTracker® Yellow HCK-123 *1 mM solution in DMSO* *special packaging*	20 x 50 µL	12.3	None
M14206	mag-fluo-4, AM *cell permeant* *special packaging*	10 x 50 µg	19.3, 19.6	191
M14205	mag-fluo-4, tetrapotassium salt *cell impermeant*	500 µg	19.3, 19.6	191
M1292	mag-fura-2, AM *cell permeant* *special packaging*	20 x 50 µg	19.2, 19.6	None
M1291	mag-fura-2, AM *cell permeant*	1 mg	19.2, 19.6	None
M1290	mag-fura-2, tetrapotassium salt *cell impermeant*	1 mg	19.2, 19.6	None
M3105	mag-fura-5, AM *cell permeant* *special packaging*	20 x 50 µg	19.2, 19.6	None
M3103	mag-fura-5, tetrapotassium salt *cell impermeant*	1 mg	19.2, 19.6	None
M24050	mag-fura-C_{18}, tripotassium salt	1 mg	19.4, 19.6	None
M6892	Mag-Fura Red™, tripotassium salt *cell impermeant*	1 mg	19.6	None
M1295	mag-indo-1, AM *cell permeant* *special packaging*	20 x 50 µg	19.2, 19.6	None
M1293	mag-indo-1, tetrapotassium salt *cell impermeant*	1 mg	19.2, 19.6	None
M3735	Magnesium Green™, AM *cell permeant* *special packaging*	20 x 50 µg	19.3, 19.6	None
M3733	Magnesium Green™, pentapotassium salt *cell impermeant*	1 mg	19.3, 19.6	None
M6890	Magnesium Orange™, tripotassium salt *cell impermeant*	1 mg	19.6	None
M14214	mag-rhod-2, AM *cell permeant* *special packaging*	10 x 50 µg	19.3, 19.6	None
M14213	mag-rhod-2, dipotassium salt *cell impermeant*	500 µg	19.3, 19.6	None
M14216	mag-X-rhod-1, AM *cell permeant* *special packaging*	10 x 50 µg	19.3, 19.6	None
M14215	mag-X-rhod-1, dipotassium salt *cell impermeant*	500 µg	19.3, 19.6	None
M689	malachite green isothiocyanate	10 mg	1.6, 18.2	None
M8	2-(4′-maleimidylanilino)naphthalene-6-sulfonic acid, sodium salt (MIANS)	100 mg	2.3	None
M6026	1-(2-maleimidylethyl)-4-(5-(4-methoxyphenyl)oxazol-2-yl)pyridinium methanesulfonate (PyMPO maleimide)	5 mg	2.2	None
M1618	*N*-((4-maleimidylmethyl)cyclohexane-1-carbonyl)-1,2-dihexadecanoyl-*sn*-glycero-3-phosphoethanolamine, triethylammonium salt (MMCC DHPE)	5 mg	5.2, 13.2	None
M1602	Nα-(3-maleimidylpropionyl)biocytin	25 mg	4.2, 14.3	None
L20492	ManLev (*N*-levulinoyl-D-mannosamine)	25 mg	3.2, 16.1	None
L20493	ManLev tetraacetate (*N*-levulinoyl-D-mannosamine, tetraacetate) *5 mM solution in DMSO*	500 µL	3.2, 16.1	None
M12416	MANT-ADP (2′-(or-3′)-*O*-(*N*-methylanthraniloyl)adenosine 5′-diphosphate, disodium salt) *5 mM in buffer*	400 µL	17.3	None
M22354	MANT-AMPPNP (2′-(or-3′)-*O*-(*N*-methylanthraniloyl)-β:γ-imidoadenosine 5′-triphosphate, trisodium salt) *5 mM in buffer*	50 µL	17.3	None
M12417	MANT-ATP (2′-(or-3′)-*O*-(*N*-methylanthraniloyl)adenosine 5′-triphosphate, trisodium salt) *5 mM in buffer*	400 µL	17.3	None
M12414	MANT-GDP (2′-(or-3′)-*O*-(*N*-methylanthraniloyl)guanosine 5′-diphosphate, disodium salt) *5 mM in buffer*	400 µL	17.3	None
M22353	MANT-GMPPNP (2′-(or-3′)-*O*-(*N*-methylanthraniloyl)-β:γ-imidoguanosine 5′-triphosphate, trisodium salt) *5 mM in buffer*	50 µL	17.3	None
M12415	MANT-GTP (2′-(or-3′)-*O*-(*N*-methylanthraniloyl)guanosine 5′-triphosphate, trisodium salt) *5 mM in buffer*	400 µL	17.3	None
M12652	Marina Blue® DHPE (Marina Blue® 1,2-dihexadecanoyl-*sn*-glycero-3-phosphoethanolamine)	1 mg	13.2	192
M12652	Marina Blue® 1,2-dihexadecanoyl-*sn*-glycero-3-phosphoethanolamine (Marina Blue® DHPE)	1 mg	13.2	192
M10991	Marina Blue® goat anti-mouse IgG (H+L) *2 mg/mL*	0.5 mL	7.2	192
M10992	Marina Blue® goat anti-rabbit IgG (H+L) *2 mg/mL*	0.5 mL	7.2	192
M10432	Marina Blue® hydrazide	5 mg	3.2	192
M10165	Marina Blue® succinimidyl ester	5 mg	1.7	192
M1378	mBBr (monobromobimane)	25 mg	2.3, 14.2, 21.2	None
M20381	mBBr (monobromobimane) *FluoroPure™ grade*	25 mg	2.3, 14.2, 21.2	None
M1381MP	mBCl (monochlorobimane)	25 mg	2.3, 14.2, 15.6	None
A11760	MBDS (4-amino-4′-benzamidostilbene-2,2′-disulfonic acid, disodium salt)	100 mg	9.2, 13.5	None
M23800	MCLA (2-methyl-6-(4-methoxyphenyl)-3,7-dihydroimidazo[1,2-a]pyrazin-3-one, hydrochloride)	5 mg	10.5, 18.2	None
D10253	MDCC (7-diethylamino-3-((((2-maleimidyl)ethyl)amino)carbonyl)coumarin)	5 mg	2.3	None
M13440	[Nle^4, D-Phe^7]-α-melanocyte-stimulating hormone, fluorescein conjugate ([Nle^4, D-Phe^7]-α-MSH, fluorescein conjugate)	25 µg	16.1	None
M6886	MEQ (6-methoxy-*N*-ethylquinolinium iodide)	100 mg	21.2	None
M24571	merocyanine 540	25 mg	18.2, 22.3	None
M14943	Methods in Enzymology, Volume 291: Caged Compounds. Gerard Marriott, ed. Academic Press (1998); 529 pages, hard cover	each	5.3, 23.6	None
M23271	methotrexate, Alexa Fluor® 488, inner salt (Alexa Fluor® 488 methotrexate) *mixed isomers*	500 µg	15.6	183
M23272	methotrexate, BODIPY® FL (BODIPY® FL methotrexate)	500 µg	15.6	191
M1198MP	methotrexate, fluorescein, triammonium salt (fluorescein methotrexate)	1 mg	15.6	None
M23273	methotrexate, Texas Red®-X, ammonium salt (Texas Red®-X methotrexate)	500 µg	15.6	211
M1445	7-methoxycoumarin-3-carbonyl azide	25 mg	3.1	None
M1420MP	7-methoxycoumarin-3-carboxylic acid	100 mg	1.7	None
M1410	7-methoxycoumarin-3-carboxylic acid, succinimidyl ester	25 mg	1.7	None
M6886	6-methoxy-*N*-ethylquinolinium iodide (MEQ)	100 mg	21.2	None
X6493	2,3-bis-(2-methoxy-4-nitro-5-sulfophenyl)-2*H*-tetrazolium-5-carboxanilide (XTT)	100 mg	15.2, 18.2	None

For current prices or to order online, visit probes.invitrogen.com

Cat #	Product Name	Unit Size	Sections	Limited Use Label License #
M440	6-methoxy-*N*-(3-sulfopropyl)quinolinium, inner salt (SPQ)	100 mg	21.2	None
M395	8-methoxypyrene-1,3,6-trisulfonic acid, trisodium salt (MPTS)	100 mg	14.3	None
M688	*N*-(6-methoxy-8-quinolyl)-*p*-toluenesulfonamide (TSQ)	25 mg	19.7	None
R351	methoxyresorufin (resorufin methyl ether)	5 mg	10.6	None
M7913	*trans*-1-(2′-methoxyvinyl)pyrene	1 mg	18.2	None
M12416	2′-(or-3′)-*O*-(*N*-methylanthraniloyl)adenosine 5′-diphosphate, disodium salt (MANT-ADP) *5 mM in buffer*	400 µL	17.3	None
M12417	2′-(or-3′)-*O*-(*N*-methylanthraniloyl)adenosine 5′-triphosphate, trisodium salt (MANT-ATP) *5 mM in buffer*	400 µL	17.3	None
M12414	2′-(or-3′)-*O*-(*N*-methylanthraniloyl)guanosine 5′-diphosphate, disodium salt (MANT-GDP) *5 mM in buffer*	400 µL	17.3	None
M12415	2′-(or-3′)-*O*-(*N*-methylanthraniloyl)guanosine 5′-triphosphate, trisodium salt (MANT-GTP) *5 mM in buffer*	400 µL	17.3	None
M22354	2′-(or-3′)-*O*-(*N*-methylanthraniloyl)-β:γ-imidoadenosine 5′-triphosphate, trisodium salt (MANT-AMPPNP) *5 mM in buffer*	50 µL	17.3	None
M22353	2′-(or-3′)-*O*-(*N*-methylanthraniloyl)-β:γ-imidoguanosine 5′-triphosphate, trisodium salt (MANT-GMPPNP) *5 mM in buffer*	50 µL	17.3	None
M7906	N^G-methyl-D-arginine, acetate salt (D-NMMA)	25 mg	18.3	None
M7898	N^G-methyl-L-arginine, acetate salt (L-NMMA)	25 mg	18.3	None
M7114	*N*-methyl-D-aspartic acid, β-(α-carboxy-2-nitrobenzyl) ester, trifluoroacetic acid salt (β-(CNB-caged) NMDA)	1 mg	5.3, 16.2	246
M13652	*N*-methyl-D-aspartic acid, β-(2,2′-dinitrobenzhydryl) ester, trifluoroacetic acid salt (β-(DNBH-caged) NMDA)	1 mg	5.3, 16.2	None
M20490	*N*-methyl-4-hydrazino-7-nitrobenzofurazan (NBD methylhydrazine)	25 mg	3.2, 10.5, 18.3, 21.2	None
M25	*N*-methylisatoic anhydride *high purity*	1 g	1.8, 3.1	None
M23800	2-methyl-6-(4-methoxyphenyl)-3,7-dihydroimidazo[1,2-a]pyrazin-3-one, hydrochloride (MCLA)	5 mg	10.5, 18.2	None
M1489MP	4-methylumbelliferyl β-D-galactopyranoside (MUG)	1 g	10.2	None
M1490	4-methylumbelliferyl β-D-glucuronide (MUGlcU)	100 mg	10.2	None
M8425	4-methylumbelliferyl phosphate, dicyclohexylammonium salt, trihydrate (MUP DCA salt)	1 g	10.3	None
M6491	4-methylumbelliferyl phosphate, free acid (MUP)	1 g	10.3	None
M8	MIANS (2-(4′-maleimidylanilino)naphthalene-6-sulfonic acid, sodium salt)	100 mg	2.3	None
D7156	micro-emerald (dextran, fluorescein and biotin, 3000 MW, anionic, lysine fixable)	5 mg	4.3, 14.5	None
D7162	micro-ruby (dextran, tetramethylrhodamine and biotin, 3000 MW, lysine fixable)	5 mg	4.3, 14.5	None
D7178	mini-emerald (dextran, fluorescein and biotin, 10,000 MW, anionic, lysine fixable)	10 mg	4.3, 14.5	None
D3312	mini-ruby (dextran, tetramethylrhodamine and biotin, 10,000 MW, lysine fixable)	10 mg	4.3, 14.5	None
M22430	mitochondrial proteins (human heart) for SDS-polyacrylamide gel electrophoresis *2 mg/mL*	100 µL	9.4, 12.2	None
M7502	MitoFluor™ Green	1 mg	12.2	217
M22424	MitoFluor™ Red 589	1 mg	12.2	154
M22422	MitoFluor™ Red 594	1 mg	12.2	None
M34151	MitoProbe™ $DiIC_1(5)$ Assay Kit *for flow cytometry* *100 assays*	1 kit	15.5, 22.3	None
M34150	MitoProbe™ $DiOC_2(3)$ Assay Kit *for flow cytometry* *100 assays*	1 kit	15.5, 22.3	None
M34152	MitoProbe™ JC-1 Assay Kit *for flow cytometry* *100 assays*	1 kit	15.5, 22.3	None
M34153	MitoProbe™ Transition Pore Assay Kit (MTP by Flow) *for flow cytometry* *100 assays*	1 kit	15.5	223
M22426	MitoTracker® Deep Red 633 *special packaging*	20 x 50 µg	12.2	217
M7514	MitoTracker® Green FM *special packaging*	20 x 50 µg	12.2	217
M7511	MitoTracker® Orange CM-H_2TMRos *special packaging*	20 x 50 µg	12.2, 18.2	217
M7510	MitoTracker® Orange CMTMRos *special packaging*	20 x 50 µg	12.2	217
M22425	MitoTracker® Red 580 *special packaging*	20 x 50 µg	12.2	217
M7513	MitoTracker® Red CM-H_2XRos *special packaging*	20 x 50 µg	12.2, 18.2	217
M7512	MitoTracker® Red CMXRos *special packaging*	20 x 50 µg	12.2, 15.5	217
M1618	MMCC DHPE (*N*-((4-maleimidylmethyl)cyclohexane-1-carbonyl)-1,2-dihexadecanoyl-*sn*-glycero-3-phosphoethanolamine, triethylammonium salt)	5 mg	5.2, 13.2	None
M6248	mono-*N*-(*t*-BOC)-propylenediamine	1 g	3.3	None
M1378	monobromobimane (mBBr)	25 mg	2.3, 14.2, 21.2	None
M20381	monobromobimane (mBBr) *FluoroPure™ grade*	25 mg	2.3, 14.2, 21.2	None
M1380	monobromotrimethylammoniobimane bromide (qBBr)	25 mg	2.3, 14.2	None
M1381MP	monochlorobimane (mBCl)	25 mg	2.3, 14.2, 15.6	None
M7926	3-morpholinosydnonimine, hydrochloride (SIN-1) *special packaging*	20 x 1 mg	18.3	None
M7891	3-morpholinosydnonimine, hydrochloride (SIN-1)	25 mg	18.3	None
M25500	mouse IgG agarose *sedimented bead suspension*	1 mL	7.3	None
M395	MPTS (8-methoxypyrene-1,3,6-trisulfonic acid, trisodium salt)	100 mg	14.3	None
E3101	MQAE (*N*-(ethoxycarbonylmethyl)-6-methoxyquinolinium bromide)	100 mg	21.2	None
M34153	MTP by Flow (MitoProbe™ Transition Pore Assay Kit) *for flow cytometry* *100 assays*	1 kit	15.5	223
M6494	MTT (3-(4,5-dimethylthiazol-2-yl)-2,5-diphenyltetrazolium bromide)	1 g	15.2, 18.2	None
M1489MP	MUG (4-methylumbelliferyl β-D-galactopyranoside)	1 g	10.2	None
M1490	MUGlcU (4-methylumbelliferyl β-D-glucuronide)	100 mg	10.2	None

For current prices or to order online, visit probes.invitrogen.com

Cat #	Product Name	Unit Size	Sections	Limited Use Label License #
M33307	Multiplexed Proteomics® Glycoprotein Gel Stain Kit *with 1 L each of Pro-Q® Emerald 300 and SYPRO® Ruby (S12000) gel stains*	1 kit	9.4	223, 190
MPM33305	Multiplexed Proteomics® Phosphoprotein Gel Stain Kit *includes MPP33300 and S12000*	1 kit	9.4	204, 190
MPM33306	Multiplexed Proteomics® Phosphoprotein Gel Stain Kit *includes MPP33301 and S12001*	1 kit	9.4	204, 190
M33305	Multiplexed Proteomics® Phosphoprotein Gel Stain Kit #1 *with 1 L each of Pro-Q® Diamond (P33300) and SYPRO® Ruby (S12000) gel stains*	1 set	9.4	223, 204, 190
M33306	Multiplexed Proteomics® Phosphoprotein Gel Stain Kit #2 *with 200 mL each of Pro-Q® Diamond (P33301) and SYPRO® Ruby (S12001) gel stains*	1 set	9.4	223, 204, 190
M33308	Multiplexed Proteomics® Transmembrane Protein Gel Stain Kit *with 500 mL each of Pro-Q® Amber and SYPRO® Ruby gel stains*	1 kit	9.4	223, 190
M7901	MultiSpeck™ Multispectral Fluorescence Microscopy Standards Kit *in suspension*	1 kit	23.1	227
M6491	MUP (4-methylumbelliferyl phosphate, free acid)	1 g	10.3	None
M8425	MUP DCA salt (4-methylumbelliferyl phosphate, dicyclohexylammonium salt, trihydrate)	1 g	10.3	None
M23400	muscimol, BODIPY® TMR-X conjugate	1 mg	16.2	193
M7006	MycoFluor™ Mycoplasma Detection Kit	1 kit	15.4	None
N7622	NAADP (β-nicotinic acid adenine dinucleotide phosphate)	10 µg	17.2	None
N1384	naloxone fluorescein	5 mg	16.2	None
N1385	naltrexone fluorescein	5 mg	16.2	None
N24915	NANOGOLD® Fab' fragment of goat anti-mouse IgG *80 µg protein/mL*	1 mL	7.2	231
N24916	NANOGOLD® Fab' fragment of goat anti-rabbit IgG *80 µg protein/mL*	1 mL	7.2	231
N24917	NANOGOLD® Fab' fragment of rabbit anti-goat IgG *80 µg protein/mL*	1 mL	7.2	231
N20345	NANOGOLD® monomaleimide *special packaging*	5 x 6 nmol	2.2	231
N24918	NANOGOLD® streptavidin (streptavidin, NANOGOLD® conjugate) *80 µg protein/mL*	1 mL	7.6	231
N6666	NanoOrange® Protein Quantitation Kit *200-2000 assays*	1 kit	9.2	190
N1138	naphthalene-2,3-dicarboxaldehyde (NDA)	100 mg	1.8, 9.3, 15.6, 21.2	None
N7897	naphthalene-1,4-dipropionic acid, disodium salt	25 mg	18.2	None
N2461	2-(2,3-naphthalimino)ethyl trifluoromethanesulfonate	100 mg	3.3	None
T411	naphthoyltrifluoroacetone (2-((trifluoroacetyl)acetyl)naphthalene)	100 mg	14.3, 19.7	None
N1154	NBD C_6-ceramide (6-((*N*-(7-nitrobenz-2-oxa-1,3-diazol-4-yl)amino)hexanoyl)sphingosine)	1 mg	12.4, 13.3, 17.4	None
N22651	NBD C_6-ceramide complexed to BSA	5 mg	12.4, 13.3, 17.4	None
C20260	NBD chloride; 4-chloro-7-nitrobenzofurazan (4-chloro-7-nitrobenz-2-oxa-1,3-diazole) *FluoroPure™ grade*	100 mg	1.8, 2.2	None
N1148	NBD cholesterol (22-(*N*-(7-nitrobenz-2-oxa-1,3-diazol-4-yl)amino)-23,24-bisnor-5-cholen-3β-ol)	10 mg	13.3	None
N3786	NBD C_6-HPC (2-(6-(7-nitrobenz-2-oxa-1,3-diazol-4-yl)amino)hexanoyl-1-hexadecanoyl-*sn*-glycero-3-phosphocholine)	5 mg	13.2, 17.4	None
N3787	NBD C_{12}-HPC (2-(12-(7-nitrobenz-2-oxa-1,3-diazol-4-yl)amino)dodecanoyl-1-hexadecanoyl-*sn*-glycero-3-phosphocholine)	5 mg	13.2, 17.4	None
N3524	NBD C_6-sphingomyelin (6-((*N*-(7-nitrobenz-2-oxa-1,3-diazol-4-yl)amino)hexanoyl)sphingosyl phosphocholine)	1 mg	12.4, 13.3, 17.4	None
D69	NBD dihexadecylamine (4-dihexadecylamino-7-nitrobenz-2-oxa-1,3-diazole)	100 mg	13.5	None
F486	NBD fluoride; 4-fluoro-7-nitrobenzofurazan (4-fluoro-7-nitrobenz-2-oxa-1,3-diazole)	25 mg	1.8, 2.2	None
N13195	2-NBDG (2-(*N*-(7-nitrobenz-2-oxa-1,3-diazol-4-yl)amino)-2-deoxyglucose)	5 mg	15.2, 16.1	None
N23106	6-NBDG (6-(*N*-(7-nitrobenz-2-oxa-1,3-diazol-4-yl)amino)-6-deoxyglucose)	5 mg	15.2, 16.1	None
M20490	NBD methylhydrazine (*N*-methyl-4-hydrazino-7-nitrobenzofurazan)	25 mg	3.2, 10.5, 18.3, 21.2	None
N360	NBD-PE (*N*-(7-nitrobenz-2-oxa-1,3-diazol-4-yl)-1,2-dihexadecanoyl-*sn*-glycero-3-phosphoethanolamine, triethylammonium salt)	10 mg	13.2	None
N354	NBD phallacidin (*N*-(7-nitrobenz-2-oxa-1,3-diazol-4-yl)phallacidin)	300 U	11.1	None
N316	NBD-X (6-(*N*-(7-nitrobenz-2-oxa-1,3-diazol-4-yl)amino)hexanoic acid)	100 mg	1.8, 13.2	None
S1167	NBD-X, SE (succinimidyl 6-(*N*-(7-nitrobenz-2-oxa-1,3-diazol-4-yl)amino)hexanoate)	25 mg	1.8	None
N6495	NBT (nitro blue tetrazolium chloride)	1 g	10.3, 15.2, 18.2	None
N6547	NBT/BCIP Reagent Kit	1 kit	10.3	None
C428	NCD-4 (*N*-cyclohexyl-*N'*-(4-(dimethylamino)naphthyl)carbodiimide)	25 mg	3.3	None
N1138	NDA (naphthalene-2,3-dicarboxaldehyde)	100 mg	1.8, 9.3, 15.6, 21.2	None
S13430	neurokinin-A, fluorescein conjugate (substance K, fluorescein conjugate)	25 µg	16.2	None
N13437	neuromedin C, Alexa Fluor® 488 conjugate	25 µg	16.2	183
N13436	neuromedin C, fluorescein conjugate	25 µg	16.2	None
N21479	NeuroTrace® 435/455 blue fluorescent Nissl stain *solution in DMSO*	1 mL	8.1, 8.6, 14.3	228
N21480	NeuroTrace® 500/525 green fluorescent Nissl stain *solution in DMSO*	1 mL	8.1, 8.6, 14.3	154
N21481	NeuroTrace® 515/535 yellow fluorescent Nissl stain *solution in DMSO*	1 mL	8.1, 8.6, 14.3	228
N21482	NeuroTrace® 530/615 red fluorescent Nissl stain *solution in DMSO*	1 mL	8.1, 8.6, 14.3	None
N21483	NeuroTrace® 640/660 deep-red fluorescent Nissl stain *solution in DMSO*	1 mL	8.1, 8.6, 14.3	228
N7167	NeuroTrace® BDA-10,000 Neuronal Tracer Kit	1 kit	14.5	None
N22883	NeuroTrace® CM-DiI tissue-labeling paste	100 mg	14.4	None

For current prices or to order online, visit probes.invitrogen.com

Cat #	Product Name	Unit Size	Sections	Limited Use Label License #
N22882	NeuroTrace® DiD tissue-labeling paste	500 mg	14.4	None
N22880	NeuroTrace® DiI tissue-labeling paste	500 mg	14.4	None
N22881	NeuroTrace® DiO tissue-labeling paste	500 mg	14.4	None
N22884	NeuroTrace® Multicolor Tissue-Labeling Kit *DiO, DiI, DiD pastes, 500 mg each*	1 kit	14.4	None
N3246	neutral red *high purity*	25 mg	12.3, 15.2	None
N7991	Newport Green™ DCF diacetate *cell permeant*	1 mg	19.7	191
N7990	Newport Green™ DCF, dipotassium salt *cell impermeant*	1 mg	19.7	191
N24190	Newport Green™ PDX	1 mg	19.7	191
N24191	Newport Green™ PDX acetoxymethyl ether	1 mg	19.7	191
H2249	NHSS (*N*-hydroxysulfosuccinimide, sodium salt)	100 mg	3.3, 5.2	None
N7622	β-nicotinic acid adenine dinucleotide phosphate (NAADP)	10 µg	17.2	None
N1495	nigericin, free acid	10 mg	20.2, 21.2	None
N1142	nile red	25 mg	11.2, 13.5	None
N1148	22-(*N*-(7-nitrobenz-2-oxa-1,3-diazol-4-yl)amino)-23,24-bisnor-5-cholen-3β-ol (NBD cholesterol)	10 mg	13.3	None
N13195	2-(*N*-(7-nitrobenz-2-oxa-1,3-diazol-4-yl)amino)-2-deoxyglucose (2-NBDG)	5 mg	15.2, 16.1	None
N23106	6-(*N*-(7-nitrobenz-2-oxa-1,3-diazol-4-yl)amino)-6-deoxyglucose (6-NBDG)	5 mg	15.2, 16.1	None
N678	12-(*N*-(7-nitrobenz-2-oxa-1,3-diazol-4-yl)amino)dodecanoic acid	100 mg	13.2	None
N3787	2-(12-(7-nitrobenz-2-oxa-1,3-diazol-4-yl)amino)dodecanoyl-1-hexadecanoyl-*sn*-glycero-3-phosphocholine (NBD C_{12}-HPC)	5 mg	13.2, 17.4	None
N316	6-(*N*-(7-nitrobenz-2-oxa-1,3-diazol-4-yl)amino)hexanoic acid (NBD-X)	100 mg	1.8, 13.2	None
N3786	2-(6-(7-nitrobenz-2-oxa-1,3-diazol-4-yl)amino)hexanoyl-1-hexadecanoyl-*sn*-glycero-3-phosphocholine (NBD C_6-HPC)	5 mg	13.2, 17.4	None
N1154	6-((*N*-(7-nitrobenz-2-oxa-1,3-diazol-4-yl)amino)hexanoyl)sphingosine (NBD C_6-ceramide)	1 mg	12.4, 13.3, 17.4	None
N3524	6-((*N*-(7-nitrobenz-2-oxa-1,3-diazol-4-yl)amino)hexanoyl)sphingosyl phosphocholine (NBD C_6-sphingomyelin)	1 mg	12.4, 13.3, 17.4	None
N360	*N*-(7-nitrobenz-2-oxa-1,3-diazol-4-yl)-1,2-dihexadecanoyl-*sn*-glycero-3-phosphoethanolamine, triethylammonium salt (NBD-PE)	10 mg	13.2	None
N354	*N*-(7-nitrobenz-2-oxa-1,3-diazol-4-yl)phallacidin (NBD phallacidin)	300 U	11.1	None
N6495	nitro blue tetrazolium chloride (NBT)	1 g	10.3, 15.2, 18.2	None
N6803	*o*-nitrophenyl EGTA, AM (NP-EGTA, AM) *cell permeant* *special packaging*	20 x 50 µg	5.3, 17.2, 19.8	None
N6802	*o*-nitrophenyl EGTA, tetrapotassium salt (NP-EGTA) *cell impermeant*	1 mg	5.3, 17.2, 19.8	None
N7065	1-(2-nitrophenyl)ethyl phosphate, diammonium salt (NPE-caged phosphate)	5 mg	5.3, 20.2	None
N6613	4-nitrophenyl phosphate, disodium salt, hexahydrate (PNPP)	5 g	10.3	None
N7892	*S*-nitroso-*N*-acetylpenicillamine (SNAP)	25 mg	18.3	None
N7927	*S*-nitroso-*N*-acetylpenicillamine (SNAP) *special packaging*	20 x 1 mg	18.3	None
M13440	[Nle^4, D-Phe^7]-α-MSH, fluorescein conjugate ([Nle^4, D-Phe^7]-α-melanocyte-stimulating hormone, fluorescein conjugate)	25 µg	16.1	None
M7906	D-NMMA (N^G-methyl-D-arginine, acetate salt)	25 mg	18.3	None
M7898	L-NMMA (N^G-methyl-L-arginine, acetate salt)	25 mg	18.3	None
A1372	nonyl acridine orange (acridine orange 10-nonyl bromide)	100 mg	12.2, 15.5	None
N6356	norbiotinamine, hydrochloride	10 mg	4.2	None
A7056	NPE-caged ADP (adenosine 5′-diphosphate, P^2-(1-(2-nitrophenyl)ethyl) ester, monopotassium salt)	5 mg	5.3, 17.3	None
A1048	NPE-caged ATP (adenosine 5′-triphosphate, P^3-(1-(2-nitrophenyl)ethyl) ester, disodium salt)	5 mg	5.3, 17.3	None
C7074	NPE-caged cADP-ribose (cyclic adenosine 5′-diphosphate ribose, 1-(1-(2-nitrophenyl)ethyl) ester) *mixed isomers*	50 µg	5.3, 17.2	None
I23580	NPE-caged Ins 1,4,5-P_3 (D-*myo*-inositol 1,4,5-triphosphate, $P_{4(5)}$-(1-(2-nitrophenyl)ethyl) ester, tris(triethylammonium) salt)	25 µg	5.3, 17.2	None
N7065	NPE-caged phosphate (1-(2-nitrophenyl)ethyl phosphate, diammonium salt)	5 mg	5.3, 20.2	None
N6802	NP-EGTA (*o*-nitrophenyl EGTA, tetrapotassium salt) *cell impermeant*	1 mg	5.3, 17.2, 19.8	None
N6803	NP-EGTA, AM (*o*-nitrophenyl EGTA, AM) *cell permeant* *special packaging*	20 x 50 µg	5.3, 17.2, 19.8	None
N21485	nuclear yellow (Hoechst S769121, trihydrochloride, trihydrate)	10 mg	8.1, 8.6	None
N7565	Nucleic Acid Stains Dimer Sampler Kit	1 kit	8.1, 15.2	228
O7703	1-octacosanyl-2-(1-pyrenehexanoyl)-*sn*-glycero-3-phosphomethanol, ammonium salt (C_{28}-O-PHPM)	250 µg	17.4	None
O322	5-octadecanoylaminofluorescein	100 mg	13.5	None
O3852	*N*-octadecyl-*N′*-(5-(fluoresceinyl))thiourea (F18)	25 mg	13.5	None
O246	octadecyl rhodamine B chloride (R18)	10 mg	13.5, 14.4	None
O2892	5-octanoylaminofluorescein di-β-D-galactopyranoside (C_8FDG)	5 mg	10.2	None
O21561	oligodeoxythymidine-18, Alexa Fluor® 555 conjugate (Alexa Fluor® 555 dT_{18})	10 nmol	8.2	183
O21562	oligodeoxythymidine-18, Alexa Fluor® 594 conjugate (Alexa Fluor® 594 dT_{18})	10 nmol	8.2	183
O21563	oligodeoxythymidine-18, Alexa Fluor® 647 conjugate (Alexa Fluor® 647 dT_{18})	10 nmol	8.2	183
O11492	OliGreen® ssDNA Assay Kit	1 kit	8.1, 8.3, 8.4	154
O7582	OliGreen® ssDNA reagent	1 mL	8.1, 8.3, 8.4	154
O24751	ONCYTE® MultiWells, one well, 13 mm diameter, with slide and matching gasket *set of 20*	1 set	23.3	None
O24750	ONCYTE® MultiWells, 12 wells, 5 mm diameter, with slide and matching gasket *set of 20*	1 set	23.3	None

For current prices or to order online, visit probes.invitrogen.com

Cat #	Product Name	Unit Size	Sections	Limited Use Label License #
P2331MP	OPA (*o*-phthaldialdehyde) *high purity*	1 g	1.8, 9.2, 9.3, 15.6, 21.2	None
D6145	Oregon Green® 488 (2',7'-difluorofluorescein)	10 mg	1.5	191
O6807	Oregon Green® 488 BAPTA-1, AM *cell permeant* *special packaging*	10 x 50 µg	19.3	191
O6798	Oregon Green® 488 BAPTA-1 dextran, potassium salt, 10,000 MW, anionic	5 mg	19.4	191
O6797	Oregon Green® 488 BAPTA-1 dextran, potassium salt, 70,000 MW, anionic	5 mg	19.4	191
O6806	Oregon Green® 488 BAPTA-1, hexapotassium salt *cell impermeant*	500 µg	19.3	191
O6809	Oregon Green® 488 BAPTA-2, AM *cell permeant* *special packaging*	10 x 50 µg	19.3	191
O6808	Oregon Green® 488 BAPTA-2, octapotassium salt *cell impermeant*	500 µg	19.3	191
O6813	Oregon Green® 488 BAPTA-5N, AM *cell permeant* *special packaging*	10 x 50 µg	19.3	191
O6812	Oregon Green® 488 BAPTA-5N, hexapotassium salt *cell impermeant*	500 µg	19.3	191
O23991	Oregon Green® 488 BAPTA-6F, AM *cell permeant* *special packaging*	10 x 50 µg	19.3	191
O23990	Oregon Green® 488 BAPTA-6F, hexapotassium salt *cell impermeant*	500 µg	19.3	191
O12920	Oregon Green® 488 biocytin (biocytin Oregon Green® 488)	5 mg	4.3, 14.3	191
O10465	Oregon Green® 488 cadaverine *5-isomer*	5 mg	3.3	191
O6146	Oregon Green® 488 carboxylic acid *5-isomer*	5 mg	1.5, 14.3, 20.3	191
O6151	Oregon Green® 488 carboxylic acid diacetate (carboxy-DFFDA) *6-isomer*	5 mg	15.2, 20.3	191
O34550	Oregon Green® 488 carboxylic acid diacetate, succinimidyl ester (carboxy-DFFDA, SE) *mixed isomers*	1 mg	14.2, 15.4	191
O6147	Oregon Green® 488 carboxylic acid, succinimidyl ester *5-isomer*	5 mg	1.5, 20.4	191
O6149	Oregon Green® 488 carboxylic acid, succinimidyl ester *6-isomer*	5 mg	1.5, 20.4	191
O12650	Oregon Green® 488 DHPE (Oregon Green® 488 1,2-dihexadecanoyl-*sn*-glycero-3-phosphoethanolamine)	1 mg	13.2, 20.4	191
O12650	Oregon Green® 488 1,2-dihexadecanoyl-*sn*-glycero-3-phosphoethanolamine (Oregon Green® 488 DHPE)	1 mg	13.2, 20.4	191
O6380	Oregon Green® 488 goat anti-mouse IgG (H+L) *2 mg/mL*	0.5 mL	7.2	191
O11033	Oregon Green® 488 goat anti-mouse IgG (H+L) *highly cross-adsorbed* *2 mg/mL*	0.5 mL	7.2	191
O6381	Oregon Green® 488 goat anti-rabbit IgG (H+L) *2 mg/mL*	0.5 mL	7.2	191
O11038	Oregon Green® 488 goat anti-rabbit IgG (H+L) *highly cross-adsorbed* *2 mg/mL*	0.5 mL	7.2	191
O6382	Oregon Green® 488 goat anti-rat IgG (H+L) *2 mg/mL*	0.5 mL	7.2	191
O6010	Oregon Green® 488 iodoacetamide *mixed isomers*	5 mg	2.2	191
O6080	Oregon Green® 488 isothiocyanate (F_2FITC) *mixed isomers*	5 mg	1.5	191
O6034	Oregon Green® 488 maleimide	5 mg	2.2	191
O7466	Oregon Green® 488 phalloidin	300 U	11.1	191
O10241	Oregon Green® 488 Protein Labeling Kit *3 labelings*	1 kit	1.2, 1.5	191
P22310	Oregon Green® 488 Taxol; Flutax-2 (paclitaxel, Oregon Green® 488 conjugate)	100 µg	11.2	191
O6185	Oregon Green® 488-X, succinimidyl ester *6-isomer*	5 mg	1.5, 4.2	191
O6135	Oregon Green® 500 carboxylic acid *5-isomer*	5 mg	1.5, 14.3, 20.3	191
O6138	Oregon Green® 514 carboxylic acid	5 mg	1.5, 14.3, 20.3	191
O6139	Oregon Green® 514 carboxylic acid, succinimidyl ester	5 mg	1.5, 20.4	191
E7498	Oregon Green® 514 EGF (epidermal growth factor, Oregon Green® 514 conjugate)	20 µg	16.1	191
O6383	Oregon Green® 514 goat anti-mouse IgG (H+L) *2 mg/mL*	0.5 mL	7.2	191
O7465	Oregon Green® 514 phalloidin	300 U	11.1	191
O14804	O-rings for Attofluor® cell chamber, set of 10	each	23.3	232
O34781	ovalbumin, Alexa Fluor® 488 conjugate	2 mg	14.7	183
O34782	ovalbumin, Alexa Fluor® 555 conjugate	2 mg	14.7	183
O34783	ovalbumin, Alexa Fluor® 594 conjugate	2 mg	14.7	183
O34784	ovalbumin, Alexa Fluor® 647 conjugate	2 mg	14.7	183
O23020	ovalbumin, fluorescein conjugate	5 mg	14.7	None
O23021	ovalbumin, Texas Red® conjugate	5 mg	14.7	None
O266	oxonol V (bis-(3-phenyl-5-oxoisoxazol-4-yl)pentamethine oxonol)	100 mg	22.3	None
O267	oxonol VI (bis-(3-propyl-5-oxoisoxazol-4-yl)pentamethine oxonol)	100 mg	22.3	None
D2935	OxyBURST® Green H_2DCFDA, SE (2',7'-dichlorodihydrofluorescein diacetate, succinimidyl ester)	5 mg	16.1, 18.2	None
O13291	OxyBURST® Green H_2HFF BSA *special packaging*	5 x 1 mg	16.1, 18.2	191
P22652	Pacific Blue™ 1,2-ditetradecanoyl-*sn*-glycero-3-phosphoethanolamine, triethylammonium salt (Pacific Blue™ DMPE)	1 mg	13.2	192
P22652	Pacific Blue™ DMPE (Pacific Blue™ 1,2-ditetradecanoyl-*sn*-glycero-3-phosphoethanolamine, triethylammonium salt)	1 mg	13.2	192
P10993	Pacific Blue™ goat anti-mouse IgG (H+L) *2 mg/mL*	0.5 mL	7.2	192
P10994	Pacific Blue™ goat anti-rabbit IgG (H+L) *2 mg/mL*	0.5 mL	7.2	192
P10163	Pacific Blue™ succinimidyl ester	5 mg	1.7	192
P3456	paclitaxel (Taxol equivalent) *for use in research only*	5 mg	11.2	None
P7501	paclitaxel, BODIPY® 564/570 conjugate (BODIPY® 564/570 Taxol)	10 µg	11.2	193
P7500	paclitaxel, BODIPY® FL conjugate (BODIPY® FL Taxol)	10 µg	11.2	193

For current prices or to order online, visit probes.invitrogen.com

Cat #	Product Name	Unit Size	Sections	Limited Use Label License #
P22310	paclitaxel, Oregon Green® 488 conjugate (Oregon Green® 488 Taxol; Flutax-2)	100 µg	11.2	191
A1122	panacyl bromide (4-(9-anthroyloxy)phenacyl bromide)	100 mg	3.3	None
P21679	Panomer™ 9 random oligodeoxynucleotide, Alexa Fluor® 350 conjugate	10 nmol	8.5	183
P21680	Panomer™ 9 random oligodeoxynucleotide, Alexa Fluor® 488 conjugate	10 nmol	8.5	183
P32925	Panomer™ 9 random oligodeoxynucleotide, Alexa Fluor® 532 conjugate	10 nmol	8.5	183
P21681	Panomer™ 9 random oligodeoxynucleotide, Alexa Fluor® 546 conjugate	10 nmol	8.5	183
P21687	Panomer™ 9 random oligodeoxynucleotide, Alexa Fluor® 555 conjugate	10 nmol	8.5	183
P21682	Panomer™ 9 random oligodeoxynucleotide, Alexa Fluor® 594 conjugate	10 nmol	8.5	183
P21683	Panomer™ 9 random oligodeoxynucleotide, Alexa Fluor® 633 conjugate	10 nmol	8.5	183
P21686	Panomer™ 9 random oligodeoxynucleotide, Alexa Fluor® 647 conjugate	10 nmol	8.5	183
P21684	Panomer™ 9 random oligodeoxynucleotide, Alexa Fluor® 660 conjugate	10 nmol	8.5	183
P21685	Panomer™ 9 random oligodeoxynucleotide, Alexa Fluor® 680 conjugate	10 nmol	8.5	183
P21689	Panomer™ 9 random oligodeoxynucleotide, biotin-XX conjugate	10 nmol	4.3, 8.5	None
P21678	Panomer™ 9 random oligodeoxynucleotide, Pacific Blue™ conjugate	10 nmol	8.5	192
P21688	Panomer™ 9 random oligodeoxynucleotide, QSY® 7 conjugate	10 nmol	8.5	259
P32934	PARAGON™ DNA Microarray QC Hybridization Kit #1 *with Alexa Fluor® 555 dye*	1 kit	8.5	154
P32937	PARAGON™ DNA Microarray QC Hybridization Kit #2 *with Alexa Fluor® 647 dye*	1kit	8.5	183
P32930	PARAGON™ DNA Microarray QC Stain Kit *with SYBR® 555 stain and control slide*	1 kit	8.5	154
P32944	PARAGON™ dye ratio calibration slide	each	8.5	183
P32938	PARAGON™ Genomic DNA Hybridization Test Kit #1 *with Alexa Fluor® 555 labeled genomic DNA*	1 kit	8.5	183
P32942	PARAGON™ Genomic DNA Hybridization Test Kit #2 *with Alexa Fluor® 647 labeled genomic DNA*	1 kit	8.5	183
P32927	PARAGON™ microarray scanner calibration slide *with intensity arrays of four Alexa Fluor® dyes*	each	8.5	183
P36005	*cis*-parinaric acid *3 mM in ethanol*	10 mL	13.2, 15.5, 18.2	None
P23012	parvalbumin from codfish, Alexa Fluor® 488 conjugate	1 mg	14.7	183
H1387	patman (6-hexadecanoyl-2-(((2-(trimethylammonium)ethyl)methyl)amino)naphthalene chloride)	5 mg	13.5	None
P1267MP	PBFI, AM *cell permeant* *special packaging*	20 x 50 µg	21.1	None
P1265MP	PBFI, tetraammonium salt *cell impermeant*	1 mg	21.1	None
P1405	PDAM (1-pyrenyldiazomethane)	25 mg	3.3	None
P1619MP	PDP DHPE (*N*-((2-pyridyldithio)propionyl)-1,2-dihexadecanoyl-*sn*-glycero-3-phosphoethanolamine, triethylammonium salt)	5 mg	5.2, 13.2	None
P14825	PeakFlow™ Blue flow cytometry reference beads, 2.5 µm *460 nm emission*	3 mL	23.2	None
P14826	PeakFlow™ Blue flow cytometry reference beads, 6 µm *460 nm emission*	3 mL	23.2	None
P14831	PeakFlow™ Carmine flow cytometry reference beads, 2.5 µm *620 nm emission*	3 mL	23.2	227
P14832	PeakFlow™ Carmine flow cytometry reference beads, 6 µm *620 nm emission*	3 mL	23.2	227
P24670	PeakFlow™ Claret flow cytometry reference beads, 6 µm *680 nm emission*	3 mL	23.2	227, 193
P14827	PeakFlow™ Green flow cytometry reference beads, 2.5 µm *515 nm emission*	3 mL	23.2	227
P14828	PeakFlow™ Green flow cytometry reference beads, 6 µm *515 nm emission*	3 mL	23.2	227
P24672	PeakFlow™ Infrared flow cytometry reference beads, 6 µm *770 nm emission*	3 mL	23.2	227, 193
P14829	PeakFlow™ Orange flow cytometry reference beads, 2.5 µm *575 nm emission*	3 mL	23.2	227, 193
P14830	PeakFlow™ Orange flow cytometry reference beads, 6 µm *575 nm emission*	3 mL	23.2	227, 193
P24671	PeakFlow™ Ultra Red flow cytometry reference beads, 6 µm *695 nm emission*	3 mL	23.2	227, 193
A35111	R-PE annexin V (annexin V, R-phycoerythrin conjugate) *50 assays*	250 µL	6.4, 15.5	213
P6317	PEAS; AET (*N*-((2-pyridyldithio)ethyl)-4-azidosalicylamide)	10 mg	5.3	None
D23739	PED6 (*N*-((6-(2,4-dinitrophenyl)amino)hexanoyl)-2-(4,4-difluoro-5,7-dimethyl-4-bora-3a,4a-diaza-*s*-indacene-3-pentanoyl)-1-hexadecanoyl-*sn*-glycero-3-phosphoethanolamine, triethylammonium salt)	1 mg	13.2, 17.4	193
P13290	5-(pentafluorobenzoylamino)dihydrofluorescein diacetate (PFB-H_2FDA)	5 mg	14.2, 16.1, 18.2	212
P12925	5-(pentafluorobenzoylamino)fluorescein (PFB-F)	5 mg	10.1, 14.3, 15.6	212
P12880	5-(pentafluorobenzoylamino)fluorescein diacetate (PFB-FDA)	5 mg	14.2, 15.2	212
P11948	5-(pentafluorobenzoylamino)fluorescein di-β-D-galactopyranoside (PFB-FDG)	5 mg	10.2	212
P11947	5-(pentafluorobenzoylamino)fluorescein di-β-D-glucopyranoside (PFB-FDGlu)	5 mg	10.2	212
P11949	5-(pentafluorobenzoylamino)fluorescein di-β-D-glucuronide (PFB-FDGlcU)	5 mg	10.2	212
P21315	Penta·His™ mouse IgG_1, monoclonal antibody (anti-pentahistidine) *BSA free*	100 µg	7.5, 9.4	None
R1147	pentoxyresorufin (resorufin pentyl ether)	5 mg	10.6	None
P33350	PeppermintStick™ phosphoprotein molecular weight standards *200 gel lanes*	400 µL	9.4	None
P27167	PeppermintStick™ phosphoprotein molecular weight standards	40 µL	9.4	None
P12271	pepstatin A, BODIPY® FL conjugate	25 µg	10.4, 15.5	193
P917	peroxidase from horseradish, biotin-XX conjugate	10 mg	4.3, 7.6	None
P7071	(µ-peroxo) (µ-hydroxo)bis(bis(bipyridyl)cobalt(III)) perchlorate (caged oxygen)	25 mg	5.3, 18.2	None
P646	3-perylenedodecanoic acid	10 mg	13.2	None

For current prices or to order online, visit probes.invitrogen.com

Cat #	Product Name	Unit Size	Sections	Limited Use Label License #
P1692	PETG (phenylethyl β-D-thiogalactopyranoside)	10 mg	10.2	None
P12925	PFB-F (5-(pentafluorobenzoylamino)fluorescein)	5 mg	10.1, 14.3, 15.6	212
P12880	PFB-FDA (5-(pentafluorobenzoylamino)fluorescein diacetate)	5 mg	14.2, 15.2	212
P11948	PFB-FDG (5-(pentafluorobenzoylamino)fluorescein di-β-D-galactopyranoside)	5 mg	10.2	212
P11949	PFB-FDGlcU (5-(pentafluorobenzoylamino)fluorescein di-β-D-glucuronide)	5 mg	10.2	212
P11947	PFB-FDGlu (5-(pentafluorobenzoylamino)fluorescein di-β-D-glucopyranoside)	5 mg	10.2	212
P13290	PFB-H_2FDA (5-(pentafluorobenzoylamino)dihydrofluorescein diacetate)	5 mg	14.2, 16.1, 18.2	212
P3457	phalloidin	1 mg	11.1	None
D7779	5,5′-Ph_2-$DiIC_{18}(3)$ (1,1′-dioctadecyl-5,5′-diphenyl-3,3,3′,3′-tetramethylindocarbocyanine chloride)	5 mg	13.4, 14.4	None
P6878	*N*-(1,10-phenanthrolin-5-yl)bromoacetamide	5 mg	2.3, 18.2	None
P6879	*N*-(1,10-phenanthrolin-5-yl)iodoacetamide	5 mg	2.3, 18.2	None
P6763	Phen Green™ FL, diacetate *cell permeant*	1 mg	19.7	245
P14313	Phen Green™ SK, diacetate	1 mg	19.7	245
P14312	Phen Green™ SK, dipotassium salt	1 mg	19.7	245
P1692	phenylethyl β-D-thiogalactopyranoside (PETG)	10 mg	10.2	None
P459	3-(4-(6-phenyl)-1,3,5-hexatrienyl)phenylpropionic acid (DPH propionic acid)	25 mg	13.5	None
P3900	*N*-((4-(6-phenyl-1,3,5-hexatrienyl)phenyl)propyl)trimethylammonium *p*-toluenesulfonate (TMAP-DPH)	5 mg	13.5, 16.1	None
P65	*N*-phenyl-1-naphthylamine	1 g	13.5	None
P6466	phospholipase C, phosphatidylinositol-specific *from *Bacillus cereus* * *100 U/mL*	50 µL	17.4	None
O7703	C_{28}-O-PHPM (1-octacosanyl-2-(1-pyrenehexanoyl)-*sn*-glycero-3-phosphomethanol, ammonium salt)	250 µg	17.4	None
P2331MP	*o*-phthaldialdehyde (OPA) *high purity*	1 g	1.8, 9.2, 9.3, 15.6, 21.2	None
P800	B-phycoerythrin *4 mg/mL*	0.5 mL	6.4, 14.7, 18.2	None
P801	R-phycoerythrin *4 mg/mL*	0.5 mL	6.4, 14.7, 18.2	None
P811	R-phycoerythrin, biotin-XX conjugate *4 mg/mL*	0.5 mL	4.3, 6.4	None
P21129	R-phycoerythrin goat anti-mouse IgG_1 (γ_1) conjugate *1 mg/mL*	250 µL	6.4, 7.2	None
P21139	R-phycoerythrin goat anti-mouse IgG_{2a} (γ_{2a}) conjugate *1 mg/mL*	250 µL	6.4, 7.2	None
P21149	R-phycoerythrin goat anti-mouse IgG_{2b} (γ_{2b}) conjugate *1 mg/mL*	250 µL	6.4, 7.2	None
P852	R-phycoerythrin goat anti-mouse IgG (H+L) *1 mg/mL*	1 mL	6.4, 7.2	None
P2771MP	R-phycoerythrin goat anti-rabbit IgG (H+L) *1 mg/mL*	0.5 mL	6.4, 7.2	None
P806	R-phycoerythrin, pyridyldisulfide derivative *2 mg/mL*	1 mL	6.4	None
P7589	PicoGreen® dsDNA Assay Kit	1 kit	8.1, 8.3	154
P11496	PicoGreen® dsDNA Quantitation Kit *200-2000 assays* *special packaging*	1 kit	8.1, 8.3	154
P7581	PicoGreen® dsDNA reagent	1 mL	8.1, 8.3	154
P11495	PicoGreen® dsDNA quantitation reagent *200-2000 assays* *special packaging*	10 x 100 µL	8.1, 8.3	154
P23748	PIP Array™ membranes *set of 2*	1 set	17.4	None
P23749	PIP Array™ membranes *set of 5*	1 set	17.4	None
P23740	PIP Beads™, PtdIns-labeled *sedimented agarose bead suspension*	1 mL	17.4	None
P23741	PIP Beads™, PtdIns(3)P-labeled *sedimented agarose bead suspension*	1 mL	17.4	None
P23742	PIP Beads™, PtdIns(4)P-labeled *sedimented agarose bead suspension*	1 mL	17.4	None
P23743	PIP Beads™, PtdIns(5)P-labeled *sedimented agarose bead suspension*	1 mL	17.4	None
P23744	PIP Beads™, PtdIns(3,4)P_2-labeled *sedimented agarose bead suspension*	1 mL	17.4	None
P23745	PIP Beads™, PtdIns(3,5)P_2-labeled *sedimented agarose bead suspension*	1 mL	17.4	None
P23746	PIP Beads™, PtdIns(4,5)P_2-labeled *sedimented agarose bead suspension*	1 mL	17.4	None
P22061	P_iPer™ Phosphate Assay Kit *1000 assays*	1 kit	10.3, 10.5, 21.2	260
P22062	P_iPer™ Pyrophosphate Assay Kit *1000 assays*	1 kit	10.3, 10.5, 21.2	260
P23752	PIP MicroStrips™ membranes *set of 10*	1 set	17.4	None
P23750	PIP Strips™ membranes *set of 2*	1 set	17.4	None
P23751	PIP Strips™ membranes *set of 10*	1 set	17.4	None
P35901	*O*-pivaloyloxymethyl umbelliferone (C-POM) *lipase substrate* *special packaging*	5 x 100 µg	10.6	None
P6867	Pluronic® F-127 *low UV absorbance*	2 g	19.8, 21.1	None
P3000MP	Pluronic® F-127 *20% solution in DMSO*	1 mL	19.8, 21.1	None
P6866	Pluronic® F-127 *10% solution in water* *0.2 µm filtered*	30 mL	19.8, 21.1	None
P226	PMC oleate (1-pyrenemethyl 3β-(*cis*-9-octadecenoyloxy)-22,23-bisnor-5-cholenate)	10 mg	13.3	None
P2007MP	PMIA amide (*N*-(1-pyrenemethyl)iodoacetamide)	25 mg	2.3	None
P4	PMIA ester (1-pyrenemethyl iodoacetate)	100 mg	2.3	None
N6613	PNPP (4-nitrophenyl phosphate, disodium salt, hexahydrate)	5 g	10.3	None
P6281	poly(ethylene glycol) methyl ether, amine-terminated, average MW 5000	1 g	3.3	None
P13235	polymyxin B, BODIPY® FL conjugate, trifluoroacetic acid salt *mixed species*	100 µg	15.2, 17.3	193

For current prices or to order online, visit probes.invitrogen.com

Cat #	Product Name	Unit Size	Sections	Limited Use Label License #
P13238	polymyxin B, dansyl conjugate, trifluoroacetic acid salt *mixed species*	100 µg	15.2, 17.3	None
P13236	polymyxin B, Oregon Green® 514 conjugate, trifluoroacetic acid salt *mixed species*	100 µg	15.2, 17.3	191
P13237	polymyxin B, Texas Red®-X conjugate, trifluoroacetic acid salt *mixed species*	100 µg	15.2, 17.3	211
P3584	POPO™-3 iodide (534/570) *1 mM solution in DMF*	200 µL	8.1, 8.4, 8.7	228
P3580	POPO™-1 iodide (434/456) *1 mM solution in DMSO*	200 µL	8.1, 8.7	228
P3581	PO-PRO™-1 iodide (435/455) *1 mM solution in DMSO*	1 mL	8.1	209
P3585	PO-PRO™-3 iodide (539/567) *1 mM solution in DMSO*	1 mL	8.1	209
P18174	Press-to-Seal™ silicone isolator, one well, 20 mm diameter, 0.5 mm deep *set of 50*	1 set	23.3	None
P18175	Press-to-Seal™ silicone isolator, one well, 20 mm diameter, 1.0 mm deep *set of 50*	1 set	23.3	None
P24743	Press-to-Seal™ silicone isolator with adhesive, eight wells, 9 mm diameter, 0.5 mm deep *set of 25*	1 set	23.3	None
P24744	Press-to-Seal™ silicone isolator with adhesive, eight wells, 9 mm diameter, 1.0 mm deep *set of 25*	1 set	23.3	None
P24740	Press-to-Seal™ silicone isolator with adhesive, one well, 20 mm diameter, 0.5 mm deep *set of 50*	1 set	23.3	None
P24741	Press-to-Seal™ silicone isolator with adhesive, one well, 20 mm diameter, 1.0 mm deep *set of 50*	1 set	23.3	None
P24742	Press-to-Seal™ silicone isolator with adhesive, 24 wells, 2.5 mm diameter, 2.0 mm deep *set of 25*	1 set	23.3	None
P18178	Press-to-Seal™ silicone sheet, 13 cm x 18 cm, 0.5 mm thick *set of 5*	1 set	23.3	None
P18179	Press-to-Seal™ silicone sheet, 13 cm x 18 cm, 1.0 mm thick *set of 5*	1 set	23.3	None
P24745	Press-to-Seal™ silicone sheet with adhesive, 13 cm x 18 cm, 0.5 mm thick *set of 5*	1 set	23.3	None
P248	prodan (6-propionyl-2-dimethylaminonaphthalene)	100 mg	11.2, 13.5	None
P7481	ProLong® Antifade Kit	1 kit	23.1	None
P36930	ProLong® Gold antifade reagent	10 mL	23.1	223
P36934	ProLong® Gold antifade reagent *special packaging*	5 x 2 mL	23.1	223
P36931	ProLong® Gold antifade reagent with DAPI	10 mL	8.6, 23.1	223
P36935	ProLong® Gold antifade reagent with DAPI *special packaging*	5 x 2 mL	8.6, 23.1	223
P1304MP	propidium iodide	100 mg	8.1, 8.6, 14.3, 15.2	None
P21493	propidium iodide *FluoroPure™ grade*	100 mg	8.1, 8.6, 14.3, 15.2	None
P3566	propidium iodide *1.0 mg/mL solution in water*	10 mL	8.1, 8.6, 15.2	None
P248	6-propionyl-2-dimethylaminonaphthalene (prodan)	100 mg	11.2, 13.5	None
P37001	ProPlate™ multi-array slide module *set of 2*	1 set	23.3	None
P37004	ProPlate™ multi-array system *includes four 16-well slide modules, one tray and cover, ten seal-strips and one applicator*	1 set	23.3	None
P37002	ProPlate™ adhesive seal-strips *set of 50 seal-strips and one applicator*	1 set	23.3	None
P37003	ProPlate™ tray and cover *includes one tray and cover*	1 set	23.3	None
O267	bis-(3-propyl-5-oxoisoxazol-4-yl)pentamethine oxonol (oxonol VI)	100 mg	22.3	None
P33203	Pro-Q® Diamond LC Phosphopeptide Detection Kit	1 kit	9.2	223, 204
P33356	Pro-Q® Diamond Phosphoprotein Blot Stain Kit *20 minigel blots*	1 kit	9.4	223, 204
P33310	Pro-Q® Diamond phosphoprotein gel destaining solution	1 L	9.4	None
P33311	Pro-Q® Diamond phosphoprotein gel destaining solution *bulk packaging*	5 L	9.4	None
P33301	Pro-Q® Diamond phosphoprotein gel stain	200 mL	9.4	223, 204
P33300	Pro-Q® Diamond phosphoprotein gel stain	1 L	9.4	223, 204
P33302	Pro-Q® Diamond phosphoprotein gel stain *bulk packaging*	5 L	9.4	223, 204
MPP33301	Pro-Q® Diamond Phosphoprotein Gel Staining Kit *includes 200 mL stain and 40 µL standard*	1 kit	9.4	223, 204
MPP33300	Pro-Q® Diamond Phosphoprotein Gel Staining Kit *includes 1 L stain and 40 µL standard*	1 kit	9.4	223, 204
MPP33302	Pro-Q® Diamond Phosphoprotein Gel Staining Kit *includes 5 L stain and 400 µL standard*	1 kit	9.4	223, 204
P33706	Pro-Q® Diamond Phosphoprotein/Phosphopeptide Microarray Stain Kit	1 kit	9.3, 10.3, 17.3	223, 204
P21857	Pro-Q® Emerald 300 Glycoprotein Gel and Blot Stain Kit *10 minigels or minigel blots*	1 kit	9.4	223
P21855	Pro-Q® Emerald 300 Glycoprotein Gel Stain Kit *with SYPRO® Ruby protein gel stain* *10 minigels*	1 kit	9.4	223
P20495	Pro-Q® Emerald 300 Lipopolysaccharide Gel Stain Kit *10 minigels*	1 kit	3.2	223
P21875	Pro-Q® Emerald 488 Glycoprotein Gel and Blot Stain Kit *10 minigels or minigel blots*	1 kit	9.4	223
P21872	Pro-Q® Glycoprotein Blot Stain Kit #5 *with *Griffonia simplicifolia* lectin II (GS-II) and DDAO phosphate* *>20 minigel blots*	1 kit	9.4	234
P21861	Pro-Q® Western Blot Stain Kit #4 *with goat anti-rabbit IgG, DDAO phosphate and SYPRO® Ruby protein blot stain* *10-20 minigel blots*	1 kit	9.4	234, 190
P21878	Pro-Q® Oligohistidine Blot Stain Kit #1 *with biotin NTA, streptavidin and DDAO phosphate* *20 minigel blots*	1 kit	9.4	234
P21879	Pro-Q® Oligohistidine Blot Stain Kit #2 *with biotin NTA, streptavidin and ELF® 39 phosphate* *20 minigel blots*	1 kit	9.4	253
P21876	Pro-Q® Sapphire 365 oligohistidine gel stain *20 minigels*	500 mL	9.4	223
P21877	Pro-Q® Sapphire 488 oligohistidine gel stain *20 minigels*	500 mL	9.4	223
P33354	Pro-Q® Sapphire 532 oligohistidine gel stain *20 minigels*	500 mL	9.4	223, 193
P21860	Pro-Q® Western Blot Stain Kit #2 *with goat anti-mouse IgG, DDAO phosphate and SYPRO® Ruby protein blot stain* *10-20 minigel blots*	1 kit	9.4	234, 190
P21864	Pro-Q® Western Blot Stain Kit #3 *with goat anti-rabbit IgG and DDAO phosphate* *>20 minigel blots*	1 kit	9.4	234
P21865	Pro-Q® Western Blot Stain Kit #5 *with streptavidin and DDAO phosphate* *>20 minigel blots*	1 kit	9.4	234

For current prices or to order online, visit probes.invitrogen.com

Cat #	Product Name	Unit Size	Sections	Limited Use Label License #
P21862	Pro-Q® Western Blot Stain Kit #6 *with streptavidin, DDAO phosphate and SYPRO® Ruby protein blot stain* *10-20 minigel blots*	1 kit	9.4	234, 190
P11047	protein A, Alexa Fluor® 488 conjugate	1 mg	7.2	183
P11049	protein A, Alexa Fluor® 546 conjugate	1 mg	7.2	183
P11050	protein A, Alexa Fluor® 568 conjugate	1 mg	7.2	183
P11051	protein A, Alexa Fluor® 594 conjugate	1 mg	7.2	183
P21107	protein A, Alexa Fluor® 633 conjugate	1 mg	7.2	183
P21462	protein A, Alexa Fluor® 647 conjugate	1 mg	7.2	183
P11065	protein G, Alexa Fluor® 488 conjugate	1 mg	7.2	183
P21041	protein G, horseradish peroxidase conjugate	1 mg	7.2, 10.5	None
P7432	protein kinase C *from rat brain* *6.7 ng/µL*	2 x 75 µL	17.3	None
P6649	protein molecular weight standards *broad range* *200 gel lanes*	400 µL	9.3	None
P6305	Protein-Protein Crosslinking Kit *3 conjugations*	1 kit	5.2	None
C7924	proxyl fluorescamine (5-(2-carboxyphenyl)-5-hydroxy-1-((2,2,5,5-tetramethyl-1-oxypyrrolidin-3-yl)methyl)-3-phenyl-2-pyrrolin-4-one, potassium salt)	5 mg	18.2	None
P7220	PS-Speck™ Microscope Point Source Kit *blue, green, orange and deep red fluorescent beads*	1 kit	23.1	227, 193
H3818	β-py-C_6-HPC (1-hexadecanoyl-2-(1-pyrenehexanoyl)-*sn*-glycero-3-phosphocholine)	1 mg	13.2, 17.4	None
H361	β-py-C_{10}-HPC (1-hexadecanoyl-2-(1-pyrenedecanoyl)-*sn*-glycero-3-phosphocholine)	1 mg	13.2, 17.4	None
H3810	β-py-C_{10}-HPM (1-hexadecanoyl-2-(1-pyrenedecanoyl)-*sn*-glycero-3-phosphomethanol, sodium salt)	1 mg	13.2, 17.4	None
H3809	β-py-C_{10}-PG (1-hexadecanoyl-2-(1-pyrenedecanoyl)-*sn*-glycero-3-phosphoglycerol, ammonium salt)	1 mg	13.2, 17.4	None
E6051	PyMPO epoxide (1-(2,3-epoxypropyl)-4-(5-(4-methoxyphenyl)oxazol-2-yl)pyridinium trifluoromethanesulfonate)	5 mg	2.2	None
M6026	PyMPO maleimide (1-(2-maleimidylethyl)-4-(5-(4-methoxyphenyl)oxazol-2-yl)pyridinium methanesulfonate)	5 mg	2.2	None
S6110	PyMPO, SE (1-(3-(succinimidyloxycarbonyl)benzyl)-4-(5-(4-methoxyphenyl)oxazol-2-yl)pyridinium bromide)	5 mg	1.7	None
P6115	1-pyreneacetic acid, succinimidyl ester	25 mg	1.7	None
P1903MP	1-pyrenebutanoic acid *high purity*	100 mg	13.2	None
P101	1-pyrenebutanoic acid, hydrazide	100 mg	3.2	None
P10167	1-pyrenebutanoic acid, STP ester, sodium salt	5 mg	1.7	None
P130	1-pyrenebutanoic acid, succinimidyl ester	100 mg	1.7	None
P244	1-pyrenebutanol	100 mg	3.3, 13.5, 18.2	None
P6114	*N*-(1-pyrenebutanoyl)cysteic acid, succinimidyl ester, potassium salt	5 mg	1.7	None
P31	1-pyrenedecanoic acid	25 mg	13.2	None
P96	1-pyrenedodecanoic acid	25 mg	13.2	None
P243	1-pyrenehexadecanoic acid	5 mg	13.2	None
P3840	1-pyrenehexanoic acid	100 mg	13.2	None
P29	*N*-(1-pyrene)iodoacetamide	100 mg	2.3, 11.1	None
P28	*N*-(1-pyrene)maleimide	100 mg	2.3	None
P2421	1-pyrenemethylamine, hydrochloride (1-aminomethylpyrene, hydrochloride)	100 mg	3.3	None
P2007MP	*N*-(1-pyrenemethyl)iodoacetamide (PMIA amide)	25 mg	2.3	None
P4	1-pyrenemethyl iodoacetate (PMIA ester)	100 mg	2.3	None
P226	1-pyrenemethyl 3β-(*cis*-9-octadecenoyloxy)-22,23-bisnor-5-cholenate (PMC oleate)	10 mg	13.3	None
P394	1-pyrenenonanol	25 mg	13.5, 18.2	None
P6254	1-pyrenepropylamine, hydrochloride	5 mg	3.3	None
P80	1-pyrenesulfonic acid, sodium salt	1 g	13.5	None
P24	1-pyrenesulfonyl chloride	100 mg	1.7	None
P58	*N*-(1-pyrenesulfonyl)-1,2-dihexadecanoyl-*sn*-glycero-3-phosphoethanolamine, triethylammonium salt (pyS DHPE)	25 mg	13.2, 17.4	None
P349	1,3,6,8-pyrenetetrasulfonic acid, tetrasodium salt	100 mg	14.3	None
P1405	1-pyrenyldiazomethane (PDAM)	25 mg	3.3	None
P6317	*N*-((2-pyridyldithio)ethyl)-4-azidosalicylamide (PEAS; AET)	10 mg	5.3	None
P1619MP	*N*-((2-pyridyldithio)propionyl)-1,2-dihexadecanoyl-*sn*-glycero-3-phosphoethanolamine, triethylammonium salt (PDP DHPE)	5 mg	5.2, 13.2	None
P58	pyS DHPE (*N*-(1-pyrenesulfonyl)-1,2-dihexadecanoyl-*sn*-glycero-3-phosphoethanolamine, triethylammonium salt)	25 mg	13.2, 17.4	None
M1380	qBBr (monobromotrimethylammoniobimane bromide)	25 mg	2.3, 14.2	None
Q10464	QSY® 7 amine, hydrochloride	5 mg	3.3, 9.5	259
Q10193	QSY® 7 carboxylic acid, succinimidyl ester	5 mg	1.6, 8.3, 9.5	259
Q21930	$N^ε$-(QSY® 7)-Nα-(9-fluorenylmethoxycarbonyl)-L-lysine (α-FMOC-ε-QSY® 7-L-lysine)	5 mg	9.5	259
Q10257	QSY® 7 C_5-maleimide	5 mg	2.2, 9.5	259
Q20131	QSY® 9 carboxylic acid, succinimidyl ester	5 mg	1.6, 8.3, 9.5	259
Q30457	QSY® 9 C_5-maleimide	5 mg	2.2	259
Q30626	QSY® 9 hydrazide	5 mg	3.2	259
Q20132	QSY® 21 carboxylic acid, succinimidyl ester	5 mg	1.6, 8.3, 9.5	259

For current prices or to order online, visit probes.invitrogen.com

Cat #	Product Name	Unit Size	Sections	Limited Use Label License #
Q20133	QSY® 35 acetic acid, succinimidyl ester	5 mg	1.8, 8.3, 9.5	259
Q21931	N^{β}-(QSY® 35)-$N\alpha$-(9-fluorenylmethoxycarbonyl)-L-alanine (α-FMOC-β-QSY® 35-L-alanine)	5 mg	9.5	259
Q20348	QSY® 35 iodoacetamide	5 mg	2.2, 9.5	259
Q20540	QSY® 35 methylamine	5 mg	3.3, 9.5	259
Q33130	Quant-iT™ DNA Assay Kit, Broad Range *2-1000 ng*	1 kit	8.3	223
Q33120	Quant-iT™ DNA Assay Kit, High Sensitivity *0.2-100 ng*	1 kit	8.3	154
Q33210	Quant-iT™ Protein Assay Kit *1000 assays*	1 kit	9.2	190
Q33140	Quant-iT™ RNA Assay Kit *5-100 ng*	1 kit	8.3	223
Q1289	quin-2, AM *cell permeant* *special packaging*	10 x 1 mg	19.2	None
Q23918	quin-2, free acid *cell impermeant*	5 mg	19.2	None
R21458	rabbit anti-goat IgG (H+L), alkaline phosphatase conjugate	1 mg	7.2	None
R21459	rabbit anti-goat IgG (H+L), horseradish peroxidase conjugate	1 mg	7.2	None
R21455	rabbit anti-mouse IgG (H+L), horseradish peroxidase conjugate	1 mg	7.2	None
R35100	RediPlate™ 96 EnzChek® Caspase-3 Assay Kit *Z-DEVD-R110 substrate* *one 96-well microplate*	1 kit	10.4, 15.5	None
R22130	RediPlate™ 96 EnzChek® Protease Assay Kit *green fluorescence* *one 96-well microplate*	1 kit	10.4	203, 193
R22132	RediPlate™ 96 EnzChek® Protease Assay Kit *red fluorescence* *one 96-well microplate*	1 kit	10.4	203, 193
R33700	RediPlate™ 96 EnzChek® Serine/Threonine Phosphatase Assay Kit *one 96-well microplate*	1 kit	10.3, 17.3	192
R22067	RediPlate™ 96 EnzChek® Tyrosine Phosphatase Assay Kit *one 96-well microplate*	1 kit	10.3, 17.3	192
R36904	RediPlate™ 96 microplate intensity standards, far red fluorescent (660/675) *one 96-well microplate*	each	23.1	183
R36901	RediPlate™ 96 microplate intensity standards, green fluorescent (490/510) *one 96-well microplate*	each	23.1	183
R36902	RediPlate™ 96 microplate intensity standards, orange fluorescent (565/580) *one 96-well microplate*	each	23.1	183
R36903	RediPlate™ 96 microplate intensity standards, red fluorescent (590/605) *one 96-well microplate*	each	23.1	None
R36910	RediPlate™ 96 microplate intensity standards set *includes one each of R36901, R36902, R36903 and R36904*	1 set	23.1	183
R32715	RediPlate™ 96 nucleic acid stain sampler *one 96-well microplate*	each	8.1	228, 154
R32716	RediPlate™ 96 PicoGreen® dsDNA Quantitation Kit *one 96-well microplate* *with separate DNA standard*	1 kit	8.1, 8.3	154
R21495	RediPlate™ 96 PicoGreen® dsDNA Quantitation Kit *one 96-well microplate*	1 kit	8.1, 8.3	154
R32700	RediPlate™ 96 RiboGreen® RNA Quantitation Kit *one 96-well microplate*	1 kit	8.1, 8.3	154
R14060	RedoxSensor™ Red CC-1 *special packaging*	10 x 50 µg	12.2, 12.3, 15.2, 18.2	None
R14782	Reference Dye Sampler Kit *five 1 mM solutions, 1 mL each*	1 kit	23.1	None
R2931	Renin Substrate 1 (Arg-Glu(EDANS)-Ile-His-Pro-Phe-His-Leu-Val-Ile-His-Thr-Lys(dabcyl)-Arg)	1 mg	10.4	None
R12204	resazurin, sodium salt	10 mg	10.6, 15.2	None
R441	resorufin benzyl ether (benzyloxyresorufin)	10 mg	10.6	None
R6564	Resorufin Ether Sampler Kit	1 kit	10.6	None
R352	resorufin ethyl ether (ethoxyresorufin)	5 mg	10.6	None
R1159	resorufin β-D-galactopyranoside	25 mg	10.2	None
R1161	resorufin β-D-glucuronide, potassium salt	5 mg	10.2	None
R351	resorufin methyl ether (methoxyresorufin)	5 mg	10.6	None
R1147	resorufin pentyl ether (pentoxyresorufin)	5 mg	10.6	None
R363	resorufin, sodium salt *reference standard*	100 mg	10.1	None
R6922	RGA-30	5 mg	16.2, 22.2	None
R1114	RH 155	25 mg	22.2	None
S1109	RH 237 (*N*-(4-sulfobutyl)-4-(6-(4-(dibutylamino)phenyl)hexatrienyl)pyridinium, inner salt)	5 mg	22.2	None
T1111	RH 414 (*N*-(3-triethylammoniumpropyl)-4-(4-(4-(diethylamino)phenyl)butadienyl)pyridinium dibromide)	5 mg	14.4, 16.1, 22.2	None
S1108	RH 421 (*N*-(4-sulfobutyl)-4-(4-(4-(dipentylamino)phenyl)butadienyl)pyridinium, inner salt)	25 mg	22.2	None
R649	RH 795	1 mg	22.2	None
R33400	Rhinohide™ polyacrylamide gel strengthener concentrate *sufficient additive for 1 L of 30% acrylamide/bis-acrylamide (37.5:1)*	200 mL	9.3, 9.4	None
R33410	Rhinohide™ Polyacrylamide Gel Strengthener Kit *makes 1 L of Rhinohide™ 30% acrylamide/bis-acrylamide (37.5:1)*	1 kit	9.3, 9.4	None
R1244	rhod-2, AM *cell permeant*	1 mg	19.3	204
R1245MP	rhod-2, AM *cell permeant* *special packaging*	20 x 50 µg	19.3	204
R14220	rhod-2, tripotassium salt *cell impermeant*	1 mg	19.3	204
R6479	rhodamine 110 (R110) *reference standard*	25 mg	10.1	None
R22122	rhodamine 110, bis-(L-aspartic acid amide), trifluoroacetic acid salt	1 mg	10.4, 15.5	None
R6513	rhodamine 110, bis-(*t*-BOC-L-leucyl-L-methionine amide)	5 mg	10.4	None
R6504	rhodamine 110, bis-(CBZ-L-alanyl-L-alanine amide)	5 mg	10.4	None
R6506	rhodamine 110, bis-(CBZ-L-alanyl-L-alanyl-L-alanyl-L-alanine amide)	5 mg	10.4	None
R6508	rhodamine 110, bis-(CBZ-L-alanyl-L-arginine amide), dihydrochloride	5 mg	10.4	None
R6501	rhodamine 110, bis-(CBZ-L-arginine amide), dihydrochloride (BZAR)	5 mg	10.4	None

For current prices or to order online, visit probes.invitrogen.com

Cat #	Product Name	Unit Size	Sections	Limited Use Label License #
R22120	rhodamine 110, bis-(*N*-CBZ-L-aspartyl-L-glutamyl-L-valyl-L-aspartic acid amide) (Z-DEVD-R110) *bulk packaging*	20 mg	10.4, 15.5	None
R22126	rhodamine 110, bis-(*N*-CBZ-L-isoleucyl-L-glutamyl-L-threonyl-L-aspartic acid amide) (Z-IETD-R110) *bulk packaging*	20 mg	10.4, 15.5	None
R22125	rhodamine 110, bis-(*N*-CBZ-L-isoleucyl-L-glutamyl-L-threonyl-L-aspartic acid amide) (Z-IETD-R110)	2 mg	10.4, 15.5	None
R6505	rhodamine 110, bis-(CBZ-L-isoleucyl-L-prolyl-L-arginine amide), dihydrochloride (BZiPAR)	5 mg	10.4	None
R6502	rhodamine 110, bis-(CBZ-L-phenylalanyl-L-arginine amide), dihydrochloride	5 mg	10.4	None
R6507	rhodamine 110, bis-(CBZ-L-prolyl-L-arginine amide), dihydrochloride	5 mg	10.4	None
R6577	rhodamine 110, bis-(L-phenylalanine amide), di(trifluoroacetic acid) salt	5 mg	10.4	None
R33752	rhodamine 110, bis-(*N*-CBZ-L-alanyl-L-alanyl-L-aspartic acid amide) (Z-AAD-R110)	2 mg	10.4, 15.5	None
R33753	rhodamine 110, bis-(*N*-CBZ-L-leucyl-L-glutamyl-L-glutamyl-L-aspartic acid amide) (Z-LEED-R110)	2 mg	10.4, 15.5	None
R33751	rhodamine 110, bis-(*N*-CBZ-L-leucyl-L-glutamyl-L-histidinyl-L-aspartic acid amide) (Z-LEHD-R110)	2 mg	10.4, 15.5	None
R33750	rhodamine 110, bis-(*N*-CBZ-L-tyrosinyl-L-valyl-L-alanyl-L-aspartic acid amide) (Z-YVAD-R110)	2 mg	10.4, 15.5	None
R33755	rhodamine 110, bis-(*N*-CBZ-L-valyl-L-aspartyl-L-valyl-L-alanyl-L-aspartic acid amide) (Z-VDVAD-R110)	2 mg	10.4, 15.5	None
R33754	rhodamine 110, bis-(*N*-CBZ-L-valyl-L-glutamyl-L-isoleucyl-L-aspartic acid amide) (Z-VEID-R110)	2 mg	10.4, 15.5	None
R22124	rhodamine 110, bis-(p-tosyl-L-glycyl-L-prolyl-L-arginine amide)	2 mg	10.4	None
R6560	rhodamine 110, 4-(chloromethyl)benzoyl amide, CBZ-L-arginine amide, hydrochloride (CMB-R110, CBZ-Arg)	1 mg	10.4	None
R302	rhodamine 123	25 mg	12.2, 15.2, 15.5, 22.3	None
R22420	rhodamine 123 *FluoroPure™ grade*	25 mg	12.2, 15.2, 15.5, 22.3	None
R634	rhodamine 6G chloride	1 g	12.2	None
R648MP	rhodamine B, hexyl ester, perchlorate (R 6)	10 mg	12.2	None
L1392	rhodamine DHPE (Lissamine™ rhodamine B 1,2-dihexadecanoyl-*sn*-glycero-3-phosphoethanolamine, triethylammonium salt)	5 mg	13.2	None
E3481	rhodamine EGF (epidermal growth factor, tetramethylrhodamine conjugate)	20 µg	16.1	None
R6107	Rhodamine Green™ carboxylic acid, succinimidyl ester, hydrochloride (5(6)-CR 110, SE) *mixed isomers*	5 mg	1.5	None
R6112	Rhodamine Green™ carboxylic acid, trifluoroacetamide, succinimidyl ester (5(6)-CR 110 TFA, SE) *mixed isomers*	5 mg	1.5	None
R6113	Rhodamine Green™-X, succinimidyl ester, hydrochloride *mixed isomers*	5 mg	1.5	None
R415	rhodamine phalloidin	300 U	11.1	None
R6029	Rhodamine Red™ C_2-maleimide	5 mg	2.2	None
R7712	Rhodamine Red™-X DHPE (Rhodamine Red™-X 1,2-dihexadecanoyl-*sn*-glycero-3-phosphoethanolamine, triethylammonium salt)	1 mg	13.2	258
R7712	Rhodamine Red™-X 1,2-dihexadecanoyl-*sn*-glycero-3-phosphoethanolamine, triethylammonium salt (Rhodamine Red™-X DHPE)	1 mg	13.2	258
R6393	Rhodamine Red™-X goat anti-mouse IgG (H+L) *2 mg/mL*	0.5 mL	7.2	258
R6394	Rhodamine Red™-X goat anti-rabbit IgG (H+L) *2 mg/mL*	0.5 mL	7.2	258
R6160	Rhodamine Red™-X, succinimidyl ester *5-isomer*	5 mg	1.6, 4.2	258
R34676	rhod dextran, potassium salt, 10,000 MW, anionic (high-affinity version)	5 mg	19.4	None
R34677	rhod dextran, potassium salt, 10,000 MW, anionic (low-affinity version)	5 mg	19.4	206
R23983	rhod-FF, AM *cell permeant* *special packaging*	10 x 50 µg	19.3	204
R23982	rhod-FF, tripotassium salt *cell impermeant*	500 µg	19.3	204
R14208	rhod-5N, AM *cell permeant* *special packaging*	10 x 50 µg	19.3	204
R14207	rhod-5N, tripotassium salt *cell impermeant*	500 µg	19.3	204
R6152	Rhodol Green™ carboxylic acid, hydrochloride (5(6)-CRF 492) *mixed isomers*	5 mg	20.3	261
R24187	RhodZin™-1, AM *cell permeant* *special packaging*	10 x 50 µg	19.7	None
R24186	RhodZin™-1, potassium salt *cell impermeant*	500 µg	19.7	None
R36351	RhodZin™-3, AM *cell permeant* *special packaging*	10 x 50 µg	19.7	223
R36350	RhodZin™-3, dipotassium salt *cell impermeant*	500 µg	19.7	223
R11490	RiboGreen® RNA Assay Kit	1 kit	8.1, 8.3	154
R11491	RiboGreen® RNA reagent	1 mL	8.1, 8.3	154
R7454	rim-1	1 mg	17.3	None
R14000	rose bengal diacetate	5 mg	18.2	None
C6124	5-ROX (5-carboxy-X-rhodamine, triethylammonium salt) *single isomer*	10 mg	1.6	None
C6156	6-ROX (6-carboxy-X-rhodamine) *single isomer*	10 mg	1.6	None
C6126	6-ROX, SE (6-carboxy-X-rhodamine, succinimidyl ester) *single isomer*	5 mg	1.6	None
C1309	5(6)-ROX, SE (5-(and-6)-carboxy-X-rhodamine, succinimidyl ester) *mixed isomers*	25 mg	1.6	None
C6125	5-ROX, SE (5-carboxy-X-rhodamine, succinimidyl ester) *single isomer*	5 mg	1.6	None
R7478	ryanodine *free of dehydroryanodine*	1 mg	16.3, 17.2	None
A685	SAMSA fluorescein (5-((2-(and-3)-S-(acetylmercapto)succinoyl)amino)fluorescein) *mixed isomers*	25 mg	5.2	None
S866	SAPE (streptavidin, R-phycoerythrin conjugate) *1 mg/mL*	1 mL	6.4, 7.6	None
S21388	SAPE (streptavidin, R-phycoerythrin conjugate) *premium grade* *1 mg/mL*	1 mL	6.4, 7.6	None
S1553	SATA (succinimidyl acetylthioacetate)	100 mg	5.2	None

For current prices or to order online, visit probes.invitrogen.com

Important Licensing Information
These products may be covered by one or more Limited Use Label Licenses (See the Invitrogen Web site, www.invitrogen.com, or the Molecular Probes Web site, probes.invitrogen.com). By the use of these products you accept the terms and conditions of all applicable Limited Use Label Licenses. All products are for research use only. CAUTION: Not intended for human or animal diagnostic or therapeutic uses.

Cat #	Product Name	Unit Size	Sections	Limited Use Label License #
S1263	SBFI, AM *cell permeant*	1 mg	21.1	206
S1264	SBFI, AM *cell permeant* *special packaging*	20 x 50 µg	21.1	206
S1262	SBFI, tetraammonium salt *cell impermeant*	1 mg	21.1	206
C7933	SECCA (coumarin-3-carboxylic acid, succinimidyl ester)	25 mg	10.6, 18.2	None
S24732	Secure-Seal™ hybridization chamber gasket, eight chambers, 9 mm diameter, 0.8 mm deep *set of 20*	1 set	8.5, 23.3	None
S24733	Secure-Seal™ hybridization chamber gasket, eight chambers, 9 mm diameter, 1.3 mm deep *set of 20*	1 set	8.5, 23.3	None
S24730	Secure-Seal™ hybridization chamber gasket, one chamber, 20 mm diameter, 0.8 mm deep *set of 40*	1 set	8.5, 23.3	None
S24731	Secure-Seal™ hybridization chamber gasket, one chamber, 20 mm diameter, 1.3 mm deep *set of 40*	1 set	8.5, 23.3	None
S24734	Secure-Seal™ hybridization chamber gasket, one chamber, 22 mm x 22 mm, 0.8 mm deep *set of 50*	1 set	8.5, 23.3	None
S24737	Secure-Seal™ spacer, eight wells, 9 mm diameter, 0.12 mm deep *set of 100*	1 set	8.5, 23.3	None
S24735	Secure-Seal™ spacer, one well, 13 mm diameter, 0.12 mm deep *set of 100*	1 set	8.5, 23.3	None
S24736	Secure-Seal™ spacer, one well, 20 mm diameter, 0.12 mm deep *set of 100*	1 set	8.5, 23.3	None
S35115	SelectFX™ Alexa Fluor® 488 Cytochrome *c* Apoptosis Detection Kit *for fixed cells*	1 kit	7.5, 12.2, 15.5	183
S34200	SelectFX™ Alexa Fluor® 488 Endoplasmic Reticulum Labeling Kit *for fixed cells*	1 kit	7.5, 12.4	183
S34201	SelectFX™ Alexa Fluor® 488 Peroxisome Labeling Kit *for fixed cells*	1 kit	7.5, 12.3	183
S1129	SFDA (5-sulfofluorescein diacetate, sodium salt)	25 mg	14.3, 15.2, 20.2	None
F2181	5(6)-SFX (6-(fluorescein-5-(and-6)-carboxamido)hexanoic acid, succinimidyl ester) *mixed isomers*	10 mg	1.5, 4.2	None
F6106	5-SFX (6-(fluorescein-5-carboxamido)hexanoic acid, succinimidyl ester) *single isomer*	5 mg	1.5	None
F6129	5(6)-SFX (6-(fluorescein-5-(and-6)-carboxamido)hexanoic acid, succinimidyl ester) *mixed isomers* *special packaging*	10 x 1 mg	1.5	None
S23731	Shuttle PIP™ carrier-1 *histone H1* *0.5 mM in water*	200 µL	17.4	None
S23733	Shuttle PIP™ carrier-1, Oregon Green® 488 conjugate *histone H1* *0.5 mM in water*	200 µL	17.4	191
S23732	Shuttle PIP™ carrier-1, tetramethylrhodamine conjugate *histone H1* *0.5 mM in water*	200 µL	17.4	None
S35900	Shuttle PIP™ carrier-2 *neomycin B sulfate*	2 x 50 nmol	17.4	None
M7926	SIN-1 (3-morpholinosydnonimine, hydrochloride) *special packaging*	20 x 1 mg	18.3	None
M7891	SIN-1 (3-morpholinosydnonimine, hydrochloride)	25 mg	18.3	None
S36002	Singlet Oxygen Sensor Green *special packaging*	10 x 100 µg	18.2	223
A339	SITS (4-acetamido-4′-isothiocyanatostilbene-2,2′-disulfonic acid, disodium salt)	100 mg	16.3	None
S2828	*SlowFade®* Antifade Kit	1 kit	23.1	None
S24635	*SlowFade®* Antifade Kit with DAPI	1 kit	8.1, 8.6, 23.1	None
S7461	*SlowFade® Light* Antifade Kit	1 kit	23.1	None
S24636	*SlowFade® Light* Antifade Kit with DAPI	1 kit	8.1, 8.6, 23.1	None
S1534	SMCC (succinimidyl *trans*-4-(maleimidylmethyl)cyclohexane-1-carboxylate)	100 mg	5.2	None
N7892	SNAP (*S*-nitroso-*N*-acetylpenicillamine)	25 mg	18.3	None
N7927	SNAP (*S*-nitroso-*N*-acetylpenicillamine) *special packaging*	20 x 1 mg	18.3	None
S22801	SNARF®-1 carboxylic acid, acetate, succinimidyl ester *special packaging*	10 x 50 µg	14.2, 15.4, 20.4	208
S23920	SNARF®-4F 5-(and-6)-carboxylic acid	1 mg	20.2	208
S23921	SNARF®-4F 5-(and-6)-carboxylic acid, acetoxymethyl ester, acetate *special packaging*	20 x 50 µg	20.2	208
S23922	SNARF®-5F 5-(and-6)-carboxylic acid	1 mg	20.2	208
S23923	SNARF®-5F 5-(and-6)-carboxylic acid, acetoxymethyl ester, acetate *special packaging*	20 x 50 µg	20.2	208
S6901	Sodium Green™ tetraacetate *cell permeant* *special packaging*	20 x 50 µg	21.1	206
S6900	Sodium Green™, tetra(tetramethylammonium) salt *cell impermeant*	1 mg	21.1	206
S460	SPA (*N*-(3-sulfopropyl)acridinium, inner salt)	100 mg	21.2	None
D7777	SP-DiIC_{18}(3) (1,1′-dioctadecyl-6,6′-di(4-sulfophenyl)-3,3,3′,3′-tetramethylindocarbocyanine)	5 mg	13.4, 14.4	None
D7778	SP-DiOC_{18}(3) (3,3′-dioctadecyl-5,5′-di(4-sulfophenyl)oxacarbocyanine, sodium salt)	5 mg	13.4, 14.4	None
S1531	SPDP (succinimidyl 3-(2-pyridyldithio)propionate)	100 mg	5.2	None
S7916	spermine NONOate	10 mg	18.3	None
S23753	SphingoStrips™ membranes *set of 10*	1 set	17.4	None
M440	SPQ (6-methoxy-*N*-(3-sulfopropyl)quinolinium, inner salt)	100 mg	21.2	None
S2860	*Staphylococcus aureus* BioParticles® opsonizing reagent	1 U	16.1	None
S23371	*Staphylococcus aureus* (Wood strain without protein A) BioParticles®, Alexa Fluor® 488 conjugate	2 mg	16.1	183
S23372	*Staphylococcus aureus* (Wood strain without protein A) BioParticles®, Alexa Fluor® 594 conjugate	2 mg	16.1	183
S2854	*Staphylococcus aureus* (Wood strain without protein A) BioParticles®, BODIPY® FL conjugate	10 mg	16.1	193
S2851	*Staphylococcus aureus* (Wood strain without protein A) BioParticles®, fluorescein conjugate	10 mg	16.1	None
S2852	*Staphylococcus aureus* (Wood strain without protein A) BioParticles®, tetramethylrhodamine conjugate	10 mg	16.1	None
S2859	*Staphylococcus aureus* (Wood strain without protein A) BioParticles®, unlabeled	100 mg	16.1	None
S7445	ST-BODIPY® (-)-dihydropyridine *high affinity enantiomer*	25 µg	16.3	193
S10490	STP (4-sulfo-2,3,5,6-tetrafluorophenol, sodium salt)	100 mg	3.3	None
S888	streptavidin	5 mg	7.6	None

For current prices or to order online, visit probes.invitrogen.com

Cat #	Product Name	Unit Size	Sections	Limited Use Label License #
S21379	streptavidin acrylamide	1 mg	7.6, 9.2	None
S951	streptavidin agarose *sedimented bead suspension*	5 mL	7.6, 9.2	None
S21002	streptavidin, Alexa Fluor® 680–allophycocyanin conjugate (Alexa Fluor® 680–allophycocyanin streptavidin) *1 mg/mL*	100 µL	6.4, 7.6	183
S21005	streptavidin, Alexa Fluor® 700–allophycocyanin conjugate (Alexa Fluor® 700–allophycocyanin streptavidin) *1 mg/mL*	100 µL	6.4, 7.6	183
S21008	streptavidin, Alexa Fluor® 750–allophycocyanin conjugate (Alexa Fluor® 750–allophycocyanin streptavidin) *1 mg/mL*	100 µL	6.4, 7.6	183
S11249	streptavidin, Alexa Fluor® 350 conjugate	1 mg	7.6	183
S32351	streptavidin, Alexa Fluor® 405 conjugate	1 mg	7.6	183
S11237	streptavidin, Alexa Fluor® 430 conjugate	1 mg	7.6	None
S11223	streptavidin, Alexa Fluor® 488 conjugate	1 mg	7.6	183
S32354	streptavidin, Alexa Fluor® 488 conjugate *2 mg/mL*	0.5 mL	7.6	183
S32352	streptavidin, Alexa Fluor® 500 conjugate	1 mg	7.6	183
S32353	streptavidin, Alexa Fluor® 514 conjugate	1 mg	7.6	183
S11224	streptavidin, Alexa Fluor® 532 conjugate	1 mg	7.6	183
S11225	streptavidin, Alexa Fluor® 546 conjugate	1 mg	7.6	183
S21381	streptavidin, Alexa Fluor® 555 conjugate	1 mg	7.6	183
S32355	streptavidin, Alexa Fluor® 555 conjugate *2 mg/mL*	0.5 mL	7.6	183
S11226	streptavidin, Alexa Fluor® 568 conjugate	1 mg	7.6	183
S11227	streptavidin, Alexa Fluor® 594 conjugate	1 mg	7.6	183
S32356	streptavidin, Alexa Fluor® 594 conjugate *2 mg/mL*	0.5 mL	7.6	183
S32359	streptavidin, Alexa Fluor® 610 conjugate	1 mg	7.6	183
S21375	streptavidin, Alexa Fluor® 633 conjugate	1 mg	7.6	183
S32364	streptavidin, Alexa Fluor® 635 conjugate	1 mg	7.6	183
S21374	streptavidin, Alexa Fluor® 647 conjugate	1 mg	7.6	183
S32357	streptavidin, Alexa Fluor® 647 conjugate *2 mg/mL*	0.5 mL	7.6	183
S21377	streptavidin, Alexa Fluor® 660 conjugate	1 mg	7.6	183
S21378	streptavidin, Alexa Fluor® 680 conjugate	1 mg	7.6	183
S32358	streptavidin, Alexa Fluor® 680 conjugate *2 mg/mL*	0.5 mL	7.6	183
S21383	streptavidin, Alexa Fluor® 700 conjugate	1 mg	7.6	183
S21384	streptavidin, Alexa Fluor® 750 conjugate	1 mg	7.6	183
S20982	streptavidin, Alexa Fluor® 610–R-phycoerythrin conjugate (Alexa Fluor® 610–R-phycoerythrin streptavidin) *1 mg/mL*	100 µL	6.4, 7.6	183
S20992	streptavidin, Alexa Fluor® 647–R-phycoerythrin conjugate (Alexa Fluor® 647–R-phycoerythrin streptavidin) *1 mg/mL*	100 µL	6.4, 7.6	183
S20985	streptavidin, Alexa Fluor® 680–R-phycoerythrin conjugate (Alexa Fluor® 680–R-phycoerythrin streptavidin) *1 mg/mL*	100 µL	6.4, 7.6	183
S32363	streptavidin, Alexa Fluor® 750–R-phycoerythrin conjugate (Alexa Fluor® 750–R-phycoerythrin streptavidin) *1 mg/mL*	100 µL	6.4, 7.6	183
S921	streptavidin, alkaline phosphatase conjugate *2 mg/mL*	0.5 mL	7.6	None
S32362	streptavidin, allophycocyanin conjugate *premium grade* *1 mg/mL*	250 µL	6.4, 7.6	None
S868	streptavidin, allophycocyanin, crosslinked, conjugate *1 mg/mL*	0.5 mL	6.4, 7.6	None
C21476	streptavidin, Captivate™ ferrofluid conjugate (Captivate™ ferrofluid streptavidin) *0.5 mg Fe/mL*	1 mL	7.6, 9.2	233
S11228	streptavidin, Cascade Yellow™ conjugate	1 mg	7.6	None
S32385	streptavidin, DyeMer™ 488/605 conjugate	500 µg	7.6	183
S32386	streptavidin, DyeMer™ 488/615 conjugate	500 µg	7.6	183
S32387	streptavidin, DyeMer™ 488/630 conjugate	500 µg	7.6	183
S869	streptavidin, fluorescein conjugate	1 mg	7.6	None
S931	streptavidin, β-galactosidase conjugate	1 mg	7.6, 10.2	None
S911	streptavidin, horseradish peroxidase conjugate	1 mg	7.6	None
S11221	streptavidin, Marina Blue® conjugate	1 mg	7.6	192
N24918	streptavidin, NANOGOLD® conjugate (NANOGOLD® streptavidin) *80 µg protein/mL*	1 mL	7.6	231
S6368	streptavidin, Oregon Green® 488 conjugate	1 mg	7.6	191
S6369	streptavidin, Oregon Green® 514 conjugate	1 mg	7.6	191
S11222	streptavidin, Pacific Blue™ conjugate	1 mg	7.6	192
S32350	streptavidin, B-phycoerythrin conjugate *1 mg/mL*	1 mL	6.4, 7.6	None
S866	streptavidin, R-phycoerythrin conjugate (SAPE) *1 mg/mL*	1 mL	6.4, 7.6	None
S871	streptavidin, rhodamine B conjugate	1 mg	7.6	None
S6366	streptavidin, Rhodamine Red™-X conjugate	1 mg	7.6	258
S21388	streptavidin, R-phycoerythrin conjugate (SAPE) *premium grade* *1 mg/mL*	1 mL	6.4, 7.6	None
S870	streptavidin, tetramethylrhodamine conjugate	1 mg	7.6	None
S872	streptavidin, Texas Red® conjugate	1 mg	7.6	None
S6370	streptavidin, Texas Red®-X conjugate	1 mg	7.6	211
S13430	substance K, fluorescein conjugate (neurokinin-A, fluorescein conjugate)	25 µg	16.2	None

For current prices or to order online, visit probes.invitrogen.com

Cat #	Product Name	Unit Size	Sections	Limited Use Label License #
S13426	substance P, Alexa Fluor® 488 conjugate	25 µg	16.2	183
S13424	substance P, fluorescein conjugate	25 µg	16.2	None
S13427	substance P, Oregon Green® 488 conjugate	25 µg	16.2	191
S13428	substance P, tetramethylrhodamine conjugate	25 µg	16.2	None
S1553	succinimidyl acetylthioacetate (SATA)	100 mg	5.2	None
B1513	succinimidyl D-biotin (D-biotin, succinimidyl ester)	100 mg	4.2, 14.3	None
S1534	succinimidyl *trans*-4-(maleimidylmethyl)cyclohexane-1-carboxylate (SMCC)	100 mg	5.2	None
S128	succinimidyl *N*-methylanthranilate	100 mg	1.8	None
S1167	succinimidyl 6-(*N*-(7-nitrobenz-2-oxa-1,3-diazol-4-yl)amino)hexanoate (NBD-X, SE)	25 mg	1.8	None
S6110	1-(3-(succinimidyloxycarbonyl)benzyl)-4-(5-(4-methoxyphenyl)oxazol-2-yl)pyridinium bromide (PyMPO, SE)	5 mg	1.7	None
S1531	succinimidyl 3-(2-pyridyldithio)propionate (SPDP)	100 mg	5.2	None
S1109	*N*-(4-sulfobutyl)-4-(6-(4-(dibutylamino)phenyl)hexatrienyl)pyridinium, inner salt (RH 237)	5 mg	22.2	None
S1108	*N*-(4-sulfobutyl)-4-(4-(4-(dipentylamino)phenyl)butadienyl)pyridinium, inner salt (RH 421)	25 mg	22.2	None
S1129	5-sulfofluorescein diacetate, sodium salt (SFDA)	25 mg	14.3, 15.2, 20.2	None
B6353	Sulfo-NHS-LC-Biotin; biotin-X, SSE (6-((biotinoyl)amino)hexanoic acid, sulfosuccinimidyl ester, sodium salt)	25 mg	4.2, 14.3	None
S460	*N*-(3-sulfopropyl)acridinium, inner salt (SPA)	100 mg	21.2	None
S359	sulforhodamine 101	25 mg	14.3, 16.1	None
S1307	sulforhodamine B	5 g	14.3	None
S6957	sulforhodamine G	5 g	14.3	None
S10490	4-sulfo-2,3,5,6-tetrafluorophenol, sodium salt (STP)	100 mg	3.3	None
S7550	SYBR® DX DNA blot stain *1000X concentrate in DMA*	1 mL	8.1, 8.5	154
S11494	SYBR® Gold nucleic acid gel stain *10,000X concentrate in DMSO*	500 µL	8.1, 8.4, 8.7	154
S7563	SYBR® Green I nucleic acid gel stain *10,000X concentrate in DMSO*	500 µL	8.1, 8.3, 8.4, 8.7	154
S7585	SYBR® Green I nucleic acid gel stain *10,000X concentrate in DMSO* *special packaging*	20 x 50 µL	8.1, 8.3, 8.4, 8.7	154
S7567	SYBR® Green I nucleic acid gel stain *10,000X concentrate in DMSO*	1 mL	8.1, 8.3, 8.4, 8.7	154
S7564	SYBR® Green II RNA gel stain *10,000X concentrate in DMSO*	500 µL	8.1, 8.4	154
S7568	SYBR® Green II RNA gel stain *10,000X concentrate in DMSO*	1 mL	8.1, 8.4	154
S7586	SYBR® Green II RNA gel stain *10,000X concentrate in DMSO* *special packaging*	20 x 50 µL	8.1, 8.4	154
S7580	SYBR® Green Nucleic Acid Gel Stain Starter Kit	1 kit	8.1, 8.4	154
S7569	SYBR® photographic filter	each	8.4, 23.4	None
S21500	SYBR® 101, succinimidyl ester	1 mg	8.1, 8.2	154
S21501	SYBR® 102, succinimidyl ester	1 mg	8.1, 8.2	154
S21502	SYBR® 103, succinimidyl ester	1 mg	8.1, 8.2	154
S33101	SYBR Safe™ DNA gel stain in 0.5X TBE	4 L	8.1, 8.4	223, 188
S33102	SYBR Safe™ DNA gel stain *10,000X concentrate in DMSO*	400 µL	8.1	223, 188
S33111	SYBR Safe™ DNA gel stain in 1X TAE	1 L	8.1	223, 188
S33112	SYBR Safe™ DNA gel stain in 1X TAE	4 L	8.1	223, 188
S33100	SYBR Safe™ DNA gel stain in 0.5X TBE	1 L	8.1, 8.4	223, 188
S33110	SYBR Safe™ DNA Gel Stain Starter Kit *with 1 L of SYBR Safe™ DNA gel stain in 0.5X TBE (S33100) and one photographic filter (S37100)*	1 kit	8.1, 8.4	223, 188
S37100	SYBR Safe™ photographic filter	each	8.4, 23.4	None
S6651	SYPRO® Orange protein gel stain *5000X concentrate in DMSO* *special packaging*	10 x 50 µL	9.3	190
S6650	SYPRO® Orange protein gel stain *5000X concentrate in DMSO*	500 µL	9.3	190
S6656	SYPRO® photographic filter	each	9.3, 9.4, 23.4	None
S12012	SYPRO® Protein Gel Stain Starter Kit	1 kit	9.3	190
S6653	SYPRO® Red protein gel stain *5000X concentrate in DMSO*	500 µL	9.3	190
S6654	SYPRO® Red protein gel stain *5000X concentrate in DMSO* *special packaging*	10 x 50 µL	9.3	190
S12011	SYPRO® Rose Plus Protein Blot Stain Kit *10-40 blots*	1 kit	9.3	190
S11791	SYPRO® Ruby protein blot stain *10-40 blots*	200 mL	9.3, 9.4	190
S12001	SYPRO® Ruby protein gel stain	200 mL	9.3, 9.4	190
S21900	SYPRO® Ruby protein gel stain *bulk packaging*	5 L	9.3, 9.4	190
S12000	SYPRO® Ruby protein gel stain	1 L	9.3, 9.4	190
S12010	SYPRO® Tangerine protein gel stain *5000X concentrate in DMSO*	500 µL	9.3	190
S11351	SYTO® 40 blue fluorescent nucleic acid stain *5 mM solution in DMSO*	250 µL	8.1	154
S11352	SYTO® 41 blue fluorescent nucleic acid stain *5 mM solution in DMSO*	250 µL	8.1	154
S11353	SYTO® 42 blue fluorescent nucleic acid stain *5 mM solution in DMSO*	250 µL	8.1	154
S11354	SYTO® 43 blue fluorescent nucleic acid stain *5 mM solution in DMSO*	250 µL	8.1	154
S11355	SYTO® 44 blue fluorescent nucleic acid stain *5 mM solution in DMSO*	250 µL	8.1	154

For current prices or to order online, visit probes.invitrogen.com

Cat #	Product Name	Unit Size	Sections	Limited Use Label License #
S11356	SYTO® 45 blue fluorescent nucleic acid stain *5 mM solution in DMSO*	250 µL	8.1	154
S11350	SYTO® Blue Fluorescent Nucleic Acid Stain Sampler Kit *SYTO® dyes 40-45* *50 µL each*	1 kit	8.1, 15.2	154
S32704	SYTO® 10 green fluorescent nucleic acid stain *5 mM solution in DMSO*	100 µL	8.1, 15.2	154
S32705	SYTO® 26 green fluorescent nucleic acid stain *5 mM solution in DMSO*	100 µL	8.1, 15.2	154
S32706	SYTO® 27 green fluorescent nucleic acid stain *5 mM solution in DMSO*	100 µL	8.1, 15.2	154
S34854	SYTO® 9 green fluorescent nucleic acid stain *5 mM solution in DMSO*	100 µL	8.1, 15.2	154
S7573	SYTO® 11 green fluorescent nucleic acid stain *5 mM solution in DMSO*	250 µL	8.1, 8.6	154
S7574	SYTO® 12 green fluorescent nucleic acid stain *5 mM solution in DMSO*	250 µL	8.1, 8.6	154
S7575	SYTO® 13 green fluorescent nucleic acid stain *5 mM solution in DMSO*	250 µL	8.1, 15.2, 15.5	154
S7576	SYTO® 14 green fluorescent nucleic acid stain *5 mM solution in DMSO*	250 µL	8.1, 8.6	154
S7577	SYTO® 15 green fluorescent nucleic acid stain *5 mM solution in DMSO*	250 µL	8.1	154
S7578	SYTO® 16 green fluorescent nucleic acid stain *1 mM solution in DMSO*	250 µL	8.1, 8.6, 15.5	154
S7555	SYTO® 20 green fluorescent nucleic acid stain *1 mM solution in DMSO*	250 µL	8.1	154
S7556	SYTO® 21 green fluorescent nucleic acid stain *5 mM solution in DMSO*	250 µL	8.1	154
S7557	SYTO® 22 green fluorescent nucleic acid stain *5 mM solution in DMSO*	250 µL	8.1	154
S7558	SYTO® 23 green fluorescent nucleic acid stain *5 mM solution in DMSO*	250 µL	8.1	154
S7559	SYTO® 24 green fluorescent nucleic acid stain *5 mM solution in DMSO*	250 µL	8.1	154
S7560	SYTO® 25 green fluorescent nucleic acid stain *5 mM solution in DMSO*	250 µL	8.1	154
S34855	SYTO® BC green fluorescent nucleic acid stain *5 mM solution in DMSO*	100 µL	8.1, 15.2	154
S7572	SYTO® Green Fluorescent Nucleic Acid Stain Sampler Kit #1 *SYTO® dyes 11-16* *50 µL each*	1 kit	8.1, 8.6, 15.2	154
S7554	SYTO® Green Fluorescent Nucleic Acid Stain Sampler Kit #2 *SYTO® dyes 20-25* *50 µL each*	1 kit	8.1, 8.6, 15.2	154
S11361	SYTO® 80 orange fluorescent nucleic acid stain *5 mM solution in DMSO*	250 µL	8.1	154
S11362	SYTO® 81 orange fluorescent nucleic acid stain *5 mM solution in DMSO*	250 µL	8.1	154
S11363	SYTO® 82 orange fluorescent nucleic acid stain *5 mM solution in DMSO*	250 µL	8.1	154
S11364	SYTO® 83 orange fluorescent nucleic acid stain *5 mM solution in DMSO*	250 µL	8.1	154
S11366	SYTO® 85 orange fluorescent nucleic acid stain *5 mM solution in DMSO*	250 µL	8.1	154
S11365	SYTO® 84 orange fluorescent nucleic acid stain *5 mM solution in DMSO*	250 µL	8.1	154
S32707	SYTO® 86 orange fluorescent nucleic acid stain *5 mM solution in DMSO*	100 µL	8.1, 15.2	154
S11360	SYTO® Orange Fluorescent Nucleic Acid Stain Sampler Kit *SYTO® dyes 80-85* *50 µL each*	1 kit	8.1, 8.6, 15.2	154
S7579	SYTO® 17 red fluorescent nucleic acid stain *5 mM solution in DMSO*	250 µL	8.1, 8.6, 15.5	154
S11341	SYTO® 59 red fluorescent nucleic acid stain *5 mM solution in DMSO*	100 µL	8.1, 8.6	154
S11342	SYTO® 60 red fluorescent nucleic acid stain *5 mM solution in DMSO*	250 µL	8.1	154
S11343	SYTO® 61 red fluorescent nucleic acid stain *5 mM solution in DMSO*	250 µL	8.1	154
S11344	SYTO® 62 red fluorescent nucleic acid stain *5 mM solution in DMSO*	250 µL	8.1	154
S11345	SYTO® 63 red fluorescent nucleic acid stain *5 mM solution in DMSO*	250 µL	8.1	154
S11346	SYTO® 64 red fluorescent nucleic acid stain *5 mM solution in DMSO*	100 µL	8.1	154
S11340	SYTO® Red Fluorescent Nucleic Acid Stain Sampler Kit *SYTO® dyes 17 and 59-64* *50 µL each*	1 kit	8.1, 8.6, 15.2	154
S32703	SYTO® RNASelect™ green fluorescent cell stain *5 mM solution in DMSO*	100 µL	8.1, 15.2	223
S7529	SYTO® 18 yeast mitochondrial stain *5 mM solution in DMSO*	250 µL	12.2	154
S11348	SYTOX® Blue nucleic acid stain *5 mM solution in DMSO*	250 µL	8.1, 8.6, 15.2	154
S7020	SYTOX® Green nucleic acid stain *5 mM solution in DMSO*	250 µL	8.1, 8.6, 15.2, 15.4	154
S11368	SYTOX® Orange nucleic acid stain *5 mM solution in DMSO*	250 µL	8.1, 8.7, 15.2	154
C300	5(6)-TAMRA (5-(and-6)-carboxytetramethylrhodamine) *mixed isomers*	100 mg	1.6	None
C6121	5-TAMRA (5-carboxytetramethylrhodamine) *single isomer*	10 mg	1.6	None
C6122	6-TAMRA (6-carboxytetramethylrhodamine) *single isomer*	10 mg	1.6	None
C1171	5(6)-TAMRA, SE (5-(and-6)-carboxytetramethylrhodamine, succinimidyl ester) *mixed isomers*	25 mg	1.6	None
C2211	5-TAMRA, SE (5-carboxytetramethylrhodamine, succinimidyl ester) *single isomer*	5 mg	1.6	None
C6123	6-TAMRA, SE (6-carboxytetramethylrhodamine, succinimidyl ester) *single isomer*	5 mg	1.6	None
T6105	5(6)-TAMRA-X, SE (6-(tetramethylrhodamine-5-(and-6)-carboxamido)hexanoic acid, succinimidyl ester) *mixed isomers*	10 mg	1.6, 4.2	None
P3456	Taxol equivalent (paclitaxel) *for use in research only*	5 mg	11.2	None
T2556	TCEP (tris-(2-carboxyethyl)phosphine, hydrochloride)	1 g	2.1, 5.2	None
T6931	TCPP (tetrakis-(4-carboxyphenyl)porphine)	5 mg	14.3, 19.7	None
T11493	20X TE buffer *RNase free*	100 mL	8.3	None
A7923	TEMPO-9-AC (4-((9-acridinecarbonyl)amino)-2,2,6,6-tetramethylpiperidin-1-oxyl, free radical)	5 mg	18.2	None
D530	TEMPO choline (4-(*N,N*-dimethyl-*N*-(2-hydroxyethyl))ammonium-2,2,6,6-tetramethylpiperidine-1-oxyl chloride)	25 mg	14.3	None
T1247	terbium(III) chloride, hexahydrate	1 g	14.3, 17.2, 19.7	None
T7017	2′,4′,5′,7′-tetrabromo-4,5,6,7-tetrafluorofluorescein diacetate (Br_4TFFDA)	5 mg	14.2	None
T3168	5,5′,6,6′-tetrachloro-1,1′,3,3′-tetraethylbenzimidazolylcarbocyanine iodide (JC-1; $CBIC_2(3)$)	5 mg	12.2, 15.2, 15.5, 22.3	None

For current prices or to order online, visit probes.invitrogen.com

Important Licensing Information
These products may be covered by one or more Limited Use Label Licenses (See the Invitrogen Web site, www.invitrogen.com, or the Molecular Probes Web site, probes.invitrogen.com). By the use of these products you accept the terms and conditions of all applicable Limited Use Label Licenses. All products are for research use only. CAUTION: Not intended for human or animal diagnostic or therapeutic uses.

Cat #	Product Name	Unit Size	Sections	Limited Use Label License #
T6931	tetrakis-(4-carboxyphenyl)porphine (TCPP)	5 mg	14.3, 19.7	None
T1210	tetrakis-(2-pyridylmethyl)ethylenediamine (TPEN)	100 mg	19.8	None
T6932	tetrakis-(4-sulfophenyl)porphine (TSPP)	5 mg	14.3	None
T12921	5-(and-6)-tetramethylrhodamine biocytin (biocytin TMR)	5 mg	4.3, 14.3	None
T1175	tetramethylrhodamine α-bungarotoxin (α-bungarotoxin, tetramethylrhodamine conjugate)	500 µg	16.2	None
A1318	tetramethylrhodamine cadaverine (5-(and-6)-((*N*-(5-aminopentyl)amino)carbonyl)tetramethylrhodamine) *mixed isomers*	10 mg	3.3	None
T6219	tetramethylrhodamine-5-carbonyl azide	5 mg	3.1	None
T6105	6-(tetramethylrhodamine-5-(and-6)-carboxamido)hexanoic acid, succinimidyl ester (5(6)-TAMRA-X, SE) *mixed isomers*	10 mg	1.6, 4.2	None
T669	tetramethylrhodamine, ethyl ester, perchlorate (TMRE)	25 mg	12.2, 15.2, 15.5, 22.3	None
T2762	tetramethylrhodamine goat anti-mouse IgG (H+L) *2 mg/mL*	0.5 mL	7.2	None
T2769	tetramethylrhodamine goat anti-rabbit IgG (H+L) *2 mg/mL*	0.5 mL	7.2	None
T6006	tetramethylrhodamine-5-iodoacetamide dihydroiodide (5-TMRIA) *single isomer*	5 mg	2.2	None
T1480	tetramethylrhodamine-5-isothiocyanate (5-TRITC; G isomer)	5 mg	1.6	None
T1481	tetramethylrhodamine-6-isothiocyanate (6-TRITC; R isomer)	5 mg	1.6	None
T490	tetramethylrhodamine-5-(and-6)-isothiocyanate (5(6)-TRITC) *mixed isomers*	10 mg	1.6	None
T6027	tetramethylrhodamine-5-maleimide *single isomer*	5 mg	2.2	None
T6028	tetramethylrhodamine-6-maleimide *single isomer*	5 mg	2.2	None
T668	tetramethylrhodamine, methyl ester, perchlorate (TMRM)	25 mg	12.2, 15.2, 15.5, 22.3	None
T1391	*N*-(6-tetramethylrhodaminethiocarbamoyl)-1,2-dihexadecanoyl-*sn*-glycero-3-phosphoethanolamine, triethylammonium salt (TRITC DHPE)	1 mg	13.2	None
T639	tetramethylrosamine chloride	25 mg	12.2	None
T7284	TetraSpeck™ Fluorescent Microspheres Sampler Kit	1 kit	23.1	227, 193
T14792	TetraSpeck™ Fluorescent Microspheres Size Kit *mounted on slides*	1 kit	23.1	227, 183
T7280	TetraSpeck™ microspheres, 0.2 µm, fluorescent blue/green/orange/dark red	0.5 mL	23.1	227, 193
T7282	TetraSpeck™ microspheres, 1.0 µm, fluorescent blue/green/orange/dark red	0.5 mL	23.1	227, 193
T7281	TetraSpeck™ microspheres, 0.5 µm, fluorescent blue/green/orange/dark red	0.5 mL	23.1	227, 193
T7283	TetraSpeck™ microspheres, 4.0 µm, fluorescent blue/green/orange/dark red	0.5 mL	23.1	227, 193
T7279	TetraSpeck™ microspheres, 0.1 µm, fluorescent blue/green/orange/dark red	0.5 mL	23.1	227, 193
C20092	6-TET, SE (6-carboxy-2',4,7,7'-tetrachlorofluorescein, succinimidyl ester) *single isomer*	5 mg	1.5	None
T30200	Texas Red® C_2-dichlorotriazine	5 mg	1.6, 3.1	None
T6008	Texas Red® C_2-maleimide	5 mg	2.2	None
T2425	Texas Red® C_5 (Texas Red® cadaverine)	5 mg	3.3	None
T6009	Texas Red® C_5-bromoacetamide	5 mg	2.2	None
T2425	Texas Red® cadaverine (Texas Red® C_5)	5 mg	3.3	None
T1395MP	Texas Red® DHPE (Texas Red® 1,2-dihexadecanoyl-*sn*-glycero-3-phosphoethanolamine, triethylammonium salt)	1 mg	13.2	None
T1395MP	Texas Red® 1,2-dihexadecanoyl-*sn*-glycero-3-phosphoethanolamine, triethylammonium salt (Texas Red® DHPE)	1 mg	13.2	None
E3480	Texas Red® EGF complex (epidermal growth factor, biotinylated, complexed to Texas Red® streptavidin)	100 µg	4.3, 16.1	None
T862	Texas Red® goat anti-mouse IgG (H+L) *2 mg/mL*	0.5 mL	7.2	None
T2767	Texas Red® goat anti-rabbit IgG (H+L) *2 mg/mL*	0.5 mL	7.2	None
T6256	Texas Red® hydrazide *>90% single isomer*	5 mg	3.2	None
T353	Texas Red® sulfonyl chloride *mixed isomers*	10 mg	1.6	None
T1905	Texas Red® sulfonyl chloride *mixed isomers* *special packaging*	10 x ~1 mg	1.6	None
T7710	Texas Red®-X DHPE (Texas Red®-X 1,2-dihexadecanoyl-*sn*-glycero-3-phosphoethanolamine, triethylammonium salt)	1 mg	13.2	211
T7710	Texas Red®-X 1,2-dihexadecanoyl-*sn*-glycero-3-phosphoethanolamine, triethylammonium salt (Texas Red®-X DHPE)	1 mg	13.2	211
T6390	Texas Red®-X goat anti-mouse IgG (H+L) *2 mg/mL*	0.5 mL	7.2	211
T6391	Texas Red®-X goat anti-rabbit IgG (H+L) *2 mg/mL*	0.5 mL	7.2	211
T6392	Texas Red®-X goat anti-rat IgG (H+L) *2 mg/mL*	0.5 mL	7.2	211
M23273	Texas Red®-X methotrexate (methotrexate, Texas Red®-X, ammonium salt)	500 µg	15.6	211
T7471	Texas Red®-X phalloidin	300 U	11.1	211
T10244	Texas Red®-X Protein Labeling Kit *3 labelings*	1 kit	1.2, 1.6	211
T10125	Texas Red®-X, STP ester, sodium salt *mixed isomers*	5 mg	1.6, 4.2	211
T6134	Texas Red®-X, succinimidyl ester *mixed isomers*	5 mg	1.6, 4.2	211
T20175	Texas Red®-X, succinimidyl ester *single isomer*	2 mg	1.6, 4.2	211
A6311	TFPAM-SS1 (*N*-(2-((2-(((4-azido-2,3,5,6-tetrafluoro)benzoyl)amino)ethyl)dithio)ethyl)maleimide)	5 mg	5.3	None
T7458	thapsigargin	1 mg	17.2	None
T7459	thapsigargin *special packaging*	20 x 50 µg	17.2	None
T6060	Thiol and Sulfide Quantitation Kit *50-250 assays*	1 kit	2.1, 5.2, 21.2	None
T204	TMA-DPH (1-(4-trimethylammoniumphenyl)-6-phenyl-1,3,5-hexatriene *p*-toluenesulfonate)	25 mg	13.5, 16.1	None

For current prices or to order online, visit probes.invitrogen.com

Cat #	Product Name	Unit Size	Sections	Limited Use Label License #
P3900	TMAP-DPH (*N*-((4-(6-phenyl-1,3,5-hexatrienyl)phenyl)propyl)trimethylammonium *p*-toluenesulfonate)	5 mg	13.5, 16.1	None
T669	TMRE (tetramethylrhodamine, ethyl ester, perchlorate)	25 mg	12.2, 15.2, 15.5, 22.3	None
T6006	5-TMRIA (tetramethylrhodamine-5-iodoacetamide dihydroiodide) *single isomer*	5 mg	2.2	None
T668	TMRM (tetramethylrhodamine, methyl ester, perchlorate)	25 mg	12.2, 15.2, 15.5, 22.3	None
T7601	TNP-ADP (2′-(or-3′)-*O*-(trinitrophenyl)adenosine 5′-diphosphate, disodium salt) *5 mg/mL in water*	2 mL	17.3	None
T7624	TNP-AMP (2′-(or-3′)-*O*-(trinitrophenyl)adenosine 5′-monophosphate, sodium salt) *5 mg/mL in buffer*	2 mL	17.3	None
T7602	TNP-ATP (2′-(or-3′)-*O*-(trinitrophenyl)adenosine 5′-triphosphate, trisodium salt) *5 mg/mL in buffer*	2 mL	17.3	None
T7600	TNP-GTP (2′-(or-3′)-*O*-(trinitrophenyl)guanosine 5′-triphosphate, trisodium salt) *5 mg/mL in water*	1 mL	17.3	None
T53	2,6-TNS (2-(*p*-toluidinyl)naphthalene-6-sulfonic acid, sodium salt)	100 mg	13.5	None
T53	2-(*p*-toluidinyl)naphthalene-6-sulfonic acid, sodium salt (2,6-TNS)	100 mg	13.5	None
T3605	TO-PRO®-3 iodide (642/661) *1 mM solution in DMSO*	1 mL	8.1, 8.4, 8.6, 15.4	209
T7596	TO-PRO®-5 iodide (745/770) *1 mM solution in DMSO*	1 mL	8.1	209
T3602	TO-PRO®-1 iodide (515/531) *1 mM solution in DMSO*	1 mL	8.1, 8.4	209
T3604	TOTO®-3 iodide (642/660) *1 mM solution in DMSO*	200 µL	8.1, 8.4, 8.6, 15.4	228
T3600	TOTO®-1 iodide (514/533) *1 mM solution in DMSO*	200 µL	8.1, 8.4, 8.6, 8.7, 15.4	228
T1210	TPEN (tetrakis-(2-pyridylmethyl)ethylenediamine)	100 mg	19.8	None
T13342	transferrin from human serum, Alexa Fluor® 488 conjugate	5 mg	16.1	183
T23364	transferrin from human serum, Alexa Fluor® 546 conjugate	5 mg	16.1	183
T35352	transferrin from human serum, Alexa Fluor® 555 conjugate	5 mg	16.1	183
T23365	transferrin from human serum, Alexa Fluor® 568 conjugate	5 mg	16.1	183
T13343	transferrin from human serum, Alexa Fluor® 594 conjugate	5 mg	16.1	183
T23362	transferrin from human serum, Alexa Fluor® 633 conjugate	5 mg	16.1	183
T23366	transferrin from human serum, Alexa Fluor® 647 conjugate	5 mg	16.1	182
T23363	transferrin from human serum, biotin-XX conjugate	5 mg	4.3, 16.1	None
T2873	transferrin from human serum, BODIPY® FL conjugate	5 mg	16.1	193
T2871	transferrin from human serum, fluorescein conjugate	5 mg	16.1	None
T13341	transferrin from human serum, Oregon Green® 488 conjugate	5 mg	16.1	191
T2872	transferrin from human serum, tetramethylrhodamine conjugate	5 mg	16.1	None
T2875	transferrin from human serum, Texas Red® conjugate	5 mg	16.1	None
T8864	TransFluoSpheres® carboxylate-modified microspheres, 0.04 µm (488/560) *2% solids*	0.5 mL	6.5	227, 193
T8865	TransFluoSpheres® carboxylate-modified microspheres, 0.04 µm (488/605) *2% solids*	0.5 mL	6.5	227
T8867	TransFluoSpheres® carboxylate-modified microspheres, 0.04 µm (488/645) *2% solids*	0.5 mL	6.5	227
T8868	TransFluoSpheres® carboxylate-modified microspheres, 0.04 µm (488/685) *2% solids*	0.5 mL	6.5	227
T8869	TransFluoSpheres® carboxylate-modified microspheres, 0.04 µm (488/720) *2% solids*	0.5 mL	6.5	227
T8870	TransFluoSpheres® carboxylate-modified microspheres, 0.04 µm (633/720) *2% solids*	0.5 mL	6.5	227, 193
T8872	TransFluoSpheres® carboxylate-modified microspheres, 0.1 µm (488/560) *2% solids*	0.5 mL	6.5	227, 193
T8876	TransFluoSpheres® carboxylate-modified microspheres, 0.1 µm (488/685) *2% solids*	0.5 mL	6.5	227
T8874	TransFluoSpheres® carboxylate-modified microspheres, 0.1 µm (543/620) *2% solids*	0.5 mL	6.5	227
T8878	TransFluoSpheres® carboxylate-modified microspheres, 0.1 µm (633/720) *2% solids*	0.5 mL	6.5	227
T8880	TransFluoSpheres® carboxylate-modified microspheres, 1.0 µm (488/560) *2% solids*	0.5 mL	6.5	227, 193
T8883	TransFluoSpheres® carboxylate-modified microspheres, 1.0 µm (488/645) *2% solids*	0.5 mL	6.5	227, 193
T8882	TransFluoSpheres® carboxylate-modified microspheres, 1.0 µm (543/620) *2% solids*	0.5 mL	6.5	227
T8860	TransFluoSpheres® NeutrAvidin™ labeled microspheres, 0.04 µm (488/605) *1% solids*	0.4 mL	6.5, 7.6	227
T8861	TransFluoSpheres® NeutrAvidin™ labeled microspheres, 0.1 µm (488/605) *1% solids*	0.4 mL	6.5, 7.6	227, 193
T13090	TransFluoSpheres® polystyrene microspheres, 2.0 µm (633/760) *for tracer studies* *1.0x10^9 beads/mL*	0.5 mL	6.5, 14.6	227
T10711	TransFluoSpheres® streptavidin-labeled microspheres, 0.04 µm (488/645) *0.5% solids*	0.4 mL	6.5, 7.6	227, 183
T6615	tricyclodecan-9-yl xanthogenate, potassium salt (D 609)	5 mg	17.4	None
T3163	*N*-(3-triethylammoniumpropyl)-4-(4-(dibutylamino)styryl)pyridinium dibromide (FM® 1-43)	1 mg	14.4, 16.1	None
T35356	*N*-(3-triethylammoniumpropyl)-4-(4-(dibutylamino)styryl)pyridinium dibromide (FM® 1-43) *special packaging*	10 x 100 µg	14.4, 16.1	None
T1111	*N*-(3-triethylammoniumpropyl)-4-(4-(4-(diethylamino)phenyl)butadienyl)pyridinium dibromide (RH 414)	5 mg	14.4, 16.1, 22.2	None
T13320	*N*-(3-triethylammoniumpropyl)-4-(6-(4-(diethylamino)phenyl)hexatrienyl)pyridinium dibromide (FM® 4-64) *special packaging*	10 x 100 µg	12.3, 14.4, 16.1	None
T3166	*N*-(3-triethylammoniumpropyl)-4-(6-(4-(diethylamino)phenyl)hexatrienyl)pyridinium dibromide (FM® 4-64)	1 mg	12.3, 14.4, 16.1	None
T7508	*N*-(3-triethylammoniumpropyl)-4-(4-(diethylamino)styryl)pyridinium dibromide (FM® 2-10)	5 mg	16.1	None
T3164	*N*-(3-triethylammoniumpropyl)-4-(4-(dipentylamino)styryl)pyridinium dibromide (FM® 1-84)	1 mg	16.1	None
T411	2-((trifluoroacetyl)acetyl)naphthalene (naphthoyltrifluoroacetone)	100 mg	14.3, 19.7	None
T24220	4-trifluoromethyl BAPTA, tetrapotassium salt	5 mg	19.8	None
T659	β-trifluoromethylumbelliferone (7-hydroxy-4-trifluoromethylcoumarin) *reference standard*	100 mg	10.1	192

For current prices or to order online, visit probes.invitrogen.com

Cat #	Product Name	Unit Size	Sections	Limited Use Label License #
T657	β-trifluoromethylumbelliferyl β-D-galactopyranoside	100 mg	10.2	192
T658	β-trifluoromethylumbelliferyl β-D-glucuronide	25 mg	10.2	192
T204	1-(4-trimethylammoniumphenyl)-6-phenyl-1,3,5-hexatriene *p*-toluenesulfonate (TMA-DPH)	25 mg	13.5, 16.1	None
T23360	*N*-(3-trimethylammoniumpropyl)-4-(6-(4-(diethylamino)phenyl)hexatrienyl)pyridinium dibromide (FM® 5-95)	1 mg	12.3, 14.4, 16.1	None
T506	4-trimethylammonium-2,2,6,6-tetramethylpiperidine-1-oxyl iodide (CAT 1)	100 mg	14.3	None
T7601	2′-(or-3′)-*O*-(trinitrophenyl)adenosine 5′-diphosphate, disodium salt (TNP-ADP) *5 mg/mL in water*	2 mL	17.3	None
T7624	2′-(or-3′)-*O*-(trinitrophenyl)adenosine 5′-monophosphate, sodium salt (TNP-AMP) *5 mg/mL in buffer*	2 mL	17.3	None
T7602	2′-(or-3′)-*O*-(trinitrophenyl)adenosine 5′-triphosphate, trisodium salt (TNP-ATP) *5 mg/mL in buffer*	2 mL	17.3	None
T7600	2′-(or-3′)-*O*-(trinitrophenyl)guanosine 5′-triphosphate, trisodium salt (TNP-GTP) *5 mg/mL in water*	1 mL	17.3	None
T2556	tris-(2-carboxyethyl)phosphine, hydrochloride (TCEP)	1 g	2.1, 5.2	None
T490	5(6)-TRITC (tetramethylrhodamine-5-(and-6)-isothiocyanate) *mixed isomers*	10 mg	1.6	None
T1481	6-TRITC; R isomer (tetramethylrhodamine-6-isothiocyanate)	5 mg	1.6	None
T1480	5-TRITC; G isomer (tetramethylrhodamine-5-isothiocyanate)	5 mg	1.6	None
T1391	TRITC DHPE (*N*-(6-tetramethylrhodaminethiocarbamoyl)-1,2-dihexadecanoyl-*sn*-glycero-3-phosphoethanolamine, triethylammonium salt)	1 mg	13.2	None
T1323	true blue chloride	5 mg	14.3	None
T23011	trypsin inhibitor from soybean, Alexa Fluor® 488 conjugate	1 mg	10.4, 14.7, 16.1	183
T20911	TSA™ Kit #1 *with HRP–goat anti-mouse IgG and biotin-XX tyramide* *50-150 slides*	1 kit	6.2	235
T20912	TSA™ Kit #2 *with HRP–goat anti-mouse IgG and Alexa Fluor® 488 tyramide* *50-150 slides*	1 kit	6.2	235, 183
T20913	TSA™ Kit #3 *with HRP–goat anti-mouse IgG and Alexa Fluor® 546 tyramide* *50-150 slides*	1 kit	6.2	235, 183
T20914	TSA™ Kit #4 *with HRP–goat anti-mouse IgG and Alexa Fluor® 568 tyramide* *50-150 slides*	1 kit	6.2	235, 183
T20915	TSA™ Kit #5 *with HRP–goat anti-mouse IgG and Alexa Fluor® 594 tyramide* *50-150 slides*	1 kit	6.2	235, 183
T20916	TSA™ Kit #6 *with HRP–goat anti-mouse IgG and Alexa Fluor® 647 tyramide* *50-150 slides*	1 kit	6.2	235, 183
T20917	TSA™ Kit #7 *with HRP–goat anti-mouse IgG and Alexa Fluor® 350 tyramide* *50-150 slides*	1 kit	6.2	235, 183
T20918	TSA™ Kit #8 *with HRP–goat anti-mouse IgG and Alexa Fluor® 532 tyramide* *50-150 slides*	1 kit	6.2	235, 183
T20919	TSA™ Kit #9 *with HRP–goat anti-mouse IgG and Oregon Green® 488 tyramide* *50-150 slides*	1 kit	6.2	235, 191
T20920	TSA™ Kit #10 *with HRP–goat anti-mouse IgG and Pacific Blue® tyramide* *50-150 slides*	1 kit	6.2	235, 192
T20921	TSA™ Kit #11 *with HRP–goat anti-rabbit IgG and biotin-XX tyramide* *50-150 slides*	1 kit	6.2	235
T20922	TSA™ Kit #12 *with HRP–goat anti-rabbit IgG and Alexa Fluor® 488 tyramide* *50-150 slides*	1 kit	6.2	235, 183
T20923	TSA™ Kit #13 *with HRP–goat anti-rabbit IgG and Alexa Fluor® 546 tyramide* *50-150 slides*	1 kit	6.2	235, 183
T20924	TSA™ Kit #14 *with HRP–goat anti-rabbit IgG and Alexa Fluor® 568 tyramide* *50-150 slides*	1 kit	6.2	235, 183
T20925	TSA™ Kit #15 *with HRP–goat anti-rabbit IgG and Alexa Fluor® 594 tyramide* *50-150 slides*	1 kit	6.2	235, 183
T20926	TSA™ Kit #16 *with HRP–goat anti-rabbit IgG and Alexa Fluor® 647 tyramide* *50-150 slides*	1 kit	6.2	235, 223
T20927	TSA™ Kit #17 *with HRP–goat anti-rabbit IgG and Alexa Fluor® 350 tyramide* *50-150 slides*	1 kit	6.2	235, 183
T20928	TSA™ Kit #18 *with HRP–goat anti-rabbit IgG and Alexa Fluor® 532 tyramide* *50-150 slides*	1 kit	6.2	235, 183
T20930	TSA™ Kit #20 *with HRP–goat anti-rabbit IgG and Pacific Blue® tyramide* *50-150 slides*	1 kit	6.2	235, 192
T20931	TSA™ Kit #21 *with HRP–streptavidin and biotin-XX tyramide* *50-150 slides*	1 kit	6.2	235
T20932	TSA™ Kit #22 *with HRP–streptavidin and Alexa Fluor® 488 tyramide* *50-150 slides*	1 kit	6.2	235, 183
T20933	TSA™ Kit #23 *with HRP–streptavidin and Alexa Fluor® 546 tyramide* *50-150 slides*	1 kit	6.2	235, 183
T20934	TSA™ Kit #24 *with HRP–streptavidin and Alexa Fluor® 568 tyramide* *50-150 slides*	1 kit	6.2	235, 183
T20935	TSA™ Kit #25 *with HRP–streptavidin and Alexa Fluor® 594 tyramide* *50-150 slides*	1 kit	6.2	235, 183
T20936	TSA™ Kit #26 *with HRP–streptavidin and Alexa Fluor® 647 tyramide* *50-150 slides*	1 kit	6.2	235, 183
T20937	TSA™ Kit #27 *with HRP–streptavidin and Alexa Fluor® 350 tyramide* *50-150 slides*	1 kit	6.2	235, 183
T20938	TSA™ Kit #28 *with HRP–streptavidin and Alexa Fluor® 532 tyramide* *50-150 slides*	1 kit	6.2	235, 183
T20939	TSA™ Kit #29 *with HRP–streptavidin and Oregon Green® 488 tyramide* *50-150 slides*	1 kit	6.2	235, 191
T20941	TSA™ Kit #31 *with HRP–goat anti-mouse IgG and DSB-X™ biotin tyramide* *50-150 slides*	1 kit	6.2	235
T20942	TSA™ Kit #32 *with HRP–goat anti-rabbit IgG and DSB-X™ biotin tyramide* *50-150 slides*	1 kit	6.2	235
T20943	TSA™ Kit #33 *with HRP–streptavidin and DSB-X™ biotin tyramide* *50-150 slides*	1 kit	6.2	235
T20944	TSA™ Kit #34 *with HRP–goat anti-mouse IgG and DNP-X tyramide* *50-150 slides*	1 kit	6.2	235
T20945	TSA™ Kit #35 *with HRP–goat anti-rabbit IgG and DNP-X tyramide* *50-150 slides*	1 kit	6.2	235
T20946	TSA™ Kit #36 *with HRP–streptavidin and DNP-X tyramide* *50-150 slides*	1 kit	6.2	235
T30950	TSA™ Kit #37 *with HRP–goat anti-mouse IgG and Alexa Fluor® 405 tyramide* *50-150 slides*	1 kit	6.2	235, 183
T30951	TSA™ Kit #38 *with HRP–goat anti-rabbit IgG and Alexa Fluor® 405 tyramide* *50-150 slides*	1 kit	6.2	235, 183
T30952	TSA™ Kit #39 *with HRP–streptavidin and Alexa Fluor® 405 tyramide* *50-150 slides*	1 kit	6.2	235, 183
T30953	TSA™ Kit #40 *with HRP–goat anti-mouse IgG and Alexa Fluor® 555 tyramide* *50-150 slides*	1 kit	6.2	235, 183
T30954	TSA™ Kit #41 *with HRP–goat anti-rabbit IgG and Alexa Fluor® 555 tyramide* *50-150 slides*	1 kit	6.2	235, 183
T30955	TSA™ Kit #42 *with HRP–streptavidin and Alexa Fluor® 555 tyramide* *50-150 slides*	1 kit	6.2	235, 183
T30502	TS-Link™ bimane thiosulfate, sodium salt	5 mg	2.3	223
T30456	TS-Link™ BODIPY® 630/650 C_5-thiosulfate, sodium salt	5 mg	2.2	223, 193

For current prices or to order online, visit probes.invitrogen.com

Cat #	Product Name	Unit Size	Sections	Limited Use Label License #
T30453	TS-Link™ BODIPY® FL C_2-thiosulfate, sodium salt	5 mg	2.2	223, 193
T30454	TS-Link™ BODIPY® TMR C_5-thiosulfate, sodium salt	5 mg	2.2	223, 193
T30455	TS-Link™ BODIPY® TR C_5-thiosulfate, sodium salt	5 mg	2.2	223, 193
T30754	TS-Link™ desthiobiotin-X C_5-thiosulfate, sodium salt (TS-Link™ DSB-X™ biotin C_5-thiosulfate)	5 mg	4.2	223
T30754	TS-Link™ DSB-X™ biotin C_5-thiosulfate (TS-Link™ desthiobiotin-X C_5-thiosulfate, sodium salt)	5 mg	4.2	223
T30875	TS-Link™ TFP-X thiosulfate, sodium salt	5 mg	5.2	223
T6932	TSPP (tetrakis-(4-sulfophenyl)porphine)	5 mg	14.3	None
M688	TSQ (*N*-(6-methoxy-8-quinolyl)-*p*-toluenesulfonamide)	25 mg	19.7	None
T12391	tubulin from bovine brain, Oregon Green® 514 conjugate *10 mg/mL*	10 µL	11.2	191
T13361	tuftsin, fluorescein conjugate (FITC tuftsin)	100 µg	16.1	None
D7760	U-6 (4-(*N*,*N*-dimethyl-*N*-tetradecylammonium)methyl-(7-hydroxycoumarin) chloride)	10 mg	13.5	None
U21650	ULYSIS® Alexa Fluor® 488 Nucleic Acid Labeling Kit *20 labelings*	1 kit	1.2, 1.3, 8.2	183
U21651	ULYSIS® Alexa Fluor® 532 Nucleic Acid Labeling Kit *20 labelings*	1 kit	1.2, 1.3, 8.2	183
U21652	ULYSIS® Alexa Fluor® 546 Nucleic Acid Labeling Kit *20 labelings*	1 kit	1.2, 1.3, 8.2	183
U21653	ULYSIS® Alexa Fluor® 568 Nucleic Acid Labeling Kit *20 labelings*	1 kit	1.2, 1.3, 8.2	183
U21654	ULYSIS® Alexa Fluor® 594 Nucleic Acid Labeling Kit *20 labelings*	1 kit	1.2, 1.3, 8.2	183
U21660	ULYSIS® Alexa Fluor® 647 Nucleic Acid Labeling Kit *20 labelings*	1 kit	1.2, 1.3, 8.2	183
U21656	ULYSIS® Alexa Fluor® 660 Nucleic Acid Labeling Kit *20 labelings*	1 kit	1.2, 1.3, 8.2	183
U21657	ULYSIS® Alexa Fluor® 680 Nucleic Acid Labeling Kit *20 labelings*	1 kit	1.2, 1.3, 8.2	183
U21659	ULYSIS® Oregon Green® 488 Nucleic Acid Labeling Kit *20 labelings*	1 kit	1.2, 1.5, 8.2	191
U21658	ULYSIS® Pacific Blue™ Nucleic Acid Labeling Kit *20 labelings*	1 kit	1.2, 1.7, 8.2	192
U23692	uridine 5′-triphosphate, P^3-(5-sulfo-1-naphthylamide), tetra(triethylammonium) salt (UTP γ-AmNS) *5 mM in water*	400 µL	17.3	None
U23692	UTP γ-AmNS (uridine 5′-triphosphate, P^3-(5-sulfo-1-naphthylamide), tetra(triethylammonium) salt) *5 mM in water*	400 µL	17.3	None
V1644	valinomycin	25 mg	21.1	None
V34850	vancomycin, BODIPY® FL conjugate (BODIPY® FL vancomycin)	100 µg	15.2	193
V7023	ViaGram™ Red+ Bacterial Gram Stain and Viability Kit *200 assays*	1 kit	15.3	251, 211, 154
V12390	vinblastine, BODIPY® FL conjugate (BODIPY® FL vinblastine)	100 µg	11.2, 15.6	193
V34403	Vybrant® Alexa Fluor® 488 Lipid Raft Labeling Kit *50 labelings*	1 kit	13.3, 17.4	183
V34404	Vybrant® Alexa Fluor® 555 Lipid Raft Labeling Kit *50 labelings*	1 kit	13.3, 17.4	183
V34405	Vybrant® Alexa Fluor® 594 Lipid Raft Labeling Kit *50 labelings*	1 kit	13.3, 17.4	183
V13240	Vybrant® Apoptosis Assay Kit #1 *Alexa Fluor® 488 annexin V/SYTOX® Green* *50 assays*	1 kit	15.5	213, 183, 154
V13241	Vybrant® Apoptosis Assay Kit #2 *Alexa Fluor® 488 annexin V/propidium iodide* *50 assays*	1 kit	15.5	213, 183
V13242	Vybrant® Apoptosis Assay Kit #3 *FITC annexin V/propidium iodide* *50 assays*	1 kit	15.5	213
V13243	Vybrant® Apoptosis Assay Kit #4 *YO-PRO®-1/propidium iodide* *200 assays*	1 kit	15.5	209
V13244	Vybrant® Apoptosis Assay Kit #5 *Hoechst 33342/propidium iodide* *200 assays*	1 kit	15.5	None
V23200	Vybrant® Apoptosis Assay Kit #6 *biotin-X annexin V/Alexa Fluor® 350 streptavidin/propidium iodide* *50 assays*	1 kit	15.5	213, 183
V23201	Vybrant® Apoptosis Assay Kit #7 *Hoechst 33342/YO-PRO®-1/propidium iodide* *200 assays*	1 kit	15.5	209
V35112	Vybrant® Apoptosis Assay Kit #8 *R-phycoerythrin annexin V/SYTOX® Green* *50 assays*	1 kit	15.5	213, 154
V35113	Vybrant® Apoptosis Assay Kit #9 *allophycocyanin annexin V/SYTOX® Green* *50 assays*	1 kit	15.5	213, 154
V35114	Vybrant® Apoptosis Assay Kit #10 *allophycocyanin annexin V/C_{12}-resazurin/SYTOX® Green* *50 assays*	1 kit	15.5	213, 154
V35116	Vybrant® Apoptosis Assay Kit #11 *Alexa Fluor® 488 annexin V/MitoTracker® Red CMXRos* *50 assays*	1 kit	15.5	213, 183
V13181	Vybrant® Cell Adhesion Assay Kit	1 kit	15.6	154
V22915	Vybrant® Cell Lineage Tracing Kit	1 kit	14.5	218, 183
V23110	Vybrant® Cell Metabolic Assay Kit *with C_{12}-resazurin* *500-1000 assays*	1 kit	15.3	None
V12883	Vybrant® CFDA SE Cell Tracer Kit	1 kit	14.2, 15.4	None
V22888	Vybrant® CM-DiI cell-labeling solution	1 mL	14.4, 15.4	None
V23111	Vybrant® Cytotoxicity Assay Kit *G6PD release assay* *1000 assays*	1 kit	10.6, 15.3	None
V22887	Vybrant® DiD cell-labeling solution	1 mL	14.4, 15.4	None
V22885	Vybrant® DiI cell-labeling solution	1 mL	14.4, 15.4	None
V22886	Vybrant® DiO cell-labeling solution	1 mL	14.4, 15.4	None
V35118	Vybrant® FAM Caspase-3 and -7 Assay Kit *for flow cytometry* *25 assays*	1 kit	15.5	None
V35119	Vybrant® FAM Caspase-8 Assay Kit *for flow cytometry* *25 assays*	1 Kit	15.5	None
V35117	Vybrant® FAM Poly Caspases Assay Kit *for flow cytometry* *25 assays*	1 kit	15.5	None
V13154	Vybrant® MTT Cell Proliferation Assay Kit *1000 assays*	1 kit	15.4	None
V22889	Vybrant® Multicolor Cell-Labeling Kit *DiO, DiI, DiD solutions, 1 mL each*	1 kit	14.4	None
V13180	Vybrant® Multidrug Resistance Assay Kit	1 kit	15.6	215
V6694	Vybrant® Phagocytosis Assay Kit *250 assays*	1 kit	16.1	None
W11263	wheat germ agglutinin, Alexa Fluor® 350 conjugate	5 mg	7.7, 12.4	183

For current prices or to order online, visit probes.invitrogen.com

Cat #	Product Name	Unit Size	Sections	Limited Use Label License #
W11261	wheat germ agglutinin, Alexa Fluor® 488 conjugate	5 mg	7.7, 12.4	183
W11262	wheat germ agglutinin, Alexa Fluor® 594 conjugate	5 mg	7.7, 12.4	183
W21404	wheat germ agglutinin, Alexa Fluor® 633 conjugate	5 mg	7.7, 12.4	183
W21407	wheat germ agglutinin, Alexa Fluor® 660 conjugate	5 mg	7.7, 12.4	183
W834	wheat germ agglutinin, fluorescein conjugate	5 mg	7.7, 12.4	None
W11260	wheat germ agglutinin, Marina Blue® conjugate	5 mg	7.7, 12.4	192
W6748	wheat germ agglutinin, Oregon Green® 488 conjugate	5 mg	7.7, 12.4	191
W7024	Wheat Germ Agglutinin Sampler Kit *four fluorescent conjugates, 1 mg each*	1 kit	7.7, 12.4, 15.3	None
W849	wheat germ agglutinin, tetramethylrhodamine conjugate	5 mg	7.7, 12.4	None
W21405	wheat germ agglutinin, Texas Red®-X conjugate	1 mg	7.7, 12.4	211
W435	WW 781, triethylammonium salt	25 mg	16.3, 22.2	None
B1690	X-Gal (5-bromo-4-chloro-3-indolyl β-D-galactopyranoside)	1 g	10.2	None
B22015	X-Gal (5-bromo-4-chloro-3-indolyl β-D-galactopyranoside) *bulk packaging*	25 g	10.2	None
B1691	X-GlcU, CHA (5-bromo-4-chloro-3-indolyl β-D-glucuronide, cyclohexylammonium salt)	100 mg	10.2	None
B1689	X-Glu (5-bromo-4-chloro-3-indolyl β-D-glucopyranoside)	100 mg	10.2	None
X14210	X-rhod-1, AM *cell permeant* *special packaging*	10 x 50 µg	19.3	204
X14209	X-rhod-1, tripotassium salt *cell impermeant*	500 µg	19.3	204
X23985	X-rhod-5F, AM *cell permeant* *special packaging*	10 x 50 µg	19.3	204
X23984	X-rhod-5F, tripotassium salt *cell impermeant*	500 µg	19.3	204
X14212	X-rhod-5N, AM *cell permeant* *special packaging*	10 x 50 µg	19.3	204
X14211	X-rhod-5N, tripotassium salt *cell impermeant*	500 µg	19.3	204
X491	X-rhodamine-5-(and-6)-isothiocyanate (5(6)-XRITC) *mixed isomers*	10 mg	1.6	None
X34675	X-rhod dextran, potassium salt, 10,000 MW, anionic	5 mg	19.4	None
X23987	X-rhod-FF, AM *cell permeant* *special packaging*	10 x 50 µg	19.3	204
X491	5(6)-XRITC (X-rhodamine-5-(and-6)-isothiocyanate) *mixed isomers*	10 mg	1.6	None
X6493	XTT (2,3-bis-(2-methoxy-4-nitro-5-sulfophenyl)-2*H*-tetrazolium-5-carboxanilide)	100 mg	15.2, 18.2	None
X1525	*p*-xylene-bis-pyridinium bromide (DPX)	1 g	14.3	None
Y7530	Yeast Mitochondrial Stain Sampler Kit	1 kit	12.2	217, 154
Y7531	Yeast Vacuole Marker Sampler Kit	1 kit	12.3	212
Y7536	yeast vacuole membrane marker MDY-64	1 mg	12.3	None
Y3603	YO-PRO®-1 iodide (491/509) *1 mM solution in DMSO*	1 mL	8.1, 8.4, 15.5	209
Y3607	YO-PRO®-3 iodide (612/631) *1 mM solution in DMSO*	1 mL	8.1	209
Y3601	YOYO®-1 iodide (491/509) *1 mM solution in DMSO*	200 µL	8.1, 8.4, 8.6, 8.7, 15.4	228
Y3606	YOYO®-3 iodide (612/631) *1 mM solution in DMSO*	200 µL	8.1	228
R33752	Z-AAD-R110 (rhodamine 110, bis-(*N*-CBZ-L-alanyl-L-alanyl-L-aspartic acid amide))	2 mg	10.4, 15.5	None
A22121	Z-DEVD-AFC (7-amino-4-trifluoromethylcoumarin, *N*-CBZ-L-aspartyl-L-glutamyl-L-valyl-L-aspartic acid amide)	5 mg	10.4, 15.5	None
R22120	Z-DEVD-R110 (rhodamine 110, bis-(*N*-CBZ-L-aspartyl-L-glutamyl-L-valyl-L-aspartic acid amide)) *bulk packaging*	20 mg	10.4, 15.5	None
Z25400	Zenon® Alexa Fluor® 350 Human IgG Labeling Kit *50 labelings*	1 kit	1.2, 1.3, 1.7, 7.3	223, 183
Z25000	Zenon® Alexa Fluor® 350 Mouse IgG_1 Labeling Kit *50 labelings*	1 kit	1.2, 1.3, 1.7, 7.3	223, 183
Z25100	Zenon® Alexa Fluor® 350 Mouse IgG_{2a} Labeling Kit *50 labelings*	1 kit	1.2, 1.3, 1.7, 7.3	223, 183
Z25200	Zenon® Alexa Fluor® 350 Mouse IgG_{2b} Labeling Kit *50 labelings*	1 kit	1.2, 1.3, 1.7, 7.3	223, 183
Z25300	Zenon® Alexa Fluor® 350 Rabbit IgG Labeling Kit *50 labelings*	1 kit	1.2, 1.3, 1.7, 7.3	223, 183
Z25013	Zenon® Alexa Fluor® 405 Mouse IgG_1 Labeling Kit *50 labelings*	1 kit	1.2, 1.3, 1.7, 7.3	223, 183
Z25113	Zenon® Alexa Fluor® 405 Mouse IgG_{2a} Labeling Kit *50 labelings*	1 kit	1.2, 1.3, 1.7, 7.3	223, 183
Z25213	Zenon® Alexa Fluor® 405 Mouse IgG_{2b} Labeling Kit *50 labelings*	1 kit	1.2, 1.3, 1.7, 7.3	223, 183
Z25313	Zenon® Alexa Fluor® 405 Rabbit IgG Labeling Kit *50 labelings*	1 kit	1.2, 1.3, 1.7, 7.3	223, 183
Z25001	Zenon® Alexa Fluor® 430 Mouse IgG_1 Labeling Kit *50 labelings*	1 kit	1.2, 1.3, 1.7, 7.3	223, 183
Z25301	Zenon® Alexa Fluor® 430 Rabbit IgG Labeling Kit *50 labelings*	1 kit	1.2, 1.3, 1.7, 7.3	223, 183
Z25602	Zenon® Alexa Fluor® 488 Goat IgG Labeling Kit *50 labelings*	1 kit	1.2, 1.3, 7.3	223, 183
Z25402	Zenon® Alexa Fluor® 488 Human IgG Labeling Kit *50 labelings*	1 kit	1.2, 1.3, 7.3	223, 183
Z25002	Zenon® Alexa Fluor® 488 Mouse IgG_1 Labeling Kit *50 labelings*	1 kit	1.2, 1.3, 7.3	223, 183
Z25090	Zenon® Alexa Fluor® 488 Mouse IgG_1 Labeling Kit *enhanced with TSA™ technology* *25 labelings*	1 kit	1.2, 1.3, 6.2, 7.3	235, 223, 183
Z25102	Zenon® Alexa Fluor® 488 Mouse IgG_{2a} Labeling Kit *50 labelings*	1 kit	1.2, 1.3, 7.3	223, 183
Z25202	Zenon® Alexa Fluor® 488 Mouse IgG_{2b} Labeling Kit *50 labelings*	1 kit	1.2, 1.3, 7.3	223, 183
Z25302	Zenon® Alexa Fluor® 488 Rabbit IgG Labeling Kit *50 labelings*	1 kit	1.2, 1.3, 7.3	223, 183
Z25003	Zenon® Alexa Fluor® 532 Mouse IgG_1 Labeling Kit *50 labelings*	1 kit	1.2, 1.3, 7.3	223, 183
Z25303	Zenon® Alexa Fluor® 532 Rabbit IgG Labeling Kit *50 labelings*	1 kit	1.2, 1.3, 7.3	223, 183
Z25004	Zenon® Alexa Fluor® 546 Mouse IgG_1 Labeling Kit *50 labelings*	1 kit	1.2, 1.3, 7.3	223, 183

For current prices or to order online, visit probes.invitrogen.com

Cat #	Product Name	Unit Size	Sections	Limited Use Label License #
Z25104	Zenon® Alexa Fluor® 546 Mouse IgG_{2a} Labeling Kit *50 labelings*	1 kit	1.2, 1.3, 7.3	223, 183
Z25204	Zenon® Alexa Fluor® 546 Mouse IgG_{2b} Labeling Kit *50 labelings*	1 kit	1.2, 1.3, 7.3	223, 183
Z25304	Zenon® Alexa Fluor® 546 Rabbit IgG Labeling Kit *50 labelings*	1 kit	1.2, 1.3, 7.3	223, 183
Z25605	Zenon® Alexa Fluor® 555 Goat IgG Labeling Kit *50 labelings*	1 kit	1.2, 1.3, 7.3	223, 183
Z25405	Zenon® Alexa Fluor® 555 Human IgG Labeling Kit *50 labelings*	1 kit	1.2, 1.3, 7.3	223, 183
Z25005	Zenon® Alexa Fluor® 555 Mouse IgG_1 Labeling Kit *50 labelings*	1 kit	1.2, 1.3, 7.3	223, 183
Z25105	Zenon® Alexa Fluor® 555 Mouse IgG_{2a} Labeling Kit *50 labelings*	1 kit	1.2, 1.3, 7.3	223, 183
Z25205	Zenon® Alexa Fluor® 555 Mouse IgG_{2b} Labeling Kit *50 labelings*	1 kit	1.2, 1.3, 7.3	223, 183
Z25305	Zenon® Alexa Fluor® 555 Rabbit IgG Labeling Kit *50 labelings*	1 kit	1.2, 1.3, 7.3	223, 183
Z25606	Zenon® Alexa Fluor® 568 Goat IgG Labeling Kit *50 labelings*	1 kit	1.2, 1.3, 7.3	223, 183
Z25006	Zenon® Alexa Fluor® 568 Mouse IgG_1 Labeling Kit *50 labelings*	1 kit	1.2, 1.3, 7.3	223, 183
Z25091	Zenon® Alexa Fluor® 568 Mouse IgG_1 Labeling Kit *enhanced with TSA™ technology* *25 labelings*	1 kit	1.2, 1.3, 6.2, 7.3	235, 223, 183
Z25106	Zenon® Alexa Fluor® 568 Mouse IgG_{2a} Labeling Kit *50 labelings*	1 kit	1.2, 1.3, 7.3	223, 183
Z25206	Zenon® Alexa Fluor® 568 Mouse IgG_{2b} Labeling Kit *50 labelings*	1 kit	1.2, 1.3, 7.3	223, 183
Z25306	Zenon® Alexa Fluor® 568 Rabbit IgG Labeling Kit *50 labelings*	1 kit	1.2, 1.3, 7.3	223, 183
Z25607	Zenon® Alexa Fluor® 594 Goat IgG Labeling Kit *50 labelings*	1 kit	1.2, 1.3, 7.3	223, 183
Z25407	Zenon® Alexa Fluor® 594 Human IgG Labeling Kit *50 labelings*	1 kit	1.2, 1.3, 7.3	223, 183
Z25007	Zenon® Alexa Fluor® 594 Mouse IgG_1 Labeling Kit *50 labelings*	1 kit	1.2, 1.3, 7.3	223, 183
Z25107	Zenon® Alexa Fluor® 594 Mouse IgG_{2a} Labeling Kit *50 labelings*	1 kit	1.2, 1.3, 7.3	223, 183
Z25207	Zenon® Alexa Fluor® 594 Mouse IgG_{2b} Labeling Kit *50 labelings*	1 kit	1.2, 1.3, 7.3	223, 183
Z25307	Zenon® Alexa Fluor® 594 Rabbit IgG Labeling Kit *50 labelings*	1 kit	1.2, 1.3, 7.3	223, 183
Z25020	Zenon® Alexa Fluor® 610–R-Phycoerythrin Mouse IgG_1 Labeling Kit *10 labelings*	1 kit	1.2, 1.3, 6.4, 7.3	223, 183
Z25608	Zenon® Alexa Fluor® 647 Goat IgG Labeling Kit *50 labelings*	1 kit	1.2, 1.3, 7.3	223, 183
Z25408	Zenon® Alexa Fluor® 647 Human IgG Labeling Kit *50 labelings*	1 kit	1.2, 1.3, 7.3	223, 183
Z25008	Zenon® Alexa Fluor® 647 Mouse IgG_1 Labeling Kit *50 labelings*	1 kit	1.2, 1.3, 7.3	223, 183
Z25108	Zenon® Alexa Fluor® 647 Mouse IgG_{2a} Labeling Kit *50 labelings*	1 kit	1.2, 1.3, 7.3	223, 183
Z25208	Zenon® Alexa Fluor® 647 Mouse IgG_{2b} Labeling Kit *50 labelings*	1 kit	1.2, 1.3, 7.3	223, 183
Z25308	Zenon® Alexa Fluor® 647 Rabbit IgG Labeling Kit *50 labelings*	1 kit	1.2, 1.3, 7.3	223, 183
Z25021	Zenon® Alexa Fluor® 647–R-Phycoerythrin Mouse IgG_1 Labeling Kit *10 labelings*	1 kit	1.2, 1.3, 6.4, 7.3	223, 183
Z25121	Zenon® Alexa Fluor® 647–R-Phycoerythrin Mouse IgG_{2a} Labeling Kit *10 labelings*	1 kit	1.2, 1.3, 6.4, 7.3	223, 183
Z25221	Zenon® Alexa Fluor® 647–R-Phycoerythrin Mouse IgG_{2b} Labeling Kit *10 labelings*	1 kit	1.2, 1.3, 6.4, 7.3	223, 183
Z25009	Zenon® Alexa Fluor® 660 Mouse IgG_1 Labeling Kit *50 labelings*	1 kit	1.2, 1.3, 7.3	223, 183
Z25109	Zenon® Alexa Fluor® 660 Mouse IgG_{2a} Labeling Kit *50 labelings*	1 kit	1.2, 1.3, 7.3	223, 183
Z25209	Zenon® Alexa Fluor® 660 Mouse IgG_{2b} Labeling Kit *50 labelings*	1 kit	1.2, 1.3, 7.3	223, 183
Z25309	Zenon® Alexa Fluor® 660 Rabbit IgG Labeling Kit *50 labelings*	1 kit	1.2, 1.3, 7.3	223, 183
Z25010	Zenon® Alexa Fluor® 680 Mouse IgG_1 Labeling Kit *50 labelings*	1 kit	1.2, 1.3, 7.3	223, 183
Z25110	Zenon® Alexa Fluor® 680 Mouse IgG_{2a} Labeling Kit *50 labelings*	1 kit	1.2, 1.3, 7.3	223, 183
Z25210	Zenon® Alexa Fluor® 680 Mouse IgG_{2b} Labeling Kit *50 labelings*	1 kit	1.2, 1.3, 7.3	223, 183
Z25310	Zenon® Alexa Fluor® 680 Rabbit IgG Labeling Kit *50 labelings*	1 kit	1.2, 1.3, 7.3	223, 183
Z25022	Zenon® Alexa Fluor® 680–R-Phycoerythrin Mouse IgG_1 Labeling Kit *10 labelings*	1 kit	1.2, 1.3, 6.4, 7.3	223, 183
Z25011	Zenon® Alexa Fluor® 700 Mouse IgG_1 Labeling Kit *50 labelings*	1 kit	1.2, 1.3, 7.3	223, 183
Z25311	Zenon® Alexa Fluor® 700 Rabbit IgG Labeling Kit *50 labelings*	1 kit	1.2, 1.3, 7.3	223, 183
Z25030	Zenon® Alexa Fluor® 700–Allophycocyanin Mouse IgG_1 Labeling Kit *10 labelings*	1 kit	1.2, 1.3, 6.4, 7.3	223, 183
Z25312	Zenon® Alexa Fluor® 750 Rabbit IgG Labeling Kit *50 labelings*	1 kit	1.2, 1.3, 7.3	223, 183
Z25031	Zenon® Alexa Fluor® 750–Allophycocyanin Mouse IgG_1 Labeling Kit *10 labelings*	1 kit	1.2, 1.3, 6.4, 7.3	223, 183
Z25050	Zenon® Alkaline Phosphatase Mouse IgG_1 Labeling Kit *25 labelings*	1 kit	1.2, 7.3	223
Z25150	Zenon® Alkaline Phosphatase Mouse IgG_{2a} Labeling Kit *25 labelings*	1 kit	1.2, 7.3	223
Z25250	Zenon® Alkaline Phosphatase Mouse IgG_{2b} Labeling Kit *25 labelings*	1 kit	1.2, 7.3	223
Z25350	Zenon® Alkaline Phosphatase Rabbit IgG Labeling Kit *25 labelings*	1 kit	1.2, 7.3	223
Z25451	Zenon® Allophycocyanin Human IgG Labeling Kit *25 labelings*	1 kit	1.2, 6.4, 7.3	223
Z25051	Zenon® Allophycocyanin Mouse IgG_1 Labeling Kit *25 labelings*	1 kit	1.2, 6.4, 7.3	223
Z25151	Zenon® Allophycocyanin Mouse IgG_{2a} Labeling Kit *25 labelings*	1 kit	1.2, 6.4, 7.3	223
Z25251	Zenon® Allophycocyanin Mouse IgG_{2b} Labeling Kit *25 labelings*	1 kit	1.2, 6.4, 7.3	223
Z25351	Zenon® Allophycocyanin Rabbit IgG Labeling Kit *25 labelings*	1 kit	1.2, 6.4, 7.3	223
Z25452	Zenon® Biotin-XX Human IgG Labeling Kit *50 labelings*	1 kit	1.2, 4.3, 7.3	223
Z25052	Zenon® Biotin-XX Mouse IgG_1 Labeling Kit *50 labelings*	1 kit	1.2, 4.3, 7.3	223
Z25152	Zenon® Biotin-XX Mouse IgG_{2a} Labeling Kit *50 labelings*	1 kit	1.2, 4.3, 7.3	223
Z25252	Zenon® Biotin-XX Mouse IgG_{2b} Labeling Kit *50 labelings*	1 kit	1.2, 4.3, 7.3	223

For current prices or to order online, visit probes.invitrogen.com

Cat #	Product Name	Unit Size	Sections	Limited Use Label License #
Z25352	Zenon® Biotin-XX Rabbit IgG Labeling Kit *50 labelings*	1 kit	1.2, 4.3, 7.3	223
Z25053	Zenon® DSB-X™ Biotin Mouse IgG$_1$ Labeling Kit *50 labelings*	1 kit	1.2, 4.3, 7.3	223
Z25042	Zenon® Fluorescein Mouse IgG$_1$ Labeling Kit *50 labelings*	1 kit	1.2, 1.5, 7.3	223
Z25342	Zenon® Fluorescein Rabbit IgG Labeling Kit *50 labelings*	1 kit	1.2, 1.5, 7.3	223
Z25454	Zenon® Horseradish Peroxidase Human IgG Labeling Kit *25 labelings*	1 kit	1.2, 6.2, 7.3	223
Z25054	Zenon® Horseradish Peroxidase Mouse IgG$_1$ Labeling Kit *25 labelings*	1 kit	1.2, 6.2, 7.3	223
Z25154	Zenon® Horseradish Peroxidase Mouse IgG$_{2a}$ Labeling Kit *25 labelings*	1 kit	1.2, 6.2, 7.3	223
Z25254	Zenon® Horseradish Peroxidase Mouse IgG$_{2b}$ Labeling Kit *25 labelings*	1 kit	1.2, 6.2, 7.3	223
Z25354	Zenon® Horseradish Peroxidase Rabbit IgG Labeling Kit *25 labelings*	1 kit	1.2, 6.2, 7.3	223
Z25040	Zenon® Marina Blue® Mouse IgG$_1$ Labeling Kit *50 labelings*	1 kit	1.2, 1.7, 7.3	223, 192
Z25340	Zenon® Marina Blue® Rabbit IgG Labeling Kit *50 labelings*	1 kit	1.2, 1.7, 7.3	223, 192
Z25043	Zenon® Oregon Green® 488 Mouse IgG$_1$ Labeling Kit *50 labelings*	1 kit	1.2, 1.5, 7.3	223, 191
Z25343	Zenon® Oregon Green® 488 Rabbit IgG Labeling Kit *50 labelings*	1 kit	1.2, 1.5, 7.3	223, 191
Z25041	Zenon® Pacific Blue™ Mouse IgG$_1$ Labeling Kit *50 labelings*	1 kit	1.2, 1.7, 7.3	223, 192
Z25455	Zenon® R-Phycoerythrin Human IgG Labeling Kit *25 labelings*	1 kit	1.2, 6.4, 7.3	223
Z25055	Zenon® R-Phycoerythrin Mouse IgG$_1$ Labeling Kit *25 labelings*	1 kit	1.2, 6.4, 7.3	223
Z25155	Zenon® R-Phycoerythrin Mouse IgG$_{2a}$ Labeling Kit *25 labelings*	1 kit	1.2, 6.4, 7.3	223
Z25255	Zenon® R-Phycoerythrin Mouse IgG$_{2b}$ Labeling Kit *25 labelings*	1 kit	1.2, 6.4, 7.3	223
Z25355	Zenon® R-Phycoerythrin Rabbit IgG Labeling Kit *25 labelings*	1 kit	1.2, 6.4, 7.3	223
Z25045	Zenon® Texas Red®-X Mouse IgG$_1$ Labeling Kit *50 labelings*	1 kit	1.2, 1.6, 7.3	223, 211
Z25345	Zenon® Texas Red®-X Rabbit IgG Labeling Kit *50 labelings*	1 kit	1.2, 1.6, 7.3	223, 211
Z25460	Zenon® Tricolor Human IgG Labeling Kit #1 *for green, orange and deep red fluorescence imaging* *3 x 10 labelings*	1 kit	1.2, 7.3	223, 183
Z25470	Zenon® Tricolor Human IgG Labeling Kit #2 *for blue, green and red fluorescence imaging* *3 x 10 labelings*	1 kit	1.2, 7.3	223, 183
Z25060	Zenon® Tricolor Mouse IgG$_1$ Labeling Kit #1 *for green, orange and deep red fluorescence imaging* *3 x 10 labelings*	1 kit	1.2, 7.3	223, 183
Z25070	Zenon® Tricolor Mouse IgG$_1$ Labeling Kit #2 *for blue, green and red fluorescence imaging* *3 x 10 labelings*	1 kit	1.2, 7.3	223, 183
Z25080	Zenon® Tricolor Mouse IgG$_1$ Labeling Kit #3 *for flow cytometry, 488 nm excitation* *3 x 10 labelings*	1 kit	1.2, 7.3	223, 183
Z25160	Zenon® Tricolor Mouse IgG$_{2a}$ Labeling Kit #1 *for green, orange and deep red fluorescence imaging* *3 x 10 labelings*	1 kit	1.2, 7.3	223, 183
Z25170	Zenon® Tricolor Mouse IgG$_{2a}$ Labeling Kit #2 *for blue, green and red fluorescence imaging* *3 x 10 labelings*	1 kit	1.2, 7.3	223, 183
Z25180	Zenon® Tricolor Mouse IgG$_{2a}$ Labeling Kit #3 *for flow cytometry, 488 nm excitation* *3 x 10 labelings*	1 kit	1.2, 7.3	223, 183
Z25260	Zenon® Tricolor Mouse IgG$_{2b}$ Labeling Kit #1 *for green, orange and deep red fluorescence imaging* *3 x 10 labelings*	1 kit	1.2, 7.3	223, 183
Z25270	Zenon® Tricolor Mouse IgG$_{2b}$ Labeling Kit #2 *for blue, green and red fluorescence imaging* *3 x 10 labelings*	1 kit	1.2, 7.3	223, 183
Z25280	Zenon® Tricolor Mouse IgG$_{2b}$ Labeling Kit #3 *for flow cytometry, 488 nm excitation* *3 x 10 labelings*	1 kit	1.2, 7.3	223, 183
Z25360	Zenon® Tricolor Rabbit IgG Labeling Kit #1 *for green, orange and deep red fluorescence imaging* *3 x 10 labelings*	1 kit	1.2, 7.3	223, 183
Z25370	Zenon® Tricolor Rabbit IgG Labeling Kit #2 *for blue, green and red fluorescence imaging* *3 x 10 labelings*	1 kit	1.2, 7.3	223, 183
A22128	Z-IETD-AFC (7-amino-4-trifluoromethylcoumarin, *N*-CBZ-L-isoleucyl-L-glutamyl-L-threonyl-L-aspartic acid amide)	5 mg	10.4, 15.5	None
A22127	Z-IETD-AMC (7-amino-4-methylcoumarin, *N*-CBZ-L-isoleucyl-L-glutamyl-L-threonyl-L-aspartic acid amide)	5 mg	10.4, 15.5	None
R22126	Z-IETD-R110 (rhodamine 110, bis-(*N*-CBZ-L-isoleucyl-L-glutamyl-L-threonyl-L-aspartic acid amide)) *bulk packaging*	20 mg	10.4, 15.5	None
R22125	Z-IETD-R110 (rhodamine 110, bis-(*N*-CBZ-L-isoleucyl-L-glutamyl-L-threonyl-L-aspartic acid amide))	2 mg	10.4, 15.5	None
R33753	Z-LEED-R110 (rhodamine 110, bis-(*N*-CBZ-L-leucyl-L-glutamyl-L-glutamyl-L-aspartic acid amide))	2 mg	10.4, 15.5	None
R33751	Z-LEHD-R110 (rhodamine 110, bis-(*N*-CBZ-L-leucyl-L-glutamyl-L-histidinyl-L-aspartic acid amide))	2 mg	10.4, 15.5	None
R33755	Z-VDVAD-R110 (rhodamine 110, bis-(*N*-CBZ-L-valyl-L-aspartyl-L-valyl-L-alanyl-L-aspartic acid amide))	2 mg	10.4, 15.5	None
R33754	Z-VEID-R110 (rhodamine 110, bis-(*N*-CBZ-L-valyl-L-glutamyl-L-isoleucyl-L-aspartic acid amide))	2 mg	10.4, 15.5	None
Z2850	zymosan A BioParticles® opsonizing reagent	1 U	16.1	None
Z23373	zymosan A (*S. cerevisiae*) BioParticles®, Alexa Fluor® 488 conjugate	2 mg	16.1	183
Z23374	zymosan A (*S. cerevisiae*) BioParticles®, Alexa Fluor® 594 conjugate	2 mg	16.1	183
Z2844	zymosan A (*S. cerevisiae*) BioParticles®, BODIPY® FL conjugate	10 mg	16.1	193
Z2841	zymosan A (*S. cerevisiae*) BioParticles®, fluorescein conjugate	10 mg	16.1	None
Z2843	zymosan A (*S. cerevisiae*) BioParticles®, Texas Red® conjugate	10 mg	16.1	None
Z2849	zymosan A (*S. cerevisiae*) BioParticles®, unlabeled	100 mg	16.1	None
R33750	Z-YVAD-R110 (rhodamine 110, bis-(*N*-CBZ-L-tyrosinyl-L-valyl-L-alanyl-L-aspartic acid amide))	2 mg	10.4, 15.5	None

For current prices or to order online, visit probes.invitrogen.com

Index

A

B

C

D

E

F

G

K

L

M

N

O

P

Q

R

T

U

V

W

X

Y

Z

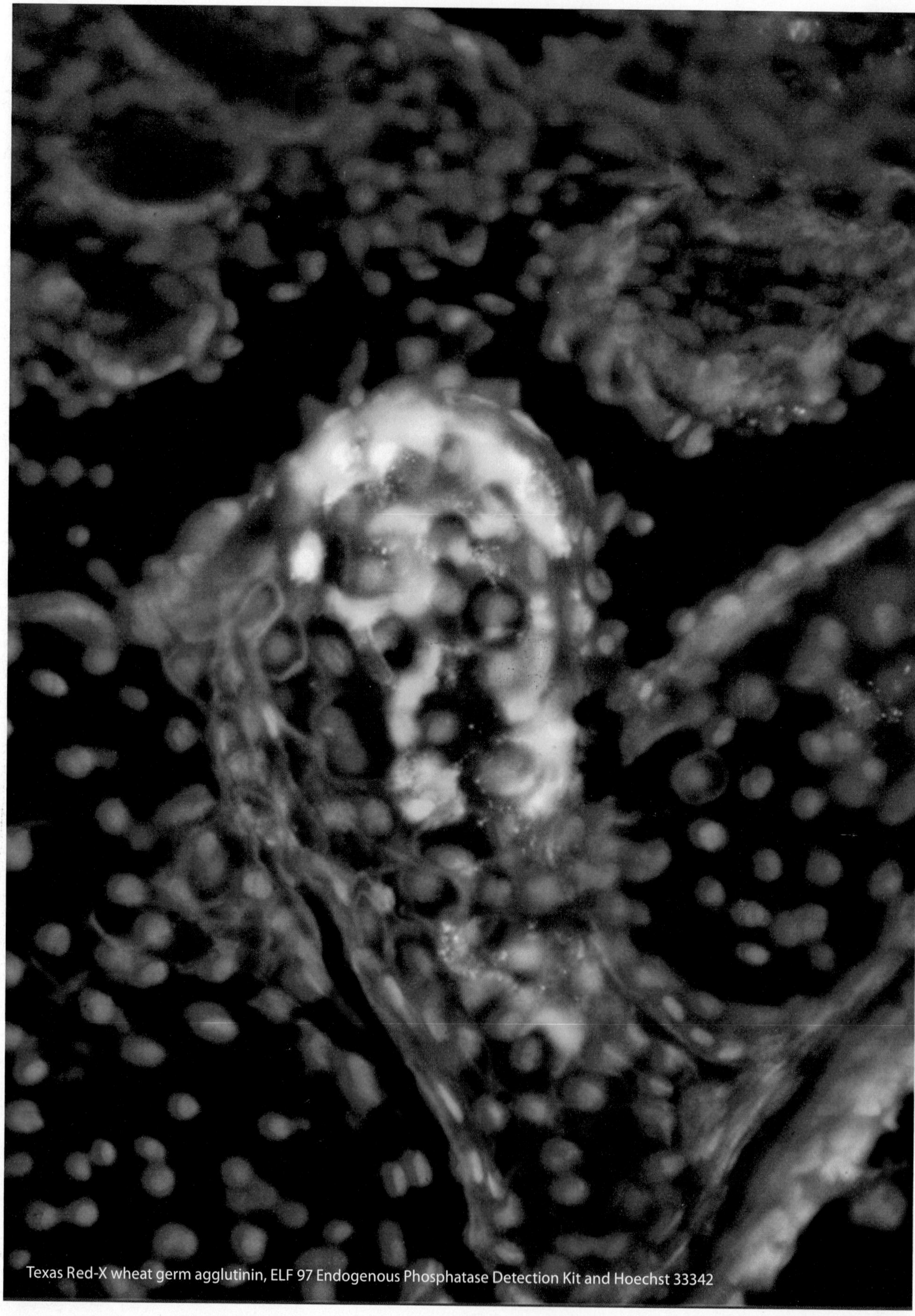

Texas Red-X wheat germ agglutinin, ELF 97 Endogenous Phosphatase Detection Kit and Hoechst 33342